Pages of Support for
Each Student Lesson.

Why choose anything less?

1. Motivate and Teach
2. Check Understanding
3. Practice and Apply

for pages 68-69

PRACTICE

Add.

1.	46.8 +59.7 106.5	**2.**	37.8 + 9.6 47.4	**3.**	6.27 +2.88 9.15	**4.**	0.85 +4.36 5.21	**5.**	3.7 +2.46 6.16
6.	7.386 +0.049 7.435	**7.**	36.35 +19.2 55.55	**8.**	4.180 +3.675 7.855	**9.**	$5.63 + 2.48 $8.11	**10.**	8.985 +4.69 13.675
11.	36.8 19.3 +26.4 82.5	**12.**	128.7 36.480 + 9.867 175.047	**13.**	1.869 2.088 +3.548 7.505	**14.**	0.687 0.975 0.836 +0.548 3.046	**15.**	$124.73 642.80 376.57 +290.17 $1,434.27

16. 26.6 + 42.9 69.5 **17.** $16.37 + $17.96 $34.33 **18.** 6.478 + 0.7 + 2.85 10.028

Estimate each sum to the place value of the underlined digit.

19. 0.34 + 0.67 1.0 **20.** 7.6 + 6.9 15 **21.** 43.62 + 9.47 53 **22.** 21.97 + 37.41 59

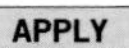

APPLY

MATH REASONING

Without adding, tell whether each sum is greater than or less than 2.

23. 0.875 + 1.105 < 2 **24.** 1.086 + 0.92 > 2 **25.** 1.006 + 0.999 > 2

PROBLEM SOLVING

26. Ian had 46.2 mg of vitamin C. Which two items from the chart did he have? baked potato and green beans

27. Loran had beans, corn, and a tomato. How much vitamin C did she get? 55.43 mg

28. Health and Fitness Data Bank Find the number of milligrams of vitamin C in three things you like to eat. What is the total amount of vitamin C you would get from one serving of each? See page 474. Answers will vary.

► CALCULATOR

Use a calculator to change the first number into the second number. Use the addition or subtraction key only once for each problem.

29. first: 6.78 → second: 6.38 −.4 **30.** first: 43.5 → second: 73.5 +30

31. first: 0.545 → second: 0.245 −.3 **32.** first: 2.37 → second: 2.49 +.12

More Practice, page 503, set A

69

3. Practice and Apply

Basic	1-10, 23-32
Average	1-32
Extended	11-32

PRACTICE

What steps should you follow to solve Exercises 1-15? (Write one or more zeros to the right of the decimal point if needed, add columns beginning from the first place at the right, make trades when a total is 10 or greater.)

APPLY

MATH REASONING ► What helpful information can you gain from studying the addends in each problem? (Possible answer: One addend is a little more and the other is a little less than 1.

PROBLEM SOLVING ► How is the graph used differently in Problems 26 and 27? (In Problem 26, it is used to find a value for each food; in Problem 27, to find two values with a sum of 46.2.)

CALCULATOR ► How can you determine which number key to press to solve each problem? (Determine the difference between the two digits in corresponding places that differ.)

3-6

Close and Assess

WRITE WHAT YOU THINK Have students write all the steps involved in doing the following exercise.
4.367 + 2.098 + 3.6

Quick Quiz

1. 11.4 + 6.31 (17.71) **2.** 6.94 + 2.73 (9.67) **3.** 4.32 + 1.09 (5.41)

...And 2 Pages Of Teaching Steps

An easy-to-teach lesson plan with questions and teaching actions.

LESSON PLAN 3-6

OBJECTIVE 3-6
To add decimals

Grouping Suggestion: pairs

1. MOTIVATE AND TEACH

LEARN ABOUT IT

EXPLORE Have student pairs work together to solve the problem and then compare their work with the procedure shown in the text.

TALK ABOUT IT ► **How many trades were made in this problem?** (3) **What were they?** (trading 14 hundredths for 1 tenth 4 hundredths, trading 18 tenths for 1 one 8 tenths, and trading 19 ones for 1 ten 9 ones)
Student Edition answers: **1.** so that we add digits that have the same place value **2.** Rounding addends to the nearest whole number gives an estimated sum of 50, which is close to 49.84. **3.** The three foods would provide 49.84 mg of vitamin C.
Have students do the other examples on paper and compare their answers with those in the text.
► **Which example required the most trades?** (C required 3 trades.) **Which required the fewest?** (A and B required 1 trade each.)
► **In which example could placing zeros be helpful?** (D) **Where?** (in the thousandths place in 4.69 and in the hundredths and thousandths places in 1.8) **Why?** (Placing zeros there makes addition easier without changing the values.)

2. CHECK UNDERSTANDING

TRY IT OUT

ERROR ALERT Exercises 3, 5: Adding incorrectly when addends have a different number of places.
Trading incorrectly.

Adding Decimals

LEARN ABOUT IT

EXPLORE **Analyze the Process**
Suppose you chose chicken, a sliced tomato, and corn for a meal. How many milligrams (mg) of vitamin C would they provide?

To solve this problem add 8.75, 28.39 and 12.7.

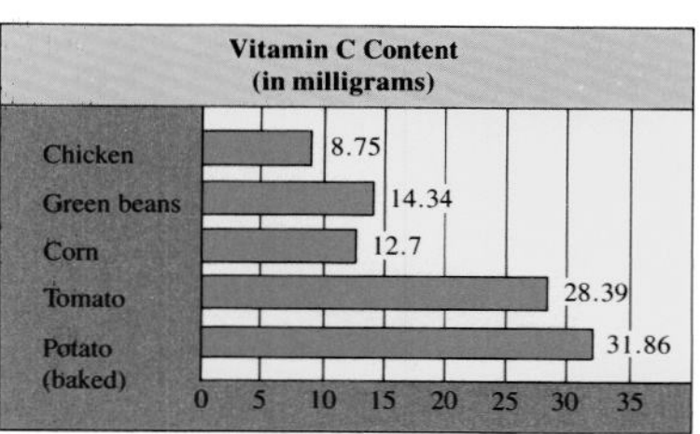

Line up the decimal points.	Add the hundredths. Trade if necessary.	Add the tenths. Trade if necessary.	Add the whole numbers. Write the decimal point.
8.75 28.39 +12.7	8.75 38.39 +12.7 4	8.75 28.39 +12.7 84	8.75 28.39 +12.7 49.84

TALK ABOUT IT See teaching notes.

1. Why do we line up decimal points?
2. Use estimation to show that the answer is reasonable.
3. Give the answer to the Explore problem in a complete sentence.

Other Examples

A $7.80 + 9.65 = $17.45

B 9.576 + 0.489 = 10.065

C 0.763 + 4.69 + 1.8 = 7.253

TRY IT OUT

Add.

1. $0.76 + 1.34 ($2.10)
2. 1.746 + 0.205 (1.951)
3. 1.6 + 0.753 (2.353)
4. 7.864 + 0.189 (8.053)
5. 6.478 + 0.7 + 2.85 (10.028)

68

TEACHING OPTIONS

RETEACHING TIPS For the first error, have students line up the decimal points and then write a zero in each empty place to the right of the decimal point. For the second error, have students use Reteaching Supplement 25.

ENRICHMENT **More Teasers from Tobbs, Sunburst, 1985** For all levels of students.
Decimal addition presents a 2 × 2 grid involving one (level 1) or 2 (level 2) operations. Students complete the empty square by ading two decimals. May consist of sessions of varied length.

Addison-Wesley
Components for

Success

- **Student Editions K-8 (K-6 Spanish*)**
These editions include a broad range of topics, stimulating lessons that help motivate students for learning mathematics, plus ample practice and application lessons to build success.

- **Teacher's Edition K-8 (K-6 Spanish*)**
They provide maximum support and options that save time through program manageability and teaching flexibility.

"I think it's an outstanding program. My rep is great and he's only a phone call away. I can always get the materials or information I need."

(Middle School Teacher)

- **Supplements**

Practice Workbook*
Extra practice pages that provide reinforcement for mastery of concepts and computational competence

Reteaching Workbook*
Opportunities to reteach and review concepts to ensure student success before moving to new ideas.

Challenges Workbook*
Mathematical situations for all students that motivate students to have fun with mathematics.

Building Thinking Skills Workbook*
Opportunities to build critical thinking and mathematical reasoning power which foster independent decision-making abilities.

Family Math Letters*
Positive communication with students' families that provide information and math experiences for families to be enjoyed at home.

Transparency Package - Teaching Aids
Items such as geometric shapes and graph paper to help make teaching and learning concepts easier in transparency and blackline master formats.

Kindergarten Big Book
Enlarged format to facilitate interactive whole group teaching.

Storybooks (K, 1, 2)
Beautifully illustrated stories for each chapter in a 17" x 22" format that deepens understanding of concepts through the mathematics and language arts connection.

Computer-Assisted Problem Solving Software
Exciting software that allows students to enter the variables in a word problem and have the computer compute the correct answer.

Manipulative Kits
Ample materials in a convenient, easy to manage fomat. The package is designed for ease in storing, distributing, and retrieving materials.

Overhead Manipulatives
These frequently requested overhead materials save teaching time by making classroom demonstrations colorful, exciting, and easy for all students to see.

Assessment Options*
A variety of options from which to choose for easy and efficient assessment of understanding and computational competence.
-Multiple Choice Test Booklets*
-Free Response Test Booklets*
-Alternative tests to use with manipulatives and critical thinking situations.

Record Keeping
Blackline masters, including Observation Checklists, that provide efficient and time-saving record keeping devices.

Cumulative Record Card
An easy to use record card that makes recording students' math progress from grades K-8 practical and easy to review and store.

Calculator Kits
Conveniently packaged calculators and resourse materials.

***Available in Spanish K-6**
Las Matemáticas de Addison-Wesley ©1991

CONTENTS

Two pages of lesson options preceed every lesson.

The options include:

Quick Review	**Problem of the Day**	**Practice Supplement**
Prior Knowledge	**Subject Integration**	**Reteaching Supplement**
Communication	**Life Skills**	**Challenge Supplement**
Explore and Connect	**Math Connection**	**Building Thinking Skills Supplement**
	Creative Thinking	**Options for Individual Needs**

Two pages of lesson options preceed every lesson.

The options include:

- **Quick Review**
- **Prior Knowledge**
- **Communication**
- **Explore and Connect**
- **Problem of the Day**
- **Subject Integration**
- **Life Skills**
- **Math Connection**
- **Creative Thinking**
- **Practice Supplement**
- **Reteaching Supplement**
- **Challenge Supplement**
- **Building Thinking Skills Supplement**
- **Options for Individual Needs**

CHAPTER 3 Addition and Subtraction of Whole Numbers

CHAPTER 4 Data, Graphs, and Probability

CONTENTS

Two pages of lesson options preceed every lesson.

The options include:

Quick Review	**Problem of the Day**	**Practice Supplement**
Prior Knowledge	**Subject Integration**	**Reteaching Supplement**
Communication	**Life Skills**	**Challenge Supplement**
Explore and Connect	**Math Connection**	**Building Thinking Skills Supplement**
	Creative Thinking	**Options for Individual Needs**

CONTENTS

Two pages of lesson options preceed every lesson.

The options include:	Problem of the Day	Practice Supplement
Quick Review	Subject Integration	Reteaching Supplement
Prior Knowledge	Life Skills	Challenge Supplement
Communication	Math Connection	Building Thinking Skills Supplement
Explore and Connect	Creative Thinking	Options for Individual Needs

CHAPTER 13 Decimal Concepts

CHAPTER 14 Metric Measurement

CHAPTER 15 Addition and Subtraction Fractions and Decimals

CHAPTER 16 Division 2-Digit Divisors

REAR MATTER

Robert E. Eicholz
Addison-Wesley Author
Woodinville, Washington

Phares G. O'Daffer
Professor Emeritus of Mathematics
Illinois State University
Normal, Illinois

Charles R. Fleenor
Addison-Wesley Author
Sunnyvale, California

Sharon L. Young
Addison-Wesley Author
Palm Harbor, Florida

Randall I. Charles
Associate Professor and Chairperson
Department of Mathematics and
Computer Science
San Jose State University
San Jose, California

Carne S. Barnett
Principle Investigator and
Program Director
Far West Laboratory for Educational
Research and Development
San Francisco, California

Stanley R. Clemens
Professor of Mathematics
Bluffton College
Bluffton, Ohio

Andy Reeves
Elementary Mathematics Consultant
Florida Department of Education
Tallahassee, Florida

Carol A. Thornton
Professor, Department of Mathematics
Illinois State University
Normal, Illinois

Joan E. Westley
Addison-Wesley Author
San Francisco, California

PROGRAM ADVISORS

John A. Dossey
Professor of Mathematics
Illinois State University
Bloomington, Illinois

David C. Brummett
Educational Consultant
Palo Alto, California

Betty C. Lee
Assistant Principal
Ferry Elementary School
Detroit, Michigan

Rosalie Whitlock
Educational Consultant
Stanford, California

Freddy Renfro
K-12 Mathematics Coordinator
La Porte Independent School District
La Porte, Texas

William J. Driscoll
Mathematics Education Consultant
Burlington, Connecticut

Irene Medima
Mathematics Coordinator
Tom Brown Middle School
Corpus Christi, Texas

Contributing Writers

Betsy Franco
Mary Heinrich
Penny Holland
Marilyn Jacobson
Michael E. Jay
Judit N. Moschkovich
Ann Muench
Gini Shimabukuro
Julie Sitomer
Marny Sorgen
Connie Thorpe
Sandra Ward
Judith K. Wells

Teacher Reviewers and Consultants

Michele Acker-Hopevar
New Port Richey, Florida

Gerald Alford
Bellingham, Washington

Mary Altieri
Shrub Oak, New York

Carol Ballentine
Jacksonville, Florida

Gini Bergstresser
Fort Myers, Florida

Donna Bibbins
Watertown, New York

Beth Bishop
Houston, Texas

Janet Boatman
Tampa, Florida

Teresa Bonderson
Euless, Texas

Inga Borowski
Hoffman Estates, Illinois

Kathryn Bowden
Palo Alto, California

Linda Braham
Seattle, Washington

Mary Ann Bravo
San Mateo, California

Richard Breen
Soring Lake, Michigan

Virginia Burdick
San Antonio, Texas

Lynn Callahan
Melbourne, Florida

Linda Cantrell
Seattle, Washington

Jeanne Cantu
San Antonio, Texas

Bernie Capuano
Greenwich, Connecticut

Norm Carter
Santa Clara, California

Ginger Cartwright
Grand Prairie, Texas

Richard Caulfield
Westfield, Indiana

Holly Cavanaugh
St. Petersburg, Florida

Darlene Choe
Tampa, Florida

Toni Coclin
Winchester, Massachusetts

Laura Cohen
Palo Alto, California

Howard Cohn
Jacksonville, Florida

Anna Corbett
Zebulon, North Carolina

Elizabeth Correll
Hanahan, South Carolina

Cathy J. Davenport
San Antonio, Texas

Robert Davies
Stamford, Connecticut

Bill Davis
Dallas, Texas

Linda Deal
Kent, Washington

Leola Deboise
Dallas, Texas

Paul Dillenberger
Minneapolis, Minnesota

Nancy Diorio
Liverpool, New York

Candace Doherty
Palm Harbor, Florida

Nancy Doll-Ugrin
Fort Bragg, California

Joan Drennan
San Antonio, Texas

Patty Dunham
Pembroke Pines, Florida

Peggy Eddy
San Antonio, Texas

Dawn Lynn Eibel
Virginia Beach, Virginia

Barbara Elliott
El Cajon, California

Margaret Erdman
Hingham, Massachusetts

Lynda Evans
Houston, Texas

Carol Farr
Bonne Terre, Missouri

Floyd Flack
Temple City, California

Joseph Floyd
Opa Locka, Florida

Jim Foley
Anoka, Minnesota

Anne Franzmann
Bellingham, Washington

Pat Freda
Zephyrhills, Florida

George Frye
East Bridgewater, Massachusetts

Jean Fuhrman
Dolton, Illinois

Eileen Fukunaga
Santa Clara, California

Ponzella Fuller
Birmingham, Alabama

Deborah Gerretsen
Tinley Park, Illinois

Sylvia Geshell
Missoula, Montana

Patty J. Gillentine
Grand Prairie, Texas

Richard Giuliano
Hamilton, Ohio

Deborah Glynn
Largo, Florida

Cara Gordon
Mount Airy, North Carolina

Patricia Guzylak
Rochester, New York

Mary Gwinn
Covington, Virginia

Barbara Hackney
Madison, Tennessee

Sylvia Hale
South Daytona, Florida

Sandra Hall
Largo, Florida

Polly C. Hamm
Zephyrhills, Florida

Aida Haro
Houston, Texas

Mary Alice Harrington
Hingham, Massachusetts

Don Hastings
Stratford, Connecticut

Francis Hernandez
San Antonio, Texas

Nancy Hildebrand
Bellingham, Washington

Shyoko Hiraga
Seattle, Washington

Hector Hirigoyen
Miami, Florida

Beverly Horne
San Antonio, Texas

Catherine Howard
Palo Alto, California

Carole Ireland
Chicago, Illinois

Roberta Irwin
South San Francisco, California

Brenda Jacobs
Port Charlotte, Florida

Helen Jacobson
Kent, Washington

JoAnn Jeffreys
Darien, Illinois

Cora Johns
Lancaster, Texas

Cynthia Johnson
Hollywood, Florida

Marianne Johnson
Palo Alto, California

Cheryl Johnson
Reno, Nevada

Marcia A. Jones
Springfield, Ohio

Ellenore Mary Jordon
Bloomfield, Connecticut

Beva Karay
Palm Harbor, Florida

Lelo Kassel
Nanuet, New York

Rosemary Kavner
Reno, Nevada

Vicki Kayusa
Fort Myers, Florida

Janet King
Tampa, Florida

Michelle Klupchak
Chicago Heights, Illinois

Debra Knowles
Hayward, California

Charles LaBarbera
Liverpool, New York

Annette LaLonde
Kent, Washington

Esther A. Lamb
Park Forest, Illinois

Susan Lapworth
Indianapolis, Indiana

Susan Larson
Elk Grove, California

Virgina Lazidis
San Antonio, Texas

Josephine Leece
Tampa, Florida

Peggy Leftakis
Orlando, Florida

)lga Leonard
Katy, Texas
)orothy Ling
Lansing, Michigan
etty Looney
Grand Prairie, Texas
oAnne MacAdam
Tampa, Florida
nn Madonia
Liverpool, New York
Iarilyn Majer
Clearwater, Florida
)ebra L. Martins
Cincinnati, Ohio
Iary Martocci
Burlingame, California
arbara Mathers
St. Petersburg, Florida
Ielissa Mathews
Orlando, Florida
ue Mattioli
Elk Grove Village, Illinois
usan McCartney
Rockledge, Florida
Iaureen McClain
Natick, Massachusetts
)ebbie McCleskey
Palo Alto, California
anet McGregor
Port Charlotte, Florida
wendolyn McMullen
St. Louis, Missouri
aren Mead
South San Francisco, California
icki Meredith
Largo, Florida
arol Midgett
Southport, North Carolina
anice Miller
Fairport, New York
atricia Miller
St. Petersburg, Florida
Iargo Morrison
San Mateo, California
an Mosier
Tampa, Florida
arol Newman
Lauderdale Lakes, Florida
olores Norris
Port Charlotte, Florida
atricia O'Brien
Liverpool, New York
aDonne Oaldon
Orlando, Florida
ugenia Oeser
Arcadia, California
ally Olson
Olympia, Washington
aren Opsomer
Ballwin, Missouri
Iegan Ormiston
Hoffman Estates, Illinois
Iillicent Osburn
Varico, Florida
Iarlys J. Otis
White Bear Lake, Minnesota
atrick Page
Oneida, New York

Beverly Peterson
Hingham, Massachusetts
Paula Phelps
Plano, Texas
Claire M. Piccinelle
Redway, California
Laura Pitts
Mexico, Missouri
Michael Pomara
Lake Grove, New York
Diana Price-Stone
Philomath, Oregon
Susan Pulisci
Palo Alto, California
Violet T. Pullara
Tampa, Florida
Michael Rapalje
Shrub Oak, New York
Jeanie Reed
Houston, Texas
Ann Reimer
Rochester, New York
Donna Ritchie
Elk Grove, Illinois
Linda S. Rittle
Tampa, Florda
Kathleen Roberson
Chicago Heights, Illinois
Martha Rosewell
East Bridgewater, Massachusetts
Beverly Saylor
South San Francisco, California
Philip Schmidt
Maple Grove, Minnesota
Mark Schumacher
Ballwin, Missouri
Margaret Scordias
Richmond Heights, Missouri
Michele Scott
Palo Alto, California
Jody Scott
Silverdale, Washington
Mary Sessler
Cupertino, California
John D. Shea
East Bridgewater, Massachusetts
Susan K. Skeiber
East Bridgewater, Massachusetts
Pearl Solomon
Pearl River, New York
Lynn Spadaccini
Melbourne, Florida
Karen Stafford
Garland, Texas
Les Steinberger
Plainview, New York
Jerry Stenson
San Bruno, California
Mary Ann Stine
Kennewick, Washington
Tom Stone
Eugene, Oregon
Lydia Stoopenkoff
San Francisco, California
Biruta Strausser
Menlo Park, California

Nancy Strodtbeck
Fairfield, Ohio
Maggie Sullivan
Chicago, Illinois
Linda Talford
Houston, Texas
Joyce Tarowsky
Indianapolis, Indiana
Elizabeth Travis
Seattle, Washington
Marie Trevino
San Antonio, Texas
Susan Troutman
Sugarland, Texas
Gloria Valenti
Tampa, Florida
Debbie Valentine
Houston, Texas
Elizabeth Von Rotz
Centralia, Washington
Karen Wade
Dade City, Florida
Anne Walters
Fort Meyers, Florida
Mary Ann Ward
Pontiac, Michigan
Edna Wayne
Sparks, Nevada
Christine West
Sullivan's Island, South Carolina
Mildred Wester
Indio, California
Sylvia White
Chicago, Illinois
Susan Widsten
San Antonio, Texas
Pat Wiemann
Kent, Washington
Joyce Wiley
Seminole, Florida
Gloria Williams
Palo Alto, California
Jo Helen Williams
Dayton, Ohio
Tamara L. Wilson
Hoffman Estates, Illinois
May Wiza
Park Forest, Illinois
Susan Wolfe
Easley, South Carolina
Dorothy Wood
Larkspur, California
Jean Worsh
Marshfield, Massachusetts
Bonnie Wrazien
Strousburg, Pennsylvania
Huretta Wright
Daytona Beach, Florida
Jane Wright
San Mateo, California
Sister Marla Yeck
St. Louis, Missouri
Jane Zarate
San Antonio, Texas
Mary Ann Zatlikal
West Nyack, New York
Margaret Zehnder
Bellingham, Washington

OBJECTIVES Grade 4

CHAPTER 1 Addition and Subtraction Concepts and Basic Facts

Objective	Lesson
To understand the operations of addition and subtraction	1-1
To understand and use basic properties for addition	1-2
To use addition to find basic subtraction facts	1-3
To use the 6-point problem solving checklist to solve problems	1-4
To use critical thinking to solve number riddles	1-
To use the mental math technique of break apart to find sums	1-
To use the mental math technique of compensation to find sums	1-

CHAPTER 2 Place Value and Money

Objective	Lesson
To read and write 3- and 4-digit numbers	2-1
To read and write 5- and 6-digit numbers	2-2
To compare and order numbers	2-3
To explore algebra by understanding equality	2-4
To solve problems using the strategy Draw a Picture	2-5
To round numbers to the nearest ten, nearest hundred, and nearest dollar	2-6
To round to the nearest thousand	2-
To read and write 7-, 8-, and 9-digit numbers	2-
To count change	2-
To estimate using the visual estimation technique to compare an amount of money to a reference point	2-1

CHAPTER 3 Addition and Subtraction of Whole Numbers

Objective	Lesson
To use mental math to find sums and differences of multiples of 10 and 100	3-1
To use the estimation technique of rounding to estimate sums and differences	3-2
To use objects to develop an understanding of adding 3-digit numbers	3-3
To add 3-digit numbers	3-4
To add a column of 3 or more numbers	3-5
To solve problems using the strategy Make an Organized List	3-6
To use the estimation technique of front-end estimation to estimate sums	3-7
To use objects to devlop an understanding of subtracting 2- and 3-digit numbers	3-8
To subtract whole numbers of 2, 3, and 4 digits	3-
To subtract whole numbers when there are one or more middle zeros	3-1
To use the mental math technique of compensation to find sums and differences	3-1
To solve multiple step problems	3-1
To add and subtract 4- and 5-digit numbers	3-1
To decide if you need an exact answer or an estimate to a problem	3-1

CHAPTER 4 Data, Graphs, and Probability

Objective	Lesson
To get information from a bar graph and a pictograph	4-1
To read and make a bar graph	4-2
To read and make a pictograph	4-3
To read, and make a line graph	4-4
To use critical thinking to analyze a graphical situation	4-5
To solve problems with extra data	4-
To determine whether or not a game is fair	4-
To determine whether the probability of something happening is high or low and to predict an outcome	4-
To solve problems using the strategy Guess and Check	4-

CHAPTER 5 Multiplication and Basic Facts

To understand the operation of multiplication 5-1
To review properties and find products when 0 or 1 is a factor 5-2
To find products when 2 or 5 is a factor 5-3
To find products when 9 is a factor 5-4
To find products when 3 or 4 is a factor 5-5
To explore algebra by using a variable that represents only 1 number 5-6
To understand the question in a problem 5-7
To use the mental math technique of break apart to find multiplication facts 5-8
To find the last six facts, 6 x 6, 7 x 7, 8 x 8, 6 x 7, 6 x 8, and 7 x 8 5-9
To identify and produce multiples of a number 5-10
To solve problems using the strategy Make a Table 5-11

CHAPTER 6 Multiplication 1-Digit Factors

To use mental math to find the product of a 1-digit number times a multiple of 10, 100, or 1,000 6-1
To use the estimation technique of rounding to estimate a product and compare it with a reference point 6-2
To use mental math to multiply two 1-digit numbers and add to the product a 1-digit number 6-3
To use objects to devlop an understanding of multiplying 1-digit numbers 6-4
To multiply a 2-digit by a 1-digit number, 1 trade 6-5
To multiply a 3-digit by a 1-digit number, 1 trade 6-6
To multiply a 3-digit by a 1-digit number, 2 or more trades 6-7
To use critical thinking to solve number riddles 6-8
To use mental math and the multiplication grouping property to find the product of 3 factors 6-9
To solve addition problems using a calculator 6-9
To multiply a 4-digit by a 1-digit number 6-10
To multiply an amount of money less than $100 by a 1-digit number 6-11
To solve problems using the strategy Look for a Pattern 6-12

CHAPTER 7 Multiplication 2-Digit Factors

To use mental math to find the product of a multiple of 10 times a multiple of 10 7-1
To adjust and then use the estimation technique of rounding to estimate the products of 2-digit and 3-digit factors 7-2
To multiply a 2-digit number by a 2-digit multiple of 10 7-3
To multiply a 2-digit by a 2-digit number 7-4
To multiply a 3-digit by a 2-digit number 7-5
To use critical thinking to find the number that multiplied by itself gives the square 7-6
To solve problems using the strategy Use Logical Reasoning 7-7
To multiply an amount of money less than $10 and a 2-digit number 7-8
To choose an appropriate method of calculation 7-9
To solve multiple step problems 7-10

CHAPTER 8 Time and Customary Measurement

To tell time to the minute, past the hour, and to the next hour 8-1
To identify a given time as a.m. or p.m. 8-2
To read a calendar 8-2
To use mental math to calculate ending times and elapsed times 8-3
To solve problems with more than one answer 8-4
To estimate and measure length, using nonstandard units 8-5
To measure length in inch, foot, yard and to relate inch, foot, yard 8-6
To decide whether an actual measurement is needed or whether an estimate is sufficient 8-7
To estimate lengths in miles 8-8
To measure perimeter and to add to find perimeter; to estimate length, width, and perimeter using a benchmark 8-9
To solve problems using data from a chart 8-10
To estimate, measure, and compare capacity using nonstandard units and gallon, half gallon, quart, pint, cup, fluid ounce 8-11
To estimate, measure, and compare weights in pounds and ounces 8-12
To measure temperature in degrees Fahrenheit 8-12

OBJECTIVES Grade 4

CHAPTER 9 Division Concepts and Basic Facts

Objective	Lesson
To understand the operation of division	9-1
To use multiplication to find quotients	9-2
To use missing factors to divide by 2 and 3	9-3
To use missing factors to divide by 4 and 5	9-4
To determine by estimation whether answers to problems are reasonable	9-5
To understand 0 and 1 in division	9-6
To use missing factors to divide by 6 and 7	9-
To use missing factors to divide by 8 and 9	9-
To use critical thinking to discover function rules	9-
To solve problems using the strategy Work Backward	9-1

CHAPTER 10 Division 1-Digit Divisors

Objective	Lesson
To find and check quotients and remainders	10-1
To use mental math to find the quotient of a multiple divided by a 1-digit number	10-2
To use the estimation technique of rounding and substituting compatible numbers to estimate quotients	10-3
To use objects to develop an understanding of dividing a 2-digit number by a 1-digit number	10-4
To find 2-digit quotients by dividing 1-digit divisors into 2-digit dividends	10-5
To solve problems by interpreting the remainder	10-
To find 3-digit quotients by dividing 1-digit divisors and 3-digit dividends	10-
To find the average of 3 or more numbers	10-
To develop skill in deciding where to start in division	10-
To divide 3-digit numbers when there is a 0 in the quotient	10-1
To choose an appropriate method of calculation	10-1
To divide an amount of money less than $10 by a 1-digit divisor	10-1

CHAPTER 11 Geometry

Objective	Lesson
To identify space figures and plane figures	11-1
To name polygon plane figures and compare their angles to 90°	11-2
To identify parallel and perpendicular lines	11-3
To make symmetric figures and identify lines of symmetry	11-4
To classify triangles and angles	11-5
To classify quadrilaterals as squares, rectangles, parallelograms, or trapezoids	11-6
To decide if two figures are congruent	11-
To identify and draw simple closed curves and circles	11-
To use number pairs to make coordinate graphs	11-
To identify and graph similar figures	11-1
To solve problems using data from a diagram	11-1

CHAPTER 12 Fraction Concepts

Objective	Lesson
To understand the region interpretation of a fraction	12-1
To understand the set interpretation of a fraction	12-2
To estimate parts of a whole as fractions	12-3
To practice problem solving	12-3
To understand the concept of equivalent fractions	12-4
To find equivalent fractions by multiplying	12-5
To reduce fractions to lowest terms	12-
To compare fractions	12-
To explore algebra by finding and graphing ordered pairs that make true equations	12-
To use mental math to find a fraction of a number	12-
To understand a mixed number	12-1
To solve problems by measuring to a fractional part of an inch	12-1

CHAPTER 13 Decimal Concepts

To read and write decimals with tenths 13-1
To read and write decimals with hundredths 13-2
To find the decimal when counting by tenths or hundredths 13-3
To compare and order decimals 13-4
To round decimals to a whole number 13-5
To relate fractions and decimals 13-6
To determine by estimation whether answers to problems are reasonable 13-7

CHAPTER 14 Metric Measurement

To measure length in cm, dm, m and km and to relate these units 14-1
To use the estimation technique of unitizing to estimate length in centimeters 14-2
To measure length in millimeters 14-3
To decide whether an actual measurement is needed or whether an estimate is sufficient 14-4
To measure area in square centimeters and to multiply to find area 14-5
To measure volume in cubic centimeters and to multiply to find volume 14-6
To solve problems by finding related problems 14-7
To estimate and measure capacity in mL and L 14-8
To estimate and measure mass in kilograms and grams 14-9
To measure temperature in degrees Celsius 14-9

CHAPTER 15 Addition and Subtraction Fractions and Decimals

To use objects to develop an understanding of adding and subtracting fractions with like denominators 15-1
To add and subtract fractions with like denominators 15-2
To solve problems using data from a recipe 15-3
To use objects to add fractions with unlike denominators 15-4
To use objects to subtract fractions with unlike denominators 15-5
To explore algebra to state verbal patterns and to understand that a variable can represent a range of numbers 15-6
To use objects to develop an understanding of adding and subtracting decimals 15-7
To add and subtract decimals 15-8
To add and subtract decimals in situations involving annexation of zeros 15-9
To use the estimation techniques of rounding and front-end estimation to estimate the sum or difference of two decimals and compare to a reference point 15-10
To use critical thinking to analyze and follow a flow chart 15-11
To analyze, organize, and make decisions using relevant data 15-12

CHAPTER 16 Division 2-Digit Divisors

To use mental math to divide by 2-digit divisors that are multiples of 10 16-1
To find 1-digit quotients by dividing with 2-digit divisors that are multiples of 10 16-2
To find 1-digit quotients by dividing with 2-digit divisors 16-3
To change the estimated quotient when actual division proves it to be too large or too small 16-4
To practice problem solving 16-5
To find 2-digit quotients by dividing with 2-digit divisors that are multiples of 10 16-6
To find 2-digit quotients by dividing with 2-digit divisors that are not rounded 16-7
To solve 2-digit division problems using a calculator 16-8

PACING Grade 4

This pacing chart will help you plan your school year. It gives a suggested amount of time to spend on each chapter. You can adjust the times suggested to meet the needs of the students in your class.

Chapter	Pages	Number of Days
1 Addition and Subtraction: Concepts and Basic Facts	2-23	8
2 Place Value and Money	24-51	11
3 Addition and Subtraction of Whole Numbers	52-87	15
4 Data, Graphs, and Probability	88-113	10
5 Multiplication: Concepts and Basic Facts	114-143	12
6 Multiplying by 1-Digit Factors	144-175	13
7 Multiplying by 2-Digit Factors	176-203	11
8 Time and Customary Measurement	204-235	13
9 Division: Concepts and Basic Facts	236-263	11
10 Division: 1-Digit Divisors	264-295	13
11 Geometry	296-325	12
12 Fraction Concepts	326-355	12
13 Decimal Concepts	356-377	8
14 Metric Measurement	378-403	10
15 Addition and Subtraction: Fractions and Decimals	404-433	12
16 Division: 2-Digit Divisors	434-457	9

Total number of days: 180

	Chapter															
	1	2	3	4	5	6	7	8	9	10	11	12	13	14	15	16
Balance scale and weights								■						■		
Cards																
Compass*																
Containers (capacity)								■						■		
Counters, 2-color*	■				■				■							
Cube-a-links*	■															
Fraction bars															■	
Fraction circles*															■	
Geoboards*												■				
Geometric solids											■					
Number cubes*				■		■										
Place-value materials		■	■			■				■			■	■	■	
Play money*		■														
Protractor*																
Spinners*			■	■		■				■					■	
Tangrams											■					
Tape measures (cust. and metric)*								■						■		
Thermometers														■		

***This item can be found in the Addison-Wesley Manipulative Kit.**

SCOPE AND SEQUENCE

Addison-Wesley Mathematics (©1991) fully integrates *motivation, understanding, problem solving, math reasoning, communication, subject integration, strand integration, group work* and *use of manipulatives* with all mathematical topics in the Scope and Sequence chart.

Algebra	**K**	**1**	**2**	**3**	**4**	**5**	**6**	**7**	**8**
Missing numbers and number sentences									
Variables and equations									
Patterns, functions, and relations									
Expressions									
Formulas									
Inequalities									
Informal proof									
Calculator Skills	**K**	**1**	**2**	**3**	**4**	**5**	**6**	**7**	**8**
Counting									
Whole numbers									
Decimals									
Fractions									
Integers									
Order of operations									
Constant key									
Memory key									
Error messages									
Ratio, proportion, percent									
Powers and roots									
Patterns									
Computer Technology	**K**	**1**	**2**	**3**	**4**	**5**	**6**	**7**	**8**
Computer programs									
Computer software									

TEACH **REINFORCE**

Grade 4

Algebra

Missing numbers and number sentences 8-9, 21, 23, 27, 71, 75, 77, 79, 103, 118-119, 121, 123, 125, 126, 133, 135, 151, 157, 181, 235, 240, 245, 250-251, 252, 255, 267, 285, 307, 337, 338, 421, 441, 443, 504
Variables 55, 93, 126, 416, 443
Equations 32, 55, 159, 441, 491
Graph equations 342
Patterns, functions, and relations 29, 41, 55, 61, 73, 84, 86, 120-121, 122-123, 134-135, 140, 142, 145, 168-169, 187, 193, 232, 254-255, 275, 279, 285, 294, 315, 317, 339, 349, 354, 362, 371, 376, 384-385, 416, 484, 495
Expressions 93
Properties of equality 32, 126

Calculator Skills

Counting 484
Whole numbers 9, 16, 29, 57, 71, 73, 78-79, 81, 121, 135, 151, 157, 163, 166, 187, 188, 202, 211, 222, 225, 251, 271, 280, 317, 385, 449, 450-451, 484, 485, 486, 487, 488, 489, 491
Money 71, 166-167, 451, 489
Decimals 361, 362, 421, 451, 489, 490
Fractions 337, 345, 368, 490, 491
Constant key 9, 135, 271, 484, 486, 487
Order of operations 362, 488
Memory keys 385, 488
Error messages 484, 487
Choose a calculation method 157, 162, 194-195, 286-287
Powers and roots 188-189
Convert decimals and fractions 368-369, 490, 491
Simplify fractions 490
Patterns 61, 121, 135, 187, 362, 484
Convert fractions and mixed numbers 345, 490, 491

Computer Technology

Computer programs 492, 493, 494, 495, 496, 497, 498, 499
Computer software 11, 15, 37, 43, 61, 73, 97, 107, 129, 135, 160, 169, 188, 197, 213, 225, 247, 256, 273, 287, 305, 311, 333, 347, 363, 373, 386, 399, 409, 427, 445, 453

Note: Red type indicates that a topic is being introduced for the first time.

Addison-Wesley Mathematics (©1991) fully integrates *motivation, understanding, problem solving, math reasoning, communication, subject integration, strand integration, group work* and *use of manipulatives* with all mathematical topics in the Scope and Sequence chart.

Concepts & Computation	K	1	2	3	4	5	6	7	8
Number, Number Properties, Numeration, Number Sense									
Numbers and counting		Teach	Teach	Teach/Reinforce	Reinforce	Reinforce	Reinforce		
Compare and order									
whole numbers	Teach	Teach	Teach	Reinforce	Reinforce	Reinforce	Reinforce	Reinforce	Reinforce
decimals				Teach	Teach	Teach/Reinforce	Reinforce	Reinforce	Reinforce
fractions				Teach	Teach	Teach/Reinforce	Reinforce	Reinforce	Reinforce
integers							Teach	Teach	Teach/Reinforce
rational numbers									Teach
Ordinal numbers	Teach	Teach	Teach	Teach/Reinforce	Reinforce	Reinforce	Reinforce	Reinforce	Reinforce
Whole number place value	Teach	Teach	Teach	Teach/Reinforce	Reinforce	Reinforce	Reinforce	Reinforce	Reinforce
Decimal place value					Teach	Teach/Reinforce	Reinforce	Reinforce	Reinforce
Roman numerals			Teach	Teach	Teach	Teach	Teach	Reinforce	Reinforce
Exponents						Teach	Teach	Teach	Teach/Reinforce
Prime and composite numbers					Teach	Teach	Teach	Teach	Teach/Reinforce
Scientific notation						Teach	Teach	Teach	Teach/Reinforce
Square numbers and square roots					Teach	Teach	Teach	Teach	Teach/Reinforce
Whole Number Properties									
Properties of addition		Teach	Teach	Teach/Reinforce	Reinforce	Reinforce	Reinforce	Reinforce	Reinforce
Properties of subtraction		Teach	Teach	Teach/Reinforce	Reinforce	Reinforce	Reinforce	Reinforce	Reinforce
Properties of multiplication			Teach	Teach	Teach	Reinforce	Reinforce	Reinforce	Reinforce
Properties of division			Teach	Teach	Teach	Reinforce	Reinforce	Reinforce	Reinforce
Adding Whole Numbers									
Understand addition concept	Teach	Teach	Teach	Teach/Reinforce	Reinforce	Reinforce	Reinforce	Reinforce	Reinforce
Concrete and pictorial models	Teach	Teach	Teach	Teach/Reinforce	Reinforce				
Fact strategies		Teach	Teach	Teach					
Basic facts and fact families		Teach	Teach	Teach/Reinforce	Reinforce				
Problem solving	Teach	Teach	Teach	Teach/Reinforce	Reinforce	Reinforce	Reinforce	Reinforce	Reinforce
Estimate sums		Teach	Teach	Teach/Reinforce	Reinforce	Reinforce	Reinforce	Reinforce	Reinforce
2- and 3-digit numbers		Teach	Teach	Teach/Reinforce	Reinforce	Reinforce	Reinforce		
3- and 4-digit numbers			Teach	Teach	Reinforce	Reinforce	Reinforce		
Larger numbers				Teach	Teach	Reinforce	Reinforce		

TEACH REINFORCE

Grade 4

Concepts & Computation

Number, Number Properties, Numeration, Number Sense

Numbers and counting 4-5, 12, 40-41, 42-43, 48, 49, 120, 165, 200, 243, 298-299, 313, 362, 365, 484

Compare and order

whole numbers 6, 30-31, 33, 36, 49, 53, 63, 73, 79, 88-89, 113, 119, 123, 125, 155, 159, 167, 176-177, 187, 269, 437, 443, 488, 500

decimals 362, 364-365, 374, 375, 383, 403, 405, 421, 425, 433, 509

fractions 329, 334-335, 336-337, 339, 340-341, 343, 353, 354, 369, 377, 383, 403, 409, 413, 415, 433, 457, 508, 509

Ordinal numbers 209

Whole number place value 26-27, 28-29, 30-31, 33, 36-37, 38-39, 40-41, 48, 49, 51, 53, 58-59, 61, 63, 67, 68-69, 72, 79, 87, 95, 113, 152-153, 154, 156, 158, 164, 182, 184, 186, 272-273, 274, 278, 282, 284, 293, 433, 439, 446, 448, 460, 462, 464, 465, 500, 512

Decimal place value 360-361, 362, 363, 364-365, 366, 374, 375, 439

Roman numerals 50

Prime and composite numbers

Square numbers and square roots 132, 188

Whole Number Properties

Properties of addition 6-7, 20, 21, 45, 51, 62-63, 113, 130, 133

Properties of subtraction 8, 51

Properties of multiplication 118-119, 130, 141, 162, 172

Properties of division 248

Adding Whole Numbers

Understanding addition concept 4-5, 13, 17, 20, 197

Concrete models 4-5, 58-59, 61, 84, 197

Pictorial models 4-5, 58-59, 61, 222, 462

Fact families 8-9, 13, 15, 20, 21, 39, 51, 63, 79, 113

Basic facts 4-5, 6-7, 13, 14-15, 16-17, 21, 39, 45, 51, 54-55, 95, 113, 163, 339, 461, 485, 500

Problem solving 3, 5, 7, 9, 10-11, 15, 17, 20, 21, 35, 37, 55, 57, 61, 63, 65, 67, 76-77, 85, 101, 107, 129, 137, 169, 181, 190, 191, 197, 224, 225, 243, 247, 256, 277, 280, 287, 292, 293, 295, 299, 301, 311, 333, 339, 349, 371, 393, 411, 425, 514, 515

Estimate sums 56-57, 61, 62, 63, 66, 107, 137, 143, 149, 183, 247, 492

2-digit numbers 3, 11, 14-15, 16-17, 54-55, 58-59, 62-63, 65, 67, 74-75, 76-77, 85, 86, 87, 95, 103, 107, 129, 131, 133, 137, 149, 163, 181, 191, 195, 211, 243, 256, 263, 277, 280, 286, 287, 292, 295, 299, 311, 349, 377, 411, 425, 462, 485, 501, 502

3-digit numbers 7, 54-55, 58-59, 60-61, 62-63, 65, 67, 74-75, 76-77, 78-79, 85, 86, 87, 95, 101, 119, 143, 149, 163, 165, 169, 181, 183, 191, 195, 197, 280, 286, 293, 301, 325, 333, 377, 393, 485, 488, 501, 502, 514

4-digit numbers 55, 60-61, 62-63, 65, 67, 85, 89, 129, 149, 165, 169, 247, 286, 333, 371, 485, 501

Larger numbers 65, 78-79, 85, 87, 95, 149, 169, 224, 225, 371, 502

Note: Red type indicates that a topic is being introduced for the first time.

Addison-Wesley Mathematics (©1991) fully integrates *motivation, understanding, problem solving, math reasoning, communication, subject integration, strand integration, group work* and *use of manipulatives* with all mathematical topics in the Scope and Sequence chart.

Concepts & Computation cont.	K	1	2	3	4	5	6	7	8
Subtracting Whole Numbers									
Understand subtraction concept									
Concrete and pictorial models									
Fact strategies									
Basic facts and fact families									
Problem solving									
Estimate differences									
2- and 3-digit numbers									
3- and 4-digit numbers									
Larger numbers									
Multiplying Whole Numbers									
Understand multiplication concept									
Concrete and pictorial models									
Basic facts and fact families									
Problem solving									
Estimating products									
2- and 3-digit numbers									
3- and 4-digit numbers									
Larger numbers									

TEACH REINFORCE

Grade 4

Concepts & Computation cont.

Subtracting Whole Numbers
Understand subtraction concept 4-5, 13, 20, 101
Concrete models4-5, 68-69, 84, 101
Pictorial models 4-5, 68-69, 464
Fact families 8-9, 13, 15, 20, 21, 39, 51, 63, 79, 113
Basic facts 4-5, 8-9, 13, 15, 21, 39, 51, 54-55, 187, 339, 463
Problem solving 3, 5, 9, 10-11, 13, 20, 21, 35, 57, 65, 67, 71, 73, 75, 76-77, 85, 93, 100-101, 107, 129, 137, 149, 155, 157, 159, 165, 179, 181, 183, 185, 190, 191, 197, 201, 224, 225, 235, 246, 247, 257, 277, 283, 287, 319, 333, 339, 371, 385, 515
Estimate differences 56-57, 70, 71, 72, 73, 87, 149, 246, 247
2-digit numbers 3, 8-9, 10-11, 13, 15, 53, 54-55, 57, 65, 67, 70-71, 72-73, 74-75, 76-77, 85, 87, 93, 101, 111, 143, 149, 159, 163, 181, 183, 185, 190, 191, 257, 286, 287, 319, 333, 464, 485, 501, 502, 515
3-digit numbers 54-55, 57, 65, 67, 68-69, 70-71, 72-73, 74-75, 76-77, 85, 87, 89, 107, 111, 113, 119, 128, 143, 149, 155, 157, 179, 185, 195, 197, 224, 283, 287, 488, 496, 501, 502
4-digit numbers 55, 65, 70-71, 72-73, 78-79, 85, 89, 113, 129, 143, 149, 165, 191, 195, 196, 201, 224, 235, 257, 277, 287, 385, 501, 502
Larger numbers 78-79, 95, 197, 225, 246, 371, 501

Multiplying Whole Numbers
Understand multiplication concept 116-117, 141, 161, 178-179
Concrete models 116-117, 118, 130, 132, 134, 152-153, 155, 161
Pictorial models 116-117, 130, 132, 134, 152-153, 161, 240-241
Fact families 240-241, 242-243, 244-245, 249, 250-251, 252-253, 260, 261, 269, 295
Basic facts 114-115, 118-119, 120-121, 122-123, 124-125, 126, 127, 129, 130-131, 132-133, 134-135, 137, 140, 141, 142, 150, 151, 157, 161, 162, 173, 175, 181, 185, 201, 203, 235, 504
Problem solving 116-117, 119, 121, 123, 127, 129, 131, 133, 135, 137, 141, 147, 149, 151, 155, 157, 159, 165, 169, 173, 179, 181, 183, 185, 187, 189, 191, 194-195, 196-197, 201, 213, 217, 235, 237, 241, 243, 246, 251, 263, 265, 267, 289, 319, 349, 393, 425, 427, 443, 444
Estimate products 148-149, 154, 157, 158, 159, 161, 164, 165, 167, 173, 179, 180-181, 182, 184, 186, 189, 200, 201, 235, 246, 263, 295
By a 1-digit number 131, 147, 151, 152-153, 154-155, 156-157, 158-159, 161, 164-165, 166-167, 169, 172, 173, 181, 185, 191, 193, 194-195, 203, 213, 217, 224, 227, 235, 237, 241, 243, 263, 265, 504, 505
By a 2-digit number 163, 178-179, 182-183, 184-185, 186-187, 188, 189, 191, 192-193, 194-195, 196, 197, 200, 201, 202, 213, 217, 227, 235, 246, 263, 427, 444, 505

Note: Red type indicates that a topic is being introduced for the first time.

Addison-Wesley Mathematics (©1991) fully integrates *motivation, understanding, problem solving, math reasoning, communication, subject integration, strand integration, group work* and *use of manipulatives* with all mathematical topics in the Scope and Sequence chart.

Concepts & Computation cont.	K	1	2	3	4	5	6	7	8
Dividing Whole Numbers									
Understand division concept									
Concrete and pictorial models									
Basic facts and fact families									
Problem solving									
Estimating quotients									
1-digit divisors									
With remainders									
2-digit divisors									
Zero in quotients									
3-digit divisors									
2-digit quotients									
3-digit quotients									
Fraction Concepts									
Understand fractions									
Concrete and pictorial models									
Compare and order									
Equivalent fractions									
Lowest-terms fractions									
Greatest common factor									
Least common multiple/denominator									
Convert improper fractions and mixed numbers									
Reciprocals									

TEACH **REINFORCE**

Grade 4

Concepts & Computation cont.

Dividing Whole Numbers
Understand division concept 238-239, 249
Concrete models 238-239, 240-241, 272-273, 279, 309
Pictorial models 238-239, 240-241, 261, 272-273
Fact families 240-241, 242-243, 244-245, 249, 250-251, 252-253, 260, 261, 269, 295
Basic facts 238-239, 240-241, 242-243, 244-245, 247, 249, 250-251, 252-253, 254-255, 257, 261, 267, 279, 295, 309, 325, 355, 455, 506, 507
Problem solving 238-239, 243, 245, 247, 249, 251, 253, 257, 261, 267, 271, 275, 276-277, 279, 281, 285, 289, 293, 301, 318, 333, 349, 371, 393, 437, 439, 441, 443, 444, 445, 447, 455
1-digit divisors 266-267, 268-269, 270-271, 274-275, 276-277, 278-279, 280, 281, 282-283, 284-285, 286, 287, 288-289, 292, 293, 295, 301, 309, 318, 325, 331, 333, 349, 355, 371, 377, 393, 507
Estimate quotients 261, 266, 270-271, 274, 275, 278, 279, 281, 282, 283, 284, 293, 329, 437, 440-441, 442-443, 446, 447, 448, 449
With remainders 266-267, 272-273, 274-275, 276-277, 278-279, 281, 282-283, 284-285, 301, 438-439, 440-441, 442-443, 445, 446-447, 448-449, 450-451, 487, 507, 511
Interpret remainders 266-267, 292, 450, 454, 455
2-digit divisors 436-437, 438-439, 440-441, 442-443, 444, 445, 446-447, 448-449, 450-451, 455, 457, 488, 511, 512
Zeros in the quotient 283, 284-285, 288, 289, 293, 441, 445, 447, 449, 455, 508
2-digit quotients 272-273, 274-275, 276-277, 281, 282-283, 284-285, 287, 292, 293, 295, 301, 318, 333, 349, 355, 377, 393, 437, 441, 446-447, 448-449, 450-451, 455
3-digit quotients 278-279, 280, 281, 283, 284-285, 301, 325, 331, 333, 355, 377, 437

Fraction Concepts
Understand fractions 328-329, 330-331
Concrete models 328-329, 334, 337, 340, 346-347, 358-359, 368-369, 406-407, 412-413, 414-415, 417, 466, 467
Pictorial models 328-329, 330-331, 332, 334-335, 336, 340-341, 343, 344-345, 346-347, 358-359, 368-369, 377, 406-407, 412-413, 415, 466, 467
Compare and order 329, 340-341, 343, 353, 383, 403, 409, 413, 509
Equivalent fractions 334-335, 336-337, 339, 340-341, 342, 343, 352, 353, 354, 369, 377, 404, 409, 433, 490, 508
Lowest-terms fractions 338-339, 343, 352, 353, 403, 408-409, 417, 431, 433, 447, 508
Convert improper fractions and mixed numbers 346-347, 383, 509
Find a fraction of a number 344-345, 353, 377, 403, 433, 497

Note: Red type indicates that a topic is being introduced for the first time.

Addison-Wesley Mathematics (©1991) fully integrates *motivation, understanding, problem solving, math reasoning, communication, subject integration, strand integration, group work* and *use of manipulatives* with all mathematical topics in the Scope and Sequence chart.

Concepts & Computation cont.	K	1	2	3	4	5	6	7	8
Computation with Fractions and Mixed Numbers									
Estimate				TEACH	TEACH/REINFORCE	TEACH/REINFORCE	REINFORCE	REINFORCE	REINFORCE
Problem solving				TEACH	TEACH/REINFORCE	TEACH/REINFORCE	REINFORCE	REINFORCE	REINFORCE
Add fractions									
like denominators				TEACH	TEACH	TEACH/REINFORCE	TEACH/REINFORCE	REINFORCE	REINFORCE
unlike denominators					TEACH	TEACH	TEACH/REINFORCE	TEACH/REINFORCE	REINFORCE
Subtract fractions									
like denominators				TEACH	TEACH	TEACH/REINFORCE	TEACH/REINFORCE	REINFORCE	REINFORCE
unlike denominators					TEACH	TEACH	TEACH/REINFORCE	TEACH/REINFORCE	REINFORCE
Multiply						TEACH	TEACH	TEACH/REINFORCE	TEACH/REINFORCE
Divide						TEACH	TEACH	TEACH/REINFORCE	TEACH/REINFORCE
Convert decimals, fractions				TEACH	TEACH	TEACH	TEACH/REINFORCE	REINFORCE	REINFORCE
Convert decimals, fractions, and percents						TEACH	TEACH	TEACH/REINFORCE	REINFORCE
Add mixed numbers					TEACH	TEACH/REINFORCE	TEACH/REINFORCE	REINFORCE	REINFORCE
Subtract mixed numbers					TEACH	TEACH	TEACH/REINFORCE	TEACH/REINFORCE	REINFORCE
Multiply mixed numbers						TEACH	TEACH	TEACH/REINFORCE	TEACH/REINFORCE
Divide mixed numbers						TEACH	TEACH	TEACH/REINFORCE	TEACH/REINFORCE
Decimal Concepts									
Understand decimals				TEACH	TEACH	TEACH	TEACH/REINFORCE	REINFORCE	REINFORCE
Models				TEACH	TEACH	TEACH	TEACH/REINFORCE		
Place value				TEACH	TEACH	TEACH	TEACH/REINFORCE	REINFORCE	REINFORCE
Compare and order				TEACH	TEACH	TEACH	TEACH/REINFORCE	REINFORCE	REINFORCE
Round decimals				TEACH	TEACH	TEACH	TEACH/REINFORCE	REINFORCE	REINFORCE
Relate decimals to money concepts				TEACH	TEACH	TEACH	TEACH/REINFORCE	REINFORCE	REINFORCE
Convert decimals, fractions				TEACH	TEACH	TEACH	TEACH/REINFORCE	REINFORCE	REINFORCE
Convert decimals, fractions, and percents						TEACH	TEACH	TEACH/REINFORCE	REINFORCE
Terminating and repeating decimals							TEACH	TEACH	TEACH
Non-repeating decimals									TEACH
Computation with Decimals									
Estimate				TEACH	TEACH	TEACH	TEACH	TEACH/REINFORCE	REINFORCE
Problem solving				TEACH	TEACH	TEACH	TEACH/REINFORCE	REINFORCE	REINFORCE
Add				TEACH	TEACH	TEACH	TEACH/REINFORCE	REINFORCE	REINFORCE
Subtract				TEACH	TEACH	TEACH	TEACH/REINFORCE	REINFORCE	REINFORCE
Multiply						TEACH	TEACH	TEACH/REINFORCE	REINFORCE
Divide									
with whole number divisors						TEACH	TEACH	TEACH/REINFORCE	REINFORCE
with decimal divisors							TEACH	TEACH	TEACH
repeating quotients								TEACH	TEACH
Integers, Rational Numbers, and Real Numbers									
Negative numbers				TEACH	TEACH	TEACH	TEACH	TEACH/REINFORCE	TEACH/REINFORCE
Understand integers							TEACH	TEACH/REINFORCE	TEACH/REINFORCE
Problem solving						TEACH	TEACH	TEACH/REINFORCE	TEACH/REINFORCE

TEACH REINFORCE

Grade 4

Concepts & Computation cont.

Computation with Fractions and Mixed Numbers
Estimate 332, 408, 415
Problem solving 329, 339, 341, 343, 347, 348, 349, 353, 369, 395, 409, 410-411, 413, 415, 417
Add fractions with like denominators 406-407, 408-409, 410-411, 417, 431, 444, 447, 457, 466, 491, 510
Add fractions with unlike denominators 411, 412-413, 415, 417, 431, 510
Subtract fractions with like denominators 406-407, 408-409, 410-411, 417, 431, 457, 467, 491, 510
Subtract fractions with unlike denominators 414-415, 431, 510
Convert decimals and fractions 358-359, 360-361, 363, 368-369, 374, 375, 376, 403, 433, 490, 491, 509
Add mixed numbers with like denominators 409, 410, 411, 417, 444, 447
Add mixed numbers with unlike denominators 491
Subtract mixed numbers with like denominators 409, 417, 444
Subtract mixed numbers with unlike denominators 347, 491
Decimal Concepts
Understand decimals 358-359, 360-361, 374, 375, 409
Models 358-359, 360-361, 364, 375, 418-419
Place value 359, 360-361, 363, 403, 433, 439
Compare and order 362, 364-365, 374, 375, 383, 405, 457, 509
Round decimals 366-367, 375, 383, 403, 424-425, 427, 439, 457, 509
Round with money 36, 37
Relate decimals to money concepts 166-167, 288-289, 492
Convert decimals and fractions 358-359, 360-361, 363, 368-369, 374, 375, 376, 403, 433, 490, 491, 509
Computation with Decimals
Estimate 367, 370, 420, 422, 424-425, 492
Problem solving 359, 361, 363, 369, 371, 375, 421, 423, 425, 427, 431, 444, 451, 457
Add 361, 418-419, 420-421, 422-423, 424-425, 426, 430, 431, 444, 457, 489, 492, 510, 511
Subtract 361, 367, 420-421, 422-423, 424-425, 431, 444, 451, 457, 489, 510, 511
Integers, Rational Numbers, and Real Numbers
Negative numbers 234

Note: Red type indicates that a topic is being introduced for the first time.

Addison-Wesley Mathematics (©1991) fully integrates *motivation, understanding, problem solving, math reasoning, communication, subject integration, strand integration, group work* and *use of manipulatives* with all mathematical topics in the Scope and Sequence chart.

Concepts & Computation cont.	K	1	2	3	4	5	6	7	8
Integers on a number line									
Compare and order									
Properties of integers									
Models									
Integer Operations									
Absolute value									
Solve linear equations									
Graph									
Rational numbers									
compute with rational numbers									
scientific notation									
Scientific notation									
Exponents									
Irrational numbers									

Consumer Math	K	1	2	3	4	5	6	7	8
Problem solving									
Consumer information sources									
Decision making									
Purchasing									
Travel									
Percent applications									
Misleading statistics									
Checking account/savings account/credit cards									
Discounts									

Critical Thinking & Logic	K	1	2	3	4	5	6	7	8
Compare or contrast									
Classify and sort									
Patterns									
Spatial visualization									
Logical reasoning									
Reasoning from graphs									
Explain your reasoning									
Predict and verify									
Evaluate evidence and conclusions									
Make generalizations									

TEACH REINFORCE

Grade 4

Consumer Math

Problem solving 35, 42-43, 44-45, 62-63, 65, 66, 71, 76-77, 80-81, 85, 97, 106-107, 121, 123, 125, 127, 129, 137, 138-139, 146, 147, 148, 149, 151, 157, 160, 161, 162, 166-167, 169, 191, 192-193, 196-197, 198-199, 201, 213, 218-219, 246-247, 256-257, 258-259, 261, 275, 276-277, 285, 288-289, 295, 349, 370-371, 372-373, 375, 393, 411, 425, 429, 437, 444, 449, 451, 457, 489, 492, 512, 514, 517, 520, 521

Consumer information sources 35, 37, 65, 66, 76-77, 80-81, 97, 100-101, 106-107, 136-137, 139, 160-161, 168-169, 191, 192, 196-197, 198-199, 211, 224-225, 246-247, 256-257, 258-259, 277, 285, 370-371, 372-373, 393, 425, 429, 489, 492

Decision making 18-19, 46-47, 82-83, 108-109,138-139, 170-171, 198-199, 230-231, 258-259, 290-291, 320-321, 372-373, 398-399, 428-429, 452-453

Purchasing (unit pricing, better buys) 42-43, 44-45, 82-83, 160, 191, 247, 277, 372-373

Travel (interpret maps, schedules, rates) 40, 48, 91, 97, 204-205, 220, 393, 408, 424, 425

Checking account/savings account 289, 489

Critical Thinking & Logic

Compare or contrast 228, 233, 253, 269, 279, 98, 311, 313, 319, 323. 389, 392-393, 427

Classify and sort 108-109, 300-301, 306-307, 308-309, 311, 335, 369, 409

Patterns 29, 41, 61, 73, 84, 86, 120-121, 122-123, 135, 140, 142, 145, 168-169, 187, 193, 232, 275, 279, 285, 315, 339, 349, 354, 362, 371, 376, 384, 385, 416, 484

Spatial visualization 31, 341, 391

Logical reasoning 12, 17, 20, 25, 37, 48, 53, 84, 89, 98, 110, 123, 135, 140, 145, 160, 172, 177, 187, 188, 200, 205, 232, 237, 243, 251, 254-255, 260, 267, 292, 297, 322, 327, 335, 352, 359, 374, 379, 400, 405, 413, 415, 426, 430, 435, 441, 454, 455

Explain your reasoning 3, 10, 53, 55, 66, 70, 71, 75, 77, 80-81, 93, 99, 115, 129, 140, 154, 194-195, 199, 215, 217, 218-219, 231, 281, 286-287, 300, 303, 332, 343, 344, 357, 370, 379, 392, 394, 396, 399, 405, 411, 452-453

Predict and verify 19, 104-105, 108-109, 110, 112, 230, 265, 290, 350-351, 398

Evaluate evidence and conclusions 3, 46-47, 75, 83, 109, 139, 147, 171, 199, 231, 232, 254-255, 291, 319, 350-351, 372, 441, 453

Make generalizations 25, 254-255, 285, 339, 416, 495

Note: Red type indicates that a topic is being introduced for the first time.

Addison-Wesley Mathematics (©1991) fully integrates *motivation, understanding, problem solving, math reasoning, communication, subject integration, strand integration, group work* and *use of manipulatives* with all mathematical topics in the Scope and Sequence chart.

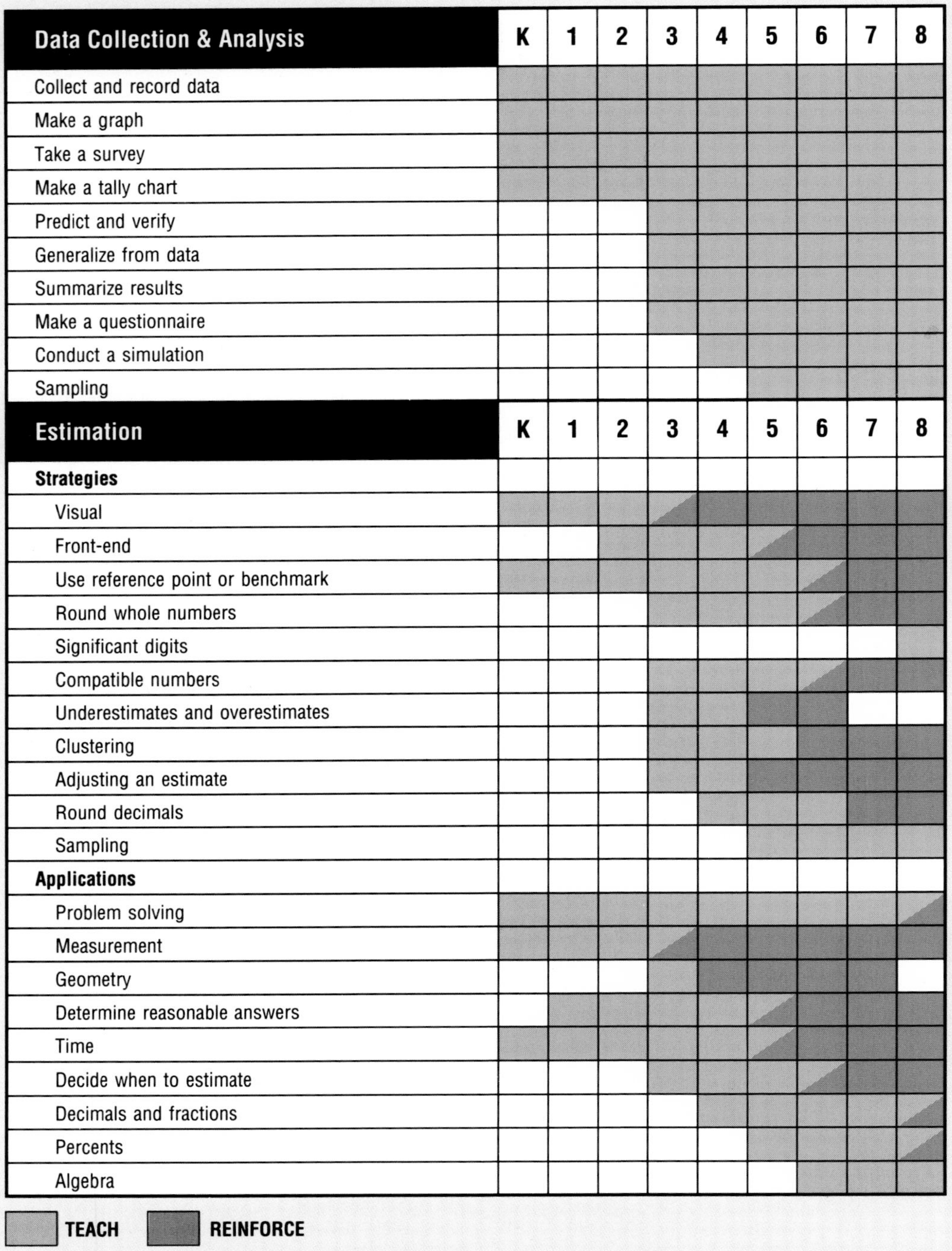

Data Collection & Analysis	K	1	2	3	4	5	6	7	8
Collect and record data									
Make a graph									
Take a survey									
Make a tally chart									
Predict and verify									
Generalize from data									
Summarize results									
Make a questionnaire									
Conduct a simulation									
Sampling									

Estimation	K	1	2	3	4	5	6	7	8
Strategies									
Visual									
Front-end									
Use reference point or benchmark									
Round whole numbers									
Significant digits									
Compatible numbers									
Underestimates and overestimates									
Clustering									
Adjusting an estimate									
Round decimals									
Sampling									
Applications									
Problem solving									
Measurement									
Geometry									
Determine reasonable answers									
Time									
Decide when to estimate									
Decimals and fractions									
Percents									
Algebra									

TEACH **REINFORCE**

Grade 4

Data Collection & Analysis

Collect and record data 15, 37, 46-47, 57, 108-109, 125, 170-171, 200, 230-231, 232, 267, 290-291, 350-351, 398-399, 423, 452-453
Make a graph 92-93, 94-95, 96-97, 99, 109, 110, 231, 269, 397, 399
Take a survey 46-47, 108-109, 170-171, 291, 398-399
Make a tally chart 47, 112, 171, 351, 452-453
Predict and verify 19, 104-105, 108-109, 230-231, 290, 350-351, 398-399
Generalize from data 47, 171, 199, 230-231, 290-291, 351, 399, 453
Summarize results 47, 109, 171, 351, 399, 453
Make a questionnaire 46-47, 170-171, 290-291, 389-399, 452-453
Conduct a simulation 498

Estimation

Strategies
Visual estimation 31, 44-45, 207, 214-215, 226-227, 275, 329, 332, 377, 381
Front-end 66, 84, 85, 143, 183, 424-425, 437, 438, 440-441, 501
Use reference point or benchmark 44-45, 61, 148-149, 161, 181, 223, 381, 394, 396, 424-425
Round whole numbers 84, 87, 95, 148-149, 161, 180-181, 183, 187, 189, 200, 227, 235, 263, 270-271, 275, 279, 281, 293, 295, 377, 439, 440-441, 500, 501, 505, 507
Compatible numbers 270-271, 281, 293, 325, 437, 438
Underestimates and overestimates 66, 180-181, 189, 201, 270-271, 281, 293, 325, 424-425, 442-443
Clustering 146, 183
Unitizing 275, 382-383, 387, 401
Adjusting an estimate 66, 143, 180-181, 189, 424-425, 442-443, 455, 511
Round decimals 366-367, 375, 424-425, 439, 457, 509, 511
Round with money 56, 113, 149, 161, 167, 173, 193, 389, 457, 509, 511, 227, 433, 500
Applications
Problem solving 10, 67, 80-81, 85, 107, 137, 159, 189, 191, 197, 218-219, 246-247, 261, 271, 279, 386, 425, 427, 441, 443,
Measurement 48, 57, 214-215, 217, 220, 221, 223, 226-227, 228, 233, 279, 381, 382-383, 386, 396, 400, 424-425, 457, 493, 494
Geometry 307, 402
Determine reasonable answers 81, 189, 246-247, 370, 433, 438, 439, 449, 455
Time 207, 211
Decide when to estimate 80-81, 175, 218-219, 386, 401
Decimals 367, 370, 420, 422, 424-425, 492
Fractions 332, 408, 415
See also CONCEPTS AND COMPUTATION, Add Whole Numbers, Estimate sums; Subtract Whole Numbers, Estimate differences; Multiply Whole Numbers, Estimate products; Divide Whole Numbers, Estimate quotients; Computation with Fractions and Mixed Numbers, Estimate fractions; and Computation with Decimals, Estimate

Note: Red type indicates that a topic is being introduced for the first time.

Addison-Wesley Mathematics (©1991) fully integrates *motivation, understanding, problem solving, math reasoning, communication, subject integration, strand integration, group work* and *use of manipulatives* with all mathematical topics in the Scope and Sequence chart.

Geometry	K	1	2	3	4	5	6	7	8
Explore geometry									
Concrete models									
Identify plane figures									
Identify space figures									
Relate plane figures to space figures									
Patterns									
Symmetry									
Congruent figures									
Sides and corners									
Inside, outside, and on									
Points, lines, and segments									
Classify angles									
Classify polygons									
Classify polyhedrons									
Measure/estimate angles									
Coordinate geometry									
Similar figures									
Formulas									
perimeter									
circumference									
area									
volume									
surface area									
Pythagorean relationship									
translations (slides)									
rotations (turns)									
reflections (flips)									
Circles, radius and diameter									
Circles, circumference and area									
Constructions									
Build/draw geometric solids									
Central angles									
Tangent, sine, and cosine ratios									
Topology									
Applications									

TEACH **REINFORCE**

Grade 4

Geometry

Explore geometry 298, 299, 300, 301, 307, 313, 318, 389, 391
Concrete models 298, 300, 301, 302, 303, 304, 305, 306, 308, 310, 311, 314, 316, 317, 322, 324
Identify plane figures 298-299, 313, 331, 347, 367, 520
Identify space figures (geometric solids) 298-299, 313, 323, 355, 367, 403, 521
Relate place figures to solid figures 298-299, 313, 367
Patterns 317, 416
Symmetry 304-305, 323, 347, 355
Congruent figures 310-311, 322, 323, 377
Points, lines, and segments 302-303, 313, 355, 521
Classify angles 300-301, 306-307, 313, 369, 403, 522
Classify polygons 300-301, 302, 306-307, 308-309, 311, 313, 317, 323, 331, 347, 355, 403, 521, 522
Measurement 222, 307, 317, 323, 388-389, 390-391, 401
Coordinate geometry 313-315, 322, 323, 342, 377
Similar figures 316-317, 322, 377, 523
Motion geometry (slides, turns, flips) 308-309, 310-311, 324
Circles 312, 323, 523
Build geometric solids 303
Draw geometric solids and cross-sections 299
Applications 299, 301, 302, 303, 305, 307, 309, 311, 313, 315, 317, 323

Note: Red type indicates that a topic is being introduced for the first time.

Addison-Wesley Mathematics (©1991) fully integrates *motivation, understanding, problem solving, math reasoning, communication, subject integration, strand integration, group work* and *use of manipulatives* with all mathematical topics in the Scope and Sequence chart.

Graphs & Graphing	K	1	2	3	4	5	6	7	8
Pictographs									
Bar graphs									
Line graphs									
Circle graphs									
Double bar graphs									
Multiple line graphs									
Divided bar graphs									
Scattergrams									
Reasoning from a graph									
Stem and leaf plots									
Box and whisker graphs									
Frequency tables and histograms									
Graphing ordered pairs									
Graphing linear equations									
Graphing inequalities									
Measurement	**K**	**1**	**2**	**3**	**4**	**5**	**6**	**7**	**8**
Explore using concrete objects									
Problem solving									
Precision in measurement									
Estimation									
Non-standard units									
Length									
customary units									
metric units									
Perimeter									
Area									
Area/perimeter relationships									
Surface area									
Weight (mass)									
Volume									
Capacity									
Circumference									
Convert units									
Temperature									
Indirect measurement									
use scale drawings									
use geometric relationships									

TEACH **REINFORCE**

Grade 4

Graphs & Graphing

Pictographs
- interpret 90-91, 94-95, 99, 101
- make 94-95, 99

Bar graphs
- interpret 3, 7, 90-91, 92-93, 100-101, 111, 231, 269, 291, 319, 351, 378, 385, 399, 438, 453,
- make 92-93, 109, 231, 291, 351, 397, 399, 453

Line graphs
- interpret 96-97, 99, 111, 175, 379, 381
- make 96-97, 99

Circle graphs
- interpret 349

Reasoning from a graph 3, 91, 92-93, 94, 99, 109, 231, 453

Algebra and graphing
- graphing ordered pairs 314-315, 322, 342

Measurement

Explore using concrete objects 214-215, 216-217, 223, 226, 228, 231, 232, 279, 380-381, 382-383, 390, 394-395, 396, 493

Problem solving 73, 155, 215, 217, 218-219, 224-225, 227, 233, 286, 287, 293, 301, 307, 309, 319, 348, 349, 381, 385, 386, 387, 389, 391, 393, 395, 401, 410-411, 421, 423, 425, 427, 431, 444

Estimation 57, 214-215, 217, 218-219, 220-221, 223, 226-227, 228, 233, 279, 381, 382-383, 386, 387, 396, 401, 402, 424-425, 457, 493, 494

Nonstandard units 214-215, 221, 222, 226, 233, 295, 394

Length
- customary 155, 216-217, 220, 221, 222, 223, 224-225, 230-231, 233, 295, 301, 307, 318, 319, 325, 348-349, 364-365, 408-409, 417, 423
- metric 378-379, 380-381, 382-383, 384-385, 386, 387, 393, 401, 433, 457, 518, 519, 526, 424-425, 427

Perimeter 222, 223, 233, 263, 301, 307, 313, 318, 323, 387, 389, 519

Area 388-389, 401, 402

Volume 390-391, 401

Weight
- customary 57, 191, 228, 269, 279, 309, 325, 520
- metric/mass 155, 396, 401, 421, 423, 427, 526

Capacity
- customary 226-227, 253, 309, 410-411, 494, 519
- metric 394-395, 400, 401, 423, 433, 457, 526

Convert units
- customary 215, 216-217, 221, 226-227, 228, 233, 253, 263, 269, 295, 325, 423
- metric 380-381, 384-385, 387, 389, 394-395, 423

Area/perimeter relationships 389, 401

Temperature
- Fahrenheit 229, 234, 520
- Celsius 397, 433, 526

Indirect measurement (scale drawings) 93, 220, 316-317, 318, 320-321

Geometric relationships 222, 233

Note: Red type indicates that a topic is being introduced for the first time.

Addison-Wesley Mathematics (©1991) fully integrates *motivation, understanding, problem solving, math reasoning, communication, subject integration, strand integration, group work* and *use of manipulatives* with all mathematical topics in the Scope and Sequence chart.

Time & Money	K	1	2	3	4	5	6	7	8
Time									
Calendar									
Tell and show time									
to the hour									
to the half hour									
to the quarter hour									
to 5-minute intervals									
to 1-minute intervals									
Estimate time									
Problem solving									
Elapsed time									
a.m. or p.m.									
Time zones									
Money									
Count and show amounts of money									
Problem solving									
Add									
Subtract									
Multiply									
Divide									
Estimate									
Relate to decimals									

Mental Math	K	1	2	3	4	5	6	7	8
Count on or back									
Skip counting									
Basic fact patterns and strategies									
special sums and differences									
doubles									
special products									
special quotients									
Use properties									
Break apart									
Compatible numbers									
Compensation									
Multiply/divide decimals by 10, 100, 1,000									
Find a fraction of a number									
Find a percent of a number									
Algebraic expressions, equations									
Measurement									

TEACH REINFORCE

Grade 4

Time & Money

Time
Calendar 209, 221, 233, 263, 518
Tell and show time to quarter hour 206-207, 221, 241, 253
Tell and show time to 5-minute intervals 206-207, 221, 241, 517
Tell and show time to 1-minute intervals 206-207, 221, 233, 241, 517
Estimate 207, 211
Problem solving 76, 213, 319, 451
Elapsed time 210-211, 221, 233, 263, 451
a.m. and p.m. 208, 221, 233, 295, 517
Time zones 204-205, 207, 211
Money
Problem solving 43, 45, 49, 65, 76-77, 80-81, 106, 123, 138-139, 167, 169, 191, 196-197, 213, 246-247, 256-257, 277, 285, 289, 349, 370-371, 393, 411, 444, 449, 451
Count change 42-43, 49, 65
Add 56, 57, 60, 61, 62, 63, 65, 67, 71, 76, 80, 81, 85, 106, 119, 139, 169, 196, 197, 199, 256-257, 277, 295, 370-371, 411, 431, 451, 489, 492
Subtract 65, 70, 71, 73, 76, 77, 106, 139, 196, 197, 201, 277, 371, 411, 425, 431, 451, 489
Multiply 139, 144, 151, 160, 161, 166-167, 169, 173, 191, 192-193, 196, 197, 201, 213, 246, 256-257, 263, 289, 295, 349, 371, 375, 393, 406, 411, 433, 451
Divide 277, 285, 288-289, 331, 371, 411, 444, 449, 455, 457, 508
Estimate 44-45, 51, 66, 80-81, 161, 246-247, 425, 492
Relate to decimals 288-289, 492

Mental Math

Count on, back 43, 150, 165, 365
Skip counting 43, 120
Basic fact patterns and strategies
special sums 54-55, 67, 95
special differences 54-55, 67, 95
doubles 14, 15, 16, 17, 120-121, 124-125, 131, 193
special products 146-147, 157, 161, 178-179, 180, 183, 185, 188, 189, 193, 201, 263, 395
special quotients 268-269, 270-271, 275, 436-437, 439, 441, 445, 447, 455
Use properties 162, 173
Break apart 14-15, 21, 23, 45, 103, 105, 130-131, 141, 165, 283, 285, 293, 421, 500, 503
Compatible numbers 54-55, 87, 103, 133, 165, 413
Compensation 16-17, 21, 45, 51, 74-75, 84, 113, 143, 165, 423, 500, 502
Find a fraction of a number 344-345, 353, 377, 403, 433, 497
Algebraic expressions, equations 36, 147, 151, 129
Measurement 215, 381

Note: Red type indicates that a topic is being introduced for the first time.

Scope and Sequence

Addison-Wesley Mathematics (©1991) fully integrates *motivation, understanding, problem solving, math reasoning, communication, subject integration, strand integration, group work* and *use of manipulatives* with all mathematical topics in the Scope and Sequence chart.

Patterns, Relations & Functions	K	1	2	3	4	5	6	7	8
Number patterns									
Spatial/positional/geometric patterns									
Color patterns									
Exponents									
Problem solving strategies									
find a pattern									
make a table									
Functions									
Make a generalization									
Ordered pairs									
Graph functions									
Geometric progressions									
Pascal's triangle									
Harmonic triangle									
Fibonacci sequence									
Napier's Bones									
Problem Solving	**K**	**1**	**2**	**3**	**4**	**5**	**6**	**7**	**8**
Strategy and Skill Lessons									
Act it out									
Use objects									
Choose the operation									
Draw a picture									
Make an (organized) list									
Guess and check									
Make a table									
Look for a pattern									
Use logical reasoning									
Solve a simpler problem									
Work backwards									
Write/use equations									
Understand the operations									
Tell or write a story									
Determine reasonable answers									
Estimate the answer									
Decide when to estimate									
Find related problems									
Interpret remainders									
Multiple-step problems									

TEACH REINFORCE

Grade 4

Patterns, Relations & Functions

Number patterns 29, 41, 55, 61, 73, 84, 86, 120-121, 122-123, 135, 140, 142, 145, 168-169, 187, 193, 232, 275, 279, 285, 294, 339, 349, 354, 362, 371, 376, 384, 385, 416, 484
Geometric patterns 317, 382, 416, 432
Problem solving strategy
look for a pattern 168-169, 349
make a table 46-47, 108-109, 125, 134-135, 136-137, 168-169, 185, 262, 285 342, 383, 384, 385, 416
Functions 134-135, 140, 254-255, 285, 315, 339, 495
Make a generalization 254-255, 285, 339, 416, 495
Ordered pairs 314-315, 322, 342, 377
Graph functions 314-315, 322, 342
Geometric progressions 404-405, 416
See also CRITICAL THINKING AND LOGIC

Problem Solving

Strategy and Skill Lessons
Choose an operation 10-11
Draw a picture 34-35
Make an organized list 64-65
Guess and check 106-107
Make a table 136-137
Look for a pattern 168-169
Use logical reasoning 190-191
Work backward 256-257
Understanding the question 128-129
Determining reasonable answers 370-371
Estimate the answer 246-247
Extra data 100-101
Finding related problems 392-393
Interpreting remainders 276-277
Measuring to a fractional part of an inch 348-349
Multiple-step problems 76-77, 196-197

Note: Red type indicates that a topic is being introduced for the first time.

Addison-Wesley Mathematics (©1991) fully integrates *motivation, understanding, problem solving, math reasoning, communication, subject integration, strand integration, group work* and *use of manipulatives* with all mathematical topics in the Scope and Sequence chart.

Problem Solving cont.	K	1	2	3	4	5	6	7	8
Problems with more than one answer									
Problems with two or more questions									
Problems without solutions									
Use/write a number sentence									
Use a calculator									
Use data sources									
from a story									
from a chart or table									
from a graph									
from other data sources									
Choose/use strategies									
Computational Methods									
choose a calculation method									
use objects									
mental math									
calculators									
computers									
Estimation									
decide when to estimate									
determine reasonable answers									
use estimation									
Six-Point Checklist									
Introduction to the checklist									
1. **UNDERSTAND THE SITUATION**									
understand the question									
understand the operation									
finish/write a problem									

TEACH **REINFORCE**

Grade 4

Problem Solving cont.

Problems with more than one answer 212-213
Using a calculator 163, 450-451
Data from a chart, 224-225
Data from a diagram, 318-319
Data from a recipe 410-411
Choose/use strategies 11, 35, 65, 77, 81, 101, 107, 129, 137, 169, 191, 195, 197, 213, 219, 225, 247, 257, 277, 287, 319, 333, 349, 371, 393, 411, 427, 444

Computational Methods

Choose a calculation method 194-195, 286-287
Use objects 197
Mental math 15, 17, 55, 75, 131, 147, 151, 179, 211
Calculators 163, 450-451, 484-491
Computers 492-499

Estimation

Decide when to estimate 80-81, 218-219, 386, 439
Determine reasonable answers 81, 341, 370-371, 439
Use estimation 10, 67, 85, 107, 137, 159, 189, 191, 197, 246-247, 261, 271, 279, 425, 427, 441, 443

Six-Point Checklist

Introduction to the checklist 10-11

UNDERSTAND THE SITUATION

Understand the question 105, 121, 128-128, 243, 247
Understand the operations 4-5, 101, 117, 147, 238-239
Write your own problem 5, 11, 26, 55, 117, 126, 239, 269, 287, 425

Note: Red type indicates that a topic is being introduced for the first time.

Addison-Wesley Mathematics (©1991) fully integrates *motivation, understanding, problem solving, math reasoning, communication, subject integration, strand integration, group work* and *use of manipulatives* with all mathematical topics in the Scope and Sequence chart.

Problem Solving cont.	K	1	2	3	4	5	6	7	8
2. **FIND DATA NEEDED/ANALYZE DATA**									
missing data		T	T	T/R	R	R	R	R	R
extra data		T	T	T/R	R	R	R	R	R
use data	T	T	T	T/R	R	R	R	R	R
3. **PLAN WHAT TO DO**									
understand the operations		T	T	T	T	R	R	R	R
develop a plan				T	T	T	T/R	R	R
decide when to estimate				T	T	T	T/R	R	R
choose a calculation method		T	T	T/R	R	R	R	R	R
find related problems				T	T	T	T/R	R	R
4. **ESTIMATE THE ANSWER**									
estimate the answer	T	T	T	T/R	T/R	R	R	R	R
determine reasonable answers		T	T	T	T	T/R	R	R	R

TEACH (T) **REINFORCE** (R)

Grade 4

Problem Solving cont.

FIND DATA NEEDED

Missing data 123, 283, 345, 391, 413

Extra data 100-101, 147, 227, 371, 415, 444, 451

Use data

from a chart 11, 35, 63, 65, 77, 80, 107, 129, 136-137, 165, 191, 196-197, 213, 224-225, 247, 277, 365, 427, 451

from a diagram 65, 249, 305, 318, 371

from a recipe 410-411

from a map 204-205, 207, 211, 393

from a graph 99, 100, 101, 269, 319, 349

from a data bank 2-3, 7, 24-25, 29, 39, 52-53, 71, 79, 88-89, 91, 97, 114-115, 119, 133, 144-145, 155, 159, 176-177, 183, 204-205, 207, 211, 236-237, 245, 251, 264-265, 271, 279, 296, 311, 317, 326-327, 331, 337, 356-357, 361, 367, 378-379, 381, 385, 404-405, 409, 421, 434-435, 441, 447

from a data hunt 15, 37, 57, 125, 267, 423

PLAN WHAT TO DO

Develop a plan 217, 275, 339

Decide when to estimate 80-81, 218-219, 386

Choose a calculation method 194-195, 286-287

Find related problems 392-393

Measure to a fractional part of an inch 348-349

Multiple-step problems 76-77, 196-197

See also PROBLEM SOLVING: Strategy and Skill Lessons

ESTIMATE THE ANSWER

Estimate the answer 246-247

Determine reasonable answers 370-371

Note: Red type indicates that a topic is being introduced for the first time.

Addison-Wesley Mathematics (©1991) fully integrates *motivation, understanding, problem solving, math reasoning, communication, subject integration, strand integration, group work* and *use of manipulatives* with all mathematical topics in the Scope and Sequence chart.

Problem Solving cont.	K	1	2	3	4	5	6	7	8
5. **SOLVE THE PROBLEM**									
solve/use number sentences/equations									
use a calculator									
use formulas									
more than one answer									
problems without solutions									
interpret remainders									
6. **CHECK/EXAMINE THE ANSWER**									
determine reasonable answers									
think/talk/write about the solution									
Applications									
applied problem solving lessons									
data collection and analysis lessons									

Ratio, Proportion, & Percent	K	1	2	3	4	5	6	7	8
Understand concept or ratio									
Equal ratios									
Tangent ratio									
Problem solving									
Estimate ratio									
Cross products									
Similar figures									
Understand concept of proportion									
Solve proportions									
Unit price									
Understand concept of percent									
Interest									
Discounts and sales prices									
Commission									
Circle graphs									
Estimate percent									
Convert fractions, decimals, percents									
Find a percent of a number									
Calculator, using percent key									
Find what percent one number is of another									
Find a number when a percent is known									
Percent of increase or decrease									

TEACH REINFORCE

Grade 4

Problem Solving cont.

SOLVE THE PROBLEM
Write/use number sentences/equations 11, 55, 269, 287, 339
Use a calculator 163, 225, 248, 251, 450-451
More than one answer 43, 212-213
Interpret remainders 276-277
CHECK THE ANSWER
Determine reasonable answers 81, 341, 370-371, 439
Think/talk about your solution 77, 129, 319, 411
Applications
Use data sources *See* PROBLEM SOLVING, Six-Point Checklist: Find Data Needed
Applied problem solving lessons 82-83, 138-139, 198-199, 258-259, 320-321, 372-373, 428-429
Data collection and analysis lessons 46-47, 108-109, 170-171, 230-231, 290-291, 350-351, 398-399, 452-453
See also DATA COLLECTION AND ANALYSIS
Consumer math and life skills *See* CONSUMER MATH

Note: Red type indicates that a topic is being introduced for the first time.

Addison-Wesley Mathematics (©1991) fully integrates *motivation, understanding, problem solving, math reasoning, communication, subject integration, strand integration, group work* and *use of manipulatives* with all mathematical topics in the Scope and Sequence chart.

Statistics & Probability	K	1	2	3	4	5	6	7	8
Collect and organize data									
Present data graphically									
Tally charts									
Graphs									
Charts and tables									
Misleading statistics/biased representation									
Mean, median, mode, range									
Statistical sampling									
Scattergrams									
Stem and leaf plots									
Box and whisper graphs									
Frequency tables and histograms									
Understand probability									
Equally likely outcomes									
Probability and prediction									
Fair and unfair games									
Mathematical and experimental probabilities									
Compound events and tree diagrams									
Permutations and combinations									
Simulations									
Cooperative Group Learning Skills	**K**	**1**	**2**	**3**	**4**	**5**	**6**	**7**	**8**
Listen to others									
Encourage and respect others									
Explain and summarize									
Disagree in an agreeable way									
Check for understanding									

TEACH REINFORCE

Grade 4

Statistics & Probability

Collect and organize data 15, 37, 46-47, 57, 108-109, 125, 170-171, 230-231, 267, 290-291, 350-351, 398-399, 423, 452-453

Present data graphically 47, 92, 93, 94-95, 96-97, 99, 109, 171, 231, 291, 342, 351, 399, 452-453, 499

Make or interpret tally charts 47, 112, 171, 203, 351, 453

Make or interpret graphs 3, 7, 90-91, 92-93, 94-95, 96-97, 98, 99, 100-101, 109, 231, 232, 269, 291, 319, 351, 378-379, 385, 397, 399, 438, 453, 499

Make or interpret charts and tables 11, 22, 24-25, 26, 28, 30, 40, 47, 52-53, 60, 63, 65, 70, 71, 72, 74, 77, 78, 80, 88-89, 94, 95, 96, 97, 99, 106, 107, 114-115, 129, 134-135, 136-137, 139, 140, 142, 144-145, 167, 171, 172, 176-177, 191, 194, 197, 207, 211, 212, 213, 214, 224-225, 231, 233, 242, 244, 247, 250, 252, 255, 259, 264, 265, 272, 277, 285, 326-327,351, 356-357, 364, 365, 366, 372, 383, 384, 385, 398-399, 404-405, 406, 416, 418, 426, 429, 434-435, 499

Understand probability 92-93, 102-103, 104-105, 498

Equally likely outcomes 92-93, 102-103, 498

Probability and prediction 104-105, 108, 109, 110, 111, 112, 498

Fair and unfair games 102-103, 110, 498

Simulations 498

See also DATA COLLECTION AND ANALYSIS; GRAPHS AND GRAPHING

Note: Red type indicates that a topic is being introduced for the first time.

Addison-Wesley Mathematics

Teacher's Edition

Grade 4

Addison-Wesley Publishing Company

Menlo Park, California ▪ Reading, Massachusetts ▪ New York
Don Mills, Ontario ▪ Wokingham, England ▪ Amsterdam ▪ Bonn
Sydney ▪ Singapore ▪ Tokyo ▪ Madrid ▪ San Juan

ISBN 0-201-27401-9

ABCDEFGHIJKL-VH- 943210

Dear Student:

Welcome to an exciting world of mathematics. We have many activities for you to enjoy—activities that will increase your skill with numbers.

You are going to take the ideas you have already learned and apply them in interesting, new ways. You will do problem solving activities by drawing pictures. You will learn to estimate with money, a very useful skill. You will discover interesting things about circles, triangles and squares. You will explore numbers from fractions to millions.

You are going to become a whiz at multiplication this year! You will start on division. You will also work in groups to share your learning experience with others. That will make mathematics fun for everyone.

This is a very important year for you. We know you will enjoy all these new ways to use math.

From your friends at Addison-Wesley.

1

Chapter Management

OVERVIEW

Lesson	Pages	Objectives	Subject Integration	Strand Integration
Chapter Opener	2-3	To introduce chapter 1	science-animals	graphing
Problem Solving: Understanding Addition and Subtraction	4-5	1-1 To understand the operations of addition and subtraction	science-squirrels	algebra
Addition Properties	6-7	1-2 To understand and use basic properties for addition	science-toads	mathematical reasoning
Using Addition to Subtract	8-9	1-3 To use addition to find basic subtraction facts	science-snail shells	calculators
Problem Solving: Introduction	10-11	1-4 To use the 6-point problem solving checklist to solve problems	science-animals	computation
Using Critical Thinking Midchapter Review/Quiz	12-13	1-5 To use critical thinking to solve number riddles	language arts-riddles	problem solving
Mental Math: Breaking Apart Numbers	14-15	1-6 To use the mental math technique of break apart to find sums	science-animal stamps	mathematical reasoning
Mental Math: Using Compensation	16-17	1-7 To use the mental math technique of compensation to find sums	fine arts-video camera	logic
Group Decision Making	18-19	1-8 To practice group skills in problem solving	art-patterns	geometry

MATHEMATICAL BACKGROUND

Addition
In Lesson 1-2, students review three addition properties: Grouping Property, Order Property, and Zero Property.

Subtraction
Lesson 1-3 teaches students to look for the missing addend when subtracting.

Mental Math
Students are introduced to three mental math addition strategies: making 10 plus a number, making a double plus 1, and using compensation.

Problem Solving
Students are introduced to the problem solving checklist in Lesson 1-4.

TIPS FROM TEACHERS

As part of the morning activity, have fun ''exploding the day.'' Put up a blank sheet of butcher paper, with the day's date (without the year) written along the top. Have students make up addition and subtraction problems that use the date as the answer. Record students' suggestions on the paper.

Linda Cantrell
Lake Forest Park School
Seattle, WA

September 18

9 + 9 = 18
10 + 8 = 18
20 − 2 = 18

ASSESSMENT

Pretest — Chapter 1, page 1

Multiple-Choice Format

Name ______

1. There are 5 girls and 3 boys in the Reading Club. How many more girls than boys are there? Choose the equation that records the action.
   Think: ● ● ● ● ● ○ ○ ○
   a. 5 − 3 = 8 b. 5 + 3 = 8 c. 5 − 3 = 2 d. 5 + 3 = 2 — 1. c
2. Find (4 + 2) + 6.
   a. 12 b. 14 c. 24 d. 1 — 2. a
3. Add. 7 + 0
   a. 70 b. 0 c. 7 d. 700 — 3. c
4. Find 9 − 5. Think about finding the missing addend.
   a. 14 b. 4 c. 3 d. 45 — 4. b
5. Find 12 − 3. Think about finding the missing addend.
   a. 15 b. 4 c. 8 d. 9 — 5. d
6. Find 8 − 5. Think about finding the missing addend.
   a. 13 b. 3 c. 12 d. 2 — 6. b
7. Alan had 12 boxes to deliver. He delivered 6. How many boxes does he still have to deliver?
   a. 18 boxes b. 2 boxes c. 6 boxes d. 72 boxes — 7. c

MCT 4 1

Pretest — Chapter 1, page 2

Multiple-Choice Format

Name ______

8. Marsha received 9 birthday gifts at school. Her parents gave her 3 more. How many gifts did she receive?
   a. 12 gifts b. 6 gifts c. 3 gifts d. 27 gifts — 8. a
9. Solve this number riddle. "I'm a double. I'm between 6 and 12. You don't say me when you count by fours. What number am I?"
   a. 8 b. 10 c. 12 d. 6 — 9. b
10. Solve this number riddle. "I'm a 2-digit number. I am odd. I could not be any greater. What number am I?"
   a. 98 b. 18 c. 11 d. 99 — 10. d
11. Use mental math to find 6 + 7. If you need help, break apart an addend.
   a. 11 b. 12 c. 13 d. 14 — 11. c
12. Use mental math to find 15 + 3. If you need help, break apart an addend.
   a. 8 b. 9 c. 13 d. 18 — 12. d
13. Compensate and use mental math to find 9 + 7. (9 down 1, + 7 up 1)
   a. 15 b. 13 c. 16 d. 17 — 13. c
14. Compensate and use mental math to find 6 + 8. (6 up 1, + 8 down 1)
   a. 2 b. 14 c. 15 d. 16 — 14. b

2 MCT 4

Posttest — Chapter 1, page 1

Multiple-Choice Format

Name ______

1. There are 5 boys and 2 girls in the Spanish Club. How many more boys than girls are there? Choose the equation that records the action.
   Think: ● ● ● ● ● ○ ○
   a. 5 − 2 = 7 b. 5 + 2 = 7 c. 5 − 2 = 3 d. 5 + 2 = 3 — 1. c
2. Find 3 + (2 + 5).
   a. 12 b. 13 c. 10 d. 11 — 2. c
3. Add. 9 + 0
   a. 0 b. 9 c. 90 d. 900 — 3. b
4. Find 10 − 8. Think about finding the missing addend.
   a. 80 b. 2 c. 18 d. 9 — 4. b
5. Find 7 − 3. Think about finding the missing addend.
   a. 10 b. 4 c. 21 d. 5 — 5. b
6. Find 13 − 7. Think about finding the missing addend.
   a. 8 b. 10 c. 9 d. 6 — 6. d
7. Joan had 9 marbles. She gave away 3 of them. How many marbles did she have then?
   a. 27 marbles b. 12 marbles c. 6 marbles d. 3 marbles — 7. c

MCT 4 3

Posttest — Chapter 1, page 2

Multiple-Choice Format

Name ______

8. Lupe bought 6 cans of cat food and 9 cans of dog food. How many cans of pet food did she buy?
   a. 15 cans b. 54 cans c. 3 cans d. 27 cans — 8. a
9. Solve this number riddle. "I'm even. I'm between 10 and 18. You don't say me when you count by fours. What number am I?"
   a. 12 b. 14 c. 16 d. 18 — 9. b
10. Solve this number riddle. "I'm a 2-digit number. I am odd. I could not be any less. What number am I?"
   a. 9 b. 10 c. 11 d. 99 — 10. c
11. Use mental math to find 8 + 7. If you need help, break apart an addend.
   a. 13 b. 14 c. 15 d. 16 — 11. c
12. Use mental math to find 11 + 3. If you need help, break apart an addend.
   a. 8 b. 13 c. 14 d. 15 — 12. c
13. Compensate and use mental math to find 7 + 3. (7 down 2, + 3 up 2)
   a. 10 b. 8 c. 12 d. 11 — 13. a
14. Compensate and use mental math to find 3 + 5. (3 up 1, + 5 down 1)
   a. 8 b. 6 c. 7 d. 2 — 14. a

4 MCT 4

ITEM ANALYSIS

Items	Objectives
1	1-1
2, 3	1-2
4-6	1-3
7, 8	1-4
9-10	1-5
11, 12	1-6
13, 14	1-7

Note: The item analysis is the same for all pretests and posttests for this chapter.

ALSO AVAILABLE

- Free Response Tests
- Alternative Tests
- Thinking Strategies
- Concrete Materials

Optional Chapter Activities

PROJECT AND BULLETIN BOARD

Use a title such as ''Addition and Subtraction— How We Use Them.'' Exhibit student pictures showing math in everyday life. Pictures may be drawn or cut from old magazines. They should show people using addition, subtraction, or both in real life.

Have students mount their pictures on construction paper and write captions or add speech balloons. Each student should be prepared to tell the story that his or her picture illustrates and explain the math that is needed. Some students may want to role play the situations.

Change the display during the chapter until all students have displayed their work. After all pictures have been displayed, students may want to categorize the pictures by situation or by the process(es) required. Any categorization that students can justify should be accepted.

ADDITION AND SUBTRACTION - HOW WE USE THEM
That will be $17 please.
Here's $20, so my change should be $3.
Well, folks, we had 6 inches of snow today, and we are predicting another 6 tomorrow and 5 on Friday, so get out your sleds, kids. There will be 17 big inches of snow.

COOPERATIVE LEARNING

Divide the class into groups of three or four. Identify the group skill: listen to others. Have each group make up a number series for another group to identify. For example, the first group might make up the series 5, 15, 13, 23, 21. The spokesperson for the first group recites the series orally for the second group to identify. The students in the second group are not allowed to write the series down. They are to listen to what is being said. They may request to have the series repeated. However, an extra point is awarded to the group that finds the series pattern the first time it is recited.

Allow time for the second group to discuss the series and to determine the pattern. To identify the series, a volunteer from the second group would have to say the two numbers that would come next in the series and to state the pattern of addition and/or subtraction that was used to construct the series.

Award one point for finding the next two numbers in the series and another point for finding the pattern. Then have the groups switch roles. One group recites the series, the other group listens.

You will find grouping suggestions and cooperative learning activities in most lessons throughout this chapter.

LITERATURE

Fritz, Jean. *What's the Big Idea, Ben Franklin?* New York: Coward McCann, 1976.

Children will enjoy this brief but entertaining biography of the Eighteenth Century inventor, writer, and statesman. Benjamin was intrigued by mathematics. In spite of this, he failed math in his last year of school. One of his hobbies was constructing magic (number) squares.
Children can use the example from the story and create their own magic squares that add up to different sums.

Leighton, Ralph and Carl Feynman. *How to Count Sheep Without Falling Asleep.* Englewood Cliffs, NJ: Prentice-Hall, 1976.

Sandburg, Carl. "Arithmetic". from: *Reflections on a Gift of Watermelon Pickle . . . and Other Modern Verse.* Compiled by Dunning, Leuders, & Smith. New York: Lothrop, Lee & Shepard, 1967.

Whitney, David C. *Let's Find Out About Addition.* New York: Franklin Watts, 1966.

English as a Second Language

ESL students often misinterpret fact families because they do not understand the relationship between the three numbers in each fact family. They will often introduce extra numbers into the family. For example, they might write:
$4 + 5 = 9$ $5 + 9 = 14$ $14 - 9 = 5$ $14 - 5 = 9$
It is helpful to point out that there are only three different numbers in a fact family, unless two addends are equal. Have students come to the chalkboard to point to each addend and to each sum. Indicate that the sum in the addition problem is used as the number from which to subtract in the subtraction problem.

Pair students. One student chooses two numbers for which the other writes one fact family. Then the first student uses the same two numbers to write a second fact family. For example, if the first student suggests the numbers nine and one, the two fact families are:
$9 + 1 = 10$ $10 - 1 = 9$ $8 + 1 = 9$ $9 - 8 = 1$
$1 + 9 = 10$ $10 - 9 = 1$ $1 + 8 = 9$ $9 - 1 = 8$

Gifted

Use real-world or imaginary situations to provide applications of the skills for this chapter for your mathematically talented students. The following situation may be enjoyable for your students. Each student has been hired as a personal shopper for Ms. Johnson, a busy executive. His/her job is to purchase gifts for Ms. Johnson's family members for different occasions: a birthday gift for an aunt, a graduation gift for a brother, a father's day gift for her father, and a baby gift for her best friend's new-born baby. Ms. Johnson is willing to spend a maximum of $350 for the four gifts.

Instruct each student to make a chart to submit to Ms. Johnson for her approval. The chart should include the name of the person, the relationship to Ms. Johnson, the occasion, the gift item, and the price. Have them determine whether or not Ms. Johnson will receive any change, and the amount of the change.

Students may enjoy exchanging their charts to compare the gift items they have chosen.

Students at Risk

Students at risk typically need ongoing review of basic addition and subtraction facts, and many opportunities to internalize facts that they may not memorize easily. Emphasizing various thinking strategies may help these students master the facts.

Provide manipulative experiences and realistic examples to strengthen the idea of doubles, and to provide visual memory cues. For instance, use tracings of hands to represent $5 + 5$, egg cartons for $6 + 6$, two weeks on a calendar for $7 + 7$, legs of 2 spiders for $8 + 8$, and 2 baseball teams for $9 + 9$. Such realistic images may help students recall doubles and enable them to use the facts to find doubles $+ 1$ or doubles $- 1$.

Stress addend combinations with sums of 10. Using two colors of snap cubes and 10-frames, have students demonstrate addend patterns such as $1 + 9 = 10$, $2 + 8 = 10$, $3 + 7 = 10$, . . . Present the activity as missing addends, such as $1 + ? = 10$, $2 + ? = 10$, . . ., to reinforce relationships between addition and subtraction visually and manipulatively and to help students reach the goal of rapid recall of basic facts.

You may also use the Reteaching Supplements and the specific Reteaching Tips from each lesson in this chapter.

INTRODUCING THE CHAPTER

SUBJECT INTEGRATION The closeup photograph of a box turtle represents the chapter theme of natural science. Students identify and compare data on the life spans of various animals in captivity and in the wild. Various lessons will incorporate other animal facts to apply addition and subtraction concepts and facts to the chapter theme.

USING DATA The Science Data Bank on page 468 of the Student Edition contains a table entitled "Life Spans of Small Wild Animals." The data compares possible number of years 5 animals could live in the wild and in captivity. Daytime Activity of Red-Backed Salamander is a bar graph showing the number of active minutes per hour in 12 daytime hours for this amphibian.

QUESTION 1 ► **Identify 2 categories of life-span data given in the table.** (possible number of years the animal could live in the wild; possible number of years in captivity)
► **Explain the difference between the 2 categories.** (*In the Wild* means animals live in their natural environment; *In Captivity* means animals live in a circus, in a zoo, on a farm, as family pets, or in any controlled setting cared for by people.)
► **Explain how to locate the data you need to answer the question.** (Find squirrel and box turtle in the left column, then find the number of years they could live in the column labeled *In the Wild*.) Student Edition answer: box turtle

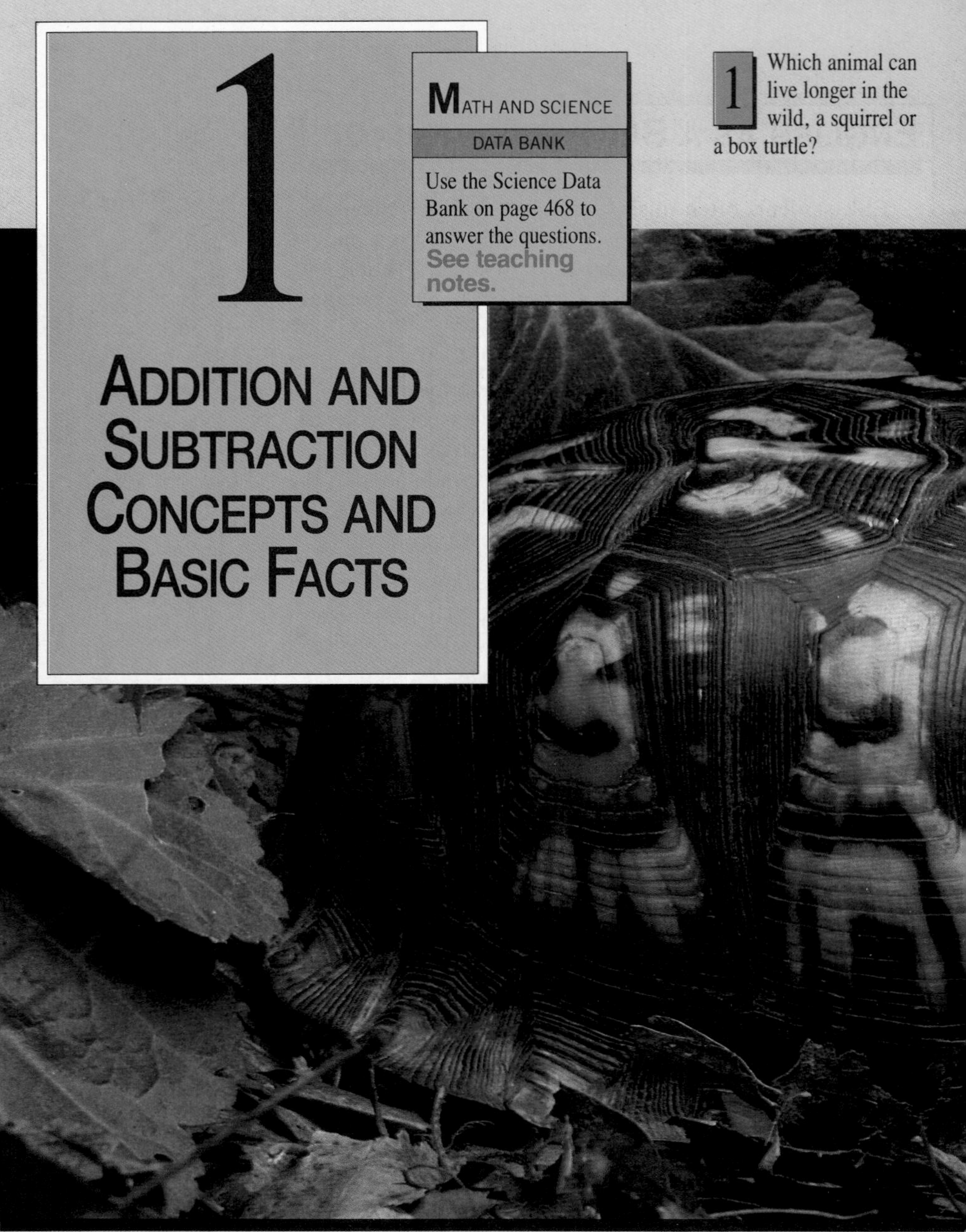

1
ADDITION AND SUBTRACTION CONCEPTS AND BASIC FACTS
MATH AND SCIENCE
DATA BANK
Use the Science Data Bank on page 468 to answer the questions.
See teaching notes.
1 Which animal can live longer in the wild, a squirrel or a box turtle?

TEACHING OPTIONS

LANGUAGE DEVELOPMENT Write the word **compare** on the chalkboard and have students explain its meaning. (Possible answer: Determine how 2 or more objects or facts are alike and different.) Have students find a word or phrase in each Chapter Opener question to signal that facts must be compared. (**1.** *longer* **2.** *how much longer* **3.** *10 years more than* **4.** *least active*)

2 In captivity, how much longer can a raccoon live than a cottontail rabbit?

3 In the wild, the life span of a chipmunk can be 10 years more than that of a white-footed mouse. What is the life span of a wild chipmunk?

4 **Use Critical Thinking** Look at the graph and tell what part of the day the red-backed salamander is least active. Can you think of a reason why?

3

QUESTION 2 ► **Identify the data you need.** (A raccoon may live 14 years; a cottontail rabbit may live 5 years.)
► **Decide how to use the data to answer the question.** (Subtract 5 from 14.) Student Edition answer: 9 years

QUESTION 3 ► **Explain how to combine data from the table with data given in the question to find the life span of a wild chipmunk.** (Find the life span of a white-footed mouse in the table; add 10 years to that number, based on the fact given in the question.) Student Edition answer: 12 years

QUESTION 4 ► **Explain how the bar graph shows data about the salamander.** (Each bar shows how many minutes per hour a red-backed salamander is active, starting at 6 a.m. and ending at 6 p.m.)
► **Analyze which bars on the graph represent the least-active hours.** (11 a.m. to 3 p.m., because those bars are the shortest)
► **Identify a characteristic of those hours that explains why a salamander may be least active then.** (Those hours are usually the warmest part of a day, so the salamander might rest in a shady spot to keep cool.) Student Edition answer: 11 a.m. to 3 p.m. is the warmest part of the day.

SUBJECT INTEGRATION PROJECT Have students collect data from their own experiences with the life spans of pets. They may begin with data about their own pets, then conduct simple interviews of friends and relatives to gather additional data. Students can use the data they find to make a table from which to formulate comparison questions, such as: Which pet lived longest? How many more years did Peg's cat live than David's hamster?

LESSON OPTIONS 1-1

Problem Solving: Understanding Addition and Subtraction

OBJECTIVE 1-1 To understand the operations of addition and subtraction

PREBOOK ACTIVITIES

QUICK REVIEW

Add.

1. 2 + 2 (4)	**2.** 3 + 3 (6)	**3.** 4 + 4 (8)
4. 5 + 5 (10)	**5.** 2 + 4 (6)	**6.** 3 + 5 (8)
7. 6 + 4 (10)	**8.** 1 + 3 (4)	**9.** 5 + 2 (7)
10. 4 + 5 (9)	**11.** 6 + 1 (7)	**12.** 3 + 2 (5)

PRIOR KNOWLEDGE

Have students recall real-life situations when they have added or subtracted and ask volunteers to write a number expression on the chalkboard to fit each situation. (Answers will vary. Students write 4 + 3 = 7, 5 − 2 = 3, and so on, based on the situations.) Have students explain in their own words what it means to add and to subtract. (Possible answers: ''to put together,'' ''to combine,'' ''to take away'')

COMMUNICATION

Writing Math Have each student make a Math Journal in which to record math writing throughout the year. Provide each student with 32 pages of Teaching Aid (TA) 1 (Math Journal) and construction paper or tagboard folders for covers. Students should bind the pages, then decorate and label the cover. As the first entry in their new Math Journals, have students write 1 addition and 1 subtraction equation relating to themselves or to a special interest. Have them accompany each equation with a sentence explaining its significance.

EXPLORE AND CONNECT

COOPERATIVE ACTIVITY

Grouping Suggestion: small groups

3 boys and 3 girls are drawing a chalk design on the playground. 4 children have chalk sets. How many more sets are needed?

TEACHING ACTIONS

Have students work in small groups to act out the situation, plan a solution, and discuss the results.

▶ **Explain the situation.** (Some children are decorating the playground but not all of them have chalk sets to use.)

▶ **Analyze the question.** (You must find how many children need chalk sets.)

DURING

▶ **Plan what to do first.** (Add to see how many children in all.)

▶ **Justify the operation that can help answer the question.** (Subtract to find how many more chalk sets are needed.)

▶ **Decide how to write an equation that fits the question.** (6 − 4 = 2)

AFTER

▶ **Evaluate your solution to see if it makes sense.** (Of the 6 children, 4 had chalk sets; you need 2 more sets so everyone can work on the design; act out the situation to check the answer.)

CONNECTIONS Use these anytime.

Problem of the Day

Creative Thinking 10 birds are sitting on a wire. 2 birds fly away, but 1 returns. Then 3 birds fly away, but 2 return. Then 4 fly away, but 3 return. How many birds are now on the wire? (7)

Life Skills

Admission Tickets You win 1 free pass to the movies. If your entire family decides to go to the movies with you, write an equation that shows how many tickets to buy. (Answers will vary.)

Number Sense

Mental Math A king wears rings on both of his pinkies and thumbs. How many of his fingers do not have rings? (6)

Classwork and Homework Supplements

Practice

Manipulatives 1-1

Name ______________________

Problem Solving: Understanding Addition and Subtraction

Use counters to find each answer. Then complete the equation that gives the same answer.

1. 4 children are jumping rope. 2 children join them. How many are there in all?
   4 + 2 = ? 4 − 2 = ?
   4 + 2 = 6
2. 7 boys are running in the marathon. 3 boys stop to rest. How many are still running?
   7 + 3 = ? 7 − 3 = ?
   7 − 3 = 4
3. 10 girls are needed for a basketball game. There are 5 girls. How many more are needed?
   10 − 5 = ? 10 + 5 = ?
   10 − 5 = 5
4. Some children are playing volleyball. 5 are on one side of the net. 4 are playing on the other side. How many are there in all?
   5 + 4 = ? 5 − 4 = ?
   5 + 4 = 9
5. There are 5 swings. Children are on 3 of them. How many swings are empty?
   5 + 3 = ? 5 − 3 = ?
   5 − 3 = 2

PS-4 Use with text pages 4–5. 1

Building Thinking Skills

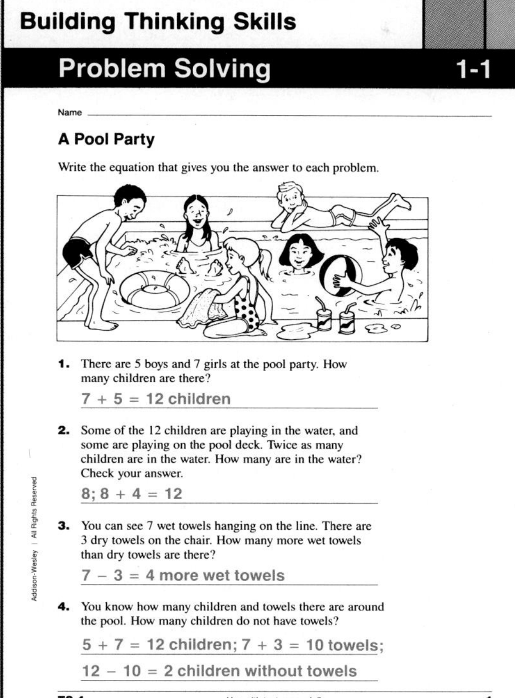

Problem Solving 1-1

Name ______________________

A Pool Party

Write the equation that gives you the answer to each problem.

1. There are 5 boys and 7 girls at the pool party. How many children are there?
   7 + 5 = 12 children
2. Some of the 12 children are playing in the water, and some are playing on the pool deck. Twice as many children are in the water. How many are in the water? Check your answer.
   8; 8 + 4 = 12
3. You can see 7 wet towels hanging on the line. There are 3 dry towels on the chair. How many more wet towels than dry towels are there?
   7 − 3 = 4 more wet towels
4. You know how many children and towels there are around the pool. How many children do not have towels?
   5 + 7 = 12 children; 7 + 3 = 10 towels;
   12 − 10 = 2 children without towels

TS-4 Use with text pages 4–5. 1

Reteaching

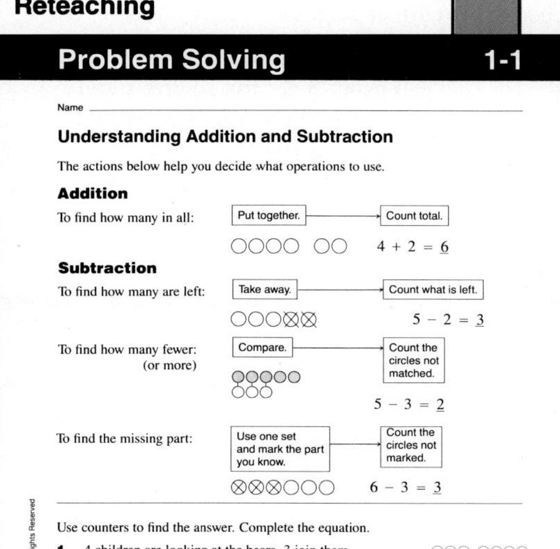

Problem Solving 1-1

Name ______________________

Understanding Addition and Subtraction

The actions below help you decide what operations to use.

Addition

To find how many in all: Put together. → Count total.
4 + 2 = 6

Subtraction

To find how many are left: Take away. → Count what is left.
5 − 2 = 3

To find how many fewer: (or more) Compare. → Count the circles not matched.
5 − 3 = 2

To find the missing part: Use one set and mark the part you know. → Count the circles not marked.
6 − 3 = 3

Use counters to find the answer. Complete the equation.

1. 4 children are looking at the bears. 3 join them. How many children are there in all? 4 + 3 = 7
2. 6 zookeepers are needed to wash an elephant. 2 are there now. How many more are needed? 6 − 2 = 4
3. You see 8 baby male zebras and 5 female zebras. How many fewer are females? 8 − 5 = 3

RS-4 Use with text pages 4-5. 1

Challenges

Reading Math 1-1

Name ______________________

Whitewater Fun

Read the diary entry. Write a question about the rafting trip that fits each equation. Then answer the questions. Use counters to help you.

Dear Diary,
We went whitewater rafting. Of the 12 rafters in our group, 5 were from my family. At the shore, there were 9 rafts, but we used only 2. The guide in our raft said she takes about 7 trips a summer and has worked 2 summers. She told 3 people to paddle on the left and 3 to paddle on the right. We went through 9 sets of rapids before lunch and 7 after. 4 people from 1 raft and 3 from the other jumped out to swim. The first night of our trip I slept 3 hours, but afterward, I slept 9!

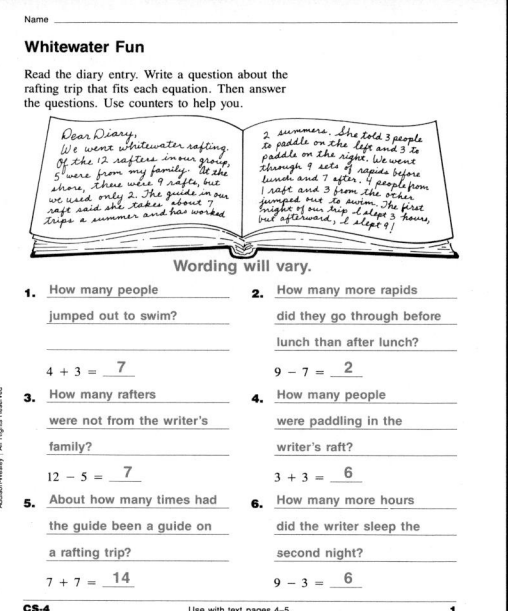

Wording will vary.

1. How many people jumped out to swim?
   4 + 3 = 7
2. How many more rapids did they go through before lunch than after lunch?
   9 − 7 = 2
3. How many rafters were not from the writer's family?
   12 − 5 = 7
4. How many people were paddling in the writer's raft?
   3 + 3 = 6
5. About how many times had the guide been a guide on a rafting trip?
   7 + 7 = 14
6. How many more hours did the writer sleep the second night?
   9 − 3 = 6

CS-4 Use with text pages 4–5. 1

Options for Individual Needs

1-1

Basic

Exercises 1-7
Skills Bank, pp. 461, 463
Calculator Bank, pp. 484, 485
More Practice, p. 512, set C

Supplements
Reteaching 1 or
Practice 1

Average

Exercises 1-7
Skills Bank, pp. 461, 463
Calculator Bank, pp. 484, 485
More Practice, p. 512, set C

Supplements
Practice 1
Challenges 1 or
Thinking Skills 1

Extended

Exercises 1-7
Calculator Bank, pp. 484, 485

Supplements
Challenges 1
Thinking Skills 1

Other Resources:
Problem-Solving Experiences in Mathematics, Grade 4, Problem 9
Mathematics, A Way of Thinking, Lessons 4-1, 4-3
Math In Stride, Grade 4, pp. 22, 23

LESSON PLAN 1-1

OBJECTIVE 1-1
To understand the operations of addition and subtraction

Materials: counters

Grouping Suggestion: pairs

1. MOTIVATE AND TEACH

LEARN ABOUT IT

► **Analyze the Put Together and Take Away equations to find a relationship among the numbers.** (Put Together has 2 addends that give a sum; Take Away has that sum minus 1 addend to give the other addend.)
► **Explain what clues signal you to subtract.** (actions such as *compare*, *find the missing part*, *find how many more are needed*)
► **Explain what is known and what is missing in the tree-squirrel situation.** (You know that of 6 squirrels, 2 are male; you must find out how many are female.)

► **Justify using subtraction to find a missing part.** (You know how many squirrels in all, which is a sum. You subtract 2 known squirrels, which is an addend, to find the number of female squirrels, which is the other addend.)

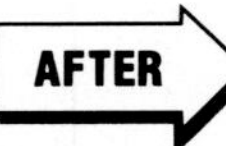

► **Explain how to check your answer.** (Possible answers: Act it Out; Draw a Picture; Use Models.)

2. CHECK UNDERSTANDING

TRY IT OUT

ERROR ALERT Choosing the wrong operation.

Problem Solving
Understanding Addition and Subtraction

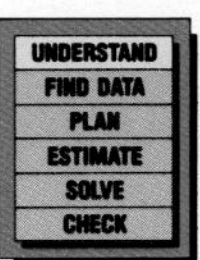

LEARN ABOUT IT

These actions help you understand addition and subtraction.

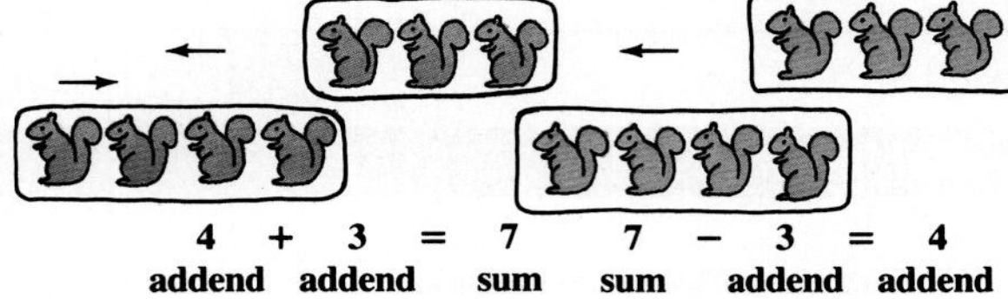

4	+	3	=	7		7	−	3	=	4
addend		addend		sum		sum		addend		addend

The actions below also help you decide what operation to use. Show the actions with counters. Complete the equations.

Problem	Action	Operation
	Compare	Subtract
On a nature walk, you count 5 red squirrels and 3 gray ones. How many fewer are gray?		5 − 3 = ▥
	Find the Missing Part	
A tree squirrel has 6 young squirrels. 2 are male. How many are female?		6 − 2 = ▥
	How Many More Are Needed?	
You want to find pictures of 6 kinds of squirrels. You have found 4 kinds. How many more must you find?		6 − 4 = ▥

TRY IT OUT

Use counters to find the answer. Choose the correct equation.

1. The Wildlife Rescue Center is caring for 7 flying squirrels and 4 fox squirrels. How many more flying squirrels are there?
   a. 7 + 4 = 11 **b.** 7 − 4 = 3

2. You see 5 squirrels near your campsite. 3 are fox squirrels and the rest are gray squirrels. How many are gray?
   a. 5 − 3 = 2 **b.** 5 + 3 = 8

4

TEACHING OPTIONS

RETEACHING TIPS A student draws a picture to fit a problem, using the problem as a caption. Have the student label each part of the picture, then explain it to a partner to clarify the situation so, together, they can choose the correct operation. Assign Reteaching Supplement 1.

ENRICHMENT Have students look through old magazines to find 2 interesting photographs of groups of people, animals, or objects. Have them formulate 1 addition and 1 subtraction problem for each picture. Display the pictures and problems on a bulletin board. Invite students to solve each other's problems.

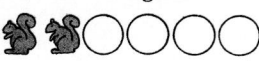

PRACTICE

Use counters to find each answer. Then complete the equation that gives the same answer.

1. 5 squirrels are hiding nuts. 3 squirrels join them. How many squirrels are there?

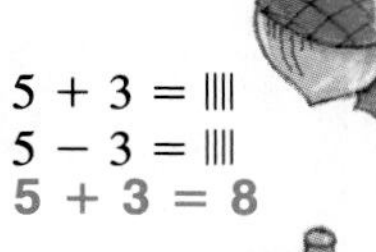

$5 + 3 = \square$
$5 - 3 = \square$
$5 + 3 = 8$

2. 7 chipmunks are eating seeds. A noise scares 2 away. How many are still eating?

$7 + 2 = \square$
$7 - 2 = \square$
$7 - 2 = 5$

3. You count 8 red squirrels in the park. Then you count 3 gray squirrels. How many more red squirrels are there?

$8 - 3 = \square$
$8 + 3 = \square$
$8 - 3 = 5$

4. It takes 6 beavers to build a dam. 2 are working now. How many more are needed?

$6 + 2 = \square$
$6 - 2 = \square$
$6 - 2 = 4$

5. 7 ground squirrels are in a nest. 2 are parents. How many are young?

$7 - 2 = \square$
$7 + 2 = \square$
$7 - 2 = 5$

▶ **WRITE YOUR OWN PROBLEM** Answers will vary.

6. Write a story problem that can be solved by adding.
7. Write a story problem that can be solved by subtracting.

More Practice, page 512, set C

Close and Assess

WRITE WHAT YOU THINK In their Math Journals, have students write a sentence to explain when to add. Then have them write another sentence that gives the 3 actions that suggest subtraction. (Answers may vary. Check students' writing.)

Quick Quiz

Write *add* or *subtract*.

1. How many are left? (subtract)
2. How many in all? (add)
3. How many more are needed? (subtract)

3. Practice and Apply

Basic	1-7
Average	1-7
Extended	1-7

1-1

PRACTICE

Summarize the choices given for each story problem. (1 addition and 1 subtraction equation that each use the same 2 numbers) *Tell how you would begin to solve Problem 1.* (Show 5 counters.) *In Problem 2, should you put together or take away counters?* (take away) *What action does Problem 3 suggest?* (compare) *In Problem 4, how many beavers are at work?* (2) *In Problem 5, what is unknown?* (how many of the 7 squirrels are young)

WRITE YOUR OWN PROBLEM

▶ **Generalize about when to add.** (in any situation involving putting groups together)

▶ **Generalize about when to subtract.** (in any situation involving comparing, finding a missing part, or finding how many more are needed)

LESSON OPTIONS 1-2

Addition Properties

OBJECTIVE 1-2 To understand and use basic properties for addition

PREBOOK ACTIVITIES

QUICK REVIEW

1. Write any two numbers whose sum is 7.
(Possible answers: 5 + 2, 6 + 1, 7 + 0)
2. Write any two numbers whose sum is 9.
(Possible answers: 4 + 5, 2 + 7, 3 + 6)
3. Write any three numbers whose sum is 10.
(Possible answers: 4 + 1 + 5, 3 + 6 + 1)

PRIOR KNOWLEDGE

Show three groups of objects. Have students verbalize different methods they might use to find the total number of objects. (Possible answers: Count every object; combine two groups to make a larger group, then add the third group.) Ask students to think of situations in which three groups of numbers are added. (Possible answer: money amounts at a store)

COMMUNICATION

Discussing and Reading Math Write these words on the chalkboard: **grouping, order.** Have students read the words aloud. Then ask them to suggest different groupings that would include all students in the class. (Students might suggest groups based on eye color, gender, age, or neighborhood.) Ask students to relate their groupings to the total number of students in the class. (The total remains the same regardless of the grouping.) Then have students suggest different orders for lining everyone up. (Possible order: by height, alphabetical order, age) Again, have students generalize how order affects the total number of students in the line. (The total remains unchanged.)

EXPLORE AND CONNECT

Materials: TA 2 (Number Cubes numbered 0-5), counters, paper and pencil
Grouping Suggestion: cooperative learning teams of 4
Play ''Order Groupings.'' Teams need a number cube, counters, and paper and pencil. One student rolls, then puts that many counters in a group. The next teammate rolls, then puts that many counters in another group. The other two teammates each write a complete addition number sentence by themselves. The team earns a point whenever writers give addends in a different **order.** If writers use the same **order** of addends, no point is scored. Students switch tasks for each round. They should play some rounds with two addends and some with three addends. When playing with three addends, writers can show any **grouping** they wish. The team with the most points wins. Discuss how students decided to **order** or **group** their addends and how their decisions affected sums.

CONNECTIONS Use these anytime.

Problem of the Day

Combinations List as many groups of three numbers as you can that total your age. (Answers may vary. Samples for age 9 include 3 + 4 + 2; 1 + 2 + 6; 2 + 3 + 4; 5 + 4 + 0; 9 + 0 + 0; 3 + 3 + 3; 5 + 3 + 1.)

Life Skills

Postage Stamps Postcards need 15-cents postage. Jared has 10-cent, 6-cent, and 3-cent stamps. Explain how he can mail a postcard without buying a 15-cent stamp. (Possible combination: 6 + 6 + 3 = 15)

Math Connection

Algebra Find a number to make each statement true.
$\square + 5 = 5$ (0)
$5 + \triangle = \triangle + 5$ (any number)

Classwork and Homework Supplements

Practice

Skills Maintenance 1-2

Name

Addition Properties

Add.

1. 4 + 6 = 10	2. 6 + 4 = 10	3. 2 + 5 = 7	4. 5 + 2 = 7	5. 3 + 7 = 10	6. 7 + 3 = 10
7. 7 + 7 = 14	8. 9 + 1 = 10	9. 1 + 9 = 10	10. 8 + 4 = 12	11. 4 + 8 = 12	12. 0 + 5 = 5
13. 5 + 0 = 5	14. 6 + 6 = 12	15. 7 + 8 = 15	16. 8 + 7 = 15	17. 5 + 9 = 14	18. 9 + 5 = 14
19. 9 + 9 = 18	20. 8 + 6 = 14	21. 6 + 8 = 14	22. 4 + 7 = 11	23. 7 + 4 = 11	24. 8 + 8 = 16

25. (4 + 6) + 2 = 12	26. 4 + (6 + 2) = 12
27. (4 + 2) + 6 = 12	28. (5 + 7) + 3 = 15
29. 5 + (3 + 7) = 15	30. (5 + 3) + 7 = 15
31. (9 + 1) + 3 = 13	32. 9 + (1 + 3) = 13
33. (9 + 3) + 1 = 13	34. (4 + 0) + 6 = 10
35. (4 + 6) + 0 = 10	36. 4 + (0 + 6) = 10
37. (7 + 3) + 4 = 14	38. 7 + (3 + 4) = 14
39. (7 + 4) + 3 = 14	40. (9 + 7) + 2 = 18
41. 9 + (2 + 7) = 18	42. (9 + 2) + 7 = 18

Building Thinking Skills

Math Reasoning 1-2

Name

Examining Properties

The three properties of addition you have learned are:

- Grouping Property
  (2 + 6) + 3 = 11, so 2 + (6 + 3) = 11
- Order Property
  9 + 6 = 15, so 6 + 9 = 15
- Zero Property
  7 + 0 = 7

Use the following sets of numbers to create equations that demonstrate each property. You may use the numbers more than once. Answers may vary.

A 0 1 2 6 7 9

B 0 1 2 8 9 11

Sample answers are shown.

1. Grouping Property	A	(6 + 2) + 1 = 9	6 + (2 + 1) = 9
	B	(2 + 8) + 1 = 11	2 + (8 + 1) = 11
2. Order Property	A	7 + 2 = 9	2 + 7 = 9
	B	9 + 2 = 11	2 + 9 = 11
3. Zero Property	A	9 + 0 = 9	
	B	11 + 0 = 11	

Reteaching

Skills Review 1-2

Name

Addition Properties

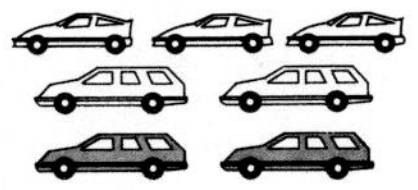

Adding Down

3 } 5 white cars
2
+ 2 2 black cars
7 7 cars in all

Adding Up

3 3 small cars
2 } 4 big cars
+ 2
7 7 cars in all

When you add, you get the same sum even when you change the grouping.

Find the sums.

1. 5 + 6 + 7 = 18	2. 8 + 6 + 2 = 16	3. 9 + 1 + 5 = 15	4. 7 + 6 + 3 = 16	5. 5 + 6 + 5 = 16	6. 1 + 2 + 7 = 10
7. 8 + 9 + 2 = 19	8. 6 + 1 + 7 = 14	9. 4 + 8 + 3 = 15	10. 3 + 6 + 9 = 18	11. 8 + 5 + 2 = 15	12. 4 + 4 + 9 = 17
13. 5 + 4 + 3 = 12	14. 9 + 3 + 4 = 16	15. 6 + 2 + 7 = 15	16. 5 + 3 + 2 = 10	17. 7 + 8 + 3 = 18	18. 6 + 4 + 2 = 12

Solve.

19. 6 + 3 + 4 = 13	20. 5 + 7 + 4 = 16	21. 8 + 6 + 3 = 17
22. 6 + 9 + 4 = 19	23. 9 + 3 + 5 = 17	24. 7 + 8 + 2 = 17

Challenges

Math Reasoning 1-2

Name

Domino Addition

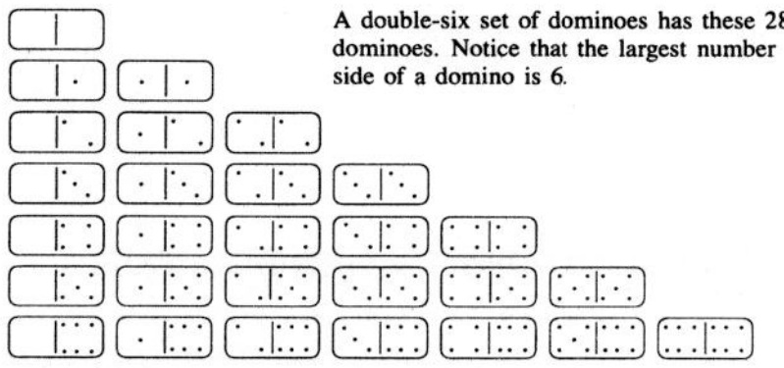

A double-six set of dominoes has these 28 dominoes. Notice that the largest number on one side of a domino is 6.

Draw dots in the dominoes below to create addition problems that are true. Then write each problem. Answers will vary.

Examples: 1 + 2 = 3; 1 + 3 + 1 = 5

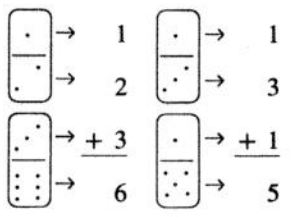

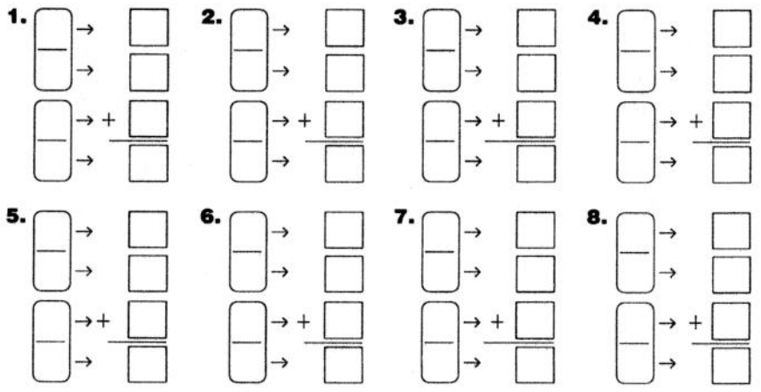

1. 2. 3. 4. 5. 6. 7. 8.

Options for Individual Needs

Basic

Exercises 1-12, 19-35
Data Bank, p 468
Skills Bank, pp. 461
More Practice, p. 500, set A

Supplements
Reteaching 2 or
Practice 2
Challenges 2

Average

Exercises 1-37
Data Bank, p 468
Skills Bank, p. 461
More Practice, p. 500, set A

Supplements
Practice 2
Challenges 2 or
Thinking Skills 2

Extended

Exercises 11-29, 34-36
Data Bank, p. 468

Supplements
Challenges 2
Thinking Skills 2

Other Resources:
Problem-Solving Experiences in Mathematics, Grade 4, Problem 2
Mathematics, A Way of Thinking, Lesson 4-2
Math In Stride, Grade 4, p. 24

LESSON PLAN 1-2

OBJECTIVE 1-2
To understand and use basic properties for addition

Materials: counters

1. MOTIVATE AND TEACH

LEARN ABOUT IT

▶ **Can you predict what would happen if you added the same two numbers in a different order?** (The sums would be the same.)

EXPLORE ▶ **Prove that 12 counters may be added in any order. Say the number sentences.** (Check students' models as they verbalize counting, grouping, and adding the numbers in their example.)
▶ **Do you notice another grouping that Hans or Will might have added first?** (3 + 5)

TALK ABOUT IT ▶ **If Hans had added 4 + 3 instead of 3 + 4, would the grouping change? Explain.** (No, only the order of that group would change.)
▶ **What rule can you give for adding three numbers?** (A sum does not change if a grouping or the order changes.)
▶ **When might you add zero and a number?** (Possible answer: when adding scores)
Student Edition answers: **1.** Hans: 3 + 4; Will: 4 + 5. **2.** No, the order or grouping does not change the sum.

2. CHECK UNDERSTANDING

TRY IT OUT

ERROR ALERT Giving a sum of zero when zero is an addend. Correctly adding numbers in parentheses but then forgetting to add the third number.

Addition Properties

LEARN ABOUT IT

EXPLORE Think About the Situation
In Germany, some roads have underpasses so that frogs can cross safely. Hans and Will watched for an hour and saw 3 frogs, 4 toads, and 5 newts come through the underpass. To find the total number Hans thought:

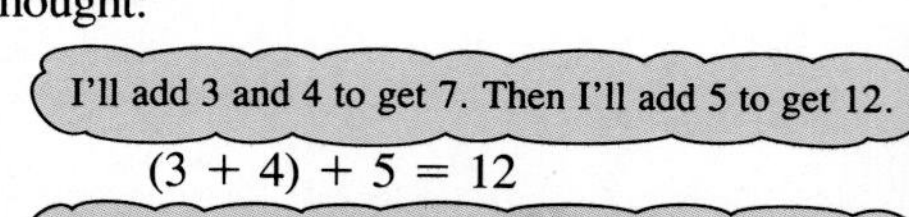

I'll add 3 and 4 to get 7. Then I'll add 5 to get 12.

(3 + 4) + 5 = 12

Will thought: I'll add 4 and 5 to get 9. Then I'll add 3 to get 12.

(4 + 5) + 3 = 12

The parentheses ( ) tell which numbers are added first.

TALK ABOUT IT See teaching notes.

1. Which two numbers did Hans add first? Which did Will add first?
2. Does adding 3 and 5 first give a different sum?

The grouping property helps when you have 3 addends.

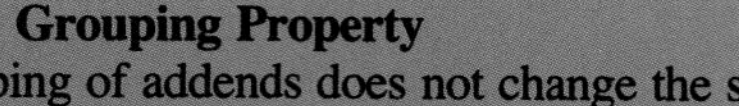

Grouping Property
Changing the grouping of addends does not change the sum.
(2 +3) + 4 = 9, so 2 + (3 + 4) = 9

You may remember other properties that help in finding addition facts.

Order Property	**Zero Property**
Changing the order of addends does not change the sum. 7 + 3 = 10, so 3 + 7 = 10	The sum of a number and zero is that number. 8 + 0 = 8

TRY IT OUT

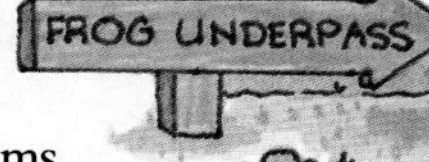

Find these sums.

1. 7 + 0 7
2. 0 + 7 7
3. 5 + (2 + 3) 10
4. (5 + 2) + 3 10

TEACHING OPTIONS

RETEACHING TIPS Students exhibiting the first error should form a group of counters and tell how many are in the group. Then ask students how many counters they have when nothing (zero) is added to that group. (Adding zero does not change the size of that group.) Assign Reteaching Supplement 2.

ENRICHMENT Have students move *one* number to a different row so that each row will have the same sum. Rows do not need equal amounts of numbers. (Move 9 to the top row.)

PRACTICE

Add.

1. 8 + 3 = 11	**2.** 3 + 8 = 11	**3.** 7 + 9 = 16	**4.** 9 + 7 = 16	**5.** 6 + 5 = 11	**6.** 5 + 6 = 11
7. 9 + 0 = 9	**8.** 0 + 9 = 9	**9.** 8 + 8 = 16	**10.** 0 + 6 = 6	**11.** 6 + 0 = 6	**12.** 7 + 7 = 14
13. 4 + 5 = 9	**14.** 5 + 4 = 9	**15.** 8 + 9 = 17	**16.** 9 + 8 = 17	**17.** 9 + 2 = 11	**18.** 2 + 9 = 11

19. (2 + 4) + 7 — 13 **20.** 2 + (4 + 7) — 13 **21.** (2 + 7) + 4 — 13

APPLY

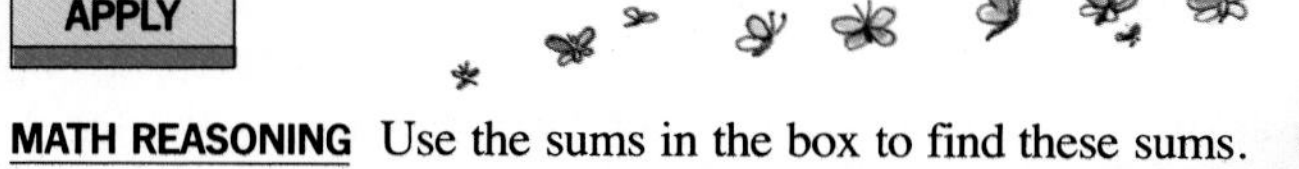

MATH REASONING Use the sums in the box to find these sums.

22. 249 + 368 — 617
23. 537 + (368 + 249) — 1,154
24. 368 + 537 — 905
25. 537 + 249 + 368 — 1,154

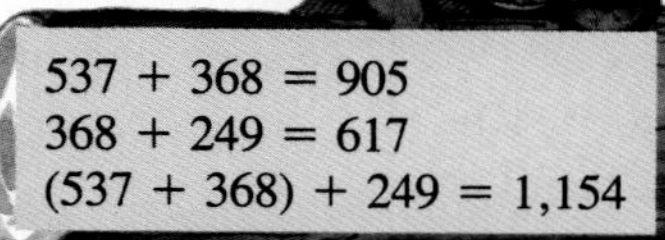

537 + 368 = 905
368 + 249 = 617
(537 + 368) + 249 = 1,154

PROBLEM SOLVING

26. Amy's backyard frog, Slurpy, ate 3 more flies one night than it had eaten that morning. If Slurpy ate 6 flies in the morning, how many did it eat that day? **15 flies**

27. Science Data Bank How many minutes is a red-backed salamander active from 6 a.m. to 8 a.m.? See page 468. **15 minutes**

DATA BANK

MIXED REVIEW

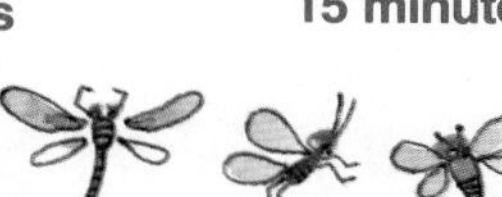

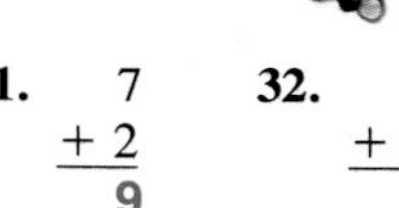

Add.

28. 8 + 5 = 13	**29.** 5 + 8 = 13	**30.** 2 + 7 = 9	**31.** 7 + 2 = 9	**32.** 3 + 0 = 3	**33.** 8 + 0 = 8

34. (2 + 6) + 5 — 13 **35.** 2 + (6 + 5) — 13 **36.** (7 + 3) + 0 — 10 **37.** 4 + 5 + 8 — 17

More Practice, page 500, set A

3. PRACTICE AND APPLY

Basic	1-12, 19-35
Average	1-37
Extended	11-29, 34-36

PRACTICE

How can the properties of order and grouping help you solve Exercises 19-21? (The properties tell you that changing the grouping or order of addends does not change the sum.)

APPLY

MATH REASONING ▶ **How are order and grouping related?** (The order property allows different groupings.)

PROBLEM SOLVING ▶ **Explain why you must add twice to solve Problem 26.** (6 + 3 tells how many flies were eaten at night; 6 + (6 + 3) tells how many flies were eaten in all.) ▶ **Explain your answer to Problem 27.** (Add 7 + 8 minutes to get a total of 15 minutes.)

MIXED REVIEW ▶ **Which exercises use the zero property?** (Exercises 32, 33, and 36)

CLOSE AND ASSESS

PROVE WHAT YOU KNOW

Have students use counters to verify the addition properties of grouping, order, and zero. Have them verbalize what they are showing as they model each property. (Check students' models.)

QUICK QUIZ

Fill in the blanks.
1. 35 + 29 = 29 + (35)
2. (9 + 8) + 7 = 9 + (___ + ___)
(Either (8 + 7) or (7 + 8) works.)
3. 500 + 0 = 0 + (500)

LESSON OPTIONS 1-3

Using Addition to Subtract

OBJECTIVE 1-3 To use addition to find basic subtraction facts

PREBOOK ACTIVITIES

QUICK REVIEW

1. Write three different addition facts whose sum is your age. (Answers will vary. Samples for 9 include 3 + 6, 4 + 5, 2 + 7.)
2. Write three addition equations whose sum is 15. (Answers will vary. Samples include 3 + 4 + 8, 1 + 8 + 6, 6 + 0 + 9, 5 + 5 + 5.)

PRIOR KNOWLEDGE

Ask volunteers to use the numbers 2, 8, and 10 to form as many different addition and subtraction number sentences as possible. Record equations on the chalkboard. (2 + 8 = 10; 8 + 2 = 10; 10 − 2 = 8; 10 − 8 = 2) Ask if students recall a name for the group of number facts that use 2, 8, and 10. (fact family)

COMMUNICATION

Discussing and Listening to Math Discuss what it means to talk about a *family of wolves* and *the Ray family*. (Possible answer: wolves that live or hunt together; people who are related) Ask students to infer what a **fact family** is. (Possible answer: number facts that are related or go together in some way)
Pronounce the word **addend** as students listen for a part that is familiar. (add) Have a volunteer tell what an addend is. (a number you add) Ask students how they use the word **difference** in real life as well as in math. (Possible answers: to describe ways in which people or things are not alike; the answer to a subtraction problem)

EXPLORE AND CONNECT

Materials: snap cubes
Grouping Suggestion: cooperative learning pairs
Have students select a work partner. Each pair needs a strip of nine snap cubes. One student places the strip behind his or her back. This student breaks the strip in two pieces of any size, then shows one piece to the other student. The first asks, "How many cubes am I hiding?" When the partner guesses correctly, the first student reveals the hidden **addend** to verify the answer. Students take turns at each role and repeat the game several times. As they become more familiar with the game, students may play with a greater number of cubes.

CONNECTIONS Use these anytime.

Problem of the Day

Money Rosa buys an apple for 28 cents. She gives the clerk a quarter and a dime. How much change will Rosa get? (7 cents)

Creative Thinking

Strategy Work in pairs. Start with 21 counters. Take turns subtracting 1, 2, or 3 counters. Whoever takes the last counter wins. Play until you find a strategy. (Whoever leaves 4 counters will always win.)

Number Sense

Mental Math I am thinking of a number sentence. The sum is 13. One addend is 4. What is the missing addend? (9)

Classwork and Homework Supplements

Practice

Skills Maintenance 1-3

Name ______________________

Using Addition to Subtract

Subtract. Think about finding the missing addend.

1. 9 − 2 = 7	**2.** 10 − 4 = 6	**3.** 2 − 2 = 0	**4.** 6 − 5 = 1	**5.** 10 − 1 = 9
6. 13 − 9 = 4	**7.** 11 − 5 = 6	**8.** 15 − 9 = 6	**9.** 12 − 9 = 3	**10.** 15 − 7 = 8
11. 11 − 2 = 9	**12.** 13 − 5 = 8	**13.** 1 − 0 = 1	**14.** 8 − 1 = 7	**15.** 16 − 8 = 8
16. 7 − 0 = 7	**17.** 10 − 5 = 5	**18.** 8 − 8 = 0	**19.** 16 − 9 = 7	**20.** 0 − 0 = 0
21. 9 − 4 = 5	**22.** 14 − 6 = 8	**23.** 7 − 7 = 0	**24.** 10 − 2 = 8	**25.** 16 − 7 = 9
26. 9 − 8 = 1	**27.** 3 − 3 = 0	**28.** 12 − 8 = 4	**29.** 9 − 7 = 2	**30.** 14 − 5 = 9

31. 15 − 8 = 7	**32.** 12 − 7 = 5	**33.** 10 − 3 = 7
34. 3 − 0 = 3	**35.** 11 − 8 = 3	**36.** 7 − 3 = 4
37. 8 − 3 = 5	**38.** 1 − 1 = 0	**39.** 6 − 3 = 3

PS-4 Use with text pages 8-9. 3

Building Thinking Skills

Critical Thinking 1-3

Name ______________________

Formulating Questions

Write a question that matches the data given. Then, in the box, write two related number facts to show how to find the answer. Ring each answer to the question.

1. Darryl had 12 baseball cards. After his first trade, he ended up with 7 cards.
How many cards did Darryl trade?
12 − 7 = (5)
7 + (5) = 12

Answer will vary. Samples given.

2. Mrs. Rivera planted 6 fewer tulips than Mrs. Borden who had 11 tulips in her garden.
How many tulips did Mrs. Rivera plant?
11 − 6 = (5)
6 + (5) = 11

3. Miori's kite shop sold 18 kites on Wednesday. This was 9 more kites than the store usually sells in one day.
How many kites does Miori usually sell in a day?
18 − 9 = (9)
9 + (9) = 18

4. Billy rode his bike 9 miles on Saturday. This is 7 miles less than the distance he rode on Sunday.
How many miles did Billy ride on Sunday?
9 + 7 = (16)
(16) − 9 = 7

TS-4 Use with text pages 8-9. 3

Reteaching

Math Reasoning 1-3

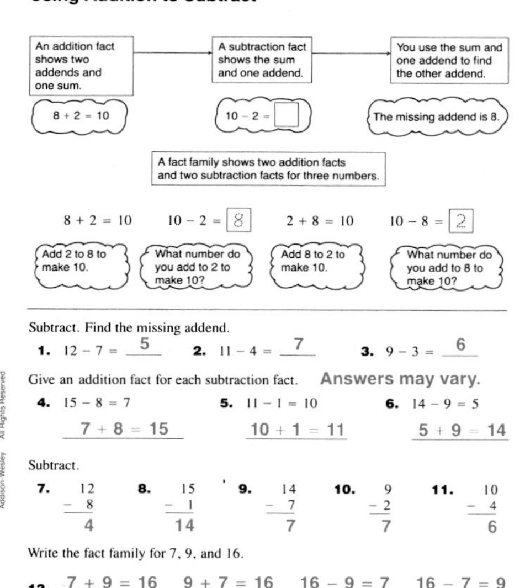

Name ______________________

Using Addition to Subtract

An addition fact shows two addends and one sum. → A subtraction fact shows the sum and one addend. → You use the sum and one addend to find the other addend.

8 + 2 = 10 | 10 − 2 = ☐ | The missing addend is 8.

A fact family shows two addition facts and two subtraction facts for three numbers.

8 + 2 = 10 (Add 2 to 8 to make 10.) | 10 − 2 = 8 (What number do you add to 2 to make 10?) | 2 + 8 = 10 (Add 8 to 2 to make 10.) | 10 − 8 = 2 (What number do you add to 8 to make 10?)

Subtract. Find the missing addend.

1. 12 − 7 = 5 **2.** 11 − 4 = 7 **3.** 9 − 3 = 6

Give an addition fact for each subtraction fact. Answers may vary.

4. 15 − 8 = 7 → 7 + 8 = 15 **5.** 11 − 1 = 10 → 10 + 1 = 11 **6.** 14 − 9 = 5 → 5 + 9 = 14

Subtract.

7. 12 − 8 = 4 **8.** 15 − 1 = 14 **9.** 14 − 7 = 7 **10.** 9 − 2 = 7 **11.** 10 − 4 = 6

Write the fact family for 7, 9, and 16.

12. 7 + 9 = 16 9 + 7 = 16 16 − 9 = 7 16 − 7 = 9

RS-4 Use with text pages 8-9. 3

Challenges

Math Reasoning 1-3

Name ______________________

Name That Number

Decide what number belongs in each shape. The same shape always stands for the same number.

1. ◇3 + ◇3 + ◇3 = 9

2. △5 + ⬡4 = 9 and 8 − ⬡4 = ⬡4

3. ☐7 − △5 = 2 and △5 + ☐7 = 12

4. ☆2 + ◇3 = △5 and ◠6 − ☆2 = 4

5. ⏢8 + ○9 = 17 and ⏢8 + ⏢8 = 16

6. ▱0 + 1 = ▭1 and ▭1 + △5 = ◠6

7. ◠6 + ☆2 + ☆2 = ☐7 + ◇3 − ▱0

CS-4 Use with text pages 8-9. 3

Options for Individual Needs

1-3

Basic

Exercises 3-21, 29-34
Skills Bank, p. 463
Calculator Bank, p. 485
More Practice, p. 512, set D

Supplements
Reteaching 3 or
Practice 3
Thinking Skills 3

Average

Exercises 1-36
Skills Bank, p. 463
Calculator Bank, p. 485
More Practice, p. 512, set D

Supplements
Practice 3
Challenges 3 or
Thinking Skills 3

Extended

Exercises 3-36
Calculator Bank, p. 485

Supplements
Challenges 3
Thinking Skills 3

Other Resources:
Problem-Solving Experiences in Mathematics, Grade 4, Problem 8
Mathematics, A Way of Thinking, Lesson 4-5
Math In Stride, Grade 4, p. 19

LESSON PLAN 1-3

OBJECTIVE 1-3
To use addition to find basic subtraction facts

Materials: snap cubes, calculators

Alternative Materials: counters, number lines

Grouping Suggestion: small groups

1. MOTIVATE AND TEACH

LEARN ABOUT IT

Show a strip of 12 snap cubes made from 8 red cubes and 4 blue cubes.
▶ **What addition facts do you notice?** (8 + 4 = 12; 4 + 8 = 12)
▶ **What subtraction facts do you notice?** (12 − 4 = 8; 12 − 8 = 4)

EXPLORE Give groups 20 snap cubes, 10 each of two different colors.
▶ **What action with snap cubes shows addition?** (connecting them)
▶ **What action with snap cubes shows subtraction?** (separating them)
▶ **Show that 7 + 3 = 10.** (Connect 7 cubes and 3 cubes.)
▶ **Show that 10 − 3 = 7.** (Separate 3 cubes from the strip of 10.)

TALK ABOUT IT ▶ **Use snap cubes to show that addition and subtraction are related.** (Using the same cubes, join two sticks to show addition; separate to show subtraction.) Student Edition answers: **1.** Connect for addition; separate for subtraction. **2.** In a fact family, two addends added make a sum. Subtracting one addend from the sum leaves the other addend.

2. CHECK UNDERSTANDING

TRY IT OUT

ERROR ALERT Needing to review basic addition facts in order to apply them to find missing addends. Adding rather than subtracting.

Using Addition to Subtract

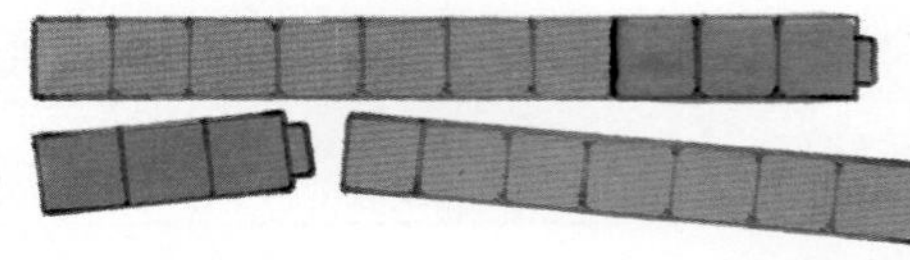

LEARN ABOUT IT

EXPLORE Use Snap Cubes

Since addition and subtraction are related, you can use addition to find differences. Work in groups. Use red and blue snap cubes to show the parts of this fact family.

Now use 10 cubes with another combination of red and blue to show a different fact family.

Fact Family
7 + 3 = 10
10 − 3 = 7
3 + 7 = 10
10 − 7 = 3

Math Point

When 0 is subtracted from a number, the difference is that number.
6 − 0 = 6
When a number is subtracted from itself, the difference is 0.
6 − 6 = 0

TALK ABOUT IT See teaching notes.

1. Look at one of your fact families. What action did you use to show each fact?
2. Use the 10 cubes and a fact family to explain how addition and subtraction are related.

An addition fact shows two addends and their sum. The related subtraction fact shows the sum and one addend. You use the sum and this addend to find the other addend.

What number adds to 9 to give 12?

12 − 9 = ▯

The missing addend is 3.

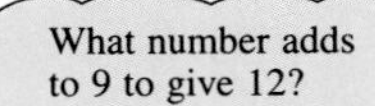

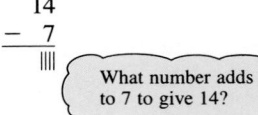

$$\begin{array}{r} 14 \\ -\ 7 \\ \hline ▯ \end{array}$$

What number adds to 7 to give 14?

The missing addend is 7.

TRY IT OUT

Subtract. Think about finding the missing addend.

1. 11 − 3 = ▯ 8
2. 12 − 6 = ▯ 6
3. 10 − 4 = ▯ 6
4. 16 − 8 = ▯ 8

TEACHING OPTIONS

RETEACHING TIPS Students who need to practice addition facts may work in small groups. One student picks a sum from 0 to 18. Everyone writes an addition fact for that sum. Students may use snap cubes or number lines to verify all the facts for a given sum. Assign Reteaching Supplement 3.

ENRICHMENT Family Math At home, students work with a family member to list every possible two-number combination for each sum from 2 to 10, including 0 as an addend. Then they try to find a pattern in the number of combinations for any sum. (Any sum [n] has n + 1 combinations.)

PRACTICE

Give an addition fact for each subtraction fact.

1. 11 − 9 = 2 9 + 2 = 11
2. 12 − 3 = 9 3 + 9 = 12
3. 8 − 5 = 3 5 + 3 = 8
4. 7 − 4 = 3 4 + 3 = 7

Subtract. Think about finding the missing addend.

5. 18 − 9 = 9
6. 12 − 7 = 5
7. 10 − 8 = 2
8. 16 − 7 = 9
9. 9 − 6 = 3
10. 11 − 8 = 3
11. 15 − 6 = 9
12. 13 − 8 = 5
13. 14 − 6 = 8
14. 17 − 8 = 9
15. 11 − 6 = 5
16. 14 − 8 = 6
17. 6 − 4 2
18. 18 − 9 9
19. 16 − 7 9
20. 15 − 7 8
21. 12 − 3 9
22. 14 − 9 5
23. 16 − 5 11
24. 13 − 6 7
25. 7 − 5 2
26. 10 − 6 4

APPLY

MATH REASONING Give the fact family for each pair of addends. See Additional Answers.

27. 4, 9
28. 6, 8
29. 3, 6
30. 7, 7

PROBLEM SOLVING

31. Keri has 8 animal stickers. How many more will she need to put one on each month of a calendar she is making? 4 stickers

32. Tim's sister gave him 7 snail shells. He found 6 more. How many more than a dozen does he have? 1 snail shell

▶ CALCULATOR

Enter the number 18 into a calculator and push these keys. [−] [9] [=] [=]

If 0 appears, your calculator has a subtraction constant. Estimate how many times you will have to subtract to reach 0 in each problem. Check.

33. Enter 24. Subtract 6. 4
34. Enter 144. Subtract 12. 12
35. Enter 48. Subtract 3. 16
36. Enter 56. Subtract 4. 14

More Practice, page 512, set D

3. Practice and Apply

Basic	3-21, 29-34
Average	1-36
Extended	3-36

1-3

Additional Answers: See p. T79.

PRACTICE

Look at Exercises 5-26. Which two methods could you use to find the answers? (subtract the second number from the first; find the missing addend)

APPLY

MATH REASONING ▶ In Exercises 27-30, which has only one addition and one subtraction fact? (Example 30)

PROBLEM SOLVING ▶ What must you know to solve Problem 31? (There are 12 months on a calendar.) **To solve Problem 32?** (There are 12 in a dozen.)

CALCULATOR ▶ Predict which exercises will allow you to subtract many times before reaching 0. Explain. (Exercises 34-36; The greater the difference between the numbers, the more times you can subtract.)

Close and Assess

SAY WHAT YOU THINK *Have students respond to this question: How are subtraction and addition related?* (Possible answer: To add, you join two parts to make a total. To subtract, you take away one of the parts from the total and leave the other part.)

Quick Quiz

Find each answer.

What number minus 3 equals 7? (10)
What number minus 6 equals 5? (11)
What number minus 0 equals 9? (9)
What number minus 7 equals 5? (12)

LESSON OPTIONS 1-4

Problem Solving: Introduction

OBJECTIVE 1-4 To use the 6-point problem solving checklist to solve problems

PREBOOK ACTIVITIES

QUICK REVIEW

Add or subtract.

1.	6 + 7 (13)	**2.**	15 − 8 (7)
3.	4 + 9 (13)	**4.**	5 + 5 (10)
5.	7 − 0 (7)	**6.**	5 + 3 + 8 (16)
7.	11 − 3 (8)	**8.**	0 + 9 (9)
9.	9 + 7 (16)	**10.**	4 + 8 + 0 (12)

PRIOR KNOWLEDGE

Have students suggest types of lists they have used. (Possible answers: shopping list; class telephone list; homework assignment sheet; spelling words to study) Have them explain how such lists can be useful. (Possible answers: to help you remember things; to compare things already done with things that still need to be done; to record things in a certain order)

COMMUNICATION

Discussing and Writing Math Have students list the following 6 steps in their Math Journals: (1) Understand the situation. (2) Find data. (3) Plan the solution. (4) Estimate the answer. (5) Solve the problem. (6) Check the answer. Have students express the meaning of each step in their own words. (Answers may vary.) Have them justify the order of the steps. (Possible answer: First, you must understand what the problem is asking. Next, it makes sense to find the data to consider and to plan how to solve the problem. Then, if you estimate an answer, you can tell if your solution seems reasonable. After solving a problem, you check that the answer makes sense.)

EXPLORE AND CONNECT

COOPERATIVE ACTIVITY

Grouping Suggestion: small groups

12 science club members share a microscope to look very closely at a strand of hair. So far, 7 students have seen the hair, which looks like a tree branch. How many students are still waiting their turn?

TEACHING ACTIONS

Organize students into small groups. Groups work together to discuss steps and decisions related to the solution.

BEFORE

► **Explain the situation in your own words.** (You want to know how many students in a science club have not yet looked in the microscope to see the strand of hair.)

► **Analyze the problem for the important data.** (12 students in the club; 7 have already looked)

DURING

► **How would you plan a solution?** (Choose an operation that will result in the difference between the 2 numbers.)

► **Justify the operation to use.** (Subtraction gives a difference between 2 numbers.)

► **Identify the number fact that can help.** (5 + 7 = 12)

AFTER

► **How can you check that your answer makes sense?** (5 + 7 = 12, so 12 − 7 = 5; 5 members have not seen the hair.)

► **How else might you have solved the problem?** (Answers may vary.)

CONNECTIONS Use these anytime.

Problem of the Day

Creative Thinking Solve the following problem, then explain your solution: 2 coins have a value of 6¢. 1 coin is not a penny. What are the 2 coins? (a penny and a nickel; although *one* is not a penny, the *other* is.)

Math Connection

Calculator What keystrokes would you use to solve this problem? Kay's new puppy howled for 25 min. Then he chewed on her slippers for 15 min. How long did the puppy annoy Kay? (Enter 25; press +, enter 15, press =.)

Subject Integration

Language Arts Create a story problem about chipmunks that uses the equation 8 + 9 + 6 = 23. (Sample problem: *One afternoon, a chipmunk gathered 8 acorns and 9 chestnuts. His brother gathered 6 acorns. How many nuts did the 2 chipmunks collect all together?*)

Classwork and Homework Supplements

Practice

Problem Solving 1-4

Name

Problem Solving: Introduction

Ring the letter of the number sentence you could use to solve these problems. Do not solve.

Heights of Some Buildings

Buildings	Location	Height
Sears Tower	Chicago	443 m
Empire State Building	New York	381 m
Transamerica Pyramid	San Francisco	260 m
Peachtree Plaza	Atlanta	229 m
Terminal Tower	Cleveland	216 m

1. How much higher is the Empire State Building than Peachtree Plaza?
   (A) 381 − 229
   B 381 + 229
2. What is the sum of the heights of Peachtree Plaza and Terminal Tower?
   A 229 − 216
   (B) 229 + 216
3. Sears Tower is how much higher than the Transamerica Pyramid?
   A 443 + 260
   (B) 443 − 260
4. What is the difference in height between Sears Tower and Peachtree Plaza?
   (A) 443 − 229
   B 443 + 229

Solve these problems.

5. The Fox Building has 16 floors. The Harris Building has 9 floors. How many more floors does the Fox Building have? 7 floors
6. Josh got on the elevator on floor 5. He went up 7 floors to the top. How many floors are in the building? 12 floors

Building Thinking Skills

Problem Solving 1-4

Name

Playground Problems

Fill in the blanks with numbers so that the answer in the box is correct. Then use the 3 numbers to create an equation. Answers will vary.

1. There were _____ children playing on the swings and _____ children playing on the slide. How many children were playing on the swings and slides altogether? [11]
2. _____ fourth graders were jumping rope. _____ of them went inside. How many were left? [15]
3. Team A scored _____ runs in the kickball game. Team B scored _____ runs. How many more runs did Team B score? [5]
4. There were _____ boys and _____ girls playing basketball on the court. How many children were playing basketball? [12]
5. _____ fourth graders and _____ third graders were getting drinks at the fountain. How many children were getting drinks? [14]

Reteaching

Problem Solving 1-4

Name

Introduction

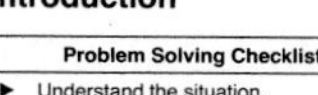

Problem Solving Checklist
► Understand the situation.
► Find data.
► Plan the solution.
► Estimate the answer.
► Solve the problem.
► Check.

The checklist can help you solve problems.

Ring the number sentence you could use to solve each problem.

1. Robin picked 15 apples. She ate 6 of them. How many did she have left?
   Understand: How many apples left?
   Data: apples to start: 15; apples eaten: 6
   Plan: To find the number left, you subtract.
   a. (15 − 6) **b.** 15 + 6
2. John picked 10 bushels of oranges one week. The next week he picked 14 bushels. How many bushels did he pick?
   Understand: How many in all?
   Data: oranges one week: 10 bushels; next week: 14 bushels
   Plan: To find the number in all, you add.
   a. (10 + 14) **b.** 14 − 10

Solve these problems.

3. Sandy sold 7 bushels of apples one day and 8 bushels the next. How many bushels did she sell? 15 bushels
4. Tom sold 12 bags of potatoes. Larry sold 7 bags. How many more bags did Tom sell? 5 bags
5. Sally bought 16 ears of yellow corn and 9 ears of white corn. How many fewer ears of white corn did she have? 7 ears
6. Bill sold 8 squash and Patty sold 6. How many did they sell altogether? 14 squash

Challenges

Cooperative Activities 1-4

Name

Let's Write a Script

Work in small groups to create story problems.
Exchange problems with other groups to solve.
You may use the ideas below or make up some of your own.

Settings
Planet Jupiter
Haunted house
King Arthur's court
Hot air balloon race

Characters
Monsters
Aliens
Ghosts
Knights
Ordinary people

Operations
Addition
Subtraction

Numbers
2 through 18

Answers will vary. Sample answer shown.

1. At the hot air balloon race Pia saw 3 red balloons go up. Then she saw 5 blue balloons. How many did she see in all?
2.
3.
4.
5.
6.

Options for Individual Needs

1-4

Basic

Exercises 1-6, 8a
Skills Bank, pp. 461, 463
More Practice, p. 512, set E

Supplements
Reteaching 4 or
Practice 4

Average

Exercises 1-8
Skills Bank, pp. 461, 463
More Practice, p. 512, set E

Supplements
Practice 4
Challenges 4 or
Thinking Skills 4

Extended

Exercises 1-4, 6-8

Supplements
Challenges 4
Thinking Skills 4

Other Resources:
Problem-Solving Experiences in Mathematics, Grade 4, Problem 10
Mathematics, A Way of Thinking, Lesson 4-9
Math In Stride, Grade 4, p. 15

LESSON PLAN 1-4

OBJECTIVE 1-4
To use the 6-point problem-solving checklist to solve problems

Grouping Suggestion: pairs

1. MOTIVATE AND TEACH

LEARN ABOUT IT

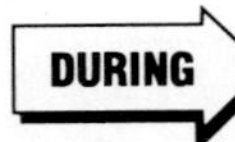

► **Explain the goal of the problem.** (to compare the different numbers of hours 2 animals usually sleep in a day)
► **Analyze the problem for the important data.** (the opposum sleeps 19 h; the wolf sleeps 13 h.)

► **Explain which operation makes sense to use to solve the problem.** (subtraction; You want to compare 2 times.)
► **Analyze why this is called a 1-step problem.** (You can solve it by the 1 operation of subtraction.)
► **How would you estimate the answer?** (Estimates may vary.)
► **Justify your calculation method.** (Methods may vary.)

AFTER

► **How would you present the solution?** (Possible response: A North American opossum sleeps 6 hours a day longer than a gray wolf.)
► **Explain how to check if the answer makes sense.** (6 + 13 = 19; use models; count on)

2. CHECK UNDERSTANDING

TRY IT OUT

► **How can you decide which number sentences fit the problems?** (Understand the situation to determine which action is required, then choose the operation related to that action.)

ERROR ALERT Choosing the wrong operation.

Problem Solving
Introduction

LEARN ABOUT IT

Problems you can solve using one addition or one subtraction equation are called one-step problems. For one-step problems, you can use the strategy **Choose the Operation.**

A North American opossum sleeps 19 hours a day. A gray wolf sleeps 13 hours a day. How many more hours does an opossum sleep than a gray wolf?

The checklist can help you solve problems.

Understand the Situation — I want to compare the number of hours each animal sleeps.

Find Data — North American opossum: 19 hours
Gray wolf: 13 hours

Plan the Solution — Since I want to compare the two numbers, I should subtract.

Estimate the Answer — 19 − 13 is about 20 − 15 or 5.

Solve the Problem — 19 − 13 = 6
An opossum sleeps 6 hours more than a gray wolf.

Check the Answer — 6 is close to the estimate of 5, so 6 hours is a reasonable answer.

TRY IT OUT

Pick the number sentence you could use to solve the problem. Do not solve.

1. A giant armadillo sleeps 18 out of 24 hours. How long is it awake?
   a. 24 − 18 **b.** 24 + 18

2. A roe deer sleeps 730 hours in a year. A rhesus monkey sleeps 2,555 more hours than a roe deer. How long does a rhesus monkey sleep in a year?
   a. 2,555 − 730 **b.** 2,555 + 730

TEACHING OPTIONS

RETEACHING TIPS Have students verbalize how each given equation would relate to the situation. For instance, in Problem 1, 24 + 18 would mean that the giant armadillo sleeps 24 h *and* 18 h, which does not fit the situation. For additional review, assign Reteaching Supplement 4.

COMPUTER Puzzle Tanks, Sunburst Communications, Copyright 1985 For use with all levels of students. Students add or subtract the amount of liquid contained in 2 tanks to fill a third to a given level. They should be urged to use paper-and-pencil strategies. The game requires 15-20 min.

MIXED PRACTICE

Pick the number sentence you could use to solve these problems.

1. How much more sleep does a giant sloth get than a mountain beaver?
   a. <u>20 − 11</u> **b.** 20 + 11
2. The black bear weighed 346 pounds when it went into hibernation. It lost 112 pounds in hibernation. How much does it weigh now?
   a. 346 + 112 **b.** <u>346 − 112</u>
3. During winter vacation, Melissa slept 70 hours the first week. She slept 72 hours the second week. How much sleep did she get during vacation?
   a. <u>70 + 72</u> **b.** 72 − 70

Animal	Hours of Sleep Per Day
Arctic ground squirrel	16
Giant armadillo	18
Giant sloth	20
Goat	3
Gray seal	6
Mountain beaver	11
North American opossum	19
Owl monkey	17
Rhesus monkey	9

Solve these problems.

4. The owl monkey has already slept 9 hours. How many more hours will he sleep today? **8 hours**
5. Lincoln the cat slept 7 hours during the day. Then he slept 7 hours at night. How many hours did he sleep all together? **14 hours**
6. There were 12 newborn chincilla rabbits sleeping in a hutch. 5 woke up. How many were still asleep? **7 rabbits**
7. How many fewer hours a day does a goat sleep than a North American opossum? **16 hours**
8. **Write Your Own Problem** Write two questions that can be answered using the data given in the table and the equations below.
   a. 20 − 3 **b.** 6 + 6 **Answers will vary.**

More Practice, page 512, set E

for pages 10-11

1-4

3. Practice and Apply

Basic	1-6, 8a
Average	1-8
Extended	1-4, 6-8

Sample Solutions: See p. T79.

PRACTICE

▶ **Explain how Problems 1 and 7 relate.** (Both use subtraction.)

▶ **Explain the situation in Problem 2 by restating it in your own words.** (Possible answer: *While a black bear had its long winter nap, it lost 112 of its 346 lb. What does the bear weigh now?)*

▶ **Justify the operation to use to solve Problem 5.** (Add to find the total amount of sleep.)

▶ **Explain how the equations in Problem 8 relate to data in the table.** (The numbers 20, 3, and 6 relate to hours of sleep for a giant sloth, a goat, and a gray seal.)

Close and Assess

SAY WHAT YOU THINK Have students work in pairs. They decide together how each step of the problem-solving checklist may be used to solve this problem: A gray seal sleeps 6 hours a day. How much sleep does it get in 2 days? (12 h; Check students' explanations.)

Quick Quiz

Solve the problem: Diane counted birds that fed at her new bird feeder. She saw 13 larks and 7 wrens. How many birds did she see? How many more larks fed than wrens? (20; 6)

LESSON OPTIONS 1-5

Using Critical Thinking/Midchapter Review/Quiz

OBJECTIVE 1-5 To use critical thinking to solve number riddles

PREBOOK ACTIVITIES

QUICK REVIEW

Give the numbers.

1. odd number from 1 to 13 (1, 3, 5, 7, 9, 11, 13)
2. even numbers from 2 to 14 (2, 4, 6, 8, 10, 12 ,14)
3. the least and the greatest 2-digit numbers (10, 99)
4. the least and the greatest 3-digit numbers (100, 999)

PRIOR KNOWLEDGE

Have students explain what a riddle is. (Possible answer: "a question you solve using whatever clues are given") Have volunteers pose some riddles they know and call on individuals to respond. Have students identify any clues in the riddles that specifically relate to the answers.

COMMUNICATION

Discussing Math Point out that silly riddles are meant to be entertaining, while serious riddles are meant to involve reasoning or logical thinking. Have students classify the riddles their classmates shared into these 2 categories, generalizing how they are alike and different. Have students tell why it is important to accout for *all* clues when you attempt to solve a serious riddle. (Possible answer: If you leave out a clue, you might miss the real answer or not notice multiple answers.) You may wish to share with students several riddles and mind challengers from the following books: *The Biggest Riddle Book in the World* by Joseph Rosenbloom (New York: Sterling, 1976) and *Mind Benders* by Anita Harnadek (Pacific Grove, CA: Midwest Publications, 1978).

EXPLORE AND CONNECT

Materials: TA 3 (Number Cards 0-9)
Grouping Suggestion: 10 cooperative learning groups
Students formulate simple riddles for the digits 0-9. Divide the class into 10 groups. Give each group a number card and ask that its members not reveal the number to other groups. Each group member writes 1 clue that will be part of a riddle whose answer is the given digit. Students may use math-related clues or clues based on any other real-life application. For instance, clues for 3 might be: *This is an odd number. This is how many sides in a triangle. This is how many vowels in the word* Idaho.
Conclude by having groups pose their riddles for others to guess until all 10 digits have been revealed.

CONNECTIONS Use these anytime.

Problem of the Day

Impossible Riddle Roland made up a riddle for the number 20: You say this number when you count by fives; it is more than 2 tens. When his sister tried to solve it, she found that it was impossible. Discover Roland's mistake. (The second clue should say *equal to 2 tens*)

Math Connection

Calculator On a calculator display, one group of digits look the same upside-down or right-side up, while another group looks different when upside-down compared to right-side up. Which group has a greater number of digits? Prove your solution. (The groups have equal numbers of digits; same: 0, 1, 2, 5, 8; different: 3, 4, 6, 7, 9.)

Subject Integration

Social Studies Make up a riddle whose answer is your state. Use a U.S. map or a list of the states to help you think of special clues that fit only your state. (Answers will vary.)

Classwork and Homework Supplements

Practice

Math Reasoning 1-5

Name

Using Critical Thinking

Solve these secret number riddles.

1. I am odd.
I am between 10 and 20.
You say me when you count by 3s.
What number am I? 15

2. I am a 3-digit number.
All 3 digits are the same.
I could not be any greater.
What number am I? 999

3. I am even.
I am between 10 and 20.
You multiply two of the same numbers by each other to get me as a product.
What number am I? 16

4. I am a 2-digit number.
My digits are the same.
You say me when you count by 5s.
What number am I? 55

5. I am even.
I am between 20 and 30.
You say me when you count by 4s and 6s.
What number am I? 24

6. I am odd.
You say me when you count by 5s.
You multiply two of the same numbers by each other to get me as a product.
What number am I? 25

7. I am a 3-digit number.
I am odd.
Add my digits and you get 3.
What number am I? 201; 111

8. I am a 2-digit number.
I am even.
Add my digits and you get 4.
What number am I? 22; 40

PS-4 Use with text page 12. 5

Building Thinking Skills

Family Math 1-5

Name

Be a Puzzle Writer

Dear Family,
Your child has been learning how to use thinking skills to solve riddles. Here is an activity that you can do together to help sharpen the skill.

Have you ever wondered who writes the puzzles in newspapers or magazines? Anybody can, including you! Try writing one yourself with your family.

[1] 1	5			

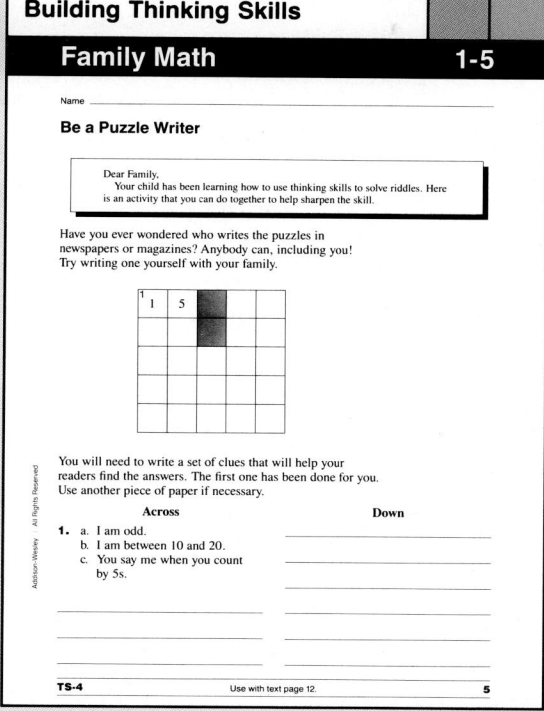

You will need to write a set of clues that will help your readers find the answers. The first one has been done for you. Use another piece of paper if necessary.

Across

1. a. I am odd.
b. I am between 10 and 20.
c. You say me when you count by 5s.

Down

TS-4 Use with text page 12. 5

Reteaching

Critical Thinking 1-5

Name

Using Critical Thinking

What number am I?

1. I am a 2-digit number between 9 and 19.
2. I am odd.
3. I could not be any less.

Write answers for sentence 1. → Write answers for sentence 2. → Write answers for sentence 3.

10, 11, 12, 13, 14, 15, 16, 17, 18 → 11, 13, 15, 17 → 11 The least 2-digit, odd number is...11

Solve these secret number riddles.

1. a. I am a 3-digit number.
b. All my digits are the same.
c. I could not be any greater.
What number am I? 999

2. a. I am an even number.
b. I am between 1 and 10.
c. I could not be any smaller.
What number am I? 2

3. a. I am between 20 and 30.
b. I am odd.
c. You say me when you count by fives.
What number am I? 25

4. a. I am an odd number.
b. I am between 10 and 20.
c. My difference with 8 is less than 4.
What number am I? 11

5. a. I am not a 2-digit number.
b. I am even.
c. My sum with 9 is between 15 and 20.
What number am I? 8

6. a. I am less than 10.
b. I am a double.
c. My product with 4 is more than 25.
What number am I? 8

7. Make up a secret number riddle. Give it to a classmate to solve.

RS-4 Use with text pages 12-13. 5

Challenges

Math Reasoning 1-5

Name

Incomplete Clues

Complete the clues below so that there is only one answer for each problem. Answers may vary.

1.
1. I am odd.
2. I am a 2-digit number.
3. I could not be any smaller.
Who am I? 11

2.
1. I am a double.
2. If you add 3 to me, my sum is not a 2-digit number.
3. I am a 1-digit number.
4. When you count by 3s, you say me.
Who am I? 6

3.
1. I am even.
2. I am a double.
3. I am between 10 and 18.
4. If you subtract 9 from me, the difference is greater than 5.
Who am I? 16

4.
1. I am greater than 99.
2. I am less than 900.
3. I am even.
4. I am the largest number I could be.
Who am I? 898

5.
1. When you count by 3s, you say me.
2. I am between 4 and 16.
3. I am not an odd number.
4. I am a 1-digit number.
Who am I? 6

6.
1. I am not an even number.
2. I am a 3-digit number.
3. I am the largest number I could be.
4. I have no tens.
Who am I? 909

CS-4 Use with text page 12. 5

Options for Individual Needs

1-5

Basic

Exercises 1-3; 1-16, 21-29
Computer Bank, p. 495

Supplements
Reteaching 5 or
Practice 5

Average

Exercises 1-3; 1-29
Computer Bank, p. 495

Supplements
Practice 5
Challenges 5 or
Thinking Skills 5

Extended

Exercises 1-3; 4-16, 22-29
Computer Bank, p. 495

Supplements
Challenges 5
Thinking Skills 5

Other Resources:

Problem-Solving Experiences in Mathematics, Grade 4, Problem 27
Mathematics, A Way of Thinking, Lesson 4-10

LESSON PLAN 1-5

OBJECTIVE 1-5
To use critical thinking to solve number riddles

Materials: TA 4 (Hundred Chart)

1. MOTIVATE AND TEACH

LEARN ABOUT IT

TALK ABOUT IT ► **Explain in your own words what Teri asked her friends.** (She asked them to use 3 clues to figure out a secret number.)
► **Explain why the first clue does not give enough information to solve the riddle.** (Even numbers are all numbers ending in 0, 2, 4, 6, or 8.)
► **Explain how the second clue narrows the choices.** (It eliminates 10 and 20 as possibilities.)
► **How would you consider 10 and 20?** (Think of numbers *greater* than 10 and *less* than 20.)
► **Interpret the third clue.** (Count by fours, eliminate numbers you *do* say, then see which numbers remain.)
► **Explain a way Teri could avoid 2 answers to her riddle.** (Add a fourth clue to exclude a number.)
Student Edition answers: **1.** a number riddle; Bill answers quickly, thinking the riddle is easy; Jessica sees 2 answers. **2.** all even numbers; 12, 14, 16, 18; 14, 18 **3.** Yes, neither 14 nor 18 is a multiple of 4. **4.** Answers may vary. Sample clue: *You do say me when you count by threes.*

2. CHECK UNDERSTANDING

TRY IT OUT

ERROR ALERT **Exercises 1 and 2** Failing to combine all clues. **Exercise 3** Making up an impossible riddle.

Using Critical Thinking

LEARN ABOUT IT

Teri gave this secret number riddle to Jessica and Bill.
"Well," said Bill, after thinking a minute. "This riddle is easy. The answer is the same number as my brother's age, 14!"
"Not so fast, Bill," said Jessica. "I think you missed something. This riddle has two answers!"

1. I'm even.
2. I am not 10 or 20 but I am between them.
3. You don't say me when you count by fours.

What number am I?

TALK ABOUT IT See teaching notes.

1. What does Teri ask? How do her friends reply?
2. What numbers are possible after the first clue? the second? the third?
3. Do you agree with Jessica that the riddle has two answers? Explain.
4. Can you give one more clue that would make the riddle have only one answer?

TRY IT OUT

Solve these secret number riddles.

1. a. I'm a double.
   b. I'm not a 2-digit number but I'm less than 100.
   c. My sum with 4 is more than 10.
   What number am I? 8
2. a. I'm a 3-digit number.
   b. I'm not odd.
   c. I couldn't be any greater.
   What number am I? 998
3. Make up a secret number riddle. Write 3 clues for your riddle. Give it to a classmate to solve. Answers will vary.

12

TEACHING OPTIONS

RETEACHING TIPS For Exercise 1, students circle numbers on a hundred chart that fit the first clue (all even numbers). Eliminate circled numbers that do *not* fit the next clue. (all 2-digit numbers; 100) Fit the third clue. (2, 4, 6, 8) Use Reteaching Supplement 5.

ENRICHMENT **Family Math** At home, students pick a mystery number that family members try to guess by asking questions that can be answered *Yes* or *No*. Suppose that a student picks 75 and a family member asks, *Is it a 3-digit number?* (No.) Guessers can ask 20 questions.

Midchapter Review/Quiz

Find the sums.

1. 4 + 7 = 11
2. 7 + 4 = 11
3. 2 + 3 + 4 = 9
4. 5 + 0 + 6 = 11
5. 7 + 3 + 4 = 14

6. 8 + 0 — 8
7. 9 + 3 — 12
8. 3 + 4 — 7
9. (2 + 3) + 5 — 10
10. 8 + (2 + 3) — 13
11. (8 + 2) + 3 — 13
12. 8 + 0 + 5 — 13
13. 5 + 3 + 3 — 11

Write the addition fact you could use to answer each subtraction problem.

14. 12 − 7 = ? — 7 + 5 = 12
15. 8 − 8 = ? — 8 + 0 = 8
16. 5 − 4 = ? — 4 + 1 = 5
17. 16 − 9 = ? — 9 + 7 = 16

Find the differences.

18. 8 − 5 = 3
19. 18 − 9 = 9
20. 10 − 6 = 4
21. 4 − 0 = 4
22. 6 − 6 = 0
23. 14 − 8 = 6

Decide if you would add or subtract to answer each question.

24. 6 robins are in a tree. 4 cardinals join them.
 a. How many birds are in the tree? add
 b. How many fewer cardinals are there than robins? subtract

25. 7 baby foxes live in a den. 4 are playing inside the den. 1 leaves the den to be with the foxes outside.
 a. How many baby foxes are in the den? subtract
 b. How many baby foxes are not in the den? add and subtract

PROBLEM SOLVING

26. Today Jeno found 3 starfish. Yesterday he found 6. How many starfish has he found? 9 starfish

27. Liz needs 5 more shells to have as many as Tim has. If Liz has 8 shells, how many does Tim have? 13 shells

28. Two numbers have a sum of 15. One number is 9. What is the other number? 6

29. Find two numbers whose sum is 12. What is the difference between the two numbers? Answers will vary.

13

Close and Assess

WRITE WHAT YOU THINK To solve this number riddle, have students explain all possible answers to each clue to show how their reasoning led them to the answer.
1. I am a 2-digit number.
2. I am not even.
3. I am a coin value.
(25; Check students' writing.)

Quick Quiz

What number am I?
1. I am a 2-digit number. **2.** I am the same backward and forward. **3.** My sum with 1 is a 3-digit number. (99)

3. Practice and Apply

1-5

Basic	1-3; 1-16, 21-29
Average	1-3; 1-29
Extended	1-3; 4-16, 22-29

PRACTICE

How are Exercises 1-2 and 3-5 alike and different? (All are vertical addition; 3-5 have 3 addends.) *How do Exercises 12 and 13 differ from Exercises 9-11?* (Exercises 9-11 include parentheses; in Exercises 12 and 13 you choose the grouping.) *How do you solve Problems 24 and 25?* (choose the operations)

ITEM ANALYSIS The following table correlates the Midchapter Review/Quiz items with the lesson objectives.

Items	Objectives
1-13	1-2
14-23	1-3
24, 25	
(26-29)	1-1
26-29	1-4

LESSON OPTIONS 1-6

Mental Math: Breaking Apart Numbers

OBJECTIVE 1-6 To use the mental math technique of break apart to find sums

PREBOOK ACTIVITIES

QUICK REVIEW

Find the sum of each pair of doubles.

1. 3 + 3 (6)	**2.** 6 + 6 (12)	**3.** 9 + 9 (18)
4. 4 + 4 (8)	**5.** 8 + 8 (16)	**6.** 7 + 7 (14)
7. 2 + 2 (4)	**8.** 5 + 5 (10)	**9.** 1 + 1 (2)

PRIOR KNOWLEDGE

Write 4 + 4 + 6 and 8 + 6 on the chalkboard. Have students invent two related situations in which those numbers would be added. (For example: Ed buys 4 comics, 4 magazines, and 6 markers; Ed buys 8 things to read and 6 drawing tools.) Have students recall what they know about grouping and order in addition. (You can group and add numbers in any order without changing the sum.)

COMMUNICATION

Discussing and Writing in Math Have students describe what it means to break apart a jigsaw puzzle. (Possible answer: to separate the pieces) Have students contrast that kind of breaking apart with the breaking apart of an egg. (Possible answer: Puzzle pieces can be put back together, a broken egg cannot.) Ask which kind of breaking apart makes sense in terms of a number amount, such as 10. (Breaking apart a number amount is like the puzzle: It can be put back together.) Have students write an explanation in their Math Journals of how they might break apart a group of 10 objects without changing the total. (Check students' writing.)

EXPLORE AND CONNECT

Materials: snap cubes, TA 3 (Number Cards 5-9)
Alternative Materials: counters
Grouping Suggestion: small cooperative learning groups
Divide students into groups. Each group needs snap cubes and number cards 5-9. A student randomly draws two number cards to form a pair of addends. Students use their knowledge of order and grouping to experiment breaking apart and rearranging the addends to see which arrangements make addition easier. They model the addends with snap cubes or counters, demonstrate the rearrangements they find, and then discuss which ones facilitate addition. A group member records the addends, how they were broken apart and rearranged, and which kinds of rearrangements worked best. Students take turns drawing addends, rearranging them, demonstrating the groupings with snap cubes or counters, and recording findings.

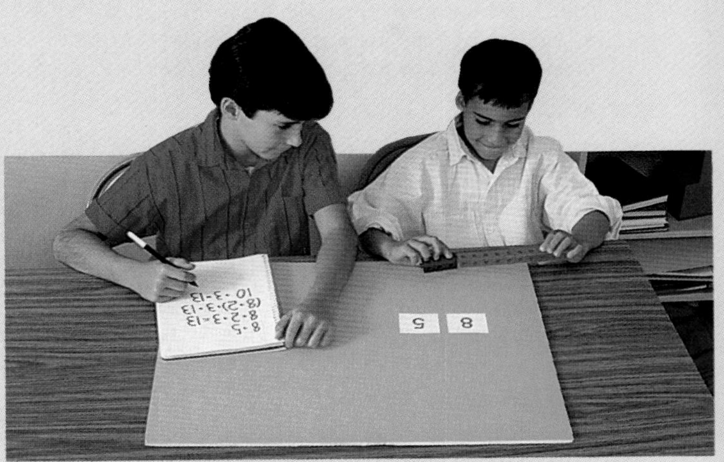

CONNECTIONS Use these anytime.

Problem of the Day

Darts Pam scored 19. How much was each dart throw worth? (Answers may vary. Sample is 9, 5, and 5.)

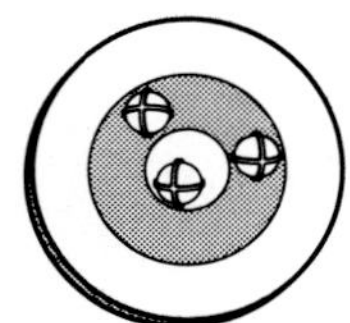

Patterns

Sequence Study the pattern and then give the next three numbers: 1, 1, 2, 3, 5, 8, 13, 21, ______, ______, ______. (Fibonacci sequence: A number is the sum of the two numbers before it; 34, 55, 89.)

Math Connection

Mental Math Break apart each of the following numbers to show them as sums of three consecutive numbers: 3, 9, 15. (0 + 1 + 2 = 3; 2 + 3 + 4 = 9; 4 + 5 + 6 = 15)

Classwork and Homework Supplements

Practice

Mental Math 1-6

Name ______

Breaking Apart Numbers

Use mental math to add.
If you need help, break apart an addend.

1. 7 + 6 = 13	**2.** 3 + 8 = 11	**3.** 6 + 5 = 11	**4.** 5 + 7 = 12	**5.** 9 + 3 = 12
6. 15 + 3 = 18	**7.** 9 + 7 = 16	**8.** 5 + 9 = 14	**9.** 7 + 3 = 10	**10.** 14 + 5 = 19
11. 4 + 7 = 11	**12.** 11 + 6 = 17	**13.** 2 + 9 = 11	**14.** 8 + 7 = 15	**15.** 8 + 5 = 13
16. 6 + 8 = 14	**17.** 9 + 4 = 13	**18.** 13 + 6 = 19	**19.** 9 + 5 = 14	**20.** 8 + 3 = 11
21. 4 + 8 = 12	**22.** 6 + 9 = 15	**23.** 8 + 8 = 16	**24.** 12 + 5 = 17	**25.** 3 + 6 = 9

26. 12 + 3 = 15 **27.** 6 + 7 = 13 **28.** 15 + 4 = 19

29. 7 + 5 = 12 **30.** 11 + 4 = 15 **31.** 2 + 9 = 11

32. 6 + 6 = 12 **33.** 3 + 8 = 11 **34.** 5 + 6 = 11

Building Thinking Skills

Mental Math 1-6

Name ______

Crafts and Bake Sale

Carolyn's 4-H Club is having a crafts-and-bake sale. The girls are making craft items such as potholders and placemats. They are also baking cookies and cakes.

Use mental math to solve each problem below. Use the numbers in the boxes to write the addends as a **Double + 1** or **Make 10 plus a number.** The first one has been done for you. Answers may vary.

1 2 3 4 5
6 7 8 9

1. Carolyn needs 8 tables for the craft items and 9 tables for the baked goods. How many tables does she need altogether?

8 + 8 + 1 = 17 (9)

2. Sumi made 4 potholders on Thursday and 5 potholders on Friday. How many potholders did she make altogether?

4 + 4 + 1 = 9

3. Tamara sold 8 placemats and 6 potholders. How many items did she sell?

8 + 2 + 4 = 14

4. Angelina made 8 dolls with yellow hair and 5 dolls with brown hair. How many dolls did she make?

8 + 2 + 3 = 13

5. During the first hour, 8 people drank lemonade, and 4 people drank juice. How many people had something to drink during that hour?

8 + 2 + 2 = 12

6. Dominique made 9 big birdhouses and 6 little birdhouses. How many birdhouses did she make?

9 + 1 + 5 = 15

Reteaching

Mental Math 1-6

Name ______

Breaking Apart Numbers

12 + 5 = 10 + 2 + 5
12 equals 10 plus 2
10 plus 2 plus 5 = 17

Use mental math to add.
It may help to break apart an addend.

1. 4 + 9 = 13 **2.** 14 + 3 = 17 **3.** 12 + 4 = 16

4. 11 + 6 = 17 **5.** 17 + 2 = 19 **6.** 8 + 6 = 14

Use mental math to add.
If you need help, break apart an addend.

7. 9 + 3 = 12	**8.** 8 + 9 = 17	**9.** 4 + 5 = 9	**10.** 6 + 7 = 13	**11.** 6 + 5 = 11
12. 11 + 6 = 17	**13.** 14 + 5 = 19	**14.** 12 + 6 = 18	**15.** 10 + 9 = 19	**16.** 7 + 8 = 15

Use mental math and the doubles in the table to find these sums.

138 + 138 = 276
26 + 26 = 52
87 + 87 = 174

17. 27 + 26 = 53

18. 86 + 87 = 173

19. 138 + 139 = 277

Challenges

Family Math 1-6

Name ______

Sum Crossouts

Dear Family:
Our class has just learned how to break apart numbers as a strategy for addition. The game below gives your child an opportunity to share the skill with you.

Two or three people can play this game. You will need two number cubes and a calculator.

Make one playing strip for each player for each game.

1	2	3	4	5	6	7	8	9	10	11	12

Rules

1. Take turns rolling one number cube to decide who goes first.
2. When it is your turn, roll both number cubes and find the sum.
3. On your playing strip, either cross off the sum **or** any group of numbers that add up to the sum.

Example: You roll a sum of 11.
Here are two possibilities:

1	2	3	4	5	6	7	8	9	10	X	12

or

1	X	3	X	X	6	7	8	9	10	11	12

4. The second player rolls the number cubes and crosses off numbers on his or her playing strip.
5. The game ends when each player has had three turns.
6. Add up the numbers on your playing strip that are not crossed off. Use a calculator if you need to. The player with the lowest score wins!

Options for Individual Needs

1-6

Basic

Exercises 7-18, 22-35
Skills Bank, pp. 461, 463
Calculator Bank, p. 485
More Practice, p. 500, set B

Supplements
Reteaching 6 or
Practice 6

Average

Exercises 1-35
Calculator Bank, p. 485
More Practice, p. 500, set B

Supplements
Practice 6
Challenges 6 or
Thinking Skills 6

Extended

Exercises 9-15, 19-35
Calculator Bank, p. 485

Supplements
Challenges 6
Thinking Skills 6

Other Resources:
Problem-Solving Experiences in Mathematics, Grade 4, Problem 30
Mathematics, A Way of Thinking, Lessons 4-12, 4-13

LESSON PLAN 1-6

OBJECTIVE 1-6
To use the mental math technique of break apart to find sums

Materials: snap cubes, number lines, ten tracks, addition fact cards for sums between 11 and 18

1. MOTIVATE AND TEACH

LEARN ABOUT IT

▶ **Explain why breaking apart a number does not change its value.** (Possible answer: When you break apart a number, you make a pair of addends, which can be combined in any order without changing the sum.)

EXPLORE ▶ **As you break apart and rearrange the 9 cubes, what rule can you say about a sum and the order of its addends?** (No matter how you order addends, the sum stays the same.)

TALK ABOUT IT ▶ **Tell how making doubles can help you find sums of addends that *are not* doubles.** (Regroup addends to form doubles, which are easy to remember, then add any remaining amount.)
▶ **Tell which addends that equal 10 can help you add 8 + 9.** (8 + 2 or 9 + 1)
Student Edition answers: **1.** 0 + 9, 9 + 0, 1 + 8, 8 + 1, 2 + 7, 7 + 2, 3 + 6, 6 + 3, 4 + 5, 5 + 4; 10 ways **2.** Answers will vary: 8 + 1 helps you make a double + 1 [8 + 8 + 1]; breaking apart 9 into 7 + 2 helps you make a 10, then add 7 [(8 + 2) + 7].

2. CHECK UNDERSTANDING

TRY IT OUT

ERROR ALERT Finding a double or a grouping of ten but forgetting to add on the remaining amount.

Mental Math
Breaking Apart Numbers

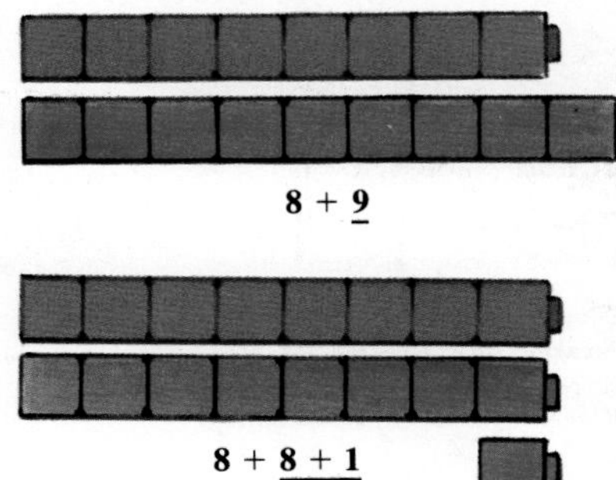

LEARN ABOUT IT

EXPLORE **Use Snap Cubes**
To help add numbers using mental math, you can break apart one of the addends. The snap cubes show one way to break apart the 9 in the sum 8 + 9.
Use snap cubes to show as many other ways as you can of breaking apart the 9.

TALK ABOUT IT See teaching notes.

1. Describe the ways you found. How many were there?
2. Which way helped you most in finding 8 + 9? Explain.

Here are two addition strategies that are useful when you need to break apart an addend.

Make a double + 1.

7 + 8 → 7 + 1
Break 8 into 7 + 1.
Find 7 + 7 plus 1.

Make 10 plus a number.

8 + 5 → 2 + 3
Break 5 into 2 + 3.
Find 8 + 2 plus 3.

13 + 2 → 10 + 3
Break 13 into 10 + 3.
Find 10 plus 3 + 2.

TRY IT OUT

Use mental math to add. It may help to break apart an addend.

1. 6 + 7 (13)	**2.** 8 + 5 (13)	**3.** 13 + 2 (15)	**4.** 7 + 6 (13)	**5.** 15 + 3 (18)
6. 5 + 11 (16)	**7.** 9 + 12 (21)	**8.** 13 + 6 (19)	**9.** 4 + 9 (13)	**10.** 7 + 11 (18)

14

TEACHING OPTIONS

RETEACHING TIPS When finding doubles, have students match snap-cube doubles to a number line, then add on remaining cubes. When they make groups of ten, students first fill a 10 track with snap cubes, then snap on any remaining cubes beyond ten. Assign Reteaching Supplement 6.

COMPUTER **Addition Magician, MECC, Copyright 1984** For students who need extra practice. Students use problem-solving skills and select the number of addends to group numbers to add up to the target number. The game requires 15 minutes to complete.

PRACTICE

Use mental math to add. If you need help, break apart an addend.

1.	2.	3.	4.	5.	6.
9 + 5	7 + 6	14 + 5	6 + 5	12 + 7	11 + 6
14	13	19	11	19	17

7.	8.	9.	10.	11.	12.
8 + 6	12 + 4	8 + 9	11 + 8	16 + 3	7 + 8
14	16	17	19	19	15

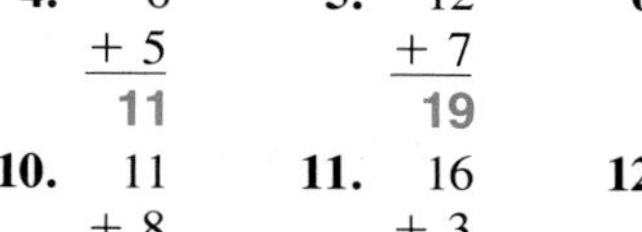

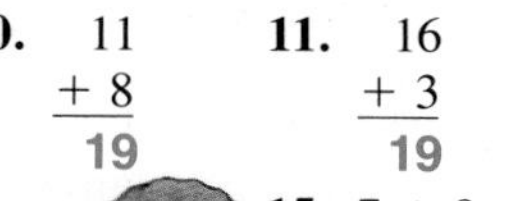

13. 14 + 5 = n
19
14. 11 + 6 = n
17
15. 7 + 9 = n
16

APPLY

MATH REASONING Use mental math and the doubles in the table to find these sums.

36 + 36 = 72
57 + 57 = 114
79 + 79 = 158
126 + 126 = 252

16. 36 + 37
73
17. 58 + 57
115
18. 78 + 78
156
19. 127 + 127
254
20. 35 + 37
72
21. 58 + 56
114

PROBLEM SOLVING

22. **Data Hunt** Add the number of letters in your first and last names. Find a classmate whose name sum is larger than yours. Find one whose name sum is smaller. **Answers will vary.**

23. Tim bought 6 animal stamps to put with the 9 he had already collected. How many did he then have?
15 stamps

MIXED REVIEW

Subtract. Think about finding the missing addend.

24.	25.	26.	27.	28.	29.
13 − 7	10 − 2	15 − 6	8 − 5	14 − 8	18 − 9
6	8	9	3	6	9

Add. If it is useful, break apart an addend.

30.	31.	32.	33.	34.	35.
13 + 0	6 + 9	12 + 7	9 + 8	2 + 16	15 + 4
13	15	19	17	18	19

More Practice, page 500, set B

15

3. PRACTICE AND APPLY

Basic	7-18, 22-35
Average	1-35
Extended	9-15, 19-35

1-6

PRACTICE

Look at Exercises 1-15. When would it be unnecessary to find a sum by breaking apart and then regrouping one of the addends to make ten plus a number? (when one of the addends is already ten or more)

APPLY

MATH REASONING ► **You do not need a calculator for Exercises 16-21. Why?** (knowing the boxed information is enough)

PROBLEM SOLVING ► **How can estimation help you answer Problem 22?** (Possible answer: estimate classmates' name lengths before you question them)

MIXED REVIEW ► **How can you use doubles or groups of ten when you subtract?** (Think of subtraction as finding missing addends and then use strategies to break apart and regroup.)

CLOSE AND ASSESS

SHOW WHAT YOU KNOW

Distribute snap cubes and addition fact cards for sums from 11-18 to groups of students. Students take turns using the cubes to model a way to find the sum by breaking apart and regrouping addends. (Check students' models.)

QUICK QUIZ

Find each sum using mental math.

1. 6 + 9 (15) **2.** 7 + 8 (15)
3. 15 + 4 (19) **4.** 6 + 13 (19)
5. 19 + 1 (20) **6.** 16 + 4 (20)
7. 9 + 3 (12) **8.** 7 + 5 (12)

LESSON OPTIONS 1-7

Mental Math: Using Compensation

OBJECTIVE 1-7 To use the mental math technique of compensation to find sums

PREBOOK ACTIVITIES

QUICK REVIEW

Add or subtract as quickly as you can.

1. 7 + 2 (9)	**2.** 9 − 1 (8)	**3.** 8 − 3 (5)
4. 9 + 1 (10)	**5.** 8 + 3 (11)	**6.** 7 + 3 (10)
7. 7 − 2 (5)	**8.** 9 − 3 (6)	**9.** 15 − 2 (13)

PRIOR KNOWLEDGE

Have students imagine lunch tables that seat eight. But one table has ten chairs and another has six. Ask students how each table differs from the standard tables. (One has two chairs too many, the other has two chairs too few.) Ask what students could do to get the standard number of seats at the tables. (Move two chairs from the table with too many and put them at the table with too few.) Have students relate the rearrangements to addition and subtraction. (Subtract two from the group that is too large, add that two to the group that is too small.) Ask how rearranging chairs affects the total number of chairs. (The total does not change.)

COMMUNICATION

Discussing and Writing in Math Write the word **compensation** on the chalkboard and pronounce it. Explain that compensation means making a balanced adjustment. Ask students to explain how compensation was used in the table scenario. (Chairs were rearranged: two were taken from the table with too many and added to the table with too few.) In their Math Journals, have students write an explanation of compensation.

EXPLORE AND CONNECT

Materials: counters or snap cubes, balance scales
Grouping Suggestion: small cooperative learning groups
Start with the whole group. Put eight counters or snap cubes in a pan on one side of a balance scale and four in the other pan. Have volunteers suggest ways to balance the scale without changing the sum, explaining their ideas as they try them. (**compensate** to make doubles) Then place the sets of eight and four on a table and have students explain how to *compensate* to make a grouping of ten. (Add or subtract from one addend to make ten, then *compensate* by adding or subtracting the same amount from the other addend.)
Now ask students to work in small groups with counters or snap cubes. One student makes two sets to be added. Another student rearranges the sets to make doubles or groups of ten by *compensation*. Another records a number sentence. Have students take turns at each task.

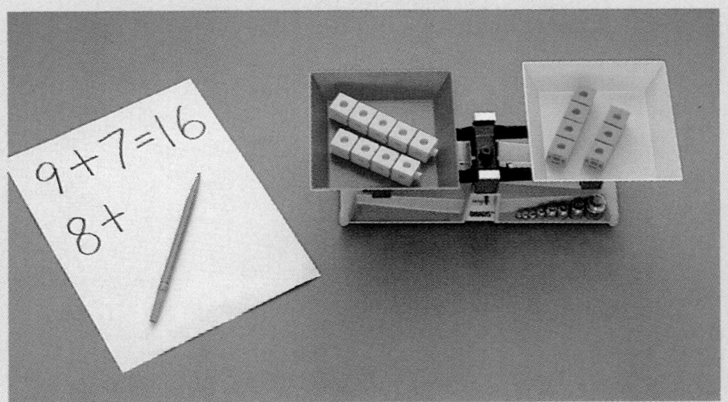

CONNECTIONS Use these anytime.

Problem of the Day

Clock Compensation Juan knows his watch runs fast. It speeds ahead 5 minutes for every hour. He resets his watch every day at noon. When Juan's watch says 3:00 p.m., what time is it really? (2:45 p.m.)

Math Connection

Time Janet swam for 45 minutes on Friday. The next day she swam for an hour and a quarter. Compensate and add to find out how long she swam in all. (2 hours)

Subject Integration

Music Jeff records music on tapes of 30 minutes per side. Two new works are 35 and 25 minutes long. Will they fit on a tape? Explain. (No; the sum is 60, but one work is too long to fit on a side.)

Classwork and Homework Supplements

Practice

Mental Math 1-7

Name ____________________

Using Compensation

Compensate and use mental math to find the sum.

1. 7 + 9 = 16 (7 up 1, 9 down 1)
2. 11 + 9 = 20 (11 down 1, 9 up 1)
3. 4 + 8 = 12 (4 up 2, 8 down 2)
4. 7 + 5 = 12 (7 down 1, 5 up 1)
5. 6 + 4 = 10 (6 down 1, 4 up 1)
6. 7 + 13 = 20 (7 up 3, 13 down 3)
7. 13 + 7 = 20 (13 down 3, 7 up 3)
8. 6 + 8 = 14 (6 up 1, 8 down 1)
9. 3 + 7 = 10 (3 up 2, 7 down 2)
10. 12 + 8 = 20 (12 down 2, 8 up 2)
11. 8 + 13 = 21 (8 up 2, 13 down 2)
12. 9 + 7 = 16 (9 down 1, 7 up 1)
13. 8 + 6 = 14 (8 down 1, 6 up 1)
14. 5 + 9 = 14 (5 up 2, 9 down 2)
15. 8 + 4 = 12 (8 down 2, 4 up 2)

Add. Use compensation if it is helpful.

16. 4 + 9 = 13
17. 7 + 9 = 16
18. 11 + 7 = 18
19. 13 + 8 = 21
20. 5 + 7 = 12
21. 8 + 9 = 17
22. 8 + 4 = 12
23. 8 + 11 = 19

Building Thinking Skills

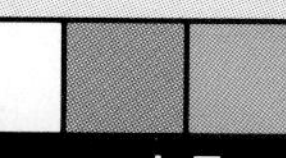

Critical Thinking 1-7

Name ____________________

Up and Down

Work from the sum and use compensation to find the addends. Analyze the clues. Find the addends and then show the example.

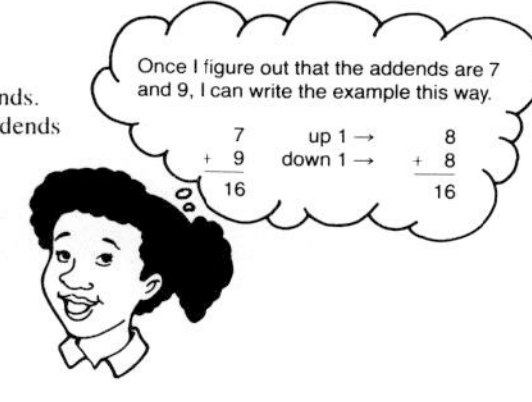

Once I figure out that the addends are 7 and 9, I can write the example this way.
7 + 9 = 16
up 1 →
down 1 →
8 + 8 = 16

1. The sum of these two addends is 18. The addends can be changed to a double by a down-up 2.
   Write the addends. 11, 7
   Now show the example:
   11 + 7 = 18; 11 down 2 → 9, 7 up 2 → 9; 9 + 9 = 18
2. The sum of these two addends is 25. One of the addends can be changed to a ten by an up 3.
   Write the addends. 7, 18
   Now show the example:
   7 + 18 = 25; 7 up 3 → 10, 18 down 3 → 15; 10 + 15 = 25
3. The sum of these two addends is 21. One of the addends can be changed to a ten by an up 3.
   Write the addends. 14, 7
   Now write the example:
   14 + 7 = 21; 14 down 3 → 11, 7 up 3 → 10; 11 + 10 = 21
4. The sum of these two addends is 200. The addends can be changed to a double by an up-down 3.
   Write the addends. 97, 103
   Now write the example:
   97 + 103 = 200; 97 up 3 → 100, 103 down 3 → 100; 100 + 100 = 200

Reteaching

Mental Math 1-7

Name ____________________

Using Compensation

Choose any two addends. 6 + 8	→ Add a chosen amount to the first addend. Subtract the same amount from the second addend. Find and compare the sums.	6 + 8 = 14; 6 up 1 → 7, 8 down 1 → 7; 7 + 7 = 14

Change to a Double.

(Think: 6 + 6 is a double.) 4 + 8 = 12; 4 up 2, 8 down 2; 6 + 6 = 12

Change to a Ten.

(Think: It is easier to change 12 to 10.) 12 + 7 = 19; 12 down 2, 7 up 2; 10 + 9 = 19

Compensate as shown and use mental math to find the sum.

1. 5 + 3 = 8 (5 down 1, 3 up 1)
2. 11 + 9 = 20 (11 down 1, 9 up 1)
3. 5 + 9 = 14 (5 up 2, 9 down 2)
4. 6 + 12 = 18 (6 up 3, 12 down 3)
5. 13 + 9 = 22 (13 down 1, 9 up 1)
6. 9 + 4 = 13 (9 up 1, 4 down 1)

Add. Change to a double.

7. 5 + 7 = 12
8. 9 + 11 = 20
9. 12 + 8 = 20
10. 13 + 9 = 22
11. 16 + 4 = 20

Add. Change to a ten.

12. 11 + 5 = 16
13. 13 + 5 = 18
14. 15 + 5 = 20
15. 8 + 6 = 14
16. 9 + 6 = 15

Challenges

Patterns 1-7

Name ____________________

Spot a Pattern

Complete the patterns.

1. 7, 9, 11, 13, 15, 17, 19, 21
2. 18, 15, 12, 9, 6, 3, 0
3. 1, 2, 4, 7, 11, 16, 22, 29
4. 25, 21, 17, 13, 9, 5, 1
5. 8, 10, 12, 14, 16, 18
6. 6, 7, 12, 13, 18, 19, 24, 25, 30
7. 23, 33, 43, 53, 63, 73
8. 5, 9, 13, 17, 21, 25
9. 21, 32, 43, 54, 65, 76, 87
10. 1, 2, 4, 8, 16, 32
11. 9 + 7, 8 + 6, 7 + 5, 6 + 4, 5 + 3, 4 + 2
12. 1, 1, 2, 3, 5, 8, 13, 21

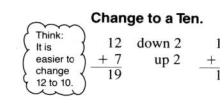

Options for Individual Needs

1-7

Basic

Exercises 1-4, 9-14, 21-26
Calculator Bank, p. 488
More Practice, p. 500, set C

Supplements
Reteaching 7 or
Practice 7

Average

Exercises 1-26
Calculator Bank, p. 488
More Practice, p. 500, set C

Supplements
Practice 7
Challenges 7 or
Thinking Skills 7

Extended

Exercises 5-26
Calculator Bank, p. 488

Supplements
Challenges 7
Thinking Skills 7

Other Resources:

Problem-Solving Experiences in Mathematics, Grade 4, Problem 12
Mathematics, A Way of Thinking, Lesson 4-14
Math In Stride, Grade 4, p. 10

LESSON PLAN 1-7

OBJECTIVE 1-7
To use the mental math technique of compensation to find sums

Materials: counters, calculators

Grouping Suggestion: pairs

1. MOTIVATE AND TEACH

LEARN ABOUT IT

EXPLORE Write 13 + 9 on the chalkboard.

▶ **Use counters to regroup addends to make an easier problem.** (Possible answers: Break apart 13 as 10 + 3, then add 10 + (3 + 9); or add 1 to 9 to make 10, subtract 1 from 13 to make 12, then add 10 + 12.)

▶ **How does compensation relate to number rules you know?** (Possible answer: Changing a grouping or order of addends, or using compensation, does not change the sum.)

TALK ABOUT IT ▶ **Why was two chosen as the compensation amount in the example 5 + 9?** (to form doubles)

▶ **Explain why you must adjust addends by the same amount.** (Possible answer: Compensating by balanced adjustments will not change sums.)

Student Edition answers: **1.** Adding 2 to one addend and subtracting 2 from the other did not change the sum. **2.** No, sums do not change with balanced adjustments. **3.** Sums did not change.

2. CHECK UNDERSTANDING

TRY IT OUT

ERROR ALERT Losing track of the up/down or down/up relationship when compensating. Having trouble when sums go into the next decade.

Mental Math
Using Compensation

LEARN ABOUT IT

EXPLORE **Discover a Relationship**
Follow these directions with 10 different pairs of addends. Use a calculator for larger numbers.

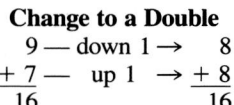

Choose any two addends.

$$\begin{array}{r} 5 \\ +\ 9 \\ \hline \end{array}$$

Add a chosen amount to the first addend.
Subtract the same amount from the second addend.
Find and compare the sums.

$$\begin{array}{rl} 5 & \text{up } 2 \rightarrow 7 \\ +\ 9 & \text{down } 2 \rightarrow \underline{7} \\ \hline \end{array}$$

TALK ABOUT IT See teaching notes.

1. Tell what happened in the above example.
2. If you add 3 to one addend and subtract 3 from the other, will the sum change? Explain.
3. What did you discover when you tried this with other addends?

You can sometimes change a sum into an easier sum that has the same answer. To do this, you make one addend larger and **compensate** by making the other addend smaller.

Change to a Double

$$\begin{array}{rcr} 9 & \text{— down } 1 \rightarrow & 8 \\ +\ 7 & \text{— up } 1 \rightarrow & +\ 8 \\ \hline 16 & & 16 \end{array}$$

Change to a Ten

$$\begin{array}{rcr} 14 & \text{— down } 2 \rightarrow & 12 \\ +\ 8 & \text{— up } 2 \rightarrow & +\ 10 \\ \hline 22 & & 22 \end{array}$$

TRY IT OUT

Compensate as shown and use mental math to find the sum.

1. $\begin{array}{rl} 8 & \text{down } 2 \\ +\ 4 & \text{up } 2 \\ \hline 12 & \end{array}$
2. $\begin{array}{rl} 8 & \text{up } 2 \\ +\ 12 & \text{down } 2 \\ \hline 20 & \end{array}$
3. $\begin{array}{rl} 14 & \text{down } 3 \\ +\ 7 & \text{up } 3 \\ \hline 21 & \end{array}$
4. $\begin{array}{rl} 9 & \text{up } 1 \\ +\ 7 & \text{down } 1 \\ \hline 16 & \end{array}$

16

TEACHING OPTIONS

RETEACHING TIPS Students rearrange addends before making adjustments. They write the addend that *increases* on top, with an up arrow showing compensation *up*. They write the addend that *decreases* below, with an arrow showing compensation *down*. Assign Reteaching Supplement 7.

ENRICHMENT Have students use mental math to compensate and find the sums.

1. 48 + 54 (102)
2. 103 + 98 (201)
3. 502 + 499 (1,001)
4. 1,004 + 996 (2,000)
5. 803 + 1,008 (1,811)
6. 2,775 + 1,005 (2,780)

PRACTICE

Compensate and use mental math to find the sum.

1. 7 down 2 + 3 up 2 10	**2.** 9 up 1 + 11 down 1 20	**3.** 6 up 1 + 8 down 1 14	**4.** 11 down 2 + 7 up 2 18
5. 9 up 1 + 11 down 1 20	**6.** 11 down 1 + 9 up 1 20	**7.** 8 down 2 + 4 up 2 12	**8.** 12 down 2 + 8 up 2 20

Add. If it is helpful, use compensation.

9. 9 + 7 16	**10.** 8 + 15 23	**11.** 14 + 8 22	**12.** 12 + 9 21	**13.** 6 + 9 15	**14.** 11 + 7 18
15. 13 + 9 22	**16.** 9 + 4 13	**17.** 11 + 8 19	**18.** 7 + 12 19	**19.** 15 + 9 24	**20.** 6 + 12 18

APPLY

MATH REASONING

21. 9 + 7 can be changed to a double by compensating down-up 1. Give 2 more facts like this. Answers will vary.

22. Use compensation to find 52 + 48. down-up 2; answer: 100

PROBLEM SOLVING

23. Jill made 8 wildlife video tapes in the summer. She made 6 more in the fall. How many tapes did she make? 14 tapes

24. Tom ran the video camera for 9 minutes. Then he ran it for 15 more minutes. How long was the total video? 24 minutes

▶ **USING CRITICAL THINKING Logical Reasoning**

Is the statement about addition with whole numbers always, sometimes, or never true?

25. The sum is less than either addend. never

26. Different sums must have different addends. always

More Practice, page 500, set C

3. Practice and Apply

Basic	1-4, 9-14, 21-26
Average	1-26
Extended	5-26

1-7

PRACTICE

Look at the exercises. When would it be most helpful to use compensation? (Possible answers: when one addend is close in value to 10; when you can make doubles)

APPLY

MATH REASONING ▶ **Can all addends be made into doubles? Explain.** (no, only addends whose difference is even)

PROBLEM SOLVING ▶ **In which problem would you be more likely to make a 10? Explain.** (Problem 24; 9 easily becomes 10 by adding 1. Then subtract 1 from 15.)

USING THINKING SKILLS ▶ **What can you conclude if you cannot think of an example for each statement that works?** (The statement is never true or you need to try more examples.)

Close and Assess

SAY WHAT YOU THINK Have students explain to a partner how to use compensation and when it may be a useful technique. (Answers may vary. Sample answer: Compensate to make easy addends, such as doubles or groups of ten, that you can add in your head.)

QUICK QUIZ

Add. Compensate if it is helpful.

1. 6 + 11 (17)
2. 5 + 7 (12)
3. 12 + 6 (18)
4. 4 + 9 (13)

CHAPTER 1

APPLIED PROBLEM SOLVING
GROUP DECISION MAKING

OBJECTIVE To practice group skills in problem solving

This open-ended math activity is designed to encourage students to work together cooperatively, to channel behavior and actions to achieve a favorable outcome, and to recognize and respect the value of individual contributions.

Have students read the group skills listed in the box. Ask them to express each skill in their own words and to explain its importance to the success of a group activity. (Answers will vary.) *How can the group check that everyone understands an activity?* (Have students restate ideas in their own words; give examples to help clarify ideas.) *Suggest a way to disagree and still be agreeable.* (Possible answer: Give facts or reasons for a disagreement, but do not make fun of or argue with someone for having a different view from your own.)

COOPERATIVE ACTIVITY

► **Justify having everyone in the group work on the same task.** (Possible answer: Different students may find different patterns.)

► **Summarize the rule for the patterns.** (Every square must touch along 1 whole edge of at least 1 other square.)

► **Explain how to decide if a pattern has already been discovered.** (Flip, turn, or rotate 2 patterns that seem similar; if you can make 1 fit on top of the other, the pattern is a repeat.)

Group Decision Making

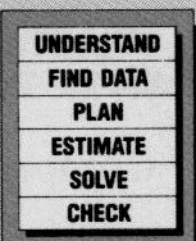

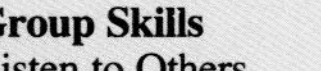

Group Skills
Listen to Others
Encourage and Respect Others
Explain and Summarize
Check for Understanding
Disagree in an Agreeable Way

You will work as part of a team for many lessons in this book. It is important for a team to listen to everyone's ideas before making decisions. The group skills in this chart are some of the ways your group can show that they appreciate everyone's ideas.

18

TEACHING OPTIONS

COOPERATIVE LEARNING

Grouping Suggestions: cooperative learning groups of 3 to 5

Explain that this is the first of many cooperative learning activities students will do throughout the year. This activity emphasizes 1 of the group skills on the student page.

Divide the class into groups. Discuss ways for members to contribute ideas that can lead to an exploration of the task. Groups may select a clerk to gather materials, a moderator to help members speak and respond in turn, and a secretary to record group findings.

Work with your group. Think of at least 3 examples of how you know when a group member is not listening to others. When you do the cooperative activity, look for ways to show you are a good listener.

Cooperative Activity

Each person in your group will need 5 small paper squares and some graph paper. Your goal is to make patterns so that the edge of each square touches the edge of another square. Touching only by corners or by part of an edge is not allowed. All five squares must be used for each pattern.

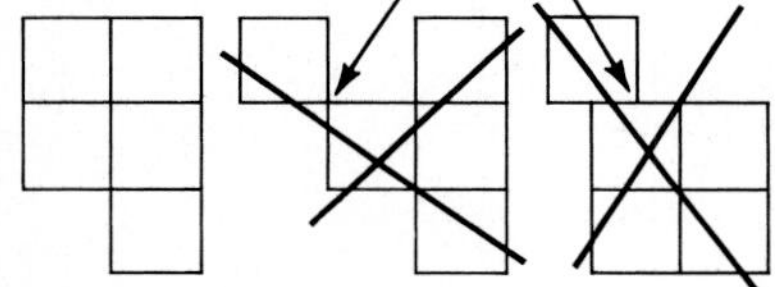

See if your group can find at least 10 different patterns. Cut each pattern out of graph paper. Patterns are different if they do not fit on top of each other no matter which way they are turned or flipped. Put the ones that are alike together.

Some Questions to Answer

1. How did you make sure everyone in your group understood what to do?
2. How many ways did your group find?
3. Did your group agree about which patterns were the same and which were different? What did you do if you did not agree?
4. Predict which of your patterns will fold to become the size of one of the squares. Try it to check your predictions.

Check Your Group Skills

5. What could your group do to improve how you listen to each other?

SOME QUESTIONS TO ANSWER

▶ **Explain how you sorted the number of different patterns your group found.** (Methods will vary.)

▶ **Explain how disagreements about patterns among group members can help improve the accuracy of the whole group's findings.** (Possible answer: When members disagree, everyone in the group is forced to look more closely at the pattern to make sure it really fits the requirements.)

▶ **Explain what you might visualize in order to form a box.** (Answers will vary. Sample answer: folds along the edge lines)

CHECK YOUR GROUP SKILLS

▶ **Summarize any problems your group encountered, and suggest ways to avoid the problems next time.** (Answers will vary.)

You and the class may decide that groups work best with a student leader who acts as moderator. This role should alternate in future Group Decision Making activities so that all students eventually have the opportunity to take on the responsibility of leadership. *Cooperative Learning in Mathematics: A Handbook for Teachers* (Addison-Wesley Publishing Company, 1990) provides useful assistance in organizing cooperative learning groups specifically for mathematics.

CHAPTER 1

WRAP UP

INTRODUCTION The Wrap Up provides activities emphasizing math language and thinking skills for the chapter and a project that integrates those skills with other math strands.

USING PAGE 20

Operation Sort Have students complete this section independently. When they finish, have pairs compare answers and make up simple number examples for each sentence to verify the chosen operation.

Sometimes, Always, Never ► How can you evaluate the statements? (Possible answer: Statements that give a math rule must *always* be true; statements that contradict a math rule must *never* be true; statements are *sometimes* true if you can find at least one true and one false example.)
► Identify a statement that is a math rule. Explain your reasoning. (11; it describes the Order Property of Addition.)

Project Students work in pairs to discuss the given information and to verify each other's story problems.
► Analyze which animal fact compares information. (The first fact compares lengths of time 2 animals can survive without food.)
► How could you find other interesting animal facts? (Possible answer: Look in science books or in nature magazines.)

Additional Answers: See p. T79.

WRAP UP

Operation Sort

If you saw these sentences in story problems, would you need to add or subtract?

1. How many are there in all? **add**
2. How many more are needed? **subtract**
3. Who is older? **subtract**
4. How much is it all together? **add**
5. Compare the weights. **subtract**
6. How many are still here? **subtract**
7. Calculate the sum. **add**
8. How many are left over? **subtract**
9. What is the total? **add**
10. Find the difference. **subtract**

Sometimes, Always, Never

Which word should go in the blank, sometimes, always, or never?

11. You may __?__ add numbers in any order. **always**
12. Fact families __?__ have two subtraction and two addition equations. **sometimes**
13. You __?__ use compensation to change sums. **never**

Project

14. Use one of these facts to make up an addition problem and the other to make up a subtraction problem. Then find one more interesting animal fact and use it to make up another addition or subtraction problem. **See Additional Answers.**

- The poisonous tarantula spider can live 2 years without food and 7 months without water. The snail can go 5 years without food.
- If you have been sprayed by a skunk, you can get rid of the odor with tomato juice! It takes 3 large cans of juice each to make one boy and one dog smell all right again.

20

TEACHING OPTIONS

ENRICHMENT Have each student select a different animal for a cooperative animal fact display. Students should locate any interesting information about their chosen animal that can be represented as a math fact. They write the fact on a 3-by-12 strip of colored paper and draw or paste a picture of the animal at an end of the strip. For instance, a math fact for a giraffe might be: An adult giraffe may grow to be 18 feet tall. Students arrange the facts in an attractive display. They may use the facts to formulate original story problems.

CHAPTER REVIEW/TEST

Part 1 Understanding

Write a number sentence for each.

1. 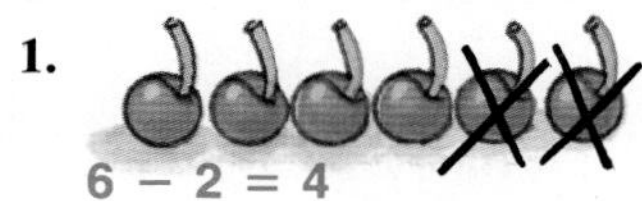
6 − 2 = 4

2. 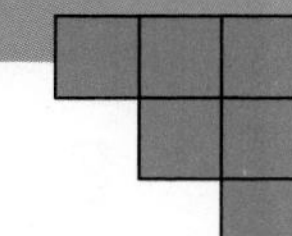
5 + 2 = 7

3. △ + (○ + □) = 12 **12**
What does (△ + ○) + □ equal?

4. If you add zero to a number, the sum will be the number. Why? **zero property of addition**

5. Write the rest of the fact family for: ○ + △ = □
See Additional Answers.

6. Use compensation to change 7 + 13 to a double. Write the new addends and sum. **10 + 10 = 20**

Part 2 Skills

Add or subtract.

7. 6 + 8 **14** 8. 15 − 9 **6** 9. 11 − 0 **11** 10. 13 − 5 **8** 11. 14 + 9 **23** 12. 16 − 8 **8**

Give the fact family for each pair of addends. **See Additional Answers.**

13. 4, 7 14. 5, 9 15. 6, 6

Add, using mental math. Break apart an addend.

16. 7 + 4 **11** 17. 8 + 4 **12** 18. 11 + 7 **18**

Part 3 Applications

19. A rabbit ate 17 carrots and 9 turnips. What number sentence could you use to find how many more carrots than turnips it ate? **17 − 9 = 8**

20. A snail crawled 9 inches in an hour. Then it crawled 6 more inches to a tidal pool. How far did the snail crawl? **15 inches**

21. Two numbers give a sum of 13 and a difference of 1. What are the numbers? **6 and 7**

22. **Challenge** Use compensation and mental math to find the sum of 227 and 273. Compensate up-down 3, then break apart addends. **500**

21

INFORMAL ASSESSMENT

Using Manipulatives Have students use counters to show 2 different addition and subtraction facts. Ask them to write equations for each fact and to give the related fact family verbally. Observe students' work and have them explain how they developed the fact families. (Answers will vary.)

Communication *Explain why you can break apart addends to add them more easily.* (Possible answer: In addition, you can change order or grouping without changing the sum; when you break apart an addend, you make a new grouping that is easier to add.)

Critical Thinking *Find the smallest 3-digit odd number that does not have a 0 in it. (111)*

CHAPTER REVIEW/TEST

INTRODUCTION The Review/Test is provided to review and evaluate the skills and concepts presented in Chapter 1.

USING PAGE 21
If you prefer to use this page for review, you may want to use the **Multiple-Choice Posttest** (pages 3-4) or the **Free-Response Posttest** (pages 3-4) to evaluate mastery of chapter objectives.

ITEM ANALYSIS The table below correlates the Chapter Review/Test items with the lesson objectives for the chapter.

Items	Objectives
1, 2	1-1
3, 4, 7, 9	1-2
5, 8, 10, 12-15	1-3
6, 22	1-7
11, 16-18	1-6
19, 20	1-4
21	1-5

Additional Answers: See p. T79.

ENRICHMENT

INTRODUCTION As students examine the data in a magic square, they sharpen their ability to recognize and continue patterns, to analyze data, and to make generalizations.

USING PAGE 22
This enrichment page is provided for all students. You may wish to use it after the students have completed the Chapter Review/Test on page 21.
Before students work through the page, discuss the basic terminology required to understand and analyze flow charts.

► **Explain what each shape in the flow chart signals.** (Rectangles with rounded corners signal to start or stop; rectangles with straight corners signal what to do next; diamonds ask questions that then direct you either to stop or to move to another instruction.)

► **Analyze each flow chart to determine the number of instructions and questions in each.** (Watch a TV Show: 3 instructions, 1 question; Try a Number Surprise: 5 instructions, 1 question)

► **Explain what links each shape.** (An arrow points from 1 shape to the next to indicate in which direction to move.)

EXTENSION Partners make a flow chart cooperatively. First they choose a simple situation to illustrate, such as checking out a library book. Together, students then list the necessary steps and decide what is to be an instruction or a question. Partners take turns writing the steps on a flow chart, then they verify the use of each shape and the direction of the arrows. Students may challenge other sets of partners to work their flow chart.

ENRICHMENT
Using and Making Flow Charts

Flow charts give directions for doing things. Special shapes signal different parts of the flow chart.

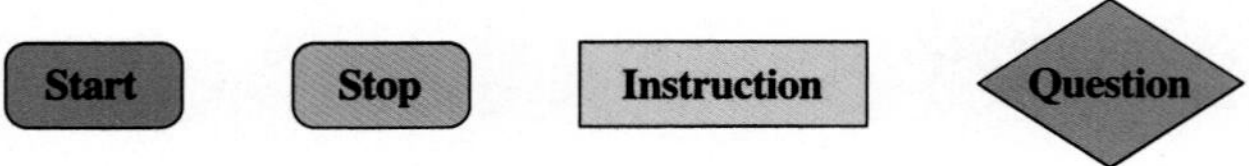

Here are two flow charts for you to copy and complete by giving the missing instructions or numbers.

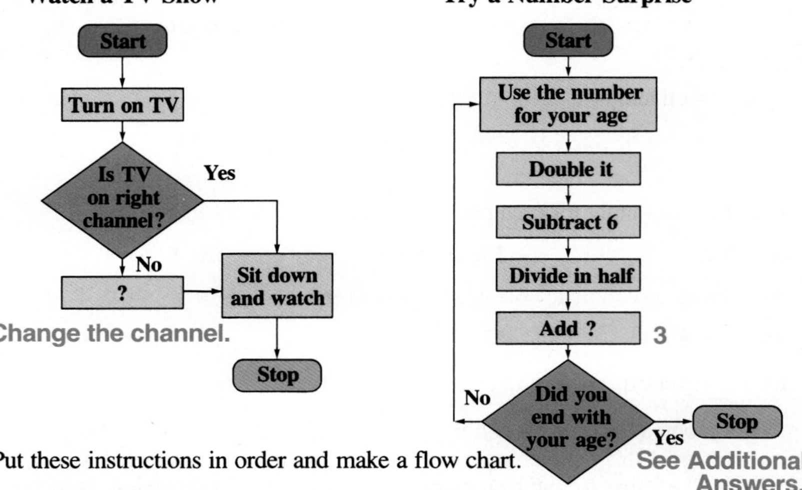

Put these instructions in order and make a flow chart. See Additional Answers.

1. Crossing the Street

Is anything coming?
Start. Stop.
Cross the street.
Wait at the corner.
Look both ways.

2. Calling on the Phone

Hang up. Start. Stop.
Does anyone answer?
Talk.
Pick up the receiver.
Dial the number.

22

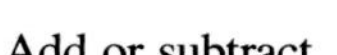

CUMULATIVE REVIEW

Add or subtract.

1. $\begin{array}{r} 5 \\ +9 \\ \hline \end{array}$

   (A) 13 B 15
   C 14 D 4

2. $\begin{array}{r} 15 \\ -6 \\ \hline \end{array}$

   (A) 9 B 10
   C 11 D 21

3. $\begin{array}{r} 12 \\ -8 \\ \hline \end{array}$

   A 6 (B) 4
   C 20 D 3

4. $\begin{array}{r} 5 \\ +6 \\ \hline \end{array}$

   A 7 (B) 11
   C 10 D 12

Which property does each number sentence show?

5. 3 + (6 + 7) = 3 + (7 + 6)

   A grouping (B) order
   C multiplication D zero

6. 6 + (4 + 5) = (6 + 4) + 5

   (A) grouping B order
   C multiplication D zero

The mental math break apart method would be helpful in solving these problems. Choose the best way to break apart an addend.

7. 8 + 9

   A 3 + 6 B 4 + 4
   (C) 8 + 1 D 9 + 8

8. 13 + 6

   A 3 + 3 B 10 + 4
   (C) 10 + 3 D 5 + 8

9. Lia must mail 15 letters. She has 8 stamps. How many stamps should she buy?

   A 23 B 6
   C 8 (D) 7

10. Ron found 79 + 36 = 115 with his calculator. Which sum can he now find using mental math?

    (A) 76 + 39 B 88 + 63
    C 97 + 67 D 115 + 179

CUMULATIVE REVIEW

INTRODUCTION The purpose of this Cumulative Review is to maintain previously taught skills and concepts. The emphasis in this Cumulative Review is on addition and subtraction concepts and basic facts, Chapter 1.

ITEM ANALYSIS The table below correlates the Cumulative Review items with the lesson objectives.

Items	Objectives
1	1-2
2,3	1-3
4-6	1-2
7,8	1-6
9	1-4
10	1-7

Chapter Management

OVERVIEW

Lesson	Pages	Objectives	Subject Integration	Strand Integration
Chapter Opener	24-25	To introduce chapter 2	social studies-Native Americans	patterns
Understanding Place Value	26-27	2-1 To read and write 3- and 4-digit numbers	language arts: writing	computation
Using Larger Numbers	28-29	2-2 To read and write 5- and 6-digit numbers	social studies-Long House	calculators
Comparing and Ordering Numbers	30-31	2-3 To compare and order numbers	social studies-geography	estimation
Exploring Algebra/Midchapter Review/Quiz	32-33	2-4 To explore algebra by understanding equality	science-scales	problem solving
Problem Solving: Draw a Picture	34-35	2-5 To solve problems using the strategy Draw a Picture	social studies-arrowheads	computation
Rounding	36-37	2-6 To round numbers to the nearest ten, hundred, and dollar	social studies-cliff dwelling	critical thinking logic
More About Rounding	38-39	2-7 To round to the nearest thousand	social studies-Richard Wetherill	problem solving
Understanding Millions	40-41	2-8 To read and write 7-, 8-, and 9-digit numbers	social studies-map skills	critical thinking
Counting Change	42-43	2-9 To count change	social studies-consumer costs	mental math
Estimating With Money: Using a Reference Point	44-45	2-10 To estimate using the visual estimation technique to compare an amount of money to a reference point	social studies-cliff dwellings	problem solving
Data Collection and Analysis: Group Decision Making	46-47	2-11 To collect, organize, and present data	health/fitness-eating preferences	statistics

MATHEMATICAL BACKGROUND

Place Value
Lesson 2-1 explains that any number can be written using the digits 0 to 9. Depending on the place a digit occupies in a number, it can represent ones, tens, hundreds, thousands, and so on. Place value models are used to help students understand the concept of place value.

Comparing and Ordering Numbers
Lesson 2-3 teaches students how to compare two numbers to find which is greater or less and to order a list of numbers from least to greatest or from greatest to least.

Problem Solving
Students learn to use the Draw a Picture strategy in Lesson 2-5.

TIPS FROM TEACHERS

Use bugs (little cars), buses, and boats to teach the concept of place value. Explain that a bug holds 1 person, a bus holds 10 people, and a boat holds 100 people. Only 9 people at a time can travel in a 9-bug caravan. If a tenth person wants to join the group, then all 10 must ride in one bus.

Polly Hamm
Woodland Elementary School
Zephyrhills, FL

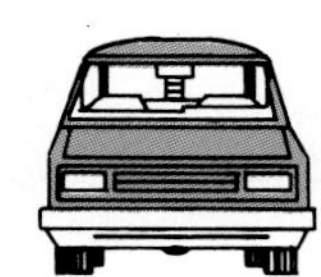

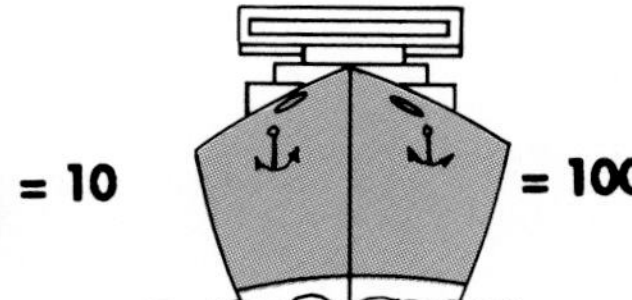

ASSESSMENT

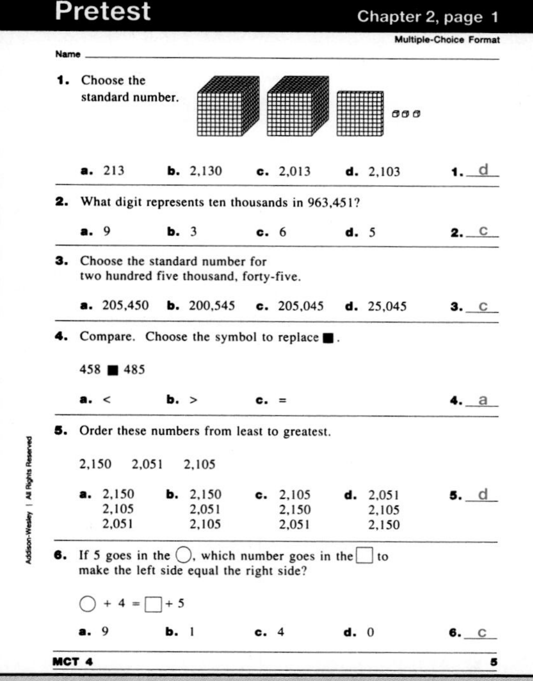

Pretest — Chapter 2, page 1

Multiple-Choice Format

Name ____________

1. Choose the standard number.

a. 213 b. 2,130 c. 2,013 d. 2,103 — 1. d

2. What digit represents ten thousands in 963,451?

a. 9 b. 3 c. 6 d. 5 — 2. c

3. Choose the standard number for two hundred five thousand, forty-five.

a. 205,450 b. 200,545 c. 205,045 d. 25,045 — 3. c

4. Compare. Choose the symbol to replace ■.

458 ■ 485

a. < b. > c. = — 4. a

5. Order these numbers from least to greatest.

2,150 2,051 2,105

a. 2,150, 2,105, 2,051 b. 2,150, 2,051, 2,105 c. 2,105, 2,150, 2,051 d. 2,051, 2,105, 2,150 — 5. d

6. If 5 goes in the ◯, which number goes in the ☐ to make the left side equal the right side?

◯ + 4 = ☐ + 5

a. 9 b. 1 c. 4 d. 0 — 6. c

Pretest — Chapter 2, page 2

Multiple-Choice Format

Name ____________

7. Four students stood in a line. Luis was in front of Ann and behind Martha. Ken was last in line. Who was second in line?

a. Luis b. Ann c. Martha d. Ken — 7. a

8. Round 8,381 to the nearest hundred.

a. 8,300 b. 8,380 c. 8,400 d. 8,000 — 8. c

9. Round $25.38 to the nearest dollar.

a. $25 b. $20 c. $30 d. $26 — 9. a

10. Round 3,429 to the nearest thousand.

a. 3,400 b. 4,000 c. 3,000 d. 3,430 — 10. c

11. What digit represents hundred millions in 598,706,321?

a. 5 b. 7 c. 3 d. 0 — 11. a

12. You buy an item for $3.74. You give the clerk $5.00. What would the clerk say to count the change out loud?

$3.74 ? ? ?

a. $3.75, $4.00, $4.25, $5.00 b. $3.74, $3.75, $4.00, $5.00
c. $3.74, $3.75, $3.95, $5.00 d. $3.74, $3.95, $4.00, $5.00 — 12. b

13. Is this enough money to buy a magazine costing $1.50?

a. Yes b. No — 13. b

Posttest — Chapter 2, page 1

Multiple-Choice Format

Name ____________

1. Choose the standard number.

a. 347 b. 3,470 c. 3,047 d. 3,407 — 1. c

2. What digit represents hundreds in 245,307?

a. 3 b. 5 c. 7 d. 2 — 2. a

3. Choose the standard number for three hundred six thousand, twenty-six.

a. 306,026 b. 300,626 c. 306,260 d. 36,260 — 3. a

4. Compare. Choose the symbol to replace ■.

321 ■ 312

a. < b. > c. = — 4. b

5. Order these numbers from least to greatest.

3,495 3,954 3,945

a. 3,495, 3,954, 3,945 b. 3,495, 3,945, 3,954 c. 3,954, 3,495, 3,945 d. 3,954, 3,945, 3,495 — 5. b

6. If 3 goes in the ◯, which number goes in the ☐ to make the left side equal the right side?

6 + ◯ = 3 + ☐

a. 3 b. 6 c. 9 d. 0 — 6. b

Posttest — Chapter 2, page 2

Multiple-Choice Format

Name ____________

7. Four students stood in a line. Pam was in front of Max and Bert. Mona was first in line. Who was second in line?

a. Pam b. Burt c. Max d. Mona — 7. a

8. Round 6,749 to the nearest hundred.

a. 7,000 b. 6,700 c. 6,000 d. 6,800 — 8. b

9. Round $67.50 to the nearest dollar.

a. $67 b. $68 c. $70 d. $60 — 9. b

10. Round 6,748 to the nearest thousand.

a. 6,000 b. 7,000 c. 6,700 d. 6,800 — 10. b

11. What digit represents millions in 918,453,027?

a. 9 b. 1 c. 3 d. 8 — 11. d

12. You buy an item for $3.98. You give the clerk $5.00. What would the clerk say to count the change out loud?

$3.98 ? ? ?

a. $3.99, $4.00, $4.25, $5.00 b. $3.98, $3.99, $4.50, $5.00
c. $3.98, $3.99, $4.00, $5.00 d. $3.99, $4.00, $4.25, $5.00 — 12. c

13. Is this enough money to buy a notebook costing $1.50?

a. Yes b. No — 13. b

ITEM ANALYSIS

Items	Objectives
1	2-1
2, 3	2-2
4, 5	2-3
6	2-4
7	2-5
8, 9	2-6
10	2-7
11	2-8
12	2-9
13	2-10

Note: The item analysis is the same for all pretests and posttests for this chapter.

ALSO AVAILABLE

- **Free Response Tests**
- **Alternative Tests**
- **Thinking Strategies**
- **Concrete Materials**

Optional Chapter Activities

PROJECT AND BULLETIN BOARD

students have completed Lesson 8, have them look in newspapers and magazines for sentences containing large numbers. They will generally find that many large numbers, especially money amounts in the millions, are written as a combination of numbers and words, such as $100 million. Have students copy the sentences on construction paper strips, then post them on the bulletin board. Next to each sentence, challenge students to write the number using only digits and commas in the appropriate places. When all students have contributed at least one sentence, have the class order the sentences and numbers from highest to lowest. Partners may practice reading these numbers aloud to each other.

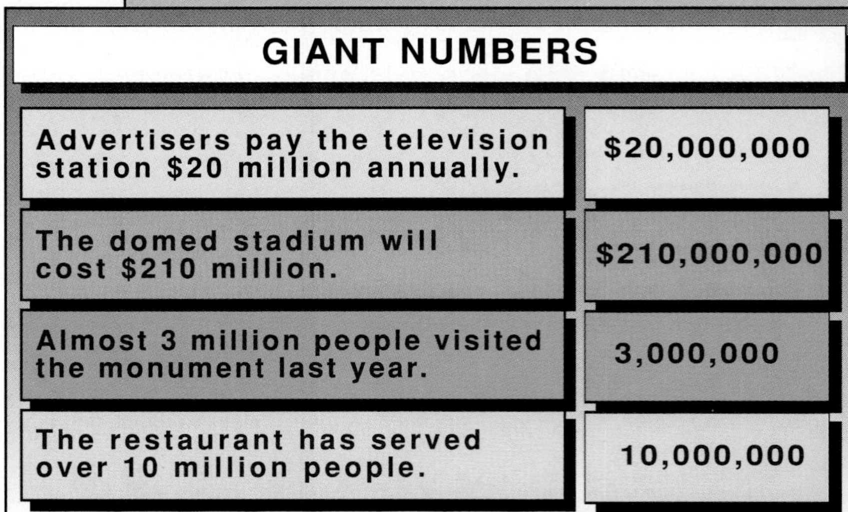

GIANT NUMBERS
Advertisers pay the television station $20 million annually.
$20,000,000
The domed stadium will cost $210 million.
$210,000,000
Almost 3 million people visited the monument last year.
3,000,000
The restaurant has served over 10 million people.
10,000,000

COOPERATIVE LEARNING

Divide the class into groups of three or four. Identify the group skill: encourage and respect others. Give each group number sentences using the *not equal to* sign. For example:

$4 + 3 \neq 9 - 3$

Tell the group to think of at least three ways to change the sentence so that they can use an equal sign. One way is to perform an operation on the left-hand side of the number sentence, $(4 + 3) - 1 = 9 - 3$. Another way is to perform an operation on the right-hand side of the number sentence. Still another way is to perform operations on both sides. They must make both sides of the number sentence equal by performing operations, not by changing existing numbers.

Tell the groups that there are many possible ways in which to do this, and that they should encourage each other to suggest ideas. As the group agrees on a method, one member should work it out to be sure it works. Then a second member should record the solution. Have the third member show the work to the rest of the class and explain what was done.

You will find grouping suggestions and cooperative learning activities in most lessons throughout this chapter.

LITERATURE

Robertson, Keith. *Henry Reed, Inc.* New York: Puffin Books, Viking Penguin, 1989.

Henry has gone into business with a neighborhood girl named Midge. One of the things they sell are fishing worms at 25¢ per dozen.
Children could use the story and figure out how many worms would have to be sold to earn different amounts of money: $20, $30, . . . Then they could draw pictures and write number stories.

Gag, Wanda. *Wanda Gag's Jorinda and Joringel.* New York: Coward, McCann & Geoghegan, 1975.

Hertzberg, Hendrik. *One Million.* New York: Simon & Schuster, 1970.

Shulman, Alix. *Bosley on the Number Line.* New York: David McKay, 1970.

English as a Second Language

It is helpful to explain to ESL students how to read numbers in terms of place value and what the role of the comma is. Preproduction children (those that can understand more than they can speak), can begin by pointing to the ten thousands, thousands, hundreds, tens, and ones as the teacher reads numbers aloud. Then do the following activity.

Write a 3-digit number on the chalkboard. Ask students to read the number, starting with the hundreds place. Then write a 4-digit number on the board and remind children to begin reading on the left. With your hand or an index card, cover everything except the thousands place. Ask students to read that digit. Uncover the comma and explain that the comma tells you to say ''thousand'', then read the rest of the number. Repeat, using larger numbers with as many as nine digits. Remember to use examples with zero to help students understand the role of zero as a place holder.

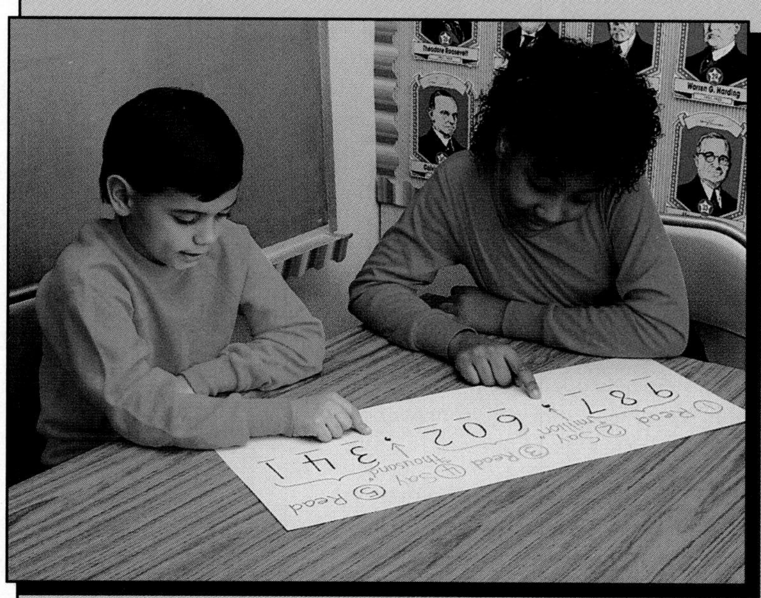

Gifted

Your students are cashiers in a company called ''Super School Store,'' which sells educational items. It is their job to list each customer's purchase, decide the total, and give the customer the correct change. Instruct the students to create a list of 15 items that might be sold in the store, and to give each item a price that is less than $5. Set the following scene: 5 customers are in line to purchase items. Each person will be buying 10 items, some of which could be duplicates.

Have the students create a sales slip for each of the 5 customers. Have them list each item, its cost, the number purchased, and the purchase total. They may use a calculator to check their math. On a separate piece of paper, have them list three different ways each customer might pay, and the coins and/or the bills they would use to make the change.

Invite students to explore the possibility of starting a real school or classroom store. What would they want to sell? Explain ''profit'' and ''mark up.'' Have them determine how much profit they would want to make on each item, and what they would do with the profit. Have them draw up a plan on how to get started.

Students at Risk

The place value, numeration, and rounding skills in this chapter are essential for understanding the rules of our number system and for success in later calculations. Some students have trouble switching between standard notation, place value models, word form, and expanded form. Provide frequent opportunities to use place value materials to internalize place order and to stress the 10-for-1 relationship between adjacent places. Have some blank index cards, jigsaw-puzzle style. On one half, write a standard 2- to 4-digit number; on the other half, draw the appropriate place value materials. The puzzles self-check, so they can be used by individuals or partners. Set up a work center with the puzzles or use parts of the puzzles in variations such as these: **1.** Show the number as students build it with place value models. **2.** Show the picture as students say the number. **3.** Say a number as students find an example of it.

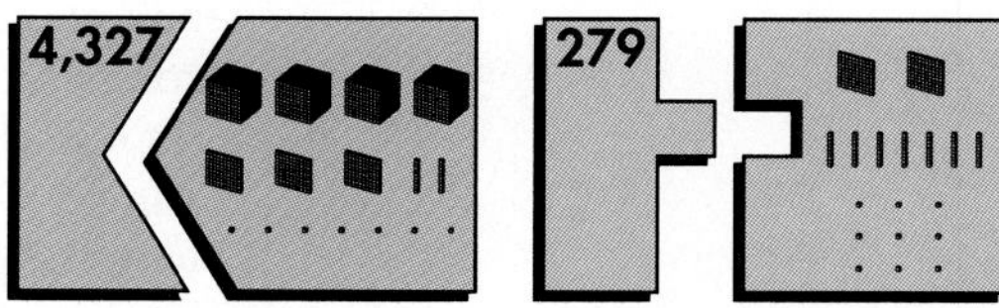

You may also use the Reteaching Supplements and the specific Reteaching Tips from each lesson in this chapter.

CHAPTER 2

INTRODUCING THE CHAPTER

SUBJECT INTEGRATION The photograph of the ruins of the cliff dwellings in Mesa Verde National Park in Colorado relates to the chapter theme of social studies. Various lessons include facts about Indians of the southwestern United States to relate place value and money concepts to the chapter theme.

USING DATA The Social Studies Data Bank on page 472 of the Student Edition presents a table entitled Old Indian Dwellings in the Southwest. It gives data on numbers of rooms found in various dwellings at Canyon de Chelly (pronounced *d'shay*), Chaco Canyon, and Mesa Verde. Students will compare and order the given numbers to answer the Chapter Opener questions.

QUESTION 1 ► **Explain what you need to recognize to be able to answer the question.** (the greatest number from among all numbers listed) Student Edition answer: Pueblo Bonito

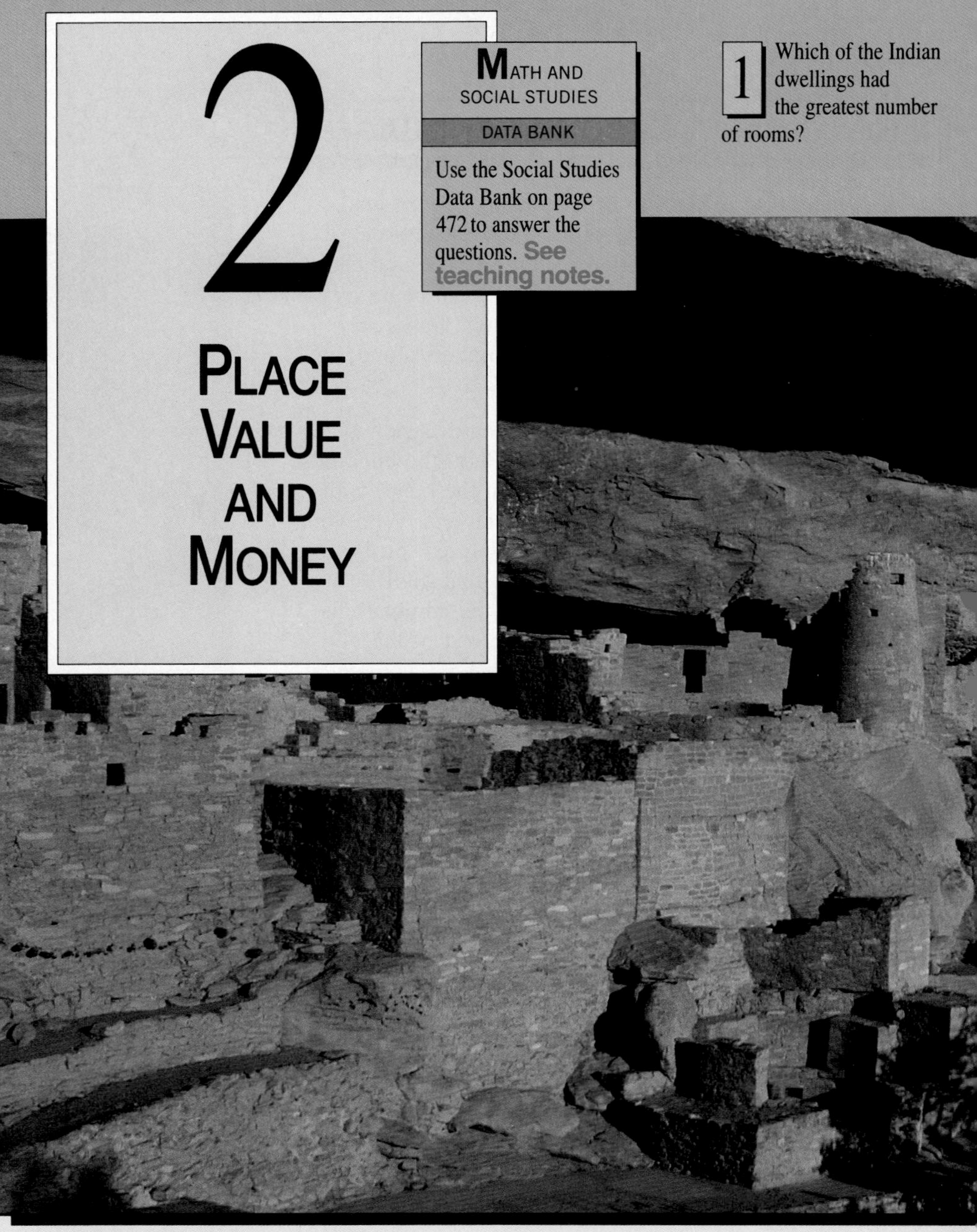

2

PLACE VALUE AND MONEY

MATH AND SOCIAL STUDIES

DATA BANK

Use the Social Studies Data Bank on page 472 to answer the questions. See teaching notes.

1 Which of the Indian dwellings had the greatest number of rooms?

TEACHING OPTIONS

LANGUAGE DEVELOPMENT
Write the words **rank** and **order** on the chalkboard. Ask students to use both words in a sentence about comparing a list of numbers. (Possible answers: You can *rank* numbers in *order* of size by starting with the greatest number and listing all the other numbers as they get smaller and smaller; you can *rank* numbers in the opposite *order* by starting with the smallest number and listing numbers as they increase.)

2 Name a building that had fewer than 90 rooms.

3 Name two buildings that had about the same number of rooms.

4 **Use Critical Thinking** What can you say about the sizes of Indian groups living in Canyon de Chelly, Chaco Canyon, and Mesa Verde? Explain.

25

QUESTION 2 ► **Decide how to rank all 7 Indian dwellings in the table from largest to smallest.** (Pueblo Bonito, Cliff Palace, Long House, Spruce Tree House, White House, Antelope House, or Mummy Cave) Student Edition answer: White House, Antelope House, or Mummy Cave

QUESTION 3 ► **Explain the meaning of the phrase *about the same number*.** (''not necessarily identical, but close to equal size'') Student Edition answer: Antelope House and Mummy Cave

QUESTION 4 ► **Estimate the relative sizes of the Indian dwellings by comparing them to buildings whose sizes you know.** (Answers will vary.)
Student Edition answer: Based on the number of rooms the dwellings provided, the largest Indian community probably lived at Pueblo Bonito in Chaco Canyon. The second largest group probably lived in the buildings at Mesa Verde, and the smallest group probably lived in the buildings at Canyon de Chelly.

SUBJECT INTEGRATION PROJECT Have students research the different styles of homes built by various American Indian tribes. Begin by brainstorming the types of Indian dwellings that may be familiar to students, such as the tepee, longhouse, and adobe. Research groups can use encyclopedias or other library sources to find information about these and other dwellings. Have students draw pictures or build models of the dwellings, noting how many rooms they usually had or how many people lived in them. Have students display their completed work, with pertinent facts, on index cards.

LESSON OPTIONS 2-1

Understanding Place Value

OBJECTIVE 2-1 To read and write 3- and 4-digit numbers

PREBOOK ACTIVITIES

QUICK REVIEW

Add 10 to each number.

1. 3 (13)	**2.** 5 (15)	**3.** 8 (18)
4. 2 (12)	**5.** 7 (17)	**6.** 4 (14)
7. 1 (11)	**8.** 10 (20)	**9.** 26 (36)

PRIOR KNOWLEDGE

Write the numbers 43 and 34 on the chalkboard. Ask students to explain how 43 and 34 are different, even though both have the same digits. (43 is greater because it has 4 tens and 3 ones; 34 has 3 tens and 4 ones.) Have a volunteer explain how the digit 4 has a different value in 43 and 403. (It means 4 tens in 43 but 4 hundreds in 403.)

COMMUNICATION

Discussing and Reading Math Write these pairs of math words on the chalkboard: **digit/place value, standard form/expanded form.** Have students read the words aloud. Have them suggest synonyms for *standard* (*normal, regular, usual*) and for *expanded* (*stretch out, spread out*). Discuss relationships between the pairs of words. (Possible answers: Numbers are made up of *digits;* a digit gets its *value* from its *place;* numbers in expanded form are written place by place instead of in the usual way, or standard form.) Ask students how they can write so many different numbers with just ten digits. (Possible answer: Digits can be combined in many ways.)

EXPLORE AND CONNECT

Materials: place value blocks, TA 3 (Number Cards 0-9), TA 5 (4-Digit Place Value Charts)
Alternative Materials: TA 6 (Place Value Models)
Grouping Suggestion: small cooperative learning groups
Students take turns at each task in 4-Digit High-Low. A student picks any four number cards at random and uses the **digits** to form the largest and smallest possible numbers. Another student checks and records the numbers in **standard form** while a third shows both numbers with place value blocks or models. Then students write the two numbers on a **place value** chart and, finally, in **expanded form.** It may help to work through one round with the whole class so students clearly understand each task. As the groups work together, ask members to verbalize their actions and ideas and to listen to verify each other's thinking.

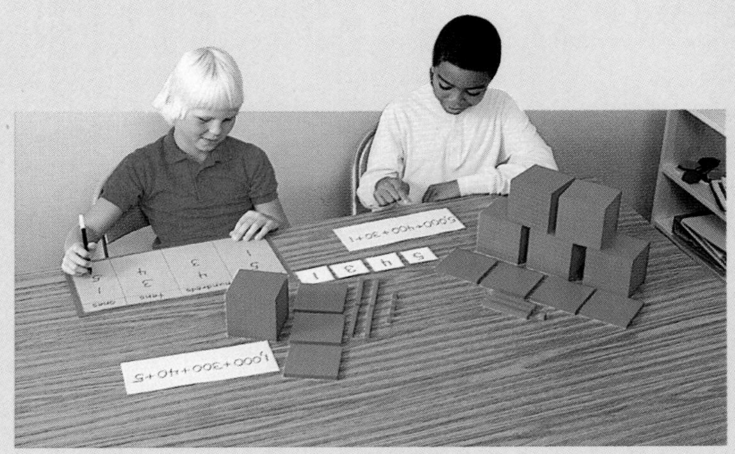

CONNECTIONS Use these anytime.

Problem of the Day

Patterns How many different 4-digit numbers are there that use each of the digits 7, 8, 9, and 0? Make a list or look for patterns to find all possibilities. (18; 0 is not used in the thousands place.)

Creative Thinking

Logic What 4-digit number fits the following rules? **1)** Digits do not repeat and 2 is not used. **2)** The ones digit is 3 more than the tens digit. **3)** The hundreds digit is odd and is a sum of the other digits. (4,703; 6,903)

Math Connection

Measurement A standard mile has five thousand, two hundred eighty feet. Draw place value models to show the number. Then write it in standard form. (5,280; Check students' models.)

Classwork and Homework Supplements

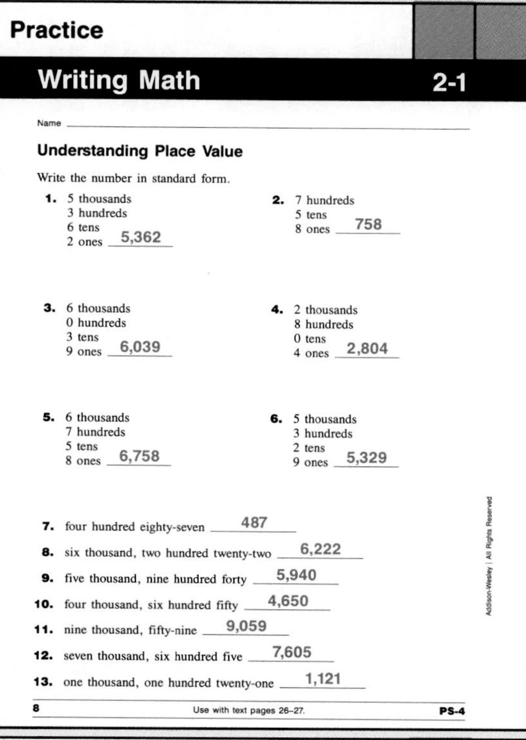

Practice

Writing Math 2-1

Name ______________________

Understanding Place Value

Write the number in standard form.

1. 5 thousands, 3 hundreds, 6 tens, 2 ones 5,362
2. 7 hundreds, 5 tens, 8 ones 758
3. 6 thousands, 0 hundreds, 3 tens, 9 ones 6,039
4. 2 thousands, 8 hundreds, 0 tens, 4 ones 2,804
5. 6 thousands, 7 hundreds, 5 tens, 8 ones 6,758
6. 5 thousands, 3 hundreds, 2 tens, 9 ones 5,329
7. four hundred eighty-seven 487
8. six thousand, two hundred twenty-two 6,222
9. five thousand, nine hundred forty 5,940
10. four thousand, six hundred fifty 4,650
11. nine thousand, fifty-nine 9,059
12. seven thousand, six hundred five 7,605
13. one thousand, one hundred twenty-one 1,121

8 Use with text pages 26–27. PS-4

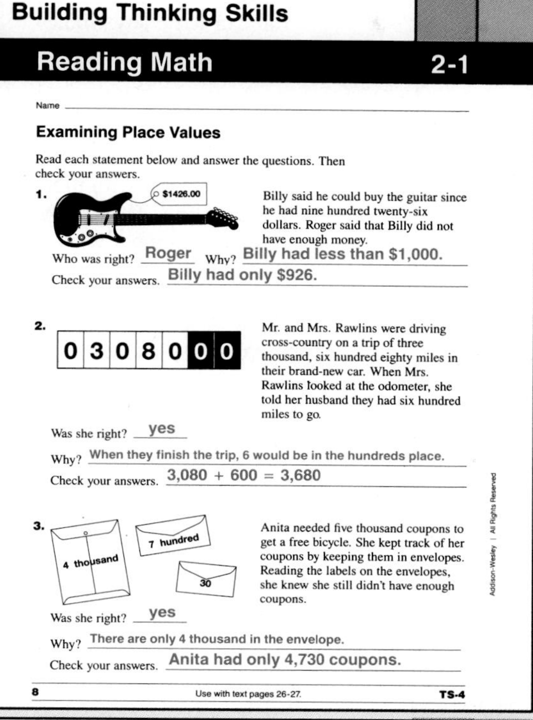

Building Thinking Skills

Reading Math 2-1

Name ______________________

Examining Place Values

Read each statement below and answer the questions. Then check your answers.

1. Billy said he could buy the guitar since he had nine hundred twenty-six dollars. Roger said that Billy did not have enough money.

   Who was right? Roger Why? Billy had less than $1,000.

   Check your answers. Billy had only $926.

2. Mr. and Mrs. Rawlins were driving cross-country on a trip of three thousand, six hundred eighty miles in their brand-new car. When Mrs. Rawlins looked at the odometer, she told her husband they had six hundred miles to go.

   Was she right? yes

   Why? When they finish the trip, 6 would be in the hundreds place.

   Check your answers. 3,080 + 600 = 3,680

3. Anita needed five thousand coupons to get a free bicycle. She kept track of her coupons by keeping them in envelopes. Reading the labels on the envelopes, she knew she still didn't have enough coupons.

   Was she right? yes

   Why? There are only 4 thousand in the envelope.

   Check your answers. Anita had only 4,730 coupons.

8 Use with text pages 26–27. TS-4

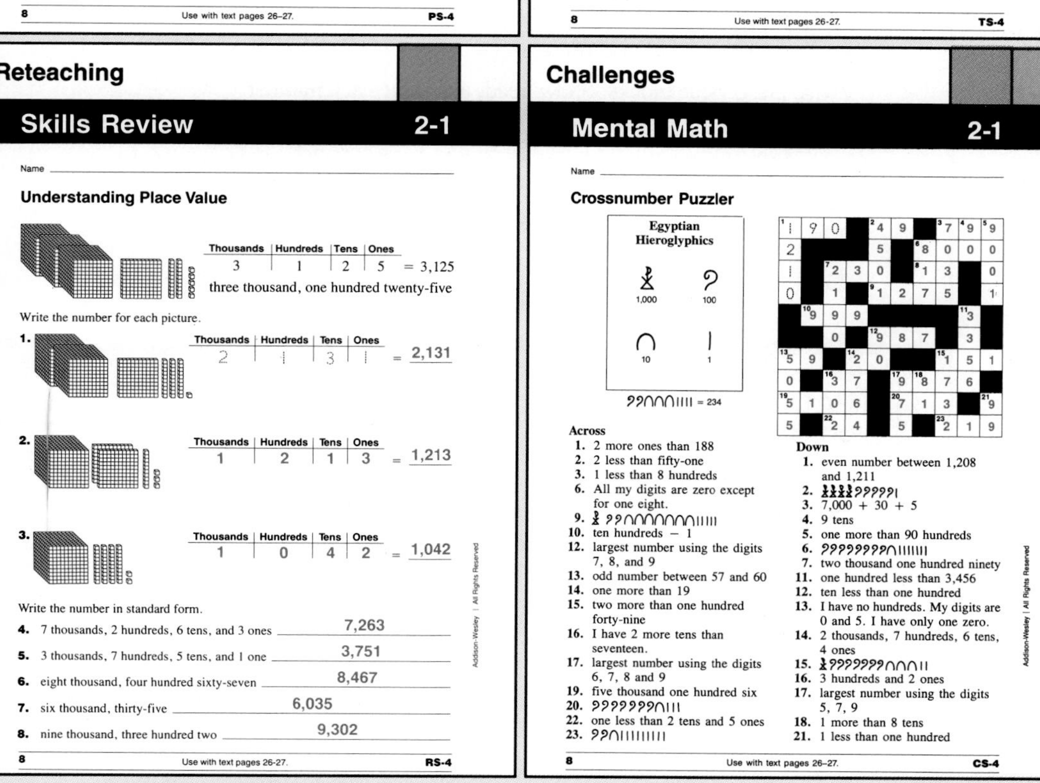

Reteaching

Skills Review 2-1

Name ______________________

Understanding Place Value

Thousands	Hundreds	Tens	Ones	
3	1	2	5	= 3,125

three thousand, one hundred twenty-five

Write the number for each picture.

	Thousands	Hundreds	Tens	Ones	
1.	2	1	3	1	= 2,131
2.	1	2	1	3	= 1,213
3.	1	0	4	2	= 1,042

Write the number in standard form.

4. 7 thousands, 2 hundreds, 6 tens, and 3 ones 7,263
5. 3 thousands, 7 hundreds, 5 tens, and 1 one 3,751
6. eight thousand, four hundred sixty-seven 8,467
7. six thousand, thirty-five 6,035
8. nine thousand, three hundred two 9,302

8 Use with text pages 26-27. RS-4

Challenges

Mental Math 2-1

Name ______________________

Crossnumber Puzzler

Egyptian Hieroglyphics

𓆼 1,000 𓍢 100 𓎆 10 𓏺 1

𓍢𓍢𓎆𓎆𓎆𓏺𓏺𓏺𓏺 = 234

(1) 1	9	0	■	(2) 4	9	■	(3) 7	(4) 9	(5) 9
2	■	■	■	5	■	(6) 8	0	0	0
1	■	(7) 2	3	0	■	(8) 1	3	■	0
0	■	1	■	(9) 1	2	7	5	■	1
■	(10) 9	9	9	■	■	■	■	(11) 3	■
■	■	0	■	(12) 9	8	7	■	3	■
(13) 5	9	■	(14) 2	0	■	■	(15) 1	5	1
0	■	(16) 3	7	■	(17) 9	(18) 8	7	6	■
(19) 5	1	0	6	■	(20) 7	1	3	■	(21) 9
5	■	(22) 2	4	■	5	■	(23) 2	1	9

Across

1. 2 more ones than 188
2. 2 less than fifty-one
3. 1 less than 8 hundreds
6. All my digits are zero except for one eight.
9. 𓆼𓍢𓍢𓎆𓎆𓎆𓎆𓎆𓎆𓎆𓏺𓏺𓏺𓏺𓏺
10. ten hundreds − 1
12. largest number using the digits 7, 8, and 9
13. odd number between 57 and 60
14. one more than 19
15. two more than one hundred forty-nine
16. I have 2 more tens than seventeen.
17. largest number using the digits 6, 7, 8 and 9
19. five thousand one hundred six
20. 𓍢𓍢𓍢𓍢𓍢𓍢𓍢𓎆𓏺𓏺𓏺
22. one less than 2 tens and 5 ones
23. 𓍢𓍢𓎆𓏺𓏺𓏺𓏺𓏺𓏺𓏺𓏺𓏺

Down

1. even number between 1,208 and 1,211
2. 𓆼𓆼𓆼𓆼𓍢𓍢𓍢𓍢𓍢𓏺
3. 7,000 + 30 + 5
4. 9 tens
5. one more than 90 hundreds
6. 𓍢𓍢𓍢𓍢𓍢𓍢𓍢𓍢𓎆𓏺𓏺𓏺𓏺𓏺𓏺
7. two thousand one hundred ninety
11. one hundred less than 3,456
12. ten less than one hundred
13. I have no hundreds. My digits are 0 and 5. I have only one zero.
14. 2 thousands, 7 hundreds, 6 tens, 4 ones
15. 𓆼𓍢𓍢𓍢𓍢𓍢𓍢𓍢𓎆𓎆𓏺𓏺
16. 3 hundreds and 2 ones
17. largest number using the digits 5, 7, 9
18. 1 more than 8 tens
21. 1 less than one hundred

8 Use with text pages 26–27. CS-4

Options for Individual Needs

Basic

Exercises 1-4, 6-11
Skills Bank, p. 460
More Practice, p. 512, set F

Supplements
Reteaching 8 or
Practice 8

Average

Exercises 1-12
Skills Bank, p. 460
More Practice, p. 512, set F

Supplements
Practice 8
Challenges 8 or
Thinking Skills 8

Extended

Exercises 3-12

Supplements
Challenges 8
Thinking Skills 8

Other Resources:
Problem-Solving Experiences in Mathematics, Grade 4, Problem 17
Math In Stride, Grade 4, pp. 1-4

LESSON PLAN 2-1

OBJECTIVE 2-1
To read and write 3- and 4-digit numbers

Materials: place value blocks, TA 5 (4-Digit Place Value Charts)

Alternative Materials: TA 6 (Place Value Models)

Grouping Suggestion: small groups

1. MOTIVATE AND TEACH

LEARN ABOUT IT

▶ **Order place value blocks from least to greatest.** (one, ten, hundred, thousand)
▶ **Generalize how any block compares with a block of the next greater size.** (Ten of any block equals one of the next greater size.)

EXPLORE ▶ **Suppose you did not have any more thousand blocks. How could you show another thousand?** (Use 10 hundreds.)

TALK ABOUT IT ▶ **In the number with no hundreds, how many places are there? Explain.** (still four; The hundreds need a zero to hold the place.)
▶ **How can you be sure to write a number properly if a place is empty?** (Possible answer: Record the value of every place.)
Student Edition answers: **1.** Add one or more thousand cubes to the sample model. **2.** used no hundred models **3.** Write a zero in the hundreds place; write a zero in the tens place.

2. CHECK UNDERSTANDING

TRY IT OUT

ERROR ALERT Omitting zeros in numbers that have empty places. Confusing standard and expanded form.

Understanding Place Value

LEARN ABOUT IT

EXPLORE **Use a Place Value Model**

You can write any whole number using the **digits** 1, 2, 3, 4, 5, 6, 7, 8, 9, 0, and place value.

thousands hundreds tens ones

Work in groups. Use place value blocks to show a number with more thousands than are in the picture. Then show a number with fewer tens and a number with no hundreds. Write each number after you show it.

These blocks show a number.

You write, **2,347**.

You read, "**two thousand, three hundred forty-seven.**"

TALK ABOUT IT See teaching notes.

1. What did you do to show more thousands than are in 2,347?
2. How did your blocks show a number with no hundreds?
3. How do you write a number with no hundreds? with no tens?

You can find the **place value** of a digit by looking at its place in the number. The chart shows the place values for the digits in 5,698.

The expanded form helps you see the value of each place.

	Thousands		Hundreds		Tens		Ones
standard form →	5	,	6		9		8
expanded form →	5,000	+	600	+	90	+	8

TRY IT OUT Check students' models.

Use place value blocks. Show, read, and write each number.

1. 4 hundreds, 4 tens, and 3 ones
443
2. 2 thousands, 4 hundreds, and 2 ones
2,402
3. 2 thousands, 3 hundreds, and 6 tens
2,360
4. 1 thousand and 9 tens
1,090
5. Write 3 thousands, 9 hundreds, and 6 ones in expanded form.
3,000 + 900 + 6

26

TEACHING OPTIONS

RETEACHING TIPS Students who omit zeros should use place value charts as they model numbers. One place at a time, they should write how many of each place value block they use for a given number. Show them how standard form follows the chart, place by place. Assign Reteaching Supplement 8.

ENRICHMENT Have students find each standard number.
1. 13 hundreds, 22 ones (1,322)
2. 14 hundreds, 14 tens, 14 ones (1,554)
3. 9 hundreds, 19 tens, 19 ones (1,109)
4. 11 hundreds, 544 ones (1,644)
5. 22 hundreds, 10 tens (2,300)

PRACTICE

How many thousands, hundreds, tens, and ones are in each number? Write the number. See Additional Answers.

1.

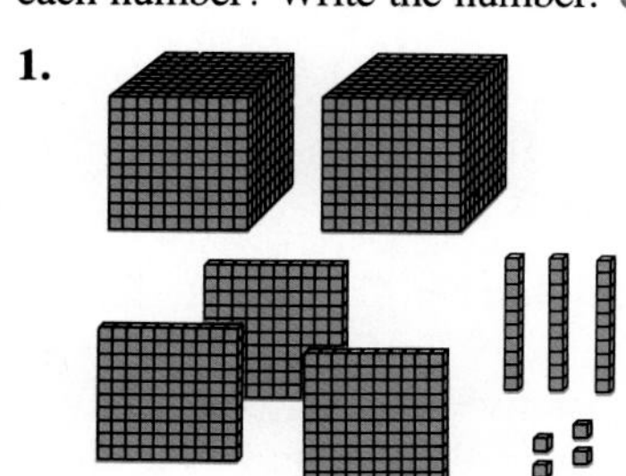

2.

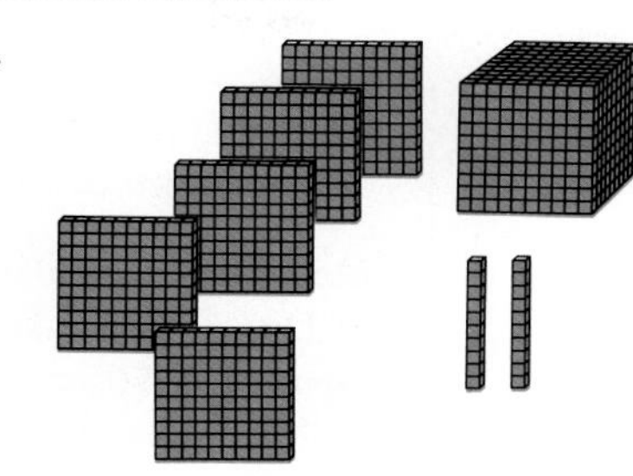

Write the number in standard form and in expanded form.

3. five thousand, eight hundred seventy-five
5,875; 5,000 + 800 + 70 + 5

4. nine thousand, ninety-nine
9,099; 9,000 + 90 + 9

5. two thousand, four hundred ten
2,410; 2,000 + 400 + 10

APPLY

MATH REASONING Give the numbers from the box in which the digit 7 has the given value.

3,875	6,704	5,713
7,025	1,847	2,427
4,725	7,023	9,378

6. 700
6,704; 4,725; 5,713

7. 70
3,875; 9,378

8. 7
1,847; 2,427

PROBLEM SOLVING

9. What number would this picture show if it had 2 more hundreds? if it had 3 more tens? 1,515; 1,345

► **ALGEBRA**

Use models to find the number you can put in the box to make the sentence true.

Tens, hundreds, and thousands are related.

10 tens = 1 hundred

10 hundreds = 1 thousand

10. 3 thousands = ▒ hundreds 30

11. 3 thousands = ▒ tens 300

12. 3 thousands = ▒ ones 3,000

More Practice, page 512, set F

3. Practice and Apply

Basic	1-4, 6-11
Average	1-12
Extended	3-12

Additional Answers: See p. T79.

PRACTICE

When writing the numbers for Exercises 1 and 2, what do you need to watch for? (The place value models are not always drawn showing the largest amount first, so you have to be careful not to give a digit the wrong value.)

APPLY

MATH REASONING ► **Compare the numbers with 7 thousands.** (Both have no hundreds and 2 tens, but the ones are different.)

PROBLEM SOLVING ► **What strategy could help you visualize the problem?** (Possible answers: use blocks, models, or a place value chart; draw a picture)

ALGEBRA ► **Restate the equation as a question.** (Sample question: How many hundreds equal 3 thousands?)
► **What is a simpler way to solve each problem?** (Find the missing number for 1 thousand and triple it.)

Close and Assess

WRITE WHAT YOU THINK
Have students choose any 4-digit number that has no repeated digits. First, they draw place value models to show the number. Next, they write the number in standard form and in expanded form. Last, they write the number in word form. (Check students' drawings and writing.)

QUICK QUIZ

Give expanded form, standard form, and word form. (Answers will vary.)
1. your telephone area code
2. the year you were born

LESSON OPTIONS 2-2

Using Larger Numbers

OBJECTIVE 2-2 To read and write 5- and 6-digit numbers

PREBOOK ACTIVITIES

QUICK REVIEW

Give the value of each digit.

1. 7 in 7,001 (7 thousands) **2.** 5 in 1,053 (5 tens) **3.** 6 in 126 (6 ones)

Write the digit that is in the given place in 9,706.

4. hundreds (7) **5.** tens (0) **6.** thousands (9)

PRIOR KNOWLEDGE

Have students describe how they have used place value models. (Possible answer: to understand place value of 3- and 4-digit numbers) Then write several 5- and 6-digit numbers on the chalkboard. Ask students to compare these numbers to 3- and 4-digit numbers. (Possible answer: 5- and 6-digit numbers have more places.) Ask students what they would need to show these larger numbers with place value models. (Possible answer: You would need place value models for ten thousands and hundred thousands.) Finally, ask students to recall where they have seen 5- and 6-digit numbers used. (Possible answers: as population figures; as the price of items such as cars)

COMMUNICATION

Discussing Math Write the word **period** on the chalkboard. Ask a volunteer to explain what *period* means in a writing class. (a punctuation mark used to end a statement) Explain that in math a period is a group of three places. Write a 6-digit number on the board. Ask students to name the places that make up each period. (ones, tens, hundreds; thousands, ten thousands, hundred thousands)

EXPLORE AND CONNECT

Materials: calculators, TA 3 (Number Cards 2-9), TA 5 (4-Digit Place Value Charts)

Grouping Suggestion: cooperative learning pairs

Students randomly pick number cards to form two 2-digit numbers. Then they make the calculator display each number, using *only* the 0, 1, +, and = keys. (For example, 23 is displayed by entering 1 + 1 + 1 + 10 + 10.) Partners record on a place value chart how many 1s and 10s they used to form each 2-digit number. When both partners have made a 2-digit number by this method, they should attempt 3- and 4-digit numbers. Encourage partners to discuss how to show greater places. (Add 100s or 1,000s.) Then have students share strategies and tell how they kept track of the addition. (Answers will vary.) Challenge students to explain how to display 5- and 6-digit numbers. (Use the same method but repeat 10,000s or 100,000s.)

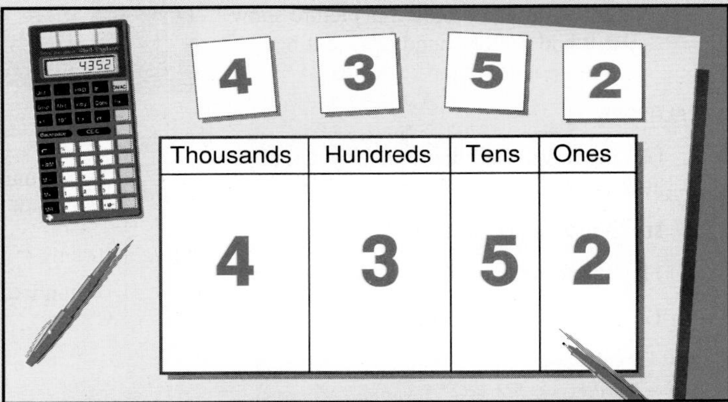

CONNECTIONS Use these anytime.

Problem of the Day

Logic Which 6-digit number fits the rules? **1.** It has only 2 digits but they repeat. **2.** The digits appear in the same order in both periods. **3.** The sum of the digits is 28. **4.** The ones digit is 7 more than the tens digit. (707,707)

Math Connection

Place Value Write each number: **1.** A number that goes one place into the thousands. **2.** A number that fills all the places in the thousands period. (Answers may vary.)

Subject Integration

Social Studies Which city has the most people? the least?

Birmingham, Alabama 277,510
San Antonio, Texas 914,350
Tampa, Florida 277,580
(most—San Antonio; least—Birmingham)

Classwork and Homework Supplements

Practice

Skills Maintenance 2-2

Name

Using Larger Numbers

Write the digit for the given place in the number 607,258.

1. thousands 7
2. tens 5
3. ten thousands 0
4. hundreds 2
5. ones 8
6. hundred thousands 6

Ring the numbers in the box in which the digit 6 has the given value.

7. 60,000 — 451,673 962,048 68,524 860,231
8. 600 — 807,653 56,059 840,627 900,674
9. 600,000 — 723,076 650,378 612,890 423,005
10. 6,000 — 536,219 267,743 86,830 72,400

Write the number.

11. twenty thousand, nine hundred ten 20,910
12. sixty-one thousand, eight hundred seven 61,807
13. seven hundred thousand, one hundred fifty 700,150
14. thirty-six thousand, seven hundred eighteen 36,718
15. five hundred twelve thousand, forty-nine 512,049

PS-4 Use with text pages 28–29. 9

Building Thinking Skills

Patterns 2-2

Name

Predict the Amount

People often study the changes in numbers over a period of time to help them understand what has happened as well as what might happen.

Predict the next amount and write it in the chart. Then fill in the answers to explain your thinking.

Echo Records—Number of Albums Sold			
Week 1	Week 2	Week 3	Week 4
101,535	101,646	101,757	101,868

1. The number of albums sold each week increased by 111 albums.
2. If the sales pattern continues, the company will sell 101,979 albums in Week 5.

Boppo Toy Company—Toys Manufactured			
Year 1	Year 2	Year 3	Year 4
750,500	550,500	350,500	150,500

3. The number of toys manufactured each year decreased by 200,000.
4. If the manufacturing pattern continues, in Year 5 the company will no longer manufacture toys.

TS-4 Use with text pages 28-29. 9

Reteaching

Skills Review 2-2

Name

Using Larger Numbers

The thousands period is the next greater period after the ones. Follow these steps to read a number in the thousands.

- ▶ Read the digits in the thousands period as a number and say the word "thousand" after it.
- ▶ Then read the digits in the ones period.

Thousands Period			Ones Period		
Hundred Thousands	Ten Thousands	Thousands	Hundreds	Tens	Ones
5	2	4	6	3	7

"five hundred twenty-four thousand" "six hundred thirty-seven"

You read: "five hundred twenty-four thousand, six hundred thirty-seven."
You write: 524,637.

1. Write a 5-digit number with 4 in the ten thousands place and 7 in the thousands place. 4 7, _ _ _
2. Write a 6-digit number with 8 in the hundred thousands place and 4 in the ten thousands place. 8 4 _, _ _ _

Other digits may vary.

Write the number.

3. sixteen thousand, four hundred eight 16,408
4. eighty-seven thousand, one hundred two 87,102

Ring the correct number.

5. four hundred seventeen thousand, three hundred one — 417,301 417,300 400,017 17,301
6. six hundred twelve thousand, twenty-four — 612,240 612,024 612,000 600,024

RS-4 Use with text pages 28-29. 9

Challenges

Reading Math 2-2

Name

Place Value Story

Complete this activity with a partner. Take turns being player 1 and player 2. Player 1 keeps the story hidden and reads aloud the clues under each blank. Player 1 writes down the numbers Player 2 picks. Player 1 then reads the story out loud. Answers will vary.

Last week I had a strange day. When I woke up, I had a spider bite on my toe. The toe was swollen ______ (2-digit number) times as large as usual. I limped over to my closet and picked out one of my ______ (5-digit number) outfits. Then I hopped on my skateboard and whizzed to school in ______ (3-digit number) minutes flat.

At recess, I was a real hotshot. I made ______ (6-digit number with 8 in hundreds place) baskets and ______ (5-digit number with 9 in thousands place) home runs. The teacher spoiled my mood by giving us some extra homework that she said would take about ______ (4-digit number with 3 in hundreds place) hours to complete.

After school I went to my friend Pat's house, and we ate ______ (3-digit number) pieces of pizza. Then Pat taught me ______ (5-digit number) tricks on my skateboard.

When I got home, I gulped down ______ (4-digit number) glasses of milk and started my ______ (5-digit number with 2 in hundreds place) pages of homework.

CS-4 Use with text pages 28–29. 9

Options for Individual Needs

2-2

Basic

Exercises 1-8, 11-16
Data Bank, p. 472
Skills Bank, p. 460
More Practice, p. 513, set A

Supplements
Reteaching 9 or
Practice 9
Challenges 9

Average

Exercises 1-18
Data Bank, p. 472
Skills Bank, p. 460
More Practice, p. 513, set A

Supplements
Practice 9
Challenges 9 or
Thinking Skills 9

Extended

Exercises 2-8, 12-18
Data Bank, p. 472

Supplements
Challenges 9
Thinking Skills 9

Other Resources:
Problem-Solving Experiences in Mathematics, Grade 4, Problem 22
Math In Stride, Grade 4, p. 173

LESSON PLAN 2-2

OBJECTIVE 2-2
To read and write 5- and 6-digit numbers

Materials: TA 7 (6-Digit Place Value Charts), calculators

1. MOTIVATE AND TEACH

LEARN ABOUT IT

► **From looking at the picture, what can you generalize about representing large numbers with place value models?** (Possible answer: You may need to invent models to represent groups of 10 thousand because each larger place increases by 10 times.)

EXPLORE ► **Explain how you would use place value models to show ten thousands and hundred thousands.** (Possible answer: Use 10 thousands models to show 1 ten thousand. 10 groups of ten thousands would show 1 hundred thousand.)

TALK ABOUT IT ► **How does knowing place value help you answer the first question?** (Possible answer: 10 of one place is always equal to 1 of the next higher place. So 10 hundreds equal 1 thousand. 10 × 100 = 1,000.)

► **Compare the cube Jerry is holding with the row of cubes he is imagining.** (Possible answer: They are all the same. So if there are 1,000 ones in 1 cube, there are 10,000 ones in 10 cubes.)
Student Edition answers: **1.** Use place value. **2.** 10,000 because 1 cube has 1,000 ones and there are 10 cubes.

2. CHECK UNDERSTANDING

TRY IT OUT

ERROR ALERT Difficulty recalling place value beyond hundreds. Confusing which values belong in the ones and thousands periods.

Using Larger Numbers

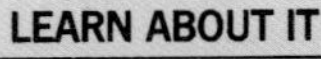

LEARN ABOUT IT

EXPLORE Think About the Situation
Jerry read that it took over 10,000 adobe blocks to build some ancient Indian homes. He thought about how he could show this large number with place value blocks.

TALK ABOUT IT See teaching notes.

1. How could you convince someone that there are 1,000 ones cubes in the thousands cube Jerry is holding?
2. How many ones are there in the long row of cubes Jerry imagined? Explain.

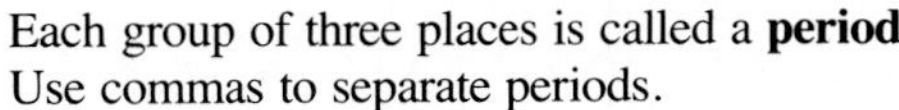

Each group of three places is called a **period**.
Use commas to separate periods.

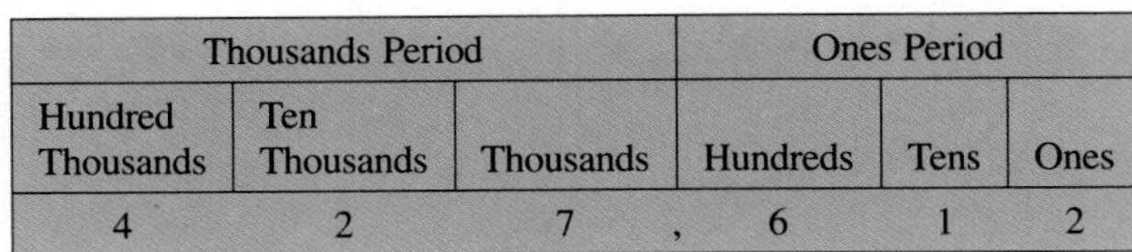

Thousands Period			Ones Period		
Hundred Thousands	Ten Thousands	Thousands	Hundreds	Tens	Ones
4	2	7 ,	6	1	2

400,000 + 20,000 + 7,000 + 600 + 10 + 2

You write, **427,612**. You read, "**four hundred twenty-seven thousand, six hundred twelve**."

TRY IT OUT Answers may vary.

1. Write and read a 5-digit number with 3 in the ten thousands place and 4 in the thousands place.
3 4, ___ ___ ___
2. Write and read a 6-digit number with 7 in the hundred thousands place and 2 in the hundreds place.
___ ___ ___, ___ ___ ___

28

TEACHING OPTIONS

RETEACHING TIPS Students having difficulty recalling place value beyond hundreds should use a place value chart. Have students find the place on the chart before they insert the number, beginning with the ones place and moving higher. Assign Reteaching Supplement 9.

ENRICHMENT Have students work in pairs to make up two 5- or 6-digit numbers. One adds the numbers using paper and pencil as the other adds the numbers using a calculator. They do as many sets of numbers as there is time for, trading roles and comparing answers after each set.

PRACTICE

Write and read each number. Answers may vary.

1. A 5-digit number with 6 in the thousands place and 0 in the hundreds place

2. A 6-digit number with 9 in the ten thousands place and 5 in the tens place

Write the digit for the given place in the number 384,019.

3. hundreds 0
4. ten thousands 8
5. thousands 4
6. hundred thousands 3

Write the numbers from the box in which the digit 3 has the given value. See Additional Answers.

385,219	463,218
443,276	538,425
832,104	645,318
221,378	308,467

7. 300
8. 300,000
9. 3,000
10. 30,000

Write the number.

11. seventy thousand, three hundred four 70,304

12. two hundred sixty-three thousand, four hundred eighty-two 263,482

APPLY

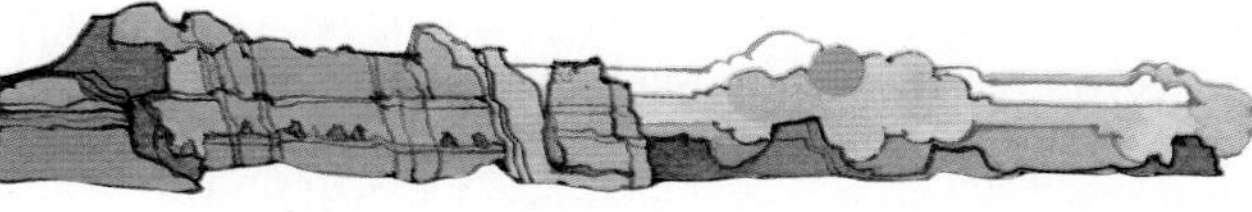

MATH REASONING

13. Give the next number in this pattern. 203 2,004 20,005 200,006

PROBLEM SOLVING

14. One ancient Indian building used about 34,000 blocks. How many thousands cubes would Jerry need to show this? 34 cubes

15. **Social Studies Data Bank** DATA BANK How many tens are in the number of rooms in Long House? See page 472. 15 tens

▶ CALCULATOR

Change the digit by adding or subtracting just once. The other digits stay the same. Tell how you made each change.

16. Change the 8 in 586,204 to 0. − 80,000

17. Change the 4 in 234,198 to 0. − 4,000

18. Change the 3 in 765,382 to 4. + 100

More Practice, page 513, set A

3. Practice and Apply

Basic	1-8, 11-16
Average	1-18
Extended	2-8, 12-18

Additional Answers: See p. T79.

2-2

PRACTICE

How many periods are in a 5- or 6-digit number? (two) *What mark separates the periods?* (a comma) *What is the order of places in the thousands period?* (thousands, ten thousands, hundred thousands)

APPLY

MATH REASONING ▶ **Explain the pattern.** (2 is moved to the next highest place and 1 more is added in the ones place.)

PROBLEM SOLVING ▶ **Explain how you arrived at your answer to Problem 14.** (One cube equals 1,000, so 34 cubes equal 34,000.)
▶ **Explain how you solved Problem 15.** (Determine that 100 ones = 10 tens. 10 tens + 5 tens = 15 tens.)

CALCULATOR ▶ **Decide if addition or subtraction is needed in each example.** (−, −, +)

Close and Assess

SHOW WHAT YOU KNOW

Write a 5-digit and a 6-digit number on the chalkboard. Have each student draw place value models to show the value of each digit in each number. Then have them write the numbers in expanded form. (Check students' models and writing.)

QUICK QUIZ

Write each number.

1. two hundred ninety thousand, four hundred seventy-three (290,473)
2. forty thousand, fifty (40,050)
3. one hundred thousand (100,000)

LESSON OPTIONS 2-3

Comparing and Ordering Numbers

OBJECTIVE 2-3 To compare and order numbers

PREBOOK ACTIVITIES

QUICK REVIEW

1. Circle the number in the ten thousands place.
107,829 68,031 861,592 22,175 945,324
(0, 6, 6, 2, 4)
2. Circle the number in the hundreds place.
72,609 414 547,184 38,576 3,210
(6, 4, 1, 5, 2)

PRIOR KNOWLEDGE

Have students suggest times when they have needed to compare and order numbers. (Possible answer: to find which distance is farther; to find the least costly item) Ask students to explain how they can use what they know about place value to compare numbers. (Possible answer: By comparing the digits in each place in two numbers, you can tell if one number is greater than or less than another.)

COMMUNICATION

Listening and Writing in Math List on the chalkboard the following symbols: <, >, =, ≠. Call on students to explain each symbol in their own words. (< could be less than, smaller than, fewer than; > could be greater than, bigger than, larger than; = could be equal to or the same as; ≠ could be not equal to or not the same as.) Ask students to write one sentence for each symbol in their Math Journals. Suggest they compare simple things. For example, they could compare the number of their family members or their age to a friend's. (Possible sentences: There are 4 people in my family, which is = to the 4 people in Joe's family; My age is < than Sally's.)

EXPLORE AND CONNECT

Materials: blank index cards
Grouping Suggestion: cooperative learning groups of 5
One student is the customer and the other four are businesses, such as the telephone and cable companies. Each customer starts with $100. Each business writes an amount greater than $5 but less than $30 on an index card and gives it to the customer as a bill. The customer handles each bill separately. The student compares the first bill to the $100, pays it by subtracting the amount, then does the same with the second and third bills. Before paying the fourth bill, the customer compares it with the balance in the book to see if the balance is greater than or less than the bill. If it is less than, the student determines how much to deposit to cover the bill. Repeat until each group member has had a turn as customer. Finally, have each group order its bills from greatest to least amount.

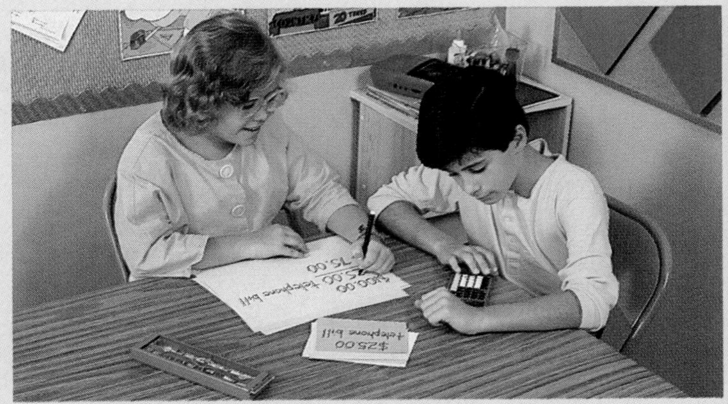

CONNECTIONS Use these anytime.

Problem of the Day

Comparing Numbers Use > and < to compare the numbers below. What is the greatest number of two-number comparisons that can be made? (20)
7,041 77,041 1,407
741 77,001

Patterns

Order Think about each pattern. Then fill in the next two numbers. 610, 620, 630, 640, (650), (660)
903, 906, 909, 912, (915), (918)
1,000; 1,040; 1,080; 1,120; (1,160); (2,000)

Math Connection

Money Compare these lunch receipts. Which grade spent the most on lunches? Which grade spent the least?

Grade 3	$72.25	
Grade 4	$87.25	(most)
Grade 5	$71.05	(least)

Classwork and Homework Supplements

Practice

Math Reasoning 2-3

Name

Comparing and Ordering Numbers

Compare. Write < or > for each □.

1. 32 [>] 28 2. 57 [<] 61 3. 97 [>] 94
4. 469 [<] 470 5. 285 [>] 258 6. 791 [>] 789
7. 672 [<] 682 8. 439 [>] 394 9. 850 [>] 849
10. 5,361 [>] 5,300 11. 6,000 [<] 6,010 12. 9,327 [>] 9,237

Order these numbers from least to greatest.

13. 8,685 927 8,698 8,740
927 8,685 8,698 8,740

14. 52,721 5,760 6,047 52,463
5,760 6,047 52,463 52,721

15. 20,561 24,385 24,279 4,890
4,890 20,561 24,279 24,385

16. 195 1,095 951 1,905
195 951 1,095 1,905

Use the numbers in the box. 10,400 1,705 7,410 4,277

17. Which number is less than 2,560? 1,705
18. Which number is greater than 9,718? 10,400
19. Which number is between 3,000 and 5,500? 4,277

Building Thinking Skills

Data Analysis 2-3

Name

Longer or Longest

Major Rivers of the World	Length (miles)
Amazon	3,915
Mississippi	2,348
Nile	4,145
Ohio-Allegheny	1,306
Rio Grande	1,885
St. Lawrence	1,900
Snake	1,000
Volga	2,194

Put these rivers in order from the shortest to the longest.

1. Snake 2. Ohio-Allegheny
3. Rio Grande 4. St. Lawrence
5. Volga 6. Mississippi
7. Amazon 8. Nile

Put > or < in the ○ to complete each problem.

9. Volga (<) Mississippi 10. Nile (>) Amazon
11. Rio Grande (<) St. Lawrence 12. Ohio-Allegheny (>) Snake

Use the data from the chart to fill in the blanks.

13. The St. Lawrence River is almost twice as long as the Snake River.
14. The Amazon and the Nile are both about 4 times as long as the Snake river.
15. The lengths of the three rivers, Ohio-Allegheny, Rio Grande, Snake, when added together, come closest to the length of the Nile.

Reteaching

Skills Review 2-3

Name

Comparing and Ordering Numbers

Which is greater, 5,839 or 5,845?

To compare these numbers, start at the left. Find the first place where the digits are different. → Compare these digits. Which digit is greater? → The numbers compare the same way the digits compare.

(same) 5,839 / (different) 5,845 — 3 / 4 (4 is greater than 3.) — 5,839 / 5,845 (5,845 is greater than 5,839. 5,845 > 5,839)

Put these numbers in order, from least to greatest or greatest to least.

5,485 5,839 583 5,893

To order a list of numbers, compare the numbers two at a time. → Then list them from least to greatest or greatest to least.

583 < 5,839 5,839 < 5,845
5,845 < 5,893

583 5,389 5,845 5,893 (583 is least.)
5,893 5,845 5,839 583 (5,893 is greatest.)

Compare. Write < or > for each ○.

1. 467 (<) 469 2. 4,805 (>) 4,580 3. 54,876 (<) 543,876

Order these numbers from least to greatest.

4. 546 1,564 678 1,546
546 678 1,546 1,564

5. 22,876 786 876 22,799
786 876 22,799 22,876

Order these numbers from greatest to least.

6. 2,876 876 222,876 28,766
222,876 28,766 2,876 876

7. 543 345 2,432 2,345
2,432 2,345 543 345

Challenges

Cooperative Activities 2-3

Name

Larger or Smaller?

Play this game in a small group. You will need a spinner with the numbers 0 through 9 on it.

Rules

1. Take turns spinning the spinner.
2. Write the number in any box. (You cannot change your mind later.)
3. Spin the spinner 5 times.
4. Each player reads his or her 5-digit number out loud.
5. The winner is the player who has the largest or smallest number and has read the number correctly.

Largest Number Wins.

Game 1 □□,□□□
Game 2 □□,□□□
Game 3 □□,□□□
Game 4 □□,□□□
Game 5 □□,□□□

Smallest Number Wins.

Game 1 □□,□□□
Game 2 □□,□□□
Game 3 □□,□□□
Game 4 □□,□□□
Game 5 □□,□□□

Evaluate as a group each member's strategies for creating the largest and smallest numbers.

Options for Individual Needs

2-3

Basic

Exercises 1-4, 8-16
More Practice, p. 500, set D

Supplements
Reteaching 10 or
Practice 10

Average

Exercises 1-16
More Practice, p. 500, set D

Supplements
Practice 10
Challenges 10 or
Thinking Skills 10

Extended

Exercises 5-16

Supplements
Challenges 10
Thinking Skills 10

Other Resources:
Problem-Solving Experiences in Mathematics, Grade 4, Problem 19
Math In Stride, pp. 8, 9
Mathematics, A Way of Thinking, Lessons 2-1, 2-2, 2-3, 2-4

LESSON PLAN 2-3

OBJECTIVE 2-3
To compare and order numbers

Materials: TA 7 (6-Digit Place Value Charts)

1. MOTIVATE AND TEACH

LEARN ABOUT IT

▶ **From looking at the chart, what can you say about the numbers?** (Possible answers: They are all different. Most have four digits.)

EXPLORE ▶ **Explain the method you would use to compare these numbers.** (Possible answers: Compare two at a time. Start with the digits in the largest place and compare values.)
▶ **Is there only one way to order numbers? Explain.** (No, numbers can be ordered from greatest to least or from least to greatest.)

TALK ABOUT IT ▶ **Can understanding number periods help answer Exercise 1? Explain.** (Possible answer: Yes, because 745 is the only number that stays in the ones period, so it must be smallest.)
▶ **When comparing numbers, why do you look for the first place where digits are not equal?** (Possible answer: If all digits are the same, then the numbers are equal in value.)
Student Edition answers: **1.** El Paso, because it has no thousands digit. **2.** Boston is farthest because its hundreds digit is greater in value.

2. CHECK UNDERSTANDING

TRY IT OUT

ERROR ALERT Forgetting to start at the left of the number when comparing. Confusing the meaning of the symbols $>$ and $<$.

Comparing and Ordering Numbers

LEARN ABOUT IT

EXPLORE **Study the Data**
You can compare these numbers to find which is greater or less. Then you can put them in order by size.

Distances from Houston, Texas to	
El Paso, Texas	745 miles
Boston, Massachusetts	1,804 miles
Seattle, Washington	2,274 miles
Miami, Florida	1,190 miles

TALK ABOUT IT See teaching notes.

1. Can you tell quickly which distance is the shortest? How?
2. Which is the greatest distance from Houston—Boston or Miami? Explain how you know.

Use these symbols to compare numbers.

$<$ means *is less than*
$>$ means *is greater than*
$=$ means *is equal to*
$\neq$ means *is not equal to*

You can use place value to compare numbers such as 7,289 and 7,294.

To compare, start at the left. Find the first place where the digits are not equal.	7,289 7,294
Compare the digits in that place.	$8 < 9$
The numbers compare the same way.	$7{,}289 < 7{,}294$
To order this list of numbers, 7,289 798 7,294 6,813, compare the numbers two at a time.	$798 < 6{,}813$ $6{,}813 < 7{,}289$ $7{,}289 < 7{,}294$
Then list them from least to greatest or greatest to least.	798 6,813 7,289 7,294 7,294 7,289 6,813 798

TRY IT OUT

Compare. Write $<$ or $>$ for each ▥.

1. 578 ▥ 579 ($>$)
2. 3,407 ▥ 3,470 ($<$)
3. 72,885 ▥ 72,588 ($>$)
4. Order these numbers. 5,817 587 5,871 5,819 See Additional Answers.

30

TEACHING OPTIONS

RETEACHING TIPS For the first error, students should insert each number in a 6-digit place value chart. Then they draw an arrow over the number from left to right to remind them to begin with the digits showing the greatest value as they compare each place. Assign Reteaching Supplement 10.

ENRICHMENT Have students use mental math to figure the sums or differences. Then fill in each ○ with $>$, $<$, or $=$.

1. 700 + 800 ○ 600 + 500
2. 90 + 90 + 10 ○ 100 + 60 + 30
3. 202 − 101 ○ 553 − 447

(**1.** $>$ **2.** $=$ **3.** $<$)

PRACTICE

Compare. Write < or > for each ▥.

1. 197 ▥ 179 **>**
2. 678 ▥ 868 **<**
3. 98 ▥ 111 **<**
4. 2,734 ▥ 2,785 **<**
5. 769 ▥ 2,032 **<**
6. 5,524 ▥ 5,454 **>**

Order these numbers from least to greatest. **See Additional Answers.**

7. 1,501 369 1,522 1,487
8. 34,967 4,967 5,867 34,867

Use the numbers in the box. **See Additional Answers.**

3,218	5,500
7,081	5,411
10,000	2,480
3,692	9,035

9. List the numbers greater than 8,371.
10. List the numbers less than 5,419.
11. List the numbers between 4,500 and 9,050.

APPLY

MATH REASONING Think about the number 5,000. Then write the numbers. **Answers may vary.**

12. Write 3 numbers that are a little more than 5,000.
13. Write 3 numbers that are much more than 5,000.

PROBLEM SOLVING

14. St. Louis is 779 miles from Houston. Atlanta is 789 miles from Houston. Which city is nearest to Houston? **St. Louis**
15. Use these digits. What is the greatest 4-digit number you can write? What is the least 4-digit number you can write? **8,642; 2,468**

2	4
6	8

▶ **ESTIMATION**

16. Without counting, list the pictures in order from most dots to fewest dots. **D > B > A > C**

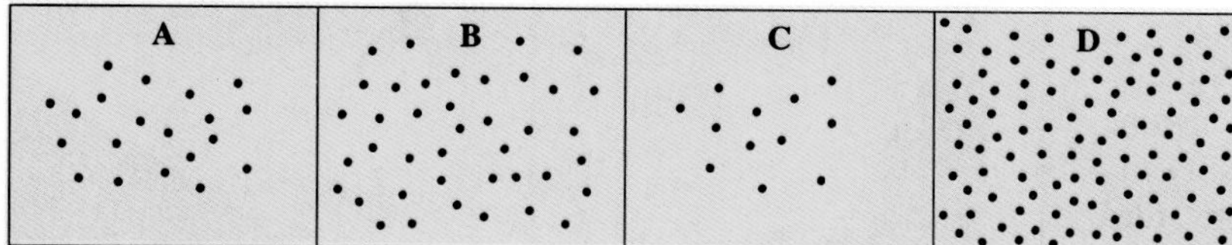

More Practice, page 500, set D

3. PRACTICE AND APPLY

Basic	1-4, 8-16
Average	1-16
Extended	5-16

Additional Answers: See p. T79.

PRACTICE

What could you do to help you answer Exercises 9-11? (Possible answer: List the boxed numbers in order from least to greatest before you begin.)

APPLY

MATH REASONING ▶ **Explain how you chose your numbers.** (Possible answer: I thought about what *little* and *much* mean.)

PROBLEM SOLVING ▶ **How can restating the question help you solve Problem 14?** (Possible answer: Thinking about which is fewer miles may make comparing easier.)

ESTIMATION ▶ **Which boxes would you compare first? Why?** (Possible answer: D and B, because they clearly have the most dots.)

2-3

CLOSE AND ASSESS

WRITE WHAT YOU KNOW Ask students to make up two different 5-digit numbers. They compare the two numbers using the greater than or less than symbol. Then, in complete sentences, each student writes an explanation of why one number is greater than the other. (Check students' writing.)

QUICK QUIZ

Order these numbers from least to greatest:
307, 3,980, 410, 389, 370, 398
(307, 370, 389, 398, 410, 3,980)

LESSON OPTIONS 2-4

Exploring Algebra/Midchapter Review/Quiz

OBJECTIVE 2-4 To explore algebra by understanding equality

PREBOOK ACTIVITIES

QUICK REVIEW

Find the missing number.

1. 6 = 3 + (3) **2.** 7 + (3) = 10
3. (5) + 4 = 9 **4.** 11 = (7) + 4
5. 8 + 5 = (13) **6.** 9 + (5) = 14
7. (9) + 4 = 13 **8.** (13) = 7 + 6

PRIOR KNOWLEDGE

Have students think of situations in which balance is important. (Possible answers: children playing on a see-saw; objects hanging from a mobile) Ask students to explain how they can tell when objects are out of balance and to describe and compare the unbalanced amounts. (Possible answer: The 2 sides will not be level; heavier objects will hang lower than lighter ones.)

COMMUNICATION

Discussing and Reading Math Have students suggest synonyms for the word **balanced.** (*equal, fair, even, steady*) Then write the word **equality** on the chalkboard. Have students identify a familiar related word within it. (equal) Have students tell what they think equality means in math as well as in real life. (Math: There is equality when numbers have the same value, such as 2 + 2 = 4; Real life: There is equality when a person has the same opportunities or chances as anyone else.) Have students relate the ideas of balance and equality in math. (Possible answer: If you put two things on opposite sides of a balance scale and the sides balance, there is equality between the objects.)

EXPLORE AND CONNECT

Materials: counters in four different colors, index cards
Alternative Materials: paper squares in 4 different colors
Grouping Suggestion: cooperative learning pairs
Students use color codes to explore **equality.** Partners assign a value from 1-4 to each of the four colors of materials they have. For instance, they might have red = 1, blue = 2, green = 3, and yellow = 4. Next, they use blank index cards to create one card with an equal sign (=) and two cards with addition symbols (+). Students create color-coded equations with values that **balance** around the equal sign. For example, given the above values, 1 green = 1 red + 1 blue. Then students show why the equation would *balance* by substituting the assigned number values in an equation, such as 3 = 1 + 2. Partners take turns formulating *equalities* and recording equations. Have students generalize about *equality* and *balance*. (In an *equality,* both sides are *balanced* or equal.)

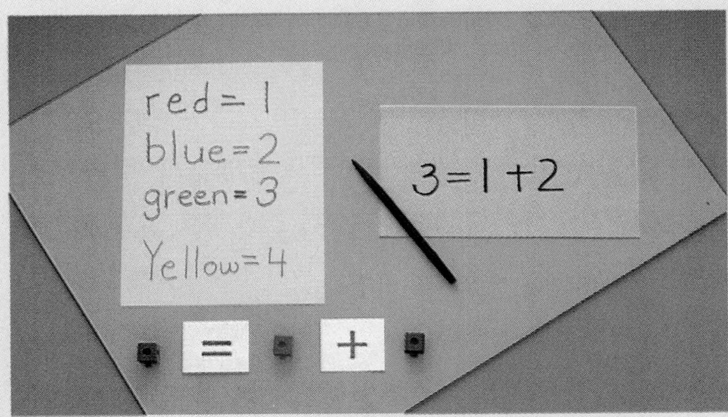

CONNECTIONS Use these anytime.

Problem of the Day

Coins Mr. O'Hara agreed to split his loose change equally between his twin daughters. When he emptied his pockets, he found 5 quarters, 3 dimes, and 3 nickels. How can the girls share the money fairly? (If one girl gets 3 quarters and 1 dime and the other gets 2 quarters, 2 dimes, and 3 nickels, each will have 85 cents.)

Creative Thinking

Logic Ed must row across a lake with a fox, a hen, and some corn. He can carry only *one* thing at a time in his row boat. PROBLEMS: The fox cannot be left with the hen. The hen cannot be left with the corn. How many trips must Ed make, and what does he bring each time? (4; 1: bring hen 2: bring fox, take hen back 3: bring corn 4: bring hen.)

Math Connection

Calculator When Lynn wrote the equation below, she accidentally wrote one + that should have been =. Use a calculator to decide where the missing = sign belongs. 43 + 87 + 19 + 63 + 86 (Change the third + to = so that both sides total 149.)

Classwork and Homework Supplements

Practice

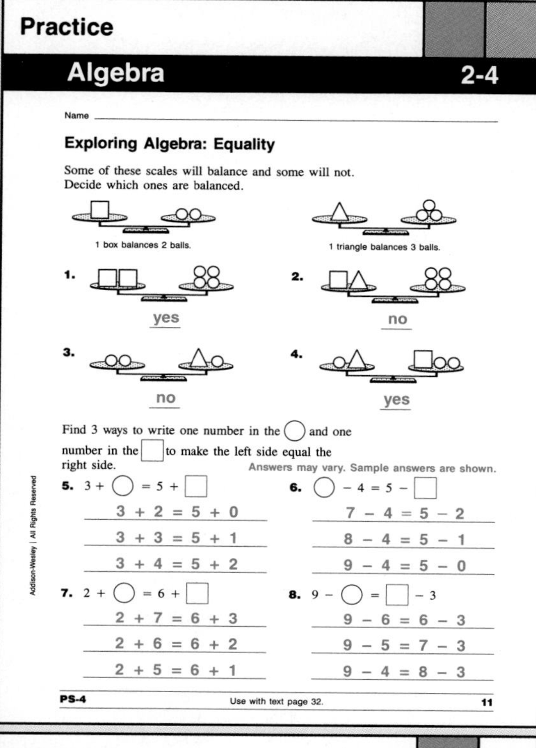
Algebra 2-4

Name

Exploring Algebra: Equality

Some of these scales will balance and some will not. Decide which ones are balanced.

1 box balances 2 balls. 1 triangle balances 3 balls.

1. yes
2. no
3. no
4. yes

Find 3 ways to write one number in the ○ and one number in the □ to make the left side equal the right side. Answers may vary. Sample answers are shown.

5. 3 + ○ = 5 + □
   - 3 + 2 = 5 + 0
   - 3 + 3 = 5 + 1
   - 3 + 4 = 5 + 2
6. ○ − 4 = 5 − □
   - 7 − 4 = 5 − 2
   - 8 − 4 = 5 − 1
   - 9 − 4 = 5 − 0
7. 2 + ○ = 6 + □
   - 2 + 7 = 6 + 3
   - 2 + 6 = 6 + 2
   - 2 + 5 = 6 + 1
8. 9 − ○ = □ − 3
   - 9 − 6 = 6 − 3
   - 9 − 5 = 7 − 3
   - 9 − 4 = 8 − 3

PS-4 Use with text page 32. 11

Building Thinking Skills

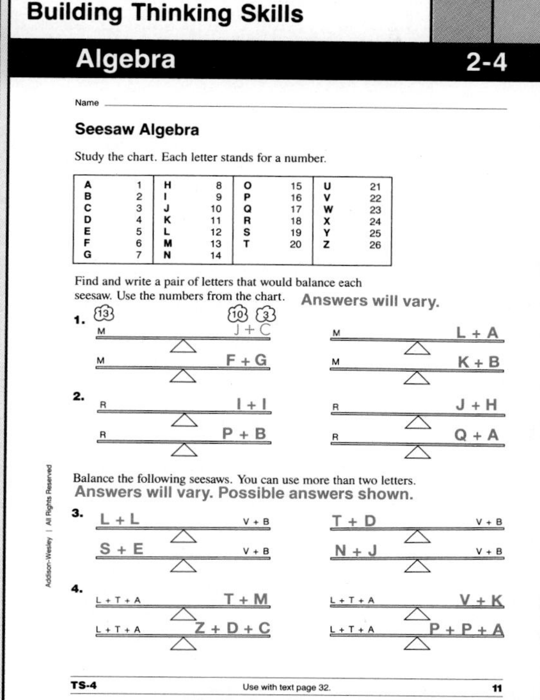
Algebra 2-4

Name

Seesaw Algebra

Study the chart. Each letter stands for a number.

A	1	H	8	O	15	U	21
B	2	I	9	P	16	V	22
C	3	J	10	Q	17	W	23
D	4	K	11	R	18	X	24
E	5	L	12	S	19	Y	25
F	6	M	13	T	20	Z	26
G	7	N	14				

Find and write a pair of letters that would balance each seesaw. Use the numbers from the chart. Answers will vary.

1. M — J + C (13 = 10 + 3); M — L + A; M — F + G; M — K + B
2. R — I + I; R — J + H; R — P + B; R — Q + A

Balance the following seesaws. You can use more than two letters. Answers will vary. Possible answers shown.

3. L + L — V + B; T + D — V + B; S + E — V + B; N + J — V + B
4. L + T + A — T + M; L + T + A — V + K; L + T + A — Z + D + C; L + T + A — P + P + A

TS-4 Use with text page 32. 11

Reteaching

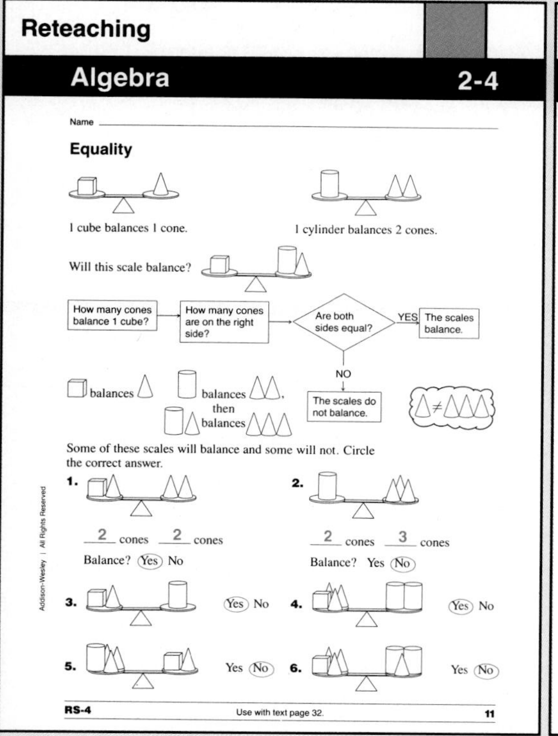
Algebra 2-4

Name

Equality

1 cube balances 1 cone. 1 cylinder balances 2 cones.

Will this scale balance?

How many cones balance 1 cube? → How many cones are on the right side? → Are both sides equal? YES → The scales balance. NO → The scales do not balance.

□ balances △. Cylinder balances △△, then □ and cylinder balances △△△.

Some of these scales will balance and some will not. Circle the correct answer.

1. 2 cones 2 cones Balance? (Yes) No
2. 2 cones 3 cones Balance? Yes (No)
3. (Yes) No
4. (Yes) No
5. Yes (No)
6. Yes (No)

RS-4 Use with text page 32. 11

Challenges

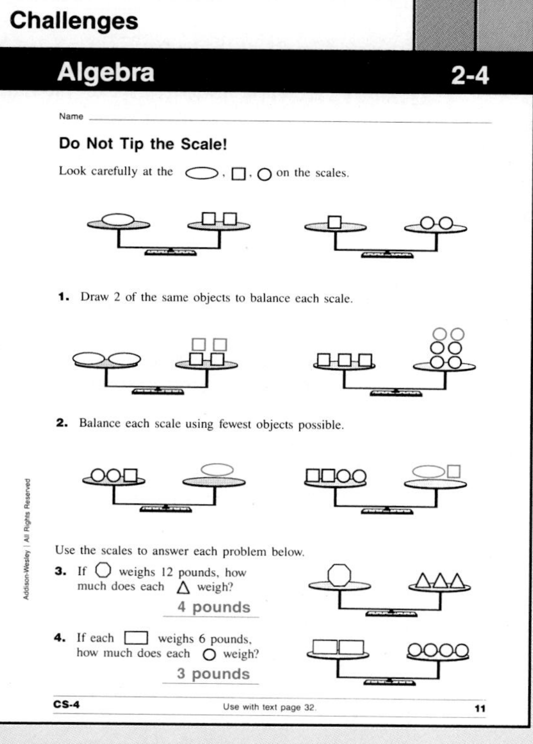
Algebra 2-4

Name

Do Not Tip the Scale!

Look carefully at the ⬭, □, ○ on the scales.

1. Draw 2 of the same objects to balance each scale.
2. Balance each scale using fewest objects possible.

Use the scales to answer each problem below.

3. If ○ weighs 12 pounds, how much does each △ weigh? 4 pounds
4. If each □ weighs 6 pounds, how much does each ○ weigh? 3 pounds

CS-4 Use with text page 32. 11

Options for Individual Needs

2-4

Basic

Exercises 1-4, 6; 1-13, 15-19

Supplements
Reteaching 11 or
Practice 11

Average

Exercises 1-6; 1-20

Supplements
Practice 11
Challenges 11 or
Thinking Skills 11

Extended

Exercises 2-6; 3-13, 15-19

Supplements
Challenges 11
Thinking Skills 11

Other Resources:
Problem-Solving Experiences in Mathematics, Grade 4, Problems 14, 15
Math In Stride, Grade 4, p. 5

LESSON PLAN 2-4

OBJECTIVE 2-4
To explore algebra by understanding equality

Materials: index cards

1. MOTIVATE AND TEACH

LEARN ABOUT IT

EXPLORE ► **Compare the value of 1 ball with the value of 1 box.** (1 ball must weigh half as much as 1 box because it takes 2 balls to balance 1 box.)
► **Would 1 box still balance 2 balls if the objects were on opposite sides of the scale? Explain.** (Yes, if the two sets of objects are equal, it makes no difference which side they are on.)
► **What math symbol would make sense in the center base of the scale to reflect how the sides balance? Explain.** (=; if the two sides balance, they must be equal in weight.)

TALK ABOUT IT ► **Decide which is heavier, a box or a triangle, and give your reasoning.** (A triangle because it takes 3 balls to balance it; it only takes 2 balls to balance a box.)
► **Give number values to the ball, box, and triangle. Explain your reasoning.** (Possible answer: triangle = 3, box = 2, ball = 1; you get balanced equations that model the scales: 2 = 1 + 1; 3 = 1 + 1 + 1.)
Student Edition answers: **1.** No, 1 box = 2 balls; 1 triangle = 3 balls **2.** 4

2. CHECK UNDERSTANDING

TRY IT OUT

ERROR ALERT Exercises 1-6: Failing to see the relationship between the box and the triangle.

Exploring Algebra

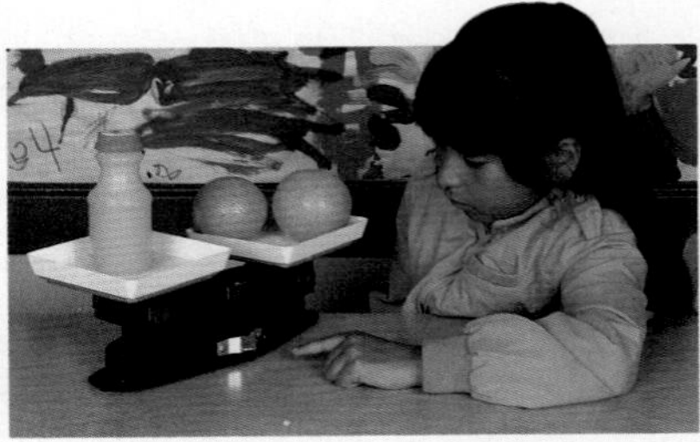

LEARN ABOUT IT

The first two scales below are balanced. All the shapes are the same in all the pictures.

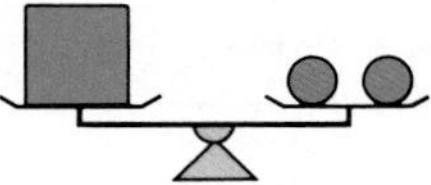

1 box balances 2 balls.

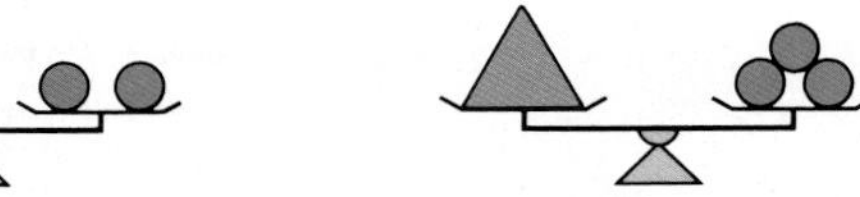

1 triangle balances 3 balls.

TALK ABOUT IT See teaching notes.

1. Would a box balance a triangle? Explain.
2. How many balls would balance 2 boxes?

TRY IT OUT

Some of these scales will balance and some will not. Decide which ones are really balanced.

1. yes

2. yes
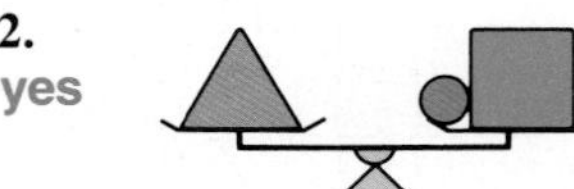

3. no

4. yes
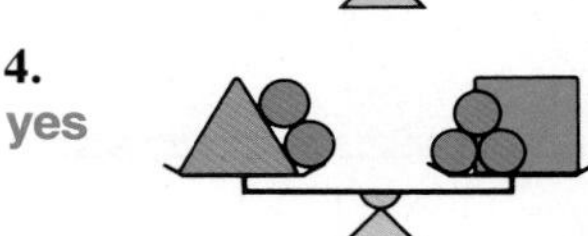

Find 3 ways to write one number in the ◯ and one number in the □ to make the left side equal the right side. Answers may vary.

5. 5 + ◯ = 2 + □

6. ◯ − 3 = 6 − □

TEACHING OPTIONS

RETEACHING TIPS Students draw a scale tipped lower on the right. They draw a box with 2 balls in it on the high (left) end and a triangle with 3 balls in it on the low (right) end. Have them use the picture as a point of reference. Assign Reteaching Supplement 11.

ENRICHMENT **Family Math** At home, students use packaged foods to create 3 balanced food equations using the weights given on the labels. For instance, they might find that 3 soup cans would balance 1 ketchup bottle and 1 mustard jar. Have them ask a family member to check their equations.

Midchapter Review/Quiz

Write the number in standard form.

1. a 3-digit number with 4 in the tens place and 1 in the hundreds place **Answers will vary.**
2. a 6-digit number with 2 in the ten-thousands place and 0 in the ones place **Answers will vary.**
3. seven hundred twenty-one **721**
4. five thousand, ninety **5,090**
5. four hundred thousand, seventy-eight **400,078**
6. six hundred thousand, forty-one **600,041**

Write the numbers from the box in which the digit 4 has the given value.

425,708	5,452
139,645	243,100
34,231	38,467
42,689	372,040

7. 40,000 **243,100 42,689**
8. 40 **372,040 139,645**
9. 400 **5,452 38,467**
10. 400,000 **425,708**
11. Which of these numbers are less than 5,000?
    5,476   4,567   672   5,027
12. Which of these numbers are between 3,050 and 4,500?
    4,507   4,075   5,423   3,250
13. Order these numbers from least to greatest. **See Additional Answers.**
    26,341   26,355   2,989   13,289

Write < or > for each ▥.

14. 2,150 ▥ 2,015 **>**
15. 48,720 ▥ 4,872 **>**
16. 62,758 ▥ 62,785 **<**

PROBLEM SOLVING

Use the digits in the box. A digit may be used only once in a problem.

1	5	8	2

17. What is the greatest 3-digit number you can write? **852**
18. What is the least 4-digit number you can write? **1,258**
19. What 3-digit number can you write that is less than 251? **Answers will vary.**
20. How many 4-digit numbers can you write that are greater than 5,812? **6**

33

3. Practice and Apply

Basic	1-4, 6; 1-13, 15-19
Average	1-6; 1-20
Extended	2-6; 3-13, 15-19

Additional Answers: See p. T79.

PRACTICE

How are Exercises 1-6 and 7-10 similar? (All use place value.) *How would you solve Exercises 11-13?* (Compare given numbers with the rule in the question.) *How are Problems 17 and 18 different from 19 and 20?* (17 and 18 have one answer; 19 and 20 have many possible answers.)

ITEM ANALYSIS The following table correlates the Midchapter Review/Quiz items with the lesson objectives.

Items	Objectives
1, 3, 4, 8, 9, 17, 18	2-1
2, 5-7, 10	2-2
11-16, 19, 20	2-3

2-4

Close and Assess

SHOW WHAT YOU KNOW

Have students write an equation that uses the numbers 2, 4, 6, and 8 with math symbols + and =. They should draw a picture to show how the equation might balance on a scale. (Possible answer: 2 + 8 = 4 + 6; check students' drawings.)

Quick Quiz

Find 3 ways to fill the ○ and the △ to make the equation balance.
4 + ○ = 2 + △
(Answers may vary; samples include 2 and 4, 4 and 6, 5 and 7)

LESSON OPTIONS 2-5

Problem Solving: Draw A Picture

OBJECTIVE 2-5 To solve problems using the strategy Draw A Picture

PREBOOK ACTIVITIES

QUICK REVIEW

Draw each situation.

1. a circle under a square

(□ ○)

2. 1 four between 2 sevens

(747)

PRIOR KNOWLEDGE

Have students tell about times when they have drawn a picture to figure out a situation or to solve a problem. (Answers will vary.) Have students explain how a picture can be a helpful tool. (Possible answer: A picture can help organize information to clarify a complicated situation.) Have students suggest types of pictures that are used in real life to help people solve problems. (Possible answers: maps; assembly directions; floor plans; seating charts)

COMMUNICATION

Discussing Math Draw a 4-point compass rose on the chalkboard and ask volunteers to label it with the directions *North*, *South*, *East*, and *West*. Have students tell how to use this simple picture to solve a problem. Example: *What lake is west of Springfield?* (Possible answer: Find Springfield on a map; look west from it, based on which way *west* is on the compass rose, until you see a lake.)

EXPLORE AND CONNECT

COOPERATIVE ACTIVITY

Grouping Suggestion: cooperative learning groups of 3

A photographer takes pictures of groups of 3 students. In each group, she puts the tallest person on the left and the middle-sized person to the right of the shortest person. How would your group stand?

TEACHING ACTIONS

Encourage groups to discuss and plan a strategy to solve the problem.

► **Explain the standing arrangement each group uses.** (The tallest person stands on the left, the middle-sized person stands to the right of the shortest person.)

► **Explain which strategies might help you solve the problem.** (Possible answers: Act It Out; Use Objects; Draw a Picture.)

► **Explain how a picture would help sort the data.** (You could follow the photographer's plan to draw where each person would stand.)

► **Explain how to use logical reasoning and position words to plan the picture.** (If the tallest person stands on the left and the middle-sized person is to the right of the shortest person, the shortest person must be in the center.)

► **Explain how to check if your picture makes sense.** (Test it to see if the arrangements matches the photographer's rules.)

CONNECTIONS Use these anytime.

Problem of the Day

Directions When Malik left for school, he walked 1 block north to mail a letter. He turned east and walked 1 block to pick up his friend, then they turned and walked 1 block south. At that point, Malik realized he had left his science project at home. How many blocks and in what direction(s) is the shortest route back to his house? (1 block west)

Patterns

Borders Sheila decorates objects with sea shells. She used 12 scallop shells and 4 snail shells to decorate one side of a square picture frame. Draw how the picture frame might look if Sheila repeats the same pattern on each side. (Solutions may vary.)

Life Skills

Gardening Amos is planning a garden. He will plant a row of marigolds along the edges and between every row of vegetables to keep away rabbits. He plans a row each of beans, corn, peas, and onions. What will grow in the middle row of Amos' garden? (marigolds)

Classwork and Homework Supplements

Practice

Problem Solving 2-5

Name

Draw a Picture

Draw a picture to help you solve each problem. Check students' drawings.

1. The largest city in Montana is Billings. Billings is east of Butte. Butte is west of Bozeman. Bozeman is west of Billings. Which city is in the middle? Bozeman

2. More people live in Helena, the state capital, than in Kalispell, a farm area. Kalispell has a larger population than Miles City. Helena has only about half the population of Great Falls. Which of the cities has the largest population? Great Falls

3. Yellowstone National Park, the oldest and largest park, is west of Bighorn Canyon National Recreational Area. Big Hole National Battlefield is west of Yellowstone. Which area is farthest east? Bighorn

4. Six Montana counties border North Dakota. Fallon is north of Carter. Roosevelt is south of Sheridan and north of Fallon. Which county is farthest south? Carter

5. Several mountains are in southern Montana. Lone Mountain is east of Sphinx Mountain. Mt. Douglas is east of Mt. Blackmore. Lone Mountain is to its west. Which mountain is farthest west? Sphinx

6. Highway 12 runs through Golden Valley, Musselshell, and Rosebud Counties. Rosebud County is larger than Musselshell County. Golden Valley is smaller than Musselshell. Which of the three is the largest? Rosebud

12 Use with text pages 34-35. PS-4

Building Thinking Skills

Problem Solving 2-5

Name

Pet Display

Draw a picture to help you solve each problem.
Check students' drawings.

1. At Bryan's Pet Shop there is a shelf with cedar chips, water bottles, salt blocks, alfalfa bales, food dishes, and guinea pig pellets. The pellets are between the food dish and the alfalfa bales. The cedar chips are last on the shelf and are next to the alfalfa bales. There are items on only one side of the salt blocks. List the order of the items on the shelf from left to right. salt blocks, water bottles, food dishes, guinea pig pellets, alfalfa bales, cedar chips

2. Bryan's Pet Shop is shaped like a rectangle. The store is 40 feet wide and 60 feet long. What is the perimeter of the store? 200 ft

3. Elizabeth is waiting in line to buy fish food. There are 3 people in front of her and twice as many people behind her. How many people are in line? 10 people

4. There are 26 legs in the display window. There are dogs and birds on display. Find 3 combinations of animals that could be in the window. 2d, 9b; 3d, 7b; 4d, 5b; 5d, 3b

12 Use with text pages 34-35. TS-4

Reteaching

Problem Solving 2-5

Name

Draw a Picture

To solve some problems, you may find it helpful to draw a picture.

There are four towers.
A is taller than B.
C is shorter than B.
D is shorter than C.
Which tower is the tallest?

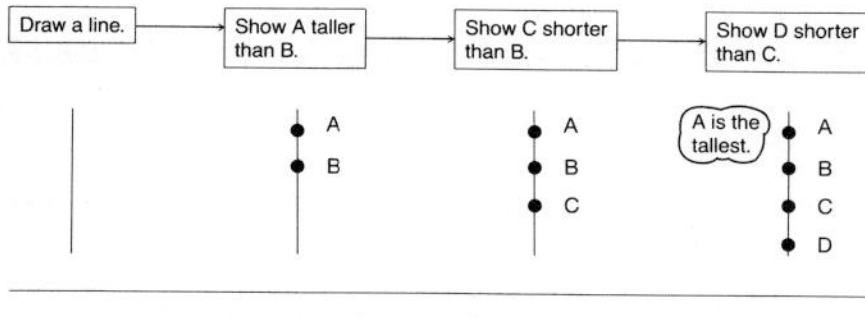

Draw a line.
Show A taller than B.
Show C shorter than B.
Show D shorter than C.
A
B
C
D
A is the tallest.

Draw a picture to help you solve each problem.

1. Tower E is taller than Tower F. Tower G is shorter than Tower F. Tower H is taller than Tower E. Which tower is the shortest? Tower G

2. Tower J is shorter than Tower K. Tower J is taller than Tower L. The height of Tower M is between Towers J and L. Which tower is the shortest? Tower L

3. Tim is shorter than Peter. John is taller than Peter. Roger is shorter than Tim. Who is the tallest? John

4. Laurie is older than Ken. Jill is younger than Ken. Chris's age is between Ken's and Jill's. Who is the oldest? Laurie

12 Use with text pages 34-35. RS-4

Challenges

Family Math 2-5

Name

Crazy Climbers

Dear Family,
Your child has been learning to draw pictures to solve problems. Work the problems below together.

Draw a picture to solve each problem.

1. A frog and a grasshopper are jumping down a flight of 12 steps. The frog jumps down 2 steps at a time. The grasshopper jumps down 3 at a time.
   a. Which step do they both land on before reaching the ground? 6
   b. Which steps do neither land on? 11, 7, 5, 1

2. A snail is climbing up a pole. Every day he climbs up 5 feet. Every night he slips back 2 feet. The pole is 17 feet high. On what day will the snail reach the top? Day 5

12 Use with text pages 34-35. CS-4

Options for Individual Needs

2-5

Basic

Exercises 1-7
More Practice, p. 513, set B

Supplements
Reteaching 12 or
Practice 12

Average

Exercises 1-8
More Practice, p. 513, set B

Supplements
Practice 12
Challenges 12 or
Thinking Skills 12

Extended

Exercises 1-8

Supplements
Challenges 12
Thinking Skills 12

Other Resources:
Math In Stride, Grade 4, pp. 11, 12
Mathematics, A Way of Thinking, Lesson 3-6

LESSON PLAN 2-5

OBJECTIVE 2-5
To solve problems using the strategy Draw a Picture

Materials: index cards

1. MOTIVATE AND TEACH

LEARN ABOUT IT

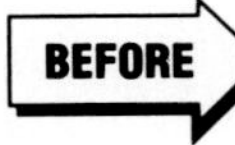

▶ **Explain the goal of the problem.** (to find the tree under which an arrowhead is buried)
▶ **Analyze the problem for direction or position words to help organize the data.**
(*west of, between, east of, farthest west*)

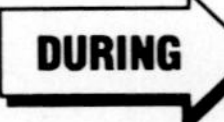

▶ **Explain how a picture can help solve the problem.** (It can show the order of the trees on the path to tell which tree is farthest west.)
▶ **Decide how to plan your drawing.** (Start with a fact you can easily draw, then add other facts to the picture as you sort them.)
▶ **Is there another way to state the relationship between the birch and the fig? Explain.** (Yes, the fig is west of the birch.)

▶ **Explain how to tell if your picture makes sense.** (Reread the situation to see if it matches the picture.)

2. CHECK UNDERSTANDING

TRY IT OUT

▶ **Decide how many animals to add to the drawing.** (2)
▶ **Explain why the beaver cannot be on top.** (It is under the thunderbird.)
▶ **Could the bear be on top? Explain.** (No, it is *under* the eagle.)

ERROR ALERT Interpreting information incorrectly.

Problem Solving
Draw a Picture

UNDERSTAND
FIND DATA
PLAN
ESTIMATE
SOLVE
CHECK

LEARN ABOUT IT

To solve some problems, you may find it helpful to **Draw a Picture**.

Four trees grow along a path. The birch tree is west of the pine. The oak is between the fig and the pine. The birch is east of the fig. The Indian arrowhead is buried under the tree that is farthest to the west. Where is the arrowhead buried?

First, I'll draw the trail.
The birch is west of the pine.
The oak is between the birch and the pine.
The birch is east of the fig.

The arrowhead is buried under the fig tree!

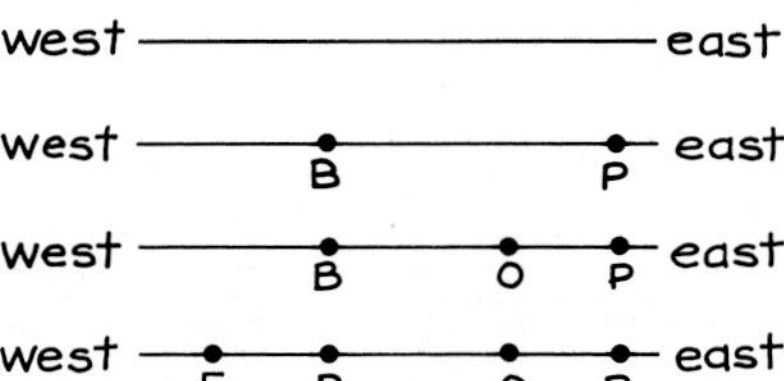

TRY IT OUT

Read this problem and finish the solution.

On the Indian totem pole, the bear is above the thunderbird. The beaver is under the thunderbird. The bear is under the eagle. Which animal is on top? **eagle**

- Since the bear is above the thunderbird, could the thunderbird be on top? **no**
- Which animal is just under the eagle? **bear**
- Copy the picture and finish drawing it to solve the problem. **Check students' drawings.**

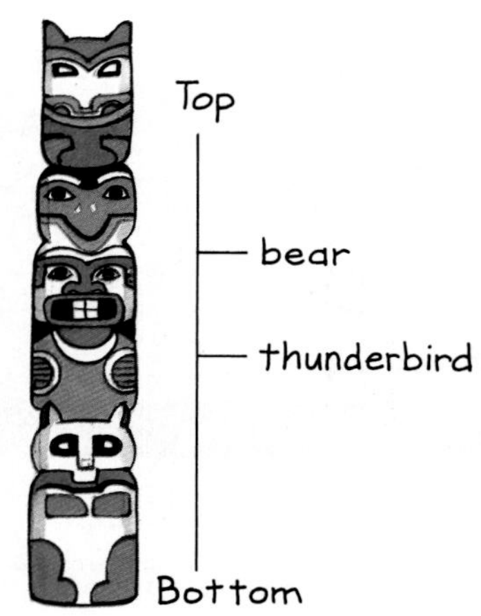

34

TEACHING OPTIONS

RETEACHING TIPS Have students write the name of each animal on a separate index card. Students can move the cards around to test possible arrangements until they find the one that matches the problem. Assign Reteaching Supplement 12.

ENRICHMENT Family Math Students act out this problem at home. *Ari, Ben, Cara, Donna, and Eleo are in line for lunch. Donna is not first in line, but she is ahead of Ari. Eleo is last. Cara is behind Ari. Give the order of the students to tell who gets lunch first.* (First to last: Ben, Donna, Ari, Cara, Eleo)

PRACTICE

Draw a picture to help you solve each problem.

1. At the Indian Festival, there were 4 booths in a row. Sand painting was east of jewelry. Drinks were west of jewelry. Belts were between jewelry and sand painting. Which booth was farthest east? sand painting

2. Dan was between Joe and Tae in the line for the Kachina doll booth. Dan was ahead of Tae. Tae was ahead of Luis. Who was third in line? Tae

MIXED PRACTICE

Solve. Choose a strategy from the list or use other strategies that you know.

Some Strategies
Act It Out
Use Objects
Choose an Operation
Draw a Picture

3. On one totem pole, the beaver's head is 17 inches high. Its mouth is 8 inches high. How high is the rest of the head? 9 inches

4. Michelle has 6 arrowheads in her collection. Her father has 15. How many more arrowheads does the father have than the daughter? 9 arrowheads

5. How many major Indian tribes are in Oklahoma and Alaska? 15 tribes

6. How many major Indian tribes in all are there in California, New Mexico, and Arizona? 14 tribes

7. On a leather bookmark, there are 4 symbols. The sun is above the rain. The mountain is above the sun. The rain is above the bird. Which picture is on the bottom? bird

8. Kara was sitting in the middle on a bench full of people watching the Indian dancing. She had 6 people to her left. How many people were on the bench? 13 people

State	Number of Major Indian Tribes
Alaska	6
Arizona	6
California	5
Florida	2
Montana	5
New Mexico	3
New York	4
Oklahoma	9
Oregon	6

More Practice, page 513, set B

3. Practice and Apply

Basic	1-7
Average	1-8
Extended	1-8

Sample Solutions: See p. T79.

PRACTICE

How are Problems 1 and 2 similar? (Both will have pictures that show 4 objects or people. (*How are they different?* (Problem 1 uses directions; Problem 2 uses positions.)

MIXED PRACTICE

► **Explain how Problems 3 and 4 are related.** (Possible answer: Both can be solved by subtraction.)

► **Explain how Problems 5 and 6 are related.** (Both require using the table about Indian tribes; both can be solved by addition.)

► **Which problem-solving strategy would you use to solve Problem 7? Explain.** (Draw a Picture; it can most easily help you sort out the information.)

► **Identify a strategy to solve Problem 8.** (anything that helps visualization)

2-5

Close and Assess

SHOW WHAT YOU KNOW

Have students draw a picture to solve this problem:
You make a 4-block tower. A red block is between the blue block and the green block. A white block is on the bottom, but it is not next to the green block. Give the order of the blocks from top to bottom. (green, red, blue, white)

Quick Quiz

Solve by drawing a picture.
4 cousins sit on a bench. Ann sits on Sam's left. Hal is to Tema's right. Tema is between Sam and Hal. Who is sitting farthest to the right? (Hal)

LESSON OPTIONS 2-6

Rounding

OBJECTIVE 2-6 To round numbers to the nearest ten, nearest hundred, and nearest dollar

PREBOOK ACTIVITIES

QUICK REVIEW

Name the highest place in each number:
1. 461 (hundreds) **2.** 1,970 (thousands)
3. 77 (tens) **4.** 592 (hundreds)
Write the digit(s) that show the number of dollars in each amount:
5. $6.87 (6) **6.** $12.95 (12) **7.** $0.43 (0)

PRIOR KNOWLEDGE

Ask students how they have used a number line. (Possible answer: to count and skip count) Ask how they would use a number line to compare and order numbers. (Possible answer: Place numbers to show the correct relationship from one point to another.) Ask students to imagine placing the following pairs of numbers on a number line. Have them tell which number in each pair would be closer to 100: 87, 79 (87); 104, 94 (104); 52, 49 (52); 72, 120 (120); 103, 110 (103). Ask students to explain how they arrived at their answers. (Possible answer: Compare each number's placement in relation to 100 to see which is closer.) Finally, ask students how a number line can help them round numbers. (It shows how far a number is from a set point so that you know whether to round up or down.)

COMMUNICATION

Discussing and Writing in Math Have students suggest times when they have had to round numbers. (Possible answers: when estimating, when shopping) Ask them to write in their Math Journals how to round a 2-digit number to the nearest ten. After the lesson students may revise their entry if necessary.

EXPLORE AND CONNECT

Materials: number lines, markers of 5 different colors
Grouping Suggestion: cooperative learning pairs
Pairs explore positioning of numbers on a tens number line from 10 to 100. One student chooses five 2-digit numbers between 11 and 89. The partner writes the numbers in place on the number line. The pair decides if each number is closest to 10, 20, 30, 40, 50, 60, 70, 80, or 90, then circles the number and the multiple it is nearest to with the same color marker. Partners trade roles and use a number line marked in hundreds. One student chooses five 3-digit numbers between 101 and 500. The partner writes them on a hundreds number line from 100 to 500. They decide if each number is closest to 100, 200, 300, 400, or 500. Again they circle the number and the multiple with the same color marker. Discuss if numbers ending in 5 or 50 are closer to the multiple before or after it. (same) Discuss why we round up if the digit is 5 or more.

CONNECTIONS Use these anytime.

Problem of the Day

Math Language A *decade* means 10 years. For example, 1900, 1910, 1950, and 1990 are decade years. Give the decade nearest to today's date, to your birth year, and to the birth year of one of your family members. (Answers will vary.)

Life Skills

Money Damien has 7 quarters and 3 dimes. Does he have enough money to take a $2 ride on the Zoom-Mobile at the county fair? Explain your decision. (Yes; he has $2.05, which is more than the cost of the ride.)

Math Connection

Logical Reasoning Solve the riddle: It is an odd money amount. It rounds to 5 dimes. You can form the amount using only nickels. What is the amount? (45¢)

Classwork and Homework Supplements

Practice

Life Skills 2-6

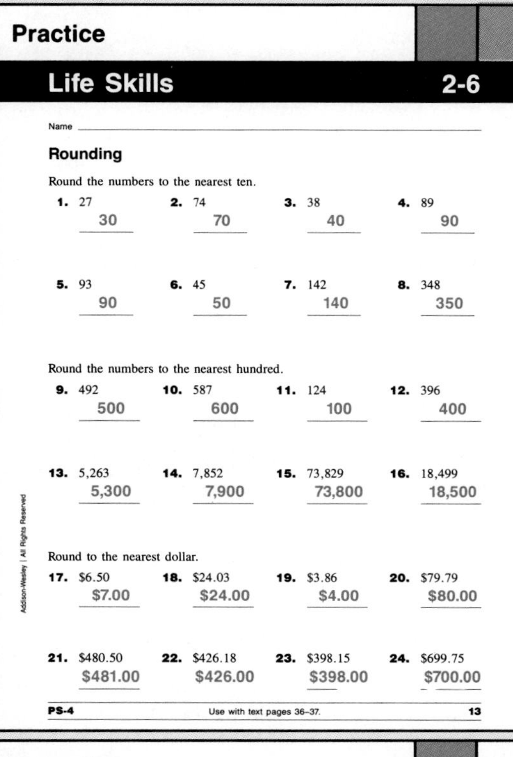

Name

Rounding

Round the numbers to the nearest ten.

1. 27 — 30
2. 74 — 70
3. 38 — 40
4. 89 — 90
5. 93 — 90
6. 45 — 50
7. 142 — 140
8. 348 — 350

Round the numbers to the nearest hundred.

9. 492 — 500
10. 587 — 600
11. 124 — 100
12. 396 — 400
13. 5,263 — 5,300
14. 7,852 — 7,900
15. 73,829 — 73,800
16. 18,499 — 18,500

Round to the nearest dollar.

17. $6.50 — $7.00
18. $24.03 — $24.00
19. $3.86 — $4.00
20. $79.79 — $80.00
21. $480.50 — $481.00
22. $426.18 — $426.00
23. $398.15 — $398.00
24. $699.75 — $700.00

PS-4 Use with text pages 36-37. 13

Building Thinking Skills

Family Math 2-6

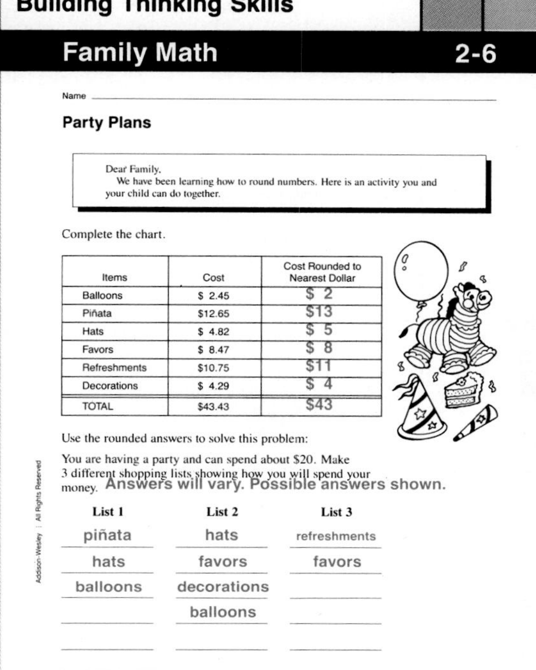

Name

Party Plans

Dear Family,
We have been learning how to round numbers. Here is an activity you and your child can do together.

Complete the chart.

Items	Cost	Cost Rounded to Nearest Dollar
Balloons	$ 2.45	$ 2
Piñata	$12.65	$13
Hats	$ 4.82	$ 5
Favors	$ 8.47	$ 8
Refreshments	$10.75	$11
Decorations	$ 4.29	$ 4
TOTAL	$43.43	$43

Use the rounded answers to solve this problem:

You are having a party and can spend about $20. Make 3 different shopping lists showing how you will spend your money. Answers will vary. Possible answers shown.

List 1	List 2	List 3
piñata	hats	refreshments
hats	favors	favors
balloons	decorations	
	balloons	

TS-4 Use with text pages 36-37. 13

Reteaching

Skills Review 2-6

Name

Rounding

Rounding to the Nearest Ten: 260 261 262 263 264 265 266 267 268 269 270 — 261 through 264 round to 260. 265 through 269 round to 270.

Rounding to the Nearest Hundred: 2,600 2,610 2,620 2,630 2,640 2,650 2,660 2,670 2,680 2,690 2,700 — 2,601 through 2,649 round to 2,600. 2,650 through 2,699 round to 2,700.

Ring the nearest ten for each number.

1. 78 → 70 or (80)
2. 57 → 50 or (60)
3. 45 → 40 or (50)
4. 234 → (230) or 240
5. 882 → (880) or 890
6. 374 → (370) or 380

Round to the nearest ten. (88 is between 80 and 90. 88 is closer to 90.) (43 is between 40 and 50. 43 is closer to 40.)

7. 88 → 90
8. 43 → 40
9. 76 → 80
10. 29 → 30
11. 215 → 220
12. 501 → 500
13. 354 → 350
14. 296 → 300

Ring the nearest hundred for each number.

15. 1,852 → 1,500 or (1,600)
16. 2,341 → (2,300) or 2,400

Ring the nearest dollar.

17. $7.49 → ($7.00) or $8.00
18. $59.90 → $59.00 or ($60.00)

Round to the nearest hundred.

19. 2,184 → 2,200
20. 632 → 600
21. 3,845 → 3,800

Round to the nearest dollar.

22. $12.99 → 13.00
23. $76.15 → $76.00
24. $45.55 → $46.00

RS-4 Use with text pages 36-37. 13

Challenges

Math Reasoning 2-6

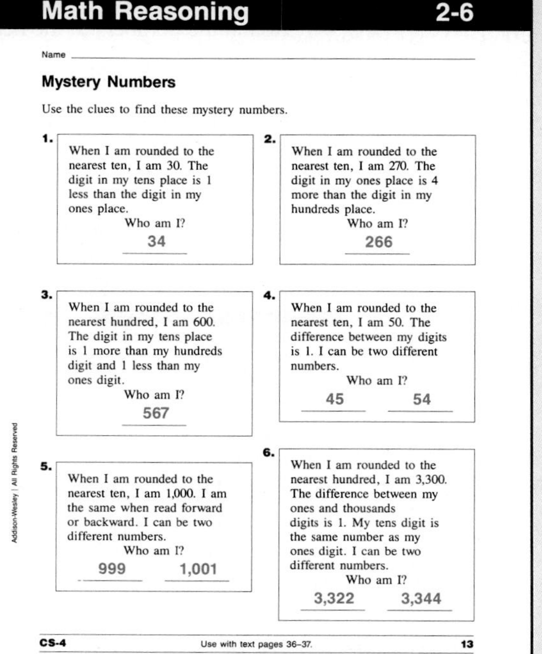

Name

Mystery Numbers

Use the clues to find these mystery numbers.

1. When I am rounded to the nearest ten, I am 30. The digit in my tens place is 1 less than the digit in my ones place. Who am I? 34

2. When I am rounded to the nearest ten, I am 270. The digit in my ones place is 4 more than the digit in my hundreds place. Who am I? 266

3. When I am rounded to the nearest hundred, I am 600. The digit in my tens place is 1 more than my hundreds digit and 1 less than my ones digit. Who am I? 567

4. When I am rounded to the nearest ten, I am 50. The difference between my digits is 1. I can be two different numbers. Who am I? 45 54

5. When I am rounded to the nearest ten, I am 1,000. I am the same when read forward or backward. I can be two different numbers. Who am I? 999 1,001

6. When I am rounded to the nearest hundred, I am 3,300. The difference between my ones and thousands digits is 1. My tens digit is the same number as my ones digit. I can be two different numbers. Who am I? 3,322 3,344

CS-4 Use with text pages 36-37. 13

Options for Individual Needs

Basic

Exercises 6-15, 21-27, 31-35
More Practice, p. 500, set E

Supplements
Reteaching 13 or
Practice 13

Average

Exercises 1-35
More Practice, p. 500, set E

Supplements
Practice 13
Challenges 13 or
Thinking Skills 13

Extended

Exercises 6-35

Supplements
Challenges 13
Thinking Skills 13

Other Resources:
Problem-Solving Experiences in Mathematics, Grade 4, Problem 20
Math In Stride, Grade 4, p. 229

2-6

LESSON PLAN 2-6

OBJECTIVE 2-6
To round numbers to the nearest ten, nearest hundred, and nearest dollar

Materials: TA 5 (4-Digit Place Value Chart)

Grouping Suggestion: pairs

1. MOTIVATE AND TEACH

LEARN ABOUT IT

EXPLORE ► **How could you define a number that is closer to 300 than to 200 or to 400?** (Possible answer: It is 250 or greater, but less than 350.)

TALK ABOUT IT ► **Explain why your numbers should not fall on the number line below 250 or beyond 350.** (Possible response: Then they would round to 200 or 400, not to 300.)
► **How could you find numbers close to 290?** (Possible answer: Identify the range, 285 to 294, in which numbers rounded to the nearest ten can fall.)
► **Why is 5 used as the comparison digit when rounding?** (Possible answer: 5 is exactly half of 10.)
► **Explain why you round up if a number is 5 or greater and round down if the number is less than 5.** (Possible answer: That is the rounding method everyone uses to be consistent.)
Student Edition answers: **1.** None of either. Other numbers will not round to 300. **2.** any numbers from 285 to 294

2. CHECK UNDERSTANDING

TRY IT OUT

ERROR ALERT Difficulty finding the correct place to which a number rounds. Being confused about whether a number rounds up or down.

Rounding

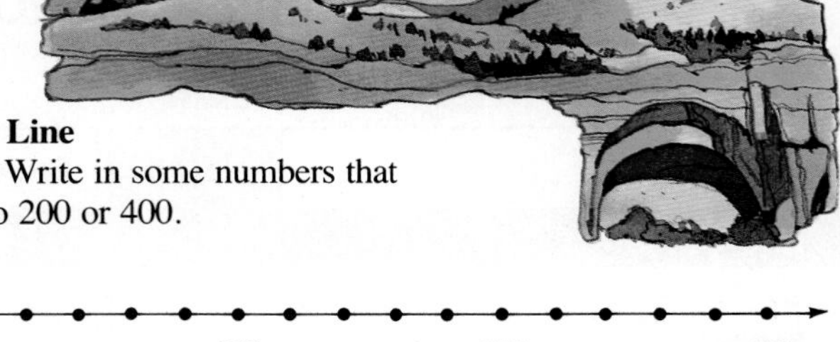

LEARN ABOUT IT

EXPLORE Use a Number Line
Draw this number line. Write in some numbers that are closer to 300 than to 200 or 400.

200 250 300 350 400

TALK ABOUT IT See teaching notes.

1. Are any of your numbers less than 250? greater than 350? Explain.
2. Give some numbers that are about 290. They should be closer to 290 than to 280 or 300.

Use this method to round numbers to any place.

Find the place to which you are rounding. →	Look at the digit to the right of that place. Compare it to 5. →	**Round up** if it is 5 or greater. **Round down** if it is less than 5.

Round to the **nearest ten.**	43 365	43 365	43 round to 40. 365 rounds to 370.
Round to the **nearest hundred.**	343 4,789	343 4,789	343 rounds to 300. 4,789 rounds to 4,800.
Round to the **nearest dollar.**	\$3.26 \$8.61	\$3.26 \$8.61	\$3.26 rounds to \$3.00. \$8.61 rounds to \$9.00.

TRY IT OUT

Round the numbers to the nearest ten. Then round them to the nearest hundred.

1. 589 590; 600
2. 831 830; 800
3. 219 220; 200
4. 450 450; 500
5. 98 100; 100
6. 6,720 6,720, 6700

Round to the nearest dollar.

7. \$4.39 \$4.00
8. \$1.74 \$2.00
9. \$11.50 \$12.00

36

TEACHING OPTIONS

RETEACHING TIPS For help finding the place to which a number rounds, students should use a 4-digit place value chart to write each number. They locate the place to which to round (tens or hundreds), then find the digit to the right in the ones or tens place. Assign Reteaching Supplement 13.

COMPUTER **Math Strategies: Estimation, SRA, Copyright 1985** For use with all levels of students. In lessons 1 and 2, students practice rounding numbers to the nearest tens and hundreds. They receive help if they answer incorrectly. The lessons takes 10 minutes.

PRACTICE

First round the numbers to the nearest ten. Then round them to the nearest hundred.

1. 168 170 200	**2.** 345 350 300	**3.** 256 260 300	**4.** 793 790 800	**5.** 487 490 500
6. 862 860 900	**7.** 104 100 100	**8.** 151 150 200	**9.** 496 500 500	**10.** 634 630 600

Round to the nearest hundred.

11. 3,576 3,600	**12.** 4,083 4,100	**13.** 7,449 7,400	**14.** 8,888 8,900	**15.** 13,175 13,200
16. 2,083 2,100	**17.** 8,450 8,500	**18.** 1,080 1,100	**19.** 5,111 5,100	**20.** 47,289 47,300

Round to the nearest dollar.

21. \$5.50 \$6.00	**22.** \$43.04 \$43.00	**23.** \$8.46 \$8.00	**24.** \$93.75 \$94.00	**25.** \$49.49 \$49.00
26. \$180.50 \$181.00	**27.** \$346.17 \$346.00	**28.** \$498.15 \$498.00	**29.** \$150.63 \$151.00	**30.** \$799.85 \$800.00

APPLY

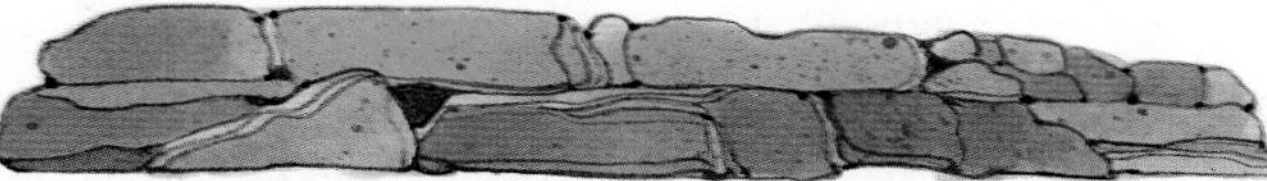

MATH REASONING

31. Give the smallest number that rounds to 170 when rounded to the nearest ten. 165

32. Give the largest amount of money that rounds to \$8.00 when rounded to the nearest dollar. \$8.49

PROBLEM SOLVING

33. An explorer found 8 rooms in a cliff dwelling on a ledge and 9 more rooms in a cave. What is the total number of rooms rounded to the nearest ten? 20

34. Data Hunt Look in a newspaper. Find 3 numbers that have been rounded. Find 3 numbers that have not. If it makes sense, round these. Answers will vary.

► **USING CRITICAL THINKING Draw Conclusions**

35. I am a 3-digit number. Use these clues to find me.

- I am greater than 500.
- I am less than 557.
- My ones digit is a 2.
- I am 600 when rounded to the nearest hundred. 552

More Practice, page 500, set E

3. Practice and Apply

Basic	6-15, 21-27, 31-35
Average	1-35
Extended	6-35

PRACTICE

Look at Exercises 1-10. How many answers do you need to give for each one? (2) *Will any of Exercises 11-20 cause the digit to the left of the hundreds place to change? Why?* (No, because no exercise has 950 or more in its ones place.)

APPLY

MATH REASONING ► **What similarity will the answers to Exercises 31 and 32 share?** (Each is one extreme of the numbers that round to 170 and \$8.)

PROBLEM SOLVING ► **Analyze how to solve Problem 33.** (Possible answer: Round each number, then add.) ► **How can you tell if a number has been rounded?** (Possible answers: It has *about* in front of it; it often has zeros on the end.)

USING THINKING SKILLS ► **How does the last statement help you?** (It tells it cannot be less than 550.)

2-6

Close and Assess

WRITE WHAT YOU THINK Ask students to write the steps required to round a number to the nearest hundred. Then have them exchange papers with a partner. Write a 3-digit number on the chalkboard. Have students round the number to the nearest hundred by following their partner's instructions.

QUICK QUIZ

Round to the nearest ten, then to the nearest hundred:
1. 182 **2.** 567 **3.** 106 **4.** 854
(**1.** 180, 200 **2.** 570, 600 **3.** 110, 100 **4.** 850, 900)

LESSON OPTIONS 2-7

More About Rounding

OBJECTIVE 2-7 To round to the nearest thousand

PREBOOK ACTIVITIES

QUICK REVIEW

Fill in the missing numbers.

1. 250, 260, 270, 280, ______, ______ (290, 300)
2. 2,600, 2,700, 2,800, ______, ______ (2,900, 3,000)
3. 37,000, 38,000, 39,000, ______, ______ (40,000, 41,000)
4. 206,000, 207,000, ______, ______, ______ (208,000, 209,000, 210,000)

PRIOR KNOWLEDGE

Write the following numbers on the board: 1,200; 709; 5,998; 850. Have students read the numbers aloud, then analyze which ones may have been rounded (1,200; 850), and which ones probably have not (709; 5,998). Ask students to explain how they judged each number. (Possible answers: Rounded amounts often end in zeros; numbers with digits other than zero in the ones place may be exact numbers.)

COMMUNICATION

Discussing Math Have students discuss similarities and differences between **rounding up** and **rounding down.** Ask them to compare the value of numbers rounded up or down with the exact value. (Possible answers: Both kinds of rounding give estimated amounts; both often result in numbers that end in one or more zeros; numbers rounded up are greater than the exact number; numbers rounded down are less than the exact number.)

EXPLORE AND CONNECT

Materials: number lines from 1,000 to 2,000, segmented by hundreds; blank index cards
Grouping Suggestion: small cooperative-learning groups
Students explore **rounding** to the nearest thousand. Each group member writes a 4-digit number greater than 1,000 but less than 2,000 on an index card. Each group also makes a set of cards that gives directions to **round** to the nearest hundred or thousand. The hundreds direction is written on each of 4 cards; the thousands direction on 2. All 6 cards are shuffled. The number cards and *rounding* cards are placed facedown in 2 piles. A student chooses a number card, reads it aloud, then writes the number on the number line. A second student picks a *rounding* card, reads it aloud, then follows its direction by circling the place on the number line that shows the previous student's number **rounded up** or **down.** Members verify actions and discuss *rounding* to the nearest thousand.

CONNECTIONS Use these anytime.

Problem of the Day

Estimation When you round this number to the nearest ten, it is 750. When you round this number to the nearest hundred, it is 700. It is read the same forward and backward. What is the number? (747)

Math Connection

Math Reasoning Think about rounding rules, then find the number that does not belong:
a. 570 **b.** 590 **c.** 630
d. 650
Explain how you chose your answer. (d, 650 rounds to 700; or c, it is the one that rounds down.)

Subject Integration

Social Studies Round each date to the nearest decade: 1733, 1865, 1902, 1988, 2007. (1730, 1870, 1900, 1990, 2010)

Classwork and Homework Supplements

Practice

Life Skills 2-7

Name

More About Rounding

Round to the nearest thousand.

1. 6,183 — 6,000	2. 8,937 — 9,000	3. 2,529 — 3,000	4. 9,482 — 9,000
5. 37,508 — 38,000	6. 54,211 — 54,000	7. 641,724 — 642,000	8. 329,899 — 330,000

Ring the numbers in the box that round to the given number when rounded to the nearest thousand.

9. 8,000	7,932	8,902	8,234	8,499	7,316
10. 5,000	4,299	4,607	5,515	4,998	5,457
11. 7,000	6,117	7,642	7,893	6,638	7,394
12. 2,000	1,541	2,562	1,997	2,001	1,004
13. 10,000	10,500	9,502	10,020	9,400	9,777
14. 56,000	56,230	55,999	56,471	56,405	55,395
15. 84,000	83,611	84,572	84,499	83,298	83,502

14 Use with text pages 38–39. PS-4

Building Thinking Skills

Data Analysis 2-7

Name

Analyze the Clues

Mikey Trackson, Bill Hollins, Jitney Lewston, and Adonna are famous singers. Each of them recently gave sold-out concerts. Read the clues to find about how many tickets each singer sold. Use the chart to help you track your clues and determine the exact number of tickets sold for each concert. Each time you can completely rule out matching a person to a number, mark an **X** in the box. When you find a match, put a check mark.

Clues:

▶ Mikey Trackson, Adonna, and Jitney Lewston each sold about 10,000 tickets.

▶ Bill Hollins sold about 1,000 fewer tickets than Adonna did.

▶ Mikey Trackson sold about 200 more tickets than Jitney Lewston did.

Number of Tickets Sold	9,116	9,503	9,684	10,002
Mikey Trackson	X	X	✓	X
Bill Hollins	✓	X	X	X
Jitney Lewston	X	✓	X	X
Adonna	X	X	X	✓

14 Use with text pages 38–39. TS-4

Reteaching

Skills Review 2-7

Name

More About Rounding

Round 4,623 to the nearest thousand.

Look at the digit to the right of the place to which you will round. → Note whether the digit is 5 or more. → If the digit is 5 or more, round up. If it is less than 5, round down.

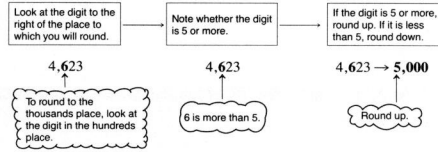

4,623 — To round to the thousands place, look at the digit in the hundreds place.

4,623 — 6 is more than 5.

4,623 → 5,000 — Round up.

Round each number to the nearest thousand. Ring the digit you will look at. Write the rounded number.

1. 7,345 — 7,000	2. 1,805 — 2,000
3. 6,734 — 7,000	4. 6,346 — 6,000
5. 1,250 — 1,000	6. 2,731 — 3,000

Ring the nearest thousand for each number.

7. 5,632: 5,000 or 6,000	8. 2,745: 2,000 or 3,000
9. 3,158: 3,000 or 4,000	10. 7,501: 7,000 or 8,000

Ring the numbers in the box that round to 4,000.

11. 4,000	4,002	3,403	3,222	4,466	3,892

14 Use with text pages 38-39. RS-4

Challenges

Number Sense 2-7

Name

Newspaper Numbers

You are a news reporter. In each report, you must decide whether to round the number to the tens, hundreds, or thousands place. Use the number in the parentheses and write the rounded number in the blank. Answers will vary. Samples given.

1. Nearly 3,000 (2,862) students went to the outdoor concert. The park was packed.

2. Jim Chin is participating in the nonstop jump-rope contest. He has only about 150 (154) minutes to go to break the world record.

3. About 200 (207) students from Oak School were in the parade. About the same number came from Pine School. Together they made a formation two blocks long.

4. Thanks to the generous contributions of local whale lovers, the bowhead whale population has increased to almost 4,500 (4,482) whales.

5. Over 1,700 (1,720) killer bees entered the state, prompting local officials to issue a red alert.

6. The students worked hard all week distributing the fliers to the homes in the village. At the end of the week, they had about 20 (23) homes left to go.

14 Use with text pages 38–39. CS-4

Options for Individual Needs

2-7

Basic

Exercises 5-23, 26-28
Data Bank, p. 472
More Practice, p. 500, set F

Supplements
Reteaching 14 or
Practice 14

Average

Exercises 1-31
Data Bank, p. 472
More Practice, p. 500, set F

Supplements
Practice 14
Challenges 14 or
Thinking Skills 14

Extended

Exercises 6-23, 26-29
Data Bank, p. 472

Supplements
Challenges 14
Thinking Skills 14

Other Resources:
Problem-Solving Experiences in Mathematics, Grade 4, Problem 21
Math In Stride, Grade 4, p. 230

LESSON PLAN 2-7

OBJECTIVE 2-7
To round to the nearest thousand

Materials: TA 7 (6-Digit Place Value Chart)

1. MOTIVATE AND TEACH

LEARN ABOUT IT

EXPLORE ► **Why did Daryl round the numbers of beads to the nearest thousand?** (Possible answer: Thousands was the greatest place.)

TALK ABOUT IT ► **How is rounding helpful?** (Possible answer: Rounded numbers are easier to work with.)
► **Justify why Daryl rounded down the numbers of beads.** (Possible answer: Both were less than the halfway amounts—2,500 and 3,500.)
► **Explain how you think Daryl would round 3,525.** (4,000; The 5 in the hundreds place would lead him to round up to the next thousand.)
► **Explain what to do if a 9 is in the place to which you are rounding and you want to round up.** (Regroup; trade 10 for 1 of the next higher place.)
Student Edition answers: **1.** Possible answer: An estimate gives a good idea of how many beads were found. **2.** 3,317 is closer to 3,000. **3.** No, he would round up to 4,000 because 3,525 is greater than the halfway point of 3,500.

2. CHECK UNDERSTANDING

TRY IT OUT

ERROR ALERT Rounding thousands to the wrong place. Rounding all numbers to the greater place, even when a smaller place is called for.

More About Rounding

LEARN ABOUT IT

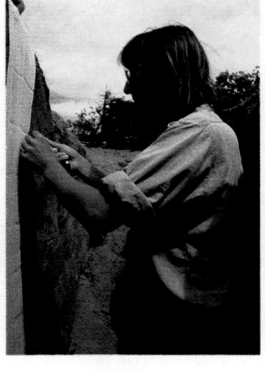

EXPLORE **Think About the Situation**
Daryl gave a report on Richard Wetherill, a famous explorer of Southwest Indian ruins. In 1895 in Pueblo Bonito, Wetherill discovered a burial room with a basket containing 2,150 turquoise beads and 3,317 shell beads. Daryl decided to round these numbers to 2,000 turquoise beads and 3,000 shell beads.

TALK ABOUT IT See teaching notes.

1. Why did it make sense for Daryl to round the numbers of beads?
2. Why did he round the number of shell beads to 3,000 instead of 4,000?
3. Would he have used the same number if there had been 3,525 shell beads? Why?

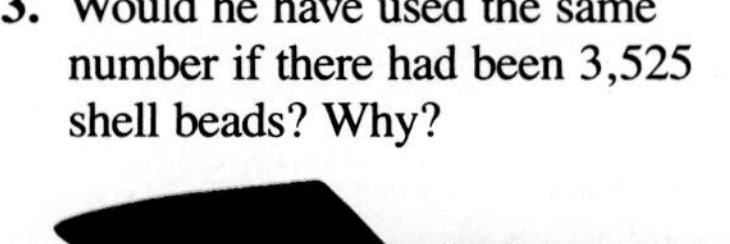

Remember! Find the digit to the right of the place to which you are rounding. **Round up** if the digit is 5 or more. **Round down** if the digit is less than 5.

Round to the **nearest thousand**.
8,296 → 8,000 8,500 → 9,000 15,494 → 15,000

Be careful when you round up with the digit 9 in the place to which you are rounding.

Round to the nearest hundred. 975 → 1,000
Round to the nearest thousand. 9,858 → 10,000

TRY IT OUT

Round to the nearest thousand.

1. 3,586 4,000
2. 6,413 6,000
3. 9,620 10,000
4. 8,500 9,000
5. 19,613 20,000
6. 224,318 224,000

38

TEACHING OPTIONS

RETEACHING TIPS When rounding to thousands, students circle the thousands place and underline the hundreds place on a 6-digit place value chart. (They apply the rounding rule to the hundreds digit, then replace the remaining 3 digits with zeros.) Assign Reteaching Supplement 14.

ENRICHMENT Have students round each car price to the nearest thousand dollars:

Model R13	$5,299.99	($5,000)
Model X33	$6,789.50	($7,000)
Model J50	$17,187.77	($17,000)
Model Z77	$19,563.00	($20,000)
Model QR5	$25,698.98	($26,000)
Model SS1	$29,999.99	($30,000)

PRACTICE

Round to the nearest thousand.

1. 4,163 4,000	2. 3,200 3,000	3. 7,685 8,000	4. 6,500 7,000
5. 3,850 4,000	6. 4,075 4,000	7. 6,304 6,000	8. 8,987 9,000
9. 5,372 5,000	10. 9,634 10,000	11. 39,499 39,000	12. 39,500 40,000
13. 216,530 217,000	14. 499,821 500,000	15. 52,819 53,000	16. 39,499 39,000

APPLY

MATH REASONING

5 3 4 2

17. Use all the digits on these cards to make two numbers that each round to 2,500 as the nearest hundred, and round to 3,000 as the nearest thousand. 2,543; 2,534

PROBLEM SOLVING

18. A room full of pottery the explorer Wetherill found in Chaco Canyon had 114 jars, 22 bowls, and 21 jar covers. If you wanted to report about how many of each he had found, what would your numbers be?
20 bowls, 20 jar covers

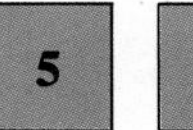

19. **Social Studies Data Bank** What are the numbers of rooms in each of the Mesa Verde dwellings rounded to the nearest ten? to the nearest hundred? See page 472.
230, 150, 110; 200, 200, 100

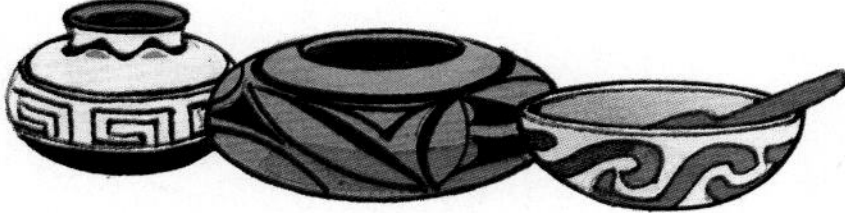

MIXED REVIEW

Add.

20. 9 + 4 = 13
21. 4 + 9 = 13
22. 8 + 6 = 14
23. 6 + 8 = 14
24. 7 + 0 = 7
25. 2 + 0 = 2

Subtract. Think about finding the missing addend.

26. 12 − 4 = 8
27. 11 − 5 = 6
28. 9 − 2 = 7
29. 14 − 7 = 7
30. 10 − 4 = 6
31. 17 − 9 = 8

More Practice, page 500, set F

3. Practice and Apply

Basic	5-23, 26-28
Average	1-31
Extended	6-23, 26-29

PRACTICE

Compare Exercises 5 to 10 to Exercises 11 to 16. How are they different? (Exercises 5 to 10 have 4-digit numbers; Exercises 11 to 16 have 5- and 6-digit numbers.)

APPLY

MATH REASONING ► What strategy could you use to solve Exercise 17? Explain. (Possible answer: work backward; determine the thousands digit first, then the hundreds, then the tens, then the ones.)

PROBLEM SOLVING ► Explain why it is reasonable to round in Problem 18. (Possible answer: The word *about* tells that an exact answer is not required.)

MIXED REVIEW ► How can finding missing addends help in Exercises 26 to 31? (Possible answer: think □ + △ = ○; so ○ − △ = □ or ○ − □ = △.)

2-7

Close and Assess

SAY WHAT YOU THINK

Challenge students to explain why the following numbers round to the nearest thousand as shown:
7,499 rounds to 7,000
7,501 rounds to 8,000
Urge them to support their explanations with rules, number lines, or drawings.

QUICK QUIZ

Round to the nearest thousand:
1. 5,280 (5,000)
2. 5,555 (6,000)
3. 9,550 (10,000)
4. 109,555 (110,000)

LESSON OPTIONS 2-8

Understanding Millions

OBJECTIVE 2-8 To read and write 7-, 8-, and 9-digit numbers

PREBOOK ACTIVITIES

QUICK REVIEW

1. Give the value of each underlined digit.
21,639 (1 thousand) 314,876 (3 hundred thousands)
491,362 (9 ten thousands) 800,999 (0 thousands)
2. Write the number nine hundred fifteen thousand, twenty-six. (915,026)

PRIOR KNOWLEDGE

On the chalkboard, draw a place value table showing the ones and thousands periods. Ask students to recall the number of digits that make up each period. (3) Have volunteers think of 5- and 6-digit numbers and write them in the proper places on the table. Then write a 7-, an 8-, and a 9-digit number on the board. Ask students to count the digits in each number. Have them infer what is needed in order to show these numbers on the table. (another period) Ask students to suggest places where they have seen large numbers such as these used. (Possible answers: in science books, in newspapers)

COMMUNICATION

Discussing and Reading Math Write the word **million** on the chalkboard. Ask a volunteer to use the word in a sentence. (Possible answer: *I wish I had a million dollars.)* Ask students to share what they know about the amount a million. (Possible answers: It is a very large amount; if you have a million dollars, you are rich.) Then ask students how they think the quantity one million compares with the quantities one hundred and one thousand. (Possible answer: A million is greater than one thousand and much greater than one hundred.)

EXPLORE AND CONNECT

Materials: calculators
Grouping Suggestion: cooperative learning pairs
Partners explore number relationships into the **millions** using a calculator. Pairs may use only the 1, 0, and × keys on their calculators. To begin, they use those digits and the × function to show a relationship between number places in the ones and thousands periods. As one partner punches in the numbers, the other counts and records the number of digits displayed and the answer. For example: 1 × 10 = 10; 10 × 10 = 100; 100 × 10 = 1,000; 1,000 × 10 = 10,000; 10,000 × 10 = 100,000. Then pairs continue the pattern to find the relationship between 100,000 and 1 **million** (100,000 × 10 = 1,000,000). Conclude by having students discuss what they noticed about place value relationships, even among larger numbers. (10 of one place = 1 of the next higher place, no matter what the value.)

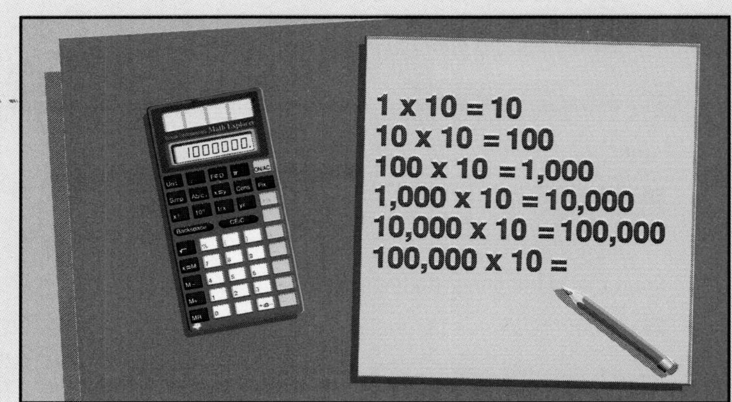

CONNECTIONS Use these anytime.

Problem of the Day

Calculator Patterns Find the pattern, then use a calculator to find the next three numbers: 201; 302; 1,312; 11,413; ____; ____; ____. (The first number was increased by 101; the next by 1,010; the next by 10,101; and so on: 112,423; 1,122,524; 11,223,534.)

Math Connection

Money Three expensive cars are being introduced at a car show. One is $25,000. The second has a price tag that is $5,000 less. The third has a price tag that is $20,000 more. What is the price of all three cars, from the most expensive to the least expensive? ($45,000; $25,000; $20,000)

Life Skills

House Hunting Martha's parents are looking for a new house to buy. They do not want to spend more than a 5-digit amount. What is the most expensive house a real estate agent could show them? ($99,999)

Classwork and Homework Supplements

Practice

Skills Maintenance 2-8

Name ______

Understanding Millions

Match.

1. 5,340,000 __E__ A fifty-three million, two hundred thousand
2. 50,420,000 __D__ B five million, four hundred thousand
3. 53,200,000 __A__ C five hundred thirty-four million
4. 532,000,000 __F__ D fifty million, four hundred twenty thousand
5. 534,000,000 __C__ E five million, three hundred forty thousand
6. 5,400,000 __B__ F five hundred thirty-two million

Write the number.

7. five million, six hundred twelve thousand __5,612,000__
8. thirty million, eight hundred forty thousand __30,840,000__
9. seventeen million, nine hundred thousand __17,900,000__
10. two hundred million, five hundred thousand __200,500,000__
11. eight hundred eighty million __880,000,000__
12. nine million, forty-three thousand __9,043,000__
13. one hundred million, two hundred thousand __100,200,000__
14. eight hundred fifty-seven million __857,000,000__

PS-4 Use with text pages 40–41. 15

Building Thinking Skills

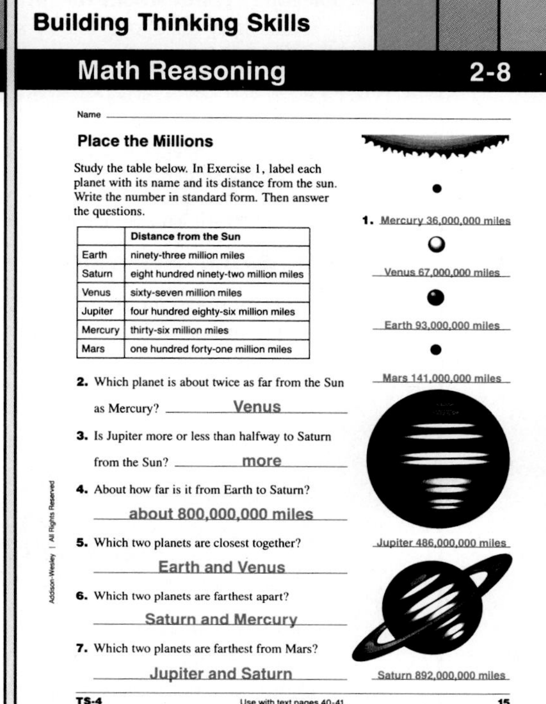

Math Reasoning 2-8

Name ______

Place the Millions

Study the table below. In Exercise 1, label each planet with its name and its distance from the sun. Write the number in standard form. Then answer the questions.

	Distance from the Sun
Earth	ninety-three million miles
Saturn	eight hundred ninety-two million miles
Venus	sixty-seven million miles
Jupiter	four hundred eighty-six million miles
Mercury	thirty-six million miles
Mars	one hundred forty-one million miles

1. Mercury 36,000,000 miles
Venus 67,000,000 miles
Earth 93,000,000 miles
Mars 141,000,000 miles
Jupiter 486,000,000 miles
Saturn 892,000,000 miles

2. Which planet is about twice as far from the Sun as Mercury? __Venus__
3. Is Jupiter more or less than halfway to Saturn from the Sun? __more__
4. About how far is it from Earth to Saturn? __about 800,000,000 miles__
5. Which two planets are closest together? __Earth and Venus__
6. Which two planets are farthest apart? __Saturn and Mercury__
7. Which two planets are farthest from Mars? __Jupiter and Saturn__

TS-4 Use with text pages 40–41. 15

Reteaching

Skills Review 2-8

Name ______

Understanding Millions

The millions period is the third period.
Follow these steps to read a number in the millions.

- ▶ Read the digits in the millions period as a number and say the word "million" after it.
- ▶ Read the digits in the thousands period as a number and say the word "thousand" after it.
- ▶ Read the digits in the ones period, if necessary

Millions Period			Thousands Period			Ones Period		
hundred millions	ten millions	millions	hundred thousands	ten thousands	thousands	hundreds	tens	ones
4	1	8 ,	6	3	5 ,	0	0	0

"four hundred eighteen million" "six hundred thirty-five thousand"

You read: "four hundred eighteen million, six hundred thirty-five thousand."
You write: 418,635,000.

1. Write an 8-digit number with 5 in the ten millions place and 3 in the thousands place.
__5__ __ , __ __ __3__ , __ __ __
Other digits may vary.
2. Write a 7-digit number with 4 in the millions place and 8 in the hundred thousands place.
__4__ , __8__ __ __ , __ __ __
Other digits may vary.

Ring the correct number.

3. thirty-two million, eight hundred five thousand
32,805 (32,805,000)
4. two hundred sixty-three million, two hundred thousand
(263,200,000) 263,200
5. fifty-eight million, forty-eight thousand
(58,048,000) 58,048

RS-4 Use with text pages 40-41. 15

Challenges

Math Reasoning 2-8

Name ______

Creating Numbers

Use all the digits 1 through 9 to create the following numbers.

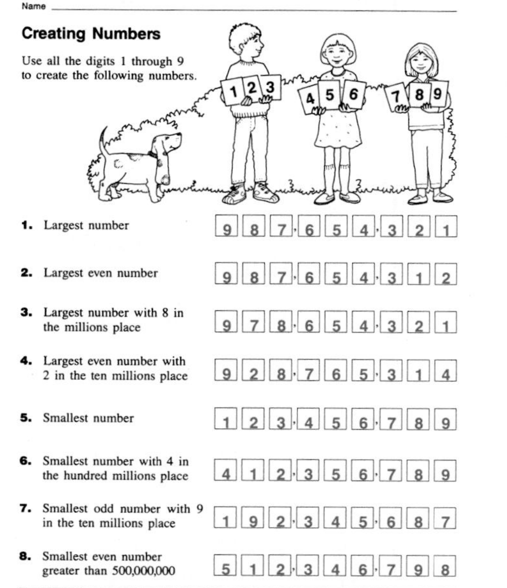

1. Largest number 9 8 7 , 6 5 4 , 3 2 1
2. Largest even number 9 8 7 , 6 5 4 , 3 1 2
3. Largest number with 8 in the millions place 9 7 8 , 6 5 4 , 3 2 1
4. Largest even number with 2 in the ten millions place 9 2 8 , 7 6 5 , 3 1 4
5. Smallest number 1 2 3 , 4 5 6 , 7 8 9
6. Smallest number with 4 in the hundred millions place 4 1 2 , 3 5 6 , 7 8 9
7. Smallest odd number with 9 in the ten millions place 1 9 2 , 3 4 5 , 6 8 7
8. Smallest even number greater than 500,000,000 5 1 2 , 3 4 6 , 7 9 8

CS-4 Use with text pages 40–41. 15

Options for Individual Needs

Basic

Exercises 1-17, 20-22
Skills Bank, p. 460
More Practice, p. 513, set C

Supplements
Reteaching 15 or
Practice 15
Thinking Skills 15

Average

Exercises 1-22
Skills Bank, p. 460
More Practice, p. 513, set C

Supplements
Practice 15
Challenges 15 or
Thinking Skills 15

Extended

Exercises 2-22

Supplements
Challenges 15
Thinking Skills 15

Other Resources:
Kids Are Consumers, Too!, pp. 94, 95, 97
Mathematics, A Way of Thinking, Lesson 8-25

2-8

LESSON PLAN 2-8

OBJECTIVE 2-8
To read and write 7-, 8- and 9-digit numbers

Materials: TA 8 (3-Digit Place Value Charts)

Grouping Suggestion: pairs

1. MOTIVATE AND TEACH

LEARN ABOUT IT

EXPLORE ► **From looking at the map, what can you conclude about the distance from San Antonio to Fort Walton Beach?** (It is quite far.)
► **How many students do you think it would take to stretch across our classroom? across the cafeteria?** (Answers will vary.)

TALK ABOUT IT ► **If each school has 1,000 students, how many schools would you need to stretch from San Antonio to Fort Walton Beach? Explain.** (1,000; 1,000 thousands = 1 million.)
► **How can you use the table to help you understand the relationship between different places?** (The name given to each place within a period is a reminder that each place to the left is 10 times the place next to it on the right.)
Student Edition answers: **1.** 1,000; If 100 thousands are 100,000, then 1,000 thousands are 1,000,000. **2.** 10; 10,000,000 has just one more zero than 1,000,000.

2. CHECK UNDERSTANDING

TRY IT OUT

ERROR ALERT Incorrectly reading or writing a large number when most of the digits are zeros. Confusing the periods.

Understanding Millions

LEARN ABOUT IT

EXPLORE Think About the Situation
Think how far a long line of students could reach.

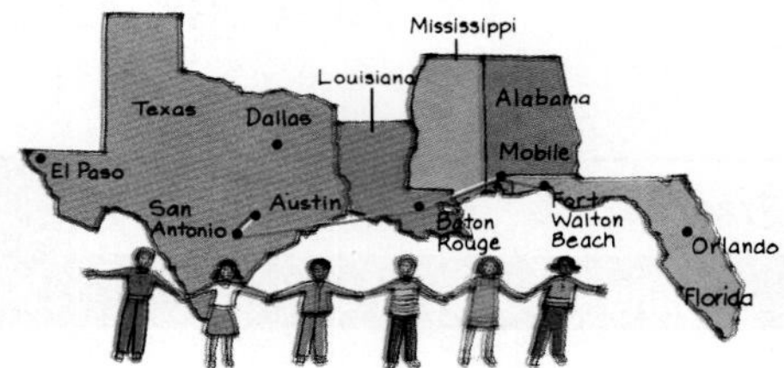

1,000 students → about 8 blocks
10,000 students → about 8 miles
100,000 students → from San Antonio to Austin (blue line)
1,000,000 students → from San Antonio to Fort Walton Beach (red line)

TALK ABOUT IT See teaching notes.

1. How many thousands do you think are in one million? Explain your thinking.
2. Would a line of 10,000,000 students be 10 or 100 times as long as a line of 1,000,000 students? How do you know?

This table shows the place values for larger numbers.

Millions Period			Thousands Period			Ones Period		
Hundred Millions	Ten Millions	Millions	Hundred Thousands	Ten Thousands	Thousands	Hundreds	Tens	Ones
6	3	2 ,	5	8	7 ,	1	4	5

You write, **632,587,145**.

You read, "**six hundred thirty-two million, five hundred eighty-seven thousand, one hundred forty-five**."

TRY IT OUT Answers will vary. Sample answers are shown.

1. Write and read a 7-digit number with 5 in the millions place and 4 in the hundred thousands place.
   5, 4 2 7, 1 3 0
2. Write and read a 9-digit number with 3 in the hundred millions place and 0 in the millions place.
   3 6 0, 1 2 4, 8 7 5

40

TEACHING OPTIONS

RETEACHING TIPS Tape together three 3-digit place value charts to represent ones, thousands, and millions periods. Students write the number in the chart, then write it in expanded form to show each digit's value. Last, they write it in standard form and read it aloud. Assign Reteaching Supplement 15.

ENRICHMENT Have students solve this number riddle: *I fill all the periods from ones to millions. The sum of my digits is 81, yet any place minus the place next to it would equal 0. Add 1 to me and I would be pushed right out of the millions period on to billions! Who am I?* (999,999,999)

PRACTICE

Write the number. **Answers will vary. Sample answers are shown.**

1. a 5-digit number with 2 in the ten thousands place and 4 in the tens place **26,341**
2. fifty-three million, four hundred eighty-two thousand, one hundred six **53,482,106**

Write the digit for the given place in 817,623,954.

3. millions **7**
4. ten thousands **2**
5. hundreds **9**
6. hundred millions **8**
7. ones **4**
8. hundred thousands **6**

Write two numbers from the box in which the digit 9 has the given value.
See Additional Answers.

98,345,012	89,540,813
387,592,041	576,908,442
639,817,430	235,975,762
493,003,561	194,318

9. 900,000
10. 9,000,000
11. 90,000,000
12. 90,000

APPLY

MATH REASONING Give a number that is 1,000,000 more and another that is 1,000,000 less. **See Additional Answers.**

13. 23,418,000
14. 516,050,000
15. 9,300,000
16. 49,750,000

PROBLEM SOLVING

17. A calculator display shows 97,216,543. How can you add or subtract once to change the 7 to 8? Explain your method. **Add 1,000,000.**
18. Use only the digits 1, 2, 3, 4, 5, 6, and 7. What are five 7-digit numbers between 4,000,000 and 5,000,000? **Answers will vary.**

▶ USING CRITICAL THINKING Discover a Pattern

Think about the pattern for the list of numbers. If you continued this pattern, which of these numbers would you use?

918,453,015
917,453,015
916,453,015
915,453,015

19. 902,453,015 **yes**
20. 899,453,015 **yes**
21. 899,000,000 **no**
22. 1,453,015 **yes**

More Practice, page 513, set C

3. Practice and Apply

Basic	1-17, 20-22
Average	1-22
Extended	2-22

Additional Answers: See p. T79.

PRACTICE

Look at Exercise 2. Decide how the commas can help you write the number. (The commas separate the periods, so you can write period by period.)

APPLY

MATH REASONING ▶ **When do you add a place to write a million more? Explain.** (when the millions digit is 9, because one more than 9 is 10; You cannot have two digits in one place, so you trade 10 millions for 1 ten million, leaving a 0 in the millions place.)

PROBLEM SOLVING ▶ **How do you decide whether to add or subtract in Problem 17? Explain.** (Subtracting means taking away. Since you want a larger digit in the millions place, you add.)

USING CRITICAL THINKING
▶ **Analyze the pattern.** (The digits in the ones and thousands periods stay the same; those in the millions change.)

Close and Assess

WRITE WHAT YOU THINK
Have each student write on a sheet of paper a number that goes into the millions period. Students then exchange papers with a partner. The partner first verifies that the number is in the millions period. Then that student writes the number in words and reads it aloud.

Quick Quiz

1. Write the number: seven hundred million, eight hundred six thousand, nine hundred fifty-five. (700,806,955)
2. Write the value of the underlined place in 134,862,983. (ten millions)

LESSON OPTIONS 2-9

Counting Change

OBJECTIVE 2-9 To count change

PREBOOK ACTIVITIES

QUICK REVIEW

Give the value of the coin combinations.

1. 4 dimes, 6 nickels, 2 pennies ($0.72)
2. 1 quarter, 2 dimes, 3 nickels, 4 pennies ($0.64)
3. 3 quarters, 2 dimes, 3 nickels, 2 pennies ($1.12)
4. 3 quarters, 5 dimes, 3 nickels, 4 pennies ($1.44)
5. 2 quarters, 12 pennies ($0.62)

PRIOR KNOWLEDGE

Using play money, show students pennies, dimes, nickels, and quarters. Have a pair of students role-play a customer giving a cashier a one-dollar bill for a purchase of $0.55. Ask students the coins the cashier might give as change. (Possible answer: 2 dimes and 1 quarter) Ask why a cashier might give the change as 4 nickels and 1 quarter or as 5 nickels and 2 dimes. (Possible answer: The cashier might not have any dimes or quarters.)

COMMUNICATION

Writing in Math Write the following paragraph on the chalkboard, omitting the words in parentheses. Write the answers in a scrambled list elsewhere on the board. Have students copy the paragraph, using the answer list to fill in the blanks to explain how to make change for a customer who pays for a $2.53 item with a ten-dollar bill.

When I count change, I start with the (cost) of the item. I start counting with the (coins) of (lesser) value. I count up by (adding) coins and bills of (greater) value. I stop when I get to ($10.00). Doing this will help me give the correct (change).

EXPLORE AND CONNECT

Materials: TA 9 (Play Money—Coins and Dollars), TA 10 (Play Money—Larger Bills)

Grouping Suggestion: cooperative learning groups of 3

Students count change up to $1 and explore counting change from larger bills. Each group sets up a "store" by tagging a pencil, eraser, and pen with the following prices: pencil—$0.25, eraser—$0.35, pen—$0.57. Students take turns playing customer, clerk, and store manager. The customer purchases one item, states the price, then gives the clerk a $1 bill. Starting from the purchase price, the clerk counts the change with coins of lesser value and proceeds to coins of greater value. The store manager verifies that the correct change has been given or corrects the change if necessary. Roles are switched until all three items have been purchased. Then members work together to decide the change they would get if they used a $5 bill to pay for a $3.25 notebook.

CONNECTIONS Use these anytime.

Problem of the Day

Making Change Leah received change of $5.90 from a purchase. Give three different coin-and-bill combinations she could have received. (Answers will vary; samples: 1 $5 bill, 3 quarters, 1 dime, 1 nickel; 5 $1 bills, 3 quarters, 1 dime, 1 nickel; 4 $1 bills, 4 quarters, 9 dimes.)

Patterns

Money Determine the patterns. Fill in the missing amounts.

1. $4.10, $4.15, $4.20, ______ ($4.25)
2. $3.26, ______, $3.46, $3.56 ($3.36)
3. $4.12, $4.17, $4.22, ______ ($4.27)
4. $1.50, $1.75, $2.00, $2.25, ______ ($2.50)

Number Sense

Estimation Jared wants to buy 4 pens that cost $2.12 each and a pencil that is $0.69. He has a ten-dollar bill. Estimate to see whether he has enough money. Explain your answer. (Yes; the pens are about $8 and the pencil is about $1, equaling $9.00.)

Classwork and Homework Supplements

Practice

Life Skills 2-9

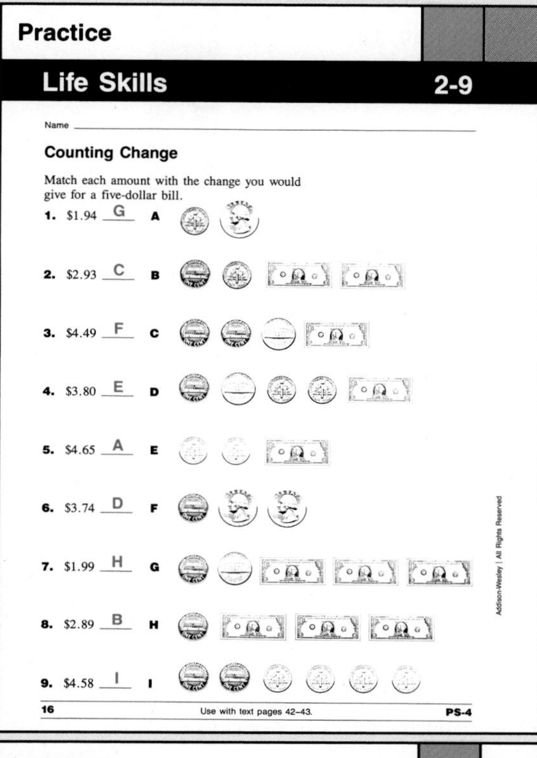

Name

Counting Change

Match each amount with the change you would give for a five-dollar bill.

1. $1.94 G — A
2. $2.93 C — B
3. $4.49 F — C
4. $3.80 E — D
5. $4.65 A — E
6. $3.74 D — F
7. $1.99 H — G
8. $2.89 B — H
9. $4.58 I — I

16 Use with text pages 42-43. PS-4

Addison-Wesley | All Rights Reserved

Building Thinking Skills

Life Skills 2-9

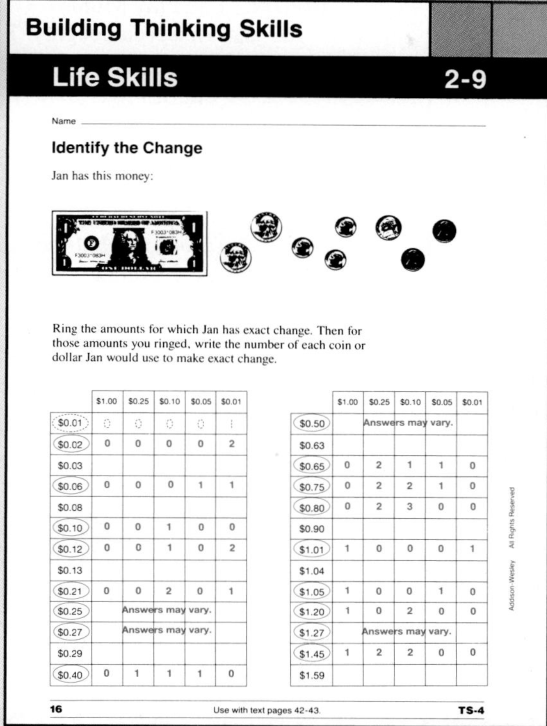

Name

Identify the Change

Jan has this money:

Ring the amounts for which Jan has exact change. Then for those amounts you ringed, write the number of each coin or dollar Jan would use to make exact change.

	$1.00	$0.25	$0.10	$0.05	$0.01
$0.01	0	0	0	0	1
$0.02	0	0	0	0	2
$0.03					
$0.06	0	0	0	1	1
$0.08					
$0.10	0	0	1	0	0
$0.12	0	0	1	0	2
$0.13					
$0.21	0	0	2	0	1
$0.25	Answers may vary.				
$0.27	Answers may vary.				
$0.29					
$0.40	0	1	1	1	0

	$1.00	$0.25	$0.10	$0.05	$0.01
$0.50	Answers may vary.				
$0.63					
$0.65	0	2	1	1	0
$0.75	0	2	2	1	0
$0.80	0	2	3	0	0
$0.90					
$1.01	1	0	0	0	1
$1.04					
$1.05	1	0	0	1	0
$1.20	1	0	2	0	0
$1.27	Answers may vary.				
$1.45	1	2	2	0	0
$1.59					

16 Use with text pages 42-43. TS-4

Addison-Wesley All Rights Reserved

Reteaching

Skills Review 2-9

Name

Counting Change

To count change, start with the cost. → Count up. Use coins of least value first. → End with the amount given.

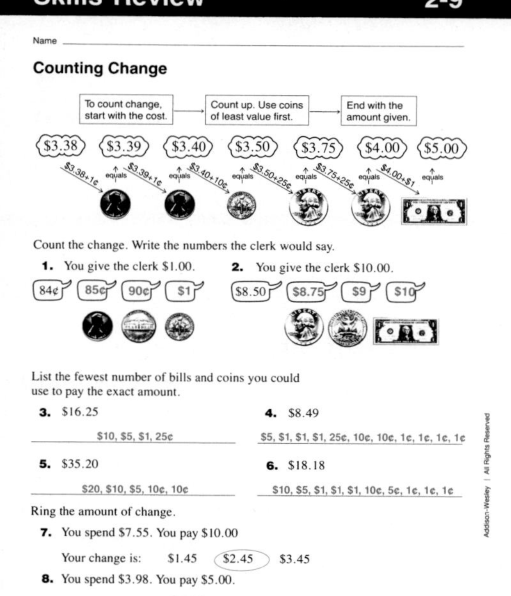

Count the change. Write the numbers the clerk would say.

1. You give the clerk $1.00. 84¢ 85¢ 90¢ $1
2. You give the clerk $10.00. $8.50 $8.75 $9 $10

List the fewest number of bills and coins you could use to pay the exact amount.

3. $16.25 — $10, $5, $1, 25¢
4. $8.49 — $5, $1, $1, $1, 25¢, 10¢, 10¢, 1¢, 1¢, 1¢, 1¢
5. $35.20 — $20, $10, $5, 10¢, 10¢
6. $18.18 — $10, $5, $1, $1, $1, 10¢, 5¢, 1¢, 1¢, 1¢

Ring the amount of change.

7. You spend $7.55. You pay $10.00.
   Your change is: $1.45 ($2.45) $3.45
8. You spend $3.98. You pay $5.00.
   Your change is: ($1.02) $2.02 $3.02

16 Use with text pages 42-43. RS-4

Addison-Wesley | All Rights Reserved

Challenges

Life Skills 2-9

Name

Change, Anyone?

Work in a small group to meet this challenge.

Twilly is the cashier at the Dizzy-Daffy Café. Mr. Dude gave her $2.00 to pay for his bill of $1.75. Twilly kept him waiting 10 minutes while she told him 12 different ways she could give him his change. Can you find 12 ways?

Use this chart to record your answer.
One row has been done for you.
Answers will vary. Samples given.

penny			5		5	10		15	5	20		10
nickel	1			5	4	3	3	2	2	1	1	1
dime	2		2				1		1		2	1
quarter		1										

Do you really want to get dizzy? Try this problem.

Mr. Toad's bill is $4.50. He gives Twilly a $5.00 bill. Find all the different ways she could give him his change. Develop with your group strategies for solving this problem in an organized way.

16 Use with text pages 42-43. CS-4

Addison-Wesley | All Rights Reserved

Options for Individual Needs

2-9

Basic

Exercises 1-11
Calculator Bank, p. 485
Computer Bank, p. 492
More Practice, p. 513, set D

Supplements
Reteaching 16 or
Practice 16

Average

Exercises 1-11
Calculator Bank, p. 485
Computer Bank, p. 492
More Practice, p. 513, set D

Supplements
Practice 16
Challenges 16 or
Thinking Skills 16

Extended

Exercises 1-11
Calculator Bank, p. 485
Computer Bank, p. 492

Supplements
Challenges 16
Thinking Skills 16

Other Resources:
Problem-Solving Experiences in Mathematics, Grade 4, Problems 30, 34
Kids Are Consumers, Too!, p. 111
Math In Stride, Grade 4, p. 39

LESSON PLAN 2-9

OBJECTIVE 2-9
To count change

Materials: play money (dollars, quarters, dimes, nickels, pennies)

Alternative Materials: TA 9 (Play Money—Coins and Dollars)

Grouping Suggestion: pairs

1. MOTIVATE AND TEACH

LEARN ABOUT IT

EXPLORE ▶ **Is there more than one way to show how Jeff paid $6.49? Explain.** (Yes. Several different coin-and-bill combinations equal $6.49.) ▶ **Explain how several people could each buy a T-shirt for $6.49 and each get a different amount in change.** (Each could give the clerk a different amount to pay for the shirt.)

TALK ABOUT IT ▶ **Explain why there are many ways to form a dollar with coins.** (Possible answer: Coins of set values can be combined in different quantities to equal a dollar.) ▶ **Could Tina have received a $5 bill in her change? Explain.** (No; the change owed her was only $3.51.) Student Edition answers: **1.** Answers will vary. Possible answer: 1 $5 bill, 1 $1 bill, 1 quarter, 2 dimes, 4 pennies **2.** Answers will vary. Possible answer: 1 penny, 2 quarters, 3 $1 bills

2. CHECK UNDERSTANDING

TRY IT OUT

ERROR ALERT Forgetting to start with the coin of least value. Forgetting to add the dollar when change owed is greater than one dollar.

Counting Change

LEARN ABOUT IT

EXPLORE Use Play Money
Jeff and Tina each bought a T-shirt for $6.49. Jeff used exact change to pay. Tina used a ten-dollar bill. The clerk gave her some change.

Use play money to show how Jeff paid for the shirt. Then show how the clerk gave Tina her change.

TALK ABOUT IT See teaching notes.

1. What coins and bills could Jeff use? How many ways did you find to show the amount?
2. What coins and bills might Tina have received in change? Explain how you decided.

Later Jeff used a ten-dollar bill to buy a game that cost $8.54. The clerk counted the change.

Start with the cost. **Count up, using coins of least value first.** **End with the amount given.**

$8.54

Jeff received 1 penny, 2 dimes, 1 quarter, and a one-dollar bill in change.

TRY IT OUT

Count the change out loud. Write the numbers the clerk would say.

1. You give the clerk $1.00.

78¢

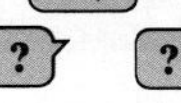

79¢ 80¢ 90¢ $1.00

2. You give the clerk $5.00.

$3.69

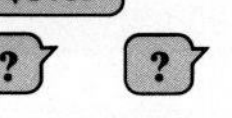

$3.70 $3.75 $4.00 $5.00

TEACHING OPTIONS

RETEACHING TIPS Arrange coins and dollars in separate piles by value from least to greatest going from left to right. Students can practice making change by always starting on the left and working toward the right. Assign Reteaching Supplement 16.

COMPUTER **Magic Cash Register, Avant-Garde, Copyright 1983** Reinforces decimals with all students. Read the introduction to the students. Students open the cash register, deal with customers, and close the cash register. Students supply customer information. A session takes 15 minutes.

PRACTICE

Count the change out loud. Write the numbers the clerk would say.

1. You give the clerk $1.00.
64¢ 65¢ 75¢ $1.00

2. You give the clerk $10.00.
$8.85 $8.90 $9.00 $10.00

List the bills and coins you could use to pay the exact amount. List the bills and coins you could receive for a twenty-dollar bill.
See Additional Answers.

3. 

4. 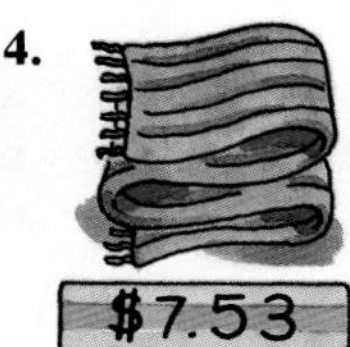

APPLY

MATH REASONING

5. Suppose you buy a belt for $6.89 and give the clerk a ten-dollar bill. Without counting, tell how much change you will get.
   a. $1.11
   b. $2.11
   (c.) $3.11

PROBLEM SOLVING

6. A clerk counts your change as "$3.44, $3.45, $3.50, $3.75, $4, $5." How much did the item cost? What did you give the clerk? What bills and coins do you get back?
See Additional Answers.

7. **More Than One Answer** How many ways can you show $1.00 using only quarters and dimes?
10 dimes; 2 quarters and 5 dimes; 4 quarters

▶ MENTAL MATH Counting On

Sometimes you can use mental math and count on by hundreds to add two numbers. To add 465 + 300, think: 465: 565, 665, 765.

Use mental math. Count on by hundreds to find these sums.

8. 294 + 200 494
9. 481 + 300 781
10. 318 + 100 418
11. 850 + 300 1,150

More Practice, page 513, set D

43

3. Practice and Apply

Basic	1-11
Average	1-11
Extended	1-11

Additional Answers: See p. T79.

PRACTICE

Look at Exercises 1 and 2. What is the amount in the first balloon under each statement? (the cost of what was purchased)

APPLY

MATH REASONING ▶ How can you solve this problem without counting? (Possible answer: Estimate the price of the belt at $7. $10 − $7 = $3. The change is at least $3.)

PROBLEM SOLVING ▶ Explain a strategy for finding the cost of the item in Problem 6. (Look at the first amount the clerk says and subtract $0.01.)

MENTAL MATH ▶ How can looking at the hundreds place help you solve each exercise? (It is the digit that will change when you count by hundreds.)

2-9

Close and Assess

SHOW WHAT YOU KNOW

Have students work in pairs with play money. They take turns creating problems for their partners to solve that require giving change from a five-, ten-, and twenty-dollar bill. (Check students' problems.)

Quick Quiz

Write the change from $1 for each purchase price using the fewest coins.
1. $0.52 **2.** $0.21 **3.** $0.94
(**1.** 3 pennies, 2 dimes, 1 quarter **2.** 4 pennies, 3 quarters **3.** 1 penny, 1 nickel)

Estimating with Money: Using a Reference Point

OBJECTIVE 2-10 To estimate using the visual estimation technique to compare an amount of money to

PREBOOK ACTIVITIES

QUICK REVIEW

Write the value of each coin combination.
1. 3 quarters ($0.75) **2.** 5 nickels ($0.25)
3. 4 dimes ($0.40) **4.** 4 quarters, 3 dimes ($1.30)
5. 3 quarters, 2 dimes, 5 nickels ($1.20)
6. 2 quarters, 1 dime, 3 nickels, 2 pennies ($0.77)

PRIOR KNOWLEDGE

Have students describe where they save their money at home. (Possible answer: in a coin bank) Then ask why they might want to open their banks. (Possible answer: to buy something) Ask students to explain how they could find out how much money they have without counting every coin. (Possible answer: Estimate.) Ask how they could make it easier to estimate the money in their bank. (Possible answer: Put coins of the same value in piles.)

COMMUNICATION

Discussing Math Ask students where they have seen the word **reference** used before. (Possible answer: in a library) Write $2.25 on the chalkboard. Explain that if $2.25 is an amount of money you need or are referring to, it is called a **reference point**. Have students work in small groups to create diagrams that show several coin combinations they could use to reach the reference point $2.25. Ask students how estimating coins can help them decide whether an amount is more or less than a reference point. (Possible answer: Compare rounded amount to the reference point.) Have students analyze ways they could estimate using their diagrams. (Answers will vary.)

EXPLORE AND CONNECT

Materials: coin cards (see activity below), TA 9 (Play Money—Coins and Dollars)
Grouping Suggestion: small cooperative learning groups
Students practice estimating amounts $5 or less. Make coin cards by writing coins marked P (penny), N (nickel), D (dime), and Q (quarter) in sets that each total $5 or less. Each group has a small stack of the coin cards, turned face down in a pile. One student writes a *reference point* amount from $1–$5 on paper, such as $1.27. A second student turns over a coin card, then estimates the amount to see if it is equal to, greater than, or less than the *reference point*. A third student verifies the answer by finding the value of the coins on the card. Other group members may suggest different ways to estimate. Group members switch roles until everyone has had a turn at each task. Conclude by discussing different ways to estimate money amounts. (Answers will vary.)

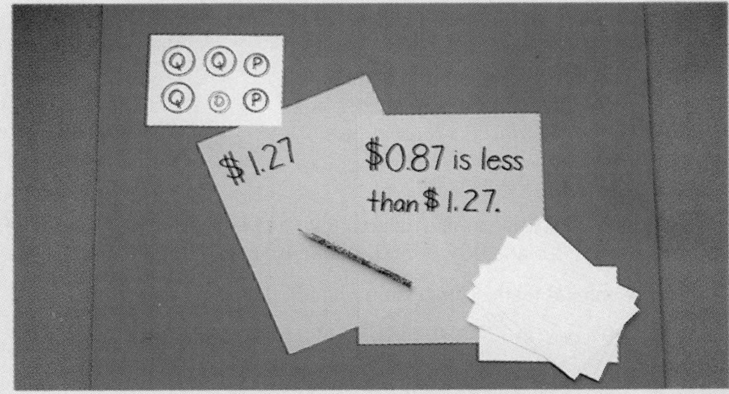

CONNECTIONS Use these anytime.

Problem of the Day

Milk Money Mitchell's mother gave him 5 quarters, 5 dimes, and 5 nickels to buy a gallon of milk at the store. If a gallon of milk costs $1.89, does Mitchell have enough money? Explain. (yes, because he has $2)

Number Sense

Math Reasoning When Carmen went to pay for her purchases, the clerk had to give her the change all in coins. The change was $1.35 and she received 10 coins. What coins did Carmen get as her change? (4 quarters, 1 dime, 5 nickels)

Life Skills

Transportation Costs A single bus ride costs $1.50. Jerry and Jay have 6 quarters, 2 dimes, 7 nickels, and 15 pennies between them. What coins do they still need in order for both boys to ride the bus? (Answers will vary. To equal $0.80, possible answers: 2 quarters and 3 dimes; 8 dimes; 16 nickels) a reference point

Classwork and Homework Supplements

Practice

Estimation 2-10

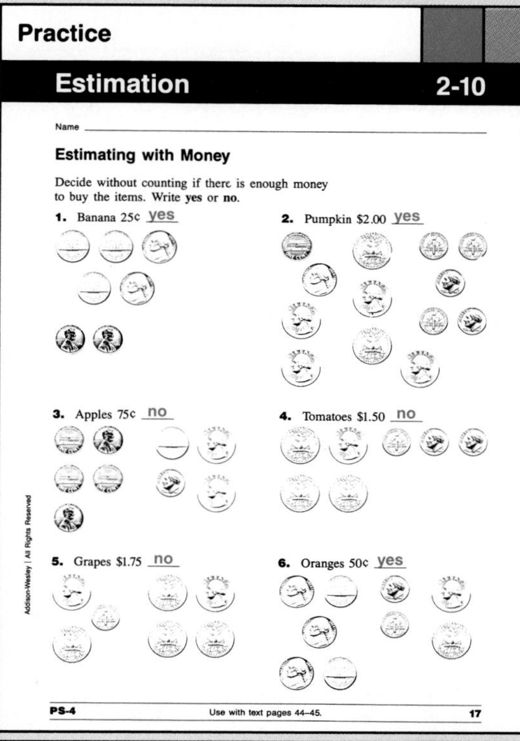

Name ______

Estimating with Money

Decide without counting if there is enough money to buy the items. Write **yes** or **no.**

1. Banana 25¢ yes
2. Pumpkin $2.00 yes
3. Apples 75¢ no
4. Tomatoes $1.50 no
5. Grapes $1.75 no
6. Oranges 50¢ yes

PS-4 Use with text pages 44-45. 17

Building Thinking Skills

Problem Solving 2-10

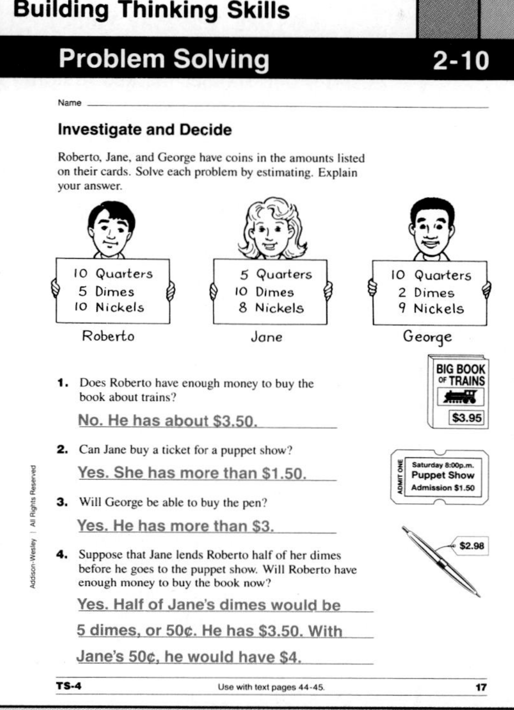

Name ______

Investigate and Decide

Roberto, Jane, and George have coins in the amounts listed on their cards. Solve each problem by estimating. Explain your answer.

10 Quarters
5 Dimes
10 Nickels
Roberto
5 Quarters
10 Dimes
8 Nickels
Jane
10 Quarters
2 Dimes
9 Nickels
George
BIG BOOK OF TRAINS
$3.95
ADMIT ONE
Saturday 8:00p.m.
Puppet Show
Admission $1.50
$2.98

1. Does Roberto have enough money to buy the book about trains?
   No. He has about $3.50.
2. Can Jane buy a ticket for a puppet show?
   Yes. She has more than $1.50.
3. Will George be able to buy the pen?
   Yes. He has more than $3.
4. Suppose that Jane lends Roberto half of her dimes before he goes to the puppet show. Will Roberto have enough money to buy the book now?
   Yes. Half of Jane's dimes would be 5 dimes, or 50¢. He has $3.50. With Jane's 50¢, he would have $4.

TS-4 Use with text pages 44-45. 17

Reteaching

Estimation 2-10

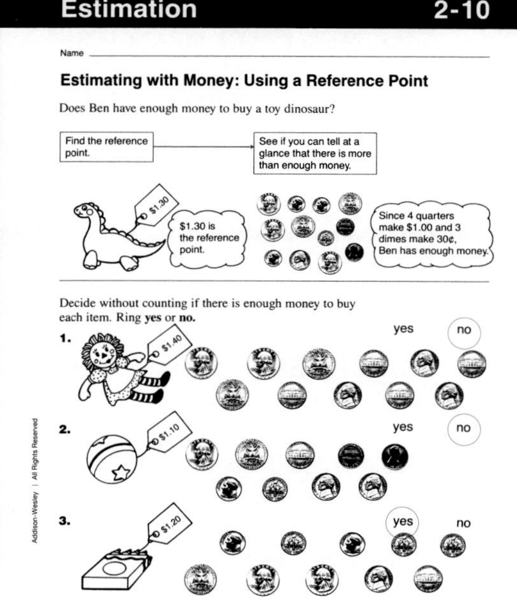

Name ______

Estimating with Money: Using a Reference Point

Does Ben have enough money to buy a toy dinosaur?

Find the reference point.
See if you can tell at a glance that there is more than enough money.
$1.30
$1.30 is the reference point.
Since 4 quarters make $1.00 and 3 dimes make 30¢, Ben has enough money.

Decide without counting if there is enough money to buy each item. Ring **yes** or **no.**

1. $1.40 yes (no)
2. $1.10 yes (no)
3. $1.20 (yes) no

RS-4 Use with text pages 44-45. 17

Challenges

Manipulatives 2-10

Name ______

Pocket Change Game

Play this game in 2 teams with 2 players on each team. You will need play money quarters, dimes, and nickels.

Rules

1. Team 1 follows these steps:
   - Pick 6 coins. (The value cannot be exactly $0.50, $1.00, or $1.50.)
   - Tell Team 2 the estimated value of the coins:

Example:

The coins are worth between $0.50 and $1.00.

2. Team 2 tries to guess the 6 coins by following these steps:
   - Put out 6 possible coins.
   - Ask three questions whose answers are yes or no.

Examples:

Are there more than 3 quarters?
Is the value less than $0.80?
Are there fewer than 5 dimes?

3. Switch sides. Team 2 picks coins and Team 1 guesses.

When you get better, try playing using 8 coins and 5 guesses.

CS-4 Use with text pages 44-45. 17

Options for Individual Needs

2-10

Basic

Exercises 1-3, 5-16
Calculator Bank, pp. 485, 486
Computer Bank, p. 492
More Practice, p. 513, set E

Supplements
Reteaching 17 or
Practice 17

Average

Exercises 1-18
Calculator Bank, pp. 485, 486
Computer Bank, p. 492
More Practice, p. 513, set E

Supplements
Practice 17
Challenges 17 or
Thinking Skills 17

Extended

Exercises 2-18
Calculator Bank, pp. 485, 486
Computer Bank, p. 492

Supplements
Challenges 17
Thinking Skills 17

Other Resources:

Problem-Solving Experiences in Mathematics, Grade 4, Problem 31
Math In Stride, Grade 4, p. 40
Kids Are Consumers, Too!, pp. 112, 113

LESSON PLAN 2-10

OBJECTIVE 2-10
To estimate using the visual estimation technique to compare an amount of money to a reference point

Materials: TA 9 (Play Money—Coins and Dollars), TA 11 (Blank Spinners—marked in dollar amounts less than $5)

Grouping Suggestion: pairs

1. MOTIVATE AND TEACH

LEARN ABOUT IT

EXPLORE ▶ **Explain how you made your decision each time you compared coins to the reference point.** (Possible answer: visually grouped like coins together, then estimated the value of all the coins)
▶ **Which coins did you look at first when estimating? Explain.** (Possible answer: started with the coins of greatest value because they usually make up most of the estimated amount)

TALK ABOUT IT ▶ **Explain why grouping coins helps you estimate.** (Possible answer: Groups of coins are easy to work with mentally.)
▶ **Explain why it is better to make groups of coins of greater value first.** (Possible answer: Those coins give an estimate faster than coins of less value.)
Student Edition answers: **1.** Possible answer: looked for a group of coins that could be added easily **2.** if you are making a purchase with limited funds

2. CHECK UNDERSTANDING

TRY IT OUT

ERROR ALERT Having difficulty remembering to group coins of the same value when estimating. Overestimating or underestimating money amounts.

Estimating with Money
Using a Reference Point

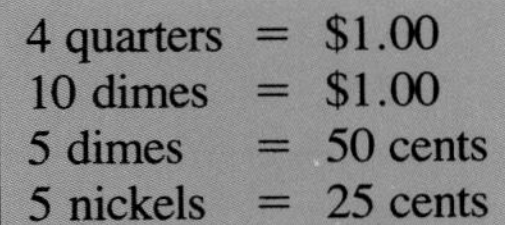

4 quarters	=	$1.00
10 dimes	=	$1.00
5 dimes	=	50 cents
5 nickels	=	25 cents

You can use the table to help estimate.

LEARN ABOUT IT

EXPLORE **Use Play Money**
Lay out a pile of play money coins. Spin a paper clip spinner marked in dollar amounts. Decide, without counting, if there is more or less than the spinner amount in the pile. Count to check. Try this several times.

TALK ABOUT IT See teaching notes.

1. How did you decide if your pile of coins was more or less than $1.00 without counting the total?
2. Why would you want to know if you have more or less than a given amount of money?

You can estimate to decide if an amount is more or less than a given amount. The given amount is called a **reference point**.

Look at the coins. Since 4 quarters make $1.00 and 5 dimes make 50¢, it is easy to see at a glance that there is more than enough money to buy the sports cards.

Sports Cards $1.50

TRY IT OUT

Decide without counting if there is enough money to buy the item.

1. no

44

TEACHING OPTIONS

RETEACHING TIPS For the first error, students separate play-money coins into groups of the same value. Then they estimate each group, starting with the coin of greatest value. Last, they add the estimated amounts together to get a total. Assign Reteaching Supplement 17.

ENRICHMENT Students work in pairs taking turns shopping. Working with a catalog and a calculator, students imagine having $1,000 to spend. They cannot go over the amount and must come within $99. They list items to buy, add the amounts on a calculator, then verify their partner's total.

PRACTICE

Decide without counting if there is enough money to buy the items.

1. Pencils $1.00
no

2. Whistle $1.50
yes

APPLY

MATH REASONING Use play money to decide. Could the pile of coins be more than $4.00? Explain your thinking. **See Additional Answers.**

3. The pile has fewer than 9 quarters, fewer than 11 dimes, and fewer than 11 nickels.
4. The pile has fewer than 5 quarters, fewer than 31 dimes, and fewer than 6 nickels.

PROBLEM SOLVING

5. Ria had 6 quarters, 10 dimes, and fewer than 5 nickels in her pocket. Did she have enough to buy a $3.00 photo book of Indian cliff dwellings? Explain.
no; she has at most $2.75
6. Lea had twice as many nickels as dimes. She had 30 coins, all dimes and nickels. Can she buy a map that costs $2.00? **yes; 20 nickels and 10 dimes make $2.00**

MIXED REVIEW

Use mental math to add.

7. (3 + 5) + 7
15
8. (5 + 3) + 7
15
9. 2 + (6 + 4)
12
10. (2 + 6) + 4
12

Use mental math. Break apart an addend if needed.

11. 7 + 5
12
12. 8 + 7
15
13. 12 + 6
18
14. 13 + 5
18

Add. Use compensation if needed.

15. 8 + 5
13
16. 9 + 6
15
17. 6 + 4
10
18. 7 + 9
16

More Practice, page 513, set E

3. PRACTICE AND APPLY

Basic	1-3, 5-16
Average	1-18
Extended	2-18

Additional Answers: See p. T79.

PRACTICE

Look at Exercises 1 and 2. What is the reference point in each exercise? (the cost of the item)

APPLY

MATH REASONING ► **What strategy did you use to answer Exercise 3?** (Possible answer: estimated one less than the number given for each coin)

PROBLEM SOLVING ► **How does knowing the relationship between a dime and a nickel help you solve Problem 6?** (If you know a dime is twice a nickel, you know that twice as many nickels as dimes equals the same amount; 10 dimes = 20 nickels, both = $1.)

MIXED REVIEW ► **Explain a strategy to answer Exercises 7-14.** (make doubles or find compatible numbers)

CLOSE AND ASSESS

SHOW WHAT YOU KNOW

Have students use play money and work in pairs to show from 10 to 20 coins that together are worth less than $3 but more than $2. Pairs may use quarters, dimes, and nickels only. (Possible answer: 8 quarters, 1 dime, and 1 nickel)

QUICK QUIZ

Which group of coins is enough to buy an item that costs $2.75?

7 quarters, 8 dimes, 5 nickels (yes)
8 quarters, 4 dimes, 5 nickels (no)
5 quarters, 12 dimes, 5 nickels (no)

CHAPTER 2

DATA COLLECTION AND ANALYSIS

GROUP DECISION MAKING

OBJECTIVE To collect, organize, and present data

Arrange students in groups, then ask them these questions to focus their thinking.

COLLECTING DATA

► **Explain what a survey is in your own words.** (Possible answer: asking 1 or more questions to many people to get their opinions on a particular subject)

► **How would you make a reasonable list of eating-place choices in your area?** (Possible answer: Ask your group first, then check local ads for other places.)

► **How could you determine other reasons for liking a place to eat besides the 3 listed?** (Possible answer: Brainstorm with your own group.)

► **Why ask so many children to respond to your survey?** (Possible answer: The more people you ask, the more reliable will be the information you receive.)

► **What should you do if someone you survey likes a place other than those on your list or has a different reason than any you included? Explain your reasoning.** (Answers may vary; students may insist that answers be chosen from ones already on the survey to make tabulating easier.)

Data Collection and Analysis

Group Decision Making

UNDERSTAND
FIND DATA
PLAN
ESTIMATE
SOLVE
CHECK

Doing a Survey
Group Skill:
Encourage and Respect Others

Your school newspaper has a section called "Kids Eating Out." Your group is in charge of that section and you are going to conduct a survey to find where your schoolmates like to eat and why.

Collecting Data

1. Work with your group to make a list of 5 places in your area that you think children like to eat.
2. What are some reasons children use to decide where they like to eat? Think of one or two more reasons to add to the list.

   a. I like the food.
   b. My friends go there.
   c. The service is quick.
   d. ________________
   e. ________________

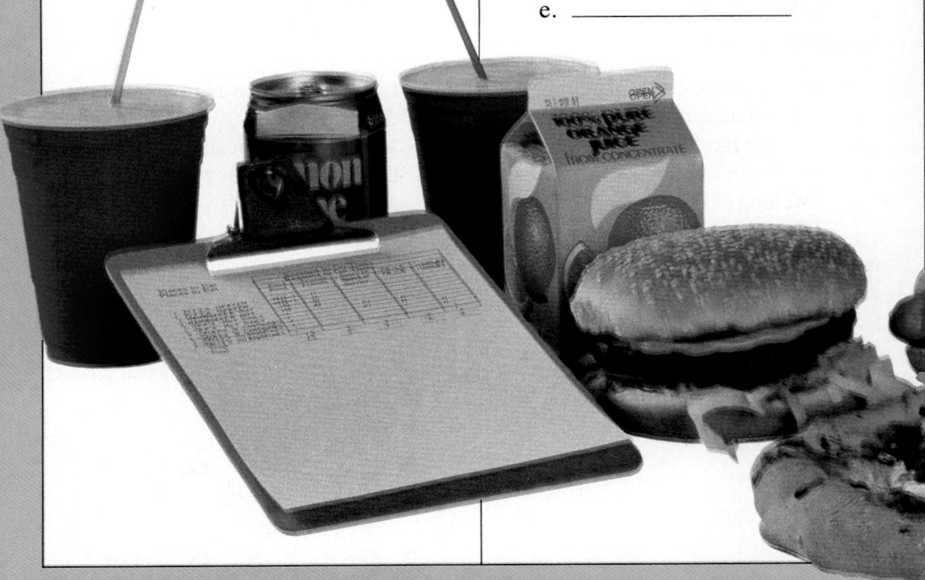

46

TEACHING OPTIONS

COOPERATIVE LEARNING

Grouping Suggestions:
cooperative learning groups of 3-5

Before dividing the class into small groups, discuss and list the steps required to complete a survey, such as list eating places and reasons for favorite places; decide who and how many people group members should survey; plan how to record answers; and determine how to total, present, and analyze results. Individual groups may decide how to divide up the tasks, but 1 group member should act as coordinator to make sure that all tasks are assigned and completed.

3. Ask at least 15 children in your school which of the five places on your list is their favorite. Then ask them to choose the 1 reason on your list which most describes why they like that particular place. Record the answers of each person you ask.

Organizing Data

4. Count how many people liked each eating place. Then mark the most popular place number 1, the next most popular place number 2, and so on.
5. Make a table. On the left hand side of the table, write the names of the 5 places to eat, in order, from the most popular place to the least popular.

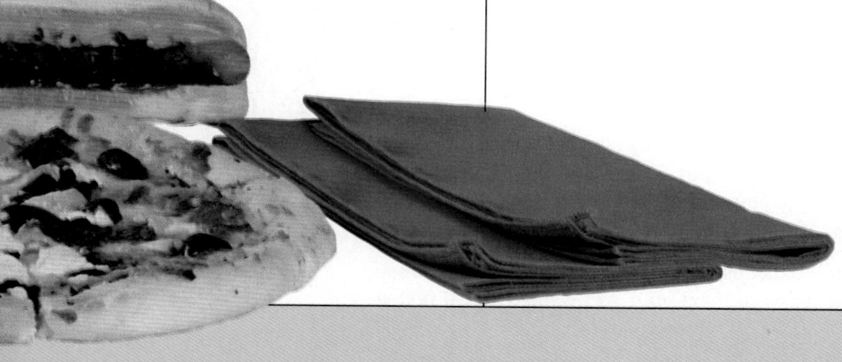

6. Make tally marks in the table to show the reasons why people eat at each restaurant.

Presenting Your Analysis

7. What can you conclude from your table? What seems to be the most important reason for choosing a place to eat? Did most children agree on their favorite place to eat or were there many different responses?

   Write a short paragraph for the school newspaper to summarize your results.

   Use the data to write 5 true statements.

47

EXTENSION Have students spread the good news. Ask each group to write a letter to the manager of the most popular eating place in the group's survey. Suggest that students tell the manager what their group found and include copies of their table of results to prove their conclusions.

ORGANIZING DATA

▶ **How will you keep track of answers to the survey?** (Possible answer: Use tally marks.)

▶ **Predict why all group members must use the same questions and reasons to survey children around school.** (You need to be able to organize responses at the end.)

▶ **Explain how to handle a tie.** (You could show 2 places numbered the same.)

▶ **Explain why a table is a useful way to present results.** (Possible answer: Results are organized in easy-to-read rows and columns.)

PRESENTING YOUR ANALYSIS

▶ **Compare the results with your group's own responses.** (Answers may vary.)

▶ **What conclusions can be drawn from the survey?** (Answers may vary; students should point to response patterns to support any statements.)

▶ **Devise a way to write a newspaper article based on the survey.** (Plans may vary. Each group member could contribute a sentence about a different eating place or preference. Group members could break the survey into parts so that each student can write about a different aspect of the activity.)

WRAP UP

INTRODUCTION The Wrap Up provides activities emphasizing math language and thinking skills for the chapter and a project that integrates those skills with other math strands.

USING PAGE 48

Estimation Language Match Have students complete this section independently. When they finish, have partners compare answers and discuss any discrepancies they may find.

Sometimes, Always, Never

▶ **Identify something that may help you evaluate the statements in Problems 7 and 8.** (place value charts)

▶ **How can you prove that a statement is *sometimes* true?** (Find one true and one false example.)

Project Have students work in small cooperative learning groups to discuss strategies and plan methods to solve the problems posed in the project.

▶ **Compare the length of string that shows how far 10 steps is to the length of string that shows how far 100 steps is.** (100 is 10 times greater than 10, so the string that shows 100 steps is 10 times longer than the string that shows 10 steps.)

▶ **Compare the length of string that shows 1,000 steps to the strings that show 100 steps and 10 steps.** (1,000 is 10 times greater than 100 and 100 times greater than 10, so the string that shows 1,000 steps is 10 times longer than the string that shows 100 steps and 100 times longer than the string that shows 10 steps.)

WRAP UP

Estimation Language Match

Match each phrase on the left with the correct amount of money or time on the right. Justify your choices.

1. just less than an hour **d** — a. $18.70
2. a little less than fifty minutes **e** — b. $20.56
3. a little over twenty dollars **b** — c. $79.05
4. a little under eighty dollars **c** — d. 59 minutes
5. almost twenty dollars **a** — e. 48 minutes

Sometimes, Always, Never **Explanations will vary.**

Which word should go in the blank, sometimes, always, or never? Explain your choices.

6. 387 __?__ rounds to 400. **sometimes**
7. The millions period __?__ has more places than the ones period. **always**
8. 6 hundred thousands is __?__ greater than 6 ten thousands. **always**

Project

How far do you walk every day?

- Use string to show how far 10 steps is. How could you show 100 steps with string? How could you show 1,000 steps?
- Now estimate how many steps you take on the way to the school restroom. If you walked 100 steps from where you are now, where do you think you would be? What if you walked 1,000 steps?
- A million steps is about 400 miles. Look at a map. How far would you go if you walked 1,000,000 steps?

48

TEACHING OPTIONS

ENRICHMENT Discuss successful strategies students used to complete the Project. Then have students choose several different locations on a map of their local area and estimate how many steps they would have to take to get to those destinations from their homes or from school.

CHAPTER REVIEW/TEST

Part 1 Understanding

1. Order these numbers from least to greatest.

4,628 43,628 43,816 4,682 4,628; 4,682; 43,628; 43,816

Write the digit for the given place in 691,073,582.

2. millions 1
3. ten millions 9
4. hundred thousands 0

Part 2 Skills

Write each number in standard form.

5. seven thousand, nine hundred fourteen 7,914
6. seventy-eight thousand, one hundred sixteen 78,116
7. forty-two million, eight hundred thousand 42,800,000

Write < or > for each ▥.

8. 9,584 ▥ 9,484 >
9. 31,772 ▥ 31,780 <
10. 567,890 ▥ 586,998 <

Write true or false.

11. To the nearest hundred, 182 rounds to 180. false
12. To the nearest thousand, 74,495 rounds to 70,000. false
13. To the nearest dollar, $7.82 rounds to $7 false

Part 3 Applications

14. Ed piled up 4 cubes. A red cube is above a blue cube. A green cube is on a pink cube. The blue cube is above the pink cube. Draw the pile.
See Additional Answers.

15. Kay first gives you a penny as she says, "$8.99." She continues to give you change and counts, "$9, $10." What did your purchase cost? How much did you give Kay? What is your change?
$8.98, $10, $1.02

CHAPTER REVIEW/TEST

INTRODUCTION The Review/Test is provided to review and evaluate the skills and concepts presented in Chapter 2.

USING PAGE 49
If you prefer to use this page for review, you may want to use the **Multiple-Choice Posttest** (pages 7-8) or the **Free-Response Posttest** (pages 7-8) to evaluate mastery of Chapter objectives.

ITEM ANALYSIS The table below correlates the Chapter Review/Test items with the lesson objectives for the chapter.

Items	Objectives
1	2-3
2, 3	2-8
4	2-2
5	2-1
6	2-2
7	2-8
8-10	2-3
11	2-6
12	2-7
13	2-6
14	2-5
15	2-9

Additional Answers: See p. T79.

INFORMAL ASSESSMENT

Using Manipulatives Have students pick 5 number cards (TA 3) at random, use them to form the greatest and smallest possible numbers, and read each number aloud. Then have them round each number to the nearest thousand. (Answers will vary.)

Communication *Explain how to tell which is the greater of 2 numbers with the same number of digits.* (Possible answer: Compare digits place by place, starting in the greatest place. When you find 2 digits in the same place that differ, the digit with the greater value is the greater number.)

Critical Thinking *Which 4-digit number has a digit sum of 11; rounds to 2,800 to the nearest hundred; but rounds to 3,000 to the nearest thousand?* (2,801 or 2,810)

CHAPTER 2

ENRICHMENT

INTRODUCTION Students gain an appreciation for the consistency and simplicity of our numeration system by comparing standard numbers with Roman numerals.

USING PAGE 50
This Enrichment page is provided for all students. You may wish to use it after they have completed the Chapter Review/Test on page 49.
Ask students where they may have seen Roman numerals used. (Possible answers: clocks, building corner stones, introductory book pages)

▶ **Analyze Roman numerals 1 to 3 for a pattern.** (Each has one more I, which is almost like what you do when you make tallies.)

▶ **Explain how the pattern changes for 4.** (It shows IV, which means 1 before 5.)

▶ **Compare Roman numerals 4 to 6.** (IV is 1 *before* 5, V is 5 exactly, VI is 1 *after* 5.)

▶ **Apply the same reasoning to explain the Roman numeral for 11.** (XI is 1 after 10.)

▶ **Relate the symbol C for 100 to words you know that begin with C and relate to 100.** (Possible answers: *c*entury, *c*entimeter)

Have students complete the page independently, then compare answers with a partner.

EXTENSION Introduce additional Roman numerals: D for 500 and M for 1,000. Guide students to compare 500 with 5 and 1,000 with 100 to determine how to write greater Roman numerals. Have them write their birth year, the current year, and the number of the last page of their Student Edition using all necessary Roman numerals. (Answers will vary; MCMXC— is the beginning of year 199—.)

Additional Answers: See p. T79.

ENRICHMENT
Roman Numerals

I = 1
V = 5
X = 10

The Romans wrote numbers with letter symbols instead of digits. We still use Roman numerals, mostly for clocks and dates.

To read and write Roman numerals, add and subtract symbols.

III = 3	IV = 4	XV = 15
1 + 1 + 1 Add to get 3.	5 − 1 Subtract to get 4.	10 + 5 Add to get 15.

Think how many tens and ones you need. Put them together.

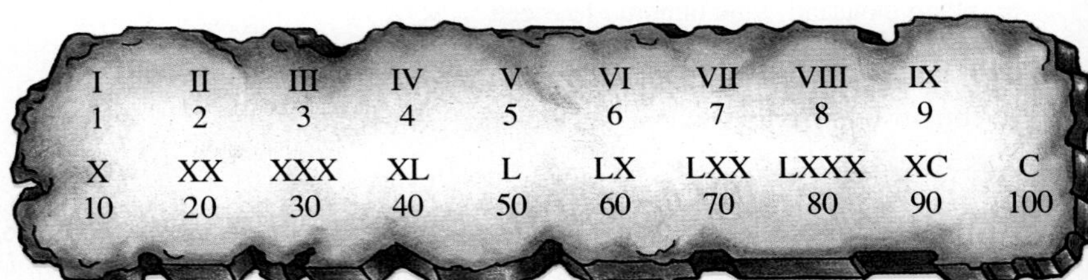

I	II	III	IV	V	VI	VII	VIII	IX	
1	2	3	4	5	6	7	8	9	
X	XX	XXX	XL	L	LX	LXX	LXXX	XC	C
10	20	30	40	50	60	70	80	90	100

Here's how to write the Roman numeral for the standard number.

38 You need 30 and 8. XXXVIII
54 You need 50 and 4. LIV
99 You need 90 and 9. XCIX

1. What patterns do you see that tell when to add and when to subtract? **See Additional Answers.**
2. Find two Roman numerals that use addition. **See Additional Answers.**
3. Find two Roman numerals that use subtraction. **See Additional Answers.**

Write the Roman numeral for the standard number.

4. 27 **XXVII**
5. 34 **XXXIIII**
6. 76 **LXXVI**
7. 149 **CIVIX**

Write the standard number for the Roman numeral.

8. XXXV **35**
9. XVI **16**
10. CCI **201**

50

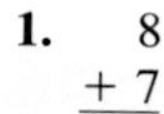

CUMULATIVE REVIEW

1. $8 + 7$

   A 1 | B 6
   (C) 15 | D 16

2. $16 - 9$

   (A) 7 | B 8
   C 10 | D 25

3. 7 + 4

   A 3 | (B) 11
   C 12 | D 10

4. 13 − 5

   A 18 | B 7
   C 9 | (D) 8

5. Which number sentence belongs with the fact family for 5 + 6 = 11?

   (A) 11 − 5 = 6 | B 6 − 5 = 11
   C 8 + 3 = 11 | D 16 − 5 = 11

6. Which number fact could help you solve 6 + 7?

   A 5 + 3 = 8 | (B) 6 + 6 = 12
   C 11 − 8 = 3 | D 7 + 3 = 10

7. What sum helps you find 8 + 4 if you use down-up 2?

   (A) 6 + 6 | B 7 + 3
   C 4 + 8 | D 10 + 2

8. Find the missing number.
   12 − ▯ = 5

   A 17 | B 8
   (C) 7 | D 6

9. Add. Use the grouping strategy.
   7 + 4 + 3

   A 11 | B 743
   (C) 14 | D 21

10. Use the zero property to find 7 − 0.

   A 0 | (B) 7
   C 70 | D 6

11. Tanya counted the money in her purse and rounded it to $10. What is the largest amount she could have?

   A $9.49 | B $9.99
   (C) $10.49 | D $10.43

12. Which number has a 4 in the thousands place, a 9 in the hundreds place, and no tens?

   A 490 | B 4,950
   (C) 34,901 | D 94,004

CUMULATIVE REVIEW

INTRODUCTION The purpose of this Cumulative Review is to maintain previously taught skills and concepts. The emphasis in this Cumulative Review is on addition and subtraction concepts and basic facts, Chapter 1; and on place value and money, Chapter 2.

ITEM ANALYSIS The table below correlates the Cumulative Review Items with the lesson objectives.

Items	Objectives
1	1-6
2	1-3
3	1-7
4-6	1-3
7	1-7
8	1-3
9, 10	1-2
11	2-6
12	2-2

Chapter Management

OVERVIEW

Lesson	Pages	Objectives	Subject Integration	Strand Integration
Chapter Opener	52-53	To introduce chapter 3	science-planets	estimation
Mental Math: Special Sums and Differences	54-55	3-1 To find sums and differences of multiples of 10 and 100	language arts-writing	algebra
Estimating Sums and Differences	56-57	3-2 To round to estimate sums and differences	science-computers	calculators
Adding Whole Numbers: Making the Connection	58-59	3-3 To understand adding 3-digit numbers	social studies-partner skills	place value
Adding Whole Numbers	60-61	3-4 To add 3-digit numbers	health/fitness-calories	problem solving
Column Addition	62-63	3-5 To add a column of 3 or more numbers	science-astronomy	mathematical reasoning
Problem Solving: Make an Organized List	64-65	3-6 To solve problems using the strategy Make an Organized List	science-Big Dipper	statistics
Front-End Estimation/Midchapter Review/Quiz	66-67	3-7 To estimate sums and differences	health/fitness-food choices	problem solving
Subtracting Whole Numbers: Making the Connection	68-69	3-8 To understand adding 2- and 3-digit numbers	social studies-partner skills	place value
Subtracting Whole Numbers	70-71	3-9 To subtract whole numbers of 2, 3, and 4 digits	science-space flights	calculators
Subtracting With Middle Zeros	72-73	3-10 To subtract with middle zeros	science-telescopes	mathematical reasoning
Mental Math: Using Compensation	74-75	3-11 To use compensation to find sums and differences	science-rocket launches	critical thinking
Problem Solving: Multiple-Step Problems	76-77	3-12 To solve multiple-step problems	health/fitness-lunch food	consumer math
Adding and Subtracting Larger Numbers: Using a Calculator	78-79	3-13 To add and subtract 4- and 5-digit numbers	science-planets	mathematical reasoning
Problem Solving: Deciding When to Estimate	80-81	3-14 To decide if you need an exact answer or an estimate	social studies-Fun Fair	consumer math
Applied Problem Solving: Group Decision Making	82-83	3-15 To analyze, organize, and make decisions	science-kittens	consumer math

MATHEMATICAL BACKGROUND

Addition
Place value models help students understand the process of adding larger numbers. Lesson 3-5 teaches students to add three or more numbers in a column.

Subtraction
Place value models are used to help students understand the process of trading in subtraction. Trading across a middle zero is taught in Lesson 3-10.

Estimation
Students learn two methods: rounding and front-end estimation.

Problem Solving
Students learn a new strategy—Make an Organized List. They also solve multiple-step problems and estimate.

TIPS FROM TEACHERS

Use the alphabet to play an addition game. Assign a money value to each letter: A = 1¢, B = 2¢, C = 3¢, . . . Challenge students to find a combination of letters or of words that add up to an amount between 95¢ and $1.05.

Floyd Flack
Cloverly School
Temple City, CA

Y = 25¢
O = 15¢
Y = 25¢
O = 15¢
S = 19¢
99¢

ASSESSMENT

Pretest — Chapter 3, page 1

Multiple-Choice Format

Name ____________

1. Use mental math to find 15,000 − 9,000.
   a. 600 b. 6,000 c. 2,400 d. 24,000 — 1. b
2. Estimate $5.78 − $3.29 by rounding to the nearest dollar.
   a. $2 b. $3 c. $9 d. $8 — 2. b
3. Find 165 + 129. Think: [Trade]
   a. 294 b. 36 c. 284 d. 46 — 3. a
4. Find 782 + 98.
   a. 770 b. 870 c. 780 d. 880 — 4. d
5. Find 458 + 129.
   a. 587 b. 507 c. 607 d. 577 — 5. c
6. Find 49 + 27 + 58.
   a. 114 b. 124 c. 134 d. 144 — 6. c
7. In the class play, Jorge wears disguises. He has 2 wigs and 3 hats. How many different ways can Jorge wear these disguises?
   a. 3 b. 5 c. 6 d. 9 — 7. c
8. Use front-end estimation to estimate 732 + 978.
   a. 170 b. 160 c. 1,700 d. 16,000 — 8. c

MCT 4 — 9

Pretest — Chapter 3, page 2

Multiple-Choice Format

Name ____________

9. Find 327 − 135. Think:
   a. 192 b. 212 c. 292 d. 112 — 9. a
10. Find 2,748 − 1,376.
    a. 1,372 b. 1,432 c. 1,478 d. 1,472 — 10. a
11. Find 847 − 508.
    a. 341 b. 339 c. 349 d. 338 — 11. b
12. Find 9,005 − 3,841.
    a. 6,844 b. 5,164 c. 6,264 d. 5,264 — 12. b
13. Use compensation to find 198 + 346.
    a. 546 b. 548 c. 544 d. 542 — 13. c
14. Eddie had 100 school play tickets to sell. His sister sold 26 and Eddie sold 35. How many were left to sell?
    a. 74 tickets b. 65 tickets c. 39 tickets d. 61 tickets — 14. c
15. Find 6,385 − 1,769.
    a. 4,616 b. 5,616 c. 5,424 d. 5,624 — 15. a
16. Decide whether you need an exact answer or an estimate. Allison has $5.00. She wants to buy toothpaste for $1.89 and a toothbrush for $1.58. Does she have enough money?
    a. Exact answer b. Estimate — 16. b

10 — MCT 4

Posttest — Chapter 3, page 1

Multiple-Choice Format

Name ____________

1. Use mental math to find 8,000 + 5,000.
   a. 1,300 b. 3,00 c. 13,000 d. 3,000 — 1. c
2. Estimate $3.45 + $2.74 by rounding to the nearest dollar.
   a. $5 b. $6 c. $7 d. $1 — 2. b
3. Find 235 + 156. Think: [Trade]
   a. 3,811 b. 381 c. 391 d. 3,881 — 3. c
4. Find 458 + 129.
   a. 587 b. 507 c. 607 d. 331 — 4. a
5. Find 673 + 118.
   a. 791 b. 781 c. 555 d. 705 — 5. a
6. Find 39 + 46 + 27.
   a. 112 b. 122 c. 102 d. 92 — 6. a
7. Keiko can choose from 2 kinds of bread–white or rye. Her 3 choices of meat are turkey, roast beef, or ham. How many different sandwiches can she make?
   a. 3 b. 4 c. 5 d. 6 — 7. d
8. Use front-end estimation to estimate 968 + 537.
   a. 149 b. 150 c. 1,500 d. 14,000 — 8. c

MCT 4 — 11

Posttest — Chapter 3, page 2

Multiple-Choice Format

Name ____________

9. Find 85 − 47. Think:
   a. 48 b. 38 c. 42 d. 122 — 9. b
10. Find 4,485 − 2,236.
    a. 2,251 b. 2,249 c. 2,259 d. 2,241 — 10. b
11. Find 319 − 97.
    a. 382 b. 282 c. 222 d. 322 — 11. c
12. Find 4,002 − 1,438.
    a. 3,436 b. 2,564 c. 3,674 d. 2,674 — 12. b
13. Use compensation to find 297 + 345.
    a. 542 b. 642 c. 645 d. 648 — 13. b
14. Dan had $5.00 He bought lunch for $2.59 and an apple after school for $0.35. How much money did he have left?
    a. $2.16 b. $3.06 c. $2.06 d. $2.94 — 14. c
15. Find 7,389 + 2,711.
    a. 10,000 b. 9,090 c. 10,100 d. 9,100 — 15. c
16. Decide whether you need an exact answer or an estimate. How much money will the cashier collect if you buy an item for $2.76 and another item for $4.68?
    a. Exact answer b. Estimate — 16. a

12 — MCT 4

ITEM ANALYSIS

Items	Objectives
1	3-1
2	3-2
3	3-3
4, 5	3-4
6	3-5
7	3-6
8	3-7
9	3-8
10, 11	3-9
12	3-10
13	3-11
14	3-12
15	3-13
16	3-14

Note: The item analysis is the same for all pretests and posttests for this chapter.

ALSO AVAILABLE

- Free Response Tests
- Alternative Tests
- Thinking Strategies
- Concrete Materials

Optional Chapter Activities

PROJECT AND BULLETIN BOARD

Display a map showing the imaginary route that the Jones family followed on their vacation driving from Springville to New City. Show the distance from one town to the next, but do not post the total mileage. Cut out the shape of a car from oaktag and use a pushpin to move the car to a new location each day that students work on this chapter. Students make entries on the chart showing the total distance the Joneses have traveled so far, how many miles they still have to go, and the total mileage traveled by the end of their trip. As students progress through the chapter, encourage them to practice strategies learned, such as finding special sums, estimating, and using compensation.

A second route can be posted showing a family heading home. The total distance is known and students subtract to find how much farther the family has to travel daily before reaching home.

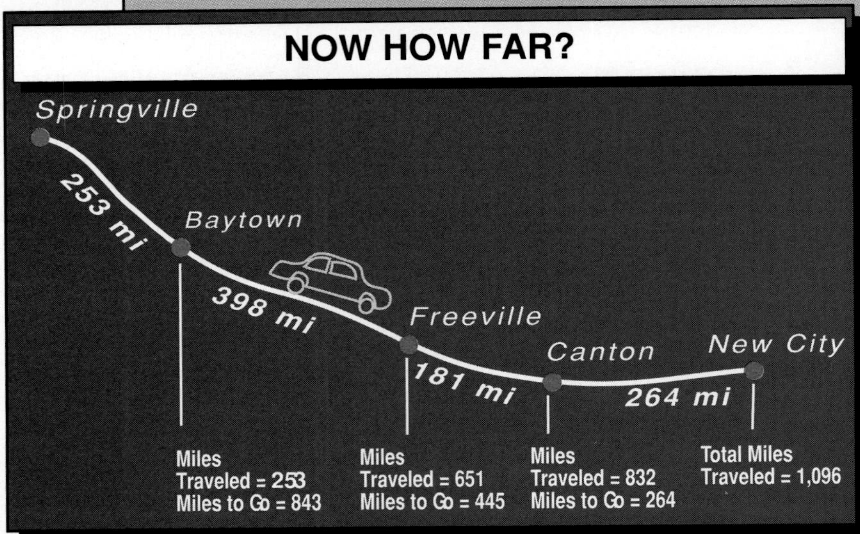

COOPERATIVE LEARNING

Divide the class into groups of three or four. Identify the group skill: check for understanding. Give each group an incomplete magic square and tell the group what the sum of each row and column should be. Assign a leader to make sure that everyone in the group understands how a magic square works. The numbers in all the rows and columns add up to the same sum. Have the group work together to complete the square. After each number has been chosen, the leader should check to make sure that the number works and that everyone in the group understands why the number was chosen.

You will find grouping suggestions and cooperative learning activities in most lessons throughout this chapter.

LITERATURE

Sachar, Louise. "Dana." from: *Sideways Stories From Wayside School.* New York: Avon Books, 1985.

In this humorous story, Dana is covered with mosquito bites. She informs her teacher that she is too itchy to even consider doing her math lessons. Cleverly, her teacher uses her bites to make up addition and subtraction problems.

Children could work in pairs creating their own number problems. One child could use a calculator, the other pencil and paper. They check each other's answers and then trade places.

Adler, David A. *Calculator Fun.* New York: Franklin Watts, 1981.

Sarnoff, Jane and Reynold Ruffins. *The Code and Cipher Book.* New York: Charles Scribner's Sons, 1975.

English as a Second Language

Include a vocabulary lesson in the introduction to each new concept to aid the ESL Student.

In this lesson, teach the word "digit." Begin by writing this definition on the chalkboard: **A digit is any one of the numerals 0, 1, 2, 3, 4, 5, 6, 7, 8, or 9.** Read the definition aloud with the class and then use the new word carefully. For example, you might say: *Five is a digit between four and six* or *Nine is the largest digit*. Then test for comprehension by asking follow-up questions, such as: *What is a digit between one and three? What is the smallest digit?*

Allow preproduction students to answer by pointing or writing. Then write a 2-digit number, such as 24, and ask: *What are the digits in the number 24?* Have students point to each digit as they say them. Continue by having students practice identifying digits in other 2- and 3-digit numbers.

Gifted

Have the students work in pairs. Pairs prepare 30 index cards that each have a different 4-digit number. The students shuffle the cards and place them face down in a pile. Each partner draws five cards. They list the numbers on the cards on a sheet of paper for column addition, then estimate the total and write down the estimate. They then compute the actual total and compare it with the estimate. Partners exchange their papers to check each other's work.

Students repeat this process for another two rounds. Students may want to use an egg timer or stop watch to see how quickly they can do the column addition. Accuracy counts! Have students award themselves a point for each correct addition answer.

Students at Risk

Learning disabled students make many computation errors due to weak spatial and/or visual organization. As these students work with larger numbers that often require several trades, the need for visual and spatial organizational aids increases. Provide structured worksheets that offer color- or design-coding, or boxes that highlight aspects of the addition and subtraction process.

For adding 3-digit numbers, highlight the ones place with a color or a simple symbol to visually emphasize the correct starting place. For subtraction, color highlight the top number to help students avoid the tendency to subtract any smaller digit from a larger one, regardless of position. Draw small boxes to remind students to record trades and to keep regrouped numbers aligned.

You may also use the Reteaching Supplements and the specific Reteaching Tips from each lesson in this chapter.

```
                      9
                   2 10 16
   926              306          611
   421            - 189         - 84
 + 725
```

CHAPTER 3

INTRODUCING THE CHAPTER

SUBJECT INTEGRATION The photograph of the telescope at Las Campanes Observatory represents the chapter theme of astronomy. Various lessons include facts about telescopes, planets, satellites, stars, and space flight to provide situations for whole-number addition and subtraction.

USING DATA The Science Data Bank on page 470 of the Student Edition provides a table entitled "Planets in Our Solar System." The data compares the length of orbit, number of satellites, and diameter of the nine known planets. A model shows the planets in size proportion and in order of distance from the Sun.

QUESTION 1 ▶ **Identify the column in the table that has the data you need to answer the question.** (*Number of Earth Days to Go Around the Sun*)
▶ **Identify the number of days it takes Earth to go around the Sun and relate that measure to a unit you know.** (365 days; 1 year)
Student Edition answer: Mercury, Venus; all other planets—Mars, Jupiter, Saturn, Uranus, Neptune, Pluto

3 ADDITION AND SUBTRACTION OF WHOLE NUMBERS

MATH AND SCIENCE
DATA BANK

Use the Science Data Bank on page 470 to answer the questions. See teaching notes.

1 Name two planets that take less time than Earth to go around the sun. Name two planets that take more time.

TEACHING OPTIONS

LANGUAGE DEVELOPMENT
Write the word **diameter** on the chalkboard. Tell students that a soccer ball has a greater diameter than a golf ball, then ask them to infer the meaning of *diameter*. ("width of something round") Explain to students that although an object may not be perfectly round, its diameter is usually measured at the widest part. Have students use the word *diameter* to compare familiar objects. (Sample answer: A grapefruit has a greater diameter than a plum.)

2 In 1610, Galileo discovered 4 satellites of Jupiter with a simple telescope. How many more of Jupiter's satellites can now be seen?

3 List the names and diameters of the planets in order from smallest to largest.

4 **Use Critical Thinking** Which numbers in the chart about planets have probably been rounded? Which have not? Explain your thinking.

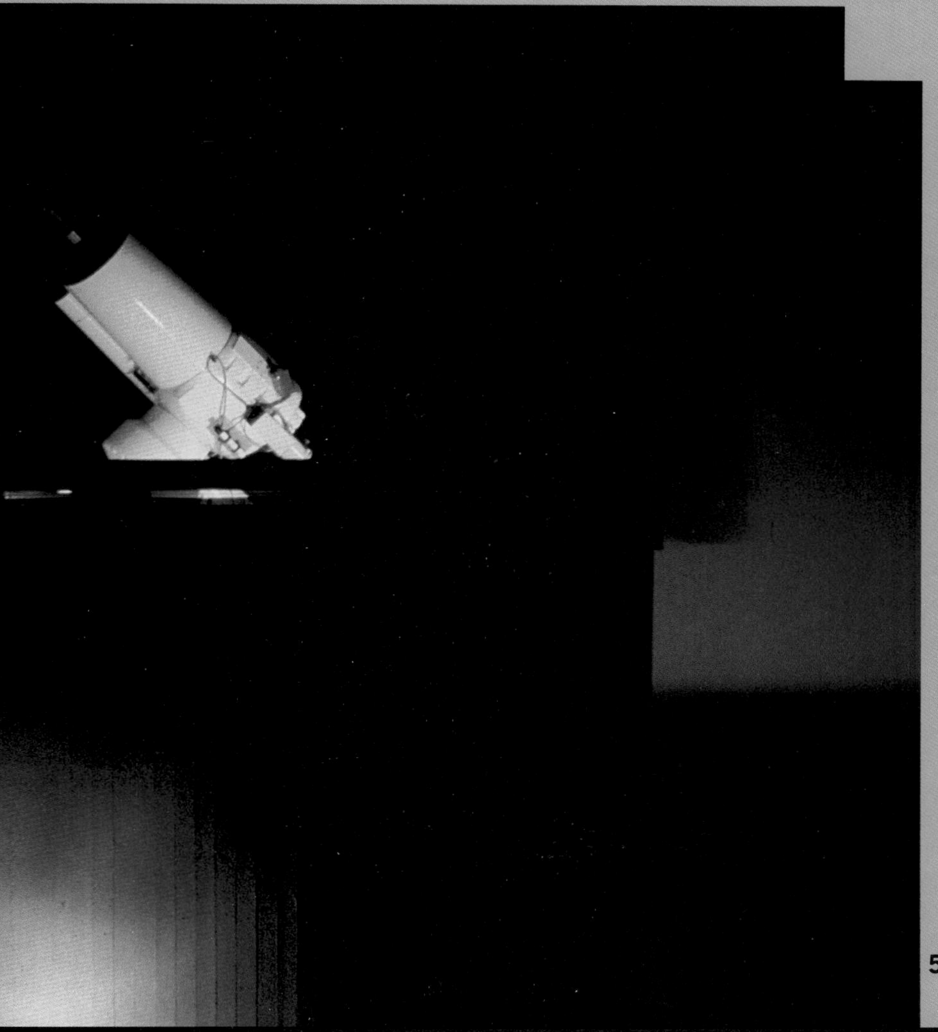

53

QUESTION 2 ► **Decide about how long ago Galileo made his discovery.** (about 400 years ago)
► **Explain the question in other words.** (Possible answer: Of all Jupiter's satellites, how many others have been found since Galileo found 4?)
Student Edition answer: 12

QUESTION 3 ► **Decide on a plan to use to answer Question 3.** (Possible answer: Look in the column *Diameter in km* for the smallest number, read across to see which planet it matches; keep finding each larger diameter until you rank all 9 planets.)
Student Edition answer: Pluto—3,000 km; Mercury—5,000 km; Mars—7,000 km; Venus—12,000 km; Earth—13,000 km; Neptune—45,000 km; Uranus—51,000 km; Saturn—121,000 km; Jupiter—143,000 km

QUESTION 4 ► **Compare the kinds of numbers given in the 3 columns of data.** (Column 1 has a variety of 2-through 5-digit numbers; column 2 numbers are the smallest, only from 0 to 23; column 3 has numbers to the nearest thousand or ten thousand.)
Student Edition answer: Diameters have probably been rounded because each ends with 3 zeros, and it is unlikely that all planets have diameters that measure to exact thousands. Satellite numbers are probably exact because they are too small to need rounding. Days around the Sun seems to use exact numbers except for Pluto, which seems rounded because of the zeros in the tens and ones places.

SUBJECT INTEGRATION PROJECT Have small groups of students "adopt" a planet, then use library resources to research data about their chosen planet, such as its size, weight, minimum and maximum distance from the Sun, length of rotation, temperature, color, orbital speed, and any other interesting data. Groups begin by selecting a planet and brainstorming to formulate a list of questions they would like to answer. Allow research time as students work through Chapter 3. Conclude by having a planet show in which groups present data orally.

LESSON OPTIONS 3-1

Mental Math: Special Sums and Differences

OBJECTIVE 3-1 To use mental math to find sums and differences of multiples of 10 and 100

PREBOOK ACTIVITIES

QUICK REVIEW

Add or subtract.

1. 6 + 7 (13) **2.** 7 + 7 (14) **3.** 3 + 9 (12)
4. 15 − 6 (9) **5.** 11 − 8 (3) **6.** 18 − 9 (9)
7. 5 + 6 (11) **8.** 15 − 8 (7) **9.** 12 − 9 (3)

PRIOR KNOWLEDGE

Write the term **mental math** on the chalkboard. Have students explain the term in their own words. (Possible answer: solving problems in your head without pencil, paper, or calculators) Ask for real-life situations in which students have used mental math. (Possible answer: to total a purchase price at a store) Have them describe any strategies they know to do mental math. (Possible answers: finding doubles or tens, compensating, changing grouping or order) Have a volunteer state the grouping principle for addition. (Numbers are grouped in any order; sum remains the same.)

COMMUNICATION

Discussing and Reading Math Under the heading **Compatible** write *pitcher* and *catcher, peanut butter* and *jelly, movies* and *popcorn*. Have students deduce what *compatible* means. (goes well together) Then have them infer what the mental math strategy of finding **compatible numbers** is. (Compatible numbers are pairs of numbers whose sum is easy to find in your head.) Have students give examples of compatible numbers whose sum is 100. (Possible answers: 50 + 50, 40 + 60)

EXPLORE AND CONNECT

Materials: TA 11 (Blank Spinner—divide into quarters showing ones, tens, hundreds, and thousands), flashcards with addition and subtraction facts

Grouping Suggestion: cooperative learning groups of four

Have students take turns at each task. One student spins to pick the place value, and another student selects a flashcard. A third student adjusts the fact to suit the place value, stating the problem aloud and completing it with the sum or difference. For example, if the spinner shows *tens* with a flashcard for 14 − 9, a student says, "14 tens minus 9 tens equals 5 tens." A fourth student then records the problem by writing **14**0 − **9**0 = **5**0. Other group members verify the answer, helping as needed. As a variation, have students make up three numbers of a given place value to add, such as 700 + 600 + 300. Encourage each group member to look for pairs of **compatible numbers,** such as 700 + 300.

CONNECTIONS Use these anytime.

Problem of the Day

Subtracting Ten How many times can you subtract 10 from 129? Explain your reasoning. (You can subtract 10 twelve times, which leaves 9. 9 is not enough to subtract another 10.) Try it using your calculator.

Math Connection

Geometry Use mental math to find the total length of the three sides of the triangle below. (175 in.)

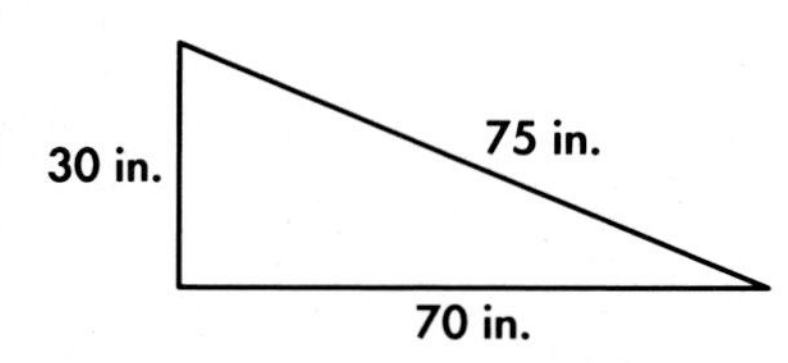

Subject Integration

Physical Education Pancho is a runner. He competes in the 1,500-meter race and in the 5,000-meter race. How many meters does he run in one day of competition? (6,500 meters)

Classwork and Homework Supplements

Practice

Mental Math 3-1

Name

Special Sums and Differences

Use mental math to find these sums and differences.

1. 40 + 50 = 90
2. 6,000 + 7,000 = 13,000
3. 900 − 200 = 700
4. 7,000 + 8,000 = 15,000
5. 14,000 − 8,000 = 6,000
6. 80 − 50 = 30
7. 1,200 − 400 = 800
8. 6,000 + 9,000 = 15,000
9. 5,000 + 4,000 = 9,000
10. 300 + 600 = 900
11. 9,000 − 7,000 = 2,000
12. 1,300 − 800 = 500
13. 700 + 500 = 1,200
14. 500 − 300 = 200
15. 2,000 + 9,000 = 11,000
16. 16,000 − 8,000 = 8,000
17. 10 + 9 + 10 = 29
18. 30 + 26 + 70 = 126
19. 87 + 90 + 10 = 187
20. 20 + 124 + 80 = 224
21. 50 + 50 + 312 = 412
22. 73 + 60 + 40 = 173

18 Use with text pages 54-55. PS-4

Building Thinking Skills

Family Math 3-1

Name

Spin and Formulate

Dear Family,
In our math class we have been learning about using mental math to find sums and differences of special numbers. Here is an activity you can do together.

Use pencils and paper clips to make 2 spinners like the ones below. Spin 1 number on each spinner. Create 1 addition and 1 subtraction problem with these numbers. Then show the mental math you could use to find the sum or difference. One example has been done for you.

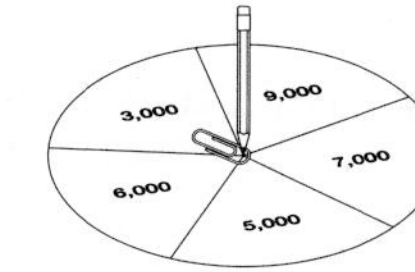

Example: 3,000 + 4,000 — Mental Math: 3 thousand + 4 thousand
4,000 − 3,000 — 4 thousand − 3 thousand

	Addition	Subtraction
1.		
2.		
3.		

18 Use with text pages 54-55. TS-4

Reteaching

Mental Math 3-1

Name

Special Sums and Differences

1 ten = 10 (1 zero)	1 hundred = 100 (2 zeros)	1 thousand = 1,000 (3 zeros)

To Find	Think	Say
70 + 50	7 + 5 tens = 12 tens	120
6,000 + 8,000	6 + 8 thousands = 14 thousands	14,000
1,200 − 300	12 − 3 hundreds = 9 hundreds	900
11,000 − 4,000	11 − 4 thousands = 7 thousands	7,000

Use mental math to fill in the blanks.

1. 60 + 70 = 6 + 7 tens = 13 tens = 130
2. 4,000 + 9,000 = 4 + 9 thousands = 13 thousands = 13,000
3. 600 − 500 = 6 − 5 hundreds = 1 hundred = 100

Use mental math to find these sums and differences.

4. 300 + 500 = 800
5. 3,000 − 2,000 = 1,000
6. 13,000 + 13,000 = 26,000
7. 24,000 − 10,000 = 14,000

Use mental math to find these sums and differences.

8. 500 + 400 = 900
9. 70 − 20 = 50
10. 12,000 − 3,000 = 9,000
11. 8,000 + 2,000 = 10,000
12. 17,000 − 9,000 = 8,000
13. 5,000 + 9,000 = 14,000
14. 40 + 30 = 70
15. 200 + 600 = 800
16. 13,000 − 5,000 = 8,000
17. 8,000 − 5,000 = 3,000

18 Use with text pages 54-55. RS-4

Challenges

Cooperative Activities 3-1

Name

Archery at Surewood Forest

Complete these challenges with a small group.

In the archery contest at Surewood Forest, Robin Hoodwink scored 140 points using two arrows. Little Juan said that Robin must have hit the bull's-eye. Prove that Little Juan is wrong by listing all the different ways the arrows could have landed. Let each person in your group contribute at least one way.

	Arrow 1	Arrow 2
1.	100 points	40 points
2.	90 points	50 points
3.	80 points	60 points
4.	70 points	70 points
5.	60 points	80 points
6.	50 points	90 points
7.	40 points	100 points

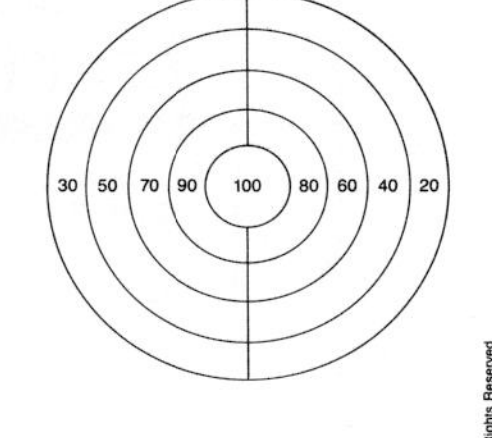

For the final contest, Robin Hoodwink used three arrows. Little Juan told him that to find his score, he could add the two points equaling 100 before adding the points from the third arrow. Try adding these scores and decide if Juan gave a good advice.

8. 20 + 40 + 80 = 140
9. 70 + 50 + 30 = 150
10. 30 + 60 + 40 = 130
11. 90 + 70 + 10 = 170
12. 50 + 20 + 50 = 120
13. 80 + 70 + 20 = 170

18 Use with text pages 54-55. CS-4

Options for Individual Needs

3-1

Basic

Exercises 1-5, 11-16, 14-26
Skills Bank, pp. 460-461
Calculator Bank, p. 484
More Practice, p. 501, set A

Supplements
Reteaching 18 or
Practice 18

Average

Exercises 1-26
Skills Bank, pp. 460- 461
Calculator Bank, p. 484
More Practice, p. 501, set A

Supplements
Practice 18
Challenges 18 or
Thinking Skills 18

Extended

Exercises 4-26
Calculator Bank, p. 484

Supplements
Challenges 18
Thinking Skills 18

Other Resources:
Problem-Solving Experiences in Mathematics, Grade 4, Problem 4
Math In Stride, Grade 4, p. 4

LESSON PLAN 3-1

OBJECTIVE 3-1
To use mental math to find sums and differences of multiples of 10 and 100

Materials: place value blocks, TA 7 (6-Digit Place Value Charts)

Alternative Materials: TA 6 (Place Value Models)

1. MOTIVATE AND TEACH

LEARN ABOUT IT

EXPLORE ► **What do the zeros mean in 600 and 300?** (no ones or tens)
► **How would you describe a special sum or difference?** (Sum or difference of numbers that are multiples of 10, 100, or 1,000.)

TALK ABOUT IT ► **How does adding only the hundreds relate to rules for breaking apart and grouping numbers?** (Break apart numbers into places, as in expanded form, then group and add place by place.)
► **What addition rules relate to compatible numbers?** (finding groups of 10; order; grouping)
► **Explain why you can subtract 400 from 700 by looking only at the hundreds place.** (There are no ones or tens.)
Student Edition answers: **1.** Apply 6 + 3 = 9 to 6 hundreds + 3 hundreds = 9 hundreds. **2.** Apply 7 − 4 = 3 to 7 hundreds − 4 hundreds = 3 hundreds.

2. CHECK UNDERSTANDING

TRY IT OUT

ERROR ALERT Using the wrong number of zeros with special sums or differences. Not noticing compatible number pairs.

Mental Math
Special Sums and Differences

LEARN ABOUT IT

EXPLORE Think About the Situation
To help you make good estimates, you need to be able to use mental math to find sums like 600 + 300. You can think about hundred-dollar bills to help you find such sums.

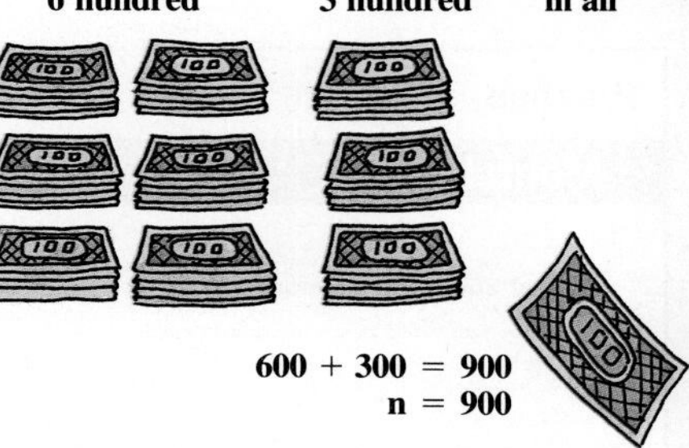

TALK ABOUT IT See teaching notes.

1. Explain how the sum of 6 and 3 helps you figure out the sum of 600 and 300 without using pencil and paper.
2. How would you use hundred-dollar bills to explain how to find 700−400?

You can use mental math to find special sums and differences by thinking about basic addition and subtraction facts.

To Find	Think	Say
90 + 70	9 + 7 tens	160
4,000 + 8,000	4 + 8 thousands	12,000
1,300 − 700	13 − 7 hundreds	600
16,000 − 9,000	16 − 9 thousands	7,000

To find the sum of 3 or more numbers, it sometimes helps to look for pairs of **compatible numbers** like 60 and 40 that can be easily found using mental math.

158
60 + 58 + 40

TRY IT OUT

Use mental math to find these sums and differences.

1. 80 + 50 **130**
2. 160 − 90 **70**
3. 400 + 800 **1,200**
4. 900 − 500 **400**
5. 1,600 − 700 **900**
6. 14,000 − 9,000 **5,000**
7. 50 + 96 + 50 **196**
8. 80 + 69 + 20 **169**

54

TEACHING OPTIONS

RETEACHING TIPS Using one kind of place value block or model per exercise, students should name the place on a 6-digit place value chart as they add or subtract, then write a zero after the sum or difference for each place to the *right* of it on the chart. Assign Reteaching Supplement 18.

ENRICHMENT Have students combine mental math strategies to find the sums.
1. 3,333 + 4,444 (7,777)
2. 8,888 + 2,000 (10,888)
3. 500 + 492 + 500 (1,492)
4. 3,000 + 4,000 + 7,000 + 4,000
5. 25,000 + 11,000 + 75,000
(Answers: **4.** 18,000; **5.** 111,000)

PRACTICE

Use mental math to find these sums and differences.

1. 80 + 50 = **130**	**2.** 7,000 + 8,000 = **15,000**	**3.** 900 − 400 = **500**	**4.** 7,000 + 3,000 = **10,000**	**5.** 15,000 − 9,000 = **6,000**
6. 90 − 50 = **40**	**7.** 1,600 − 700 = **900**	**8.** 12,000 − 3,000 = **9,000**	**9.** 3,000 + 5,000 = **8,000**	**10.** 400 + 900 = **1,300**
11. 50 + 40 = **90**	**12.** 4,500 − 300 = **4,200**	**13.** 800 − 200 = **600**	**14.** 2,300 + 400 = **2,700**	**15.** 600 − 200 = **400**

16. 50 + 78 + 50 **178** **17.** 80 + 256 + 20 **356** **18.** 96 + 60 + 40 **196**

APPLY

MATH REASONING Use mental math to find these sums and differences. Explain how you found each answer.

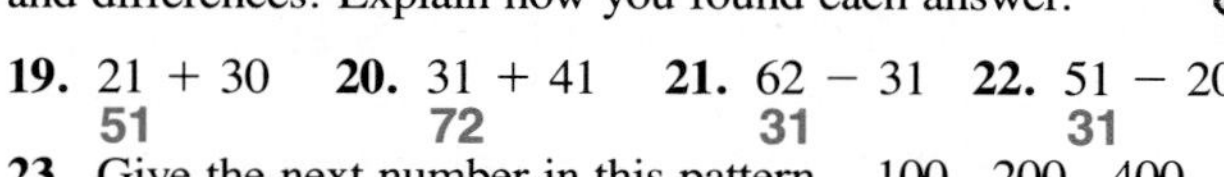

19. 21 + 30 **51** **20.** 31 + 41 **72** **21.** 62 − 31 **31** **22.** 51 − 20 **31**

23. Give the next number in this pattern. 100 200 400 700 **1,100**

PROBLEM SOLVING

24. Juan doubled his starting score and then scored 100 more points to get a total of 900 points. What was his starting score? **400 points**

25. Write Your Own Problem Use the following data to write a problem. Nan scored 800 points in the first game. She scored 500 points in the second game. **See Additional Answers.**

► **ALGEBRA**

26. A pair of numbers from this list has been written in the □ and △ to make a true number sentence. Show as many other ways as you can to do this.

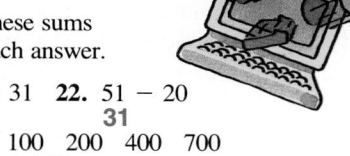

10	20	30	40	50	60	70	80	90

30 − 10, 40 − 20, 50 − 30, 60 − 40, 80 − 60, 90 − 70

More Practice, page 501, set A

3. PRACTICE AND APPLY

Basic	1-5, 11-16, 19-26
Average	1-26
Extended	4-26

Additional Answers: See p. T79.

PRACTICE

Look at Exercises 16-18. What will you be looking for to add first? (compatible numbers)

APPLY

MATH REASONING ► **What operation is used in Exercise 23? Explain.** (addition, because numbers get bigger)

PROBLEM SOLVING ► **How do you know to work backward in Problem 24?** (You are finding the starting score.)
► **Can you use addition or subtraction in Problem 25? Explain.** (both; add to find a total or subtract to compare scores)

ALGEBRA ► **Can □ and △ use the same number? Explain.** (No, because a number minus itself is always 0.)

3-1

CLOSE AND ASSESS

WRITE WHAT YOU THINK Ask each student to write a letter to a friend, telling how to find special sums and differences. In the letter, students should explain the thinking process involved and tell how to use basic addition and subtraction facts and compatible numbers. (Check students' writing.)

QUICK QUIZ

Make up an addition problem that uses each number as one of two compatible numbers: 50, 80, 400, and 1,200. Solve each problem. (Answers will vary. Check students' work.)

LESSON OPTIONS 3-2

Estimating Sums and Differences

OBJECTIVE 3-2 To use the estimation technique of rounding to estimate sums and differences

PREBOOK ACTIVITIES

QUICK REVIEW

Round to the nearest ten and nearest hundred.
1. 265 (270; 300) **2.** 612 (610; 600)
3. 975 (980; 1,000) **4.** 3,752 (3,750; 3,800)
Round to the nearest thousand.
5. 5,297 (5,000) **6.** 9,872 (10,000)
7. 25,388 (25,000) **8.** 584,673 (585,000)

PRIOR KNOWLEDGE

Have students share what they already know about rounding and estimation. (Possible responses: rounding to the nearest ten, hundred, thousand, and dollar; estimating money amounts using reference points) Have them relate rounding and estimation. (Possible response: Like estimates, rounded numbers are not exact amounts.) Ask students for examples of situations in which rounding might be useful. (Answers will vary.)

COMMUNICATION

Discussing and Reading Math Write the following sentence on the chalkboard: When you **estimate** a sum, be sure your **estimate** is reasonable. Read the sentence aloud. Have students compare the two uses of the word *estimate*. (Though spelled alike and related in meaning, they are pronounced differently.) Discuss with students the meaning of the verb and the noun. (The verb means to determine an amount close to an exact amount; the noun names that amount.) Ask students to suggest verb and noun synonyms for estimate. (verb: *guess, approximate;* noun: *approximation*)

EXPLORE AND CONNECT

Materials: blank index cards
Grouping Suggestion: small cooperative learning groups
Give each group member two blank index cards. Have each write a 2-digit number on one and a 3-digit number on the other. Groups then shuffle all members' cards together and stack them face down. A student draws two cards, reads them, then rounds the numbers to the nearest ten or hundred, based on the number of places in the smaller number. Another student records the rounded numbers while others verify the rounding. A third student **estimates** the sum or difference of the numbers. Groups earn 1 point for **estimated** sums of 1,000 or more *or* for differences of 300 or less. (Encourage students to discuss whether adding or subtracting will earn the group a point.) After students have determined whether a point can be scored, the round ends. A new round begins with two new cards and with students trading tasks.

CONNECTIONS Use these anytime.

Problem of the Day

Rounding Riddle Find 2 numbers to fit all these rules: 1) To the nearest ten and hundred, both round to the same number. 2) The estimated sum is 200. 3) The estimated difference is 0. (any 2 numbers from 95 to 104)

Life Skills

Checkbook Marla adds $409 to the $287.59 in her checking account. She owes 3 bills, totaling around $700. Can she pay them? Explain. (Not all 3; although the sum of her checking account balance and deposit rounds to $700, she will really have under $700, which may not cover her bills in *full*.)

Number Sense

Estimation Gizmo the Great has $50 to spend at the magic shop. If a set of magic rings costs $37.50, how many $5 silk scarves can Gizmo also afford? (2)

Classwork and Homework Supplements

Practice

Estimation 3-2

Name ______________________

Estimating Sums and Differences

Estimate the sum or difference. Answers may vary. Sample answers given.

1. 56 + 34 → 60 + 30 = 90
2. 28 + 51 → 30 + 50 = 80
3. 67 − 36 → 70 − 40 = 30
4. 83 + 66 → 80 + 70 = 150
5. 59 − 15 → 60 − 20 = 40
6. 71 − 28 → 70 − 30 = 40
7. 75 + 23 → 80 + 20 = 100
8. 88 + 12 → 90 + 10 = 100
9. 326 + 198 → 300 + 200 = 500
10. 828 − 594 → 800 − 600 = 200
11. 485 + 509 → 500 + 500 = 1,000
12. 603 − 186 → 600 − 200 = 400
13. 592 − 311 → 600 − 300 = 300
14. 458 + 279 → 500 + 300 = 800
15. 620 + 301 → 600 + 300 = 900
16. 295 + 831 → 300 + 800 = 1,100
17. \$5.58 + 3.16 → \$6.00 + 3.00 = \$9.00
18. \$5.15 − 1.88 → \$5.00 − 2.00 = \$3.00
19. \$6.11 − 2.77 → \$6.00 − 3.00 = \$3.00
20. \$7.72 + 1.38 → \$8.00 + 1.00 = \$9.00
21. 8,525 + 2,606 → 9,000 + 3,000 = 12,000
22. 6,283 + 1,796 → 6,000 + 2,000 = 8,000
23. 4,322 + 1,709 → 4,000 + 2,000 = 6,000
24. 6,432 − 1,265 → 6,000 − 1,000 = 5,000

PS-4 Use with text pages 56-57. 19

Building Thinking Skills

Estimation 3-2

Name ______________________

Baseball Card-o-Rama

Estimate to solve each problem. Estimates will vary. Possible answers given.

1. Miguel has 376 baseball cards. Tony has 293 baseball cards. About how many more cards does Miguel have than Tony?
   about 100 cards
2. Stefan has about half the number of baseball cards that Miguel has. Miguel, Tony, and Stefan are going to a Baseball Card-o-Rama. About how many cards will they take altogether?
   about 900 cards
3. Many people attended the Baseball Card-o-Rama. There were 1,295 people from Illinois, 3,363 people from Michigan, and 2,642 people from Indiana. About how many people attended the Baseball Card-o-Rama?
   about 7,000 people
4. At the Baseball Card-o-Rama, Miguel spent \$8.27. Tony spent \$5.81, and Stefan spent about twice as much as Tony. About how much money did the boys spend altogether?
   about \$26
5. At the Baseball Card-o-Rama, the boys had lunch. It cost them about \$6. At the lunch stand, there were hamburgers, hot dogs, tacos, and pizza. Hamburgers cost \$2.89 each. Hot dogs cost \$1.05 each. Tacos cost \$1.79 each. Pizza cost \$1.25 a slice. Miguel bought a hamburger, and Tony bought a hot dog. What did Stefan buy?
   taco
6. It took 2 hours to travel to the Baseball Card-o-Rama. The boys spent 4 hours at the show and 45 minutes eating. It was 5 o'clock when they got back home. About what time did they leave in the morning?
   8 o'clock

TS-4 Use with text pages 56-57. 19

Reteaching

Mental Math 3-2

Name ______________________

Estimating Sums and Differences

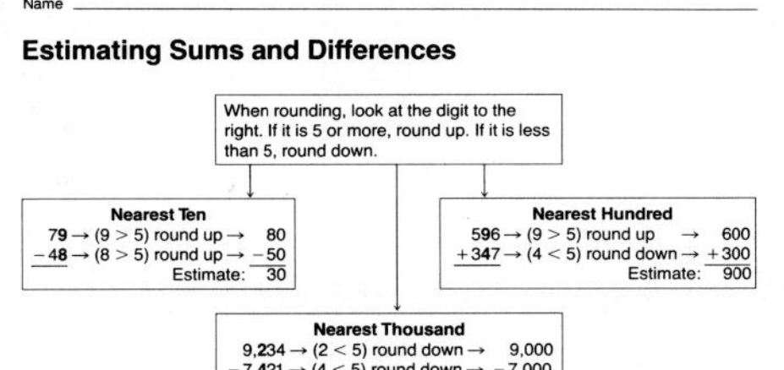

When rounding, look at the digit to the right. If it is 5 or more, round up. If it is less than 5, round down.
Nearest Ten
79 → (9 > 5) round up → 80
−48 → (8 > 5) round up → −50
Estimate: 30
Nearest Hundred
596 → (9 > 5) round up → 600
+347 → (4 < 5) round down → +300
Estimate: 900
Nearest Thousand
9,234 → (2 < 5) round down → 9,000
−7,421 → (4 < 5) round down → −7,000
Estimate: 2,000

Estimate the sum or difference.
Round to the nearest ten and then add or subtract.

1. 38 + 53 → 40 + 50 = 90
2. 32 + 88 → 30 + 90 = 120
3. 81 − 39 → 80 − 40 = 40

Round to the nearest hundred and then add or subtract.

4. 483 + 209 → 500 + 200 = 700
5. 325 − 225 → 300 − 200 = 100
6. 613 − 198 → 600 − 200 = 400

Round to the nearest thousand and then add or subtract.

7. 3,682 + 9,009 → 4,000 + 9,000 = 13,000
8. 8,698 − 7,598 → 9,000 − 8,000 = 1,000
9. 6,504 + 7,002 → 7,000 + 7,000 = 14,000

RS-4 Use with text pages 56-57. 19

Challenges

Estimation 3-2

Name ______________________

Four in a Row

Play this game with a partner.
Each player needs a set of about 10 markers.

Rules
When it is your turn:
1. Choose two numbers from the circle.
2. Estimate their sum or difference and find it on the game board.
3. Place a marker on the correct answer. (Only one marker can be on each numeral.)
4. The winner is the first player to get 4 markers in a row, across or down.

Circle: 33, 78, 61, 129, 152, 72, 48, 143

GAME BOARD

170	100	210	140	80	160
150	130	60	180	200	230
110	10	40	120	90	280
50	220	150	270	70	130
100	30	10	20	190	290

CS-4 Use with text pages 56-57. 19

Options for Individual Needs

Basic

Exercises 1-28
Computer Bank, p. 492
More Practice, p. 501, set B

Supplements
Reteaching 19 or
Practice 19

Average

Exercises 1-28
Computer Bank, p. 492
More Practice, p. 501, set B

Supplements
Practice 19
Challenges 19 or
Thinking Skills 19

Extended

Exercises 3-28
Computer Bank, p. 492

Supplements
Challenges 19
Thinking Skills 19

Other Resources:
Math In Stride, Grade 4, p. 229
Problem-Solving Experiences in Mathematics, Grade 4, Problem 36

LESSON PLAN 3-2

OBJECTIVE 3-2
To use the estimation technique of rounding to estimate sums and differences

Materials: calculators, TA 5 (4-Digit Place Value Charts)

1. MOTIVATE AND TEACH

LEARN ABOUT IT

EXPLORE ► **Are the computer game scores rounded or exact numbers? Explain.** (probably exact, because they do not end in zeros)
► **Would you add or subtract to solve Pat's problem? Explain.** (Add to find a total.)

TALK ABOUT IT ► **Why does it make sense to round the scores to the nearest hundred rather than to the nearest ten?** (Both numbers are in the hundreds.)
► **Do the scores round up or down? Explain how this could affect the total.** (226 rounds down; 297 rounds up. 297 is very close to 300, so the total should be more than 500.)
Student Edition answers: **1.** 200, 300 **2.** The score in Game 1 rounds down to 200, but it still has 26 additional points. The score in Game 2 is nearly 300. Therefore the total will be more than 500.

2. CHECK UNDERSTANDING

TRY IT OUT

ERROR ALERT Rounding numbers of unlike place value to different places. Confusing which digits round up or down.

Estimating Sums and Differences

LEARN ABOUT IT

EXPLORE Read the Information
Sometimes you only need to **estimate** an answer that is close to the exact answer. One way to estimate is to round the numbers before you add or subtract.

Pat played a computer game. The computer showed the points for each game. Pat wanted to score over 500 points in two games.

TALK ABOUT IT See teaching notes.

1. To the nearest hundred, how many points did Pat score in the first game? in the second game?
2. Do you think the total number of points is more or less than 500? Explain.

You can estimate a sum or difference by rounding the numbers to the highest place of the smaller number and then adding or subtracting.

Nearest Ten	Nearest Hundred	Nearest Thousand
161 → 160	789 → 800	8,798 → 9,000
− 74 → − 70	+ 518 → + 500	− 4,559 → − 5,000
Estimate: 90	Estimate: 1,300	Estimate: 4,000

You can also estimate dollar amounts by rounding to the nearest dollar.

$6.57 → $7
+ $5.43 → + $5
Estimate: $12

TRY IT OUT

Estimate. Round to the highest place of the smaller number.

1.	2.	3.	4.	5.
143	697	4,246	$9.56	9,178
− 56	+ 436	+ 3,879	− 4.98	− 2,687
est. 80	est. 1,100	est. 8,000	est. $5.00	est. 6,000

56

TEACHING OPTIONS

RETEACHING TIPS For the first error, students should use a 4-Digit Place Value Chart to show addends. They identify the smaller number, name its highest place, then circle that place in both numbers. They round both numbers to the named place, then add or subtract. Assign Reteaching Supplement 19.

ENRICHMENT Ask students to solve this problem: *Suppose your parent's car weighs 2,895 pounds. Estimate the total weight, car included, if your whole family were out for a drive. Record the steps you use to find your estimate and explain your reasoning.* (Solutions will vary.)

PRACTICE

Estimate the sum or difference. Answers may vary. Sample answers are given.

1.	2.	3.	4.	5.	6.
78 + 53 = 130	43 − 29 = 10	52 + 169 = 220	472 − 309 = 200	17 + 82 = 100	614 − 264 = 300

7.	8.	9.	10.	11.	12.
823 − 396 = 400	914 − 573 = 300	789 + 127 = 900	\$2.41 − 1.07 = \$1.00	421 − 333 = 100	2,473 + 536 = 3,000

13.	14.	15.	16.	17.	18.
\$8.65 + 5.29 = \$14.00	4,741 − 2,098 = 3,000	7,343 − 2,196 = 5,000	3,731 − 1,602 = 2,000	5,264 + 7,913 = 13,000	\$9.29 − 4.75 = \$4.00

APPLY

MATH REASONING Without finding the sums, decide which is greater.

19. 29 + 19 or 31 + 21 **20.** 59 + 34 or 56 + 26 **21.** 72 + 46 or 82 + 44

PROBLEM SOLVING

22. Data Hunt Find your weight in pounds. Choose a partner. Estimate the sum of your weights and the difference of your weights. Answers will vary.

23. Tim weighed 127 pounds and Tami weighed 89 pounds. About what was the difference of their weights? about 40 pounds

24. Jeff weighs more than Ann. Tina weighs less than Ann. Meg weighs more than Jeff. Who weighs most? Meg

▶ CALCULATOR

Draw squares like this and write the digits 4, 5, 6, 7, 8, and 9 in them to make these sums. Use your calculator to check.

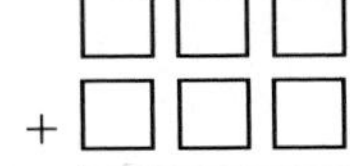

25. the largest sum possible 1,839

26. the smallest sum possible 1,047

27. the sum as close to 1,500 as possible 1,506

28. the sum as close to 2,000 as possible 1,839

More Practice, page 501, set B

3. Practice and Apply

Basic	1-28
Average	1-28
Extended	3-28

PRACTICE

Look at Exercise 12. What rule about rounding do you need to remember? (to round both numbers to the highest place in the smaller number)

APPLY

MATH REASONING ▶ Explain how two sets of addends could have the same rounded sums yet have different exact sums. (Possible answer: Rounded numbers are determined by a range within which numbers fall, so two numbers that are just slightly different might fall within the range for the same rounded number.)

PROBLEM SOLVING ▶ How can you do Problem 22 without knowing your exact weight? (Possible answer: Estimate it using the weight of someone about your size.)

CALCULATOR ▶ How can estimation help with Exercises 27 and 28? (Estimate addends with sums of 1,500 and 2,000.)

Close and Assess

WRITE WHAT YOU THINK Ask students to play the teacher. Have them write the steps, in order, that they would use to show a class of fourth graders how to use rounding to estimate a sum or a difference. They should also give several examples. (Check students' writing and examples.)

Quick Quiz

Estimate the sum or difference.

1. 86 − 43 (50)
2. 588 + 936 (1,500)
3. 6,338 + 7,701 (14,000)
4. \$8.33 − \$1.70 (\$6.00)

LESSON OPTIONS 3-3

Adding Whole Numbers: Making the Connection

OBJECTIVE 3-3 To use objects to develop an understanding of adding 3-digit numbers

PREBOOK ACTIVITIES

QUICK REVIEW

Add mentally.

1.	60 + 80	(140)	**2.**	300 + 600	(900)
3.	800 + 700	(1,500)	**4.**	40 + 90	(130)
5.	90 + 90	(180)	**6.**	120 + 50	(170)
7.	310 + 310	(620)	**8.**	250 + 250	(500)
9.	500 + 700	(1,200)	**10.**	20 + 90	(110)

PRIOR KNOWLEDGE

Have students name the 3 places in the ones period, from least to greatest. (ones, tens, hundreds) Ask them to recall the rules of trading in addition. (Possible answer: Whenever you have 10 or more in a certain place, trade for 1 of the next-greater place.) Ask students when they might have to add 2- or 3-digit numbers. (Possible answer: when totaling shopping purchases)

COMMUNICATION

Writing and Discussing Math Write the word **trade** on the chalkboard and have students write synonyms for it in their Math Journals. (Possible answers: *exchange, switch, swap, convert*) Have students explain what justifies a fair trade. (if both quantities in the trade are equivalent) Have students predict a problem that would arise if they added without making necessary trades. (Possible answer: It would be difficult to record the sum in a meaningful way.)

EXPLORE AND CONNECT

Materials: place value blocks, TA 3 (Number Cards 0-9), TA 5 (4-Digit Place Value Charts)
Alternative Materials: TA 6 (Place Value Models)
Grouping Suggestion: cooperative learning pairs
Students explore addition by making up problems with various **trades.** Partners select 6 number cards, then form two 3-digit numbers to add with place value materials. The first problem should require *no trades,* such as 123 + 456 = 579. Partners discuss how to formulate the problem and how to show its addition with place value materials. Then partners create 4 other problems with *trades* as follows: (1) ones for a ten, (2) tens for a hundred, (3) hundreds for a thousand, (4) *trades* in all places. Partners alternate formulating and showing problems. Conclude by having students generalize how to predict when *trades* are needed. (whenever the sum in a place is 10 or more)

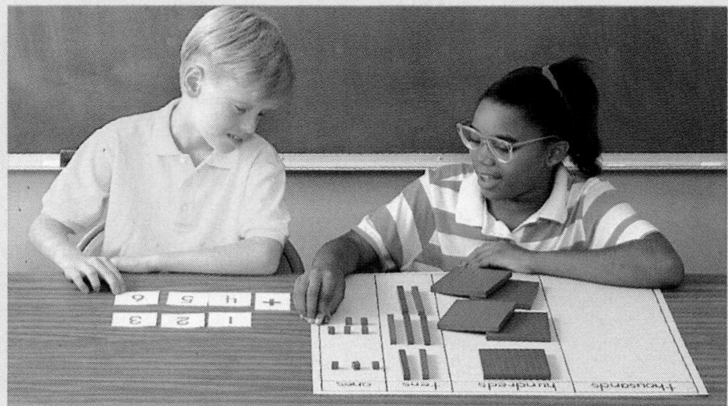

CONNECTIONS Use these anytime.

Problem of the Day

Lost and Found When Ms. Klein moved the math cupboard, she discovered some lost place value blocks behind it. She found 47 ones, 34 tens, and 10 hundreds. What is the total value of the lost blocks? (1,387)

Math Connection

Logical Reasoning All the missing digits are the same. What are the addends?

$$\begin{array}{r} \square\square \\ +\square\square \\ \hline 1\,3\,2 \end{array}$$

(66 + 66)

Patterns

Calculator Use a calculator to discover the pattern, then continue it 3 more times:
39, 68, 97, 126, (155), (184), (213)
(Pattern: Add 29.)

CLASSWORK AND HOMEWORK SUPPLEMENTS

Practice

Manipulatives 3-3

Name ____________________

Adding Whole Numbers: Making the Connection

Use blocks to find the sum.

1. 254 + 163 = 417

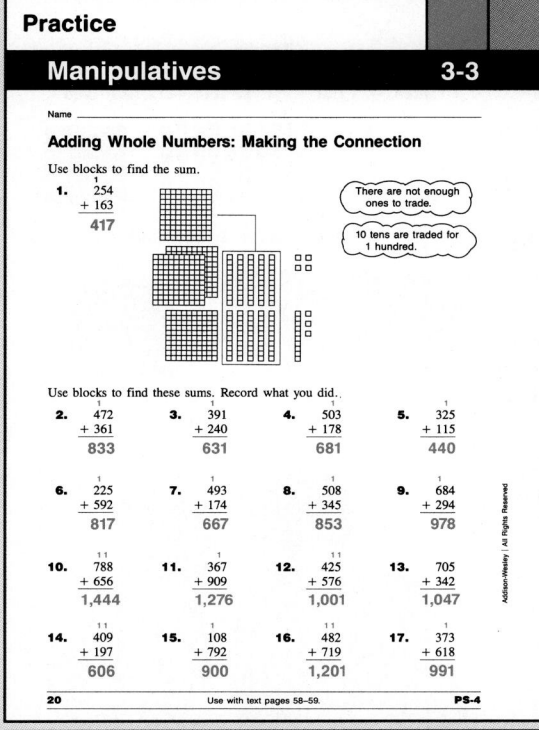

There are not enough ones to trade.

10 tens are traded for 1 hundred.

Use blocks to find these sums. Record what you did.

2. 472 + 361 = 833	**3.** 391 + 240 = 631	**4.** 503 + 178 = 681	**5.** 325 + 115 = 440
6. 225 + 592 = 817	**7.** 493 + 174 = 667	**8.** 508 + 345 = 853	**9.** 684 + 294 = 978
10. 788 + 656 = 1,444	**11.** 367 + 909 = 1,276	**12.** 425 + 576 = 1,001	**13.** 705 + 342 = 1,047
14. 409 + 197 = 606	**15.** 108 + 792 = 900	**16.** 482 + 719 = 1,201	**17.** 373 + 618 = 991

Building Thinking Skills

Math Reasoning 3-3

Name ____________________

It's How You Play the Game

This is a game of skill and strategy for two people. The object is to accumulate as many points as you can.

You will need: two number cubes, pencil and paper.

To play:

- Each player starts with the number 100.
- Take turns. Roll the two number cubes to form a 2-digit number. *Either digit may be in either place*—it is the player's decision.
- The player adds this number to his or her number.
- The game ends when one player reaches a sum of 500.

To score:

- Reaching at least 500 is worth 50 points.
- Along the way to 500, reaching any of these numbers *exactly* is worth 10 points: 150, 200, 250, 300, 350, 400, 450.
- Reaching any of these numbers is worth 20 points: 111, 222, 333, 444.

Example:

Suppose you have 299 and you roll a 4 and a 3. Add 43, and you will get closer to 500. But if you add 34, you will get 333, a number worth 20 points. Which would you do?

The first player to reach 500 is the winner. If both players have not had an equal number of turns when 500 has been reached, the second player may roll again to try for a tie.

Reteaching

Manipulatives 3-3

Name ____________________

Adding Whole Numbers: Making the Connection

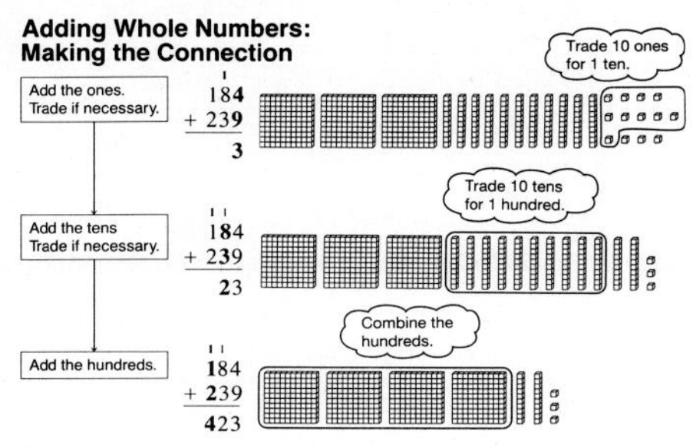

Use blocks to find these sums. Record what you did.

1. 758 + 65 = 823 **2.** 467 + 474 = 941 **3.** 683 + 287 = 970

Use blocks to find these sums.

4. 568 + 284 = 852 (1 + 5 + 2 = 8 Trade? no) **5.** 168 + 540 = 708 (6 + 4 = 10 Trade?) **6.** 437 + 478 = 915 (7 + 8 = 15 Trade? no)

7. 457 + 386 = 843 **8.** 528 + 396 = 924 **9.** 403 + 279 = 682 **10.** 268 + 540 = 808 **11.** 664 + 258 = 922

Challenges

Manipulatives 3-3

Name ____________________

The Letter Store

Gena's Letter Store sells letters at the following prices.

A $50	E $54	I $58	M $62	Q $66	U $70	Y $74
B $51	F $55	J $59	N $63	R $67	V $71	Z $75
C $52	G $56	K $60	O $64	S $68	W $72	
D $53	H $57	L $61	P $65	T $69	X $73	

Complete each chart. Estimate first. Then use place value blocks to help you find the exact sum.

1. Write some words that cost more than $100 but less than $175.

Word	Estimated Cost	Exact Cost

2. Write some 3-letter words that cost more than $188.

Word	Estimated Cost	Exact Cost

3. How much would your first name cost? ____________

OPTIONS FOR INDIVIDUAL NEEDS

Basic

Exercises 1-5
Skills Bank, p. 460
Calculator Bank, pp. 484, 485

Supplements
Reteaching 20 or
Practice 20

Average

Exercises 1-5
Skills Bank, p. 460
Calculator Bank, pp. 484, 485

Supplements
Practice 20
Challenges 20 or
Thinking Skills 20

Extended

Exercises 1-5
Calculator Bank, pp. 484, 485

Supplements
Challenges 20
Thinking Skills 20

Other Resources:
Problem-Solving Experiences in Mathematics, Grade 4, Problem 11
Math In Stride, Grade 4, pp. 1, 2

LESSON PLAN 3-3

OBJECTIVE 3-3
To use objects to develop an understanding of adding 3-digit numbers

Materials: TA 11 (Blank Spinners), place value blocks, TA 5 (4-Digit Place Value Charts), index cards

Alternative Materials: TA 6 (Place Value Models)

Grouping Suggestions: small groups, pairs

1. MOTIVATE AND TEACH

LEARN ABOUT IT

EXPLORE ► **Explain why groups must spin 3 times.** (They must spin once for each place.)
► **Explain what to show if a 0 is spun.** (0 in that place on the chart and no blocks of that value)

TALK ABOUT IT ► **Explain where to begin to make any possible trades.** (Begin with ones because it is the smallest place. If needed, trade ones for tens; tens for hundreds; hundreds for thousands.)
► **Do all problems require trades? Explain.** (No, only when the sum of any place is 10 or more.)
► **Relate the action of putting piles together to an operation. Explain your reasoning.** (addition, because the action represents making a total)
Student Edition answers: **1.** Answers will vary. **2.** 0 if the sum in each place is below 10; 3 if the sum in each place is 10 or more. **3.** The combined pile is the sum of the 2 numbers that represented the original piles.

2. CHECK UNDERSTANDING

ERROR ALERT Failing to make all possible trades.

Adding Whole Numbers
Making the Connection

LEARN ABOUT IT

EXPLORE Use a Place Value Model
Work in groups. Use a spinner with the digits 0–9 and make piles of blocks.

- Spin 3 times. The first spin gives the number of hundreds blocks for a pile. The second gives the number of tens and the third gives the number of ones. Make the pile and write the number for it in a table like the one given. Then repeat the steps.
- Push the two piles together and make all possible trades. When you get 10 or more of one type, trade for a larger block. Write the number for the resulting pile.
- Do this several times with different numbers.

Trades

10 ones = 1 ten 10 tens = 1 hundred

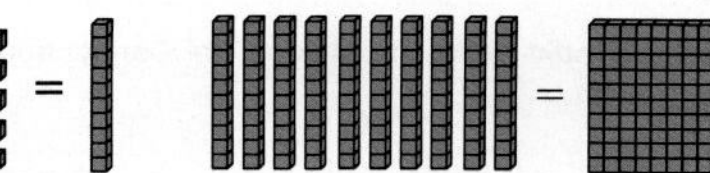

10 hundreds = 1 thousand

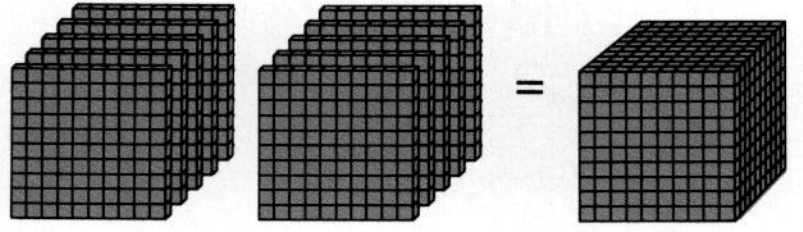

Put together and trade.

TALK ABOUT IT See teaching notes.

1. Use blocks and describe the trades that can be made.
2. Suppose you spin to make two piles of blocks and push them together. What are the smallest number of trades possible? the largest number? Explain using the blocks.
3. How does the number for the combined pile compare with the numbers for the original piles? Explain.

58

TEACHING OPTIONS

RETEACHING TIPS Each student writes this hint on an index card: 10 or more? If YES, then TRADE. They put the cards above each place on the place value chart as they put together blocks of that value. Before moving to the next place, they apply the hint. Assign Reteaching Supplement 20.

ENRICHMENT Have students use the digits 2, 4, and 6 as often as needed to formulate four 3-digit addition problems with 0, 1, 2, or 3 trades. Tell them to find the sums with place value materials, verify the number of trades they planned, and record what they do.

You have pushed blocks together, traded, and figured out how many in all. Now you will see a way to record what you have done. This process can help you find sums such as 382 + 256.

What You Do **What You Record**

1. Lay out the blocks.

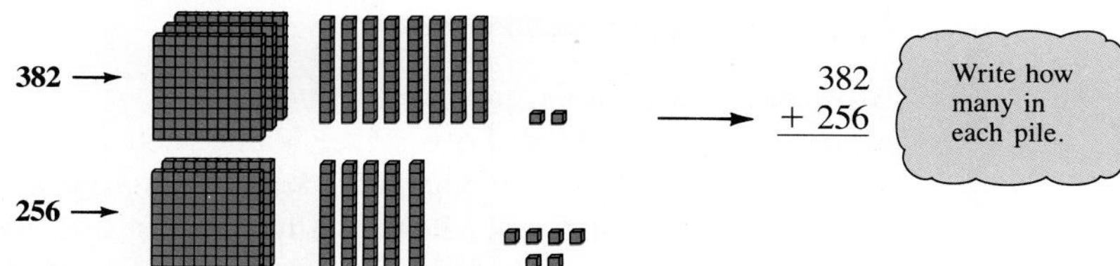

382
+ 256

Write how many in each pile.

2. Put the ones together. Trade if possible.

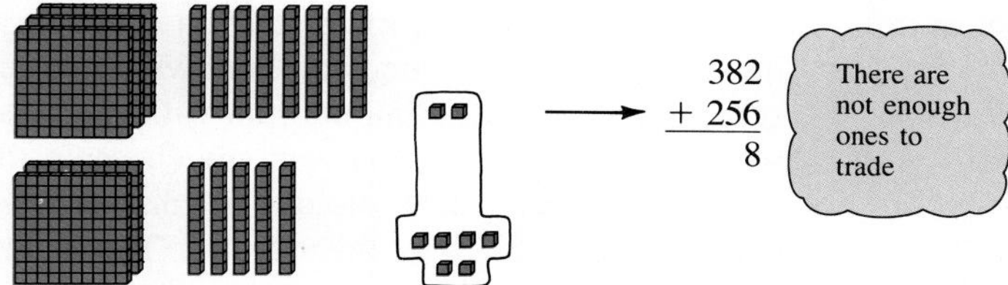

382
+ 256
8

There are not enough ones to trade

3. Put the tens together. Trade if possible.

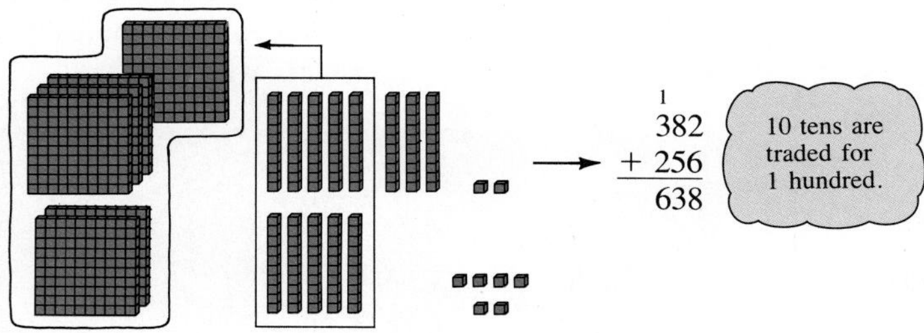

1
382
+ 256
638

10 tens are traded for 1 hundred.

TRY IT OUT

Use blocks to find these sums. Record what you did.

1. 53 + 29 **82** **2.** 173 + 48 **221** **3.** 358 + 276 **634** **4.** 367 + 475 **842**

5. Use blocks to find the sum of two 3-digit numbers of your choice. **See Additional Answers.**

59

Close and Assess

SHOW WHAT YOU KNOW

Have students work in pairs. The first student shows how to find the sum of 354 and 277, explaining each step to follow. Then the other student shows how to find the sum of 286 and 345, explaining the steps involved. (Both sums are 631.)

Quick Quiz

Find the sums. Use place value materials if necessary and record what you do.

1. 149 + 244 (393)
2. 475 + 428 (903)

3. Practice and Apply

Basic	1-5
Average	1-5
Extended	1-5

Additional Answers: See p. T79.

PRACTICE

Explain the connection between What You Do and What You Record on page 59. (Lay out models of 382 and 256 to be combined; write the same numbers in vertical form with a plus sign and a bar below the bottom number.) *Link the ones in the loop to the 8 below the bar.* (The loop has 8 ones; write 8 in the ones place of the problem.) *Explain the box around 10 tens with an arrow pointing to the hundreds place.* (8 tens and 5 tens are 13 tens; trade 10 tens for 1 hundred.) *How do you record the trade?* (Write a 1 over the hundreds place to show the trade; write the 3 other tens below the bar.) *What does 6 written under the bar in the hundreds place show?* (the addition of 1 traded hundred + 3 hundreds + 2 hundreds) *Continue working with a partner to complete the Try It Out exercises.*

LESSON OPTIONS 3-4

Adding Whole Numbers

OBJECTIVE 3-4 To add 3-digit numbers

PREBOOK ACTIVITIES

QUICK REVIEW

Estimate the sums. (Answers may vary. Sample answers given.)

1. 52 + 38 (90)
2. 25 + 53 (80)
3. 79 + 79 (160)
4. 411 + 388 (800)
5. 861 + 652 (1,600)
6. 46 + 348 (400)
7. 170 + 710 (900)
8. 993 + 972 (2,000)
9. 4,321 + 272 (4,600)
10. 741 + 1,025 (1,700)

PRIOR KNOWLEDGE

Have students suggest situations when they have added numbers. (Answers will vary. Samples: pages read; miles traveled; total cost) Have students tell different ways they know to find totals. (models; pencil and paper; mental math; calculator) Ask students to generalize about aspects of addition that would be the same regardless of the calculation method chosen. (Possible answers: the exact sum; combine places of the same value; make trades of 10 of a place for 1 of the next greater place.)

COMMUNICATION

Discussing Math Have students relate trades, place value, and numbers written in standard form. (Possible answer: You can write only 1 digit in any given place. When a place has 10 or more, you must trade 10 for 1 of the next greater place. Then you will be able to represent the sum in standard form.)

EXPLORE AND CONNECT

Materials: calculators, place value blocks
Alternative Materials: TA 6 (Place Value Models)
Grouping Suggestion: cooperative learning groups of 4
Students explore different calculation methods to find and compare sums. Write the following addends on the chalkboard: 77, 95, 129, 246, 364, 458. A group member selects 2 addends and uses them in an addition equation, such as 246 + 458 = ? That student finds the sum with a calculator, while other group members find the sum with place value materials, with paper and pencil, and with any chosen estimation strategy. Students compare sums, discuss any discrepancies, and evaluate the accuracy of the estimate. They trade tasks and repeat the activity three times, then generalize about adding 2 numbers with a different number of places. (Line up places to get the correct sum.) Have students tell the calculation method they prefer and why. (Answers will vary.)

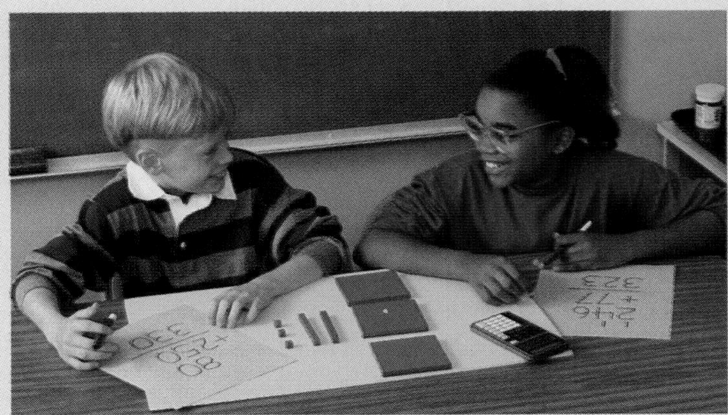

CONNECTIONS Use these anytime.

Problem of the Day

Logical Reasoning Find the missing digits.

```
  □ □ 7
+ 5 4 □
-------
  8 7 5
```

Number Sense

Mental Math Determine a quick way to find the sum of the following numbers. Explain your method.
1 + 2 + 3 + 4 + 5 + 6 + 7 + 8 + 9 = ? (Possible answer: 1 + 9, 2 + 8, 3 + 7, and 4 + 6 all equal 10; 4 tens is 40; add the unpaired 5 to get 45)

Life Skills

Bus Fare Diego and his mother plan a bus trip to another city. A regular adult fare is $66.00 and a child's fare is half that. But they could buy a family Night Owl pass for the 2 of them for $99.50 if they travel after 9:00 p.m. Decide which fare is better. (Diego and his mother would pay $99 for regular tickets, so the special fare actually costs $0.50 more.)

Classwork and Homework Supplements

Practice

Skills Maintenance 3-4

Name ______

Adding Whole Numbers

Find the sums.

1. 64 + 59 = 123
2. 67 + 84 = 151
3. 658 + 82 = 740
4. 849 + 689 = 1,538
5. 429 + 873 = 1,302
6. 4,614 + 3,747 = 8,361
7. 168 + 96 = 264
8. 489 + 578 = 1,067
9. 2,937 + 1,758 = 4,695
10. 5,807 + 956 = 6,763
11. 238 + 77 = 315
12. 6,821 + 59 = 6,880
13. $7.43 + 5.48 = $12.91
14. $74.36 + 7.45 = $81.81
15. $56.21 + 33.79 = $90.00
16. $6.24 + 0.87 = $7.11
17. $8.43 + 6.69 = $15.12
18. $57.65 + 39.38 = $97.03
19. $67.63 + 7.77 = $75.40
20. $20.64 + 53.47 = $74.11
21. 526 + 83 = 609
22. 9,758 + 162 = 9,920
23. 5,941 + 3,864 = 9,805
24. $0.46 + $3.88 = $4.34
25. $26.53 + $61.74 = $88.27
26. $54.08 + $30.29 = $84.37

Building Thinking Skills

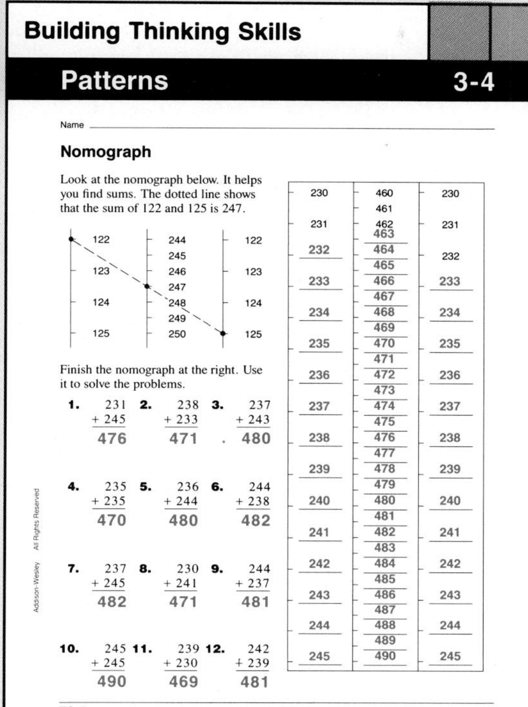

Patterns 3-4

Name ______

Nomograph

Look at the nomograph below. It helps you find sums. The dotted line shows that the sum of 122 and 125 is 247.

Finish the nomograph at the right. Use it to solve the problems.

1. 231 + 245 = 476
2. 238 + 233 = 471
3. 237 + 243 = 480
4. 235 + 235 = 470
5. 236 + 244 = 480
6. 244 + 238 = 482
7. 237 + 245 = 482
8. 230 + 241 = 471
9. 244 + 237 = 481
10. 245 + 245 = 490
11. 239 + 230 = 469
12. 242 + 239 = 481

Reteaching

Skills Review 3-4

Name ______

Adding Whole Numbers

Add the ones. Trade if necessary. → Add the tens. Trade if necessary. → Add the hundreds.

H	T	O
	6	8	7

687 + 245: 7 + 5 = 12 ones = 1 ten 2 ones → 2; 1 + 8 + 4 = 13 tens = 1 hundred 3 tens → 32; 1 + 6 + 2 = 9 hundreds → 932

Find the sums.

1. 37 + 48 = 85 (7 + 8 = 15 Trade.)
2. 347 + 82 = 429 (4 tens + 8 tens = 12 tens)
3. 208 + 564 = 772 (8 + 4 = 12 ones)
4. 376 + 214 = 590
5. 734 + 562 = 1,296
6. 475 + 538 = 1,013
7. 6,321 + 2,789 = 9,110
8. $68.75 + 94.88 = $163.63
9. 286 + 485 = 771
10. $42.79 + 99.54 = $142.33
11. 681 + 608 = 1,289
12. 926 + 85 = 1,011
13. 4,627 + 3,895 = 8,522

Line up the ones digit. Then add.

14. 436 + 872 = 1,308
15. 9,234 + 398 = 9,632
16. $73.00 + $42.85 = $115.85

Challenges

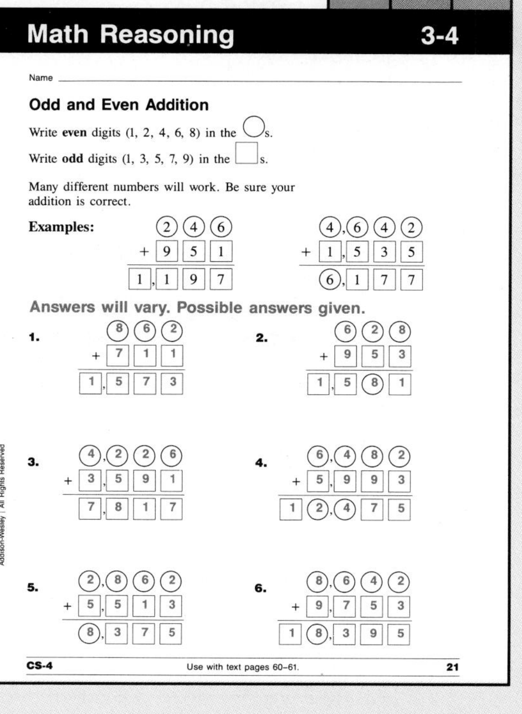

Math Reasoning 3-4

Name ______

Odd and Even Addition

Write **even** digits (1, 2, 4, 6, 8) in the ○s.

Write **odd** digits (1, 3, 5, 7, 9) in the □s.

Many different numbers will work. Be sure your addition is correct.

Examples: 246 + 951 = 1,197; 4,642 + 1,535 = 6,177

Answers will vary. Possible answers given.

1. 862 + 711 = 1,573
2. 628 + 953 = 1,581
3. 4,226 + 3,591 = 7,817
4. 6,482 + 5,993 = 12,475
5. 2,862 + 5,513 = 8,375
6. 8,642 + 9,753 = 18,395

Options for Individual Needs

Basic

Exercises 1-23, 29-33
More Practice, p. 501, set C

Supplements
Reteaching 21 or
Practice 21
Challenges 21

Average

Exercises 1-33
More Practice, p. 501, set C

Supplements
Practice 21
Challenges 21 or
Thinking Skills 21

Extended

Exercises 6-15, 24-33

Supplements
Challenges 21
Thinking Skills 21

Other Resources:
Problem-Solving Experiences in Mathematics, Grade 4, Problem 16
Mathematics, A Way of Thinking, Lesson 8-11
Kids Are Consumers, Too!, pp. 131, 132

LESSON PLAN 3-4

OBJECTIVE 3-4
To add 3-digit numbers

Materials: calculators, place value blocks, TA 5 (4-Digit Place Value Charts)
Alternative Materials: TA 6 (Place Value Models)

1. MOTIVATE AND TEACH

LEARN ABOUT IT

EXPLORE ► **Justify addition as the correct operation.** (You add to put together amounts to find a total.)
► **Analyze the information to explain where the addends come from.** (A half hour to bicycle to the tennis court plus a half hour to return = 475 calories for 1 h; 1 h of tennis = 450 calories.)

TALK ABOUT IT ► **Explain the trade in the tens place.** (7 + 5 = 12; trade 10 tens for 1 hundred; record 2 tens.)
► **Why is there 1 thousand in Other Example A?** (6 + 8 = 14; trade 10 hundreds for 1 thousand.)
► **Justify how Other Example B is written.** (Line up ones and tens to add digits with the same place value; 9 hundreds line up with the empty hundreds place of the bottom addend.)
Student Edition answers: **1.** to add numbers of the same place value **2.** Answers may vary. **3.** You use 925 calories to ride a bike for 1 h and play tennis for 1 h.

2. CHECK UNDERSTANDING

TRY IT OUT

ERROR ALERT Exercises 2 and 4: Lining up numbers incorrectly. Failing to make all possible trades.

Adding Whole Numbers

LEARN ABOUT IT

EXPLORE Think About the Process
Suppose you ride your bicycle for half an hour to get to the tennis court. You play tennis for an hour and then ride home. How many calories do you use?

You add because you need to put together amounts to find the total.

Activity	Calories/hour
Bicycling	475
Rollerskating	370
Running	620
Swimming	425
Tennis	450

Add the ones. Trade if necessary.	Add the tens. Trade if necessary.	Add the hundreds.
475 + 450 = 5	(1) 475 + 450 = 25	(1) 475 + 450 = 925

TALK ABOUT IT See teaching notes.

1. Why do you need to line up the digits?
2. How would you have estimated the sum?
3. Use a complete sentence to give a reasonable answer to the story problem.

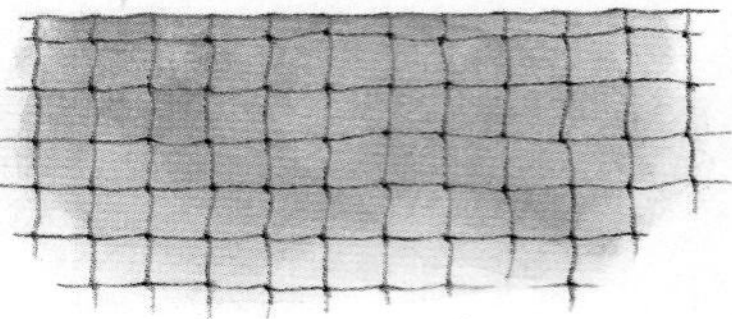

Other Examples

14 hundreds equal 1 thousand and 4 hundreds

A 624 + 845 = 1,469 **B** 987 + 38 = 1,025 **C** 3,754 + 5,489 = 9,243 **D** $76.87 + 81.16 = $158.03

TRY IT OUT

Add.

1. 39 + 26 = 65 2. 364 + 72 = 436 3. 576 + 385 = 961 4. 4,586 + 635 = 5,221 5. 7,674 + 1,768 = 9,442 6. $25.89 + 52.34 = $78.23

60

TEACHING OPTIONS

RETEACHING TIPS Have students who are not lining up digits correctly write each exercise in a 4-digit place value chart. They use the chart to verify that digits appear in the proper places and that those of the same value align. Assign Reteaching Supplement 21.

COMPUTER **Addition Logician, MECC, Copyright 1984** For use with all levels of students. In "Repeat After Me," students answer 5 addition problems with 2- to 4-digit addends. After 5 problems, students test their logic and problem-solving skills. The time for this activity varies.

PRACTICE

Find the sums.

1. 59 + 36 = 95	**2.** 493 + 21 = 514	**3.** 812 + 560 = 1,372	**4.** \$5.45 + 3.76 = \$9.21	**5.** 9,052 + 876 = 9,928
6. 316 + 287 = 603	**7.** 1,486 + 3,039 = 4,525	**8.** 275 + 91 = 366	**9.** \$63.45 + 7.36 = \$70.81	**10.** 6,525 + 7,680 = 14,205
11. 213 + 99 = 312	**12.** \$3.02 + 6.78 = \$9.80	**13.** 9,163 + 708 = 9,871	**14.** 547 + 145 = 692	**15.** 2,568 + 3,846 = 6,414

16. 78 + 95
173

17. 467 + 295
762

18. \$83.00 + \$61.75
\$144.75

19. 9,154 + 258
9,412

20. 843 + 89
932

21. 3,556 + 82
3,638

22. 749 + 541
1,290

23. \$32.09 + \$4.78
\$36.87

24. 85 + 46
131

25. 425 + 81
506

26. 2,518 + 605
3,123

27. \$16.48 + \$5.02
\$21.50

APPLY

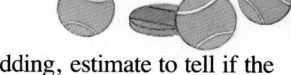

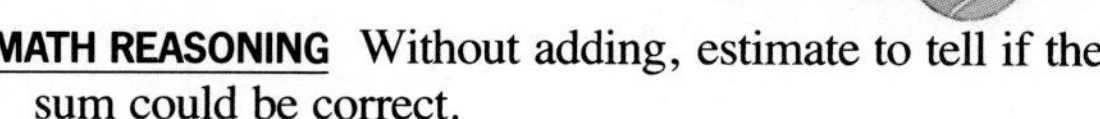

MATH REASONING Without adding, estimate to tell if the sum could be correct.

28. 57 + 39 = 67
no

29. 525 + 236 = 651
no

30. 354 + 128 = 482
yes

PROBLEM SOLVING

31. A ham sandwich is 365 calories and a serving of hash brown potatoes is 197 calories. Would these foods together have more or less than 500 calories?
more calories

32. Use a calculator to find the next 3 numbers in this pattern. The same number is always added to get the next number. 28, 157, 286, ___?___, ___?___, ___?___
415, 544, 673

► **COMMUNICATION Write to Learn**

33. Write a paragraph that tells how you would use these place value blocks to show 346 + 182 = 528.
See Additional Answers.

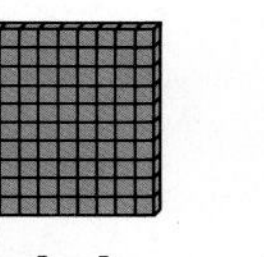
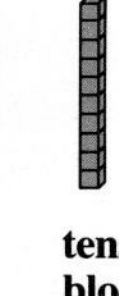

hundreds block   tens block   ones block

More Practice, page 501, set C

61

3. PRACTICE AND APPLY

Basic	1-23, 29-33
Average	1-33
Extended	6-15, 24-33

Additional Answers: See p. T79.

PRACTICE

How do Exercises 16-27 differ from 1-16? (It may help to rewrite 16-27 vertically.)

APPLY

MATH REASONING ► **Explain how to use number sense to judge the sums.** (Possible answer: round; estimate the sum; compare it to the given sum to check for reasonableness.)

PROBLEM SOLVING ► **Explain a way to uncover the pattern in Problem 32.** (Possible answer: 157 − 28 will help find the missing addend.)

COMMUNICATION ► **Explain the process you would follow to model the addition.** (Lay out 2 groups of blocks; push them together; combine blocks of the same place value; record any necessary trades.)

3-4

CLOSE AND ASSESS

SHOW WHAT YOU KNOW

Have students use place value materials or place value charts to compare the sum of \$4.56 + \$0.78 with the sum of 78 + 456. (\$5.34, 534; the answers are the same but the money amount needs a dollar sign and decimal point to show dollars and cents.)

QUICK QUIZ

Find the sums.

1. 39 + 43 (82)
2. 536 + 81 (617)
3. 406 + 858 (1,264)
4. \$3.10 + \$5.95 (\$9.05)

LESSON OPTIONS 3-5

Column Addition

OBJECTIVE 3-5 To add a column of 3 or more numbers

PREBOOK ACTIVITIES

QUICK REVIEW

Add mentally.

1. 3 + 6 + 4 + 5 (18)
2. 7 + 3 + 6 + 3 (19)
3. 3 + 5 + 1 + 7 (16)
4. 9 + 7 + 5 + 1 (22)
5. 2 + 7 + 8 + 7 (24)
6. 5 + 3 + 6 + 8 (22)
7. 1 + 0 + 8 + 5 (14)
8. 6 + 6 + 7 + 7 (26)

PRIOR KNOWLEDGE

Write this example on the chalkboard: 4,152 + 981 + 95. Have students explain how they would find the sum of the numbers without a calculator. (Rewrite vertically; line up places; add the ones, tens, hundreds, and thousands, trading as needed.) Ask them to compare adding 2 addends with adding 3 addends. (Possible answer: Both apply the same basic number facts, same rules of grouping, order, trading.) Have students suggest real-life situations in which lists of numbers are added. (Possible answers: test scores, sales slips)

COMMUNICATION

Discussing and Writing in Math Ask each student to write an example of what comes to mind when you ask for a **column** of numbers. Ask students to compare a vertical column of numbers to other types of columns, such as a column of a building or a column of smoke. (Possible answer: They all go up and down.) Have students conclude a general meaning of *column*. (Possible answer: an often long, vertical line) Then, have students write in their Math Journals a sentence explaining what they think **column addition** means. (to add a line of numbers in vertical form)

EXPLORE AND CONNECT

Materials: TA 6 (Place Value Models)
Grouping Suggestion: cooperative learning groups of 5
Students explore **column** addition using place value models. Two students in a group each think of a 2-digit number using the digits 1–5, such as 42 and 35. A third student thinks of a 3-digit number, such as 123. A fourth student records the numbers in a vertical *column* so that places align. A fifth student uses place value models to form each number, modeling the placement on the paper. For example, 123 would have 3 ones, 2 tens, and 1 hundred; 42 would have 2 ones and 4 tens; and 35 would have 5 ones and 3 tens. Then members work together to count the models in each place. If any place totals 10 or more, a trade is made and the extra ten or hundred model is placed above the next *column*. The recorder writes the final total on the paper. Groups trade roles until each member has done each task.

CONNECTIONS Use these anytime.

Problem of the Day

The Hungry Toad A toad ate 75 bugs on Sunday. On Monday, the toad ate 5 more than 75, and it continued to increase its meals at the same rate every day. How many bugs did the hungry toad eat in a week? You can use a calculator if you need help. (630)

Life Skills

Hobbies Michael wants to add another model airplane to his collection. He buys a $10.95 kit and a $6.95 set of paints at Hal's Hobby Shop. But Hal is out of glue for putting the kit together. So Michael stops at Moe's Model Shop, where he buys a tube of glue for $3.45. How much does Michael spend on his new model? ($21.35)

Math Connection

Logic The fourth-graders at Super School entered a read-a-thon. Jamie read 10 books. Marcia read 10 more than Jamie. Nancy read the same number of books as Marcia. And Diane read 10 more books than Marcia. What was the total number of books read by these 4 students? (80)

Classwork and Homework Supplements

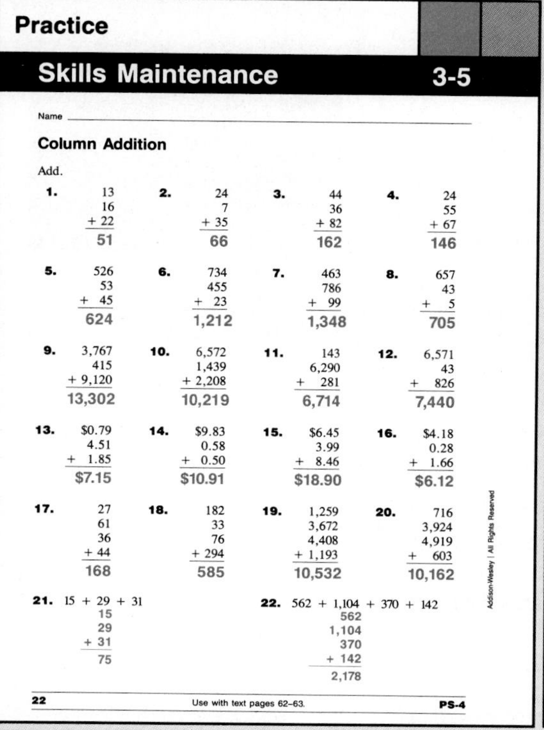

Practice

Skills Maintenance 3-5

Name ______________________________

Column Addition

Add.

1.	2.	3.	4.
13 16 + 22 51	24 7 + 35 66	44 36 + 82 162	24 55 + 67 146

5.	6.	7.	8.
526 53 + 45 624	734 455 + 23 1,212	463 786 + 99 1,348	657 43 + 5 705

9.	10.	11.	12.
3,767 415 + 9,120 13,302	6,572 1,439 + 2,208 10,219	143 6,290 + 281 6,714	6,571 43 + 826 7,440

13.	14.	15.	16.
$0.79 4.51 + 1.85 $7.15	$9.83 0.58 + 0.50 $10.91	$6.45 3.99 + 8.46 $18.90	$4.18 0.28 + 1.66 $6.12

17.	18.	19.	20.
27 61 36 + 44 168	182 33 76 + 294 585	1,259 3,672 4,408 + 1,193 10,532	716 3,924 4,919 + 603 10,162

21. 15 + 29 + 31	22. 562 + 1,104 + 370 + 142
15 29 + 31 75	562 1,104 370 + 142 2,178

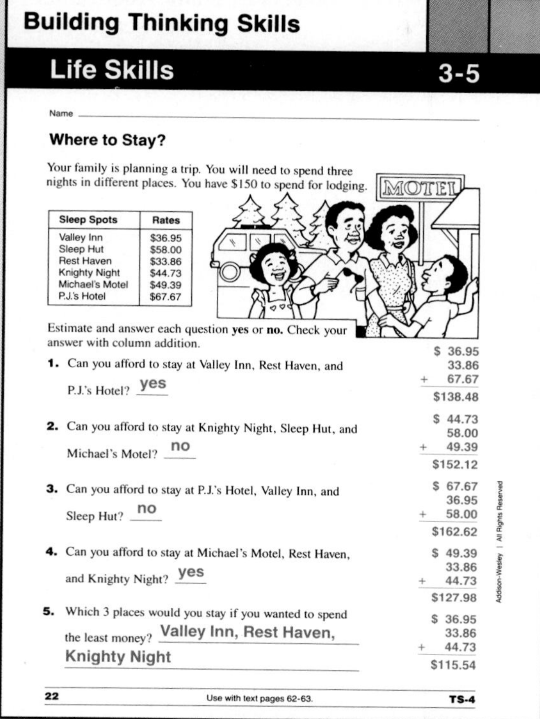

Building Thinking Skills

Life Skills 3-5

Name ______________________________

Where to Stay?

Your family is planning a trip. You will need to spend three nights in different places. You have $150 to spend for lodging.

Sleep Spots	Rates
Valley Inn	$36.95
Sleep Hut	$58.00
Rest Haven	$33.86
Knighty Night	$44.73
Michael's Motel	$49.39
P.J.'s Hotel	$67.67

Estimate and answer each question **yes** or **no**. Check your answer with column addition.

1. Can you afford to stay at Valley Inn, Rest Haven, and P.J.'s Hotel? yes — $ 36.95 + 33.86 + 67.67 = $138.48
2. Can you afford to stay at Knighty Night, Sleep Hut, and Michael's Motel? no — $ 44.73 + 58.00 + 49.39 = $152.12
3. Can you afford to stay at P.J.'s Hotel, Valley Inn, and Sleep Hut? no — $ 67.67 + 36.95 + 58.00 = $162.62
4. Can you afford to stay at Michael's Motel, Rest Haven, and Knighty Night? yes — $ 49.39 + 33.86 + 44.73 = $127.98
5. Which 3 places would you stay if you wanted to spend the least money? Valley Inn, Rest Haven, Knighty Night — $ 36.95 + 33.86 + 44.73 = $115.54

Reteaching

Skills Review 3-5

Name ______________________________

Column Addition

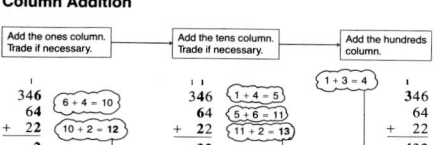

Add the ones column. Trade if necessary.	Add the tens column. Trade if necessary.	Add the hundreds column.
346 64 + 22 2 (6 + 4 = 10) (10 + 2 = 12)	346 64 + 22 32 (1 + 4 = 5) (5 + 6 = 11) (11 + 2 = 13)	346 64 + 22 432 (1 + 3 = 4)

Add.

1.	2.	3.	4.	5.
66 14 + 56 136	54 43 + 85 182	365 297 + 357 1,019	268 345 + 463 1,076	222 468 + 387 1,077

6.	7.	8.	9.	10.
4,365 262 1,634 + 303 6,564	$3.76 2.15 6.43 + 4.09 $16.43	6,532 78 202 + 5,732 12,544	$2.66 5.43 0.44 + 4.62 $13.15	34 776 1,345 + 74 2,229

11. 32 + 456 + 73 = 561

12. $42.78 + $8.29 + $2.34 = $53.41

13. 472 + 387 + 908 = 1,767

14. 3,405 + 3,026 + 5,408 = 11,839

Which sum is greater? Ring the answer.

15. (68 + 45 + 32) or 86 + 34 + 12

16. (458 + 82 + 20) or 333 + 88 + 71

Challenges

Family Math 3-5

Name ______________________________

Calendar Addition

Dear Family:
Our class just learned how to add a column of 3 or more numbers. Complete the activity below with your child.

1. These four squares are taken from a two-by-two section of the calendar. Add the numbers on each diagonal. Write the sums in the circles.

Sun.	Mon.	Tues.	Wed.	Thurs.	Fri.	Sat.
		1	2	3	4	5
6	7	8	9	10	11	12
13	14	15	16	17	18	19
20	21	22	23	24	25	26
27	28	29	30	31		

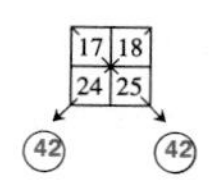

(42) (42)

2. Try this for other two-by-two sections of the calendar.
Answers will vary. Some possible answers are given.

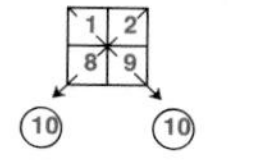

(10) (10)

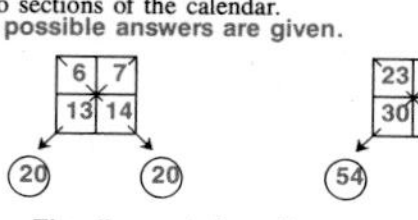

(20) (20)

23 24
30 31

(54) (54)

3. What pattern do you find? The diagonals have the same sum.

4. Now try three-by-three and four-by-four calendar sections.
Answers will vary. Some possible answers are given.

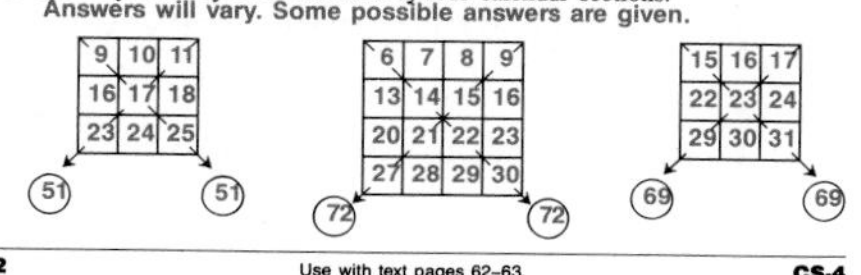

(51) (51) (72) (72)

15 16 17
22 23 24
29 30 31

(69) (69)

Options for Individual Needs

Basic

Exercises 1-5, 8-21
More Practice, p. 501, set D

Supplements
Reteaching 22 or
Practice 22

Average

Exercises 1-21
More Practice, p. 501, set D

Supplements
Practice 22
Challenges 22 or
Thinking Skills 22

Extended

Exercises 3-21

Supplements
Challenges 22
Thinking Skills 22

Other Resources:
Problem-Solving Experiences in Mathematics, Grade 4, Problem 6
Math In Stride, Grade 4, p. 13

LESSON PLAN 3-5

OBJECTIVE 3-5

To add a column of 3 or more numbers

Materials: place value blocks

Alternative Materials: TA 6 (Place Value Models)

1. MOTIVATE AND TEACH

LEARN ABOUT IT

EXPLORE ▶ **How can place value help you write numbers to add?** (Possible answer: It helps you align digits of the same value before adding.)
▶ **Must 9 + 5 be added first? Explain.** (No, order rules say you can add any two digits in the ones place.)
▶ **What does the 2 mean over the tens column?** (There were 21 ones—2 tens were traded.)

TALK ABOUT IT ▶ **What would happen if you did not line up places as you rewrote the numbers?** (You might add digits with different values and get a wrong answer.)
▶ **Explain why the sum should be the same whether you add columns up or down.** (Order does not change an addition sum.)
▶ **To what place would you round the prices? Explain.** (tens; It is the highest place of the smaller numbers.) Student Edition answers: **1.** Numbers with the same value should be added place by place. **2.** yes **3.** Answers may vary. Sample estimation: 170 + 80 + 40 = 290 **4.** The 3 items cost $282.

2. CHECK UNDERSTANDING

TRY IT OUT

ERROR ALERT Being confused about trading when the sum of a column is 20 or more. Having trouble lining up numbers of different place value in columns.

Column Addition

LEARN ABOUT IT

EXPLORE Think About the Process

Tyrone's father bought a telescope for $169, a tripod for $75, and a special color picture book about astronomy for $38. How much did these 3 items cost?

How do you know that you can add to solve this problem? Here is how to find the correct sum.

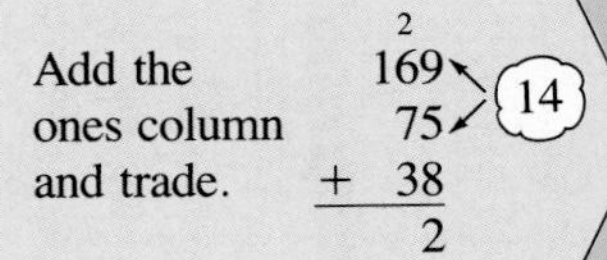

Add the ones column and trade.	2 169 75 + 38 2 (14)	Add the other columns. Trade if you can.	12 169 75 + 38 282 (14)

TALK ABOUT IT See teaching notes.

1. Why is it important to line up ones, tens, and hundreds when writing the numbers to be added?
2. Do you get the same sum if you begin at the bottom of a column and add up? Use this idea to check the addition.
3. How would you have estimated the sum?
4. Use a complete sentence to give a reasonable answer to the story problem.

TRY IT OUT

Add.

1.	2.	3.	4.	5.
42	27	346	725	$1.49
69	9	78	6,348	2.98
+ 38	+ 37	265	1,642	3.56
149	**73**	+ 39	+ 76	+ 4.75
		728	**8,791**	**$12.78**

TEACHING OPTIONS

RETEACHING TIPS Have students use place value blocks or models to add columns. Tell them not to trade until they have added the entire column. If a column sum is 20 or more, they will see 2 groups of 10 to trade. Assign Reteaching Supplement 22.

ENRICHMENT Have students use mental math to find the sums.
1. 47 + 53 + 48 + 52 (200)
2. 550 + 25 + 1,000 + 75 + 450 (2,100)
3. 698 + 97 + 400 + 702 + 103 (2,000)
4. $6.75 + $9.50 + $3.25 + $.50 ($20.00)

PRACTICE

1.	2.	3.	4.	5.
59	35	635	349	283
78	47	786	8	4,475
+ 36	+ 22	+ 429	67	3,864
173	**104**	**1,850**	+ 123	+ 88
			547	**8,710**

6.	7.	8.	9.	10.
346	$1.75	$5.45	36	2,946
69	2.68	2.98	948	79
+ 287	3.19	+ 3.76	+ 213	483
702	+ 0.79	**$12.19**	**1,197**	+ 605
	$8.41			**4,113**

11. 78 + 95 + 37 **210**

12. 4,627 + 5,748 + 1,236 **11,611**

APPLY

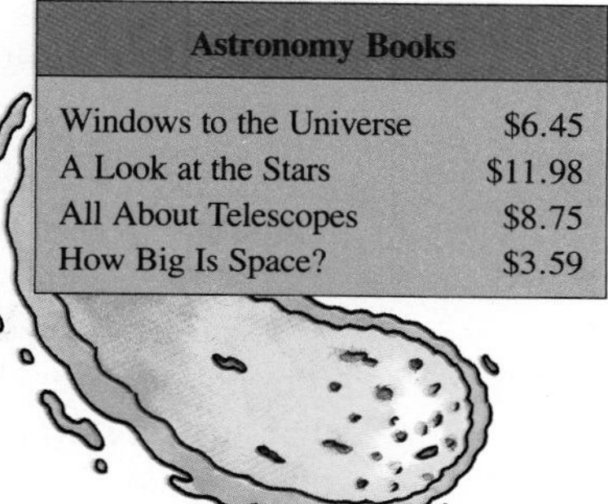

MATH REASONING Which sum is greater? Decide without finding the sum.

13. 89 + 75 + 42   79 + 65 + 32

14. 518 + 649 + 298   524 + 651 + 305

PROBLEM SOLVING

Astronomy Books	
Windows to the Universe	$6.45
A Look at the Stars	$11.98
All About Telescopes	$8.75
How Big Is Space?	$3.59

15. Tad bought 3 books about astronomy. He paid for them with a twenty-dollar bill and got some change back. Which 3 books did he buy? **See Additional Answers.**

16. Write a problem that you can solve using the data from this chart. **Answers will vary.**

MIXED REVIEW

Give a subtraction fact for each addition fact. **See Additional Answers.**

17. 8 + 3 = 11   **18.** 7 + 8 = 15   **19.** 6 + 9 = 15   **20.** 9 + 9 = 18

Say and write this number.

21. 3 thousands, 6 hundreds, 4 tens, and 9 ones **3,649**

More Practice, page 501, set D

3. PRACTICE AND APPLY

Basic	1-5; 8-21
Average	1-21
Extended	3-21

Additional Answers: See p. T79.

PRACTICE

Look at Exercises 11 and 12. What might you want to do before adding the numbers in each exercise? (Rewrite the numbers in vertical columns so that digits with the same value line up.)

APPLY

MATH REASONING ► **How can comparing addends help you to predict a sum?** (Possible answer: Greater addends will give a greater sum.)

PROBLEM SOLVING ► **Explain how to quickly find the answer to Problem 15.** (Possible answer: Round each price, then look for three that together total less than $20.00.)

MIXED REVIEW ► **How do Exercises 17-19 differ from Exercise 20?** (Exercises 17-19 have two possible answers, but Exercise 20 has only one answer.)

3-5

CLOSE AND ASSESS

SAY WHAT YOU THINK

Students find the sum of 5,439 + 741 + 762 + 58. Then they identify the mental math and addition rules that helped them. (7,000; Explanations may vary. Students may make groups of 10, find doubles, use other orders or groupings, or add the numbers place by place.)

QUICK QUIZ

1.	2.	3.
489	6,307	$8.42
54	965	4.08
+ 667	+ 8,844	+ 9.95
(1,210)	(16,116)	($22.45)

LESSON OPTIONS 3-6

Problem Solving: Make an Organized List

OBJECTIVE 3-6 To solve problems using the strategy Make an Organized List

PREBOOK ACTIVITIES

QUICK REVIEW

Add or subtract.

1. 4917 − 500 (4,417)
2. 154 + 451 (605)
3. $5.00 − $1.77 ($3.23)
4. 105 + 468 (573)
5. $0.79 + $1.80 ($2.59)
6. 502 − 408 (94)
7. 13,456 + 2,468 (15,924)
8. 47 − 29 (18)

PRIOR KNOWLEDGE

Have students give examples of times they have used lists. (Possible answers: for shopping, for taking attendance, for recording homework assignments, for making gift wishes) Have them explain how lists can be useful. (Possible answers: help in recalling details; account for possibilities; provide something to check off)

COMMUNICATION

Discussing Math Have students explain in their own words what it means to account for all possibilities. (Possible answer: to consider each different choice there could be) Discuss how accounting for all possibilities relates to making successful plans or to being prepared for events that might happen. Have students relate this idea to their own experience. (Possible answers: plan supplies for a trip; think about "best" and "worst" situations to imagine how to handle either case)

EXPLORE AND CONNECT

COOPERATIVE ACTIVITY

Grouping Suggestion: small cooperative learning groups
Liz is getting a puppy from the animal shelter. Collies and retrievers are available now. There are males and females of both. How many different choices does Liz have for the puppy?

TEACHING ACTIONS

Organize students into small groups. Students work together and discuss possible solution strategies for the problem.

► **Explain Liz's options.** (She must decide if she wants a collie or a retriever puppy and whether she wants a male or female.)

► **Sort Liz's choices into groups.** (collie or retriever; male or female)

► **Explain how a list could help you track choices.** (List every possible combination, then count them.)

► **Explain your strategy for finding all of Liz's choices.** (Possible answer: List all choices in each group separately, then match each choice in one group with every choice in the other group.)

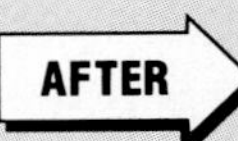

► **Compare lists with another group. Verify each solution.** (Liz can pick a male or a female collie as 2 choices, or a male or a female retriever as 2 more choices; the total number of choices is 4.)

CONNECTIONS Use these anytime.

Problem of the Day

Sports Car Rex is taking three friends for a ride in his new car. One friend can sit in front with Rex and two can sit in back. If Rex always drives, how many seating arrangements of 2 passengers in back and 1 in front are there? (3)

Creative Thinking

A Sock Story In her drawer, Inez has only pink or red socks. One morning the light bulb blew in her room before she had put on her socks. She could not see the colors. To save time, how many socks did Inez pull from her drawer to be sure she would have a matching pair to put on in the light downstairs? Explain. (3; two would have to be the same color)

Life Skills

Family Pictures Ned and Ted are having their picture taken together. Fred the photographer says each boy may stand or sit, and the boys may be in any order they choose. How many different ways can the boys be arranged, if order counts? (8)

Classwork and Homework Supplements

Practice

Problem Solving 3-6

Name

Make an Organized List

Make an organized list to help you solve each problem.

1. The Holton School has gym uniforms. Tops consist of white T-shirts, blue T-shirts, or blue sweatshirts. Bottoms include white shorts, blue shorts, or blue sweatpants. How many different combinations of tops and bottoms are there? 9
white T, white shorts; white T, blue shorts; white T, blue sweats; blue T, white shorts; blue T, blue shorts; blue T, blue sweats; sweatshirt, white shorts; sweatshirt, blue shorts; sweatshirt, sweatpants

2. There are 4 soccer teams in the school league: red, blue, green, and orange. How many different combinations of teams can play against each other? 6
red-blue; red-green; red-orange; blue-green; blue-orange; green-orange

3. After-school sports begin at 3:30 and 4:30. Students can play softball or tennis. How many different choices do they have? 4
3:30 softball; 3:30 tennis; 4:30 softball; 4:30 tennis

4. Each student needs to complete 2 events in the gymnastics tournament. They include the horse, balance beam, uneven parallel bars, and trampoline. How many different choices does each student have? 6
h, bb; h, upb; h, t; bb, upb; bb, t; upb, t

5. Winter activities include basketball, square dancing, and volleyball. Each activity is offered in January and February. How many choices are there? 6
Jan. basketball; Jan. square dancing; Jan. volleyball; Feb. basketball; Feb. square dancing; Feb. volleyball

6. The 2 physical education teachers are Ms. Akona and Mr. Moses. Classes meet at 10:00, 11:00, 1:00, or 2:00. How many different classes are there? 8
10:00 Ms. Akona; 10:00 Mr. Moses; 11:00 Ms. Akona; 11:00 Mr. Moses; 1:00 Ms. Akona; 1:00 Mr. Moses; 2:00 Ms. Akona; 2:00 Mr. Moses

Building Thinking Skills

Problem Solving 3-6

Name

What's Your Order?

Make an organized list to solve each problem.

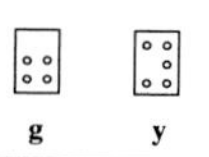

1. Paula's Pizza Paradise serves pizza with cheese, sausage, pepperoni, and ham toppings. The drink choices are milk, grape juice, and lemonade. How many combinations of single-topping pizzas and drinks can the customer order? Write your list.

cheese, milk	sausage, milk
cheese, grape juice	sausage, grape juice
cheese, lemonade	sausage, lemonade
pepperoni, milk	ham, milk
pepperoni, grape juice	ham, grape juice
pepperoni, lemonade	ham, lemonade

2. Last week Paula added onions to her list of toppings. How many combinations do her customers have to choose from now? 15

3. This week Kristen, Jamie, Megan, and Valerie all went out to Paula's Pizza Paradise for lunch. Paula was having a special that day. Customers could order any two toppings on a pie for free. How many different combinations of toppings are possible? Write your list.

cheese, pepperoni	pepperoni, onions
cheese, sausage	pepperoni, ham
cheese, onions	ham, onions
cheese, ham	ham, sausage
pepperoni, sausage	onions, sausage

Reteaching

Problem Solving 3-6

Name

Make an Organized List

Using the data in a problem to make an organized list may help you solve the problem.

Tom could buy one baseball glove and one bat. One glove was brown, the other was black. He had three colors of bats to choose from—brown, tan, and black. How many choices did he have?

For each color of glove, there are three possible colors of bats.

Gloves	Bats
brown	brown
	tan
	black
black	brown
	tan
	black

Tom has 6 choices.

Make an organized list to help you solve each problem.

1. Bill can buy one box of balls and one tennis racquet. The three colors of balls are orange, green, and white. The two types of racquets are wood and metal. How many choices does Bill have? 6

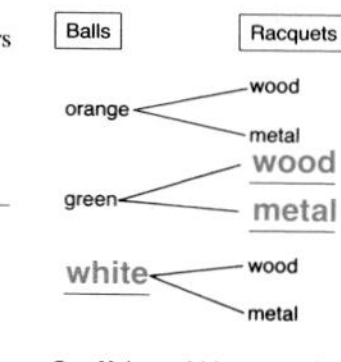

2. The three lengths of fishing poles were 5 feet, 6 feet, and 7 feet. The three styles of reels were bait casting, open faced, and fly. Dick could buy only one fishing pole and one reel. How many choices did Dick have? 9

3. Kris could buy one sleeping bag and one tent. The two kinds of sleeping bags were box and mummy. The three choices of tents were pup, umbrella, and dome. How many choices did Kris have? 6

Challenges

Critical Thinking 3-6

Name

Braille Discoveries

Each letter in the Braille system is made up of a combination of 6 or fewer dots.

Examples: d g y

1. Some letters, such as g, have 4 dots. What are all the possible combinations of 4 dots? Make an organized list to find them. The first one is done for you.

Combinations with dots along left side	Combinations with dots along right side	Combinations with 2 dots on top	Combinations with 2 dots in middle	Combinations with 2 dots on bottom

2. Cross out any repeats. How many combinations are here? 15

3. Look up Braille letters in the encyclopedia. See which combinations of 4 dots are actual letters in Braille.

Options for Individual Needs

Basic

Exercises 1-8
Calculator Bank, pp. 485, 488
More Practice, p. 513, set F

Supplements
Reteaching 23 or
Practice 23

Average

Exercises 1-8
Calculator Bank, pp. 485, 488
More Practice, p. 513, set F

Supplements
Practice 23
Challenges 23 or
Thinking Skills 23

Extended

Exercises 1-8
Calculator Bank, pp. 485, 488

Supplements
Challenges 23
Thinking Skills 23

3-6

Other Resources:
Math In Stride, Grade 4, p. 12
Problem-Solving Experiences in Mathematics, Grade 4, Problems 9, 10, 44, 45

Lesson Plan 3-6

OBJECTIVE 3-6
To solve problems using the strategy Make an Organized List

Materials: colored pencils or markers

1. Motivate and Teach

LEARN ABOUT IT

▶ **Restate the problem in your own words.** (Possible answer: Joey and his sister must decide which of two events to attend at one of three different times.)

▶ **How can the data be sorted?** (into 2 groups: demonstration or star show; 9:30, 10:30, or 11:30)

▶ **Analyze how the list is organized.** (It matches each event to each possible starting time.)

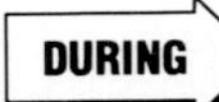

▶ **How can a list help answer the question?** (You can record all choices.)

▶ **What other list could help solve the problem?** (List each time and match both events to it.)

▶ **How can you confirm that all choices are listed?** (Check that all times are listed for each event.)

▶ **Find a link between the number of events, the times per event, and the total number of choices.** (2 events × 3 times per event = 6 choices.)

2. Check Understanding

TRY IT OUT

▶ **What strategy could you use to find all the ways to sort the family members into groups?** (Make an Organized List; Use Objects; Act It Out)

ERROR ALERT Missing some possible choices.

Problem Solving
Make an Organized List

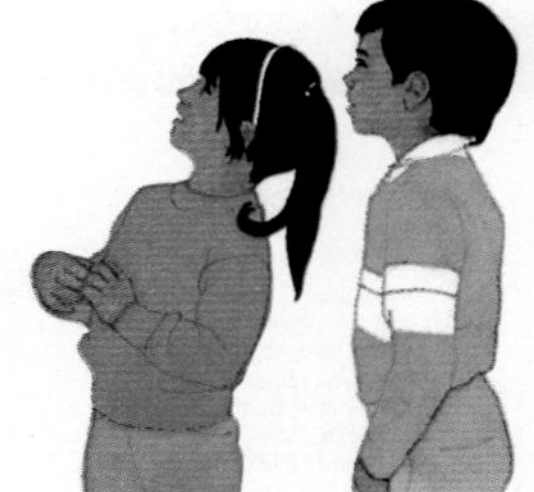

LEARN ABOUT IT

To solve some problems, you might need to make a list using the data in the problem. This strategy is called **Make an Organized List**.

The morning events at the Adler Planetarium begin at 9:30, 10:30, and 11:30. At each time Joey and his sister can either see the star show or the demonstration on making navigation tools. How many different choices do they have?

If they choose the Star Show they can go at 3 different times.

If they choose the demonstration they can go at 3 different times.

Event	Time
Star Show	9:30 a.m.
Star Show	10:30 a.m.
Star Show	11:30 a.m.
Demonstration	9:30 a.m.
Demonstration	10:30 a.m.
Demonstration	11:30 a.m.

They have 6 different choices.

TRY IT OUT

Joey visited the planetarium with his sister Teresa, his mother, and his father. They went to the events in pairs, with one adult and one child going together. How many different ways could they pair up?

- How many different adults can Joey choose? **2**
- Can Joey and Teresa go together? **no**
- Copy and complete the list below to solve the problem.

Joey - mother   **Teresa - mother**
Joey - father   **Teresa - father**

64

Teaching Options

RETEACHING TIPS Have students use one color to write one child's name from the list and the matching facts, then use another color to write the other child's name and the matching facts. Different colors often help students verify that all matches are made. Assign Reteaching Supplement 23.

ENRICHMENT Ask students to solve: *Tuesdays at Dinah's Diner, Dinah serves sandwich specials. You can choose chicken salad, tuna salad, or ham salad on white, rye, oat, or whole wheat bread, with or without lettuce. How many different sandwich choices does Dinah offer?* (24)

PRACTICE

Make an organized list to help you solve each problem.

1. The 3 kinds of sandwiches served at the planetarium lunch stand were chicken, ham, and cheese. The 2 choices of drinks were fruit juice and milk. How many different lunches could you choose? **6 different lunches**

2. Leroy could buy one book and one postcard in the planetarium shop. The books he liked were *The Life of a Star* and *Find That Constellation*. The postcards he liked were a photo of the earth and a drawing of Saturn. How many choices did he have? **4 choices**

MIXED PRACTICE

Solve. Choose a strategy from the list or use other strategies that you know.

3. Joe gave the clerk a $5 bill. He bought juice and a sandwich for $3.28. How much change did he get back? **$1.72**

4. Shirley wanted to write 50 facts in her star journal by New Year's Day. In October she had 21 facts. In November she had 15. How many facts did she need to write in her journal in December? **14 facts**

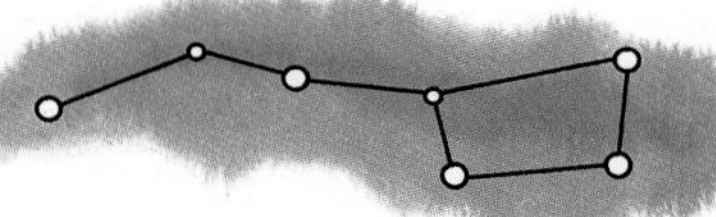

5. The Big Dipper is the easiest star group to find. There are 4 stars in its handle. The star Alioth is closer to the cup than Alkaid. Mizar is between Alioth and Alkaid. Alioth is farther from the cup than Megrez. Which star is at the end of the handle? **Alkaid**

6. Yuri Gagarin was the first person to travel in space. His flight in April, 1961, lasted 108 minutes. Alan Shepard was the second. His flight in May, 1961, lasted 19 minutes. How many minutes did these 2 men fly in space? **127 minutes**

Some Strategies
Act It Out
Use Objects
Choose an Operation
Draw a Picture
Make an Organized List

John Young Planetarium (Orlando, Florida)

	Attendance in June	Attendance in January
laser show	3,000	3,526
star show	11,483	11,000

7. How many more people saw the laser show in January than in June? **526 more people**

8. What was the January attendance at the laser show and the star show? **14,526 people**

More Practice, page 513, set F

3. PRACTICE AND APPLY

Basic	1-8
Average	1-8
Extended	1-8

Additional Answers and Sample Solutions: See p. T79.

PRACTICE

For Problems 1 and 2, how many groups of data are given and how many choices are there per group? (2 data groups, 1 with 3 choices, 1 with 2; 2 groups of 2 choices each)

MIXED PRACTICE

▶ **How are Problems 3 and 4 related?** (Possible answer: Both can be solved using 1 or more operations.)

▶ **Identify a strategy you might use to solve Problem 5.** (Draw a Picture; Use Objects; Act It Out)

▶ **Is the order in which the astronauts flew important to the solution of Problem 6? Explain.** (No; addends can be added in any order to find a total.)

▶ **How are Problems 7 and 8 alike? How are they different?** (Both use data from the same table, but it takes different operations to solve each problem.)

CLOSE AND ASSESS

SHOW WHAT YOU KNOW Give students this information and have them make an organized list to find all the choices: *You can wear a blue sweatshirt with black pants, white sweatpants, or jeans. Or you could wear any of those pants with your new T-shirt. How many different outfits can you wear?* (6)

QUICK QUIZ

Solve this problem: Hayes has corn flakes, oatmeal, cream of wheat, and bran. He has bananas and berries. How many different cereal-and-fruit breakfasts can he make? (8)

LESSON OPTIONS 3-7

Front-End Estimation/Midchapter Review/Quiz

OBJECTIVE 3-7 To use the estimation technique of front-end estimation to estimate sums

PREBOOK ACTIVITIES

QUICK REVIEW

Round to the greatest place.

1. 57 (60)	**2.** 344 (300)
3. $7.28 ($7)	**4.** 5,802 (6,000)
5. 419 (400)	**6.** 1,499 (1,000)
7. 150 (200)	**8.** 507 (500)
9. 965 (1,000)	**10.** 851 (900)

PRIOR KNOWLEDGE

Ask students when they might want to use an estimated sum. (Answers will vary. Samples: to find about how much a purchase will be, about how many calories eaten, about how many people at an event) Have students review some estimation strategies they have used. (Possible answers: break apart numbers; compensate; round; count on; use a reference point; find compatible numbers)

COMMUNICATION

Discussing Math Write the word *front* on the chalkboard and ask students what it means in such phrases as the *front of a line,* the *front-end of a car,* or *a front porch.* (Possible answers: "beginning"; "head or leading place"; "first part") Challenge students to identify **front-end digits** in the numbers 742 and $7.42 and to justify their thinking. (Possible answer: 7; it is the digit in the greatest place and the first digit you consider when you compare the numbers.)

EXPLORE AND CONNECT

Materials: TA 6 (Place Value Models)
Grouping Suggestion: cooperative learning pairs
Students explore estimating sums using **front-end digits.** Write this addend list on the chalkboard: 330, 440, 550, 660, 770. Partners pick 2 addends. They combine hundreds using Place Value Models, then use mental math to find the sum of the rest of the broken-apart addends. For instance, to estimate the sum of 330 + 550, students break apart addends to total the *front-end digits:* 3 hundreds + 5 hundreds = 8 hundreds. Then they add 30 + 50 = 80. Pairs discuss how to adjust the partial estimate (800) to take into account the 80 not considered. (Possible answer: 30 + 50 is nearly another hundred, so adjust 800 *up* by adding 1 more hundred; now the estimated sum is 900.) Have students summarize how to use *front-end digits* to find estimated sums. (Add the digits in the greatest place, then adjust *up* to account for the other places.)

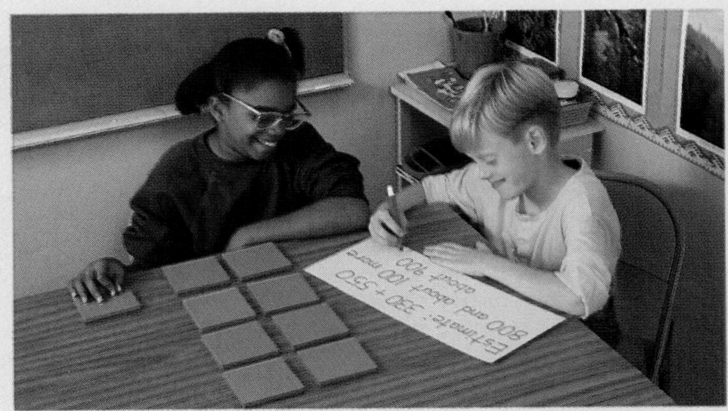

CONNECTIONS Use these anytime.

Problem of the Day

Money Celeste has $4.00. If she buys a notebook for $2.09 and a marker for $1.77, will she have a quarter left to call home? What would you advise her to do? (no; although she has enough to buy the 2 items, she would not have 25¢ left for the phone call; Possible answer: if it is available, buy a slightly cheaper marker or notebook.)

Number Sense

Estimation Find 2 different ways to estimate the sum of $4.89 and $3.19 and explain your thinking. (Possible answers: Round to the nearest dollar: $5 + $3 = $8; use only front-end digits: $4 + $3 = $7; use front-end digits, then adjust: $4 + $3 + $1 = $8)

Subject Integration

Health and Fitness Zeke estimated the calories in a fast-food lunch. He consulted a chart in his science class to learn that his super burger had 605 calories, his large French fries had 212 calories, and his big drink had 370 calories. About how many calories did the meal have? (about 1,200)

Classwork and Homework Supplements

Practice

Estimation 3-7

Name ____________

Front-End Estimation

Use front-end estimation to estimate each sum. **Answers will vary.**

1. \$5.58 + 3.38 = **\$9.00**
2. \$9.72 + 1.05 = **\$11.00**
3. 521 + 277 = **800**
4. 256 + 435 = **700**
5. 2,212 + 6,594 = **8,800**
6. 4,115 + 6,794 = **10,900**
7. 3,297 + 8,375 = **11,700**
8. 5,029 + 7,362 = **12,400**
9. 121 + 875 + 269 = **1,300**
10. 525 + 708 + 195 = **1,400**
11. 678 + 431 + 506 = **1,600**
12. 999 + 389 + 689 = **2,100**
13. 2,659 + 6,122 + 4,075 = **12,900**
14. 4,395 + 3,319 + 2,004 = **9,700**
15. 105 + 532 + 214 = **800**
16. 7,635 + 8,192 = **15,800**

17. Is \$10 enough for a \$4.85 notebook binder, a \$2.20 package of paper, and a \$2.49 pen? **yes**

18. Is \$11 enough for a \$9.50 pizza and \$1.95 pitcher of lemonade? **no**

19. Which is greater, 294 + 397 or 249 + 399? **294 + 397**

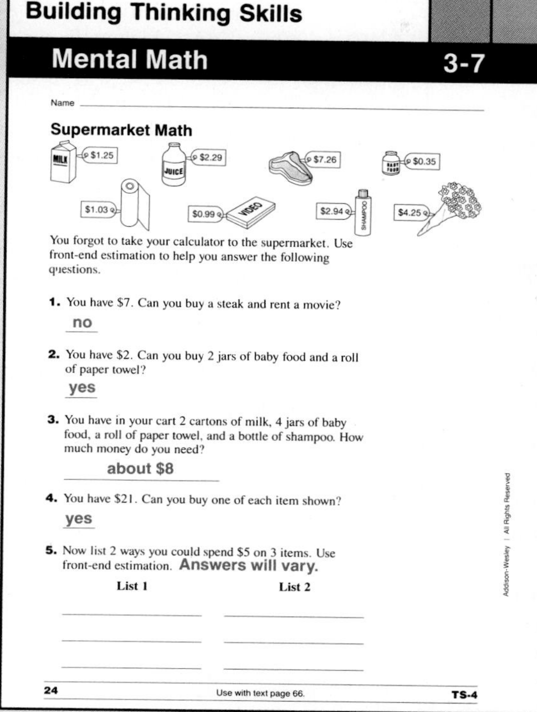

Building Thinking Skills

Mental Math 3-7

Name ____________

Supermarket Math

You forgot to take your calculator to the supermarket. Use front-end estimation to help you answer the following questions.

1. You have \$7. Can you buy a steak and rent a movie? **no**
2. You have \$2. Can you buy 2 jars of baby food and a roll of paper towel? **yes**
3. You have in your cart 2 cartons of milk, 4 jars of baby food, a roll of paper towel, and a bottle of shampoo. How much money do you need? **about \$8**
4. You have \$21. Can you buy one of each item shown? **yes**
5. Now list 2 ways you could spend \$5 on 3 items. Use front-end estimation. **Answers will vary.**

List 1	List 2

Reteaching

Estimation 3-7

Name ____________

Front-End Estimation

To find a close estimation, use **front-end estimation.**

Estimate the far left numbers. → Estimate the remaining numbers. → Add the two estimates.

476 + 432: 4 + 4 = 8; 76 + 32 is about 100; 800 + 100 = 900. The estimate is 900.

Use front-end estimation to estimate each sum.

1. 364 + 227: 3 + 2 = 5; 64 + 27 is about 100. Estimate: **600**
2. 3,584 + 4,127: 3 + 4 = 7; 584 + 127 is about 700. Estimate: **7,700**
3. 726 + 354 = **1,100**
4. \$6.38 + 8.95 = **\$15.00**
5. 7,832 + 4,136 = **11,900**
6. 2,136 + 9,764 = **11,900**
7. 127 + 286 + 865 = **1,300**
8. Is \$4 enough for a \$2.95 book and a \$1.35 magazine? **no**
9. Is \$8 enough for a \$5.95 game and a \$1.35 pad of paper? **yes**
10. Which is greater, **(495 + 194)** or 486 + 139?
11. Which is greater, 285 + 521 or **(284 + 596)**?

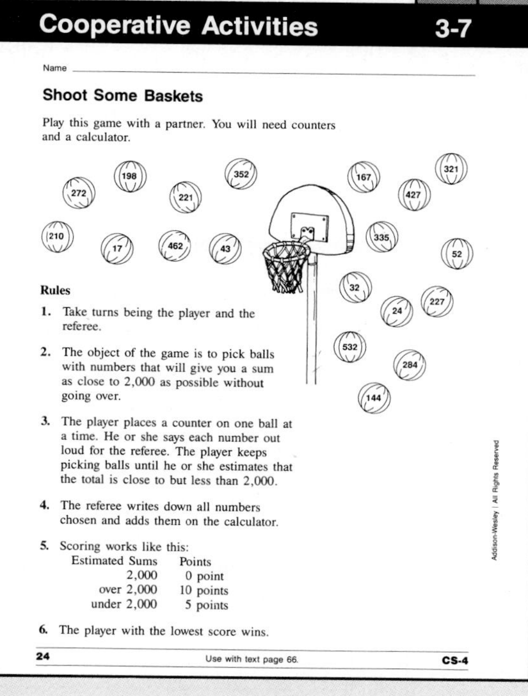

Challenges

Cooperative Activities 3-7

Name ____________

Shoot Some Baskets

Play this game with a partner. You will need counters and a calculator.

Rules

1. Take turns being the player and the referee.
2. The object of the game is to pick balls with numbers that will give you a sum as close to 2,000 as possible without going over.
3. The player places a counter on one ball at a time. He or she says each number out loud for the referee. The player keeps picking balls until he or she estimates that the total is close to but less than 2,000.
4. The referee writes down all numbers chosen and adds them on the calculator.
5. Scoring works like this:

Estimated Sums	Points
2,000	0 point
over 2,000	10 points
under 2,000	5 points

6. The player with the lowest score wins.

Options for Individual Needs

Basic

Exercises 1-6; 2-10, 19-34
Computer Bank, p. 492
More Practice, p. 501, set E

Supplements
Reteaching 24 or
Practice 24

Average

Exercises 1-6; 1-34
Computer Bank, p. 492
More Practice, p. 501, set E

Supplements
Practice 24
Challenges 24 or
Thinking Skills 24

Extended

Exercises 1-6; 5-10, 21-34
Computer Bank, p. 492

Supplements
Challenges 24
Thinking Skills 24

Other Resources:
Problem-Solving Experiences in Mathematics, Grade 4, Problem 30
Math In Stride, Grade 4, p. 229
Kids Are Consumers, Too!, pp. 114, 115

LESSON PLAN 3-7

OBJECTIVE 3-7
To use the estimation technique of front-end estimation to estimate sums

Materials: colored markers

1. MOTIVATE AND TEACH

LEARN ABOUT IT

EXPLORE ▶ **Analyze the data in the menu to explain which numbers Cindy used.** (She used the given dollar amounts and ignored the cents in the cost of the 2 dinners.)

▶ **Explain how you would estimate the cost of the dinners.** (Possible answer: Round to the nearest dollar—$5 + $5 = $10.)

TALK ABOUT IT ▶ **Analyze whether Cindy over- or underestimated. Explain your reasoning.** (Underestimated, because she did not account for the cents, which together would be at least $1.)

▶ **Explain how Cindy could fix her estimate to make it more reasonable.** (Possible answer: Adjust up to account for cents.)

▶ **Generalize how to adjust a front-end estimate.** (Possible answer: Adjust up to reflect an estimated sum of the other places.)

Student Edition answers: **1.** less; She ignored cents. **2.** yes; It never considers cents. **3.** Answers may vary; adjust up.

2. CHECK UNDERSTANDING

TRY IT OUT

ERROR ALERT Failing to adjust after finding the sum of front-end digits.

Front-End Estimation

MENU
Dinner Specials
(Drink, salad, and tax included)

Shrimp Basket	$4.79
Steak Supreme	$6.45
Chicken Teriyaki	$5.35
Giant Pork Ribs	$3.69

LEARN ABOUT IT

EXPLORE Examine the Data
To estimate the total cost of a shrimp dinner and a chicken dinner, Cindy added $4 and $5.

Think about her method. Try it with other pairs of dinners and decide if it is a good way to estimate the total.

TALK ABOUT IT **See teaching notes.**

1. Is Cindy's estimate for the shrimp and chicken dinners more or less than the actual total? How do you know?
2. Does Cindy's method always give a low estimate? Explain.
3. Can you think of a way to improve Cindy's estimate?

Here is how you can use **front-end estimation** and adjust to find a closer estimate.

Estimate	Adjust
$ 8.57	$ 8.57
+ 7.39	+ 7.39
15	about $1

Estimate: $16

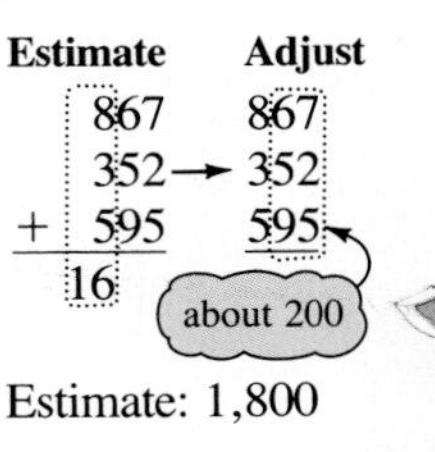

Estimate: 1,800

PRACTICE

Use front-end estimation to estimate each sum.

1. $9.45 + 5.69 — **$15.00**
2. 856 + 438 — **1,300**
3. 232 + 985 + 361 — **1,600**
4. 6,511 + 7,295 — **14,000**
5. 3,128 + 8,693 — **12,000**

Answers may vary. Sample answers given.

6. Is $7 enough for a $5.49 dinner and a $1.98 dessert? **no**

66

More Practice, page 501, set E

TEACHING OPTIONS

RETEACHING TIPS Students highlight the front-end digits in 1 color and the other digits in another color. After they add front-end digits, they adjust for the amount in the other color, then add that adjustment to the front-end sum. Assign Reteaching Supplement 24.

ENRICHMENT **Family Math** At home, students cover the sum on a cash-register receipt. They find the approximate column sum using front-end estimation, adjusting as necessary. They compare the estimate with the exact sum to see how close they were. A family member checks their estimate.

Midchapter Review/Quiz

Find the sums and differences using mental math.

1.	2.	3.	4.	5.	6.
60	400	80	600	7,000	500
+ 30	+ 900	− 50	− 200	+ 4,000	− 500
90	**1,300**	**30**	**400**	**11,000**	**0**

Estimate the sum or difference. **Answers may vary. Sample answer given.**

7.	8.	9.	10.	11.	12.
232	837	728	583	$7.23	644
+ 741	− 256	− 64	+ 77	− 4.75	+ 365
973	**600**	**670**	**660**	**$2.00**	**1,000**

Find the sums.

13.	14.	15.	16.	17.	18.
84	367	402	$3.57	843	975
+ 19	+ 221	+ 689	+ 4.99	+ 79	+ 268
103	**588**	**1,091**	**$8.56**	**922**	**1,243**

19.	20.	21.	22.	23.	24.
27	68	452	$8.95	9,632	846
45	13	68	4.21	906	3,257
+ 63	+ 9	+ 541	+ 2.58	+ 1,843	+ 2,182
135	**90**	**1,061**	**$15.74**	**12,381**	**6,285**

25. 50 + 16 + 50
26. 80 + 45 + 20
27. 16 + 20 + 10
28. 89 + 458 + 35
29. 961 + 422 + 5
30. 1,356 + 15 + 408

PROBLEM SOLVING

31. Becky used place value blocks to show the addends 32 + 168. How many hundreds, tens, and ones pieces did she use? Which pieces did she need for the sum? **See Additional Answers.**
32. George has six place value blocks. He has two each of the hundreds, tens, and ones pieces. How many 3-digit numbers can he show if he does not use zero? **8**
33. Dana's mom bought her 3 shirts, a white one, a blue one, and a red one. She also bought her a pair of blue jeans and a pair of white jeans. How many different outfits can Dana make? **6**
34. Bob estimated that he would use 555 calories by rollerskating for one and a half hours and use 425 calories by swimming for one hour. Is this more or less than 1,000 calories? **less**

67

3. Practice and Apply

Basic	1-6; 2-10, 19-34
Average	1-6; 1-34
Extended	1-6; 5-10, 21-34

Additional Answers: See p. T79.

PRACTICE

In the Midchapter Review/Quiz, how will you do Exercises 1-6? (Use mental math.) *How are Exercises 7-12 different from Exercises 13-24?* (Exercises 7-12 are estimates; Exercises 13-24 are exact sums.)

ITEM ANALYSIS The following table correlates the Midchapter Review/Quiz items with the lesson objectives.

Items	Objectives
1-6	3-1
7-12	3-2
13-18	3-4
19-30	3-5
32, (33)	3-3
33, 34	3-6
35	3-2

3-7

Close and Assess

WRITE WHAT YOU THINK

Have students write paragraphs explaining how to estimate the sum of 663 and 737 using front-end estimation. They should explain how to look at the addends and how to make any necessary adjustments. (600 + 700 = 1,300; 60 + 40 = 100; 1,300 + 100 = 1,400)

Quick Quiz

Estimate sums. (Answers may vary.)

1.	2.
$7.59	4,307
+ 8.45	+7,613
($16)	(12,000)

LESSON OPTIONS 3-8

Subtracting Whole Numbers: Making the Connection

OBJECTIVE 3-8 To use objects to develop an understanding of subtracting 2- and 3-digit numbers

PREBOOK ACTIVITIES

QUICK REVIEW

Subtract mentally.

1. 130 − 50 (80)	**2.** 110 − 40 (70)
3. 500 − 100 (400)	**4.** 900 − 300 (600)
5. 1,400 − 700 (700)	**6.** 1,500 − 600 (900)
7. 160 − 90 (70)	**8.** 1,200 − 800 (400)
9. 1,200 − 400 (800)	**10.** 1,700 − 900 (800)

PRIOR KNOWLEDGE

Have students suggest situations when they might need to subtract. (Possible answers: to find how many are left; to compare amounts) Have students relate the 2 numbers in a subtraction problem in terms of size. (Possible answer: You subtract the smaller number from the larger number.)

COMMUNICATION

Discussing Math Write 35 and 17 on the chalkboard. Ask a volunteer to add the numbers, showing any trades needed. (52; trade 10 ones for 1 ten.) Then have another volunteer subtract the same 2 numbers and point out the necessary trade. (Trade 1 ten for 10 ones, showing 2 tens and 15 ones, then subtract; 18.) Have students compare and contrast the 2 trades. (Possible answer: Both trades link 10 of one place to 1 of the next greater place. In addition, you trade *up* when you have 10 or more in a place; in subtraction, you trade *down* to get 10 or more in a place so you can subtract the other number.)

EXPLORE AND CONNECT

Materials: TA 6 (Place Value Models), TA 3 (Number Cards 1-9), TA 8 (3-Digit Place Value Charts)

Grouping Suggestion: cooperative learning pairs

Students explore subtraction by formulating problems with various trades. Partners select 6 number cards, then use them to form two 3-digit numbers to subtract with place value materials. The first problem should require *no* trades, such as 357 − 126 = 231. Partners discuss how to create the problems and how to show the subtraction with models. Then partners make up 3 other subtraction problems with the following trades: 1) trade 1 ten for 10 ones, 2) trade 1 hundred for 10 tens, 3) trade 1 hundred for 10 tens *and* trade 1 ten for 10 ones. Partners take turns formulating, showing, and checking the problems. Conclude by having students generalize how to know when a trade is needed in subtraction. (In any place, trade whenever the bottom digit is greater than the top digit.)

CONNECTIONS Use these anytime.

Problem of the Day

Number Sense Danielle has 4 hundreds, 3 tens, and 6 ones blocks. Identify the greatest and the least possible 3-digit numbers she could subtract from that number. Then give the greatest and least possible 2-digit numbers she could subtract. (436, 100; 99, 10)

Math Connections

Logical Reasoning All missing digits are the same. Complete the problem.

```
  □ 9 2
− 2 □ □
  6 0 4
```

(Substitute 8: 892 − 288)

Patterns

Calculator Use a calculator to discover the pattern, then continue it 3 more times.

547, 498, 449, 400, (351), (302), (253)

(Pattern: Subtract 49.)

Classwork and Homework Supplements

Practice

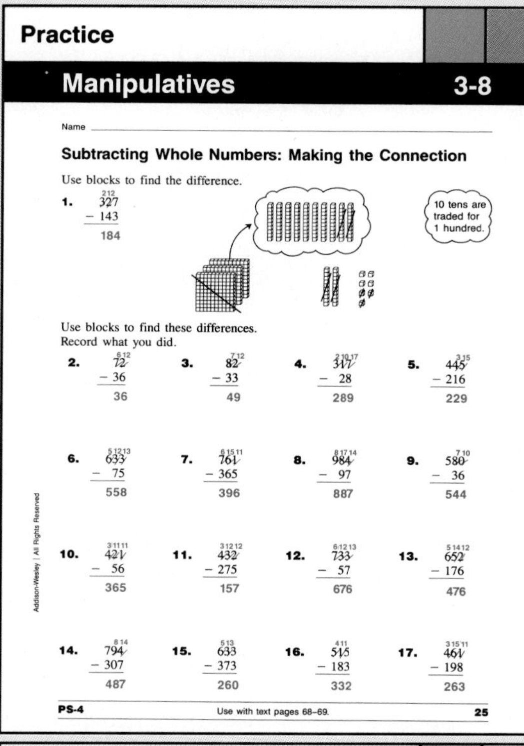
Manipulatives 3-8

Name

Subtracting Whole Numbers: Making the Connection

Use blocks to find the difference.

1. 327 − 143 = 184

10 tens are traded for 1 hundred.

Use blocks to find these differences. Record what you did.

2. 72 − 36 = 36	3. 82 − 33 = 49	4. 317 − 28 = 289	5. 445 − 216 = 229
6. 633 − 75 = 558	7. 761 − 365 = 396	8. 984 − 97 = 887	9. 580 − 36 = 544
10. 421 − 56 = 365	11. 432 − 275 = 157	12. 733 − 57 = 676	13. 652 − 176 = 476
14. 794 − 307 = 487	15. 633 − 373 = 260	16. 515 − 183 = 332	17. 461 − 198 = 263

PS-4 Use with text pages 68–69. 25

Building Thinking Skills

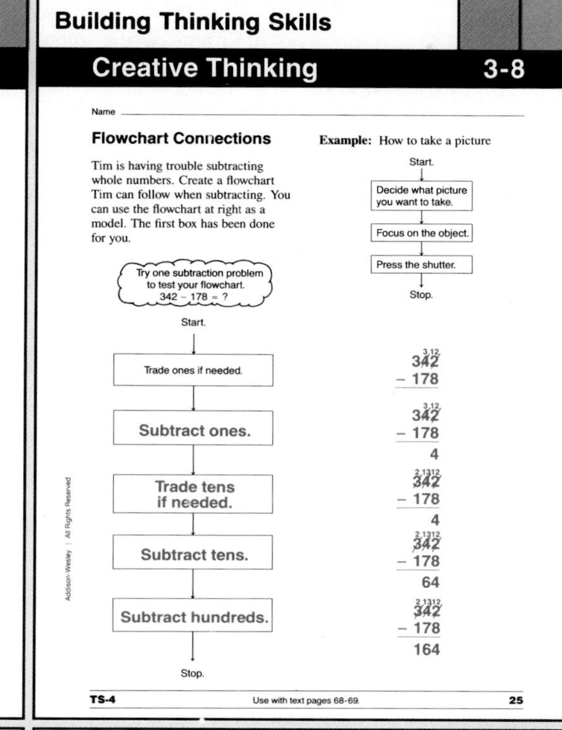
Creative Thinking 3-8

Name

Flowchart Connections

Tim is having trouble subtracting whole numbers. Create a flowchart Tim can follow when subtracting. You can use the flowchart at right as a model. The first box has been done for you.

Example: How to take a picture

Start.
Decide what picture you want to take.
Focus on the object.
Press the shutter.
Stop.
Try one subtraction problem to test your flowchart. 342 − 178 = ?
Start.
Trade ones if needed.
Subtract ones.
Trade tens if needed.
Subtract tens.
Subtract hundreds.
Stop.
342 − 178
342 − 178 4
342 − 178 4
342 − 178 64
342 − 178 164

TS-4 Use with text pages 68–69. 25

Reteaching

Manipulatives 3-8

Name

Subtracting Whole Numbers: Making the Connection

53 − 28

Start with 53.

Subtract the ones. Trade if necessary.

Trade 1 ten for 10 ones. Cross out 8 ones.

5 ones left — 5

Subtract the tens.

Cross out 2 tens.

2 tens left — 25

Use blocks to find these differences. Record what you did.

1. 38 − 19 = 19
2. 443 − 181 = 262
3. 632 − 327 = 305

Use blocks to find these differences.

4. 45 − 27 = 18 (Trade 1 ten for 10 ones.)
5. 76 − 9 = 67 (Trade 1 ten for 10 ones.)
6. 329 − 87 = 242 (Trade 1 hundred for 10 tens.)

7. 45 − 27 = 18	8. 23 − 15 = 8	9. 64 − 26 = 38	10. 92 − 57 = 35	11. 85 − 38 = 47
12. 155 − 36 = 119	13. 479 − 287 = 192	14. 326 − 146 = 180	15. 173 − 55 = 118	16. 896 − 263 = 633

RS-4 Use with text pages 68–69. 25

Challenges

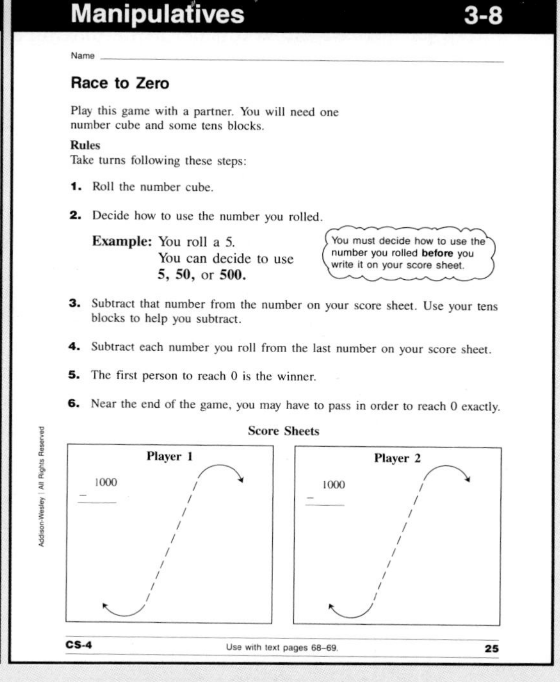
Manipulatives 3-8

Name

Race to Zero

Play this game with a partner. You will need one number cube and some tens blocks.

Rules

Take turns following these steps:

1. Roll the number cube.
2. Decide how to use the number you rolled.

   Example: You roll a 5. You can decide to use **5, 50,** or **500.**

   You must decide how to use the number you rolled **before** you write it on your score sheet.
3. Subtract that number from the number on your score sheet. Use your tens blocks to help you subtract.
4. Subtract each number you roll from the last number on your score sheet.
5. The first person to reach 0 is the winner.
6. Near the end of the game, you may have to pass in order to reach 0 exactly.

Score Sheets

Player 1
1000
Player 2
1000

CS-4 Use with text pages 68–69. 25

Options for Individual Needs

3-8

Basic

Exercises 1-5
Skills Bank, pp. 463, 464

Supplements
Reteaching 25 or
Practice 25

Average

Exercises 1-5
Skills Bank, pp. 463, 464

Supplements
Practice 25
Challenges 25 or
Thinking Skills 25

Extended

Exercises 1-5

Supplements
Challenges 25
Thinking Skills 25

Other Resources:
Problem-Solving Experiences in Mathematics, Grade 4, Problem 7
Math In Stride, Grade 4, p. 14
Mathematics, A Way of Thinking, Lessons 8-20, 8-21

LESSON PLAN 3-8

OBJECTIVE 3-8

To use objects to develop an understanding of subtracting 2- and 3-digit numbers

Materials: TA 11 (Blank Spinners), place value blocks, TA 8 (3-Digit Place Value Charts), index cards

Alternative Materials: TA 6 (Place Value Models)

Grouping Suggestion: pairs

1. MOTIVATE AND TEACH

LEARN ABOUT IT

EXPLORE ► **Explain why the take-away number must be less than the top number.** (You cannot take away more than the number with which you began.)
► **Identify places in the take-away number that may have greater digits than those places in the top number. Explain why.** (The value of the hundreds in the top number must be greater than that in the take-away number, but the take-away number can have more tens and ones; trade to subtract those places.)

TALK ABOUT IT ► **In the example shown, explain how to subtract tens.** (Trade 1 hundred for 10 tens; 12 tens − 7 tens = 5 tens.)
Student Edition answers: **1.** 1 hundred for 10 tens **2.** ones; It is the place of least value and you start on the right and move left.

2. CHECK UNDERSTANDING

ERROR ALERT Taking the top number away from the bottom number instead of trading. Making incorrect trades.

Subtracting Whole Numbers
Making the Connection

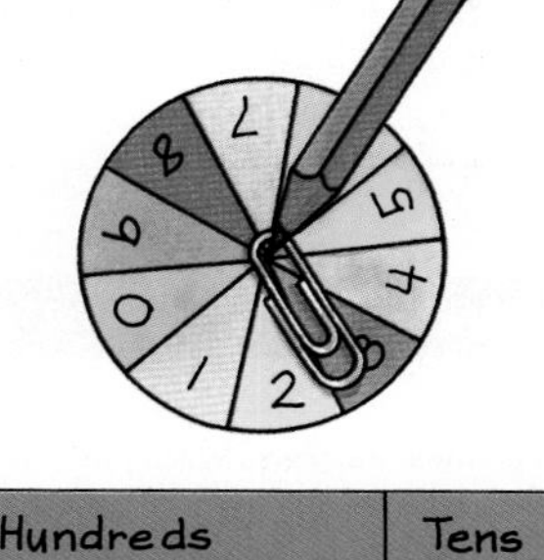

LEARN ABOUT IT

EXPLORE Use a Place Value Model
Work in groups. Use a spinner with the digits 0–9 and make piles of blocks.

- Each partner spins 3 times. The first spin gives the number of hundreds blocks for your pile. The second gives the numbers of tens and the third gives the number of ones. Make your pile and write the number for it in the top row of a table like the one given.
- Each partner now spins 3 times to give the number of hundreds, tens, and ones to take away from your pile.
- Spin again as needed until the take away number is less than the number in your pile. Write the take away number in the table.
- Take from your pile the number of blocks shown. Trade if you need to. In the table write the number of blocks left.
- Do this several times.

Hundreds	Tens	Ones
6	2	5
Take Away 4	7	3
Number Left		

Take away.
Trade if needed.

TALK ABOUT IT See teaching notes.

1. Describe a trade you might make when taking blocks from the pile.
2. Is it better to start taking away the ones or should you start with the hundreds? Explain.

TEACHING OPTIONS

RETEACHING TIPS Have each student write this hint on an index card: Enough to subtract? If NO, then TRADE. To guide them, students put the cards above each place on a place value chart *before* they subtract. Assign Reteaching Supplement 25.

ENRICHMENT In the subtraction problem below, each different letter stands for a different digit. Students replace the letters with digits to make it work. (Answers will vary. Sample: 864 − 432 = 432.)

```
  TWO
 −ONE
 ----
  ONE
```

You have laid out blocks, taken some away, and found how many were left. Now you will see a way to record what you have done. This procedure can help you find differences such as 428 − 153.

What You Do | **What You Record**

1. Lay out the blocks. Write how many you want to take away.

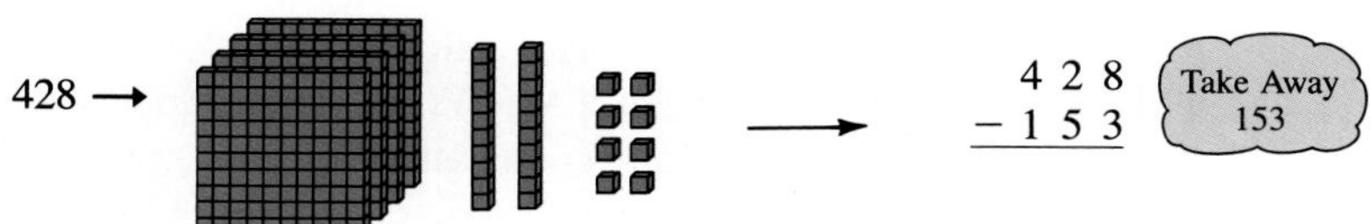

2. Take away 3 ones. Trade if needed.

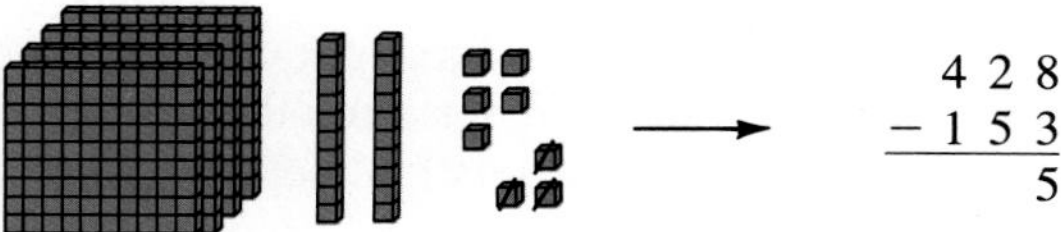

3. Take away 5 tens. Trade if needed.
Take away 1 hundred.

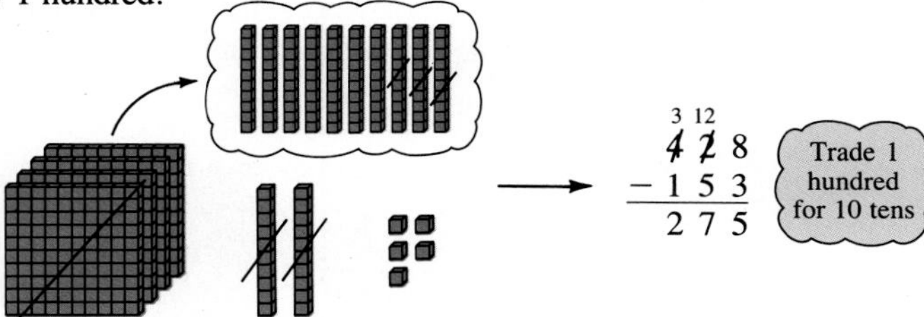

TRY IT OUT See Additional Answers.

Use blocks to find these differences. Record what you did.

1. 82 − 37 **2.** 175 − 58 **3.** 362 − 137 **4.** 436 − 271

5. Use blocks to find the difference of two 3-digit numbers of your choice.

69

3. Practice and Apply

Basic	1-5
Average	1-5
Extended	1-5

Additional Answers: See p. T79.

PRACTICE

Relate What You Do to What You Record in Step 1. (The top number tells how many blocks to lay out; the bottom number is how many you subtract.) *Why are 3 ones crossed out in Step 2?* (to show 3 ones taken away) *Why is a trade made in Step 3?* (not enough tens to take away 5; by trading 1 hundred for 10 tens, the total value of 428 is unchanged, but you get enough tens to take away 5.) *How is the trade recorded?* (Cross out 1 hundred, leaving 3 hundreds; put 10 new tens with the 2 tens already there for 12 tens.) *Continue working with a partner to complete the Try It Out exercises.*

3-8

Close and Assess

WRITE WHAT YOU THINK

Have students write paragraphs explaining how to do this subtraction problem: 243 − 180. They should list each step to follow, explain any trades to make, and give the difference. (63; Check students' writing.)

Quick Quiz

Find the differences. Use place value materials as needed. Record what you do.

1. 74 − 28 (46)
2. 381 − 146 (235)

LESSON OPTIONS 3-9

Subtracting Whole Numbers

OBJECTIVE 3-9 To subtract whole numbers of 2, 3, and 4 digits

PREBOOK ACTIVITIES

QUICK REVIEW

Tell how many trades are needed. Do not subtract.

1. $\begin{array}{r} 80 \\ -52 \\ \hline \end{array}$ (1) **2.** $\begin{array}{r} 148 \\ -96 \\ \hline \end{array}$ (1) **3.** $\begin{array}{r} 334 \\ -187 \\ \hline \end{array}$ (2) **4.** $\begin{array}{r} 796 \\ -686 \\ \hline \end{array}$ (0) **5.** $\begin{array}{r} 215 \\ -109 \\ \hline \end{array}$ (1)

PRIOR KNOWLEDGE

Have students make up situations for comparing numbers. (Possible answers: how much older one person is than another; how much more one object weighs than another) Have students justify subtraction as the correct operation in such cases. (Possible answer: Subtract to compare 2 amounts because the difference tells how much greater or less one number is than the other.

COMMUNICATION

Discussing and Reading Math Write these phrases on the chalkboard: *older than, longer than, smaller than, hotter than, heavier than.* Have students read the phrases to determine how they are alike. (All make comparisons using the suffix *-er* with a describing root word, followed by *than.*) Have students link such phrases to an operation. (Subtract to compare 2 amounts.) Ask students to suggest other phrases that compare. (Possible answers: *shorter than, colder than, faster than*)

EXPLORE AND CONNECT

Materials: calculators, place value blocks
Alternative Materials: TA 6 (Place Value Models)
Grouping Suggestion: cooperative learning groups of 4
Students use various calculation methods to find differences. Write these 2 number lists on the chalkboard: 824, 713, 642, 531; 187, 296, 378, 469. A group member picks 1 number from each list to form a subtraction equation, such as 824 − 187. That student subtracts on a calculator while other group members find the difference in other ways: using models, paper and pencil, or any estimation method. When they finish, students compare differences, discuss any discrepancies, and evaluate the estimate. Trading tasks, students repeat the activity 3 times. Conclude by having students summarize how they indicated trades. (Answers will vary.) Have students tell their preferred calculation method and give a reason. (Answers will vary.)

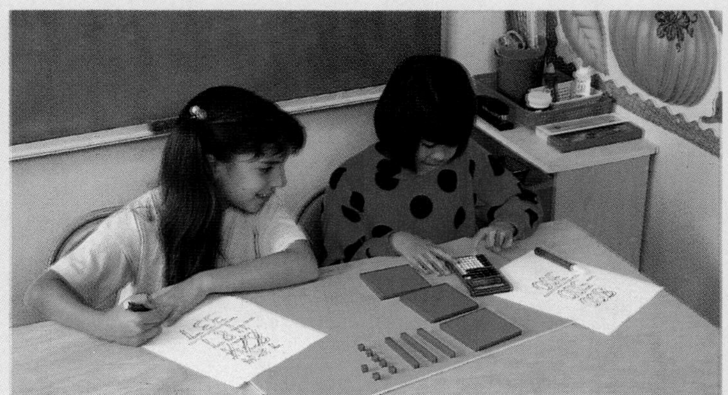

CONNECTIONS Use these anytime.

Problem of the Day

The Grand Tour Jean-Louis and his family are visiting the United States from France. They want to tour by car. They plan to drive from New York to Washington, D.C. (237 mi), on to Boston (448 mi), and then back to New York. If they will travel a total of 893 mi, how far is the distance from Boston to New York? (208 mi)

Math Connection

Calculator Predict how many times you can subtract 113 from 850. Then use a calculator to test your prediction. (You can subtract it 7 times, leaving 59.)

Patterns

Subtract? Find the pattern. Continue it as far as you can before reaching zero. You can use a calculator after you do the first 3. 852 − 39 = 813; 813 − 49 = 764; 764 − 59 = 705 (Subtract 10 more each time—705 − 69 = 636; 636 − 79 = 557; 557 − 89 = 468; 468 − 99 = 369; 369 − 109 = 260; 260 − 119 = 141; 141 − 129 = 12)

Classwork and Homework Supplements

Practice — Skills Maintenance 3-9

Name

Subtracting Whole Numbers

Find the differences.

1. 68 − 19 = 49
2. 51 − 18 = 33
3. 82 − 27 = 55
4. 66 − 48 = 18
5. 573 − 81 = 492
6. 455 − 128 = 327
7. 937 − 19 = 918
8. 762 − 481 = 281
9. 721 − 256 = 465
10. 537 − 169 = 368
11. 385 − 196 = 189
12. 444 − 285 = 159
13. 5,556 − 2,658 = 2,898
14. 4,392 − 1,774 = 2,618
15. 6,432 − 265 = 6,167
16. 4,324 − 427 = 3,897
17. 6,442 − 2,795 = 3,647
18. 6,314 − 5,719 = 595
19. 8,735 − 5,787 = 2,948
20. 4,744 − 3,658 = 1,086
21. $42.38 − 9.39 = $32.99
22. $17.71 − 2.88 = $14.83
23. $92.63 − 65.94 = $26.69
24. $15.35 − 13.69 = $ 1.66
25. 846 − 51 = 795
26. 444 − 328 = 116
27. $5.72 − $0.90 = $4.82

Building Thinking Skills — Problem Solving 3-9

Name

Disappearing Cups

The Great Eatery ordered 1,325 packages of cups for the year. Complete the table to show how many packages of cups were left at the end of each month. Then answer the questions.

Month	Number of Packages Used	Number of Packages Left
Jan.	36	1,289
Feb.	74	1,215
March	57	1,158
April	43	1,115
May	146	969
June	139	830
July	119	711
Aug.	128	583
Sept.	120	463
Oct.	131	332
Nov.	112	220
Dec.	186	34

1. How many more packages of cups were used in the second half of the year than the first half? 301 packages
2. How many more packages were used in December than in June? 47 packages
3. During which month did the Great Eatery finish using half of its supply of cups? August

Reteaching — Manipulatives 3-9

Name

Subtracting Whole Numbers

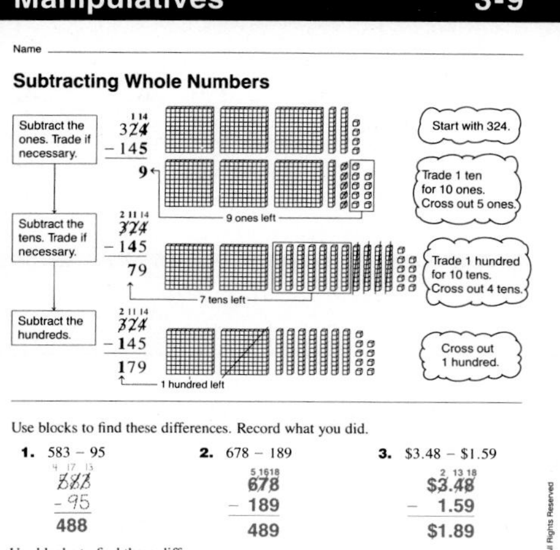

Subtract the ones. Trade if necessary.
Start with 324.
Trade 1 ten for 10 ones. Cross out 5 ones.
9 ones left
Subtract the tens. Trade if necessary.
Trade 1 hundred for 10 tens. Cross out 4 tens.
7 tens left
Subtract the hundreds.
Cross out 1 hundred.
1 hundred left

Use blocks to find these differences. Record what you did.

1. 583 − 95 = 488
2. 678 − 189 = 489
3. $3.48 − $1.59 = $1.89

Use blocks to find these differences.

4. 835 − 276 = 559 (Trade tens and hundreds.)
5. 375 − 87 = 288 (Trade 1 hundred for 10 tens.)
6. $7.34 − 3.68 = $3.66 (Trade.)
7. 914 − 456 = 458
8. 853 − 386 = 467
9. 772 − 475 = 297
10. 683 − 94 = 589
11. $5.72 − 1.86 = $3.86

Challenges — Patterns 3-9

Name

Hotel Hunt

Below are the numbers on some of the doors of a 6-story hotel. The other numbers have fallen off the doors.

(You can move up↑, down↓, or diagonally↗↙.)

1. Analyze the number pattern. Then number the hotel doors whose numbers are missing.

280	289	298	307	316
230	239	248	257	266
180	189	198	207	216
130	139	148	157	166
80	89	98	107	116
30	39	48	57	66

2. Describe the number patterns:
   What happens when you move → ? 9 is added.
   What happens when you move ↓ ? 50 is subtracted.
3. What happens for each of these moves?
   ↑→ add 59 ↓→ subtract 59
   ↗ add 59 ↗ subtract 59
4. Show with arrows two ways to get from 148 to 266. For each way, write a number sentence that describes what is happening. Answers will vary.
   ↗ ↗ 148 + 59 + 59 = 266
   ↑ → ↗ 148 + 50 + 9 + 59 = 266

Options for Individual Needs

3-9

Basic

Exercises 1-9, 14-22
Data Bank, p. 470
Skills Bank, p. 464
More Practice, p. 502, set A

Supplements
Reteaching 26 or
Practice 26
Thinking Skills 26

Average

Exercises 1-22
Data Bank, p. 470
Skills Bank, p. 464
More Practice, p. 502, set A

Supplements
Practice 26
Challenges 26 or
Thinking Skills 26

Extended

Exercises 4-22
Data Bank, p. 470

Supplements
Challenges 26
Thinking Skills 26

Other Resources:

Mathematics, A Way of Thinking, Lesson 8-23
Problem-Solving Experiences in Mathematics, Grade 4, Problem 1
Math In Stride, Grade 4, p. 16

LESSON PLAN 3-9

OBJECTIVE 3-9
To subtract whole numbers of 2, 3, and 4 digits

Materials: calculators, colored pencils

1. MOTIVATE AND TEACH

LEARN ABOUT IT

EXPLORE ► **Why is 514 compared to 365?** (The space flight would take 514 days, and a year has 365 days.)

TALK ABOUT IT ► **Explain the first trade needed.** (4 ones are not enough to take away 5 ones; trade 1 ten for 10 ones, combine the 10 new ones with the 4 ones already in place, then subtract 5.)
► **Why is a second trade needed?** (too few tens)
► **Explain how to use another operation to verify the difference.** (Add the difference to the take-away number; the sum should equal the top number.)
► **Compare Other Example D to Other Examples A-C.** (Other Example D uses money amounts, but you trade and subtract as you do with whole numbers.)
Student Edition answers: **1.** too few ones to take away 5 **2.** The first trade leaves 0 tens; trade 1 hundred for 10 tens, leaving 4 hundred. **3.** Answers may vary. **4.** A flight to Mars takes 149 more days than a year.

2. CHECK UNDERSTANDING

TRY IT OUT

ERROR ALERT Failing to indicate an amount traded away. Subtracting from the bottom up.

Subtracting Whole Numbers

LEARN ABOUT IT

EXPLORE **Analyze the Process**
How many days longer than a year would a space flight to Mars take? A year is 365 days.
You subtract because you need to take away one amount from another to find the difference.

Space Flight from Earth	
to Mercury	206 days
to Venus	288 days
to Mars	514 days

Subtract the ones. Trade if necessary.
$$\begin{array}{r} {}^{0\,14} \\ 5\,\cancel{1}\,\cancel{4} \\ -\,3\,6\,5 \\ \hline 9 \end{array}$$

Subtract the tens. Trade if necessary.
$$\begin{array}{r} {}^{4\;9\,14} \\ \cancel{5}\,\cancel{1}\,\cancel{4} \\ -\,3\,6\,5 \\ \hline 4\,9 \end{array}$$

Subtract the hundreds.
$$\begin{array}{r} {}^{4\;9\,14} \\ \cancel{5}\,\cancel{1}\,\cancel{4} \\ -\,3\,6\,5 \\ \hline 1\,4\,9 \end{array}$$

TALK ABOUT IT See teaching notes.

1. Why is it necessary to trade in the first step?
2. Explain the other trades.
3. How would you have estimated the difference?
4. Use a complete sentence to give a reasonable answer to the story problem.

Other Examples

A
$$\begin{array}{r} {}^{5\,13\,12} \\ \cancel{6}\,\cancel{4}\,\cancel{2} \\ -\,1\,7\,9 \\ \hline 4\,6\,3 \end{array}$$
Check: 463 + 179 = 642

B
$$\begin{array}{r} {}^{0\,11\,14} \\ \cancel{1}\,\cancel{2}\,\cancel{4} \\ -\,7\,8 \\ \hline 4\,6 \end{array}$$

C
$$\begin{array}{r} {}^{4\;15\,12\,14} \\ \cancel{5},\cancel{6}\,\cancel{3}\,\cancel{4} \\ -\,2,9\,5\,6 \\ \hline 2,6\,7\,8 \end{array}$$

D
$$\begin{array}{r} {}^{3\;\;15\,10} \\ \$5\,\cancel{4}.\,\cancel{6}\,\cancel{0} \\ -\,2\,1.\,8\,5 \\ \hline \$3\,2.\,7\,5 \end{array}$$

TRY IT OUT

1. 64 − 48 = **16**
2. 548 − 73 = **475**
3. 462 − 235 = **227**
4. 6,825 − 409 = **6,416**
5. 7,256 − 6,184 = **1,072**
6. $25.42 − 18.65 = **$6.77**

TEACHING OPTIONS

RETEACHING TIPS Students indicate both parts of a trade with a colored pencil. First they cross out the digit *from* which a trade is made, then show that the traded 10 goes *to* an amount already in place. After the trade is recorded, students subtract in that place. Assign Reteaching Supplement 26.

ENRICHMENT Have students use the digits 1-6 to build two 3-digit numbers whose sum is 957 and whose difference is 267. (612 and 345)

PRACTICE

Find the differences.

1. 59 − 45 = **14**	**2.** 238 − 69 = **169**	**3.** 593 − 465 = **128**	**4.** $8.26 − 3.81 = **4.45**	**5.** 4,529 − 635 = **3,894**

6. 78 − 45 **33** **7.** 230 − 149 **81** **8.** $62.08 − $38.52 **$23.56** **9.** 9,126 − 7,241 **1,885**

10. 6,843 − 2,589 **4,254** **11.** $3.59 − $1.29 **$2.30** **12.** 8,942 − 1,385 **7,557**

13. 456 − 94 **362** **14.** 1,549 − 425 **1,124** **15.** 6,961 − 4,682 **2,279**

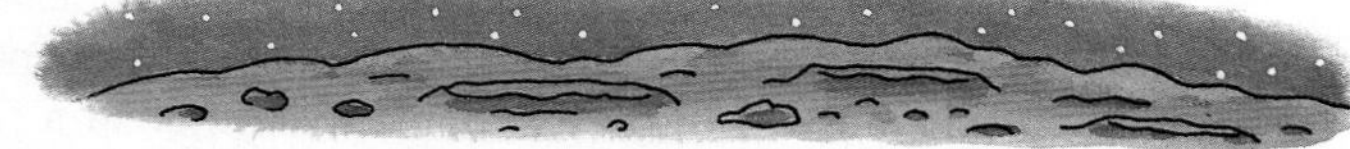

MATH REASONING Decide without subtracting if the difference is correct. Tell how you know. **See Additional Answers.**

16. 142 − 59 = 107 **17.** 356 − 28 = 298 **18.** 532 − 216 = 316

PROBLEM SOLVING

19. Science Data Bank Compare the number of days it takes Mars and Earth to go around the sun. Which takes longer? How many more days? See page 470. **Mars, 322 days**

DATA BANK

20. Temperatures on Venus can reach 850 degrees Fahrenheit. How much hotter is that than Earth's high temperature of 136 degrees? **714 degrees**

► **CALCULATOR**

When Jerry bought booklets about the planets, the price of the Mars booklet had been marked out. He discovered an easy way to use his calculator to find it. Here is what he did.

Booklets

Venus	$2.49
Mercury	$1.98
Mars	▬
Total	$5.64

Push	Enter	Push	Enter	Push	Enter	Push
ON/AC	5.64	−	1.98	−	2.49	=

Use Jerry's method to find the missing numbers.

21. Find the Mars book price. **$1.17**

22. 57 + 86 + ▥ = 237 **94**

More Practice, page 502, set A

71

3. Practice and Apply

Basic	1-9, 14-22
Average	1-22
Extended	4-22

Additional Answers: See p. T79.

PRACTICE

Of Exercises 1-5, which needs no trades? (Exercise 1)

APPLY

MATH REASONING ► **Explain how to use number sense to judge Exercise 16.** (142 minus 59 must have a difference less than 100, so 107 must be wrong.)

PROBLEM SOLVING ► **What clue suggests how to solve Problem 19? Explain.** (*Which takes longer* suggests a comparison; comparison suggests subtraction.)

CALCULATOR ► **Analyze how Jerry's method relates to the situation. Explain your reasoning.** (Jerry began with the total, then subtracted each known price; the difference is how much of the total cost remains, which gives the price of the Mars booklet.)

3-9

Close and Assess

WRITE WHAT YOU THINK

Have students write paragraphs explaining how to predict the number of trades required to subtract 524 − 118 and 426 − 168. Then have them subtract to verify their ideas and to find the differences. (406, 1 trade; 258, 2 trades; Check students' writing.)

Quick Quiz

Find the differences.
1. 473 − 180 (293)
2. 734 − 432 (302)
3. 831 − 378 (453)
4. $32.57 − $30.98 ($1.59)

LESSON OPTIONS 3-10

Subtracting with Middle Zeros

OBJECTIVE 3-10 To subtract whole numbers when there are one or more middle zeros

PREBOOK ACTIVITIES

QUICK REVIEW

Give the number that is 10 less.
1. 78 (68) **2.** 326 (316) **3.** 705 (695)
Give the number that is 100 less.
4. 543 (443) **5.** 9,601 (9,501) **6.** 3,020 (2,920)

PRIOR KNOWLEDGE

Have students tell what zero means. (nothing, no amount) List some numbers with zeros in the middle, such as 603 or 1,002. Ask students to identify the value of each place and to explain the importance of the zeros in the numbers. (Possible answer: A zero tells that a place is empty.) Review the rules about adding zero to or subtracting zero from any number. (Adding or subtracting zero does not change a number.) Have students guess what it means to subtract a number *from* zero. (Students may say that it is impossible to subtract something from nothing.) Explain that in this lesson they will learn a method for subtracting a number from zero in a given place.

COMMUNICATION

Discussing Math Explain to students that our number system often uses zero as a placeholder. Discuss the meaning of placeholder by writing the numbers 63 and 603 on the chalkboard. Have students explain what is the same about the 6 in 63 and the 0 in 603. (Both are in the tens place.) Ask what each of those numbers tells us. (6 tells there are 6 tens; 0 tells there are no tens.) Have students explain the relationship between the 6 and 0 in 603. (It shows there are 60 tens.)

EXPLORE AND CONNECT

Materials: TA 8 (3-Digit Place Value Charts), TA 5 (4-Digit Place Value Charts)
Grouping Suggestion: small cooperative learning groups
Students explore relationships between adjacent places with place value materials. Groups first generate a list of 3-digit numbers with a middle zero. Members take turns writing the numbers on a 3-digit place value chart in expanded form. Then students represent each number in a different way by trading all hundreds for an equivalent number of tens. For example, in the number 308, 3 hundreds are traded for 30 tens. Students should record the trades on the place value chart. Groups expand the activity to 4-digit numbers with 2 middle zeros. They take turns regrouping the numbers on a 4-digit place value chart and verbalizing the trades. For example, 2,003 has 2 thousands, 20 hundreds, or 200 tens. Encourage groups to discuss these relationships.

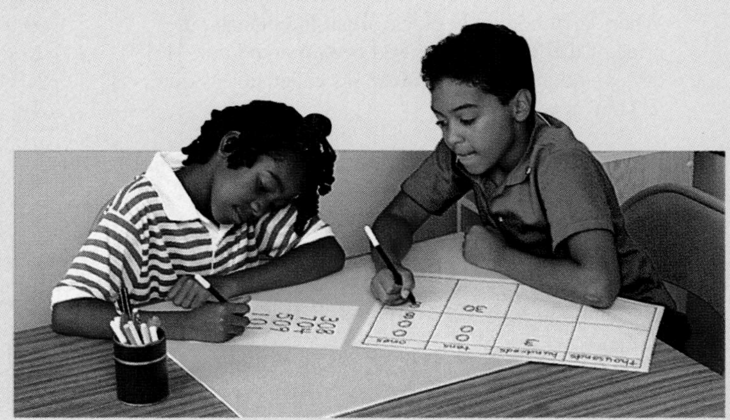

CONNECTIONS Use these anytime.

Problem of the Day

Patterns How many possible 3 digit numbers are there that have a middle zero? How many possible 4-digit numbers are there that have two middle zeros? Explain your answers. (90; 90. Forms of answers may vary: Students may write out all the numbers. They may also multiply the number of patterns per digit—10—by 9.)

Subject Integration

Social Studies The year 2001 is the first year of the twenty-first century. How many years is that from the year when you were born? (Answers will vary.)

Creative Thinking

Number Puzzle Substitute an even number for each letter to make a correct subtraction problem.

```
  S 0 T
- U S 2
  1 U S   (608 − 462 = 146)
```

Classwork and Homework Supplements

Practice

Skills Maintenance 3-10

Name ______

Subtracting with Middle Zeros

Find the differences.

1. 300 − 25 = 275
2. 805 − 49 = 756
3. 508 − 98 = 410
4. 406 − 176 = 230
5. 200 − 164 = 36
6. 502 − 159 = 343
7. 404 − 126 = 278
8. 800 − 347 = 453
9. 4,307 − 439 = 3,868
10. 5,900 − 1,375 = 4,525
11. 8,206 − 1,937 = 6,269
12. 9,501 − 187 = 9,314
13. $6.05 − 5.87 = $0.18
14. $7.07 − 2.38 = $4.69
15. $8.00 − 5.16 = $2.84
16. $3.50 − 1.25 = $2.25
17. $9.04 − 5.78 = $3.26
18. $4.00 − 0.66 = $3.34
19. $86.08 − 24.31 = $61.77
20. $47.01 − 8.44 = $38.57
21. 900 − 51: 900 − 51 = 849
22. 806 − 142: 806 − 142 = 664
23. 702 − 88: 702 − 88 = 614
24. 5,604 − 328: 5,604 − 328 = 5,276
25. 8,002 − 351: 8,002 − 351 = 7,651
26. $5.07 − $3.28: $5.07 − 3.28 = $1.79

Building Thinking Skills

Critical Thinking 3-10

Name ______

Draw Conclusions

Changes in school enrollment from year to year are recorded and studied because schools need to have enough teachers, equipment, and space for students.

Elementary School Enrollment in Greenvale County

School	1990	1991
Sunnyside	578	705
Greenwood	950	1,084
Briarpatch	2,009	1,262
Oak Tree	889	3,000

Study the chart and read the statements. If you agree with the conclusion, circle **Agree** and tell why. If you disagree, circle **Disagree** and tell why. Use the space below for computation. Answers may vary. Samples are given.

1. The combined increase in enrollment at Sunnyside and Greenwood is greater than the decrease at Briarpatch. Agree (Disagree)
   The total increase in the two schools is less than Briarpatch's decrease.
   705 − 578 = 127; 1,084 − 950 = 134; 127 + 134 = 261; 2,009 − 1,262 = 747; 747 > 261
2. Oak Tree gained almost three times as many students as Briarpatch lost. (Agree) Disagree
   When you compare the differences, 2,111 is almost three times 747.
   3,000 − 889 = 2,111; 2,009 − 1,262 = 747
3. The combined enrollment of Greenwood and Briarpatch in 1991 is about 700 less than that of Oak Tree. (Agree) Disagree
   The difference between the enrollments is 654.
   1,084 + 1,262 = 2,346; 3,000 − 2,346 = 654

Reteaching

Skills Review 3-10

Name ______

Subtracting with Middle Zeros

Subtract the ones. Trade if necessary. → Subtract the tens. Trade if necessary. → Subtract the hundreds.

607 − 238 = 9 (Trade 60 tens 7 ones for 59 tens and 17 ones.) → 607 − 238 = 69 (9 tens − 3 tens = 6 tens) → 607 − 238 = 369 (5 hundreds − 2 hundreds = 3 hundreds)

Find the differences.

1. 804 − 176 = 628 (Trade 80 tens 4 ones for 79 tens 14 ones.)
2. 909 − 68 = 841 (Do not need to trade ones.)
3. $6.05 − 1.47 = $4.58 (Trade 60 tens 5 ones for 59 tens 15 ones.)
4. 706 − 369 = 337
5. 503 − 219 = 284
6. 400 − 138 = 262
7. $9.01 − 4.76 = $4.25
8. 700 − 348 = 352
9. 503 − 259 = 244
10. 601 − 464 = 137
11. $8.05 − 5.77 = $2.28

Line up the ones digits. Then subtract.

12. 505 − 86: 505 − 86 = 419
13. 300 − 185: 300 − 185 = 115
14. $4.00 − $2.25: $4.00 − 2.25 = $1.75

Challenges

Computers 3-10

Name ______

Reverso

Read the flow chart to understand a trick called "Reverso."

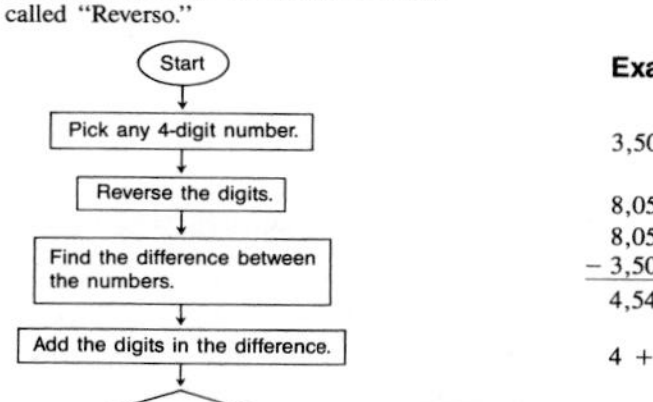

Start
Pick any 4-digit number.
Reverse the digits.
Find the difference between the numbers.
Add the digits in the difference.
Does the sum have only one digit?
no
Keep adding the digits.
yes
Stop

Example:

3,508

8,053

8,053 − 3,508 = 4,545

4 + 5 + 4 + 5 = 18

1 + 8 = 9

Try "Reverso" on these 4-digit numbers.

1. 5,002; 2,005; 5,002 − 2,005 = 2,997; 2 + 9 + 9 + 7 = 27; 2 + 7 = 9
2. 6,104; 4,016; 6,104 − 4,016 = 2,088; 2 + 0 + 8 + 8 = 18; 1 + 8 = 9
3. 4,055; 5,504; 5,504 − 4,055 = 1,449; 1 + 4 + 4 + 9 = 18; 1 + 8 = 9
4. 9,909; 9,099; 9,909 − 9,099 = 810; 8 + 1 + 0 = 9

5. What pattern do you find? The answer is always 9.

Pick a 4-digit number of your own and try "Reverso."

6. Does the pattern work for it, too? yes

Options for Individual Needs

Basic

Exercises 5-20
Computer Bank, p. 496
Calculator Bank, p. 485
More Practice, p. 502, set B

Supplements
Reteaching 27 or
Practice 27

Average

Exercises 1-20
Computer Bank, p. 496
Calculator Bank, p. 485
More Practice, p. 502, set B

Supplements
Practice 27
Challenges 27 or
Thinking Skills 27

Extended

Exercises 6-20
Computer Bank, p. 496
Calculator Bank, p. 485

Supplements
Challenges 27
Thinking Skills 27

Other Resources:
Problem-Solving Experiences in Mathematics, Grade 4, Problem 13
Math In Stride, Grade 4, p. 231

LESSON PLAN 3-10

OBJECTIVE 3-10
To subtract whole numbers when there are one or more middle zeros

Materials: TA 5 (4-Digit Place Value Charts)

1. MOTIVATE AND TEACH

LEARN ABOUT IT

EXPLORE ► **What is another way to state the question to show that you need to subtract?** (Possible answer: What is the difference in diameter of the two mirrors?)
► **How can you trade for more ones if there are no tens?** (Trade twice: trade 1 hundred for 10 tens, then trade 1 new ten for 10 ones.)
► **Why not trade 1 hundred for 100 ones? Explain your reasoning.** (Possible answer: You would have more ones than you need.)

TALK ABOUT IT ► **How does thinking about 40 tens help you subtract?** (It helps when trading 1 ten from 40 tens so that you can subtract from 39.)
Student Edition answers: **1.** 1 hundred = 10 tens, so 4 hundreds = 40 tens. **2.** Possible estimate: 400 − 250 = 150. **3.** The mirror at Kitt Peak Observatory has a diameter 147 cm greater than that of the mirror at Hooker Observatory.

2. CHECK UNDERSTANDING

TRY IT OUT

ERROR ALERT Misunderstanding how to regroup to trade tens for ones in a number with a middle zero. Changing middle zeros to nines and forgetting to trade from the first digit.

Subtracting with Middle Zeros

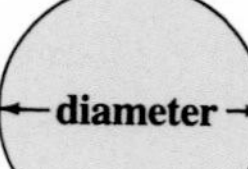

LEARN ABOUT IT

EXPLORE Analyze the Process
Some of the most powerful telescopes use circular mirrors to collect light from planets. How much greater is the diameter of the mirror at Kitt Peak Observatory than that of the mirror at Hooker Observatory?

How do you know that you can subtract to solve this problem?

Observatory	Diameter of mirror (cm)
Hale (California)	508
Kitt Peak (Arizona)	401
Lick (California)	305
McDonald (Texas)	272
Hooker (California)	254
Mauna Kea (Hawaii)	223

Subtract the ones. Trade if necessary.	Subtract the tens. Trade if necessary.	Subtract the hundreds.
(9 11) 4 0̸ 1̸ − 2 5 4 = 7	(3 9 11) 4̸ 0̸ 1̸ − 2 5 4 = 4 7	(3 9 11) 4̸ 0̸ 1̸ − 2 5 4 = 1 4 7

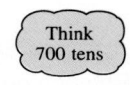

TALK ABOUT IT See teaching notes.

1. How do you know that 4 hundreds and 0 tens are 40 tens?
2. How would you have estimated the sum?
3. Use a complete sentence to give a reasonable answer to the story problem.

Other Examples

A (4 9 13) 5̸ 0̸ 3̸ − 68 = 435

B (9 14) 1 0̸ 4̸ − 67 = 37

C (7 9 10) 8̸ 0̸ 0̸ − 764 = 36

D (6 9 9 13) 7̸, 0̸ 0̸ 3̸ − 2,568 = 4,435

Think 700 tens

TRY IT OUT

1. 604 − 37 = 567
2. 408 − 246 = 162
3. 6,005 − 246 = 5,759
4. 402 − 164 = 238
5. $6.04 − 2.59 = $3.45

72

TEACHING OPTIONS

RETEACHING TIPS Have students use 4-digit place value charts to show the double trades when subtracting with middle zeros. Have them verbalize, then record each part of the trade on their papers. Assign Reteaching Supplement 27.

COMPUTER Math Practice Level II, IBM Educational Systems, Copyright 1985 For use with all levels of students. In lessons 4 and 6, students practice solving subtraction with 2- and 3-digit minuends. The digit of the answer is entered before the tens. Each lesson requires 15 minutes.

PRACTICE

Find the differences.

1. 703 − 58 = 645	**2.** 809 − 528 = 281	**3.** 501 − 316 = 185	**4.** 1,006 − 981 = 25	**5.** 2,308 − 924 = 1,384
6. 8,003 − 2,416 = 5,587	**7.** 4,602 − 2,537 = 2,065	**8.** 2,037 − 428 = 1,609	**9.** $67.08 − 4.63 = $62.45	**10.** $6.00 − 5.25 = $0.75

11. 6,403 − 378 6,025 **12.** 2,004 − 621 1,383 **13.** 502 − 81 421 **14.** $20.35 − $16.48 $3.87

APPLY

MATH REASONING Show that these differences are all the same. Give the next 3 differences. **See Additional Answers.**

15. 104 − 67 **16.** 204 − 167 **17.** 304 − 267 **18.** 404 − 367

PROBLEM SOLVING

19. Unfinished problem Choose the question or questions that can be answered using the following data. The diameter of the largest mirror in a Russian telescope is 600 cm, in an Australian telescope, 389 cm, and in a Chilean telescope, 401 cm.

(a.) How much larger is the Russian telescope mirror than the Australian?

b. Which telescope mirror is the largest in the world?

▶ **ESTIMATION**

20. Draw squares like this. Write the digits 4, 5, 6, 7, 8, and 9 in them to make the smallest difference, the largest difference, and the difference closest to 100. Check with your calculator.

745 − 698 987 − 456 586 − 479

More Practice, page 502, set B

73

3. Practice and Apply

Basic	5-20
Average	1-20
Extended	6-20

Additional Answers: See p. T79.

PRACTICE

Look at Exercises 9 and 10. Do the same rules apply for subtracting across a middle zero when working with dollar amounts? (yes)

APPLY

MATH REASONING ▶ **Explain the pattern of change in Exercises 15 to 18.** (Both numbers in each exercise increase by 100 each time.)

PROBLEM SOLVING ▶ **Is there data to answer both questions? Explain.** (There is data to answer Question **a.**, but you need sizes of all mirror telescopes in the world to answer Question **b.**)

ESTIMATION ▶ **For a larger difference, should the two numbers be closer or farther apart? Explain.** (farther apart, so the difference between them increases)

3-10

Close and Assess

SHOW WHAT YOU KNOW

Have students use 4-digit place value charts to show how to subtract when there are middle zeros. Each student makes up 2 sample problems, then uses the chart to show the trades. Pick students at random to explain the process they are following.

Quick Quiz

Find the difference.

1. 502 − 79 (423)
2. 7,007 − 3,575 (3,432)
3. 1,006 − 827 (179)
4. $9.00 − $1.04 ($7.96)

LESSON OPTIONS 3-11

Mental Math: Using Compensation

OBJECTIVE 3-11 To use the mental math technique of compensation to find sums and differences

PREBOOK ACTIVITIES

QUICK REVIEW

Add or subtract mentally.

1. 97 + 3 (100) **2.** 394 + 6 (400)
3. 32 − 2 (30) **4.** 804 − 4 (800)
5. 296 + 4 (300) **6.** 703 − 3 (700)
7. 912 − 12 (900) **8.** 695 + 5 (700)

PRIOR KNOWLEDGE

Have students explain the compensation strategy for finding sums. (Possible answer: Adjust addends up or down to form easier numbers to work with.) Write 19 + 7 on the chalkboard. Ask a volunteer to use compensation to find the sum, verbalizing the steps involved. (Possible answer: Add 1 to 19, making 20; subtract 1 from 7, making 6; 20 + 6 = 26.) Then write **increase** and **decrease** on the board. Ask volunteers to define each. (Possible answers: Increase is to make bigger; decrease is to make smaller.) Finally, have students relate these terms to compensation. (Possible answer: Increase or decrease addends by the same amount when compensating.)

COMMUNICATION

Discussing and Writing in Math Ask students to relate the terms **increase** and **decrease** to addition and subtraction. (Increase relates to addition, decrease relates to subtraction.) Have students complete each statement in their Math Journals: To increase a number, ______. To decrease a number, ______. (Answers will vary. Sample answers: add an amount to make the number greater; subtract an amount to make the number smaller.)

EXPLORE AND CONNECT

Materials: place value blocks
Alternative Materials: TA 6 (Place Value Models)
Grouping Suggestion: small cooperative learning groups
Write 405 + 295 (700) and 405 − 295 (110) on the chalkboard. For the first example, 2 students each use place value blocks to show one of the numbers. A third student demonstrates how to use compensation to add 5 ones to 295 and to remove 5 ones from 405 to make 300 + 400 = 700. Groups then review how they **increased** and **decreased** the numbers by the same amount. Next, the group explores how to use compensation to create an easier subtraction problem. Members discuss, adjust, show, and record their method. (Sample method: Add 5 to 295 to get 300; add 5 to 405 to get 410; subtract.) Students then use the standard method to do the subtraction. Last, students compare the accuracy and efficiency of different methods.

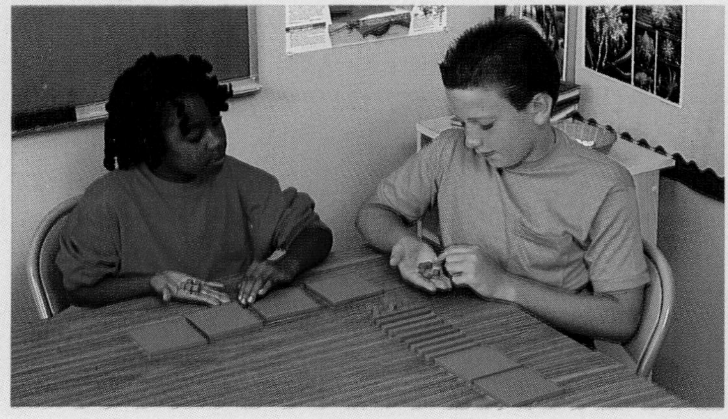

CONNECTIONS Use these anytime.

Problem of the Day

Money Duane is shopping. He buys 2 pairs of socks at $1.98 each and 2 T-shirts at $4.98 each. Use mental math to find his total bill. ($13.92)

Creative Thinking

Algebra A butcher has an old balance scale that he uses to weigh meat. With only a 2−, a 4−, and a 5− lb weight, how can he measure 3 lb of hamburger? (Use the 2− and 5−lb weights. Place the 2 lb in one pan and the 5 lb in the other. Then add meat to the 2−lb pan until the scale balances.)

Patterns

Add or Subtract? Study the pattern, then continue it by filling in the next 4 numbers: 398, 387, 365, 332, 288, ______, ______, ______, ______,. (The pattern decreases by 11 more each time: 233, 167, 90, 2.)

Classwork and Homework Supplements

Practice

Mental Math 3-11

Name ______________________

Using Compensation

Use compensation to find these sums and differences.

1. 48 + 52 = 100
2. 29 + 121 = 150
3. 253 + 67 = 320
4. 16 + 199 = 215
5. 82 − 42 = 40
6. 92 − 12 = 80
7. 324 − 99 = 225
8. 663 − 403 = 260
9. 429 + 97 = 526
10. 758 − 204 = 554

Estimate these sums and differences. Use any method you wish. Answers may vary. Sample answers given.

11. 298 + 53 350
12. 355 − 101 250
13. 679 + 111 800
14. 694 + 86 800
15. 97 − 49 50
16. 352 − 47 300
17. 810 − 386 400
18. 11 + 119 + 60 190
19. 512 − 298 200
20. 36 + 22 + 431 490

28 Use with text pages 74–75. PS-4

Building Thinking Skills

Mental Math 3-11

Name ______________________

Reasonable Answers?

Use mental math to determine if the following answers would be reasonable answers to see displayed on your calculator. Write **yes** or **no.** If the answer is no, write the correct answer.

1. 125 + 199 — no; 324 — 325.
2. 97 − 41 — yes — 56.
3. 302 + 61 — yes — 363.
4. 558 + 299 — no; 857 — 757.
5. 86 − 31 — no; 55 — 45.
6. 95 − 28 — yes — 67.
7. 245 − 97 — yes — 148.
8. 143 − 39 — no; 104 — 114.
9. 224 − 196 — no; 28 — 19.
10. 339 + 296 — no; 635 — 535.
11. 428 + 98 — yes — 526.
12. 345 − 29 — no; 316 — 326.

28 Use with text pages 74–75. TS-4

Reteaching

Mental Math 3-11

Name ______________________

Using Compensation

Use compensation to find 348 + 202.

Change one of the numbers so that it has 0 as the last digit. 348 + 202 (Looks easier to change 202 to 200.)	→	Compensate—increase one addend and decrease the other addend the same amount. 348 → up 2 → + 202 → down 2 →	→	Add. 350 + 200 = 550

Use compensation to find 468 − 299.

Change one of the numbers so that it has 0 as the last digit. 468 − 299 (Looks easier to change 299 to 300.)	→	Compensate—increase or decrease each number the same amount. 368 → up 1 → − 299 → up 1 →	→	Subtract. 469 − 300 = 169

Use compensation to find these sums or differences. Write the number you used to increase or decrease.

1. 18 + 42 = 60 2
2. 154 + 46 = 200 4
3. 125 − 87 = 38 3
4. 296 + 222 = 518 4

Use compensation to find these sums or differences. Write the number you used to increase or decrease.

5. 74 + 26 = 100 4
6. 29 − 14 = 15 1
7. 21 + 49 = 70 1
8. 78 − 23 = 55 2

Use compensation to find these sums or differences.

9. 15 + 45 = 60
10. 86 − 22 = 64
11. 98 + 452 = 550
12. 505 − 82 = 423

28 Use with text pages 74–75. RS-4

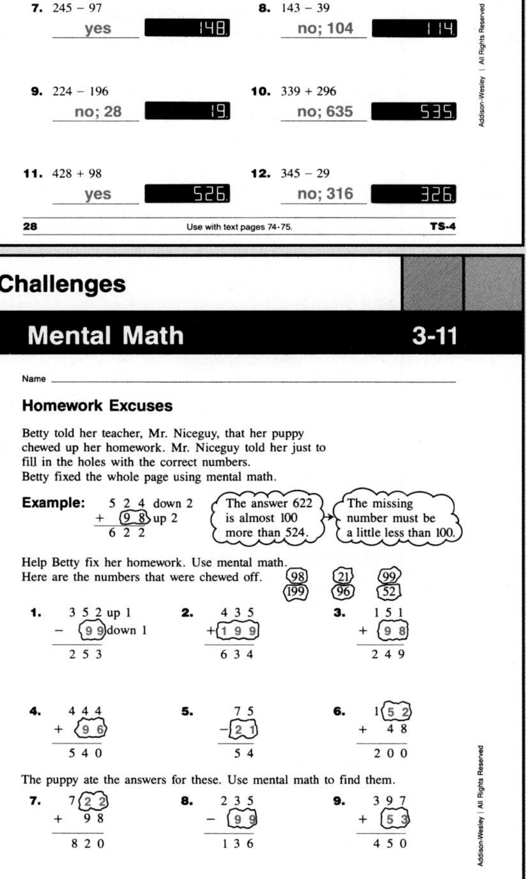

Challenges

Mental Math 3-11

Name ______________________

Homework Excuses

Betty told her teacher, Mr. Niceguy, that her puppy chewed up her homework. Mr. Niceguy told her just to fill in the holes with the correct numbers. Betty fixed the whole page using mental math.

Example: 5 2 4 down 2 + (9 8) up 2 = 6 2 2 — (The answer 622 is almost 100 more than 524.) → (The missing number must be a little less than 100.)

Help Betty fix her homework. Use mental math. Here are the numbers that were chewed off. 98 199 21 96 99 52

1. 3 5 2 up 1 − (9 9) down 1 = 2 5 3
2. 4 3 5 + (1 9 9) = 6 3 4
3. 1 5 1 + (9 8) = 2 4 9
4. 4 4 4 + (9 6) = 5 4 0
5. 7 5 − (2 1) = 5 4
6. 1(5 2) + 4 8 = 2 0 0

The puppy ate the answers for these. Use mental math to find them.

7. 7(2 2) + 9 8 = 8 2 0
8. 2 3 5 − (9 9) = 1 3 6
9. 3 9 7 + (5 3) = 4 5 0
10. 5(4 2) + 1 9 8 = 7 4 0
11. 6 4 + (1 9) = 8 3
12. 2 4 6 − (9 7) = 1 4 9

28 Use with text pages 74–75. CS-4

Options for Individual Needs

3-11

Basic

Exercises 1-24
Computer Bank, p. 496
More Practice, p. 502, set C

Supplements
Reteaching 28 or
Practice 28

Average

Exercises 1-28
Computer Bank, p. 496
More Practice, p. 502, set C

Supplements
Practice 28
Challenges 28 or
Thinking Skills 28

Extended

Exercises 5-28
Computer Bank, p. 496

Supplements
Challenges 28
Thinking Skills 28

Other Resources:
Problem-Solving Experiences in Mathematics, Grade 4, Problem 18
Math In Stride, Grade 4, p. 17

Lesson Plan 3-11

OBJECTIVE 3-11
To use the mental math technique of compensation to find sums and differences

Materials: counters

1. Motivate and Teach

LEARN ABOUT IT

EXPLORE ► **How could you change the numbers in the table to make them easier to work with? Explain.** (Possible answer: You could round them to the nearest ten—300, 180, 240, 200, and 350.)

TALK ABOUT IT ► **Explain how compensation affects addends and sums.** (It balances the addends without changing the sum.)
► **Explain what would happen if Ben decreased 243 by 3, then subtracted.** (He would get 40, an incorrect answer.)
► **Explain why Ben should increase 243 by the same amount that he increased 197.** (Possible answer: If he did not, he would subtract 3 fewer ones from 243 and his answer would be 3 more than 243 − 197.)
► **Compare compensating to find a sum with compensating to find a difference.** (Possible answer: To add, you increase one addend and decrease the other by the same amount. To subtract, you increase or decrease both numbers by the same amount.)
Student Edition answers: **1.** Decrease 176 by 2. **2.** Increase 243 by 3.

2. Check Understanding

TRY IT OUT

ERROR ALERT Applying the up-down compensation for addition when they subtract. Forgetting to adjust both addends when compensating.

Mental Math
Using Compensation

LEARN ABOUT IT

You have learned how to use compensation to find smaller sums. The same idea can be used to find larger sums and differences.

EXPLORE **Examine the Data**
Tom counted the number of vacationers who watched rocket launchings from a large park near Cape Canaveral. He made this table to show the data.

Rocket Launch	Number of People Watching
1	298
2	176
3	243
4	197
5	356

TALK ABOUT IT See teaching notes.

1. Tom used mental math to find how many watched the first two launches. He increased 298 to 300. How should he change 176 before he adds?
2. Ben used mental math to find how many more people watched launch 3 than watched launch 4. He increased 197 to 200. How should he change 243 before he subtracts?

To use **compensation** to add, you increase one addend and decrease the other addend the same amount. To subtract, you increase or decrease each number the same amount.

■ Use compensation to find 256 + 198.

198 + **256** = 454
Increase 198 by 2.
Decrease 256 by 2.

■ Use compensation to find 243 − 197.

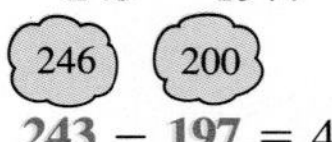

243 − **197** = 46
Increase 243 by 3.
Increase 197 by 3.

TRY IT OUT

Use compensation to find these sums or differences.

1. 97 + 538 **635**
2. 253 − 99 **154**
3. 38 + 56 **94**
4. 63 − 29 **34**

74

Teaching Options

RETEACHING TIPS Have students make a reminder chart like the one below. As they compensate to subtract, they put counters on the chart to keep track of the adjustment.

increase by	to subtract *extra*
decrease by	to subtract *less*

Assign Reteaching Supplement 28.

ENRICHMENT **Family Math** Students ask a family member to write any 3-digit number to 500. The student mentally figures a number to add to it that will give a sum of 504. The family member verifies it. If correct, a point is earned. They trade roles and continue until 10 points are earned.

PRACTICE

Use compensation to find these sums or differences.

1. 19 + 63 **82**
2. 52 + 133 **185**
3. 147 + 31 **178**
4. 97 + 568 **665**
5. 125 + 198 **323**
6. 356 + 99 **455**
7. 439 + 296 **735**
8. 496 + 132 **628**
9. 96 − 52 **44**
10. 75 − 21 **54**
11. 135 − 97 **38**
12. 243 − 39 **204**

Estimate these sums or differences. Choose any method you wish.
Answers may vary. Sample answers given.

13. 148 + 52 **200**
14. 496 + 45 **550**
15. 16 + 42 + 129 **190**
16. 876 + 114 **1,000**

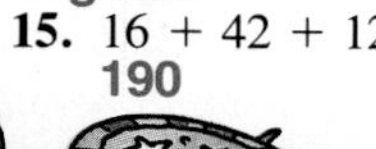

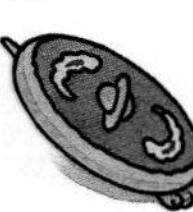

APPLY

MATH REASONING

17. To find 76 + 98, Ted first found 76 + 100 = 176. How must he change 176 to get the correct sum for 76 + 98? **Subtract 2.**

18. To find 72 − 37, Jan first found 72 − 40 = 32. How must she change 32 to get the correct difference for 72 − 37? **Add 3.**

PROBLEM SOLVING

19. In the morning, 196 cars entered Cape Canaveral. In the afternoon, 348 cars entered. How many cars entered that day? **544**

20. Jenny put 26 rocket buttons in one pile and 34 buttons in another pile. How many must she move from the large pile to the small pile to have the same number in each pile? **4 buttons**

▶ USING CRITICAL THINKING Draw Conclusions

Find the missing digits. Complete the calculation. **See Additional Answers.**

21. □ 2 □ + 5 □ 7 = 8 7 5
22. 3 □ 9 − 1 8 □ = □ 4 7
23. 3 □ □ + □ 4 8 = 7 5 3
24. □ 6 2 + 4 □ □ = 1, 0 7 1
25. 4 □ 5 − □ 1 6 = 1 8 □
26. □ 5 □ + 4 2 7 = 1,2 □ 2
27. 5 8 □ − □ 3 2 = 1 □ 4
28. 1 7 4 + 6 □ □ = □ 0 9

More Practice, page 502, set C

3. Practice and Apply

Basic	1-24
Average	1-28
Extended	5-28

Additional Answers: See p. T79.

PRACTICE

In Exercises 13-16, what might you look for first to make estimating easier and more accurate? (Possible response: exercises for which you can use compensation and mental math)

APPLY

MATH REASONING ▶ Compare the compensation method in Exercises 17 and 18 with the way you have been compensating. (The sum or difference is adjusted after adding or subtracting.)

PROBLEM SOLVING ▶ What operation is called for in Problem 19? Explain. (Addition; you need a total.)

USING THINKING SKILLS
▶ Explain a strategy you could use to solve missing-digit problems.
(Possible answers: Guess and check; use the opposite operation to work backward; notice which facts are given to determine what step to take next.)

3-11

Close and Assess

SHOW WHAT YOU KNOW
Have students use counters to show and explain why compensation works. Give them these two exercises: 567 + 397 and 714 − 98. (964; 616; Check each student's demonstration and explanation or have pairs of students check each other.)

QUICK QUIZ

Add or subtract using compensation.
1. 295 + 437 (732)
2. 430 − 198 (232)
3. 891 − 201 (690)
4. 674 + 403 (1,077)

LESSON OPTIONS 3-12

Problem Solving: Multiple-Step Problems

OBJECTIVE 3-12 To solve multiple-step problems.

PREBOOK ACTIVITIES

QUICK REVIEW

Add or subtract.

1.	**2.**	**3.**	**4.**
58	308	\$2.77	515
+76	−129	+ 7.03	−308
(134)	(179)	(\$9.80)	(207)

PRIOR KNOWLEDGE

Using the numbers 35 and 28, have students make up a problem to solve by adding and a problem to solve by subtracting. (Sample problems: *If 35 girls and 28 boys play freeze tag, how many children play?* add; *How many more girls than boys play?* subtract) Have students justify the operation used in each problem. (Add for a total: subtract to compare.) Explain that some problems may need more than 1 operation, such as finding a total cost and figuring out how much change you get. Challenge students to make up such a problem, then analyze the operations needed to solve it. (Sample problem: *If you buy a 25¢ stamp and a 15¢ postcard, how much change do you get from \$1?* add, subtract)

COMMUNICATION

Discussing and Reading Math Write **multiple** on the chalkboard and ask students to relate the word to an operation they know. (multiplication) Have students infer the meaning of *multiple* based on such phrases as multiple-choice quiz or multiple-step problem. (more than 1) Have students predict what multiple-step problems may need. (more than 1 step to find an answer)

EXPLORE AND CONNECT

COOPERATIVE ACTIVITY

Grouping Suggestion: small groups
7 adults and 12 children line up to order at Chuck 'n' Chicken. After 8 people get their meals, how many are still waiting?

TEACHING ACTIONS

Have students work together to discuss the problem and to check that they understand the steps involved in its solution.

▶ **Explain the situation in your own words.** (The line has 7 adults and 12 children; after a while, 8 people get their food.)

▶ **Decide how you could solve the problem.** (Add, then subtract.)
▶ **Plan an order of operations.** (Add to find the total number of people in line, then subtract the number of people who get their food to see how many are left waiting.)

▶ **Examine your solution to see if it makes sense.** (7 + 12 = 19; 19 − 8 = 11; 11 people still need to order.)
▶ **Justify calling this a multiple-step problem.** (Both addition and subtraction were used to find the solution.)

CONNECTIONS Use these anytime.

Problem of the Day

Field Trip 78 students took a tour of an underground cave. 57 students rode to the cave site in school buses. 15 students were driven there by their parents. Some students met the others at the cave site because they lived close enough to walk there. How many students got to the cave site by walking? (6)

Math Connection

Money Claude brought \$8.00 to the cave. He spent \$3.75 for his ticket, \$2.25 on hot dogs, and \$0.75 on lemonade. Decide if Claude has enough money for a souvenir booklet that costs \$1.00. (Yes, and he will have \$0.25 left.)

Number Sense

Mental Math Geraldine takes attendance for the underground cave tours. At 9:00 a.m., 50 people enter the cave. At 9:30 a.m., 30 people leave and 20 more enter. At 10:00 a.m., 40 people leave and 20 more enter. How many people are on cave tours at that moment? (20)

Classwork and Homework Supplements

Practice

Problem Solving 3-12

Name ____________________

Multiple-Step Problems

Solve. Show your work.

1. There are 44 students at the Book Fair. After making purchases, 15 students leave. Another 21 students enter. How many students are there now?
   50 students
   44 − 15 = 29
   29 + 21 = 50

2. Jason brought $8.15 to the Book Fair. He spent $2.95 on *Mr. Popper's Penguins* and $3.95 on *Homer Price*. How much money did he have left?
   $1.25
   $2.95 + $3.95 = $6.90
   $8.15 − $6.90 = $1.25

3. Elena has $4.95. She bought a book for $2.50. She wants to buy another book for $2.75. How much more money does she need?
   $0.30
   $2.50 + $2.75 = $5.25
   $5.25 − $4.95 = $0.30

4. The Book Fair had 60 books by E. B. White. 14 were sold the first day and 23 the next day. How many E. B. White books were left?
   23 books
   14 + 23 = 37
   80 − 37 = 23

5. Jill's class has 25 minutes to visit the fair. Jill spends 6 minutes looking at animal books and 12 minutes looking at fiction. If she spends 5 minutes buying a book, how much time does she have left to browse?
   2 minutes
   6 + 12 + 5 = 23
   25 − 23 = 2

6. *The Secret Garden* is 298 pages long. Becky read 36 pages on Tuesday and 54 pages on Wednesday. How many pages does she have left to read?
   208 pages
   36 + 54 = 90
   298 − 90 = 208

Building Thinking Skills

Problem Solving 3-12

Name ____________________

A Day at the Zoo

Solve the following problems.

1. Admission to the Riverside Zoo is $2.50 for adults and $1.50 for children. Mary and both her parents visit the zoo. Her mother pays their admission with a $10 bill. How much change should she receive?
   $3.50

2. At the zoo there are many kinds of animals. There are 27 monkeys and 8 gorillas in the jungle house. There are 187 birds in the bird house. How many more animals are in the bird house than in the jungle house?
   152 more animals

3. At the herpetarium 110 animals are displayed. There are 23 poison arrow frogs, 55 snakes, 4 giant tortoises, and 8 crocodiles. The rest of the animals in the herpetarium are lizards. How many lizards are there?
   20 lizards

4. Mary and her parents visited the gift shop at the zoo. Mary bought an animal puzzle that cost $5.25. Her father bought a hat for himself and one for Mary. The hats were $3 each. Her mother bought a panda poster for $8. They gave the cashier the exact change. They used 6 bills and 3 coins. What bills and coins did they use?
   1 $10 bill, 1 $5 bill, and 4 $1 bills,
   2 dimes, 1 nickel

ZOO
TICKETS

Reteaching

Problem Solving 3-12

Name ____________________

Multiple-Step Problems

Sometimes a problem must be solved using more than one operation. These problems are called **multiple-step problems.**

Peter had 124 books in his store. He sold 63 of them on Monday. On Tuesday 12 books were returned. How many books did he have then?

Step 1 Find how many books were left on Monday. Subtract the number sold from the total number of books. 124 − **63** = 61

Step 2 Find how many books there were after 12 were returned. Add the number of books returned. 61 + **12** = 73

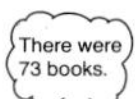

Solve.

1. Tracy brought $9.25 to the bookstore. She bought two books, one for $3.75 and another for $4.28. How much money did she have left?
   Step 1 Add to find the total cost of the books.
   $4.28 + $3.75 = **$8.03**
   Step 2 Subtract to find how much is left.
   $9.25 − **$8.03** = **$1.22**

2. Sue ordered 274 books. 118 books came on Thursday, and 120 came on Friday. How many books have not arrived yet?
   30 books

3. There are 152 books on the shelves. 58 are fiction books, and 64 are nonfiction books. How many other kinds of books are on the shelves?
   36 books

Challenges

Calculators 3-12

Name ____________________

Get Out the Calculator

When the numbers get large, it is faster to use the calculator than to "push the pencil."
Solve.

1. Sara is a volunteer at the Wildlife Rescue Center. The center rescued 12,426 hurt creatures in the 4 years, 1988 through 1991. How many were rescued in 1991?
   2,886

Year	Creatures Rescued
1988	3,137
1989	3,550
1990	2,853
1991	?
Total	12,426

2. The number of injured songbirds at the center was 438 more than the number of hummingbirds, waterbirds, doves, and pigeons combined. How many songbirds were there?
   1,564

Type of Bird	Number Injured
hummingbirds	52
waterbirds	337
doves/pigeons	737
songbirds	?

3. How many more birds than mammals were cared for in 4 years at the center?
   9,296

Year	Birds	Mammals
1988	2,476	389
1989	3,157	371
1990	2,538	313
1991	2,540	342
Totals	?	?

4. In 4 years, 849 mammals and 5,343 birds were treated then released. How many creatures in all were not released?
   5,934

Options for Individual Needs

3-12

Basic

Exercises 1-8
More Practice, p. 514, set A

Supplements
Reteaching 29 or
Practice 29

Average

Exercises 1-8
More Practice, p. 514, set A

Supplements
Practice 29
Challenges 29 or
Thinking Skills 29

Extended

Exercises 1-8

Supplements
Challenges 29
Thinking Skills 29

Other Resources:
Kids Are Consumers, Too!, p. 122
Math In Stride, Grade 4, p. 11
Problem-Solving Experiences in Mathematics, Grade 4, Problem 27

LESSON PLAN 3-12

OBJECTIVE 3-12
To solve multiple-step problems

Grouping Suggestion: pairs

1. MOTIVATE AND TEACH

LEARN ABOUT IT

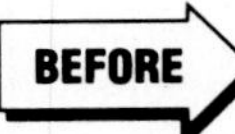

▶ **Explain your goal in solving this problem.** (to find how many servings of peas were eaten)

▶ **Analyze the problem for the important data.** (176 lunches sold; 37 older students and 42 younger ones left their peas)

DURING

▶ **Justify addition as one of the steps.** (Add 37 and 42 to find the total number of servings of peas that were not eaten.)

▶ **Justify the need for a subtraction step.** (Subtract the sum of 37 and 42 from the 176 lunches sold to find how many servings were eaten.)

▶ **Explain a way to check your solution.** (97 + 79 = 176, so the answer that 97 students ate servings of peas is reasonable.)

▶ **Justify calling this a multiple-step problem.** (Possible answer: It took both addition and subtraction to solve the problem, so it required multiple steps.)

2. CHECK UNDERSTANDING

TRY IT OUT

ERROR ALERT Choosing the wrong operation. Adding all given numbers.

Problem Solving
Multiple-Step Problems

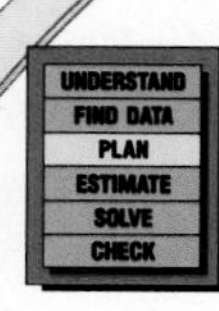

LEARN ABOUT IT

Some problems can be solved by using both addition and subtraction. These problems are called **Multiple-Step Problems.**

The cafeteria sold 176 hot lunches of chicken and peas. The older students left 37 servings of peas untouched. The younger students left 42 servings of peas untouched. How many servings of peas were eaten?

First I'll add to find out how many students left their peas uneaten. $37 + 42 = 79$

Then I'll subtract to find out how many students ate their peas. $176 - 79 = 97$

The students ate 97 servings of peas.

TRY IT OUT

1. Roman's lunch break at school is 55 minutes long. He spent 17 minutes in the hot lunch line and 19 minutes eating lunch. How much time did he have left? **19 minutes**
2. Guido had $1.05 for lunch. He bought a taco for $0.89. Then he borrowed $0.65 from John. How much more money does he need to buy another taco? **$0.08**
3. There are 47 students standing in the hot lunch line. 29 students are served and leave the line. 18 new students get in line. How many students are in the line now? **36 students**
4. Joann brought $2.60 for lunch. She spent $1.37 on a hamburger and $0.68 on a lemonade. How much money did she have left? **$0.55**

76

TEACHING OPTIONS

RETEACHING TIPS Have students work in pairs. To help them visualize the steps needed to solve the problem before they try to calculate a solution, encourage students to verbalize each situation in their own words or to act it out. Assign Reteaching Supplement 29.

ENRICHMENT Have students use the numbers $7.99, $3.60, and $15.00 to formulate a multiple-step problem that uses addition and subtraction. Tell them to write the problem on an index card and give the solution on the back. Then students exchange problems with a partner. (Problems will vary.)

MIXED PRACTICE

Solve. Use any problem solving strategy. Use the survey for problems 1 and 2.

Survey questions: What is your favorite hot lunch?
What is your least favorite hot lunch?

Favorite	Votes	Least Favorite	Votes
Pizza	98	Hot Dogs	123
Hamburgers	83	Sloppy Joes	63
Tacos	||||	Bean Tortillas	52

1. A total of 248 students voted for either tacos, hamburgers, or pizza as their favorite food. How many voted for tacos? **67 students**
2. How many votes did hot dogs and sloppy joes get for least favorite lunch? **186 votes**
3. A book of lunch tickets for one week cost Jorge $6.85. Without the tickets, a week of lunches would cost $8.30. How much does Jorge save by buying tickets? **$1.45**
4. Ralph finished lunch before Josie. Matt finished after Josie. Vince finished between Josie and Matt. Who finished last? **Matt**
5. On Tuesday, 224 students bought pizza, 140 students bought hamburgers, and 187 students brought their own bag lunches. How many more students bought pizza than ate a bag lunch? **37 more students**

Milk Cartons Sold in a Week	
Day	**Cartons**
Monday	132
Tuesday	173
Wednesday	148
Thursday	131
Friday	138

6. How many more milk cartons were sold on Tuesday and Wednesday than on Thursday and Friday? **52 more milk cartons**
7. Students bought 689 milks in January and 726 in February. How many did they buy in those two months? **1,415 milks**
8. **Talk About Your Solution** Solve. Then explain your solution to a classmate. One rectangular cafeteria table seats 8 people. Two tables are pushed together to make one long table. How many people can be seated? **See Additional Answers.**

More Practice, page 514, set A

3. Practice and Apply

Basic	1-8
Average	1-8
Extended	1-8

Additional Answers and Sample Solutions: See p. T79.

MIXED PRACTICE

▶ **Explain how to find the missing data in Problem 1.** (Use the total number of votes to find how many students voted for tacos.)

▶ **Analyze how Problems 2 and 7 are alike.** (Both can be solved by addition.)

▶ **Analyze how Problems 3 and 5 are alike.** (Both can be solved by subtraction.)

▶ **Which strategy could you use to solve Problem 4?** (Possible answer: Draw a Picture.)

▶ **Explain the steps you need to solve Problem 6.** (Add 2 totals; subtract to compare.)

3-12

Close and Assess

SAY WHAT YOU THINK Have students work in pairs. The first student tells the second why this is a multiple-step problem and how to solve it. *Marc and Jill spent $9.50 at China Inn. Marc had wonton soup for $1.10 and chicken chow mein for $3.75. How much did Jill's meal cost?* ($1.10 + $3.75 = 4.85; $9.50 − $4.85 = $4.65)

QUICK QUIZ

Fawn was at a restaurant for 1 h. She spent 10 min waiting for a table, 5 min choosing what to order, and 40 min eating. How much time was left to pay the bill? (5 min)

LESSON OPTIONS 3-13

Adding and Subtracting Larger Numbers: Using a Calculator

OBJECTIVE 3-13 To add and subtract 4- and 5-digit numbers

PREBOOK ACTIVITIES

QUICK REVIEW

Read each number aloud, then identify the place with a 7.

1. 13,579 (tens)
2. 7,654,321 (millions)
3. 47,032 (thousands)
4. 950,711 (hundreds)
5. 50,447 (ones)
6. 172,000 (ten thousands)
7. 768,952 (hundred thousands)

PRIOR KNOWLEDGE

Discuss real-life situations where students use calculators or see others using them. Have students suggest reasons for using a calculator rather than another solution method. (Possible answers: speed, accuracy, or ease of calculation with large or complicated numbers) Ask students how a calculator could give the wrong answer. (Possible answer: User may enter numbers incorrectly or choose the wrong operation.) Tell students that in this lesson, they will use calculators to solve problems, but they must first make some math decisions about how to use the calculators.

COMMUNICATION

Discussing Math Tell students that the verb **calculate** comes from an old Latin word for a counting stone. Have them name other forms of the word *calculate*. (Possible answers: *calculation, calculator, miscalculate*) Ask students to explain what a **calculator** is, based on the early meaning of *calculate*. (Possible answer: a counting machine) Have them suggest other words that mean calculate. (Possible answers: *compute, figure, add*)

EXPLORE AND CONNECT

Materials: calculators
Grouping Suggestion: cooperative learning pairs
Students combine skills in listening and following directions and knowledge of place value with **calculator** practice. Each student first secretly writes several 3-, 4-, and 5-digit numbers on paper. For each round, one student is the speaker and the other is the listener. The speaker uses two of his or her numbers to create an addition or subtraction problem for the listener to enter on a *calculator*. The speaker may repeat the numbers, if necessary. The speaker solves the problem on a second *calculator* to verify the listener's work. If solutions differ, the listener **recalculates** the numbers. If solutions still differ, the listener may write the numbers down before entering them. Students take turns at each role. Close by discussing possible reasons why a *calculator* sometimes gives a wrong answer. (Possible answer: User makes an error.)

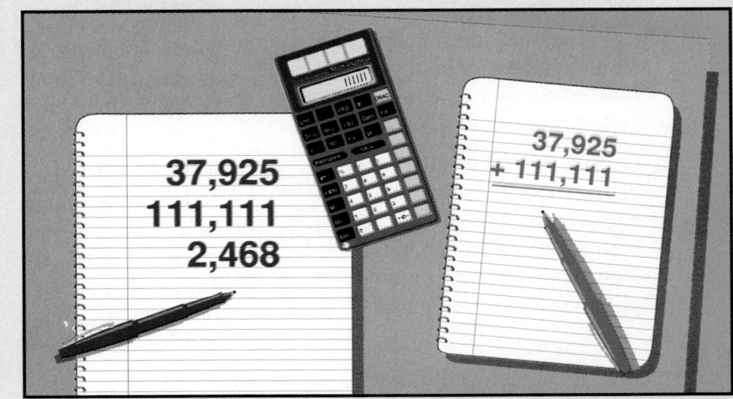

CONNECTIONS Use these anytime.

Problem of the Day

Broken 4 Ellen cannot use the 4 key on her calculator. How can she add 984 + 741 + 495? Explain your answer. (Possible answer: She can compensate by adding 1 more in each place with a 4, then subtract the extra from the total to get the final answer; 2,220.)

Patterns

Calculator Calculations Use a calculator to discover the pattern. Then find the next 4 numbers: 29, 86, 143, 200, ____, ____, ____, ____.
(The pattern is to add 57 each time: 257, 314, 371, 428.)

Number Sense

Plus or Minus Enter 987 on your calculator. Add or subtract one number to make the calculator show 123. (subtract 864)

Classwork and Homework Supplements

Practice

Calculators 3-13

Name ______

Adding and Subtracting Larger Numbers

Population of Places in Massachusetts	
City or Village	Estimated Population
Amherst	17,773
Concord	4,680
Essex	2,998
Marblehead	20,126
Plymouth	7,232
Salem	38,600

Use the table to solve the problems. Decide whether to use paper and pencil or a calculator.

1. How much greater is the population of Plymouth than Concord? 2,552
2. How many more people live in Marblehead than in Amherst? 2,353
3. What is the difference in population between the largest and smallest places? 35,602
4. Is the population of Plymouth more or less than 3 times the population of Essex? less
5. What is the difference in population between Amherst and Concord? 13,093
6. What is the sum of the populations of Salem and Marblehead? 58,726

Building Thinking Skills

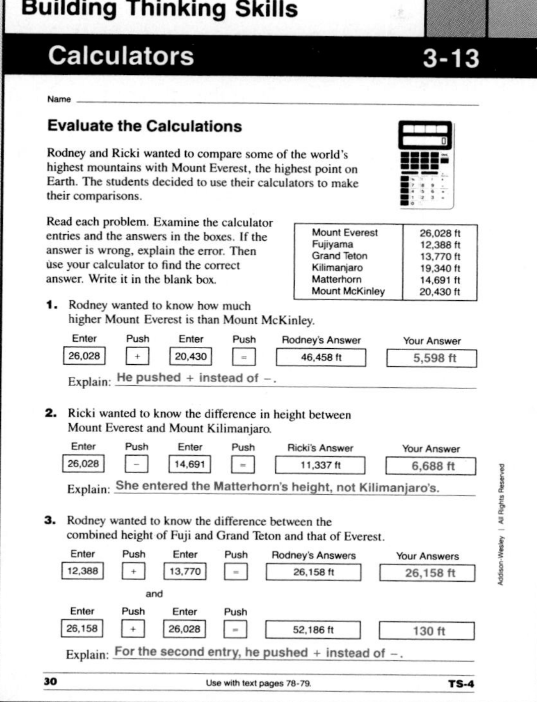

Calculators 3-13

Name ______

Evaluate the Calculations

Rodney and Ricki wanted to compare some of the world's highest mountains with Mount Everest, the highest point on Earth. The students decided to use their calculators to make their comparisons.

Read each problem. Examine the calculator entries and the answers in the boxes. If the answer is wrong, explain the error. Then use your calculator to find the correct answer. Write it in the blank box.

Mountain	Height
Mount Everest	26,028 ft
Fujiyama	12,388 ft
Grand Teton	13,770 ft
Kilimanjaro	19,340 ft
Matterhorn	14,691 ft
Mount McKinley	20,430 ft

1. Rodney wanted to know how much higher Mount Everest is than Mount McKinley.

Enter	Push	Enter	Push	Rodney's Answer	Your Answer
26,028	+	20,430	=	46,458 ft	5,598 ft

Explain: He pushed + instead of −.

2. Ricki wanted to know the difference in height between Mount Everest and Mount Kilimanjaro.

Enter	Push	Enter	Push	Ricki's Answer	Your Answer
26,028	−	14,691	=	11,337 ft	6,688 ft

Explain: She entered the Matterhorn's height, not Kilimanjaro's.

3. Rodney wanted to know the difference between the combined height of Fuji and Grand Teton and that of Everest.

Enter	Push	Enter	Push	Rodney's Answers	Your Answers
12,388	+	13,770	=	26,158 ft	26,158 ft
and					
26,158	+	26,028	=	52,186 ft	130 ft

Explain: For the second entry, he pushed + instead of −.

Reteaching

Calculators 3-13

Name ______

Adding and Subtracting Larger Numbers

Find the sum of 35,466 and 14,967. Find their difference.

Use a Calculator

To Add

Enter	Push	Enter	Push
35,466	+	14,967	=

To subtract

Enter	Push	Enter	Push
35,466	−	14,967	=

50,433

Use Pencil and Paper

Add each place. Trade when necessary.

```
  1 1  1 1
  35,466
+ 14,967
  50,433
```

Subtract each place. Trade when necessary.

```
  4  13 15 16
  35,466
− 14,967
  20,499
```

Add or subtract. Use a calculator or pencil and paper.

1. 160,743 + 26,895 = 187,638
2. 531,922 − 56,435 = 475,487
3. 3,768 − 1,386 = 2,382
4. 4,532 + 2,487 = 7,019
5. 77,468 − 12,589 = 64,879
6. 96,304 − 12,659 = 108,963
7. 17,345 + 22,986 = 40,331
8. 552,667 − 324,759 = 227,908

Use a calculator. Find the number for the [ ].

9. [71,463] − 7,965 = 63,498
10. [63,825] + 12,398 = 76,223
11. [80,449] + 43,876 = 124,325
12. [306,474] − 62,765 = 243,709
13. 625,340 − 347,289 = [278,051]
14. 498,764 + 232,434 = [731,198]

Challenges

Calculators 3-13

Name ______

Palindrome Fun

The words *Mom, Bob, radar,* and *kayak* are called word palindromes. Numbers such as 1,551, 464, and 81 are called number palindromes. What do you think a palindrome is?

a word or number that reads the same backward or forward

Try these. Keep going until you arrive at a palindrome. Use your calculator for larger numbers. The first one has been done for you.

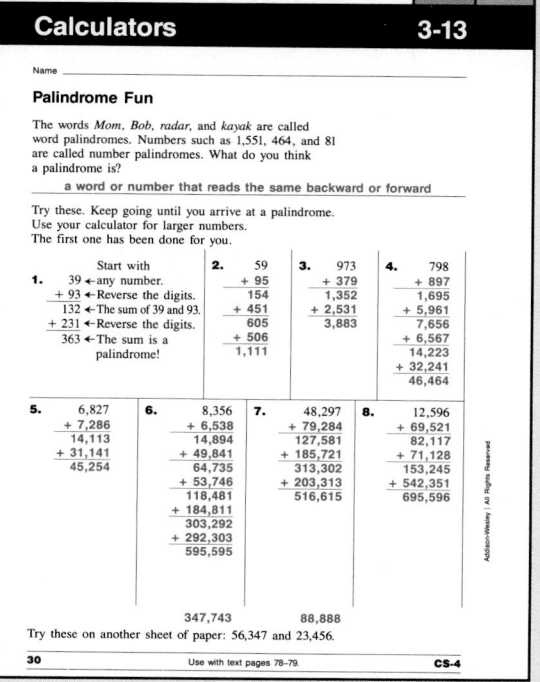

1. Start with
```
   39  ← any number.
 + 93  ← Reverse the digits.
  132  ← The sum of 39 and 93.
+ 231  ← Reverse the digits.
  363  ← The sum is a palindrome!
```

2.
```
   59
 + 95
  154
+ 451
  605
+ 506
1,111
```

3.
```
   973
 + 379
 1,352
+ 2,531
 3,883
```

4.
```
    798
  + 897
  1,695
+ 5,961
  7,656
+ 6,567
 14,223
+32,241
 46,464
```

5.
```
   6,827
 + 7,286
  14,113
+ 31,141
  45,254
```

6.
```
    8,356
  + 6,538
   14,894
 + 49,841
   64,735
 + 53,746
  118,481
+ 184,811
  303,292
+ 292,303
  595,595
```

7.
```
   48,297
 + 79,284
  127,581
+ 185,721
  313,302
+ 203,313
  516,615
```

8.
```
   12,596
 + 69,521
   82,117
 + 71,128
  153,245
+ 542,351
  695,596
```

347,743 88,888

Try these on another sheet of paper: 56,347 and 23,456.

Options for Individual Needs

Basic

Exercises 3-18
Data Bank, p. 470
Calculator Bank, p. 485
More Practice, p. 502, set D

Supplements
Reteaching 30 or
Practice 30

Average

Exercises 1-18
Data Bank, p. 470
Calculator Bank, p. 485
More Practice, p. 502, set D

Supplements
Practice 30
Challenges 30 or
Thinking Skills 30

Extended

Exercises 3-18
Data Bank, p. 470
Calculator Bank, p. 485

Supplements
Challenges 30
Thinking Skills 30

Other Resources:
Problem-Solving Experiences in Mathematics, Grade 4, Problem 3
Math In Stride, Grade 4, p. 230
Mathematics, A Way of Thinking, Lesson 8-35

LESSON PLAN 3-13

OBJECTIVE 3-13
To add and subtract 4- and 5-digit numbers

Materials: calculators

1. MOTIVATE AND TEACH

LEARN ABOUT IT

► **Explain how to enter numbers on a calculator.** (Enter digits one at a time, reading from left to right.)
► **How do you enter two or more numbers with different place values?** (Enter them the same way; the calculator lines them up.)
► **Explain why you press =.** (to get the solution to an entered problem)

EXPLORE ► **To find the diameter of a ball, do you measure around the widest part or through the ball at the widest part?** (through the ball at the widest part)

TALK ABOUT IT ► **How does place value help you to compare diameters?** (Numbers with more places are larger.)
► **What operation helps you determine how much larger or smaller a planet is?** (subtraction)
Student Edition answers: **1.** Jupiter; Pluto **2.** Answers will vary; subtract **3.** Answers will vary; add the smaller number to itself and compare with larger number.

2. CHECK UNDERSTANDING

TRY IT OUT

ERROR ALERT Entering numbers in the wrong order, so that larger numbers are subtracted from smaller numbers. Entering numbers inaccurately.

Adding and Subtracting Larger Numbers
Using a Calculator

LEARN ABOUT IT

EXPLORE Read the Information
The diameter of a ball is the distance from one side to the other at the widest part. Even though the planets are far away, astronomers have invented ways to measure their diameters.

Planet	Diameter in Kilometers
Mercury	4,878
Venus	12,102
Earth	12,756
Mars	6,794
Jupiter	142,880
Saturn	120,500
Uranus	51,400
Neptune	48,600
Pluto	3,000

TALK ABOUT IT See teaching notes.

1. Which planet is the largest? the smallest?
2. Pick 2 planets. How can you find how much larger the diameter of one is than the diameter of the other?
3. Estimate to pick 2 planets so that the diameter of one is double the diameter of the other. How can you check this?

Here is a way to calculate answers to the questions above.

Use a Calculator

To Add

Enter	Push	Enter	Push
6,794	+	6,794	=

To Subtract

Enter	Push	Enter	Push
51,400	−	12,102	=

13588

or

Use Pencil and Paper

Add or subtract in each place. Trade when necessary.

```
  1  1             4 11  3 9 10
  6, 7 9 4          5 1, 4 0 0
+ 6, 7 9 4        − 1 2, 1 0 2
 13, 5 8 8          3 9, 2 9 8
```

TRY IT OUT

How much greater is the diameter? Choose pencil and paper or a calculator.

1. Jupiter than Saturn **22,380 kilometers**
2. Mars than Mercury **1,916 kilometers**
3. Earth than Mars **5,962 kilometers**

78

TEACHING OPTIONS

RETEACHING TIPS To correct the first error, have students identify the numbers to compare and write them as a subtraction problem before entering them on the calculator. When students verify that the larger number must be entered first, they calculate the difference. Assign Reteaching Supplement 30.

ENRICHMENT Students use a calculator and the Science Data Bank on page 470 to answer these questions: *Which planet takes about 3 earth months to go around the sun? about 12 earth years? about 30 earth years? about 165 earth years? about 250 earth years?* (Mercury; Jupiter; Saturn; Neptune; Pluto)

PRACTICE

How much greater is the diameter? Use the chart on page 78. Decide whether to use pencil and paper or a calculator.

1. Uranus than Neptune **2,800 kilometers**
2. Saturn than Earth **107,744 kilometers**
3. Mercury than Pluto **1,878 kilometers**
4. Jupiter than Uranus **91,480 kilometers**
5. Venus than Mercury **7,224 kilometers**
6. Earth than Pluto **9,756 kilometers**
7. Is the diameter of Jupiter more or less than 3 times the diameter of Neptune? **less**
8. Is the diameter of Earth more or less than 2 times the diameter of Mercury? **more**

APPLY

MATH REASONING Use a calculator. Find the number for the ||||.

9. |||| − 6,276 = 57,698 **63,974**
10. |||| + 5,897 = 87,629 **81,732**

PROBLEM SOLVING **See Additional Answers.**

11. **Science Data Bank** How does the number of satellites circling Jupiter compare to the number circling Saturn? See page 470.

12. Mercury travels 170,500 kilometers per hour around the sun. The earth travels 107,220 kilometers per hour around the sun. How much faster does Mercury travel?

MIXED REVIEW

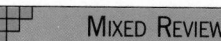

Give an addition fact for each subtraction fact.

13. 15 − 7 = 8 **7 + 8 = 15**
14. 11 − 6 = 5 **6 + 5 = 11**
15. 17 − 9 = 8 **9 + 8 = 17**
16. 14 − 8 = 6 **8 + 6 = 14**

Write the number in standard form.

17. eight hundred thirty-nine thousand, three hundred one **839,301**
18. 600,000 + 80,000 + 2,000 + 40 + 9 **682,049**

More Practice, page 502, set D

3. Practice and Apply

Basic	3-18
Average	1-18
Extended	3-18

Additional Answers: See p. T79.

PRACTICE

Look at Exercise 3. Why might you use paper and pencil to find the answer? (The numbers are easy to subtract.) *Look at Exercises 7 and 8. Why might a calculator be the best choice for these?* (Possible answer: The numbers are large.)

APPLY

MATH REASONING ▶ **What operation will you use to solve Exercise 9. Why?** (Addition; you are given 2 parts and must find the whole.)

PROBLEM SOLVING ▶ **Is there more than one way to answer Problem 11? Explain.** (Possible answer: You can find out which planet has more satellites or which has fewer satellites.)

MIXED REVIEW ▶ **Explain the place value errors you could make in Exercises 17 and 18.** (Possible answers: You could forget 0 as a place holder; you could put digits in the wrong place.)

3-13

Close and Assess

WRITE WHAT YOU THINK

Have each student write a paragraph explaining why a calculator is a good tool to use to find certain sums and differences. Have students include ideas for using a calculator accurately and effectively. (Answers will vary.)

QUICK QUIZ

Choose paper and pencil or calculator to add or subtract.

1. 80,694 + 13,799 (94,493)
2. 45,002 − 30,005 (14,997)
3. 75,875 + □ = 98,783 (22,908)

LESSON OPTIONS 3-14

Problem Solving: Deciding When to Estimate

OBJECTIVE 3-14 To decide if you need an exact answer or an estimate to a problem

PREBOOK ACTIVITIES

QUICK REVIEW

Estimate. (Answers may vary. Samples are given.)

1. \$6.85 + \$2.09 (\$9.00)
2. \$103.50 − \$68.75 (\$30.00)
3. \$1.29 + \$1.67 (\$3.00)
4. \$58.64 − \$29.33 (\$30.00)
5. \$5.88 + \$2.22 + \$7.75 (\$16.00)

PRIOR KNOWLEDGE

Have students tell when they have used estimation and have them justify its use. (Possible answers: to determine an approximate answer; to see if an exact answer is reasonable) Have them generalize about the relationship between the exact answer and the estimate for a particular problem. (Possible answer: The estimate and the exact answer should be similar.)

COMMUNICATION

Discussing and Reading Math Write this sentence on the chalkboard: Is \$1.00 enough money to buy a yogurt and an apple? Have students identify the reference point and analyze its role in the question. (\$1.00; compare it to the total cost to see if it is more or less than \$1.00) Ask students to give reasonable prices for a yogurt and an apple. Have them estimate *and* give an exact answer based on those numbers, then compare the sums to the reference point to answer the question. (Answers will vary.)

EXPLORE AND CONNECT

COOPERATIVE ACTIVITY

Grouping Suggestion: small groups
It costs \$0.85 to take a photo in a silly photo booth. How much will 3 silly photos cost? Is \$3.00 enough money?

TEACHING ACTIONS

Have students work together to check their understanding.

▶ **Explain the situation.** (Determine whether \$3.00 is enough to cover the cost of 3 silly photos.)
▶ **Compare the 2 questions.** (One asks for the cost of 3 photos; the other asks a reference-point question.)

▶ **Decide which question needs an exact answer. Explain why.** (cost of 3 photos; You must pay the actual cost.)
▶ **Explain why you could use an estimate to answer the reference-point question.** (Possible answer: A reference point is a number used for comparing, so an estimated answer would be sufficient.)
▶ **Explain how you would solve the problem.** (Add \$0.85 three times, then compare to \$3.00.)

▶ **Evaluate your solutions to see if they seem reasonable.** (\$0.85 + \$0.85 + \$0.85 = \$2.55; estimate: 3 photos at about \$1.00 each = \$3.00; \$2.55 makes sense; \$3.00 is enough if you overestimated.)

CONNECTIONS Use these anytime.

Problem of the Day

Safe Sailing A boat can safely carry 800 lb. Without making anyone weigh in before getting in the boat, how can you estimate how many fourth graders can sail safely at once? (Possible answer: Overestimate based on the weight of a typical-size student, then assume the exact weight is less than the estimate.)

Math Connection

Calculator Find the total cost of 2 yogurts at 75¢ each, 2 apples at 33¢ each, and 1 bag of popcorn at \$1.49. Enter only 3 numbers in your calculator. (First double the yogurt and apple prices mentally, then add \$1.50 + \$0.66 + \$1.49 = \$3.65)

Number Sense

Estimation Randy read that 40,000 fans were at a football game. He wondered how a reporter found out the number of people at the game. Justify an exact *and* an estimated way to determine that number. (Possible answer: Estimate the number based on how many seats are in the stadium; ask the ticket takers for the exact number, then round it.)

Classwork and Homework Supplements

Practice

Problem Solving 3-14

Name

Deciding When to Estimate

Tell if you can estimate the answer or if you need to find an exact answer. Explain why.

SILVER DINER MENU

Sandwiches		Side Orders		Beverages	
hamburger	$2.50	french fries	$0.80	lemonade	$0.65
hot dog	$1.75	cole slaw	$0.70	juice	$0.75
grilled cheese	$1.45	salad	$1.25	milk shake	$1.50

Answers will vary.

1. The diner seats 195 people. If 159 seats are filled, how many more people can be seated?
   Exact; the diner needs to know exactly how many seats are left.
2. Lance ordered french fries and a milk shake. What is his total bill?
   Exact; Lance needs to know how much to pay.
3. Arturo has $3.50 to spend on lunch. He orders a hamburger and juice. Does he have enough money to buy a milk shake rather than juice?
   Estimate; he needs to know if he can change his order.
4. Tao's mother gave her money to buy lunch at the diner. She ordered a salad and juice. How much change should she return to her mother?
   Exact; Tao needs to know the exact amount to return.
5. Mrs. Cole wants to buy dinner for 5 people in her family. If she orders a hot dog and lemonade for each person, will $15 cover the cost of the meal?
   Estimate; Mrs. Cole needs to know if she has enough money.
6. The Molinas spent 74 minutes having dinner at the diner on Friday and 37 minutes for lunch on Sunday. What amount should she use to tell a friend how much longer they were at the diner on Friday?
   Estimate; the friend needs to know only about how long.

Building Thinking Skills

Problem Solving 3-14

Name

Menu Decisions

Entree		Fruit	
Hamburger	$2.25	Apple	$0.55
Grilled Cheese	$1.50	Orange	$0.45
Hot Dog	$1.30	Pear	$0.40
Chicken Fingers	$2.15	Banana	$0.35
Ham Sandwich	$2.55		

Beverage	
Milk	
Large	$0.95
Small	$0.70

Decide whether you need an exact answer or an estimate for each problem. Then solve. Answers may vary.

1. Chad orders a hamburger, an apple, and a large glass of milk. How much does he have to pay for his meal?
   exact; $3.75
2. Kelly has $5. She orders two hot dogs for lunch. Does she have enough money left to treat her friend to a grilled cheese sandwich?
   estimate; yes
3. Mr. Williams places an order for the track team. He needs 6 hamburgers, 5 chicken fingers, and 3 grilled cheese sandwiches. He pays for lunch with a $20 bill and a $10 bill. How much change should he receive?
   exact; $1.25
4. The Ajayi family orders 4 chicken fingers and 4 large glasses of milk. They pay with a $10 bill and a $5 bill. About how much change should they receive?
   estimate; $3
5. You spend exactly $3 on lunch. You buy 1 entree, 1 fruit, and 1 beverage. What is your lunch?
   grilled cheese, apple, large milk
6. You have $4 to spend on a meal. List what you will order.
   Answers will vary.

Reteaching

Problem Solving 3-14

Name

Deciding When to Estimate

When you solve problems, you can estimate when you need to

- compare with a **reference point.**

or

- decide **about** how many.

In other situations, you need to find the exact answer.

Alison wants to buy 2 books for $2.95 each. She has $6. Does she have enough money?

(You can estimate because all Alison needs to know is if she has enough money.)

Alison bought 2 books for $2.95 each. What amount should she pay the cashier?

(You need an exact answer because she has to pay the correct amount.)

Tell if you can estimate the answer or if you need to find an exact answer. Explain why. Then solve the problem. Wording for reasons will vary.

1. Sally's mom gave her $5 to buy 3 pens for $0.89 each. What amount should she use to tell how much change she needs to return to her mom?
   exact; $2.33
2. Bill bought 2 pads of paper for $1.85 each. What amount should he use to tell a friend about the total cost?
   estimate; about $4.00
3. Laurie has $25. Is that enough to buy 3 books at $6.95 each?
   estimate; less than $21.00
4. Roger's dad drove 78 miles on Friday and 129 miles on Saturday. What amount should he use to tell a friend how many miles he drove on both days?
   estimate; about 200 miles

Challenges

Reading Math 3-14

Name

Garage Sale

Read the story. Then list all situations that require an exact answer and all situations for which only estimates are needed.

Georgia's family had a huge garage sale to earn the money to buy her a new bike at $159.99 and a helmet at $39.95. The first customer paid for a chair at $15.50 with a $50 bill, and Georgia had trouble giving her change. Little Polly Jones asked her mother if a $10 bill was enough to buy 3 dolls at $2.75 each. Mrs. Jones wanted to buy 4 chairs at $6.95 each with a $20 bill. A radio Georgia originally bought for $49.95 sold for about half as much. She also sold 63 comics at 10¢ each. Throughout the sale, Georgia sold popcorn at 55¢ per bag. One large family took 12 bags and asked how much they owed. At the end of the day, Georgia anxiously counted the money.

Wording will vary.

Estimates needed:

1. They need to make about $200.
2. Polly had enough to buy 3 dolls.
3. Mrs. Jones did not have enough money for the chairs.
4. Radio sold for about $25.

Exact answers needed:

1. change for $50
2. Georgia made exactly $6.30 on comics.
3. cost of 12 bags of popcorn
4. Georgia's family needed to count exactly how much they made.

Options for Individual Needs

3-14

Basic

Exercises 1-4, 7-10
More Practice, p. 514, set B

Supplements
Reteaching 31 or
Practice 31

Average

Exercises 1-10
More Practice, p. 514, set B

Supplements
Practice 31
Challenges 31 or
Thinking Skills 31

Extended

Exercises 2-10

Supplements
Challenges 31
Thinking Skills 31

Other Resources:
Mathematics, A Way of Thinking, Lesson 8-37
Problem-Solving Experiences in Mathematics, Grade 4, Problem 25

LESSON PLAN 3-14

OBJECTIVE 3-14
To decide if you need an exact answer or an estimate to a problem

1. MOTIVATE AND TEACH

LEARN ABOUT IT

► **Analyze the chart for the cost of adult and child tickets.** (adult: $2.45; child: $1.75)
► **Explain how you would estimate the cost of 5 adult tickets.** (5 × $2 = $10)
► **Is your estimate over or under the exact cost? Explain.** (Under, because you have ignored the cents in each price.)

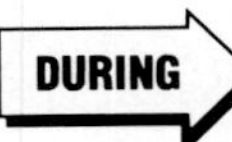

► **Explain how to use the estimate to answer the reference-point question.** (An underestimate of $10 means the exact cost is over $10; it is not enough for 5 adult tickets.)
► **Justify the operation to use to find the cost of 1 adult and 1 child ticket.** (Add, because you need a total amount.)

► **Analyze why one question needed an exact answer and the other needed only an estimate.** (Possible answer: You can estimate to find *about* how many or to compare with a reference point; to find a more specific amount, such as how much to pay, you must find an exact answer.)

2. CHECK UNDERSTANDING

TRY IT OUT

ERROR ALERT Finding only exact answers. Making inappropriate decisions about whether to estimate or to find an exact answer.

Problem Solving
Deciding When to Estimate

UNDERSTAND
FIND DATA
PLAN
ESTIMATE
SOLVE
CHECK

LEARN ABOUT IT

When you solve problems, you sometimes need an exact answer. Other times you only need to know about how much or how many and you can make an estimate.

Fun Fair Tickets	
Adults	$2.45
Children	$1.75
Senior Citizens	$1.25
Special Tickets	
Cake Walk	$0.75
Lunch	$3.25

You have a ten-dollar bill. Is that enough to buy 5 adult tickets?

All I need to know is whether I have enough money. I can estimate the total cost.

What will you have to pay the ticket seller for 1 adult ticket and 1 child ticket?

The ticket seller must receive the exact amount. I need to find the exact answer.

When you need to decide about how many, or to compare an amount with a reference point, you can estimate. In other situations, you should find the exact answer.

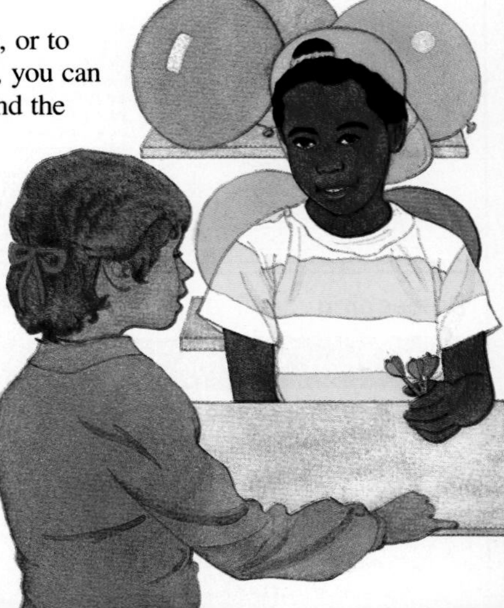

TRY IT OUT See Additional Answers.

Decide whether you need an exact answer or an estimate. Tell why.

1. Is $5 enough to pay for 5 cakewalk tickets?
2. What should you pay the ticket taker for 3 student tickets?

80

TEACHING OPTIONS

RETEACHING TIPS Students find which exercises have a reference point and identify it. (Exercise 1: $5; Exercise 3: $15) Help them state a relationship between estimating and comparing with a reference point. (Estimate to compare with a reference point.) Assign Reteaching Supplement 31.

ENRICHMENT Have students justify estimating *and* finding an exact answer: *Ann has $10.00. She wants a $6.79 hat, a $1.39 scarf, and a $2.00 bracelet. Does she have enough money?* (Estimate first: $10.00. The estimate is very close, so find the exact answer: $10.18 is more than she has.)

MIXED PRACTICE

Tell if you can estimate the answer or if you need to find an exact answer. Explain why. See Additional Answers.

1. On Friday, 148 people came to the Fun Fair. On Saturday, 156 people came. To tell her mother how successful the fair was, how many tickets should Janell say were sold?
2. The first night ticket sales were $144.55 for adult tickets and $155.75 for child tickets. What should the school newspaper report about the total ticket sales?
3. Mr. Thornquist wanted to buy lunch at the Fun Fair for 4 people in his family. He had $20. Was that enough?
4. Megan ordered balloons for the Fun Fair. Last year, 78 balloons were used. She wanted to order twice as many this year. How many should Megan order?
5. William bought a child's ticket and a lunch ticket. How much should he pay the ticket seller?
6. There were 26 fourth grade and 27 fifth grade Fun Fair workers who received free tickets. How many free tickets should Erica report to the ticket takers? Would she give the same number to the person figuring the profits?
7. Sue bought 2 Fun Fair T-shirts for $4.98 each. What amount should she use to tell a friend about the total cost?
8. Jake's father gave him money to spend at the fair. Jake bought a student ticket, walked for a cake, and ate lunch. What amount should he use to tell how much change he needed to return to his father?
9. Bo recorded the amount of time he spent at the Fun Fair. He was there 29 minutes on Friday and 116 minutes on Saturday. What amount should he use to tell a friend how much longer he was at the fair on Saturday than on Friday?
10. **Determining Reasonable Answers** Tell if the calculator answer for this problem is reasonable. If it is not reasonable, tell why. Jerod bought one ticket of each type at the Fun Fair. What was his total cost?

More Practice, page 514, set B

3. PRACTICE AND APPLY

Basic	1-4, 7-10
Average	1-10
Extended	2-10

Additional Answers and Sample Solutions: See p. T79.

MIXED PRACTICE

► **Find a problem that uses a reference point. Explain your reasoning.** (Problem 3; you need to compare the cost of 4 lunches with $20.)

► **Analyze how Problems 1, 7, and 9 are alike.** (Possible answer: Estimate each answer because the people getting the data need to know only *about* how much.)

► **Explain how Problems 2 and 8 are related.** (Both are about money costs, so exact answers make sense.)

► **Explain how you know that in Problem 10, Jerod was trying to find an exact answer.** (He used a calculator.)

3-14

CLOSE AND ASSESS

WRITE WHAT YOU THINK

Have students write a paragraph responding to this statement: Estimating is silly because you never find an exact amount. Students should tell whether they agree or disagree and give reasons to support their ideas. (Check students' writing.)

QUICK QUIZ

Solve. Tell why you estimated or found the exact answer. At the fair, Vic got lunch for $3.75 and 4 pens for $0.80 each. Did he spend over $8? (No, estimate with a reference point.)

CHAPTER 3

APPLIED PROBLEM SOLVING
GROUP DECISION MAKING

OBJECTIVE To analyze, organize, and make decisions using relevant data
Did you ever want a pet? (Answers will vary.) *Did you convince your family to get one? How?* (Answers will vary.)

FACTS TO CONSIDER

▶ **Classify Facts 1, 2, 4, 5, and 6 as weekly or one-time expenses.** (Facts 1, 4, and 5—shots, a cat door, and a litter box— are one-time costs; Facts 2 and 6—food and litter—are weekly expenses.)
▶ **Evaluate Fact 3 according to importance and frequency.** (You must replace flea collars every so often, making the cost an occasional one but an important one to a cat's health; the name tag is a one-time cost meant to help if your cat gets lost.
▶ **Analyze which costs could be cut back and explain how.** (Possible answers: Buy cat food on sale; buy a simple litter box or use an old dishpan instead; do without a cat door; investigate whether larger bags of litter cost less than smaller bags.)
▶ **Identify costs that cannot be changed. Explain your reasoning.** (shots, office visit; those are controlled by the animal pound.)

Applied Problem Solving
Group Decision Making

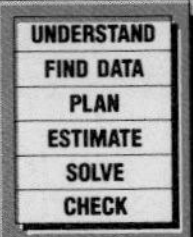

Group Skill:
Check for Understanding

You want to get a kitten from the animal pound. Your parents are concerned about the costs and problems of having a cat in the house. How can you convince them to let you have the kitten?

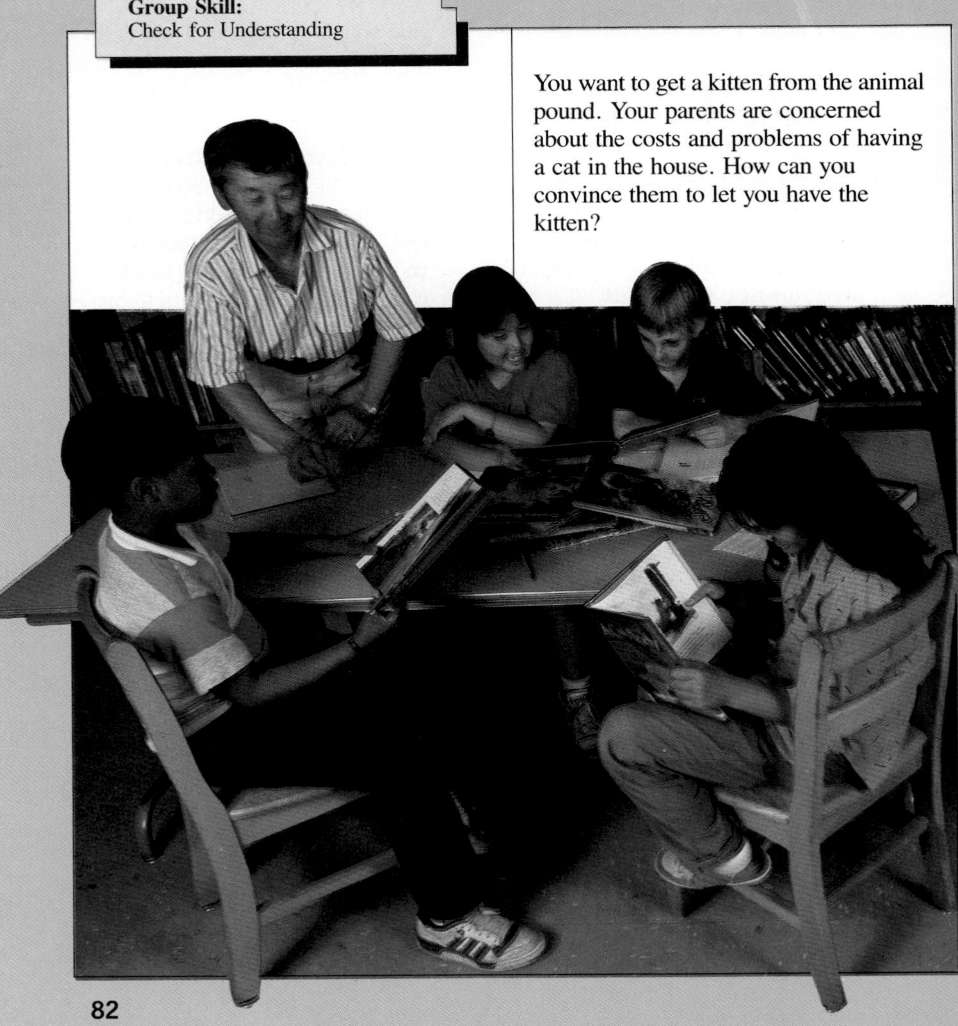

82

TEACHING OPTIONS

COOPERATIVE LEARNING

Grouping Suggestion: cooperative learning groups of 3-5
If possible, divide the class into groups in which at least 1 member already has a cat. Discuss plans that encourage all group members to contribute opinions and ideas that will lead to a good decision. For instance, a group may select a moderator to call on students in turn, a secretary to write down important ideas, a timer to see that too much time is not spent on any one point, and a calculator operator to check computations.

Facts to Consider

1. Before you can take the kitten home, it must have its shots. The pound charges $17 for the shots plus $10 for the office visit.
2. The kitten will need to eat 2 times a day. It will eat about 1 small can of cat food a day. Cat food costs about $0.35 a can.
3. A flea collar for the cat costs $3.29. A name tag for the collar costs $3.79.
4. A cat door costs $9.98.
5. A simple litter box costs $8.69. A fancy one that keeps the cat from kicking litter out costs $13.99.
6. A medium-sized bag of litter costs $2.89. It lasts about 1 week.

Some Questions to Answer

1. If you got the kitten, what things would you need to buy right away?
2. How would the cost change if you decided to buy only the necessary items? if you choose the cheaper litter box? What effects could these decisions have once the kitten had lived with you for a while?
3. How much would it cost to get the kitten's shots and buy all the things you would need to get started? Estimate the amount.
4. How much would it cost for food and litter each week? Estimate.

What Is Your Decision?

Write out a plan to give your parents. List the things you will need that will cost money. Show how much you estimate the kitten will cost in the beginning. Show the weekly cost. Tell how you plan to take care of the kitten.

83

WHAT IS YOUR PLAN? Some groups may role-play a family meeting about the kitten decision, in which some students present the plan as others act as parents or other family members.

▶ **Evaluate your plan. If you were a parent, what else would you ask your child?** (Answers may vary.)

▶ **Compare the advantages and disadvantages of having a kitten, other than cost.** (Possible advantages: Kittens can be lovable and entertaining companions. Possible disadvantages: Kittens can break things, scratch you, and make messes.)

SOME QUESTIONS TO ANSWER

▶ **What might you ask an experienced cat owner to help evaluate having a kitten?** (That person could judge your plan for a kitten, tell about other factors you should know, and verify whether your ideas and decisions make sense.)

▶ **Judge whether to overestimate or underestimate.** (It would be unrealistic to underestimate; if you overestimate, you will get an idea of maximum costs.)

▶ **Consider other questions that members of your family might ask.** (Answers may vary.)

WHAT IS YOUR DECISION?

Encourage groups to discuss ways to prepare the written plan. For instance, 1 group member could list and total weekly expenses while another lists and totals initial expenses. Some students could work out a kitten-care plan as others suggest ways to earn extra money to help pay for the initial costs.

CHAPTER 3

WRAP UP

INTRODUCTION The Wrap Up provides activities emphasizing math language and thinking skills for the chapter and a project that integrates those skills with other math strands.

USING PAGE 84

Strategy Search Have students complete this section independently. When they finish, have them discuss their answers in small groups, taking turns explaining their choices and telling how to finish each problem using the chosen strategy.

Sometimes, Always, Never

▶ **Visualize adding two 3-digit numbers to evaluate the statement in Exercise 4.** (Students should recall trading whenever they have 10 or more blocks in a place.)

▶ **Explain how a calculator gives an answer.** (The user must enter the correct numbers and operations.)

Project Have students work in pairs to discuss patterns that emerge.

▶ **Compare the addition and subtraction facts given.** (The same pairs of numbers are added and subtracted.)

▶ **Identify each number as odd or even.** (2, 4, and 6 are even; 3 and 5 are odd.)

▶ **Analyze the number pairs to find a pattern.** (Each operation uses numbers that are odd/odd, even/even, and even/odd.)

Additional Answers: See p. T79.

WRAP UP

Strategy Search

Match each situation with one of the techniques or strategies that it suggests. Justify your choices.

1. To subtract 562 − 304, first subtract 4 from each number to make 558 − 300. **d**
2. To estimate the difference of 628 and 312, subtract 300 from 600. **c**
3. To decide if $4 is enough money to buy tape for $1.69 and glue for $2.77, add $1 + $2. Then add an estimate of $0.69 + 77. **b**

a. using basic facts to find special sums
b. front-end estimation
c. estimating by rounding
d. using compensation

Sometimes, Always, Never

Which word should go in the blank, sometimes, always, or never? Explain your choices.

4. When adding whole numbers, if you have 10 or more ones blocks, tens blocks, or hundreds blocks, you should __?__ trade for a larger block. **always**
5. A calculator __?__ gives the correct answer. **sometimes**

Project

Even numbers end in 2, 4, 6, 8, or 0.
Odd numbers end in 1, 3, 5, 7, or 9.

6. Use counters to show and then answer these addition and subtraction problems. **Check students' work.**

5 + 3   4 + 2   6 + 3   5 − 3   4 − 2   6 − 3

7. If you add two odd numbers is your answer odd or even? If you subtract two odd numbers is your answer odd or even? **even, even**
8. Check your answers to problem 7 by showing several examples with your counters. What other patterns can you find for adding and subtracting odd and even numbers? **See Additional Answers.**

84

TEACHING OPTIONS

ENRICHMENT Have pairs of students use a calculator to test the generalizations they made in the project with greater numbers. Pairs formulate 3 addition and 3 subtraction cases like the ones in the project, but with numbers of at least 6 digits. For example, to verify that 2 odd numbers give an even sum, students might enter 999,999 + 777,777. (even sum: 1,777,776)

CHAPTER 3

CHAPTER REVIEW/TEST

Part 1 Understanding

Use mental math to find the sum or difference.
Explain how you found each answer. **See Additional Answers.**

1. 399 + 464
2. 1,500 − 700
3. 400 + 335 + 600

Part 2 Skills

Estimate the sum or difference. **Answers will vary. Sample answers given.**

4. 86 + 43 **130**
5. 730 − 285 **400**
6. 668 − 45 **620**

Use front-end estimation to find the sum or difference.

7. $7.88 + 5.25 = **$13**
8. 5,709 − 1,383 = **4,300**
9. 386 + 977 + 591 = **2,000**
10. 425 − 210 = **220**

Add or subtract.

11. 427 + 368 = **795**
12. 548 − 399 = **149**
13. 603 − 357 = **246**
14. 12,536 + 40,805 = **53,341**
15. 54 + 793 **847**
16. 762 − 465 **297**
17. 8,006 − 541 **7,465**
18. 1,608 + 523 **2,131**
19. 872 + 333 + 164 + 21 **1,390**
20. 3,608 + 753 + 6,551 **10,912**

Part 3 Applications

21. Ed writes on a computer. He writes 234 words on page 1 and 188 words on page 2. How many more words does he need for a 500-word story? **78 words**

22. Last year Rita used 27 cups at her party. This year she needs to double the number of cups. Should she find an estimate or an exact answer? How many cups should she buy? **estimate; about 60 cups**

85

INFORMAL ASSESSMENT

Using Manipulatives Students work in pairs to create 2 addition and 2 subtraction problems with randomly drawn number cards. As they take turns finding the sums or differences, have partners explain the steps they follow to each other and use place value materials to verify their answers.

Communication *How do you decide when to use compensation?* (Possible answer: when you notice that 1 addend is nearly a multiple of 10 or 100)

Critical Thinking *Explain which has the greater difference: 587 − 396 or 587 − 346.* (587 − 346; both problems show an amount subtracted from 587, so the case in which *less* is taken away shows the greater difference.)

CHAPTER REVIEW/TEST

INTRODUCTION The Review/Test is provided to review and evaluate the skills and concepts presented in Chapter 3.

USING PAGE 85
If you prefer to use this page for review, you may want to use the **Multiple-Choice Posttest** (pages 11-12) or the **Free-Response Posttest** (pages 11-12) to evaluate mastery of chapter objectives.

ITEM ANALYSIS The table below correlates the Chapter Review/Test items with the lesson objectives for the chapter.

Items	Objectives
1	3-11
2, 3	3-1
4-6	3-2
7-10	3-7
11, 15	3-4
12, 13, 16, 17	3-9
(13), (17)	3-10
14, (17), 18	3-13
19, 20	3-5
21	3-12
22	3-14

Additional Answers: See p. T79.

ENRICHMENT

INTRODUCTION Exploring an interesting pattern called the palindrome, which appears in words and numbers, will sharpen students' visual and mental acuity.

USING PAGE 86
This Enrichment page is provided for all students. You may wish to use it after the students have completed the Chapter Review/Test on page 85.
► **Analyze the words and numbers in Exercise 1 to discover the palindrome pattern, then explain it in your own words.** (A palindrome is a number or word that reads the same forward and backward.)
► **Explain how the flowchart guides you after you answer the question in the diamond-shaped box.** (If you answer *Yes,* follow the arrow to *Stop;* if you answer *No,* follow the arrow back to the step it points to and keep going until you can answer *Yes.*)
Have students complete the Enrichment lesson on their own. Then have them form small groups to discuss answers, share their word palindromes, and compare the number of steps they used to create their number palindromes.

EXTENSION Have students determine if any class member has a palindrome in his or her name, such as Eve, Otto, and Hannah. Then challenge them to list the times when a digital clock would show a palindrome during the school day, such as 8:48 and 9:19. (Answers will vary.)

Additional Answers: See p. T79.

ENRICHMENT
Palindromes

The words and numbers below are called palindromes. Palindromes have a special pattern.

1. What is the pattern? See Additional Answers.

dad	toot	level	deed	madam
66	747	3,883	52,125	753,357

2. Tell which of the following are not palindromes. Why not? See Additional Answers.

505   12,345   yoyo   mom   moon

3. Make up a word palindrome with 2 vowels.
Answers will vary. Sample answers: eye, peep.

The flow chart steps tell how to create a number palindrome.

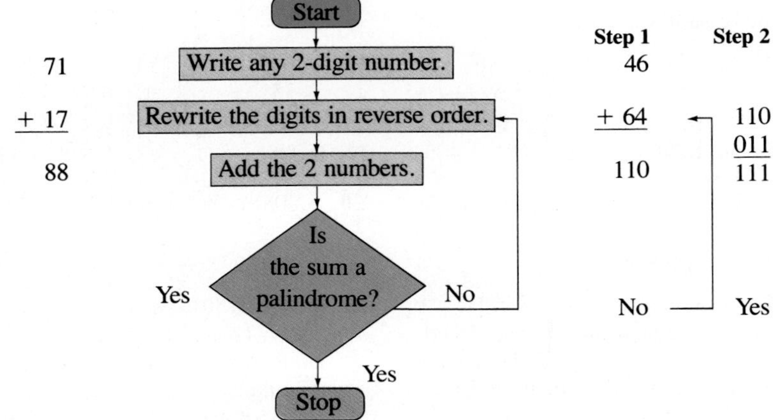

4. Follow the flow chart. Use 5 different starting numbers. Does it always work? Do you always use the same number of steps to make a palindrome? Explain. See Additional Answers.

86

CUMULATIVE REVIEW

1. 47 − 28

A 21 (B) 19
C 29 D 55

2. 37 + 56

A 81 B 19
C 83 (D) 93

3.
$$\begin{array}{r} 134 \\ -\ 39 \\ \hline \end{array}$$

(A) 95 B 115
C 105 D 173

4. To find 698 + 965, how many trades must you make?

A 0 (B) 2
C 1 D 3

5. What odd number is greater than 10, rounds to 20, and is said when you count by 5?

A 11 (B) 15
C 13 D 20

6. In 300 + 177 + 700, which are compatible numbers?

(A) 300 + 700 B 100 + 77
C 177 + 700 D 177 + 300

7. Estimate the difference between 783 and 231.

A 500 B 900
(C) 600 D 1,000

8. Which number is two hundred thousand, seventy-five?

A 275 B 275,000
C 20,750 (D) 200,075

9. What is 45,682 rounded to the nearest hundred?

(A) 45,700 B 46,000
C 45,600 D 45,000

10. In the city election, Ms. Ryan got 36,348 votes and the only other candidate, Mr. Sanchez, got 40,659 votes. How many people voted?

A 76,007 B 4,311
C 76,907 (D) 77,007

11. Rico made posters that were either blue, white, or red. Each poster had a single large star, eagle, or banner. How many poster combinations were there?

A 3 (B) 9
C 6 D 12

CUMULATIVE REVIEW

INTRODUCTION The purpose of this Cumulative Review is to maintain previously taught skills and concepts. The emphasis in this Cumulative Review is on addition and subtraction concepts and basic facts, Chapter 1; on place value, Chapter 2; and on adding and subtracting whole numbers, Chapter 3.

ITEM ANALYSIS The table below correlates the Cumulative Review items with the lesson objectives.

Items	Objectives
1	3-9
2	3-4
3	3-9
4	3-3
5	1-5
6	3-1
7	3-2
8	2-2
9	2-6
10	3-13
11	3-6

CHAPTER 4 DATA, GRAPHS, AND PROBABILITY

Chapter Management

OVERVIEW

Lesson	Pages	Objectives	Subject Integration	Strand Integration
Chapter Opener	88-89	To introduce chapter 4	social studies-mountains	critical thinking
Getting Information From a Graph	90-91	4-1 To get information from a bar graph and a pictograph	social studies-campers	mathematical reasoning
Reading and Making Bar Graphs	92-93	4-2 To read and make a bar graph	science-recording results	algebra
Reading and Making Pictographs	94-95	4-3 To understand and make a pictograph	health/fitness-popcorn	mathematical reasoning
Reading and Making Line Graphs	96-97	4-4 To read and make a line graph	social studies-Rocky Mountains	problem solving
Using Critical Thinking/ Midchapter Review/Quiz	98-99	4-5 To use critical thinking to analyze a graphical situation	social studies-generations	statistics
Problem Solving: Extra Data	100-101	4-6 To solve problems with extra data	science-decibels	computation
Fair and Unfair Games	102-103	4-7 To determine whether or not a game is fair	social studies-group skills	mathematical reasoning
Probability and Prediction	104-105	4-8 To determine whether the probability of something happening is high or low and to predict an outcome	social studies-group skills	mental math
Problem Solving: Guess and Check	106-107	4-9 To solve problems using the strategy Guess and Check	language arts-magazine survey	statistics
Data Collection and Analysis: Group Decision Making	108-109	4-10 To collect, organize, and present data	science-fingerprints	statistics

MATHEMATICAL BACKGROUND

Graphs
In Chapter 4, students are taught how to read and to make bar graphs, pictographs, and line graphs. When making graphs, students learn to create a scale, label one side and the bottom of the graph, and title the graph.

Probability
Deciding whether a game is fair or unfair helps students understand and apply the concept of probability in Lesson 4-7. A game is fair when all players have an equal chance, or probability, of winning.

Problem Solving
Students learn to identify the necessary data in problems that contain extra data. In Lesson 4-9, they learn to use the Guess and Check strategy.

TIPS FROM TEACHERS

Use pennies as the basis of a graphing project. Divide the class into small cooperative learning groups and give each group a container filled with 25 to 30 pennies. Discuss ways to sort the pennies, such as by date or by degree of shine. Each group sorts, counts, then graphs the pennies. Compare the finished graphs.

Trina Hendrickson
South Bay Elementary School
Olympia, WA

OUR PENNIES
1 "○" = 2 pennies

SHINY: ○○○○○○
DULL : ●●●●●●●●

ASSESSMENT

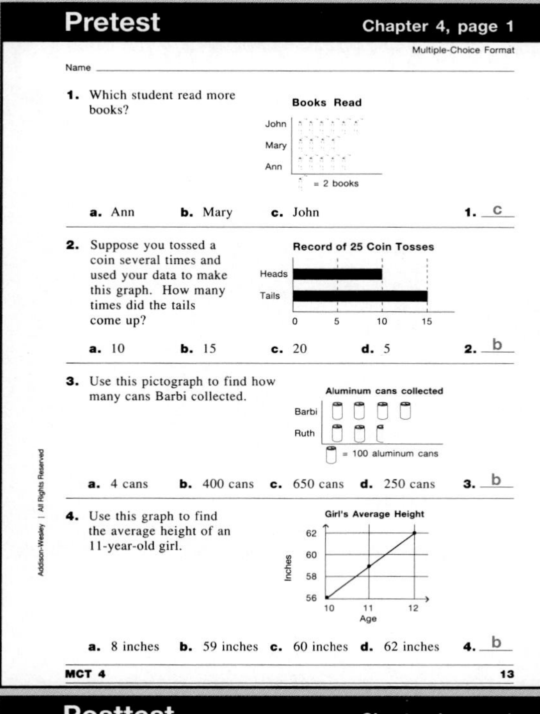

Pretest — Chapter 4, page 1

Multiple-Choice Format

Name ____________

1. Which student read more books?

a. Ann **b.** Mary **c.** John — **1.** c

2. Suppose you tossed a coin several times and used your data to make this graph. How many times did the tails come up?

a. 10 **b.** 15 **c.** 20 **d.** 5 — **2.** b

3. Use this pictograph to find how many cans Barbi collected.

a. 4 cans **b.** 400 cans **c.** 650 cans **d.** 250 cans — **3.** b

4. Use this graph to find the average height of an 11-year-old girl.

a. 8 inches **b.** 59 inches **c.** 60 inches **d.** 62 inches — **4.** b

Pretest — Chapter 4, page 2

Multiple-Choice Format

Name ____________

5. If an arrow is drawn from each person to that person's parent, which letter shows a grandparent?

a. A **b.** B **c.** C **d.** D — **5.** c

6. Some people have to travel over 25 miles to come to the school play. There were 46 fathers and 59 mothers at the play. How many parents were at the play?

a. 71 parents **b.** 130 parents
c. 84 parents **d.** 105 parents — **6.** d

7. Suppose you were to use these spinners to play a game with your classmate. Is the game fair or unfair?

Rules: Spin both spinners. If both numbers match, your team scores. If not, the other team scores. The first team to get 10 points wins.

a. Fair **b.** Unfair — **7.** b

8. Use these cards to make predictions. Is the probability you will draw a 7 higher or lower than the probability you will draw an 8?

7	7	8	7	7	8

a. Higher **b.** Lower — **8.** a

9. The sum of two numbers is 42. The difference is 14. What are the two numbers?

a. 16 and 26 **b.** 14 and 28
c. 15 and 27 **d.** 25 and 39 — **9.** b

Posttest — Chapter 4, page 1

Multiple-Choice Format

Name ____________

1. Which student read fewer books?

Books Read: John, Mary, Ann — = 2 books

a. Ann **b.** Mary **c.** John — **1.** a

2. Suppose you tossed a coin several times and used your data to make this graph. How many times did heads come up?

Record of 25 Coin Tosses: Heads, Tails — 0 5 10 15

a. 10 **b.** 15 **c.** 20 **d.** 25 — **2.** b

3. Use this pictograph to find how many cans Ruth collected.

Aluminum cans collected: Barbi, Ruth — = 100 aluminum cans

a. 200 cans **b.** 225 cans **c.** 250 cans **d.** 300 cans — **3.** c

4. Use this graph to find the average height of a 12-year-old boy.

Boy's Average Height — Inches 62, 60, 58, 56 — Age 10, 11, 12

a. 59 inches **b.** 60 inches **c.** 61 inches **d.** 62 inches — **4.** d

Posttest — Chapter 4, page 2

Multiple-Choice Format

Name ____________

5. If an arrow is drawn from each person to that person's child, which letter shows a grandchild?

A C B D

a. A **b.** B **c.** C **d.** D — **5.** d

6. Last year, there were 14 boys and 18 girls in the class play. This year there are 19 boys and 16 girls. How many more boys were in this year's play than were in last year's play?

a. 2 boys **b.** 33 boys **c.** 3 boys **d.** 5 boys — **6.** d

7. Suppose you were to use these spinners to play a game with your classmate. Is the game fair or unfair?

Rules: Spin both spinners. If both numbers are odd or both are even, your team scores. If not, the other team scores. The first team to get 10 points wins.

a. Fair **b.** Unfair — **7.** b

8. Use these cards to make predictions. Is the probability you will draw an A higher or lower than the probability you will draw a B?

A	B	A	A	B	A

a. Higher **b.** Lower — **8.** a

9. The sum of two numbers is 75. The difference is 13. What are the two numbers?

a. 37 and 38 **b.** 31 and 44
c. 37 and 50 **d.** 35 and 48 — **9.** b

ITEM ANALYSIS

Items	Objectives
1	4-1
2	4-2
3	4-3
4	4-4
5	4-5
6	4-6
7	4-7
8	4-8
9	4-9

Note: The item analysis is the same for all pretests and posttests for this chapter.

ALSO AVAILABLE

- Free Response Tests
- Alternative Tests
- Thinking Strategies
- Concrete Materials

Optional Chapter Activities

PROJECT AND BULLETIN BOARD

Have students work together to make a double bar graph of the predicted high and low temperatures for your city every day while they work on this chapter. Students should obtain the predicted high and low temperature readings by listening to radio or television reports, or by reading the newspaper. Have them color the high-reading bars red and the low-reading bars blue.

After temperatures have been graphed for several days, have students make up questions based on the graph. Questions can be posted on the bulletin board or in a packet. They may also be asked orally. Students should know the answers to their own questions and be prepared to explain to classmates any problem-solving steps needed.

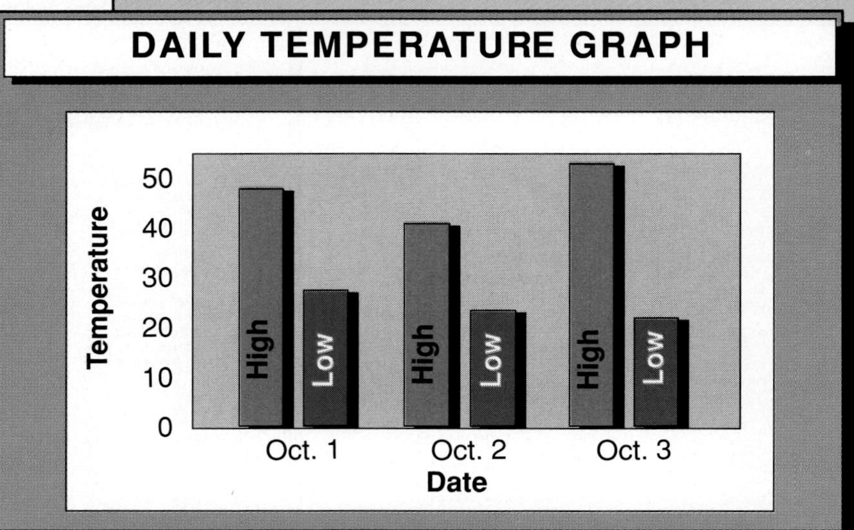

COOPERATIVE LEARNING

Divide the class into groups of three or four. Identify the group skill: listen to others. Give each group a stick two or three feet in height. Have the group insert its stick in the ground in the schoolyard, or have someone hold it steady. On a sunny day, have the group measure the length of the stick's shadow every hour from the beginning to the end of the school day. One student should be appointed to make the measurements and another to record them. Students should then plan and make a line graph showing the change in the length of the stick's shadow during the course of the day. Students may repeat the experiment with a different length stick and graph those results, too. Each group should then discuss what its graph shows. (They should find that the shadow of the stick is longest when the sun is lowest in the sky, and shortest when the sun is highest in the sky.) If two graphs were made, the results should be compared.

You will find grouping suggestions and cooperative learning activities in most lessons throughout this chapter.

LITERATURE

Tongren, Sally. ***What's For Lunch: Animal Feeding at the Zoo.*** New York: EMG Publishing, 1981.

In this delightful book children will get an inside glimpse of how and what animals are fed at the National Zoological Park in Washington, D.C. Children could draw pictographs using the animals from the story. Or they could make bar graphs to record the amount of food a particular animal needs daily, weekly, or monthly.

Anno, Mitsumasa. ***Anno's Math Games.*** New York: Philomel Books, Putnam & Grosset, 1987.

Branley, Franklyn M. ***How Much and How Little; A Book About Scales.*** New York: Young Math Book Series, Thomas Y. Crowell, 1976.

Wyler, Rose & Gerald Ames. ***Funny Number Tricks, Easy Magic with Arithmetic.*** New York: Parents' Magazine Press, 1976.

English as a Second Language

Reading and making graphs are especially good learning tools for the ESL child because graphs can be understood with limited language skills.

Begin the activity by choosing subjects that are easy to understand and that interest the children. The students participate by supplying data for different types of graphs. First use a one-to-one scale, then progress to a more complex scale, demonstrating the scales' purpose each time. For example, if a scale uses a symbol to represent two people, ask two children to come to the front of the room. Draw the symbol on the chalkboard and explain that the symbol represents those two children. Then ask the class to list different situations to show on a graph and to suggest appropriate scales. Possible situations include graphing the class's favorite foods or the modes of transportation students take to get to school.

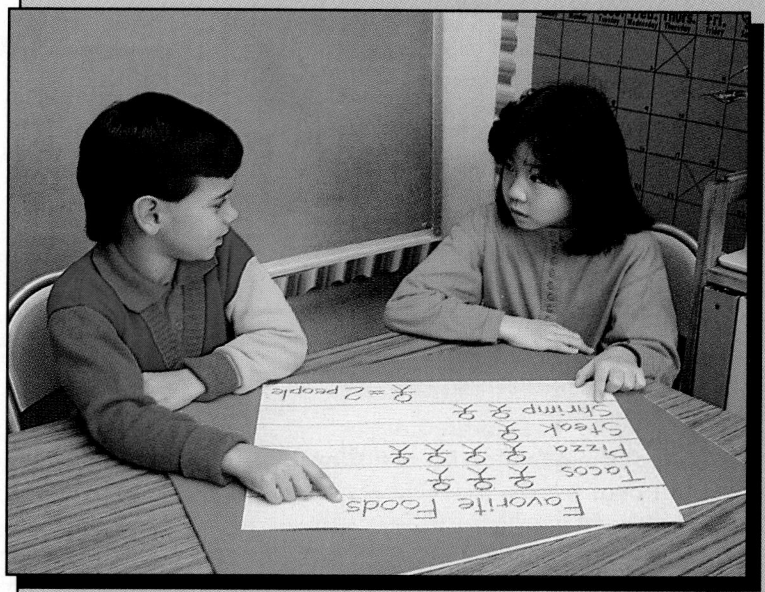

Gifted

A company called ''Birthday Magic'' is trying to determine the two calendar months in which most fourth graders have a birthday. The students have been asked to collect information about their classmates' birthdays and to display the information on a double bar graph. The double bar graph will be shown to the ''company president.''

Encourage students to think of different ways of tallying the birthday months. They should make two separate tallies, one for the boys and one for the girls. Have the students choose two different colors for the bars in the bar graph, one color for the boys and a different color for the girls. Encourage the students to give the graph a creative but appropriate title. Remind them to label the graph accurately and clearly.

Have each student write five questions that can be answered by reading the graph. Ask students to choose a partner, then to trade graphs and questions. Have students use the graphs to answer each others' questions. Partners report whether the graph provides the necessary information for ''Birthday Magic.'' Have them determine if the graphs indicate any patterns.

Students at Risk

Because graphs represent information in visual or symbolic form, students with language problems often have trouble translating visual data into words or numbers. They may have a general feel for the data, but they may need help finding the appropriate language to interpret and to draw conclusions from the data. Provide a list of words that are helpful for making comparisons about data presented in visual form, such as *most, least, increase, decrease, equal*. Less able students may feel more at ease asking questions in a small group setting. They can listen and take turns formulating general statements to describe the data. Remind them that the titles, labels, and number scales on graphs provide clues to the data.

Students with weak number sense may have trouble interpreting number scales when some intervals are not labeled. Provide them with alternate graphs of the same data with all intervals marked to allow them to work with the data more readily. As their ability increases, students can move to graphs with more complex number scales.

You may also use the Reteaching Supplements and the specific Reteaching Tips from each lesson in this chapter.

CHAPTER 4

INTRODUCING THE CHAPTER

SUBJECT INTEGRATION The photograph of a Rocky Mountain scene represents the chapter theme of American geography. Various lessons include facts about mountains and rivers to provide data in graph, table, and chart form for students to read and interpret.

USING DATA The Social Studies Data Bank on page 473 of the Student Edition provides 2 tables of facts about American land features. The first table gives state-by-state totals of mountains over 14,000 feet. The second compares 5 rivers formed in the Rocky Mountains according to length, direction of flow, and site of mouth.

QUESTION 1 ► **Explain the meaning of the question by restating it in your own words.** (Possible answer: *What is the total number of U.S. mountains over 14,000 ft?*)
► **Justify the operation to use to answer the question.** (add to join groups)
Student Edition answer: 84

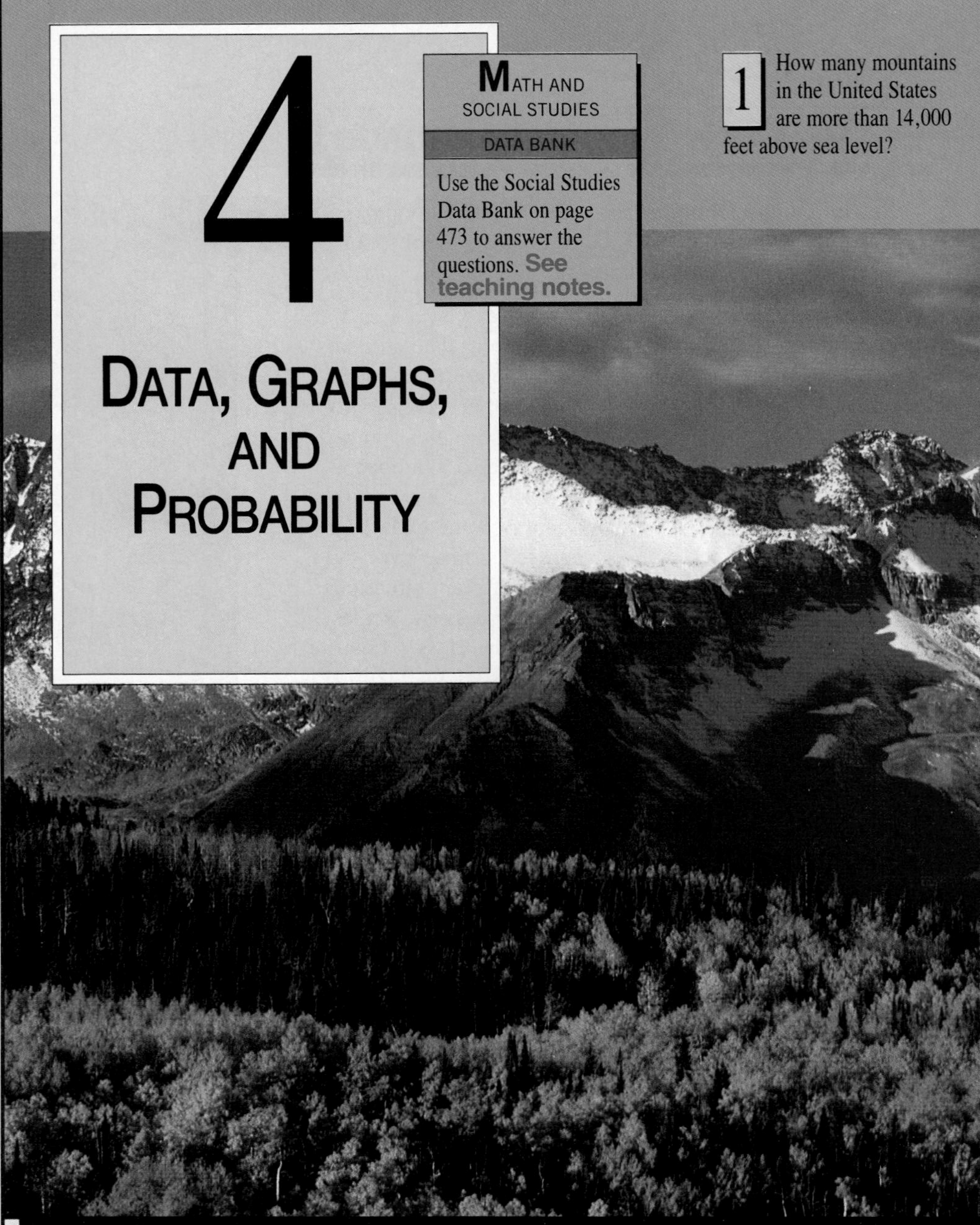

4
DATA, GRAPHS, AND PROBABILITY
MATH AND SOCIAL STUDIES
DATA BANK
Use the Social Studies Data Bank on page 473 to answer the questions. See teaching notes.
1 How many mountains in the United States are more than 14,000 feet above sea level?

TEACHING OPTIONS

LANGUAGE DEVELOPMENT
Write the word **table** on the chalkboard and have students explain its mathematical meaning. (Possible answer: ''an organized way to present data using columns and rows'') Have students explain how to interpret the kind of data a table presents. (Possible response: Read its title and the labels used to identify columns.)

2 What is the longest river formed in the Rocky Mountains? Does it flow east or west?

3 The Rio Grande River goes about 800 miles before it becomes the US/Mexico border. For about how many miles is the river a border?

4 **Use Critical Thinking** Which two rivers put end-to-end would come closest to equaling the longest river in the table?

QUESTION 2 ► **Based on its title, what conclusion can you draw about the river table?** (Possible answer: Other rivers form in the Rocky Mountains, but only 5 have been used in the table.)
Student Edition answers: Missouri; east

QUESTION 3 ► **Explain how a river can form a border between 2 countries.** (Possible answer: The first country starts on one side of the river; the second country starts across the same river.)

► **Develop a plan to answer the question.** (Find the total length of the Rio Grande River in the table, then subtract 800 miles from that number to account for the length the river goes before it becomes a border.)
Student Edition answer: 1,000 miles

QUESTION 4 ► **Identify the data you need first in order to answer the question.** (The Missouri River at 2,714 miles is the longest river.)

► **Explain how the question relates to a mathematical idea.** (Possible answer: A number + another number = about 2,714)

► **Decide on a strategy to find the best answer.** (Possible method: Use front-end digits to find two numbers that equal 27; 14 + 14 = 28; Colorado and Arkansas Rivers)
Student Edition answer: Colorado and Arkansas Rivers

SUBJECT INTEGRATION PROJECT Have students make a pictograph based on the data in the mountain table and a bar graph based on some of the data in the river table. Students decide how to present data and plan a reasonable design for the graphs. Begin by having students pose riddles based on the data in either table, using the wording of Question 4 as an example. Students can create their graphs to answer the riddles as they work through the lessons in Chapter 4. Conclude by displaying the finished graphs and by having a group discussion to compare and contrast them.

LESSON OPTIONS 4-1

Getting Information From a Graph

OBJECTIVE 4-1 To get information from a bar graph and a pictograph

PREBOOK ACTIVITIES

QUICK REVIEW

Write < or > for each ○.

1. 3,450 ○ 3,054 (>) **2.** 37,782 ○ 37,872 (<)

3. 1,732 ○ 1,730 (>)

Order these numbers from least to greatest.

4. 1,365 1,345 1,360 1,350 1,340 1,355
(1,340; 1,345; 1,350; 1,355; 1,360; 1,365)

PRIOR KNOWLEDGE

Ask students to list sports that students their age participate in after school. (Possible answers: soccer, gymnastics) Then tally how many students participate in each of the sports listed. Ask students how this information could be displayed so that it would be easy to understand. (Possible answers: make a table; make a graph) Ask students to think about where they have seen graphs before. (Possible answers: textbooks, magazines, newspapers) Then ask students to describe graphs they have used in school. (Possible answers: bar graphs, pictographs)

COMMUNICATION

Discussing, Reading, and Writing Math Arrange students into small groups. Provide each group with several graphs photocopied from magazines, newspapers, or textbooks. Have students examine them and form two generalizations explaining what the graphs have in common. (Possible answers: Each has a title, labels, and number scales.) Then write the words **title, label,** and **number scale** on the chalkboard. Groups discuss each word and write on the graph what role each one has. Allow time for each group to discuss and evaluate each word and to share their definitions with the class.

EXPLORE AND CONNECT

Grouping Suggestion: small groups

Students explore ways to show collected data. Ask students to name 3 of their favorite school lunches, then tally each child's favorite choice on the chalkboard. Ask students to name as many ways that they can to show this information, listing their suggestions on the board. (Sample answers: bar graph, pictograph, line graph, chart, table) Also ask them to name possible **titles, labels,** and **number scales.** Have students assist you in showing 3 of the formats on the board. Then arrange students into small groups to record what they feel are the advantages and the disadvantages of each format. Conclude by having each group explain which format it thinks works best. (Possible answer: A bar graph tells at a glance the favorite lunch and how many people like it, while a table or a chart gives you only numbers and a pictograph requires converting symbols to numbers to get exact answers.)

CONNECTIONS Use these anytime.

Problem of the Day

Intervals Mr. Granados was making a number scale from 0 to 12 for his bar graph. Draw a number scale with a partner to find out how many numbers he wrote on the scale if he wrote a number for every 3 marks. (5 numbers—0, 3, 6, 9, 12)

Subject Integration

Physical Education In a Physical Fitness pictograph, each symbol represents 5 jumps. Count how many times you can jump in 1 min. How many symbols would you use? (Possible answer: 30 symbols for 150 jumps in 1 min)

Patterns

Spelling Scores Jerry made a graph to track his spelling-test scores. If the first 4 numbers showing scores on the number scale are 0, 10, 20, and 30, decide what the remaining numbers are if the scale goes up to 100. (40, 50, 60, 70, 80, 90, 100)

Classwork and Homework Supplements

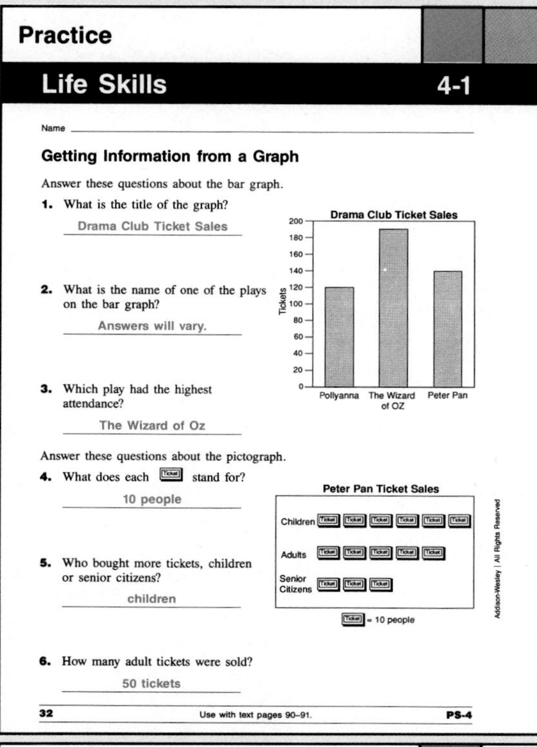

Practice

Life Skills 4-1

Name ____________

Getting Information from a Graph

Answer these questions about the bar graph.

1. What is the title of the graph? Drama Club Ticket Sales
2. What is the name of one of the plays on the bar graph? Answers will vary.
3. Which play had the highest attendance? The Wizard of Oz

Answer these questions about the pictograph.

4. What does each [ticket] stand for? 10 people
5. Who bought more tickets, children or senior citizens? children
6. How many adult tickets were sold? 50 tickets

32 Use with text pages 90-91. PS-4

Building Thinking Skills

Data Analysis 4-1

Name ____________

Data Predictions

Analyze the bar graph and next week's school lunch menu to make each prediction below.

School Lunch Menu	
Monday	Chili
Tuesday	Chicken
Wednesday	Hot Dog
Thursday	Pizza
Friday	Tacos

1. Which day would you predict the greatest number of students might eat the school lunch? Why? Thursday; the greatest number of students chose pizza as their favorite lunch.
2. Which day would you predict the fewest students might eat the school lunch? Why? Monday; the fewest number of students chose chili as their favorite.
3. On which days might the same number of students eat the school lunch? Why? Tuesday and Friday; the same numbers of students chose chicken and tacos as their favorite lunches.
4. To change the bar graph to a pictograph you would use symbols instead of bars. Write the number of symbols you would use to represent each school lunch. Include a key that tells how many lunches each symbol represents. Answers will vary. Sample answers given.

$1\frac{1}{2}$ Chili $2\frac{1}{2}$ Hot Dog   2 Tacos

2 Chicken   3 Pizza   1 symbol = 10 school lunches

32 Use with text pages 90-91. TS-4

Reteaching

Life Skills 4-1

Name ____________

Getting Information from a Graph

Use the bar graph.

Look for the correct bar. → Follow the bar to the top. → Look at the number scale to find out what the bar stands for.

Use the pictograph.

Find the correct label. → Count the number of pictures next to it. → Find out what each picture stands for. Add or multiply to get the answer.

Use the graphs to answer these questions.

1. What is the title of the bar graph? Favorite Subjects
2. What subject was liked the least? social studies
3. Which subject was liked more, math or English? English
4. In the pictograph, what does each [figure] show? 10 people
5. How many people liked the monkey bars best? 20 people
6. Do more people like the slide or swings? slide

32 Use with text pages 90-91. RS-4

Challenges

Critical Thinking 4-1

Name ____________

Tricky Graphing

The way a graph is drawn can change the message you get from it.

1. What is the same about the graphs above? title and labels
2. What is different about the graphs? scale
3. Which graph makes you think sales were very "up and down"? graph B
4. What does the other graph make you think? Sales have been a little bit up and down.

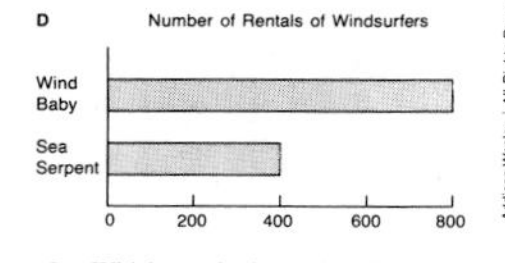

5. Which graph makes it look like very few people rent Sea Serpents? graph C
6. Which graph shows that Wind Baby rentals were double Sea Serpent rentals? graph D

32 Use with text pages 90-91. CS-4

Options for Individual Needs

Basic

Exercises 1-9
Data Bank, p. 473
Computer Bank, p. 499
More Practice, p. 514, set C

Supplements
Reteaching 32 or
Practice 32

Average

Exercises 1-9
Data Bank, p. 473
Computer Bank, p. 499
More Practice, p. 514, set C

Supplements
Practice 32
Challenges 32 or
Thinking Skills 32

Extended

Exercises 1-9
Data Bank, p. 473
Computer Bank, p. 499

Supplements
Challenges 32
Thinking Skills 32

Other Resources:
Problem-Solving Experiences in Mathematics, Grade 4, Problem 112
Math In Stride, Grade 4, p. 144
Mathematics, A Way of Thinking, Lessons 15-3, 15-4

LESSON PLAN 4-1

OBJECTIVE 4-1
To get information from a bar graph and a pictograph

Materials: calculators

Grouping Suggestion: pairs

1. MOTIVATE AND TEACH

LEARN ABOUT IT

▶ **Compare the similarities between the graphs shown.** (Possible answer: Both have a title and labels; both give information)

EXPLORE ▶ **Explain the advantages of using a graph to get information.** (Possible answer: You can quickly draw conclusions from the data and easily make comparisons.)

TALK ABOUT IT ▶ **Explain why a bar graph is good for representing mountain height.** (Possible answer: It helps you visualize height.)
▶ **Describe how to use the graph to find Mt. Whitney's height.** (Locate the bar for Mt. Whitney, compare it to the height in feet, then estimate that it is halfway between 12,000 and 16,000 ft—about 14,000 ft.)
Student Edition answers: **1.** Some Mountains in the United States; People Enjoying Mt. Rec in One Year; Possible answer: It tells what the data is about. **2.** Mt. McKinley; Guadalupe Peak **3.** Campers; Climbers **4.** Possible answers: mountain heights in feet; how many people each stick figure stands for

2. CHECK UNDERSTANDING

TRY IT OUT

ERROR ALERT Forgetting to convert stick figures to numbers of people in the key.

Getting Information From a Graph

LEARN ABOUT IT

EXPLORE Think About Graphs
Graphs give us information by showing data. They use bars, lines, or pictures. Study these two graphs.

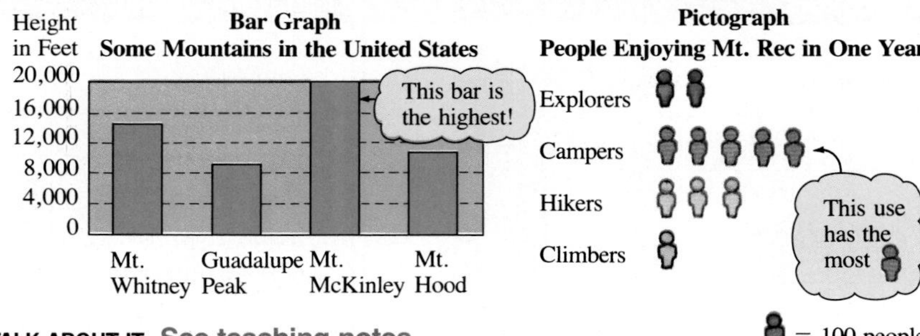

TALK ABOUT IT See teaching notes.

1. What is the title of the bar graph? the pictograph? Why do you think the title is important?
2. Which mountain in the bar graph is the highest? the lowest?
3. Who used Mt. Rec the most? the least?
4. What else do the graphs tell us?

Every graph has a title that tells what it is about. It also has labels to tell what it shows. A number scale shows the units used on the graph.

TRY IT OUT

1. In the bar graph, what numbers are used to show heights of the mountains?
   4,000; 8,000; 12,000; 16,000; 20,000
2. In the pictograph, what does the  stand for?
   100 people
3. How many hikers enjoy Mt. Rec in one year?
   1,100 people

90

TEACHING OPTIONS

RETEACHING TIPS Students exhibiting this error should point to the first stick figure next to the label for Hikers and enter 100 on a calculator. As they point to the two remaining stick figures, they should enter + 100 each time, ending with = to get a total of 300 Hikers. Assign Reteaching Supplement 32.

ENRICHMENT Have students work with a partner and use one volume of an encyclopedia to find a graph. Both students write the graph's title, number scale, and labels. Then each creates a question about the graph for his or her partner to answer. Students check each other's work.

PRACTICE

Answer these questions about this bar graph. See Additional Answers.

1. What is the title of the graph?
2. Name one of the trails on the bar graph.
3. Why do you think one of the trails is called Short Stretch?
4. Which trail is longer than 2 miles, but less than 4 miles?

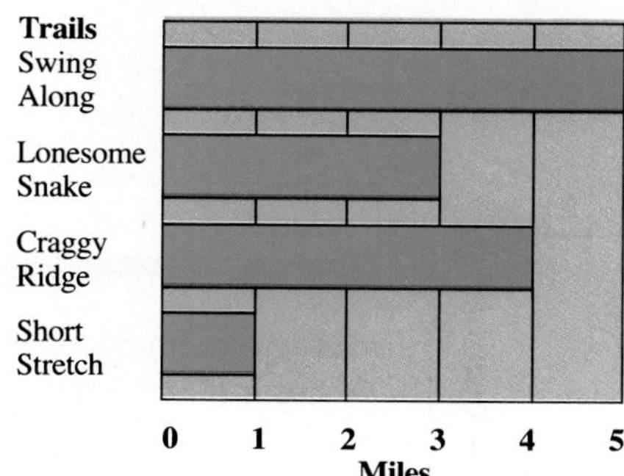

Answer these questions about this pictograph.

5. What kinds of birds does the pictograph show? eagles, hawks, vultures, and others
6. How many birds does each [bird symbol] represent? 2 birds

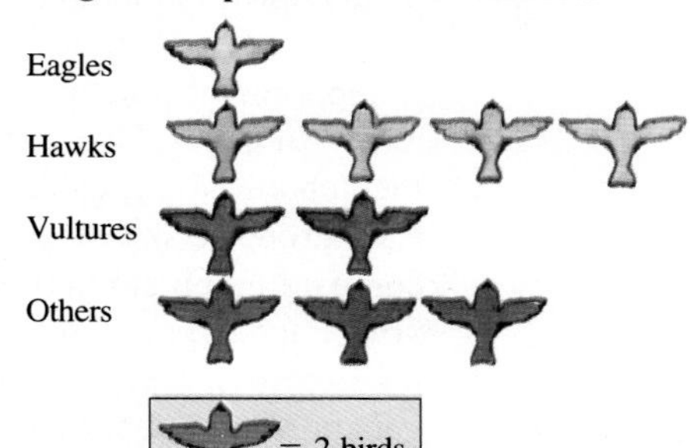

APPLY

MATH REASONING

7. What if each [bird symbol] represented 5 birds? How many hawks would the graph then show? 20 hawks

PROBLEM SOLVING

DATA BANK

8. **Social Studies Data Bank** What state would you visit to see the greatest number of high peaks? See page 473. Colorado

▶ COMMUNICATION Write About It

9. Write a short paragraph about a mountain hike. In your story, use data from the graphs shown in this lesson. Answers will vary.

More Practice, page 514, set C

91

3. PRACTICE AND APPLY

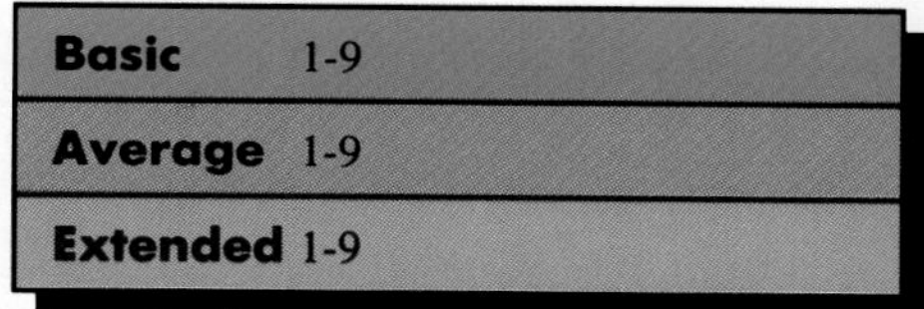

Basic	1-9
Average	1-9
Extended	1-9

Additional Answers: See p. T79.

PRACTICE

Look at the bar graph and the pictograph and decide how their number scales are different. (The bar graph's scale has intervals of one; in the pictograph, you use the key and you count by twos.)

APPLY

MATH REASONING ▶ Explain how you could count by fives to solve Problem 7. (If each picture represents 5 birds, you count by five 4 times.)

PROBLEM SOLVING ▶ Describe how ordering numbers from least to greatest helps you solve Problem 8. (Ordering 1, 12, 18, and 53 helps you quickly see there is no greater number listed than 53.)

COMMUNICATION ▶ Before you begin Exercise 9, create a sentence that uses data from both graphs. (Possible answer: I saw 2 eagles on my 5-mi walk on the Swing Along trail.)

4-1

CLOSE AND ASSESS

WRITE WHAT YOU KNOW

Distribute photocopies of both a bar graph and a pictograph, different from those you may have used in the Communication section. Ask students to write this information for each graph: the kind; the title; the labels; the number scales; and the type of information, such as the most or the least of something. Have students compare answers in a class discussion.

QUICK QUIZ

Use the graph to answer the questions.
1. Who read the most?
2. Who read 6 books?
(**1.** Sal **2.** Pam)

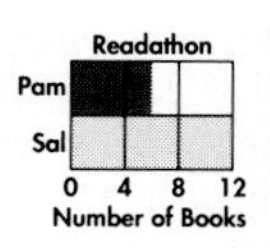

LESSON OPTIONS 4-2

Reading and Making Bar Graphs

OBJECTIVE 4-2 To read and make a bar graph

PREBOOK ACTIVITIES

QUICK REVIEW

1. Round to the nearest ten.
453 (450) 398 (400) 272 (270) 456 (460)
2. Round to the nearest hundred.
3,452 (3,500) 6,197 (6,200) 4,518 (4,500)
3. Round to the nearest thousand.
2,163 (2,000) 8,702 (9,000) 34,346 (34,000)

PRIOR KNOWLEDGE

Have students describe the kinds of graphs they have seen before. (Possible answers: bar graphs, pictographs) Then ask students to explain what these graphs have in common. (Possible answer: They have titles and labels and they tell something about numbers.) Ask students when a graph might be useful. (Possible answer: when you want to see or interpret data quickly)

COMMUNICATION

Discussing Math Write the words **horizontal** and **vertical** on the chalkboard. Then display examples of a horizontal and a vertical bar graph, identifying each. Ask students to list the graphs' similarities. (Possible answers: titles, number scales, bars, labels, data presented) Then have them discuss the differences. (Possible answers: direction of bars; the labels are reversed) Have students suggest reasons why one graph might be preferred to the other since they present the same data. (Possible answers: We read in a horizontal direction; space on a page may dictate which graph format should be used.)

EXPLORE AND CONNECT

Materials: photocopies of a paragraph
Grouping Suggestion: cooperative learning groups of 6
Students explore ways to make bar graphs. Explain that, for some word games, it helps to know the most frequently used letters in words. Give each student one copy of the photocopied paragraph, then arrange students into groups to count how many times each vowel is used. One of each group's members chooses one of the five vowels—*a, e, i, o,* or *u*—to count. The sixth student records the result. Together they choose the graph's title, labels, and number scale. Then each group records the data on 2 different bar graphs. Groups compare graph similarities (such as the number of times each vowel appears) and differences (such as showing information **vertically** or **horizontally**). Ask the class to make a generalization about the graphs. (Possible answer: The same information may be shown in different forms.)

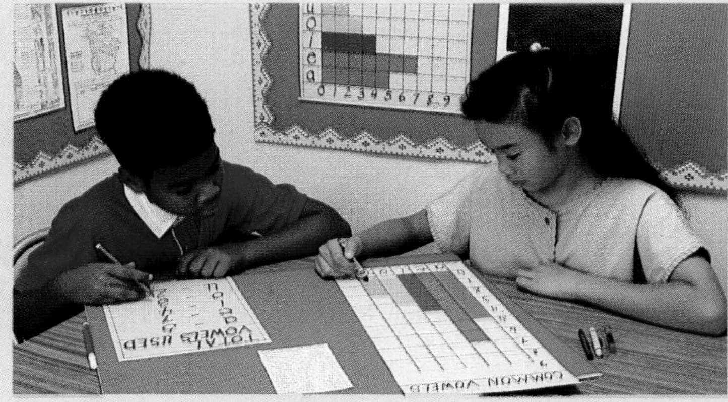

CONNECTIONS Use these anytime.

Problem of the Day

Ordering The following colored bars are on a graph with a number scale showing 0 to 20 in intervals of 2. Use each bar's location on the number scale to order the bars from least to greatest value: pink—between 4 and 6; green—between 8 and 10; yellow—between 2 and 4; red—between 6 and 8. (yellow, pink, red, green)

Math Connection

Estimating The number scale on Mr. Ali's rope-jumping bar graph is marked from 0 to 5,000 in intervals of a thousand. This week, he jumped rope 423 times on Monday, 489 times on Tuesday, and 381 times on Thursday. Between what 2 numbers will the bar for this week's total number of jumps appear? (between 1,000 and 2,000)

Number Sense

Money Each week, Paula collects milk-money envelopes from each of the 3 fourth-grade classes. She tracks each envelope on a bar graph. This week, the first envelope has a value of a half dozen dollars, the second has a value of 11 dollars, and the third has a roll of 50 dimes. Which bar on her graph is the longest? (the second)

Classwork and Homework Supplements

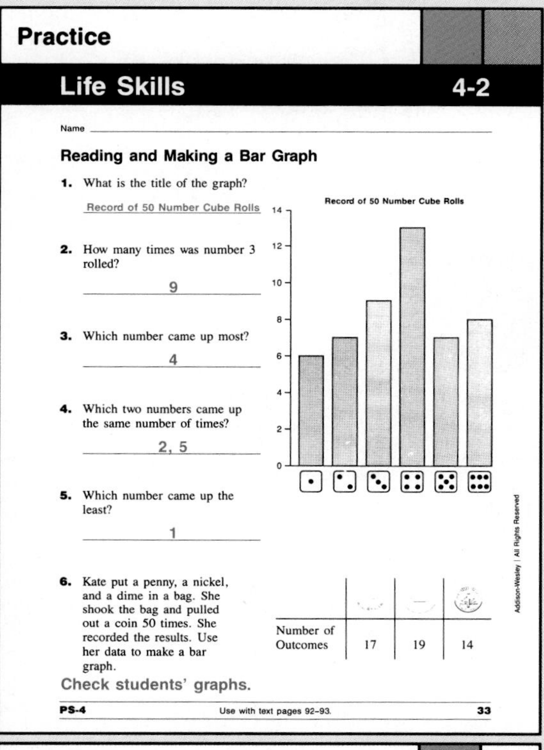

Practice

Life Skills 4-2

Name ______

Reading and Making a Bar Graph

1. What is the title of the graph? Record of 50 Number Cube Rolls
2. How many times was number 3 rolled? 9
3. Which number came up most? 4
4. Which two numbers came up the same number of times? 2, 5
5. Which number came up the least? 1
6. Kate put a penny, a nickel, and a dime in a bag. She shook the bag and pulled out a coin 50 times. She recorded the results. Use her data to make a bar graph. Check students' graphs.

Number of Outcomes	17	19	14

Addison-Wesley | All Rights Reserved

PS-4 Use with text pages 92-93. 33

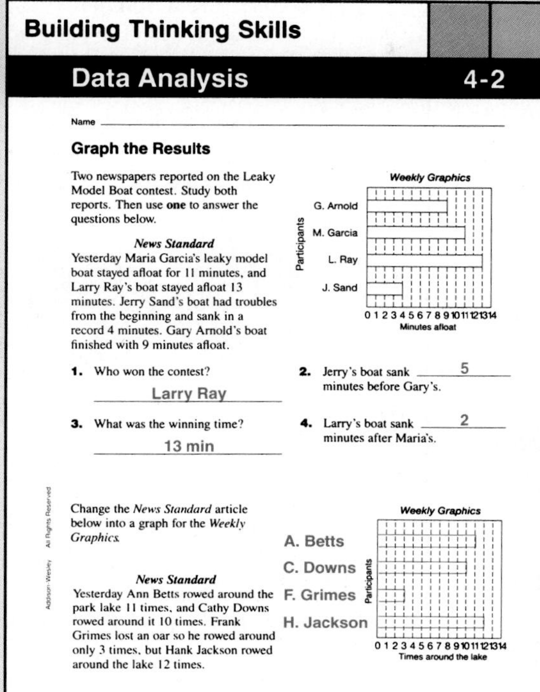

Building Thinking Skills

Data Analysis 4-2

Name ______

Graph the Results

Two newspapers reported on the Leaky Model Boat contest. Study both reports. Then use **one** to answer the questions below.

News Standard

Yesterday Maria Garcia's leaky model boat stayed afloat for 11 minutes, and Larry Ray's boat stayed afloat 13 minutes. Jerry Sand's boat had troubles from the beginning and sank in a record 4 minutes. Gary Arnold's boat finished with 9 minutes afloat.

1. Who won the contest? Larry Ray
2. Jerry's boat sank 5 minutes before Gary's.
3. What was the winning time? 13 min
4. Larry's boat sank 2 minutes after Maria's.

Change the *News Standard* article below into a graph for the *Weekly Graphics*.

News Standard

Yesterday Ann Betts rowed around the park lake 11 times, and Cathy Downs rowed around it 10 times. Frank Grimes lost an oar so he rowed around only 3 times, but Hank Jackson rowed around the lake 12 times.

Addison-Wesley All Rights Reserved

TS-4 Use with text pages 92-93. 33

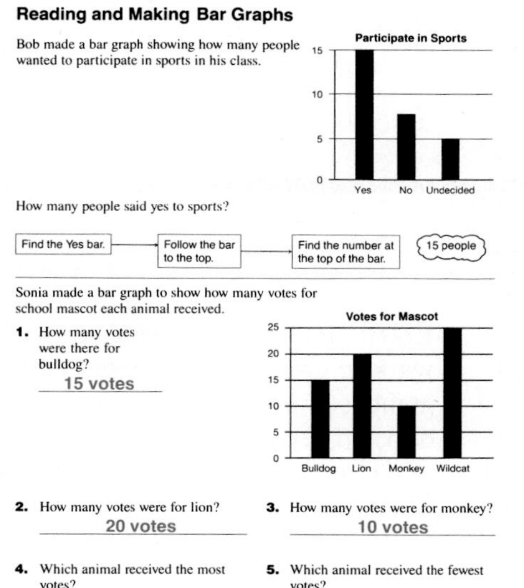

Reteaching

Life Skills 4-2

Name ______

Reading and Making Bar Graphs

Bob made a bar graph showing how many people wanted to participate in sports in his class.

How many people said yes to sports?

Find the Yes bar. → Follow the bar to the top. → Find the number at the top of the bar. → 15 people

Sonia made a bar graph to show how many votes for school mascot each animal received.

1. How many votes were there for bulldog? 15 votes
2. How many votes were for lion? 20 votes
3. How many votes were for monkey? 10 votes
4. Which animal received the most votes? wildcat
5. Which animal received the fewest votes? monkey

Addison-Wesley | All Rights Reserved

RS-4 Use with text pages 92-93. 33

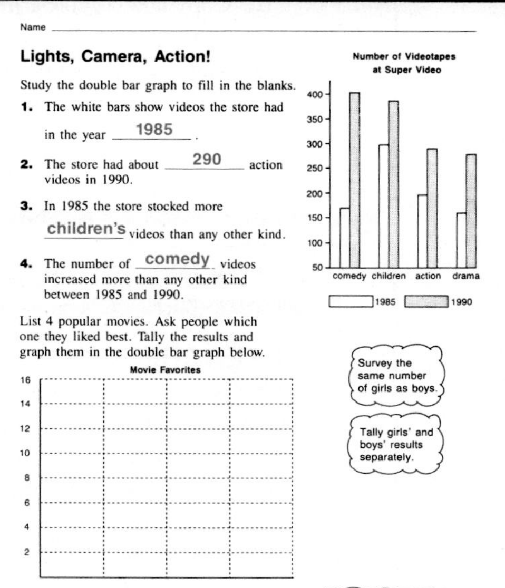

Challenges

Data Analysis 4-2

Name ______

Lights, Camera, Action!

Study the double bar graph to fill in the blanks.

1. The white bars show videos the store had in the year 1985.
2. The store had about 290 action videos in 1990.
3. In 1985 the store stocked more children's videos than any other kind.
4. The number of comedy videos increased more than any other kind between 1985 and 1990.

List 4 popular movies. Ask people which one they liked best. Tally the results and graph them in the double bar graph below.

Addison-Wesley All Rights Reserved

CS-4 Use with text pages 92-93. 33

Options for Individual Needs

Basic

Exercises 1-10
Skills Bank, pp. 461, 463
Computer Bank, pp. 498, 499
More Practice, p. 514, set D

Supplements
Reteaching 33 or
Practice 33
Challenges 33

Average

Exercises 1-10
Skills Bank, pp. 461, 463
Computer Bank, pp. 498, 499
More Practice, p. 514, set D

Supplements
Practice 33
Challenges 33 or
Thinking Skills 33

Extended

Exercises 1-10
Computer Bank, pp. 498, 499

Supplements
Challenges 33
Thinking Skills 33

Other Resources:
Math In Stride, Grade 4, pp. 142, 143
Kids Are Consumers, Too!, p. 173
Mathematics, A Way of Thinking, Lesson 15-10

4-2

LESSON PLAN 4-2

OBJECTIVE 4-2
To read and make a bar graph

Materials: TA 11 (Blank Spinners), graph paper, colored pencils or crayons

Alternative Materials: TA 12 (Centimeter Graph Paper)

Grouping Suggestions: small groups, pairs

1. MOTIVATE AND TEACH

LEARN ABOUT IT

EXPLORE ► **Explain why a spinner might land on one color more than on another.** (Possible answer: There is more of one color on the spinner than another.)
► **Explain why different people might get different results.** (Possible answer: Spinning techniques will vary.)

TALK ABOUT IT ► **What comparison can you make based on the unfinished graph?** (Possible answer: Spinner 1 landed on blue fewer times than Spinner 2 has.)
► **How might you decide on a number scale?** (Possible answer: Divide the total number of spins into equal intervals that are convenient to read.)
Student Edition answers: **1.** number of times each spinner lands on blue **2.** Spinners **3.** 25, 30 **4.** The less there is of a color on a spinner, the less chance there is that color will be chosen; results are equally likely for only Spinner 2.

2. CHECK UNDERSTANDING

TRY IT OUT

ERROR ALERT Placing the bar to meet the line on the number scale when perhaps it should fall in between. Making a poor choice of a number scale.

Reading and Making Bar Graphs

LEARN ABOUT IT

EXPLORE Use a Spinner
Work in groups. The bar graph shows the results of spinning the first two spinners 30 times each.

Use a spinner like Spinner 3 and spin it 30 times. Decide how you could use the results to complete the bar graph.

Number of times it lands on blue

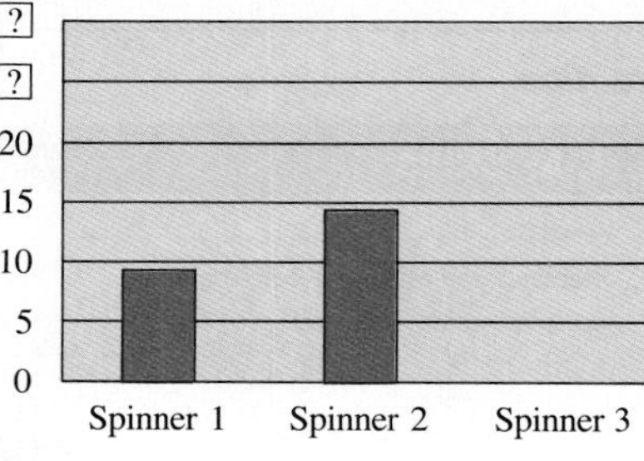

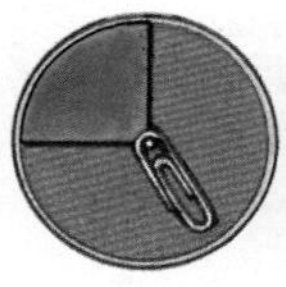
Spinner 1

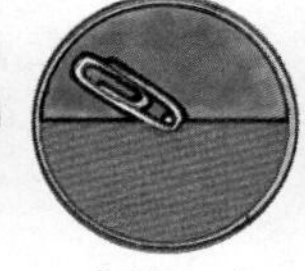
Spinner 2

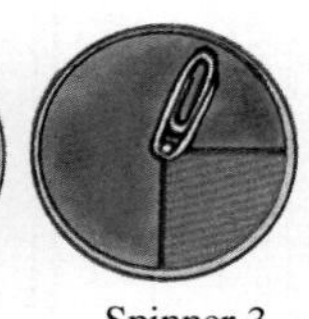
Spinner 3

TALK ABOUT IT See teaching notes.

1. What do the blue bars show?
2. How would you complete the title of the graph?
3. How would you complete the number scale?
4. What can you tell about the outcomes of spinning these spinners? Are the results equally likely or not equally likely?

Here is how to make a bar graph.

- Create a scale. Label the side and bottom of the graph.
- Draw the bars to show the data.
- Title the graph.

TRY IT OUT

Check students' graphs.

1. Copy and complete the graph above.
2. Make a bar graph using the data in this table.

	Spinner 1	Spinner 2	Spinner 3
Red Spins in 30 Tries	20	16	6

92

TEACHING OPTIONS

RETEACHING TIPS To help students place bars, they should use graph paper and a number scale from 0 to 30 with an interval of 1. They use a different color to draw in each bar to meet the correct number-scale line. Repeat using a number scale with an interval of 5. Assign Reteaching Supplement 33.

ENRICHMENT Have students work in groups of 3 to count the number of books in each of their desks. They should arrange the data in an organized list, then decide on a title, labels, and a number scale. Last, they should make a bar graph to represent their data.

PRACTICE

1. What is the title of the graph? **Record of 50 Coin Tosses**
2. How many times was the coin tossed? **50 times**
3. Which came up more, heads or tails? Is this what you would expect? **heads**
4. About how many times did each side come up? **tails 22, heads 28**
5. Jason tossed a paper cup on the table 50 times. He recorded the results. Use his data to make a bar graph. **Check students' graphs.**

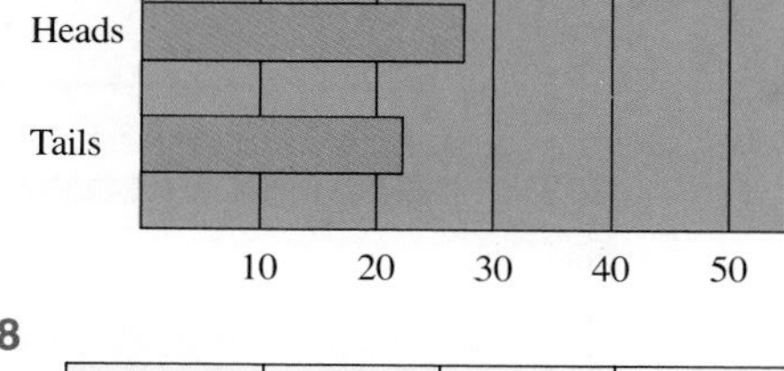

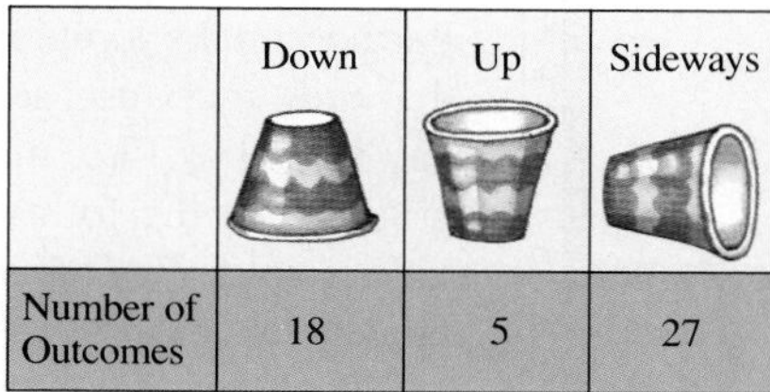

	Down	Up	Sideways
Number of Outcomes	18	5	27

APPLY

MATH REASONING

6. Suppose you spin this spinner 30 times. Do you think you would spin blue more than half the time? Why or why not? **yes; the blue area is more than half of the circle**

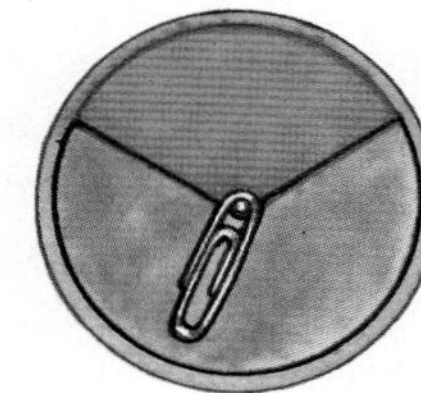

PROBLEM SOLVING

7. One bar on a graph was a little bit above 50. Another bar was a little below 20. Is the difference of the numbers the bars show more or less than 30? Tell why. **more; 50 − 20 = 30**

► ALGEBRA

Copy this number scale.

0 — 100 — 200 — x — 300 — 400 — y 500

8. Show about where X + 100 would be. **halfway between 300 and 400**
9. Show about where Y − 100 would be. **a little before 400**
10. Show about where X − 150 would be. **about 100**

More Practice, page 514, set D

Close and Assess

SHOW WHAT YOU KNOW On the chalkboard, tally students' favorite fruits. Then pair students and give each pair a sheet of graph paper. Pairs choose a title, labels, number scale, and a vertical or a horizontal format to make a bar graph. They construct the graph together, then compare their graph to other pairs'.

QUICK QUIZ

What would you look at on a bar graph to find out what it is about? (the title) What would you look at to make comparisons? (the number scale; the bars)

3. Practice and Apply

Basic	1-10
Average	1-10
Extended	1-10

PRACTICE

Look at the bar graph and decide what interval is used on the number scale. (10) *Explain what the data shows.* (how many times heads or tails came up when a coin was tossed 50 times)

MATH REASONING ► **Explain how you could increase your chances of landing on blue.** (Possible answer: Make the blue area larger.)

PROBLEM SOLVING ► **Explain how estimation could help you solve Problem 7.** (Possible answer: 50 − 20 = 30, so if one bar is above 50 and the other is below 20, the distance between them must be greater than 30.)

ALGEBRA ► **Explain your thinking to solve Problems 8-10.** (Possible answer: if X is halfway between 200 and 300, then $X + 100$ must be halfway between 300 and 400; if $Y - 100$ is a little less than 500, then $Y - 100$ must be a little less than 400; if X is about 250, $X - 150$ is about 100.)

LESSON OPTIONS 4-3

Reading and Making Pictographs

OBJECTIVE 4-3 To read and make a pictograph

PREBOOK ACTIVITIES

QUICK REVIEW

Discover each pattern and continue it three more times.

1. 3,000, 4,000, 5,000, (6,000), (7,000), (8,000)
2. 250, 300, 350, (400), (450), (500)
3. 70, 80, 90, (100), (110), 120)
4. 50, 75, 100, (125), (150), (175)
5. 65, 70, 75, (80), (85), (90)

PRIOR KNOWLEDGE

Have students summarize the steps they used to make bar graphs. (Possible answer: Choose a title, labels, and a number scale; draw bars to show data.) Then display a pictograph and have students describe the similarities and differences between the two types of graphs. (Similarities: Both have titles and labels. Differences: Bar graphs show data with bars; pictographs show data with pictures.) Ask students where they have seen pictographs before. (Possible answers: newspapers, magazines, textbooks) Tell students that in this lesson, they will read and make their own pictographs.

COMMUNICATION

Discussing and Reading Math Write the following sentence on the chalkboard: In a pictograph, each **symbol** stands for the same amount of data. Have students use context clues to determine the meaning of the word *symbol*. (''picture''; ''drawing'') Have students consider why a pictograph symbol should be simple to draw. (Possible answer: Because you will have to draw it many times to represent data in your pictograph, the symbol should not be too complicated.)

EXPLORE AND CONNECT

Materials: gummed stars, plain paper, data table (see below)
Grouping Suggestion: cooperative learning pairs
Partners make simple graphs about video sales. Tell students that they must use not more than 20 stars to show all the data any way they like, and they can write only *one* number on the graph. Post the following data in table form: *Alien Zucchini*: 18 videos sold; *Punk Dentist*: 6 videos sold; *Tuesday the Tenth*: 12 videos sold. Pairs use gummed stars as **symbols** for the data and decide how many videos each **symbol** should stand for. Then they figure out how to organize and show the data. Conclude by having students summarize the steps they used to make their graphs. Have students compare completed graphs to determine how they are alike and different. (All graphs represent the same data with star *symbols;* title, labels, and *symbol* value may vary, but a *symbol* stands for more than one video.)

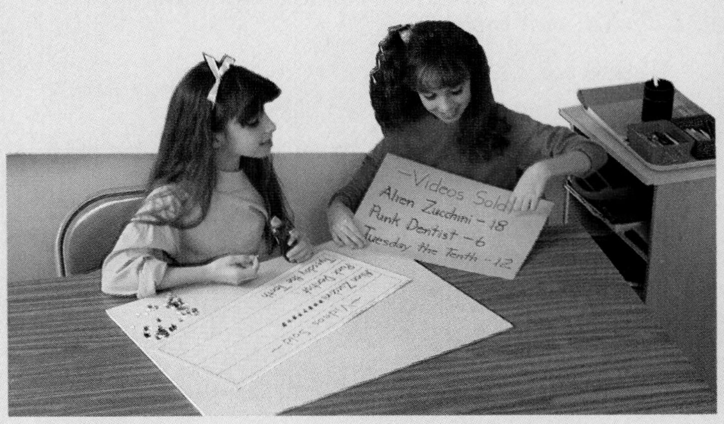

CONNECTIONS Use these anytime.

Problem of the Day

Symbols On Jake's ranch, he has 1 gray horse, 3 black horses, 19 brown horses, 65 palominos, and 997 pintos. Explain why he is having so much trouble making a pictograph about his horses. *Hint*: Remember that one symbol must equal a certain number of horses. (The numbers are so different, it is hard to pick a reasonable symbol.)

Patterns

Boxes Discover the pattern, then continue it three more times.

___ ___ ___

( )

Math Connection

Logical Reasoning If * means 20, how much is ***? (60) How much is *****? (100) How would you show 140? (*******)

Classwork and Homework Supplements

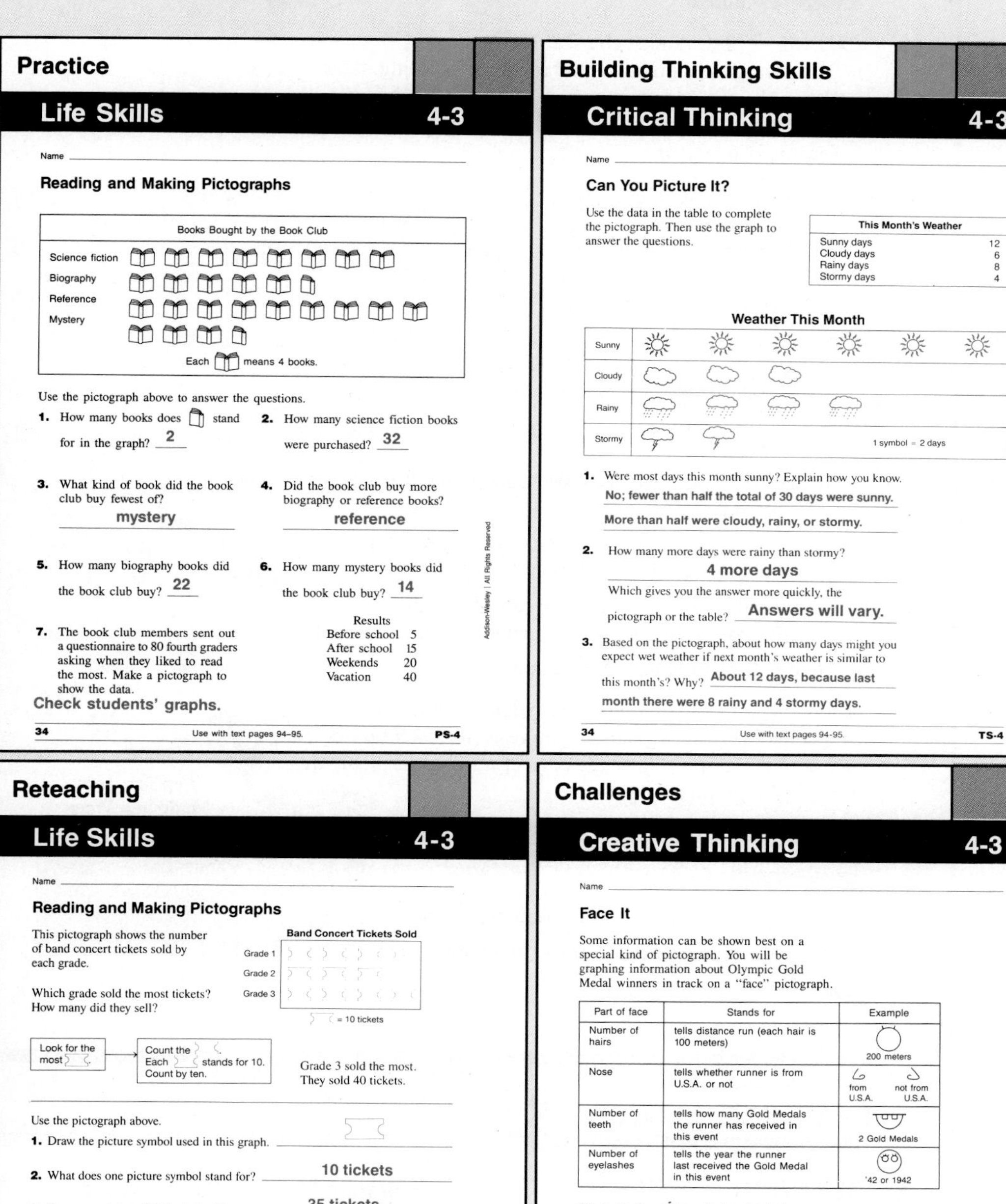

Practice

Life Skills 4-3

Name ______

Reading and Making Pictographs

Books Bought by the Book Club

Science fiction
Biography
Reference
Mystery

Each [book] means 4 books.

Use the pictograph above to answer the questions.

1. How many books does [half book] stand for in the graph? 2
2. How many science fiction books were purchased? 32
3. What kind of book did the book club buy fewest of? mystery
4. Did the book club buy more biography or reference books? reference
5. How many biography books did the book club buy? 22
6. How many mystery books did the book club buy? 14
7. The book club members sent out a questionnaire to 80 fourth graders asking when they liked to read the most. Make a pictograph to show the data. Check students' graphs.

Results	
Before school	5
After school	15
Weekends	20
Vacation	40

34 Use with text pages 94-95. PS-4

Building Thinking Skills

Critical Thinking 4-3

Name ______

Can You Picture It?

Use the data in the table to complete the pictograph. Then use the graph to answer the questions.

This Month's Weather	
Sunny days	12
Cloudy days	6
Rainy days	8
Stormy days	4

Weather This Month

Sunny
Cloudy
Rainy
Stormy

1 symbol = 2 days

1. Were most days this month sunny? Explain how you know. No; fewer than half the total of 30 days were sunny. More than half were cloudy, rainy, or stormy.
2. How many more days were rainy than stormy? 4 more days
   Which gives you the answer more quickly, the pictograph or the table? Answers will vary.
3. Based on the pictograph, about how many days might you expect wet weather if next month's weather is similar to this month's? Why? About 12 days, because last month there were 8 rainy and 4 stormy days.

34 Use with text pages 94-95. TS-4

Reteaching

Life Skills 4-3

Name ______

Reading and Making Pictographs

This pictograph shows the number of band concert tickets sold by each grade.

Which grade sold the most tickets? How many did they sell?

Band Concert Tickets Sold

Grade 1
Grade 2
Grade 3

= 10 tickets

Look for the most → Count the [ticket]. Each [ticket] stands for 10. Count by ten.

Grade 3 sold the most. They sold 40 tickets.

Use the pictograph above.

1. Draw the picture symbol used in this graph.
2. What does one picture symbol stand for? 10 tickets
3. How many tickets did Grade 1 sell? 35 tickets
4. How many tickets did Grade 2 sell? 30 tickets
5. Make a pictograph to show these data. Check students' pictographs.

Band Concert Tickets Sold Each Day	
Monday	15
Tuesday	10
Wednesday	25

34 Use with text pages 94-95. RS-4

Challenges

Creative Thinking 4-3

Name ______

Face It

Some information can be shown best on a special kind of pictograph. You will be graphing information about Olympic Gold Medal winners in track on a "face" pictograph.

Part of face	Stands for	Example
Number of hairs	tells distance run (each hair is 100 meters)	200 meters
Nose	tells whether runner is from U.S.A. or not	from U.S.A.; not from U.S.A.
Number of teeth	tells how many Gold Medals the runner has received in this event	2 Gold Medals
Number of eyelashes	tells the year the runner last received the Gold Medal in this event	'42 or 1942

Fill in the face or the missing data below.

Carl Lewis	Sebastian Coe	Evelyn Ashford
100-meter run	1,500-meter run	100-meter run
U.S.A.	Britain	U.S.A.
won 2 Gold medals	won 2 Gold Medals	won 1 Gold Medal
won in 1984, 1988	won in 1980, 1984	won in 1984

34 Use with text pages 94-95. CS-4

Options for Individual Needs

Basic

Exercises 1-11, 14-16
More Practice, p. 514, set E

Supplements
Reteaching 34 or
Practice 34
Thinking Skills 34

Average

Exercises 1-16
More Practice, p. 514, set E

Supplements
Practice 34
Challenges 34 or
Thinking Skills 34

Extended

Exercises 1-6, 8-11, 14-16

Supplements
Challenges 34
Thinking Skills 34

Other Resources:
Problem-Solving Experiences in Mathematics, Grade 4, Problem 113
Mathematics, A Way of Thinking, Lessons 15-1, 15-2

LESSON PLAN 4-3

OBJECTIVE 4-3
To read and make a pictograph

> **Materials:** place value blocks
>
> **Alternative Materials:** TA 6 (Place Value Models)

1. MOTIVATE AND TEACH

LEARN ABOUT IT

EXPLORE ► Compare the table and the pictograph. (One shows the data with numbers, the other shows that data with pictures.)

TALK ABOUT IT ► Analyze the pictograph. Explain its organization. (1 kernel of popcorn stands for each 1,000 lb of popcorn sold; four seasons of sales will be represented.)
► Justify 1,000 as the value of a kernel symbol. (Since data is given in 1,000s or 500s, one symbol for every 1,000 is easy to use.)
► Explain why half a kernel appears in the Spring row. (4 whole kernels mean 4,000 lb, the half kernel means 500 lb, so there are 4,500 lb in all.)
► Explain how to show Winter popcorn sales. (Draw $8\frac{1}{2}$ kernels.)
Student Edition answers: **1.** 1,000 lb of popcorn **2.** No, the pictograph would need too many kernels. **3.** Possible answer: A pictograph shows comparisons more easily.

2. CHECK UNDERSTANDING

TRY IT OUT

ERROR ALERT Choosing an inappropriate value for the pictograph symbol. Misunderstanding the use of half symbols.

Reading and Making Pictographs

LEARN ABOUT IT

EXPLORE Think About the Data
The pictograph illustrates the information in the table. When the pictograph is complete, it will tell how much popcorn a small popcorn company sold in each season of one year.

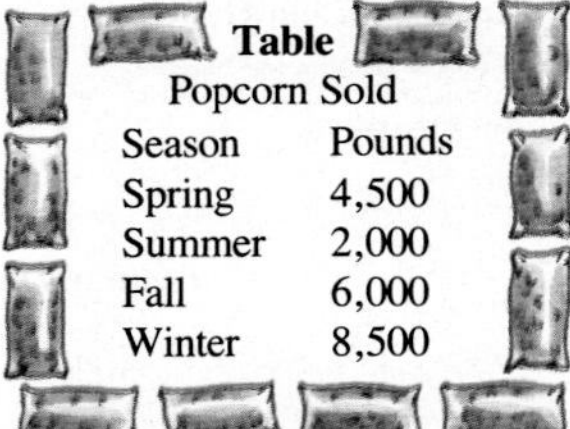

Table
Popcorn Sold

Season	Pounds
Spring	4,500
Summer	2,000
Fall	6,000
Winter	8,500

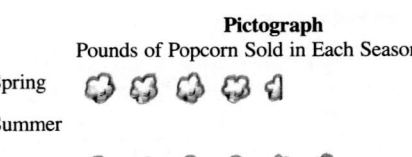

Pictograph
Pounds of Popcorn Sold in Each Season

Spring
Summer
Fall
Winter

= 1,000 pounds of popcorn

TALK ABOUT IT See teaching notes.

1. In the pictograph, what does one kernel of popcorn represent?
2. Would it be a good idea for one kernel to equal 10 pounds? Why or why not?
3. What is the difference between seeing the information in a table and seeing it in a pictograph?

Here is how to make a pictograph.

- Choose a picture symbol. Tell what it represents.
- Decide how many pictures you need for each number.
- Label the graph. Draw the correct number of pictures.
- Give the graph a title.

Popcorn Jars Made in a Week

Day	Jars
Monday	500
Tuesday	650
Wednesday	800
Thursday	350
Friday	200

TRY IT OUT Check students' graphs.

1. Copy and complete the pictograph above.
2. Make a pictograph to show this data.

94

TEACHING OPTIONS

RETEACHING TIPS Help students pick a suitable value for their pictograph symbol by having them show Thursday's data with as few place value blocks as possible. (3 hundreds, 5 tens) Then have them compare the tens to 1 hundred. (5 tens = half of 1 hundred.) Assign Reteaching Supplement 34.

ENRICHMENT Have students ask at least 15 classmates how they like to eat popcorn. They use the same 4 categories as in Problem 8—plain, with salt only, with butter only, or with butter and salt. They tally classmates' responses and make a pictograph to show the results.

PRACTICE

A class made this pictograph about a school survey. Answer these questions.

Ways We Pop Popcorn

skillet

microwave oven

popcorn popper

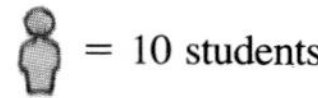 = 10 students

1. What does one picture symbol stand for on the graph? **10 students**
2. How many students make popcorn in a skillet? **40 students**
3. How many more students make their popcorn in popcorn poppers than in microwave ovens? **25 students**
4. The fourth grade sent a questionnaire asking what students most like to do while they eat popcorn. 50 students answered. These are the results. Make a pictograph to show this data. **Check students' graphs.**

Watch TV	25
Play a game	10
Read a book	15

APPLY

MATH REASONING Suppose [box] stands for 100 boxes of popcorn. Draw what would stand for these amounts.

5. 50 boxes **half a symbol**
6. 200 boxes **2 symbols**
7. 150 boxes **one and a half symbols**

PROBLEM SOLVING

8. People like to eat popcorn in different ways. In a survey, 9 people said they liked it plain, 5 liked salt only, 3 liked butter only, and 8 liked both butter and salt. How many took part in the survey? **25 people**

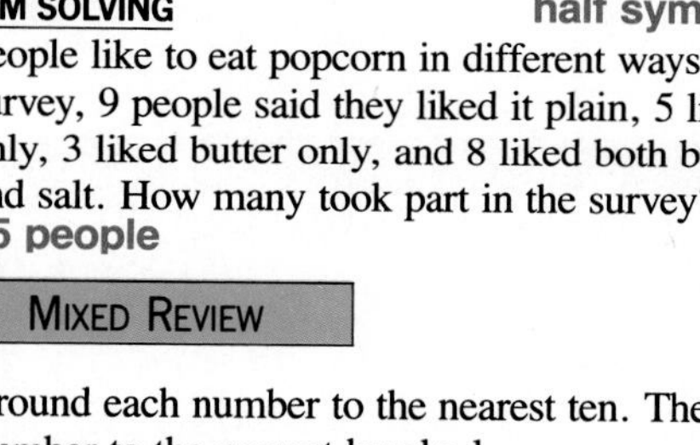

MIXED REVIEW

First round each number to the nearest ten. Then round the number to the nearest hundred.

9. 273 **270, 300**
10. 99 **100**
11. 833 **830, 800**
12. 611 **610, 600**
13. 441 **440, 400**

Find the sums and differences using mental math.

14. 60 + 70 = n **130**
15. 36,000 − 15,000 = n **21,000**
16. 400 + 500 **900**

95

3. Practice and Apply

Basic	1-11, 14-16
Average	1-16
Extended	1-6, 8-11, 14-16

PRACTICE

How many ways to pop popcorn are shown on the pictograph? (3) *What is the value of the symbol?* (10 students) *What is the value of the half symbol?* (5 students)

APPLY

MATH REASONING ► Explain how Exercises 5 and 7 are related. (Both amounts use a half symbol to represent 50.)

PROBLEM SOLVING ► Analyze Problem 8 to decide what operation to use. Explain your reasoning. (You are looking for a total, so you add to combine groups.)

MIXED REVIEW ► Explain how Exercise 10 differs from Exercises 9 and 11-13. (Possible answer: 99 rounds to 100 for both the nearest ten and nearest hundred; the other numbers round to two different numbers for the nearest ten and hundred.)

4-3

Close and Assess

WRITE WHAT YOU THINK Ask students to agree or disagree with this statement: Pictographs work only if you count by 10; 100; or 1,000. Suggest that they think of pictographs they have made or seen, then write a response. Ask students to give examples to support their opinions. (Check students' work.)

QUICK QUIZ

Make a pictograph for the number of jars of popcorn sold last week.

Pops-A-Lot	25	Captain Kernel	35
Video Pop	40	Popper's Best	30

(Check students' pictographs.)

LESSON OPTIONS 4-4

Reading and Making Line Graphs

OBJECTIVE 4-4 To read and make a line graph

PREBOOK ACTIVITIES

QUICK REVIEW

Fill in the number that is halfway between the numbers given.

1. 50 and 60 (55)
2. 300 and 500 (400)
3. 1,000 and 2,000 (1,500)
4. 150 and 200 (175)
5. 300 and 350 (325)
6. 35 and 55 (45)
7. 800 and 1,000 (900)
8. 40 and 80 (60)

PRIOR KNOWLEDGE

Have students compare pictographs and bar graphs. (Possible answer: Both show data in an easy-to-read format, organized by labels and a title; pictographs use pictures and a symbol key; bar graphs use bars and a number scale.) Ask students to describe other kinds of graphs they have seen. (Possible answers: circle graphs and line graphs) Tell students that in this lesson they will learn to read and make a line graph.

COMMUNICATION

Discussing and Reading Math Write this sentence on the chalkboard: Two lines can meet at only one **point.** Have students use the context to explain what *point* means. (''spot''; ''place''; ''intersection'') Draw an *X* and a *V* on the chalkboard and have volunteers identify the points where each of the two lines meet. Then draw a point and ask a volunteer to draw a horizontal *and* a vertical line through it. Challenge students to apply the idea of lines meeting at a point to reading graphs. (Possible answer: A point represents the spot where two number scales meet.)

EXPLORE AND CONNECT

Materials: TA 12 (Centimeter Graph Paper), data table (see below)
Grouping Suggestion: cooperative learning pairs
Students explore using **points** to show data. Write the following data in table form on the chalkboard and tell students it is the number of carnival tickets sold: Wednesday—20; Thursday—30; Friday—50, Saturday—80; Sunday—60. Partners graph the data using only *points*, then discuss the title, number scale, and labels the graph should have. After pairs have finished, display several graphs and have the class discuss a way to improve the graphs. (Possible answer: Draw lines connecting the points.) Conclude by having students evaluate the purpose of the *points* and lines in the graph. (Possible answer: Read exact data at the *points;* use lines to make the graph easier to read and to show how the data changes from day to day.)

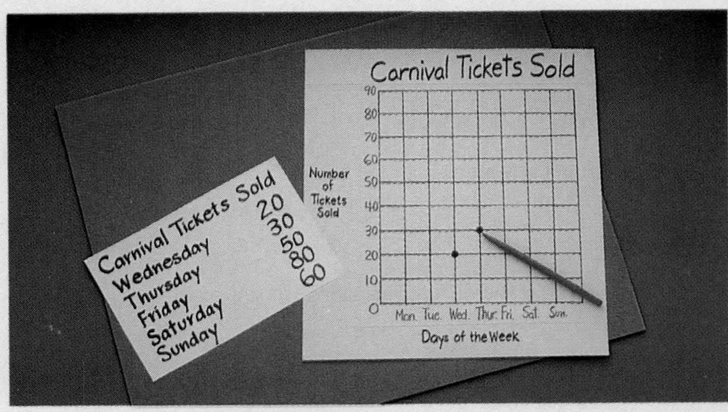

CONNECTIONS Use these anytime.

Problem of the Day

Attendance Mr. Perrone wants to graph attendance for a school week. He plans to record how many students attend school each day. How many points will he use to show the data? If the same number of students are present each day, visualize how the points will be arranged. (5; horizontally)

Number Sense

Estimation Lucy has a piece of graph paper 10 squares high and 10 squares wide that she is using to graph how much water her dog, Corky, drank each day last week. The measurements range from 25 to 275 ml. Determine a reasonable number scale for Lucy to use that will fit on her paper. (Start at 0, count by 50s to 300.)

Math Connection

Numeration Ichiro got these scores on 4 rounds of a video game: 5,362; 7,146; 7,279; and 8,111. Suggest a reasonable scale Ichiro might use to graph his scores and explain how he could indicate each one. (Possible answer: Start at 5,000 and count by 500s or 1,000s; round each score to the nearest hundred.)

Classwork and Homework Supplements

Practice

Life Skills 4-4

Name

Reading and Making Line Graphs

Answer these questions about the line graph.

1. About how many people attended the fair on Friday? 150
2. Which day had the lowest attendance? Thursday
3. On which day did about 250 people attend? Wednesday
4. On which days was the attendance greater than 250 people? Saturday, Sunday
5. Make a line graph for these data. Check students' graphs.

Attendance at Spring Fair

Profits from the Spring fair			
1987	$1,200	1988	$1,450
1989	$1,350	1990	$1,600

PS-4 Use with text pages 96–97. 35

Building Thinking Skills

Data Analysis 4-4

Name

Hamster Lines

Jack's pet hamster had two baby hamsters that Jack named Angela and Frederick. He weighed the hamsters every week and made a line graph of their weights.

Use the graph to answer these questions.

Hamster Weights

Angela ——
Frederick - - - -

1. At what ages did Angela and Frederick weigh the same? 4 weeks and 12 weeks
2. At what age was the difference in Frederick's and Angela's weights the greatest? 10 weeks
3. At 4 weeks, Frederick weighed 30 grams. How many weeks did it take him to double this weight? 4 weeks
4. Between 8 weeks and 13 weeks, did Frederick double his weight? no
5. At 12 weeks, Frederick weighed how many times as much as he did at 4 weeks? 3 times
6. Between 4 weeks and 16 weeks, which hamster gained 5 times its weight? Angela

TS-4 Use with text pages 96–97. 35

Reteaching

Data Analysis 4-4

Name

Reading and Making Line Graphs

The manager of the Sports Shop made a line graph to show the dollar amount from sales of soccer balls each month for eight months. Use the graph to solve the problems.

Soccer Sales

1. How many dollars came from the sale of soccer balls in June? (between $90 and $100) $ 95
2. How many dollars came from the sale of soccer balls in April? (between $60 and $70) $65
3. In what month was the dollar amount from sales of soccer balls the highest? July
4. In what month was the dollar amount from sales of soccer balls the lowest? October
5. If each soccer ball sold for $5 in May, how many were sold that month? 14
6. If each soccer ball sold for $10 in March, how many were sold that month? 8
7. The number of balls sold in November was the same as the number sold in October. If each ball sold for $11, what was the total number of balls sold in October and November? 10

RS-4 Use with text pages 96–97. 35

Challenges

Reading Math 4-4

Name

Graph Stories

Draw a graph to go with each story. Answers will vary. Sample answers shown.

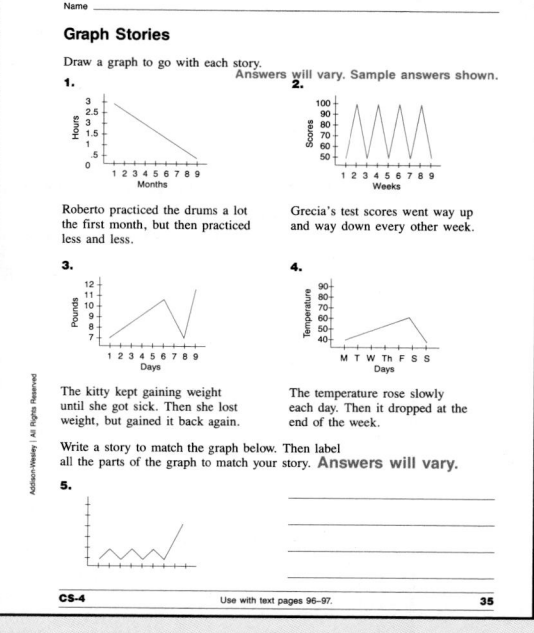

1. Roberto practiced the drums a lot the first month, but then practiced less and less.

2. Grecia's test scores went way up and way down every other week.

3.

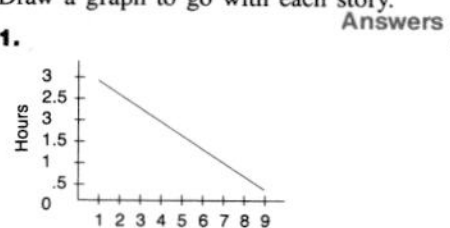

The kitty kept gaining weight until she got sick. Then she lost weight, but gained it back again.

4.

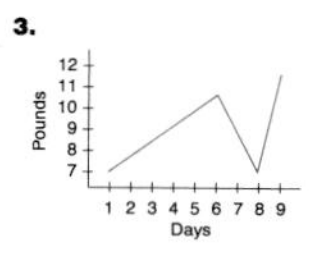

The temperature rose slowly each day. Then it dropped at the end of the week.

Write a story to match the graph below. Then label all the parts of the graph to match your story. Answers will vary.

5.

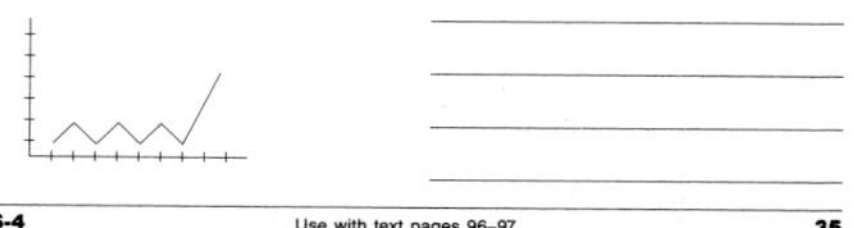

CS-4 Use with text pages 96–97. 35

Options for Individual Needs

Basic

Exercises 1-8
Data Bank, pp. 468-483
More Practice, p. 515, set A

Supplements
Reteaching 35 or
Practice 35

Average

Exercises 1-8
Data Bank, pp. 468-483
More Practice, p. 515, set A

Supplements
Practice 35
Challenges 35 or
Thinking Skills 35

Extended

Exercises 1-8
Data Bank, pp. 468-483

Supplements
Challenges 35
Thinking Skills 35

Other Resources:
Problem-Solving Experiences in Mathematics, Grade 4, Problem 131
Mathematics, A Way of Thinking, Lesson 15-13

4-4

LESSON PLAN 4-4

OBJECTIVE 4-4
To read and make a line graph

Materials: TA 12 (Centimeter Graph Paper); line graphs from books, newspapers, and magazines

1. MOTIVATE AND TEACH

LEARN ABOUT IT

EXPLORE ► **Justify the title of the graph.** (It summarizes the data.)
► **Explain the two number scales Stacy used.** (She counted by 5s to show temperature; she counted by 1,000 ft to show height.)
► **Analyze the temperature scale to determine the missing numbers. Explain.** (55, 60; that scale counts by 5.)
► **Relate the base of the mountain to a number on a graph scale. Explain.** (0 ft; The base is the lowest point.)
► **Explain the relationship between temperature and height on the graph.** (As Stacy climbs higher, the temperature falls.)

TALK ABOUT IT ► **Analyze how a line graph uses points to show data.** (Every fact is shown at the point where the two scales meet.)
► **Explain how the lines relate to the data.** (As the temperature falls, the lines go down.)
Student Edition answers: **1.** The graph shows only the first 5 temperatures
2. down; It gets colder as you go higher.

2. CHECK UNDERSTANDING

TRY IT OUT

ERROR ALERT Choosing inappropriate scales. Omitting scales, labels, or a title.

Reading and Making Line Graphs

LEARN ABOUT IT

EXPLORE Study the Graph
Stacy hiked up a mountain on her vacation. She made this line graph to show how the temperature changed. The graph uses data she recorded in the table below.

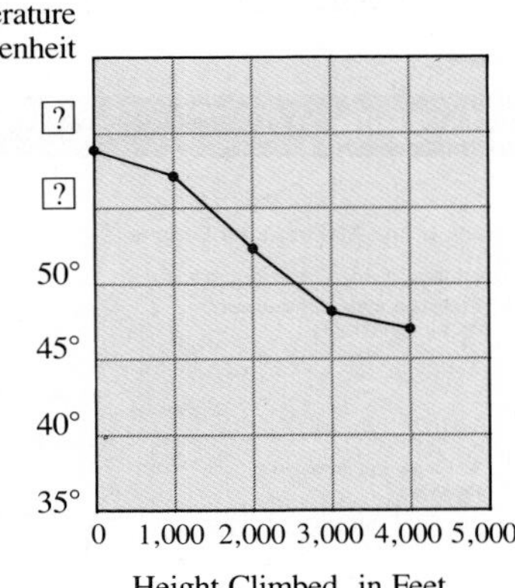

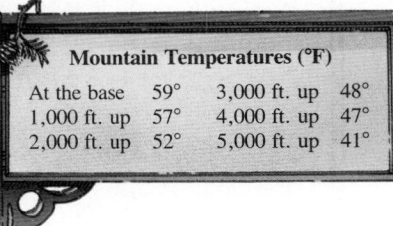

Mountain Temperatures (°F)

At the base	59°	3,000 ft. up	48°
1,000 ft. up	57°	4,000 ft. up	47°
2,000 ft. up	52°	5,000 ft. up	41°

TALK ABOUT IT See teaching notes.

1. Do the points on the graph show the data in the table? Explain.
2. Does the line on the graph go up or down? What does this tell you about the temperature?

This is how to make a line graph.

- Create scales. Label the side and bottom of the graph.
- Mark points that match the data on the bottom scale with the data on the side scale.
- Draw lines to connect the points.
- Give the graph a title.

TRY IT OUT Check students' graphs.

1. Copy and complete the line graph above.
2. Use this data to make a line graph.

Mountain Park Camp Temperatures in One Day	
8 a.m.	42°
10 a.m.	48°
12 noon	56°
2 p.m.	55°
4 p.m.	49°

96

TEACHING OPTIONS

RETEACHING TIPS Exercise 2: Have students find the highest and lowest temperatures, then round each to the nearest 10 to find a reasonable temperature range for a number scale. Have them imagine an interval that would be easy to use to plot temperature points. Assign Reteaching Supplement 35.

COMPUTER **Bumble Games, Addison-Wesley, Copyright 1985**
For use with all levels of students. In "Visit from Space," students are given a graph labeled with numbers and letters. Students select a number from the top and one from the side to find Bumble's cousin. The game takes 5 to 10 min.

PRACTICE

Answer these questions about the line graph.

Attendance at Mountain Park Camp

400
350
300
250
200
150
100
0

Feb. Mar. Apr. May June July

1. About how many attended the camp in March? **150**
2. Which month had the lowest attendance? **February**
3. In which months was the attendance greater than 200? **May, June, and July**
4. In what two months did the attendance stay about the same? **June and July**
5. Make a line graph for this data. **Check students' graphs.**

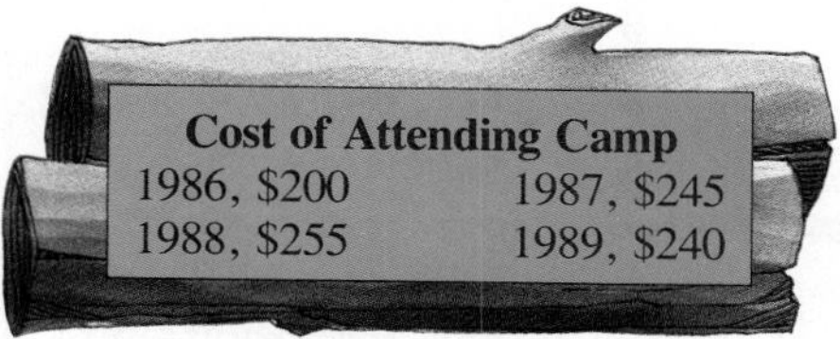
Cost of Attending Camp

1986, $200	1987, $245
1988, $255	1989, $240

APPLY

MATH REASONING

6. Match the words decrease, no change, and increase with graphs A, B, and C.

A **increase**

B **decrease**

C **no change**

PROBLEM SOLVING

7. **Social Studies Data Bank** Two rivers formed in the Rocky Mountains flow east and become part of another river. What river do they join? Which of the two flows the greater distance? See page 473. **Missouri and Arkansas; Missouri**

▶ COMMUNICATION Write About It

8. Jane recorded the temperatures as she hiked on a mountain. Write two or three sentences to describe what this graph tells about her hike. **Answers will vary.**

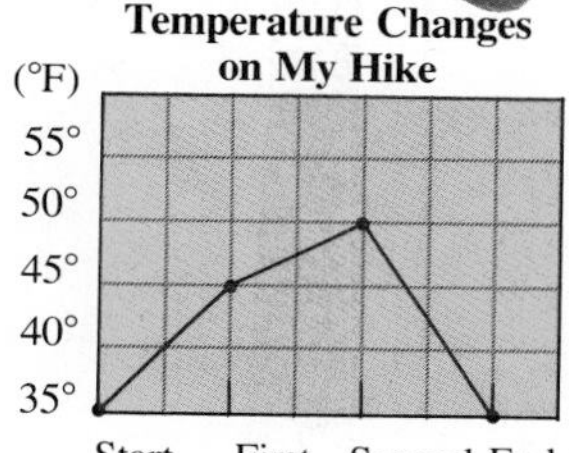

More Practice, page 515, set A

97

3. Practice and Apply

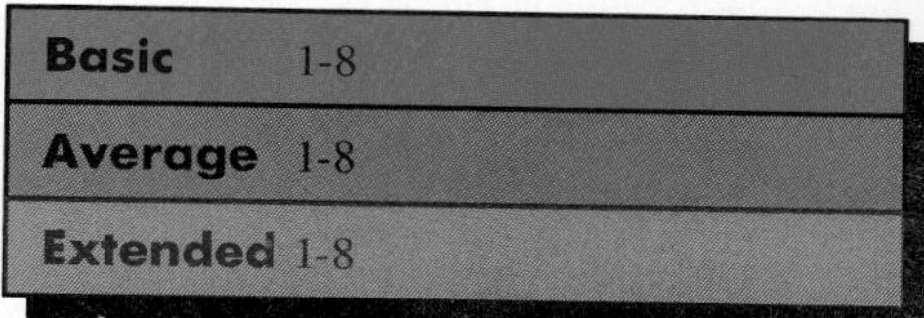

Basic	1-8
Average	1-8
Extended	1-8

PRACTICE

How does the line graph show changes in attendance? (The line starts going up, then falls, then goes up again.)

APPLY

MATH REASONING ▶ **Explain how the direction words relate to the line movements.** (*Increase* means to go up, *decrease* means to go down, and *no change* means to stay flat.)

PROBLEM SOLVING ▶ **At what columns in the Data Bank do you need to look? Explain why.** (direction of flow because the rivers flow *east* and the column labeled Mouth to find a river that the two other rivers join)

COMMUNICATION ▶ **Explain a pattern in the line graph.** (Possible answer: The temperatures were the same at the start and finish of Jane's hike because the points for both are on the same line.)

4-4

Close and Assess

WRITE WHAT YOU THINK

Have students use a line graph from a book, newspaper, or magazine. Ask each student to write 2 questions based on the data, then to trade graphs and answer the questions in complete sentences. (Check students' writing.)

QUICK QUIZ

Make a line graph of monthly snowfalls measured at the top of Nugget Peak. January: 34 in.; February: 51 in.; March: 42 in.; April: 10 in. (Check students' graphs.)

Using Critical Thinking/Midchapter Review/Quiz

OBJECTIVE 4-5 To use critical thinking to analyze a graphical situation

PREBOOK ACTIVITIES

QUICK REVIEW

Classify the following relatives as male, female, or either.

1. father (male) **2.** sister (female) **3.** grandparent (either)
4. aunt female) **5.** cousin (either) **6.** son (male)
7. brother male) **8.** mother (female) **9.** uncle (male)

PRIOR KNOWLEDGE

Have students name as many different kinds of relatives as possible. (Samples include father, mother, brother, sister, uncle, aunt, son, daughter, cousin, grandparent.) Have students describe their own relationship to their immediate family members. (Possible answers: I am my father's daughter; I am my brother's sister.)

COMMUNICATION

Discussing and Writing Math Write the word **relationship** on the chalkboard and have students explain its meaning. (Possible answer: a link between things, people, or ideas) Discuss a connection between the words *relatives* and *relationship*. (Relatives are people linked together in a family.) In their Math Journals, have students list examples from their own families of different relatives. Challenge students to describe the exact relationship between some of the relatives. (Possible answers: Uncle Al is my mother's brother; My cousin, Drew, is Aunt Sonya's son.)

EXPLORE AND CONNECT

Materials: two colors of markers
Grouping Suggestion: cooperative learning pairs
Students explore graphic ways to encode family **relationships**. List the following ''family'' on the chalkboard: Dad, Mom, JoAnne, Steve, and Marco. Have students draw a circle to represent each **relative**. Then challenge them to develop a color code with arrows that can relate the parents to their children. (For example, a red arrow points to a daughter and a blue arrow points to a son.) Partners decide which circles will be parents and which will be the children, but they should not reveal this information to other groups, nor should they explain whatever *relationship* code they invent. After they have developed their codes, have two pairs switch papers and try to identify the *relatives* as either parents or children. (Answers will vary.) Conclude by having students share how they developed, drew, and broke the codes. (Answers will vary.)

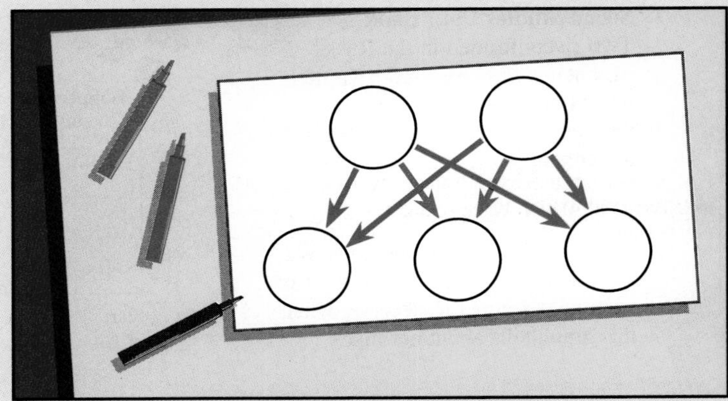

CONNECTIONS Use these anytime.

Problem of the Day

Family Riddle Mr. Wong and his daughter, Grace, were taken to the hospital in an ambulance. When they got there, the doctor said. ''Oh, no! This is my son!'' Evaluate the situation. (The doctor is Mr. Wong's mother or father and Grace's grandparent.)

Math Connection

Algebra Karim is 4 years older than Danitra, who is 2 years older than Jamaal. Only one has a 1-digit age. If the three ages total 35, determine each person's age. (Karim is 15, Danitra is 11, Jamaal is 9.)

Creative Thinking

Hand Shakes When the Browns finished moving into their new house, the four family members all shook hands. If each person shook all the other family members' hands, how many handshakes occurred? Draw a picture if it will help. (6: AB, AC, AD, BC, BD, CD)

Classwork and Homework Supplements

Practice

Critical Thinking 4-5

Name ____________________

Using Critical Thinking

Miss Ishii has 10 students in her class who participate in after-school activities. To keep track of who takes which classes, she made this arrow graph.

Music, Dance, Art
piano, violin, jazz, tap, painting
A, B, C, D, E, F, G, H, I, J

1. How many students take dance lessons? 6 students
   Which letters represent those students? E, F, B, G, J, H,
2. Which student takes music, dance, and art lessons? H
3. Which students take both art and dance lessons? G, H, J
4. How many of the students take piano lessons? 4 students
   How many take violin lessons? 3 students
   Which student takes both? C
5. Which student takes both kinds of dance? E
   Which other activity does this student participate in? violin

Building Thinking Skills

Critical Thinking 4-5

Name ____________________

A Family Tree

Ed is 10 years old. His family is having a reunion hosted by his mother's parents. Naturally, Ed's parents are there. So are his brother and sister. His mother's brother and father's twin sister are there, too. Ed is going to make a family tree for this group.

This is what his tree will look like:

SISTER <- - -> ME <- - -> BROTHER
UNCLE <-> MOTHER   FATHER <-> AUNT
GRANDMOTHER   GRANDFATHER

<- - - -> Brother or Sister ———> Parent

Help Ed complete his family tree. Trace and cut out Ed's relatives below. Paste them where they belong on the tree. Your problem is that all the male relatives and all the female relatives have the same name! But they were not born in the same years. Use the date of their births to make a correct family tree.

ED b. 1958	ED b. 1981	ED b. 1948	ED b. 1984	ED b. 1927
EDNA b. 1949	EDNA b. 1926	EDNA b. 1974	EDNA b. 1948	

Ed b. 1980, sister b. 1974, brother b. 1984, father b. 1948, mother b. 1949, uncle b. 1958, aunt b. 1948, grandmother b. 1926, grandfather b. 1927

Reteaching

Critical Thinking 4-5

Name ____________________

Using Critical Thinking

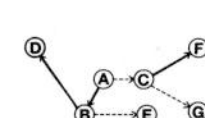

These arrow graphs illustrate the relationship between a boy (A), his parents (B, C), and his grandparents (D, E, F, G). A solid arrow points to a person's father and a dotted arrow points to a person's mother.

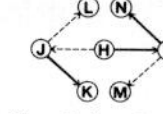

Use the graph at the right to answer the following questions.

1. What does the dotted arrow from H to J show? H's mother
2. What does the solid arrow from J to K show? J's father
3. Is person L male or female? female
4. What letters represent H's parents? J, I
5. What letters represent H's grandparents? K, L, M, N

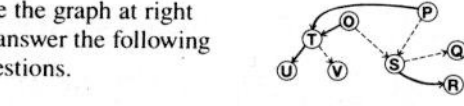

Use the graph at right to answer the following questions.

6. Which letters represent the grandparents? Q, R, U, V
7. Which letters represent the parents? T, S
8. How many children are there? 2
   Which letters represent these children? O, P

Challenges

Critical Thinking 4-5

Name ____________________

Food for Thought

This arrow graph describes a typical food chain showing different living things that feed on each other.

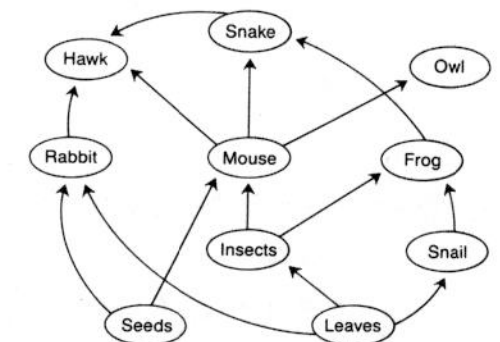

Answer each question below.

1. What does the arrow from one living thing to another show? It identifies the "eater" and the "eaten" in the food chain. The arrow points to the "eater."
2. What does the frog eat? insects, snail
3. What does the hawk eat? snake, mouse, rabbit
4. Which two animals are at the top of this food chain? hawk, owl
5. What does the mouse eat? insects, seeds
   What is the mouse eaten by? snake, hawk, owl

Use an encyclopedia to add two animals to the food chain on the arrow graph. Answers will vary: birds, small mammals, and reptiles may be included.

Options for Individual Needs

Basic

Exercises 1, 2; 1-9

Supplements
Reteaching 36 or
Practice 36

Average

Exercises 1, 2; 1-9

Supplements
Practice 36
Challenges 36 or
Thinking Skills 36

Extended

Exercises 1, 2; 1-9

Supplements
Challenges 36
Thinking Skills 36

Other Resources:
Mathematics, A Way of Thinking, Lesson 15-14
Kids Are Consumers, Too!, pp. 120, 121

LESSON PLAN 4-5

OBJECTIVE 4-5
To use critical thinking to analyze a graphical situation

Grouping Suggestion: pairs

1. MOTIVATE AND TEACH

LEARN ABOUT IT

▶ **Identify the children of grandparents using other relative words.** (They are parents of their own children.)
▶ **Compare red and blue arrows.** (Red arrows point to mothers; blue arrows point to fathers.)
▶ **Explain who the person is on the other end of a blue arrow.** (That person is the son or daughter of the father.)

TALK ABOUT IT ▶ **Explain how *I* and *C* are related.** (*C* is *I*'s mother.)
▶ **Explain how *C* and *F* are related.** (*F* is *C*'s father.)
▶ **Analyze that information to relate *I* and *F*.** (F is I's grandfather.)
▶ **Is *D* a mother or father? Explain your reasoning.** (*D* is a mother because of the red arrows pointing to her.)
▶ **Decide the parents of *D*.** (No arrows point *from* D to other people, so D must be a grandparent.)
Student Edition answers: **1.** *C* is *I*'s mother; *F* is *C*'s father. **2.** Female; red arrows point to *D*. **3.** *D*, other parents point to *D*; *F*, other parents points to *F*.

2. CHECK UNDERSTANDING

TRY IT OUT

ERROR ALERT Misinterpreting relationships. Losing track of relationships.

Using Critical Thinking

LEARN ABOUT IT

"Wow! What's that?" asked Meri, as she looked at Tim's paper.

"I call it an arrow graph," said Tim. "It tells about my grandfather, my grandmother, their children, and their grandchildren."

"It doesn't make sense to me," exclaimed Meri. "How does it work?"

"Simple," said Tim. "A red arrow points to a person's mother. A blue arrow points to a person's father."

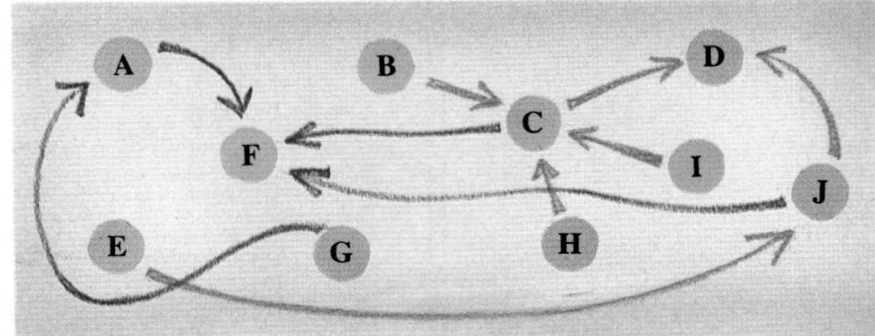

TALK ABOUT IT See teaching notes.

1. What does the red arrow from I to C show? What does the blue arrow from C to F show?
2. Is person D male or female? Explain.
3. What letter represents the grandmother? the grandfather? Explain.

TRY IT OUT

1. How many children did the grandparents have? **3**
   Which letters represent these children? **J, A, C**
2. How many grandchildren did the grandparents have? **5**
   Which letters represent these grandchildren? **E, G, B, H, I**

TEACHING OPTIONS

RETEACHING TIPS To help keep track of relationships as they are discovered, have students list each letter of the graph in alphabetical order. They can use the list to record each relationship they find. Assign Reteaching Supplement 36.

ENRICHMENT **Family Math** Have students try this activity with family members. Ask each to make an arrow graph that represents one side of his or her family. (They may use the graph on page 98 as a model.) Then they see how many family members can identify themselves in it.

MIDCHAPTER REVIEW/QUIZ

In an experiment, a table tennis ball was hidden under one of four cups. The tally chart shows which cup each person guessed.

first cup	卌 卌
second cup	卌 卌 卌 卌 卌
third cup	卌 卌 卌 卌 卌 卌 卌 卌
fourth cup	卌 卌 卌 卌

1. How many people chose each cup? How many people were guessing? **first 10, second 25, third 40, fourth 20; 95 people**

Make a pictograph of the data. Use [ball symbol] = 10 balls. **Check students' graphs.**

2. What picture did you use for 5 balls? for 8 balls? **half a symbol; three-fourths of a symbol**
3. What would [5 ball symbols and a half symbol] mean? **55 balls**
4. What title did you give your pictograph? **Answers will vary.**
5. Use the information in the tally chart to make a bar graph. **Check students' graphs.**
6. What scale did you use? How did you label the side of the graph? How did you label the bottom? **Answers will vary.**

PROBLEM SOLVING

7. The line graph will show temperatures from 6:00 a.m. until noon. Copy and complete the graph, using the temperatures in the table.

Time	Temperature °F
2 a.m.	13°
4 a.m.	14°
6 a.m.	15°
8 a.m.	15°
10 a.m.	26°
noon	32°

Check students' graphs.

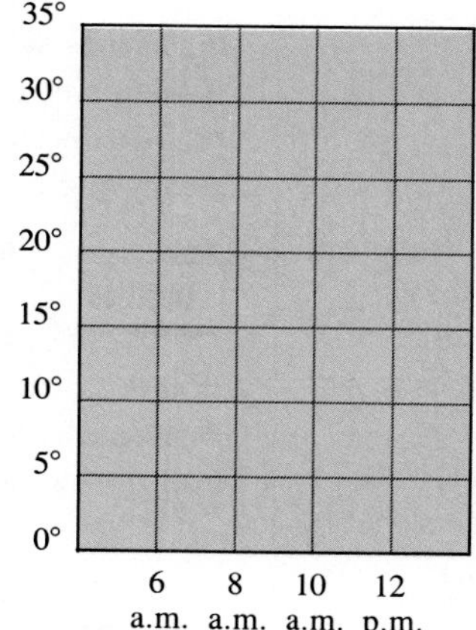

8. What was the temperature at 8 a.m.? **15°**
9. During which period of time was the temperature rising? Explain. **See Additional Answers.**

99

3. PRACTICE AND APPLY

Basic	1, 2; 1-9
Average	1, 2; 1-9
Extended	1, 2; 1-9

Additional Answers: See p. T79.

PRACTICE

Which questions relate to the tally chart? (1-6) *How do the temperature chart and the line graph go together?* (Use the data in the chart to make a line graph.)

ITEM ANALYSIS The following table correlates the Midchapter Review/Quiz items with the lesson objectives.

Items	Objectives
1-4, (6)	4-1
5-6	4-2
(2-4)	4-3
7-9	4-4

4-5

CLOSE AND ASSESS

SHOW WHAT YOU KNOW

Have students make an arrow graph to illustrate this family: Ann and Bob are the parents of Cal, Dina, and Ellen. Cal is the father of Frank and Gary. Dina is the mother of Helen and Ike. Who is Helen's uncle? (Cal) Check students' graphs.

QUICK QUIZ

Relate *A* to *D*. (*A* is *D*'s grandfather.)

A - - → B - - → D
A - - → C - - → E

- - → = father of

LESSON OPTIONS 4-6

Problem Solving: Extra Data

OBJECTIVE 4-6 To solve problems with extra data

PREBOOK ACTIVITIES

QUICK REVIEW

Add or subtract.

1. 462 + 327 (789)
2. 482 − 266 (216)
3. 86 + 137 (223)
4. 550 − 275 (275)
5. 100 − 48 (52)
6. 75 + 85 (160)
7. 16 + 9 + 8 (33)
8. 120 − 55 (65)
9. 80 + 70 + 40 (190)
10. 303 − 113 (190)

PRIOR KNOWLEDGE

Have students share experiences in which they have had to sort through more data or objects than they needed to find certain facts or items. (Possible answers: doing research for a report; searching the newspaper for a certain article; separating coins before you count all of one kind)

COMMUNICATION

Discussing Math Have students suggest synonyms for the word **extra**. (Possible answers: another, more, spare, leftover, additional, unrelated, unnecessary) Have them evaluate having *extra* as a positive as well as a negative situation. (Possible answer: It is good to have extra paper towels during a messy art project; too much extra food may go to waste.) Have students explain how math problems can have extra data. (Possible answer: A situation may include interesting facts that are not needed to answer the question the problem asks.)

EXPLORE AND CONNECT

COOPERATIVE ACTIVITY

Grouping Suggestion: small groups

Alex read that the steam engine was invented in 1705, the diesel engine was invented in 1895, and the rocket engine was invented in 1926. How long ago was the steam engine invented?

TEACHING ACTIONS

Have groups discuss and plan a solution to the problem.

► **Analyze the data Alex read.** (He found dates when three different kinds of engines were invented.)

► **Decide what you need to find out.** (How many years has it been since the steam engine was invented?)

► **Decide which fact to use to answer the question.** (The steam engine was invented in 1705.)

► **Explain a way to solve the problem.** (Subtract 1705 from this year.)

► **Justify the operation you chose.** (Subtract to find the difference.)

► **Explain how you would estimate the answer.** (round both to the nearest hundred; 2,000 − 1,700 = 300 years)

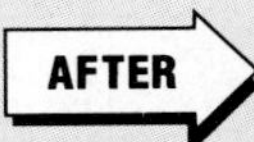

► **Evaluate your solution to see if it makes sense.** (Answers will vary.) Check students' answers.

► **Explain what data was extra.** (the dates of the diesel and rocket engines; They were not part of the question.)

CONNECTIONS Use these anytime.

Problem of the Day

Ages Mr. Miller was born in 1948. His daughter was born in 1976. Determine how much older Mr. Miller's daughter is than you are. Then find the information that is not needed to solve the problem. (Answers will vary. You do not need to know when Mr. Miller was born.)

Number Sense

Estimation Marty is the fastest reader in his class. He can read 50 pages per hour. About how many hours would it take him to read a 197 page novel if he starts at 2:45 on Sunday? (4 hours)

Creative Thinking

Coin Riddle Penny has 2 coins that total 35 cents. One of them is not a dime. What are the coins? Explain your reasoning. (quarter and dime; One is not a dime, but the other one is!)

Classwork and Homework Supplements

Practice

Problem Solving 4-6

Name

Extra Data

Underline the data that is extra.
Then solve the problem.

1. In June, the average high temperature in Beijing is 88°. There may be 8 days of rain that month. San Francisco's average high temperature in June is 66°. How much cooler is San Francisco than Beijing in June? 22°

2. New Delhi's average high temperature in June is 102°. New Delhi averages about 4 rainy days in June. The low temperature in June averages 83°. What is the difference between the average high and low June temperatures? 19°

3. Mexico City's avearge high temperature for June is 76°. There may be as many as 21 rainy days. Buenos Aires has an average of 7 rainy days. How many more rainy days does Mexico City have? 14 days

4. New York City averages 10 rainy days in June. Last June there were 14 rainy days. The year before there were 7 rainy days. How many days did it rain during both Junes? 21 days

5. Tokyo and Venice have the same average temperature in June, a high of 76° and low of 63°. Tokyo has 4 more rainy days in June than Venice. What is the difference between the average high and low temperatures in the 2 cities? 13°

6. Marrakesh has an average high temperature of 92° in June and low of 62°. It averages 1 rainy day that month. Prague has an average high of 88° in June and low of 44°. Which city has a greater difference between its average high and low temperatures? Prague

Building Thinking Skills

Problem Solving 4-6

Name

Electronic Games

Read the data about the Electronic Games Company. Decide which questions can be answered with the data given. Write the answers. Where there is not enough information, write **need more data.** Underline any data you do not need to answer the questions.

The Electronic Games Company made 3,548 electronic games in May, 3,982 in June, and 4,083 in July. 42 games were returned to the company in July.

1. How many games did they make in all three months? 11,613

2. How many more games were made in July than in May? 535

3. How many fewer games were made in January than in June? need more data

4. What data do you need to answer Question 3? the number of toys the company made in January

In August, Toys-for-All ordered 600 games, Toys Plus ordered 550 games, and Games Galore ordered 675 games. The games ordered were football games, math whiz games, and spelling whiz games.

5. Who ordered the most games? Games Galore

6. How many fewer games did Toys Plus order than Toys-for-All? 50

7. How many more games were ordered in August than in June? need more data

8. What data do you need to answer Question 7? the number of orders in June

Reteaching

Problem Solving 4-6

Name

Extra Data

The following problems have more data than you need.
Ring the data that you need and then solve each problem.

1. Ned delivers 75 morning papers and 58 evening papers. Last week he collected $56 for his paper route. How much papers does he deliver each day?

133

You don't need to know about money.

2. Ted is saving money for a new bike that costs $85. He earns $7 a week on his paper route. He has $42 now. How much more money does he need? $43

3. Pat collected $58 last week and $64 this week. He paid Todd $14. How much more did Pat collect this week than last week? $6

4. Janet's paper route took her 45 minutes on Monday and 55 minutes on Tuesday. The route is 3 km long. How many more minutes did it take her on Tuesday? 10 min

5. A daily paper costs $15 a month. A Sunday paper costs $7 a month. Sally has 42 papers. How much does it cost to buy both papers each month? $22

6. Peggy had 29 customers on her route. She added 5 new customers last week and 8 new customers this week. How many customers did she add in the last 2 weeks? 13

7. Mark has 38 homes on his route. He took 30 minutes on Monday to do his route and 27 minutes on Tuesday. How much less time did he take on Tuesday? 3 min

8. Sally delivered 48 papers on Saturday, 63 on Sunday, and 52 on Monday. How many more papers did she deliver on Sunday than on Saturday? 15

Challenges

Family Math 4-6

Name

Be a Data Detective

Dear Family,
We have been learning to pick out needed data to solve problems. Help your child find the missing data in the problems below.

Read the story. After each problem, write the letter of the data that are missing. Then solve.

When Joe found the snake's skeleton, he counted 396 bones from its back. His book on snakes says there are only about 400 kinds of poisonous snakes, not all actually dangerous to people. The longest snake ever measured is 999 cm long. The heaviest weighs 243 kg more than Joe.

After reading about snakes, Joe bought a python that was 152 cm long. He built a cage for it that fit on his desk.

- A Joe is 142 cm tall.
- B Joe's desk is 115 cm wide.
- C The cage is 70 cm high.
- D Joe weighs 29 kg.
- E A human back has 32 bones.
- F The cage is 65 cm long.
- G The shortest snake ever measured is 108 mm.
- H A snake can have as many as 500 bones in its back.
- I About 350 kinds of poisonous snakes are not dangerous to people.

1. How many more bones did the snake skeleton have in its back than a human? E 364

2. How many poisonous kinds of snakes are actually dangerous to people? I about 50

3. How much taller than Joe is the longest snake ever measured? A 857 cm

4. How much does the heaviest snake weigh? D 272 kg

5. How much longer was Joe's python than its cage? F 87 cm

Options for Individual Needs

Basic

Exercises 1-7
Skills Bank, pp. 462, 464
Calculator Bank, pp. 484, 485
More Practice, p. 515, set B

Supplements
Reteaching 37 or
Practice 37

Average

Exercises 1-7
Skills Bank, pp. 462, 464
Calculator Bank, pp. 484, 485
More Practice, p. 515, set B

Supplements
Practice 37
Challenges 37 or
Thinking Skills 37

Extended

Exercises 1-7
Calculator Bank, pp. 484, 485

Supplements
Challenges 37
Thinking Skills 37

Other Resources:
Mathematics, A Way of Thinking, Lesson 15-15
Kids Are Consumers, Too!, pp. 94, 95, 97

LESSON PLAN 4-6

OBJECTIVE 4-6
To solve problems with extra data

1. MOTIVATE AND TEACH

LEARN ABOUT IT

▶ **Explain the data in a general statement.** (Three kinds of sounds are given in units called decibels.)

▶ **Explain what decibels are.** (units to measure how loud sounds are)

▶ **Explain what the question asks you to do.** (compare the loudness of a rock band with the loudness of normal talking)

▶ **Identify the extra data and explain why it is not needed.** (Tony hears only sounds louder than 110 decibels; the question does not ask anything about Tony.)

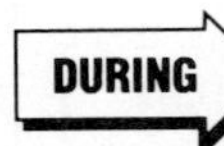

▶ **Plan a way to answer the question.** (Subtract 65 from 120.)

▶ **Justify using subtraction.** (Subtraction is used to compare two amounts.)

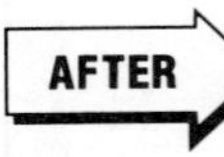

▶ **Evaluate your solution to see if it makes sense.** (120 − 65 = 55; check by adding: 55 + 65 = 120)

▶ **Justify including the extra data in the problem.** (Possible answer: It is an interesting fact related to the problem's topic.)

2. CHECK UNDERSTANDING

TRY IT OUT

ERROR ALERT Confusing extra data with the necessary data.

Problem Solving
Extra Data

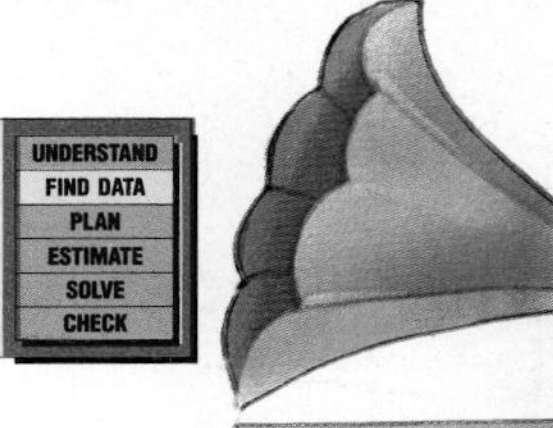

LEARN ABOUT IT

Sometimes a problem has extra data that you do not need to solve the problem.

Decibels measure the loudness of a sound. Without his hearing aid, Tony can hear only sounds louder than 110 decibels. Normal talking is about 65 decibels. A rock band is about 120 decibels. How many decibels louder than normal talking is a rock band?

I'll find the data I need to solve the problem.

Normal talking is about 65 decibels.
A rock band is about 120 decibels.

Some data is extra.

Tony hears only sounds louder than 110 decibels.

I'll solve the problem using only the data I need.

$$\begin{array}{r} 120 \\ -\ 65 \\ \hline 55 \end{array}$$

A rock band is 55 decibels louder than normal talking.

TRY IT OUT

Tell what data is extra. Then solve the problem.

1. The noise in the train station 2 miles from Ted's house is about 110 decibels. Music on Ted's headphones is about 75 decibels. How much louder is the noise in the train station? **how far the train station is from Ted's house; 35 decibels**
2. Look at the graph. How many decibels louder is loud talking than soft talking? **normal talking; 50 decibels**

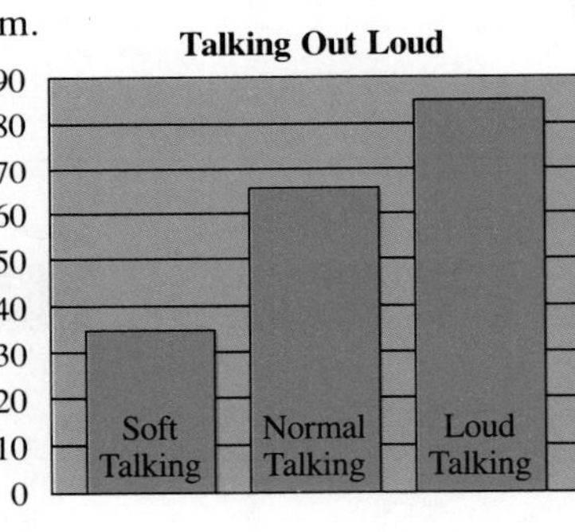

TEACHING OPTIONS

RETEACHING TIPS Exercise 3: Students locate the two bars needed to answer the question. (loud and soft talking) They use the edge of a paper to match the top of the bars to the decibel scale to determine the number of decibels for each, then do the correct operation. Assign Reteaching Supplement 37.

ENRICHMENT Have students use the pictograph on page 101 to create a story problem that compares sounds and that includes extra data. They write their problems on index cards, then post them on a math bulletin board for others to solve. (Answers will vary.) Check students' work.

MIXED PRACTICE

1. Jim, David, Rod, and Li worked in pairs to practice sign language. What are the different pairs they could form? **See Additional Answers.**

2. John's friend Ben is deaf. John and his dad decided to learn sign language. The first 2 months, they learned 128 signs. The next 2 months, they learned 168 more signs. How many did they learn in all? **296 signs**

3. Use the pictograph. How many decibels louder is the sound of talking nearby than the sound of a pencil writing? **20 decibels**

4. On the pictograph, how many decibels louder is a car horn than the sound of people talking far away? **55 decibels**

5. Without her hearing aid, Carmina can hear only sounds starting at 82 decibels. According to the pictograph, can she hear the sound of people talking nearby? **no**

6. Ferman learned how to finger sign the first 12 letters of the alphabet. Then he learned 11 more letters. How many letters did he know all together? **23 letters**

7. **Understanding the Operations** Tell the operation you would use to solve the problem. Use objects to solve. Janet learned 7 signs. There are 16 signs in her first lesson. How many more does she have to learn to know all the signs in the first lesson? **subtraction; 9 signs**

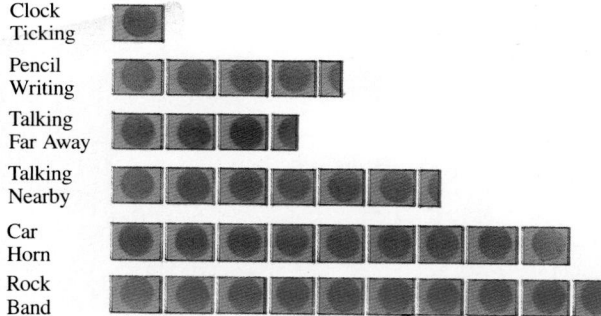

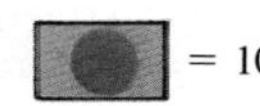

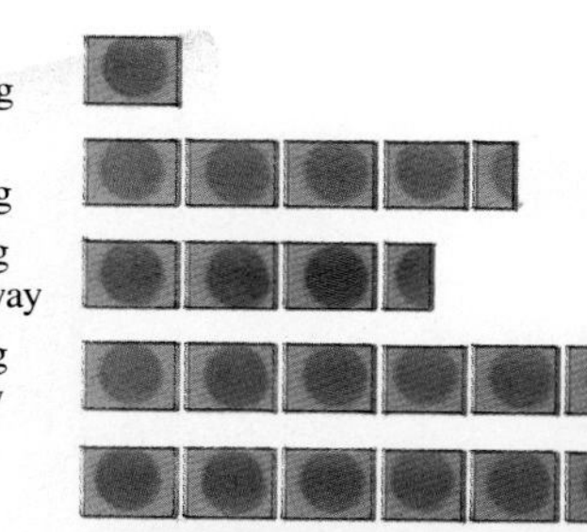

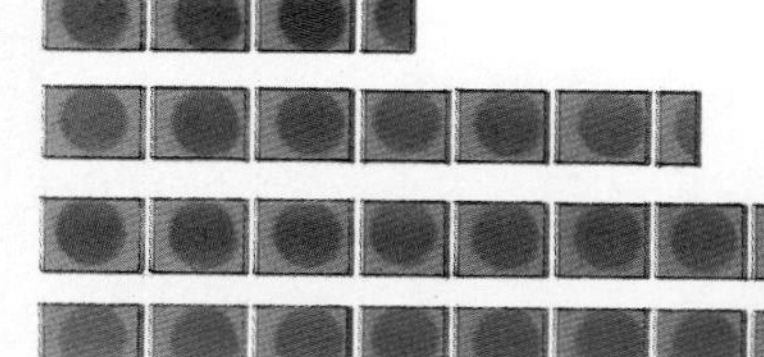

More Practice, page 515, set B

3. PRACTICE AND APPLY

Basic	1-7
Average	1-7
Extended	1-7

Additional Answers and Sample Solutions: See p. T79.

MIXED PRACTICE

▶ **Justify a strategy to use with Problem 1.** (Make an Organized List to see the possible pairs.)

▶ **Identify extra data in Problem 2.** (It took John and his dad four months to learn the signs.)

▶ **Compare Problems 3 and 4.** (Both use the pictograph and subtraction.)

▶ **Analyze the task in Problem 5.** (Use the data in the pictograph to see if Carmina can hear the sound of people talking nearby.)

▶ **Justify operations for solving Problems 6 and 7.** (Problem 6: add for a total; Problem 7: subtract to find how many more are needed)

CLOSE AND ASSESS

WRITE WHAT YOU THINK

Have students write a paragraph explaining how to solve a problem that has extra data in it. They should explain any helpful strategies or methods to use. (Answers will vary.) Check students' writing.

QUICK QUIZ

A scientist measured the loudness of a whisper at 30 decibels, an air drill at 85 decibels, and a shout at 100 decibels. How much softer is a whisper than a shout? (70 decibels)

LESSON OPTIONS 4-7

Fair and Unfair Games

OBJECTIVE 4-7 To determine whether or not a game is fair

PREBOOK ACTIVITIES

QUICK REVIEW

Identify each number as *odd* or *even*.

1. 5 (odd) **2.** 8 (even) **3.** 14 (even)
4. 13 (odd) **5.** 27 (odd) **6.** 81 (odd)
7. 132 (even) **8.** 229 (odd) **9.** 406 (even)

PRIOR KNOWLEDGE

Discuss how to make fair teams for a kickball game. (Possible answers: Give teams the same number of players; share stronger and weaker players between the teams; apply the rules equally to both teams.) Have students justify setting up fair teams. (Each team has an equal chance to win.) Have students consider how to make the kickball game unfair. (Possible answers: Give one team all the best players; apply different rules.) Have students link fair and unfair games to an ability to predict the winner. (Possible answer: In a fair game, both teams have an equal chance to win, so it is hard to predict a winner; in an unfair game, the team with an advantage will probably win.)

COMMUNICATION

Discussing Math Write this sentence on the chalkboard: There is very little **probability** of snow on July 4 in Florida. Have students read it, suggest a synonym for *probability* (chance), and identify a common word related to *probability*. (probably) Explain that mathematicians study probability to determine how likely something is to happen and point out that logical rules can help evaluate probability.

EXPLORE AND CONNECT

Materials: TA 2 (Number Cubes numbered 1 to 6)
Grouping Suggestion: cooperative learning pairs
Students explore **probability** and fairness with a simple game. Pairs start by rolling a number cube. The student who gets the higher number can earn a point in future rolls only by getting a 2 or less. The other player can earn a point in future rolls only by getting a 3 or more. Pairs take turns rolling and tallying their scores until one of them reaches 5 points. Conclude by having the whole group analyze the *probability* of either player winning the game. (The player who got points for rolling 3 or higher had a better chance of winning.) Have students develop a plan to make the game more equal for both players (Possible answer: One player earns a point for rolling 1, 2, or 3; the other earns a point for rolling 4, 5, or 6.) Have students explain why games need fair rules. (Possible answer: Games are more fun if each player has an equal chance to win.)

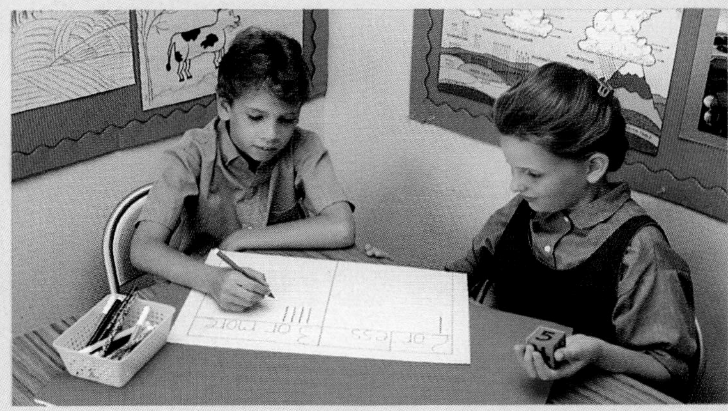

CONNECTIONS Use these anytime.

Problem of the Day

Ms. Curry plans a basketball-shooting contest for the whole school on Field Day. She wants the contest to be fair for everyone, considering their sizes, ages, and basketball experience. What rules would you suggest? (Possible answers: extra shots or points for younger students; greater distance from the basket for bigger students)

Math Connection

Logical Reasoning Mr. Sage asks party guests to guess his age and the age of his son, who he says is in kindergarten. Which age will guests be more likely to guess? Explain your reasoning. (the son; his age is probably around 5, but there are many possibilities for Mr. Sage's age.)

Creative Thinking

Tug of War The last event on Field Day was a tug of war. Although one team had 36 players and the other team had only 9, all agreed that the event was fair. How could this be? (Possible answer: 9 teachers, 36 students)

Classwork and Homework Supplements

Practice

Math Reasoning 4-7

Name

Fair and Unfair Games

Play these games with a classmate. Use spinners with the numbers 1, 2, 3, 4, 5, and 6 in equal-size regions. Tell if you think the games are fair. Try to figure out why.

1. Odds and Evens Subtraction Game

   Rules: Spin both spinners. Subtract the smaller number from the larger one. If the answer is even, one player scores. If the answer is odd, the other player scores. No one scores if the answer is zero. The first player to get 10 points wins.

   Not fair; chances of getting an odd number are greater.

2. Number Matching Game

   Rules: Spin both spinners. If both numbers match, one player scores. If the two numbers are different, the other player scores. The first to get 10 points wins.

   Not fair; chances that numbers will be different are greater.

3. Add to Get Odds and Evens Game

   Rules: Spin both spinners. Add the two numbers. If the answer is even, one player scores. The other player scores if the answer is odd. The first player to get 10 points wins.

   Fair; chances of winning are equal.

4. Multiply to Get Odds and Evens Game

   Rules: Spin both spinners. Multiply the two numbers. If the product is an even number, one player scores. The other player scores if the product is an odd number. The first player to get 10 points wins.

   Not fair; chances of getting an even number are greater.

38 Use with text pages 102–103. PS-4

Building Thinking Skills

Life Skills 4-7

Name

Should You or Shouldn't You?

Suppose you are presented with each offer below. Decide whether it would be wise for you to take it or not. Explain your decisions.

1. Either you or your brother takes out the garbage. Your brother says to you, "I will roll this number cube. If I roll a 3 or higher, you take out the garbage for a month. If I roll less than a 3, I will." Should you take this offer?

   No; chances to get 3 or greater = 4, chances to get less than 3 = 2.

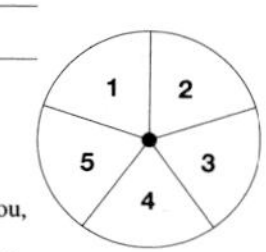

2. Either you or your sister walks the dogs. She says to you, "I will spin this spinner. If I spin an odd number, you walk the dogs this week. If I spin an even number, I will do it." Should you take her offer?

   No; 3 choices for odd, 2 for even.

3. Either you or your sister has to clean the yard. She makes you this offer: She will mix up these four number cards and place them facedown on a table. Then she will turn over two of them. If the sum is 6 or greater, she will clean the yard. Otherwise, you will. Should you take her offer?

   No; 4 combinations are less than 6; 2 combinations are 6 or greater.

38 Use with text pages 102-103. TS-4

Reteaching

Cooperative Activities 4-7

Name

Fair and Unfair Games

Rules: Spin both spinners.
If the colors match, Team 1 gets a point.
If they do not match, Team 2 gets the point.

Fair Game

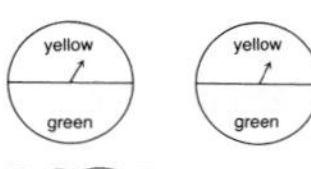

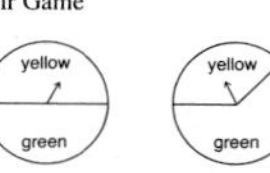

The colors on both spinners cover equal areas.

The chances of winning are equal.

Unfair Game

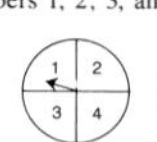

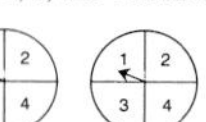

The colors on the second spinner do not cover equal areas.

The chances of winning are not equal.

Play the games below in teams. Cut 2 different colored pieces of paper into 5 strips each, and write a different number (1–10) on each strip. Place strips in a bag. Tell if you think the games are fair. Try to determine why.

1. Color-Match Game
   Rules: Each team draws a strip. If the two strips are the same color, Team 1 receives a point. If the colors do not match, Team 2 scores. The first team to get 10 points wins.

   Fair; there is an equal chance of the colors matching or not matching.

2. Sum Game
   Rules: Each team in turn draws 2 strips. If the sum of the two numbers is 10 or greater, Team 1 scores. Team 2 scores if the sum is less than 10. The first team to get 10 points wins.

   Unfair; there is a greater chance that the sum will be 10 or greater.

38 Use with text pages 102-103. RS-4

Challenges

Cooperative Activities 4-7

Name

Spin-a-Sum Game

Michiko invited Ken to play a game. They each had a spinner with the numbers 1, 2, 3, and 4 in the regions.

Michiko explained the rules. "We each spin a spinner. If the sum of the numbers is 4, 5, or 6, then I get 1 point. If the sum is any other number, you get 1 point."

1. Play this game with a partner. Spin at least 30 times.
2. Do you think the game is fair or unfair? unfair
3. Analyze the game by determining the 16 possible pairs of numbers and their sum below. Write the pairs of numbers you could spin in the triangles and the sums on the blanks. The first one is done for you.

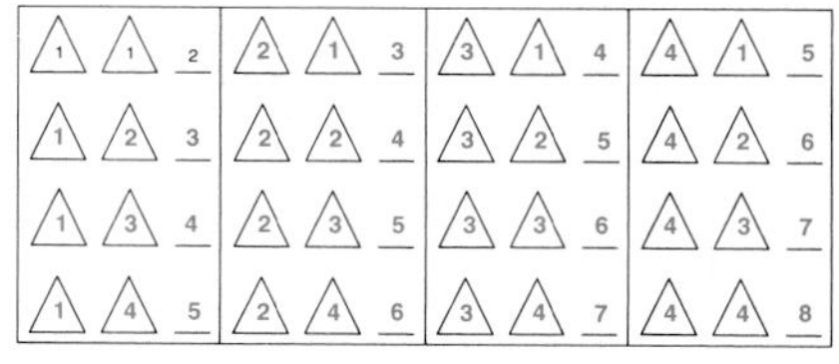

1, 1: 2	2, 1: 3	3, 1: 4	4, 1: 5
1, 2: 3	2, 2: 4	3, 2: 5	4, 2: 6
1, 3: 4	2, 3: 5	3, 3: 6	4, 3: 7
1, 4: 5	2, 4: 6	3, 4: 7	4, 4: 8

4. Count all sums of 4, 5, or 6. How many did you find? 10
5. Use your answer to Exercise 4 to decide again if the game is fair or unfair. Explain your decision. unfair; 10 out of the 16 possible sums are 4, 5, or 6.

38 Use with text pages 102–103. CS-4

Options for Individual Needs

Basic

Exercises 1-9, 12, 13
Skills Bank, p. 462
Calculator Bank, p. 485
Computer Bank, p. 498
More Practice, p. 515, set C

Supplements
Reteaching 38 or
Practice 38

Average

Exercises 1-14
Skills Bank, p. 462
Calculator Bank, p. 485
Computer Bank, p. 498
More Practice, p. 515, set C

Supplements
Practice 38
Challenges 38 or
Thinking Skills 38

Extended

Exercises 1-7, 10-13
Calculator Bank, p. 485
Computer Bank, p. 498

Supplements
Challenges 38
Thinking Skills 38

Other Resources:
Mathematics, A Way of Thinking, Lessons 17-1, 17-2, 17-3
Problem-Solving Experiences in Mathematics, Grade 4, Problem 2

LESSON PLAN 4-7

OBJECTIVE 4-7
To determine whether or not a game is fair

Materials: TA 13 (Spinners 1-4), TA 11 (Blank Spinners)

Grouping Suggestion: small groups

1. MOTIVATE AND TEACH

LEARN ABOUT IT

EXPLORE ▶ **Evaluate your chances of landing on a certain number on the spinner.** (equal, because the spinner has 4 same-size parts)
▶ **Explain whether the game relies on skill or chance.** (chance, because anyone can use a spinner)

TALK ABOUT IT ▶ **Suppose the first player spins a 3. Which is more likely, a Match or a No Match? Explain.** (a No Match, because there is only 1 chance for a Match but 3 chances for a No Match)
▶ **Explain what makes this game fair or unfair.** (The game is unfair because the No Match team has 3 times as many chances to score on each turn.)
▶ **Explain how you would make the game more fair.** (Possible answer: Make a Match worth 3 points and a No Match worth 1 point.)
Student Edition answers: **1.** Answers will vary. The No Match team probably won. **2.** No, the No Match team has 3 times as many chances to score. **3.** The game would be more fair; answers will vary.

2. CHECK UNDERSTANDING

TRY IT OUT

ERROR ALERT Exercise 2
Incorrectly evaluating game fairness.

Fair and Unfair Games

LEARN ABOUT IT

EXPLORE Use a Spinner
Work in groups. A game is fair if all players have about an equal chance or **probability** of winning. To play this game, each team needs a spinner like the one shown.

Match or No Match Game

- Two groups should play together. One is the Match team. The other is the No Match team.
- A player from each team spins the spinner. If the numbers on both spinners match, the Match team gets a point. If the numbers do not match, the No Match team scores a point.
- The first team to score 10 points wins. Play the game at least 3 times.

TALK ABOUT IT See teaching notes.

1. Who won the most games, the Match team or the No Match team? Were the game scores very close?
2. Do you think the game is fair to both teams? Explain your reasoning.
3. What would happen if you gave extra points for a match spin? How would you decide the number of extra points to give?

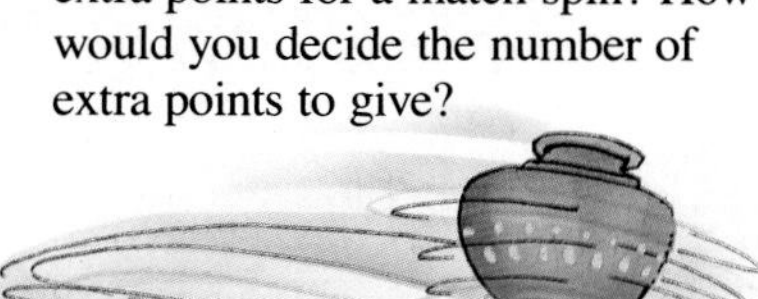

TRY IT OUT

Play Match or No Match with spinners like this.

1. Who won the game? Was the score close?
   Answers will vary.
2. Do you think this is a fair game? Why or why not?
   Yes; all players have an equal chance of winning.

102

TEACHING OPTIONS

RETEACHING TIPS Have students make an organized list of the possible spin combinations. (1-1, 1-2, 2-1, 2-2) Have them circle Matches and underline No Matches, then count how many of each can occur. Students will see that they are equally likely. Assign Reteaching Supplement 38.

ENRICHMENT **Family Math**
Students try this with a family member. They create a fair game using a penny and a nickel. They play the game twice to see if the rules are fair. If not, they adjust the rules, then play two more times. They write their rules to share with classmates.

PRACTICE

Play these games with a classmate. Use spinners like the one at the top of page 102. Are the games fair? Why?

1. Odds and Evens Match Game

   Rules: Spin both spinners. If both numbers are odd or both are even, one team scores. The other team scores if one number is odd and the other is even. The first team to get 10 points wins. **fair**

2. Odd and Even Differences Game

   Rules: Spin both spinners. If the difference between the two numbers is odd, one team scores. The other team scores if the difference is even. The first team to get 10 points wins. **not fair**

APPLY

MATH REASONING

3. Suppose the spinners in the Match or No Match game each had 10 numbered regions. Would the Match team win more often or less often? **less**

PROBLEM SOLVING

4. Joe and Victoria each flip a coin. If both coins come up heads or both come up tails, Joe wins. If one coin comes up heads and one comes up tails, Victoria wins. Is this a fair game? Why or why not? **yes; chances of winning are equal**

MIXED REVIEW

Find the sums.

5. 12 + (25 + 41) = n **78** 6. 36 + (0 + 14) = n **50** 7. (41 + 12) + 25 = n **78**

Use mental math and break apart an addend to find the sums.

8. 18 + 6 **24** 9. 36 + 9 **45** 10. 78 + 7 **85** 11. 56 + 8 **64**

Use mental math and compatible numbers to find the sums.

12. 25 + 16 + 15 **56** 13. 37 + 43 + 7 **87** 14. 38 + 12 + 21 **71**

More Practice, page 515, set C

3. PRACTICE AND APPLY

Basic	1-9, 12, 13
Average	1-14
Extended	1-7, 10-13

PRACTICE

How could you predict whether a game is fair before you play it? (List all the possible spin combinations to see if one combination is more likely to occur than another.)

APPLY

MATH REASONING ► **Analyze a relationship between the number of regions and the chance of landing on a certain one.** (As the number of regions increases, the size of each region decreases, so you are less likely to land on a certain one.)

PROBLEM SOLVING ► **Explain how to predict the winner in Problem 4.** (If the rules are fair for both, you cannot predict a winner because each player has an equal chance to win.)

MIXED REVIEW ► **Explain why parentheses are used in Exercises 5-7.** (to tell which numbers to add first)

CLOSE AND ASSESS

WRITE WHAT YOU THINK A spinner divided into 3 equal parts, 2 red and 1 blue, is used in a game. Players get 1 point for landing on red and 2 points for landing on blue. Students explain whether the game is fair. (fair; there are twice as many red parts, but blue is worth twice as much.)

QUICK QUIZ

Fill in the blanks. A game is fair if all players have an (equal) chance of winning. If one player is more likely to score than another, the (probability) of winning is not the same.

LESSON OPTIONS 4-8

Probability and Prediction

OBJECTIVE 4-8 To determine whether the probability of something happening is high or low

PREBOOK ACTIVITIES

QUICK REVIEW

Use mental math to find the missing addend.

1. 5 + (7) = 12	**2.** (20) + 54 = 74
3. 36 + (100) = 136	**4.** (25) + 25 = 50
5. 102 + (98) = 200	**6.** 44 + (50) = 94
7. (30) + 143 = 173	**8.** (11) + 989 = 1,000
9. 444 + (444) = 888	**10.** 502 + (600) = 1,102

PRIOR KNOWLEDGE

Discuss real-life situations that are based on guessing whether an event is likely to happen. (Possible answers: Our team will probably win because of our strategy; I should take my umbrella because it looks like rain; I will probably pass the spelling test because I memorized all the words.) Ask students to explain how they make predictions. (Possible answers: rely on facts, patterns, experience, probability)

COMMUNICATION

Discussing and Writing Math Have students review the meaning of probability and relate it to fair and unfair games. (chance that something will or will not happen; In a fair game, all players have an equal probability of winning; in an unfair game, the player or team with an advantage has a greater probability of winning than others.) In their Math Journals, have students write an explanation of how they might use probability to make a reasonable prediction. (Possible answer: If something has a high probability of happening, you may predict it will occur; if something has a low probability of happening, you may not predict it would occur.)

EXPLORE AND CONNECT

Materials: small same-size objects in 2 colors (counters, marbles, snap cubes, paper squares), paper bags
Grouping Suggestion: cooperative learning pairs
Students experiment with probability and prediction. Partners put 5 small objects of each color in a paper bag and give it a gentle shake. Explain that, without looking, pairs are to draw one object from the bag, record its color, then return the object to the bag and give the bag a shake, repeating this process 40 times. Before they begin, pairs predict how many times they think each color will appear. Then they perform the experiment. One student draws as the other tallies the colors, trading tasks after every 10 draws. After they complete the activity, have pairs explain how they made their predictions, share their actual outcomes of the experiment, and relate the outcomes to the original predictions. (Although the mathematical probability is $\frac{1}{2}$, actual outcomes may vary.)

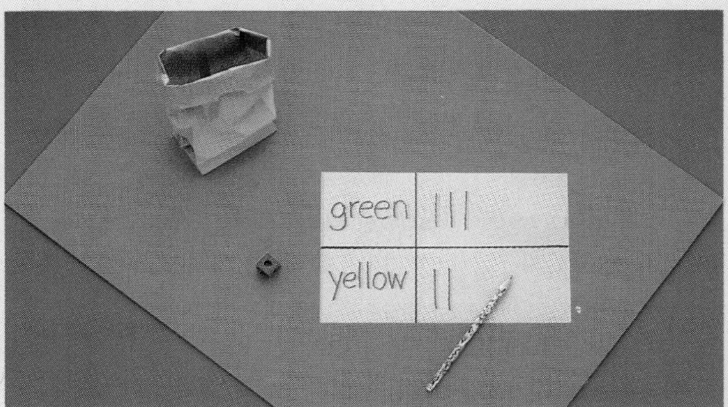

CONNECTIONS Use these anytime.

Problem of the Day

Predictions At 4:00 p.m., Joe's thermometer read 88°F. He put it in the freezer and read it every 5 min. At 4:05 p.m., it was 73°F. At 4:10 p.m., the temperature was 58°F. How would you predict the next reading? If the pattern continues, when will the temperature be below 32°F? (Subtract another 15° to get 43°F; by 4:20 p.m.)

Life Skills

Contests A sign says that to enter the contest for a free horse, you must send Mustang Stables a postcard with your name and address. Linda sends 1 card, Jackie sends 3 cards, and Viola sends 25 cards. Explain which girl has the best chance to win. (Viola, because she entered the contest more times than the others.)

Math Connection

Math Language Write two sentences using the word *chance:* one that describes a very likely event and one that describes a very unlikely event. (Answers will vary. Samples: There is a good chance that I will watch television today. There is no chance that I will ride a camel today.)

and to predict an outcome

Classwork and Homework Supplements

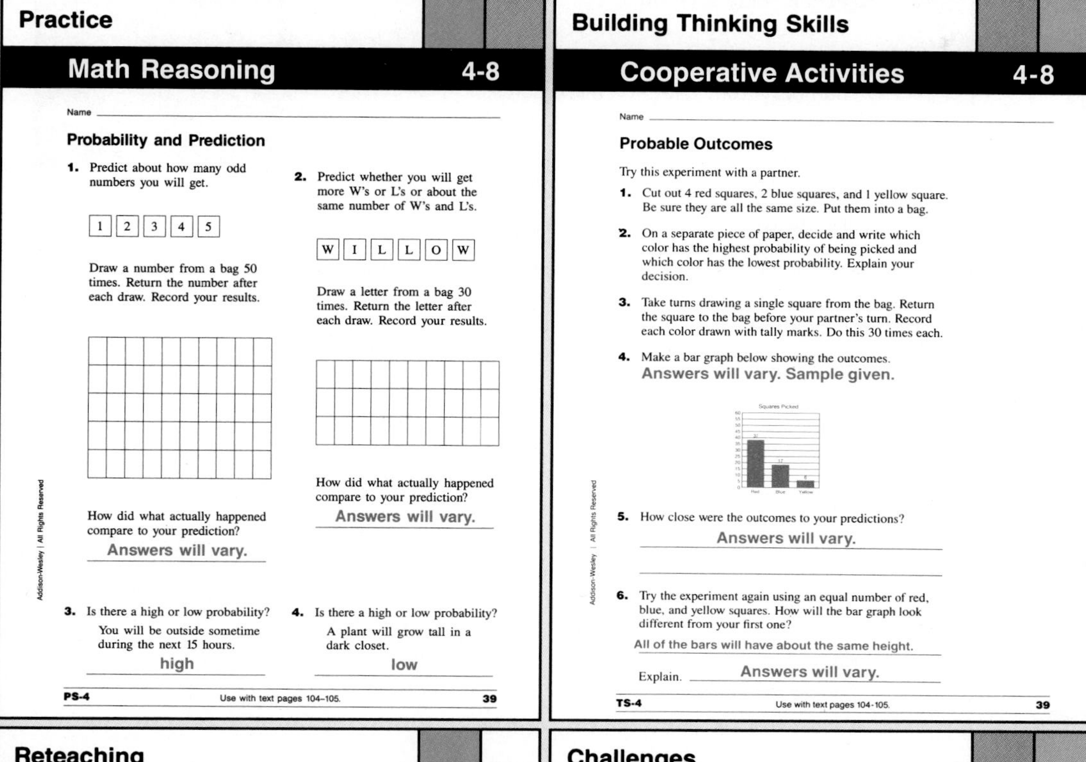

Practice

Math Reasoning 4-8

Name

Probability and Prediction

1. Predict about how many odd numbers you will get.

1 2 3 4 5

Draw a number from a bag 50 times. Return the number after each draw. Record your results.

How did what actually happened compare to your prediction? Answers will vary.

2. Predict whether you will get more W's or L's or about the same number of W's and L's.

W I L L O W

Draw a letter from a bag 30 times. Return the letter after each draw. Record your results.

How did what actually happened compare to your prediction? Answers will vary.

3. Is there a high or low probability? You will be outside sometime during the next 15 hours. high

4. Is there a high or low probability? A plant will grow tall in a dark closet. low

Addison-Wesley | All Rights Reserved

PS-4 Use with text pages 104–105. 39

Building Thinking Skills

Cooperative Activities 4-8

Name

Probable Outcomes

Try this experiment with a partner.

1. Cut out 4 red squares, 2 blue squares, and 1 yellow square. Be sure they are all the same size. Put them into a bag.
2. On a separate piece of paper, decide and write which color has the highest probability of being picked and which color has the lowest probability. Explain your decision.
3. Take turns drawing a single square from the bag. Return the square to the bag before your partner's turn. Record each color drawn with tally marks. Do this 30 times each.
4. Make a bar graph below showing the outcomes. Answers will vary. Sample given.

Squares Picked

5. How close were the outcomes to your predictions? Answers will vary.
6. Try the experiment again using an equal number of red, blue, and yellow squares. How will the bar graph look different from your first one? All of the bars will have about the same height.

Explain. Answers will vary.

Addison-Wesley | All Rights Reserved

TS-4 Use with text pages 104–105. 39

Reteaching

Math Reasoning 4-8

Name

Probability and Prediction

There are 7 marbles in this bag. Which color marble would you have a higher probability of drawing?

Count the white marbles. → Count the black marbles. → Decide if there are more black or white marbles.

5 2 white

You have a **higher probability** of drawing a white marble than a black marble.

Which color marble would you have a higher probability of drawing?

1. white
2. black
3. black
4. white

5. Predict about how many white paper strips you will get.

Draw a strip from a bag 30 times. Return the strip after each draw. How did what actually happened compare to your prediction? Answers will vary.

6. Predict whether you will get more white or black strips or about the same of white and black.

Draw a strip from a bag 20 times. Return the strip after each draw. How did what actually happened compare to your prediction? Answers will vary.

Addison-Wesley | All Rights Reserved

RS-4 Use with text pages 104-105. 39

Challenges

Manipulatives 4-8

Name

Sum Predictions

Make two spinners like these:

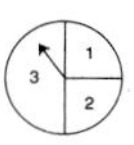

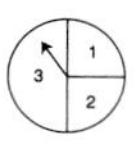

1. Suppose you spun the 2 spinners 30 times and found the sum of the two numbers each time. Make predictions about the sums you would spin:

   What sum would you spin the most? 6

   What sum would you spin the least? 2

2. Test your predictions. Spin 30 times and record your results in the table.

Sum	Tally
2	
3	
4	
5	
6	

3. How did your results compare to your predictions? Answers will vary.

4. Suppose you made 2 identical spinners. When you spun them, the sum that came up most often was 8, and the sum that came up least often was 11. Use three different numbers to show one way the spinners might look. Answers will vary.

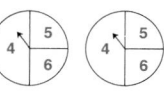

Addison-Wesley | All Rights Reserved

CS-4 Use with text pages 104–105. 39

Options for Individual Needs

Basic

Exercises 1-9
Computer Bank, p. 498
More Practice, p. 515, set D

Supplements
Reteaching 39 or
Practice 39

Average

Exercises 1-12
Computer Bank, p. 498
More Practice, p. 515, set D

Supplements
Practice 39
Challenges 39 or
Thinking Skills 39

Extended

Exercises 1-6; 9-12
Computer Bank, p. 498

Supplements
Challenges 39
Thinking Skills 39

Other Resources:
Mathematics, A Way of Thinking, Lessons 17-4, 17-5
Problem-Solving Experiences in Mathematics, Grade 4, Problem 10

4-8

LESSON PLAN 4-8

OBJECTIVE 4-8
To determine whether the probability of something happening is high or low and to predict an outcome

Materials: paper, scissors, markers, paper bags, colored counters

Grouping Suggestion: small groups

1. MOTIVATE AND TEACH

LEARN ABOUT IT

EXPLORE ► **Explain how to make the number squares to keep the game fair.** (Possible answer: All should be the same size so you cannot tell them apart by touch.)

TALK ABOUT IT ► **Compare any one number card to the total number of cards.** (Any of the numbers is 1 number out of 5 in all.)
► **Decide which number has the greatest probability of being picked. Explain your reasoning.** (There is an equal chance for all because there is only 1 card for each number.)
► **In the second game, explain why there are unequal chances to get 3s and 5s.** (There are more 5s, so the probability is greater of drawing a 5.)
Student Edition answers: **1.** same chance for both; yes, there is one of every number. **2.** no, more odd than even numbers

2. CHECK UNDERSTANDING

TRY IT OUT

ERROR ALERT Experimenting too few times to assess the prediction. Misjudging the greater probability of drawing an odd number.

Probability and Prediction

LEARN ABOUT IT

EXPLORE **Play a Game**
Work in groups.

- Cut out five small squares of paper. Write the numbers from 1 to 5 on the squares.
- Think of a lucky number from 1 to 5. Put the squares in a paper bag and shake the bag. How many draws does it take to get your lucky number?

TALK ABOUT IT See teaching notes.

1. Suppose you draw one square from the bag without looking. Are you more likely to draw a 3 or a 5? Are the chances the same? Why or why not?
2. Suppose one team gets a point every time someone draws an even number. The other team gets a point every time someone draws an odd number. Do you think this is a fair game? Why or why not?

Probability is the chance that something will or will not happen. If there are more chances of something happening, there is a higher probability.

Suppose the game is played with these pieces of paper. There are more 5s than 3s, so there is a higher probability of drawing a 5 than a 3.

TRY IT OUT

Use paper squares for this experiment.

Predict whether you will get more even numbers or more odd numbers. odd

Draw a number from a bag 30 times. Return the number after each draw.

What actually happened? Compare this to your prediction.
Answers will vary.

TEACHING OPTIONS

RETEACHING TIPS Have students who do not perform the experiment the specified number of times use tally marks to record each draw. Remind them to count the total number of tallies every so often to be sure they perform the experiment 30 times. Assign Reteaching Supplement 39.

ENRICHMENT Students work in pairs to plan a probability experiment using a calculator. They agree on fair rules, then predict what they think will happen. They try the experiment 50 times to test their prediction. They share their results with the class. (Check pairs' experiments and results.)

PRACTICE

1. Predict about how many Bs you will get.

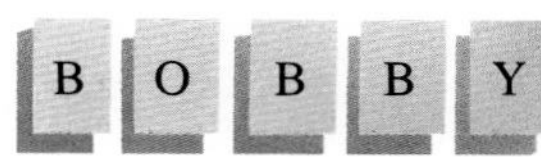

Draw a letter from a bag 50 times. Return the letter after each draw. How did what actually happened compare to your prediction?
Answers will vary.

2. Predict whether you will get more R's or E's or about the same number of R's and E's.

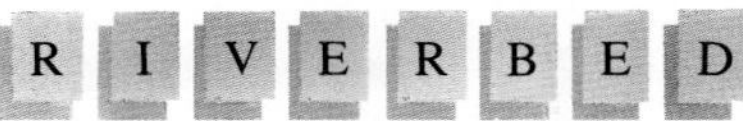

Draw a letter from a bag 30 times. Return the letter after each draw. How did what actually happened compare to your prediction?
Answers will vary.

3. Do you think there is a high or low probability that it will snow in the Sahara Desert during June? **low**

4. Do you think there is a high or low probability that you will sleep sometime during the next 24 hours? **high**

APPLY

MATH REASONING

5. You flip a penny. Is there a high probability of getting heads or of getting tails? Or are the probabilities the same? **same**

PROBLEM SOLVING

6. **Understand the Question** Ben put the letters of his name in a bag. He drew a letter out of the bag 60 times. He returned the letter after each draw. He drew the letter E 24 times. He drew the letter N 23 times. How many times did he draw the letter B? **13 times**

▶ MENTAL MATH

You can halve a number by halving its parts. For example, 118 halved = half of 100 + half of 18. So half of 118 is 50 plus 9, or 59. Find half of these numbers.

7. 56	**8.** 84	**9.** 124	**10.** 250	**11.** 450	**12.** 616
28	42	62	125	225	308

More Practice, page 515, set D

3. PRACTICE AND APPLY

Basic	1–9
Average	1–12
Extended	1–6, 9–12

PRACTICE

Compare B*s to all letters in Exercise 1.* (3 out of 5 are *B*s) *Explain how the data affects a prediction.* (The probability of getting *B*s compared to other letters is higher.) *Link Exercises 3 and 4.* (Judge each statement as likely or not.)

APPLY

MATH REASONING ▶ Explain how determining every possible way a penny can land can help answer Exercise 5. (If you know there are only two ways it can land, you know the chances of getting either are the same.)

PROBLEM SOLVING ▶ Explain what the problem asks. (It asks: Out of 60 draws, how many were the letter *B*?)

MENTAL MATH ▶ Explain how the halving method is like another mental math method you have used. (break-apart addends, because you break apart larger numbers into easier numbers to work with)

CLOSE AND ASSESS

SHOW WHAT YOU KNOW

Have students create 2 experiments using 5 counters: one with a *high* probability of drawing red and one with a *low* probability of drawing red. Ask them to explain their reasoning, then to try the experiment to see what really happens. (Check students' ideas.)

QUICK QUIZ

If you form words with letter tiles, is the probability of picking **p** *higher*, *lower*, or *equal to* picking **i**? **1.** pipe (higher) **2.** pine (equal) **3.** pig (equal) **4.** dipper (higher) **5.** icicle (lower)

LESSON OPTIONS 4-9

Problem Solving: Guess and Check

OBJECTIVE 4-9 To solve problems using the strategy Guess and Check

PREBOOK ACTIVITIES

QUICK REVIEW

Write three different pairs of addends for each sum. (Answers may vary.)

1. 12 (3 + 9, 4 + 8, 6 + 6) **2.** 15 (6 + 9, 8 + 7, 5 + 10)
3. 18 (10 + 8, 9 + 9, 11 + 7) **4.** 9 (3 + 6, 7 + 2, 1 + 8)
5. 11 (2 + 9, 4 + 7, 5 + 6) **6.** 16 (8 + 8, 7 + 9, 6 + 10)
7. 8 (2 + 6, 4 + 4, 5 + 3) **8.** 20 (11 + 9, 15 + 5, 12 + 8)

PRIOR KNOWLEDGE

Have students suggest situations based on guessing. (Possible answers: certain games or contests, some estimates, answers when facts are unknown) Have students guess a verifiable fact related to the school, such as the number of classrooms in the school or the height of the building. Ask them to explain how they could check their guesses. (Possible answer: Count the classrooms; interview the custodian.)

COMMUNICATION

Discussing Math Have students use reasoning to interpret a difference between *wild* and *educated* guesses. (Possible answer: A wild guess is anything that may pop into mind, not based on facts or careful thinking; an educated guess is based on planning, on logical reasoning, or on related facts.) Have students predict what the Guess and Check problem solving strategy might involve. (Possible answer: making a sensible guess, then checking to see if it is reasonable)

EXPLORE AND CONNECT

COOPERATIVE ACTIVITY

Grouping Suggestion: small groups

Holly is 4 years older than Brent. Their ages total 18. How old is each child?

TEACHING ACTIONS

Encourage groups to discuss and solve the problem together.

▶ **Explain what you know about Holly and Brent.** (Their ages add up to 18; Holly is 4 years older than Brent.)

▶ **Analyze what is tricky about the problem.** (You know the sum of two ages and a link between them, but both addends are missing.)

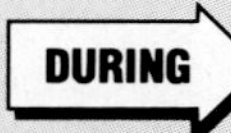

▶ **Decide on a plan to use to solve the problem.** (Possible answer: Guess any age for Brent, then add 4 to that guess for Holly's age; see if the ages total 18.)

▶ **Explain what to do if your first guess does not work.** (Guess and check again.)

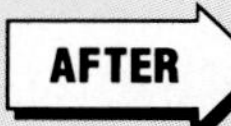

▶ **Evaluate your solution to see if it makes sense.** (If Brent is 7 and Holly is 11, their ages add up to 18.)

▶ **Justify the name Guess and Check for this problem solving strategy.** (The strategy requires making a reasonable guess, then checking it with the situation to see if it makes sense.)

CONNECTIONS Use these anytime.

Problem of the Day

Coins Libby has 3 different coins. One coin is worth twice as much as another, and the third coin is worth less than either of the others. What coins might Libby have? (4 possible combinations: penny, nickel, dime; penny, quarter, half dollar; nickel, quarter, half dollar; dime, quarter, half dollar)

Math Connection

Operations List all possible 2-digit addend pairs that give a sum of 30. (6 possibilities: 10 + 20, 11 + 19, 12 + 18, 13 + 17, 14 + 16, 15 + 15)

Subject Integration

Fine Arts The local library has 15 new works by local artists on display. There are twice as many paintings as sculptures. How many of each kind of art are in the library exhibit? (10 paintings, 5 sculptures)

Classwork and Homework Supplements

Practice

Problem Solving 4-9

Name ____________________

Guess and Check

Guess and check to help you solve each problem.

1. Mr. and Mrs. Gold thought of 14 possibilities for names for the child they are expecting. They selected 4 more boy's names than girl's names. How many girl's names did they select?
   5 girl's names
2. Last week at Suburban Hospital 18 babies were born. There were 4 more girls born than boys. How many boys were born that week?
   7 boys
3. At the hospital gift shop Sara sold 2 bouquets of flowers that totaled $21. The cost of one bouquet was twice the price of the other. How much was the more expensive bouquet?
   $14
4. Mrs. Cly bought 2 boxes of diapers for her newborn son. She bought 1 box of Softies and 1 box of Smoothies. She spent $10. Softies cost $2 more than Smoothies. How much did Softies cost?
   $6
5. David and Karen took turns baby-sitting for their sister. Together they baby-sat for 44 minutes. David baby-sat 10 minutes longer than Karen. How long did David baby-sit?
   27 minutes
6. Baby Felipe napped twice for a total of 6 hours on Friday. His morning nap was 2 hours shorter than his afternoon nap. How long did Felipe sleep in the morning?
   2 hours

Building Thinking Skills

Problem Solving 4-9

Name ____________________

At the Pond

Old Ben the bullfrog sits down by the pond and watches all that goes on there. He enjoys making up problems from what he sees around him. Here are some of his favorites for you to solve. *Hint:* Use the Guess and Check strategy.

1. Ben knows 100 of his neighbors by name. Ten are fish. The rest are frogs and turtles. He knows the names of twice as many turtles as frogs. How many turtles does he know by name?
   60 turtles
2. For 5 days Ben counted the number of people fishing in his pond. Each day he counted 4 more than the day before. He counted a total of 55 people. How many did he count each day?
   3, 7, 11, 15, 19 people
3. Ben saw that one frog ate 3 more bugs each day than he ate on the day before. If this frog ate 100 bugs in 8 days, how many did he eat each day?
   2, 5, 8, 11, 14, 17, 20, 23 bugs
4. A bigger frog ate 10 more bugs each day than on the day before. In 5 days she ate 120 bugs. How many did she eat on the first day?
   4 bugs

Reteaching

Problem Solving 4-9

Name ____________________

Guess and Check

You can use the **Guess and Check** strategy to solve some problems.

Ted has 3 more pencils than Tom.
There are 13 pencils altogether.
How many pencils did Tom have?

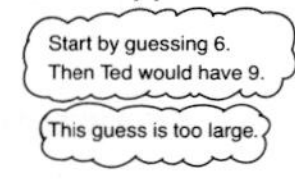
Start by guessing 6.
Then Ted would have 9.
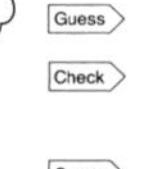
Guess

This guess is too large.
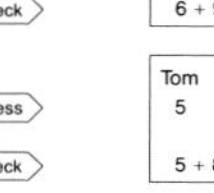
Check

Guess again.
Guess
This checks.
Check

Tom	Ted
6	6 + 3
	9
6 + 9 = 15	

Tom	Ted
5	5 + 3
	8
5 + 8 = 13	

Tom has 5 pencils.

Guess and check to help you solve each problem.

1. Dennis had 11 racquet balls. He had 3 more red balls than blue. How many red balls did he have?
   7 balls
2. Pat sold 14 tapes in two days. There were 2 more sold on the first day than on the second day. How many tapes were sold on the first day?
   8 tapes
3. There were 20 problems on Sally's English test. She got 12 more right answers than wrong answers. How many answers did Sally get right?
   16 answers
4. Bob raises ducks and sheep on his farm. The animals in one pasture have a total of 9 heads and 26 feet. How many sheep and how many ducks are there in the pasture? (Remember: sheep have 4 feet, ducks have 2 feet.)
   4 sheep, 5 ducks

Challenges

Problem Solving 4-9

Name ____________________

Math at the Movies

1. On her birthday, Sachiyo went to her favorite superhero movie with friends and relatives. The 5 tickets cost $19 in all. How many adult tickets and how many children's tickets did they buy? Guess and check to find the solution. (The first guess is done for you.) Put a ✓ next to the correct guess.

Matinee Tickets
Adult $5
Children $3

Guess		Check	
Number of Adult Tickets	Number of Children's Tickets	Cost	
0	5	$15	
1	4	$17	
2	3	$19	✓
3	2	$21	
4	1	$23	
5	0	$25	

2. Mr. Hernandez spent $4.20 for 6 boxes of popcorn for his family. He bought some larges and some super-larges. How many of each size did he buy? Put a ✓ next to the correct guess.

Popcorn
Large $0.60
Super-large $0.90

Guess		Check	
Large	Super-Large	Cost	
1	5	$5.10	
2	4	$4.80	
3	3	$4.50	
4	2	$4.20	✓
5	1	$3.90	

Options for Individual Needs

Basic

Exercises 2-7
Skills Bank, p. 463
Calculator Bank, p. 485
Computer Bank, pp. 495, 496
More Practice, p. 515, set E

Supplements
Reteaching 40 or
Practice 40

Average

Exercises 1-7
Skills Bank, p. 463
Calculator Bank, p. 485
Computer Bank, pp. 495, 496
More Practice, p. 515, set E

Supplements
Practice 40
Challenges 40 or
Thinking Skills 40

Extended

Exercises 1-7
Calculator Bank, p. 485
Computer Bank, pp. 495, 496

Supplements
Challenges 40
Thinking Skills 40

Other Resources:
Problem-Solving Experiences in Mathematics, Grade 4, Problems 59, 60, 69, 70, 74, 90, 104, 105
Mathematics, A Way of Thinking, Lesson 21-1

LESSON PLAN 4-9

OBJECTIVE 4-9
To solve problems using the strategy Guess and Check

Materials: TAs 9 and 10 (Play Money: Coins and Dollars, Larger Bills)

1. MOTIVATE AND TEACH

LEARN ABOUT IT

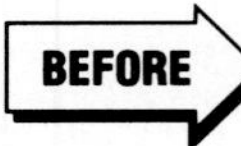

Analyze the situation. (12 computer games are in 2 piles; one pile has 2 extra games.)
▶ **Explain why finding 12 − 2 does not answer the question.** (12 − 2 = 10; 10 games in one pile and 2 in another does not fit the situation.)

▶ **Explain how the guess of 4 fits with other data.** (If Joe had 4 borrowed games, he would have 4 + 2 games of his own.)
▶ **Analyze how a wrong guess can lead to a better one.** (4 was too small; increase the next guess.)

▶ **Evaluate the correct answer.** (The guess of 5 borrowed games means 5 + 2 = 7 owned games; 5 + 7 = 12, so the guess checks.)
▶ **Explain how this strategy uses errors to lead to solutions.** (if wrong, adjust next guess)

2. CHECK UNDERSTANDING

TRY IT OUT

▶ **Analyze the table.** (It has a column for each game; guess, then use the relationship between prices to check your guess and fill in the table.)

ERROR ALERT Failing to use the given relationship between addends to check each guess.

Problem Solving
Guess and Check

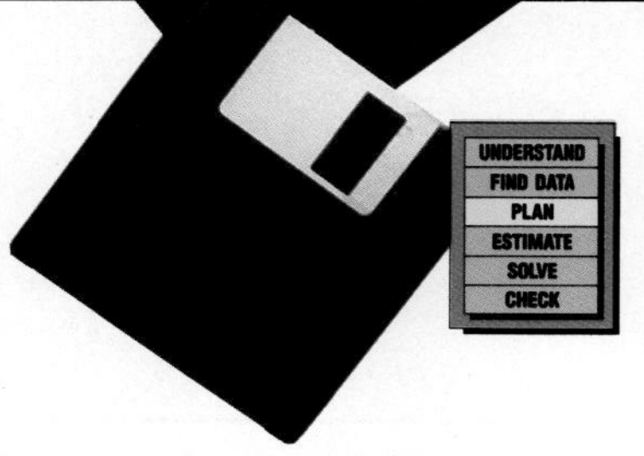

LEARN ABOUT IT

For some problems, you cannot just add or subtract to find the answer. You can sometimes use a strategy called **Guess and Check**.

Joe divided 12 computer games into two piles: games he owns and games he has borrowed. He owns 2 more games than he has borrowed. How many are in the pile of borrowed games?

I'll guess he borrowed 4. That means he owns 6. My guess is too small.

Guess: Borrowed 4
Check: Owned 4 + 2 = 6
Total 4 + 6 = 10

I'll guess again. This time I'll guess a higher number. It checks! My guess is right.

Guess: Borrowed 5
Check: Owned 5 + 2 = 7
Total 5 + 7 = 12

There were 5 games in the pile of borrowed games.

TRY IT OUT

Read the problem and finish the solution.

Jill bought 2 used computer games from Terry. Together the games cost $24. *Ghost Hunt* cost $4 more than *Home Run*. How much did *Home Run* cost? $10

- Which game cost more? Ghost Hunt
- How much did the games cost all together? $24

Copy and use this table to help.

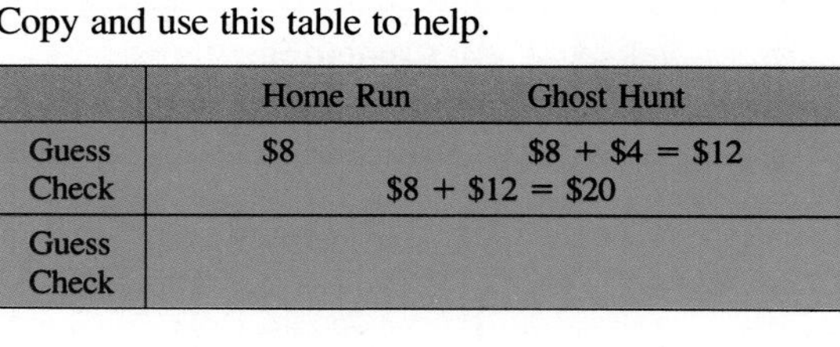

	Home Run	Ghost Hunt
Guess Check	$8 $8 + $12 = $20	$8 + $4 = $12
Guess Check		

106

TEACHING OPTIONS

RETEACHING TIPS Have students use play money to represent game prices, adjusting the two piles based on their guesses. The piles must be $4 apart and have a total of $24. Assign Reteaching Supplement 40.

COMPUTER **Building Perspective, Sunburst Communications, Copyright 1986** For all students (best played in pairs). Students determine where colored buildings are in a 3 × 3 array after looking at 4 side views. First they guess, then check answers. It requires 10-15 min.

PRACTICE

Guess and check to help you solve each problem.

1. Tena and Joan played on the computer for 20 minutes. Tena played 5 minutes longer than Joan. How long did Tena play? 12½ minutes

2. Itaro invited his friends to play computer games for his birthday. He invited 10 friends in all. There were 2 more boys than girls. How many girls were there? 4 girls

MIXED PRACTICE

Solve. Choose a strategy from the list or use other strategies that you know.

Some Strategies
Act It Out
Use Objects
Choose an Operation
Draw a Picture
Make an Organized List
Guess and Check

3. Lisa played the computer game *Adventures of Bo* for 30 minutes. She had 300 seconds to find the way out of the haunted castle. She used up 158 seconds. How many seconds did she have left? 142 seconds

4. It took Jeff 14 weeks to win *Crystal Search* and *Triple Dragon*. It took him 4 weeks longer to win *Triple Dragon* than *Crystal Search*. How long did he take to win *Crystal Search*? 5 weeks

5. Mike has 3 computer games: *Racer*, *Triple Dragon*, and *Baseball Player*. Yesterday he had time to play 2 games. List the choices. How many different choices of 2 games did he have? See Additional Answers.

6. Use the survey from Super Games Magazine. How many more votes did *Land of Zando* get than *Triple Dragon*? 45 votes

7. Use the survey from Super Games Magazine below. Estimate the total number of votes for the two most popular games. 690 votes

Super Games Magazine Survey
"What is your favorite game?"

Game	Votes
Baseball Player	359
Land of Zando	328
Triple Dragon	283
Safari Sisters	228
Crystal Search	192

3. Practice and Apply

Basic	2-7
Average	1-7
Extended	1-7

Additional Answers and Sample Solutions: See p. T79.

PRACTICE

Find the total that is known in each situation. (Problem 1: 20 minutes of computer-playing time; Problem 2: 10 friends in all)

MIXED PRACTICE

▶ **Which problem can you solve using Guess and Check.** (Problem 4)
▶ **What strategy makes sense in Problem 3? Explain your reasoning.** (Choose an Operation because you need to find a difference)
▶ **Compare Problems 3 and 6.** (Both use subtraction as a solution method.)
▶ **Analyze the situation in Problem 5 to determine a solution strategy.** (Mike can play 2 computer games; Make an Organized List to find the pairs and count choices.)
▶ **Identify extra data in Problem 7.** (The table has 5 games; you only need the most popular 2.)

4-9

Close and Assess

SHOW WHAT YOU KNOW

Have students use play money to make two piles that total $15. Have them give one pile $3 more than the other. ($6, $9)

Quick Quiz

The grocery bag ripped on Missy's way to the kitchen. She found 6 more broken eggs than whole eggs in the dozen she had just bought. How many eggs cracked? (9)

CHAPTER 4

DATA COLLECTION AND ANALYSIS

GROUP DECISION MAKING

OBJECTIVE To collect, organize, and present data

Classifying fingerprints into categories sharpens students' visual-discrimination and analytical skills. Tell students that although fingerprints can be sorted into general categories, no 2 fingers have identical marks.

COLLECTING DATA

► **Identify the part of the thumb pad that has the fingerprint.** (between the top of the thumb and the first joint)
► **Analyze the arch, circle, and loop fingerprint types to compare their differences.** (Possible answer: In an arch, lines cross the pad from side to side; lines in a circle form a spiral in the center of the pad; lines of a loop enter and leave on the same side.)
► **Explain a way to judge a print that may combine types.** (Possible answer: 2 or 3 people can examine the print, then agree on the closest type.)
► **Evaluate the kind of data contained in the sample table on page 109.** (names of people whose thumb print types are the same or different)

Data Collection and Analysis

Group Decision Making

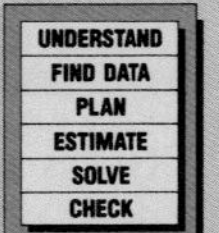

Doing a Survey
Group Skill:
Listen to Others

Look at the finger pads of the members of your group. Most fingerprints are composed of one or more of the three main types.

Look at the thumb pads of your group. Predict whether the thumb prints of both hands are the same type or different types for most people. Conduct an investigation to find out if your prediction was correct.

TEACHING OPTIONS

COOPERATIVE LEARNING

Grouping Suggestions:
cooperative learning groups of 4, 6, or 8
Within groups, have students work in pairs to verify fingerprint types. As some prints may not fit any of the 3 main categories, groups should discuss how to listen to and respect each other's judgments. Before data collection begins, have students design a table on which to record findings. Groups can divide the class list for investigation assignments. Each pair could examine 5-8 people, themselves included, to reach a group total of at least 20.

Collecting Data

1. Look at both thumb pads of at least 20 people. Record whether or not the thumb prints are the same type or different. Make a table.

Thumb Prints	
Same	Different
Angelita Gabriel Tony Penny Gina	Jerry Patrick

Organizing Data

2. Make a bar graph using the data in your table.

Title

Number of People

6
4
2
0

same ———

3. Did you label and give a title to your graph?

Presenting Your Analysis

4. Write a summary of your findings. Compare your findings with those of other groups.
5. Write at least two other questions you could ask about fingerprints.
6. Predict what you would discover if you looked at the thumb pads of 20 more people.

EXTENSION Ask students to formulate questions about fingerprints that arose during the survey or that they are just curious about. Encourage students to use encyclopedias and science books to answer their own questions and to research other fingerprint types. If possible, invite a local police officer to talk to the class about how fingerprint files are used in finding missing persons and in investigating crimes.

ORGANIZING DATA

▶ **Explain how your group can combine results to reach a group total.** (Possible method: 1 student can tally findings as another verifies that no person is listed twice.)
▶ **Compare the data to your prediction.** (Comparisons may vary.)
▶ **Compare the sample bar graph on page 109 to your findings to determine if your group should use a different number scale.** (Answers may vary.)

PRESENTING YOUR ANALYSIS

▶ **Develop a group plan for summarizing the results of your survey in a written report.** (Plans may vary. Encourage groups to devise a cooperative plan that involves every group member. For example, 1 pair can write a summary of the group's overall findings. Another pair can summarize the investigative process, discussing how the data was collected. Yet another pair can write a comparison of the 3 main print types and and discuss any fingerprints they examined that were difficult to classify.)

CHAPTER 4

WRAP UP

INTRODUCTION The Wrap Up provides activities emphasizing math language and thinking skills for the chapter and a project that integrates those skills with other math strands.

USING PAGE 110

What Are Your Chances? Have students complete this section independently. When they finish, have volunteers restate each sentence in their own words to reflect the probability they chose.

Sometimes, Always, Never ► **Explain a way to evaluate the statements in Exercises 9 to 11.** (Examine pictographs and bar graphs you have used.)
► **Analyze Exercise 12 for two phrases that contradict.** (*fair game; better chance*)

Project Have students work in small cooperative learning groups to formulate a probability experiment. Provide TA 11 (Blank Spinners).
► **Explain a way to keep track of the number of times you try the experiment.** (tally spins)
► **Predict what would happen if you did the experiment 100 times.** (You might get more accurate results.)
► **Decide on a suitable graph to use for your results.** (Possible answers: bar graph; pictograph)
Have students display their graphs on a math bulletin board. Compare results among groups to draw generalizations.

WRAP UP

What Are Your Chances?

Each sentence contains an expression associated with probability. Decide whether the expression means that the situation has a high, low, or even chance of happening.

1. There is little chance of snow tonight. **low**
2. Eve and Ruth are likely to tie. **even**
3. All experts favor the Central Division team. **high**
4. There is only a slim chance that she will come. **low**
5. Chances are great that he will get lost. **high**
6. I have a 50-50 chance of being picked. **even**
7. Mia has a clear advantage over Paco. **high**
8. Which racer is better? It's a toss-up! **even**

Sometimes, Always, Never

Which word should go in the blank, sometimes, always, or never? Explain your choices. **Explanations may vary.**

9. Pictograph symbols __?__ stand for even numbers. **sometimes**
10. Bar graphs __?__ help you compare data. **always**
11. A bar graph should __?__ use a scale that helps show information clearly. **always**
12. A fair game __?__ gives you a better chance than your opponent to win. **never**

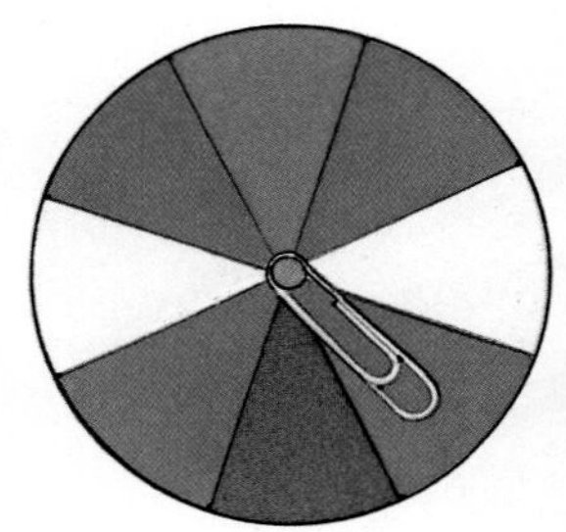

Project

Use a spinner like this one to figure out a probability experiment. Predict what might happen and then do the experiment at least 30 times. Record your results and present them in a graph. **Answers will vary.**

110

TEACHING OPTIONS

ENRICHMENT Have students use the class roster to create a probability experiment. They plan questions for outcomes, such as: Which is more likely, choosing a boy or a girl from the class list? Other questions could relate to choosing first and last names that start with the same letter or choosing 1-syllable first names. Students can write each name on an index card or slip of paper. Then they predict what might happen, experiment at least 50 times, tally the results, and share a summary of the results with the class.

CHAPTER REVIEW/TEST

Part 1 Understanding

1. Pictographs present data by using ?. **pictures**
2. Explain what it means when a game is fair. **See Additional Answers.**
3. stands for 300 ladders. Draw what a pictograph might show for 150 ladders. **Answers may vary.**
4. Describe a reasonable scale to use on a bar graph of the ages of people in your family. **Answers will vary.**

Part 2 Skills

Use the line graph to answer these questions.

5. About how many tickets were sold on Friday? **400 tickets**
6. On what day were over 800 movie tickets sold? **Saturday**
7. Estimate the total number of tickets sold. **2,400 tickets**

Use the bar graph to answer these questions.

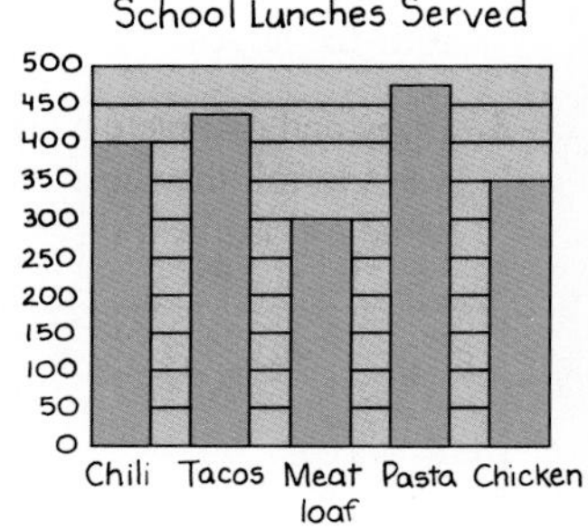

8. What does the scale tell? **See Additional Answers.**
9. Which lunch was the most popular? **pasta**
10. Which food was served in about 350 lunches? **chicken**
11. How many more taco lunches were served than chili lunches? **about 40**
12. Which lunch was the least popular? **meat loaf**

Part 3 Applications

13. Amy's and Beth's ages total 18 years. Beth is 4 years older than Amy. How old is each girl? **Amy, 7 years; Beth, 11 years**
14. **Challenge** Li flips two dimes at once. Is the probability of getting two heads the same as that of getting one head and one tail? Explain. **See Additional Answers.**

111

CHAPTER REVIEW/TEST

INTRODUCTION The Review/Test is provided to review and evaluate the skills and concepts presented in Chapter 4.

USING PAGE 111
If you prefer to use this page for review, you may want to use the **Multiple-Choice Posttest** (pages 15-16) or the **Free-Response Posttest** (pages 15-16) to evaluate mastery of chapter objectives.

ITEM ANALYSIS The table below correlates the Chapter Review/Test items with the lesson objectives for the chapter.

Items	Objectives
1	4-1, 4-3
2	4-7
3	4-1, 4-3
4	4-2
5-7	4-4
8-12	4-2
13	4-9
14	4-8

Additional Answers: See p. T79.

INFORMAL ASSESSMENT

Using Manipulatives Have students use counters to show how to solve this problem, explaining their strategy: *Zeke and Zack have 13 cats. Zeke has 3 more cats than Zack. How many cats does each person have?* (Zeke has 8, Zack has 5; check students' models.)

Communication *Write a paragraph explaining how to select a reasonable scale for a bar or line graph.* (Answers will vary. Check students' writing.)

Critical Thinking *If a game spinner has 6 red and 3 blue same-sized sections, what would be a fair point system?* (Possible answer: Make red worth 1 point and blue worth 2 points.)

CHAPTER 4

ENRICHMENT

INTRODUCTION Predicting possible outcomes before performing an experiment sharpens students' ability to analyze and plan.

USING PAGE 112
This Enrichment page is provided for all students. You may wish to use it after the students have completed the Chapter Review/Test on page 111.
Have students work in pairs or in small groups to do the RATS! experiment in the Enrichment lesson. Students will need 2 number cubes (TA 2).

▶ **Explain how the answer to Exercise 1 will help you list possible outcomes.** (If you can determine the greatest and the smallest possible sums, you will be able to list all the possibilities in between.)

▶ **Justify listing all the possible outcomes before making any predictions.** (You can see whether all sums have an equal chance of appearing; if not, you will be better able to predict which sums are more or less likely to appear.) Have the teams complete the experiment on their own. Ask each team to summarize its findings in a paragraph.

EXTENSION Have students consider how probabilities would change if they rolled 3 number cubes at once, then have them try this variation of RATS! Teams should first adjust the table to account for the changes in possible outcomes, then experiment 50 times. Conclude by having students compare the two versions of RATS!

Additional Answers: See p. T79.

ENRICHMENT
Listing Possible Outcomes

RATS! is a probability experiment. To do the experiment, you will need two number cubes labeled with the numbers 0 through 5. The letters in RATS stand for Roll, Add, and Tally the Sums.

Roll: [3] [1]

Add: 3 + 1 = 4

Tally the Sum

Sum	Tally	Total
0		
1		
2		
3		
4		

Before you do RATS!, answer these questions to learn more about the possible sums you could roll.

1. What is the smallest sum you could roll? the largest? **0, 10**
2. Can you roll a sum in more than one way? Give an example. **yes; samples will vary**
3. Copy and complete a table to list all the possible ways to roll the sums. Consider the roll [1] [3] the same roll as the roll [3] [1]. **See Additional Answers.**

Sum	Ways to Roll the Sum	Total Number of Ways to Roll the Sum
0	[0] [0]	1
1	[1] [0]	1
2	[1] [1] [2] [0]	2

4. When you do RATS!, which three sums do you predict will appear most often? least often? Explain your thinking. **See Additional Answers.**
5. Now do RATS! 50 times. Tally your results in a table like the one on this page. Tell how the outcome compares with your predictions. **Answers will vary.**

112

CUMULATIVE REVIEW

1. Which equation is in a fact family with 7 + 2 = 9?

   A 6 + 3 = 9 B 7 + 3 = 10
   (C) 9 − 7 = 2 D 9 − 9 = 0

2. Compensate to find the sum of 11 + 8.

   (A) 19 B 20
   C 18 D 3

3. Which property tells you that 5 + 4 equals 4 + 5?

   (A) order B grouping
   C zero D compensation

4. In the number 4,307, which digit is in the thousands place?

   A 0 (B) 4
   C 3 D 7

5. Which number is greater than 802,573?

   A 802,537 B 801,999
   C 802,568 (D) 802,576

6. Which number is between 6,850 and 7,200?

   A 6,720 B 6,820
   (C) 7,159 D 7,210

7. What is $45.45 rounded to the nearest dollar?

   A $40.00 (B) $45.00
   C $50.00 D $46.00

8. What is 58,620 rounded to the nearest thousand?

   (A) 59,000 B 58,600
   C 58,000 D 60,000

9. Which number has a 5 in the ten millions place?

   A 531,726,894 B 405,394,662
   C 123,456,789 (D) 952,736,104

10. You pay for a $7.75 tie with $10.00. What is your change?

    A $2.75 B $3.75
    C $3.25 (D) $2.25

11. 537 − 288

    A 825 B 351
    (C) 249 D 251

12. 786 + 409

    A 1,185 (B) 1,195
    C 1,095 D 377

113

CUMULATIVE REVIEW

INTRODUCTION The purpose of this Cumulative Review is to maintain previously taught skills and concepts. The emphasis in this Cumulative Review is on addition and subtraction concepts and basic facts, Chapter 1; on place value and money, Chapter 2; and on adding and subtracting whole numbers, Chapter 3.

ITEM ANALYSIS The table below correlates the Cumulative Review items with the lesson objectives.

Items	Objectives
1	1-3
2	1-7
3	1-2
4	2-1
5, 6	2-3
7	2-6
8	2-7
9	2-8
10	2-9
11	3-9
12	3-4

Chapter Management

OVERVIEW

Lesson	Pages	Objectives	Subject Integration	Strand Integration
Chapter Opener	114-115	To introduce chapter 5	language arts-Tall Tales	critical thinking
Problem Solving:Understanding Multiplication	116-117	5-1 To understand the operation of multiplication	language arts-Tall Tales	problem solving
Multiplication Properties	118-119	5-2 To find products when 0 or 1 is a factor	language arts-Paul Bunyan	mathematical reasoning
Factors of 2 and 5	120-121	5-3 To find products when 2 or 5 is a factor	fine arts-patterns	calculators
A Factor of 9	122-123	5-4 To find products when 9 is a factor	science-flower seeds	consumer math
Factors of 3 and 4	124-125	5-5 To find products when 3 or 4 is a factor	social studies-consumer packaging	mental math
Exploring Algebra/Midchapter Review/Quiz	126-127	5-6 To explore algebra by using a variable that represents only 1 number	fine arts-art room	problem solving
Problem Solving: Understanding the Question	128-129	5-7 To understand the question in a problem	health/fitness-dental care	measurement: time
Mental Math: More Breaking Apart Numbers	130-131	5-8 To break apart numbers to find multiplication facts	language arts-Tall Tales Booklet	mental math
The Last Six Facts	132-133	5-9 To find 6×6, 7×7, 8×8, 6×7, 6×8, and 7×8	language arts-tall tale characters	mathematical reasoning
Multiples	134-135	5-10 To identify and produce multiples of a number	language arts-Paul Bunyan	calculators
Problem Solving: Make a Table	136-137	5-11 To solve problems using the strategy Make a Table	social studies-Bubble Festival	problem solving
Applied Problem Solving: Group Decision Making	138-139	5-12 To analyze, organize, and make decisions using relevant data	social studies-school Round-Up	problem solving

MATHEMATICAL BACKGROUND

Multiplication
In Lesson 5-1, students are helped to understand the concept of multiplication using counters and the idea of repeated addition. Students learn they can multiply when combining same-size groups. In Lesson 5-2, they learn three multiplication properties: Order Property, One Property, and Zero Property. Throughout the chapter, they practice learning basic facts.

Mental Math
Students learn to break apart factors to create easier problems they can solve mentally.

Problem Solving
Students use the strategy Make a Table to solve problems. They focus on understanding the question in Lesson 5-7.

TIPS FROM TEACHERS

To help students remember multiplication by zero, give each student 4 cups and 12 pieces of cereal. Students put 3 pieces of cereal in each cup, then write a multiplication statement ($4 \times 3 = 12$). *They eat one piece from each cup, then write a new statement* ($4 \times 2 = 8$). *Repeat this process until students find the meaning of* $4 \times 0 = 0$.

Deborah Glynn
Largo C & I Elementary School
Largo, FL

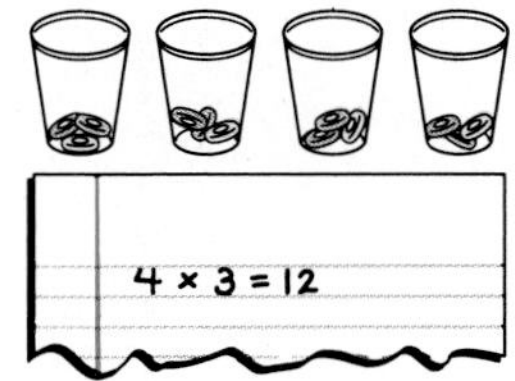

ASSESSMENT

Pretest — Chapter 5, page 1

Multiple-Choice Format

Name

1. Donna had 3 bowls of apples. There were 5 apples in each bowl. How many apples did she have altogether? Choose the equation that records the action.
Think:
a. 3 × 5 = 15 b. 3 + 5 = 8 c. 5 - 3 = 2 — 1. a

2. Find 8 × 0.
a. 8 b. 80 c. 0 d. 800 — 2. c

3. Find 9 × 1.
a. 8 b. 9 c. 10 d. 1 — 3. b

4. Find 5 × 2.
a. 7 b. 10 c. 12 d. 3 — 4. b

5. Find 9 × 8.
a. 63 b. 72 c. 17 d. 1 — 5. b

6. Find 4 × 7.
a. 28 b. 32 c. 11 d. 3 — 6. a

7. Find 8 × 4.
a. 4 b. 12 c. 32 d. 2 — 7. a

8. Each shape holds a place for just one number. Choose the number that goes in the triangle.
■ × ■ = 16
▲ + ■ = 11
a. 4 b. 5 c. 6 d. 7 — 8. d

MCT 4 17

Pretest — Chapter 5, page 2

Multiple-Choice Format

Name

9. Choose the question which asks the same thing as the one in the problem. Jim caught 47 fish. Jack caught 38 fish. How many more fish did Jim catch than Jack?
a. What is the difference in the number of fish?
b. How many fish did they catch altogether?
c. How many fish did Jack catch? — 9. a

10. Find 7 × 8. Break apart the first factor.
a. 56 b. 16 c. 40 d. 15 — 10. a

11. Find 8 × 8.
a. 64 b. 56 c. 88 d. 48 — 11. a

12. Find 6 × 7.
a. 48 b. 13 c. 56 d. 42 — 12. d

13. Choose the number that replaces ■ in this table.

Multiples of 8

x	0	1	2	3	4	5
8	0	8	16	24	32	■

a. 35 b. 45 c. 60 d. 40 — 13. d

14. Use the table to solve the problem.

tickets	5	10	15		
price	$4	$8	$12		

Five tickets cost $4. How much will it cost to buy tickets for a class of 25 students?
a. $20 b. $24 c. $16 d. $25 — 14. a

18 MCT 4

Posttest — Chapter 5, page 1

Multiple-Choice Format

Name

1. The waitress served 4 plates of eggs. There were 3 eggs on each plate. How many eggs were there in all? Choose the equation that shows the action.
Think:
a. 4 + 3 = 7 b. 4 - 3 = 1 c. 4 × 3 = 12 — 1. c

2. Find 9 × 0.
a. 9 b. 90 c. 0 d. 900 — 2. c

3. Find 3 × 1.
a. 2 b. 3 c. 4 d. 5 — 3. b

4. Find 7 × 5.
a. 25 b. 12 c. 30 d. 35 — 4. d

5. Find 9 × 7.
a. 16 b. 2 c. 63 d. 56 — 5. c

6. Find 3 × 8.
a. 21 b. 24 c. 11 d. 18 — 6. b

7. Find 4 × 4.
a. 8 b. 16 c. 12 d. 44 — 7. b

8. Each shape holds a place for just one number. Choose the number that goes in the triangle.
■ × ■ = 9
▲ + ■ = 8
a. 6 b. 5 c. 4 d. 3 — 8. b

MCT 4 19

Posttest — Chapter 5, page 2

Multiple-Choice Format

Name

9. Choose the question which asks the same thing as the one in the problem. David bought 7 boxes of crayons. Each box had 8 crayons. How many crayons did he buy?
a. What is the total number of boxes?
b. What is the total number of crayons?
c. How many crayons are in a box? — 9. b

10. Find 7 × 6. Break apart the first factor.
a. 42 b. 30 c. 12 d. 13 — 10. a

11. Find 6 × 6.
a. 36 b. 18 c. 12 d. 0 — 11. a

12. Find 7 × 8.
a. 1 b. 15 c. 64 d. 56 — 12. d

13. Choose the number that replaces ■ in this table.

Multiples of 9

x	0	1	2	3	4	5
9	0	9	18	27	■	45

a. 28 b. 32 c. 36 d. 14 — 13. c

14. Use the table to solve the problem.

tickets	9	18	27		
price	$4	$8	$12		

Nine tickets cost $4. How much will it cost to buy tickets for a class of 45 students?
a. $36 b. $20 c. $16 d. $45 — 14. b

20 MCT 4

ITEM ANALYSIS

Items	Objectives
1	5-1
2, 3	5-2
4	5-3
5	5-4
6, 7	5-5
8	5-6
9	5-7
10	5-8
11-12	5-9
13	5-10
14	5-11

Note: The item analysis is the same for all pretests and posttests for this chapter.

ALSO AVAILABLE

- **Free Response Tests**
- **Alternative Tests**
- **Thinking Strategies**
- **Concrete Materials**

Optional Chapter Activities

PROJECT AND BULLETIN BOARD

After students have completed Lesson 10, challenge them to make "Factor Pine Trees" to display on a bulletin board. Pair students and assign each pair a different multiple of a number, such as 54 or 81. Partners break apart their number into factors, then break apart each factor. For example, 54 can be broken into 6 × 9, then 6 can be broken into 2 × 3 and 9 can be broken into 3 × 3. You may wish to have students display the factors on green tree shapes cut from construction paper and draw pine cones around each number.

COOPERATIVE LEARNING

Divide the class into groups of three or four. Identify the group skill: encourage and respect others. Give each group several multiplication facts with one factor missing. Also give the group some counters or other small objects, which they can use to help them find and/or verify their answers. Tell the group that they are to find the missing factors and that they should allow everyone in the group to participate. Have the group appoint one student to record preliminary answers, which can then be verified by another student using the counters. A third student can write the completed multiplication facts.

You will find grouping suggestions and cooperative learning activities in most lessons throughout this chapter.

LITERATURE

Sloan, Sara. *The Brown Bag Cookbook: Nutritious Portable Lunches for Kids and Grownups.* Charlotte, Vermont: Williamson Publishing, 1984.

This cookbook contains many appetizing and healthy lunches that can easily be prepared by children. Children could work in small groups. Each group could select a menu. They then could multiply the number of ingredients needed to feed their group.

Blume, Judy. *Tales of a Fourth Grade Nothing.* New York: Dell Publishing, 1972.

Levy, Elizabeth. *Something Queer at the Lemonade Stand.* New York: Dell Young Yearling Book, 1982.

English as a Second Language

This activity will help students understand the concept of multiplication and memorize multiplication facts.

Prepare two-inch wide strips of oaktag. Provide each student with nine oaktag strips and designate one of the numbers from one to nine per strip. Students punch out nine groups of holes for the number that belongs to each strip. For example, the strip for number three would have nine groups of three holes to show all the factors for three. Children write a multiplication problem above each group of holes that shows the cumulative amount of holes and groups to that point. Then they write the product under each group of holes.

In pairs, students practice reciting the multiplication facts without looking at the strips. If they miss a product, they look at the blank side of the strip and recount the holes.

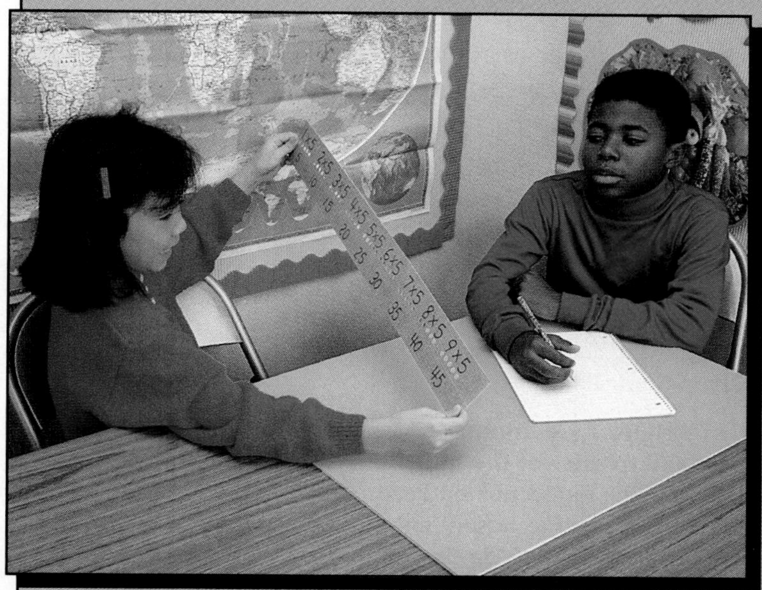

Gifted

Have students play the "Math-O" number game in groups of four. Each student creates a game card. The card should be a square with a 5-by-5 array of 25 smaller squares. In each of the 25 squares on each game card, students randomly place any of the following numbers: 4, 6, 8, 9, 10, 12, 14, 15, 16, 18, 20, 21, 24, 25, 27, 28, 30, 32, 35, 36, 40, 42, 45, 48, 49, 54, 56, 63, 64, 72, or 81. On a blank spinner (TA 11), write the numbers 2, 3, 4, 5, 6, 7, 8, and 9. Have each player either cut out 25 circles for markers or use 25 buttons or pennies.

Each player, in turn, spins the spinner twice and announces the numbers that come up to be used as factors. All players must then compute the product mentally and place a marker on that game-card number if it is on their game card. The first player to cover five squares in a horizontal, vertical, or diagonal row, and who announces "Math-O", wins the round.

To play another round, students create a new board or trade their board for a classmate's.

Students at Risk

Students with memory or language deficits typically have difficulty learning the basic multiplication facts. Although they cannot retrieve isolated facts, some students can use logical thinking skills to solve them by using related or easier facts. The following strategies may be helpful.

Clock Math Students with proficiency at telling time can use the numbers on a clock face to learn the 5 facts. They skip count by fives around the clock face, stopping at a target multiple. To find factors of 6, students may again use the clock face. They count by fives to a target multiple, then add on 1 for each number. So, to find 6 × 7, students count by fives to 35, then count on 1 more for each of the 7 numbers: 36, 37, 38, 39, 40, 41, 42. They may use a related strategy for the 4 facts: count by fives to a target multiple, then count back 1 for each number.

Skip Counting Rhythms Some students can learn an entire table of a given factor as a rhythmic or melodic skip counting pattern. They "play back" the pattern to skip count to a target multiple to solve any basic fact in that table.

You may also use the Reteaching Supplements and the specific Reteaching Tips from each lesson in this chapter.

INTRODUCING THE CHAPTER

SUBJECT INTEGRATION The photograph of cowhands on a cattle drive represents the chapter theme of American folklore. Various lessons incorporate references to wild frontier characters and to legendary tall-tale heroes to provide data for students to use with basic multiplication facts.

USING DATA The Language Arts Data Bank on page 476 of the Student Edition is called Tall Facts from American Tall Tales. It provides outrageous data in sentence form about 4 American tall-tale characters: Pecos Bill, Paul Bunyan, Joe Magarac, and Alfred Bulltop Stormalong.

QUESTION 1 ▶ **Identify the data you need to answer the question.** (Read through the section on Pecos Bill to find that he had to lasso 9 miles of the Rio Grande River each day.)
▶ **Explain how to find how many miles of river Pecos Bill lassoed in 3 days.** (Multiply 3 × 9 or add 9 + 9 + 9.)
Student Edition answer: 27 miles

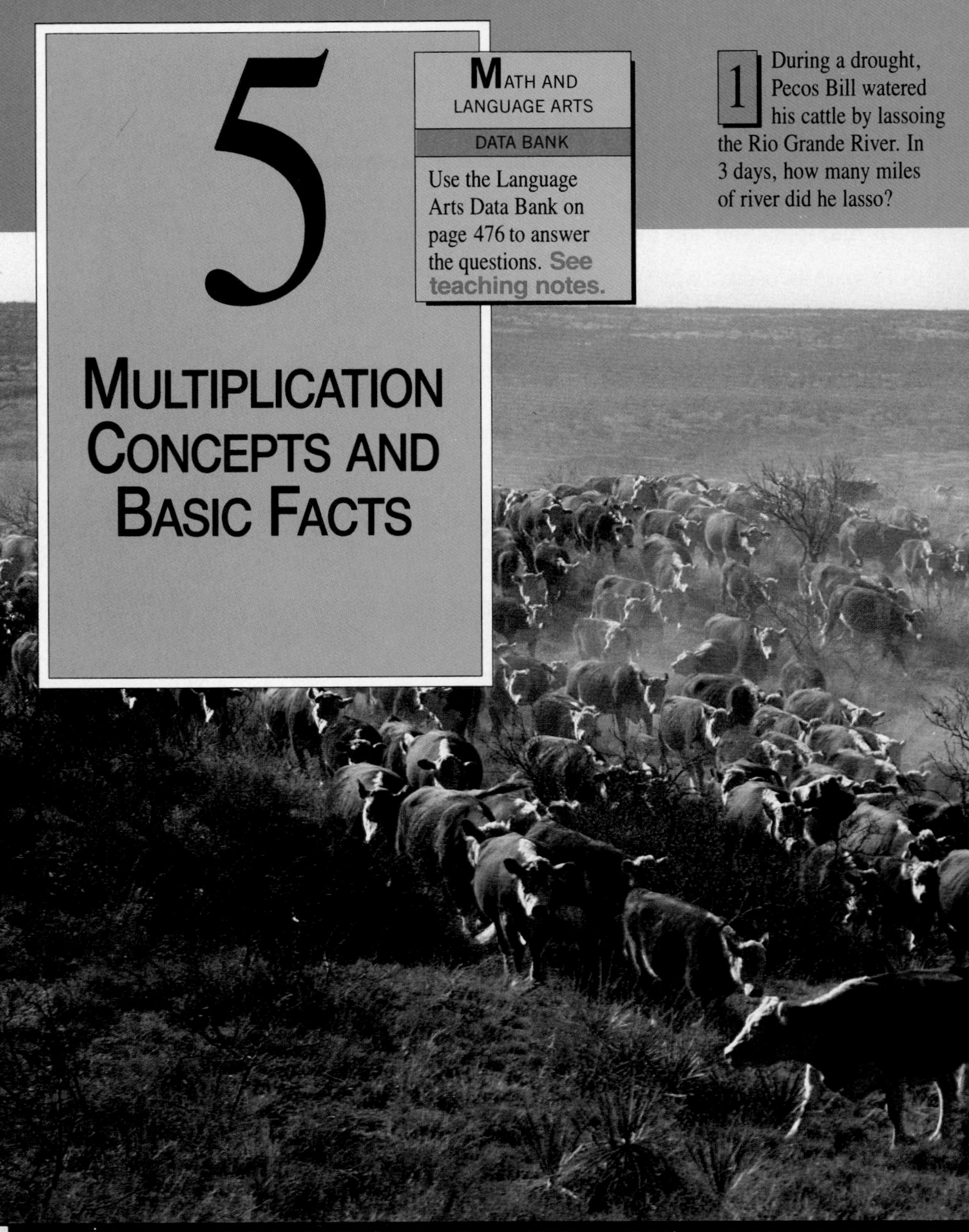

5 MULTIPLICATION CONCEPTS AND BASIC FACTS

MATH AND LANGUAGE ARTS

DATA BANK

Use the Language Arts Data Bank on page 476 to answer the questions. See teaching notes.

1 During a drought, Pecos Bill watered his cattle by lassoing the Rio Grande River. In 3 days, how many miles of river did he lasso?

TEACHING OPTIONS

LANGUAGE DEVELOPMENT
Write the phrase **count by twos** on the chalkboard and have students explain what it means. (Possible answer: Instead of saying every number when you count, you say only every other number.) Have students count by twos to 20, starting at 0. Then start again with 1 to 21. (2, 4, 6, 8, 10 . . . 20; 1, 3, 5, 7, 9 . . . 21) Ask students to count by any other numbers they can. (Answers will vary. Many students can count by fives, tens, and threes.)

2 Paul Bunyan made rubber boots from the legs of a Gumbaroo. How many rubber legs does a Gumbaroo have? Count by twos to find the answer.

3 How many steel rails did Joe Magarac make when he squeezed with both hands at once?

4 **Use Critical Thinking** Explain how you would find the number of days it took Alfred's Octopus to get untied.

115

QUESTION 2 ► **Identify and explain a fact about the Gumbaroo.** (It has 16 pairs of legs, which means 16 sets of 2 legs in each set.)
► **Decide on a sensible plan to find the total number of legs on a Gumbaroo.** (Count by twos 16 times or add 16 + 16.)
Student Edition answer: 32

QUESTION 3 ► **Analyze the question to determine what fact you must know before you can solve the problem.** (how many rails Joe Magarac could make when he squeezed 1 hand at a time)
Student Edition answer: 8

QUESTION 4 ► **Identify the tall fact related to the question.** (Alfred tied an octopus's arms in knots that took a month of Sundays to untie.)
► **Explain 3 different interpretations for the expression *a month of Sundays*. Evaluate each interpretation.** (Possible answers: a month that has only Sundays in it, which is impossible; a month in which every day is like a Sunday, which would mean as many Sundays as days in a month; the number of Sundays in 1 month, which means 1 per week, or 4 or 5, depending on when the month begins)
Student Edition answer: Answers will vary. The expression generally suggests an impossible amount of time but could be interpreted literally as about 30 days.

SUBJECT INTEGRATION PROJECT Have students make up tall-tale riddles that combine basic multiplication facts with Tall Facts in the Language Arts Data Bank. Begin by having students restate each tall fact as a number sentence, such as 1 lasso = 9 miles of river or 1 fathom = 6 feet. Have students create their riddles as they proceed through Chapter 5 so they can use a variety of factors. Conclude by having a tall-tale riddlethon in which groups ask and answer each other's riddles.

LESSON OPTIONS 5-1

Problem Solving: Understanding Multiplication

OBJECTIVE 5-1 To understand the operation of multiplication

PREBOOK ACTIVITIES

QUICK REVIEW

Add.

1. 2 + 2 + 2 + 2 + 2 (10)
2. 5 + 5 + 5 + 5 + 5 + 5 (30)
3. 7 + 7 + 7 + 7 (28)
4. 8 + 8 (16)
5. 3 + 3 + 3 + 3 (12)

PRIOR KNOWLEDGE

Have students suggest real-life examples of same-size groups that often are repeated. (Possible answers: 12 eggs in 1 dozen; 7 days in 1 week; 24 hours in 1 day; 4 quarters in 1 dollar) Based on 1 of the groups students suggest, ask them how to determine the total in 3 identical groups of that size. (Add the group size 3 times; multiply by 3.)

COMMUNICATION

Reading and Writing Math Write **multiplication** and **multiply** on the chalkboard and have students read them aloud. Then write 3 × 5 on the chalkboard as a volunteer reads it aloud. (three times five) Ask students to identify the word that means to multiply (*times*) and to describe the multiplication sign. (×) In their Math Journals, ask students to write a sentence that expresses a relationship between the 2 words, such as: Multiplication is the process of multiplying.

EXPLORE AND CONNECT

COOPERATIVE ACTIVITY

Grouping Suggestion: small groups

Lucy can balance 4 books on her head at once. Juggo the Great balances 3 times that many. How many books can Juggo balance?

TEACHING ACTIONS

Have students work together to model the situation, plan a solution, and discuss the results.

▶ **Explain the situation.** (Lucy can balance 4 books at once, but Juggo can balance 3 times that amount.)

▶ **Analyze the question.** (Find the total number of books Juggo balances.)

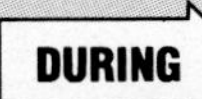

▶ **Explain what to do first.** (Possible answer: Show 1 group of 4 books.)

▶ **Compare 1 group with how many groups Juggo can balance.** (He balances 3 groups that size.)

▶ **Justify multiplying to find the answer.** (Repeat the size of the group 3 times to find the total.)

▶ **Decide how to write an equation that fits the question.** (3 × 4 = 12)

▶ **Draw a picture to evaluate whether your answer makes sense.** (Lucy balances 4 books, Juggo balances an amount 3 times greater; 3 × 4 = 12)

CONNECTIONS Use these anytime.

Problem of the Day

Scrambled Eggs Juggo the Great can now juggle 5 eggs at once. But he had to practice the trick 10 times before he could do it without dropping all the eggs. How many eggs did he break? (50)

Life Skills

Cooking A batch of Veronica's light and fluffy homemade pancakes uses 3 eggs. If Veronica plans to double the batch of pancakes, how many eggs will she need? (6)

Math Connection

Money A vending machine sells small bags of popcorn for 4 dimes. If Archie wants to buy 4 bags of popcorn, how many dimes does he need? How much money will he spend? (16; $1.60)

Classwork and Homework Supplements

Practice

Manipulatives 5-1

Name ______________________

Understanding Multiplication

Use counters to find the answer. Then write a multiplication equation that gives the same answer.

1. José bought 5 packages of juice. There were 3 boxes in each package.

   How many juice boxes did he buy? 15 boxes; 5 × 3 = 15

2. Amanda had 5 candles on her birthday cake. Her mother had 6 times as many on her cake.

   How many candles did her mother have? 30 candles; 6 × 5 = 30

3. Hoy had 4 coins in his collection. His brother Howin had 5 times as many coins.

   How many coins did Howin have? 20 coins; 5 × 4 = 20

4. Julie carried 2 bags of leaves to the trash cans. She did this 4 times.

   How many bags did she carry in all? 8 bags; 4 × 2 = 8

Building Thinking Skills

Family Math 5-1

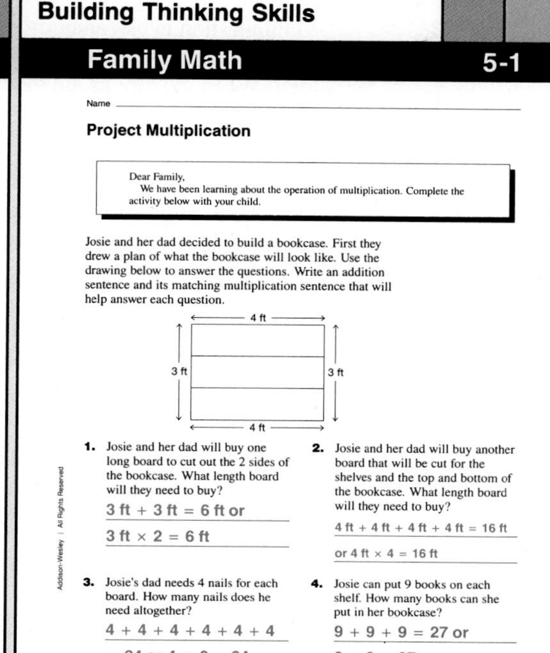

Name ______________________

Project Multiplication

Dear Family,
We have been learning about the operation of multiplication. Complete the activity below with your child.

Josie and her dad decided to build a bookcase. First they drew a plan of what the bookcase will look like. Use the drawing below to answer the questions. Write an addition sentence and its matching multiplication sentence that will help answer each question.

4 ft
3 ft
3 ft
4 ft

1. Josie and her dad will buy one long board to cut out the 2 sides of the bookcase. What length board will they need to buy?
   3 ft + 3 ft = 6 ft or
   3 ft × 2 = 6 ft

2. Josie and her dad will buy another board that will be cut for the shelves and the top and bottom of the bookcase. What length board will they need to buy?
   4 ft + 4 ft + 4 ft + 4 ft = 16 ft
   or 4 ft × 4 = 16 ft

3. Josie's dad needs 4 nails for each board. How many nails does he need altogether?
   4 + 4 + 4 + 4 + 4 + 4
   = 24 or 4 × 6 = 24

4. Josie can put 9 books on each shelf. How many books can she put in her bookcase?
   9 + 9 + 9 = 27 or
   3 × 9 = 27

Reteaching

Problem Solving 5-1

Name ______________________

Understanding Multiplication

Juanita has 4 flowers in each garden patch. How many flowers does she have in 3 patches?

4 + 4 + 4 = 12
3 × 4 = 12

When there are the same number of items in each group, you can multiply.

Use counters to find the answer. Then write a multiplication equation that gives the same answer. Order of factors will vary.

1. There are 2 frogs on one pad. How many frogs on 3 pads?
   3 × 2 = 6

2. There are 4 socks in each box. How many socks in 2 boxes?
   2 × 4 = 8

3. There are 3 birds in one cage. How many birds in 3 cages?
   3 × 3 = 9

4. There are 5 fingers on one hand. How many fingers on 2 hands?
   5 × 2 = 10

5. There are 9 muffins in each pan. How many muffins in 2 pans?
   2 × 9 = 18

6. There are 7 days in one week. How many days in 2 weeks?
   2 × 7 = 14

Challenges

Number Sense 5-1

Name ______________________

School Spirit

Rosita and Nate are in charge of setting up the items for the opening of the school spirit shop. There is a table for each group of items. Use counters to help you list all the different ways they could arrange each group of items in rows with the same number in each row.

There has to be more than one row.

1. There are 12 magnets with the school name.

Pine School

Rows	Number in Each Row
2	6
3	4
4	3
6	2

2. There are 16 bulldog mugs.

Rows	Number in Each Row
2	8
4	4
8	2

3. There are 18 bulldog sweatshirts.

Rows	Number in Each Row
2	9
3	6
6	3
9	2

4. There are 24 bulldog T-shirts.

Rows	Number in Each Row
2	12
3	8
4	6
6	4
8	3
12	2

Options for Individual Needs

Basic

Exercises 1-5
More Practice, p. 516, set A

Supplements
Reteaching 41 or
Practice 41

Average

Exercises 1-5
More Practice, p. 516, set A

Supplements
Practice 41
Challenges 41 or
Thinking Skills 41

Extended

Exercises 1-5

Supplements
Challenges 41
Thinking Skills 41

Other Resources:
Problem-Solving Experiences in Mathematics, Grade 4, Problems 32, 33
Math In Stride, Teacher Sourcebook, Grade 4, Activity 6A
Mathematics: A Way of Thinking, Lesson 5-1

LESSON PLAN 5-1

OBJECTIVE 5-1
To understand the operation of multiplication

Materials: counters

1. MOTIVATE AND TEACH

LEARN ABOUT IT

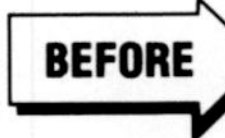

▶ **Explain how each multiplication equation relates to the action.** (Put together 3 groups of 6 for 3 × 6; repeat 4 groups of 3 for 4 × 3)

▶ **Compare putting together same-size groups to finding a number of times as many.** (In either case, you repeat same-size groups a certain number of times.)

▶ **Analyze each problem to find the size of 1 group.** (first: 6 pancakes; second: 3 pancakes)

▶ **Analyze each problem to identify the other factor.** (first: 3; second: 4)

▶ **Justify using multiplication instead of adding in these problems.** (Multiply if groups are the same size)

▶ **How do you find products when you know the factors?** (Make same-size groups; find the total.)

▶ **Explain how to verify your answer.** (Possible answers: Draw a Picture; Use Models; add)

2. CHECK UNDERSTANDING

TRY IT OUT

ERROR ALERT Making the wrong number of groups. Failing to form equal groups.

Problem Solving
Understanding Multiplication

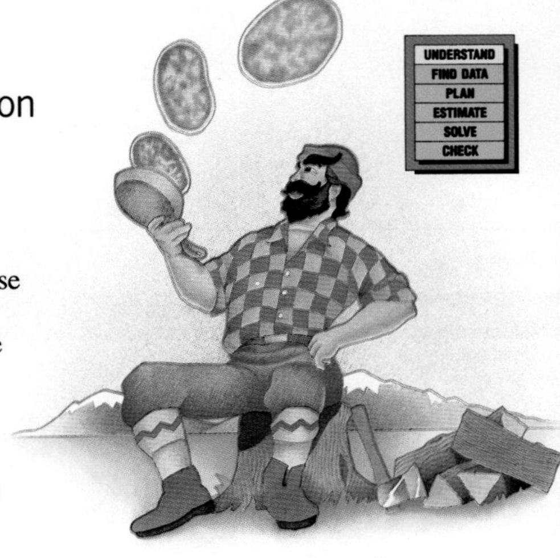

LEARN ABOUT IT

Multiplication is like addition because you put together groups to find the total. When the groups are the same size, you can multiply.

The actions below help you decide when to use multiplication. Show the actions with counters. Complete the equations.

Problem	Action	Operation
Paul Bunyan ate 6 pancakes in one bite. How many pancakes did he eat in 3 bites?	**Put Together Same-Size Groups** 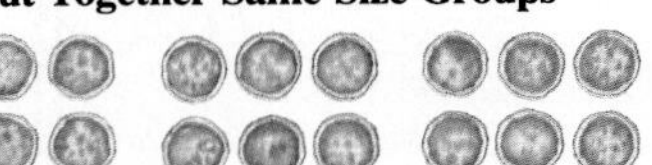	**Multiply** $3 \times 6 = ?$
Paul's friend could flip 3 bike tire-size pancakes in the air at one time. Paul could flip 4 times that many. How many could Paul flip?	**Find a Number of Times as Many** 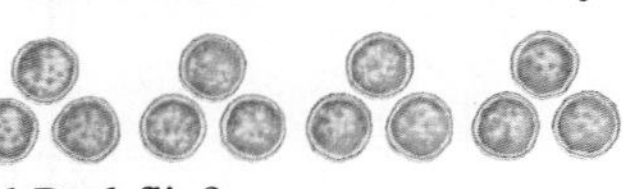	**Multiply** $4 \times 3 = ?$

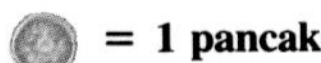 **= 1 pancake**

TRY IT OUT

Use counters to find the answer. Write an equation.

1. The lumberjacks used a griddle that could cook 9 large pancakes at once. Paul built a griddle that could cook 3 times as many tractor tire-size pancakes at once. How many pancakes could Paul cook at once? **27 pancakes; $3 \times 9 = 27$**

2. Paul had a plate so big that he could pile 6 of his giant pancakes on it. He used 3 plates piled full to start his breakfast. How many pancakes was that? **18 pancakes; $3 \times 6 = 18$**

TEACHING OPTIONS

RETEACHING TIPS Students use counters to show 1 group, explaining how it matches the situation. Then they identify how many groups are needed in all. As they make the necessary groups, have them check that each is the same size as the first group. Assign Reteaching Supplement 41.

ENRICHMENT Students look through magazines to find interesting pictures of a group of people, animals, or objects. Have them formulate 2 different story problems about the picture that use the 2 actions of multiplication. Display pictures and ask students to solve each other's problems.

PRACTICE

Use counters to find the answer. Then write a multiplication equation that gives the same answer.

1. Pecos Bill roped four cattle in each throw. He threw 3 times. How many cattle did he rope?
12 cattle; $3 \times 4 = 12$

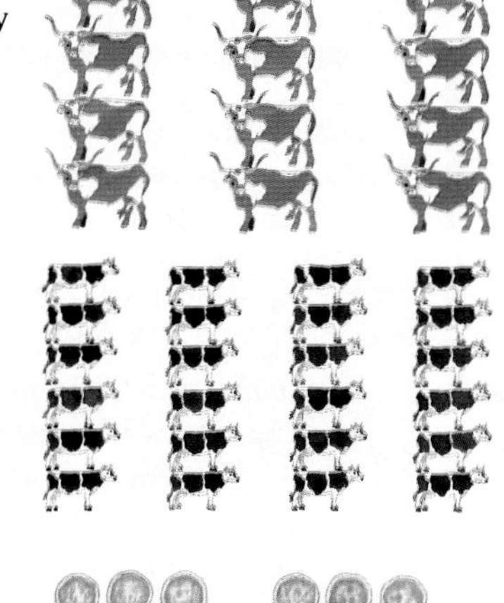

2. Pecos Bill could herd 6 cows at a time, just by looking hard at them. His dog, Norther, could herd 4 times as many. How many cows could Norther herd?
24 cows; $4 \times 6 = 24$

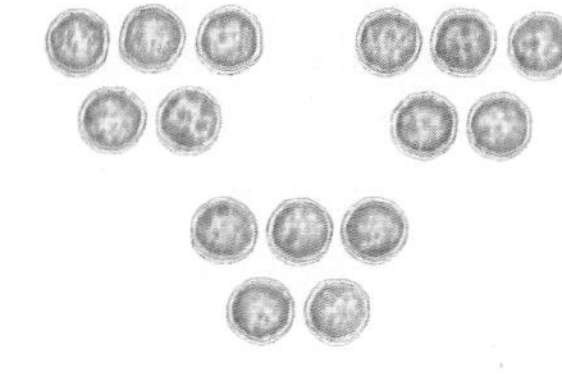

3. Pecos Bill's friend, Bean Hole, could make 5 pancakes fly into the air, turn over, and return to their exact places. Bill could do this with 3 times as many pancakes. How many pancakes could Bill make flip and return?
15 pancakes; $3 \times 5 = 15$

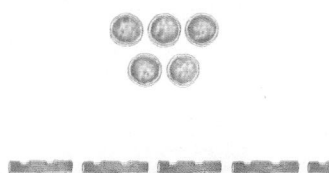

4. To build a fence from El Paso, Texas, to the Pacific Ocean, Bill bit off 4 fence posts at a time with his teeth. To begin, he took 5 bites and went to work. How many posts did he have to work with?
20 posts; $5 \times 4 = 20$

▶ WRITE YOUR OWN PROBLEM

5. Write two story problems that can be solved by multiplying. Use a different action in each. Answers will vary.

3. Practice and Apply

Basic	1-5
Average	1-5
Extended	1-5

PRACTICE

Identify the factors in Problem 1. (4, 3) *Explain a way to begin Problem 1.* (Show a group of 4 counters.) *Describe the group that repeats in Problem 2.* (6 cows) *How many times as many pancakes could Pecos Bill make, flip, and return in Problem 3?* (3 times as many) *For Problem 4, determine how many fence posts Pecos Bill could make in 1 bite.* (4)

WRITE YOUR OWN PROBLEM

▶ **Summarize the purpose of multiplying.** (to put together same-size groups; to find a number of times how many)

▶ **Compare the 2 actions.** (Possible answer: Putting together same-size groups is like adding; finding a number of times how many is like increasing something that many times.)

5-1

Close and Assess

SHOW WHAT YOU KNOW

Have students use counters to show how to multiply 4×4, 3×3, and 5×5. Ask them to give the products in equation form. (Check students' models; $4 \times 4 = 16$, $3 \times 3 = 9$, $5 \times 5 = 25$)

Quick Quiz

Write a multiplication equation for each picture.

1. XXXXXXXXX XXXXXXXXX

2. \\\\\\\\\\\\\\ \\\\\\\\\\\\\\ \\\\\\\\\\\\\\

(**1.** $2 \times 9 = 18$ **2.** $3 \times 7 = 21$)

LESSON OPTIONS 5-2

Multiplication Properties

OBJECTIVE 5-2 To review properties and find products when 0 or 1 is a factor

PREBOOK ACTIVITIES

QUICK REVIEW

Find the sums.

1. 4 + 4 + 4 (12)
2. 3 + 3 + 3 + 3 (12)
3. 2 + 2 + 2 + 2 (8)
4. 5 + 5 + 5 + 5 + 5 (25)
5. 8 + 8 + 8 (24)
6. 0 + 0 + 0 + 0 (0)
7. 6 + 6 + 6 + 6 + 6 (30)
8. 9 + 9 + 9 (27)

PRIOR KNOWLEDGE

Have students suggest objects that are packaged in fixed quantities, such as 10-packs of pencils. (Possible answers: plastic cups; canned soft drinks; tennis balls; eggs) Have them explain how they might use multiplication to find the total number of objects in more than 1 package. (Possible answer: Multiply the number of objects per package by the number of packages in all.)

COMMUNICATION

Discussing and Writing Math Have students write the words **factor** and **product** in their Math Journals. Discuss the meaning of factors and products in multiplication and have students write a sentence that relates both words. (Possible answer: *Multiply 2 factors to give a product*.) Have students form a multiplication equation with the numbers 5, 2, and 10, then identify the factors and the product. (5 × 2 = 10 or 2 × 5 = 10; 5 and 2 are factors, 10 is the product.)

EXPLORE AND CONNECT

Materials: counters, paper cups
Grouping Suggestion: cooperative learning pairs
Students explore the Order Property and the One Property of Multiplication. Write these **factors** on the chalkboard: 2 × 6, 3 × 5, 1 × 4, 3 × 3, 7 × 1. Partners put counters in paper cups to arrange the *factors* and the **products** in 2 ways, such as 6 cups with 2 counters per cup and 2 cups with 6 counters per cup. Pairs take turns showing the *factors* and recording the *products* in equation form, such as 2 × 6 = 12 and 6 × 2 = 12. Conclude by having students generalize how *factor* order affects the *product*, using an example from their exploration. (Possible answer: Changing *factor* order does not change the *product:* 2 × 6 = 12 and 6 × 2 = 12.) Then have them formulate a rule for multiplying when 1 is a *factor*, based on their exploration. (Possible answer: A number multiplied by 1 has itself as the *product*; 4 × 1 = 4 and 1 × 4 = 4.)

CONNECTIONS Use these anytime.

Problem of the Day

Logical Reasoning Each symbol stands for the same number. What number is it?
□ × □ = 4
□ + □ = 4
(2)

Patterns

Products Find each pattern, then continue it 3 times.
3, 6, 9, 12, (15), (18), (21)
4, 8, 12, 16, (20), (24), (28)
15, 20, 25, 30, (35), (40), (45)

Math Connection

Measurement As a reward for performing tricks, Pierre the circus poodle eats 3 packs of puppy treats per week. Write a multiplication equation to show how many packs of puppy treats Pierre eats in 4 wk. (3 × 4 = 12 or 4 × 3 = 12)

Classwork and Homework Supplements

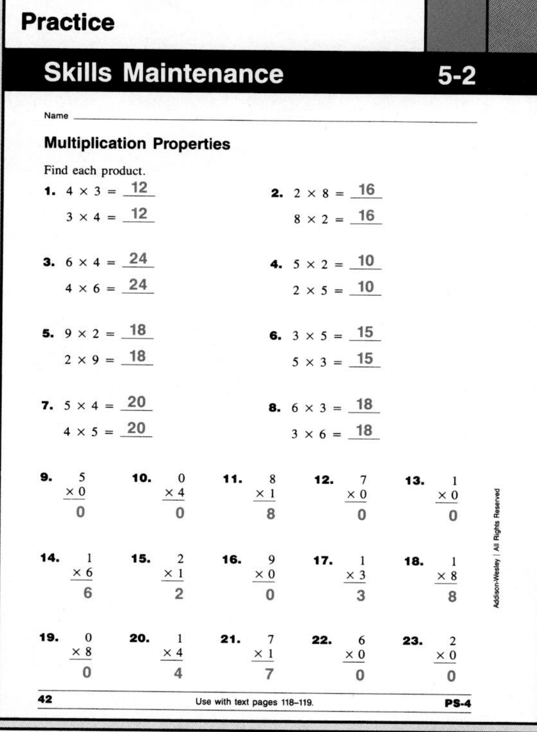

Practice

Skills Maintenance 5-2

Name ________________

Multiplication Properties

Find each product.

1. 4 × 3 = 12; 3 × 4 = 12
2. 2 × 8 = 16; 8 × 2 = 16
3. 6 × 4 = 24; 4 × 6 = 24
4. 5 × 2 = 10; 2 × 5 = 10
5. 9 × 2 = 18; 2 × 9 = 18
6. 3 × 5 = 15; 5 × 3 = 15
7. 5 × 4 = 20; 4 × 5 = 20
8. 6 × 3 = 18; 3 × 6 = 18
9. 5 × 0 = 0
10. 0 × 4 = 0
11. 8 × 1 = 8
12. 7 × 0 = 0
13. 1 × 0 = 0
14. 1 × 6 = 6
15. 2 × 1 = 2
16. 9 × 0 = 0
17. 1 × 3 = 3
18. 1 × 8 = 8
19. 0 × 8 = 0
20. 1 × 4 = 4
21. 7 × 1 = 7
22. 6 × 0 = 0
23. 2 × 0 = 0

42 Use with text pages 118–119. PS-4

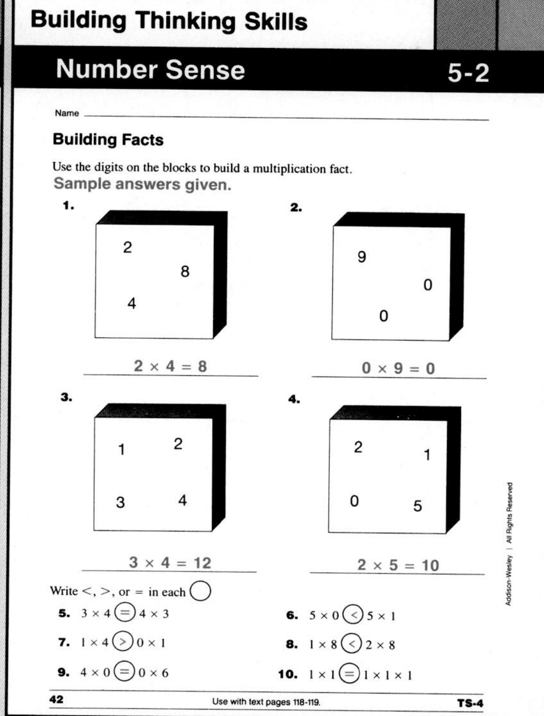

Building Thinking Skills

Number Sense 5-2

Name ________________

Building Facts

Use the digits on the blocks to build a multiplication fact.
Sample answers given.

1. 2 × 4 = 8
2. 0 × 9 = 0
3. 3 × 4 = 12
4. 2 × 5 = 10

Write $<$, $>$, or = in each ◯.

5. 3 × 4 (=) 4 × 3
6. 5 × 0 ($<$) 5 × 1
7. 1 × 4 ($>$) 0 × 1
8. 1 × 8 ($<$) 2 × 8
9. 4 × 0 (=) 0 × 6
10. 1 × 1 (=) 1 × 1 × 1

42 Use with text pages 118-119. TS-4

Reteaching

Skills Review 5-2

Name ________________

Multiplication Properties

Order Property	One Property	Zero Property
Changing the order of factors does not change the product. 2 × 4 = 8, 4 × 2 = 8; 2 × 4 = 4 × 2	The product of a number and 1 is that number. 1 × 3 = 3	The product of a number and 0 is 0. 6 × 0 = 0

Find each missing number.

1. 3 × 4 = 12; 4 × 3 = 12
2. 7 × 1 = 7; 1 × 7 = 7
3. 4 × 0 = 0; 0 × 4 = 0
4. 3 × 2 = 6; 2 × 3 = 6

Find each answer.

5. 2 × 8 = 16; 8 × 2 = n; n = 16
6. 3 × 6 = 18; 6 × 3 = n; n = 18
7. 3 × 5 = 15; 5 × 3 = n; n = 15
8. 6 × 7 = 42; 7 × 6 = n; n = 42
9. 4 × 3 = 12; 3 × 4 = n; n = 12
10. 5 × 2 = 10; 2 × 5 = n; n = 10
11. 6 × 4 = 24; 4 × 6 = n; n = 24
12. 7 × 2 = 14; 2 × 7 = n; n = 14
13. 1 × 4 = 4
14. 4 × 0 = 0
15. 3 × 1 = 3
16. 0 × 9 = 0
17. 9 × 1 = 9
18. 5 × 1 = 5
19. 0 × 6 = 0
20. 4 × 0 = 0
21. 1 × 8 = 8
22. 2 × 1 = 2

42 Use with text pages 118-119. RS-4

Challenges

Critical Thinking 5-2

Name ________________

Fact Finders

Use the clues to find the facts.

1. The product of my factors is the same as their sum. I can be two different facts. Who am I? 0 × 0 = 0; 2 × 2 = 4
2. My factors are identical. Their product is less than their sum. Who am I? 1 × 1 = 1
3. The product of my factors is 1 more than their sum. Who am I? 2 × 3 = 6
4. The product of my factors is less than 10. Their difference is 0. I can be four different facts. Who am I? 0 × 0 = 0; 1 × 1 = 1; 2 × 2 = 4; 3 × 3 = 9
5. The product of my factors is 25. Their difference is 0. Who am I? 5 × 5 = 25
6. The product of my factors is odd. It is 1 less than the sum of my factors. I can be five different facts. Who am I? 1 × 1 = 1; 3 × 1 = 3; 5 × 1 = 5; 7 × 1 = 7; 9 × 1 = 9
7. The sum of my factors is the same as one of the factors. I can be ten different facts. Who am I? 0 × 0 = 0; 1 × 0 = 0; 2 × 0 = 0; 3 × 0 = 0; 4 × 0 = 0; 5 × 0 = 0; 6 × 0 = 0; 7 × 0 = 0; 8 × 0 = 0; 9 × 0 = 0

42 Use with text pages 118–119. CS-4

Options for Individual Needs

Basic

Exercises 1-12, 14-20, 24-27
Data Bank, p. 476
Skills Bank, pp. 460, 462, 464
Calculator Bank, pp. 485, 486
More Practice, p. 502, set E

Supplements
Reteaching 42 or
Practice 42

Average

Exercises 1-27
Data Bank, p. 476
Skills Bank, pp. 462, 464
Calculator Bank, pp. 485, 486
More Practice, p. 502, set E

Supplements
Practice 42
Challenges 42 or
Thinking Skills 42

Extended

Exercises 3-8, 12-20, 25-27
Data Bank, p. 476
Calculator Bank, pp. 485, 486

Supplements
Challenges 42
Thinking Skills 42

Other Resources:
Problem-Solving Experiences in Mathematics, Grade 4, Problem 53
Math In Stride, Grade 4, Page 90
Mathematics: A Way of Thinking, Lesson 5-12
Calculator Activities, Chapter 14

LESSON PLAN 5-2

OBJECTIVE 5-2
To review properties and find products when 0 or 1 is a factor

Materials: counters, snap cubes

Alternative Materials: paper clips

Grouping Suggestion: small groups

1. MOTIVATE AND TEACH

LEARN ABOUT IT

EXPLORE ▶ **Decide how many trees Paul Bunyan cut with a stroke of his ax.** (12)

TALK ABOUT IT ▶ **Explain how making equal rows relates to multiplying.** (Multiply to put together same-size groups, which are like equal rows.)
▶ **Explain the Order Property of Multiplication.** (Possible answer: You can multiply factors in any order and get the same product.)
▶ **Explain the One Property.** (If you multiply a number by 1, the product is that number.)
▶ **Explain why the product of any number and 0 is 0.** (Possible answer: Nothing put together over and over again is still nothing.)
Student Edition answers: **1.** 6; 3 × 4, 4 × 3, 6 × 2, 2 × 6, 1 × 12, 12 × 1 **2.** yes; Either arrangement uses 12 trees in all.

2. CHECK UNDERSTANDING

TRY IT OUT

ERROR ALERT Failing to relate factors in either order to the same product. Confusing the Zero Property of Addition with the Zero Property of Multiplication.

Multiplication Properties

LEARN ABOUT IT

EXPLORE **Use Counters**
Work in groups. Paul Bunyan could chop down many trees with one stroke of his ax. Here is one way to show how many trees he chopped down. Use counters to show other ways the trees could be laid in equal rows.

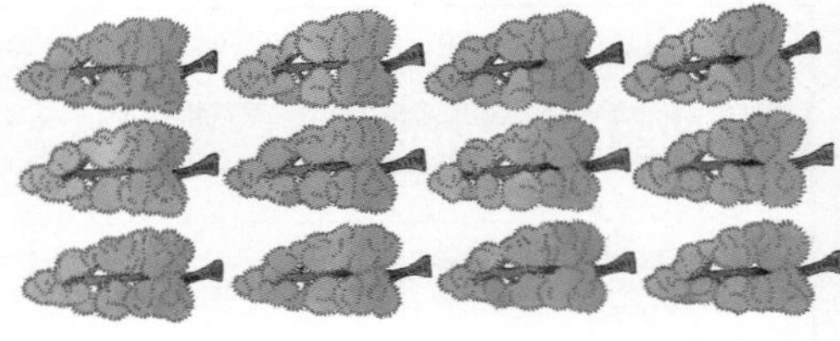

TALK ABOUT IT See teaching notes.

1. How many ways did you find? Write a multiplication fact for each way of making equal rows.
2. Do 3 × 4 and 4 × 3 give the same product? Tell how you know.

Multiplication Fact

3 × 4 = 12 (3 ← factor, 4 ← factor, 12 ← product)

```
  3  ← factor
× 4  ← factor
 12  ← product
```

These multiplication properties will help you find certain multiplication facts.

Order Property	One Property	Zero Property
Changing the order of factors does not change the product. **5 × 3 = 3 × 5**	The product of a number and 1 is that number. **8 × 1 = 8**	The product of a number and 0 is 0. **4 × 0 = 0**

TRY IT OUT

Find each missing number.

1. 2 × 4 = 8; 4 × 2 = ||| **8**
2. 3 × 2 = 6; 2 × 3 = ||| **6**
3. 5 × 4 = 20; 4 × 5 = ||| **20**
4. 6 × 1 = ||| **6**; 1 × 6 = ||| **6**
5. 3 × 0 = ||| **0**; 3 × ||| = 0 **0**

118

TEACHING OPTIONS

RETEACHING TIPS For Exercise 5, have students try to use snap cubes to show 3 rows of 0, then 0 rows of 3. Have them verbalize the situation to explain the product. (0 rows of 3 cubes per row uses 0 cubes; 3 rows of 0 cubes per row uses 0 cubes.) Assign Reteaching Supplement 42.

ENRICHMENT Have students identify and write a pair of related multiplication equations that combine the Order, One, and Zero Properties. (0 × 1 = 0 and 1 × 0 = 0)

PRACTICE

Find each answer.

1. $2 \times 9 = 18$; $9 \times 2 = n$ **18**
2. $6 \times 8 = 48$; $8 \times 6 = n$ **48**
3. $7 \times 3 = 21$; $3 \times 7 = n$ **21**
4. $4 \times 5 = 20$; $5 \times 4 = n$ **20**

5.	6.	7.	8.	9.	10.	11.
0	6	1	0	1	8	0
× 3	× 1	× 3	× 4	× 7	× 1	× 9
0	**6**	**3**	**0**	**7**	**8**	**0**

APPLY

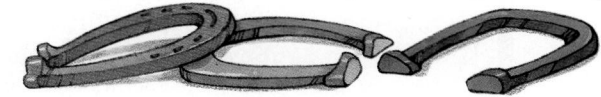

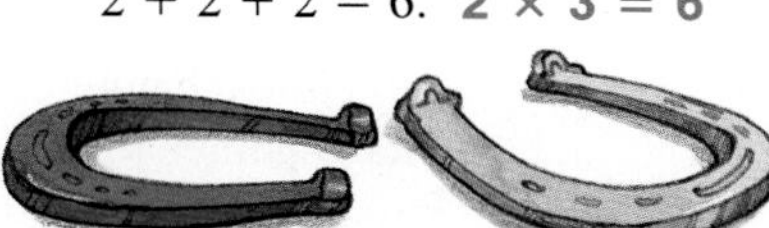

MATH REASONING

12. Write a multiplication fact for the sentence, "Two fives are ten." **2 × 5 = 10**
Write a multiplication fact for the sentence, "Five twos are ten." **5 × 2 = 10**

13. Write a multiplication fact for $2 + 2 + 2 = 6$. **2 × 3 = 6**

PROBLEM SOLVING

14. Ole could shoe 6 horses at a time. To shoe the hooves of 3 horses, how many horseshoes did he need? **12 horseshoes**

15. **Language Arts Data Bank** How many slabs of bacon did his men use to grease Paul Bunyan's hotcake griddle? See page 476. **10 slabs of bacon**

DATA BANK

MIXED REVIEW

Compare. Write < or > in each ▥.

16. 897,234 ▥ 879,234 **>**

17. 33,410 ▥ 33,401 **>**

Find each sum.

18.	19.	20.	21.	22.
476	\$2.95	809	\$3.89	812
+ 378	+ 6.50	+ 793	+ 5.67	+ 702
854	**\$9.45**	**1,602**	**\$9.56**	**1,514**

Find each difference.

23.	24.	25.	26.	27.
769	109	\$9.50	412	981
− 727	− 87	− 7.75	− 398	− 195
42	**22**	**\$1.75**	**14**	**786**

More Practice, page 502, set E

119

for pages 118-119

3. PRACTICE AND APPLY

Basic	1-12, 14-20, 24-27
Average	1-27
Extended	3-8, 12-20, 25-27

PRACTICE

In Exercises 1-4, explain how the factor pairs relate. (2 factors are given in either order, so both have the same product.)

APPLY

MATH REASONING ► **Analyze Exercise 12 to link the word *are* in the sentences with a math symbol.** (=)
► **Explain why multiplication and addition relate in Exercise 13.** (The addition equation shows same-size groups put together, the same action as in multiplication.)

PROBLEM SOLVING ► **Analyze Problem 14 to find an extra fact and a missing fact.** (Ole could shoe 6 horses at a time is not needed, but you need to know a horse needs 4 shoes.)

MIXED REVIEW ► **Which exercises will have the greatest sum? the greatest difference? Explain why.** (Exercise 20, because you are adding the largest numbers; Exercise 27, because the take-away number is so small)

5-2

CLOSE AND ASSESS

SHOW WHAT YOU KNOW

Have students use counters to illustrate each property with the multiplication fact given: the Order Property for 4×2 and 2×4, the One Property for 4×1, and the Zero Property for 4×0. (8; 4; 0; Check students' work.)

QUICK QUIZ

Find each missing number.

1. $6 \times 3 = 18$, so $3 \times 6 = \square$ (18)
2. $7 \times 2 = 14$, so $2 \times \square = 14$ (7)
3. $0 \times 5 = \square$ (0)
4. $6 \times 1 = \square$ (6)

LESSON OPTIONS 5-3

Factors of 2 and 5

OBJECTIVE 5-3 To find products when 2 or 5 is a factor

PREBOOK ACTIVITIES

QUICK REVIEW

Add.

1. 5 + 5	(10)	**2.** 2 + 2	(4)
3. 9 + 9	(18)	**4.** 3 + 3	(6)
5. 7 + 7	(14)	**6.** 4 + 4	(8)
7. 6 + 6	(12)	**8.** 8 + 8	(16)
9. 1 + 1	(2)	**10.** 0 + 0	(0)

PRIOR KNOWLEDGE

Have students suggest objects that usually come in pairs. (Possible answers: shoes; ears; bus seats) Have students explain how they could determine how many objects there are in 3 pairs. (Possible answers: Count by twos 3 times; add 2 + 2 + 2; multiply 3 × 2.) Then have students list things that come in fives. (Possible answers: fingers; pennies in a nickel; minutes per digit on a clock face) Ask students when they have counted by fives. (Possible answers: counting out nickels; counting minutes around a clock face)

COMMUNICATION

Discussing Math Have volunteers skip count by twos and by fives to 50. Have students explain why people often learn to skip count by those numbers. (Possible answers: It is faster than counting by ones; the fives are easy to remember.) Have students skip count by twos to multiply 3 × 2 and explain their thinking. (Say *2, 4, 6,* which is skip counting 3 times by 2, or 3 × 2.) Then have students skip count by fives to multiply 3 × 5, again explaining their reasoning. (Say *5, 10, 15,* which is skip counting 3 times by 5, or 3 × 5.)

EXPLORE AND CONNECT

Materials: TA 4 (Hundred Chart), crayons in 2 colors
Alternative Materials: TA 12 (Centimeter Graph Paper)
Grouping Suggestion: cooperative learning pairs
Pairs explore patterns in factors of 2 and 5. Using a hundred chart, the first partner skip counts by twos, circling each number said. Using another chart, the second partner skip counts by fives, circling each number said in a different color. Partners exchange charts to verify selections. Then students work together to describe the pattern they see in the twos. (Possible answer: All boxes contain even numbers, and they form vertical stripes on the chart, separated by blank columns of odd numbers.) Pairs do the same for the fives. (Possible answer: All numbers end in 0 or 5; half the products are odd, the other half are even.) Students generalize about products related to the factors of 2 and 5. (Products when two is a factor are even; products when five is a factor end in 0 or 5.)

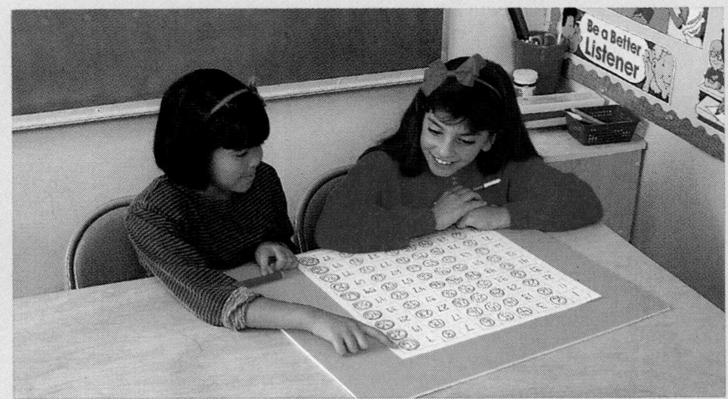

CONNECTIONS Use these anytime.

Problem of the Day

Logical Reasoning Each symbol stands for the same number. What number is it?
□ × □ = 20 + □ (5)

Math Connection

Money Stan and Fran each recycled 4 empty bottles, earning a nickel for each one. How much money did they collect in all? (40¢)

Patterns

Counting Back Find each pattern, then continue it 3 times.
45, 40, 35, (30), (25), (20)
18, 16, 14, (12), (10), (8)

CLASSWORK AND HOMEWORK SUPPLEMENTS

Practice

Skills Maintenance 5-3

Name ______

Factors of 2 and 5

Find each product.

1. 5 × 6 = 30
2. 2 × 4 = 8
3. 8 × 5 = 40
4. 3 × 2 = 6
5. 5 × 0 = 0
6. 1 × 2 = 2
7. 2 × 2 = 4
8. 2 × 5 = 10
9. 5 × 5 = 25
10. 2 × 9 = 18
11. 7 × 5 = 35
12. 5 × 3 = 15
13. 5 × 9 = 45
14. 6 × 2 = 12
15. 5 × 4 = 20
16. 2 × 7 = 14
17. 1 × 5 = 5
18. 7 × 2 = 14
19. 3 × 5 = 15
20. 2 × 1 = 2
21. 9 × 2 = 18
22. 4 × 5 = 20
23. 0 × 2 = 0
24. 8 × 2 = 16
25. 0 × 5 = 0
26. 7 × 2 = 14
27. 5 × 1 = 5
28. 5 × 7 = 35
29. 2 × 8 = 16
30. 6 × 5 = 30
31. 5 × 8 = 40
32. 9 × 5 = 45
33. 5 × 3 = 15
34. 2 × 0 = 0

Building Thinking Skills

Patterns 5-3

Name ______

Sum Patterns

Find each product. Write an addition double. Then complete each sentence. The first one is done for you.

1. 2 × 1 = 2 = 1 + 1 2 groups of 1 is 2
   2 × 2 = 4 = 2 + 2 2 groups of 2 is 4
   2 × 3 = 6 = 3 + 3 2 groups of 3 is 6
   2 × 4 = 8 = 4 + 4 2 groups of 4 is 8
   2 × 5 = 10 = 5 + 5 2 groups of 5 is 10
   2 × 6 = 12 = 6 + 6 2 groups of 6 is 12
   2 × 7 = 14 = 7 + 7 2 groups of 7 is 14
   2 × 8 = 16 = 8 + 8 2 groups of 8 is 16
   2 × 9 = 18 = 9 + 9 2 groups of 9 is 18
2. Multiplying by 2 is like adding doubles.

Find each product. Write the sum of the digits of each product.

	Product	Sum of Digits of Products		Product	Sum of Digits of Products
5 × 1 =	5	5	5 × 2 =	10	1
5 × 3 =	15	6	5 × 4 =	20	2
5 × 5 =	25	7	5 × 6 =	30	3
5 × 7 =	35	8	5 × 8 =	40	4
5 × 9 =	45	9	5 × 10 =	50	5

3. What pattern do you see? Wording will vary. The sums of the digits in odd and in even products are consecutive.

Reteaching

Skills Review 5-3

Name ______

Factors of 2 and 5

To find a 2 fact, think about adding doubles.

To find a 5 fact, think about counting nickels.

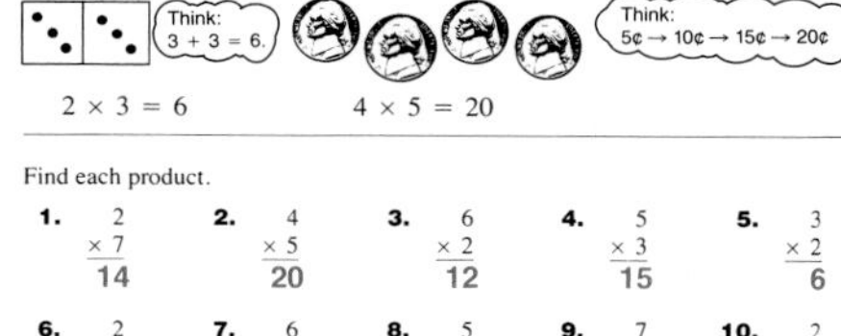

2 × 3 = 6 4 × 5 = 20

Find each product.

1. 2 × 7 = 14
2. 4 × 5 = 20
3. 6 × 2 = 12
4. 5 × 3 = 15
5. 3 × 2 = 6
6. 2 × 9 = 18
7. 6 × 5 = 30
8. 5 × 5 = 25
9. 7 × 5 = 35
10. 2 × 2 = 4
11. 5 × 4 = n n = 20
12. 7 × 2 = n n = 14
13. 2 × 9 = n n = 18
14. 8 × 5 = n n = 40
15. 2 × 5 = n n = 10
16. 7 × 2 = n n = 14
17. 6 × 5 = n n = 30
18. 5 × 3 = n n = 15

Find the missing numbers.

19. 5 × = 45 [9] × 5 = 14
20. 8 × = 18 2 × [8] = 16
21. 3 × 5 = 15 5 × [3] = 15

Find the missing numbers.

22. 4 + 4 = 8 2 × 4 = 8
23. 5 + 5 = 10 5 × 2 = 10

Challenges

Math Reasoning 5-3

Name ______

Jumbled Tables

Work in a group.

1. This multiplication table got all jumbled up. Straighten it out by filling in the blanks.
2. Compare your answers with other group members.

×	5	1	2	0
4	20	4	8	0
7	35	7	14	0
6	30	6	12	0
5	25	5	10	0

3. This multiplication table got left in the rain. Fill in the boxes that were washed out.
4. Compare your answers with other group members.

×	3	4	7	9	6
1	3	4	7	9	6
5	15	20	35	45	30
0	0	0	0	0	0
2	6	8	14	18	12

5. Make up a jumbled table for a classmate.
   a. Fill in the numbers along the left side of the table.
   b. Fill in the table.
   c. Erase the answers in the circles and give the table to a classmate to complete.
   Answers will vary.

×	0	5	1	2
	○			○
○		○	○	
	○	○		○
○	○	○		

OPTIONS FOR INDIVIDUAL NEEDS

Basic

Exercises 1-6, 15-28
More Practice, p. 502, set F

Supplements
Reteaching 43 or
Practice 43
Challenges 43

Average

Exercises 1-28
More Practice, p. 502, set F

Supplements
Practice 43
Challenges 43 or
Thinking Skills 43

Extended

Exercises 10-28

Supplements
Challenges 43
Thinking Skills 43

Other Resources:
Problem-Solving Experiences in Mathematics, Grade 4, Problem 38
Mathdroid Multiplication, pp. 27, 53
Middle Grades Mathematics Project: Factors and Multiples, p. 32
Calculator Activities, Chapter 14

LESSON PLAN 5-3

OBJECTIVE 5-3
To find products when 2 or 5 is a factor

Materials: TA 9 (Play Money—Coins and Dollars), calculators

Grouping Suggestion: pairs

1. MOTIVATE AND TEACH

LEARN ABOUT IT

EXPLORE ▶ **Analyze the pictures to decide which factor appears in each multiplication fact on the left and which appears in each on the right.** (2, 5)

TALK ABOUT IT ▶ **Explain how multiplication facts with a factor of 2 relate to addition.** (Multiplying by 2 is like adding doubles.)
▶ **Generalize about products when 2 is a factor.** (All products are even.)
▶ **Explain a pattern in the products when 5 is a factor.** (All products end in either 0 or 5.)
▶ **Analyze how to predict whether products are odd or even when 5 is a factor.** (If the other factor is odd, the product is odd; if it is even, the product is even.)
Student Edition answers: **1.** 2, 4, 6, 8, 10, 12, 14, 16, 18, 20, . . . All are even numbers. **2.** Adding doubles is like using a factor twice. **3.** 5, 10, 15, 20, 25, 30, 35, 40, 45, 50, . . . All end in 0 or 5. **4.** Visualize counting as many nickels as the other factor to multiply by 5.

2. CHECK UNDERSTANDING

TRY IT OUT

ERROR ALERT Counting by fives too many or too few times. Adding instead of multiplying.

Factors of 2 and 5

LEARN ABOUT IT

EXPLORE Discover a Pattern
Think about the pictures and equations. Do you see any patterns?

How many?

2 sixes
$2 \times 6 = n$

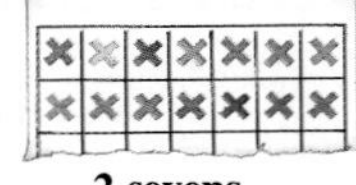

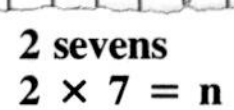

2 sevens
$2 \times 7 = n$

2 eights
$2 \times 8 = n$

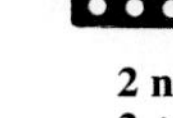

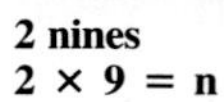

2 nines
$2 \times 9 = n$

How much money?

$2 \times 5 = n$

$3 \times 5 = n$

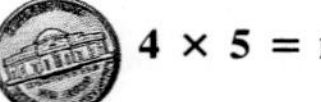

$4 \times 5 = n$

TALK ABOUT IT See teaching notes.

1. Make an ordered list for the facts of 2. What patterns do you see?
2. Explain how using addition doubles can help you multiply when 2 is a factor.
3. Make an ordered list for the facts of 5. What patterns do you see?
4. Explain how using nickel counting patterns can help you multiply when 5 is a factor.

- To find a 2 fact, you can think about addition doubles.
- To find a 5 fact, you can think about counting nickels.

TRY IT OUT

Find each product.

1. $2 \times 5 = n$ 10 **2.** $8 \times 5 = n$ 40 **3.** $2 \times 8 = n$ 16 **4.** $7 \times 5 = n$ 35

5. 5×4 = 20 **6.** 5×6 = 30 **7.** 2×7 = 14 **8.** 3×2 = 6 **9.** 6×5 = 30

120

TEACHING OPTIONS

RETEACHING TIPS For factors of 5, have students count out as many play nickels as necessary, then verbally count by fives as they touch each nickel. They record the product after they have counted the last nickel. Assign Reteaching Supplement 43.

ENRICHMENT On 2 separate index cards, have students write a story problem involving a factor of 2 and a story problem that uses a factor of 5. Have them exchange cards with a friend to solve each other's problems. (Answers will vary. Check students' story problems.)

PRACTICE

Find each product.

1.	2.	3.	4.	5.	6.
2×5 = 10	5×8 = 40	2×3 = 6	9×5 = 45	7×2 = 14	5×5 = 25

7.	8.	9.	10.	11.	12.
8×2 = 16	5×3 = 15	2×2 = 4	7×5 = 35	2×4 = 8	6×5 = 30

13. $4 \times 5 = n$ 20 **14.** $6 \times 2 = n$ 12 **15.** $5 \times 8 = n$ 40 **16.** $2 \times 7 = n$ 14

17. $5 \times 2 = n$ 10 **18.** $5 \times 9 = n$ 45 **19.** $2 \times 9 = n$ 18 **20.** $6 \times 5 = n$ 30

Find the missing numbers.

21. [9] × 5 = 45 **22.** 2 × [9] = 18 **23.** 8 × [5] = 40

APPLY

MATH REASONING

24. If 2 + 2 + 2 = 6 goes with 3 × 2 = 6, what goes with 4 × 5 = 20?
5 + 5 + 5 + 5 = 20

25. When you multiply an even number by 5, what is always true about the last digit in the product?
It is always zero.

PROBLEM SOLVING

26. Unfinished Problem
Tickets for the magic show cost $5. Juan bought 3 tickets and Emilia bought 6. Write a question to finish the problem. Answers will vary.

27. Janey put fortune cookies in packages of 5. How many cookies did she need to fill 8 packages?
40 cookies

▶ CALCULATOR

28. Give the numbers that go in the □ and △. Use your calculator and make 5 more cards like these with larger factors. What do you discover?
The products always differ by 1.

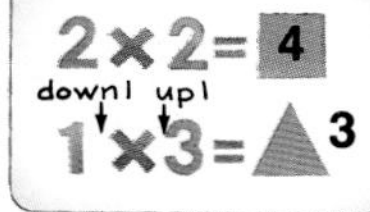

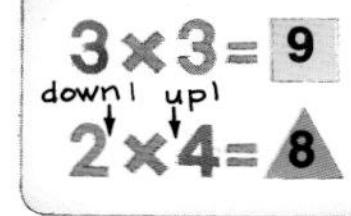

More Practice, page 502, set F

3. Practice and Apply

Basic	1-6, 15-28
Average	1-28
Extended	10-28

PRACTICE

How are Exercises 1 and 6 alike? How are they different? (Both have a factor of 5; Exercise 1 has 2 fives, Exercise 6 has 5 fives.)

APPLY

MATH REASONING ▶ **Explain how the first 2 equations in Exercise 24 relate.** (Adding 3 twos is the same as multiplying 3 × 2.)

PROBLEM SOLVING ▶ **Decide what to do first to write a question for Problem 26.** (Possible answer: Evaluate the given data.)
▶ **Analyze Problem 27 to identify factors to use.** (5 × 8)

CALCULATOR ▶ **Analyze the top factor pairs for a similarity.** (The same factor is multiplied by itself in each.)
▶ **Explain the change in the bottom pairs.** (One factor goes down 1, the other factor goes up 1 each time.)

5-3

Close and Assess

SAY WHAT YOU THINK Have students work in pairs. The first partner explains how to skip count to multiply by 2. The second partner explains how to use a clock to multiply by 5. (Count by twos as many times as the other factor; use each 5-min interval on the clock to count the number of intervals indicated by the other factor.)

Quick Quiz

Find each product.

1. 4 × 5 (20) **2.** 2 × 9 (18)
3. 5 × 9 (45) **4.** 4 × 2 (8)
5. 1 × 5 (5) **6.** 0 × 2 (0)
7. 2 × 7 (14) **8.** 7 × 5 (35)

LESSON OPTIONS 5-4

A Factor of 9

OBJECTIVE 5-4 To find products when 9 is a factor

PREBOOK ACTIVITIES

QUICK REVIEW

Find the products.

1. 4 × 10 (40) **2.** 10 × 7 (70) **3.** 2 × 10 (20)
4. 10 × 5 (50) **5.** 1 × 10 (10) **6.** 10 × 9 (90)
7. 10 × 3 (30) **8.** 6 × 10 (60) **9.** 10 × 8 (80)

PRIOR KNOWLEDGE

Have students recall the compensation mental math strategy to add a 9. (Mentally add 10, then subtract the 1 extra.) Have them think of a quick way to find 2 nines, using compensation. (Possible answer: Think of 2 tens, which is 20; subtract the 2 extra, which is 18.)

COMMUNICATION

Discussing Math Have students suggest various real-life meanings of the word **pattern.** (Possible answers: ''a repeating design,'' as in tile work; ''a mapped-out plan,'' as in football-pass patterns; ''a guide,'' as in sewing patterns) Then have students describe the meaning of a *number pattern.* (Possible answer: ''a predictable number arrangement'') Discuss how recognizing number patterns may help students learn number facts. (Possible answers: predict results; decide if answers make sense; understand how numbers go together in organized ways)

EXPLORE AND CONNECT

Materials TA 12 (Centimeter Graph Paper), scissors, crayons
Grouping Suggestion: cooperative learning groups of 5
Students explore multiplication **patterns** with factors of 9 and 10. The first student writes a multiplication fact with 10 as the first factor, such as 10 × 7. The next student shows that fact with graph paper and crayons. (Color 10 rows of 7 boxes per row.) The third student replaces the 10 with a 9 (9 × 7). The fourth student adjusts the original graph-paper model to show the new fact. (Possible solution: Cut away 1 box from each of the 7 rows.) The fifth student records both facts and finds the difference between the products. (10 × 7 = 70; 9 × 7 = 63; 7) Groups discuss the relationship between the 2 facts and formulate a rule for multiplying by 9 using products of 10. They repeat the exploration several times with other factors of 10 and 9 to test their rule, trading tasks each time. Have students share their discoveries.

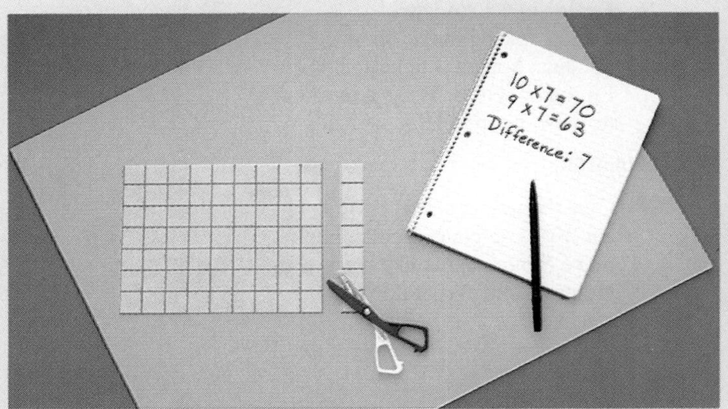

CONNECTIONS Use these anytime.

Problem of the Day

Softball Throw In a throwing contest, Ellis threw a softball 9 m. Fatima threw a softball 4 times farther. Find the distance of Fatima's throw. (36 m)

Patterns

Calculator The pattern below combines products and digit sums. Continue it 2 more times with a calculator.

19 × 1 = 19, 1 + 9 = 10, 1 + 0 = 1
19 × 2 = 38, 3 + 8 = 11, 1 + 1 = 2
19 × 3 = 57, 5 + 7 = 12, 1 + 2 = 3
(19 × 4 = 76, 7 + 6 = 13, 1 + 3 = 4;
19 × 5 = 95, 9 + 5 = 14, 1 + 4 = 5)

Math Connection

Money Rafael buys 6 baseball cards at 9¢ each. He gave the clerk a dime for each card. How much change should he get? How many nickels would Rafael use for the same purchase? What would his change be then? (6¢; 11; 1)

Classwork and Homework Supplements

Practice

Skills Maintenance 5-4

Name

A Factor of 9

Multiply.

1. 5 × 9 = 45
2. 9 × 9 = 81
3. 9 × 2 = 18
4. 5 × 7 = 35
5. 9 × 3 = 27
6. 9 × 1 = 9
7. 9 × 7 = 63
8. 6 × 9 = 54
9. 1 × 3 = 3
10. 9 × 4 = 36
11. 3 × 5 = 15
12. 8 × 9 = 72
13. 4 × 5 = 20
14. 9 × 0 = 0
15. 5 × 5 = 25
16. 9 × 8 = 72
17. 2 × 2 = 4
18. 4 × 9 = 36
19. 0 × 9 = 0
20. 9 × 4 = 36
21. 5 × 8 = 40
22. 9 × 6 = 54
23. 9 × 9 = 81
24. 3 × 9 = 27
25. 4 × 9 = 36
26. 9 × 5 = 45
27. 2 × 9 = 18
28. 0 × 5 = 0
29. 7 × 9 = 63
30. 1 × 9 = 9

31. 9 × 4 = 36
32. 2 × 9 = 18
33. 1 × 9 = 9
34. 9 × 8 = 72
35. 9 × 9 = 81
36. 9 × 6 = 54
37. 9 × 5 = 45
38. 9 × 0 = 0
39. 5 × 9 = 45
40. 9 × 3 = 27

44 Use with text pages 122–123. PS-4

Building Thinking Skills

Patterns 5-4

Name

Patterns in 9 Facts

Complete each statement about the patterns that helps you find the 9 facts. Then write a sample to demonstrate each pattern. Samples will vary. Possible answers given.

9 facts
9 × 1 = 9
9 × 2 = 18
9 × 3 = 27
9 × 4 = 36
9 × 5 = 45
9 × 6 = 54
9 × 7 = 63
9 × 8 = 72
9 × 9 = 81

1. The product of 9 and an odd factor is always odd. (odd, even)
   9 × 3 = 27
2. The sum of the digits of each product is 9.
   9 × 5 = 45; 4 + 5 = 9
3. The product of 9 and an even factor is always even. (odd, even)
   9 × 8 = 72
4. The tens digit of the product is 1 less than the non-9 factor.
   9 × 6 = 54; 6 − 1 = 5
5. Describe the pattern of the tens digits in the 9 facts.
   The numbers increase by 1.
6. Describe the pattern of the ones digits in the 9 facts.
   The numbers decrease by 1.

44 Use with text pages 122–123. TS-4

Reteaching

Patterns 5-4

Name

A Factor of 9

What is the product of 4 × 9?

Use 10 product. → Subtract the other factor from the product. → You will get the same answer using a factor of 9.

10 × 4 = 40 — 40 − 4 = 36 — 9 × 4 = 36

Multiply.

1. 4 × 9 = 36 (40 − 4)
2. 8 × 9 = 72 (80 − 8)
3. 5 × 9 = 45 (50 − 5)
4. 3 × 9 = 27
5. 9 × 9 = 81
6. 7 × 9 = 63
7. 9 × 6 = 54
8. 9 × 0 = 0
9. 9 × 3 = 27
10. 9 × 4 = 36
11. 9 × 8 = 72
12. 9 × 2 = 18
13. 9 × 6 = 54
14. 0 × 9 = 0
15. 9 × 9 = 81
16. 3 × 9 = 27
17. 9 × 0 = 0
18. 7 × 9 = 63
19. 1 × 9 = 9
20. 4 × 9 = 36
21. 6 × 9 = 54
22. 9 × 1 = 9
23. 5 × 9 = 45
24. 9 × 5 = 45
25. 9 × 3 = 27
26. 8 × 9 = 72
27. 9 × 2 = 18
28. 9 × 7 = 63
29. 2 × 9 = 18
30. 9 × 8 = 72

44 Use with text pages 122-123. RS-4

Challenges

Mental Math 5-4

Name

Star Traveler

Play this game with 2 or more players.

Rules

1. Make a spinner with the numbers 1 to 9 and the word **wild** on it.
2. Use a different marker for each player. Place your markers at **START.**
3. Take turns spinning a number. Multiply the number you spin by either 5 or 9. If the next star has your product, move your marker to that star. If it does not, your marker does not move. (**Wild** can be any number you want.)
4. The first player to reach the last star wins.

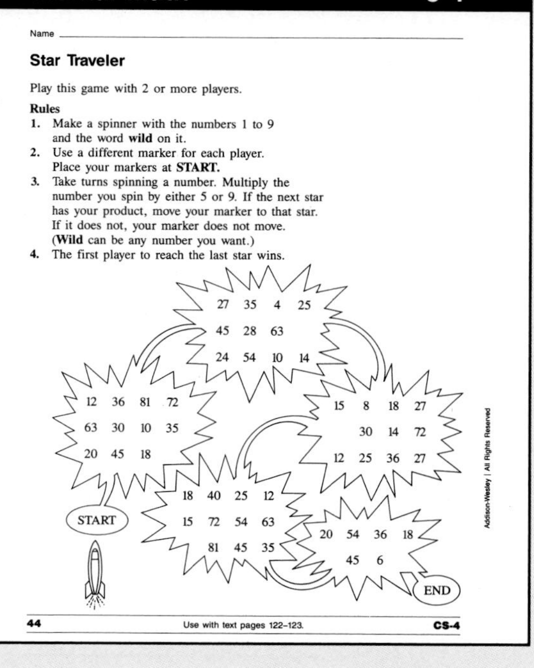

44 Use with text pages 122–123. CS-4

Options for Individual Needs

Basic

Exercises 1-27, 30-33
Calculator Bank, pp. 484, 486
More Practice, p. 503, set A

Supplements
Reteaching 44 or
Practice 44
Thinking Skills 44

Average

Exercises 1-33
Calculator Bank, pp. 484, 486
More Practice, p. 503, set A

Supplements
Practice 44
Challenges 44 or
Thinking Skills 44

Extended

Exercises 8-33
Calculator Bank, pp. 484, 486

Supplements
Challenges 44
Thinking Skills 44

Other Resources:
Problem-Solving Experiences in Mathematics, Grade 4, Problem 39
Math In Stride, Grade 4, p. 66
Mathdroid Multiplication, p. 90
Using the Math Explorer Calculator: A Sourcebook for Teachers, Chapter 14

LESSON PLAN 5-4

OBJECTIVE 5-4
To find products when 9 is a factor

Materials: snap cubes

Alternative Materials: counters

1. MOTIVATE AND TEACH

LEARN ABOUT IT

▶ **Analyze the chart to identify a relationship between the 10 facts and the 9 facts.** (The difference between products of a 10 fact and the related 9 fact is the same as the other factor.)

TALK ABOUT IT ▶ **Explain a pattern in the sum of the digits in each product for a 9 fact.** (The 2 digits always add to 9.)

▶ **Explain a relationship in each 9 fact between the factor that is not 9 and the tens digit of the product.** (The tens digit is 1 less than that multiple of 9.)

▶ **Explain how to use the patterns to find a 9 fact that you might not know, such as 9 × 7.** (According to the pattern, the product begins with a 6 and the digit sum is 9, so 9 × 7 = 63.)

▶ **Explain how to find 9 × 8 using 10 products.** (10 × 8 = 80; 9 × 8 would be 8 less than 80, or 72.)

Student Edition answers: **1.** All sums of the digits equal 9. **2.** The tens digit of the product is 1 less than the factor that is not 9. **3.** Subtract the factor in the 9 fact that is not 9 from the 10 product.

2. CHECK UNDERSTANDING

TRY IT OUT

ERROR ALERT Subtracting 9 instead of the other factor when using 10 products. Starting the product with the multiple of 9 when using the 9 pattern.

A Factor of 9

LEARN ABOUT IT

EXPLORE Discover a Pattern
Tim wrote some 9 facts and 10 products on his paper. He said he used patterns to find the 9 facts. See what patterns you can find.

Some 10 products	Some 9 facts
10 × 2 = 20	9 × 2 = 18
10 × 3 = 30	9 × 3 = 27
10 × 4 = 40	9 × 4 = 36
10 × 5 = 50	9 × 5 = 45

TALK ABOUT IT See teaching notes.

1. Look at the products for the 9 facts. What do you discover about the sum of the digits?
2. For 9 × 2, the product starts with a 1. For 9 × 3, the product starts with a 2. Tell about this pattern.
3. Look at a 10 product. Then look at a matching 9 fact. How can you use the 10 products to find the 9 facts?

Here are some ways to find a product when 9 is a factor.

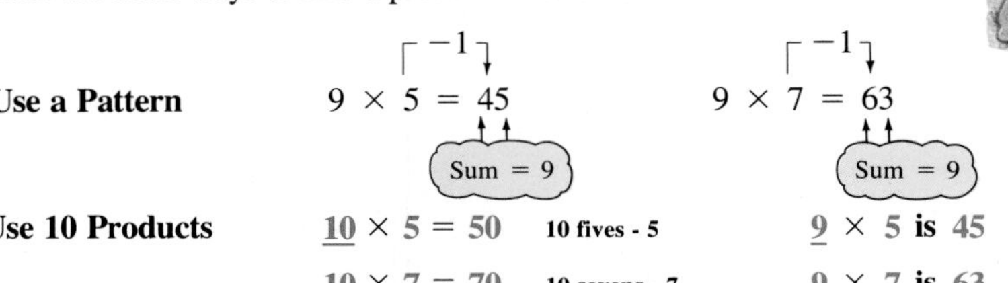

TRY IT OUT

1. $2 \times 9 = n$ 18
2. $4 \times 9 = n$ 36
3. $7 \times 9 = n$ 63
4. $9 \times 8 = n$ 72
5. $9 \times 0 = n$ 0
6. $9 \times 1 = n$ 9
7. $9 \times 3 = n$ 27
8. $0 \times 9 = n$ 0
9. 3 × 9 = 27
10. 6 × 9 = 54
11. 9 × 5 = 45
12. 9 × 9 = 81
13. 5 × 9 = 45

TEACHING OPTIONS

RETEACHING TIPS Have students use snap cubes in tracks of 10 to multiply a factor by 10, then unsnap 1 cube from each track to represent multiplying by 9. Students should verbalize the amount subtracted and relate it to the 9 fact. Assign Reteaching Supplement 44.

ENRICHMENT On an index card, have each student write a number riddle whose answer is the product of any 9 fact, then write 3 clues. Have students exchange papers to solve each other's riddles. (Riddles will vary. Check students' work.)

PRACTICE

Multiply.

1. $9 \times 5 = $ **45**
2. $3 \times 9 = $ **27**
3. $9 \times 6 = $ **54**
4. $2 \times 5 = $ **10**
5. $0 \times 9 = $ **0**
6. $4 \times 9 = $ **36**
7. $0 \times 5 = $ **0**
8. $9 \times 9 = $ **81**
9. $9 \times 7 = $ **63**
10. $1 \times 9 = $ **9**
11. $5 \times 2 = $ **10**
12. $5 \times 5 = $ **25**
13. $1 \times 9 = $ **9**
14. $9 \times 8 = $ **72**

15. $4 \times 9 = a$ **36** **16.** $9 \times 7 = a$ **63** **17.** $5 \times 9 = a$ **45** **18.** $1 \times 9 = a$ **9**

Find the missing numbers.

19. $9 \times \square = 36$ **4** **20.** $9 \times \square = 72$ **8** **21.** $\square \times 9 = 27$ **3** **22.** $\square \times 9 = 9$ **1**

23. Find the product of 9 times 3. **27** **24.** Multiply 10 by 9. **90**

APPLY

MATH REASONING Give the number just before and just after each product.

25. 7×9 **62, 64** **26.** 6×5 **29, 31** **27.** 2×9 **17, 19** **28.** 8×9 **71, 73** **29.** 9×9 **80, 82**

30. Give the next six numbers in this pattern. 0 9 18 27 **36, 45, 54, 63, 72, 81**

PROBLEM SOLVING

31. Missing Data What data is needed? Tina earned $9 each week helping her father. How much did she earn? **how many weeks she worked**

32. Cindy sold 9 boxes of flower seeds that had 6 packs of seeds in each. How many packs did she sell? **54 packs**

▶ **USING CRITICAL THINKING Logical Reasoning**

33. Can you find the secret number? Here are some clues.

- It is odd and it is a 5 fact.
- It is not more than 30.
- If you had half that many eggs, then you would still have more than a dozen. **25**

More Practice, page 503, set A

3. Practice and Apply

Basic	1-27, 30-33
Average	1-33
Extended	8-33

PRACTICE

Explain how each of Exercises 15 to 18 relates to another of Exercises 1 to 14. (The Order Property links 15 to 6, 16 to 9, 17 to 1, and 18 to 13.)

APPLY

MATH REASONING ▶ **Explain what you would do first to solve Exercises 25 to 29.** (Find the product of each.)

▶ **Explain the pattern in Exercise 30.** (Each number is 9 more than the one before.)

PROBLEM SOLVING ▶ **Analyze the situation in Problem 31 to determine the missing data.** (You must know how long Tina worked to find her earnings.)

USING THINKING SKILLS

▶ **Explain why the first clue is really 2 clues.** (Not all 5 facts are odd.)

▶ **Explain the meaning of the next clue.** (It is 30 or less.)

5-4

Close and Assess

WRITE WHAT YOU THINK

Have students write paragraphs explaining 2 different methods to use to find the product of 8 × 9. They should also explain which method they prefer and why. (Answers may vary. Check students' writing.)

Quick Quiz

Find the products.

1. 7 nines (63) **2.** 4 nines (36)
3. 9 nines (81) **4.** 6 nines (54)
5. 9 × 5 (45) **6.** 9 × 0 (0)
7. 1 × 9 (9) **8.** 3 × 9 (27)

LESSON OPTIONS 5-5

Factors of 3 and 4

OBJECTIVE 5-5 To find products when 3 or 4 is a factor

PREBOOK ACTIVITIES

QUICK REVIEW

Find the products.

1. 2 × 2 = (4)	**2.** 5 × 3 = (15)	**3.** 9 × 2 = (18)
4. 2 × 8 = (16)	**5.** 5 × 5 = (25)	**6.** 9 × 3 = (27)
7. 2 × 6 = (12)	**8.** 5 × 4 = (20)	**9.** 9 × 5 = (45)

PRIOR KNOWLEDGE

Ask students what we do when we multiply. (Possible answer: Add one factor to itself as many times as the other factor tells us to.) Have students state a situation when it is useful to use multiplication. (Possible answer: when you buy several of one item in a grocery store and you want to find the total cost) Have students explain how they might find the total cost of 3 boxes of cereal each marked $2.00. (Possible answer: Multiply 3 × $2.00 to get $6.00.)

COMMUNICATION

Discussing and Writing in Math Ask students to develop several word problems using multiples of common classroom items—for example: 3 students each have 2 pencils. How many pencils are there in all? (6) Ask one student to write the problem in English sentence form on the chalkboard. Ask another student to write a number sentence to match. (2 + 2 + 2 or 2 × 3 = 6) Have students discuss how they would decide which form to use when writing a problem. (Possible answer: Use the English sentence form when writing a story; use a number sentence when solving an equation.)

EXPLORE AND CONNECT

Materials: TA 11 (Blank Spinners marked 2-5), counters
Grouping Suggestion: cooperative learning groups of 4
Each group gets a spinner and a set of counters. One child spins twice to get two factors. A second child uses counters to represent the multiplication. For example, 3 × 5 would be 3 groups of 5 counters. A third child counts aloud the members in each group and the number of groups, then writes a multiplication fact for it, such as 3 × 5. A fourth child writes an addition fact for the counters, such as 5 + 5 + 5. Students discuss what mental math techniques could be used to find the answer, such as grouping (5 + 5) and then adding the remaining 5 to find 15, skip counting, or multiplying 2 × 5 and adding one more group of 5 to get 15. Students play several rounds, each time switching roles. Last, they compare addition and multiplication and discuss shortcuts they may have discovered when multiplying with factors of 3 or 4.

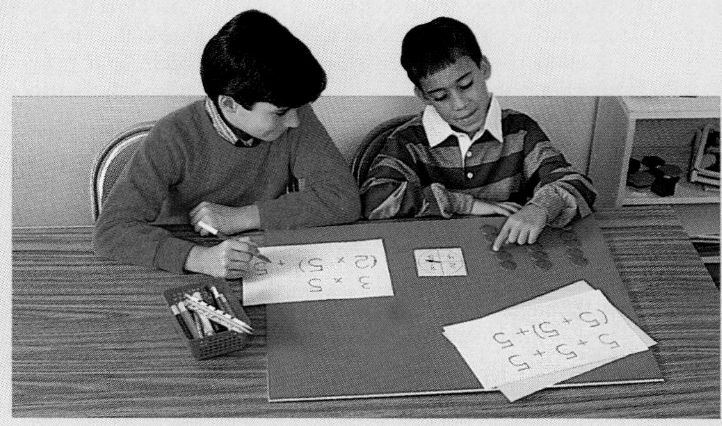

CONNECTIONS Use these anytime.

Problem of the Day

Patterns Solve the following multiplication problems. What is the pattern found in the answers?
3 × 1, 3 × 2, 3 × 3, 3 × 4, 3 × 5, 3 × 6, 3 × 7, 3 × 8, 3 × 9, 3 × 10 (3, 6, 9, 12, 15, 18, 21, 24, 27, 30; 3 is added to the preceding answer.)

Math Connection

Math Reasoning Write a multiplication sentence for each product in the following pattern. Make sure each sentence includes the number 5 as a factor at least once: 5, 10, 15, 20, 25. (Possible answers: 1 × 5 = 5, 2 × 5 = 10, 3 × 5 = 15, 4 × 5 = 20, 5 × 5 = 25)

Subject Integration

Reading Count the number of books you read last month. If you read at least as many books in each of the remaining months of this school year as you did last month, what is the least amount of books you will have read from last month to the end of the school year? (Answers will vary.)

Classwork and Homework Supplements

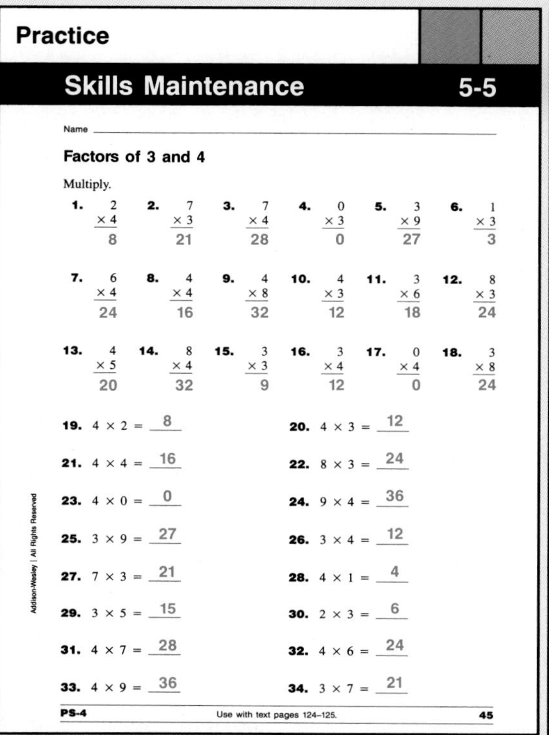

Practice

Skills Maintenance 5-5

Name ____________________

Factors of 3 and 4

Multiply.

1. $2 \times 4 = 8$	2. $7 \times 3 = 21$	3. $7 \times 4 = 28$	4. $0 \times 3 = 0$	5. $3 \times 9 = 27$	6. $1 \times 3 = 3$
7. $6 \times 4 = 24$	8. $4 \times 4 = 16$	9. $4 \times 8 = 32$	10. $4 \times 3 = 12$	11. $3 \times 6 = 18$	12. $8 \times 3 = 24$
13. $4 \times 5 = 20$	14. $8 \times 4 = 32$	15. $3 \times 3 = 9$	16. $3 \times 4 = 12$	17. $0 \times 4 = 0$	18. $3 \times 8 = 24$

19. $4 \times 2 =$ 8 — 20. $4 \times 3 =$ 12
21. $4 \times 4 =$ 16 — 22. $8 \times 3 =$ 24
23. $4 \times 0 =$ 0 — 24. $9 \times 4 =$ 36
25. $3 \times 9 =$ 27 — 26. $3 \times 4 =$ 12
27. $7 \times 3 =$ 21 — 28. $4 \times 1 =$ 4
29. $3 \times 5 =$ 15 — 30. $2 \times 3 =$ 6
31. $4 \times 7 =$ 28 — 32. $4 \times 6 =$ 24
33. $4 \times 9 =$ 36 — 34. $3 \times 7 =$ 21

PS-4 — Use with text pages 124–125. — 45

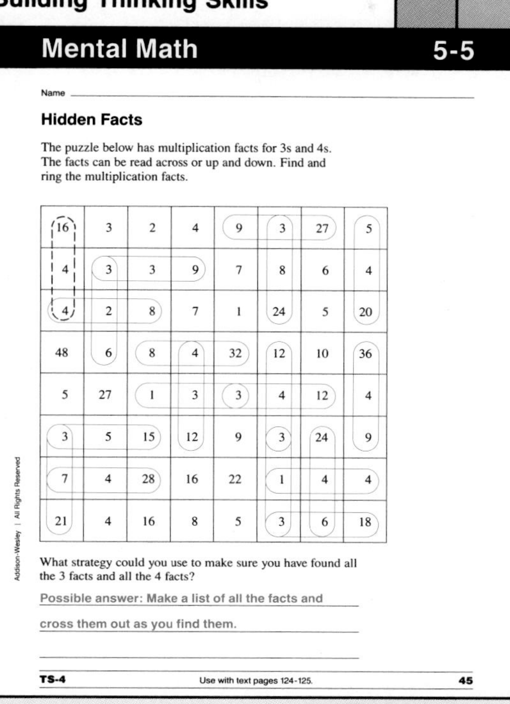

Building Thinking Skills

Mental Math 5-5

Name ____________________

Hidden Facts

The puzzle below has multiplication facts for 3s and 4s. The facts can be read across or up and down. Find and ring the multiplication facts.

16	3	2	4	9	3	27	5
4	3	3	9	7	8	6	4
4	2	8	7	1	24	5	20
48	6	8	4	32	12	10	36
5	27	1	3	3	4	12	4
3	5	15	12	9	3	24	9
7	4	28	16	22	1	4	4
21	4	16	8	5	3	6	18

What strategy could you use to make sure you have found all the 3 facts and all the 4 facts?

Possible answer: Make a list of all the facts and cross them out as you find them.

TS-4 — Use with text pages 124–125. — 45

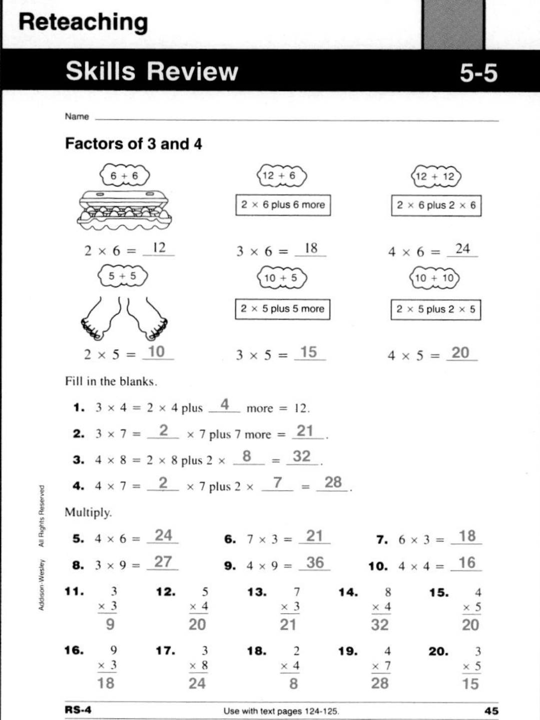

Reteaching

Skills Review 5-5

Name ____________________

Factors of 3 and 4

6 + 6 — 12 + 6 — 12 + 12
2 × 6 plus 6 more — 2 × 6 plus 2 × 6

$2 \times 6 =$ 12 — $3 \times 6 =$ 18 — $4 \times 6 =$ 24

5 + 5 — 10 + 5 — 10 + 10
2 × 5 plus 5 more — 2 × 5 plus 2 × 5

$2 \times 5 =$ 10 — $3 \times 5 =$ 15 — $4 \times 5 =$ 20

Fill in the blanks.

1. $3 \times 4 = 2 \times 4$ plus 4 more $= 12$.
2. $3 \times 7 =$ 2 $\times 7$ plus 7 more $=$ 21.
3. $4 \times 8 = 2 \times 8$ plus $2 \times$ 8 $=$ 32.
4. $4 \times 7 =$ 2 $\times 7$ plus $2 \times$ 7 $=$ 28.

Multiply.

5. $4 \times 6 =$ 24 — 6. $7 \times 3 =$ 21 — 7. $6 \times 3 =$ 18
8. $3 \times 9 =$ 27 — 9. $4 \times 9 =$ 36 — 10. $4 \times 4 =$ 16

11. $3 \times 3 = 9$	12. $5 \times 4 = 20$	13. $7 \times 3 = 21$	14. $8 \times 4 = 32$	15. $4 \times 5 = 20$
16. $9 \times 3 = 18$	17. $3 \times 8 = 24$	18. $2 \times 4 = 8$	19. $4 \times 7 = 28$	20. $3 \times 5 = 15$

RS-4 — Use with text pages 124–125. — 45

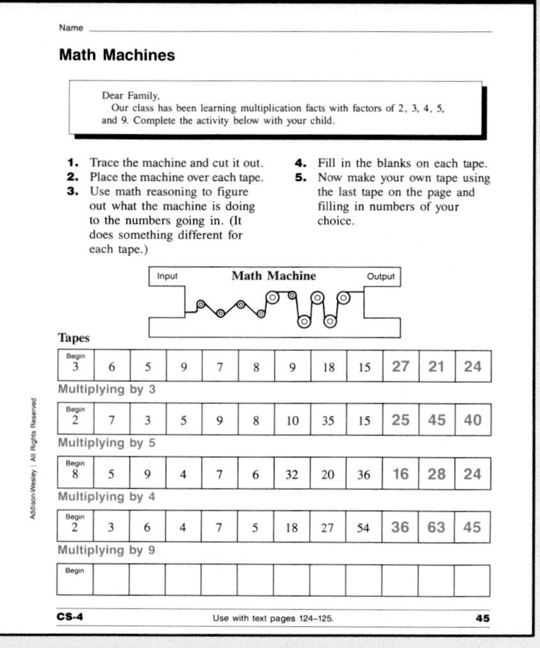

Challenges

Family Math 5-5

Name ____________________

Math Machines

Dear Family,
Our class has been learning multiplication facts with factors of 2, 3, 4, 5, and 9. Complete the activity below with your child.

1. Trace the machine and cut it out.
2. Place the machine over each tape.
3. Use math reasoning to figure out what the machine is doing to the numbers going in. (It does something different for each tape.)
4. Fill in the blanks on each tape.
5. Now make your own tape using the last tape on the page and filling in numbers of your choice.

Tapes

Begin											
3	6	5	9	7	8	9	18	15	27	21	24

Multiplying by 3

Begin											
2	7	3	5	9	8	10	35	15	25	45	40

Multiplying by 5

Begin											
8	5	9	4	7	6	32	20	36	16	28	24

Multiplying by 4

Begin											
2	3	6	4	7	5	18	27	54	36	63	45

Multiplying by 9

Begin											

CS-4 — Use with text pages 124–125. — 45

Options for Individual Needs

Basic

Exercises 1-10, 15-20, 28-34
Computer Bank, p. 492
More Practice, p. 503, set B

Supplements
Reteaching 45 or
Practice 45
Challenges 45

Average

Exercises 1-37
Computer Bank, p. 492
More Practice, p. 503, set B

Supplements
Practice 45
Challenges 45 or
Thinking Skills 45

Extended

Exercises 4-14, 21-34
Computer Bank, p. 492

Supplements
Challenges 45
Thinking Skills 45

Other Resources:
Problem-Solving Experiences in Mathematics, Grade 4, Problem 37
Mathdroid Multiplication, pp. 35, 46
Middle Grades Mathematics Project: Factors and Multiples, p. 31
Using the Math Explorer Calculator: A Sourcebook for Teachers, Chapter 14

LESSON PLAN 5-5

OBJECTIVE 5-5
To find products when 3 or 4 is a factor

Materials: counters, paper cups

Grouping Suggestion: small groups

1. MOTIVATE AND TEACH

LEARN ABOUT IT

EXPLORE ► **What do you know about breaking apart numbers in addition that can help you with multiplication?** (Possible answer: The order or grouping of addends or factors does not change the sum or product.)

TALK ABOUT IT ► **Why might breaking apart a factor to multiply by 3 and 4 be useful?** (Possible answer: It makes it easy mentally to multiply by 2 and add another group or to multiply by 2 twice and add the sums.)
► **What might you do to help you break apart the factors in Exercise 3?** (Possible answers: Draw pictures; use counters.)
► **Explain why doubling a double is the same as multiplying the original number by 4.** (Possible answer: Doubling is multiplying by 2. Doubling again is multiplying by 2 again. $2 \times 2 = 4$)
Student Edition answers: **1.** It shows 3 groups of 8. **2.** It shows 4 groups of 8. **3.** $(2 \times 6) + 6$; $(2 \times 6) + (2 \times 6)$ **4.** 2 times a number is a double. 4 times a number equals 2 times that number twice.

2. CHECK UNDERSTANDING

TRY IT OUT

ERROR ALERT Forgetting the steps to break apart a factor of 3 or 4 before multiplying.

Factors of 3 and 4

LEARN ABOUT IT

EXPLORE Study the Pictures
You can break apart a factor and use the 2 facts to multiply by 3 or 4.

TALK ABOUT IT See teaching notes.

1. How do the pictures show that 3×8 is 2×8 and 8 more?
2. How do the pictures show that 4×8 is 2×8 and 2×8?
3. How would you use the same ideas to find 3×6 and 4×6?
4. Lenny said, "To multiply by 4, I just double a double!" What did he mean?

To multiply a number by 3, add the number to its double.
To multiply a number by 4, double it, then double again.

2×7 plus 7 more
$3 \times 7 = 21$
Double the 7 to get 14.
Add 7 more to get 21.

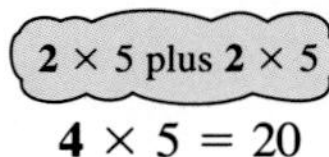

2×5 plus 2×5
$4 \times 5 = 20$
Double the 5 to get 10.
Double the 10 to get 20.

TRY IT OUT

Find the products mentally.

2×5 plus 5 more
1. 3×5 15

2×7 plus 2×7
2. 4×7 28

2×9 plus 9 more
3. 3×9 27

4. $3 \times 7 =$ |||| 21
5. $4 \times 3 =$ |||| 12
6. $4 \times 8 =$ |||| 32
7. $3 \times 9 =$ |||| 27

TEACHING OPTIONS

RETEACHING TIPS Students model the process using paper cups and counters. To show 3×6 they put 6 counters in each of 3 cups. They group 2 cups to find $2 \times 6 = 12$, then add 6 more to get 18. They do the same to break apart 4×6 into $(2 \times 6) + (2 \times 6) = 24$. Assign Reteaching Supplement 45.

ENRICHMENT Give pairs of students 12 blank index cards. Write 6 products on the chalkboard; half divisible by 3, half by 4. Pairs write on a card a multiplication fact for each product, then write the fact broken apart. They mix the cards, place them in rows face down, then take turns trying for a match.

PRACTICE

Multiply.

1. 3 × 6 = 18	**2.** 4 × 7 = 28	**3.** 9 × 3 = 27	**4.** 5 × 4 = 20	**5.** 4 × 8 = 32	**6.** 3 × 7 = 21	**7.** 8 × 3 = 24
8. 6 × 5 = 30	**9.** 9 × 8 = 72	**10.** 6 × 7 = 42	**11.** 9 × 9 = 81	**12.** 7 × 8 = 56	**13.** 6 × 6 = 36	**14.** 6 × 8 = 48

15. 3 × 7 21	**16.** 4 × 6 24	**17.** 2 × 0 0	**18.** 3 × 1 3	**19.** 5 × 8 40	**20.** 7 × 3 21
21. 4 × 5 20	**22.** 4 × 3 12	**23.** 3 × 8 24	**24.** 1 × 4 4	**25.** 9 × 3 27	**26.** 7 × 9 63

APPLY

MATH REASONING What number goes in the box to show a multiplication fact?

27. [8] × 3 = 24 **28.** [8] × 4 = 32 **29.** 3 × [7] = 21

30. 3 × 8 is a name for the number 24. Write three other names for 24.
1 × 24, 2 × 12, 4 × 6

PROBLEM SOLVING

31. Data Hunt Make a table of items that come in packages, showing how many are in each package. For each item, how many are in 3 packages? in 4 packages?
Answers will vary.

► **MENTAL MATH**

To do mental math, it helps if you can remember one number while computing with other numbers. To practice this, do these without pencil and paper. Which fact is greater?

32. 4 × 3 or 2 × 7 **33.** 3 × 5 or 4 × 4 **34.** 2 × 9 or 4 × 6

35. 4 × 7 or 9 × 3 **36.** 6 × 5 or 4 × 8 **37.** 7 × 3 or 5 × 4

More Practice, page 503, set B

3. PRACTICE AND APPLY

Basic	1-10; 15-20; 28-34
Average	1-37
Extended	4-14; 21-34

PRACTICE

How are Exercises 1-14 different from Exercises 15-26? (Exercises 1-14 are written vertically while Exercises 15-26 are written horizontally.)

APPLY

MATH REASONING ► **How might you find the missing factors in Exercises 27-29?** (Possible answer: Divide the product by the known factor.)

PROBLEM SOLVING ► **Explain a mental math method to find how many items are in 3 packages and then in 4 packages.** (For 3 packages, add the amount in 1 package to its double; for 4 packages, double the amount in 1 package, then double it again.)

MENTAL MATH ► **What strategies might help you answer Exercises 32-37?** (Possible answer: When multiplying by 3, add the number to its double; when multiplying by 4, double the number twice, then add.)

5-5

CLOSE AND ASSESS

SAY WHAT YOU THINK

Arrange students into groups of 3. One student states a multiplication fact in which one factor is either 3 or 4. Another student tells how the fact could be broken apart. A third child decides if the facts have the same product. Students switch roles for several rounds.

QUICK QUIZ

Break apart the facts to solve each exercise mentally.

3 × 7 = (21)	4 × 4 = (16)
9 × 4 = (36)	3 × 8 = (24)
3 × 5 = (15)	6 × 4 = (24)

Exploring Algebra/Midchapter Review/Quiz

OBJECTIVE 5-6 To explore algebra by using a variable that represents only 1 number

PREBOOK ACTIVITIES

QUICK REVIEW

Find the products.

1. 2 × 2 (4) **2.** 3 × 3 (9)
3. 4 × 4 (16) **4.** 5 × 5 (25)
5. 1 × 1 (1) **6.** 1 × 7 (7)
7. 8 × 0 (0) **8.** 0 × 0 (0)

PRIOR KNOWLEDGE

Write this equation on the chalkboard: △ × 3 = 12. Have students tell how they could find the missing factor. (Possible answers: Use 12 counters; make groups of 3 until all counters are used; think *What times 3 is 12?*) Then write a second equation on the chalkboard: □ + □ = 12. Explain that □ must always be replaced with the same number. Have students find a solution, then identify and analyze the important clue they used to solve the equation. (6; both addends were the same.)

COMMUNICATION

Writing Math In their Math Journals, have students write an explanation for what the term **relationship** means. (Possible answer: "a connection between 2 or more people, things, or ideas") Tell students that some number relationships are very easy to recognize, such as 2 + 2 = 4. However, other number relationships must be explored and analyzed to discover their connection, such as 4 × □ = 24. (6)

EXPLORE AND CONNECT

Materials: TA 3 (Number Cards 0-9), markers or crayons
Grouping Suggestion: cooperative learning pairs
Students create equation puzzles to explore number **relationships**. Partners pick 3 number cards. One student uses 2 of the numbers in an addition, a subtraction, or a multiplication equation, recording it on paper. For instance, given 4 and 7, a student might show 7 − 4 = 3. The partner uses the same numbers in a different equation, also recording it on paper. The second student might use only the 4 to write 4 × 4 = 16. Partners turn the 2 equations into a puzzle, drawing a different-colored box for each number to the left of the equal sign, using the *same* color for the digit that repeats. They should show operation and equal signs and the answer. Pairs exchange puzzles and try to find the missing numbers. Have students describe number **relationships** they used to solve the puzzles. (Answers will vary.)

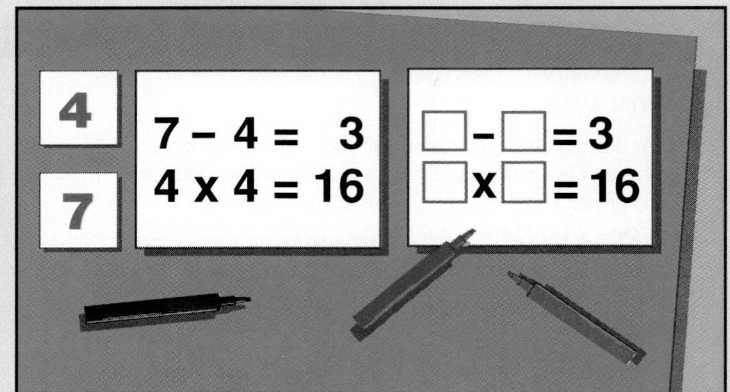

CONNECTIONS Use these anytime.

Problem of the Day

Number Riddle Solve the number riddle.
1. I am an odd number.
2. Both my digits are the same.
3. I am less than 40 but more than 10.
4. Someone this age would be an adult.
What number am I?
(33)

Math Connection

Algebra Find a number that you can triple to equal 24, or increase by the smallest odd number to equal 9. (8)

Number Sense

Mental Math Every missing digit is the same. Complete the equations.
□ + □ = 2
□ × □ = □
□ − □ = 0
(1)

Classwork and Homework Supplements

Practice

Algebra 5-6

Name ____

Exploring Algebra

In each set of equations, each shape represents a number. Find the number that goes in each shape.

1. [2] + △7 = 9; [2] × [2] = 4
2. 8 − [6] = 2; [6] + (4) = 10
3. 4 × △2 = 8; △2 + [8] = 10
4. △4 + [1] = (5); △4 + △4 = 8; (5) × [1] = (5)
5. 10 − △5 − 2 = [3]; [3] × [3] = 9; [3] + 2 = △5
6. [7] + 1 = 8; △2 + 5 = (7); [6] × △2 = 12
7. △3 + 3 = 6; [7] × △3 = 21; (9) − [7] = 2
8. 5 + [4] = △9; △9 − [4] = 5; [4] × [4] = 16
9. △3 × [1] = △3; 5 + △3 = 9 − 1; △3 + 4 = (7)
10. [4] × [4] = 16; 8 − [4] = [4]
11. (8) + [1] = 9; [1] × (8) = (8)
12. [6] × △4 = 24; △4 × △4 = 16
13. [6] + △2 = 8; △2 × △2 = 4
14. 7 + △0 = 7; 5 − △0 = 5
15. [4] × (2) = 8; [4] + [4] = 8
16. Make up a problem like the ones on this page. Exchange with a classmate and find the missing numbers. Answers will vary.

46 Use with text page 126. PS-4

Building Thinking Skills

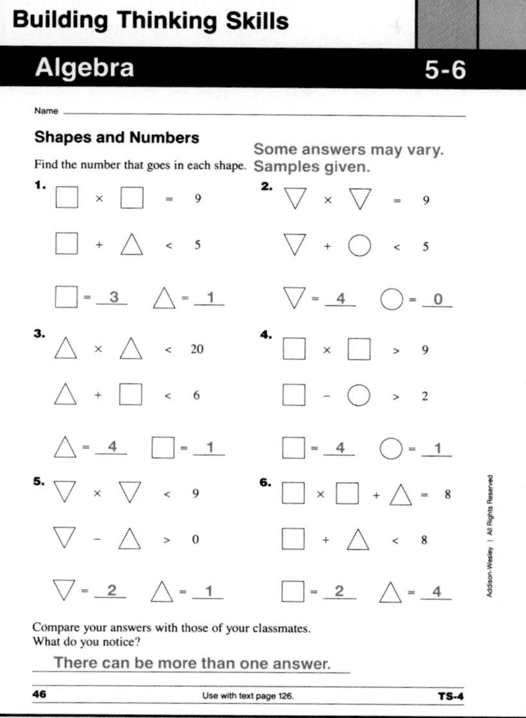

Algebra 5-6

Name ____

Shapes and Numbers

Find the number that goes in each shape. Some answers may vary. Samples given.

1. □ × □ = 9; □ + △ < 5; □ = 3, △ = 1
2. ▽ × ▽ = 9; ▽ + ○ < 5; ▽ = 4, ○ = 0
3. △ × △ < 20; △ + □ < 6; △ = 4, □ = 1
4. □ × □ > 9; □ − ○ > 2; □ = 4, ○ = 1
5. ▽ × ▽ < 9; ▽ − △ > 0; ▽ = 2, △ = 1
6. □ × □ + △ = 8; □ + △ < 8; □ = 2, △ = 4

Compare your answers with those of your classmates. What do you notice?

There can be more than one answer.

46 Use with text page 126. TS-4

Reteaching

Algebra 5-6

Name ____

Exploring Algebra

In these equations, △ stands for one number and □ stands for a different number. Find the number that goes in each shape.

Solve one equation.
□ × □ = 4
2 × 2 = 4;
therefore □ = 2.

Solve the second equation.
△ + □ = 11
△ + 2 = 11;
therefore △ = 9.

Think which equation looks easier to solve.

Find the number that goes in each shape.

1. □ + △ = 7; △ × △ = 16; △ = 4, □ = 3
2. ○ + △ = 8; ○ × ○ = 4; △ = 6, ○ = 2
3. △ + △ = 8; △ × □ = 4; △ = 4, □ = 1
4. ◇ × ◇ = 25; ◇ × □ = 30; ◇ = 5, □ = 6
5. △ + 7 = 8; □ − △ = ◇; ◇ + ◇ = 6; △ = 1, □ = 4, ◇ = 3
6. □ + △ = ○; 4 × △ = 4; ○ + ○ = 10; △ = 1, ○ = 5, □ = 4
7. □ × △ = 24; □ − △ = 2; □ = 6, △ = 4
8. ◇ + □ = ○ + 4; ○ + ◇ = 3; □ × ◇ = 6; □ = 3, ◇ = 2, ○ = 1

46 Use with text page 126. RS-4

Challenges

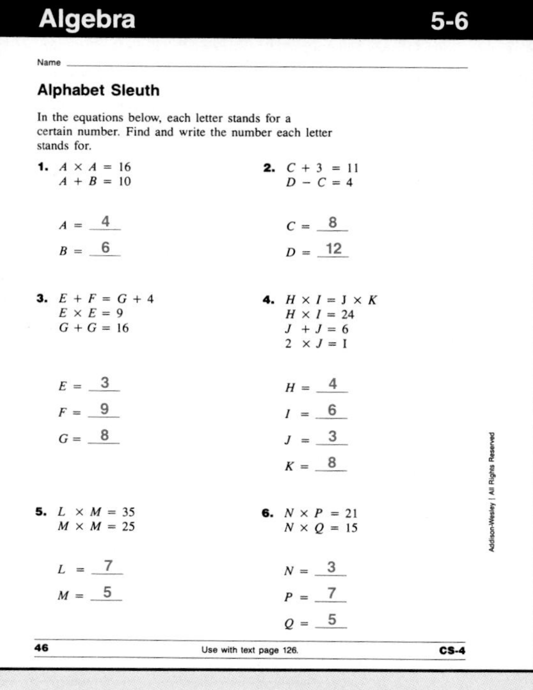

Algebra 5-6

Name ____

Alphabet Sleuth

In the equations below, each letter stands for a certain number. Find and write the number each letter stands for.

1. $A \times A = 16$; $A + B = 10$; $A = 4$, $B = 6$
2. $C + 3 = 11$; $D - C = 4$; $C = 8$, $D = 12$
3. $E + F = G + 4$; $E \times E = 9$; $G + G = 16$; $E = 3$, $F = 9$, $G = 8$
4. $H \times I = J \times K$; $H \times I = 24$; $J + J = 6$; $2 \times J = I$; $H = 4$, $I = 6$, $J = 3$, $K = 8$
5. $L \times M = 35$; $M \times M = 25$; $L = 7$, $M = 5$
6. $N \times P = 21$; $N \times Q = 15$; $N = 3$, $P = 7$, $Q = 5$

46 Use with text page 126. CS-4

Options for Individual Needs

Basic

Exercises 1-3, 6, 7; 1-17, 30-38

Supplements
Reteaching 46 or
Practice 46

Average

Exercises 1-7; 1-38

Supplements
Practice 46
Challenges 46 or
Thinking Skills 46

Extended

Exercises 3-7; 1-10, 30-38

Supplements
Challenges 46
Thinking Skills 46

Other Resources:
Problem-Solving Experiences in Mathematics, Grade 4, Problem 44
Math In Stride, Grade 4, pp. 108, 109
Middle Grades Mathematics Project: Factors and Multiples, Activity 1

5-6

LESSON PLAN 5-6

OBJECTIVE 5-6
To explore algebra by using a variable that represents only 1 number

Materials: colored pencils

Grouping Suggestion: pairs

1. MOTIVATE AND TEACH

LEARN ABOUT IT

EXPLORE ► **Explain a relationship between the 2 equations.** (The multiplication fact uses a double to equal 9; the addition fact equal to 10 has one of the factors as an addend.)

TALK ABOUT IT ► **Analyze how many number combinations exist when you consider only the addition equation.** (10)
► **Explain why it makes sense to solve the multiplication equation first.** (There are fewer number combinations that equal 9, and only 1 that is a double.)
► **Explain how you know that the factors are the same number but the addends are not.** (by the symbols used; 2 boxes indicate doubles; A box and a triangle indicate 2 different digits, 1 being a factor of 9.)
► **Explain how to find a missing addend if you know the sum and 1 addend.** (Subtract the known addend from the sum to give the missing addend.)
Student Edition answers: **1.** 2; 3 × 3, 1 × 9 **2.** same; It must be 3 × 3. **3.** Subtract one addend from the sum; 10 − 3 = 7.

2. CHECK UNDERSTANDING

TRY IT OUT

ERROR ALERT Substituting digits inconsistently in the same exercise. Failing to relate all equations in one exercise.

Exploring Algebra

LEARN ABOUT IT

In these equations, each shape holds a place for just one number. Find the number that goes in each shape.

□ × □ = 9
△ + □ = 10

TALK ABOUT IT See teaching notes.

1. Look at the first equation. How many basic facts have a product of 9?
2. In the first equation, will the factors be the same or will they be different? Why is this important?
3. If you know what □ equals, how can you find △? Tell why.

TRY IT OUT

Find the number that goes in each shape.

1. □ + △ = 7   (5, 2)
   △ × △ = 4   (2, 2)
2. △ + 8 = 8   (0)
   □ − △ = 6   (6, 0)
3. □ × △ = 27   (9, 3)
   □ − △ = 6   (9, 3)
4. □ × △ = 30   (6, 5)
   □ × □ = 36   (6, 6)
5. △ + △ = ○ + 3   (5, 5, 7)
   ○ + □ = 8   (7, 1)
   □ × △ = △   (1, 5, 5)
6. □ + △ = ○   (3, 1, 4)
   5 × △ = 5   (1)
   □ + □ = 6   (3, 3)
7. Make up a problem like the one on this page. Exchange with a classmate and find the missing numbers. Answers will vary.

TEACHING OPTIONS

RETEACHING TIPS Be sure students who are substituting digits inconsistently realize that the same shape may have a different value in different exercises. Have students use colored pencils to write a digit in every identical shape in the same exercise. Assign Reteaching Supplement 46.

ENRICHMENT Have students find the number that goes in each shape.
○ × □ = 24
□ + ○ = 11
□ − ○ = 5
4 + ○ = □ − 1
(○ = 3; □ = 8)

Midchapter Review/Quiz

Draw a picture to show that the key action is **put together same-size groups**.

1. May planted 3 rows of tulips. She put 5 tulips in each row. How many tulips did she plant? **Check drawings. 15**
2. The pet store has 2 bowls of goldfish. There are 6 goldfish in each bowl. How many goldfish are in the bowls? **Check drawings. 12**
3. Liz has 9 nickels. How much money does she have? **Check drawings. 45¢**

Find the products.

4. 4×1 **4**
5. 2×5 **10**
6. 5×9 **45**
7. 0×2 **0**
8. 3×5 **15**
9. 1×3 **3**
10. 9×2 **18**
11. 9×1 **9**
12. 3×2 **6**
13. 4×9 **36**
14. 2×8 **16**
15. 1×5 **5**
16. 5×0 **0**
17. 8×9 **72**
18. 2×3 **6**
19. 4×5 **20**
20. 0×9 **0**
21. 2×2 **4**
22. 7×9 **63**
23. 4×2 **8**
24. 0×3 **0**
25. 5×6 **30**
26. 7×5 **35**
27. 1×0 **0**
28. 9×6 **54**
29. 6×2 **12**
30. 9×9 **81**
31. 8×5 **40**
32. 9×3 **27**
33. 2×7 **14**
34. 5×5 **25**

PROBLEM SOLVING

35. The art room has 9 tables. 4 students sit at each table. How many students can sit at the tables? **36 students**
36. A quarter is worth 5 nickels. Ray has 7 quarters. How many nickels can Ray get for his 7 quarters? **35 nickels**
37. June has 3 nickels, 2 dimes, and 2 quarters. How much money does she have? **85¢**
38. Ben has 3 pairs of tennis shoes and 1 pair of dress shoes. How many pairs of shoes does he have? How many shoes is that? **4 pairs; 8 shoes**

3. Practice and Apply

Basic	1-3, 6, 7; 1-17, 30-38
Average	1-7; 1-38
Extended	3-7; 1-10, 30-38

PRACTICE

How are Exercises 4, 9, 11, 15, and 27 related? (All use the One Property.)

ITEM ANALYSIS The following table correlates the Midchapter Review/Quiz items with the lesson objectives.

Items	Objectives
1-3	5-1
4, 7, 9, 11, 15, 16, 20, 24, 27	5-2
(1-3), 5, 6, 8, 10, 12, 14, (15, 16), 18, 19, 21, 23, 25, 26, 29, 31, 33, 34, 36, 38	5-3
(6, 10, 11), 13, 17, (20), 22, 28, 30, 32, 35	5-4
(1, 4, 8, 9, 12, 13, 18, 19, 23, 24, 32, 35, 38)	5-5

5-6

Close and Assess

WRITE WHAT YOU THINK
Have students solve the equations below. Then have them write paragraphs explaining the order of the steps they followed and describing the number relationships they noticed. (△ = 5, ○ = 6)
△ + ○ = 11
△ × △ = 25

QUICK QUIZ

Solve.
□ − △ = 1
△ × □ = 6
(□ = 3; △ = 2)

LESSON OPTIONS 5-7

Problem Solving: Understanding the Question

OBJECTIVE 5-7 To understand the question in a problem

PREBOOK ACTIVITIES

QUICK REVIEW

Add or subtract.

1. 462 + 5,622 + 3,019 (9,103)
2. 5,002 − 3,527 (1,475)
3. 85 − 39 (46)
4. 4,320 + 337 (4,657)
5. 4,112 − 804 (3,308)

PRIOR KNOWLEDGE

Have students share experiences of trying to explain something to a very young child. Ask them to recall what they did to help the child understand the ideas. (Possible answer: Use simple words; repeat the idea; try several different ways of explaining.)

COMMUNICATION

Discussing Math Have students give a synonym for *different*. (Possible answer: *unlike*) Explain that 2 things may be so different that they are opposites, such as cold and hot. Other times, 2 things that are different may be somewhat alike, such as ovals and circles. Still other times, an idea is described using different words, such as a glass that is half empty or half full. Have students suggest things that are described by different words. (Possible answers: graph paper or grid paper; sneakers or athletic shoes; doctor or physician) Then have students give different math words for the same operations. (Sample answers for *add: plus, find a sum, total, combine;* for *subtract: minus, take away, find a difference*)

EXPLORE AND CONNECT

COOPERATIVE ACTIVITY

Grouping Suggestion: small groups

In 35 y of work, a dentist in Italy collected 2,000,744 teeth. In 35 y of work, a school nurse in Ohio collected 472 teeth. How many more teeth did the dentist collect?

TEACHING ACTIONS

Encourage group members to respect others as they work together.

▶ **Explain the situation in your own words.** (2 people collected teeth over 35 y at their jobs.)

▶ **Decide what you need to find out.** (How many more teeth did the dentist collect?)

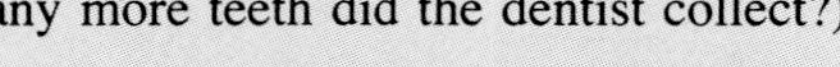

▶ **Analyze the question to understand the operation it suggests.** (compare 2 different amounts, so subtract)

▶ **Formulate a similar question about the problem using other words.** (Sample question: *What is the difference in the sizes of the 2 collections?*)

▶ **Justify your calculation method.** (Possible answer: I used a calculator to find 2,000,272 because one number was so large.)

▶ **Explain how asking the same question in other words can help.** (It can help you more clearly understand what a problem is asking.)

CONNECTIONS Use these anytime.

Problem of the Day

Tall Buildings Read the problem, decide how to solve it, then find the answer. In Houston, the Texas Commerce Tower is 340 ft taller than the First City Tower, which is 662 ft tall. Find the height of the larger building. (You are given the height difference, so add 662 and 340; 1,002 ft)

Number Sense

Mental Math What is the question? Read the facts and the answer, then determine a reasonable question: There are 5 six-ounce cans in a juice pack. Stan bought 3 juice packs. Answer: 30. (How many ounces of juice are in 1 juice pack?)

Math Connection

Calculator In 1987, a total of 14,781,222 passengers used the Orlando airport. During the same year, almost twice as many people used the airport in San Francisco. Tell the keystrokes to use to find how many twice as many people would be and the number the calculator would display. (Enter 14781222 × 2 = 29562444.)

CLASSWORK AND HOMEWORK SUPPLEMENTS

Practice

Problem Solving 5-7

Name

Understanding the Question

Read each problem. Underline the question that asks the same thing. Then solve the problem.

1. Scientists believe that 38 million years ago the average height of horses was 24 inches. Today's horses are about 66 inches high. What is the difference in height?
   a. How much taller are today's horses?
   b. What is the total height of today's horses and horses of long ago?
2. Thoroughbred horses weigh up to 1,300 pounds. Cleveland Bays may weigh as much as 2,200 pounds. What is the total weight of the two kinds of horses?
   a. How much more does the Cleveland Bay weigh?
   b. How much would a Thoroughbred and a Cleveland Bay weigh together?
3. Shetland ponies are about 11 hands high. Welsh ponies may be as high as 14 hands. What is the difference in height of the two hands of ponies?
   a. How high are a Shetland and Welsh pony together?
   b. How much higher is a Welsh pony?
4. Berta loves to horseback ride. She tries to ride 3 days a week. In 4 weeks, how many days does she ride altogether?
   a. How many times does she ride each week?
   b. What is the total number of days she rides in 4 weeks?

Write a question for each statement. Then solve. Answers will vary. Examples given.

5. There were 187 tickets sold at the horse show on Saturday. Ticket sales for Sunday's show totaled 213.
   How many tickets were sold altogether? 400
6. A total of 9 different horses were ridden in the show. Each horse was ridden by 3 different riders in different events.
   What is the total number of events? 27

PS-4 Use with text pages 128–129. 47

Building Thinking Skills

Reading Math 5-7

Name

What Is the Question?

Read the two questions for each data card below. Draw lines from each data card to the questions that go with it. Then write +, −, or × in the box beside each question to show the operation needed to find the answer. Finally, answer each question.

Data cards:
- Ridge sold 126 boxes on Thursday and 142 boxes on Friday.
- Lily stacked 5 rows of boxes with 6 boxes in each row.
- Thomas delivered 9 boxes in 25 minutes on Monday and four times as many boxes on Tuesday in 123 minutes.
- Tammy wrote 42 bills in 3 hours. It took her twice as long to do 84 bills.

1. How many boxes did Thomas deliver on Tuesday? × 36
2. What is the difference in the number of bills Tammy wrote at the different times? − 42
3. How many boxes did Lily stack altogether? × 30
4. How many more boxes did Ridge sell on Friday? − 16
5. How many hours did it take Tammy to write 84 bills? × 6
6. How many boxes did Lily stack in 2 rows? × 12
7. How many boxes did Ridge sell in all? + 268
8. How many minutes less did it take Thomas to deliver the boxes on Monday than on Tuesday? − 98

TS-4 Use with text pages 128–129. 47

Reteaching

Problem Solving 5-7

Name

Understanding the Question

Read the question carefully. → Ask the question in a different way. → Solve the problem.

Ben sold 7 baseballs and 5 basketballs. What is the difference between the number of baseballs he sold and the number of basketballs he sold? — How many more baseballs did Ben sell? — Ben sold 2 more baseballs.

Ring the letter of the question that asks the same thing.

1. Sandy saw 6 robins and 8 bluebirds. How many birds did she see?
   (a.) How many birds did Sandy see in all?
   b. How many fewer robins than bluebirds did Sandy see?
2. Danny bought 9 goldfish and 7 striped fish. What is the difference in the number of fish?
   a. How many fish did Danny buy in all?
   (b.) How many more goldfish than striped fish did Danny buy?

Write each question in a different way. Then solve.

3. Cindy planted 8 bean plants and 5 corn plants. How many fewer corn plants than bean plants did Cindy plant?
   wording will vary; 3
4. Tom has 2 black cats and 7 gray cats. What is the total number of cats that Tom has?
   wording will vary; 9

RS-4 Use with text pages 128–129. 47

Challenges

Reading Math 5-7

Name

Teacher for a Day

You are the math teacher today. One of your students did not solve the problems correctly because he did not understand the questions. In your comments, explain his mistakes and write the correct answer.

Comments: Wording will vary.

1. At the pet parade, there were 176 entries last year and 267 this year. How many more entries were there this year? 443
   You added to find the total for 2 years. You should subtract to find the difference. Answer: 91
2. Jeff bought a bandanna for $3.74 and a leash for $7.49 for his dog to wear in the parade. How much money did he spend? $3.75
   You subtracted to find out how much more the leash cost instead of adding to find the total cost. Answer: $11.23
3. There were 5 floats in the parade with 8 people on each float. How many people were on floats altogether? 13
   You needed to multiply, not add, to find the number of people on 5 floats. Answer:40
4. At the refreshment stand, 247 drinks were sold the first hour, 482 the second hour, and 67 the third hour. How many drinks were sold in all? 729
   You needed to find the sum of 3 numbers, not 2. Answer: 796

CS-4 Use with text pages 128–129. 47

OPTIONS FOR INDIVIDUAL NEEDS

Basic

Exercises 1-8
Skills Bank, pp. 461, 462
Calculator Bank, p. 485
Computer Bank, p. 492
More Practice, p. 516, set B

Supplements
Reteaching 47 or
Practice 47

Average

Exercises 1-8
Skills Bank, p. 462
Calculator Bank, p. 485
Computer Bank, p. 492
More Practice, p. 516, set B

Supplements
Practice 47
Challenges 47 or
Thinking Skills 47

Extended

Exercises 1-8
Calculator Bank, p. 485
Computer Bank, p. 492

Supplements
Challenges 47
Thinking Skills 47

Other Resources:
Problem-Solving Experiences in Mathematics, Grade 4, Problem 1
Math in Stride, Grade 4, pp. 94, 95
Mathematics Book A, p. 43
Using the Math Explorer Calculator: A Sourcebook for Teachers, Chapter 14

LESSON PLAN 5-7

OBJECTIVE 5-7
To understand the question in a problem

Grouping Suggestion: pairs

1. MOTIVATE AND TEACH

LEARN ABOUT IT

BEFORE ▶ **Summarize Matt's situation in your own words.** (Matt has already worn his headgear for some time and must keep wearing it for more time.)

▶ **Analyze the problem for important data.** (2,142 h already; 5,523 h to go)

DURING ▶ **Identify a key phrase in the question that suggests an action. Explain your reasoning.** (*total amount*; It suggests putting groups together.

▶ **Explain which operation to use.** (addition; put together different-size groups)

▶ **Formulate a related question that asks the same thing.** (Possible answer: *How long must Matt wear his headgear all together?*)

▶ **Find the answer. Explain what you did.** (7,665; add the time Matt has already worn the headgear to the time still to go.)

▶ **Evaluate your answer to determine if it makes sense.** (Based on an estimate of 2,000 + 6,000 = 8,000, 7,655 is a reasonable answer.)

2. CHECK UNDERSTANDING

TRY IT OUT

ERROR ALERT Misinterpreting key operation words.

Problem Solving
Understanding the Question

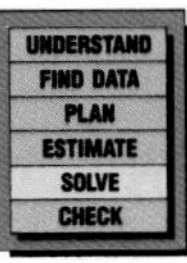
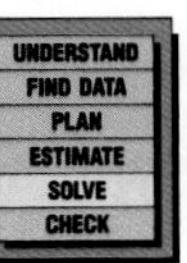

LEARN ABOUT IT

One of the first things you must do when you solve a problem is to understand the question. Sometimes it helps to put the question in your own words or to ask it in a different way.

Matt calculated that he has worn his headgear for 2,142 hours. He has 5,523 hours to go. What is the total amount of time he will wear his headgear?

First I'll read the question. — What is the total amount of time he will wear his headgear?

Then I'll ask the question in a different way. — How many hours must Matt wear his headgear in all?

TRY IT OUT

Read each problem. Then decide which question asks the same thing.

1. An adult human has 32 teeth. A whale shark can have 4,000 teeth. What is the difference in the number of teeth?
   (a.) How many more teeth does a whale shark have?
   b. How many teeth do humans and whale sharks have all together?

2. Dr. Li is a children's dentist. She takes care of 15 patients a day. What is the total number of patients she sees in 5 days?
   a. How many patients does she see each day?
   (b.) In 5 days, how many patients does she see all together?

Write each question in a different way. Then solve. **See Additional Answers.**

3. Dr. Verne, the orthodontist, saw 365 patients in August. He saw 287 patients in September. How many fewer patients did he see in September?

4. Dr. Mudd displays pictures of some of his patients. There are 9 rows of pictures with 9 pictures in each row. What is the total number of pictures?

TEACHING OPTIONS

RETEACHING TIPS Group students in pairs. In Exercises 1 and 2, have partners identify the key word in each question and relate it to a math operation. Then have students find another phrase or word from the choices that means the same. Assign Reteaching Supplement 47.

COMPUTER **Teasers by Tobb, Sunburst Communications, Copyright 1985** For all students. Choose multiplication and difficulty levels one or two. An incomplete 2-by-2 multiplication table is presented in which empty squares must be filled. It requires 10-15 min.

MIXED PRACTICE

Write each question in a different way. Then solve. See Additional Answers.

Dr. Fisher's Dental Office Number of Patients		
	Adults	Children
1989	2,177	1,334
1990	2,189	1,399
1991	2,161	1,442

1. How many more adults than children did Dr. Fisher see in 1990?
2. How many children did Dr. Fisher see all together from 1989 to 1991?
3. Did Dr. Fisher see fewer than 6,000 adults from 1989 to 1991? Tell how you know.
4. For the first 3 nights, Charlie wore his headgear for 6 hours each night. For the next 4 nights, he wore it for 8 hours each night. How long did he wear it in all?
5. For her prize box, Dr. Rose bought 5 packages of rings with 8 rings in each package. She also bought 36 stickers. How many rings did she buy?
6. Jose waited in the dentist's waiting room 20 minutes. His checkup took 45 minutes. What is the total amount of time Jose was at the dentist's office?

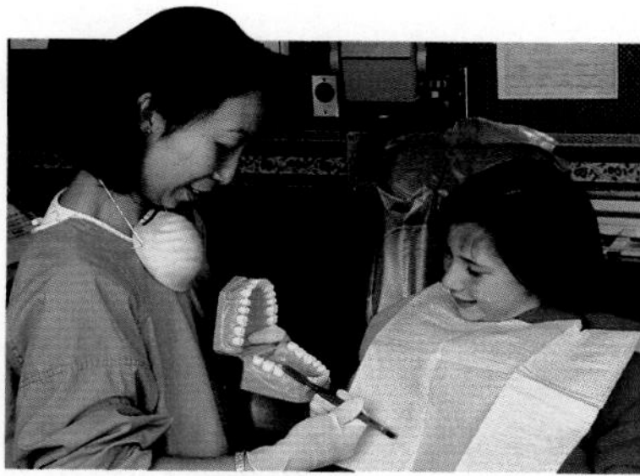

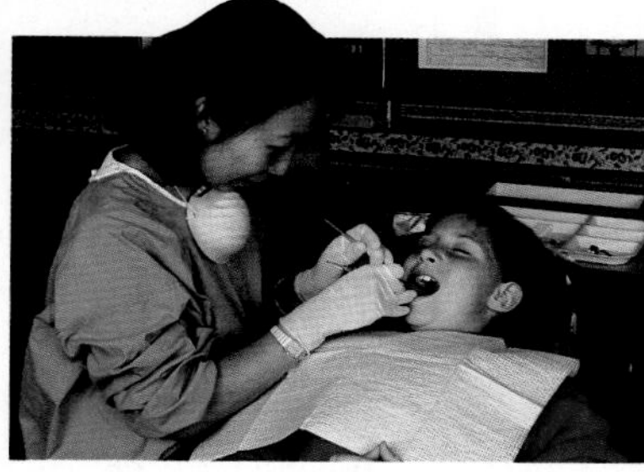

7. Mrs. Osawa has 8 times as many teeth as baby Keisi. Keisi has 4 teeth. How many teeth does Mrs. Osawa have?
8. **Think About Your Solution**
A wire on Judy's braces came loose. She could see Dr. Brown, Dr. Pan, or Dr. Bernstein. She could get an appointment during school or after school. How many choices does she have?
   - **a.** Show the steps you took to solve the problem.
   - **b.** Write your answer in a complete sentence.
   - **c.** Tell the strategy or strategies you used to solve the problem.

More Practice, page 516, set B

3. Practice and Apply

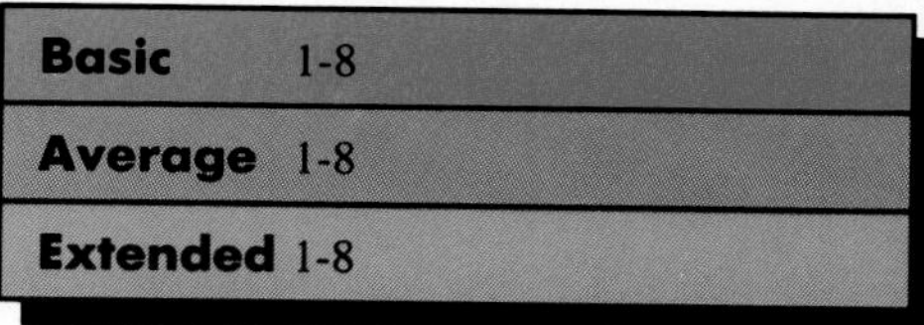

Basic	1-8
Average	1-8
Extended	1-8

Additional Answers and Sample Solutions: See p. T79.

MIXED PRACTICE

▶ **Analyze the chart for the data you need in Problem 1.** (2,189 adults; 1,399 children)

▶ **Analyze the similarity between Problems 2, 3, and 6.** (All involve finding a total of 2 or more numbers.)

▶ **Which problem requires multiplying, then adding? Explain why.** (Problem 4; multiply to find same-size groups, then add the products.)

▶ **Justify a solution strategy for Problem 8.** (Choose Make an Organized List to track choices.)

5-7

Close and Assess

WRITE WHAT YOU THINK

Have students write each question another way.

1. How many more molars than baby teeth?
2. How much dental floss on 6 rolls?
3. What is the total amount of mouthwash? (Answers may vary. Check students' writing.)

QUICK QUIZ

Rewrite the question, then solve. Dr. Yanks charges $20 for a checkup, $25 for X rays, and $30 per filling. How much would a checkup and 2 fillings cost? ($80; Check students' questions.)

LESSON OPTIONS 5-8

Mental Math: More Breaking Apart Numbers

OBJECTIVE 5-8 To use the mental math technique of break apart to find multiplication facts

PREBOOK ACTIVITIES

QUICK REVIEW

Add, using mental math strategies.

1. 32 + 16 (48)	**2.** 24 + 12 (36)	**3.** 21 + 21 (42)
4. 35 + 15 (50)	**5.** 14 + 21 (35)	**6.** 42 + 12 (54)
7. 18 + 18 (36)	**8.** 40 + 16 (56)	**9.** 36 + 24 (60)

PRIOR KNOWLEDGE

Have students suggest how they might break apart factors to multiply 3 × 6 and 4 × 7. (Possible answer: Find 2 × 6, then add 6 more to get 18; find 2 × 7, then double the product to get 28.) Have students review the order-of-operations rule for adding and multiplying. (First multiply, then add.) Tell students that they will use the break-apart strategy with the order-of-operations rule to find products of greater factors.

COMMUNICATION

Discussing Math Have students break apart a factor to find the product of 4 × 6 by using doubles. (2 × 6 and 2 × 6; 4 × 3 and 4 × 3) Have students analyze how the order-of-operations rule applies to the doubling strategy. (Possible answer: First multiply 2 × 6 and 2 × 6; then add the two products, 12 + 12, to get the product of 24.)

EXPLORE AND CONNECT

Materials: graph paper, scissors, TA 11 (Blank Spinners divided into sixths marked 3-8)
Grouping Suggestion: cooperative learning pairs
Have each pair of students cut 8 strips of graph paper six units long. They spin to determine how many times to multiply by 6. For example, if they spin 5, one student takes 5 strips and the other gives the product. (5 × 6 = 30) Then partners break apart the 5 strips to form 2 groups in as many ways as possible. (3 strips + 2 strips; 1 strip + 4 strips) They record these groupings as expressions with parentheses. [(3 × 6) + (2 × 6); (1 × 6) + (4 × 6)] They take turns computing the partial and complete products. [(3 × 6) + (2 × 6) = 18 + 12 = 30; (1 × 6) + (4 × 6) = 6 + 24 = 30] They verify that breaking apart factors and computing partial products will give the same complete product. Conclude by having students summarize how to use break-apart factors.

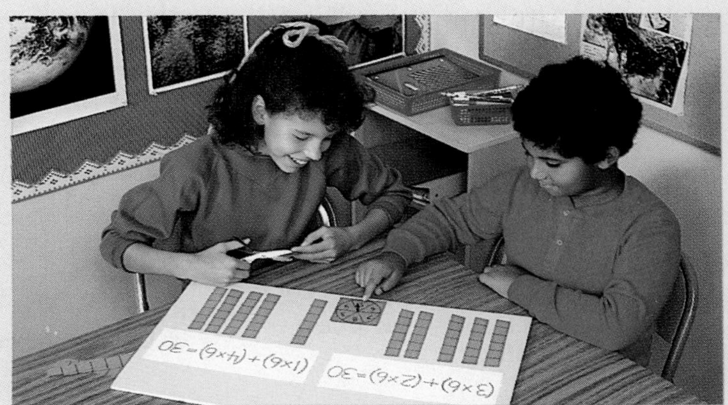

CONNECTIONS Use these anytime.

Problem of the Day

Patterns Find each sum, then figure out how it relates to addends and factors.
(1 × 3) + (2 × 3) + (3 × 3) = ? (18)
(1 × 4) + (2 × 4) + (3 × 4) = ? (24)
(1 × 5) + (2 × 5) + (3 × 5) = ? (30)
(1 + 2 + 3 = 6; sums are 6 times the repeating factor.)

Math Connection

Time A class has 30 minutes of math time every morning and a half-hour of math time each afternoon. How many hours of math time does the class have in a regular school week? (5 hours)

Number Sense

Riddles I am one 6 less than 5 × 6. What number am I? (4 × 6 or 24)
I am one 7 more than 5 × 7. What number am I? (6 × 7 or 42) Make up more riddles like these.

Classwork and Homework Supplements

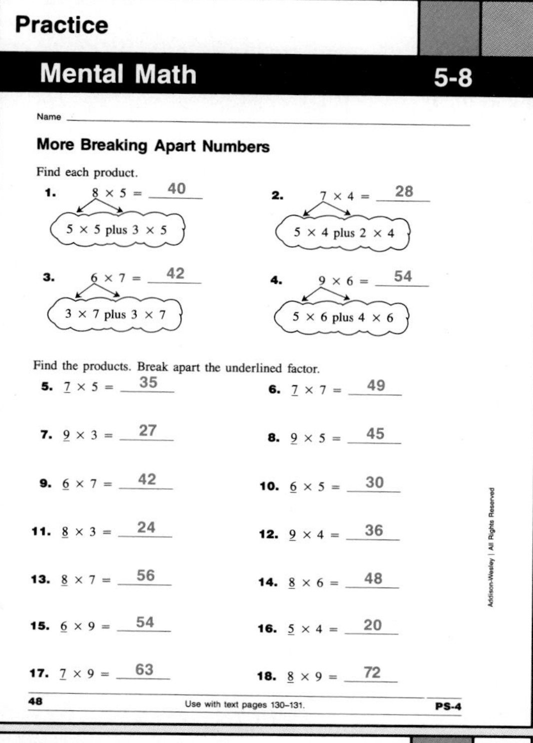

Practice

Mental Math 5-8

Name ______

More Breaking Apart Numbers

Find each product.

1. 8 × 5 = 40 (5 × 5 plus 3 × 5)
2. 7 × 4 = 28 (5 × 4 plus 2 × 4)
3. 6 × 7 = 42 (3 × 7 plus 3 × 7)
4. 9 × 6 = 54 (5 × 6 plus 4 × 6)

Find the products. Break apart the underlined factor.

5. 7 × 5 = 35	6. 7 × 7 = 49
7. 9 × 3 = 27	8. 9 × 5 = 45
9. 6 × 7 = 42	10. 6 × 5 = 30
11. 8 × 3 = 24	12. 9 × 4 = 36
13. 8 × 7 = 56	14. 8 × 6 = 48
15. 6 × 9 = 54	16. 5 × 4 = 20
17. 7 × 9 = 63	18. 8 × 9 = 72

48 Use with text pages 130–131. PS-4

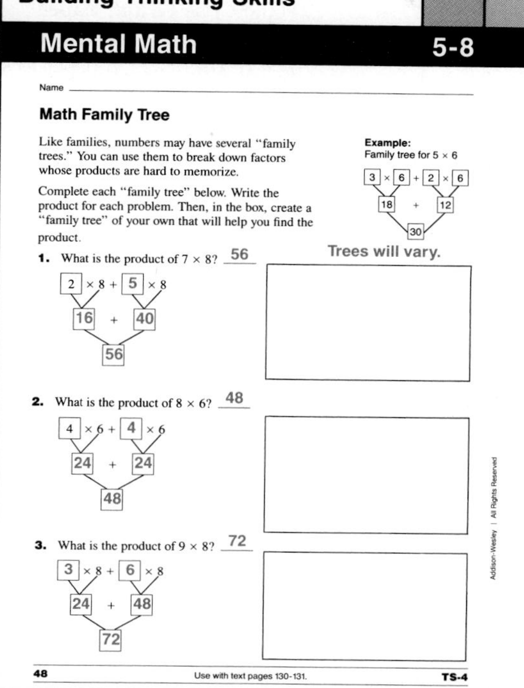

Building Thinking Skills

Mental Math 5-8

Name ______

Math Family Tree

Like families, numbers may have several "family trees." You can use them to break down factors whose products are hard to memorize.

Complete each "family tree" below. Write the product for each problem. Then, in the box, create a "family tree" of your own that will help you find the product.

Example: Family tree for 5 × 6: 3 × 6 + 2 × 6; 18 + 12; 30

Trees will vary.

1. What is the product of 7 × 8? 56
   2 × 8 + 5 × 8; 16 + 40; 56
2. What is the product of 8 × 6? 48
   4 × 6 + 4 × 6; 24 + 24; 48
3. What is the product of 9 × 8? 72
   3 × 8 + 6 × 8; 24 + 48; 72

48 Use with text pages 130-131. TS-4

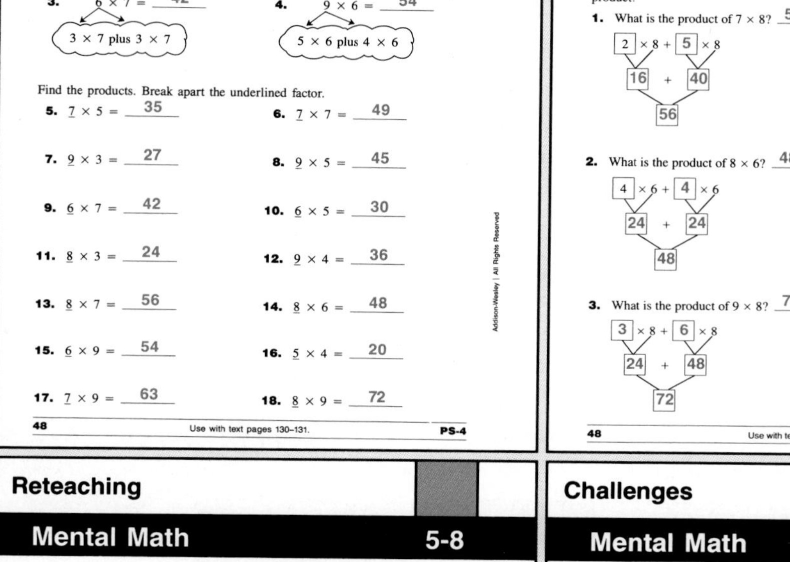

Reteaching

Mental Math 5-8

Name ______

More Breaking Apart Numbers

Multiplication-Addition Property
When you multiply, you can break apart a factor.

8 × 7 = ?
Break apart 8. — 5 plus 3
Multiply both factors by 7. — (5 × 7) plus (3 × 7)
Add the products. — 35 plus 21
Their sum is the total product. — 56

Find each product. Show how you break apart one factor.

1. 9 × 4 = 5 × 4 plus 4 × 4 = 36
2. 6 × 5 = 3 × 5 plus 3 × 5 = 30
3. 7 × 6 = 3 × 6 plus 4 × 6 = 42

Find the products.

4. 3 × 6 = 18	5. 5 × 8 = 40	6. 8 × 4 = 32
7. 7 × 5 = 35	8. 6 × 6 = 36	9. 9 × 7 = 63
10. 7 × 1 = 7	11. 8 × 0 = 0	12. 4 × 9 = 36
13. 3 × 9 = 27	14. 4 × 7 = 28	15. 0 × 5 = 0

Give the missing number. Then give the product.

16. 5 × 8 is 40, so 6 × 8 is 40 + 8, which is 48
17. 4 × 7 is 28, so 5 × 7 is 28 + 7, which is 35
18. 5 × 9 is 45, so 6 × 9 is 45 + 9, which is 54

48 Use with text pages 130-131. RS-4

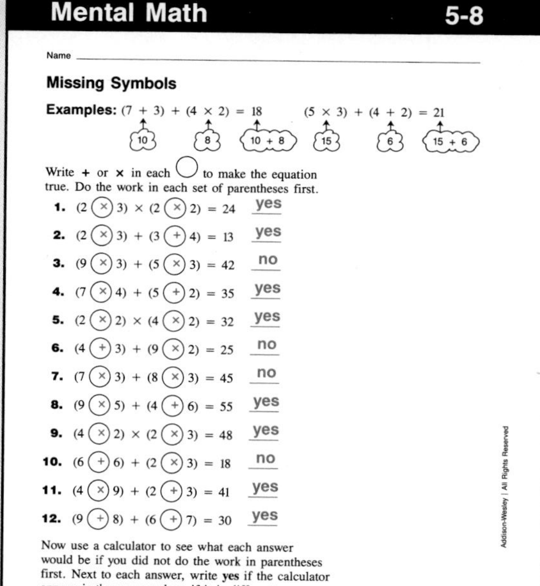

Challenges

Mental Math 5-8

Name ______

Missing Symbols

Examples: (7 + 3) + (4 × 2) = 18 [10, 8, 10 + 8] (5 × 3) + (4 + 2) = 21 [15, 6, 15 + 6]

Write + or × in each ◯ to make the equation true. Do the work in each set of parentheses first.

1. (2 × 3) × (2 × 2) = 24 yes
2. (2 × 3) + (3 + 4) = 13 yes
3. (9 × 3) + (5 × 3) = 42 no
4. (7 × 4) + (5 + 2) = 35 yes
5. (2 × 2) × (4 × 2) = 32 yes
6. (4 + 3) + (9 × 2) = 25 no
7. (7 × 3) + (8 × 3) = 45 no
8. (9 × 5) + (4 + 6) = 55 yes
9. (4 × 2) × (2 × 3) = 48 yes
10. (6 + 6) + (2 × 3) = 18 no
11. (4 × 9) + (2 + 3) = 41 yes
12. (9 + 8) + (6 + 7) = 30 yes

Now use a calculator to see what each answer would be if you did not do the work in parentheses first. Next to each answer, write **yes** if the calculator answer is the same and **no** if it is different.

Example: For problem **1**, enter 2 × 3 × 2 × 2 = 24

48 Use with text pages 130–131. CS-4

Options for Individual Needs

Basic

Exercises 1-9, 16-26
Skills Bank, p. 461
Calculator Bank, p. 488
More Practice, p. 503, set C

Supplements
Reteaching 48 or
Practice 48

Average

Exercises 1-26
Calculator Bank, p. 488
More Practice, p. 503, set C

Supplements
Practice 48
Challenges 48 or
Thinking Skills 48

Extended

Exercises 1-6, 16-26
Calculator Bank, p. 488

Supplements
Challenges 48
Thinking Skills 48

Other Resources:
Problem-Solving Experiences in Mathematics, Grade 4, Problem 63
Math in Stride, Teacher Sourcebook, Grade 4, Activity 60
Mathematics: A Way of Thinking, Lesson 5-5
Using the Math Explorer Calculator: A Sourcebook for Teachers, Chapter 14

5-8

LESSON PLAN 5-8

OBJECTIVE 5-8

To use the mental math technique of break apart to find multiplication facts

Materials: graph paper, crayons or markers, snap cubes, TA 15 (Dot Paper)

1. MOTIVATE AND TEACH

LEARN ABOUT IT

EXPLORE ► **Why show 7 × 6 on graph paper?** (You can break apart the boxes to find the product.)
► **Explain why 7 × 6 and 6 × 7 have equal numbers of boxes.** (Factor order has no effect on the product.)

TALK ABOUT IT ► **Explain how to use two easy facts to find a hard fact.** (Find the two easy products, then add to get the final product.)
► **How can (5 × 6) + (2 × 6) help you find 7 × 6?** (5 × 6 and 2 × 6 are easier facts than 7 × 6.)
► **Describe another easy fact to use for 7 × 6.** (Possible answer: 6 × 6 = 36, plus 1 more group of 6.)
► **Develop a rule for finding products by breaking apart a factor.** (Break apart one factor, multiply each part by the other factor, add those products to get the final product.)
Student Edition answers: **1.** Find two easier products, then add. **2.** Possible answers: 1, 6; 2, 5; 3, 4 **3.** (1 × 6) + (6 × 6); (2 × 6) + (5 × 6); (3 × 6) + (4 × 6)

2. CHECK UNDERSTANDING

TRY IT OUT

ERROR ALERT Breaking apart both factors. Adding incorrectly.

Mental Math
More Breaking Apart Numbers

LEARN ABOUT IT

EXPLORE Use Graph Paper
Here is one way to break apart the factor 7 in 7 × 6. Color graph paper to show as many other ways to do this as you can.

7 × 6
7 sixes

2 sixes
2 × 6

5 sixes
5 × 6

TALK ABOUT IT See teaching notes.

1. How can you use this idea to find 7 × 6?
2. Complete the following in 3 different ways.
   7 sixes = __?__ sixes and __?__ sixes.
3. Show how each way can be used to find 7 × 6.

Multiplication-Addition Property
When you multiply, you can break apart a factor.

You can find a product by breaking apart a factor, multiplying twice and then adding.

Break apart the factor.	Multiply twice, then add.
Break 7 into 5 and 2.	5 × 6 plus 2 × 6 7 × 6 is 30 plus 12, or 42.

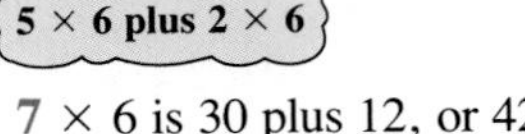

TRY IT OUT

Find each product.

1. 6 × 6 = n (3 × 6 plus 3 × 6) 36
2. 7 × 8 = n (5 × 8 plus 2 × 8) 56
3. 8 × 6 = n (5 × 6 plus 3 × 6) 48

Find each product. Break apart the red factor.

4. 8 × 4 32
5. 9 × 2 18
6. 4 × 9 36
7. 7 × 7 49
8. 6 × 4 24

130

TEACHING OPTIONS

RETEACHING TIPS For help with the first error, give students snap cubes. To show 4 × 9, for example, students use snap cubes to make 4 sticks, each with 9 cubes. They may combine sticks any way that gives easy facts, but they cannot break apart a stick. Assign Reteaching Supplement 48.

ENRICHMENT Tell students that it can help to break apart a factor to make 3 smaller facts, like this: 15 × 8 = (5 × 8) + (5 × 8) + (5 × 8). Then have them find the products.
1. 24 × 4 **2.** 27 × 7
[**1.** (8 × 4) + (8 × 4) + (8 × 4) = 96 **2.** (9 × 7) + (9 × 7) + (9 × 7) = 189]

PRACTICE

Find each product.

(3 × 6 plus 2 × 6) (6 × 5 plus 1 × 5) (5 × 6 plus 4 × 6)

1. 5 × 6 = *n* 30 **2.** 7 × 5 = *n* 35 **3.** 9 × 6 = *n* 54

Find the products. Break apart the red factor.

4. 5 × 7 35 **5.** 6 × 3 18 **6.** 4 × 5 20 **7.** 6 × 8 48 **8.** 8 × 8 64 **9.** 7 × 4 28
10. 5 × 8 40 **11.** 4 × 7 28 **12.** 8 × 9 72 **13.** 3 × 9 27 **14.** 5 × 9 45 **15.** 6 × 4 24

APPLY

MATH REASONING Give the missing number. Then give the underlined product.

16. 5 × 6 is 30, so 6 × 6 is 30 + ? 6, 36

17. 5 × 7 is 35, so 6 × 7 is 35 + ? 7, 42

PROBLEM SOLVING

18. Each member of a group made up 8 short tall tales. There were 4 members in the group. How many tall tales were there? 32 tall tales

19. A class Tall Tales Booklet had 9 pages. Each page except the first had 6 tall tales on it. The first page had 3 tall tales. How many tall tales were in the booklet? 51 tall tales

▶ **MENTAL MATH**

Use mental math. First find the larger doubles in Exercises 21–25. Then use your skill in finding larger doubles to find the products in Exercises 26 and 27.

20. 12 + 12 24 **21.** 14 + 14 28 **22.** 15 + 15 30 **23.** 16 + 16 32 **24.** 18 + 18 36

25. **14** × 3 = (**7** × 3) plus (**7** × 3) = ? 42

26. **16** × 5 = (**8** × 5) plus (**8** × 5) = ? 80

More Practice, page 503, set C

3. Practice and Apply

Basic	1-9, 16-26
Average	1-26
Extended	1-6, 16-26

PRACTICE

Look at Exercises 1-15. What do you think would happen if you broke apart the other *factor instead of the red one?* (You would have the same final product.)

APPLY

MATH REASONING ▶ **Analyze how each new pair of factors differs from the first factor.** (In each case, one factor repeats and the other factor increases by 1.)

PROBLEM SOLVING ▶ **What operation do you use to solve Problem 18? Explain why.** (Multiplication. You are putting together same-size groups.)

▶ **Identify a clue that tells Problem 19 has more than one step.** (The pages do not all have the same number of tall tales.)

MENTAL MATH ▶ **Explain two ways to double a number.** (Multiply by 2; add the number to itself.)

Close and Assess

SHOW WHAT YOU KNOW

Have students use dot paper to demonstrate how they can break apart 6 × 9 in 3 different ways and always get the same product. Ask them to write equations to go with their pictures to identify each break-apart arrangement. (Students may break apart either factor in different ways.)

Quick Quiz

Break apart factors to find each product. (Breakdowns may vary.)

1. 8 × 8 (64) **2.** 8 × 6 (48)
3. 7 × 4 (28) **4.** 5 × 6 (30)
5. 8 × 4 (32) **6.** 6 × 6 (36)

LESSON OPTIONS 5-9

The Last Six Facts

OBJECTIVE 5-9 To find the last six facts, 6 × 6, 7 × 7, 8 × 8, 6 × 7, 6 × 8, and 7 × 8

PREBOOK ACTIVITIES

QUICK REVIEW

Write the products.

1. 1 × 1 (1)	**2.** 5 × 5 (25)	**3.** 3 × 3 (9)
4. 4 × 4 (16)	**5.** 2 × 2 (4)	**6.** 5 × 8 (40)
7. 3 × 6 (18)	**8.** 4 × 7 (28)	**9.** 8 × 3 (24)
10. 4 × 6 (24)	**11.** 7 × 5 (35)	**12.** 0 × 0 (0)

PRIOR KNOWLEDGE

Have students describe a square as a volunteer draws a picture of one on the chalkboard. Ask students to give some common characteristics of all squares. (Possible answers: four corners, four equal sides, four right angles) Write an estimated measure along one side of the square. Ask students what they can say about the other sides of the square, based on the given fact. (They would have the same estimated length.) Tell students that they will be learning some special multiplication facts called square facts.

COMMUNICATION

Discussing Math Discuss the word **square** in phrases such as a *square table* (the shape), a *square meal* (balanced), *square dance* (four dance couples stand like sides of a square), *square mile* (large area a mile long on each of four sides), and *win fair and square* (honestly following the rules). Point out that many phrases use the idea of balanced or equal size. Challenge students to apply the idea of squares to guess what a square multiplication fact is. (factors such as 3 × 3 or 4 × 4)

EXPLORE AND CONNECT

Materials: counters, TA 14 (Practice Table)
Grouping Suggestion: cooperative learning pairs
Students complete a 10-by-10 **square** multiplication table to see how many facts they know and to find new ones. Before partners begin, they determine how many empty boxes make up the table. (10 rows by 10 columns = 100 **squares**) To start, one student says the products across the 0 row while his or her partner records them. They do the 0 column together. Then pairs trade tasks for the next row and column. Students do the easier rows and columns first—1, 2, 3, 5, and 9—then count how many facts remain. (16) They do the row and column for 4 next, again counting how many facts remain. (9) Partners should examine the 9 facts to see how many use different factors. (6) Then pairs use counters or mental math to figure out the remaining facts. Last, the group verifies products and describes mental math strategies they used.

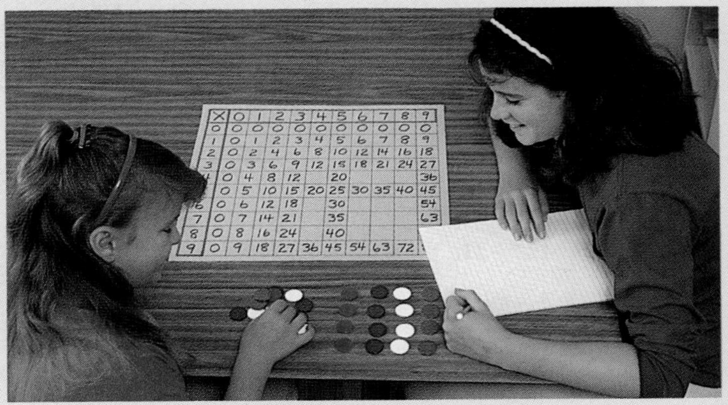

CONNECTIONS Use these anytime.

Problem of the Day

Creative Thinking Laura invented a way to remember the product of 7 × 8. She said, "All I do is count 5, 6, 7, 8." Figure out Laura's idea. (Use 5, 6, 7, 8 to write the equation 56 = 7 × 8.)

Patterns

Multiples of 8 Find the pattern, then write the remaining equations through 9 × 8.
1 × 8 = 10 − 2
2 × 8 = 20 − 4
3 × 8 = 30 − 6
(4 × 8 = 40 − 8; 5 × 8 = 50 − 10; 6 × 8 = 60 − 12; 7 × 8 = 70 − 14; 8 × 8 = 80 − 16; 9 × 8 = 90 − 18)

Math Connection

Algebra A small 2 written above a number is a special way to show a square fact. 4^2 says "four squared" and means 4 × 4. Read each number aloud, tell what number fact it means, and give its product. 5^2 6^2 7^2 8^2 9^2
(5 × 5 = 25; 6 × 6 = 36; 7 × 7 = 49; 8 × 8 = 64; 9 × 9 = 81)

Classwork and Homework Supplements

Practice

Skills Maintenance 5-9

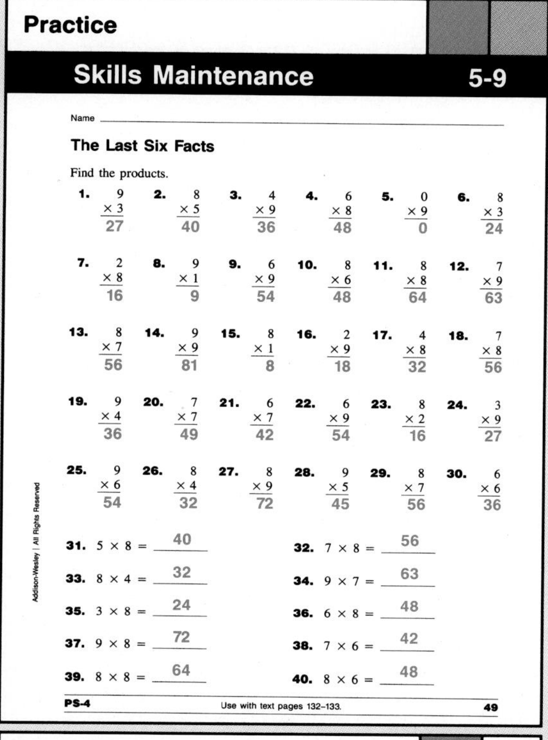

Name

The Last Six Facts

Find the products.

1. 9 × 3 = 27	2. 8 × 5 = 40	3. 4 × 9 = 36	4. 6 × 8 = 48	5. 0 × 9 = 0	6. 8 × 3 = 24
7. 2 × 8 = 16	8. 9 × 1 = 9	9. 6 × 9 = 54	10. 8 × 6 = 48	11. 8 × 8 = 64	12. 7 × 9 = 63
13. 8 × 7 = 56	14. 9 × 9 = 81	15. 8 × 1 = 8	16. 2 × 9 = 18	17. 4 × 8 = 32	18. 7 × 8 = 56
19. 9 × 4 = 36	20. 7 × 7 = 49	21. 6 × 7 = 42	22. 6 × 9 = 54	23. 8 × 2 = 16	24. 3 × 9 = 27
25. 9 × 6 = 54	26. 8 × 4 = 32	27. 8 × 9 = 72	28. 9 × 5 = 45	29. 8 × 7 = 56	30. 6 × 6 = 36

31. 5 × 8 = 40 32. 7 × 8 = 56
33. 8 × 4 = 32 34. 9 × 7 = 63
35. 3 × 8 = 24 36. 6 × 8 = 48
37. 9 × 8 = 72 38. 7 × 6 = 42
39. 8 × 8 = 64 40. 8 × 6 = 48

PS-4 Use with text pages 132–133. 49

Building Thinking Skills

Manipulatives 5-9

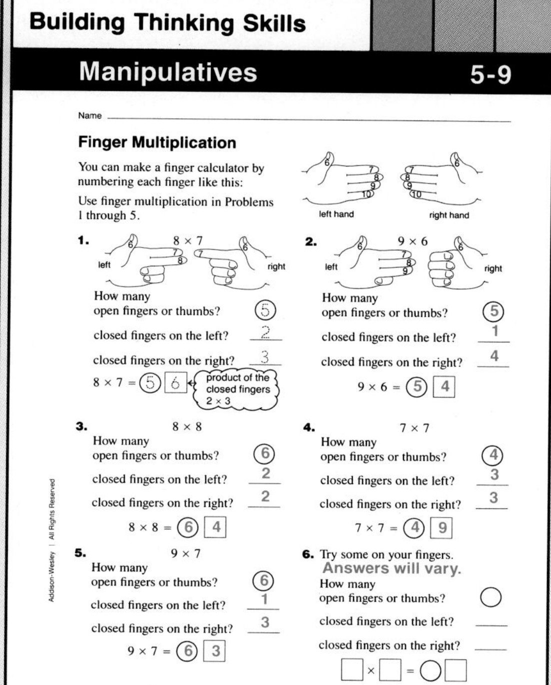

Name

Finger Multiplication

You can make a finger calculator by numbering each finger like this:

Use finger multiplication in Problems 1 through 5.

1. 8 × 7
How many open fingers or thumbs? 5
closed fingers on the left? 2
closed fingers on the right? 3
8 × 7 = 5 6 (product of the closed fingers 2 × 3)

2. 9 × 6
How many open fingers or thumbs? 5
closed fingers on the left? 1
closed fingers on the right? 4
9 × 6 = 5 4

3. 8 × 8
How many open fingers or thumbs? 6
closed fingers on the left? 2
closed fingers on the right? 2
8 × 8 = 6 4

4. 7 × 7
How many open fingers or thumbs? 4
closed fingers on the left? 3
closed fingers on the right? 3
7 × 7 = 4 9

5. 9 × 7
How many open fingers or thumbs? 6
closed fingers on the left? 1
closed fingers on the right? 3
9 × 7 = 6 3

6. Try some on your fingers. Answers will vary.
How many open fingers or thumbs? ○
closed fingers on the left? ___
closed fingers on the right? ___
□ × □ = ○□

TS-4 Use with text pages 132–133. 49

Reteaching

Mental Math 5-9

Name

The Last Six Facts

To find the last six facts,

Break apart factors. → Use the facts you already know. → Add the facts.

6 × 6 → 3 and 3 → 3 × 6 = 18, 3 × 6 = 18 → 18 + 18 = 36 → 6 × 6 = 36

6 × 7 → 3 × 7 plus 3 × 7
6 × 8 → 3 × 8 plus 3 × 8
7 × 7 → 5 × 7 plus 2 × 7
8 × 7 → 4 × 7 plus 4 × 7
8 × 8 → 4 × 8 plus 4 × 8

(Use mental math and the facts you already know.)

Find each product.

1. 6 × 6 = 36	2. 8 × 7 = 56	3. 7 × 8 = 56	4. 9 × 7 = 63	5. 5 × 6 = 30
6. 9 × 6 = 54	7. 9 × 1 = 9	8. 7 × 7 = 49	9. 8 × 9 = 72	10. 4 × 8 = 32
11. 5 × 9 = 45	12. 9 × 7 = 63	13. 8 × 8 = 64	14. 7 × 6 = 42	15. 6 × 9 = 54

16. 8 × 8 = 64 17. 9 × 5 = 45 18. 6 × 7 = 42

Which product is greater? Ring the factors.

19. 9 × 7 or (8 × 9) 20. 5 × 8 or (6 × 7) 21. 6 × 7 or (8 × 6)
22. (8 × 8) or 7 × 9 23. 9 × 0 or (8 × 1) 24. 6 × 9 or (8 × 7)

RS-4 Use with text pages 132–133. 49

Challenges

Patterns 5-9

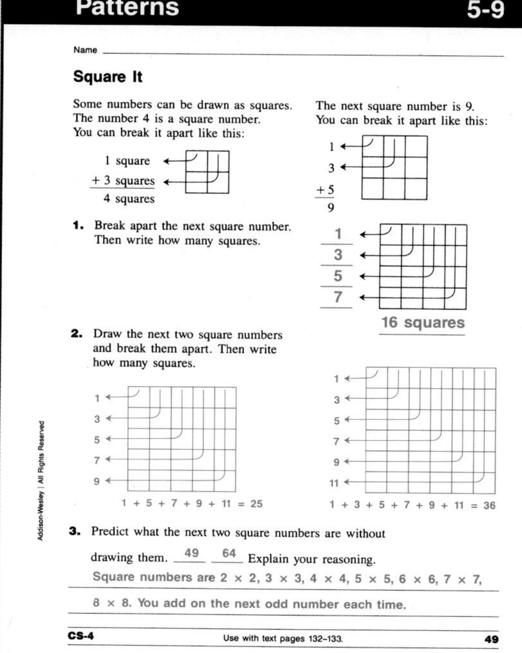

Name

Square It

Some numbers can be drawn as squares. The number 4 is a square number. You can break it apart like this:

1 square
+ 3 squares
4 squares

The next square number is 9. You can break it apart like this:

1
3
+ 5
9

1. Break apart the next square number. Then write how many squares.

1
3
5
7
16 squares

2. Draw the next two square numbers and break them apart. Then write how many squares.

3. Predict what the next two square numbers are without drawing them. 49 64 Explain your reasoning.
Square numbers are 2 × 2, 3 × 3, 4 × 4, 5 × 5, 6 × 6, 7 × 7, 8 × 8. You add on the next odd number each time.

CS-4 Use with text pages 132–133. 49

Challenges & Games—Grade 4, Chapter 5, Page 49

Options for Individual Needs

Basic

Exercises 3-25, 28-30
Data Bank, p. 476
Calculator Bank, p. 488
More Practice, p. 503, set D

Supplements
Reteaching 49 or
Practice 49
Thinking Skills 49

Average

Exercises 1-31
Data Bank, p. 476
Calculator Bank, p. 488
More Practice, p. 503, set D

Supplements
Practice 49
Challenges 49 or
Thinking Skills 49

Extended

Exercises 1-7, 15-31
Data Bank, p. 476
Calculator Bank, p. 488

Supplements
Challenges 49
Thinking Skills 49

Other Resources:
Problem-Solving Experiences in Mathematics, Grade 4, Problem 40
Math In Stride, Grade 4, pp. 60-65
Middle Grades Mathematics Project: Factors and Multiples, p. 29
Using the Math Explorer Calculator: A Sourcebook for Teachers, Chapter 14

LESSON PLAN 5-9

OBJECTIVE 5-9
To find the last six facts, 6 × 6, 7 × 7, 8 × 8, 6 × 7, 6 × 8, 7 × 8

Materials: graph paper, TA 14 (Practice Table)

Alternative Materials: TA 15 (Dot Paper)

1. MOTIVATE AND TEACH

LEARN ABOUT IT

EXPLORE ► **Justify what makes a shape a square.** (Possible answer: four equal sides)
► **Explain why 6 × 6 = 36 is a square fact.** (It relates to a square shape with 6 units per side.)
► **Link the size of a square to multiplication factors.** (A factor is the number of units along one side; for a square fact, multiply the factor by itself.)

TALK ABOUT IT ► **Do all square facts have even products? Explain.** (Square facts of even numbers have even products; odd square facts have odd products.)
► **How can knowing 6 × 6 help you find 6 × 7?** [Possible answer: break apart 6 × 7 as (6 × 6) + (6 × 1).]
► **How could you break apart numbers to find 8 × 7?** [Possible answer: Think (7 × 7) + (7 × 1).]
Student Edition answers: **1.** 8 square facts, 2 are new **2.** Count all small squares. **3.** The dark line splits the square in half, with 3 rows of 6 in each.

2. CHECK UNDERSTANDING

TRY IT OUT

ERROR ALERT Failing to apply mental math strategies. Forgetting harder facts.

The Last Six Facts

LEARN ABOUT IT

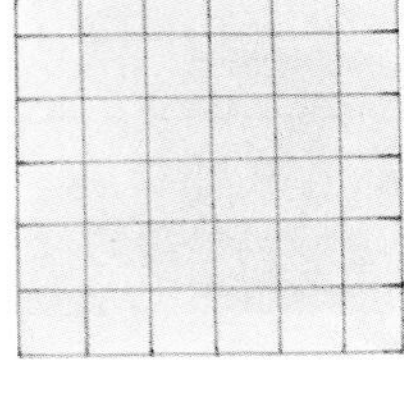

EXPLORE Use Graph Paper
This square piece of graph paper shows a square fact. It has 6 rows of 6 small squares, or 36 squares in all.

Draw squares on graph paper to show as many other square facts as you can. Write a number sentence for each fact. Circle those facts not presented in earlier lessons.

TALK ABOUT IT See teaching notes.

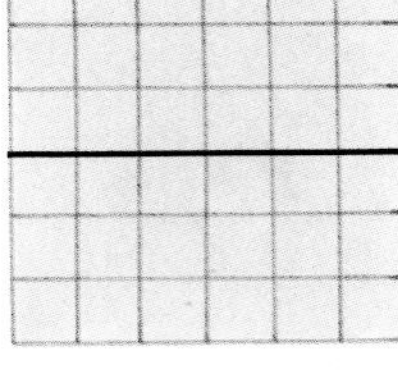

1. How many square facts did you find? How many of these are new facts?
2. How could you use the graph paper square to help find 6 × 6?
3. Explain how this square shows that 6 × 6 is 3 × 6 plus 3 × 6.

Here is one way to break apart factors to find the last six facts. Use mental math and the facts you already know.

6 facts
6 × 6 3 × 6 plus 3 × 6
6 × 6 is a square fact.
6 × 7 3 × 7 plus 3 × 7
6 × 8 3 × 8 plus 3 × 8

7 fact
7 × 7 5 × 7 plus 2 × 7
7 × 7 is a square fact.

8 facts
8 × 7 4 × 7 plus 4 × 7
8 × 8 4 × 8 plus 4 × 8
8 × 8 is a square fact.

TRY IT OUT

Find each product.

1. 8 × 7 = 56
2. 7 × 7 = 49
3. 6 × 6 = 36
4. 8 × 8 = 64
5. 7 × 8 = 56
6. 6 × 8 = 48

132

TEACHING OPTIONS

RETEACHING TIPS Let students who fail to apply mental math strategies fill in facts through the 4s on a multiplication table. Have them verbalize how to combine easier facts to find harder ones, such as (3 × 8) + (3 × 8) to find 6 × 8. Assign Reteaching Supplement 49.

ENRICHMENT Family Math With a family member, students create funny story problems for 7 × 8, 6 × 7, and 7 × 7. Students write each one on a separate sheet of paper. They cut out pictures from old magazines to decorate their problems. Students write each solution on the back.

PRACTICE

Find each product.

1. 8 × 6 = 48
2. 6 × 7 = 42
3. 7 × 7 = 49
4. 8 × 7 = 56
5. 9 × 7 = 63
6. 6 × 6 = 36
7. 8 × 8 = 64
8. 6 × 9 = 54
9. 8 × 9 = 72
10. 4 × 8 = 32
11. 7 × 6 = 42
12. 9 × 9 = 81
13. 7 × 8 = 56
14. 3 × 7 = 21

15. 6 × 7 42 16. 8 × 9 72 17. 7 × 8 56 18. 6 × 9 54 19. 9 × 7 63 20. 4 × 4 16

21. Find the product of 6 and 8. 48

22. What times 6 is equal to 54? 9

APPLY

MATH REASONING Find each product.

23. I am a square fact. One of my factors is 8. What is my product? 64

24. One of my factors is 6. My other factor is 2 more than the first. What is my product? 48

PROBLEM SOLVING

25. Stormalong was 4 fathoms tall. He fought the sea monster Guznod who was 10 fathoms long. A fathom is 6 feet. How many feet longer than Stormalong's height was Guznod's length? 36 feet

26. **Language Arts Data Bank** If Joe Magarac squeezed 7 times, how many steel rails did he make? See page 476. 28 steel rails

DATA BANK

MIXED REVIEW

Give the missing number.

27. (15 + 25) + 36 = (36 + ▥) + 15 25

28. 9 + (43 + 37) = (37 + 43) + ▥ 9

Use mental math.

29. 40 + 63 + 60 163 30. 50 + 89 + 50 189 31. 80 + 58 + 20 158

More Practice, page 503, set D

3. Practice and Apply

Basic	3-25, 28-30
Average	1-31
Extended	1-7, 15-31

PRACTICE

Look at Exercises 1-22. Which ones are square facts? (Exercises 3, 6, 7, 12, and 20.) *Which of those square facts will have odd products?* (Exercises 3 and 12)

APPLY

MATH REASONING ▶ **What is true about factors of square facts?** (Both are the same number.)

▶ **Explain how to find the missing factor in Problem 24.** (Add 2 + 6.)

PROBLEM SOLVING ▶ **Identify a key fact in Problem 25.** (A fathom is 6 feet.)

▶ **Before checking the Data Bank, predict the operation you will need to use to solve Problem 26. Explain.** (Possible answer: Probably multiplication, because Joe squeezes 7 times.)

MIXED REVIEW ▶ **Describe a mental math method for solving Exercises 29-31.** (Find addends that make 100.)

5-9

Close and Assess

SAY WHAT YOU THINK Ask students to pretend that a third grader told them that 8 × 7 is the hardest multiplication fact in the world. If they agree, they should tell why and give a way to find the product. If they disagree, they should tell how to find the product easily. (Answers will vary.)

QUICK QUIZ

Write the products.

1. 6 × 6 (36)
2. 7 × 7 (49)
3. 8 × 8 (64)
4. 6 × 8 (48)
5. 8 × 7 (56)
6. 6 × 7 (42)

LESSON OPTIONS 5-10

Multiples

OBJECTIVE 5-10 To identify and produce multiples of a number

PREBOOK ACTIVITIES

QUICK REVIEW

Find the products.

1. 7 × 0 (0) **2.** 7 × 1 (7) **3.** 7 × 2 (14)
4. 7 × 3 (21) **5.** 7 × 4 (28) **6.** 7 × 5 (35)
7. 7 × 6 (42) **8.** 7 × 7 (49) **9.** 7 × 8 (56)
10. 7 × 9 (63) **11.** 7 × 10 (70)

PRIOR KNOWLEDGE

Have students classify different numbers as being odd or even and explain how they made their decisions. (Possible answers: Odd numbers end in 1, 3, 5, 7, or 9; even numbers end in 0, 2, 4, 6, or 8; even amounts can be made into 2 equal groups.) Ask students to identify some 5 facts as odd or even. (Examples for odd: 5, 15, 25, 35, 45; examples for even: 10, 20, 30, 40)

COMMUNICATION

Discussing and Reading Math Write **multiple** on the chalkboard and ask students to give 2 other words related to it. (*multiplication, multiply)* Tell students that the multiples of a number are any products of that number and another factor. For instance, 15 is a multiple of 5 because it is the product of 5 and 3. Challenge students to explain why 20 is a multiple of 5. (20 is the product of 5 and 4.) Ask students to predict how many multiples the number 5 has. (an endless number; You can keep multiplying 5 by greater and greater factors.)

EXPLORE AND CONNECT

Materials: calculators
Grouping Suggestion: cooperative learning pairs
Students explore **multiples** of odd and even numbers with calculators. One student picks any 1-digit *odd* number greater than 2. Partners use the calculator to generate a list of any 7 *multiples* of that number and record them as products of multiplication facts. (Given 3, students could list 3 × 1 = 3, 3 × 2 = 6, 3 × 3 = 9, and so on.) When students have found and listed 7 *multiples,* have them classify the *multiples* as odd or even. Partners repeat the activity with any 1-digit *even* number greater than 2. Conclude by having students examine any patterns in the *multiples* related to odd and even numbers. (Possible answer: Odd numbers have odd *and* even *multiples,* but even numbers have only even *multiples*.)

CONNECTIONS Use these anytime.

Problem of the Day

Multiples Lew and Sue agree on a schedule for cleaning their rooms. Lew will clean once every 3 d and Sue will clean once every 5 d. If they both clean their rooms on Saturday, April 1, give the next time they will clean on the same day. (Sunday, April 16)

Patterns

Mental Math Discover the pattern, then continue it 4 more times.
70, 63, 56, 49, (42), (35), (28), (21)
(Pattern: descending multiples of 7)

Math Connection

Number Theory What is the only number whose multiples are all the same? (0)

Classwork and Homework Supplements

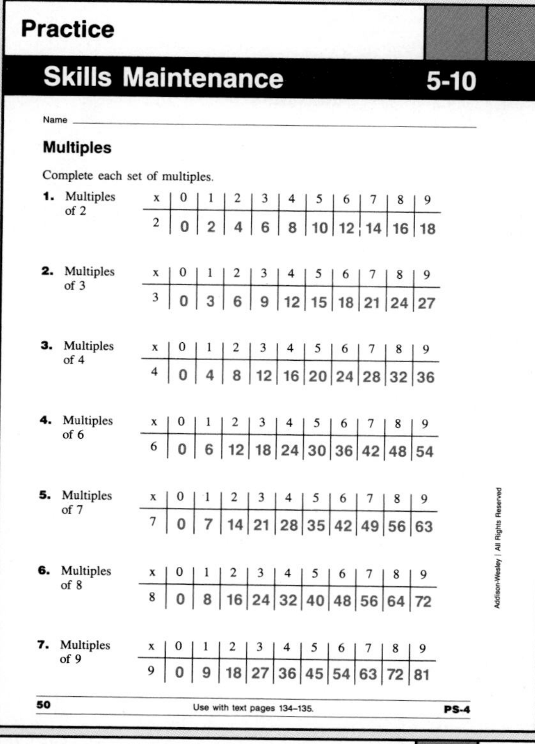
Practice

Skills Maintenance 5-10

Name ______________________

Multiples

Complete each set of multiples.

1. Multiples of 2

x	0	1	2	3	4	5	6	7	8	9
2	0	2	4	6	8	10	12	14	16	18

2. Multiples of 3

x	0	1	2	3	4	5	6	7	8	9
3	0	3	6	9	12	15	18	21	24	27

3. Multiples of 4

x	0	1	2	3	4	5	6	7	8	9
4	0	4	8	12	16	20	24	28	32	36

4. Multiples of 6

x	0	1	2	3	4	5	6	7	8	9
6	0	6	12	18	24	30	36	42	48	54

5. Multiples of 7

x	0	1	2	3	4	5	6	7	8	9
7	0	7	14	21	28	35	42	49	56	63

6. Multiples of 8

x	0	1	2	3	4	5	6	7	8	9
8	0	8	16	24	32	40	48	56	64	72

7. Multiples of 9

x	0	1	2	3	4	5	6	7	8	9
9	0	9	18	27	36	45	54	63	72	81

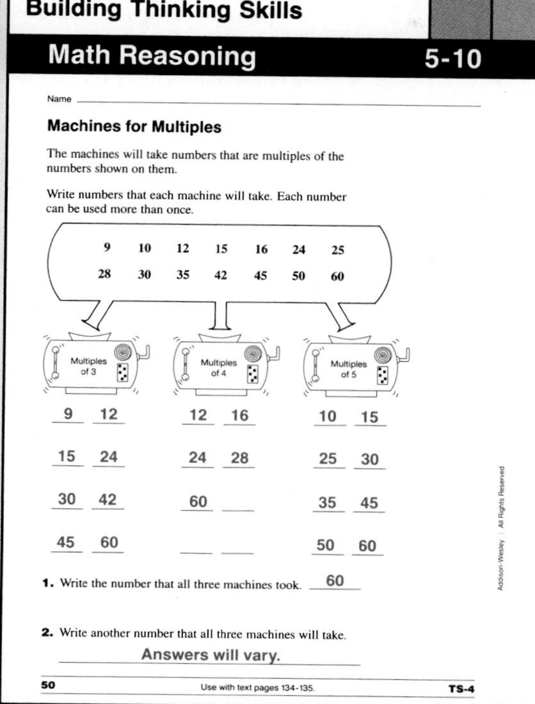
Building Thinking Skills

Math Reasoning 5-10

Name ______________________

Machines for Multiples

The machines will take numbers that are multiples of the numbers shown on them.

Write numbers that each machine will take. Each number can be used more than once.

Multiples of 3		Multiples of 4		Multiples of 5	
9	12	12	16	10	15
15	24	24	28	25	30
30	42	60		35	45
45	60			50	60

1. Write the number that all three machines took. 60

2. Write another number that all three machines will take.
Answers will vary.

Reteaching

Skills Review 5-10

Name ______________________

Multiples

Look for the pattern in the chart.

Multiples of 4	
1 × 4	4
2 × 4	8
3 × 4	12
4 × 4	16
5 × 4	20

Think: 1 × 4 = 4
Think: 2 × 4 = 8
Think: 3 × 4 = 12
Think: 4 × 4 = 16
Think: 5 × 4 = 20

4, 8, 12, 16, and 20 are **multiples** of 4. You can get these products by multiplying 4 by another number. Continue the pattern to name 3 other multiples of 4. 24, 28, 32

Fill in the charts to find the multiples.

1.

Multiples of 5	
1 × 5	5
2 × 5	10
3 × 5	15
4 × 5	20
5 × 5	25

2.

Multiples of 6	
1 × 6	6
2 × 6	12
3 × 6	18
4 × 6	24
5 × 6	30

3.

Multiples of 7	
1 × 7	7
2 × 7	14
3 × 7	21
4 × 7	28
5 × 7	35

Find the products.

4. 3 × 4 = 12 5. 4 × 5 = 20 6. 3 × 6 = 18 7. 5 × 7 = 35

8. 7 × 3 = 21 9. 5 × 7 = 35 10. 8 × 6 = 48 11. 7 × 2 = 14

12. 9 × 4 = 36 13. 6 × 6 = 36 14. 3 × 9 = 27 15. 7 × 9 = 63

Challenges

Critical Thinking 5-10

Name ______________________

Prime Number Search

Work in a small group to complete this activity.

Directions

1. Circle the first number, 2. Then cross out all the multiples of 2.
2. Circle the next number not crossed out, 3. Then cross out all the multiples of 3 that are not already crossed out.
3. Circle the next number not crossed out. Then cross out all the multiples of that number that are not already crossed out.
4. Repeat Step 3 and keep doing it until all numbers are circled or crossed out.

	2	3	4	5	6	7	8	9	10
11	12	13	14	15	16	17	18	19	20
21	22	23	24	25	26	27	28	29	30
31	32	33	34	35	36	37	38	39	40
41	42	43	44	45	46	47	48	49	50
51	52	53	54	55	56	57	58	59	60
61	62	63	64	65	66	67	68	69	70
71	72	73	74	75	76	77	78	79	80
81	82	83	84	85	86	87	88	89	90
91	92	93	94	95	96	97	98	99	100

The numbers that are circled are called **prime numbers**. Write your own definition of a prime number.

A prime number is a number that can be divided only by itself and 1.

Options for Individual Needs

Basic

Exercises 1-10
Calculator Bank, p. 484
Computer Bank, p. 495
More Practice, p. 503, set E

Supplements
Reteaching 50 or
Practice 50

Average

Exercises 1-12
Calculator Bank, p. 484
Computer Bank, p. 495
More Practice, p. 503, set E

Supplements
Practice 50
Challenges 50 or
Thinking Skills 50

Extended

Exercises 1-12
Calculator Bank, p. 484
Computer Bank, p. 495

Supplements
Challenges 50
Thinking Skills 50

Other Resources:
Problem-Solving Experiences in Mathematics, Grade 4, Problem 41
Math In Stride, Grade 4, pp. 41, 42
Using the Math Explorer Calculator: A Sourcebook for Teachers, Chapter 14

LESSON PLAN 5-10

OBJECTIVE 5-10
To identify and produce multiples of a number

Materials: TA 12 (Centimeter Graph Paper), calculators

Grouping Suggestion: pairs

1. MOTIVATE AND TEACH

LEARN ABOUT IT

EXPLORE ► **Compare the even-number shapes with the odd-number shapes.** (All even-number shapes are rectangles or squares, but only 1 is a square among the odd-number shapes; the rest each have a leftover box.)
► **Analyze why multiples of 2 should be even numbers.** (Anything times 2 is a double.)
► **If you skip count by 2s, do you always say multiples of 2? Explain.** (only if you start with an even number; If you start with an odd number, you skip multiples of 2.)

TALK ABOUT IT ► **Can you skip count by any number? Explain.** (Yes, say multiples of any number by starting at 0 and skip counting by that number.)
► **Compare graph-paper boxes showing multiples of 3 with those showing multiples of 4.** (Multiples of 3 would have 3 boxes in each row increasing by 3 each time; multiples of 4 would have 4 boxes in each row increasing by 4 each time.)
Student Edition answers: **1.** multiples of 3: 3, 6, 9, 12, . . . **2.** 4 squares per row

2. CHECK UNDERSTANDING

TRY IT OUT

ERROR ALERT Exercise 1: Using the wrong factor as the multiple. Exercise 2: Omitting multiples.

Multiples

LEARN ABOUT IT

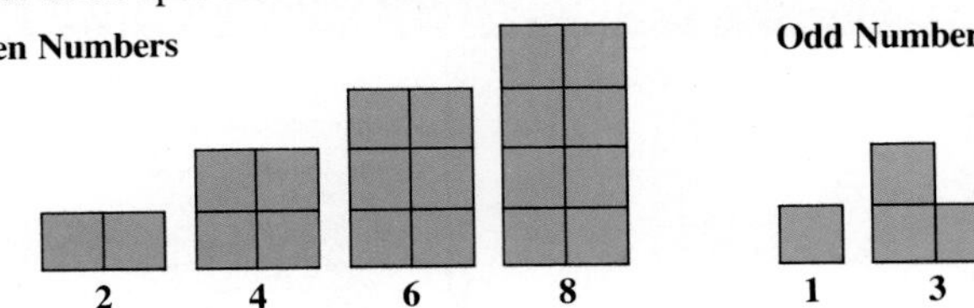

EXPLORE Use Graph Paper
Graph paper strips can help you learn about some special sets of numbers.

Even Numbers 0 2 4 6 8 **Odd Numbers** 1 3 5 7

The numbers that can be shown with rectangular strips of graph paper with 2 squares in each row, along with 0, are also called **multiples of 2** or **even numbers**. All other whole numbers are called **odd numbers**. You can start at 0 and skip count by twos to get the multiples of 2.

TALK ABOUT IT See teaching notes.

1. Suppose you cut some rectangular strips of graph paper with 3 squares in each row. How could you describe these numbers? How would you skip count to say these numbers?
2. What would strips that showed multiples of 4 look like?

The **multiples** of a number are the products when the number is one of the factors.

Multiples of 5	×	0	1	2	3	4	5	6	7	8	9	10
	5	0	5	10	15	20	25	30	35	40	45	50

TRY IT OUT

1. Cut graph paper strips to show multiples of 4. Check students' work.
2. Make a multiple table for 3. See Additional Answers.

134

TEACHING OPTIONS

RETEACHING TIPS Using the Multiples of 5 Table as a guide, have students draw a table, label it, write a × symbol and the numbers 0-9 along the top row. In the bottom row, one student skip counts by 3, starting at 0, as a partner fills in each number in the proper space. Assign Reteaching Supplement 50.

COMPUTER Number Munchers, MECC, Copyright 1986 For use with all levels of students. In ''Multiples,'' move the 'Number Muncher' around the grid to eat expressions that are multiples of the target before 'Toggle Monster' eats the 'Number Muncher.' The game takes 10 min.

PRACTICE

Copy and complete these multiple tables. Look at your tables. What patterns do you see?

1.

Multiples of 4	×	0	1	2	3	4	5	6	7	8	9	10
	4	0	4	8	12	16	20	24	28	32	36	40

2.

Multiples of 6	×	0	1	2	3	4	5	6	7	8	9	10
	6	0	6	12	18	24	30	36	42	48	54	60

3.

Multiples of 9	×	0	1	2	3	4	5	6	7	8	9	10
	9	0	9	18	27	36	45	54	63	72	81	90

4. Write the first 10 even numbers. 2, 4, 6, 8, 10, 12, 14, 16, 18, 20

5. Write the first 10 odd numbers. 1, 3, 5, 9, 11, 13, 15, 17, 19

APPLY

MATH REASONING

6. Solve this riddle. "Of the numbers with two digits, I'm the smallest with this fate. I'm a multiple of 6 and a multiple of 8. Who am I?" 24

PROBLEM SOLVING

7. Paul Bunyon's blacksmith made shoes for Babe the Blue Ox only in groups of 4. Paul thought between 40 and 50 shoes would last Babe for about a week, so he asked a friend to buy a week's supply. How many do you think he bought? 44 or 48 shoes

USE A CALCULATOR

These keystrokes will give some multiples of 8:

[ON/AC] 0 + [8] [=] [=]

Use the constant function on your calculator to find multiples of the numbers given below. Record the first 10 multiples of each. See Additional Answers.

8. 8 **9.** 9 **10.** 12 **11.** 13 **12.** 15

More Practice, page 503, set E

3. Practice and Apply

Basic	1-10
Average	1-12
Extended	1-12

Additional Answers: See p. T79.

PRACTICE

How is the table in Exercise 3 different from the tables in Exercise 1 and 2? (The tables in 1 and 2 are started.) *What is the first multiple in each table?* (0)

APPLY

MATH REASONING ► **Analyze the riddle for useful data.** (It has 2 digits; it is a multiple of 6 and 8.) ► **Explain how you would solve the riddle.** (List the multiples of 6 and of 8; find the smallest 2-digit number in both lists.)

PROBLEM SOLVING ► **What set of multiples can help you solve Problem 7? Explain your reasoning.** (multiples of 4, because the shoes are made in sets of 4)

USE A CALCULATOR ► **Justify using repeated addition to find multiples.** (Multiplication is repeated addition.)

Close and Assess

WRITE WHAT YOU THINK Ask students to pretend that a friend needs help learning the 8 facts. Have them write letters explaining how to use multiples to organize the facts. They should tell how to relate skip counting and multiples. (Check students' writing.)

QUICK QUIZ

Make a multiples table for 7. (top row factors: 0, 1, 2, 3, 4, 5, 6, 7, 8, 9, 10; corresponding bottom row products: 0, 7, 14, 21, 28, 35, 42, 49, 56, 63, 70)

LESSON OPTIONS 5-11

Problem Solving: Making a Table

OBJECTIVE 5-11 To solve problems using the strategy Make a Table

PREBOOK ACTIVITIES

QUICK REVIEW

Continue the pattern 5 more times.

1. 1, 3, 5, 7, (9), (11), (13), (15), (17)
2. 4, 8, 12, 16, (20), (24), (28), (32), (36)
3. 6, 12, 18, 24, (30), (36), (42), (48), (54)
4. 11, 22, 33, 44, (55), (66), (77), (88), (99)
5. 20, 40, 60, 80, (100), (120), (140), (160), (180)

PRIOR KNOWLEDGE

Have students look around the classroom for any tables of data that may be on display. Have students identify the parts of the table, such as rows, columns, title, labels, and individual units of data. Challenge them to look for any possible relationships between rows or columns.

COMMUNICATION

Discussing Math Have students explain a relationship between the numbers in this statement: At a speed of 1 mi every 10 min, Craig can run 3 mi in a half hour. (Possible answer: For every 10 min Craig runs, he goes 1 mi. Since a half hour is 30 min, or 3 tens, he would go 3 mi.) Challenge students to determine a way to show a step-by-step change in the numbers during Craig's run. (Possible answer: Make a table of how far he has run after 10, 20, and 30 min.) Have a volunteer draw a horizontal table with data about Craig's run in 10-min intervals.

(

Minutes Craig Has Run	10	20	30
Miles He Has Covered	1	2	3

)

EXPLORE AND CONNECT

COOPERATIVE ACTIVITY

Grouping Suggestion: small groups

Every minute, 8 fans call radio station KXYZ to request their favorite songs. How long will it take 40 people to call?

TEACHING ACTIONS

Have students work together to discuss and plan a solution strategy.

▶ **Explain the situation in your own words.** (During each minute, a radio station gets 8 request calls.)

▶ **Decide what you need to find out.** (how long it takes for 40 people to call)

▶ **Analyze the problem for 2 kinds of data to compare.** (minutes; number of callers)

▶ **How could a table help organize the data?** (Make a row for minutes and another for number of callers; show the change as minutes pass.)

▶ **Determine the rate of change in the table.** (Count by minutes; at each new minute, add on the new calls.)

▶ **Predict how long the table will be.** (long enough to show 40 callers)

▶ **Analyze whether your answer makes sense.** (At 8 callers per minute, it will take 5 min for 40 calls.)

▶ **Explain how to check your answer.** (Use the number fact $8 \times 5 = 40$.)

CONNECTIONS Use these anytime.

Problem of the Day

Word Processing Part of Celia's job is to type reports on a word processor. If she types steadily, she can do 3 pages in 5 min. How long will it take her to finish a 12-page report? (20 min)

Patterns

Recipe Table Discover the pattern, then extend the table 3 more columns.

Number of Pancakes	12	24	36
Ounces of Mix	5	10	15

(pancakes: 48, 60, 72; ounces: 20, 25, 30)

Math Connection

Money Terry buys a roll of 40 quarters to use when he does his laundry. It takes 4 quarters for the washer and 4 quarters for the dryer for each load. After how many loads will Terry run out of money? (5)

CLASSWORK AND HOMEWORK SUPPLEMENTS

Practice

Problem Solving 5-11

Name ______

Make a Table

Complete the table to help you solve each problem.

1. The recipe for honey cups calls for 4 cups of corn flakes and 2 tablespoons of honey. How many tablespoons of honey will Doug need if he uses 20 cups of corn flakes?
   10 tablespoons

corn flakes	4	8			
honey	2	4			

2. Doug plans to sell the honey cups at a neighborhood block party. If 5 honey cups sell for $1, how much will he earn by selling 25 honey cups?
   $5

honey cups	5	10	15	20	25
money	$1	$2	$3	$4	$5

3. A ride at the party holds 8 children. If the ride lasts 3 minutes, how many children can ride in 15 minutes?
   40 children

children	8	16	24	32	40
minutes	3	6	9	12	15

4. The moon bounce holds 10 people at a time and earns $5. How much will be earned if 60 people ride?
   $30

people	10	20	30	40	50	60
money	$5	$10	$15	$20	$25	$30

5. The disc jockey plays 7 songs in 30 minutes. How many songs will she play in 120 minutes?
   28 songs

songs	7	14	21	28
minutes	30	60	90	120

6. A book of 5 raffle tickets cost $2. How much would it cost to buy 25 tickets?
   $10

tickets	5	10	15	20	25
price	$2	$4	$6	$8	$10

PS-4 Use with text pages 136–137. 51

Building Thinking Skills

Problem Solving 5-11

Name ______

How Much Is Too Much Lasagne?

Juan's 4-H Club is having a dinner for which he is going to make lasagne. He has decided that if he doubles his recipe and then triples the doubled recipe, he will have enough lasagne.

Here is the recipe. Help Juan double the recipe and then triple the double recipe. Help him record the information on the chart.

Lasagne
9 lasagne noodles
2 quarts spaghetti sauce
1 pound ground beef
2 cups mozzarella cheese
1 cup parmesan cheese

Ingredient	Single Recipe	Double Recipe	Triple the Double Recipe
noodles	9	18	54
spaghetti sauce (quarts)	2	4	12
ground beef (pounds)	1	2	6
mozzarella cheese (cups)	2	4	12
parmesan cheese (cups)	1	2	6

Use the table to answer these questions.

1. How many people will Juan's lasagne serve if the original recipe serves 6 people?
   36
2. How many more cups of mozzarella cheese than parmesan cheese will Juan need to serve 36 people?
   6
3. Juan's lasagne was a big success at the 4-H Club dinner. He decided to make lasagne for his parents' anniversary party. 18 people will be invited. How should he figure out how much of each ingredient he will need?
   Triple the single recipe or halve the triple/double recipe.

TS-4 Use with text pages 136–137. 51

Reteaching

Problem Solving 5-11

Name ______

Make a Table

A **table** can be used to organize data and to help solve some problems.

Fujiko is making play dough. The dough recipe calls for 2 cups of flour and 1 cup of salt. How many cups of salt will she use with 6 cups of flour?

Flour	2	4	6		
Salt	1	2	3	4	5

There is always twice as much flour as salt.

For 6 cups of flour, Fujiko will need 3 cups of salt.

Use the table above to answer Questions 1 and 2.

1. How many cups of flour will Fujiko use with 2 cups of salt?
   4
2. How many cups of flour will Fujiko use with 5 cups of salt?
   10

Jon is going to make mayonnaise. He needs 3 eggs, and 2 cups of oil. Complete the table, then solve these problems.

Eggs	3	6	9	12	15
Oil	2	4	6	8	10

3. Jon needs 8 cups of oil. How many eggs will he need?
   12
4. Jon needs 15 eggs. How many cups of oil will he need?
   10

RS-4 Use with text pages 136–137. 51

Challenges

Cooperative Activities 5-11

Name ______

Do-It-Yourself Rhymes

Complete the tables to find the solutions.

1. Peter Piper picked 26 pickles in 3 hours. How many did he pick in 15 hours?
   130 pickles

pickles	26	52	78	104	130
hours	3	6	9	12	15

2. Jack jumped over the candlestick 15 times in 4 days. How many times did he jump over the candlestick in 28 days?
   105 times

jumps	15	30	45	60	75	90	105
days	4	8	12	16	20	24	28

3. 48 blackbirds were baked in 2 pies. How many were baked in 6 pies?
   144 blackbirds

blackbirds	48	96	144
pies	2	4	6

Finish Problems 4 and 5. Then give them to a partner to solve. Check your partner's answers. Problems and answers will vary.

4. Little Bo Peep lost ____ sheep in ____ hours.
   How many did she lose in ____ hours? ______
5. Simple Simon paid ____ for ____ pies.
   How much did he pay for ____ pies? ______

CS-4 Use with text pages 136–137. 51

OPTIONS FOR INDIVIDUAL NEEDS

Basic

Exercises 1-6
Calculator Bank, p. 484
Computer Bank, p. 495
More Practice, p. 516, set C

Supplements
Reteaching 51 or
Practice 51

Average

Exercises 1-6
Calculator Bank, p. 484
Computer Bank, p. 495
More Practice, p. 516, set C

Supplements
Practice 51
Challenges 51 or
Thinking Skills 51

Extended

Exercises 1-6
Calculator Bank, p. 484
Computer Bank, p. 495

Supplements
Challenges 51
Thinking Skills 51

Other Resources:
Problem-Solving Experiences in Mathematics, Grade 4, Problem 90
Make It Simpler, Problem 123
Using the Math Explorer Calculator: A Sourcebook for Teachers, Chapter 14

LESSON PLAN 5-11

OBJECTIVE 5-11
To solve problems using the strategy Make a Table

1. MOTIVATE AND TEACH

LEARN ABOUT IT

▶ **Explain the situation.** (Jim adds dishwashing soap and glycerine to water to make bubble mix.)

▶ **Explain a relationship between the ingredients.** (For every 2 c of soap, Jim must use 6 tbsp of glycerine.)

DURING

▶ **Explain why the table begins with 2 and 6.** (A basic batch uses 2 c of soap and 6 tbsp of glycerine.)

▶ **Justify the numbers that follow in each row.** (The rows use multiples of 2 and 6.)

▶ **Explain why the table ends after four columns.** (The goal was to see how much soap goes with 24 tbsp of glycerine; 4 columns gives enough data—8 c.)

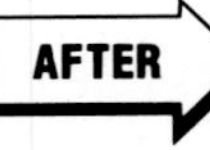

▶ **Analyze the table for a pattern.** (Each top number times 3 equals the bottom number.)

▶ **Explain how to verify the answer.** (Possible answers: Use Models; Draw a Picture; make sure $8 \times 3 = 24$ fits the pattern.)

2. CHECK UNDERSTANDING

TRY IT OUT

▶ **Analyze the situation to find related data.** (2 bubble shows every 10 min)

▶ **Explain how you will complete the table.** (Continue the multiples of 10 until you reach 60; fill in the same number of multiples of 2.)

ERROR ALERT Continuing the multiples incorrectly.

Problem Solving
Make a Table

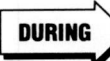

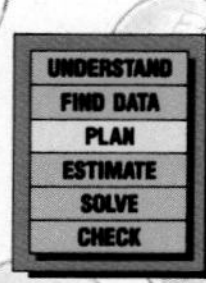

LEARN ABOUT IT

To solve some problems, you may need to make a table using the data in the problem. This strategy is called **Make a Table**.

Jim is making a batch of bubble mixture for making giant bubbles. He uses water, 2 cups of dishwashing soap, and 6 tablespoons of glycerine. How many cups of soap does he need if he uses 24 tablespoons of glycerine?

First I'll make a table and write what I know.

cups of soap	2
tablespoons of glycerine	6

Now I'll fill in the table to find the solution to the problem.

Add 2 more cups. +2 +2 +2

cups of soap	2	4	6	8
tablespoons of glycerine	6	12	18	24

Add 6 more tablespoons. +6 +6 +6

Jim will need 8 cups of soap.

TRY IT OUT

Read this problem and finish the solution.

At the Pinewood Bubble Festival, there were 2 bubble demonstrations every 10 minutes. How many shows were there in 60 minutes? **12 shows**

- How many demonstrations are given at a time? **2**
- How long does it take to give 2 demonstrations? **10 minutes**
- Copy and complete the table to solve the problem.

demonstrations	2	4	6	**8**	**10**	**12**
minutes	10	20	30	**40**	**50**	**60**

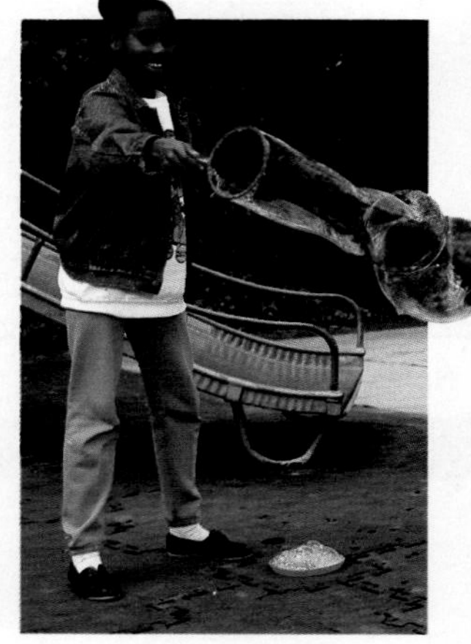

136

TEACHING OPTIONS

RETEACHING TIPS Have students identify which row will contain the target multiple. (minutes) They should finish that row first with the multiples of 10. Then they complete the multiples of 2, ending at the same column that has the 60. Assign Reteaching Supplement 51.

ENRICHMENT **Family Math** At home, students can make a batch of modeling dough with 8 oz of flour, 6 oz of salt, 3 oz of hot water, and $\frac{1}{2}$ tbsp of powdered alum. They should find how much of each ingredient they would use with 32 oz of flour. (24 oz of salt, 12 oz of water, 2 tbsp of alum)

PRACTICE

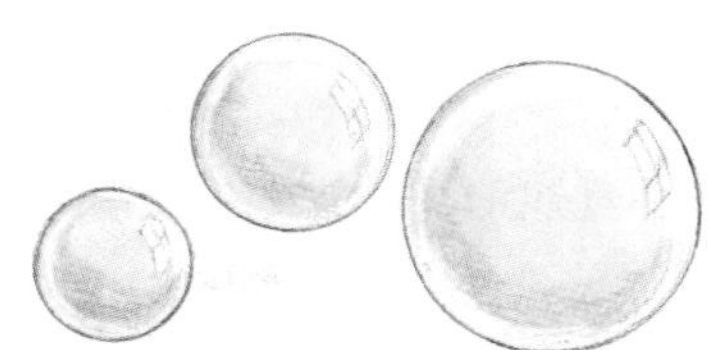

Copy and complete each table to help you solve these problems.

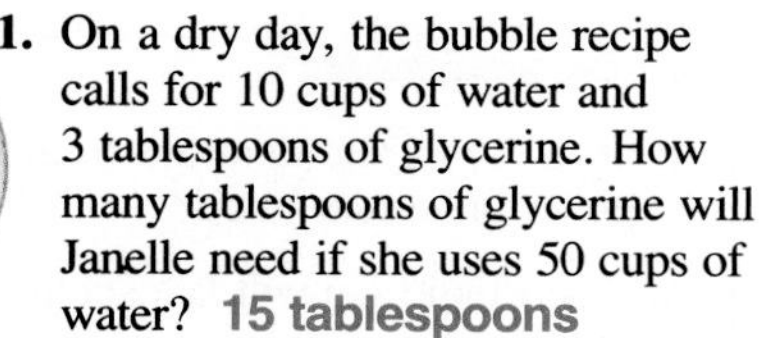

1. On a dry day, the bubble recipe calls for 10 cups of water and 3 tablespoons of glycerine. How many tablespoons of glycerine will Janelle need if she uses 50 cups of water? **15 tablespoons**

water	10	20	30	40	50
glycerine	3	6	9	12	15

2. Five tickets to the Bubble Festival cost $4. How much would it cost to buy tickets for a class of 25 students? **$20**

tickets	5	10	15	20	25
price	$4	8	12	16	20

MIXED PRACTICE

Choose a strategy from the list or use other strategies you know to solve these problems.

Some Strategies
Act It Out
Use Objects
Choose an Operation
Draw a Picture
Make an Organized List
Guess and Check
Make a Table

3. Jimbo made 3 bubble chains with 7 bubbles in each chain. Then he made 5 bubble chains with 9 bubbles each. How many bubbles in all were in both chains? **66 bubbles**

4. To make bubbles with her bubble wand, Juanita needs dishwashing soap. The 3 different brands it comes in are Glow, Sparkle, and Lemon Clear. The 2 sizes are large and small. How many different choices does Juanita have? **6 choices**

5. About how many people attended these three demonstrations? **Answers may vary.**

Demonstration	Number of Spectators
Walking Through Bubbles	682
Barehanded Bubble Making	478
Building Bubble Castles	394

6. A Bubble Pack contains 2 bubble blowers and 8 ounces of bubbles. Janell bought enough packs to get 32 ounces of bubbles. How many blowers did she get? **8 blowers**

blowers	2	4	6	8
bubbles	8	16	24	32

More Practice, page 516, set C

3. Practice and Apply

Basic	1-6
Average	1-6
Extended	1-6

Sample Solutions: See p. T79.

PRACTICE

Read Problems 1 and 2. For each problem, identify the set of multiples you will need to use to complete the table. (Problem 1: 10, 3; Problem 2: 5, 4)

MIXED PRACTICE

▶ **Identify a problem you could solve with the Make a Table strategy. Explain your reasoning.** (Problem 6, because it gives 2 kinds of related data.)

▶ **Explain how you might solve Problem 3.** (Multiply 3 × 7 and 5 × 9, then add the 2 products.)

▶ **Analyze Problem 4 to determine a solution method.** (Possible answer: Make an Organized List to sort the choices.)

▶ **Explain whether you need an estimate or an exact answer for Problem 5.** (An estimate—*about* is the clue.)

5-11

Close and Assess

SHOW WHAT YOU KNOW

Have students make a table to solve this problem: Chen buys 3 packs of blank tapes for $5. How many can he buy for $20? (12)

Tapes	3	6	9	12
Prices	$5	$10	$15	$20

Quick Quiz

How many pictures can Ty take with 5 rolls of film?

Film	1	(2)	(3)	(4)	(5)
Photos	20	(40)	(60)	(80)	(100)

CHAPTER 5

APPLIED PROBLEM SOLVING
GROUP DECISION MAKING

OBJECTIVE To analyze, organize, and make decisions using relevant data

FACTS TO CONSIDER

▶ **Evaluate the accuracy of Facts 1 and 2.** (Fact 1 is an estimated range, so you may actually award more or fewer prizes every hour; Fact 2 gives an estimated length of time, so the Round-Up may last more or less than 6 h.)
▶ **Interpret Fact 3.** (You cannot spend any more than $140 although you could decide to spend less.)
▶ **Explain why you probably cannot buy only one kind of prize.** (Fact 4 says that the store has only 9 packages of each kind of prize, so you will probably need several kinds of prizes; besides, winners may enjoy choosing from a variety of prizes.)
▶ **Examine the prize list to make some comparisons about price and number of prizes per package.** (Answers will vary. Sample answers: Skeletons are the most expensive, but the package has the most prizes in it; rings and small dinosaurs are of equal value; bouncy balls are twice as expensive as silly glasses.)

Applied Problem Solving
Group Decision Making

UNDERSTAND
FIND DATA
PLAN
ESTIMATE
SOLVE
CHECK

Group Skill:
Encourage and Respect Others

At the school Round-Up, your class is going to run the ball-tossing booth. First decide how many prizes you will need all together. Then decide how many of each type of prize you want to buy.

Facts to Consider

1. You can expect to award from 15 to 25 prizes each hour.
2. The Round-Up will last about 6 hours.
3. You have only $140 to spend.
4. There are only 9 packages of each type of prize at Max's Variety Store.

138

TEACHING OPTIONS

COOPERATIVE LEARNING

Grouping Suggestion: cooperative learning groups of 4 or 6
If possible, form groups with even numbers of students so they can work in pairs. Point out that there are many possible prize plans. Pairs in each group work to determine their own plan, written in the form of an itemized sales slip. Then the group reconvenes to compare and evaluate all the plans. Groups may decide whether to select a plan as is or to create a combined plan using elements from every pair's plan. Provide calculators so groups can verify their computations.

Max's Variety Store		
Prize	Number in a Package	Cost per Package
Skeletons	8 per package	$7
Rings	6 per package	$4
Whistles	5 per package	$2
Small spiders	5 per package	$4
Small dinosaurs	6 per package	$4
Finger monsters	7 per package	$4
Tiny race cars	4 per package	$2
Bouncy balls	3 per package	$4
Silly glasses	3 per package	$2

Some Questions to Answer

1. How many prizes will you need to buy if you award 15 prizes each hour?
   Hint:
   $15 + 15 + 15 + 15 + 15 + 15 = n$
2. How many prizes will you need to buy if you award 25 prizes each hour?
3. Suppose you bought 5 packages of rings at Max's Variety Store. How many prizes would you have? How much would they cost?
4. Suppose you bought 8 packages of silly glasses at Max's Variety Store. How many prizes would you have? How much would they cost?
5. How would a table or list help you to keep track of the number of prizes you will buy and the amount they will cost?

What Is Your Decision?

Show the prizes you have decided to buy.
Show how much money you will spend on each type of prize.
Show how much the prizes will cost all together.

139

EXTENSION Ask students how they might change their prize plans if they had more money to spend on the same number of prizes. (Answers will vary.) Begin with the same facts, but allow groups to spend up to $200. Students should use their original plans, then adjust them as they wish to suit the new data.

SOME QUESTIONS TO ANSWER

► **Relate Questions 1 and 2.** (The questions work together to give the least and the greatest number of prizes likely to be given per hour.)
► **Relate Questions 3 and 4.** (The questions make comparisons between price and number of prizes per package.)
► **Explain whether a $2 package of prizes is a better buy than a more costly package.** (It depends on how many prizes are in a package.)
► **Justify using a table or a list.** (You can record how many prizes and how much money you have.)

WHAT IS YOUR DECISION?

► **Explain how you developed your prize plan.** (Answers will vary.)
► **Evaluate your decision based on cost and variety of prizes.** (Answers will vary.)
► **Explain how the decision could have been made easier.** (Possible answer: If you knew what other booths were giving away, you could eliminate some prizes to avoid duplicating others.)
► **How would you choose to spend any leftover money?** (Answers will vary.) Have groups post their final sales slips on a bulletin board so others can see the variety of decisions that were made.

WRAP UP

INTRODUCTION The Wrap Up provides activities emphasizing math language and thinking skills for the chapter and a project that integrates those skills with other math strands.

USING PAGE 140

Operation Classification Have students complete this section independently. Then have partners compare answers and discuss any discrepancies they find.

Sometimes, Always, Never

► **Develop a strategy to help you evaluate the statements in Exercises 6 to 8.** (Possible answer: Formulate examples based on the first part of each sentence, then examine the outcomes to complete the sentences.)

Project Have students work in pairs to complete the Project.

► **Explain a pattern in Row A.** (Numbers increase by 1.)

► **Analyze Row B for a pattern.** (Numbers increase by 2.)

► **If the number chart had a Row C, predict what its pattern would be.** (Numbers would increase by 3.)

Have students create an alternative way to show the same patterns on a visual chart using stickers, drawings, or small objects in each box in place of numbers. Make a display of students' ideas.

WRAP UP

Operation Classification

Decide whether you might add, subtract, or multiply to solve a problem about each situation. Some situations may suggest more than one operation. Justify your choices.

1. The class has 5 sets of markers with 8 in a set. multiply
2. Gene took 28 photos. An album holds 50. subtract
3. The art room has 452 tubes of paint, but 26 have dried out. subtract
4. Tina counted 9 spiders, each with 8 legs. multiply
5. Ky is 13. His sister is 6 years younger. subtract

Sometimes, Always, Never

Which word should go in the blank, sometimes, always, or never? Explain your choices. Explanations will vary.

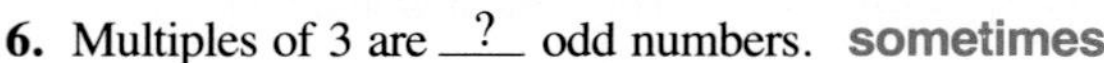

6. Multiples of 3 are __?__ odd numbers. sometimes
7. The product of two odd factors is __?__ odd. always
8. The product of two even factors is __?__ odd. never

Project

9. Look at the pattern in row A and in row B and complete this number chart.

Row A	2	3	4	5	6	7	8	9	10
Row B	4	6	8	10	12	14	16	18	20

10. What is the relationship between each pair of numbers in a column? Row B numbers are doubles of row A numbers.
11. Using the rule you found, add 5 more columns to your chart.

11	12	13	14	15
22	24	26	28	30

140

TEACHING OPTIONS

ENRICHMENT On blank index cards, have students create number charts that reflect a secret number pattern of their choice. Have them complete 4 columns of their charts, leaving 4 to 6 more columns blank. Store the pattern cards in a file box labeled Math Patterns and encourage students to solve independently.

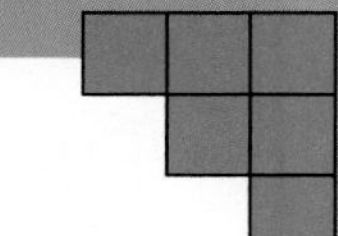

CHAPTER REVIEW/TEST

Part 1 Understanding

Write a multiplication equation that is an example of each property. **Answers will vary. Sample answers given.**

1. order property
   2 × 7 = 7 × 2
2. one property
   5 × 1 = 5
3. zero property
   4 × 0 = 0

Match each word with an example.

4. factors **b**
5. multiplication equation **c**
6. multiples **a**

a. 3, 6, 9, 12
b. 6 × 5
c. 5 × 5 = 25

7. Complete the sentence.

   To break apart 7 × 6, you might use the sets of factors ▯ and ▯. **Answers will vary. Samples answer: 5 × 6 and 2 × 6**

Part 2 Skills

Find the products.

8. 2 × 8 = **16**
9. 4 × 9 = **36**
10. 6 × 8 = **48**
11. 7 × 3 = **21**
12. 9 × 4 = **36**
13. 6 × 0 **0**
14. 4 × 8 **32**
15. 7 × 7 **49**
16. 5 × 8 **40**
17. 8 × 1 **8**

Find a number to fill the squares and another number to fill the triangles.

18. □ × △ = 18 (□ = **2**, △ = **9**)
19. △ − □ = 7 (△ = **9**, □ = **2**)

Part 3 Applications

20. A fruit salad recipe calls for 5 apples and 2 oranges. If Ray wants to use 35 apples, how many oranges does he need? **14 oranges**
21. Write the question another way, then solve. On Monday, Amir's Restaurant served 357 lunches and 464 dinners. What is the total number of meals served? **See Additional Answers.**

141

CHAPTER REVIEW/TEST

INTRODUCTION The Review/Test is provided to review and evaluate the skills and concepts presented in Chapter 5.

USING PAGE 141
If you prefer to use this page for review, you may want to use the **Multiple-Choice Posttest** (pages 19-20) or the **Free-Response Posttest** (pages 19-20) to evaluate mastery of chapter objectives.

ITEM ANALYSIS The table below correlates the Chapter Review/Test items with the lesson objectives for the chapter.

Items	Objectives
1-5, 13, 17	5-2
6	5-10
7	5-8
8, 16, 20	5-3
9, 12	5-4
10, 15	5-9
(9), 11, (12), 14	5-5
18, 19	5-6
(20)	5-11
21	5-7

Additional Answers: See p. T79.

INFORMAL ASSESSMENT

Using Manipulatives Have students represent each factor pair on graph paper, then give the products.
6 × 8 = ? 4 × 7 = ? 9 × 3 = ? (48, 28, 27; Check students' drawings, which should be rectangles.)

Communication *Relate multiplication to doubling a number.* (Possible answer: Use that number as 1 factor and 2 as the other factor.)

Critical Thinking *Determine the missing numbers. Explain your reasoning.*
△ × □ = 21 □ − △ = 4
(□ = 7; △ = 3; They fit both equations.)

ENRICHMENT

INTRODUCTION Exploring a familiar table to discover patterns and relationships sharpens students' ability to analyze, make predictions, and draw conclusions.

USING PAGE 142
This Enrichment page is provided for all students. You may wish to use it after the students have completed the Chapter Review/Test on page 141.
▶ **Without counting each, explain how you could determine the number of products in the multiplication table.** (Multiply the number of factors across the top by the number of factors down the side: 10 × 10 = 100.)
▶ **Explain how to use the table to find the product of 4 × 7.** (Find 1 factor along the left edge and the other factor across the top, then trace across and down to the box where the 2 meet to find 28.)
Have students work in pairs to discuss and complete the Enrichment page.

EXTENSION Have students examine the diagonal that appears on the multiplication chart starting at 0 in the upper left-hand corner and ending at 81 in the lower right-hand corner. *What pattern can you describe?* (It contains products of square numbers.)

Additional Answers: See p. T79.

ENRICHMENT
Multiplication Table Patterns

You know that a multiplication table helps you find the product of a pair of factors. You can also explore the rows, columns, and diagonals of the table to discover some interesting number patterns and relationships.

x	0	1	2	3	4	5	6	7	8	9
0	0	0	0	0	0	0	0	0	0	0
1	0	1	2	3	4	5	6	7	8	9
2	0	2	4	6	8	10	12	14	16	18
3	0	3	6	9	12	15	18	21	24	27
4	0	4	8	12	16	20	24	28	32	36
5	0	5	10	15	20	25	30	35	40	45
6	0	6	12	18	24	30	36	42	48	54
7	0	7	14	21	28	35	42	49	56	63
8	0	8	16	24	32	40	48	56	64	72
9	0	9	18	27	36	45	54	63	72	81

1. How could the table help you count by 2s? by 3s? by 5s? See Additional Answers.
2. Which rows of the table have all numbers even? Does any row have all numbers odd? 2, 4, 6, 8; no
3. Use the table to help you complete these "equations."
   a. even × even = ▯ even
   b. even × odd = ▯ even
   c. odd × odd = ▯ odd
4. Compare the 3 row with the 3 column. What do you discover? Is this true for other rows and columns? They are the same. yes
5. The blue line connects two identical products. How many other pairs of identical non-zero products can you find? Explain why this happens. See Additional Answers.
6. Look at the non-zero products, such as 36, in row 9. Add the digits in each product, in this case 3 + 6. What do you discover? They all equal 9.
7. Is what you discovered in exercise 6 true for other rows? What patterns, if any, do you see in other rows? See Additional Answers.
8. Add any product in the 1 row to the product below it in the 2 row. What do you discover about the sum? Try this with other rows. Does it always work this way? See Additional Answers.

142

CUMULATIVE REVIEW

1. Which numbers can fill the box and the circle to make the equation true?
6 + □ = 3 + ○

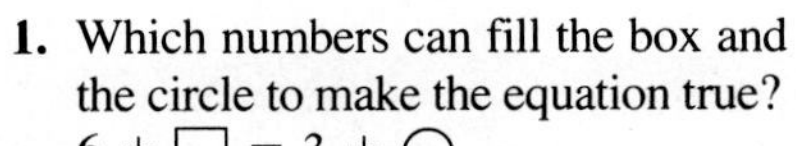

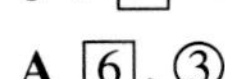

A [6], ③ B [4], ④
(C) [5], ⑧ D [2], ③

2. A, E, M, and T spell a word. T comes before E. M comes after A. The vowels are together. What is the word?

A mate (B) team
C meat D tame

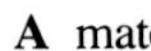

3. Use front-end estimation and adjust to estimate \$4.49 + \$8.44.

(A) \$13 B \$12
C \$14 D \$11

4. Use compensation to find the difference of 497 and 98.

A 400 B 398
(C) 399 D 401

5. 593 + 688

A 1,281 B 1,271
C 1,181 D 1,211

6. 442 + 1,296 + 375 + 803

A 2,816 (B) 2,916
C 3,016 D 17,496

7. About 10,000 fans liked which sport?

(A) tennis B basketball
C hockey D wrestling

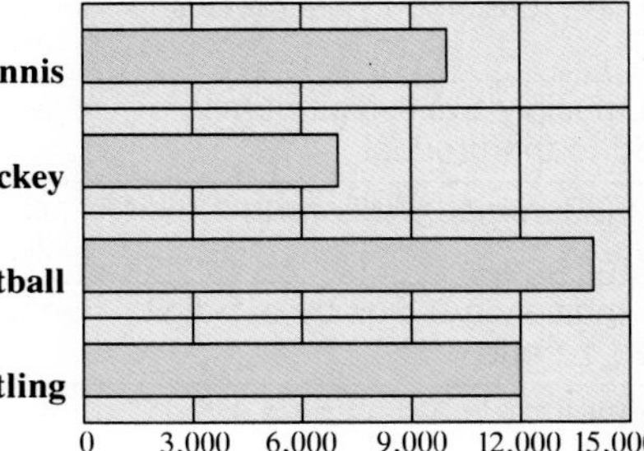

8. 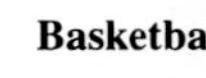 stands for 25 trees. If 250 trees are planted, how many tree symbols would a pictograph show?

A 5 (B) 10
C 50 D 25

9. A grab bag has 7 books, 2 puzzles, 2 tapes, and 1 art set. Which has the highest probability of being picked?

(A) book B puzzle
C tape D art set

CUMULATIVE REVIEW

INTRODUCTION The purpose of this Cumulative Review is to maintain previously taught skills and concepts. The emphasis in this Cumulative Review is on problem solving strategies, Chapter 2; on adding and subtracting whole numbers, Chapter 3; and on data, graphs, and probability, Chapter 4.

ITEM ANALYSIS The table below correlates the Cumulative Review items with the lesson objectives.

Items	Objectives
1	2-4
2	2-5
3	3-7
4	3-11
5	3-4
6	3-5
7	4-1
8	4-3
9	4-8

Chapter Management

OVERVIEW

Lesson	Pages	Objectives	Subject Integration	Strand Integration
Opener	144-145	To introduce chapter 6	science-birds	critical thinking
Mental Math: Special Products	146-147	6-1 To multiply by multiples of 10, 100, or 1000	science-geese	consumer math
Estimating Products	148-149	6-2 To use rounding to estimate a product	language arts-writing	measurement-money
Mental Math: Multiply and Then Add	150-151	6-3 To multiply two 1-digit numbers and add to the product	science-birds	calculators
Multiplying Whole Numbers: Making the Connection	152-153	6-4 To understand multiplying 1-digit numbers	social studies-partner skills	computation
Multiplying 2-Digit Numbers	154-155	6-5 To multiply a 2-digit by a 1-digit number, 1 trade	language arts-writing	measurement
Multiplying Larger Numbers: 1 Trade	156-157	6-6 To multiply a 3-digit by a 1-digit number, 1 trade	fine arts-puppet shows	algebra
Multiplying Larger Numbers: 2 or More Trades	158-159	6-7 To multiply a 3-digit by a 1-digit number	science-heartbeat rate	estimation
Using Critical Thinking & Midchapter Review/Quiz	160-161	6-8 To use mental math to multiply money; To review multiplication	social studies-consumer costs	number
Mental Math: Multiplying 3 Factors/Problem Solving: Using a Calculator	162-163	6-9 To find the product of 3 factors; To solve addition problems	social studies-holiday candles	life skills
Multiplying Larger Numbers: All Trades	164-165	6-10 To multiply a 4-digit by a 1-digit number	social studies-bridges	measurement
Multiplying with Money	166-167	6-11 To multiply an amount of money less than $100	social studies-consumer costs	estimation
Problem Solving: Look for a Pattern	168-169	6-12 To solve problems	language arts-school newspaper	consumer math
Data Collection and Analysis	170-171	To make a questionnaire for gathering data	language arts-writing	statistics

MATHEMATICAL BACKGROUND

Mental Math
The first mental-math skill lesson teaches students to think in terms of tens, hundreds, and thousands when multiplying with numbers such as 80, 500, or 3,000. A second mental-math skill lesson involves multiplying two 1-digit factors and then adding a third 1-digit number. A third mental-math skill lesson involves finding the product of 3 factors by multiplying any two first.

Estimation
The type of estimation used in this chapter is estimating products by rounding.

Problem Solving
Students learn to recognize and use patterns to solve problems in Lesson 6-12.

TIPS FROM TEACHERS

Play "Multiplication Frisbee." Make a frisbee by stapling together two paper plates. Construct several of them and on each one write a multiplication problem on one side and the answer on the other. The object is to answer the problem, then toss the frisbee into a box to score a point.

Mary Skeen
Denton Elementary
Denton, NC

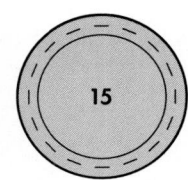

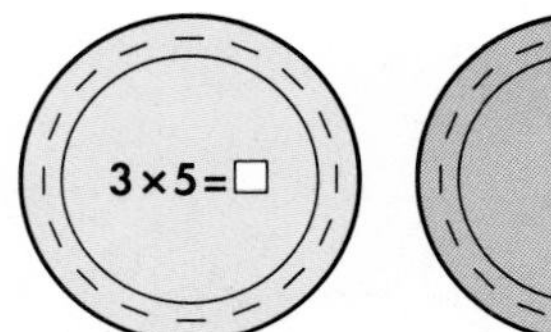

ASSESSMENT

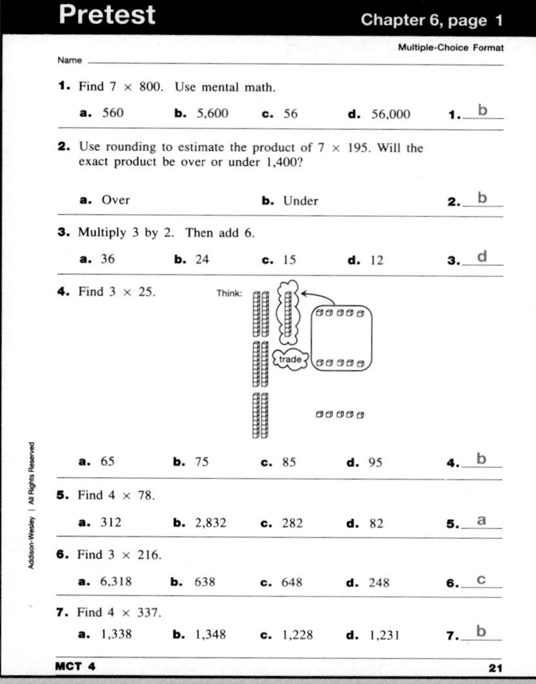

Pretest — Chapter 6, page 1

Multiple-Choice Format

Name ______

1. Find 7 × 800. Use mental math.
   a. 560 b. 5,600 c. 56 d. 56,000 — 1. b

2. Use rounding to estimate the product of 7 × 195. Will the exact product be over or under 1,400?
   a. Over b. Under — 2. b

3. Multiply 3 by 2. Then add 6.
   a. 36 b. 24 c. 15 d. 12 — 3. d

4. Find 3 × 25.

   a. 65 b. 75 c. 85 d. 95 — 4. b

5. Find 4 × 78.
   a. 312 b. 2,832 c. 282 d. 82 — 5. a

6. Find 3 × 216.
   a. 6,318 b. 638 c. 648 d. 248 — 6. c

7. Find 4 × 337.
   a. 1,338 b. 1,348 c. 1,228 d. 1,231 — 7. b

MCT 4 — 21

Pretest — Chapter 6, page 2

Multiple-Choice Format

Name ______

8. Use mental math method to find the cost of 3 notebooks at 24¢ each.
   a. 62¢ b. 72¢ c. 19¢ d. 27¢ — 8. b

9. Find (4 × 2) × 5.
   a. 40 b. 11 c. 30 d. 400 — 9. a

10. What missing number will make this a magic square?

96	12	72
36	60	84
48	?	24

   a. 180 b. 132 c. 108 d. 156 — 10. c

11. Find 3 × 3,054.
   a. 9,362 b. 9,162 c. 9,152 d. 9,062 — 11. b

12. Find 6 × $2.75.
   a. $16.20 b. $12.50 c. $12.20 d. $16.50 — 12. d

13. Baseball cards sell for $1.00 in bin 1, $1.25 in bin 2, $1.50 in bin 3, and so on. How much would a card in bin 7 cost? You can make a table to help you solve this problem.
   a. $2.75 b. $3.00 c. $2.25 d. $2.50 — 13. d

22 — MCT 4

Posttest — Chapter 6, page 1

Multiple-Choice Format

Name ______

1. Find 8 x 900. Use mental math.
   a. 720 b. 702 c. 7,200 d. 72 — 1. c

2. Use rounding to estimate the product of 9 x 784. Will the exact product be over or under 6,300?
   a. Over b. Under — 2. a

3. Multiply 2 by 5. Then add 4.
   a. 40 b. 18 c. 14 d. 13 — 3. c

4. Find 3 x 34. Think: (trade)
   a. 37 b. 92 c. 912 d. 102 — 4. d

5. Find 8 x 67.
   a. 4,856 b. 75 c. 486 d. 536 — 5. d

6. Find 4 x 233.
   a. 8,812 b. 892 c. 882 d. 862 — 6. b

7. Find 7 x 652.
   a. 4,264 b. 4,554 c. 4,254 d. 4,564 — 7. d

MCT 4 — 23

Posttest — Chapter 6, page 2

Multiple-Choice Format

Name ______

8. Use mental math method to find the cost of 2 pens at 39¢ each.
   a. 68¢ b. 41¢ c. 76¢ d. 78¢ — 8. d

9. Find 3 × (4 × 5).
   a. 60 b. 17 c. 12 d. 36 — 9. a

10. What missing number will make this a magic square?

112	?	84
42	70	98
56	126	28

   a. 98 b. 14 c. 140 d. 210 — 10. b

11. Find 3 × 2,069.
   a. 6,607 b. 6,187 c. 6,207 d. 6,007 — 11. c

12. Find 3 × $14.92.
   a. $44.76 b. $32.76 c. $34.76 d. $42.76 — 12. a

13. Baseball cards sell for $2.25 in bin 1, $2.50 in bin 2, $2.75 in bin 3, and so on. How much would a card in bin 7 cost? You can make a table to help you solve this problem.
   a. $4.00 b. $4.25 c. $3.50 d. $3.75 — 13. d

24 — MCT 4

ITEM ANALYSIS

Items	Objectives
1	6-1
2	6-2
3	6-3
4	6-4
5	6-5
6	6-6
7	6-7
8	6-8
9, 10	6-9
11	6-10
12	6-11
13	6-12

Note: The item analysis is the same for all pretests and posttests for this chapter.

ALSO AVAILABLE

- **Free Response Tests**
- **Alternative Tests**
- **Thinking Strategies**
- **Concrete Materials**

Optional Chapter Activities

PROJECT AND BULLETIN BOARD

Have each student bring a favorite recipe from home. This can be a recipe they know how to make themselves or something that an adult makes for them. Post the recipes on the bulletin board. Be sure each recipe uses only whole numbers and tells how many servings are made. Next to each recipe, have students post a list of quantities needed if the amounts of the ingredients were multiplied by 3, 4, and 5.

At another session, students may decide how to multiply to prepare enough of each recipe to feed everyone in the class.

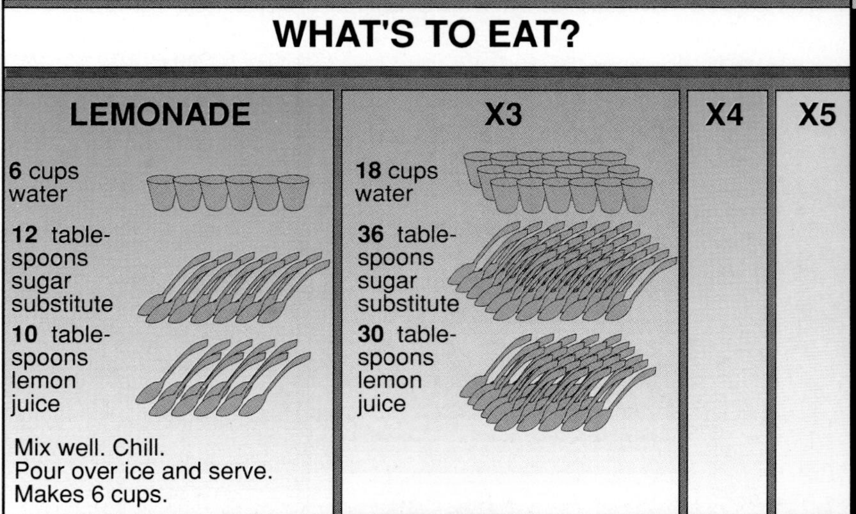

WHAT'S TO EAT?
LEMONADE
X3
X4
X5
6 cups water
12 table-spoons sugar substitute
10 table-spoons lemon juice
Mix well. Chill.
Pour over ice and serve.
Makes 6 cups.
18 cups water
36 table-spoons sugar substitute
30 table-spoons lemon juice

COOPERATIVE LEARNING

This activity may be used after Lesson 4-7. Divide the class into groups of three or four. Then identify the group skill: check for understanding. Give each group several multiplication problems in which one or more trades are necessary, such as 256 × 5. Tell each group to break apart the larger number into its component ones, tens, and hundreds. One student multiplies the ones, another the tens, and a third the hundreds. The group adds the results to get the answer to the multiplication problem. Then each member multiplies in the standard way and members compare answers to make sure everyone got the same answer. Ask students to question each other to make sure that everyone in the group understands why multiplying the ones, tens, and hundreds and then adding the results produces the same answer as multiplying directly.

You will find grouping suggestions and cooperative learning activities in most lessons throughout this chapter.

LITERATURE

Brittain, William. *All the Money in the World.* New York: Harper & Row, 1979.

Quentin Stowe stumbles upon a leprechaun. He makes a wish and it comes true—he gets all the money in the world. It's piled up all over his family's farm, and now the problems begin.

Once Quentin has all the money in the world, he cannot return it. That means no one in the town has any money of their own. The mayor calls a town meeting to discuss the problem and the people agree to use play money called dilly bills instead of real money. Everyone in Cedar Valley gets paid in dilly bills. Children could make their own dilly bills. Then they could act out the story using dilly bills to pay each other salaries and to pay debts.

MacDonald, Betty. *Mrs. Piggle-Wiggle's Farm.* New York: A Harper Trophy Book, Harper & Row, 1954.

Srivastava, Jane Jonas. *Number Families.* New York: Thomas Y. Crowell, 1979.

St. John, Glory. *How to Count Like a Martian.* New York: Henry Z. Walck, 1975.

English as a Second Language

Before learning to estimate products involving 2-digit factors and larger numbers with 2 or more trades, it is essential that children understand simple factors and products. Review the parts of a multiplication equation using a lesson such as the following where spoken language is modeled. Write several 1-digit by 1-digit multiplication number sentences on the chalkboard, such as $4 \times 3 = 12$ and $2 \times 3 = 6$. As you say the number sentences aloud, have individual children come up and point to each factor and product while other students copy the number sentences and follow along.

Next, dictate several other 1-digit by 1-digit multiplication number sentences as one child writes them on the chalkboard and the rest of the class writes them on their papers. When students have finished, pair limited English proficiency students with English proficient students and have them take turns saying the number sentences aloud to each other.

Gifted

Ask students to suppose that they have volunteered to assist with the ''Shopping for Seniors'' program which chooses groceries for homebound senior citizens. Instruct them to obtain a supermarket ad for groceries. Tell them that their senior needs one week's groceries and that $99.00 is the maximum amount they can spend.

Direct students to create a shopping list complete with prices. Inform them that multiples of less than ten are needed of some items and that they should calculate those quantities into their money total. Remind them to multiply the money carefully for their senior citizen. Have students verify that they will be able to feed one person for one week with what they will be buying. Encourage students to vary the meals and to make them nutritious.

Have students create a week's worth of menus based on the shopping list. Invite students to share these menus orally and to post the menus in the classroom. Then ask students to create an itemized grocery receipt that includes the breakdown for multiples of items and their unit price, the quantity of those items being purchased, and the dollar amount to be added into the total. Suggest that students trade receipts and check multiplication.

Students at Risk

The multiplication algorithm reviewed in this chapter is problematic for many learning disabled students because it involves sequencing and memory skills. Inadequate mastery of addition and multiplication facts and trouble aligning numbers during computation also present difficulty. Provide students with regular review of number facts and the proper sequence of multiplication steps. Have students work multiplication problems on lined paper turned widthwise to help them align numbers in columns.

On lined paper turned widthwise, have students write multiplication problems within the format illustrated below. Color highlight the ones digit as a visual reminder of the first step. The box with the addition sign serves as a reminder to trade tens and add the traded value. Students should develop the habit of crossing out each digit they have traded as they use it.

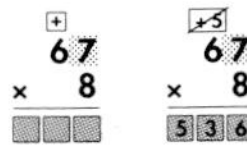

You may also use the Reteaching Supplements and the specific Reteaching Tips from each lesson in this chapter.

CHAPTER 6

INTRODUCING THE CHAPTER

SUBJECT INTEGRATION The photograph of a hummingbird feeding on a flower represents the chapter theme of Natural Science. Students explore a relationship between a hummingbird's weight and its wingbeat rate per second. Various lessons include other science facts about birds to connect multiplication with the chapter theme.

USING DATA The Science Data Bank on page 469 of the student text contains three tables about birds: Heartbeat Rates of Birds, Wingbeats Per Second, and Number of Eggs Laid. Data for heartbeat rate and eggs laid compare a variety of birds; wingbeat data compare hummingbirds by weight.

QUESTION 1 ► **Explain how to find the number of eggs a lark lays per year.** (Find how many eggs in 3 groups of 4: 12.)
► **Tell how to use the other data in the table to answer the question.** (Locate another number combination with the same product, such as 2 groups of 6.)
Student Edition answer: starling

6 MULTIPLYING BY 1-DIGIT FACTORS

MATH AND SCIENCE
DATA BANK
Use the Science Data Bank on page 469 to answer the questions. **See teaching notes.**

1 Which bird on the list lays the same number of eggs in 1 year as the lark does?

TEACHING OPTIONS

LANGUAGE DEVELOPMENT FOR MULTIPLICATION Write the word **per** on the chalkboard. Have students locate each use of *per* in the Science Data Bank on page 469 and identify two values connected by *per*. (heartbeats per minute, wingbeats per second) Have students restate each phrase with *per* to clarify its meaning. (Possible answers: heartbeats in each minute, wingbeats for every second)

2 A turkey's heart beats 28 more times per minute than an ostrich's heart does. How many times per minute does a turkey's heart beat?

3 Which of the birds lays the greatest number of eggs in 1 year? Which bird lays the least number of eggs in 1 year?

4 **Use Critical Thinking** What do you notice about the number of wingbeats per second when you compare the sizes of the hummingbirds?

145

QUESTION 2 ► **What fact do you need to answer the question? Where will you find it?** (how many ostrich heartbeats per minute; Heartbeat Rates of Birds table)
► **How can you use that fact with the other information to answer the question?** (Add: 28 + 65 = 93.)
Student Edition answer: 93 heartbeats per minute

QUESTION 3 ► **How can you answer the questions without finding the number of eggs per year for every bird on the list?** (Possible answer: Consider the greatest and least numbers of eggs per clutch, then see if any number combinations are greater or smaller.)
Student Edition answers: greatest, coot; least, king penguin

QUESTION 4 Have students explain what the *g* means in the Wingbeats list. (grams)
Student Edition answer: The smaller the hummingbird, the more times its wings beat per second.

SUBJECT INTEGRATION PROJECT Have students formulate questions about the birds featured in the Data Bank. For example: "How much does an ostrich egg weigh? How tall is a king penguin? How long does it take for coot eggs to hatch?" As they work through Chapter 6, students can research science books or encyclopedias in the school library to answer their questions. On a bulletin board or poster, have them classify and display the facts they find with pictures or drawings of the birds.

Lesson Options 6-1

Mental Math: Special Products

OBJECTIVE 6-1 To use mental math to find the product of a 1-digit number times a multiple of 10, 100, or 1,000

Prebook Activities

Quick Review

Give the products.

1. 4×7 (28)	**2.** 5×9 (45)	**3.** 1×4 (4)
4. 2×6 (12)	**5.** 8×3 (24)	**6.** 6×7 (42)
7. 8×7 (56)	**8.** 6×9 (54)	**9.** 7×7 (49)

PRIOR KNOWLEDGE

Ask volunteers to skip count by 10, 100, and 1,000. (10, 20, 30, . . . ; 100, 200, 300, . . . ; 1,000, 2,000, 3,000, . . .) Have students relate skip counting to the multiples of 10, 100, and 1,000. (Possible answer: When you skip count, you are reciting multiples.) Brainstorm to create a list of items that customarily come in groups of 10 or one of its multiples. Make similar lists for multiples of 100 and of 1,000. (Answers will vary; samples: stamps, notebook paper, paper plates) Then explain that in this lesson students will use mental math with basic multiplication facts to find products when one factor is a multiple of 10, 100, or 1,000.

COMMUNICATION

Discussing Math Have students describe a **cluster** of grapes or of houses. (things of the same kind in a group) Ask them what it means **to cluster** around a teacher. (Students form a group around a teacher.) List the numbers 48, 52, 46, 54, and 51 on the chalkboard. Ask students to look for a multiple of 10 around which the numbers cluster. (50) Then ask them to suggest a way to estimate the sum of the numbers, using the idea of the *cluster*. (Students may find 5×50.)

Explore and Connect

Materials: index cards, calculators
Grouping Suggestion: small cooperative learning groups
Students explore ways to add a series of numbers that **cluster** together. Each group member writes five 2-digit numbers on separate index cards. Group members mix the cards, then sort the set by **clustering** cards around the nearest multiple of 10. Members apply rounding rules to check their sorting. When all cards are **clustered**, students explore ways to estimate the sum of the cards that *cluster* around each multiple of 10. Encourage the groups to be open to any reasonable ideas from their members. Students may use calculators to find exact sums. Discuss how the estimated sums were found. Have students who discovered a good method for *clustering* demonstrate how it works and justify their reasoning. If time allows, students can repeat the activity with multiples of 100 and 1,000 and cards for 3- and 4-digit numbers.

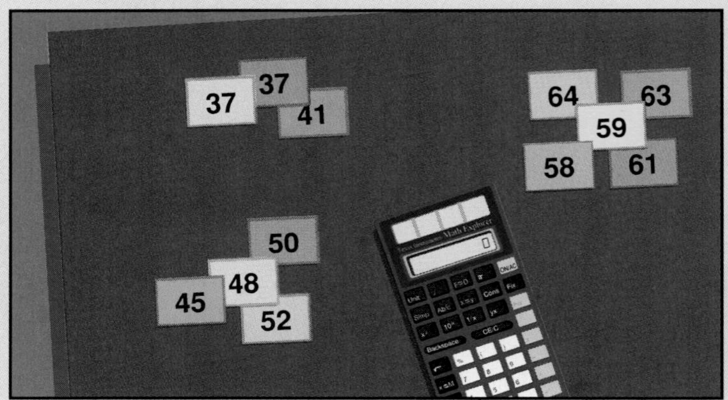

Connections Use these anytime.

Problem of the Day

Supplies Mr. Alvarez is ordering marbles for his toy store. The marbles come in packets of 10. There are 50 packets to a carton and 10 cartons to a case. How many marbles are in a case? Explain your reasoning. (10 marbles to a packet $\times$ 50 packets to a carton $\times$ 10 cartons to a case: $10 \times 50 \times 10 = 5{,}000$ marbles.)

Math Connection

Money Large numbers of coins are sorted, counted, and wrapped in rolls. Coin rolls hold 50 pennies, 40 nickels, 50 dimes, or 40 quarters. How much is each roll worth? ($0.50, $2.00, $5.00, $10.00)

Life Skills

Postage Stamps Post offices sell some 25-cent stamps in rolls of 100 stamps or in sheets of 50 stamps. How much does a roll of stamps cost? How much does a sheet cost? How might you buy 350 stamps and what would it cost? ($25.00; $12.50; Possible answer: 3 rolls and 1 sheet; $87.50)

Classwork and Homework Supplements

Practice

Mental Math 6-1

Name ____________________

Special Products

Copy each question and write the number for the □ and △.

1. Since 6 × 4 = □, then 6 × 40 = △. 6 x 4 = 24, 6 x 40 = 240
2. Since 3 × 3 = □, then 3 × 30 = △. 3 x 3 = 9, 3 x 30 = 90
3. Since 7 × 9 = □, then 7 × 900 = △. 7 x 9 = 63, 7 x 900 = 6,300
4. Since 2 × 8 = □, then 2 × 800 = △. 2 x 8 = 16, 2 x 800 = 1,600

Estimate the sums.

5. 295 + 323 + 276 + 309 = 1,200
6. 659 + 741 + 682 = 2,100
7. 158 + 170 + 212 + 235 = 800
8. 98 + 146 + 96 = 300

Find the products.

9. 2 × 50 =	100	**10.** 700 × 7 =	4,900
11. 5 × 300 =	1,500	**12.** 800 × 3 =	2,400
13. 400 × 9 =	3,600	**14.** 6 × 5,000 =	30,000
15. 6 × 7,000 =	42,000	**16.** 6,000 × 8 =	48,000
17. 9,000 × 4 =	36,000	**18.** 2,000 × 6 =	12,000

Building Thinking Skills

Critical Thinking 6-1

Name ____________________

Using Data

Study the facts on this chart.

Plane	Speed	Time
A	600 mph	2 hours
B	300 mph	6 hours
C	200 mph	8 hours

Use the chart to answer the questions below. Write how you will find the answers on the lines. Then write the answers in the boxes. Use mental math to help you where necessary.

1. Do you have enough information to find out the distance each plane traveled? Why? Yes; speed x time = distance.
2. How far did each plane travel?
   - Plane A: 600 miles per hour x 2 hours — 1,200 miles
   - Plane B: 300 miles per hour x 6 hours — 1,800 miles
   - Plane C: 200 miles per hour x 8 hours — 1,600 miles
3. How far can Plane B travel in 3 hours? 300 miles per hour x 3 hours — 900 miles
4. Plane D can travel twice as fast as Plane A. How far can Plane D travel in 4 hours? How do you know? The speed of Plane D is 1,200 mph; 1,200 miles per hour x 4 hours. — 4,800 miles

Reteaching

Mental Math 6-1

Name ____________________

Special Products

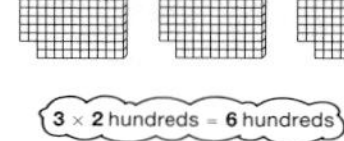

3 × 2 tens = 6 tens

3 × 20 = 60

3 × 2 hundreds = 6 hundreds

3 × 200 = 600

Use mental math to find the products.

4 × 3 tens = 12 tens

4 × 3 hundreds = 12 hundreds

1. 4 × 30 =	120	**2.** 4 × 300 =	1,200
3. 4 × 3,000 =	12,000	**4.** 2 × 40 =	80
5. 2 × 400 =	800	**6.** 2 × 4,000 =	8,000
7. 3 × 50 =	150	**8.** 3 × 500 =	1,500
9. 3 × 5,000 =	15,000	**10.** 4 × 70 =	280
11. 4 × 700 =	2,800	**12.** 4 × 7,000 =	28,000
13. 5 × 80 =	400	**14.** 5 × 800 =	4,000
15. 5 × 8,000 =	40,000	**16.** 7 × 10 =	70
17. 9 × 40 =	360	**18.** 3 × 6,000 =	18,000
19. 4 × 2,000 =	8,000	**20.** 7 × 600 =	4,200
21. 3 × 70 =	210	**22.** 8 × 30 =	240

Challenges

Cooperative Activities 6-1

Name ____________________

Product Wheels

Work with a group to complete this challenge.

1. Put 2 numbers in each spoke whose product is the center number. Compare the results within the group.
   Answers will vary. Samples given.

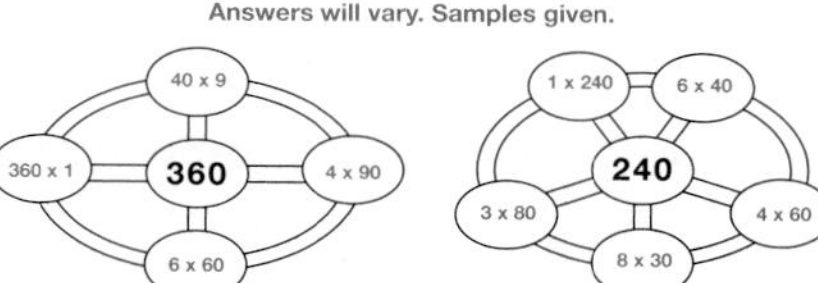

2. How many other pairs of numbers for the spokes above can your group find? Answers will vary.
3. Now work as a group to fill in each spoke with two numbers to make the product in the center of each wheel below.
   Answers will vary. Samples given.

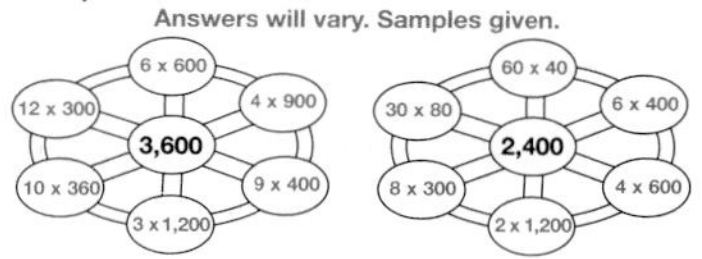

4. Compare answers for Exercise 1 to those for Exercise 3. What generalizations can you make?
   Answers will vary. Sample: You can use basic multiplication facts and what you know about place value to determine special products mentally.

Options for Individual Needs

Basic

Exercises 2-9, 11-16
Skills Bank, p. 460
More Practice, p. 503, set F

Supplements
Reteaching 52 or
Practice 52
Thinking Skills 52

Average

Exercises 1-16
More Practice, p. 503, set F

Supplements
Practice 52
Challenges 52 or
Thinking Skills 52

Extended

Exercises 3-16

Supplements
Challenges 52
Thinking Skills 52

Other Resources:
Math in Stride, 4, Teacher Sourcebook, pp. 86-88
Workbook, pp. 48-106

6-1

LESSON PLAN 6-1

OBJECTIVE 6-1
To use mental math to find the product of a 1-digit number times a multiple of 10, 100, or 1,000

Materials: colored marking pens

1. MOTIVATE AND TEACH

LEARN ABOUT IT

EXPLORE ► **Which operation would you use to answer questions about how many stickers Dana bought? Why?** (Possible answer: Multiplication; it is easier than adding amounts repeatedly.)

TALK ABOUT IT ► **Explain how to determine how many sticker sheets Dana bought in all.** (Possible answer: A package has 300 stickers with 100 stickers on a sheet, so count by hundreds up to 300 to get 3 sheets. Then multiply 3 sheets by the 4 packages bought to get 12 sheets in all.)
► **How can you skip count to find how many stickers Dana bought in all?** (Possible answer: Skip count by 3 four times; Dana got 3 hundreds for each of 4 friends.)
► **How does breaking apart 80 into 8 tens help when multiplying by 4?** (Possible answer: It is easier to multiply 4 × 8 to get 32 and then add 1 zero to get 320, than to multiply 4 × 80 to get 320.)
Student Edition answers: **1.** 3 **2.** 12; 1,200; explanations will vary

2. CHECK UNDERSTANDING

TRY IT OUT

ERROR ALERT Writing the wrong number of zeros after basic facts. Failing to notice a number around which addends cluster, as in Exercise 9.

Mental Math
Special Products

LEARN ABOUT IT

EXPLORE Think About the Situation
Dana bought a package of 300 stickers for each of 4 friends. The packages had sheets with 100 stickers on a sheet.

4 × 3 hundred stickers are ▯ hundred stickers?
4 × 300 = ▯

TALK ABOUT IT See teaching notes.

1. How many sticker sheets did Dana buy for each friend?
2. How many sticker sheets did Dana buy in all? How many stickers is this? Explain how you decided.

You can break apart numbers and use basic multiplication facts to find products like 4 × 80, 6 × 500, and 8 × 3,000.

To Find	Think	
4 × 80	4 × 8 tens	320
6 × 500	6 × 5 hundreds	3,000
8 × 3,000	8 × 3 thousands	24,000

You can use this mental math skill and a method called **clustering** to help you estimate sums of certain addends.

The addends cluster around 500. The sum is about 3 × 500, or 1,500.

496 + 508 + 487

TRY IT OUT

Use mental math to find the products.

1. 6 × 100 **600**
2. 7 × 30 **210**
3. 8 × 4,000 **32,000**
4. 4 × 500 **2,000**
5. Use clustering to estimate the sum 687 + 699 + 716 + 708. **2,800**

TEACHING OPTIONS

RETEACHING TIPS Have students isolate digits that form a basic multiplication fact by circling them with a colored pen, then write their product. Have them circle the number of zeros in the factors in another color, then write that many zeros after the basic-fact product. Assign Reteaching Supplement 52.

ENRICHMENT Have students use products to find these products:
1. 10 × 300 (3,000)
2. 90 × 90 (8,100)
3. 2,000 × 20 (40,000)
4. 600 × 400 (240,000)
5. 7,000 × 300 (2,100,000)
6. 5,000 × 2,000 (10,000,000)

PRACTICE

Copy each equation and give the numbers for the □ and the △.

1. Since $8 \times 7 = \square$, then $8 \times 70 = \triangle$. $8 \times 7 = 56, 8 \times 70 = 560$
2. Since $3 \times 8 = \square$, then $3 \times 80 = \triangle$. $3 \times 8 = 24, 3 \times 80 = 240$
3. Since $6 \times 9 = \square$, then $6 \times 900 = \triangle$. $6 \times 9 = 54, 6 \times 900 = 5{,}400$

Estimate the sums.

4. $397 + 411 + 385 + 403$ 1,600
5. $191 + 175 + 230 + 213$ 800
6. $921 + 897 + 884$ 2,700

Find the products. Write only the answers.

7. 4×600 2,400
8. 7×700 4,900
9. $9 \times 6{,}000$ 54,000
10. 800×3 2,400
11. Multiply 6 and 400. 2,400
12. Find the product of 9 and 2,000. 18,000

APPLY

MATH REASONING

13. The equation 3×40 has the same product as 4×30, 2×60, and 6×20. Give 3 equations that have the same product as 9×20.
Answers will vary. Sample answers: 2×90, 3×60, 6×30

PROBLEM SOLVING

14. **Extra Data** Solve the problem, then tell what data was not needed. Eve bought 4 sheets with 50 stickers on a sheet for 60¢. Fran bought 3 sheets of 80 stickers for 70¢. How many more stickers did Fran get?
40 stickers; cost of stickers is not needed.
15. Stan wanted to buy enough packages containing 4 sheets with 50 stickers each to have 1,000 stickers. How many packages must he buy? 5 packages

▶ USING CRITICAL THINKING Support Your Conclusion

16. Without using pencil and paper or a calculator, convince someone that a goose flying at a top speed of 63 miles per hour cannot fly 190 miles in 3 hours.
$3 \times 63 = (3 \times 60) + (3 \times 3) = 189 < 190$

More Practice, page 503, set F

3. PRACTICE AND APPLY

Basic	2-9, 11-16
Average	1-16
Extended	3-16

PRACTICE

Ask: *In Exercises 1-3, how will you know how many zeros to add to the basic product?* (In each exercise, count how many zeros each factor has. Then add that many zeros to the basic product.)

APPLY

MATH REASONING ▶ What should you do first in order to solve Exercise 13? Explain. (Possible answer: Find the product of 9×20 so you can name other factors with that product.)

PROBLEM SOLVING ▶ How does the question in Problem 14 help you identify the extra data? (Possible answer: It tells you what you need to look for so that you know what data are important.)

USING THINKING SKILLS ▶ How can you break apart the numbers to get easier numbers to work with? (Multiply 3×60 and 3×3, then add the products to get a total of 189 miles.)

6-1

CLOSE AND ASSESS

SAY WHAT YOU THINK Ask students to explain how to multiply $5 \times 7{,}000$ using mental math. Have them give the steps they would follow, and explain their reasoning. (Students explain their ideas to a partner. They should be thinking 5 × 7 thousands = 35 thousands = 35,000.)

QUICK QUIZ

1. Estimate the sum of 82, 77, 79, and 81. (Cluster; $80 \times 4 = 320$.)

Find the products using mental math.

2. 7×100 (700)
3. $6 \times 6{,}000$ (36,000)

LESSON OPTIONS 6-2

Estimating Products

OBJECTIVE 6-2 To use the estimation technique of rounding to estimate a product and compare it with

PREBOOK ACTIVITIES

QUICK REVIEW

Estimate to tell if sums are over or under $10.

1. $5.87 + $3.96 (under)
2. $4.05 + $6.50 (over)
3. $8.20 + $1.99 (over)
4. $2.60 + $7.27 (under)
5. $3.49 + $6.63 (over)

PRIOR KNOWLEDGE

Ask students to recall what a **reference point** is. (a number given for comparing) Ask a volunteer to illustrate its use by making up a question about whether someone has enough money for a purchase. For example: If you have $20, can you buy jeans for $12.99 and a shirt for $8.50? (no) Ask another volunteer to identify the reference point and to explain its use. (Possible answer: The reference point is $20. After prices are rounded and a sum estimated, the sum is compared to the reference point to see if it is under or over $20.) Ask students if reference points could be used with products as well as with sums and to explain why. (Possible answer: Yes; it is only a guide and can be used with any operation.)

COMMUNICATION

Discussing Math Have students compare **overestimates** and **underestimates.** (Overestimates are higher than the exact answer: underestimates are lower.) Ask students to generalize the relationship between an exact product and its estimated product based on how factors are rounded. (Possible answer: If you round factors up, you overestimate the product; if you round factors down, you underestimate the product.)

EXPLORE AND CONNECT

Materials: TA 3 (Number Cards 0–9), TA 2 (Number Cubes numbered 1-6), calculators

Grouping Suggestion: cooperative learning pairs

Students round and estimate products, then compare to exact answers, to discover any relationships between rounding up or down and **over-** or **underestimation.** To begin, one student draws number cards at random to form a 2- or 3-digit number and rounds the number to its highest place. The student then rolls a number cube and predicts whether the product of the number rolled and his or her rounded number is an **overestimate** or an **underestimate.** The partner finds the exact product on a calculator and checks the prediction for accuracy. Pairs take turns forming a number and completing the other steps. Encourage pairs to verify each other's estimates and to help with special products that some students may not recall. Conclude by discussing students' discoveries.

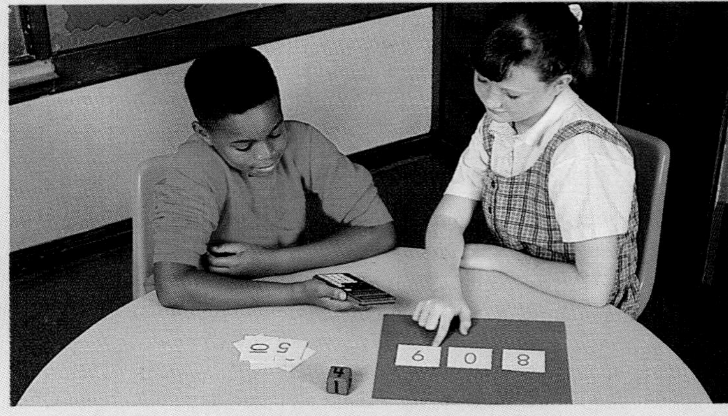

CONNECTIONS Use these anytime.

Problem of the Day

Recycling Pedro earns a nickel for every aluminum can he brings to the recycling center. If he returns a thousand cans, will he have enough money to buy 4 cassette tapes at $13 each? Explain your answer. (No; 1,000 × $.05 = $50; 4 × $13 = $52. He will be $2 short.)

Math Connection

Measurement An elevator can safely carry 1,600 pounds. Decide whether 10 adults whose average weight is 147 pounds can safely ride together. Explain your answer. (Yes; round up to overestimate: 10 × 150 = 1,500.)

Life Skills

Shopping Wes buys 9 frozen dinners at $1.99 each. Is $20 enough money? Explain your reasoning. (Yes; overestimate: 9 × $2 = $18.)

a reference point

CLASSWORK AND HOMEWORK SUPPLEMENTS

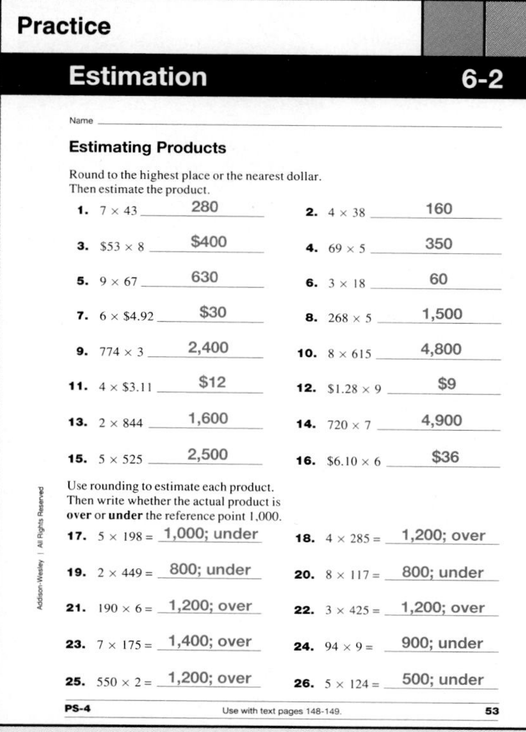

Practice

Estimation 6-2

Name

Estimating Products

Round to the highest place or the nearest dollar.
Then estimate the product.

1. 7 × 43	280	**2.** 4 × 38	160
3. $53 × 8	$400	**4.** 69 × 5	350
5. 9 × 67	630	**6.** 3 × 18	60
7. 6 × $4.92	$30	**8.** 268 × 5	1,500
9. 774 × 3	2,400	**10.** 8 × 615	4,800
11. 4 × $3.11	$12	**12.** $1.28 × 9	$9
13. 2 × 844	1,600	**14.** 720 × 7	4,900
15. 5 × 525	2,500	**16.** $6.10 × 6	$36

Use rounding to estimate each product.
Then write whether the actual product is **over** or **under** the reference point 1,000.

17. 5 × 198 =	1,000; under	**18.** 4 × 285 =	1,200; over
19. 2 × 449 =	800; under	**20.** 8 × 117 =	800; under
21. 190 × 6 =	1,200; over	**22.** 3 × 425 =	1,200; over
23. 7 × 175 =	1,400; over	**24.** 94 × 9 =	900; under
25. 550 × 2 =	1,200; over	**26.** 5 × 124 =	500; under

PS-4 Use with text pages 148-149. 53

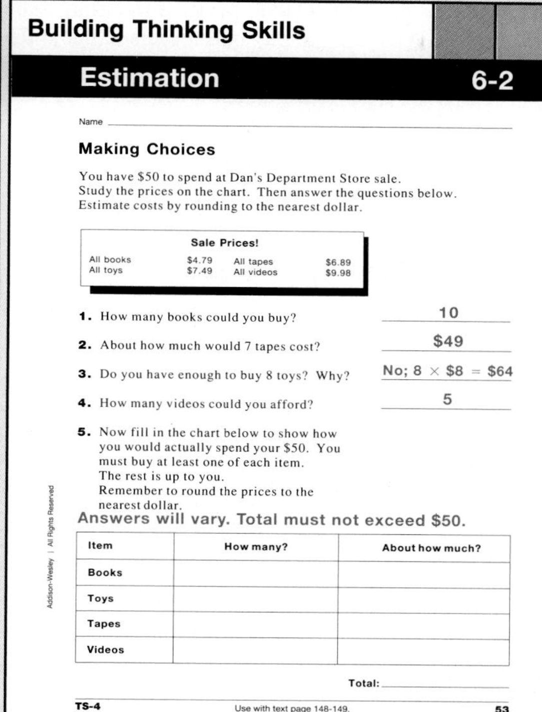

Building Thinking Skills

Estimation 6-2

Name

Making Choices

You have $50 to spend at Dan's Department Store sale.
Study the prices on the chart. Then answer the questions below.
Estimate costs by rounding to the nearest dollar.

Sale Prices!			
All books	$4.79	All tapes	$6.89
All toys	$7.49	All videos	$9.98

1. How many books could you buy? 10
2. About how much would 7 tapes cost? $49
3. Do you have enough to buy 8 toys? Why? No; 8 × $8 = $64
4. How many videos could you afford? 5
5. Now fill in the chart below to show how you would actually spend your $50. You must buy at least one of each item. The rest is up to you. Remember to round the prices to the nearest dollar.

Answers will vary. Total must not exceed $50.

Item	How many?	About how much?
Books		
Toys		
Tapes		
Videos		

Total:

TS-4 Use with text page 148-149. 53

Reteaching

Estimation 6-2

Name

Estimating Products

To **estimate** products, you should round and multiply.

Estimate to the nearest ten.	Estimate to the nearest hundred.	Estimate to the nearest dollar.
4 x 57 (Think: 7 > 5, so round up.) 4 x 60 = 240	3 x 429 (Think: 2 < 5, so round down.) 3 x 400 = 1,200	7 x $3.89 (Think: 8 > 5, so round up.) 7 x $4 = $28
About 240	About 1,200	About $28

Round to the nearest ten. Then estimate the product.

1. 3 × 21 3 × 20 = 60 **2.** 6 × 48 6 × 50 = 300
3. 4 × 77 4 × 80 = 320 **4.** 7 × 43 7 × 40 = 280
5. 5 × 78 5 × 80 = 400 **6.** 9 × 32 9 × 30 = 270

Round to the nearest hundred. Then estimate the product.

7. 2 × 732 2 × 700 = 1,400 **8.** 6 × 375 6 × 400 = 2,400
9. 5 × 425 5 × 400 = 2,000 **10.** 4 × 679 4 × 700 = 2,800
11. 3 × 211 3 × 200 = 600 **12.** 8 × 783 8 × 800 = 6,400

Round to the nearest dollar. Then estimate the product.

13. 4 × $8.40 4 × $8 = $32 **14.** 6 × $3.78 6 × $4 = $24
15. 3 × $9.42 3 × $9 = $27 **16.** 5 × $4.15 5 × $4 = $20

RS-4 Use with text pages 148-149. 53

Challenges

Estimation 6-2

Name

Factor Bowl

Play this game with a partner or in teams.
You will need a watch or a 2-minute timer.

Factor Bowl Rules

Partners or teams should take turns following these steps:

1. Choose one number from each factor bowl. Cross them out.
2. Estimate the product of the numbers you chose and record your prediction.
3. Calculate the product of the numbers you chose.
4. Your score is the difference between the actual product and your estimate. Calculate and record it.
5. As other players take their turns, crossed out numbers cannot be reused. The game is over when all the numbers in both bowls have been crossed out.
6. The partner or team with the lowest score wins.

29 63 78 11 37 54 18 92 42

7 8 3 9 8 4 5 3 6

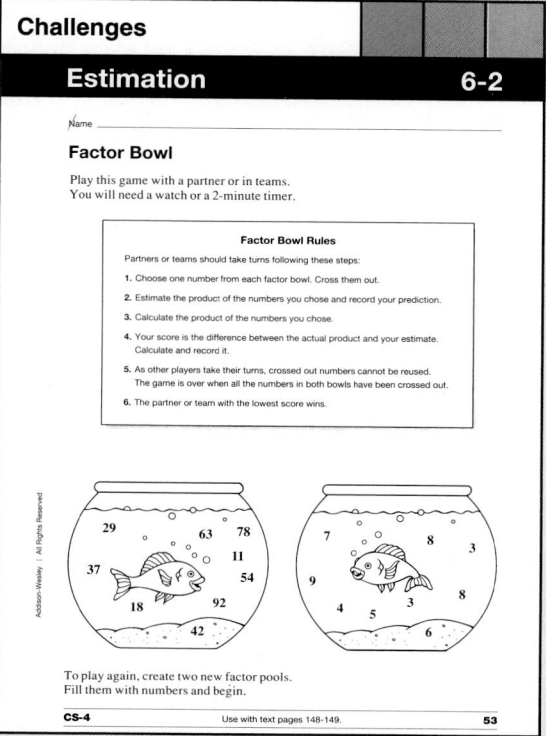

To play again, create two new factor pools.
Fill them with numbers and begin.

CS-4 Use with text pages 148-149. 53

OPTIONS FOR INDIVIDUAL NEEDS

Basic

Exercises 5-22
Skills Bank, p. 460
More Practice, p. 503, set G

Supplements
Reteaching 53 or
Practice 53
Challenges 53

Average

Exercises 1-25
More Practice, p. 503, set G

Supplements
Practice 53
Challenges 53 or
Thinking Skills 53

Extended

Exercises 7-15, 20-25

Supplements
Challenges 53
Thinking Skills 53

Other Resources:
Problem-Solving Experiences in Mathematics, Grade 4,
Problem 51

LESSON PLAN 6-2

OBJECTIVE 6-2
To use the estimation technique of rounding to estimate a product and compare it with a reference point

Materials: TA 9 (Play Money—Coins and Dollars), TA 10 (Play Money—Larger Bills), calculators

1. MOTIVATE AND TEACH

LEARN ABOUT IT

EXPLORE ▶ **Restate the question in your own words.** (Possible response: Is $150 enough money to buy 7 bird feeders that cost $19 each?)
▶ **Why would you multiply to solve this problem?** (to compare the product to the reference point)

TALK ABOUT IT ▶ **Explain how you would round the feeder price.** (Round $19 to $20; 19 is only 1 less than 20.)
▶ **Should you round the 7? Explain.** (No; you can think of 7 × 20 as a special product.)
▶ **How can you tell which number is the reference point?** (Find the total amount the club can spend—$150.)
▶ **Explain how the estimated product will compare with the exact product.** (19 rounds up to 20, so the estimated product will be greater than the exact product.)
Student Edition answers: **1.** $20; 19 is rounded up to 20. **2.** more

2. CHECK UNDERSTANDING

TRY IT OUT

ERROR ALERT Rounding both factors and getting estimates that are much too high. Forgetting dollar signs for money products, as in Exercises 3-4.

Estimating Products

LEARN ABOUT IT

EXPLORE Make a Decision Julie's nature club wanted to buy bird feeders to put at the windows in a senior citizens' home. Each feeder costs $19. The children had earned $150. Did they have enough money to buy 7 feeders?

TALK ABOUT IT See teaching notes.

1. Should the children use $10 or $20 when estimating the cost of each bird feeder? Why?
2. Will their estimate be more or less than the actual cost?

You can round numbers when you want to estimate a product to decide if it is close to a reference point.

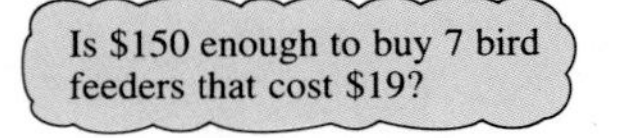
Is $150 enough to buy 7 bird feeders that cost $19?

Round to the nearest 10.	$19 × 7	⟶	$20 × 7
Estimate.			$140

The reference point is $150. The estimate, $140, is over the actual cost. So $150 is more than enough to buy the 7 bird feeders.

Other Examples

A Nearest Ten
3 × 45 (3 × 50 = 150)
About 150

B Nearest Hundred
4 × 678 (4 × 700 = 2,800)
About 2,800

C Nearest Dollar
7 × $5.89 (7 × $6)
About $42

TRY IT OUT

Round to the nearest ten, hundred, or dollar. Then estimate the product.

1. 8 × 23 — **8 × 20 = 160**
2. 9 × 855 — **9 × 900 = 8,100**
3. 5 × $6.98 — **5 × $7 = $35**
4. 7 × $3.19 — **7 × $3 = $21**

148

TEACHING OPTIONS

RETEACHING TIPS Have students who round both factors identify the 1-digit number. Then round the other number and find the special product. Students who forget dollar signs should estimate the product and count out play money to equal it. Assign Reteaching Supplement 53.

ENRICHMENT Family Math Have students solve this multiplication riddle at home: *My estimated product is 240. My exact product is 6 less. One of my factors is odd. What are my actual factors?* Students should ask a family member to check their answer. (Two possible answers: 3 × 78 or 6 × 39)

PRACTICE

Round to the highest place or the nearest dollar. Then estimate the product.

1. 5 × 68 5 × 70 = 350
2. 9 × 74 9 × 70 = 630
3. $57 × 4 $60 × 4 = $240
4. 266 × 7 300 × 7 = 2,100
5. 4 × 824 4 × 800 = 3,200
6. 341 × 3 300 × 3 = 900
7. $4.70 × 2 $5.00 × 2 = $10.00
8. 6 × 36 6 × 40 = 240

Use rounding to estimate each product. Then decide whether the actual product is over or under the reference point 800.

9. 199 × 4 200 × 4 = 800; under
10. 8 × 87 8 × 90 = 720; under
11. 390 × 2 400 × 2 = 800; under
12. 186 × 5 200 × 5 = 1000; over

APPLY

MATH REASONING

13. The product of 8 and one of these numbers is 2,456. Use estimation to find the number. Explain how you chose your answer. 307; 8 × 3 = 24, 8 × 7 = 56

398	357	298
428	264	307

PROBLEM SOLVING

14. One day in late March, Mr. Abbott counted 27 Rocky Mountain blue birds on a fence in his pasture. At this rate, how many would he see in 4 days? 108 birds

15. A kids' nature club in Florida earned $2,200 for a bald eagle exhibit by recycling aluminum cans. If they collected 3,789 cans in April, how many fewer was this than the 5,068 cans they collected in May? 1,279 fewer cans

MIXED REVIEW

Estimate the sum or difference. Answers will vary. Sample answers given.

16. 89 + 41 = 130
17. 686 − 475 = 200
18. $23.19 + 11.87 = $35.00
19. $49.89 − 37.50 = $10.00
20. 6,791 + 3,211 = 10,000

Add.

21. 527 + 8,436 + 59 = 9,022
22. $20.32 + 1.68 + .19 = $22.19
23. 678 + 45 + 123 = 846
24. 12,765 + 476 + 6,928 = 20,169
25. 32,123 + 87 + 51 = 32,261

149

3. Practice and Apply

Basic	5-22
Average	1-25
Extended	7-15, 20-25

PRACTICE

Look at Exercises 1-12. Which exercises contain factors that should be rounded to the nearest hundred? (4-6, 9, 11, 12) *How do you know you should round to hundreds?* (The largest digit should be rounded to its highest place.)

APPLY

MATH REASONING ▶ How could rounding help you find the number? (Possible answer: since 8 × 300 = 2,400, look for a number a little more than 300.)

PROBLEM SOLVING ▶ What data do you need to solve Problem 15? Explain why. (the numbers of cans collected in April and May; because you are looking for the difference of these amounts)

MIXED REVIEW ▶ Explain how Exercises 16-20 are different from 21-25. (16-20 ask for estimates; 21-25 are column addition exercises and require exact answers.)

6-2

Close and Assess

PROVE WHAT YOU KNOW

Ask students to pretend that they want to buy 5 books that cost $2.29 each. Have them use play money or a calculator to support the idea that they should overestimate prices to be sure they have enough money. (5 × $2 = $10, an underestimate; proofs may vary.)

QUICK QUIZ

Round and estimate. Is the actual product over or under $600?
1. 89 × 7 (90 × 7 = 630; over)
2. 203 × 3 (200 × 3 = 600; over)
3. 165 × 3 (200 × 3 = 600; under)

LESSON OPTIONS 6-3

Mental Math: Multiply and Then Add

OBJECTIVE 6-3 To use mental math to multiply two 1-digit numbers and add to the product a 1-digit number

PREBOOK ACTIVITIES

QUICK REVIEW

Use mental math to add.

1. 36 + 5 (41) **2.** 16 + 3 (19) **3.** 27 + 6 (33)
4. 35 + 5 (40) **5.** 32 + 5 (37) **6.** 42 + 9 (51)
7. 54 + 7 (61) **8.** 18 + 4 (22) **9.** 64 + 6 (70)

PRIOR KNOWLEDGE

Have students review some of the mental math strategies they use to add 1-digit numbers. (counting on, compensation, finding groups of 10, making doubles) Have them identify strategies they find most useful and ones they find more difficult to apply. Ask students to suggest real-life situations in which someone might add a 1-digit number to a 2-digit number. (Possible answers: sales tax, restaurant tip, extra credit on a test)

COMMUNICATION

Discussing Math Talk about the word **rules.** Have students suggest as many meanings and examples of rules as they can. (Possible answers: laws, regulations, what always happens, steps in playing a game) Ask students to justify the use of rules in games. (Possible answer: Rules help each player to understand how to play fairly.) Then have students compare game rules with mathematical rules, such as the zero rule of multiplication. (Possible answer: Mathematical rules state what is always true, while game rules give procedures.)

EXPLORE AND CONNECT

Materials: TA 2 (Number Cubes numbered 1-6)
Grouping Suggestion: cooperative learning pairs
Students use a mathematical **rule** to explore number and operation order. Tell students that one math *rule* says you must multiply numbers before you add. Then partners roll a number cube 3 times and write down the number that appears on each roll. Each partner multiplies two of the numbers and then adds the remaining number to form equations with the greatest and smallest totals. For example, using 2, 5, and 1: $5 \times 2 + 1$ gives the greatest total (11) and $1 \times 2 + 5$ gives the smallest total (7). When each partner has found totals, pairs compare their findings. Conclude the activity by discussing as a group any patterns partners discovered. (Possible pattern: Multiplying the larger numbers and adding the smallest gives the greatest total.)

CONNECTIONS Use these anytime.

Problem of the Day

Algebra Find a number for each shape that will make both equations true.
△ × □ + 5 = 17
□ × 5 + △ = 23
(△ = 3, □ = 4)

Life Skills

Tips Aunt Mae treats you and 6 of your friends to lunch at a café. Everyone orders the lunch special, which costs $5 per person. If Aunt Mae leaves a $6 tip, what is the total cost of the lunch? ($46)

Number Sense

Mental Math Find the value of each equation using mental math.
$(5 \times 5 \times 2 \times 1) + 50$ (100)
$(2 \times 2 \times 2 \times 5) + 60$ (100)
$(4 \times 5 \times 2 \times 2) + 20$ (100)

Classwork and Homework Supplements

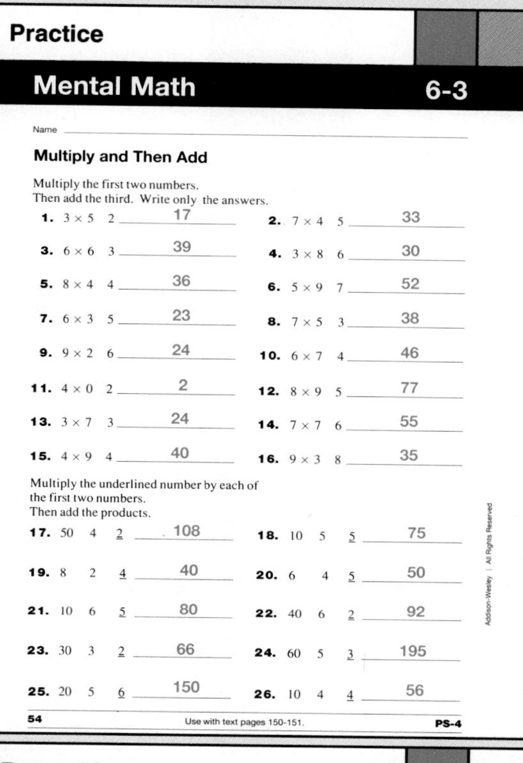

Practice

Mental Math 6-3

Name ______

Multiply and Then Add

Multiply the first two numbers.
Then add the third. Write only the answers.

1. 3 × 5 2 17
2. 7 × 4 5 33
3. 6 × 6 3 39
4. 3 × 8 6 30
5. 8 × 4 4 36
6. 5 × 9 7 52
7. 6 × 3 5 23
8. 7 × 5 3 38
9. 9 × 2 6 24
10. 6 × 7 4 46
11. 4 × 0 2 2
12. 8 × 9 5 77
13. 3 × 7 3 24
14. 7 × 7 6 55
15. 4 × 9 4 40
16. 9 × 3 8 35

Multiply the underlined number by each of the first two numbers.
Then add the products.

17. 50 4 2 108
18. 10 5 5 75
19. 8 2 4 40
20. 6 4 5 50
21. 10 6 5 80
22. 40 6 2 92
23. 30 3 2 66
24. 60 5 3 195
25. 20 5 6 150
26. 10 4 4 56

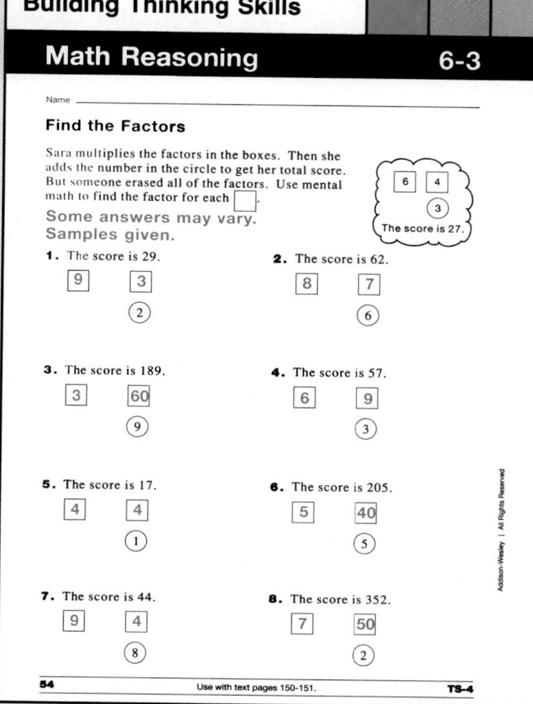

Building Thinking Skills

Math Reasoning 6-3

Name ______

Find the Factors

Sara multiplies the factors in the boxes. Then she adds the number in the circle to get her total score. But someone erased all of the factors. Use mental math to find the factor for each □.

6 4
3
The score is 27.

Some answers may vary.
Samples given.

1. The score is 29. [9] [3] (2)
2. The score is 62. [8] [7] (6)
3. The score is 189. [3] [60] (9)
4. The score is 57. [6] [9] (3)
5. The score is 17. [4] [4] (1)
6. The score is 205. [5] [40] (5)
7. The score is 44. [9] [4] (8)
8. The score is 352. [7] [50] (2)

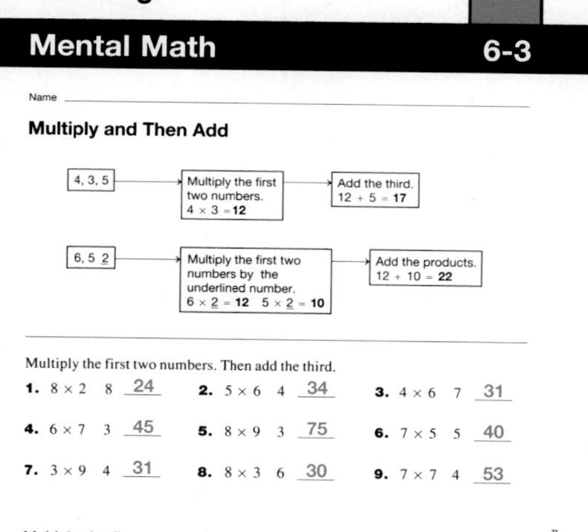

Reteaching

Mental Math 6-3

Name ______

Multiply and Then Add

4, 3, 5
Multiply the first two numbers. 4 × 3 = 12
Add the third. 12 + 5 = 17
6, 5 2
Multiply the first two numbers by the underlined number. 6 × 2 = 12 5 × 2 = 10
Add the products. 12 + 10 = 22

Multiply the first two numbers. Then add the third.

1. 8 × 2 8 24
2. 5 × 6 4 34
3. 4 × 6 7 31
4. 6 × 7 3 45
5. 8 × 9 3 75
6. 7 × 5 5 40
7. 3 × 9 4 31
8. 8 × 3 6 30
9. 7 × 7 4 53

Multiply the first two numbers by the underlined number.
Then add the products.

10. 10, 4 3 42
11. 40, 5 5 225
14. 12, 3 2 30
13. 50, 1 4 204
14. 10, 3 8 104
15. 30, 10 3 120

Write the missing number in each □.

16. 4 × 5 + [1] = 21
17. 8 × 9 + [2] = 74
18. 6 × 7 + [7] = 49
19. 4 × 6 + [6] = 30
20. 6 × 9 + [1] = 55
21. 8 × 8 + [2] = 66

Challenges

Mental Math 6-3

Name ______

Three in a Row

Play these games with a partner or in teams.
You will need different markers for each player or team.

1	4	7
2	5	8
3	6	9

Rules

1. Pick three numbers from the square at the right.
2. Find the product of two of the numbers. Then add the third number to the product.
3. If the number is on the game card, put a marker on it.
4. The first player or team with three markers on any vertical, horizontal, or diagonal row is the winner.
5. Before playing Game 4, fill in the card yourselves with numbers from 10 to 80 and a FREE square.

HINT: FREE boxes stand for any number.

Game 1

10	59	50	17	72	16
44	32	15	19	80	47
69	37	33	FREE	24	29
38	14	21	35	12	18
11	20	78	41	22	51
23	48	39	24	27	60

Game 2

45	73	39	13	79	42
61	11	60	19	22	34
38	FREE	40	28	51	81
30	36	49	33	70	23
48	20	25	21	52	16
46	14	37	75	18	12

Game 3

72	25	40	51	27	38
42	46	36	74	41	15
22	63	32	80	50	35
30	53	13	73	44	14
54	62	FREE	21	24	52
18	48	16	39	20	28

Game 4

Options for Individual Needs

Basic

Exercises 5-13, 17, 18, 21-25
Skills Bank, p. 461
Calculator Bank, p. 488
More Practice, p. 504, set A

Supplements
Reteaching 54 or
Practice 54
Thinking Skills 54

Average

Exercises 1-25
Calculator Bank, p. 488
More Practice, p. 504, set A

Supplements
Practice 54
Challenges 54 or
Thinking Skills 54

Extended

Exercises 5-12, 17-26
Calculator Bank, p. 488

Supplements
Challenges 54
Thinking Skills 54

Other Resources:
Problem-Solving Experiences in Mathematics, Grade 4,
Problems 42, 68
Challenge, Vol. I, Activity 36

6-3

LESSON PLAN 6-3

OBJECTIVE 6-3
To use mental math to multiply two 1-digit numbers and add to the product a 1-digit number

Materials: sets of number cards 1-9, index cards with + and × symbols

Alternative Materials: TA 3 (Number/Operation Cards)

Grouping Suggestion: small groups

1. MOTIVATE AND TEACH

LEARN ABOUT IT

EXPLORE ► **Make up rules for when to multiply and add that do not rely on card color.** (Possible answer: Always multiply the first two numbers you pick, then add the third number to the product.)

TALK ABOUT IT ► **What are the greatest and smallest factors you could pick? Explain.** (9 × 9 and 1 × 1; they are the greatest and smallest numbers from 1 to 9.)
► **Why is it important to follow the game rules?** (Because adding first and then multiplying gives a larger answer than the rule of multiplying first and then adding.)
► **How would the game change if the number cards included zero?** (Possible answers: You could get products of 0; sums would be smaller with addends of 0.)
Student Edition answers: **1.** 51 **2.** 90, 2

2. CHECK UNDERSTANDING

TRY IT OUT

ERROR ALERT Mixing up the order of operations. Making errors in basic addition or multiplication.

Mental Math
Multiply and Then Add

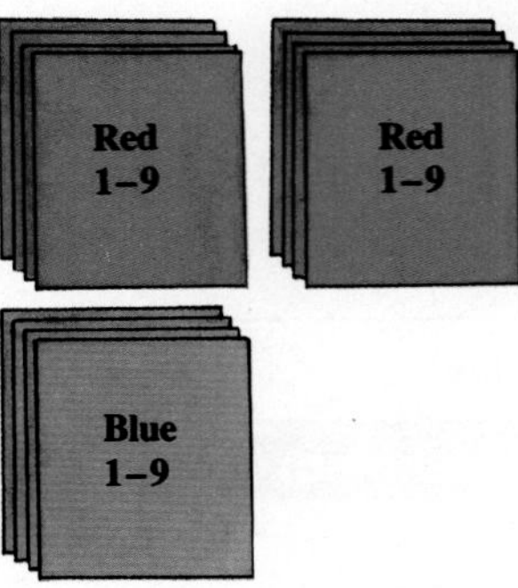

LEARN ABOUT IT

EXPLORE Use Number Cards
Work in groups. To play this game, use 3 sets of number cards. Each set should have 9 cards. Draw a card from each deck and play by the rules shown. Take turns and use mental math.

Rules ■ **Multiply red x red.**
■ **Add the blue.**

TALK ABOUT IT See teaching notes.

1. Kathy drew these cards. What was her score?
2. What is the largest possible score for this game? the smallest possible score?

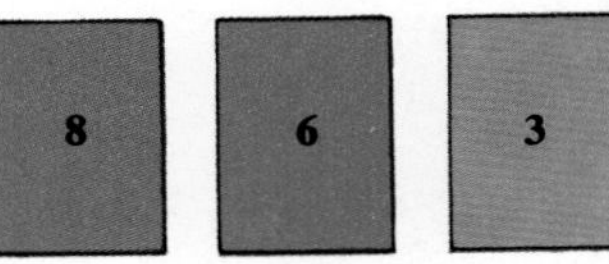

Here is how you can find a score.

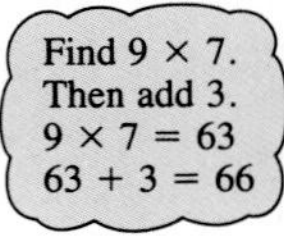

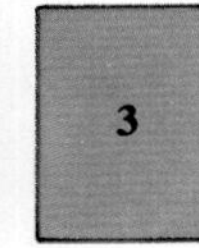

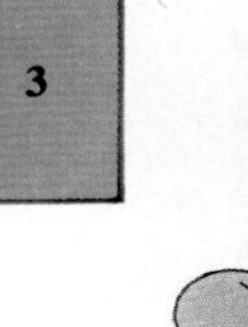

TRY IT OUT

Give the score for each turn below.

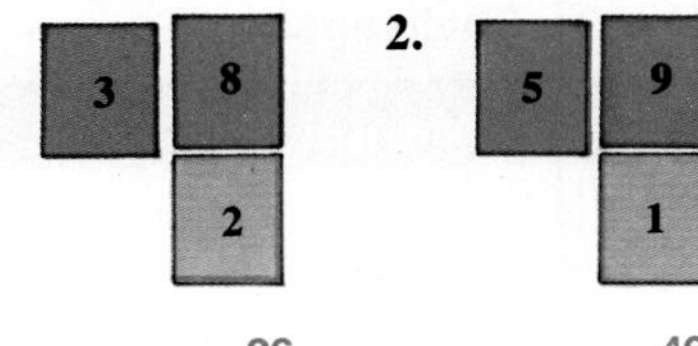

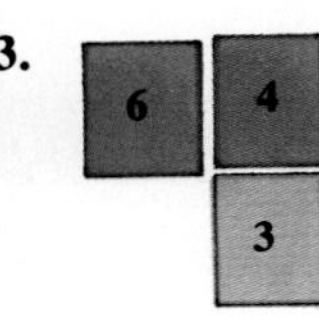

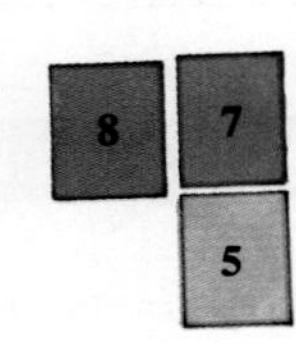

26 46 27 61

150

TEACHING OPTIONS

RETEACHING TIPS Have students use number cards to form equations. They should insert cards with the multiplication and addition symbols between numbers to remind them of the order of operations. Assign Reteaching Supplement 54.

ENRICHMENT Have students use any digits from 0 to 5 in the pattern □ × □ + □ to equal each consecutive number from 10 to 20. (Answers may vary; samples include 2 × 4 + 2 = 10; 3 × 3 + 2 = 11; 4 × 3 + 0 = 12; 5 × 2 + 3 = 13; 3 × 3 + 5 = 14.)

PRACTICE

Multiply the first 2 numbers. Then add the third. Write only the answers.

1. 7 × 3 4 25 **2.** 5 × 6 5 35 **3.** 4 × 8 7 39 **4.** 7 × 6 3 45

5. 8 × 6 3 51 **6.** 3 × 9 8 35 **7.** 8 × 8 6 70 **8.** 4 × 5 5 25

Multiply the red number by each of the first 2 numbers. Then add the products.

9. 20 3 2 46 **10.** 12 6 2 36 **11.** 9 1 8 80 **12.** 10 4 3 42

13. 60 2 4 248 **14.** 40 2 3 126 **15.** 30 4 5 170 **16.** 50 3 3 159

APPLY

MATH REASONING Give the number for each ▥.

17. 3 × 4 + ▥ = 13 1 **18.** 5 × 6 + ▥ = 34 4

19. 8 × 5 + ▥ = 45 5 **20.** 7 × 9 + ▥ = 65 2

PROBLEM SOLVING

21. Beth collects bird photos. Every time she gets a new photo she writes 3 facts to describe the bird. When she has 9 photos, how many facts will she have written? 27 facts

22. Manuel bought six 30¢ stamps and three 5¢ stamps. How much did he pay? $1.95

▶ **CALCULATOR**

Think about the 2 numbers on the top cards. Use mental math to multiply each by the blue number card. Then use the calculator to find the sum of the products.

23. 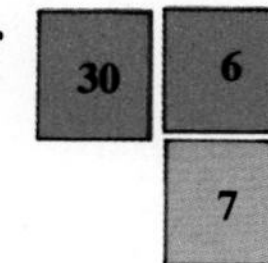

252

24. 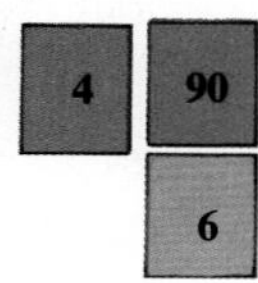

564

25. 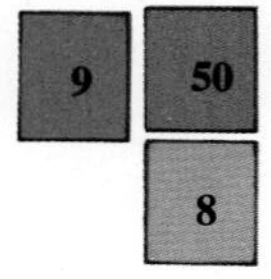

472

26. 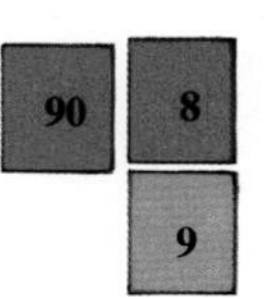

882

More Practice, page 504, set A

3. Practice and Apply

Basic	5-13, 17, 18, 21-25
Average	1-25
Extended	5-12, 17-26

PRACTICE

Look at Exercises 1-8. Are there any basic multiplication facts that you need to review before completing the exercises? (Answers may vary.)

APPLY

MATH REASONING ▶ **How can you use subtraction to find the missing number?** (Multiply to get the product of the first two numbers, then subtract from the total.)

PROBLEM SOLVING ▶ **How many steps are needed to solve Problem 22? Explain.** (Three; you need to multiply two sets of same-size groups, then add to get the total cost.)

CALCULATOR ▶ **Explain the method you would use to multiply each red number by the 2-digit number.** (Possible answer: Think of special products. For example, 7 × 3 tens = 21 tens or 210.)

Close and Assess

WRITE WHAT YOU THINK

Have each student write a paragraph explaining how to find 6 × 7 + 8 without using pencil and paper or a calculator. Students should give the steps they would follow, in order, and describe any mental math strategies they would use. (50; strategies will vary.)

Quick Quiz

Multiply, then add, using mental math.

1. 6 × 6 + 5 (41)
2. 5 × 9 + 3 (48)
3. 7 × 40 + 4 (284)
4. 50 × 3 + 3 (153)

LESSON OPTIONS 6-4

Multiplying Whole Numbers: Making the Connection

OBJECTIVE 6-4 To use objects to develop an understanding of multiplying 1-digit numbers

PREBOOK ACTIVITIES

QUICK REVIEW

Multiply mentally.

1. 4 × 30 (120)	**2.** 50 × 7 (350)	**3.** 9 × 70 (630)
4. 3 × 80 (240)	**5.** 6 × 60 (360)	**6.** 4 × 10 (40)
7. 30 × 5 (150)	**8.** 5 × 90 (450)	**9.** 2 × 60 (120)

PRIOR KNOWLEDGE

Have students review the standard place value rules for trading. (Whenever possible, trade 10 of one place for 1 of the next greater place.) Have students imagine cases that might require trading more than 10 ones for 1 ten. (Possible answer: Some column addition has sums with over 20 ones, so you could trade more than one group of 10 ones.) Have students explain the trade to make in a situation where they have 34 ones. (Trade 30 ones for 3 tens.)

COMMUNICATION

Discussing Math Have students review the action suggested by multiplication. (Put together same-size groups.) Discuss the connection between multiplication and addition. (Possible answer: Multiplying is like adding the quantity of one of the factors over and over as many times as the other factor indicates.) Ask students to visualize putting together 3 groups of 35, using models, and explain what steps they might follow. (Lay out 3 equal groups, each of which has 3 tens and 5 ones, then make any necessary trades to find the product.)

EXPLORE AND CONNECT

Materials: place value blocks, TA 2 (Number Cubes numbered 1-6)
Alternative Materials: TA 6 (Place Value Models)
Grouping Suggestion: small cooperative learning groups
Students explore the trades required in multiplication. Write 13, 24, and 36 on the chalkboard. One student rolls the number cube to determine how many groups of the first 2-digit number to find. For example, if a 4 comes up, another student writes the equation 4 × 13 = □. (52) Each group uses place value materials to make 4 groups of 13. They count place by place, making any necessary trades, to find the product. The recorder writes the product in the original equation. Students trade tasks until all three 2-digit numbers are multiplied. Students summarize what they noticed about trading in multiplication. (Possible answers: You may need to trade more than 10 of a place; you might have to trade both ones and tens.)

CONNECTIONS Use these anytime.

Problem of the Day

Patterns Figure out the pattern, then continue it 3 more times.
38, 57, 76, 95, 114, _____, _____, _____

(The pattern shows multiples of 19—tens increase by 2 as ones decrease by 1; 133, 152, 171)

Math Connection

Money At a neighborhood picnic, Zelda sold 9 cups of lemonade at 13 cents per cup, and she collected exact change each time. Explain how many penny trades she would be able to make. (2; 9 groups of 3 ones, or 9 × 3, is 27; she could trade 20 pennies for 2 dimes.)

Number Sense

Mental Math Without finding the exact product, predict how many ones you could trade if you multiplied 26 × 7. Then predict how many tens you could trade. (Trade 40 ones for 4 tens and 10 tens for 1 hundred.)

Classwork and Homework Supplements

Practice

Manipulatives 6-4

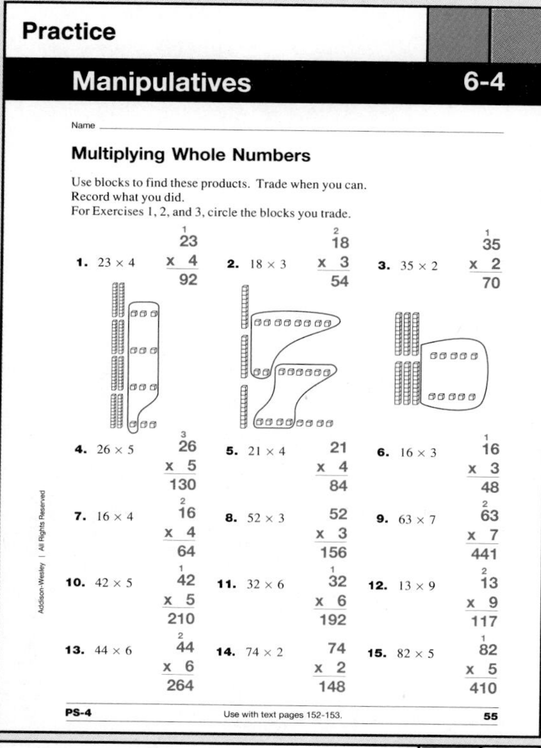

Name ______

Multiplying Whole Numbers

Use blocks to find these products. Trade when you can.
Record what you did.
For Exercises 1, 2, and 3, circle the blocks you trade.

1. 23 × 4 — 23 × 4 = 92
2. 18 × 3 — 18 × 3 = 54
3. 35 × 2 — 35 × 2 = 70
4. 26 × 5 — 26 × 5 = 130
5. 21 × 4 — 21 × 4 = 84
6. 16 × 3 — 16 × 3 = 48
7. 16 × 4 — 16 × 4 = 64
8. 52 × 3 — 52 × 3 = 156
9. 63 × 7 — 63 × 7 = 441
10. 42 × 5 — 42 × 5 = 210
11. 32 × 6 — 32 × 6 = 192
12. 13 × 9 — 13 × 9 = 117
13. 44 × 6 — 44 × 6 = 264
14. 74 × 2 — 74 × 2 = 148
15. 82 × 5 — 82 × 5 = 410

Building Thinking Skills

Number Sense 6-4

Name ______

Place the Product

Look at each multiplication exercise.
Decide whether the product is *less than 100*, *between 100 and 200*, or *greater than 200*.
Put a ☺ in the correct column.

Choose a reasonable method to help you decide:

- Use place value blocks.
- Use estimation.
- Use the break-apart and mental math strategy.
- Use paper and pencil.

	Less than 100	Between 100 and 200	More than 200
1. 36 × 3		☺	
2. 18 × 4	☺		
3. 47 × 6			☺
4. 34 × 5		☺	
5. 62 × 4			☺
6. 32 × 3	☺		
7. 76 × 2		☺	
8. 42 × 5			☺
9. 57 × 3		☺	
10. 17 × 7		☺	

Reteaching

Manipulatives 6-4

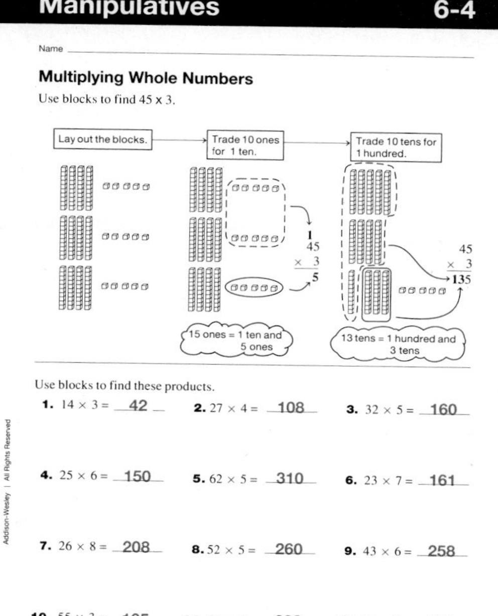

Name ______

Multiplying Whole Numbers

Use blocks to find 45 x 3.

Lay out the blocks.
Trade 10 ones for 1 ten.
Trade 10 tens for 1 hundred.
15 ones = 1 ten and 5 ones
13 tens = 1 hundred and 3 tens

Use blocks to find these products.

1. 14 × 3 = 42
2. 27 × 4 = 108
3. 32 × 5 = 160
4. 25 × 6 = 150
5. 62 × 5 = 310
6. 23 × 7 = 161
7. 26 × 8 = 208
8. 52 × 5 = 260
9. 43 × 6 = 258
10. 55 × 3 = 165
11. 46 × 5 = 230
12. 33 × 8 = 264

Challenges

Math Reasoning 6-4

Name ______

Shortcut Multiplication

You can use the table to multiply a 2-digit number. Study the example.

Example: 45 × 3 = 135

x	0	1	2	3	4	5
0	0	0	0	0	0	0
1	0	1	2	3	4	5
2	0	2	4	6	8	10
3	0	3	6	9	12	15

13 tens, 5 ones

You will have 13 tens and 5 ones.

x	0	1	2	3	4	5	6	7	8	9
0	0	0	0	0	0	0	0	0	0	0
1	0	1	2	3	4	5	6	7	8	9
2	0	2	4	6	8	10	12	14	16	18
3	0	3	6	9	12	15	18	21	24	27
4	0	4	8	12	16	20	24	28	32	36
5	0	5	10	15	20	25	30	35	40	45
6	0	6	12	18	24	30	36	42	48	54
7	0	7	14	21	28	35	42	49	56	63
8	0	8	16	24	32	40	48	56	64	72
9	0	9	18	27	36	45	54	63	72	81

Find these products using the shortcut.

1. 23 × 3 = 69
2. 45 × 2 = 90
3. 34 × 4 = 136
4. 23 × 7 = 161
5. 67 × 4 = 268
6. 78 × 3 = 234
7. 56 × 5 = 280
8. 89 × 8 = 712
9. 45 × 7 = 315

10. Shortcut multiplication works for only a special kind of problem. What is it?

The digits in each 2-digit factor must be consecutive.

Options for Individual Needs

Basic

Exercises 1-6
Skills Bank, p. 465

Supplements
Reteaching 55 or
Practice 55
Thinking Skills 55

Average

Exercises 1-6
Skills Bank, p. 465

Supplements
Practice 55
Challenges 55 or
Thinking Skills 55

Extended

Exercises 1-6

Supplements
Challenges 55
Thinking Skills 55

Other Resources:
Mathematics Book A, pp. 39 and 40

LESSON PLAN 6-4

OBJECTIVE 6-4
To use objects to develop an understanding of multiplying 1-digit numbers

Materials: TA 11 (Blank Spinners marked for 1-9), place value blocks, 1-inch strips of colored paper

Alternative Materials: TA 6 (Place Value Models), multicolored counters

Grouping Suggestion: pairs

1. MOTIVATE AND TEACH

LEARN ABOUT IT

EXPLORE ▶ **Analyze how 25 got on the chart.** (Someone first spun a 2 and took 2 tens, then spun a 5 and took 5 ones.)
▶ **Discuss the relationship between the 2- and 1-digit factors.** (Possible answer: The 1-digit number tells how many groups to make, each the value of the 2-digit number.)
▶ **Explain why the chart has hundreds in the product.** (You might trade 10 tens for 1 hundred.)

TALK ABOUT IT ▶ **How did you organize the blocks when you combined groups?** (Possible answer: Add ones, trade for tens if necessary, add tens, trade for hundreds if necessary.)
Student Edition answers: **1.** Answers may vary. **2.** Sample answers: 78 × 3 has 2 trades, 28 × 2 has 1, 43 × 2 has none.

2. CHECK UNDERSTANDING

ERROR ALERT Failing to make same-size groups. Failing to make accurate trades.

Multiplying Whole Numbers
Making the Connection

LEARN ABOUT IT

EXPLORE Use a Place Value Model
Work in groups. Use a spinner with the digits 1–9.

Hundreds	Tens	Ones
	2	5
	×	3

- Spin 2 times. The first spin gives the number of tens. The second gives the number of ones. Make a table like the one shown and record this number in the top row.
- Spin again. If you land on an even number, write 2 beside the × sign in the table. Then lay out 2 piles of blocks, each with the number of tens and ones in the top number. If you land on an odd number, write 3 and lay out 3 piles of blocks.
- Push the piles together and make all possible trades. When you get 10 or more of one type, trade for a larger block. Write the number for the resulting pile in the bottom row of the table.
- Do this several times. Make a separate table each time.

Make same size piles and put together.

TALK ABOUT IT See teaching notes.

1. Look at one of your tables and tell what trades, if any, you made when you pushed the piles together.
2. Can you show a situation in which you must make two trades to find the total? one trade? no trades?

152

TEACHING OPTIONS

RETEACHING TIPS Before students combine groups, have them check that all groups are exactly the same size. They can arrange the groups in parallel rows separated by colored paper strips to test one-to-one correspondence. Assign Reteaching Supplement 55.

ENRICHMENT Students use the digits 1, 5, and 7 to create three different multiplication problems (2-digit times 1-digit) that will require 0, 1, and 2 trades to find the product. They use models or blocks to verify the trades. (Sample answers: no trade in 57 × 1; 1 trade in 17 × 5; 2 trades in 15 × 7.)

You have pushed same-size piles of blocks together, traded, and figured out how many in all. Now you will see a way to record what you have done. This process can help you find products such as 64 × 4.

What You Do	**What You Record**

1. Lay out the blocks.

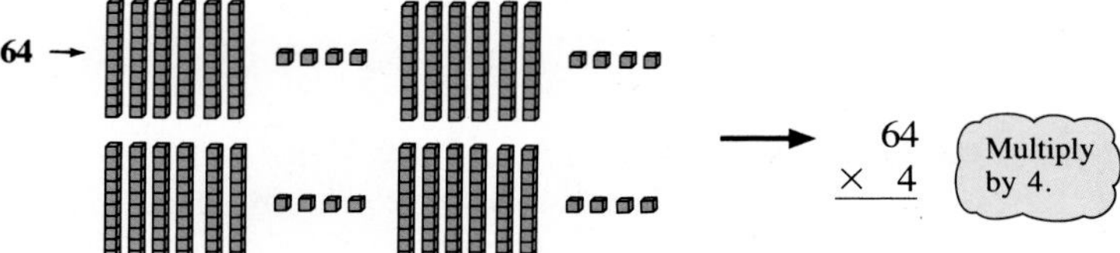

2. Trade 10 ones for 1 ten.
Trade 10 tens for 1 hundred.

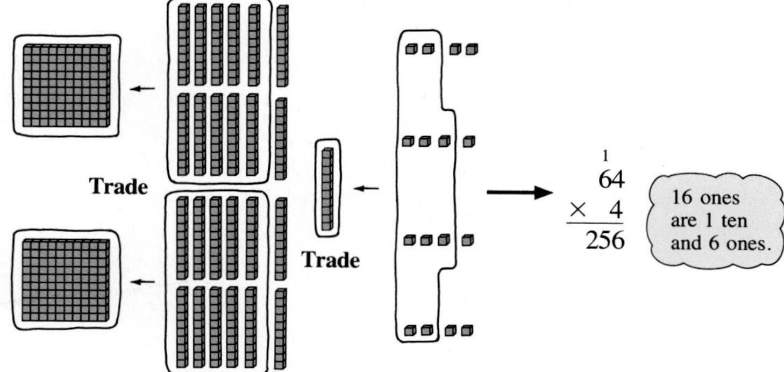

TRY IT OUT See Additional Answers.

Use blocks to find these products. Trade when you can. Record what you did.

1. 42 × 3 **2.** 17 × 4 **3.** 16 × 5 **4.** 72 × 8 **5.** 58 × 6

6. Use blocks to solve a multiplication problem of your choice.

3. Practice and Apply

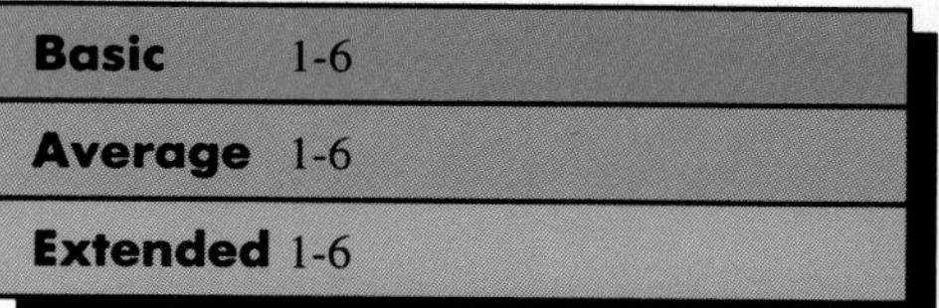

Basic	1-6
Average	1-6
Extended	1-6

Additional Answers: See p. T79.

PRACTICE

Look at the example pictured on page 153. Explain the connection between What You Do and What You Record. (The 4 repeating rows, each with 6 tens and 4 ones, match the factors 64 × 4.) *Compare the block trade of 10 ones for 1 ten with the way it is recorded.* (A traded ten appears as a small 1 over the 6 in the tens place; the other 6 below the bar means 6 ones are left after the trade.) *Analyze the picture to justify the next trade.* (Trade 20 tens for 2 hundreds.) *Continue working with a partner to complete the Try It Out exercises. If you do not have enough materials to model Exercises 4 and 5, substitute counters of different colors for the place value blocks or models.*

Close and Assess

WRITE WHAT YOU THINK Ask students to list all the steps they would follow to find the product of 54 × 3 with place value materials. Then have students exchange papers with a partner. Partners follow the steps on each other's papers to verify that the steps make sense and are in the correct order.

QUICK QUIZ

Find the product of 37 × 4. (148)
Use place value materials if you need to and record what you do.

LESSON OPTIONS 6-5

Multiplying 2-Digit Numbers

OBJECTIVE 6-5 To multiply a 2-digit by a 1-digit number, 1 trade

PREBOOK ACTIVITIES

QUICK REVIEW

Find the products using mental math.

1. 30 × 2 (60)	**2.** 10 × 7 (70)	**3.** 50 × 1 (50)
4. 40 × 3 (120)	**5.** 70 × 9 (630)	**6.** 60 × 6 (360)
7. 20 × 8 (160)	**8.** 90 × 5 (450)	**9.** 80 × 4 (320)

PRIOR KNOWLEDGE

Write this sentence on the chalkboard: Sam rides his bicycle at a speed of 23 kilometers per hour. Ask students to name two familiar points between which the distance is about one kilometer. (Sample answer: It is about one kilometer from the school to the pool.) Ask them to explain the meaning of the word **per.** (for each) Then have them paraphrase the information about Sam. (Possible answer: In about one hour, Sam travels a distance of 23 kilometers on his bike.) Next, have students explain what you do when you multiply. (put same-size groups together) Finally, ask students to formulate a multiplication question about Sam. (Sample question: How far can Sam ride in 3 hours?)

COMMUNICATION

Discussing and Writing in Math Point out that to combine same-size groups, you must know the size of one group. Have students reread the sentence about Sam. Ask them to write 3 original sentences that compare numbers using the word **per.** Then have them formulate a multiplication question based on each of their sentences. (Sample sentence: Tuna costs $0.99 per can. Sample question: How much will 5 cans cost?

EXPLORE AND CONNECT

Materials: TA 2 (Number Cubes numbered 1-6), place value blocks, calculators
Alternative Materials: TA 6 (Place Value Models)
Grouping Suggestion: cooperative learning pairs
Display these data about swimming rates **per** hour.

Sailfish	98 kilometers per hour
Flying Fish	65 kilometers per hour
Dolphin	60 kilometers per hour

Students work in pairs to determine distance for more than 1 hour. One student chooses a sea animal's water speed. The partner rolls a number cube. Together they select a calculation method—mental math, modeling with place value materials, paper and pencil, or calculator—to find the product. Pairs repeat the exploration several times using different calculation methods. Discuss preferred calculation methods.

CONNECTIONS Use these anytime.

Problem of the Day

Product Pattern Use a calculator. Multiply 9 × 11, 9 × 22, 9 × 33, and so on, to 9 × 99. Analyze the product pattern. (Tens digits = 9, ones digits decrease from 9 to 1, and hundreds digits increase from 0 to 8.)

Number Sense

Logical Reasoning The same digit fits each empty box. What is it? (0 or 1)

```
  □□
×  □
  □□
```

Math Connection

Measurement When Grandpa learned to knit, he made a scarf that was 4 yards long. How long was the scarf in inches? HINT: 1 yard = 36 inches. (144 in.)

Classwork and Homework Supplements

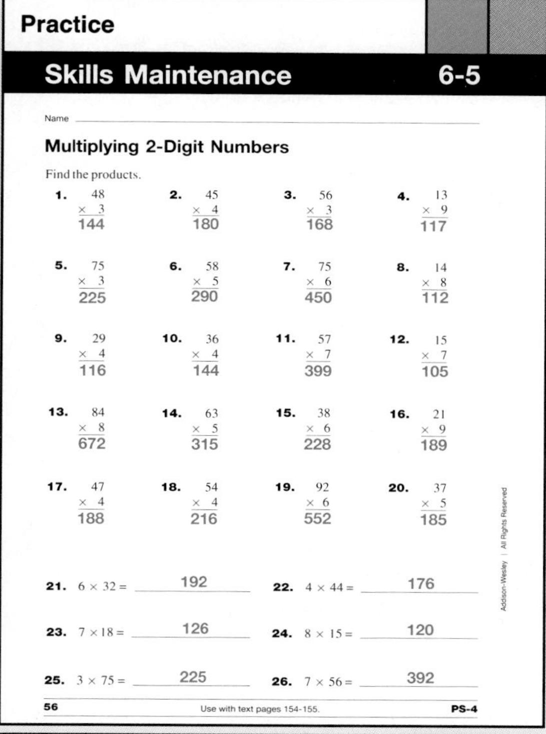

Practice

Skills Maintenance 6-5

Name

Multiplying 2-Digit Numbers

Find the products.

1. 48 × 3 = 144
2. 45 × 4 = 180
3. 56 × 3 = 168
4. 13 × 9 = 117
5. 75 × 3 = 225
6. 58 × 5 = 290
7. 75 × 6 = 450
8. 14 × 8 = 112
9. 29 × 4 = 116
10. 36 × 4 = 144
11. 57 × 7 = 399
12. 15 × 7 = 105
13. 84 × 8 = 672
14. 63 × 5 = 315
15. 38 × 6 = 228
16. 21 × 9 = 189
17. 47 × 4 = 188
18. 54 × 4 = 216
19. 92 × 6 = 552
20. 37 × 5 = 185
21. 6 × 32 = 192
22. 4 × 44 = 176
23. 7 × 18 = 126
24. 8 × 15 = 120
25. 3 × 75 = 225
26. 7 × 56 = 392

56 Use with text pages 154-155. PS-4

Building Thinking Skills

Writing Math 6-5

Name

Create Word Problems

Write a word problem that uses each set of factors. You may write about toys, animals, or any other subject you wish.

1. 75 × 5 = 375 — Answers will vary. Sample answer: A train travels 75 miles per hour. How many miles can it travel in 5 hours?

2. 36 × 4 = 144

3. Explain why the situations you chose suggested multiplication to you. If you need more space to write, use the back of your paper.

56 Use with text pages 154-155. TS-4

Reteaching

Skills Review 6-5

Name

Multiplying 2-Digit Numbers

Multiply the ones. Trade if necessary.

41 × 3 = 3 — 3 ones — 3 × 1 = 3 no trading

Multiply the tens. Add any extra tens.

41 × 3 = 123 — Trade 10 tens for 1 hundred. — 12 tens = 1 hundred and 2 tens

Find the products.

1. 22 × 8 = 176 (17 tens is 7 tens and 1 hundred.)
2. 34 × 4 = 136 (13 tens Trade.)
3. 12 × 9 = 108 (Trade?)
4. 52 × 4 = 208
5. 43 × 8 = 344
6. 34 × 2 = 68
7. 52 × 6 = 312
8. 38 × 9 = 342
9. 67 × 5 = 335
10. 52 × 7 = 364
11. 28 × 3 = 84
12. 94 × 5 = 470
13. 77 × 8 = 616

Rewrite and then find the products.

14. 6 × 43 — 43 × 6 = 258
15. 4 × 86 — 86 × 4 = 344

56 Use with text pages 154-155. RS-4

Challenges

Critcal Thinking 6-5

Name

Even and Odd Combos

Work with a partner. In each problem write one of the even digits — 0, 2, 4, 6, or 8 — for each **E**. Write one of the odd digits — 1, 3, 5, 7, or 9 — for each **O**. Then solve. There is more than one answer for each problem.

Example: EE × O = EOE; 28 × 9 = 252

1. EE + EE = EE
2. EE + EE = OE
3. EO + EO = OE
4. OO + EO = EE
5. OE + OE = OEE
6. EE × E = EE
7. OE × E = OE
8. EE × O = EE
9. OE × O = EEE
10. EE × O = OOE
11. OO × O = OO
12. EO × E = OE
13. OO × E = OOE
14. EO × O = EEO
15. OO × O = EOO

16. How do you know if a 2- or 3-digit number is even or odd? Look at the ones place.

17. Answer these questions with **sometimes** (S), **always** (A), or **never** (N).

N The sum of an even number and an odd number is an even number.

A The product of an even number and an odd number is an even number.

A The product of two odd numbers is an odd number.

56 Use with text pages 154-155. CS-4

Options for Individual Needs

Basic

Exercises 6-14, 19-28
Data Bank, p. 468-483
Skills Bank, p. 465
Computer Bank, p. 492
More Practice, p. 504, set B

Supplements
Reteaching 56 or
Practice 56
Challenges 56

Average

Exercises 1-28
Data Bank, p. 468-483
Computer Bank, p. 492
More Practice, p. 504, set B

Supplements
Practice 56
Challenges 56 or
Thinking Skills 56

Extended

Exercises 6-28
Data Bank, p. 468-483
Computer Bank, p. 492

Supplements
Challenges 56
Thinking Skills 56

Other Resources:
Problem-Solving Experiences in Mathematics, Grade 4, Skillseekers, 2, pp. 10-12

LESSON PLAN 6-5

OBJECTIVE 6-5
To multiply a 2-digit by a 1-digit number, 1 trade

Materials: place value blocks, TA 3 (Number Cards 1-4)

Alternative Materials: TA 6 (Place Value Models)

1. MOTIVATE AND TEACH

LEARN ABOUT IT

EXPLORE ▶ **Justify why you multiply 96 by 3 to solve the problem.** (Possible answer: You could add 96 + 96 + 96, but it is faster to multiply 96 × 3 to put together same-size groups.)
▶ **If the homing pigeon flew at a different speed each hour, how would the problem change?** (You could not multiply; you would add the 3 different speeds.)

TALK ABOUT IT ▶ **Explain why you find 6 × 3 first.** (Order of operations says always begin in the ones place.)
▶ **Why do you add the extra 10 after you multiply 6 × 9 tens?** (The correct order of operations is first multiply , then add.)
▶ **Is it always necessary to trade when you multiply? Explain.** (No; you trade when you have 10 or more in any place.)
Student Edition answers: **1.** 3 × 6—18—is greater than 10 **2.** 100 × 3 = 300 **3.** Sample answer: The homing pigeon flew 288 km in 3 hours.

2. CHECK UNDERSTANDING

TRY IT OUT

ERROR ALERT Confusing the order of operations. Making trading errors.

Multiplying 2-Digit Numbers

LEARN ABOUT IT

EXPLORE Think About the Process
A homing pigeon was flying from a mountain camp to headquarters. It flew 96 kilometers per hour for 3 hours. How far did it fly?

You multiply because you need to put together same-size groups.

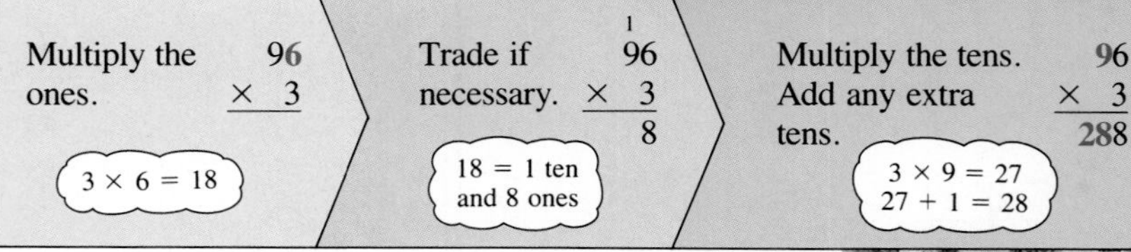

Multiply the ones.
96
× 3
3 × 6 = 18
Trade if necessary.
1
96
× 3
8
18 = 1 ten and 8 ones
Multiply the tens. Add any extra tens.
96
× 3
288
3 × 9 = 27
27 + 1 = 28

TALK ABOUT IT See teaching notes.

1. When was it necessary to trade? Why?
2. How would you have estimated the distance?
3. Give the answer in a complete sentence.

Other Examples

A 23 × 3 = 69	**B** 52 × 3 = 156	**C** (1) 43 × 6 = 258	**D** (2) 35 × 5 = 175	**E** (2) 75 × 4 = 300

TRY IT OUT

1. 36 × 4 = 144	**2.** 64 × 5 = 320	**3.** 25 × 7 = 175	**4.** 86 × 3 = 258	**5.** 18 × 6 = 108

154

TEACHING OPTIONS

RETEACHING TIPS Students verbalize the factors as they multiply the ones and choose a number card to show the trade. They place the number card to the left of the tens, then multiply the tens by the ones and add the number-card amount to find the final product. Assign Reteaching Supplement 56.

ENRICHMENT Have students make up a 1-digit factor and a 2-digit factor for each product. They may use a calculator to guess and test their factors. (Answers vary; samples given.)
1. 80 (2 × 40) **2.** 65 (5 × 13)
3. 102 (2 × 51) **4.** 175 (7 × 25)
5. 372 (6 × 62) **6.** 648 (8 × 81)

PRACTICE

Find the products.

1. 43 × 6 = 258
2. 58 × 4 = 232
3. 72 × 8 = 576
4. 94 × 7 = 658
5. 31 × 6 = 186
6. 62 × 5 = 310
7. 29 × 4 = 116
8. 47 × 3 = 141
9. 68 × 1 = 68
10. 89 × 9 = 801
11. 78 × 5 390
12. 4 × 67 268
13. 28 × 7 196
14. 0 × 35 0
15. 43 × 9 387
16. 3 × 83 249
17. 53 × 8 424
18. 84 × 6 504
19. Multiply 6 × 27. 162
20. Find the product of 43 and 8. 344

APPLY

MATH REASONING Find only the products that are over 500. Write under for the others.

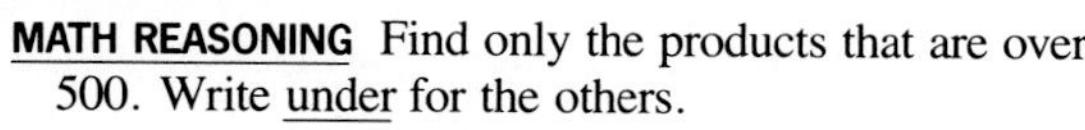

21. 49 × 3 under

22. 78 × 7 546
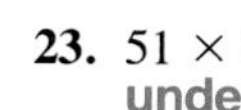
23. 51 × 9 under
24. 73 × 6 under
25. 86 × 7 602

PROBLEM SOLVING

26. A sparrow flew south at a speed of 40 kilometers per hour for 6 hours. A Canadian goose flew in the same direction at a speed of 87 kilometers per hour for 3 hours. Which bird flew farther? How much farther did it fly? Canadian goose; 21 km

27. **Science Data Bank** How many more times would a hummingbird weighing 2 grams beat its wings than a hummingbird weighing 6 grams if both birds hovered for 5 seconds? See page 000. 130 times more

▶ **COMMUNICATION Write to Learn**

28. Write a paragraph that tells how you would solve the equation 24 × 3 using blocks. Use these words: lay out, put together, trade, ones, tens, count. See Additional Answers.

More Practice, page 504, set B

3. Practice and Apply

Basic	6-14, 19-28
Average	1-28
Extended	6-28

Additional Answers: See p. T79.

PRACTICE

Look at Exercises 6-10. Do you see one exercise in which it will not be necessary to trade? (Exercise 9) *Look at Exercises 11-20. What should you do before you multiply each one?* (Rewrite the exercise in vertical form.)

APPLY

MATH REASONING ▶ **How can you identify the exercises in which you must multiply exactly?** (Round, then multiply to get an estimated product; look for products over 500.)

PROBLEM SOLVING ▶ **Explain how to predict the greater product in Problem 26.** (Possible answer: 40 × 6 = 240; 90 × 3 = 270, minus 3 × 3 = 261, so 87 × 3's product is greater.)

COMMUNICATION ▶ **Give an example of a reasonable sentence that contains 3 math words.** (Sample: *Trade* 10 *ones* for 1 *ten*.)

6-5

Close and Assess

PROVE WHAT YOU KNOW

Ask students to demonstrate why 73 × 6 = 438. They may use the multiplication-addition rule, the break-apart rule, or any other strategy they know. (Answers will vary; sample explanation: 73 = 70 + 3; 70 × 6 = 420, 3 × 6 = 18, so 420 + 18 = 438.)

QUICK QUIZ

Find the products.

1. 34 × 6 (204)
2. 17 × 8 (136)
3. 13 × 7 (91)
4. 58 × 3 (174)
5. 72 × 4 (288)

LESSON OPTIONS 6-6

Multiplying Larger Numbers: 1 Trade

OBJECTIVE 6-6 To multiply a 3-digit by a 1-digit number, 1 trade

PREBOOK ACTIVITIES

QUICK REVIEW

Find the products.

1.	**2.**	**3.**	**4.**	**5.**
35 × 2	80 × 8	61 × 4	14 × 5	72 × 3
(70)	(640)	(244)	(70)	(216)

PRIOR KNOWLEDGE

Ask a volunteer to review how to find the product of a 2-digit number and a 1-digit number, such as 26 × 3. (Possible answer: Write the factors vertically, multiply the ones, trade if necessary, multiply the tens, add any extra tens.) Discuss when students might need to multiply 2-digit and 1-digit numbers. (Possible answer: when finding how many books are needed for 3 same-size groups) Ask students to define how a trade is made. (Possible answer: 10 of one place is traded for 1 of the next higher place.) Have them explain where the adding step comes in the multiplication process. (Possible answer: always after you multiply) Then explain that multiplication with larger numbers may require trades in several places. Ask students to predict what those places might be. (Possible answer: Trade 10 ones for 1 ten; trade 10 tens for 1 hundred.)

COMMUNICATION

Writing in Math Have students write a general rule in their math journals for trading and adding the extra amount when multiplying. (Possible rule: Multiply, trade if necessary, multiply the next place, add any extra amount *after* you multiply.)

EXPLORE AND CONNECT

Materials: place value blocks, TA 3 (Number Cards 1-5)
Alternative Materials: TA 6 (Place Value Models)
Grouping Suggestion: cooperative learning pairs
Pairs use number cards, place value materials, and number sense to create multiplication exercises in which 1 trade is needed in a ones, tens, or hundreds place. One student picks 4 number cards and arranges them to form a 3-digit by 1-digit multiplication problem, with no trades. (Sample: 341 × 2) The partner models the numbers, finds the product, and confirms whether or not trades were needed. Next, partners exchange roles to try a problem that requires trading ones. Then they exchange roles again for a problem trading tens, and last, for a problem trading hundreds. (Samples: 125 × 3; 152 × 4; 514 × 2) Encourage partners to discuss number combinations to create trades, how and when to trade, and how to predict trades.

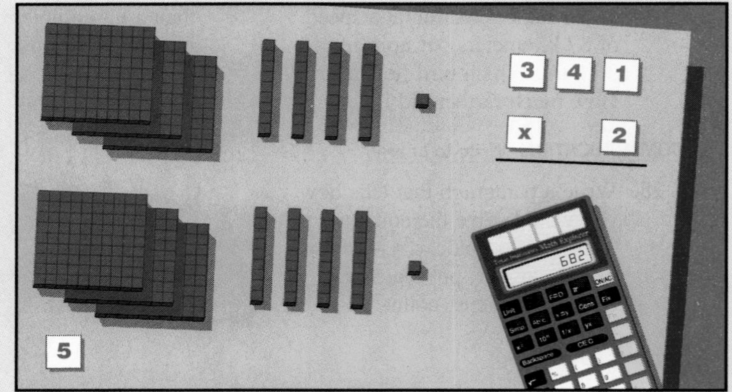

CONNECTIONS Use these anytime.

Problem of the Day

Multiplication Riddle I have an odd 3-digit product. My factors are a 1-digit number and either a 2- or a 3-digit number. My factors are odd, but neither is 1. Find my factors and my product. (41 × 3 = 123; 41 × 9 = 369; or 123 × 3 = 369)

Number Sense

Estimation Amy brushes her horse 102 times each day. About how many times is this per week? (7 × 100 = 700) Use the product to estimate how many times she brushes her horse every 4 weeks. (4 × 700 = 2,800)

Creative Thinking

Blocks Val created a large design with 241 pattern blocks. If she doubles her design, and then doubles it again, how many pattern blocks will she use in all? (964)

Classwork and Homework Supplements

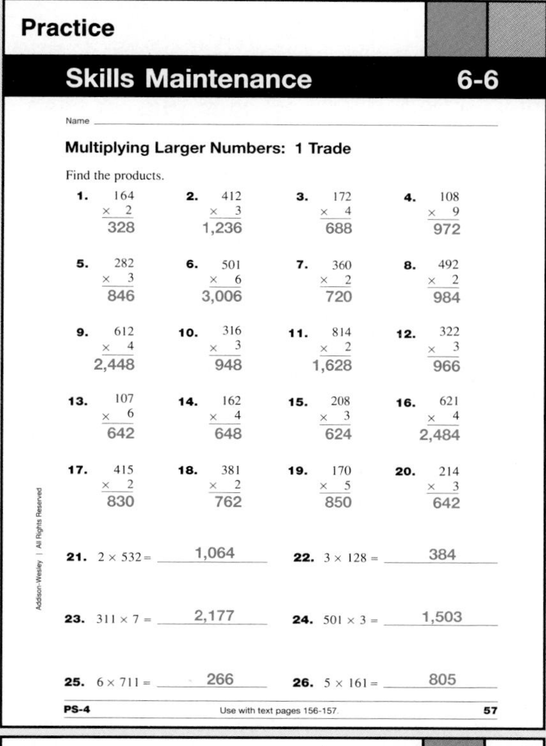

Practice

Skills Maintenance 6-6

Name

Multiplying Larger Numbers: 1 Trade

Find the products.

1. 164 × 2 = 328
2. 412 × 3 = 1,236
3. 172 × 4 = 688
4. 108 × 9 = 972
5. 282 × 3 = 846
6. 501 × 6 = 3,006
7. 360 × 2 = 720
8. 492 × 2 = 984
9. 612 × 4 = 2,448
10. 316 × 3 = 948
11. 814 × 2 = 1,628
12. 322 × 3 = 966
13. 107 × 6 = 642
14. 162 × 4 = 648
15. 208 × 3 = 624
16. 621 × 4 = 2,484
17. 415 × 2 = 830
18. 381 × 2 = 762
19. 170 × 5 = 850
20. 214 × 3 = 642
21. 2 × 532 = 1,064
22. 3 × 128 = 384
23. 311 × 7 = 2,177
24. 501 × 3 = 1,503
25. 6 × 711 = 266
26. 5 × 161 = 805

PS-4 Use with text pages 156-157. 57

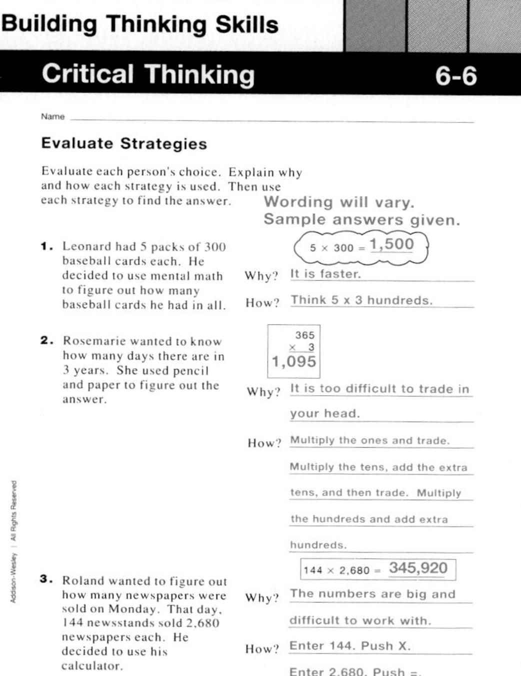

Building Thinking Skills

Critical Thinking 6-6

Name

Evaluate Strategies

Evaluate each person's choice. Explain why and how each strategy is used. Then use each strategy to find the answer. Wording will vary. Sample answers given.

1. Leonard had 5 packs of 300 baseball cards each. He decided to use mental math to figure out how many baseball cards he had in all.
   5 × 300 = 1,500
   Why? It is faster.
   How? Think 5 x 3 hundreds.

2. Rosemarie wanted to know how many days there are in 3 years. She used pencil and paper to figure out the answer.
   365 × 3 = 1,095
   Why? It is too difficult to trade in your head.
   How? Multiply the ones and trade. Multiply the tens, add the extra tens, and then trade. Multiply the hundreds and add extra hundreds.

3. Roland wanted to figure out how many newspapers were sold on Monday. That day, 144 newsstands sold 2,680 newspapers each. He decided to use his calculator.
   144 × 2,680 = 345,920
   Why? The numbers are big and difficult to work with.
   How? Enter 144. Push X. Enter 2,680. Push =.

TS-4 Use with text pages 156-157. 57

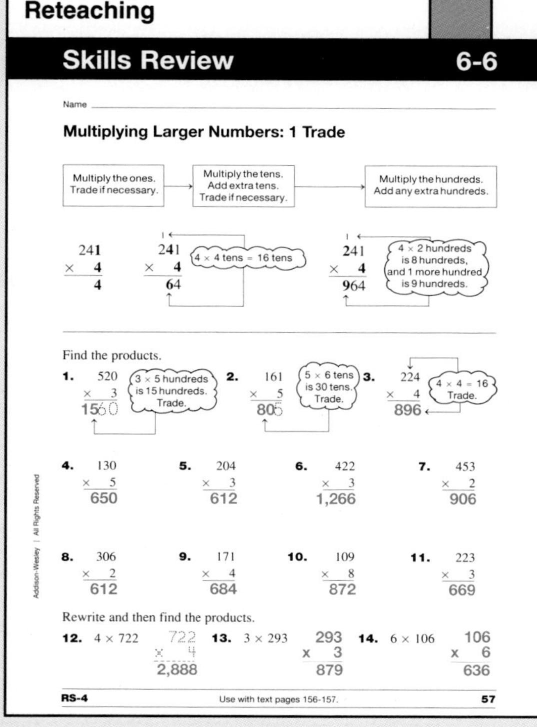

Reteaching

Skills Review 6-6

Name

Multiplying Larger Numbers: 1 Trade

Multiply the ones. Trade if necessary. → Multiply the tens. Add extra tens. Trade if necessary. → Multiply the hundreds. Add any extra hundreds.

241 × 4 = 4 → 241 × 4 = 64 (4 × 4 tens = 16 tens) → 241 × 4 = 964 (4 × 2 hundreds is 8 hundreds, and 1 more hundred is 9 hundreds.)

Find the products.

1. 520 × 3 = 1560 (3 × 5 hundreds is 15 hundreds. Trade.)
2. 161 × 5 = 805 (5 × 6 tens is 30 tens. Trade.)
3. 224 × 4 = 896 (4 × 4 = 16 Trade.)
4. 130 × 5 = 650
5. 204 × 3 = 612
6. 422 × 3 = 1,266
7. 453 × 2 = 906
8. 306 × 2 = 612
9. 171 × 4 = 684
10. 109 × 8 = 872
11. 223 × 3 = 669

Rewrite and then find the products.

12. 4 × 722 → 722 × 4 = 2,888
13. 3 × 293 → 293 × 3 = 879
14. 6 × 106 → 106 × 6 = 636

RS-4 Use with text pages 156-157. 57

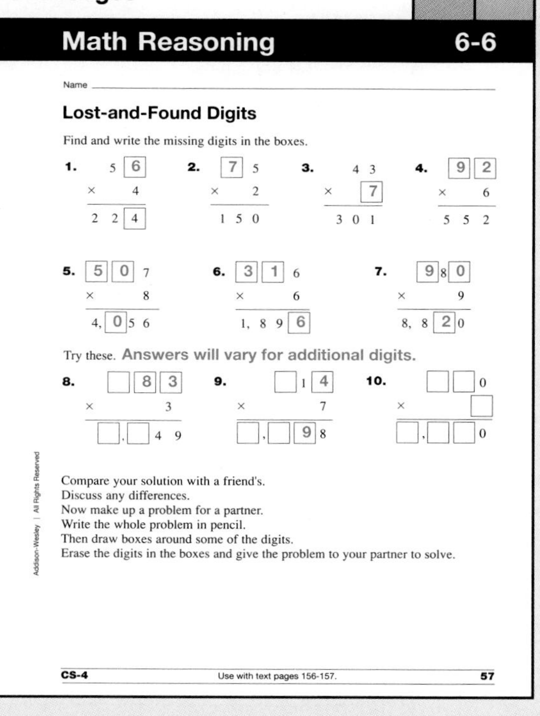

Challenges

Math Reasoning 6-6

Name

Lost-and-Found Digits

Find and write the missing digits in the boxes.

1. 5[6] × 4 = 22[4]
2. [7]5 × 2 = 150
3. 43 × [7] = 301
4. [9][2] × 6 = 552
5. [5][0]7 × 8 = 4,[0]56
6. [3][1]6 × 6 = 1,89[6]
7. [9]8[0] × 9 = 8,8[2]0

Try these. Answers will vary for additional digits.

8. [ ][ ][ ]3 × 3 = [ ],[ ]49
9. [ ]1[4] × 7 = [ ],[ ][9]8
10. [ ][ ]0 × [ ] = [ ],[ ][ ]0

Compare your solution with a friend's.
Discuss any differences.
Now make up a problem for a partner.
Write the whole problem in pencil.
Then draw boxes around some of the digits.
Erase the digits in the boxes and give the problem to your partner to solve.

CS-4 Use with text pages 156-157. 57

Options for Individual Needs

Basic

Exercises 5-14, 19-30
Skills Bank, p. 465
Calculator Bank, p. 486
More Practice, p. 504, set C

Supplements
Reteaching 57 or
Practice 57
Thinking Skills 57

Average

Exercises 1-32
Calculator Bank, p. 486
More Practice, p. 504, set C

Supplements
Practice 57
Challenges 57 or
Thinking Skills 57

Extended

Exercises 8-31
Calculator Bank, p. 486

Supplements
Challenges 57
Thinking Skills 57

Other Resources:
Problem-Solving Experiences in Mathematics, Grade 4, Problem 52

LESSON PLAN 6-6

OBJECTIVE 6-6
To multiply a 3-digit by a 1-digit number, 1 trade

Materials: red and blue pencils or markers

1. MOTIVATE AND TEACH

LEARN ABOUT IT

EXPLORE ▶ **Where do you begin to multiply? Explain.** (Ones place; order of operations says always start with the smallest place.)
▶ **What do you multiply next? Why?** (3 × 9 tens; because you continue in order from ones to tens.)
▶ **Why is there a 2 over the hundreds place?** (It shows a trade of 20 tens for 2 hundreds.)
▶ **Explain what to multiply last.** (3 × 2 hundreds, because hundreds is the highest place.)
▶ **How do you know when to add the 2 extra hundreds?** (The order of operations says always multiply first, then add any extra.)

TALK ABOUT IT ▶ **Compare the answers if you added in the hundreds place, then multiplied.** (Possible answer: You would get 12 hundreds, which would put the answer into the thousands place. The correct answer is only 879.)
Student Edition answers: **1.** 300 × 3 = 900 **2.** Sample: 879 people saw the shows.

2. CHECK UNDERSTANDING

TRY IT OUT

ERROR ALERT Adding traded amounts before multiplying factors. Being confused by zero, as in Exercise 4.

Multiplying Larger Numbers
1 Trade

LEARN ABOUT IT

EXPLORE Think About the Process
The school auditorium could seat 293 people. If the seats were full for each of 3 puppet shows, how many people saw the shows?

You multiply because you need to find the total for equal numbers of people.

Multiply the ones. Trade if necessary.	293 × 3 = 9	Multiply the tens. Add any extra tens. Trade if necessary.	(2) 293 × 3 = 79	Multiply the hundreds. Add any extra hundreds.	(2) 293 × 3 = 879

TALK ABOUT IT See teaching notes.

1. How would you estimate the number of people who saw the shows?
2. Use a complete sentence that gives a reasonable answer to the story problem.

Other Examples

Trading Ones	Trading Tens	Trading Hundreds
A (2) 216 × 4 = 864	**B** (1) 380 × 2 = 760	**C** 301 × 5 = 1,505

TRY IT OUT

1. 213 × 7 = 1,491 **2.** 652 × 3 = 1,956 **3.** 741 × 6 = 4,446 **4.** 109 × 5 = 545 **5.** 317 × 2 = 634

156

TEACHING OPTIONS

RETEACHING TIPS Have students write factors in red pencil and show the steps with blue pencil. They multiply the red numbers, then add any extra written in blue. Have students confused by zero verbalize multiplication and addition with zero: 5 × 0 = 0 and 0 + 4 = 4. Assign Reteaching Supplement 57.

ENRICHMENT Students find the missing digits in each exercise.

1. (1)(4)(2) × 3 = 426
2. (6)(0)(9) × 7 = 4,263
3. (3)(1)2 × (4) = 1,248
4. (2)(0)5 × (4) = 820

PRACTICE

Find the products.

1. 315 × 4 = **1,260**
2. 206 × 9 = **1,854**
3. 941 × 5 = **4,705**
4. 174 × 2 = **348**
5. 503 × 7 = **3,521**
6. 642 × 3 = **1,926**
7. 741 × 7 = **5,187**
8. 539 × 2 = **1,078**
9. 416 × 6 = **2,496**
10. 880 × 8 = **7,040**
11. 708 × 5 **3,540**
12. 121 × 8 **968**
13. 3 × 318 **954**
14. 861 × 4 **3,444**
15. 473 × 2 **946**
16. 6 × 712 **4,272**
17. 510 × 9 **4,590**
18. 7 × 271 **1,897**
19. Multiply 6 × 207. **1,242**
20. Find the product of 413 and 5. **2,065**

APPLY

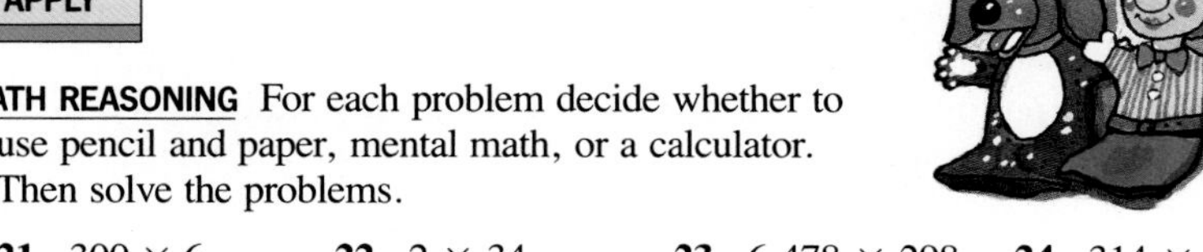

MATH REASONING For each problem decide whether to use pencil and paper, mental math, or a calculator. Then solve the problems.

21. 300 × 6 **mental math; 1,800**
22. 2 × 34 **mental math; 68**
23. 6,478 × 298 **calculator; 1,930, 444**
24. 314 × 6 **pencil and paper; 1,884**

PROBLEM SOLVING

25. Jeff sold some \$2 and some \$5 tickets to a puppet show. He sold \$35 worth of tickets all together. How many of each type ticket could he have sold? Give 3 possible combinations. **15 \$2 tickets and 1 \$5 ticket; 10 \$2 tickets and 3 \$5 tickets; 5 \$2 tickets and 5 \$5 tickets**
26. The puppet show project made \$204 for a charity. A can collection project made \$159. How much more did the puppet show make? **\$15 more**

▶ **ALGEBRA**

Estimate to find the number for the ||||. Check your estimate with a calculator.

27. 316 × |||| = 1,580 **5**
28. 832 × |||| = 3,328 **4**
29. 271 × |||| = 2,168 **8**
30. 490 × |||| = 3,430 **7**
31. 909 × |||| = 3,636 **4**
32. 826 × |||| = 2,478 **3**

More Practice, page 504, set C

3. PRACTICE AND APPLY

Basic	5-14, 19-30
Average	1-32
Extended	8-31

PRACTICE

Look at Exercises 13, 16, and 18. Does having the smaller factor first change the way you multiply? Why? (No, because factors can be arranged in any order.) *What should you do before you multiply Exercises 11-20?* (Rewrite the numbers vertically.)

APPLY

MATH REASONING ▶ **Explain when it makes sense to use mental math instead of other methods.** (when numbers are small or when they are multiples of 10, 100, or 1,000)

PROBLEM SOLVING ▶ **What operation is called for in Problem 26? Explain.** (Subtraction; you are comparing amounts.)

ALGEBRA ▶ **How can estimation help you make reasonable guesses?** (Round, then think of special products and compatible numbers)

CLOSE AND ASSESS

SAY WHAT YOU THINK Pair students. Each partner uses one of the following exercises to show the other how to multiply with 1 trade: 484 × 2 or 206 × 4. Pairs take turns explaining the steps involved in solving their problem and how to know when to trade. (968; 824; explanations will vary)

QUICK QUIZ

Find the products.

1. 271 × 3 (813)
2. 618 × 5 (3,090)
3. 192 × 4 (768)
4. 502 × 4 (2,008)
5. 741 × 6 (4,446)

LESSON OPTIONS 6-7

Multiplying Larger Numbers: 2 or More Trades

OBJECTIVE 6-7 To multiply a 3-digit by a 1-digit number, 2 or more trades

PREBOOK ACTIVITIES

QUICK REVIEW

Estimate the products.

1. 48 × 6 (300)	**2.** 92 × 7 (630)
3. 4 × 83 (320)	**4.** 5 × 96 (500)
5. 488 × 6 (3,000)	**6.** 912 × 7 (6,300)
7. 4 × 832 (3,200)	**8.** 5 × 967 (5,000)

PRIOR KNOWLEDGE

Write 161 × 4 on the chalkboard. Have students read the factors aloud and predict where trading may occur. (Trading will be needed in tens place.) Have students verbalize the steps in the multiplication process. (Possible answer: Multiply ones, trade if necessary, multiply tens, add any extra tens, trade if necessary, multiply hundreds, add any extra hundreds.) Tell students that some factors may require *more* than one trade. Have them suggest factors in which more than one trade will occur. (Answers will vary; samples include 345 × 8, 425 × 7.) Have students predict how to multiply with 2 or more trades. (Possible answer: Follow the same steps for a single trade—trade, multiply, then add as necessary.)

COMMUNICATION

Discussing Math Have students relate the importance of order to multiplication with trading. (Possible answers: Always multiply, then add; always begin multiplying in ones place, then move to each higher place.) Then ask students to predict the kinds of errors than can result if these rules of order are not followed. (Possible answer: If you add an extra amount, then multiply, the answer will be too large.)

EXPLORE AND CONNECT

Materials: poster paper, colored markers, calculators
Grouping Suggestions: small groups or pairs
Students create algorithm posters to show the general order of steps involved in multiplication with 1 or 2 trades. Assign each group a set of factors, such as 234 × 5. Use the general ability level of the group to determine whether factors requiring 1 or 2 trades are more appropriate. Groups first multiply the factors to get a product and verify the product with a calculator. Then, with one member acting as recorder, they repeat the multiplication, summarizing the essential steps in the process. These summaries can become the labels for the steps on the poster. Encourage groups to think about linking a particular color to each step or using some other visual scheme to make the process clearer. Ask each group to present its completed poster to the class. Discuss steps that repeat on all posters. (multiply, add, trade)

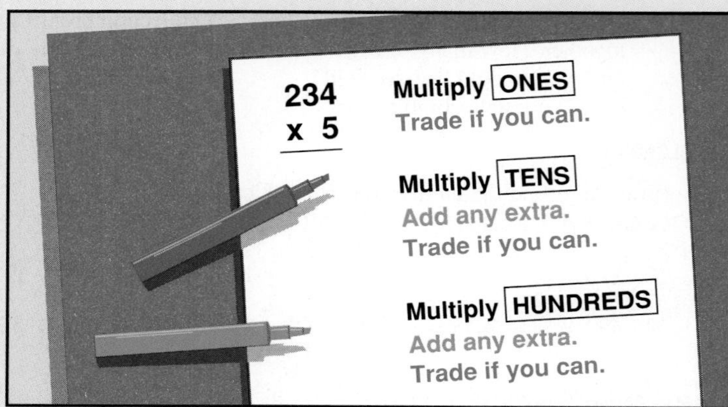

CONNECTIONS Use these anytime.

Problem of the Day

Multiplying Without × Find the product of 579 × 4 on a calculator without using the × key. Explain your strategy. (Possible strategy: Press 579 + 579 + 579 + 579 = 2,316 because 579 × 4 means finding 579 four times.)

Math Connection

Time Kyle remembers that the watch he got for his eighth birthday came with a brand-new battery. Yesterday, Kyle turned 11. He has never replaced the battery. How many days has the battery lasted so far? HINT: 1 year = 365 days. (365 × 3 = 1,095 + 1 day = 1,096 days)

Patterns

Multiply, Then Add Find the missing numbers to complete the pattern:
0 × 9 + 1 = 1
1 × 9 + 2 = 11
12 × 9 + 3 = 111
123 × 9 + 4 = (1,111)
(1,234) × 9 + (5) = (11,111)

Classwork and Homework Supplements

Practice

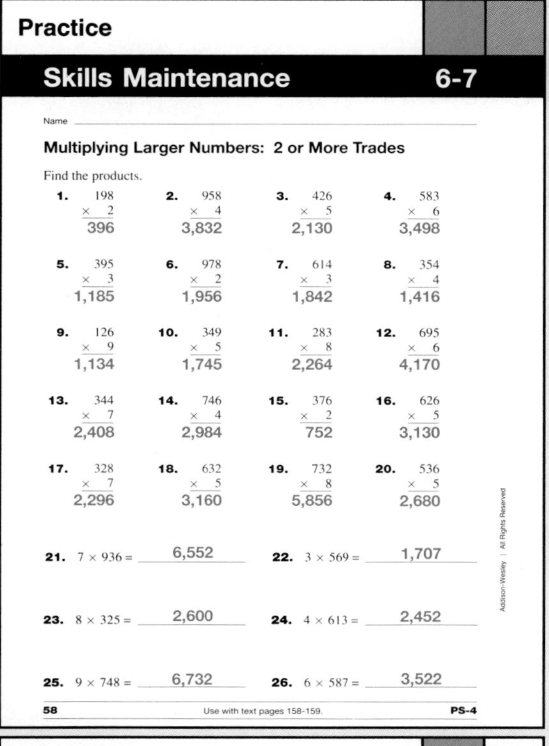

Skills Maintenance 6-7

Name ______

Multiplying Larger Numbers: 2 or More Trades

Find the products.

1. 198 × 2 = 396
2. 958 × 4 = 3,832
3. 426 × 5 = 2,130
4. 583 × 6 = 3,498
5. 395 × 3 = 1,185
6. 978 × 2 = 1,956
7. 614 × 3 = 1,842
8. 354 × 4 = 1,416
9. 126 × 9 = 1,134
10. 349 × 5 = 1,745
11. 283 × 8 = 2,264
12. 695 × 6 = 4,170
13. 344 × 7 = 2,408
14. 746 × 4 = 2,984
15. 376 × 2 = 752
16. 626 × 5 = 3,130
17. 328 × 7 = 2,296
18. 632 × 5 = 3,160
19. 732 × 8 = 5,856
20. 536 × 5 = 2,680
21. 7 × 936 = 6,552
22. 3 × 569 = 1,707
23. 8 × 325 = 2,600
24. 4 × 613 = 2,452
25. 9 × 748 = 6,732
26. 6 × 587 = 3,522

Building Thinking Skills

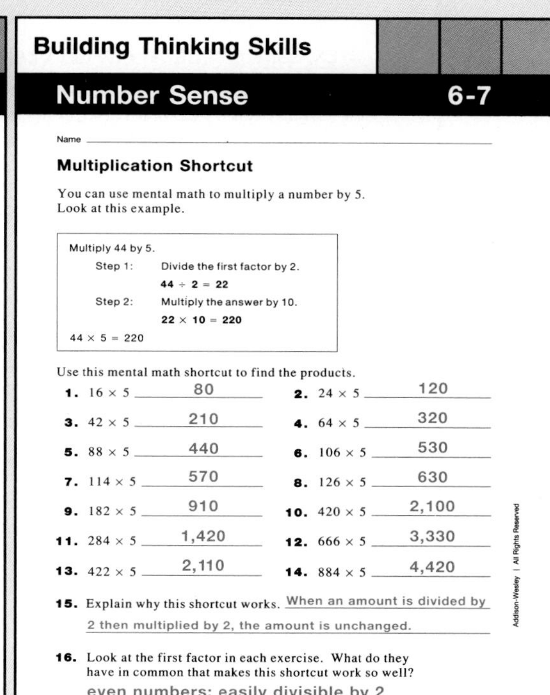

Number Sense 6-7

Name ______

Multiplication Shortcut

You can use mental math to multiply a number by 5. Look at this example.

Multiply 44 by 5.
Step 1: Divide the first factor by 2. 44 ÷ 2 = 22
Step 2: Multiply the answer by 10. 22 × 10 = 220
44 × 5 = 220

Use this mental math shortcut to find the products.

1. 16 × 5 = 80
2. 24 × 5 = 120
3. 42 × 5 = 210
4. 64 × 5 = 320
5. 88 × 5 = 440
6. 106 × 5 = 530
7. 114 × 5 = 570
8. 126 × 5 = 630
9. 182 × 5 = 910
10. 420 × 5 = 2,100
11. 284 × 5 = 1,420
12. 666 × 5 = 3,330
13. 422 × 5 = 2,110
14. 884 × 5 = 4,420
15. Explain why this shortcut works. When an amount is divided by 2 then multiplied by 2, the amount is unchanged.
16. Look at the first factor in each exercise. What do they have in common that makes this shortcut work so well? even numbers; easily divisible by 2

Reteaching

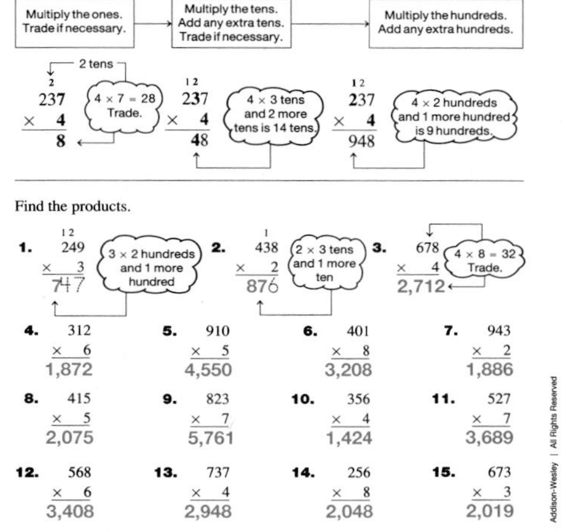

Skills Review 6-7

Name ______

Multiplying Larger Numbers: 2 or More Trades

Multiply the ones. Trade if necessary. → Multiply the tens. Add any extra tens. Trade if necessary. → Multiply the hundreds. Add any extra hundreds.

237 × 4: 4 × 7 = 28 Trade. (2 tens) → 8; 4 × 3 tens and 2 more tens is 14 tens. → 48; 4 × 2 hundreds and 1 more hundred is 9 hundreds. → 948

Find the products.

1. 249 × 3 = 747 (3 × 2 hundreds and 1 more hundred)
2. 438 × 2 = 876 (2 × 3 tens and 1 more ten)
3. 678 × 4 = 2,712 (4 × 8 = 32 Trade.)
4. 312 × 6 = 1,872
5. 910 × 5 = 4,550
6. 401 × 8 = 3,208
7. 943 × 2 = 1,886
8. 415 × 5 = 2,075
9. 823 × 7 = 5,761
10. 356 × 4 = 1,424
11. 527 × 7 = 3,689
12. 568 × 6 = 3,408
13. 737 × 4 = 2,948
14. 256 × 8 = 2,048
15. 673 × 3 = 2,019

Rewrite and then find the products.

16. 7 × 650: 650 × 7 = 4,550
17. 5 × 683: 683 × 5 = 3,415
18. 3 × 178: 178 × 3 = 534

Challenges

Family Math 6-7

Name ______

The Bamboozle Machine

Dear Family,
In our math class we have been learning how to multiply large numbers. Play the game with your child to practice the skill.

1. Put a number between 18 and 39 into the Bamboozle Machine.
2. Follow the directions to the end of the machine. The number that comes out at the end should be the same one you put in.
3. Try 3 more numbers between 18 and 39. Do they work? yes

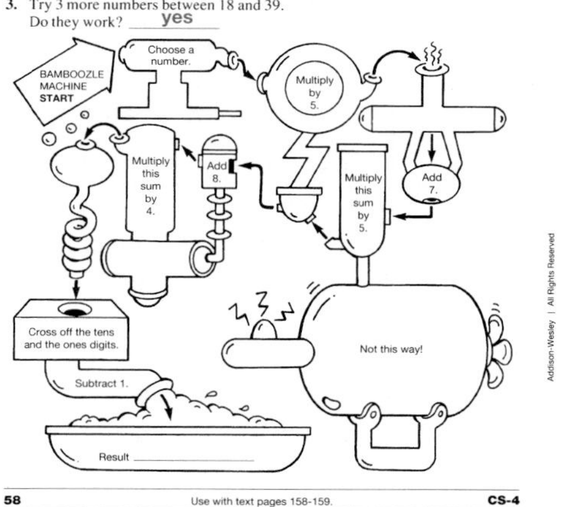

Options for Individual Needs

Basic

Exercises 3-8, 14-22
Data Bank, pp. 468-483
More Practice, p. 504, set D

Supplements
Reteaching 58 or
Practice 58
Thinking Skills 58

Average

Exercises 1-22
Data Bank, pp. 468-483
More Practice, p. 504, set D

Supplements
Practice 58
Challenges 58 or
Thinking Skills 58

Extended

Exercises 5-9, 14-22
Data Bank, pp. 468-483

Supplements
Challenges 58
Thinking Skills 58

Other Resources:
Skillseekers 2, pp. 13-18

LESSON PLAN 6-7

OBJECTIVE 6-7
To multiply a 3-digit by a 1-digit number, 2 or more trades

Materials: lined paper

1. MOTIVATE AND TEACH

LEARN ABOUT IT

EXPLORE ▶ **Explain a heartbeat rate in your own words.** (Possible answer: It is how many times a heart beats in one minute.)
▶ **Express the heartbeat rate of a robin another way.** (A robin's heart beats 4 times faster per minute than a dove's heart.)

TALK ABOUT IT ▶ **Explain why a 0 is in the ones place for 4 × 5.** (The product was 20; two tens were traded, leaving 0.)
▶ **Explain how to find the number in the tens place.** (4 × 3 tens = 12 tens, + 2 extra tens = 14 tens; trade 10 tens, leaving 4.)
▶ **Why do you write 4 and not 14?** (only 1 digit per place)
▶ **Explain how to multiply the hundreds.** (4 × 1 hundred = 4 hundreds, + 1 extra = 5 hundreds.)
▶ **Explain what is the same in both trades.** (Both places had over 10; you always multiply, then add any extra amount, then trade.)
Student Edition answers: **1.** 140 × 4 = 560 or 100 × 4 = 400 **2.** Sample answer: A robin's heart beats about 540 times per minute.

2. CHECK UNDERSTANDING

TRY IT OUT

ERROR ALERT Writing the number of the traded amount over the wrong place. Adding the extra before multiplying.

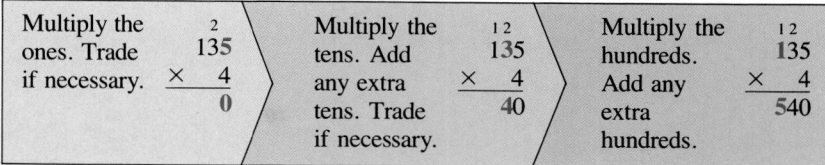

Multiplying Larger Numbers
2 or More Trades

LEARN ABOUT IT

EXPLORE Think About the Process
The heartbeat rate of a robin is about 4 times the heartbeat rate of a dove. The heartbeat rate of a dove is 135 beats a minute. About what is the heartbeat rate of a robin?

You multiply because you need a total for equal numbers of heartbeats.

Multiply the ones. Trade if necessary.	$\begin{array}{r} {}^{2}\\ 135 \\ \times\ 4 \\ \hline 0 \end{array}$	Multiply the tens. Add any extra tens. Trade if necessary.	$\begin{array}{r} {}^{1\,2}\\ 135 \\ \times\ 4 \\ \hline 40 \end{array}$	Multiply the hundreds. Add any extra hundreds.	$\begin{array}{r} {}^{1\,2}\\ 135 \\ \times\ 4 \\ \hline 540 \end{array}$

TALK ABOUT IT See teaching notes.

1. How would you have estimated the heartbeat rate of the robin?
2. Give the answer in a complete sentence.

Other Examples

A $\begin{array}{r} {}^{3}\\ 318 \\ \times\ 4 \\ \hline 1{,}272 \end{array}$ **B** $\begin{array}{r} {}^{1\,2}\\ 237 \\ \times\ 3 \\ \hline 711 \end{array}$ **C** $\begin{array}{r} {}^{1}\\ 706 \\ \times\ 2 \\ \hline 1{,}412 \end{array}$

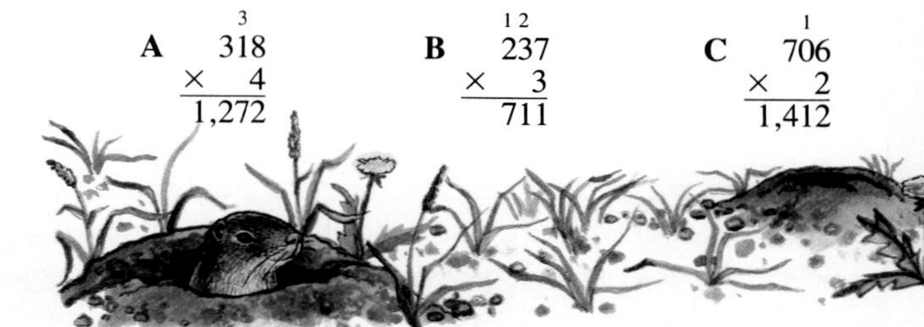

TRY IT OUT

Find the products.

1. $\begin{array}{r} 354 \\ \times\ 3 \\ \hline 1{,}062 \end{array}$ **2.** $\begin{array}{r} 572 \\ \times\ 4 \\ \hline 2{,}288 \end{array}$ **3.** $\begin{array}{r} 879 \\ \times\ 6 \\ \hline 5{,}274 \end{array}$ **4.** $\begin{array}{r} 727 \\ \times\ 3 \\ \hline 2{,}181 \end{array}$ **5.** $\begin{array}{r} 515 \\ \times\ 4 \\ \hline 2{,}060 \end{array}$

158

TEACHING OPTIONS

RETEACHING TIPS Have students who write traded amounts over the wrong place multiply on lined paper turned sideways, using the lines as columns. The lines separate the places more clearly so that students can record trades properly. Assign Reteaching Supplement 58.

ENRICHMENT Have students use a calculator or mental math to find a 3-digit and a 1-digit factor for each product:
1. 1,250 **2.** 6,464
3. 3,542
(Answers may vary; sample factors: **1.** 5 × 250 **2.** 808 × 8 **3.** 7 × 506)

PRACTICE

Find the products.

1. 456 × 3 = 1,368	**2.** 343 × 6 = 2,058	**3.** 169 × 9 = 1,521	**4.** 826 × 4 = 3,304	**5.** 369 × 7 = 2,583

6. 728 × 6 4,368 **7.** 571 × 4 2,284 **8.** 8 × 733 5,864 **9.** 879 × 3 2,637

10. 428 × 8 3,424 **11.** 2 × 683 1,366 **12.** 256 × 5 1,280 **13.** 9 × 354 3,186

14. Multiply 7 × 409. 2,863 **15.** Find the product of 537 and 9. 4,833

MATH REASONING Use estimation to choose the greater product.

16. 398 × 4 or 498 × 3 **17.** 508 × 8 or 608 × 7 **18.** 999 × 4 or 499 × 9

PROBLEM SOLVING

19. **Science Data Bank** The heartbeat rate of a hummingbird is about 3 times the heartbeat rate of a starling. About what is the heartbeat rate of a hummingbird? See page 000.
DATA BANK
about 1,200 heartbeats per minute

20. An ostrich takes 45 breaths per minute when the weather is warm. In cool weather, an ostrich takes 5 breaths per minute. How many more breaths per minute does an ostrich take in warm weather?
40 breaths per minute

MIXED REVIEW

The 2 scales are balanced. Each shape has the same value in all the pictures.

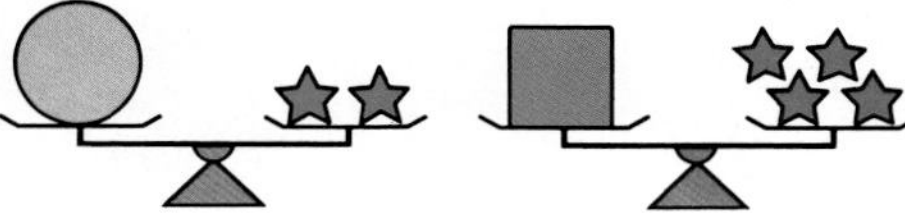

Write yes if each scale below is balanced. Write no if it is not.

21.

yes

22.

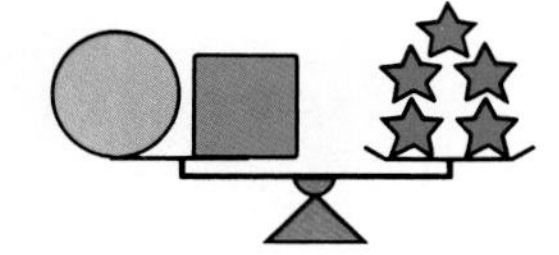

no

More Practice, page 504, set D

3. PRACTICE AND APPLY

Basic	3-8, 14-22
Average	1-22
Extended	5-9; 14-22

PRACTICE

Look at Exercise 1. How many trades? (2) *Look at Exercise 7. How many trades?* (1) *Look at Exercise 15. How do you know to multiply?* (It asks for a product.)

APPLY

MATH REASONING ▶ **Explain the method you would use to solve Exercises 16-18.** (Round, then multiply to find special products, then compare the special products.)

PROBLEM SOLVING ▶ **Explain how you know to estimate in Problem 19.** (The question asks for *about* what rate, meaning an exact answer is not needed.)

MIXED REVIEW ▶ **Explain 3 ways to show the value of 4 stars.** (1 ball = 2 stars, so 2 balls = 4 stars; 2 stars + 1 ball = 4 stars; 2 stars + 1 ball = 1 box, so 1 box = 4 stars.)

6-7

CLOSE AND ASSESS

SHOW WHAT YOU KNOW Ask students to agree or disagree with this statement and to explain their opinion: Multiplying with 2 or more trades is just like multiplying with 1 trade. Have them make up one or more sample problems to support their answer. (Answers will vary.)

QUICK QUIZ

Find the products.

1. 745 × 2 (1,490) **2.** 819 × 5 (4,095) **3.** 463 × 6 (2,778) **4.** 102 × 8 (816)

5. 7 × 419 (2,933)

Using Critical Thinking/Midchapter Review/Quiz

OBJECTIVE 6-8 To discover a mental math technique for multiplying money;

PREBOOK ACTIVITIES

QUICK REVIEW

Give the value in cents.

1. 6 pennies (6¢) **2.** 3 dimes (30¢)
3. 5 nickels (25¢) **4.** 3 quarters (75¢)
5. 7 dimes (70¢) **6.** 9 pennies (9¢)
7. 2 quarters (50¢) **8.** 8 dimes (80¢)
9. 7 nickels (35¢) **10.** 1 quarter (25¢)

PRIOR KNOWLEDGE

Have students recall any of the various mental math methods they have learned. (Answers will vary.) Have them justify using mental math to perform calculations. (Answers may vary. Possible answers: to save time, to check whether an answer seems reasonable) Have students share situations in which they have used mental math strategies. (Answers will vary.)

COMMUNICATION

Discussing Math Review the break-apart method of finding products, such as 8 × 4. (Possible answer: Break apart the numbers to form easier factors, multiply, then combine the smaller products for a final product; 8 × 4 = (4 × 4) + (4 × 4), 4 × 4 = 16, 16 + 16 = 32.) Have students generalize how they might use this method with larger factors. (Possible answer: Follow the same steps; break apart one number to form easier factors, multiply, add the smaller products to get a final product.)

EXPLORE AND CONNECT

Materials: TA 2 (Number Cubes numbered 1-6), price list (see below), TA 9 (Play Money—Coins and Dollars)
Grouping Suggestion: cooperative learning pairs
Partners pretend to buy packages of snack foods in various quantities, using mental math to multiply to find total cost. Post the following price list: Peanuts—26¢, Popcorn—19¢, Raisins—31¢. A student rolls a number cube to determine how many packages of the first snack to calculate. For example, if a 5 comes up, partners "buy" 5 packages of peanuts at 26¢ per pack. Partners discuss ways to find the total cost using any reasonable mental math method. (Possible methods: Break apart a factor; compensate.) Then they use play coins to model the problem and to verify the cost they found mentally. Partners repeat the task for each snack item. Students share mental math methods they used most often or most successfully. (Answers will vary.)

CONNECTIONS Use these anytime.

Problem of the Day

What Coins? Jeremy has $1.00 in 19 coins of 2 different values. What are the coins? How many of each coin does he have? (10 pennies, 9 dimes)

Creative Thinking

Number Riddle Use the clues to find a mystery money amount.
1. If I were a price, you would get change back from a half dollar.
2. I am a multiple of 11.
3. I am closer to 4 dimes than I am to 7 nickels. (44¢)

Math Connection

Calculator When Helen bought 8 ribbons at 49¢ each, she wanted to use her calculator to find the total cost. But the calculator's 8 key was broken. Explain how she could still use the calculator to find the total cost. (Strategies may vary. Possible answer: 4 × $.49 × 2 = $3.92) to review multiplication of 1-digit factors

Classwork and Homework Supplements

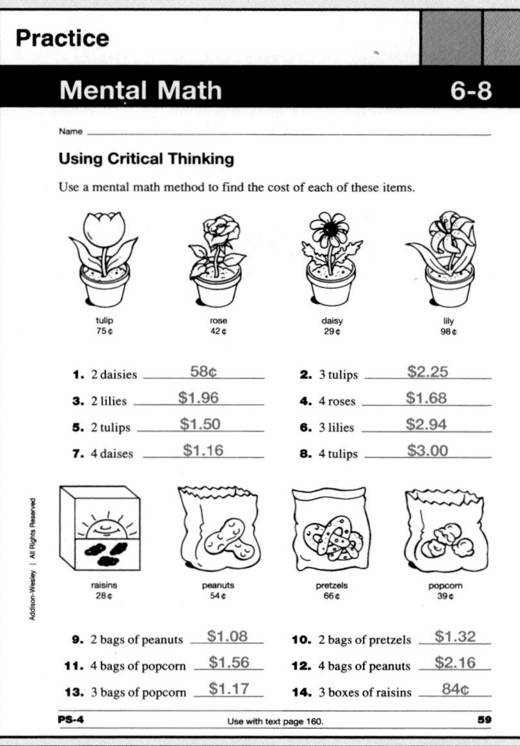

Practice

Mental Math 6-8

Name ____________

Using Critical Thinking

Use a mental math method to find the cost of each of these items.

1. 2 daisies 58¢
2. 3 tulips $2.25
3. 2 lilies $1.96
4. 4 roses $1.68
5. 2 tulips $1.50
6. 3 lilies $2.94
7. 4 daises $1.16
8. 4 tulips $3.00

9. 2 bags of peanuts $1.08
10. 2 bags of pretzels $1.32
11. 4 bags of popcorn $1.56
12. 4 bags of peanuts $2.16
13. 3 bags of popcorn $1.17
14. 3 boxes of raisins 84¢

PS-4 Use with text page 160. 59

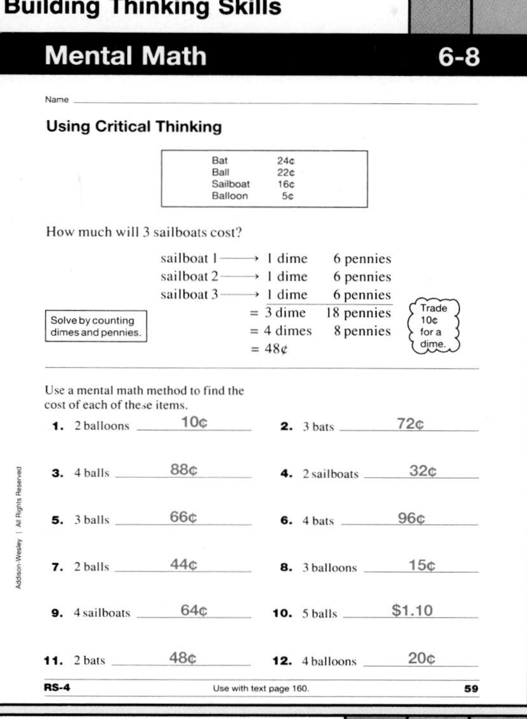

Building Thinking Skills

Mental Math 6-8

Name ____________

Using Critical Thinking

Bat	24¢
Ball	22¢
Sailboat	16¢
Balloon	5¢

How much will 3 sailboats cost?

sailboat 1 → 1 dime 6 pennies
sailboat 2 → 1 dime 6 pennies
sailboat 3 → 1 dime 6 pennies
= 3 dime 18 pennies
= 4 dimes 8 pennies
= 48¢

Solve by counting dimes and pennies.

Trade 10¢ for a dime.

Use a mental math method to find the cost of each of these items.

1. 2 balloons 10¢
2. 3 bats 72¢
3. 4 balls 88¢
4. 2 sailboats 32¢
5. 3 balls 66¢
6. 4 bats 96¢
7. 2 balls 44¢
8. 3 balloons 15¢
9. 4 sailboats 64¢
10. 5 balls $1.10
11. 2 bats 48¢
12. 4 balloons 20¢

RS-4 Use with text page 160. 59

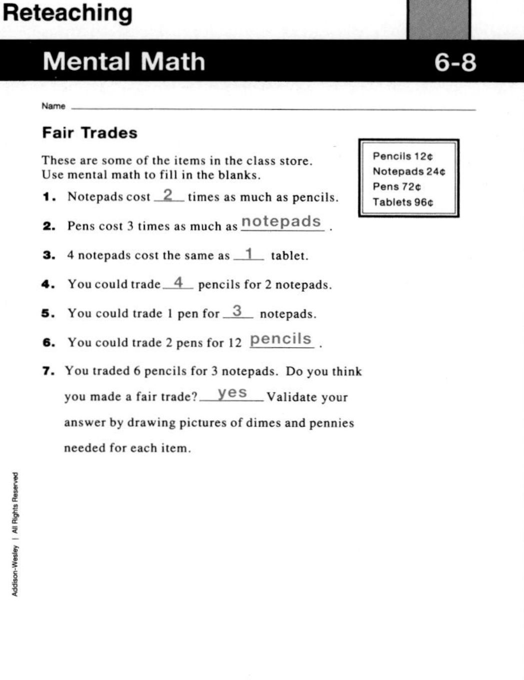

Reteaching

Mental Math 6-8

Name ____________

Fair Trades

These are some of the items in the class store. Use mental math to fill in the blanks.

Pencils 12¢
Notepads 24¢
Pens 72¢
Tablets 96¢

1. Notepads cost 2 times as much as pencils.
2. Pens cost 3 times as much as notepads.
3. 4 notepads cost the same as 1 tablet.
4. You could trade 4 pencils for 2 notepads.
5. You could trade 1 pen for 3 notepads.
6. You could trade 2 pens for 12 pencils.
7. You traded 6 pencils for 3 notepads. Do you think you made a fair trade? yes Validate your answer by drawing pictures of dimes and pennies needed for each item.

TS-4 Use with text pages 160-161. 59

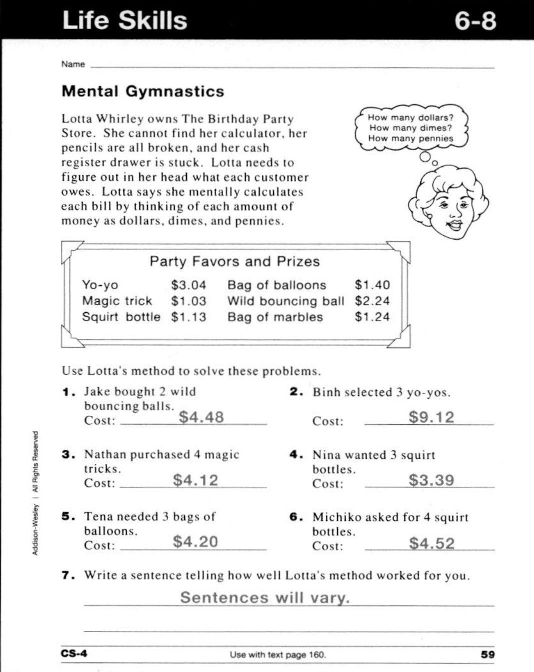

Challenges

Life Skills 6-8

Name ____________

Mental Gymnastics

Lotta Whirley owns The Birthday Party Store. She cannot find her calculator, her pencils are all broken, and her cash register drawer is stuck. Lotta needs to figure out in her head what each customer owes. Lotta says she mentally calculates each bill by thinking of each amount of money as dollars, dimes, and pennies.

Party Favors and Prizes

Yo-yo	$3.04	Bag of balloons	$1.40
Magic trick	$1.03	Wild bouncing ball	$2.24
Squirt bottle	$1.13	Bag of marbles	$1.24

Use Lotta's method to solve these problems.

1. Jake bought 2 wild bouncing balls. Cost: $4.48
2. Binh selected 3 yo-yos. Cost: $9.12
3. Nathan purchased 4 magic tricks. Cost: $4.12
4. Nina wanted 3 squirt bottles. Cost: $3.39
5. Tena needed 3 bags of balloons. Cost: $4.20
6. Michiko asked for 4 squirt bottles. Cost: $4.52
7. Write a sentence telling how well Lotta's method worked for you. Sentences will vary.

CS-4 Use with text page 160. 59

Options for Individual Needs

Basic

Exercises 1-6; 1-30, 36, 37
Computer Bank, p. 495

Supplements
Reteaching 59 or
Practice 59
Challenges 59

Average

Exercises 1-6; 1-37
Computer Bank, p. 495

Supplements
Practice 59
Challenges 59 or
Thinking Skills 59

Extended

Exercises 1-6; 3-30, 36, 37
Computer Bank, p. 495

Supplements
Challenges 59
Thinking Skills 59

Other Resources:
Problem-Solving Experiences in Mathematics, Grade 4, Problem 53

LESSON PLAN 6-8

OBJECTIVE 6-8
To discover a mental math technique for multiplying money; to review multiplication of 1-digit factors

Materials: TA 9 (Play Money—Coins and Dollars)

1. MOTIVATE AND TEACH

LEARN ABOUT IT

EXPLORE ► **Compare each price to one coin or dollar value.** (Pencils are a little over 1 dime; notepads are a little under 1 quarter; pens are a little less than 3 quarters; tablets are just under a dollar.)

TALK ABOUT IT ► **How might Rudy break apart the cost of a notepad?** (Possible answer: 2 dimes, 4 pennies)
► **How might he have used mental math to find the cost of 3 notepads?** (Possible answer: Combine 3 groups of 4 pennies to get 12 pennies; trade 10 pennies for 1 dime with 2 pennies left; combine 3 groups of 2 dimes to get 6 dimes; add the extra dime and remaining 2 pennies to get a total of 72¢.)
► **Explain how to use the relationship between a quarter and the price of a notebook to find the total cost of 3 notebooks.** (1 quarter = 25¢; 1 notebook costs 1¢ less than 1 quarter; 3 quarters = 75¢, so 3 notebooks = 3 quarters − 3¢; 75¢ − 3¢ = 72¢.)
Student Edition answers: **1.** Break apart 24¢, then triple each value. **2.** Answers will vary. **3.** 72¢; use play money.

2. CHECK UNDERSTANDING

ERROR ALERT Making mental math calculation errors. Confusing the steps in one method by applying them to another.

Using Critical Thinking

LEARN ABOUT IT

Rudy and Sara sometimes work at the class store. "How much will 3 notepads be?" asked Derrick. "I forgot my calculator!" exclaimed Sara. "I guess we'll have to use pencil and paper."
"Wait," said Rudy. "I thought about dimes and pennies and invented a way to do it in my head!"

TALK ABOUT IT See teaching notes.

1. What method might Rudy have invented?
2. Invent a method of your own for finding the product.
3. How much did the 3 notepads cost? How could you prove that your answer is correct?

TRY IT OUT

Use a mental math method to find the cost of each of these items.

1. 3 pencils 36¢
2. 4 pencils 48¢
3. 2 notepads 48¢
4. 2 pens $1.44
5. 4 notepads 96¢
6. 2 tablets $1.90

TEACHING OPTIONS

RETEACHING TIPS Have students manipulate play coins to model suitable mental math strategies before they find total costs. They might make same-size groups of prices as given, break apart factors into separate groups of pennies and dimes, or compensate. Assign Reteaching Supplement 59.

COMPUTER **Puzzle Tanks, Sunburst Communications, Copyright 1985** For use with all levels of students. Students add to or subtract from the amount of liquid in two tanks to fill a third. Encourage them to try different strategies. The game requires 15 to 20 minutes to complete.

Midchapter Review/Quiz

Find the products. Write answers only.

1. 7 × 10 70
2. 8 × 40 320
3. 500 × 6 3,000
4. 3 × 9,000 27,000

Round to the highest place and then multiply to estimate the product.

5. 4 × 909 3,600
6. 5 × $7.89 $40.00
7. 8 × 674 5,600
8. 398 × 2 800

Estimate the product. Is it less than $10?

9. 3 × $2.77 $9; yes
10. 6 × $0.98 $6; yes
11. $4.25 × 2 $8; yes
12. 5 × $2.37 $10; no

Multiply the two numbers. Then add 3. Write answers only.

13. 4 and 3 15
14. 9 and 7 66
15. 7 and 7 52
16. 6 and 8 51

Multiply each number by 4. Then add the products.

17. 30 and 2 128
18. 10 and 4 56
19. 70 and 6 304
20. 80 and 5 340

Find the products.

21. 32 × 3 = 96
22. 16 × 7 = 112
23. 783 × 2 = 1,566
24. 126 × 9 = 1,134
25. $3.75 × 8 = $30.00
26. 821 × 5 = 4,105
27. 84 × 5 = 420
28. 308 × 9 = 2,772
29. 496 × 6 = 2,976
30. 515 × 4 = 2,060
31. 632 × 7 = 4,424
32. 72 × 9 = 648
33. 36 × 8 = 288
34. 224 × 3 = 672
35. $7.77 × 4 = $31.08

PROBLEM SOLVING

36. Peter used place value blocks to show these four problems. For which problems did he trade ones for tens? For which did he trade tens for hundreds? B and D; A and D

A	61 × 7
B	27 × 3
C	32 × 3
D	42 × 5

37. Chris has 8 coins in his pocket that total 75¢. Which coins are they? Can you find another possibility? 7 dimes and 1 nickel; 1 quarter, 3 dimes and 4 nickels

161

3. Practice and Apply

Basic	1-6; 1-30, 36, 37
Average	1-6; 1-37
Extended	1-6; 3-30, 36, 37

PRACTICE

Read the direction lines on the Midchapter Review/Quiz for Exercises 5-8 and 9-12. Tell how the two groups of exercises are alike. (Both groups use estimation.)

ITEM ANALYSIS The following table correlates the Midchapter Review/Quiz items with the lesson objectives.

Items	Objectives
1-4	6-1
5-12, (38)	6-2
13-20, 37-38	6-3
36	6-4
21, 22, 27, 32, 33, (37-38)	6-5
23, 26, 28, 30, 34	6-6
24, 25, 29, 31, 35, (38)	6-7

6-8

Close and Assess

SHOW WHAT YOU KNOW Ask students to choose a mental math method to find the cost of 5 packets of tissue that are priced at 17¢ each. Have students use play coins to demonstrate that their method works. (85¢; proofs may vary; check for accuracy.)

Quick Quiz

Solve using mental math.

1. How much are 3 markers at 26¢ each? (78¢)

2. How much are 4 erasers at 18¢ each? (72¢)

LESSON OPTIONS 6-9

Mental Math: Multiplying 3 Factors

OBJECTIVE 6-9 To use mental math and the multiplication grouping property to find the product of 3 factors;

PREBOOK ACTIVITIES

QUICK REVIEW

Add.

1. 4 + 8 + 6	(18)	**2.** 6 + 7 + 6	(19)
3. 6 + 9 + 7	(22)	**4.** 8 + 8 + 8	(24)
5. 5 + 8 + 5	(18)	**6.** 9 + 9 + 8	(26)
7. 9 + 6 + 1	(16)	**8.** 3 + 3 + 4	(10)
9. 7 + 3 + 7	(17)	**10.** 5 + 3 + 5	(13)

PRIOR KNOWLEDGE

Have students give 2 methods for adding 7 + 3 + 7. (Find doubles or a group of 10) Have them justify their methods by recalling the grouping rule for addition. (You can group addends in any order without changing the sum.) Ask how order affects the product of factors such as 6 × 4 and 4 × 6. (Order does not affect the product.)

Have students recall what a magic square is. (a square in which the sum of the numbers along each row, column, and diagonal is always the same)

COMMUNICATION

Discussing Math Have students explain how parentheses organize number groupings, as in the example 4 + (7 × 3). (Do what is inside the parentheses first, then use the result to finish the equation.) Have students explain how to enter the example in a calculator without using parentheses. (Possible answer: Organize or group the numbers before entering them; first enter 7 × 3, then add 4.)

EXPLORE AND CONNECT

Materials: calculators, TA 3 (Number Cards 2-9)
Grouping Suggestion: cooperative learning groups of 3
Students explore the effect of various groupings in multiplication. One student draws any 3 number cards and lays them out on the table. Group members take turns using the calculator to find the combined product of all 3 factors, each entering a different factor first. Members compare displays after entering the equal sign each time. Students may also write down each product for comparison. (All products should be equal.) Each trio then mixes the number cards and repeats the activity, stopping after 3 more rounds. Conclude by having students generalize about how grouping affects products in multiplication. (Possible conclusion: You can group factors any way you want without changing their product.)

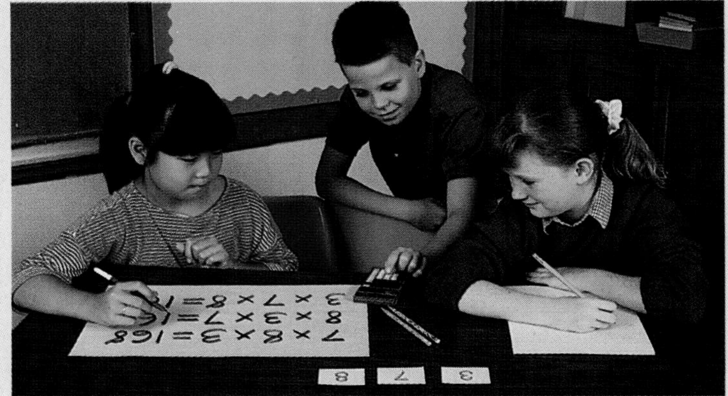

CONNECTIONS Use these anytime.

Problem of the Day

Algebra Suppose each alphabet letter has a number value such as this: A = 1, B = 2, C = 3, D = 4, and so on. Find the sum of the letters in the word *CALCULATOR*. (106)

Math Connection

Calculator There are no parentheses in this equation: 4 × 3 + 3 × 4 = □. Keep the numbers and operations in the order they are but add parentheses to group the numbers three different ways to get results of 24, 60, and 96. [(4 × 3) + (3 × 4) = 24; (4 × 3) + 3 × 4 = 60; 4 × (3 + 3) × 4 = 96]

Subject Integration

Music A metronome is a click machine. It helps musicians keep a steady beat as they practice. Mark sets his metronome to make 4 clicks for every measure. He is practicing a section of 8 measures. If he plays the selection 5 times, how many times will the metronome click? (160)

Problem Solving: Using a Calculator

to solve addition problems using a calculator

CLASSWORK AND HOMEWORK SUPPLEMENTS

Practice

Critical Thinking 6-9

Name ______________________

Mental Math: Multiplying 3 Factors

Decide whether to use mental math, pencil and paper, or a calculator. Write **m**, **p**, or **c** on the line. Then find the products.
Answers will vary. Sample answers given.

1. (2 × 5) × 4 = m; 40
2. 6 × (2 × 3) = m; 36
3. (8 × 7) × 6 = p; 336
4. 10 × (2 × 2) = m; 40
5. 9 × 8 × 54 = c; 3,888
6. 2 × 68 × 5 = m; 680
7. 3 × 6 × 4 = p; 72
8. 6 × 92 × 7 = c; 3,864
9. 4 × 2 × 10 = m; 80
10. 4 × 47 × 8 = c; 1,504
11. 4 × 25 × 9 = m; 900
12. 7 × 3 × 4 = p; 84
13. 6 × 3 × 5 = m; 90
14. 5 × 2 × 49 = m; 490
15. 7 × 45 × 8 = c; 2,520
16. 3 × 4 × 5 = m; 60
17. 2 × 4 × 5 = m; 40
18. 2 × 9 × 4 = m; 72
19. 7 × 3 × 8 = p; 168
20. 25 × 6 × 7 = c; 1,050
21. 9 × 5 × 52 = c; 2,340
22. 4 × 3 × 2 = m; 24
23. 3 × 5 × 5 = m; 75
24. 10 × 7 × 4 = m; 280
25. 4 × 2 × 100 = m; 800
26. 6 × 6 × 7 = p; 252

Write a sentence justifying one of your choices.

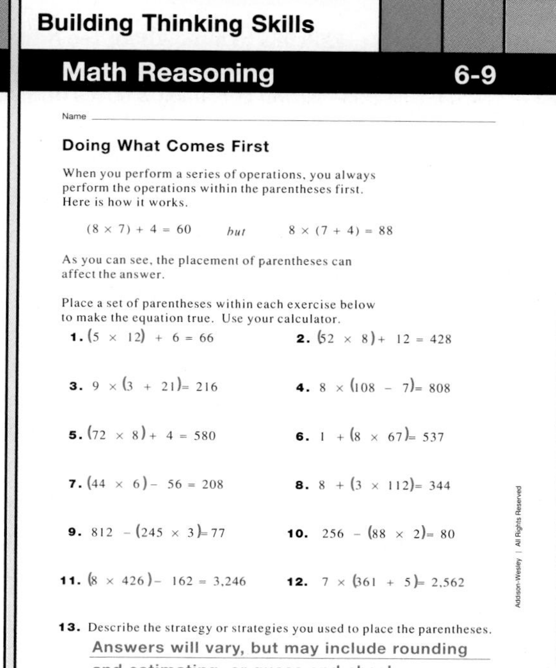

Building Thinking Skills

Math Reasoning 6-9

Name ______________________

Doing What Comes First

When you perform a series of operations, you always perform the operations within the parentheses first. Here is how it works.

(8 × 7) + 4 = 60 *but* 8 × (7 + 4) = 88

As you can see, the placement of parentheses can affect the answer.

Place a set of parentheses within each exercise below to make the equation true. Use your calculator.

1. (5 × 12) + 6 = 66
2. (52 × 8) + 12 = 428
3. 9 × (3 + 21) = 216
4. 8 × (108 − 7) = 808
5. (72 × 8) + 4 = 580
6. 1 + (8 × 67) = 537
7. (44 × 6) − 56 = 208
8. 8 + (3 × 112) = 344
9. 812 − (245 × 3) = 77
10. 256 − (88 × 2) = 80
11. (8 × 426) − 162 = 3,246
12. 7 × (361 + 5) = 2,562
13. Describe the strategy or strategies you used to place the parentheses.
Answers will vary, but may include rounding and estimating, or guess and check.

Reteaching

Mental Math 6-9

Name ______________________

Multiplying 3 Factors

Grouping Property for Multiplication
Changing the grouping of factors does not change the product.

Multiplying factors with parentheses → Multiply what is in parentheses first.

(5 × 2) × 3 = 10 × 3 = 30
5 × (2 × 3) = 5 × 6 = 30

Multiplying factors without parentheses → Pick any 2 factors to multiply first.

5 × 2 × 3 = **15** × 2 = 30 · 5 × **2 × 3** = **10** × 3 = 30 · **5** × 2 × **3** = 5 × **6** = 30

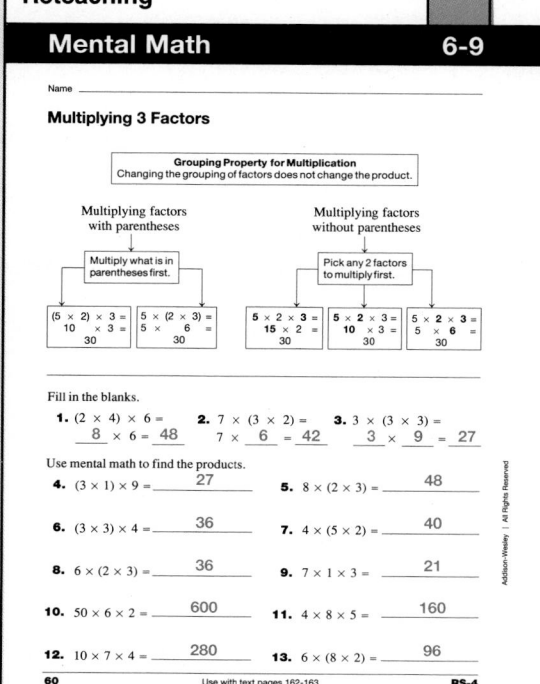

Fill in the blanks.

1. (2 × 4) × 6 = 8 × 6 = 48
2. 7 × (3 × 2) = 7 × 6 = 42
3. 3 × (3 × 3) = 3 × 9 = 27

Use mental math to find the products.

4. (3 × 1) × 9 = 27
5. 8 × (2 × 3) = 48
6. (3 × 3) × 4 = 36
7. 4 × (5 × 2) = 40
8. 6 × (2 × 3) = 36
9. 7 × 1 × 3 = 21
10. 50 × 6 × 2 = 600
11. 4 × 8 × 5 = 160
12. 10 × 7 × 4 = 280
13. 6 × (8 × 2) = 96

Challenges

Math Reasoning 6-9

Name ______________________

Number Scramble

Use three of the wacky number cards below to complete each equation. Perform operations from left to right.

Cards: 4 5 6 8

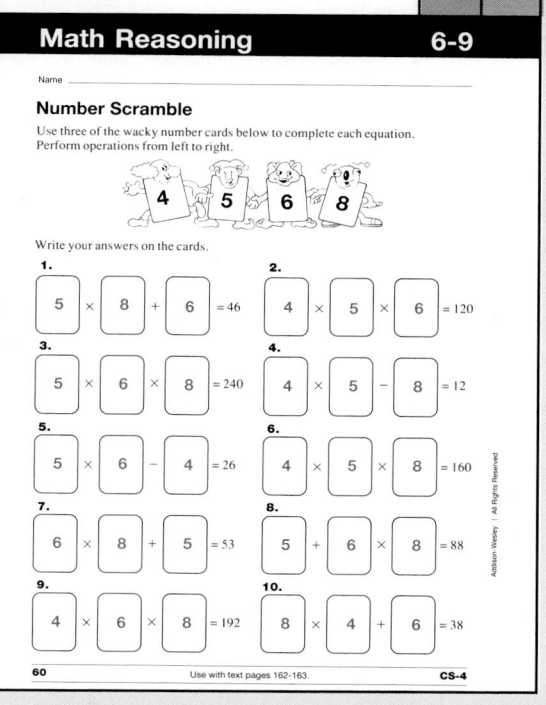

Write your answers on the cards.

1. 5 × 8 + 6 = 46
2. 4 × 5 × 6 = 120
3. 5 × 6 × 8 = 240
4. 4 × 5 − 8 = 12
5. 5 × 6 − 4 = 26
6. 4 × 5 × 8 = 160
7. 6 × 8 + 5 = 53
8. 5 + 6 × 8 = 88
9. 4 × 6 × 8 = 192
10. 8 × 4 + 6 = 38

OPTIONS FOR INDIVIDUAL NEEDS

Basic

Exercises 1-8; 1-3
Calculator Bank, p. 488
More Practice, p. 504, sets E and F

Supplements
Reteaching 60 or
Practice 60
Thinking Skills 60

Average

Exercises 1-8; 1-3
Calculator Bank, p. 488
More Practice, p. 504, sets E and F

Supplements
Practice 60
Challenges 60 or
Thinking Skills 60

Extended

Exercises 1-8; 1-3
Calculator Bank, p. 488

Supplements
Challenges 60
Thinking Skills 60

Other Resources:
Challenge, Vol II, Activity 24

LESSON PLAN 6-9

OBJECTIVE 6-9
To use mental math and the multiplication grouping property to find the product of 3 factors

1. MOTIVATE AND TEACH

LEARN ABOUT IT

EXPLORE
► **Compare the number of candles per box to the number per carton.** (3 candles per box, 6 per carton)

TALK ABOUT IT
► **If you can group factors in any order, how do you decide which ones to multiply first?** (Look for easy facts or for compatible numbers first.)
Student Edition answers: **1.** 2 × 3; multiply 6 × 4 for a total of 24. **2.** no

2. CHECK UNDERSTANDING

ERROR ALERT Multiplying two factors but adding the third.

3. PRACTICE AND APPLY

Basic	1-8
Average	1-8
Extended	1-8

PRACTICE

Look at Exercises 1-4. How are they different from Exercises 5-8? (The parentheses in Exercises 1-4 indicate that certain factors must be multiplied first. No parentheses in Exercises 5-8 means any factors can be multiplied first.) *In Exercise 5, which factors would you multiply first? Why?*
(Possible answer: 5 × 2, because multiplying by 10 helps you do the problem mentally.)

Mental Math
Multiplying 3 Factors

LEARN ABOUT IT

1 carton of
2 boxes

EXPLORE **Think About the Situation**
Liz and John sold 4 cartons of holiday candles. Each carton contained 2 boxes of 3 candles each. One box had red candles and the other had green. How many candles did Liz and John sell?

TALK ABOUT IT See teaching notes.

1. What numbers do you multiply first to find out how many candles were in each carton? What second step do you need to take?
2. If you find the total number of red candles first and then multiply by 2, will the answer change?

Grouping Property for Multiplication
Changing the grouping of factors does not change the product.

The parentheses tell which digits to multiply first. When no parentheses are shown, you can pick any 2 factors to multiply first.

1. **Multiply these.**
(3 × 2) × 4
6 × 4 = 24

2. **Multiply these.**
3 × (2 × 4)
3 × 8 = 24

3. **Pick any two. Try these.**
3 × 2 × 4
12 × 2 = 24

TRY IT OUT

Decide whether to use mental math, pencil and paper, or a calculator. Then find the products.

1. (3 × 2) × 5 mental math; 30
2. 3 × (5 × 4) mental math; 60
3. (2 × 5) × 8 mental math; 80
4. 4 × (9 × 7) pencil and paper; 25
5. 2 × 94 × 5 mental math; 940
6. 48 × 25 × 4 mental math; 4,800
7. 50 × 78 × 2 mental math; 7,800
8. 8 × 67 × 9 calculator; 4,824

162

More Practice, page 504, set E

TEACHING OPTIONS

RETEACHING TIPS Have students verbalize each number as they enter it in the calculator, then check the display *before* pressing the next operation or equal symbol. Assign Reteaching Supplement 60.

ENRICHMENT In this magic square, all rows, columns, and diagonals have a magic *product*. Have students use a calculator to find the magic product and the 3 missing factors. (3,780; 10, 2, 14)

6	15	3	14
21	2	(10)	9
10	9	21	(2)
3	(14)	6	15

Problem Solving Using a Calculator

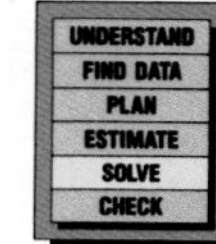

LEARN ABOUT IT

This square with numbers is a magic square because the sum of the numbers in each row, column, and diagonal is the same. The sum is called the magic number. In this square the magic number is 15. You can use a calculator to solve magic square problems.

Magic Square

8	1	6	= 15 row
3	5	7	= 15
4	9	2	= 15
= 15	= 15	= 15	

15 diagonal (both diagonals = 15); 15 15 15 column

Find the missing number to make this a magic square.

297	45	225
117	189	261
153	333	?

Here's how. Use your calculator to add any row or column to find the magic number. Then look at a row or column with the missing number. With the magic number still on your calculator, use these key strokes.

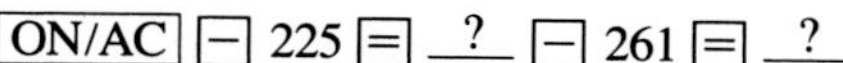

This missing number is 81.
Check by adding all 3 numbers.

TRY IT OUT

1. What missing numbers will make this a magic square?
2. Multiply each number in the square by 99. Is this still a magic square? yes
3. Add 99 to each number in the square. Is this still a magic square? yes

		36		
	414	?	360	
216	?	270	?	324
	180	?	126	
		504		

More Practice, page 504, set F

OBJECTIVE 6-9 To solve addition problems using a calculator

Materials: calculators

1. Motivate and Teach

LEARN ABOUT IT

▶ **How could you verify your answer?** (Compare the sum to the sum of other rows, columns, or diagonals because all should be the same.)

2. Check Understanding

ERROR ALERT Entering numbers incorrectly on the calculator.

3. Practice and Apply

Basic	1-3
Average	1-3
Extended	1-3

PRACTICE

In Exercise 1, what do you need to do first before you can find each missing number? (First add one row of diagonal numbers to find the magic sum of the magic square.)

6-9

Close and Assess

SHOW WHAT YOU KNOW

Have students use a calculator to show that 4 × 6 × 8 gives the same product regardless of grouping. (192) Then have them finish the row from a magic square whose magic sum is 525. (210)

280	35	(210)

Quick Quiz

1. Find the product of 5 × 6 × 7. (210)
2. Finish the addition in the magic square.

art spec
4-6-9-4-3

LESSON OPTIONS 6-10

Multiplying Larger Numbers: All Trades

OBJECTIVE 6-10 To multiply a 4-digit by a 1-digit number

PREBOOK ACTIVITIES

QUICK REVIEW

Find the products.

1.	43 × 2 (86)	**2.**	16 × 4 (64)
3.	27 × 8 (216)	**4.**	523 × 4 (2,092)
5.	926 × 6 (5,556)	**6.**	407 × 9 (3,663)
7.	237 × 5 (1,185)	**8.**	391 × 2 (782)
9.	300 × 7 (2,100)	**10.**	844 × 1 (844)

PRIOR KNOWLEDGE

Have students suggest real-life situations in which people might multiply large numbers. (Possible answers: to find the distance of a round trip; to compare the size of something many times greater than another) Have students explain how all multiplication relies on basic number facts. (Possible answer: Multiplication problems use the same 1-digit facts; you need addition facts when you need to make trades.)

COMMUNICATION

Writing and Discussing Math Write this sentence on the chalkboard: The new tunnel is 4 times longer than the old tunnel. In their Math Journals, have students write down questions they might ask based on this statement. Then have them make up reasonable data to create true problems to solve. (Sample problem: If the old tunnel is 1,234 ft long, how long is the new tunnel?) Discuss how to estimate, then how to solve the problems in terms of operations and calculations.

EXPLORE AND CONNECT

Materials: TA 3 (Number Cards 0-9)
Grouping Suggestion: cooperative learning groups of 5
Students explore break-apart multiplying with special products and column addition. Each group picks 5 number cards to form 4-digit by 1-digit factors. Four students each pick a place (ones, tens, hundreds, or thousands), then multiply the 1-digit factor by the digit in that place. The fifth member records those products for column addition. For example, for 4,321 × 6, students add 6 + 120 + 1,800 + 24,000 = 25,926. Members verify each other's products and check the addition. They rotate tasks until each group has done 5 problems. Conclude by asking groups to multiply the same factors using the regular process. Compare the break-apart method with regular multiplication in terms of order of operations. (In either method, you multiply, then add.) Ask students which method they prefer and to explain why. (Answers will vary.)

CONNECTIONS Use these anytime.

Problem of the Day

Number Sense Fill each box with a different digit so the multiplication works.

```
  □ □ □ 8
×       □
  5, 4 3 2
```

(1,358 × 4)

Life Skills

Round Trips An airline pilot flies the Boston-to-Miami route on weekends. The trip is 1,520 mi each way. If she makes 4 round trips on a weekend, how many miles does she fly? (12,160 mi)

Subject Integration

Nutrition A 22-lb baby needs about 1,050 calories a day to stay healthy. Her 220-lb father is an athlete who needs about 4 times as many calories to stay healthy. How many calories does the father need? (about 4,200)

Classwork and Homework Supplements

Practice

Calculators 6-10

Name ____

Multiplying Larger Numbers: All Trades

Find the products using a pencil. Time yourself.
Then use a calculator to do the same exercises.
Compare the time and accuracy of each method.

1. 1,413 × 4 = 5,652
2. 7,738 × 2 = 15,476
3. 6,184 × 5 = 30,920
4. 2,809 × 7 = 19,663
5. 2,023 × 6 = 12,138
6. 5,670 × 3 = 17,010
7. 2,994 × 8 = 23,952
8. 6,092 × 3 = 18,276
9. 1,232 × 4 = 4,928
10. 5,033 × 9 = 45,297
11. 2,943 × 5 = 14,715
12. 3,438 × 3 = 10,314
13. 2,886 × 8 = 23,088
14. 4,433 × 6 = 26,598
15. 1,709 × 4 = 6,836
16. 6,330 × 2 = 12,660
17. 5 × 4,606: 4,606 x 5 = 23,030
18. 4 × 2,101: 2,101 x 4 = 8,404
19. 7 × 5,123: 5,123 x 7 = 35,861
20. 3 × 6,893: 6,893 x 3 = 20,679
21. 6 × 4,105: 4,105 x 6 = 24,630
22. 8 × 7,314: 7,314 x 8 = 58,512

Time for paper and pencil ____

Time for calculator ____

Building Thinking Skills

Reading Math 6-10

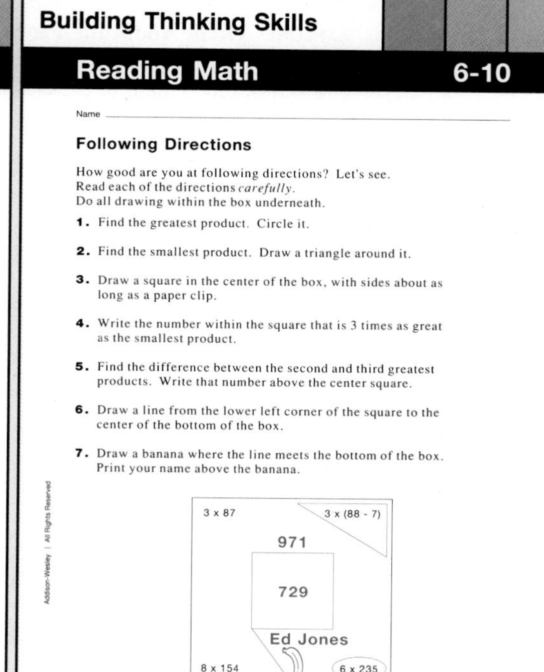

Name ____

Following Directions

How good are you at following directions? Let's see.
Read each of the directions *carefully*.
Do all drawing within the box underneath.

1. Find the greatest product. Circle it.
2. Find the smallest product. Draw a triangle around it.
3. Draw a square in the center of the box, with sides about as long as a paper clip.
4. Write the number within the square that is 3 times as great as the smallest product.
5. Find the difference between the second and third greatest products. Write that number above the center square.
6. Draw a line from the lower left corner of the square to the center of the bottom of the box.
7. Draw a banana where the line meets the bottom of the box. Print your name above the banana.

Reteaching

Skills Review 6-10

Name ____

Multiplying Larger Numbers: All Trades

Multiply the ones. Trade if necessary. → Multiply the tens. Add any extra tens. Trade if necessary. → Multiply the hundreds. Add any extra hundreds. Trade if necessary. → Multiply the thousands. Add any extra thousands. Trade if necessary.

Think: 4 × 3 = 12 — 1,034 × 3 = 2
Think: 3 × 3 = 9, 9 + 1 = 10 — 1,034 × 3 = 02
Think: 0 × 3 = 0, 0 + 1 = 1 — 1,034 × 3 = 102
Think: 3 × 1 = 3 No trade necessary. — 1,034 × 3 = 3,102

Find the products.

1. 4,328 × 4 = 17,312
2. 3,515 × 2 = 7,030
3. 2,034 × 6 = 12,204
4. 2,032 × 7 = 14,224
5. 4,824 × 5 = 24,120
6. 7,412 × 3 = 22,236
7. 8,120 × 8 = 64,960
8. 6,008 × 9 = 54,072
9. 4,022 × 6 = 24,132
10. 2,001 × 9 = 18,009
11. 8,024 × 3 = 24,072
12. 3,505 × 5 = 17,525
13. 4 × 5,602 = 22,408
14. 1,803 × 5 = 9,015
15. 1,530 × 3 = 4,590
16. 6,843 × 7 = 47,901
17. 7 × 1,001 = 7,007
18. 8 × 2,012 = 16,096

Challenges

Patterns 6-10

Name ____

Surprise!

Predict and check: How long will each pattern continue?

Find these products.

1. 142,857 × 1 = 142,857
2. 142,857 × 2 = 285,714
3. 142,857 × 3 = 428,571
4. 142,857 × 4 = 571,428
5. 142,857 × 5 = 714,285
6. 142,857 × 6 = 857,142
7. Analyze the products. What did you discover?
   The same digits rotate in the answer.

Now find these products.

8. 37 × 3 = 111
9. 37,037 × 3 = 111,111
10. 37,037,037 × 3 = 111,111,111
11. What did you discover about these products?
    All digits in the answer are 1's.
12. What is the next problem in the pattern?
    37,037,037,037 x 3 = 111,111,111,111

Options for Individual Needs

Basic

Exercises 6-25
More Practice, p. 505, set A

Supplements
Reteaching 61 or
Practice 61
Thinking Skills 61

Average

Exercises 1-25
More Practice, p. 505, set A

Supplements
Practice 61
Challenges 61 or
Thinking Skills 61

Extended

Exercises 9-25

Supplements
Challenges 61
Thinking Skills 61

Other Resources:
Mathematics . . . A Way of Thinking, Chapter 9

6-10

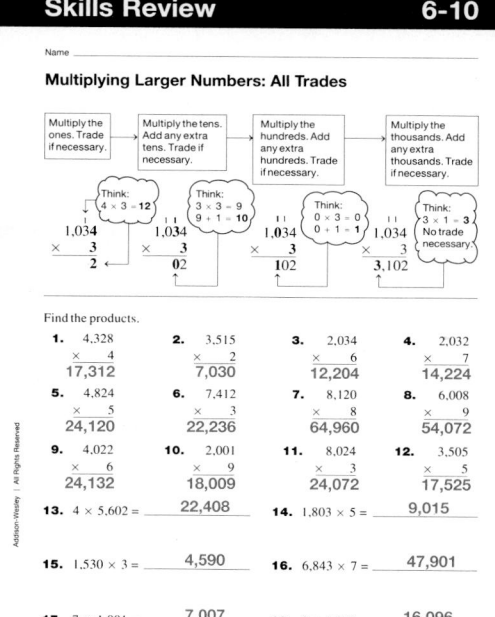

LESSON PLAN 6-10

OBJECTIVE 6-10
To multiply a 4-digit by a 1-digit number

Materials: TA 12 (Centimeter Graph Paper)

Grouping Suggestion: cooperative learning pairs

1. MOTIVATE AND TEACH

LEARN ABOUT IT

EXPLORE ▶ **Explain what the chart shows.** (lengths of 3 of the world's longest suspension bridges)

TALK ABOUT IT ▶ **Justify why you multiply to solve the problem.** (You multiply to combine same-size lengths.)
▶ **Why does the product have no ones?** (The zero property says that 5 × 0 = 0.)
▶ **What do Examples B and C have in common?** (zeros in the factors)
▶ **How does the order-of-operations rule help you find products when the zero rule is applied?** (Multiply to get zero, *then* add traded amounts.)
Student Edition answers: **1.** Estimates vary. **2.** Possible answer: The Chesapeake Bay Bridge is 6,400 m long.

2. CHECK UNDERSTANDING

TRY IT OUT

ERROR ALERT Recording trades in the wrong column. Making number-fact errors.

Multiplying Larger Numbers
All Trades

LEARN ABOUT IT

EXPLORE Think About the Process
The length of the Chesapeake Bay Bridge is 5 times the length of the Golden Gate Bridge. How long is the Chesapeake Bay Bridge?

You multiply because you need a total for equal lengths.

Lengths of World's Longest Suspension Bridges

Place	meters
Akashi-Kaykyo, Japan	1,780
Humber, England	1,410
Golden Gate, California	1,280

Multiply the ones. Trade if necessary.	Multiply the tens. Add any extra tens. Trade if necessary.	Multiply the hundreds. Add any extra hundreds. Trade if necessary.	Multiply the thousands. Add any extra thousands.
1,280 × 5 = 0	(4) 1,280 × 5 = 00	(1 4) 1,280 × 5 = 400	(1 4) 1,280 × 5 = 6,400

TALK ABOUT IT See teaching notes.

1. How would you estimate the product?
2. Give the answer in a complete sentence.

Other Examples

A (1 13) 3,428 × 4 = 13,712

B (3 3) 2,505 × 6 = 15,030

C (4 8) 1,049 × 9 = 9,441

TRY IT OUT

Find the product.

1. 3,154 × 3 = **9,462**
2. 1,578 × 4 = **6,312**
3. 3,879 × 6 = **23,274**
4. 9,221 × 7 = **64,547**

164

TEACHING OPTIONS

RETEACHING TIPS Have students write the exercises on centimeter graph paper, one digit per box. The isolated digits help students focus on one place at a time as they multiply and can help them record trades in the proper column. Assign Reteaching Supplement 61.

ENRICHMENT **Patterns** Have students note this pattern.

1,089 × 1	Product	1,089 × 9
1	1,089	9,801

(The products of 1,089 × 1 and 1,089 × 9 have the same digits in reverse order.) Have them continue with 2 and 8, 3 and 7, 4 and 6.

PRACTICE

Find the products.

1. 1,473 × 4 = 5,892
2. 6,201 × 6 = 37,206
3. 3,472 × 2 = 6,944
4. 8,307 × 7 = 58,149
5. 9,195 × 6 = 55,170
6. 3,276 × 5 = 16,380
7. 4,009 × 8 = 32,072
8. 6,428 × 3 = 19,284
9. 5,066 × 9 = 45,594
10. 7,183 × 8 = 57,464
11. 7,206 × 6 43,236
12. 2 × 7,956 15,912
13. 1,840 × 5 9,200
14. 9 × 9,074 81,666
15. Multiply 7 × 4,098. 28,686
16. Find the product of 9,537 and 9. 85,833

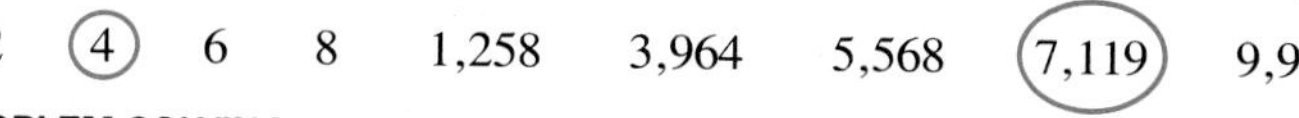

APPLY

MATH REASONING

17. Use estimation to pick the two numbers below with the product 28,476.

2 (4) 6 8 1,258 3,964 5,568 (7,119) 9,985

PROBLEM SOLVING

18. A mile is 5,280 feet. The Golden Gate Bridge is 4,199 feet long. How much more or less than a mile is the length of the Golden Gate Bridge? 1,081 feet less than a mile

19. A meter is a little more than 3 feet. Look at the table on page 164 and tell if the Akashi-Kaykyo Bridge in Japan is more or less than a mile long. more than a mile long

▶ MENTAL MATH

Choose a method or methods from this chart to answer these problems. Tell what method you used. See Additional Answers.

20. 2,010 × 3
21. 78 × 25 × 4
22. 2,198 + 3
23. 3,333 + 198
24. 2,100 × 4
25. 4,500 − 2

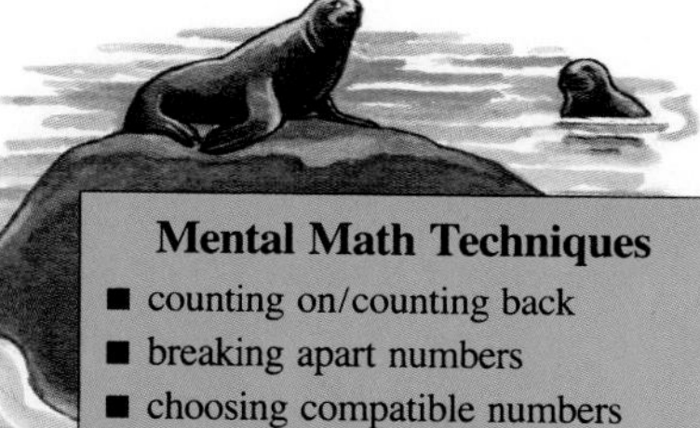

Mental Math Techniques

- counting on/counting back
- breaking apart numbers
- choosing compatible numbers
- using compensation

More Practice, page 505, set A

3. Practice and Apply

Basic	6-25
Average	1-25
Extended	9-25

Additional Answers: See p. T79.

PRACTICE

Look at Exercises 12, 14, and 15. How are they different from the others? (The smaller factor is given first.)

APPLY

MATH REASONING ▶ **How can you decide which numbers to pick?** (Possible answer: Round, then find special products.)
▶ **What number pairs are much too high or low?** (Answers may vary. Possible answers: low pairs: all 4-digit factors and 2; high pairs: 9,985 and 4, 6, or 8)

PROBLEM SOLVING ▶ **Decide how to solve Problem 18.** (The bridge is under a mile; subtract to find how much less.)

MENTAL MATH ▶ **Which exercise contains compatible numbers? Explain.** (Exercise 21; 25 × 4 = 100.)

Close and Assess

SAY WHAT YOU THINK Student pairs tell and write the steps to multiply 4,593 × 8 and 5,943 × 6. A writer records what a speaker says, then checks the product. If the product is wrong, the speaker tries to correct it. Partners trade roles to solve the other problem. (36,744; 35,658)

Quick Quiz

Find the product.
1. 2,963 × 7 (20,741)
2. 5,318 × 3 (15,954)
3. 4,607 × 2 (9,214)
4. Multiply 5,678 by 9. (51,102)

LESSON OPTIONS 6-11

Multiplying with Money

OBJECTIVE 6-11 To multiply an amount of money less than $100 by a 1-digit number

PREBOOK ACTIVITIES

QUICK REVIEW

Multiply.

1. 42 × 5 (210)
2. 516 × 3 (1,548)
3. 781 × 4 (3,124)
4. 436 × 9 (3,924)
5. 667 × 7 (4,669)
6. 907 × 6 (5,442)
7. 1,234 × 5 (6,170)
8. 7,334 × 8 (58,672)

PRIOR KNOWLEDGE

Ask students to recall times when they have needed to multiply money amounts. (Possible answer: to find the total cost of many items bought at the same price) Have students recall how to add and subtract money amounts and extend the generalization to include multiplication. (Possible answer: Use the usual rules to add and subtract number amounts, but show the answers with dollar and cent signs; so multiply as with any other number, but show the product in dollars and cents.)

COMMUNICATION

Discussing Math Write 456 and $4.56 on the chalkboard. Have students compare the money amount with the whole number. (Possible answer: $4.56 includes 4 whole dollars and 56 cents, or parts of a dollar, while 456 includes only whole units—hundreds, tens, and ones.) Have students find a case in which 456 coins and $4.56 are equal. (456 pennies is the same as $4.56, after making all possible trades.)

EXPLORE AND CONNECT

Materials: calculators, TA 3 (Number Cards 0-9)
Grouping Suggestion: cooperative learning pairs
Students compare multiplying money with and without decimal points. Partners choose any 4 number cards and arrange them like this: $____.________ × ____. Partners round the amount to the nearest dollar and estimate the product, recording the answer in a table. Then, using calculators, one partner multiplies the exact amount *without* using a decimal point while the other partner multiplies *with* a decimal point. They compare calculator displays to determine how to interpret the product as a money amount. They record the exact product, indicating dollars and cents, in the table. Partners repeat the activity several times, trading tasks. Conclude by having students generalize how to multiply with money. (Multiply as with whole numbers, show products with a dollar sign, decimal point, and two places to the right of the decimal point.)

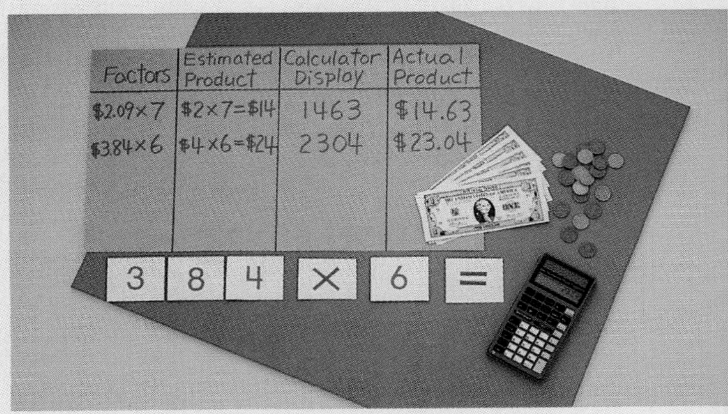

CONNECTIONS Use these anytime.

Problem of the Day

Creative Thinking Substitute a number from 1 to 5 for each shape to make the problem work.

$ △.0△
× ⬠
$ ⌷△.⌷△

($5.05 × 3 = $15.15)

Number Sense

Mental Math Each time Nick goes to the movies, he spends $2.75 for a ticket and $2.25 for a large tub of popcorn. If he goes to the movies 2 times a week for 4 wk, how much will it cost? ($40.00)

Life Skills

Book Club Penny buys science-fiction books from a mail-order book club. In October, she ordered 5 books at $2.00 each. Find the total cost of her order if she must pay $1.00 extra per book for sales tax and shipping costs. ($15.00)

Classwork and Homework Supplements

Practice

Life Skills 6-11

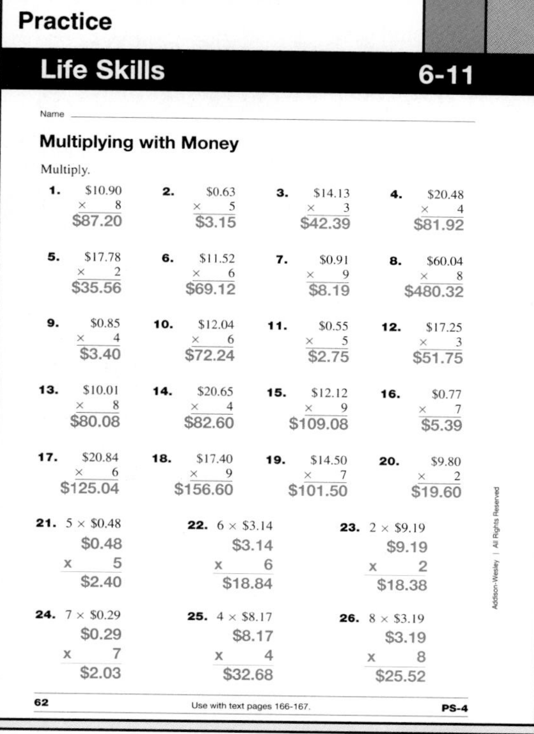

Name

Multiplying with Money

Multiply.

1. $10.90 × 8 = $87.20	**2.** $0.63 × 5 = $3.15	**3.** $14.13 × 3 = $42.39	**4.** $20.48 × 4 = $81.92
5. $17.78 × 2 = $35.56	**6.** $11.52 × 6 = $69.12	**7.** $0.91 × 9 = $8.19	**8.** $60.04 × 8 = $480.32
9. $0.85 × 4 = $3.40	**10.** $12.04 × 6 = $72.24	**11.** $0.55 × 5 = $2.75	**12.** $17.25 × 3 = $51.75
13. $10.01 × 8 = $80.08	**14.** $20.65 × 4 = $82.60	**15.** $12.12 × 9 = $109.08	**16.** $0.77 × 7 = $5.39
17. $20.84 × 6 = $125.04	**18.** $17.40 × 9 = $156.60	**19.** $14.50 × 7 = $101.50	**20.** $9.80 × 2 = $19.60

21. 5 × $0.48 — $0.48 × 5 = $2.40

22. 6 × $3.14 — $3.14 × 6 = $18.84

23. 2 × $9.19 — $9.19 × 2 = $18.38

24. 7 × $0.29 — $0.29 × 7 = $2.03

25. 4 × $8.17 — $8.17 × 4 = $32.68

26. 8 × $3.19 — $3.19 × 8 = $25.52

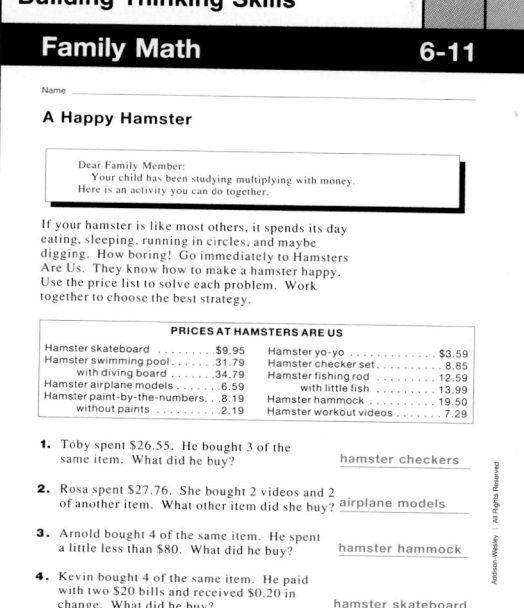

Building Thinking Skills

Family Math 6-11

Name

A Happy Hamster

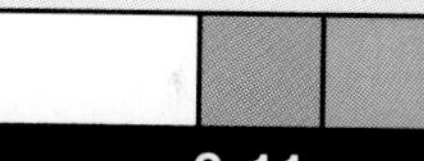

Dear Family Member:
Your child has been studying multiplying with money. Here is an activity you can do together.

If your hamster is like most others, it spends its day eating, sleeping, running in circles, and maybe digging. How boring! Go immediately to Hamsters Are Us. They know how to make a hamster happy. Use the price list to solve each problem. Work together to choose the best strategy.

PRICES AT HAMSTERS ARE US

Hamster skateboard	$9.95	Hamster yo-yo	$3.59
Hamster swimming pool	31.79	Hamster checker set	8.85
with diving board	34.79	Hamster fishing rod	12.59
Hamster airplane models	6.59	with little fish	13.99
Hamster paint-by-the-numbers	8.19	Hamster hammock	19.50
without paints	2.19	Hamster workout videos	7.29

1. Toby spent $26.55. He bought 3 of the same item. What did he buy? hamster checkers
2. Rosa spent $27.76. She bought 2 videos and 2 of another item. What other item did she buy? airplane models
3. Arnold bought 4 of the same item. He spent a little less than $80. What did he buy? hamster hammock
4. Kevin bought 4 of the same item. He paid with two $20 bills and received $0.20 in change. What did he buy? hamster skateboard
5. Toshiko bought 3 of one item and 2 of another. She spent about $80. What did she buy? Sample answer: 3 yo-yos; 2 pools with board

Reteaching

Skills Review 6-11

Name

Multiplying with Money

$2.96 × 7 = ?

Multiply as with whole numbers. → Write the product showing dollars and cents.

$2.96 × 7 — 296 × 7 = 2,072 — $2.96 × 7 = $20.72

Multiply. Write the products showing dollars and cents.

1. $5.23 × 3 = $15.69	**2.** $4.32 × 2 = $8.64	**3.** $0.84 × 5 = $4.20	**4.** $6.48 × 4 = $25.92	**5.** $2.83 × 6 = $16.98
6. $12.30 × 2 = $24.60	**7.** $14.71 × 5 = $73.55	**8.** $10.32 × 9 = $92.88	**9.** $0.78 × 7 = $5.46	**10.** $11.95 × 8 = $95.60

11. 4 × $3.26 = $13.04 **12.** 8 × $2.94 = $23.52

13. 9 × $5.06 = $45.54 **14.** 6 × $4.86 = $29.16

15. 5 × $1.75 = $8.75 **16.** 7 × $1.38 = $9.66

17. 8 × $1.78 = $14.24 **18.** 4 × $7.54 = $30.16

Challenges

Writing Math 6-11

Name

Loan Time

Radio/Tapedeck $52

Skateboard $48

Work by yourself or in a small group. Write a letter that will convince someone you know to give you a loan to buy one of these items.

Your letter should include:

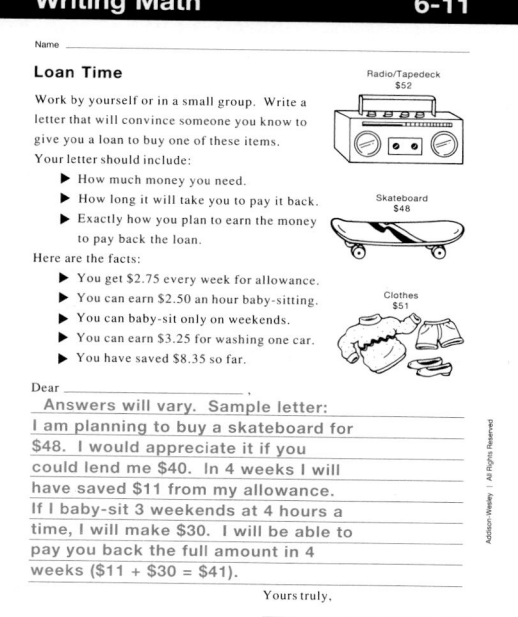

- How much money you need.
- How long it will take you to pay it back.
- Exactly how you plan to earn the money to pay back the loan.

Here are the facts:

- You get $2.75 every week for allowance.
- You can earn $2.50 an hour baby-sitting.
- You can baby-sit only on weekends.
- You can earn $3.25 for washing one car.
- You have saved $8.35 so far.

Dear ________,

Answers will vary. Sample letter: I am planning to buy a skateboard for $48. I would appreciate it if you could lend me $40. In 4 weeks I will have saved $11 from my allowance. If I baby-sit 3 weekends at 4 hours a time, I will make $30. I will be able to pay you back the full amount in 4 weeks ($11 + $30 = $41).

Yours truly,

Options for Individual Needs

Basic

Exercises 1-16
Calculator Bank, p. 487
More Practice, p. 505, set B

Supplements
Reteaching 62 or
Practice 62
Challenges 62

Average

Exercises 1-16
Calculator Bank, p. 487
More Practice, p. 505, set B

Supplements
Practice 62
Challenges 62 or
Thinking Skills 62

Extended

Exercises 1-16
Calculator Bank, p. 487

Supplements
Challenges 62
Thinking Skills 62

Other Resources:
Kids Are Consumers, Too!, Activity 6-1

LESSON PLAN 6-11

OBJECTIVE 6-11
To multiply an amount of money less than $100 by a 1-digit number

Materials: TA 12 (Centimeter Graph Paper), calculators

1. MOTIVATE AND TEACH

LEARN ABOUT IT

EXPLORE ► **If you bought one of each item, explain why multiplying would not help find the total cost.** (The items are all different prices. You multiply same-size groups but add groups of different sizes.)

TALK ABOUT IT ► **Decide how you would find the cost of 6 items priced the same. Explain your reasoning.** (Multiply 6 times the price because you are putting together same-size groups.)
► **Explain what you would enter in the calculator to find the cost of 6 perches.** (6 × 12.69 or 12.69 × 6)
► **Explain the relationship between $4.79 and 479 cents.** (They are equivalent ways to express the same amount of money.)
► **If the calculator display does not show a decimal point, explain how to decide where to place one.** (Show two places to the right of the decimal point for dimes and pennies.)
Student Edition answers: **1.** multiplied **2.** Each dollar is 100 cents, or 400 cents in all, plus 79 cents, is 479 cents. **3.** $8.56

2. CHECK UNDERSTANDING

TRY IT OUT

ERROR ALERT Misplacing the decimal point. Omitting the dollar sign or decimal point.

Multiplying with Money

LEARN ABOUT IT

EXPLORE Think About the Situation
A pet store owner checked to see what it would cost to stock items to sell to owners of parrots. Use a calculator and the information in the ad to find how much 6 of an item of your choice would cost. Do this for several items. Make a table to show the results.

TALK ABOUT IT See teaching notes.

1. What process did you use to find your answers?
2. If you changed the cost of a box of birdseed to all cents, how many cents would you have? Explain.
3. How would you write 856¢ using the $ symbol?

You can multiply money just like you multiply whole numbers. Here is an example.

How much would 6 boxes of birdseed at $4.79 each cost?

$4.79 × 6 $28.74	**Multiply as with whole numbers.** **Show dollars and cents.**

TRY IT OUT

1. $9.43 × 2 = $18.86
2. $13.59 × 5 = $67.95
3. $10.72 × 9 = $96.48
4. $0.87 × 4 = $3.48
5. $6.82 × 5 = $34.10
6. 9 × $2.98 $26.82
7. 8 × $1.25 $10.00
8. 7 × $6.08 $42.56
9. 4 × $5.16 $20.64
10. 6 × $3.05 $18.30
11. 2 × $4.36 $8.72
12. 5 × $1.32 $6.60
13. 3 × $8.54 $25.62

166

TEACHING OPTIONS

RETEACHING TIPS Students write the dollar sign, decimal point, and digit of each factor in its own graph-paper box. They put a decimal point below its place in the money factor. They multiply and then write a dollar sign in front of the product's greatest place. Assign Reteaching Supplement 62.

ENRICHMENT **Family Math** At home, students plan a meal at a restaurant. They pretend that they and 2 of their family members or friends order the same meal. They use an approximate price to find the total cost of the meal. A family member checks their work.

PRACTICE

Multiply to decode the message.

1. $4.19 × 7 R — $29.33
2. $6.05 × 8 U — $48.40
3. $3.18 × 6 Y — $19.08
4. $5.46 × 4 W — $21.84
5. $10.32 × 8 T — $82.56
6. $3.68 × 4 A — $14.72
7. $19.78 × 3 E — $59.34
8. $18.27 × 5 O — $91.35
9. $8.57 × 7 Z — $59.99
10. $38.79 × 2 H — $77.58
11. $60.94 × 6 M — $365.64
12. $14.56 × 3 I — $43.68

Message

Y	O	U	*	A	R	E	*	A
$19.08	$91.35	$48.40		$14.72	$29.33	$59.34		$14.72

M	A	T	H	*	W	H	I	Z
$365.64	$14.72	$8.60	$77.58		$21.84	$77.58	$43.68	$59.99

APPLY

MATH REASONING Estimate which product is greater. Use < or >.

13. $2.92 × 7 ▥ $1.99 × 8 >

14. $42.09 × 6 ▥ $59.67 × 5 <

PROBLEM SOLVING

15. Tammy bought 6 tropical fish that cost $4.65 each. The store reduced the total cost by $2. What did Tammy pay? $25.90

▶ **CALCULATOR**

Here are some items ordered by the manager of a pet store. Find the missing numbers.

Item	Aquarium	Book	Fish
Cost of Item	$54.98	$16.79	? ($5.75)
Number of Items	25	? (7)	12
Total Cost	? ($1,374.50)	$117.53	$69

More Practice, page 505, set B

3. Practice and Apply

Basic	1-16
Average	1-16
Extended	1-16

PRACTICE

Look at Exercises 1-12. Explain the steps to follow to complete the exercises and the message. (First multiply each exercise, then find the product in the message. Write the letter of the exercise above the matching product. Repeat for each exercise to spell the message.)

APPLY

MATH REASONING ▶ Explain the estimation method you would use to solve Exercises 13-14. (Possible answer: Round each money amount to the nearest dollar or ten dollars; multiply.)

PROBLEM SOLVING ▶ What operation would you use first? Explain. (Multiply 6 × $4.65, because you first need to know the cost of the fish before taking $2 off.)

CALCULATOR ▶ Explain the data organization. (Read down each column to find an item, its cost, how many items were ordered, and total cost.)

Close and Assess

WRITE WHAT YOU KNOW

State the following problem: *The coach bought 9 baseball bats that cost $6.23 each. What was the total bill?* Students write the calculator steps they would use to solve the problem. (Enter 9, enter ×, enter 6.23, press =.) Then students solve to get 56.07.

Quick Quiz

Multiply.

1. $7.29 × 4 ($29.16)
2. $0.89 × 6 ($5.34)
3. $25.44 × 3 ($76.32)
4. $80.13 × 5 ($400.65)

LESSON OPTIONS 6-12

Problem Solving: Look for a Pattern

OBJECTIVE 6-12 To solve problems using the strategy Look for a Pattern

PREBOOK ACTIVITIES

QUICK REVIEW

Give the next 7 multiples.

1. 4, 8, 12, . . . (16, 20, 24, 28, 32, 36, 40)
2. 6, 12, 18, . . . (24, 30, 36, 42, 48, 54, 60)
3. 7, 14, 21, . . . (28, 35, 42, 49, 56, 63, 70)
4. 8, 16, 24, . . . (32, 40, 48, 56, 64, 72, 80)
5. 9, 18, 27, . . . (36, 45, 54, 63, 72, 81, 90)

PRIOR KNOWLEDGE

Have students scan the room for things arranged in discernable patterns. (Possible answers: window panes, floor tiles, rows or groups of desks) Ask students to formulate a number relationship to describe any patterns they noticed, such as every 1 window has 4 panes. (Answers will vary.) Explain that some number patterns always repeat at a steady rate, such as 4 panes in every window. In other patterns, the important fact to recognize is *how* the numbers change so the pattern can be continued. Tell students that they can solve some pattern problems by combining the Make a Table strategy with a new strategy called Look for a Pattern.

COMMUNICATION

Discussing Math Write these numbers on the chalkboard, then challenge students to find each pattern and to continue it three more times: 1, 3, 5, 7, . . . ; 11, 22, 33, . . . ; 2, 5, 8, 11, . . . (9, 11, 13; 44, 55, 66; 14, 17, 20) Have students explain how they discovered the patterns. (Answers will vary.) Point out that number patterns can be written in table form to organize them more clearly, as in the rows of products on a multiplication table.

EXPLORE AND CONNECT

COOPERATIVE ACTIVITY

Grouping Suggestion: small groups

Cal made a cover for his science report with silver star stickers. He put 1 sticker in the first row, 3 in the second row, 5 in the third row, and so on. How many star stickers did Cal put in the sixth row?

TEACHING ACTIONS

Have students work in small groups to solve the problem together and check that they understand the situation and the strategy.

► **What information will you try to figure out?** (the number of star stickers Cal used in the sixth row)

► **What strategy might help you solve the problem?** (Find a Pattern)
► **Explain how a table can help organize the data.** (It will show how the numbers change with each row.)
► **Decide what categories your tables should have and give your reasoning.** (Categories should be Rows and Stickers in Each Row to help identify a relationship pattern.)
► **What pattern do you see? Explain how to use it to solve the problem.** (Every row has 2 more stickers; keep adding 2 stickers per row to see how many are in the sixth row.)

► **Justify your solution.** (The pattern of 2 or more per row stayed the same, so it makes sense that the sixth row has 11 stickers.)

CONNECTIONS Use these anytime.

Problem of the Day

Patterns Discover the pattern, then continue it twice: 1, 3, 9, 27, 81, ______, ______. (Numbers triple; 243, 729)

Math Connection

Calculator Jane is making a tile design with 10 rows. She used 56 tiles in the first row, 52 tiles in the second row, 48 tiles in the third row, and so on to the tenth row. Find the pattern, then use a calculator to figure out how many tiles Jane used in the entire design. (decrease each row by 4; 380)

Life Skills

Walk-A-Thon Ruth planned a walk-a-thon for charity. She told people to join as the walkers passed their street corner. 15 people started at the first corner. At the second corner, 30 people joined. At the third corner, 45 more joined, and so on. At this rate, how many walkers joined at the fifth corner? (75)

Classwork and Homework Supplements

Practice

Problem Solving 6-12

Name

Look for a Pattern

Make a table to help solve each problem.

1. Andy arranged the bookstore window. He put 1 book on the top shelf, 3 books on the second shelf, and 5 books on the third shelf. If he continues the pattern, how many books will he put on the fourth shelf? 7 books

shelf	1	2	3	4
books	1	3	5	7

2. Marta unpacked boxes at the bookstore. On the first day she unpacked 2 boxes, the second day 4 boxes, the third day 8 boxes, and the fourth day 16 boxes. If she continued in this pattern, how many boxes did she unpack on the fifth day? 32 boxes

day	1	2	3	4	5
boxes	2	4	8	16	32

3. Jaimie bought a goldfish for 50¢. The fish sell for 2 for $1.00, 3 for $1.50, and so on. At this rate, how much would Jaimie pay for 4 goldfish? $2.00

fish	1	2	3	4
price	50¢	$1	$1.50	$2

4. There are 4 kinds of notepads at the bookstore. Notepad 1 has 10 pages, notepad 2 has 30 pages, notepad 3 has 90 pages, and so on. How many pages would notepad 4 have? 270 pages

notepad	1	2	3	4
pages	10	30	90	270

5. Package 1 has 25 sheets of lined paper. Package 2 has 50 sheets, package 3 has 75 sheets, and so on. How many sheets of paper would be in package 5? 125 sheets

package	1	2	3	4	5
sheets	25	50	75	100	125

6. Notebook binder 1 sells for $1.00. Binder 2 sells for $2.50 and binder 3 sells for $4.00. What would binder 4 cost if this pattern continues? $5.50

binder	1	2	3	4
cost	$1	$2.50	$4	$5.50

PS-4 Use with text pages 168-169. 63

Building Thinking Skills

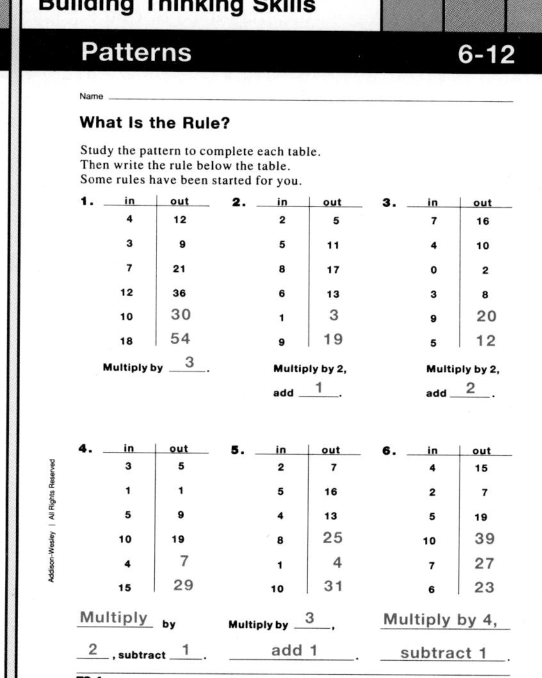

Patterns 6-12

Name

What Is the Rule?

Study the pattern to complete each table. Then write the rule below the table. Some rules have been started for you.

1.

in	out
4	12
3	9
7	21
12	36
10	30
18	54

Multiply by 3.

2.

in	out
2	5
5	11
8	17
6	13
1	3
9	19

Multiply by 2, add 1.

3.

in	out
7	16
4	10
0	2
3	8
9	20
5	12

Multiply by 2, add 2.

4.

in	out
3	5
1	1
5	9
10	19
4	7
15	29

Multiply by 2, subtract 1.

5.

in	out
2	7
5	16
4	13
8	25
1	4
10	31

Multiply by 3, add 1.

6.

in	out
4	15
2	7
5	19
10	39
7	27
6	23

Multiply by 4, subtract 1.

TS-4 Use with text pages 168-169. 63

Reteaching

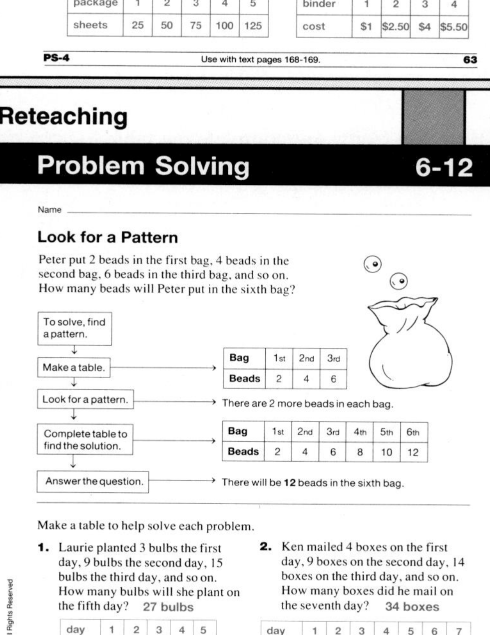

Problem Solving 6-12

Name

Look for a Pattern

Peter put 2 beads in the first bag, 4 beads in the second bag, 6 beads in the third bag, and so on. How many beads will Peter put in the sixth bag?

To solve, find a pattern.

Make a table.

Bag	1st	2nd	3rd
Beads	2	4	6

Look for a pattern. → There are 2 more beads in each bag.

Complete table to find the solution.

Bag	1st	2nd	3rd	4th	5th	6th
Beads	2	4	6	8	10	12

Answer the question. → There will be **12** beads in the sixth bag.

Make a table to help solve each problem.

1. Laurie planted 3 bulbs the first day, 9 bulbs the second day, 15 bulbs the third day, and so on. How many bulbs will she plant on the fifth day? 27 bulbs

day	1	2	3	4	5
bulbs	3	9	15	21	27

2. Ken mailed 4 boxes on the first day, 9 boxes on the second day, 14 boxes on the third day, and so on. How many boxes did he mail on the seventh day? 34 boxes

day	1	2	3	4	5	6	7
boxes	4	9	14	19	24	29	34

3. Jill's mom rode her bicycle 1 mile the first week, 3 miles the second week, 5 miles the third week, and so on. How many miles did she ride the sixth week? 11 miles

week	1	2	3	4	5	6
miles	1	3	5	7	9	11

4. Scott did 5 push-ups the first week, 8 push-ups the second week, 11 push-ups the third week, and so on. How many push-ups did he do the seventh week? 23 push-ups

week	1	2	3	4	5	6	7
push-ups	5	8	11	14	17	20	23

RS-4 Use with text pages 168-169. 63

Challenges

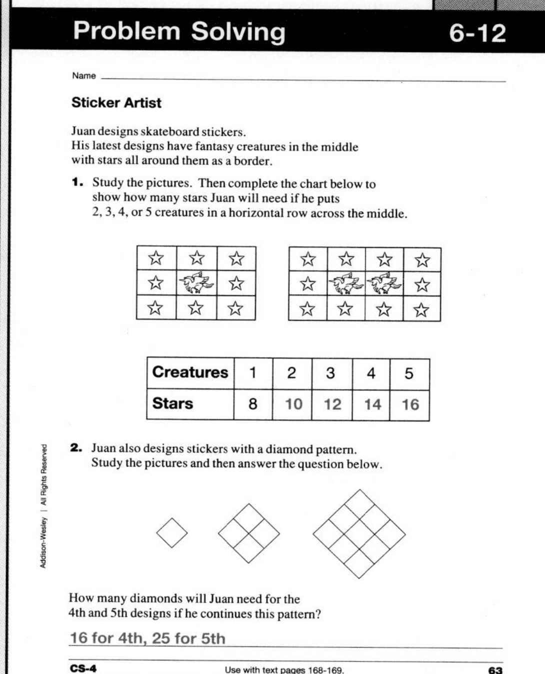

Problem Solving 6-12

Name

Sticker Artist

Juan designs skateboard stickers. His latest designs have fantasy creatures in the middle with stars all around them as a border.

1. Study the pictures. Then complete the chart below to show how many stars Juan will need if he puts 2, 3, 4, or 5 creatures in a horizontal row across the middle.

Creatures	1	2	3	4	5
Stars	8	10	12	14	16

2. Juan also designs stickers with a diamond pattern. Study the pictures and then answer the question below.

How many diamonds will Juan need for the 4th and 5th designs if he continues this pattern?

16 for 4th, 25 for 5th

CS-4 Use with text pages 168-169. 63

Options for Individual Needs

Basic

Exercises 1-8
Computer Bank, p. 495

Supplements
Reteaching 63 or
Practice 63
Thinking Skills 63

Average

Exercises 1-8
Computer Bank, p. 495

Supplements
Practice 63
Challenges 63 or
Thinking Skills 63

Extended

Exercises 1-8
Computer Bank, p. 495

Supplements
Challenges 63
Thinking Skills 63

Other Resources:
Make It Simpler, Problem 144

LESSON PLAN 6-12

OBJECTIVE 6-12
To solve problems using the strategy Look for a Pattern

1. MOTIVATE AND TEACH

LEARN ABOUT IT

► **What shape would the comic book display have? Explain.** (A triangle; because it starts with one book on top and each row spreads out with more books.)

► **Analyze what was the least number of rows Fred made.** (7)

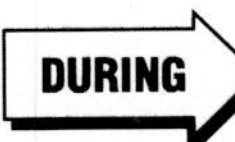

► **Why does the table need two rows of data?** (One names each display row, the other tells how many comics were put in each row.)

► **Decide how to identify a pattern.** (Possible answer: Try to find a rule to explain how the number of comics changes in each row.)

► **Explain the relationship between numbers of comics from row to row.** (Except for the first row, each row increased by 3.)

► **How can you verify the pattern?** (Answers may vary. Possible answers: Draw a Picture, Use Objects.)

2. CHECK UNDERSTANDING

TRY IT OUT

► **Explain how to use the table to find the answer.** (Identify the pattern for three months, then apply the pattern to the next three months.)

ERROR ALERT Failing to discover the number pattern.

Problem Solving
Look for a Pattern

LEARN ABOUT IT

You may need to find a pattern in the data to help you solve some problems. Making a table might help you discover the pattern. This problem solving strategy is called **Look for a Pattern.**

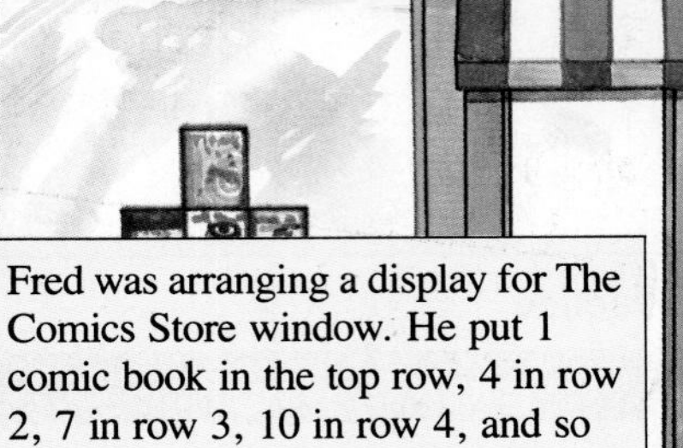

Fred was arranging a display for The Comics Store window. He put 1 comic book in the top row, 4 in row 2, 7 in row 3, 10 in row 4, and so on. How many did he put in row 7?

I'll make a table and look for a pattern.

row number	1	2	3	4
comics	1	4	7	10

I see the pattern. There are 3 more comic books in each row. I'll complete the table to row 7.

row number	1	2	3	4	5	6	7
comics	1	4	7	10	13	16	19

Fred put 19 comic books in row 7.

top row

row 2

row 3

TRY IT OUT

Read this problem and finish the solution.

Jessie is a cartoonist for the school newspaper. She drew 5 comic strips the first month, 10 the second month, 15 the third, and so on. How many did she draw the sixth month? **30 comic strips**

- How many comic strips did Jessie draw the first month? **5 comic strips**
- How many comic strips did she draw the second month? **10 comic strips**
- Copy and complete the table to solve the problem.

month	1	2	3	4	5	6
comic strips	5	10	15	**20**	**25**	**30**

168

TEACHING OPTIONS

RETEACHING TIPS Have students find the missing addend that links the first two numbers of comic strips. ($5 + n = 10$; $n = 5$) Then have students apply that missing addend to link the next two numbers. If it works, they have found the number pattern. Assign Reteaching Supplement 63.

COMPUTER **Right Turn, Sunburst Communications, Copyright 1985** For use with all levels of students. A 3-by-3 grid is used which has either colors or shapes in a pattern. Students predict how the pattern will change as it is rotated or flipped. The lesson takes 5 to 10 minutes to complete.

PRACTICE

Make a table to help solve each problem. **See Additional Answers.**

1. When The Comics Store first opened, Ben had to sort all the comics into bins. The first day he sorted 1 box, the second day 2, the third day 4, the fourth day 8, and so on. How many boxes did he sort the sixth day?

2. Comics sell for $1.50 in bin 1, $1.75 in bin 2, $2.00 in bin 3, and so on. How much would a comic book in bin 7 cost?

MIXED PRACTICE

Choose a strategy from the strategies list or use other strategies you know to solve these problems.

Some Strategies
Act It Out
Use Objects
Choose an Operation
Draw a Picture
Make an Organized List
Guess and Check
Make a Table
Look for a Pattern

3. Posters at The Comics Store cost $7.99 each. Buttons are $1.99 each. How much did Maria pay for 6 posters? **$47.94**

4. George displayed the most expensive comics on the wall behind the counter. He put 3 comics in the top row, 7 in row 2, 11 in row 3, 15 in row 4, and so on. How many comics did he put in row 9? **35 comics**

5. Joe writes a comic strip every day in the newspaper. Each strip has 4 frames in it. How many frames does he draw in a year? **1,460 frames**

6. The 4 most expensive comic books in the store cost $132.98, $115.98, $95.98, and $87.98. How much are they worth all together? **$432.92**

7. A box of 5 Rocket Ron comic books costs $6. How much would 30 Rocket Ron comic books cost? **$36**

8. Mark bought 3 comics at $1.59 each. He also bought an old comic book for $6.95. How much did he pay in all? **$11.72**

More Practice, page 516, set D

3. Practice and Apply

Basic	1-8
Average	1-8
Extended	1-8

Additional Answers and Sample Solutions: See p. T79.

PRACTICE

For each problem, determine the categories of data to be used in a table. (Problem 1: days, boxes of comics sorted; Problem 2: bins, comic price per bin)

MIXED PRACTICE

► **Identify a problem you could solve with the Look for a Pattern strategy. Explain your reasoning.** (4, because it gives data that can be used to make a table and to find a pattern to apply.)

► **Which problems require multiplication? Explain your reasoning.** (3, 5, 7, and 8, because each involves combining same-size groups)

► **Analyze Problem 5 to determine the data you need to solve it.** (You need to know the number of days per year to multiply by 4.)

Close and Assess

SHOW WHAT YOU KNOW

Have students make a table to solve the following problem: *You built a block tower with 8 rows. The top row had 4 blocks, the second row had 8 blocks, and the third row had 12 blocks. If you kept this pattern, how many blocks were on the bottom row?* (32)

QUICK QUIZ

McFast-Food is having a burger sale. During this time, 1 burger costs 25 cents, 2 burgers cost 45 cents, 3 burgers cost 65 cents, and so on. How much would 6 burgers cost? ($1.25)

CHAPTER 6

DATA COLLECTION AND ANALYSIS

GROUP DECISION MAKING

OBJECTIVE To collect, organize, and present data

COLLECTING DATA

► **Explain the importance of the questionnaire's title.** (Possible answer: It classifies the data to be collected.)

► **Justify providing answer choices on a questionnaire.** (Possible answer: It narrows the number of answers you can get for a question, which makes it easier to tally and to interpret the results.)

► **Explain why question 2 of the questionnaire uses "other" as a choice.** (Possible answer: There may be more choices than those given, but because it is not possible to include every choice, ''other'' covers anything not stated.)

► **Devise a plan to create questions.** (Plans may vary; one plan might be to list all reasonable questions, pick the 4 best, then create 3 to 4 choices for each question.)

► **Explain the value of testing your questionnaire on 2 or 3 people first.** (They can identify questions that are unclear or problems with the choices.)

► **Would your results be as reliable if you gave the questionnaire to just 5 people? Explain.** (No, you need more to see patterns in responses.)

Data Collection and Analysis

Group Decision Making

UNDERSTAND
FIND DATA
PLAN
ESTIMATE
SOLVE
CHECK

Doing a Questionnaire
Group Skill:
Check for Understanding

How do students your age like to study? Your group is in charge of making a **questionnaire** to gather information about study habits. A questionnaire is a written list of questions used to gather information.

Collecting Data

1. A **multiple choice question** is one type of question that can be used on a questionnaire. A multiple choice question usually gives 3 or 4 choices for answers. The sample questionnaire has 2 multiple choice questions. Why is it useful on question 2 to include "other" as one of the choices?

170

TEACHING OPTIONS

COOPERATIVE LEARNING

Grouping Suggestion: cooperative learning groups of 4 to 6

Discuss and list the tasks required to create and use a questionnaire: devise questions, formulate answer choices, test for problems, revise, make copies, tally results, and present the outcome. Cooperative learning groups may decide how to divide tasks, but every task should have at least 2 students who check each other's understanding of it. Students can prepare the final version of the questionnaire, making copies for at least 20 students.

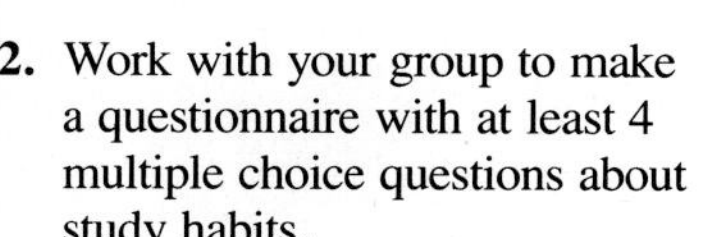

2. Work with your group to make a questionnaire with at least 4 multiple choice questions about study habits.
3. Test your questionnaire with 2 or 3 people. Revise the questions that are unclear.
4. Make at least 20 copies of your questionnaire. Give the questionnaire to 20 students.

Organizing Data

5. Make a table to show the results of each question on your questionnaire. Mark a tally for each response on your table. Count and record the total number of responses. This is an example.

1. Do you prefer to study with		Total
soft music	𝍸 𝍸	10
loud music	III	3
no music	𝍸 II	7

Presenting Your Analysis

6. Write an article for a school newspaper about what you found out from your questionnaire. Make up a headline for your article.

Circle one choice for each question.
1. Do you prefer to study with
a. soft music?
b. loud music?
c. no music?
2. Where do you like to study?
a. at a desk or table
b. on the floor
c. on the bed
d. other

ORGANIZING DATA

► **How can you use your own questionnaire to record results?** (Possible answer: Make tally marks by the answer choices.)

► **Explain how to determine what the response total should be.** (The response total should equal the number of questionnaires that were returned.)

► **How can you verify that you tallied all responses?** (Compare tally marks to the number of questionnaires you received back to make sure they are the same.)

PRESENTING YOUR ANALYSIS

► **Devise a way to write an article to summarize what you found.** (Plans may vary. Students might assign a paragraph to each group member, discuss ideas as a group secretary records them, or create a different plan of their own. Other summarizing tasks may include preparing a banner headline, organizing data in a table or graph, or creating a suitable illustration.)

► **What conclusions can be drawn from the results of the questionnaire?** (Answers may vary, but students should be able to cite patterns in study habits.)

► **What problems arose as your group tried to collect and evaluate the data? Explain what you could do to avoid these problems next time.** (Answers will vary.)

FOLLOW UP Have each group select its best question and combine it with the other group to create a class questionnaire. Make sure all questions cover a different aspect of study habits. Make enough copies to poll students in other classes or in other grades. Have students compile the new data, then compare and contrast them with the original data belonging to each group.

CHAPTER 6

WRAP UP

INTRODUCTION The Wrap Up provides activities emphasizing math language and thinking skills for the chapter and a project that integrates those skills with other math strands.

USING PAGE 172

Number Phrase Match Have students complete this section independently. When they finish, have pairs compare and discuss their choices.

Sometimes, Always, Never ► How can you use logical reasoning to evaluate the statements? (Possible answer: Look for true *and* false cases.)
► Must you consider all possible cases to decide? Explain. (No; statements that give a math rule must *always* be true; those that give the opposite of a math rule must *never* be true; statements are *sometimes* true if you can find at least one true and one false example.) Have students record an example to support each decision.

Project ► Students work in pairs to develop a strategy for completing the project.
► Explain how you would complete the project. (Possible answer: First determine your own weight in pounds and round it to the nearest ten. Then for each food, find the number that is in one pound. Multiply that number by your weight.)
Have a volunteer tell his or her rounded weight, then have the class work in groups to draw and cut out enough of each food to represent how much the volunteer would have to eat to equal his or her weight. Mount the food cut-outs on a chart or bulletin board with an appropriate title and labels.

WRAP UP

Number Phrase Match

Match each phrase with a number expression. Explain your choices.

1. six hundreds **e**
2. the product of six and twelve **a**
3. double six **h**
4. twelve groups of four each **b**
5. twelve times two **i**
6. six multiplied by four **c**
7. a pair of odd factors **d**
8. six dollars twelve cents **g**
9. two more than the product of nine and three **f**

a. 6×12
b. 12×4
c. 4×6
d. 9×3
e. 6×100
f. $(9 \times 3) + 2$
g. $6.12
h. 2×6
i. 12×2

Sometimes, Always, Never

Which word should go in the blank, <u>sometimes</u>, <u>always</u>, or <u>never</u>? Explain your choices.

10. The product of a number and 1 is __?__ that number. **always**
11. Factors __?__ may be multiplied in any order. **always**
12. Multiplying a number by a 2-digit or 3-digit factor __?__ requires trading. **sometimes**

Project

13. Has anyone ever told you that you eat like a bird? If you really ate like some songbirds, you would eat your weight in food every day. Find out how many of each of these foods you would have to eat if you had a songbird's appetite! To begin, you will need to know how much you weigh. **Answers will vary.**

Food	Number in one pound
hamburger	4
orange	3
egg	5
piece of bread	8

172

TEACHING OPTIONS

ENRICHMENT Challenge students to use the chart to figure out how much of each food is in the body weight of some really big eaters. Have pairs of students use encyclopedias to find the average weight of an elephant, blue whale, rhinoceros, hippopotamus, or other animals students select. Pairs may use a calculator, if needed, to multiply each animal's body weight by each of the four numbers on the chart. Then have each pair choose one food item and create a pictograph that compares the results for each animal. Ask students to explain their pictographs to the class.

CHAPTER REVIEW/TEST

Part 1 Understanding

Copy each equation and give the numbers for the □ and the △.

1. Since 6 × 4 = □, then 600 × 4 = △. 24 2,400

2. Since □ × 5 = 40, then △ × 5 = 400. 8 80

3. Which factors would you multiply first in 4 × 7 × 5? Why? Find the product. See Additional Answers.

Which method would you suggest using to solve each of these problems? Explain your reasoning. Answers may vary.

4. 400 × 7 a. calculator

5. 3,984 × 687 b. mental math

6. 216 × 6 c. paper and pencil

Part 2 Skills

Round, then estimate the product.

7. 7 × $5.22 $35 **8.** 6 × 88 540

Multiply and add. Use mental math.

9. (4 × 7) + 3 31 **10.** (3 × 6) + 5 23

Multiply.

11. 26 × 4 = 104 **12.** 373 × 3 = 1,119 **13.** 4,971 × 6 = 29,826 **14.** $20.77 × 3 = $62.31

Part 3 Applications

15. Roy delivers 77 papers a day. Estimate his weekly total by rounding. Is the weekly total more or less than 500? more

16. Sue is making a design. She puts 5 tiles in row 1, 11 tiles in row 2, 17 tiles in row 3, and 23 tiles in row 4. How many tiles will be in row 7? 41 tiles

CHAPTER REVIEW/TEST

INTRODUCTION The Review/Test is provided to review and evaluate the skills and concepts presented in Chapter 6.

USING PAGE 173
If you prefer to use this page for review, you may want to use the **Multiple-Choice Posttest** (pages 23-24) or the **Free-Response Posttest** (pages 23-24) to evaluate mastery of chapter objectives.

ITEM ANALYSIS The table below correlates the Chapter Review/Test items with the lesson objectives for the chapter.

Items	Objectives
1-2	6-1
3	6-9
4	6-1
6	6-6
7-8	6-2
9-10	6-3
11	6-5
12	6-6
13	6-7
14	6-11
15	6-2
16	6-12

Additional Answers: See p. T79.

INFORMAL ASSESSMENT

Using Manipulatives Using place value materials, have students create 3 multiplication problems for a partner that increase in difficulty. Have them use 2-, 3-, and 4-digit factors multiplied by 4, 5, or 6. Observe students' work and have them verbalize the steps they use. If errors occur, provide a similar example.

Communication *How is the order of operations rule for multiplication and addition like the procedure for multiplying larger numbers with trading?* (Possible answer: The rule says to multiply, then add. When you multiply after a trade, first multiply the two factors, then add the traded amount to the product.)

Critical Thinking *State a way to find the product of 53¢ × 3 in your head. Explain your method.* (Possible answer: Break apart 53 as 50 + 3, multiply each part by 3, which gives 150 + 9, 159¢, or $1.59.)

CHAPTER 6

ENRICHMENT

INTRODUCTION Recognizing what data you need to know and asking questions that may elicit the desired facts sharpen the ability to analyze given information.

USING PAGE 174

This Enrichment page is provided for all students. You may wish to use it after the students have completed the Chapter Review/Quiz on page 173.

Have volunteers read aloud the three facts at the top of the page. Before they continue through the page, have students comment on the facts.

► **Compare and contrast the facts.** (Answers may vary. Possible answers: The rocking chair and pogo stick records were set by individuals, while the sand castle record was set by a group of people; all records were set in 1986.)

► **How does asking questions relate to analyzing data?** (Possible answer: You must analyze the given data to determine what is known and what is not known, and that helps you decide what questions to ask.)

► **Justify asking questions that you cannot answer.** (Possible answer: You may not know how to answer them, but someone else may have a solution method or the necessary data.)

Students may work in pairs or small groups to complete the page. Conclude by having students share their questions and identify the kind of information needed to answer them.

EXTENSIONS Have students look through the *Guinness Book of World Records* for other unusual facts. Have them prepare a strange-facts poster, scrapbook, or mobile.

Additional Answers: See p. T79.

ENRICHMENT
What Else Do You Need to Know?

- In 1986, people in Florida built the world's tallest sand castle. It was 5 stories tall and weighed 48,400 tons.
- In 1986, a California man rocked in a rocking chair for 453 hours and 40 minutes.
- In 1986, a man in Japan set a distance record. He spent 8 hours 21 minutes climbing up and down the foothills of Mount Fuji on a pogo stick.

Rita found these facts in a book of world records. As she thought about each fact, she realized she wanted to know more. So Rita made up these questions about the sand castle.

1. How tall is a story?
2. Is the given weight exact or estimated?
3. How could someone weigh a sand castle?

Think about the three records. For each record write three questions to explore information that is missing. You do not have to answer the questions. See Additional Answers.

Then use a book of world records to find another interesting record. Write three questions you would like to ask the record holder. Answers will vary.

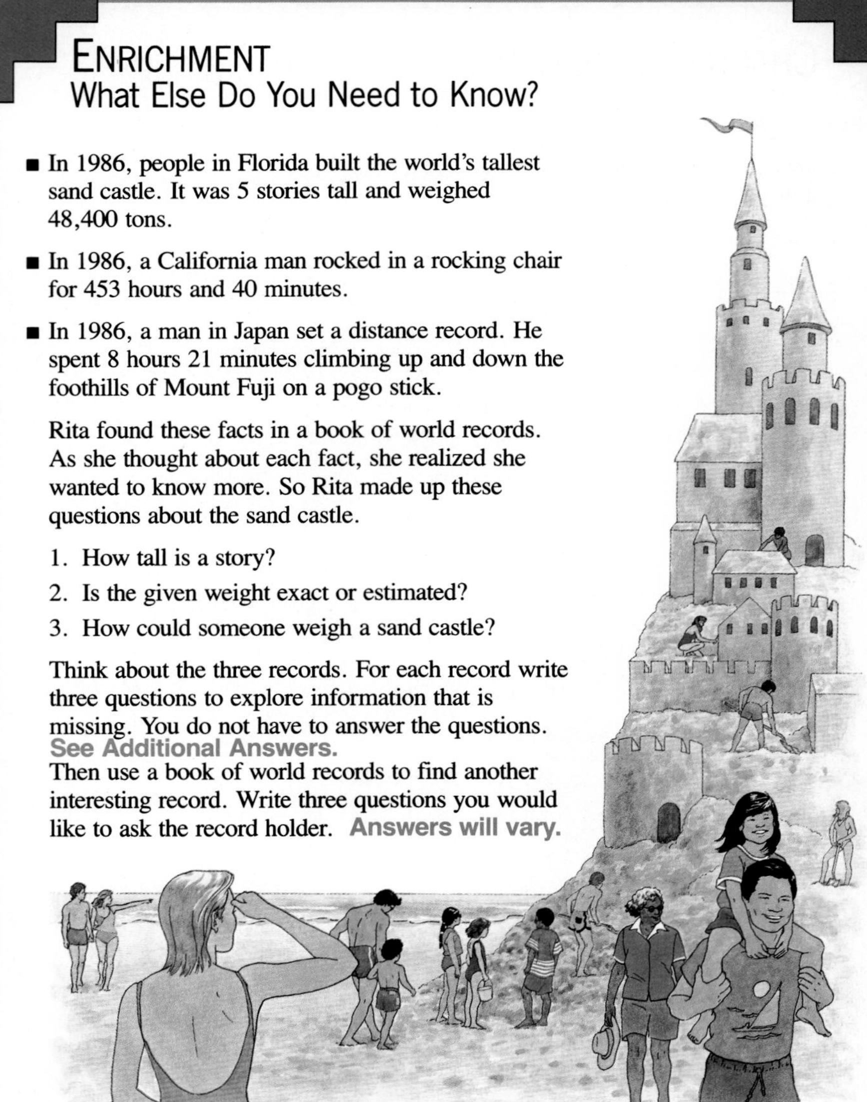

CUMULATIVE REVIEW

1. Lynette needs to trade 1 ten for 10 ones. Which number is she subtracting from 234?
   A 234 | B 181
   (C) 78 | D 34
2. Estimate the sum of 673 and 821.
   A 1,494 | (B) 1,500
   C 1,400 | D 1,600
3. To find the number of apples you need to give 2 each to 15 children, what kind of answer would be best?
   A estimate | B rounded
   C difference | (D) exact
4. Which equation fits the picture?
   A $2 + 7 = 9$ | B $7 \times 3 = 21$
   (C) $2 \times 7 = 14$ | D $14 - 7 = 7$

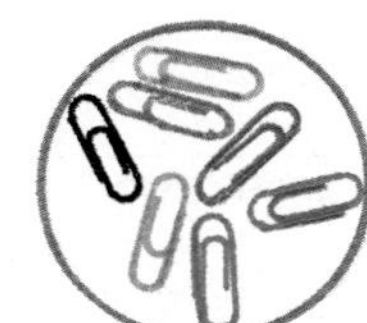

5. 9×4
   (A) 36 | B 45
   C 32 | D 40
6. 6×1
   (A) 6 | B 5
   C 7 | D 1

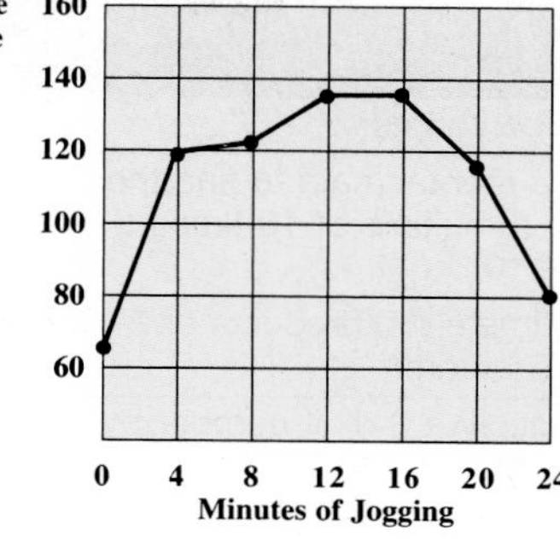

7. How is the data given in the graph?
   A bars | (B) lines
   C pictures | D words
8. Look at the graph and tell what Mary's pulse rate was after she ran 12 minutes.
   A 120 | B 130
   (C) 135 | D 140
9. During which part of her run did Mary's pulse rate change the least?
   A 0–4 min | B 4–8 min
   C 8–12 min | (D) 12–16 min
10. At what time do you think Mary began to slow down?
    (A) 16 min | B 24 min
    C 12 min | D 20 min

175

CUMULATIVE REVIEW

INTRODUCTION The purpose of this Cumulative Review is to maintain previously taught skills and concepts. The emphasis in this Cumulative Review is on addition and subtraction of whole numbers, Chapter 3; on data, graphs, and probability, Chapter 4; and on multiplication concepts and basic facts, Chapter 5.

ITEM ANALYSIS The table below correlates the Cumulative Review items with lesson objectives.

Items	Objectives
1	3-8
2	3-2
	3-7
3	3-14
4	5-1
5	5-4
	5-5
6	5-2
7-10	4-4

Chapter Management

OVERVIEW

Lesson	Pages	Objectives	Subject Integration	Strand Integration
Chapter Opener	176-177	To introduce chapter 7	health/fitness-exercise	critical thinking
Mental Math: Special Products	178-179	7-1 To use mental math to find the product of a multiple of 10 times a multiple of 10	science-hen's egg	critical thinking
Estimating Larger Products	180-181	7-2 To estimate the products of 2- and 3-digit factors	health/fitness-age	problem solving
Multiplying by Multiples of 10	182-183	7-3 To multiply a 2-digit number by a 2-digit multiple of 10	health/fitness-running	estimation
Multiplying with 2-Digit Factors	184-185	7-4 To multiply a 2-digit number by a 2-digit number	health/fitness-jumping rope	mathematical reasoning
Multiplying with 2- and 3-Digit Factors	186-187	7-5 To multiply a 3-digit number by a 2-digit number	health/fitness-jumping rope	calculators
Using Critical Thinking/ Midchapter Review/Quiz	188-189	7-6 To use critical thinking to find the number that multiplied by itself gives the square	science-animal heart rates	problem solving
Problem Solving: Use Logical Reasoning	190-191	7-7 To solve problems using the strategy Use Logical Reasoning	health/fitness-frozen yogurt	consumer math
Multiplying with Money	192-193	7-8 To multiply an amount of money less than $10	health/fitness-soccer	mental math
Problem Solving: Choosing a Calculation Method	194-195	7-9 To choose an appropriate method of calculation	language arts-writing	measurement
Problem Solving: Multiple-Step Problems	196-197	7-10 To solve multiple-step problems	language arts-book club	consumer math
Applied Problem Solving: Group Decision Making	198-199	7-11 To analyze, organize, and make decisions using relevant data	science-zoo	consumer math

MATHEMATICAL BACKGROUND

Mental Math
Lesson 7-1 teaches students to use mental math when finding the product of a multiple of 10 times a multiple of 10.

Multiplication
Students learn the steps to follow to multiply by a 2-digit number: multiply the ones first, making all necessary trades; multiply the tens next, making all necessary trades; add the two products.

Estimation
Students learn to estimate products of 2- and 3-digit numbers by rounding the factors before multiplying.

Problem Solving
Students learn to use the strategy Use Logical Reasoning.

TIPS FROM TEACHERS

Create a game board that looks like a miniature football field. Name the team at each end of the field. Write multiplication problems on the front of several cards. On the back of each, write the answer and a direction telling where to move to on the field. Students take turns answering cards until one player scores a touchdown.

Richard Wulf-McGrath
Side Creek Elementary School
Aurora, CO

ASSESSMENT

Pretest — Chapter 7, page 1

Multiple-Choice Format

Name ____________

1. Find 60 × 40. Use mental math.
   a. 2,400 b. 24 c. 240 d. 24,000 1. a

2. Estimate 31 × 49 by rounding each factor to the highest place.
   a. 120 b. 150 c. 1,200 d. 1,500 2. d

3. Estimate 27 × 381. Will the actual product be over or under 12,000?
   a. Over b. Under 3. b

4. Find 73 × 90.
   a. 657 b. 6,370 c. 6,570 d. 1,637 4. c

5. Find 29 × 80.
   a. 2,320 b. 1,620 c. 232 d. 162 5. a

6. Find 76 × 25.
   a. 1,800 b. 1,970 c. 1,900 d. 532 6. c

7. Find 45 × 26.
   a. 1,140 b. 1,040 c. 360 d. 1,170 7. d

8. Find 28 × 176.
   a. 1,760 b. 4,928 c. 5,088 d. 4,828 8. b

MCT 4 25

Pretest — Chapter 7, page 2

Multiple-Choice Format

Name ____________

9. Find 32 × 415.
   a. 13,280 b. 12,170 c. 2,075 d. 2,055 9. a

10. 4,096 is the product of a number multiplied by itself. Decide what multiples of 10 it is between.
    a. Between 30 and 40 b. Between 80 and 90
    c. Between 70 and 80 d. Between 60 and 70 10. d

11. All of the 25 students in Ms. Brown's class speak a foreign language. 20 students speak Spanish, and 19 students speak French. How many students speak both Spanish and French?
    a. 39 students b. 5 students c. 14 students d. 6 students 11. c

12. Find 27 × $0.38.
    a. $8.76 b. $10.26 c. $3.42 d. $2.92 12. b

13. Find 28 × $9.47.
    a. $94.70 b. $161.66 c. $260.66 d. $265.16 13. d

14. Choose the calculation method you would use to solve this problem. Ricardo spends $3.75 for lunch each day. How much money will he spend in 365 days?
    a. Mental math b. Paper and pencil c. Calculator 14. c

15. Ellie earned $6.72 running errands and $15.00 mowing lawns. How much more money does she need to buy a radio that costs $32.67?
    a. $21.72 b. $10.95 c. $17.67 d. $25.95 15. b

26 MCT 4

Posttest — Chapter 7, page 1

Multiple-Choice Format

Name ____________

1. Find 80 × 30. Use mental math.
   a. 240 b. 24,000 c. 2,400 d. 24 1. c

2. Estimate 22 × 79 by rounding each factor to the highest place.
   a. 140 b. 210 c. 1,600 d. 160 2. c

3. Estimate 39 × 276. Will the actual product be over or under 12,000?
   a. Over b. Under 3. b

4. Find 26 × 40.
   a. 84 b. 840 c. 104 d. 1,040 4. d

5. Find 48 × 30.
   a. 144 b. 1,240 c. 124 d. 1,440 5. d

6. Find 38 × 48.
   a. 1,744 b. 1,824 c. 1,864 d. 456 6. b

7. Find 39 × 24.
   a. 936 b. 706 c. 906 d. 194 7. a

8. Find 16 × 427.
   a. 6,832 b. 2,989 c. 2,692 d. 45,262 8. a

MCT 4 27

Posttest — Chapter 7, page 2

Multiple-Choice Format

Name ____________

9. Find 29 × 384.
   a. 4,224 b. 9,406 c. 11,136 d. 10,406 9. c

10. 7,225 is the product of a number multiplied by itself. Decide what multiples of 10 it is between.
    a. Between 30 and 40 b. Between 80 and 90
    c. Between 70 and 80 d. Between 60 and 70 10. b

11. There are 12 students in the band. 9 students can play the clarinet. 5 students can play the saxophone. How many students play both the clarinet and the saxophone?
    a. 26 students b. 7 students c. 2 students d. 3 students 11. c

12. Find 46 × $0.72.
    a. $33.12 b. $7.20 c. $33.02 d. $7.10 12. a

13. Find 46 × $8.93.
    a. $375.68 b. $310.78 c. $410.78 d. $81.20 13. c

14. Choose the calculation method you would use to solve this problem. Max spends $50 each month on clothes. How money will he spend in 4 months?
    a. Mental math b. Paper and pencil c. Calculator 14. a

15. Frank bought a notebook for $1.98 and paper for $0.98. How much change did he receive if he gave the clerk $5.00?
    a. $2.02 b. $3.02 c. $2.04 d. $4.02 15. c

28 MCT 4

ITEM ANALYSIS

Items	Objectives
1	7-1
2, 3	7-2
4, 5	7-3
6, 7	7-4
8, 9	7-5
10	7-6
11	7-7
12, 13	7-8
14	7-9
15	7-10

Note: The item analysis is the same for all pretests and posttests for this chapter.

ALSO AVAILABLE

- **Free Response Tests**
- **Alternative Tests**
- **Thinking Strategies**
- **Concrete Materials**

Optional Chapter Activities

PROJECT AND BULLETIN BOARD

At the beginning of Chapter 7, have students find their resting pulse rate by counting the number of heartbeats in 15 seconds and multiplying by 4. Each student makes an individual pulse rate bar to attach to a group bar graph. Any time after they complete Lesson 3, have students work in pairs or small groups to find their pulse rates after some active exercises, such as 1 minute of sit–ups or 5 minutes of running in place. Have students make double or triple bar graphs to compare active and resting pulse rates, and add them to the bulletin board. Then students attach heart shapes around each graph with equations or calculations that show the total number of heartbeats if they were to continue exercising for 10 minutes, 15 minutes, 20 minutes, 30 minutes, 45 minutes, or 1 hour.

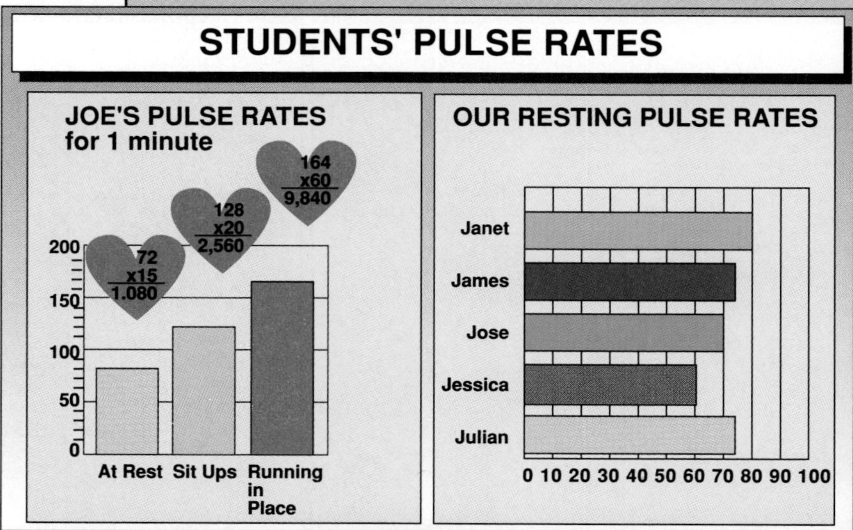

COOPERATIVE LEARNING

Divide the class into groups of three or four. Identify the group skill: explain and summarize. Assign each group four digits such as 2, 3, 4, and 5. Tell the group to multiply one digit by the other three to make as many multiplication problems as they can. The group should first decide all the possible configurations for the multiplication problems. Then someone in the group should write each problem down. For each problem, have someone in the group estimate the product and write down the estimate. Have another student perform the multiplication and a third student check it. In each case, the group should note how different the actual product is from their estimate, discuss how and why their estimate differed, and then use what they have learned to better their estimate on the next problem. Finally, have each group explain its work to the class.

You will find grouping suggestions and cooperative learning activities in most lessons throughout this chapter.

LITERATURE

Anno, Masaichiro & Mitsumasa. *Anno's Mysterious Multiplying Jar.* New York: Philomel Books, The Putnam Publishing Group, 1983.

In this beautiful and imaginative book, children are introduced to factors in a natural, easy manner. Children can create their own multiplication fact books.

Gilson, Jamie. *4B Goes Wild.* New York: Lothrop, Lee & Shepard, 1983.

Whitney, David C. *The Easy Book of Multiplication.* New York: Franklin Watts, 1969.

ENGLISH AS A SECOND LANGUAGE

Using the distributive property of multiplication can help ESL students better understand the multiplication algorithm. Working in pairs, one child uses the distributive property to expand a problem into several simpler problems, then to add the products for the final sum. For example:

$$\begin{array}{r}234\\ \underline{\times\ 52}\end{array} = \begin{array}{r}234\\ \underline{\times\ \ 2}\end{array} + \begin{array}{r}234\\ \underline{\times\ 50}\end{array} = \left(\begin{array}{r}4\\ \underline{\times 2}\end{array} + \begin{array}{r}30\\ \underline{\times\ 2}\end{array} + \begin{array}{r}200\\ \underline{\times\ \ 2}\end{array}\right) + \left(\begin{array}{r}4\\ \underline{\times 50}\end{array} + \begin{array}{r}30\\ \underline{\times 50}\end{array} + \begin{array}{r}200\\ \underline{\times\ 50}\end{array}\right)$$

That child writes the products of the expanded number as addends in vertical columns and adds them for a final sum. The partner uses the shorter form. Partners should compare steps and final results.

$$\begin{array}{r}8\\60\\ \underline{+400}\\468\end{array} \qquad \begin{array}{r}200\\1500\\ \underline{+10000}\\11700\end{array} \qquad \begin{array}{r}468\\ \underline{+11700}\\12168\end{array} \qquad \begin{array}{r}234\\ \underline{\times\ 52}\\468\\ \underline{+11700}\\12168\end{array}$$

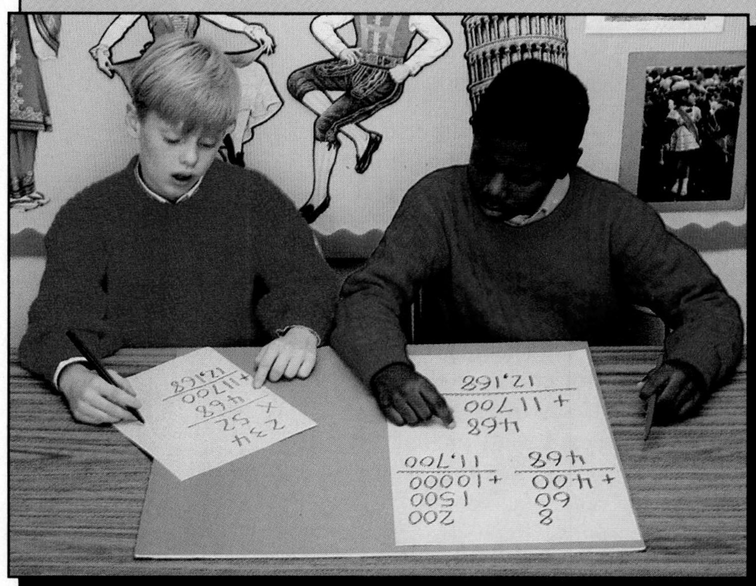

GIFTED

Inform students that they will be making some purchases at a neighborhood store. Mrs. Hobb has just opened ''Hobb-Ease'' and is selling baseball cards, stickers, stamps, model airplanes, and other hobby items. Ask them to cut out or draw pictures and create an ad for the store. Remind them to include prices, varied items, and pertinent information.

Have students role play. Two students should assume the roles of Mrs. Hobb and her assistant, while others are customers. Instruct them to look at the ads and decide what they can afford to buy. They each have $25 to spend. They each must buy 11 or more of one item and whatever else they want, including additional multiples and single items. Have students first estimate the total of their purchases, then check to see if it is reasonable when the actual total is determined. Instruct Mrs. Hobb's assistant to compute the totals for the orders. Mrs. Hobb may use a calculator to check for accuracy. Ask the customers to determine their change and have Mrs. Hobb again check for accuracy.

STUDENTS AT RISK

The extension of the multiplication algorithm to include multiplying by 2-digit factors places greater demands on students' memory, sequencing, and organizational skills. Continue using the structured worksheet format introduced in Chapter 6 (see Interleaf page 114D) to focus students' attention on the sequence of steps. Encourage students to devise their own cues, such as touching or circling starting digits or finding partial products in different colors.

Follow the Fan

Some students may need a clearer guide to the sequence of steps. A tiny ''fan'' from each digit of the multiplier may help students visualize the order of steps in the algorithm and multiply each place in each factor. You may also use the Reteaching Supplements and the specific Reteaching Tips from each lesson in this chapter.

Step 1

$$\begin{array}{r}3\,7\,2\\ \underline{\times\quad 8\,\textcircled{6}}\\2\,2\,3\,2\end{array}$$

Step 2

$$\begin{array}{r}3\,7\,2\\ \underline{\times\quad \textcircled{8}\,6}\\2\,2\,3\,2\\ \underline{2\,9\,7\,6\,\textcircled{0}}\end{array}$$

CHAPTER 7

INTRODUCING THE CHAPTER

SUBJECT INTEGRATION The photograph of children jumping rope suggests the chapter theme of health and physical fitness. Lessons include data on heart rates, aerobic points, and rope-jumping skills to provide situations in which students can multiply.

USING DATA The Health and Fitness Data Bank on page 481 of the Student Edition presents data in 2 tables and a picture. ''World Records for Fourth Graders in Single Rope Skills Events'' is a table of record numbers of jumps in seven events. ''Aerobic Points for Energy Used in Exercise'' gives the aerobic points for energy used in 1 hour doing each of 5 activities. ''Average Resting Heartbeat Levels in Heartbeats Per Minute'' is a picture that shows data for male and female adults and children.

QUESTION 1 ▶ **Justify multiplying to answer the question.** (Aerobic points are given per hour of activity and the question asks about 3 hours of baseball, so you must triple aerobic points for 1 hour of baseball.)
Student Edition answer: 1 hour of jumping rope

7 MULTIPLYING BY 2-DIGIT FACTORS

MATH AND HEALTH AND FITNESS

DATA BANK

Use the Health and Fitness Data Bank on page 481 to answer the questions. See teaching notes.

1 Which is greater, the number of aerobic points for 3 hours of playing baseball or for 1 hour of skipping rope?

TEACHING OPTIONS

LANGUAGE DEVELOPMENT
Write the word **rate** on the chalkboard and have students explain its meaning. (''steady pace at which an event occurs'') Have students describe the meaning of *heart rate*. (''pulse,'' ''how many times per minute the heart beats'') Challenge students to find a relationship between multiplication and heart rate. (Possible answer: If you know the heart rate for 1 minute, you can multiply that rate to find how many heartbeats occur in many minutes.)

2 In double unders, the rope turns 2 times per jump. Find the world record for fourth graders in this event.

3 In triple unders, the rope turns 3 times per jump. Find the world record for fourth graders in this event.

4 **Use Critical Thinking** One hour of bicycling uses 16 aerobic points. Name another activity that uses about this number of aerobic points.

177

SUBJECT INTEGRATION PROJECT Have students plan a rope-jumping contest that includes several single-rope events. Begin by having volunteers explain and discuss as many of the events listed in the Data Bank table with which they are familiar. Ask the physical education teacher to help by providing classtime for students to practice the events and discuss the fitness benefits. Hold the contest when students finish Chapter 7. They take turns jumping, counting, and recording the results. Conclude by having students display outcomes in tables or graphs.

QUESTION 2 ► **Explain a possible error that could be made when looking for data in the table.** (Possible answer: The table has three events that begin with *Double*, so you might use data for the wrong event.)
Student Edition answer: 296 jumps

QUESTION 3 ► **Explain why the record for triple unders might be so much lower than the record for double unders.** (Answers will vary. Possible explanation: Triple unders is much harder than double unders.)
Student Edition answer: 39 jumps

QUESTION 4 ► **Decide on a plan to find at least 2 activities that have aerobic points equal to an hour of riding a bicycle.** (Possible answers: You can multiply the hourly rate to find a product that is about 16; consider less than 1 hour of an activity that has more than 16 aerobic points per hour.)
Student Edition answer: Answers may vary. Possible answers: 1 hour swimming; $\frac{1}{2}$ hour running; 5 hours walking; 8 hours baseball

LESSON OPTIONS 7-1

Mental Math: Special Products

OBJECTIVE 7-1 To use mental math to find the product of a multiple of 10 times a multiple of 10

PREBOOK ACTIVITIES

QUICK REVIEW

Find each product mentally.

1. 5 × 50 (250)
2. 40 × 6 (240)
3. 800 × 4 (3,200)
4. 600 × 9 (5,400)
5. 9 × 9,000 (81,000)
6. 4,000 × 5 (20,000)
7. 6,000 × 1 (6,000)
8. 8 × 7,000 (56,000)
9. 30 × 7 (210)
10. 6 × 700 (4,200)

PRIOR KNOWLEDGE

Have students recall how to find special products, such as 4 × 600 and 3,000 × 7. (Identify basic facts, such as 4 × 6 and 3 × 7; multiply; then affix the zeros to the right of the basic fact products—2,400; 21,000.) Have students give the product of 10 × 10 and verify it by skip counting. (100) Tell students that they will be finding special products that relate to the fact 10 × 10 = 100.

COMMUNICATION

Discussing Math Discuss the relationship between the front-end digits in the factors and the first two digits in the special product of 4 × 600 = 2,400 and 3,000 × 7 = 21,000. (Possible answer: The front-end digits of the factors are the factors of a basic fact; the first two digits in the special product is the product of that basic fact.) *What is the relationship of the number of zeros in the factors and the number of zeros in the special product?* (Possible answer: In the examples, the number of zeros in the special product is equal to the number of zeros in both factors.) *When might there be one more zero in the special product?* (Possible answer: when the product for the fact has a zero, for example: 5 × 600 = 3,000)

EXPLORE AND CONNECT

Materials: TA 13 (Spinners 1-4)
Grouping Suggestion: small cooperative learning groups
Students explore zero patterns in special products. Groups choose a multiplication fact with two 1-digit factors, such as 3 × 5. One student records the fact and its product in an equation. Students spin for a number of zeros to add to either factor. Another student annexes the zeros to either factor, then records that fact and its special product. Another student rearranges the fact and the zeros to form new factors with the same special product. Members take turns forming as many different factor arrangements as possible. For example: 3 zeros can form 3,000 × 5, 3 × 5,000, 30 × 500, or 300 × 50—all equal 15,000. Conclude by having students describe a zero pattern. (Special products have as many zeros written after the basic fact product as there are in the factors, no matter where the zeros are.)

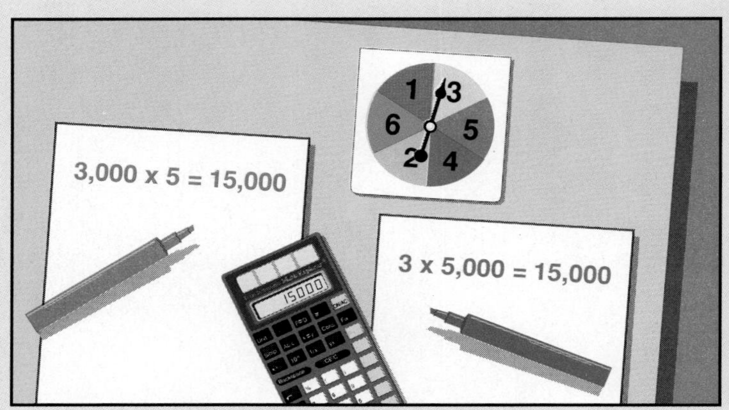

CONNECTIONS Use these anytime.

Problem of the Day

Number Sense Analyze and order the following amounts: a hundred dozen, a dozen hundreds, and ten dozen tens. (They can be arranged in any order because all are equal to 1,200.)

Subject Integration

Geography Pipe Spring National Monument in Arizona has an area of 40 acres. Tuzigoot National Monument, also in Arizona, is about 20 times bigger. Find the area of Tuzigoot. (about 800 acres)

Patterns

Multiple Zeros Find the pattern, then continue it five more times: 1; 30; 500; 7,000; ______; ______; ______; ______; ______. (Count by odd numbers, add a zero: 90,000; 1,100,000; 13,000,000; 150,000,000; 1,700,000,000.)

Classwork and Homework Supplements

Practice

Mental Math 7-1

Name ______

Special Products

Write the number for each □ and △.

1. Since 3 × 6 = □, then 30 × 60 = △. 18; 1,800
2. Since 8 × 4 = □, then 80 × 40 = △. 32; 3,200
3. Since 5 × 7 = □, then 50 × 70 = △. 35; 3,500
4. Since 2 × 9 = □, then 20 × 90 = △. 18; 1,800

Find the products.

5. 70 × 30 = 2,100	6. 20 × 50 = 1,000
7. 80 × 70 = 5,600	8. 60 × 70 = 4,200
9. 90 × 10 = 900	10. 50 × 60 = 3,000
11. 40 × 60 = 2,400	12. 20 × 40 = 800
13. 60 × 80 = 4,800	14. 70 × 90 = 6,300
15. 50 × 50 = 2,500	16. 40 × 70 = 2,800
17. 90 × 30 = 2,700	18. 80 × 60 = 4,800
19. 40 × 50 = 2,000	20. 70 × 60 = 4,200
21. 30 × 40 = 1,200	22. 40 × 90 = 3,600
23. 90 × 90 = 8,100	24. 60 × 90 = 5,400

64 Use with text pages 178-179. PS-4

Building Thinking Skills

Mental Math 7-1

Name ______

Human Calculator

You can use mental math to find the products of certain 2-digit factors.

Look at this example.

Multiply 40 × 11.
Step 1: Multiply. 40 × 10 = 400
Step 2: Multiply. 40 × 1 = 40
Step 3: Add the products. 400 + 40 = 440
40 × 11 = 440

Use mental math to find the products.

1. 90 × 21 = 1,890	2. 60 × 41 = 2,460
3. 81 × 30 = 2,430	4. 71 × 70 = 4,970
5. 40 × 61 = 2,440	6. 50 × 41 = 2,050
7. 91 × 40 = 3,640	8. 30 × 61 = 1,830
9. 30 × 21 = 630	10. 80 × 21 = 1,680
11. 71 × 60 = 4,260	12. 40 × 41 = 1,640

Look at the two factors in each multiplication problem. What does each pair of factors have in common that makes it possible for you to use mental math?

Ones place digit in one factor is 1, and ones place digit in the other factor is 0.

64 Use with text pages 178-179. TS-4

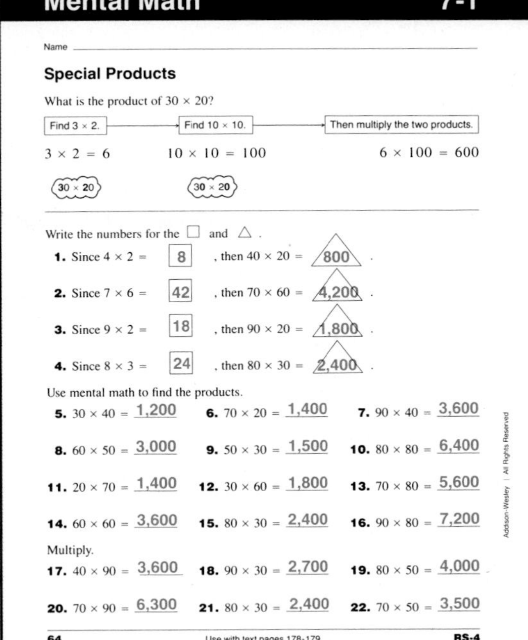

Reteaching

Mental Math 7-1

Name ______

Special Products

What is the product of 30 × 20?

Find 3 × 2. → Find 10 × 10. → Then multiply the two products.

3 × 2 = 6 10 × 10 = 100 6 × 100 = 600

30 × 20 30 × 20

Write the numbers for the □ and △.

1. Since 4 × 2 = 8, then 40 × 20 = 800.
2. Since 7 × 6 = 42, then 70 × 60 = 4,200.
3. Since 9 × 2 = 18, then 90 × 20 = 1,800.
4. Since 8 × 3 = 24, then 80 × 30 = 2,400.

Use mental math to find the products.

5. 30 × 40 = 1,200	6. 70 × 20 = 1,400	7. 90 × 40 = 3,600
8. 60 × 50 = 3,000	9. 50 × 30 = 1,500	10. 80 × 80 = 6,400
11. 20 × 70 = 1,400	12. 30 × 60 = 1,800	13. 70 × 80 = 5,600
14. 60 × 60 = 3,600	15. 80 × 30 = 2,400	16. 90 × 80 = 7,200

Multiply.

17. 40 × 90 = 3,600	18. 90 × 30 = 2,700	19. 80 × 50 = 4,000
20. 70 × 90 = 6,300	21. 80 × 30 = 2,400	22. 70 × 50 = 3,500

64 Use with text pages 178-179. RS-4

Challenges

Reading Math 7-1

Name ______

Teacher for a Day

You are the teacher for a day. Lisa, Don, and Pat turned in these papers. They each made mistakes for different reasons. Cross out the mistakes and write the correct answers. Then write a note to each student explaining his or her mistakes.

Lisa

1. 10 × 70 = 700	2. 20 × 40 = 800	3. 30 × 60 = ~~180~~ 1,800
4. 20 × 30 = 600	5. 40 × 60 = ~~240~~ 2,400	6. 50 × 80 = ~~400~~ 4,000
7. 90 × 10 = 900	8. 30 × 40 = ~~120~~ 1,200	9. 30 × 30 = 900

Lisa, whenever the answer is in the thousands, you forget a zero. Wording will vary.

Don

1. 40 × 80 = ~~1,200~~ 3,200	2. 80 × 20 = 1,600	3. 90 × 50 = 4,500
4. 40 × 50 = 2,000	5. 70 × 80 = ~~1,500~~ 5,600	6. 40 × 10 = 400
7. 60 × 50 = ~~1,100~~ 3,000	8. 90 × 40 = ~~1,300~~ 3,600	9. 30 × 20 = 600

Don, sometimes you add the tens digits instead of multiplying them.

Pat

1. 70 × 40 = 2,800	2. 80 × 30 = ~~2,100~~ 2,400	3. 80 × 50 = ~~4,300~~ 4,000
4. 90 × 40 = 3,600	5. 80 × 80 = ~~6,500~~ 6,400	6. 70 × 60 = 4,200
7. 20 × 60 = 1,200	8. 80 × 40 = ~~3,400~~ 3,200	9. 50 × 30 = 1,500

Pat, you need to practice your 8 facts.

64 Use with text pages 178-179. CS-4

Options for Individual Needs

Basic

Exercises 1-6, 11-16
Calculator Bank, p. 486
More Practice, p. 505, set C

Supplements
Reteaching 64 or
Practice 64

Average

Exercises 1-16
Calculator Bank, p. 486
More Practice, p. 505, set C

Supplements
Practice 64
Challenges 64 or
Thinking Skills 64

Extended

Exercises 7-16
Calculator Bank, p. 486

Supplements
Challenges 64
Thinking Skills 64

Other Resources:
Problem-Solving Experiences in Mathematics, Grade 4, Problems 115, 116
Math In Stride, Teacher Sourcebook, Grade 4, Activity 5A
Using the Math Explorer Calculator: A Sourcebook for Teachers, Chapter 14
Mathematics: A Way of Thinking, Activity 9-18

7-1

LESSON PLAN 7-1

OBJECTIVE 7-1
To use mental math to find the product of a multiple of 10 times a multiple of 10

Materials: TA 3 (Number Cards 0-9), TA 5 (4-Digit Place Value Charts)

1. MOTIVATE AND TEACH

LEARN ABOUT IT

EXPLORE ► **Explain the operation to use to solve both Wacky Facts Problems.** (Multiply to put together many same-size groups.)

TALK ABOUT IT ► **How might you break apart a factor to find 40 × 20?** [Possible answer: (40 × 10) + (40 × 10).]
► **Compare the product with 2 × 4.** (800 is 100 8s.)
► **Explain how to find a basic fact in the Problem 2 factors.** (Look at the front-end digits to find 3 × 2 = 6.)
► **Compare 3 × 2 to 30 × 20.** (Each factor is 10 times greater.)
► **Compare the products.** [600 is 100 times (10 × 10) greater than 6.]
► **What pattern do you see?** (Possible answer: The special product has as many zeros as both factors.)
► **Explain why 50 × 60 has 3 zeros in the product.** (5 × 6 = 30, then add 2 zeros.)
Student Edition answers: **1.** 10; 2 × 10 = 20 **2.** 10; 3 × 10 = 30 **3.** 100; 2 × 10 = 20, 3 × 10 = 30, so 10 × 10 = 100.

2. CHECK UNDERSTANDING

TRY IT OUT

ERROR ALERT Affixing the wrong number of zeros. Making basic-fact errors.

Mental Math
Special Products

LEARN ABOUT IT

EXPLORE Solve to Understand
Daniela made up these Far Out Facts problems that can be solved using mental math.

Far Out Facts Problems
1. There is enough lead in one pencil to draw a line 40 miles long. How long a line could you draw with a pack of 20 pencils?
2. The average dollar bill wears out in 20 months. How many days is this? Use 30 days in a month.

TALK ABOUT IT See teaching notes.

1. How many times as large as 40 × 2 is the answer to problem 1? Explain.
2. How many times as large as 20 × 3 is the answer to problem 2? Explain.
3. How many times as large as 2 × 3 is the answer to problem 2? Explain.

This mental math method gives you a quick way to find products like 40 × 20.

■ To find 40 × 20, find 4 × 2 and then multiply by 100.

4 tens × 2 tens = 8 hundreds

40 × 20 = 800

Here are more examples.

60 × 10 = 600   6 tens × 1 ten = 6 hundreds
50 × 60 = 3,000   5 tens × 6 tens = 30 hundreds or 3 thousands

TRY IT OUT

1. 70 × 10 700 **2.** 30 × 70 2,100 **3.** 80 × 40 3,200 **4.** 40 × 50 2,000

5. 50 × 20 1,000 **6.** 60 × 70 4,200 **7.** 40 × 90 3,600 **8.** 50 × 80 4,000

178

TEACHING OPTIONS

RETEACHING TIPS To verify how many zeros special products need, students transfer the zeros from the factors to the ones and tens places on a place value chart, then multiply the basic fact and show its product with number cards in hundreds and thousands places. Assign Reteaching Supplement 64.

ENRICHMENT Have students use mental math reasoning to find these special products.
1. 10 × 40 × 20 (8,000)
2. 40 × 30 × 20 (24,000)
3. 50 × 30 × 20 (30,000)
4. 80 × 20 × 30 (48,000)
5. 20 × 60 × 70 (84,000)
6. 30 × 30 × 30 (27,000)

PRACTICE

Copy each equation and give the numbers for the □ and △.

1. Since 9 × 4 = □, then 90 × 40 = △. 36; 3,600
2. Since 2 × 7 = □, then 20 × 70 = △. 14; 1,400

Find the products. Use pencil and paper for answers only.

3. 90 × 10 900 4. 20 × 30 600 5. 50 × 10 500 6. 40 × 40 1,600
7. 40 × 60 2,400 8. 90 × 50 4,500 9. 20 × 30 600 10. 80 × 50 4,000
11. Multiply 60 and 70. 4,200 12. Find the product of 90 and 20. 1,800

APPLY

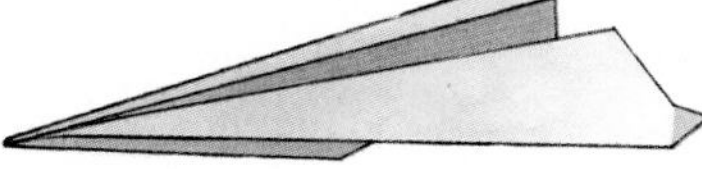

MATH REASONING See Additional Answers.

13. What product would give the best estimate for 55 × 55? Why? See Additional Answers.
    a. 60 × 60 b. 60 × 50 c. 50 × 50 d. 50 × 40

PROBLEM SOLVING

14. A hen's egg was once thrown 90 meters without being broken. The record for throwing a paper airplane is 10 times that far. How many meters did the paper airplane fly? 900 meters

15. A cat was taken away in a moving van by mistake. To get home it had to travel 640 kilometers. If it went 10 kilometers a day for 60 days, how much further would it still have to go? 40 kilometers

▶ **USING CRITICAL THINKING Discover a Sequence**

16. These cards give a shortcut for finding products such as 60 × 40. What is their correct sequence?

Add on the number of zeros in the factors. — 4

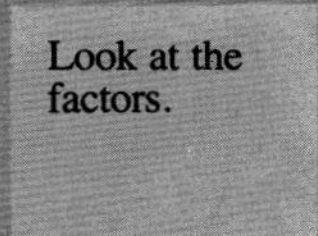

Look at the factors. — 1

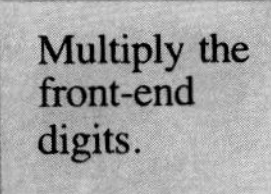

Multiply the front-end digits. — 2

Count the number of zeros in the factors. — 3

More Practice, page 505, set C

3. PRACTICE AND APPLY

Basic	1-6, 11-16
Average	1-16
Extended	7-16

Additional Answers: See p. T79.

PRACTICE

Look at Exercises 1 and 2. What do these exercises show? (Exercises 1 and 2 show how products of basic facts and special products are related.) *Look at Exercises 3-12. Will you use the same logic to solve these?* (Yes, but you must identify the basic fact on your own.)

APPLY

MATH REASONING ▶ **Analyze a sensible way to adjust your estimate.** (Round one factor up, the other down, since both are exactly in the middle.)

PROBLEM SOLVING ▶ **Analyze how many steps it takes to solve Problem 15.** (2—multiply, then subtract)

USING THINKING SKILLS ▶ **How can you verify the correct sequence?** (Possible answer: Use the steps as you ordered them to see if they help you find special products.)

CLOSE AND ASSESS

PROVE WHAT YOU KNOW

Give students the following equations. Ask them to find and to explain the errors, then to give the correct products.

1. 40 × 70 = 1,100 (multiply, not add front-end digits; 2,800)
2. 80 × 20 = 160 (too few zeros; 1,600)
3. 70 × 70 = 4,800 (basic-fact error in multiplying front-end digits; 4,900)

QUICK QUIZ

Find the products mentally.

1. 40 × 40 (1,600)
2. 90 × 50 (4,500)
3. 60 × 20 (1,200)
4. Multiply 50 and 60. (3,000)

LESSON OPTIONS 7-2

Estimating Larger Products

OBJECTIVE 7-2 To adjust and then use the estimation technique of rounding to estimate the products of

PREBOOK ACTIVITIES

QUICK REVIEW

Estimate the products. Tell if your estimate is *over* or *under* the exact answer. (Estimates may vary. Samples are given.)

1. 789 × 4 (3,200; over) **2.** 304 × 7 (2,100; under)
3. 446 × 2 (900; over) **4.** 26 × 8 (240; over)
5. 333 × 5 (1,500; under) **6.** $9.87 × 6 ($60; over)

PRIOR KNOWLEDGE

Have students explain the difference between *over*estimates and *under*estimates. (Overestimates are greater than exact answers; underestimates are less than exact answers.) Have students suggest real-life situations in which overestimates may be preferable. (Possible answers: how much money to bring to the store; how much food to serve)

COMMUNICATION

Discussing Math Discuss the meaning of the expression *common sense*. (Possible answer: to use reasonable judgment based on sensible thinking rather than on specific facts or rules) Have students explain how estimation and common sense are related. (Possible answer: Estimates are not exact answers, so common sense helps you decide how to interpret estimates to judge how close they are to exact answers or how reasonable they are.)

EXPLORE AND CONNECT

Materials: index cards, calculators
Grouping Suggestion: cooperative learning pairs
Partners round factors in different ways to find estimated products closest to exact products. On each of several index cards, write 2- and 3-digit factors, such as 35 × 85, 65 × 45, and 850 × 95. Give 1 card to each pair. Partners use a calculator to find the exact product and record it as an equation. (35 × 85 = 2,975) Then they round factors in as many different ways as possible, including non-traditional ways. Pairs find each estimated product, recording each as an equation and comparing each to the exact product. For example, for 35 × 85, estimates may include 40 × 90 = 3,600; 30 × 90 = 2,700; 30 × 80 = 2,400; and 40 × 80 = 3,200. Last, have students analyze their different estimating techniques. (Possible responses: Estimates seem to be closer when one factor rounds up and the other rounds down.)

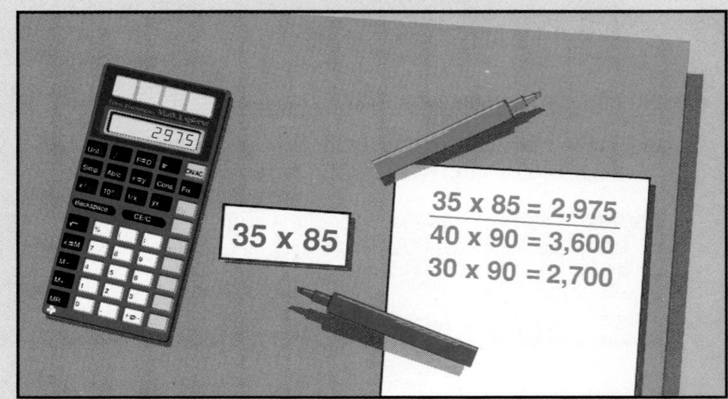

CONNECTIONS Use these anytime.

Problem of the Day

Number Sense Write 2 different pairs of factors whose estimated product is 3,600. Make 3,600 an overestimate of one factor pair and an underestimate of the other pair. (Answers will vary. Possible answer: 3,600 *over*estimates 38 × 89; 3,600 *under*estimates 64 × 62.)

Life Skills

Theater Seats A 683-seat theater accommodated 43 performances of a popular play. Each performance was sold out. About how many tickets were sold? (Estimates may vary. Possible answer: 28,000.)

Math Connection

Money Mr. Gill spends $7.50 on bridge tolls each week to drive back and forth to his job. Estimate the yearly cost. (Estimates may vary. Possible answer: about $400)

Classwork and Homework Supplements

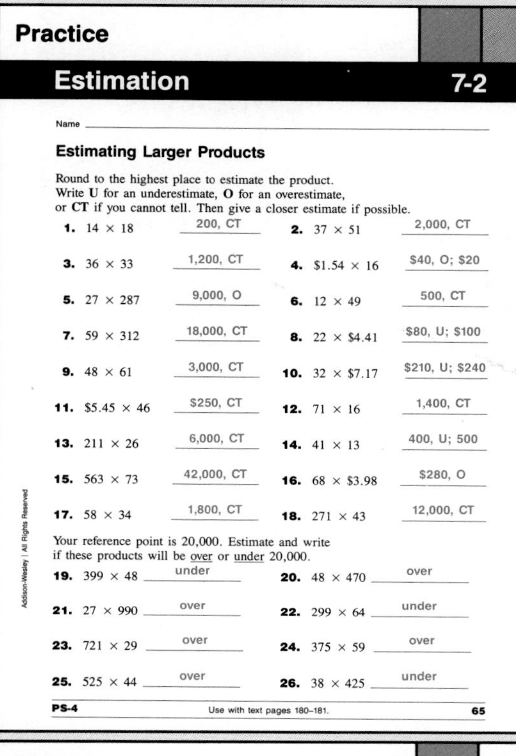

Practice

Estimation 7-2

Name ______________________

Estimating Larger Products

Round to the highest place to estimate the product.
Write **U** for an underestimate, **O** for an overestimate,
or **CT** if you cannot tell. Then give a closer estimate if possible.

1.	14 × 18	200, CT	**2.**	37 × 51	2,000, CT
3.	36 × 33	1,200, CT	**4.**	$1.54 × 16	$40, O; $20
5.	27 × 287	9,000, O	**6.**	12 × 49	500, CT
7.	59 × 312	18,000, CT	**8.**	22 × $4.41	$80, U; $100
9.	48 × 61	3,000, CT	**10.**	32 × $7.17	$210, U; $240
11.	$5.45 × 46	$250, CT	**12.**	71 × 16	1,400, CT
13.	211 × 26	6,000, CT	**14.**	41 × 13	400, U; 500
15.	563 × 73	42,000, CT	**16.**	68 × $3.98	$280, O
17.	58 × 34	1,800, CT	**18.**	271 × 43	12,000, CT

Your reference point is 20,000. Estimate and write
if these products will be over or under 20,000.

19.	399 × 48	under	**20.**	48 × 470	over
21.	27 × 990	over	**22.**	299 × 64	under
23.	721 × 29	over	**24.**	375 × 59	over
25.	525 × 44	over	**26.**	38 × 425	under

PS-4 Use with text pages 180–181. 65

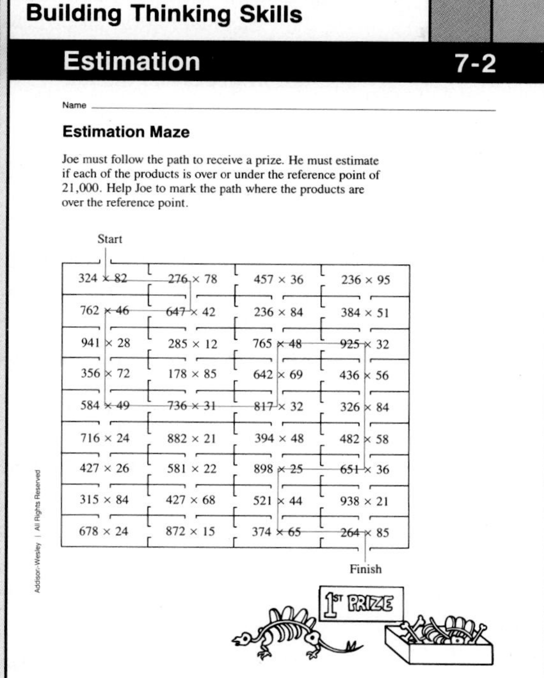

Building Thinking Skills

Estimation 7-2

Name ______________________

Estimation Maze

Joe must follow the path to receive a prize. He must estimate
if each of the products is over or under the reference point of
21,000. Help Joe to mark the path where the products are
over the reference point.

Start

324 × 82	276 × 78	457 × 36	236 × 95
762 × 46	647 × 42	236 × 84	384 × 51
941 × 28	285 × 12	765 × 48	925 × 32
356 × 72	178 × 85	642 × 69	436 × 56
584 × 49	736 × 31	817 × 32	326 × 84
716 × 24	882 × 21	394 × 48	482 × 58
427 × 26	581 × 22	898 × 25	651 × 36
315 × 84	427 × 68	521 × 44	938 × 21
678 × 24	872 × 15	374 × 65	264 × 85

Finish

TS-4 Use with text pages 180-181. 65

Reteaching

Estimation 7-2

Estimating Larger Products

Overestimation	Underestimation
Always occurs when both factors are rounded up.	Always occurs when both factors are rounded down.
36 x 47	32 x 83
40 x 50 = 2,000	30 x 80 = 2,400

Round to the highest place of each factor to estimate
the product. Circle underestimate, overestimate,
or cannot tell.

1.	23 x 18	400	underestimate overestimate (cannot tell)
2.	65 x 38	2,800	underestimate (overestimate) cannot tell
3.	93 x 75	7,200	underestimate overestimate (cannot tell)
4.	475 x 25	15,000	underestimate (overestimate) cannot tell
5.	19 x 191	4,000	underestimate (overestimate) cannot tell
6.	63 x 84	4,800	(underestimate) overestimate cannot tell
7.	72 x $2.18	$140	(underestimate) overestimate cannot tell

Your reference point is 28,000. Estimate to tell if these
products will be over or under the reference point.

8. 733 x 44 over **9.** 698 x 37 under **10.** 549 x 62 over

RS-4 Use with text pages 180-181. 65

Challenges

Calculators 7-2

Name ______________________

Pathfinder

Play this game with a partner.
You will each need markers.
Your goal is to make a path from
river to river or from mountain
to mountain.

Survival Kit: 315, 17, 29, 89, 68, 81, 197, 98

Rules
Take turns following these steps:

1. Pick 2 numbers from the survival kit.
2. Find their product using a calculator.
3. Place one of your markers on the product on the game board. Only one player's marker can be on each space.
4. The first player to cross the game board is the winner.

Try to plan your path across the game board by picking your numbers carefully. The numbers can be reused.

Game Board

1,241; 25,515; 4,964; 9,135; 3,349; 22,995; 5,508; 9,135; 1,666; 13,396; 5,913; 30,870; 2,117; 5,355; 1,972; 1,156; 5,713; 1,156; 21,420; 25,515; 15,957; 2,842; 2,349; 14,371; 1,377; 62,055; 7,938; 493

CS-4 Use with text pages 180–181. 65

Options for Individual Needs

Basic

Exercises 1-8, 15-20, 26-34
Computer Bank, p. 492
More Practice, p. 505, set D

Supplements
Reteaching 65 or
Practice 65

Average

Exercises 1-34
Computer Bank, p. 492
More Practice, p. 505, set D

Supplements
Practice 65
Challenges 65 or
Thinking Skills 65

Extended

Exercises 5-20, 26-34
Computer Bank, p. 492

Supplements
Challenges 65
Thinking Skills 65

Other Resources:
Problem-Solving Experiences in Mathematics, Grade 4, Problem 121
Math In Stride, Grade 4, pp. 100, 101

7-2

LESSON PLAN 7-2

OBJECTIVE 7-2
To adjust and then use the estimation technique of rounding to estimate the products of 2-digit and 3-digit factors

Grouping Suggestion: pairs

1. MOTIVATE AND TEACH

LEARN ABOUT IT

EXPLORE ▶ **Explain how Phil could find Patti's exact age in months. in weeks.** (12 × 12; 12 × 52)

TALK ABOUT IT ▶ **Relate the factors 12 × 52 to the situation.** (12 is Patti's age in years; there are 52 weeks per year.)
▶ **Justify Phil's rounding.** (12 is closer to 10 than to 20; 52 is closer to 50 than to 60.)
▶ **Compare Phil's rounded factors with the exact factors; relate them to an estimate.** (He rounded both factors down; the product is an underestimate.)
▶ **If one factor was rounded up, predict the effect of the change.** (The adjusted product might be closer to the actual product.)
Student Edition answers: **1.** underestimate; both factors rounded down **2.** probably; round one factor up, the other down

2. CHECK UNDERSTANDING

TRY IT OUT

ERROR ALERT Failing to adjust factors for a closer estimate. Misinterpreting whether estimates are over or under exact answers.

Estimating Larger Products

LEARN ABOUT IT

EXPLORE **Think About the Situation**
Phil was making his sister Patti a funny card for her 12th birthday. He wanted to write on it her estimated age in weeks and months.

TALK ABOUT IT See teaching notes.

1. Phil first estimated Patti's age in weeks. He rounded 12 × 52 to 10 × 50 and got 500. Is this an overestimate or an underestimate? Explain.
2. His older brother suggested he use 10 × 60 instead. Would this give a closer estimate? Explain.

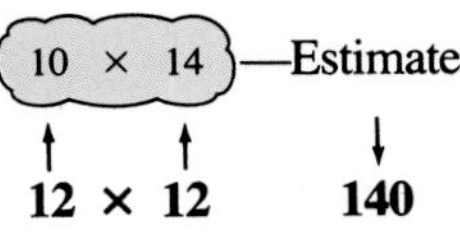

1 year = 52 weeks
1 year = 12 months

Here is how to estimate the age in months.

If you round 12 × 12 to the nearest 10, you get an underestimate.

10 × 10 = 100

To get a closer estimate, round one factor up and the other down.

10 × 14 —Estimate
↑ ↑ ↓
12 × 12 140

Look at these additional examples.

43 × 589
40 × 600
About 24,000

32 × $5.75
30 × $6
About $180

TRY IT OUT

Round to the highest place to make an estimate. Decide if the estimate is an underestimate, an overestimate, or if you can't tell. Give a closer estimate if possible See Additional Answers.

1. 53 × 84 **2.** 39 × 21 **3.** 264 × 35 **4.** 623 × 46 **5.** 54 × $3.79

180

TEACHING OPTIONS

RETEACHING TIPS Have students decide their estimate for each factor, then draw an arrow beside each to show if it is to be rounded up (↑) or down (↓). When both round the same way, students adjust one for a more balanced estimate. Assign Reteaching Supplement 65.

ENRICHMENT **Family Math** Have students do this activity with a family member. Students choose 3 items from their food cupboard or refrigerator that cost over $2.00. They estimate the cost of buying 1 dozen, 2 dozen, 3 dozen, and 4 dozen of each item.

PRACTICE

Round to the highest place to estimate the product. Write underestimate, overestimate, or can't tell. Then give a closer estimate if possible. See Additional Answers.

1. 25 × 68 2. 37 × 52 3. $5.52 × 28 4. 237 × 46
5. 24 × 834 6. 61 × 78 7. 88 × 717 8. $3.54 × 62
9. 769 × 63 10. 82 × $3.06 11. 54 × 51 12. 97 × 536

Your reference point is 24,000. Estimate to tell if these products will be over or under the reference point.

13. 399 × 57 under 14. 49 × 547 over 15. 38 × 789 over 16. 368 × 51 under

APPLY

MATH REASONING Use estimation to choose the best number for each box.

17. 49 × □ = 1,421 a. 19 (b.) 29 c. 39
18. □ × 25 = 1,100 a. 24 b. 34 (c.) 44

PROBLEM SOLVING

19. Katrina is 9 years and 15 weeks old. What is her age in weeks? 483 weeks
20. Steve is 52 months old. How many months less than 8 years is this? 44 months

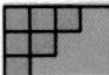

MIXED REVIEW

Find the products.

21. 3 × 2 6 22. 9 × 1 9 23. 0 × 5 0 24. 1 × 7 7 25. 4 × 0 0
26. 5 × 4 20 27. 2 × 9 18 28. 8 × 5 40 29. 7 × 2 14 30. 5 × 7 35

Multiply and then add the number given.

31. 6 × 5 8 38 32. 7 × 4 3 31 33. 3 × 9 7 34 34. 7 × 8 4 60

More Practice, page 505, set D

3. Practice and Apply

Basic	1-8, 15-20, 26-34
Average	1-34
Extended	5-20, 26-34

Additional Answers: See p. T79.

PRACTICE

Look at Exercises 1-12. Find the exercises in which both factors round to the same place. (Exercises 1, 2, 6, 11)

APPLY

MATH REASONING ► How would you begin to analyze Exercises 17 and 18? (Possible answer: Round each product and factor first. Then think of a second factor that multiplied by the rounded one would equal close to the product.)

PROBLEM SOLVING ► Identify the reference point in Problem 20 and explain how to use it to find the answer. (number of months in 8 years; Compare that amount to 52 to find the difference.)

MIXED REVIEW ► Find two number facts with the same product. Explain why. (0 × 5 and 4 × 0; Zero rule says a number multiplied by 0 is 0.)

Close and Assess

WRITE WHAT YOU THINK
Each student writes a paragraph telling how to adjust 65 × 255 to give a close estimate and whether the method produces an overestimate or an underestimate. Then have students exchange papers with a partner. Partners evaluate each other's explanation and check to make sure the estimate is reasonable. (Answers may vary. Possible answer: 60 × 300 = 18,000.)

QUICK QUIZ

Estimate products. Write *over, under,* or *cannot tell.* (Estimates may vary.)

1. 73 × 51 (3,500; under)
2. 608 × 57 (3,600; cannot tell)
3. 588 × 39 (24,000; over)

LESSON OPTIONS 7-3

Multiplying by Multiples of 10

OBJECTIVE 7-3 To multiply a 2-digit number by a 2-digit multiple of 10

PREBOOK ACTIVITIES

QUICK REVIEW

Multiply using mental math.

1. 40 × 70	(2,800)	**2.** 30 × 40	(1,200)
3. 90 × 90	(8,100)	**4.** 50 × 30	(1,500)
5. 60 × 60	(3,600)	**6.** 20 × 80	(1,600)
7. 70 × 80	(5,600)	**8.** 40 × 90	(3,600)
9. 70 × 60	(4,200)	**10.** 30 × 80	(2,400)

PRIOR KNOWLEDGE

Have students think of real-life situations involving time or days in which they might multiply by a multiple of 10. (Possible answers: Multiply by 60 to find a rate per hour if you know a rate per minute; multiply by 30 to find a rate per month if you know a rate per day.)

COMMUNICATION

Discussing Math Have students explain how they would use mental math to multiply 6 × 70. (Think of 70 as 7 tens; multiply 6 × 7 tens = 42 tens, or 420.) Then have them explain how to multiply 60 × 70. (Multiply front-end digits 6 × 7 = 42, then add 2 zeros to show 4,200.) Challenge students to imagine how to multiply 62 × 70. (Possible answers: Break apart 62 as 60 + 2, multiply each by 70, add 4,200 + 140 = 4,340; multiply 62 × 7 = 434, then multiply the product by 10.)

EXPLORE AND CONNECT

Materials: calculators, TA 11 (Blank Spinners marked 2-9)
Grouping Suggestion: cooperative learning groups of 3
Students explore relationships between products of related 1- and 2-digit factors. The first student spins 3 times to build a 2-digit by 1-digit multiplication problem, such as 57 × 4. The second student solves it with paper and pencil, as the third student uses an appropriate method to verify the product. Then students change the second factor to make it a multiple of 10. (57 × 4<u>0</u>) Group members discuss how the change in the factor should affect the product and predict the new product. One student uses a calculator to find the new product, which students compare with their prediction. (The new product will be 10 times greater than the first product.) Students trade tasks and repeat the exploration 2 more times. Conclude by having students generalize about products when a factor is a multiple of 10. (Possible answer: Products always end in 0.)

CONNECTIONS Use these anytime.

Problem of the Day

Heartbeats When Dan sleeps, his pulse rate is 63 beats per minute. If he takes a half-hour nap, how many times will his heart beat? (1,890 times)

Number Sense

Estimation Lucas is saving to buy his own horse. So far, he has eleven $20 bills. Estimate how much money he has. (about $200)

Life Skills

Stamps Winnie always buys postage stamps in rolls of 50 for her office. If a single stamp costs $0.25, what is the cost of the roll? ($12.50)

Classwork and Homework Supplements

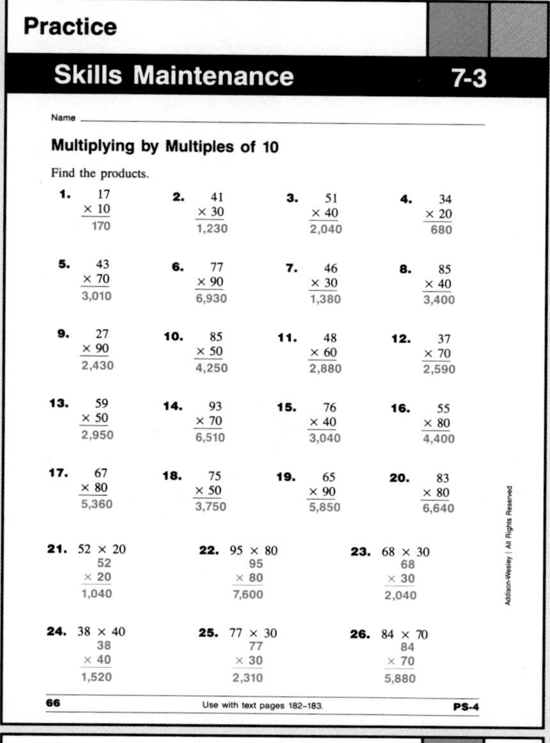

Practice

Skills Maintenance 7-3

Name ______

Multiplying by Multiples of 10

Find the products.

1. 17 × 10 = 170
2. 41 × 30 = 1,230
3. 51 × 40 = 2,040
4. 34 × 20 = 680
5. 43 × 70 = 3,010
6. 77 × 90 = 6,930
7. 46 × 30 = 1,380
8. 85 × 40 = 3,400
9. 27 × 90 = 2,430
10. 85 × 50 = 4,250
11. 48 × 60 = 2,880
12. 37 × 70 = 2,590
13. 59 × 50 = 2,950
14. 93 × 70 = 6,510
15. 76 × 40 = 3,040
16. 55 × 80 = 4,400
17. 67 × 80 = 5,360
18. 75 × 50 = 3,750
19. 65 × 90 = 5,850
20. 83 × 80 = 6,640
21. 52 × 20 — 52 × 20 = 1,040
22. 95 × 80 — 95 × 80 = 7,600
23. 68 × 30 — 68 × 30 = 2,040
24. 38 × 40 — 38 × 40 = 1,520
25. 77 × 30 — 77 × 30 = 2,310
26. 84 × 70 — 84 × 70 = 5,880

66 Use with text pages 182–183. PS-4

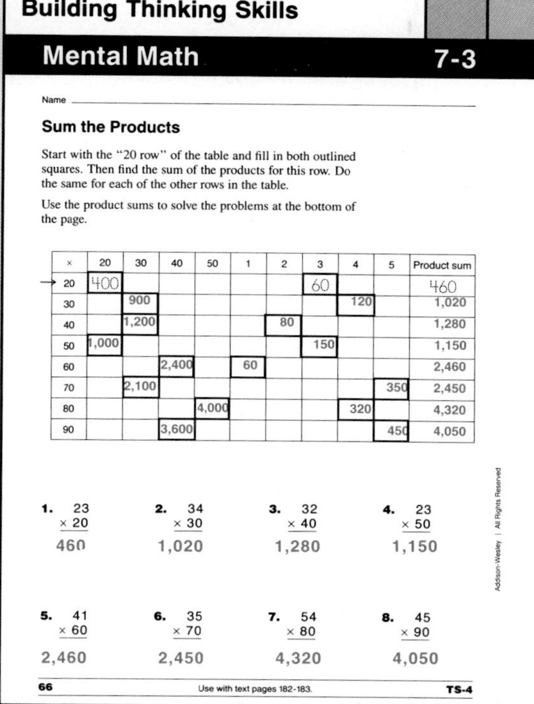

Building Thinking Skills

Mental Math 7-3

Name ______

Sum the Products

Start with the "20 row" of the table and fill in both outlined squares. Then find the sum of the products for this row. Do the same for each of the other rows in the table.

Use the product sums to solve the problems at the bottom of the page.

×	20	30	40	50	1	2	3	4	5	Product sum
→ 20	400						60			460
30		900						120		1,020
40		1,200				80				1,280
50	1,000						150			1,150
60			2,400		60					2,460
70		2,100							350	2,450
80				4,000				320		4,320
90			3,600						450	4,050

1. 23 × 20 = 460
2. 34 × 30 = 1,020
3. 32 × 40 = 1,280
4. 23 × 50 = 1,150
5. 41 × 60 = 2,460
6. 35 × 70 = 2,450
7. 54 × 80 = 4,320
8. 45 × 90 = 4,050

66 Use with text pages 182–183. TS-4

Reteaching

Skills Review 7-3

Name ______

Multiplying by Multiples of 10

To multiply by multiples of 10,

Multiply by the digit in the ones place.

69 × 50: 0 × 69 = 0 → 0

Multiply by the digit in the tens place.

69 × 50: 5 tens × 69 = 345 tens → 3,450

Find the products.

1. 73 × 10 = 730
2. 63 × 30 = 1,890
3. 54 × 80 = 4,320
4. 86 × 90 = 7,740
5. 39 × 70 = 2,730
6. 39 × 40 = 1,560
7. 47 × 20 = 940
8. 26 × 60 = 1,560
9. 95 × 30 = 2,850
10. 84 × 50 = 4,200
11. 56 × 70 = 3,920
12. 32 × 80 = 2,560
13. 52 × 20 = 1,040
14. 49 × 80 = 3,920
15. 84 × 30 = 2,520
16. 75 × 60 = 4,500
17. 26 × 40 = 1,040
18. 93 × 20 = 1,860
19. 62 × 60 = 3,720
20. 99 × 90 = 8,910

66 Use with text pages 182-183. RS-4

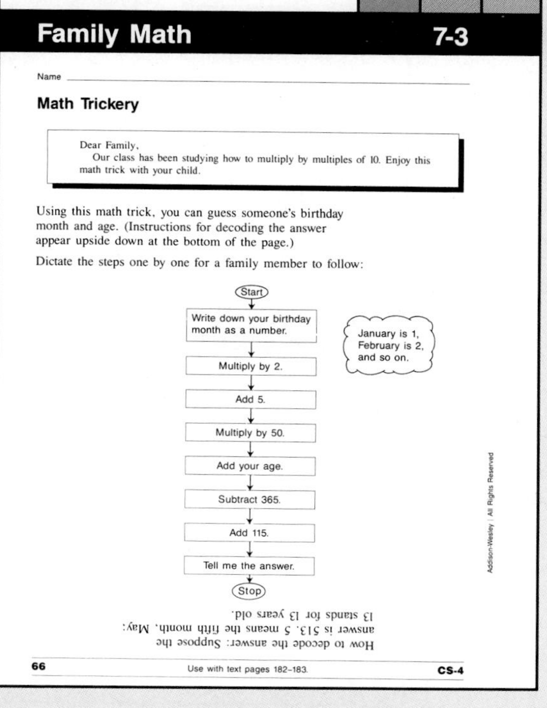

Challenges

Family Math 7-3

Name ______

Math Trickery

Dear Family,
Our class has been studying how to multiply by multiples of 10. Enjoy this math trick with your child.

Using this math trick, you can guess someone's birthday month and age. (Instructions for decoding the answer appear upside down at the bottom of the page.)

Dictate the steps one by one for a family member to follow:

Start
Write down your birthday month as a number.
January is 1, February is 2, and so on.
Multiply by 2.
Add 5.
Multiply by 50.
Add your age.
Subtract 365.
Add 115.
Tell me the answer.
Stop

How to decode the answer: Suppose the answer is 513. 5 means the fifth month, May; 13 stands for 13 years old.

66 Use with text pages 182–183. CS-4

Options for Individual Needs

Basic

Exercises 1-7, 11-20
Data Bank, p. 481
Skills Bank, p. 465
More Practice, p. 505, set E

Supplements
Reteaching 66 or
Practice 66
Challenges 66

Average

Exercises 1-20
Data Bank, p. 481
Skills Bank, p. 465
More Practice, p. 505, set E

Supplements
Practice 66
Challenges 66 or
Thinking Skills 66

Extended

Exercises 5-20
Data Bank, p. 481

Supplements
Challenges 66
Thinking Skills 66

Other Resources:
Problem-Solving Experiences in Mathematics, Grade 4, Problem 117
Math in Stride, Grade 4, pp. 98-99
Using the Math Explorer Calculator: A Sourcebook for Teachers, Chapter 14

7-3

LESSON PLAN 7-3

OBJECTIVE 7-3
To multiply a 2-digit number by a 2-digit multiple of 10

Materials: counters

Grouping Suggestion: pairs

1. MOTIVATE AND TEACH

LEARN ABOUT IT

EXPLORE ► **Explain why you must know that 1 h = 60 min to solve the problem.** (You have a rate per *minute,* you need a total per *hour.*)
► **Justify multiplication as the correct operation.** (Multiply to combine same-size groups.)

TALK ABOUT IT ► **Explain how the Zero Property affects the first step.** (0 × 84 = 0)
► **Analyze the value of the 6 in the second factor.** (It means 6 tens.)
► **Explain a relationship between 84 × 6 and 84 × 60 and between 504 and 5,040.** (60 is 10 times greater than 6, just as 5,040 is 10 times greater than 504.)
► **Explain why Example C has 3 zeros.** (The 0 on the right is for the factor that is a multiple of 10; the other zeros appear as a result of the rest of the multiplication.)
Student Edition answers: **1.** 0 × 84 **2.** 6 tens × 84 = 504 tens **3.** Answers may vary. Possible answer: 80 × 60 = 4,800; round to 5,000. **4.** At 84 beats per/min, your heart beats 5,040 times in 1 h.

2. CHECK UNDERSTANDING

TRY IT OUT

ERROR ALERT Failing to include the 0 in the ones place of the product. Multiplying only the tens digit of the top factor by the tens digits of the multiple of 10.

Multiplying by Multiples of 10

LEARN ABOUT IT

EXPLORE Think About the Process
How many times would your heart beat in one hour on a slow walk, if it beats 84 times a minute? An hour is 60 minutes.

You multiply to find the total number of heartbeats when you have an equal number per minute for 1 hour.

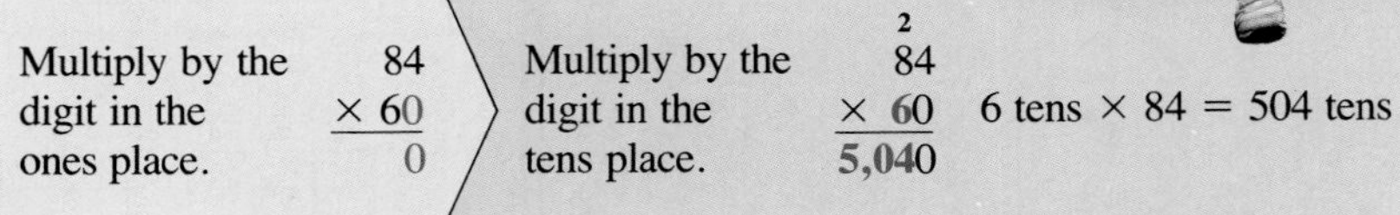

Multiply by the digit in the ones place.
84
× 60
0
Multiply by the digit in the tens place.
2
84
× 60
5,040
6 tens × 84 = 504 tens

TALK ABOUT IT See teaching notes.

1. What product does the first 0 in the answer represent?
2. Why is 504 written to the left of the 0 in the second step?
3. How would you have estimated the total?
4. Give the answer in a complete sentence.

Other Examples

A	B	C	D
64 × 10 = 640	46 × 50 = 2,300 (carry 3)	75 × 80 = 6,000 (carry 4)	40 × 30 = 1,200

TRY IT OUT

Multiply.

1.	2.	3.	4.	5.
36 × 20	76 × 50	53 × 30	89 × 40	16 × 90
720	3,800	1,590	3,560	1,440

TEACHING OPTIONS

RETEACHING TIPS Students mask the 0 in the multiple of 10 with a counter, then multiply by the tens digit as though it were a 1-digit factor. After they multiply, they remove the counter, then annex a 0 to the product to indicate that it is a multiple of 10. Assign Reteaching Supplement 66.

ENRICHMENT Have students use number sense and their understanding of multiplying by a multiple of 10 to find the following products.
1. 357 × 60 (21,420)
2. 463 × 70 (32,410)
3. 918 × 30 (27,540)
4. 502 × 80 (40,160)

PRACTICE

Find the products.

1. 52 × 20 = 1,040	**2.** 67 × 40 = 2,680	**3.** 35 × 80 = 2,800	**4.** 95 × 60 = 5,700
5. 76 × 40 = 3,040	**6.** 41 × 90 = 3,690	**7.** 26 × 10 = 260	**8.** 83 × 50 = 4,150

9. 66 × 50 3,300 **10.** 39 × 30 1,170 **11.** 46 × 60 2,760

12. Find the product when the factors are 83 and 60. 4,980

APPLY

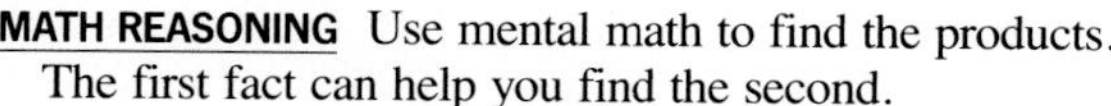

MATH REASONING Use mental math to find the products. The first fact can help you find the second.

13. **a.** 25 × 10 250 **b.** 25 × 20 500 **14.** **a.** 25 × 4 100 **b.** 25 × 40 1,000

PROBLEM SOLVING

15. While Rosella was running, her heart beat 96 times a minute. At this rate, how many times would it beat during a 30-minute run? 2,880 times

16. **Science Data Bank** Compare the average resting heartbeat for girls with that of women. How much greater is the average number of heartbeats for girls than for women? See page 481. 8 beats

DATA BANK

ESTIMATION

Use one or more of these methods to estimate the answers. Tell which method you used. Answers will vary. Sample answers given.

17. 98 × 60 6,000; rounding

18. 48 × 22 1,000; rounding

19. 579 + 617 + 589 + 624 2,400; clustering

20. 456 + 848 1,300; front-end

Choose an Estimation Method
- Front-end
- Rounding
- Clustering

More Practice, page 505, set E

183

3. PRACTICE AND APPLY

Basic	1-7, 11-20
Average	1-20
Extended	5-20

PRACTICE

What number will be in the ones place of each product? Why? (0; All exercises have 1 factor that is a multiple of 10.) *How will you begin Exercises 9 to 12?* (Rewrite each in vertical form.)

APPLY

MATH REASONING ▶ **Explain a relationship between the a and b parts of Exercises 13 and 14.** (13b is twice 13a; 14b is 10 times 14a.)

PROBLEM SOLVING ▶ **Explain how you would solve Problem 15.** (Multiply 96 × 30 to repeat the same rate per minute 30 times.)
▶ **Without using the Data Bank, predict the operation to use to solve Problem 16. Explain why.** (Subtract to compare.)

ESTIMATION ▶ **Explain why it makes sense to use clustering with one of the exercises.** (In Exercise 19, all 4 addends are near 600.)

7-3

CLOSE AND ASSESS

SAY WHAT YOU THINK Have students work in pairs. The first partner explains the steps to follow to multiply 57 × 40. The second partner explains the steps to use to multiply 54 × 70. (2,280; 3,780; Check students' explanations.)

QUICK QUIZ

Find the products.
1. 63 × 40 (2,520)
2. 76 × 30 (2,280)
3. 55 × 50 (2,750)
4. 18 × 90 (1,620)

LESSON OPTIONS 7-4

Multiplying with 2-Digit Factors

OBJECTIVE 7-4 To multiply a 2-digit by a 2-digit number

PREBOOK ACTIVITIES

QUICK REVIEW

Multiply.

1. 64 × 50 (3,200)	**2.** 93 × 80 (7,440)
3. 47 × 40 (1,880)	**4.** 52 × 70 (3,640)
5. 36 × 30 (1,080)	**6.** 18 × 90 (1,620)
7. 85 × 20 (1,700)	**8.** 29 × 10 (290)
9. 71 × 60 (4,260)	**10.** 47 × 50 (2,350)

PRIOR KNOWLEDGE

Have students suggest real-life situations when they might multiply by a 2-digit number that is *not* a multiple of 10. (Sample answers: Given the price of 1 item, find the total cost of a case of 45 items; given an hourly rate, find the total over 24 h.)

COMMUNICATION

Discussing Math Have a volunteer multiply 84 × 30 on the chalkboard as students identify the 2 parts involved in multiplying by a multiple of ten. (First multiply by the 0 ones, then multiply by the 3 tens; 2,520.) Point out that both steps are recorded together because the product of 0 × 84 is 0. Challenge students to apply the same reasoning to consider how to multiply 84 × 32, using what they know about breaking apart factors. (Possible answer: Break apart 32; multiply 84 by the 2 ones, record that product; then multiply 84 by 3 tens, record that product; then combine the 2 products.)

EXPLORE AND CONNECT

Materials: TA 3 (Number Cards 2-6)
Grouping Suggestion: cooperative learning groups of 5
Students explore multiplying by a 2-digit number by breaking apart a factor and combining partial products. One student picks 4 number cards to make a 2-digit by 2-digit problem, such as 26 × 43. The group breaks apart the second factor to multiply in 2 steps. (40 + 3) A second student multiplies the top factor by the ones of the break-apart factor and records that product. (26 × 3 = 78) A third student multiplies the top factor by the tens of the break-apart factor and records that product. (26 × 40 = 1,040) A fourth student adds the 2 products, as a fifth student verifies the product. (1,118) Groups trade tasks and repeat. Students summarize how to multiply by a 2-digit factor. (Multiply by the ones of the bottom factor, record the product; multiply by the tens, record that product; combine the products.)

CONNECTIONS Use these anytime.

Problem of the Day

Missing Digits The same digit goes in every box to give the product of 5,390. What digit is it?

```
   □ □
×  □ 0
 5,3 9 0
```

(7; 77 × 70 = 5,390)

Patterns

Calculator Discover the pattern, then continue it four more times.

12 × 99 = (1,188)
23 × 99 = (2,277)
34 × 99 = (3,366)
45 × 99 = (4,455)

(Each digit of the first factor increases by 1; 56 × 99 = 5,544; 67 × 99 = 6,633; 78 × 99 = 7,722; 89 × 99 = 8,811)

Number Sense

Estimation An arcade game uses quarters only. Ramon collects 82 quarters from the game's money box at the end of 1 day. About how much money is that? (about $20)

Classwork and Homework Supplements

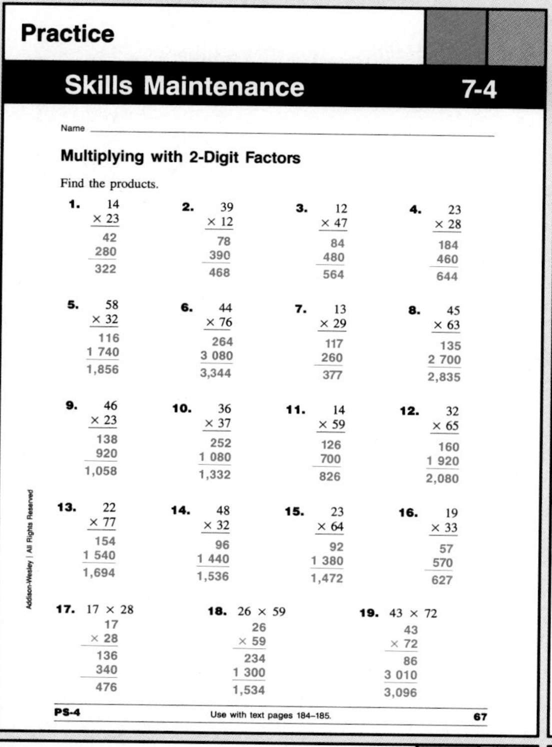

Practice
Skills Maintenance 7-4

Name ____________

Multiplying with 2-Digit Factors

Find the products.

1. 14 × 23 = 42 + 280 = 322
2. 39 × 12 = 78 + 390 = 468
3. 12 × 47 = 84 + 480 = 564
4. 23 × 28 = 184 + 460 = 644
5. 58 × 32 = 116 + 1 740 = 1,856
6. 44 × 76 = 264 + 3 080 = 3,344
7. 13 × 29 = 117 + 260 = 377
8. 45 × 63 = 135 + 2 700 = 2,835
9. 46 × 23 = 138 + 920 = 1,058
10. 36 × 37 = 252 + 1 080 = 1,332
11. 14 × 59 = 126 + 700 = 826
12. 32 × 65 = 160 + 1 920 = 2,080
13. 22 × 77 = 154 + 1 540 = 1,694
14. 48 × 32 = 96 + 1 440 = 1,536
15. 23 × 64 = 92 + 1 380 = 1,472
16. 19 × 33 = 57 + 570 = 627
17. 17 × 28 = 136 + 340 = 476
18. 26 × 59 = 234 + 1 300 = 1,534
19. 43 × 72 = 86 + 3 010 = 3,096

PS-4 Use with text pages 184-185. 67

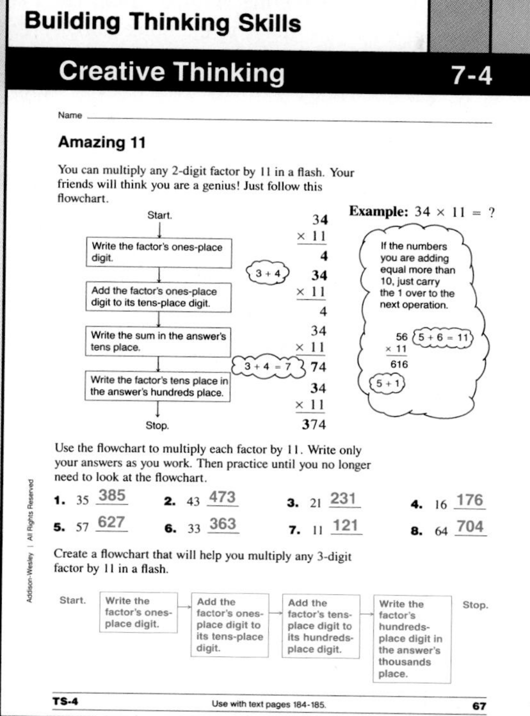

Building Thinking Skills
Creative Thinking 7-4

Name ____________

Amazing 11

You can multiply any 2-digit factor by 11 in a flash. Your friends will think you are a genius! Just follow this flowchart.

Start. → Write the factor's ones-place digit. → Add the factor's ones-place digit to its tens-place digit. → Write the sum in the answer's tens place. → Write the factor's tens place in the answer's hundreds place. → Stop.

34 × 11 = 4; 34 × 11 = 74 (3 + 4); 34 × 11 = 374 (3 + 4 = 7)

Example: 34 × 11 = ?

If the numbers you are adding equal more than 10, just carry the 1 over to the next operation. 56 × 11 = 616 (5 + 6 = 11) (5 + 1)

Use the flowchart to multiply each factor by 11. Write only your answers as you work. Then practice until you no longer need to look at the flowchart.

1. 35 385
2. 43 473
3. 21 231
4. 16 176
5. 57 627
6. 33 363
7. 11 121
8. 64 704

Create a flowchart that will help you multiply any 3-digit factor by 11 in a flash.

Start. → Write the factor's ones-place digit. → Add the factor's ones-place digit to its tens-place digit. → Add the factor's tens-place digit to its hundreds-place digit. → Write the factor's hundreds-place digit in the answer's thousands place. → Stop.

TS-4 Use with text pages 184-185. 67

Reteaching
Skills Review 7-4

Name ____________

Multiplying with 2-Digit Factors

To multiply with 2-digit factors

Multiply by the digit in the ones place. → Multiply by the digit in the tens place. → Add the two products.

65 × 32 = 130 (2 × 65 = 130)

65 × 32: 130, 1,950 (3 tens × 65 = 195 tens)

65 × 32: 130 + 1,950 = 2,080

Find the products.

1. 21 × 23 = 63 + 420 = 483
2. 19 × 35 = 95 + 570 = 665
3. 41 × 52 = 82 + 2,050 = 2,132
4. 32 × 24 = 128 + 640 = 768
5. 68 × 22 = 136 + 1,360 = 1,496
6. 94 × 35 = 470 + 2,820 = 3,290
7. 86 × 98 = 688 + 7,740 = 8,428
8. 99 × 87 = 693 + 7,920 = 8,613
9. 47 × 55 = 2,585
10. 98 × 43 = 4,214
11. 84 × 23 = 1,932
12. 75 × 31 = 2,325

RS-4 Use with text pages 184-185. 67

Challenges
Patterns 7-4

Name ____________

That Amazing 37!

Find the products for the first row of problems using 37 as a factor. Then **predict** the next row of products. Multiply to check your predictions.

1. 37 × 3 = 111
2. 37 × 6 = 222
3. 37 × 9 = 333
4. 37 × 12 = 444
5. 37 × 15 = 555
6. 37 × 18 = 666
7. 37 × 21 = 777 Predicted product: 777
8. 37 × 24 = 888 Predicted product: 888
9. 37 × 27 = 999 Predicted product: 999

Find the products below. Then put the digits of each product in order from greatest to smallest. Find the difference between the first and second digits and between the second and third digits.

Examples: 37 × 10 = 370 Order: 7 3 0 (greatest ... smallest) Differences: 4 3 (7 − 3) (3 − 0)

37 × 16 = 592 Order: 9 5 2 Differences: 4 3

10. 37 × 22 = 814 Order: 8 4 1 Differences: 4 3
11. 37 × 25 = 925 Order: 9 5 2 Differences: 4 3
12. What do you notice about the differences? The differences between the digits are always 4 and 3.

CS-4 Use with text pages 184-185. 67

Options for Individual Needs

Basic

Exercises 1-10, 14-29
Skills Bank, p. 465
Calculator Bank, p. 486
More Practice, p. 505, set F

Supplements
Reteaching 67 or
Practice 67

Average

Exercises 1-33
Skills Bank, p. 465
Calculator Bank, p. 486
More Practice, p. 505, set F

Supplements
Practice 67
Challenges 67 or
Thinking Skills 67

Extended

Exercises 6-33
Calculator Bank, p. 486

Supplements
Challenges 67
Thinking Skills 67

Other Resources:
Problem-Solving Experiences in Mathematics, Grade 4, Problem 119
Middle Grades Mathematics Project: Factors and Multiples, p. 55
Mathematics: A Way of Thinking, Activity 9-7
Using the Math Explorer Calculator: A Sourcebook for Teachers, Chapter 14

LESSON PLAN 7-4

OBJECTIVE 7-4
To multiply a 2-digit by a 2-digit number

Materials: colored pencils

1. MOTIVATE AND TEACH

LEARN ABOUT IT

EXPLORE ▶ **Explain why the problem shows 28 × 24.** (2 dozen means 2 × 12, which is 24.)
▶ **Decide which factors give the product 112 and explain why.** (4 × 28; You multiply by ones first.)
▶ **Decide which factors give the product 560 and explain why.** (28 × 20; You multiply by tens next.)
▶ **Analyze why the 2 products are added to give 672.** (Each of the 2 products was only part of the total product.)

TALK ABOUT IT ▶ **Explain a rule you could use when multiplying by a 2-digit number.** (Possible rule: First multiply by ones, then multiply by tens, then add the 2 products.)
▶ **Explain how this process relates to the order-of-operations rule.** (The rule says to multiply first, then add.)
Student Edition answers: **1.** Possible answer: Round both numbers; 30 × 20 = 600. **2.** At the rate of 28 jumps each time, Mary would make 672 jumps to go around the flower bed 2 dozen times.

2. CHECK UNDERSTANDING

TRY IT OUT

ERROR ALERT Adding trades from the first product to the second product. Forgetting that the second product is a multiple of 10.

Multiplying with 2-digit Factors

LEARN ABOUT IT

EXPLORE Think About the Process
Mary, in the book *The Secret Garden*, could only skip up to 20 when she first got her jump rope. By practicing each day she could soon jump more than 100 times. If it took her 28 jumps to go around a flower bed in the garden, how many jumps would she make after going around 2 dozen times?

You multiply because you need to find the total number of jumps in 24 trips around the flower bed.

Multiply by the digit in the ones place.	$\begin{array}{r} {}^{3}\\ 28 \\ \times 24 \\ \hline 112 \end{array}$	Multiply by the digit in the tens place.	$\begin{array}{r} {}^{1}\\ 28 \\ \times 24 \\ \hline 112 \\ 560 \end{array}$	Add the two products.	$\begin{array}{r} 28 \\ \times 24 \\ \hline 112 \\ 560 \\ \hline 672 \end{array}$

TALK ABOUT IT See teaching notes.

1. How would you have estimated the answer?
2. Give the answer in a complete sentence.

Other Examples

A $\begin{array}{r} 32 \\ \times 23 \\ \hline 96 \\ 640 \\ \hline 736 \end{array}$ B $\begin{array}{r} {}^{1}\\ 34 \\ \times 24 \\ \hline 136 \\ 680 \\ \hline 816 \end{array}$ C $\begin{array}{r} {}^{2}\\ 54 \\ \times 65 \\ \hline 270 \\ 3,240 \\ \hline 3,510 \end{array}$

TRY IT OUT

Multiply.

1. $\begin{array}{r} 26 \\ \times 34 \\ \hline \end{array}$ **884**
2. $\begin{array}{r} 74 \\ \times 25 \\ \hline \end{array}$ **1,850**
3. $\begin{array}{r} 46 \\ \times 28 \\ \hline \end{array}$ **1,288**
4. $\begin{array}{r} 67 \\ \times 42 \\ \hline \end{array}$ **2,814**
5. $\begin{array}{r} 82 \\ \times 76 \\ \hline \end{array}$ **6,232**

184

TEACHING OPTIONS

RETEACHING TIPS Have students use 2 colored pencils. They multiply by ones with the first color, indicating any trades as usual. They use the second color to cross out the trades already used. Then they multiply by tens, indicating any new trades in the second color. Assign Reteaching Supplement 67.

ENRICHMENT Given the factors 38, 41, 54, 65, 77, and 96, have students use estimation and number sense to decide how to pair the factors to give products of 2,665; 2,926; and 5,184. (65 × 41 = 2,665; 77 × 38 = 2,926; 54 × 96 = 5,184)

PRACTICE

Find the products.

1. 53 × 26 = 1,378
2. 36 × 17 = 612
3. 93 × 84 = 7,812
4. 85 × 62 = 5,270
5. 74 × 53 = 3,922
6. 66 × 58 3,828
7. 56 × 78 4,368
8. 68 × 16 1,088
9. 75 × 85 6,375
10. Multiply 36 × 47. 1,692
11. Find the product of 73 and 28. 2,044

APPLY

MATH REASONING Use mental math to make up multiplication problems of 2-digits times 2-digits with these products.
Answers will vary. Sample answers given.

12. 2,000 50 × 40
13. 4,800 60 × 80
14. 7,200 80 × 90
15. 3,000 60 × 50

PROBLEM SOLVING

16. In "Rock the Boat" you skip rope and bounce a ball at the same time. Arlene tried twice. The first time she went 58 skips without missing. The second time she skipped to 116. How much better did she do the second time? twice as well; 58 skips

17. 13 of the fourth grade girls played "Chase the Fox." They ran through the rope 3 times before anyone missed. If they each jumped once the first time through, twice the second time, and 3 times the third time, how many jumps did they make all together? 78 jumps

MIXED REVIEW

18. 3 × 6 = 18
19. 7 × 4 = 28
20. 4 × 9 = 36
21. 3 × 3 = 9
22. 3 × 4 = 12
23. 4 × 8 = 32
24. 7 × 8 = 56
25. 8 × 7 = 56
26. 6 × 6 = 36
27. 7 × 6 = 42
28. 8 × 8 = 64
29. 7 × 7 = 49
30. 36 × 6 216
31. 72 × 7 504
32. 69 × 5 345
33. 82 × 3 246

More Practice, page 505, set F

3. PRACTICE AND APPLY

Basic	1-10, 14-29
Average	1-33
Extended	6-33

PRACTICE

How would you begin to solve Exercises 6 to 9? (Rewrite each in vertical form.)

APPLY

MATH REASONING ► **Analyze the products for a clue that can help you find reasonable factors.** (Possible answer: Look at the 2 greatest digits; imagine 1-digit factors that give that number; use multiples of 10.)

PROBLEM SOLVING ► **Explain how you could compare Arlene's tries in Problem 16.** (Possible answer: Subtract to find the difference between the two attempts.)
► **Justify the operations to use in Problem 17.** (Multiply to combine the same-size groups, then add the products.)

MIXED REVIEW ► **Compare Exercises 18 to 29 with Exercises 30 to 33.** (Exercises 18 to 29 are all basic multiplication facts; Exercises 30 to 33 are not.)

CLOSE AND ASSESS

WRITE WHAT YOU THINK
Have students write organized lists of steps to follow to find the product of 24 and 63. They should show each step in a different color to match their lists. (1,512; Check students' writing.)

QUICK QUIZ

Find the products.

1. 46 × 83 (3,818)
2. 92 × 77 (7,084)
3. 51 × 85 (4,335)
4. 16 × 61 (976)
5. 80 × 49 (3,920)

7-4

LESSON OPTIONS 7-5

Multiplying with 2- and 3-Digit Factors

OBJECTIVE 7-5 To multiply a 3-digit by a 2-digit number

PREBOOK ACTIVITIES

QUICK REVIEW

Multiply.

1. 473 × 7 (3,311) **2.** 826 × 6 (4,956) **3.** 513 × 9 (4,617) **4.** 209 × 8 (1,672)

5. 706 × 4 (2,824) **6.** 785 × 3 (2,355)
7. 562 × 5 (2,810) **8.** 888 × 2 (1,776)

PRIOR KNOWLEDGE

Have students make up a real-life situation to fit the number problem 45 × 14. (Possible answer: *A bus holds 45 riders. How many people can ride in 14 buses?)* Then have students make up another situation to fit the number problem 45 × 365. (Possible answer: *Gramps walks 45 minutes per day. At that rate, how many minutes does he walk in a year?*)

COMMUNICATION

Discussing Math Have students explain how to multiply a 2-digit number by a 2-digit number. (Multiply by ones, record the product; multiply by tens, record the product; add the 2 products.) Have students use logical reasoning to explain how to multiply a 3-digit number by a 2-digit number, such as 365 × 45. (Follow all the same steps: multiply 365 × 5; record the product; multiply 365 × 40, record the product; then add the 2 products for a final product.)

EXPLORE AND CONNECT

Materials: TA 3 (Number Cards 0-9), calculators
Grouping Suggestion: cooperative learning pairs
Students estimate products of 2- and 3-digit factors. The first student in each pair picks any 5 number cards. Both partners discuss how to arrange the cards to form a 2- and a 3-digit factor that will give a product less than 10,000. When they agree on reasonable factors, the second student uses a calculator to find their product. If the product is greater than 10,000, partners may rearrange the cards and multiply again. After successfully formulating factors that give an appropriate product, students repeat the activity, trading tasks. This time they rearrange the same 5 number cards to form factors with a product greater than 20,000. Conclude by having students share their strategies and tell how they adjusted factors when products were too high or too low. (Answers will vary.)

CONNECTIONS Use these anytime.

Problem of the Day

Missing Digits Find the different missing digits.

```
   □3□
×   □6
  3,216
 48,240
 51,456
```

(536 × 96 = 51,456)

Subject Integration

Science Mars is farther from the Sun than Earth is, so a Martian year is longer than an Earth year because it takes Mars longer to travel around the Sun. A year on Mars is 687 Earth days long. Tell how to determine the number of Earth hours in a Martian year. You do not need to do the calculation. (687 × 24)

Number Sense

Estimation Camilla brushes her dog's fur 30 strokes a day with a special brush to protect him from fleas. At that rate, about how many strokes does her dog get in a year? (Estimates may vary; about 11,000)

Classwork and Homework Supplements

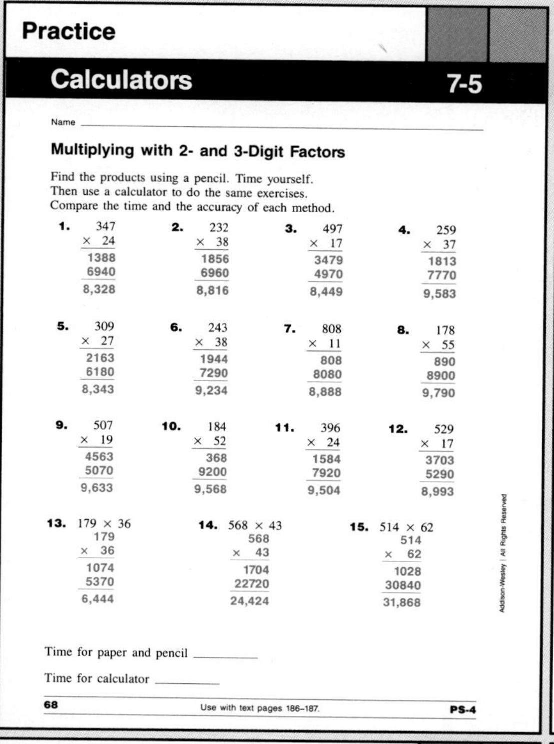

Practice
Calculators 7-5

Name ______

Multiplying with 2- and 3-Digit Factors

Find the products using a pencil. Time yourself.
Then use a calculator to do the same exercises.
Compare the time and the accuracy of each method.

1. 347 × 24 — 1388, 6940, 8,328
2. 232 × 38 — 1856, 6960, 8,816
3. 497 × 17 — 3479, 4970, 8,449
4. 259 × 37 — 1813, 7770, 9,583
5. 309 × 27 — 2163, 6180, 8,343
6. 243 × 38 — 1944, 7290, 9,234
7. 808 × 11 — 808, 8080, 8,888
8. 178 × 55 — 890, 8900, 9,790
9. 507 × 19 — 4563, 5070, 9,633
10. 184 × 52 — 368, 9200, 9,568
11. 396 × 24 — 1584, 7920, 9,504
12. 529 × 17 — 3703, 5290, 8,993
13. 179 × 36 — 179 × 36: 1074, 5370, 6,444
14. 568 × 43 — 568 × 43: 1704, 22720, 24,424
15. 514 × 62 — 514 × 62: 1028, 30840, 31,868

Time for paper and pencil ______

Time for calculator ______

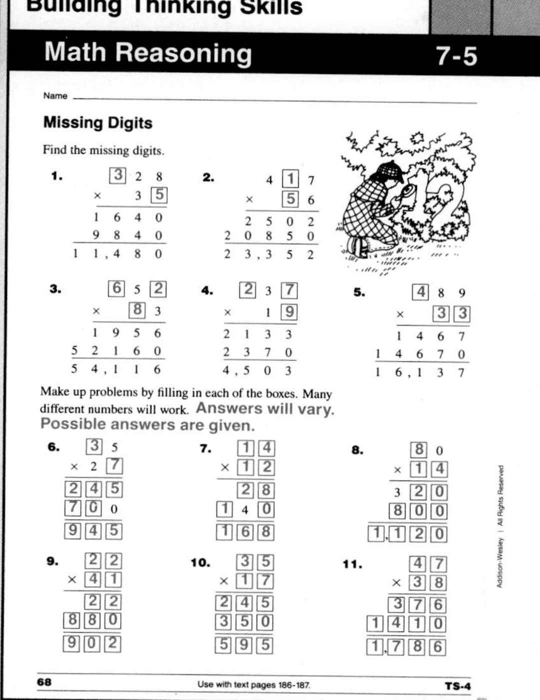

Building Thinking Skills
Math Reasoning 7-5

Name ______

Missing Digits

Find the missing digits.

1. [3] 2 8 × 3 [5] — 1 6 4 0, 9 8 4 0, 1 1 , 4 8 0
2. 4 [1] 7 × [5] 6 — 2 5 0 2, 2 0 8 5 0, 2 3 , 3 5 2
3. [6] 5 [2] × [8] 3 — 1 9 5 6, 5 2 1 6 0, 5 4 , 1 1 6
4. [2] 3 [7] × 1 [9] — 2 1 3 3, 2 3 7 0, 4 , 5 0 3
5. [4] 8 9 × [3] [3] — 1 4 6 7, 1 4 6 7 0, 1 6 , 1 3 7

Make up problems by filling in each of the boxes. Many different numbers will work. Answers will vary. Possible answers are given.

6. [3] 5 × 2 [7] — [2][4][5], [7][0] 0, [9][4][5]
7. [1][4] × [1][2] — [2][8], [1] 4 [0], [1][6][8]
8. [8] 0 × [1][4] — 3 [2][0], [8][0][0], [1],[1][2][0]
9. [2][2] × [4][1] — [2][2], [8][8][0], [9][0][2]
10. [3][5] × [1][7] — [2][4][5], [3][5][0], [5][9][5]
11. [4][7] × [3][8] — [3][7][6], [1][4][1][0], [1],[7][8][6]

Reteaching
Skills Review 7-5

Name ______

Multiplying with 2- and 3-Digit Factors

Multiply by ones. → Multiply by tens. → Add the products.

148 × 53 = 444 (3 × 148 = 444)

148 × 53: 444, 7,400 (5 tens × 148 = 740 tens)

148 × 53: 444 + 7,400 = 7,844

Find the products.

1. 423 × 45 — 2115 + 16920 = 19,035
2. 834 × 68 — 6672 + 50040 = 56,712
3. 924 × 26 — 5544 + 18480 = 24,024
4. 783 × 79 — 7047 + 54810 = 61,857
5. 752 × 25 — 3760 + 15040 = 18,800
6. 634 × 80 — 50,720
7. 763 × 47 — 5341 + 30520 = 35,861
8. 908 × 39 — 8172 + 27240 = 35,412
9. 453 × 71 — 453 + 31710 = 32,163
10. 674 × 85 — 3370 + 53920 = 57,290
11. 312 × 58 — 2496 + 1560 = 18,096

Challenges
Creative Thinking 7-5

Name ______

Digit Switcheroo

Use these digits to create each problem. Use each digit only once in each problem. 1 3 4 7 9

1. Fill in the boxes to create problems whose products are larger than 29,000.

   Answers will vary. Possible answers: 974 × 31, 941 × 37

2. Fill in the boxes to create problems whose products are less than 8,500.

   Possible answers: 173 × 49, 149 × 37

3. Fill in the boxes to create a problem whose product is close to 15,000.

   Possible answer: 479 × 31

Each problem below uses the digits 1, 2, 3, 4, 5, and 6. Predict which problem has the larger product. Check your prediction. Predictions will vary.

162 × 53 = 8,586 153 × 62 = 9,486

Options for Individual Needs

Basic

Exercises 4-16
Skills Bank, p. 465
Calculator Bank, p. 485
More Practice, p. 505, set G

Supplements
Reteaching 68 or
Practice 68

Average

Exercises 1-16
Skills Bank, p. 465
Calculator Bank, p. 485
More Practice, p. 505, set G

Supplements
Practice 68
Challenges 68 or
Thinking Skills 68

Extended

Exercises 6-16
Calculator Bank, p. 485

Supplements
Challenges 68
Thinking Skills 68

Other Resources:

Problem-Solving Experiences in Mathematics, Grade 4, Problem 122

Middle Grades Mathematics Project: Factors and Multiples, pp. 56, 57

Mathematics: A Way of Thinking, Activity 9-14

Using the Math Explorer Calculator: A Sourcebook for Teachers, Chapter 14

LESSON PLAN 7-5

OBJECTIVE 7-5
To multiply a 3-digit by a 2-digit number

Materials: TA 12 (Centimeter Graph Paper), calculators

1. MOTIVATE AND TEACH

LEARN ABOUT IT

EXPLORE ▶ **Justify the factors used in the example.** (365 is the number of days in a regular year; 48 is the number of aerobic points Mr. Suzuki earns each day he skips rope for 2 h.)
▶ **Explain which factors give the product 2,920.** (365 × 8, because you multiply by ones first)
▶ **Explain which factors give the product 14,600.** (365 × 40, because you multiply by tens next)

TALK ABOUT IT ▶ **Explain why you add the 2 products.** (You broke apart 48 to find 2 separate products, so you must put them back together by adding.)
▶ **Explain why you need to line up the products before you add them.** (to be sure to add like places)
Student Edition answers: **1.** Possible answer: Round 48 up to 50; round 365 down to 360; 18,000 **2.** At 48 aerobic points per day, Mr. Suzuki would have 17,520 aerobic points in a regular year.

2. CHECK UNDERSTANDING

TRY IT OUT

ERROR ALERT Lining up the 2 products incorrectly, causing addition errors. Forgetting that the second product is a multiple of 10.

Multiplying with 2- and 3-Digit Factors

LEARN ABOUT IT

1 regular year = 365 days
1 leap year = 366 days
Every 4th year is a leap year.

EXPLORE **Think About the Process**
Katsumi Suzuki holds world records in 3 jump rope events. Usually, Mr. Suzuki skips rope for 2 hours each day. This has an aerobic value of 48 points. How many aerobic points would he have for skipping rope every day in a year that is not a leap year?

You multiply to find the total aerobic points when the same number is earned each day for a year.

Multiply by ones.	Multiply by tens.	Add the products.
(regroup 5 4) 365 × 48 = **2,920**	(regroup 2 2) 365 × 48: 2,920; **14,600**	365 × 48: **2,920** + **14,600** = **17,520**

TALK ABOUT IT See teaching notes.

1. How would you have estimated the answer?
2. Give the answer in a complete sentence.

Other Examples

A	B	C
286 × 23	305 × 82	840 × 37
858	610	5,880
5,720	24,400	25,200
6,578	25,010	31,080

TRY IT OUT

Multiply.

1. 542 × 23 = 12,466
2. 704 × 57 = 40,128
3. 680 × 39 = 26,520
4. 500 × 24 = 12,000

186

TEACHING OPTIONS

RETEACHING TIPS Have students write each digit in a separate box on centimeter graph paper. This will help them correctly line up the products to avoid addition errors. Assign Reteaching Supplement 68.

ENRICHMENT 12,345,679 × 9 = 111,111,111
Students use number sense and the example above to find these products.
12,345,679 × 18 (222,222,222)
12,345,679 × 27 (333,333,333)
12,345,679 × 54 (666,666,666)
12,345,679 × 63 (777,777,777)
12,345,679 × 81 (999,999,999)

PRACTICE

Find the products.

1. 572 × 26	2. 813 × 94	3. 546 × 67	4. 725 × 13	5. 489 × 76
14,872	76,422	36,582	9,425	37,164

6. 360 × 47	7. 273 × 65	8. 361 × 88
16,920	17,745	31,768

Estimate the products. Answers will vary. Sample answers given.

9. 397 × 48 20,000 10. 617 × 89 60,000 11. 84 × 791 64,000

APPLY

MATH REASONING Without using pencil and paper, tell which equation has the larger product.

12. 36 × 487 or 46 × 487

13. 58 × 649 or 58 × 639

PROBLEM SOLVING

14. Manuel's fastest jump rope time was 105 times in a minute. At that rate, how many jumps would he make in 12 tries? 1,260 jumps

15. How many more hours are in a leap year than in an ordinary year? A day has 24 hours. 24 hours

▶ CALCULATOR

16. Use a calculator. Multiply any number by 9 and add together the digits in your answer. If the result is more than 1 digit, add those together until you get a 1-digit answer. Do this with several other numbers, always using 9 as a factor. Do you think it is always, sometimes, or never true that the digits in the answer will add up to 9? Would you give the same answer for multiplying by 90? always; yes

Multiply	Add the Digits
9 × 6 = 54	5 + 4 = 9
9 × 62 = 558	5 + 5 + 8 = 18 1 + 8 = 9

More Practice, page 505, set G

3. Practice and Apply

Basic	4-16
Average	1-16
Extended	6-16

PRACTICE

Predict which exercise in the top row has the smallest product. (Exercise 4)

APPLY

MATH REASONING ▶ **Compare the factors in Exercise 12.** (Both have factors of 487 multiplied by 36 or 46.) ▶ **Analyze the factor pairs in Exercise 13.** (58 is a factor in both pairs, so the larger product will belong to the pair with the larger second factor.)

PROBLEM SOLVING ▶ **Justify multiplication as the correct operation in Problem 14.** (Multiply to put together same-size groups.) ▶ **Interpret the situation in Problem 15.** (A leap year has 1 more day than a regular year, so how many more hours would it have?)

CALCULATOR ▶ **Explain why you should try the experiment a few times before you generalize.** (to see if you ever find a counterexample)

Close and Assess

SHOW WHAT YOU KNOW

Write 245 × 26 on the chalkboard. Have students unscramble the following numbers to complete the multiplication: 4,900; 6,370; 1,470.

```
   245
×   26
 1,470
 4,900
 6,370
```

QUICK QUIZ

1. 256 × 35 (8,960) 2. 183 × 96 (17,568) 3. 479 × 42 (20,118)

4. 45 × 216 (9,720)

7-5

LESSON OPTIONS 7-6

Using Critical Thinking Skills/Midchapter Review/Quiz

OBJECTIVE 7-6 To use critical thinking to find the number that multiplied by itself gives the square

PREBOOK ACTIVITIES

QUICK REVIEW

Find the products mentally.

1. 30 × 30 (900)	**2.** 50 × 50 (2,500)
3. 90 × 90 (8,100)	**4.** 20 × 20 (400)
5. 70 × 70 (4,900)	**6.** 40 × 40 (1,600)
7. 10 × 10 (100)	**8.** 80 × 80 (6,400)
9. 60 × 60 (3,600)	**10.** 0 × 0 (0)

PRIOR KNOWLEDGE

Have a volunteer draw a square on the chalkboard and relate it to the square fact 3 × 3 = 9. (Possible answer: A square has equal sides; a square fact has equal factors; draw small boxes inside the square to show 3 rows of 3 boxes each, which is 9 boxes.) Have students identify other square facts. (1 × 1, 2 × 2, 4 × 4, 5 × 5, and so on)

COMMUNICATION

Discussing and Reading Math Write this statement on the chalkboard: We can show 3 × 3 as 3^2 and say "three squared." Have students explain in their own words what it means to square a number. (to multiply a number by itself, as in 3 × 3) Ask students what 20^2 would mean and what its product would be. (twenty squared; 20 × 20; 400) Have students use the math phrase *to square a number* when they want to express the idea of multiplying a number by itself.

EXPLORE AND CONNECT

Materials: calculators

Grouping Suggestion: cooperative learning pairs

Students explore multiples of 10, special products, and **square** numbers. One student picks a multiple of 10 from 10 to 80, *squares* it, and records the product. A second student *squares* the next consecutive multiple of 10 and records its product. Students estimate the *square* of the number halfway between the 2 multiples of 10, then multiply it by itself on a calculator to check. For example, if students find 30^2 = 900 and 40^2 = 1,600, they may estimate 35^2 as about 1,250, since that number is halfway between 900 and 1,600. Partners repeat with 2 other multiples of 10, then try to estimate the *square* of the number halfway between them. Students summarize any pattern they saw. (Possible answer: The *square* of the number halfway between two multiples of 10 is 25 less than the number halfway between the 2 special products.)

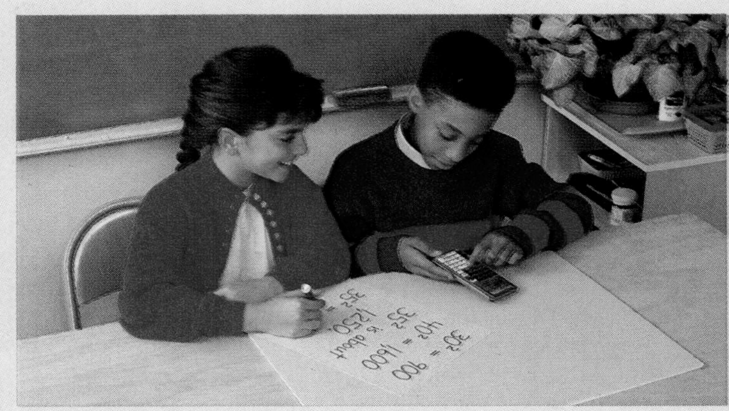

CONNECTIONS Use these anytime.

Problem of the Day

Number Riddle Find the mystery number and the product when it is multiplied by itself. 1) I am the smallest 2-digit even number whose digits add to 4. 2) I look the same backward and forward and so does my square product. 3) My square product is a 3-digit number. (22; 484)

Math Connection

Geometry Margo got a small square table for her back porch and covered the top with 1-in. square tiles. If the table measures 15 in. on each side, how many tiles did she need? Draw a picture if it will help. (225)

Life Skills

Gardening Gene cultivates a square patch of ground for his flower garden. He plants a dozen rows of tulips with 12 bulbs in each row. How many tulips does Gene plant in all? (144)

Classwork and Homework Supplements

Practice

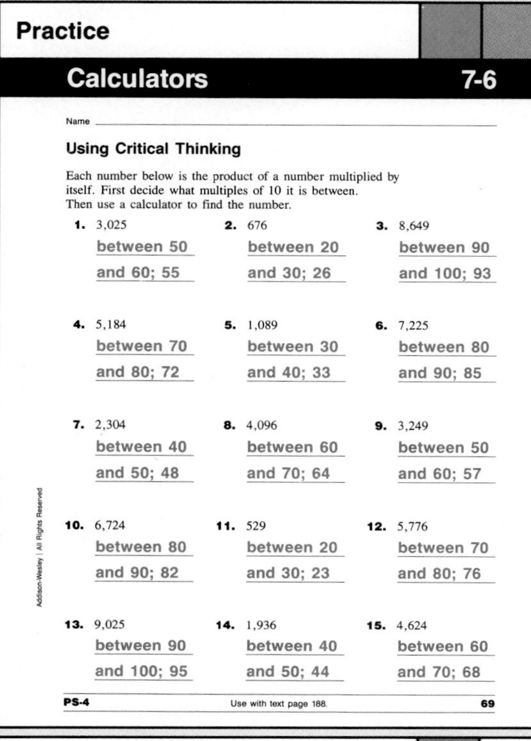

Calculators 7-6

Name

Using Critical Thinking

Each number below is the product of a number multiplied by itself. First decide what multiples of 10 it is between. Then use a calculator to find the number.

1. 3,025 between 50 and 60; 55
2. 676 between 20 and 30; 26
3. 8,649 between 90 and 100; 93
4. 5,184 between 70 and 80; 72
5. 1,089 between 30 and 40; 33
6. 7,225 between 80 and 90; 85
7. 2,304 between 40 and 50; 48
8. 4,096 between 60 and 70; 64
9. 3,249 between 50 and 60; 57
10. 6,724 between 80 and 90; 82
11. 529 between 20 and 30; 23
12. 5,776 between 70 and 80; 76
13. 9,025 between 90 and 100; 95
14. 1,936 between 40 and 50; 44
15. 4,624 between 60 and 70; 68

Addison-Wesley | All Rights Reserved

PS-4 Use with text page 188. 69

Building Thinking Skills

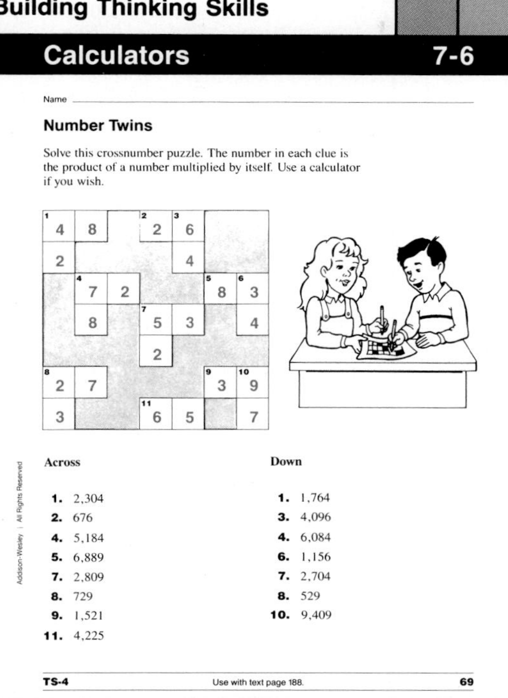

Calculators 7-6

Name

Number Twins

Solve this crossnumber puzzle. The number in each clue is the product of a number multiplied by itself. Use a calculator if you wish.

1 4	8		2 2	3 6		
2				4		
	4 7	2			5 8	6 3
	8		7 5	3		4
			2			
8 2	7				9 3	10 9
3			11 6	5		7

Across

1. 2,304
2. 676
4. 5,184
5. 6,889
7. 2,809
8. 729
9. 1,521
11. 4,225

Down

1. 1,764
3. 4,096
4. 6,084
6. 1,156
7. 2,704
8. 529
10. 9,409

Addison-Wesley | All Rights Reserved

TS-4 Use with text page 188. 69

Reteaching

Calculators 7-6

Name

Using Critical Thinking

What number multiplied by itself is 2,116?

Find the multiples of 10 it is between.		Choose numbers and find their product. Use a calculator.	
40 × 40 = 1,600	Try 45	45 × 45 = 2,025	too small
50 × 50 = 2,500	Try 47	47 × 47 = 2,209	too big
	Try 46	46 × 46 = 2,116.	

2,116 is between 1,600 and 2,500 and closer to 2,500. So the number is between 40 and 50 and closer to 50.

The number is **46.**

Find these products.

1. 10 × 10 = 100
2. 20 × 20 = 400
3. 30 × 30 = 900
4. 40 × 40 = 1,600
5. 50 × 50 = 2,500
6. 60 × 60 = 3,600
7. 70 × 70 = 4,900
8. 80 × 80 = 6,400
9. 90 × 90 = 8,100

Each number below is the product of a number multiplied by itself. First decide what multiples of 10 it is between. Use the answers to the exercises above to help you. Then use a calculator to find the number.

10. 196 Between 10 and 20. The number is 14.
11. 529 Between 20 and 30. The number is 23.
12. 2,704 50 and 60; 52
13. 1,444 30 and 40; 38
14. 5,776 70 and 80; 76
15. 3,025 50 and 60; 55

Addison-Wesley | All Rights Reserved

RS-4 Use with text page 188. 69

Challenges

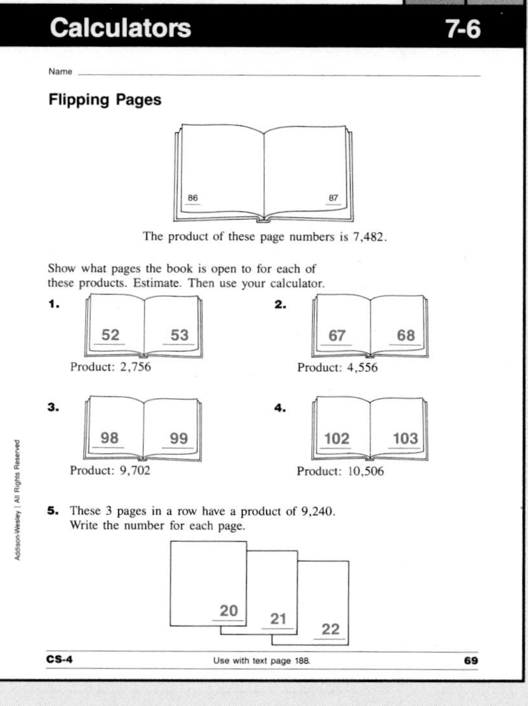

Calculators 7-6

Name

Flipping Pages

86 87

The product of these page numbers is 7,482.

Show what pages the book is open to for each of these products. Estimate. Then use your calculator.

1. 52 53 Product: 2,756
2. 67 68 Product: 4,556
3. 98 99 Product: 9,702
4. 102 103 Product: 10,506
5. These 3 pages in a row have a product of 9,240. Write the number for each page. 20 21 22

Addison-Wesley | All Rights Reserved

CS-4 Use with text page 188. 69

Options for Individual Needs

Basic

Exercises 1-5; 2-7, 13-34

Supplements
Reteaching 69 or
Practice 69

Average

Exercises 1-6; 1-34

Supplements
Practice 69
Challenges 69 or
Thinking Skills 69

Extended

Exercises 3-6; 3-7, 14-34

Supplements
Challenges 69
Thinking Skills 69

Other Resources:
Problem-Solving Experiences in Mathematics, Grade 4, Problem 40
Mathematics: A Way of Thinking, Activity 5-11
Using the Math Explorer Calculator: A Sourcebook for Teachers, Chapter 14

LESSON PLAN 7-6

OBJECTIVE 7-6
To use critical thinking to find the number that multiplied by itself gives the square

Materials: calculators

Grouping Suggestion: pairs

1. MOTIVATE AND TEACH

LEARN ABOUT IT

EXPLORE ▶ **Explain what the x^2 key does.** (It squares a number, or multiplies it by itself.)
▶ **Without an x^2 key, explain how to square a number on a calculator.** (Enter the number, press x, enter the same number, press =.)
▶ **Analyze Beth's thinking.** (She narrowed the possibilities using special products; 30^2 is less than 1,024, 40^2 is greater than 1,024; the number to square is between 30 and 40.)

TALK ABOUT IT ▶ **Decide which multiple of 10 has a square closer to Brad's product. Explain.** (30 × 30 is only about 100 less than 1,024; 40 × 40 is about 600 greater than 1,024.)
▶ **How does the ones digit in 1,024 give a clue to the secret number?** (1,024 ends in 4, so the ones place of the factor must be a square number whose product ends in 4.)
Student Edition answers: **1.** He entered a number and pressed x^2 to get 1,024; he asks Beth to find the factor he squared. **2.** It is a number between 30 and 40. **3.** 30; 1,024 is nearer to 900 than to 1,600. **4.** Possible answer: Try Guess and Check.

2. CHECK UNDERSTANDING

TRY IT OUT

ERROR ALERT Failing to determine the multiples of 10 between which the product falls.

Using Critical Thinking

LEARN ABOUT IT

Brad showed Beth his calculator. "I've used the x^2 key on my calculator to multiply a number by itself. The product is 1,024," said Brad. "Can you use my calculator and find the number? I'll tell you what multiple of 10 it's close to, so you'll know where to start!"

Beth thought for a while. "No thanks," she said. "I won't need your hint. I already know where to start!"

Beth was thinking: 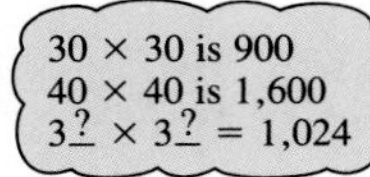
30 × 30 is 900
40 × 40 is 1,600
3? × 3? = 1,024

TALK ABOUT IT See teaching notes.

1. What did Brad do to produce 1,024 on his calculator? What did he ask Beth to do?
2. What did Beth learn about Brad's number from the products she thought about?
3. What multiple of 10 is Brad's number closest to? How do you know?
4. How would you use a calculator to find Brad's number?

TRY IT OUT

Each number below is the product of a number multiplied by itself. First decide what multiples of 10 it is between. Then use a calculator to find the number.

1. 1,849 between 40 and 50, 43
2. 5,476 between 70 and 80, 74
3. 729 between 20 and 30, 27
4. 3,136 between 50 and 60, 56
5. 6,561 between 80 and 90, 81
6. 625 between 20 and 30, 25

188 

TEACHING OPTIONS

RETEACHING TIPS Partners identify front-end digits in Exercise 1. (18) They think of square products *under* and *over* 18: 4 × 4 = 16, 5 × 5 = 25. Then they affix a zero to each factor to give special products. Pairs can now guess and check to find the ones digit. Assign Reteaching Supplement 69.

COMPUTER **Pond: Explorations in Problem Solving, Sunburst Communications, Copyright 1985** For all student levels. In Level 2, predict number and direction of steps the frog should take to hop to shore. Advanced students may try Level 3. Each level requires 10-20 min.

MIDCHAPTER REVIEW/QUIZ

Estimate each product.

1. 44 × 53 2,000
2. 29 × $7.67 $240.00
3. 72 × 429 28,000
4. 655 × 19 14,000

Decide if each estimate in red is an overestimate or an underestimate. Then give a closer estimate. See Additional Answers.

5. 37 × 28 1,200
6. 32 × $5.42 $150.00
7. 88 × 366 36,000
8. 243 × 97 20,000

Find the products. Use estimation and mental math to decide if your answer is reasonable.

9. 20 × 30 600
10. 24 × 50 1,200
11. 78 × 90 7,020
12. 90 × 30 2,700
13. 70 × 60 4,200
14. 63 × 80 5,040
15. 50 × 20 1,000
16. 80 × 70 5,600
17. 72 × 30 2,160
18. 64 × 16 1,024
19. 88 × 55 4,840
20. 32 × 75 2,400
21. 105 × 39 4,095
22. 681 × 26 17,706
23. 95 × 48 4,560
24. 37 × 18 666
25. 607 × 87 52,809
26. $7.25 × 84 $609.00
27. 28 × 35 980
28. $4.95 × 26 $128.70
29. 479 × 60 28,740
30. 700 × 41 28,700
31. $1.98 × 14 $27.72

PROBLEM SOLVING

32. If an elephant's heart beats 33 times in 1 minute, how many times does it beat in 1 hour? An hour is 60 minutes. 1,980 times

33. In one minute, a canary's heart beats about 22 times faster than an elephant's heart. Which of these 3 products give the closest estimate? b

a. 20 × 30
b. 25 × 30
c. 22 × 30

34. When Billy runs, his heart beats about twice as fast as normal. After a short rest, Billy's heart rate drops 30 beats per minute to reach 110. What is his normal heart rate? 70 beats per minute

189

3. PRACTICE AND APPLY

Basic	1-5; 2-7, 13-34
Average	1-6; 1-34
Extended	3-6; 3-7; 14-34

Additional Answers: See p. T79.

PRACTICE

How would you estimate Exercise 2? (Round $7.67 to $8, round 29 to 30, then multiply.) *How do Exercises 9-16 differ from Exercises 17-31?* (You can use special products to multiply in Exercises 9-16; Exercises 9-16 are horizontal, and Exercises 17-26 are vertical.)

ITEM ANALYSIS The following table correlates the Midchapter Review/Quiz items with the lesson objectives.

Items	Objectives
1-8, 33	7-2
9, 12, 13, 15, 16	7-1
10, 11, 14, 17, 32, (33)	7-3
18-20, 23, 24, 27	7-4
21, 22, 25, 26, 28-31	7-5

CLOSE AND ASSESS

WRITE WHAT YOU THINK

Have students list the steps to follow to discover the number that multiplied by itself equals 3,844. Then ask students to trade papers with a partner, who follows the steps exactly to verify that they make sense. (62; Check students' writing.)

QUICK QUIZ

What number multiplied by itself gives the product? Use a calculator to help you.

1. 4,624 (68) **2.** 2,209 (47)
3. 3,025 (55) **4.** 8,464 (92)

LESSON OPTIONS 7-7

Problem Solving: Use Logical Reasoning

OBJECTIVE 7-7 To solve problems using the strategy Use Logical Reasoning

PREBOOK ACTIVITIES

QUICK REVIEW

Use mental math to add or subtract.

1. 25 − 9 (16)
2. 43 + 18 (61)
3. 25 + 26 (51)
4. 34 − 14 (20)
5. 30 − 11 (19)
6. 7 + 5 + 3 (15)
7. 27 + 13 (40)
8. 28 − 12 (16)
9. 40 + 37 + 60 (137)
10. 90 − 57 (33)

PRIOR KNOWLEDGE

Pose this riddle: How much dirt is inside a hole 3 ft wide, 2 ft long, and 1 ft deep? (none; A hole has no dirt inside it.) Have students analyze the reasoning used in the riddle and in its solution. (Possible answer: At first, the question makes you imagine complicated computation, but if you think about the situation logically, you see that you do not need to calculate at all.) Invite students to share any similar riddles or jokes they may know that depend on logic. (Answers will vary.)

COMMUNICATION

Discussing Math Tell students that the word **logic** comes from the Greek word *logos,* which means "reason, word, or speech." Have students consider what it means to think **logically.** (Possible answer: "to use careful, organized reasons to support an idea") Have students suggest some ways to think logically. (Possible answers: notice patterns; recognize relationships; support points with fact; consider all sides of an argument)

EXPLORE AND CONNECT

COOPERATIVE ACTIVITY

Grouping Suggestion: small groups

9 baseball players voted for a new team captain. Wes got 7 votes and Andy got 5 votes. Explain how this could have happened.

TEACHING ACTIONS

Have students work in small groups to discuss the situation and to use logical reasoning to determine what happened.

BEFORE

► **Explain the situation.** (9 team members voted for a team captain.)

► **Analyze the problem for important data.** (9 players; 7 voted for Wes, 5 voted for Andy)

DURING

► **Analyze a fact that makes no sense.** (5 + 7 = 12, but there are only 9 members on the team.)

► **What explanation could fit the situation?** Some team members voted more than once.

► **Decide how many extra votes were cast.** (3)

AFTER

► **Explain your conclusion.** (Since there are three extra votes, 3 team members must have voted twice.)

► **Explain a way to prove the conclusion.** (12 − 3 = 9; 9 is the number of team members.)

CONNECTIONS Use these anytime.

Problem of the Day

Milk Count Each morning, the 27 students in Mr. Lin's class order whole or skim milk. One day, they ordered 10 whole milks and 25 skim milks. How many milks were ordered in all? Relate the total to the number of students in the class and explain what must have happened. (35; 8 extra milks; 8 students wanted 2 milks with their lunch.)

Math Connection

Calculator Use a calculator to solve this long equation: 348 × 7 ÷ 6 × 2 − 79 = ? Enter the numbers and operations in the order they appear. After you press =, guess what sea creature's name you would see in the display if you turned the calculator upside down. (733, EEL)

Creative Thinking

Reasonable Possibilities Lucy drops an egg 5 ft, but the egg does not break. Use logical reasoning to find three possible explanations for this amazing fact. (Possible answers: Lucy drops a plastic egg; someone catches it; the egg lands on something very soft; it is in a padded container.)

Classwork and Homework Supplements

Practice

Problem Solving 7-7

Name ______

Use Logical Reasoning

Use logical reasoning to solve each problem.

1. All 23 of Mr. Rodman's students visited the school store. 17 students bought pencils. 12 students bought paper. How many students bought both pencils and paper? 6 students

2. On Friday, 36 fourth graders visited the store. 19 students bought graph paper. 26 students bought protractors. How many students bought both graph paper and protractors? 9 students

3. During School Spirit Week, 132 students bought school bumper stickers and car window decals. 74 school bumper stickers and 78 car window decals were sold. How many students bought both bumper stickers and window decals? 20 students

4. On Tuesday, 40 students visited the store and purchased felt tip pens. 27 students purchased blue ones and 20 students purchased red ones. How many students purchased both blue and red pens? 7 students

5. For School Spirit Week, T-shirts and sweatshirts were on sale. Of the 25 students in Ms. Chin's class, 19 bought T-shirts. Sweatshirt sales totaled 11. How many students bought both kinds of shirts? 5 students

6. Blue and gold pom-poms were sold to 93 students. 62 students bought blue pom-poms and 79 students bought gold pom-poms. How many bought both blue and gold pom-poms? 48 students

Building Thinking Skills

Critical Thinking 7-7

Name ______

Numbers Get into Shape

The numbers 1-9 are placed inside the shapes.

Write the numbers that are inside:

1. the circle 1, 2, 3, 4, 8
2. the square 3, 6, 8
3. the triangle 1, 2, 9
4. the rectangle 2, 5, 6, 7, 8
5. the triangle, but not the rectangle 1, 9
6. the square, but not the circle 6
7. both the rectangle and the circle 2, 8
8. both the triangle and the circle 1, 2

Find the product of the numbers that are inside:

9. the triangle 18
10. the square and **only** the circle 576

Hint: square 3, 8, 6; only the circle 4

Reteaching

Problem Solving 7-7

Name ______

Use Logical Reasoning

Terri has 28 students in her gym class. 14 of them run around the track. 18 of them jump hurdles. How many students both run and jump?

Think logically about the data.

Add how many run or jump. → Write how many students in class. → Subtract to find how many do both.

14 run + 18 jump = 32 run and/or jump | 28 students | 32 − 28 = **4**, **4** students do both.

Use logical reasoning to solve each problem.

1. Tom has 34 students in his class. 20 of them run around the track. 18 of them throw the discus. How many do both?
   How many run and/or throw? 38
   How many students in class? 34
   How many do both? 4

2. There are 58 students on Amy's track team. 26 of them jump hurdles. 38 of them take part in the high jump. How many do both? 6

3. There are 24 judges at the track meet. 13 of them judge the shot put, and 16 judge the pole vault. How many judge both events? 5

4. There are 12 people on the track team. During practice, 9 run the 500 meter dash. 8 run cross country. How many practice both? 5

5. The coach bought shirts for the 64 students on the track team. 24 of the students want yellow. 52 of them want green. How many want both colors? 12

Challenges

Creative Thinking 7-7

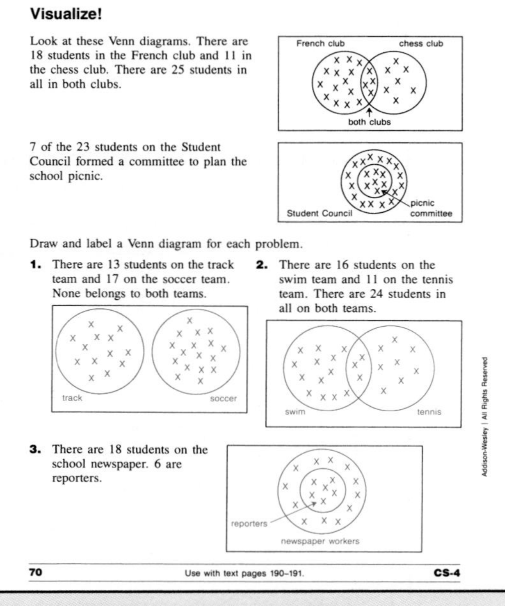

Name ______

Visualize!

Look at these Venn diagrams. There are 18 students in the French club and 11 in the chess club. There are 25 students in all in both clubs.

7 of the 23 students on the Student Council formed a committee to plan the school picnic.

Draw and label a Venn diagram for each problem.

1. There are 13 students on the track team and 17 on the soccer team. None belongs to both teams.

2. There are 16 students on the swim team and 11 on the tennis team. There are 24 students in all on both teams.

3. There are 18 students on the school newspaper. 6 are reporters.

Options for Individual Needs

Basic

Exercises 1-5, 7-8
Skills Bank, pp. 462, 465
Calculator Bank, p. 488
Computer Bank, p. 492
More Practice, p. 516, set E

Supplements
Reteaching 70 or
Practice 70

Average

Exercises 1-8
Skills Bank, p. 465
Calculator Bank, p. 488
Computer Bank, p. 492
More Practice, p. 516, set E

Supplements
Practice 70
Challenges 70 or
Thinking Skills 70

Extended

Exercises 1-7
Calculator Bank, p. 488
Computer Bank, p. 492

Supplements
Challenges 70
Thinking Skills 70

Other Resources:

Problem-Solving Experiences in Mathematics, Grade 4, Problems 69, 70
Make It Simpler, pp. 23-26
Using the Math Explorer Calculator: A Sourcebook for Teachers, Chapter 14

LESSON PLAN 7-7

OBJECTIVE 7-7
To solve problems using the strategy Use Logical Reasoning

Materials: counters

Grouping Suggestion: pairs

1. MOTIVATE AND TEACH

LEARN ABOUT IT

► **Summarize the situation.** (25 students chose from 2 different toppings for their frozen yogurts.)

► **Determine how many toppings were ordered in all. Explain.** (30; 14 + 16 = 30)

► **Compare the number of students to the number of toppings.** (25 students, 30 toppings)

► **Explain why the numbers could be different.** (Some students may have ordered 2 toppings.)

► **Find the difference of the 2 numbers, then explain how it relates to the situation.** (5; 5 students must have ordered both toppings.)

AFTER

► **Use logical reasoning to evaluate the solution.** (Possible answer: If 25 students each order 1 topping, but 5 of them order a second topping, 25 + 5 = 30, as does 16 + 14.)

2. CHECK UNDERSTANDING

TRY IT OUT

► **Use logical reasoning to explain how you know that some people have to work at both of Mrs. Fong's stores.** (12 video-store workers and 9 yogurt-shop workers equal 21, yet the problem says Mrs. Fong has only 16 workers.)

ERROR ALERT Comparing the wrong data.

Problem Solving
Use Logical Reasoning

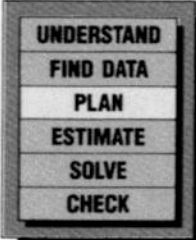

LEARN ABOUT IT

To solve some problems, you need to write down what you know and then think logically about the facts. This problem solving strategy is called **Use Logical Reasoning**.

When Judy's class went to the Frozen Yogurt Shop, all 25 students ordered toppings. 14 ordered fruit toppings and 16 ordered nut toppings. How many ordered both toppings?

14 ordered fruit toppings. 16 ordered nut toppings. So 30 toppings were ordered in all

The class ordered 30 toppings in all.

There were only 25 students. They all ordered toppings.

25 students ordered toppings.

There are 5 more toppings than students.

5 of the students must have ordered both a fruit topping and a nut topping.

5 students ordered both toppings.

TRY IT OUT

Mrs. Fong owns the Midland Video Store and the Frozen Yogurt Shop. 16 people work for Mrs. Fong all together. 9 people work at the video store and 12 people work at the yogurt shop. How many people work at both stores? **5**

- What is the total number of people who work for Mrs. Fong? **16**
- How many people work at the video store? **9**
- How many people work at the yogurt shop? **12**
- Copy the data shown. Use it to help you solve the problem logically.

People who work for Mrs. Fong	16
People who work at the video store	9
People who work at the yogurt shop	12

190

TEACHING OPTIONS

RETEACHING TIPS Have students use counters for the 16 workers, setting aside 9 as the video-store workers. The 7 counters left are not enough for the 12 yogurt-shop workers. Have students move counters to show the number that have two jobs. (5) Assign Reteaching Supplement 70.

ENRICHMENT Have students solve the question for this situation: *20 people ordered 1 or 2 snacks. 11 got raisins, 9 got popcorn, and 12 got pizza. How many people ordered 2 snack items?* (12)

PRACTICE

Use logical reasoning to solve each problem.

1. As a treat, the 27 students in Edwa's class got frozen yogurt. 18 of them had chocolate yogurt. 13 of them had vanilla. How many had both vanilla and chocolate? **4 students**

2. For the Back-to-School picnic, frozen yogurt and nachos were on sale. 57 people bought food. 36 bought yogurt and 37 bought nachos. How many bought both? **16 people**

MIXED PRACTICE

Choose a strategy from the strategies list or use other strategies you know to solve these problems.

Some Strategies

- Act It Out
- Use Objects
- Choose an Operation
- Draw a Picture
- Make an Organized List
- Guess and Check
- Make a Table
- Look for a Pattern
- Use Logical Reasoning

Frozen Yogurt

Size	Weight	Cost
child	3 ounces	$0.95
small	7 ounces	$1.35
medium	10 ounces	$1.55
large	14 ounces	$1.95
quart	32 ounces	$3.85

3. About how much would 9 quarts of frozen yogurt weigh? **about 270 ounces**

4. Jeremy's boy scout troop ordered 12 medium frozen yogurts and 11 larges. How many ounces of yogurt were ordered in all? **274 ounces**

5. There are 21 calories in each ounce of lowfat frozen yogurt. There are 15 calories in each ounce of nonfat yogurt. How many calories are in a large lowfat strawberry frozen yogurt? **294 calories**

6. How much would 7 quarts of frozen yogurt cost? **$26.95**

7. Mrs. Ramirez bought $42.35 worth of frozen yogurt for a party. She gave the clerk a $50 bill. How much change did she get? **$7.65**

8. In April and May, Mrs. Fong offered 15 flavors of frozen yogurt. She offered 12 flavors in April and 9 in May. How many were offered in both April and May? **6 flavors**

More Practice, page 516, set E

3. PRACTICE AND APPLY

Basic	1-5, 7-8
Average	1-8
Extended	1-7

Sample Solutions: See page T79.

PRACTICE

Read problems 1 and 2 before you attempt to solve them. Identify 2 choices in each problem. (**1:** chocolate or vanilla **2:** yogurt or nachos)

MIXED PRACTICE

► **To solve problems 3 and 6, explain what measurement relationship you need to know.** (1 qt = 32 oz, because you need to multiply to convert quarts to ounces)

► **Analyze the operations you need to solve Problem 4.** (multiplication, then addition)

► **Analyze problem 5 for the necessary data.** (1 oz of lowfat frozen yogurt has 21 calories.)

► **Decide if Mrs. Ramirez will get back more or less than $10 in Problem 7.** (less)

► **Analyze problem 8 to choose a solution strategy.** Use Logical Reasoning)

CLOSE AND ASSESS

SAY WHAT YOU THINK Have students work in pairs. The first partner explains how it is possible for 12 people to eat 8 hot dogs and 13 hamburgers at a picnic. The second partner explains how many had both foods. (Since 8 + 13 = 21, but there are only 12 people eating, you know that 9 people had both foods.)

QUICK QUIZ

Solve the problem: When 9 baseball players stopped for snacks after a game, they ordered 7 cheeseburgers and 6 chicken sandwiches. How many people had both kinds of food? (4)

Multiplying with Money

OBJECTIVE 7-8 To multiply an amount of money less than $10 and a 2-digit number

PREBOOK ACTIVITIES

QUICK REVIEW

Find the products.

1. $4.72 × 3 ($14.16) **2.** $15.63 × 4 (62.52) **3.** $20.90 × 6 ($125.40) **4.** $77.77 × 8 ($622.16)

5. 5 × $41.96 ($209.80) **6.** 7 × $0.64 ($4.48)

PRIOR KNOWLEDGE

Have students share situations when they have needed to multiply money amounts or have seen others do so. (Possible answer: when shopping) Ask them to create a story about multiplying $3.75 by a 2-digit number. (Possible answer: *If 26 students in a class go to a movie that costs $3.75, how much do all the tickets cost?*) Have students explain how they would solve the problem. (Possible answer: Multiply 26 × $3.75 as you would multiply whole numbers 26 × 375, but show the product with a dollar sign and decimal point.)

COMMUNICATION

Discussing and Writing Math Write 735, $7.35, and $735 on the chalkboard. Have students compare the numbers. (Possible answer: $7.35 means 7 whole dollars and 35 cents or parts of a dollar; $735 is whole dollars in hundreds, tens, and ones, with no cents; 735 is a nonmoney number with hundreds, tens, and ones.) In their Math Journals, have students write an explanation of how 735 coins could equal $7.35. (735 pennies is $7.35 after all possible trades are made.) Then ask how 735 coins could equal $735. (735 silver dollars is $735.)

EXPLORE AND CONNECT

Materials: calculators, TA 3 (Number Cards 1-9)
Grouping Suggestion: cooperative learning pairs
Students compare multiplying money with and without decimal points. Partners generate a problem by choosing any 4 number cards and arranging them like this: $0. __ __ × __ __ . Then, using calculators, the first partner multiplies the exact money amount *without* using a decimal point, while the second partner multiplies *with* a decimal point. They compare calculator displays to determine how to interpret the product as a money amount, then record it, indicating dollars and cents. Have partners repeat the activity several times, trading tasks. Conclude by asking students to summarize how to multiply money amounts. (Possible answer: Multiply as with whole numbers, show products with a dollar sign and a decimal point, always indicating 2 places for cents.)

CONNECTIONS Use these anytime.

Problem of the Day

Admission Fees Mrs. Cohen takes her hiking club to an amusement park. She plans to treat everyone to a ride on the new roller coaster. Tickets for the roller coaster cost $1.75 each, and she needs 10 tickets. Decide whether $20.00 is enough money. (yes; 10 roller-coaster tickets will cost $17.50.)

Math Connection

Calculator Determine a way to find the product of 14 × $4.01 without using the × key on your calculator. (Possible solution: Break apart the factor 14 to 10 + 4; use mental math to find 10 × $4.01, which is $40.10; enter 40.10, then add 4.01 four times; $56.14.)

Life Skills

Accounting Every evening, Dale counts and rolls the coins from his cash register and records each amount. Yesterday, he made 12 rolls of 50 pennies each and 11 rolls of 40 nickels each. If necessary, break apart numbers to find what Dale recorded for the penny and nickel coin rolls. (12 × $0.50 = $6.00; 11 × $2.00 = $22.00)

Classwork and Homework Supplements

Practice

Skills Maintenance 7-8

Name

Multiplying Money

Find the amounts. Write the answers in dollars and cents.

1. $2.57 × 23 = 771 + 5140 = $59.11
2. $0.66 × 48 = 528 + 2640 = $31.68
3. $3.91 × 12 = 782 + 3910 = $46.92
4. $5.82 × 34 = 2328 + 17460 = $197.88
5. $4.43 × 33 = 1329 + 13290 = $146.19
6. $2.61 × 25 = 1305 + 5220 = $65.25
7. $5.15 × 41 = 515 + 20600 = $211.15
8. $0.94 × 16 = 564 + 940 = $15.04
9. $3.79 × 19 = 3411 + 3790 = $72.01
10. $5.08 × 45 = 2540 + 20320 = $228.60
11. $1.83 × 53 = 549 + 9150 = $96.99
12. $4.16 × 29 = 3744 + 8320 = $120.64
13. $4.60 × 27 = 3220 + 9200 = $124.20
14. $3.02 × 48 = 2416 + 12080 = $144.96
15. $2.71 × 15 = 1355 + 2710 = $40.65
16. $1.66 × 22 = 322 + 3320 = $36.52
17. $3.43 × 64 = 1372 + 20580 = $219.52
18. $8.05 × 35 = 402 + 24150 = $281.75
19. $0.78 × 91 = 78 + 7020 = $70.98
20. $5.45 × 25 = 2725 + 10900 = $136.25

PS-4 Use with text pages 192–193. 71

Building Thinking Skills

Life Skills 7-8

Name

The Sports Sale!

The Sports Place is having a sale. Write questions about the sale. Then give an answer for each question you wrote.

Example:

Brand A bats How much money would you save on 14 brand A bats if you bought them on sale?

Answer: $5.46

Questions and answers will vary.

1. Brand B footballs ______

Answer: ______

2. Brand A and Brand B bats ______

Answer: ______

3. Brand A soccer balls ______

Answer: ______

4. Brand A and Brand B mitts ______

Answer: ______

TS-4 Use with text pages 192–193. 71

Reteaching

Skills Review 7-8

Name

Multiplying Money

You can multiply money the same way you multiply whole numbers.

$7.64 × 36 = ?

Multiply by ones. → Multiply by tens. → Add the products. → Place $ and . in product.

7.64 × 36	$7.64 × 36	$7.64 × 36	$7.64 × 36
4584	4584	4584	4584
	22920	22920	22920
		27504	$275.04

Place dollar sign and decimal point.

Find the products.

1. $2.38 × 24 = $57.12
2. $6.25 × 12 = $75.00
3. $7.84 × 63 = $493.92
4. $0.86 × 75 = $64.50
5. $6.15 × 61 = $375.15
6. $4.36 × 84 = $366.24
7. $3.76 × 22 = $82.72
8. $5.49 × 36 = $197.64
9. $49 × 60 = $2,940
10. $87 × 48 = $4,176
11. $327 × 34 = $11,118
12. $2.85 × 25 = $71.25
13. $7.29 × 43 = $313.47
14. $5.36 × 27 = $144.72

RS-4 Use with text pages 192–193. 71

Challenges

Cooperatiave Activities 7-8

Name

Boating Party

Work in small groups to complete each activity.

Types of Boat	Number of People Allowed in 1 Boat	Cost per Hour for 1 Boat
Canoe	3	$ 7.50
Pedalboat	4	$ 9.55
Sailboat	5	$14.55

You are giving a large boating party.
- 48 people are invited.
- You want everyone to be in boats at the same time.
- You want to pay the least amount of money you can.

1. Make a plan for renting the same type of boat for everyone. What type of boat will you rent and how many? How much will the rental cost? You might want to make a table or drawing to help you solve the problem.
   12 pedalboats for $114.60

2. Make another plan in which you rent at least one of each type of boat. How many of each type of boat will you rent? How much will the rental cost?
   10 pedalboats, 1 canoe, 1 sailboat for $117.55

CS-4 Use with text pages 192–193. 71

Options for Individual Needs

Basic

Exercises 1-14, 19-34
Skills Bank, p. 465
Calculator Bank, p. 489
Computer Bank, p. 495
More Practice, p. 506, set A

Supplements
Reteaching 71 or
Practice 71
Thinking Skills 71

Average

Exercises 1-39
Skills Bank, p. 465
Calculator Bank, p. 489
Computer Bank, p. 495
More Practice, p. 506, set A

Supplements
Practice 71
Challenges 71 or
Thinking Skills 71

Extended

Exercises 6-34
Calculator Bank, p. 489
Computer Bank, p. 495

Supplements
Challenges 71
Thinking Skills 71

Other Resources:
Problem-Solving Experiences in Mathematics, Grade 4, Problem 123
Mathematics Book A, (Teacher's Edition), p. 42
Using the Math Explorer Calculator: A Sourcebook for Teachers, Chapter 14

LESSON PLAN 7-8

OBJECTIVE 7-8
To multiply an amount of money less than $10 and a 2-digit number

Materials: TA 12 (Centimeter Graph Paper)

1. MOTIVATE AND TEACH

LEARN ABOUT IT

EXPLORE ► **Estimate the difference between the regular and discount trophy prices. Explain your reasoning.** ($1; round $6.59 to $6.60, $5.45 to $5.50; compare)
► **Explain why Mrs. Wingate would consider buying more trophies than she needs.** (Possible answer: She may save over $1 each; she wants the better buy.)

TALK ABOUT IT ► **Justify multiplication as the correct operation.** (Multiply to put together same-size groups.)
► **Analyze the steps to use to multiply $6.59 by 23.** (Multiply as with whole numbers: begin in ones place, multiply each place in $6.59 by 3, trade as needed; multiply each place in $6.59 by 2 tens, trade as needed; add partial products; show dollars and cents in the final product.)
Student Edition answers: **1.** Multiply 23 trophies at $6.59, multiply 25 trophies at $5.45, compare the products. **2.** 659

2. CHECK UNDERSTANDING

TRY IT OUT

ERROR ALERT Omitting dollar signs or decimal points.
Exercises 11-13 Rewriting in vertical form with 3-digit factors as multipliers.

Multiplying with Money

LEARN ABOUT IT

EXPLORE Make a Decision
Mrs. Wingate wants to order special award trophies for each of the 23 students who won sports honors during the year. She saw this ad in the school catalog. She needs to decide whether to buy 23 trophies at the regular price or to buy 25 at the reduced price.

Sports Trophies
$6.59 each
Only $5.45 each with the purchase of 25 or more

TALK ABOUT IT See teaching notes.

1. What process would you use to make the choice?
2. If you changed the single sports trophy price to all cents, how many cents would you have?

You can multiply money just like you multiply whole numbers.

$6.59	← Multiply as with whole numbers →	$5.45
× 23		× 25
1977		2725
13180		10900
$151.57	← Show dollars and cents. →	$136.25

Mrs. Wingate should buy 25 sports trophies at the cheaper price.

TRY IT OUT

Multiply.

1. $3.24 × 18 = **$58.32**
2. $9.38 × 38 = **$356.44**
3. $3.75 × 22 = **$82.50**
4. $0.75 × 44 = **$33.00**
5. $6.09 × 11 = **$66.99**
6. $2.78 × 12 = **$33.36**
7. $6.05 × 49 = **$296.45**
8. $1.99 × 20 = **$39.80**
9. $7.10 × 29 = **$205.90**
10. $4.31 × 15 = **$64.65**
11. 11 × $3.80 **$41.80**
12. 17 × $2.35 **$39.95**
13. 20 × $0.85 **$17**

TEACHING OPTIONS

RETEACHING TIPS In each of Exercises 11-13, ask students to identify the factor with more places, regardless of its value. (always the money amounts) Order does not affect the product in multiplication, so have students write the factor first to make multiplying easier. Assign Reteaching Supplement 71.

ENRICHMENT Family Math At home, students imagine they are planning a family reunion for 38 adults and 47 children. They want to order special T-shirts. With an adult, they decide a reasonable price for adult and for child T-shirts. Then they find the total shirt cost for everyone at the reunion.

PRACTICE

Find the products.

1. $3.86 × 12 — $46.32
2. $2.81 × 21 — $59.01
3. $5.79 × 32 — $185.28
4. $3.68 × 45 — $165.60
5. $8.20 × 29 — $237.80
6. $0.98 × 60 — $58.80
7. $9.00 × 71 — $639.00
8. $0.56 × 28 — $15.68
9. $7.14 × 86 — $614.04
10. $9.49 × 45 — $427.05
11. 15 × $0.89 — $13.35
12. $7.09 × 78 — $553.02
13. $4.30 × 68 — $292.40
14. 59 × $7.40 — $436.60
15. $4.28 × 23 — $98.44
16. $8.27 × 47 — $388.69
17. 17 × $0.75 — $12.75
18. $3.05 × 18 — $54.90

Estimate these products. Answers may vary. Sample answers given.

19. $1.98 × 49 — $100
20. $4.89 × 52 — $250
21. $6.07 × 19 — $120
22. $9.98 × 25 — $250

APPLY

MATH REASONING Solve. Look for a pattern and give the next 3 products.

23. $0.50 × 50 — $25.00
24. $0.51 × 49 — $24.99
25. $0.52 × 48 — $24.96
26. $0.53 × 47 — $24.91
27. $0.54 × 46 — $24.84

Next 3 products: $24.75, $24.64, $24.51

PROBLEM SOLVING

28. Award certificates for a team cost $9.75. Mrs. Wingate bought certificates for 3 teams. How much did she pay? $29.25
29. Jeff's soccer coach bought 3 trophies for $4 each. He bought some more trophies for $5 each. The total cost was $22. How many $5 trophies did he buy? 2 $5 trophies

▶ **MENTAL MATH**

Use mental math to multiply by 4. To do this, double and then double again.

30. $32 — $128
31. $2.50 — $10
32. $5.25 — $21
33. $4.15 — $16.60
34. $12.20 — $48.80
35. $16 — $64
36. $6.08 — $24.32
37. $7.10 — $28.40
38. $8.22 — $32.88
39. $92.00 — $368

More Practice, page 506, set A

3. Practice and Apply

Basic	1-14, 19-34
Average	1-39
Extended	6-34

PRACTICE

How are Exercises 19-22 different from 11-18? (Exercises 19-22 ask for estimates, not exact products.)

APPLY

MATH REASONING ▶ **Analyze the pattern in the factors of Exercises 23-27.** (The top factor increases by 1 as the bottom factor decreases by 1.)

PROBLEM SOLVING ▶ **How would you estimate Problem 28? Explain.** (Round $9.75 to $10; multiply by 3; about $30.)

▶ **Explain how you would solve Problem 29.** (Multiply 3 × $4; subtract the product from $22; decide how many $5 trophies Jeff can buy with the difference.)

MENTAL MATH ▶ **Justify doubling twice as a way to multiply by 4.** (Since 2 × 2 = 4, doubling twice is like breaking apart factors.)

Close and Assess

SHOW WHAT YOU KNOW Ask students to create sales slips for the purchase of a $1.25 comic book for each child in the class. They should write down how many comic books they need to buy, show the calculation, and circle the total. (Answers will vary. Check students' work.)

Quick Quiz

Find the products.

1. $5.06 × 19 ($96.14)
2. $0.28 × 71 ($19.88)
3. 46 × $3.14 ($144.44)
4. $9.87 × 65 ($641.55)

LESSON OPTIONS 7-9

Problem Solving: Choosing a Calculation Method

OBJECTIVE 7-9 To choose an appropriate method of calculation

PREBOOK ACTIVITIES

QUICK REVIEW

Match each mental math method with an appropriate use of it.

1. compensation	(c)	**a.** 61 + 200 + 39
2. special products	(e)	**b.** 268 + 521
3. break-apart addends	(b)	**c.** 476 − 99
4. break-apart factors	(d)	**d.** 3 × 52
5. compatible numbers	(a)	**e.** 40 × 30

PRIOR KNOWLEDGE

Have students justify using mental math to solve problems. (Possible answer: If you see special number relationships, you can often solve a problem easily and quickly in your head.) Have them justify using calculators to solve problems. (Possible answer: Calculators simplify lengthy problems and perform operations quickly.) Have students justify pencil-and-paper calculations. (Possible answer: You may not have a calculator handy, and mental math may not suit the problem.)

COMMUNICATION

Writing Math Write these mental math methods on the chalkboard: break apart, compensation, compatible numbers, special products. Have students copy each method in their Math Journals, formulate an example with which to use it, and explain how to apply the method. (Check students' writing.)

EXPLORE AND CONNECT

COOPERATIVE ACTIVITY

Materials: calculators

Grouping Suggestion: small groups

198 adults and 300 children paid $5.75 each to go to Thrill Town. Also, 43 senior citizens paid $2.00 each. How many paid $5.75? What was the total? How much did seniors pay? What was the total attendance?

TEACHING ACTIONS

Have students work together to explain and summarize ideas.

BEFORE

► **Decide what you need to find out.** (how many people paid $5.75; how much full-price ticket buyers paid; how much senior citizens paid; how many went to Thrill Town in all)

► **Analyze the data to classify computations as easy, diffficult, or in-between.** (easy: 198 + 300, $2 × 43; difficult: $5.75 × 498; in-between: 198 + 300 + 43)

DURING

► **Explain how to decide which calculation method to use.** (Possible answers: Use mental math for easy calculations; use a calculator for difficult calculations; use paper and pencil or calculator for those in-between.)

► **Evaluate your answers to decide if they make sense.** (Estimate to check answers. Exact answers: 498 people paid $5.75, total is $2,863.50; senior citizens paid $86; 541 people were at Thrill Town that day.)

CONNECTIONS Use these anytime.

Problem of the Day

Ticket Tally One Tuesday, Thrill Town ticket taker Tim Taylor tallied 232 adult, 392 child, and 28 senior-citizen tickets sold. He lost his calculator on the bumper cars, so he had to use another method to total the tally. Justify which calculation method you would tell Tim to try. (paper and pencil; No mental math method suits the numbers.)

Number Sense

Mental Math A ride on the Scream Wheel lasts 59 noisy seconds. Blair rode the Scream Wheel 8 times. Use mental math to find the total time she spent on the ride. Explain your reasoning. *Hint:* 1 minute = 60 seconds. (472 seconds; 60 seconds × 8 = 480 seconds; compensate by subtracting 8 seconds; 480 seconds − 8 seconds = 472 seconds)

Patterns

Calculator Use a number from 1-9 as the missing factor in this equation: _____ × 3 × 37,037 = ? Solve with a calculator and record the product. Try again with another 1-digit number. Can you predict the product? (The product repeats the chosen factor in a 6-digit number, such as 444,444 or 777,777.)

Classwork and Homework Supplements

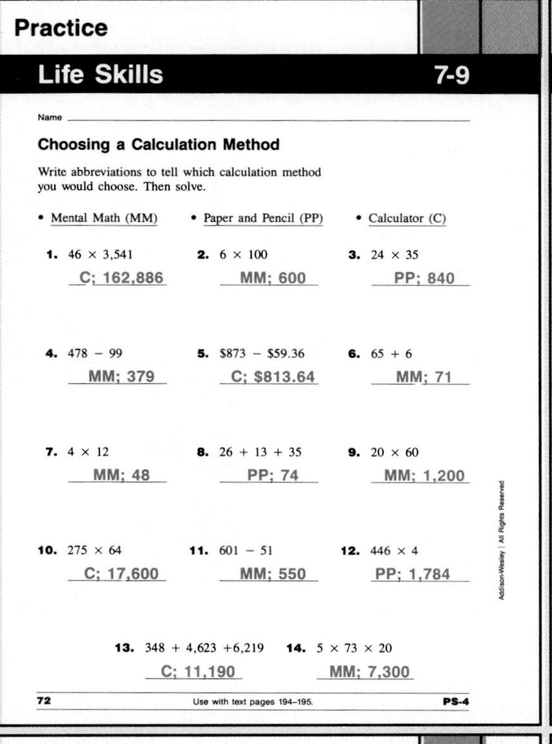

Practice

Life Skills 7-9

Name ______

Choosing a Calculation Method

Write abbreviations to tell which calculation method you would choose. Then solve.

- Mental Math (MM)
- Paper and Pencil (PP)
- Calculator (C)

1. 46 × 3,541 C; 162,886
2. 6 × 100 MM; 600
3. 24 × 35 PP; 840
4. 478 − 99 MM; 379
5. $873 − $59.36 C; $813.64
6. 65 + 6 MM; 71
7. 4 × 12 MM; 48
8. 26 + 13 + 35 PP; 74
9. 20 × 60 MM; 1,200
10. 275 × 64 C; 17,600
11. 601 − 51 MM; 550
12. 446 × 4 PP; 1,784
13. 348 + 4,623 +6,219 C; 11,190
14. 5 × 73 × 20 MM; 7,300

72 Use with text pages 194–195. PS-4

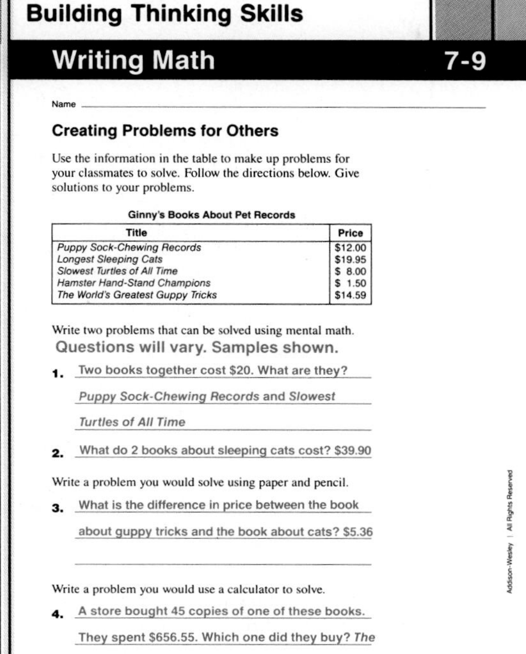

Building Thinking Skills

Writing Math 7-9

Name ______

Creating Problems for Others

Use the information in the table to make up problems for your classmates to solve. Follow the directions below. Give solutions to your problems.

Ginny's Books About Pet Records

Title	Price
Puppy Sock-Chewing Records	$12.00
Longest Sleeping Cats	$19.95
Slowest Turtles of All Time	$ 8.00
Hamster Hand-Stand Champions	$ 1.50
The World's Greatest Guppy Tricks	$14.59

Write two problems that can be solved using mental math.

Questions will vary. Samples shown.

1. Two books together cost $20. What are they? *Puppy Sock-Chewing Records* and *Slowest Turtles of All Time*
2. What do 2 books about sleeping cats cost? $39.90

Write a problem you would solve using paper and pencil.

3. What is the difference in price between the book about guppy tricks and the book about cats? $5.36

Write a problem you would use a calculator to solve.

4. A store bought 45 copies of one of these books. They spent $656.55. Which one did they buy? *The World's Greatest Guppy Tricks*

72 Use with text pages 194-195. TS-4

Reteaching

Problem Solving 7-9

Name ______

Choosing a Calculation Method

You can choose calculation methods according to the type of problem you have to solve.

Use **mental math** for easy computations.	Use **paper and pencil** for few-step computations.	Use a **calculator** for multi-step computations.
40 × 30 = 1,200	124 × 3 = 372	846 × 29 = 24,534

Write which calculation method you would choose. Then solve.

1. 10 × 50 = 500 mental math
2. 115 × 6 = 690 paper and pencil
3. 7,437 × 24 = 178,488 calculator
4. 21 × 3 = 63 mental math
5. 974 × 632 = 615,568 calculator
6. 86 + 5 = 91 mental math

Choose the most useful calculation method. Then solve.

7. Tom weighs 140 pounds. His brother weighs 70 pounds. How many pounds do they weigh altogether? mental math; 210 pounds
8. Will ordered 135 boxes of pencils. Each box cost $1.75. What is the total cost? calculator; $236.25
9. There are 165 pads of paper in one box. Tina has 4 boxes. How many pads of paper does Tina have? pencil and paper; 660 pads
10. Geri's aunt drove 305 miles one day and 156 miles the next day. How many more miles did she drive the first day? pencil and paper; 149 miles

72 Use with text pages 194-195. RS-4

Challenges

Life Skills 7-9

Name ______

Puzzling over Money

Jess kept track of the money she spent and earned for 6 months on this chart. She studied the chart to answer these questions:

Should I spend less money? Can I baby-sit less?

	Money Spent				Money Earned	
	Clothes	Movies	Gifts	Toys	Baby-Sitting	Paper Route
Jan.	$12.99	$ 7.25	0	$ 5.25	$22.90	$30.00
Feb.	$19.50	$ 5.40	$23.95	$ 4.85	$10.50	$30.00
Mar.	$27.95	0	0	$ 3.27	$17.75	$30.00
Apr.	$25.99	$12.85	$17.84	$ 6.98	$12.95	$30.00
May.	$14.29	$ 5.25	0	$17.21	$24.85	$30.00
June.	$16.49	$15.98	$ 2.13	0	$16.35	$30.00
Total	$117.21	$46.73	$43.92	$37.56	$105.30	$180.00

Complete the chart above. Then, on the chart below, help Jess find out **about** how much she spent in each category and **about** how much she earned from each job. Round the answers to the nearest dollar.

Use mental math, paper and pencil, or your calculator.

Money Jess spent in 6 months		Money Jess earned in 6 months	
Clothes	$117	Baby-Sitting	$105
Movies	$47	Paper Route	$180
Gifts	$44		
Toys	$38		
Estimated Total	$246	Estimated Total	$285

What advice would you give Jess? You can baby-sit less.

72 Use with text pages 194–195. CS-4

Options for Individual Needs

Basic

Exercises 1-10, 14-20
Skills Bank, pp. 462, 464, 465
Calculator Bank, pp. 485, 486
More Practice, p. 517, set A

Supplements
Reteaching 72 or
Practice 72

Average

Exercises 1-20
Skills Bank, pp. 464, 465
Calculator Bank, pp. 485, 486
More Practice, p. 517, set A

Supplements
Practice 72
Challenges 72 or
Thinking Skills 72

Extended

Exercises 4-20
Calculator Bank, pp. 485, 486

Supplements
Challenges 72
Thinking Skills 72

Other Resources:
Problem-Solving Experiences in Mathematics, Grade 4, Problem 118
Make It Simpler, p. 226
Using the Math Explorer Calculator: A Sourcebook for Teachers, Chapter 14

LESSON PLAN 7-9

OBJECTIVE 7-9
To choose an appropriate method of calculation

Materials: calculators

1. MOTIVATE AND TEACH

LEARN ABOUT IT

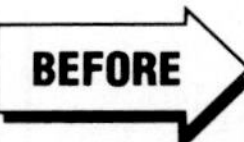

▶ **Compare each Wacky Record to a common fact to interpret the accomplishments.** (Sample answers: balanced longer than 1 day; crawled farther than a marathon; stood up almost 2 fourth graders' lifetimes; walked on hands longer than most people walk normally in the same amount of time)

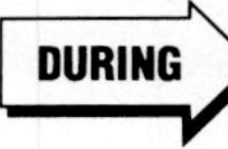

▶ **Justify using mental math to solve the Walking on Hands Record.** (You can use special products.)
▶ **Justify using a calculator to solve the Crawling Record.** (Possible answer: It involves multiplying large numbers.)

▶ **Generalize when to use a calculator to solve problems.** (with large numbers or with many steps)
▶ **Generalize when to use mental math.** (with easy computations or with recognizable number relationships)
▶ **Generalize when to use paper and pencil.** (when neither of the other methods is appropriate)

2. CHECK UNDERSTANDING

TRY IT OUT

ERROR ALERT Failing to notice easy computations that can be done with mental math.

Problem Solving
Choosing a Calculation Method

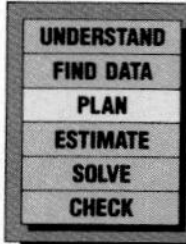

LEARN ABOUT IT

Calculation Methods
- Mental Math
- Paper and Pencil
- Calculator

When you solve a problem, you must choose which of these calculation methods is best to use.

Wacky Records adapted from the *Guinness Book of World Records*	
■ Balancing on 1 foot 34 hours —5-minute rest breaks after each hour	■ Crawling 27 miles —always moving, with one or the other knee always touching the ground
■ Standing Up 17 years —leaning against a board while sleeping	■ Walking on Hands 871 miles —in 55 daily 10-hour periods

Which methods would you use to solve these Wacky Records problems?

How many hours did it take to reach the record for walking on hands?

55 × 10 — I can do this using mental math!

How many feet did the crawling record holder crawl?

5,280 × 27 — I think I'll use a calculator.

Use these hints when you are choosing a calculation method.

- **First try mental math.** Look for easy computations.
- **Then choose paper and pencil or a calculator.** It is better to use a calculator when many steps are needed.

TRY IT OUT

Tell which calculation method you would choose and why. Then solve.
See Additional Answers.

1. 7 × 100 **2.** 362 − 99 **3.** 3 × 13 **4.** \$9.58 + \$0.42 **5.** 5,280 × 39

194

TEACHING OPTIONS

RETEACHING TIPS Students identify exercises best done with a calculator. Then they identify exercises with any special factors or addends. For remaining exercises, students use their Math Journal list of mental math techniques for hints of possible strategies. Assign Reteaching Supplement 72.

ENRICHMENT Students look through the *Guinness Book of World Records* for odd accomplishments. They use facts of interest to create 3 problems: 1 to solve by mental math, 1 to solve with a calculator, and 1 to solve with paper and pencil. Post the problems for others to solve.

MIXED PRACTICE

Tell which calculation method you choose and why. Then solve. See Additional Answers.

1. 25 × 68 × 4
2. 300 − 199
3. 967 × 346
4. 60 × 40
5. 123 × 3
6. 101 + 100 + 99
7. 155 × 5
8. $967 − $38.69
9. 86 + 5
10. 3 × 21
11. 31 × 20
12. 45 × 26

Solve. Give the calculation method you chose. Use the Wacky Records on page 194. Methods may vary. Logical sample shown.

13. Joe balanced on one foot for 3 hrs. How many hours longer than this is the official record? mental math; 31 hours
14. Between the start and the finish, how many minutes of rest did the person who set the balancing on one foot record get? paper and pencil; 165 minutes
15. How many days did the person who set the standing record stand? Use 365 days in a year. calculator; 6,205 days
16. How many more miles is the walking on hands record distance than the crawling record distance? paper and pencil; 844 miles
17. Jonathan crawled 1 mile in 30 minutes. How many minutes would it take for him to crawl as far as the world record holder did? paper and pencil; 810 minutes
18. Lila is 9 years old. How many more years did the standing record holder stand than Lila has been alive? mental math; 8 years
19. How many more miles would the record holder have had to walk on his or her hands to have walked 1,000 miles? paper and pencil; 129 miles
20. **Write Your Own Problems** Write a problem that you would solve **a.** using mental math, **b.** using paper and pencil, and **c.** using a calculator. Answers will vary.

More Practice, page 517, set A

3. Practice and Apply

Basic	1-10, 14-20
Average	1-20
Extended	4-20

Additional Answers and Sample Solutions: See p. T79.

MIXED PRACTICE

▶ **Analyze Exercises 1-12 to choose those best done on a calculator.** (Answers may vary; 1, 3, 8, 12)

▶ **What methods would suit Exercises 2, 6, and 9? Explain.** (mental math, because 6 has compatible numbers and 2 and 9 can be done using the compensation method)

▶ **Analyze how Exercises 4 and 11 are related.** (Both have special factors.)

▶ **Justify the operation to use to solve Problems 13, 16, 18, and 19.** (subtraction; All involve making comparisons.)

Close and Assess

WRITE WHAT YOU THINK Ask students to write a paragraph responding to this statement: Students should not be allowed to use calculators in school. Students should write arguments that justify why it makes sense to select the best calculation method, including using a calculator.

Quick Quiz

Solve. (possible methods suggested)

1. 45 + 55 (mental math; 100)
2. $3.89 × 34 (calculator; $132.26)
3. 446 − 268 (paper and pencil; 178)

LESSON OPTIONS 7-10

Problem Solving: Multiple-Step Problems

OBJECTIVE 7-10 To solve multiple-step problems

PREBOOK ACTIVITIES

QUICK REVIEW

Add, subtract, or multiply.

1. 54 + 27 (81)
2. 54 − 27 (27)
3. 54 × 27 (1,458)
4. 306 − 79 (227)
5. 306 + 79 (385)
6. 306 × 79 (24,174)
7. $5.46 − $0.88 ($4.58)
8. $5.46 × 88 ($480.48)

PRIOR KNOWLEDGE

Have students compare multiple-step problems with other kinds of problems. (Possible answer: Unlike 1-step problems, multiple-step problems need 2 or more operations to solve.) Have students create a multiple-step problem in which they multiply and add. (Sample problem: *If Sabina buys 3 books at $2.75 each and 2 magazines at $1.25 each, how much does she spend?)* Have students explain how they would solve such a problem. (Multiply to find the cost of each part of the purchase, then add the products; $10.75)

COMMUNICATION

Discussing Math Have students recall the order of operations rule for multiplication and addition. (Multiply, then add.) Challenge students to adapt the rule to determine an order of operations for multiplication and subtraction. (Multiply, then subtract.) Have students relate the rule to multiple-step problems. (Possible answer: In multiple-step problems, use the order of operations rule to decide which step to do first.)

EXPLORE AND CONNECT

COOPERATIVE ACTIVITY

Grouping Suggestion: small groups

Alex brought $7.00 to a video arcade. He played a game 7 times. Each play cost $0.75. How much money did he have after the 7 games?

TEACHING ACTIONS

Have students work together to explain and summarize ideas.

BEFORE

▶ **Explain the situation in your own words.** (Alex plays a video game 7 times at $0.75 a game.)

▶ **Decide what you need to find out.** (how much money is left)

DURING

▶ **Analyze the situation to determine the steps to solve it.** (2: Multiply to find the cost of 7 games; subtract the product from $7.00.)

▶ **Justify an order of operations.** (Multiply first, then subtract.)

▶ **Decide whether Alex will have money left. Explain your reasoning.** (overestimate: 7 × $1 = $7; Alex should have money left.)

AFTER

▶ **Evaluate your solution to see if it makes sense.** (7 × $0.75 = $5.25; $7.00 − $5.25 = $1.75; it makes sense that Alex has $1.75 left; use play money to check.)

CONNECTIONS Use these anytime.

Problem of the Day

Geography Mr. Sanchez is a bus driver. His route is from Dallas to Tyler, Texas, which is 101 miles each way. If he makes 2 round-trips daily, how many miles does he drive in a 5-day work week? (2,020 miles)

Number Sense

Mental Math A video arcade has 10 new games and 20 old games. If it costs $0.75 to play each new game and $0.50 to play each old game, how much would it cost to play every game once? ($17.50)

Creative Thinking

Missing Operations 2 operation signs are missing from the following equation. Decide what they are and place them where they belong so that the equation works. 3 □ 15 □ 20 = 25 (3 × 15 − 20 = 25)

Classwork and Homework Supplements

Practice

Problem Solving 7-10

Name

Multiple-Step Problems

Solve these problems.

1. Roberto had $5 to buy valentines. He bought 3 cards at $0.75 each and a $1.25 card for his mother. How much change did he receive? $1.50
2. Amy needs 32 hearts to make valentines. She can cut 4 hearts from one sheet of paper. She has 7 sheets of paper. How many more sheets does she need? 1 sheet
3. Fred wants to send valentines to 45 people. He made 6 cards a day for 7 days. How many more cards does he need to make? 3 cards
4. Louise wants to earn $15 to buy her mother a white lace heart pillow. She sold 9 roses at $1.25 each. How much more money does she need? $3.75
5. Nara bought 3 heart erasers for $0.65 each and 6 balloons for $0.19 each. How much change did she receive from a $5 bill? $1.91
6. Mr. Land agreed to make waffles for his 5 children. Everyone wanted 3 waffles, except Nan, who said she wanted 2. How many waffles does Mr. Land need to make? 14 waffles
7. Jason invited 15 friends to his party. He needs paper plates, cups, and napkins. Each package contains 8 items. How many packages should he buy in all? 6 packages
8. Sumin put stickers on 30 cards. She had 4 sheets of stickers, each with 8 stickers. How many stickers did Sumin have left? 2 stickers

PS-4 Use with text pages 196–197. 73

Building Thinking Skills

Family Math 7-10

Name

Grocery Math

Dear Family,
Your child has been learning how to solve multiple-step problems. Here is an activity you can do together.

Look at the supermarket advertisement and answer the questions.

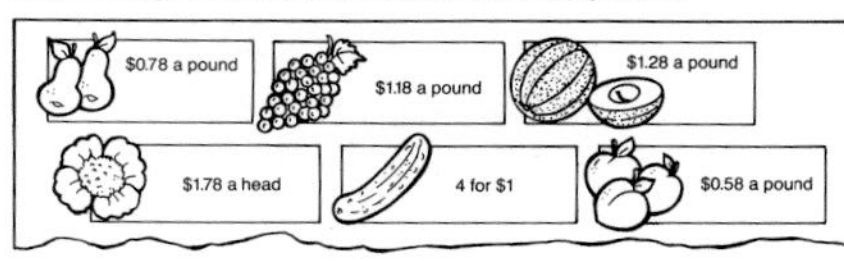

1. You have $4. Each family member finds a favorite food in the advertisement. Do you have enough money to buy all of the food items? Answers will vary.
2. You have $5. What is one item you can buy three pounds of with the least amount of change? cantaloupe
3. You are going to make a fruit salad. You need 2 pounds of cantaloupe, 3 pounds of grapes, 2 pounds of pears, and 2 pounds of peaches. How much will you have left from $10? $1.18
4. Make a shopping list of as many different items as you can without going over $10. Answers will vary.

TS-4 Use with text pages 196–197. 73

Reteaching

Problem Solving 7-10

Name

Multiple-Step Problems

Sometimes you need to use more than 1 operation to solve a problem.

Pedro bought 4 boards. He gave the cashier $10.00. How much money should he get back?

Price signs: $3.26, $9.50, $2.38, $7.49, $3.95

Step 1: **Multiply** to find the total cost. $2.38 × 4 = $9.52

Step 2: **Subtract** to find the change. $10.00 − $9.52 = $0.48

Pedro should get $0.48 back.

Use the price signs to solve these problems.

1. Sally bought 3 pounds of nails and 1 tape measure. How much did she spend?
   Step 1: Find the cost of 3 pounds of nails. 3 × $3.26 = $9.78
   Step 2: Add the cost of the nails and tape measure to find the total cost. $9.78 + $9.50 = $19.28
2. Pete bought a screwdriver and a hammer. He gave the clerk $20. How much change did he get back?
   Step 1: Find the cost of a screwdriver and a hammer. $11.44
   Step 2: Subtract to find the change. $8.56
3. Tony bought 2 hammers on sale for $12.00. How much did he save? $2.98
4. Carmen bought 3 tape measures. She gave the cashier $30. How much did she get back? $1.50

RS-4 Use with text page 196. 73

Challenges

Problem Solving 7-10

Name

Do It Your Way

Read each problem and study Carl's way of solving the problem. Then develop your own way to solve it. Show your work. The first one is started for you. Answers may vary.

1. For Terry's party, his father brought $65.00 to the Mini-Indy Racetrack. The tickets cost $23.04 and the lunches cost $11.95. How much did he have left?
   Carl's way: Subtract: $65.00 − $23.04. Subtract $11.95 from the difference.
   Your way: $23.04 + 11.95 = $34.99; $65.00 − $34.99 = $30.01
2. It costs $7.68 per child to drive the miniracers. The birthday package costs $6.95 per child. How much does the package save you for 12 children?
   Carl's way: Subtract: $7.68 − $6.95. Multiply the difference by 12.
   Your way: $7.68 × 12 = $92.16; $6.95 × 12 = $83.40; $92.16 − 83.40 = $8.76
3. Jo had a $50 bill. When he bought miniracer tickets that normally cost $38.40, he used a coupon. How much was his change?

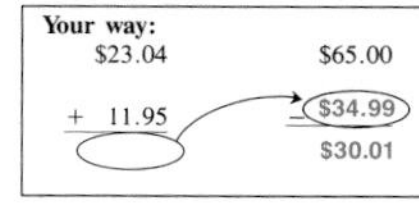

   Carl's way: Subtract: $50.00 − $38.40. Add $3.75 to the difference.
   Your way: $38.40 + 3.75 = $34.65; $50.00 − $34.65 = $15.35
4. It costs $2.55 per lap in a miniracer. A booklet of 100 laps costs only $1.40 per lap. How much do you save on 100 laps if you buy the booklet?
   Carl's way: Subtract: $2.55 − $1.40. Multiply the difference by 100.
   Your way: $2.55 × 100 = $255.00; $1.40 × 100 = $140.00; $255.00 − 140.00 = $115.00

CS-4 Use with text pages 196–197. 73

Options for Individual Needs

Basic

Exercises 1-6
Skills Bank, pp. 462, 464, 465
Calculator Bank, p. 488
Computer Bank, p. 492
More Practice, p. 517, set B

Supplements
Reteaching 73 or
Practice 73

Average

Exercises 1-6
Skills Bank, pp. 464, 465
Calculator Bank, p. 488
Computer Bank, p. 492
More Practice, p. 517, set B

Supplements
Practice 73
Challenges 73 or
Thinking Skills 73

Extended

Exercises 2-6
Calculator Bank, p. 488
Computer Bank, p. 492

Supplements
Challenges 73
Thinking Skills 73

Other Resources:

Problem-Solving Experiences in Mathematics, Grade 4, Problem 103
Make It Simpler, p. 211
Using the Math Explorer Calculator: A Sourcebook for Teachers, Chapter 14
Math In Stride, Grade 4, p. 97

LESSON PLAN 7-10

OBJECTIVE 7-10
To solve multiple step problems

Grouping Suggestion: pairs

1. MOTIVATE AND TEACH

LEARN ABOUT IT

BEFORE ▶ **Explain the situation in your own words.** (Mario wants to read 1,550 pages, so he reads 35 pages a day for 59 days.)
▶ **Analyze the situation for facts to organize and to decide how to use.** (35 pages a day for 59 days; goal of 1,550 pages)

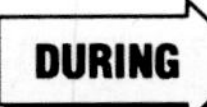

▶ **Explain why you can classify this as a multiple-step problem.** (Possible answer: Multiply 35 × 59 to find how many pages Mario read; subtract to compare the product with the goal.)
▶ **Justify the order of operations.** (Multiply, then subtract.)
▶ **Explain what calculation method makes sense.** (paper and pencil or calculator; not mental math because the numbers are not suited to a mental math strategy)

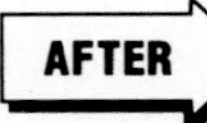

▶ **Evaluate the solution to see if it makes sense.** (35 × 59 = 2,065; 2,065 − 1,550 = 515; It makes sense that Mario passed his goal by 515 pages.)

2. CHECK UNDERSTANDING

TRY IT OUT

ERROR ALERT Failing to multiply before adding or subtracting.

Problem Solving
Multiple-Step Problems

UNDERSTAND
FIND DATA
PLAN
ESTIMATE
SOLVE
CHECK

LEARN ABOUT IT

To solve some problems, you will need to use more than one of the operations of addition, subtraction, and multiplication. These problems are called multiple-step problems.

Mario's goal in the Reading Marathon was to read 1,550 pages. He read 35 pages a day for 59 days. How many pages over his goal did he go?

First I'll multiply to find how many pages he read in all.

35 × 59 = 2,065

Then I'll subtract to find how many pages he read over his goal.

2,065 − 1,550 = 515

He read 515 pages over his goal.

TRY IT OUT

1. Mrs. Finch made a mistake when she wrote a check for \$9.02. Her daughter had ordered 2 books at \$1.69 each and 3 books at \$1.49 each. How much money should Mrs. Finch get back? **\$1.17**
2. Marta's goal was to make \$20.00 from her sponsors in the Reading Marathon. She read 23 books and collected a total of \$0.75 for each book. How much under her goal was she? **\$2.75**

Use the order form on page 197 to solve these problems.

3. How much more did the fourth grade classes spend on *The Phantom Tollbooth* by Norton Juster than on *Voyage to the Misty Isles*? **\$7.74**
4. Last month, the fourth graders spent \$35.32 on software. How much less did they spend this month? **\$9.67**

TEACHING OPTIONS

RETEACHING TIPS As a reminder, have students write the order of operations rule: Multiply, then add. Explain that because addition and subtraction are opposites, students can amend the rule to say: Multiply, then add *or* subtract. Assign Reteaching Supplement 73.

COMPUTER **Path Tactics, MECC, Copyright 1986** For use with all levels of students. Choose the operation to be practiced. Given 3 numbers, create an equation whose solution is the number of steps for the Robot to reach the end of the path. The game requires 5 to 10 min.

MIXED PRACTICE

You may need to use the book club order form below to solve these problems.

1. The longest book Stacey had ever read was 304 pages. She just finished *The Wind in the Willows* by Kenneth Grahame with 258 pages. How much shorter was this than the longest book she had read? **46 pages**
2. Last month, the fourth graders bought a total of 71 items and spent a total of $136.98 on their book club orders. How much less was spent on this book order? **$7.15**
3. There are 30 shelves in the children's section of the library. There are about 20 books on each shelf. About how many books are in the children's section? **600 books**
4. Stacey bought one each of items 3 through 6 on the book order form. How much did she spend? **$6.62**
5. A total of 16 students bought old time favorites. How many students bought both old time favorites? **4 students**
6. **Understanding the Operations** Tell what operation you would use. Use objects to solve the problem. Lita had a box of detective mysteries. She gave 9 books away. She has 8 books left. How many books did she have in the beginning? **17 books; addition**

Triangle Book Club
Order Form Rooms 6, 7, and 8

Item	Qty	Title	Cost each
Paperbacks			
1	14	James and the Giant Peach	$1.49
2	7	Little House on the Prairie	$1.69
3	11	Little Women **Old Time Favorite**	$1.95
4	3	Mystery of Slimey Gulch	$1.49
5	12	The Phantom Tollbooth	$1.49
6	6	Voyage to the Misty Isles	$1.69
7	9	Wind in the Willows **Old Time Favorite**	$1.95
Software			
8	2	Math Whiz	$8.85
9	1	Write Your Own Jokes	$7.95
Total Items	65	Total Cost	$129.83

More Practice, page 517, set B

3. Practice and Apply

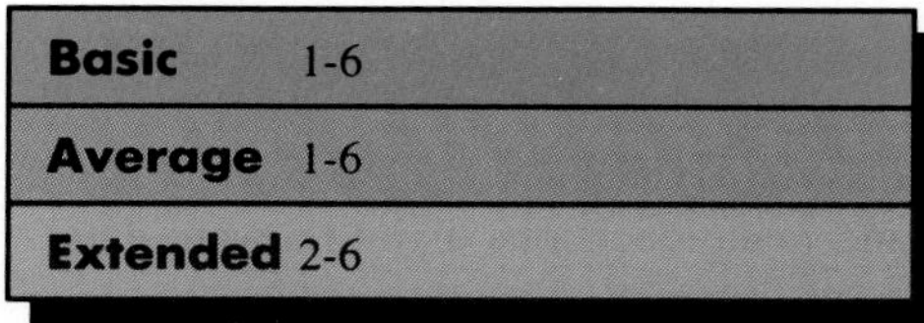

Basic	1-6
Average	1-6
Extended	2-6

Sample Solutions: See p. T79.

MIXED PRACTICE

► **How are Problems 1 and 3 related?** (Both use 1 step.)

► **Analyze Problem 2 to identify a fact you need.** (total cost of this month's order)

► **Justify the operation to use in Problems 4 and 6.** (Use addition for a total.)

► **For Problem 5, explain how to find data on Old Time Favorites.** (Find Old Time Favorite beside some titles, then look at the Qty column for the numbers you need.)

Close and Assess

WRITE WHAT YOU THINK

Have students write the steps to follow to solve this problem and give their reasoning. With $15.00 to spend on gifts, Amy buys 6 copies of *Little Women* at $1.95 each. How much money does she have left to spend on cards? ($3.30; multiply, then subtract; Check students' writing.)

Quick Quiz

A printer makes 120 copies of the same book. Each book takes 48 sheets of paper. How many sheets over 5,000 does the printer need? (760)

7-10

Chapter 7

Applied Problem Solving
Group Decision Making

OBJECTIVE To analyze, organize, and make decisions using relevant data

Discuss visits to a zoo and the purpose of zoos with the class before reading the opening paragraph together.

FACTS TO CONSIDER

► **Classify Facts 1 to 6 as having estimated or exact information. Explain your reasoning.** (Facts 1 to 3 and 5 have exact data determined by the zoo or by the family; Facts 4 and 6 give estimates that are signalled by the word *about*.)
Select the membership benefit that is good only once. (50¢ coupon for the zoo gift store) *Identify a membership benefit that would be new for Rick's family.* (subscription to zoo magazine)

► **Compare the admission to the insect and petting zoo with the other fees.** (Possible answers: It is the same as the children's fee; it is the same price for children and adults, while the general zoo admission is different for each.)

► **Predict how Fact 4 might vary.** (Possible answers: The family might go to the zoo more or less often than 3 times a year; fewer family members might go to the zoo sometimes.)

► **Predict other costs of a family visit to the zoo, and decide which, if any, are related to membership.** (Answers may vary: Sample answers: snacks; parking or transportation costs; animal food; special fees for special exhibits)

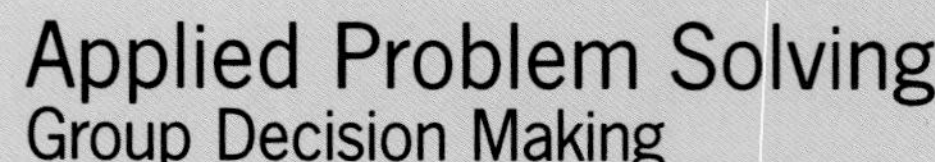

Applied Problem Solving
Group Decision Making

UNDERSTAND
FIND DATA
PLAN
ESTIMATE
SOLVE
CHECK

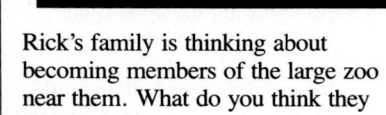

Group Skill:
Explain and Summarize

Rick's family is thinking about becoming members of the large zoo near them. What do you think they should do?

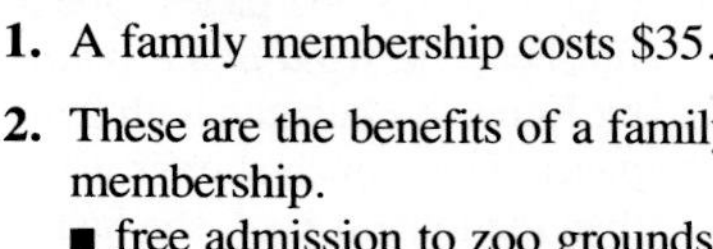

Facts to Consider

1. A family membership costs $35.
2. These are the benefits of a family membership.
   - free admission to zoo grounds
   - subscription to zoo magazine
   - free admission to insect and petting zoo
     - one 50¢ coupon for a purchase of $5.00 or more at the zoo gift store

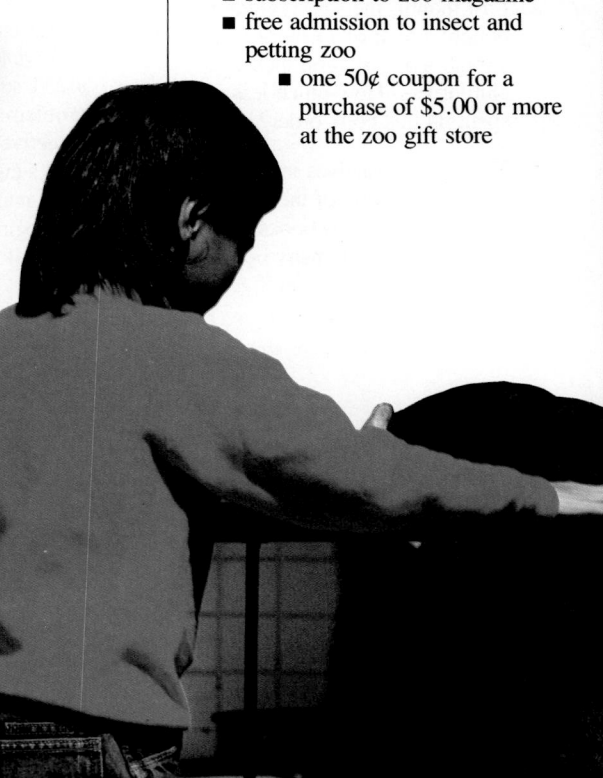

198

Teaching Options

COOPERATIVE LEARNING

Grouping Suggestion:
cooperative learning groups of 3-5
Have group members discuss, plan, and assign tasks related to the decision-making process. For example, the first student could design a chart for recording data, the second could figure total costs with paper and pencil, and the third could check the figures for accuracy and record them in the chart. Another student could write questions about the advantages and disadvantages of zoo membership for the group to consider before making its final decision.

3. These are the regular admission fees.
   - adult $2.25
   - child $0.75
   - insect and petting zoo, per person $0.75
4. Rick's entire family usually goes to the zoo about 3 times a year. There are 3 children and 2 parents in the family.
5. The family always goes to the insect and petting zoo.
6. The family usually spends about $5.00 at the zoo store each visit.

Some Questions to Answer

1. How much does Rick's family pay for admission fees each time they go to the zoo?
2. How much does his family pay to go to the insect and petting zoo?
3. How much money does Rick's family spend in all for each zoo visit, not including the zoo store?
4. How much do they spend in 2 visits?
5. If they were members, how much would they get back from the zoo store each time?

What Is Your Decision?

Make a list or chart to show why you think Rick's family should or should not become members of the zoo.

199

EXTENSION If there is a zoo in your area, have groups call or write to request information about family memberships. Students can compare costs and benefits of family membership with the usual cost of paying as you go. They should also compare advantages and disadvantages of other membership categories that may be available.

SOME QUESTIONS TO ANSWER

► **Analyze the facts to identify those that you need to answer Questions 7 and 8.** (Fact 3: fees; Fact 4: number of people in Rick's family; Fact 5: They always go to the insect and petting zoo.)
► **Explain how you would answer Question 10.** (Add all the costs for 1 visit, then double the sum or multiply it by 2.)
► **How would you consider data about the zoo store?** (Possible answer: It is the cost most likely to vary, so you may not consider it as much as other facts.)

WHAT IS YOUR DECISION?

► **Explain how you kept track of comparisons.** (Answers will vary.)
► **Summarize advantages of a family membership.** (Answers may vary. Sample answers: you save money if you visit the zoo enough times; you get a zoo magazine, some free admissions, and a 50¢ discount coupon for the zoo shop.)
► **Analyze some possible disadvantages.** (Answers may vary. Sample answers: if you do not visit the zoo often enough, the membership is not worth it; if you have a small family, it may be cheaper to pay as you go.)

CHAPTER 7

WRAP UP

INTRODUCTION The Wrap Up provides activities emphasizing math language and thinking skills for the chapter and a project that integrates those skills with other math strands.

USING PAGE 200

Multiplication Match Have students complete this section independently, then read their completed sentences aloud so that classmates can discuss the responses.

Sometimes, Always, Never

▶ **Decide on a method for completing Exercise 5.** (Multiply 2 even numbers; examine the product.)

▶ **Decide when it makes more sense to overestimate and when to underestimate.** (Overestimate when shopping; underestimate to create easier numbers to calculate mentally.)

Project Have students work in pairs to plan, discuss, and carry out the project. Pairs will need a clock or watch with a second hand or a stopwatch. They should decide whether to count an inhale and exhale as 1 or as 2 events.

▶ **Explain how to estimate hourly totals.** (Multiply the total per minute by 60.)

▶ **Explain how hourly totals relate to daily totals.** (1 day = 24 hours; multiply hourly totals by 24.)

Suggest students make booklets to represent each category of data and each method of representation: chart, bar graph, pictograph, line graph. Have students compare and display them.

WRAP UP

Multiplication Match

Use the term that best completes each sentence.

whole numbers	mental math
underestimates	multiple steps

1. When you multiply front-end digits of factors your products are usually __?__. **underestimates**
2. You can multiply with money just like you multiply with __?__. **whole numbers**
3. When numbers are easy to work with you can use __?__. **mental math**
4. If you must use more than one operation to solve a problem, the problem has __?__. **multiple steps**

Sometimes, Always, Never

Which word should go in the blank, sometimes, always, or never? Explain your choices. **Explanations will vary.**

5. The product of two even numbers is __?__ an odd number. **never**
6. It is __?__ wiser to overestimate than to underestimate. **sometimes**
7. In a multiple-step problem, you __?__ do the multiplication step first. **sometimes**

Project

For one minute, count how many times these things happen.

- your heart beats
- your eyes blink
- you swallow
- you breathe in and out

After you collect the exact data, estimate how many times you do each activity in one hour, then in one day. Explain how some of the estimates might vary over 24 hours.

200

TEACHING OPTIONS

ENRICHMENT Have students use science books or an encyclopedia to research pulse rates of 5 different animals or birds. Have them use the data to create a table, graph, or other visual representation on which to compare the rates. Display the graphs on a math bulletin board.

CHAPTER REVIEW/TEST

Part 1 Understanding

1. What fact helps you find the product for 40 × 60? 4 × 6 = 24
2. What fact helps you find the product for 70 × 80? 7 × 8 = 56
3. One way to estimate 27 × 78 is to use 30 × 80. Will your product be an overestimate or an underestimate? Why? overestimate; both factors were rounded up
4. Make the best match you can.

- to find 5,684 + 4,692 + 3,425 c
- to find 582 + 32 + 14 b
- to find 3,000 × 40 a

a. use mental math
b. use pencil and paper
c. use a calculator

Part 2 Skills

5. 50 × 70 3,500
6. 40 × 40 1,600
7. 83 × 30 2,490
8. 68 × 60 4,080
9. 48 × 75 = 3,600
10. 19 × 91 = 1,729
11. 34 × 84 = 2,856
12. 61 × 27 = 1,647
13. 804 × 39 = 31,356
14. 773 × 52 = 40,196
15. $6.15 × 89 = $547.35
16. $3.63 × 40 = $145.20

Part 3 Applications

17. A magician does 13 coin tricks using dimes and nickels. In 7 of the tricks she uses dimes. In 10 of the tricks she uses nickels. In how many tricks does she use both dimes and nickels? 4 tricks
18. The magician needs a dozen scarves that cost $2.75 each. She has a $20 bill. How much more money does she need? $13
19. A bowling ball weighs 17 times more than a 15-ounce football. How much does the bowling ball weigh? 255 oz
20. **Challenge** Ky can do 33 sit-ups a minute. If he kept that pace for 24 hours, how many sit-ups would he do? 47,520 sit-ups

201

CHAPTER REVIEW/TEST

INTRODUCTION The Review/Test is provided to review and evaluate the skills and concepts presented in Chapter 7.

USING PAGE 201
If you prefer to use this page for review, you may want to use the **Multiple-Choice Posttest** (pages 27-28) or the **Free-Response Posttest** (pages 27-28) to evaluate mastery of Chapter objectives.

ITEM ANALYSIS The table below correlates the Chapter Review/Test items with the lesson objectives for the chapter.

Items	Objectives
1, 2	7-1
3	7-2
4	7-9
5, 6	7-1
7, 8	7-3
9-12	7-4
13, 14	7-5
15, 16	7-8
17	7-7
18	7-8
(18)	7-10
19, 20	7-4

INFORMAL ASSESSMENT

Using Manipulatives Have students use 5 number cards (TA 3) to form a 3-digit factor and a 2-digit factor. They multiply, record the product, then rearrange the 5 digits to form other 2- and 3-digit factors to give a greater and a lesser product. (Answers will vary. Check students' work.)

Communication *Explain how to multiply $5.27 by 63, relating the necessary steps to multiplying a nonmoney amount.* (Follow the same steps you would use if the factors were 527 × 63—multiply 527 by 3; multiply 527 by 60; add partial products; then write the product with a dollar sign, decimal point, and 2 decimal places.)

Critical Thinking *Determine a sensible estimate for the product of 94 and 37. Explain your reasoning.* (Possible answer: Round 94 down to 90; round 37 up to 40; 90 × 40 = 3,600.)

CHAPTER 7

ENRICHMENT

INTRODUCTION Completing the multiplication table will provide students with an opportunity to apply logical reasoning, number sense, and an understanding of the link between multiplication and division.

USING PAGE 202
This Enrichment page is provided for all students. You may wish to use it after they have completed the Chapter Review/Test on page 201.

► **Explain how 49, 57, 28, and 163 are related in the table.** (All are factors.)

► **Analyze the table to determine how many products are known.** (4)

► **Decide on a plan for finding a missing factor.** (Divide a product by the known factor to find the other factor.)

► **Explain where to record the other factor you would multiply with 49 to give a product of 19,943.** (in the first empty factor box on the top row)

► **Explain how to complete the table.** (Write each factor or product as you find it, then solve the next related missing factor or product until all boxes are filled.)

► **Compare the strategy you use to complete the table with finding missing digits.** (Use the same relationship between multiplication and division to find the missing digits.)

ENRICHMENT
The Unfinished Table

The multiplication table below is incomplete. There are some missing factors and products. Find your detective hat and your calculator. Complete the table. Hint: How are multiplication and division related?

1.

X	407	62	28	163
49	19,943	3,038	1,372	7,987
94	38,258	5,828	2,632	15,322
60	24,420	3,720	1,680	9,780
57	23,199	3,534	1,596	9,291

Then find the missing digits in these examples.

2. [3][9][7] × 2 8 = 11,116

3. 2 8 3 × [6][6] = 18,678

4. [4] 78 × 25 = 11,950

CUMULATIVE REVIEW

1.

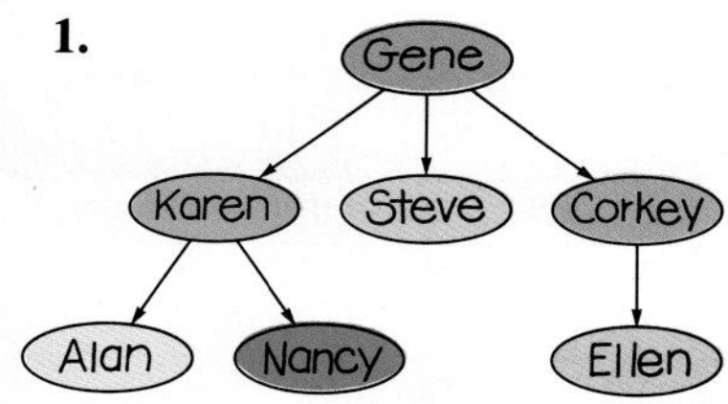

Gene made a family tree. Find the number of children Gene has.

A 5 B 4

(C) 3 D 6

2.

	Players 1	2	3
Game 1	II	𝍸	I
Game 2	III	III	𝍸
Game 3	III	II	IIII
Game 4	𝍸	𝍸	𝍸

Look at the scores of the 3 players trying each game. Which game seems the least fair?

(A) Game 1 B Game 2

C Game 3 D Game 4

3. 10 × 0

A 10 B 100

(C) 0 D 1

4. 7 × 5

A 12 (B) 35

C 0 D 70

5. Which is a muliple of 8?

A 4 B 20

C 18 (D) 32

6. Find the product of 3 and 9.

(A) 27 B 6

C 28 D 12

7. 308 × 3

A 911 B 904

(C) 924 D 964

8. 314 × 6

A 1,864 B 2,064

(C) 1,884 D 1,984

9. Find the product of 5,073 and 8.

(A) 40,584 B 45,084

C 40,544 D 44,084

10. A rubber nose costs 85¢. Use mental math to find the cost of 4 rubber noses.

(A) $3.40 B $1.70

C $3.20 D $2.60

11. Clown makeup jars are on display in rows. Row 1 has 5 jars, row 2 has 8 jars, and row 3 has 11 jars. How many jars are in row 6?

A 30 B 17

C 23 (D) 20

203

CUMULATIVE REVIEW

INTRODUCTION The purpose of this Cumulative Review is to maintain previously taught skills and concepts. The emphasis in this Cumulative Review is on data, graphs, and probability, Chapter 4; on multiplication concepts and basic facts, Chapter 5; and on multiplication of 2-, 3-, and 4-digit factors by 1-digit factors, Chapter 6.

ITEM ANALYSIS The table below correlates the Cumulative Review items with the lesson objectives.

Items	Objectives
1	4-5
2	4-7
3	5-2
4	5-3
5	5-10
6	5-4
(6)	5-5
7, 8	6-6
9	6-10
10	6-2
11	6-12

CHAPTER 8 TIME AND CUSTOMARY MEASUREMENT

Chapter Management

OVERVIEW

Lesson	Pages	Objectives	Subject Integration	Strand Integration
Chapter Opener	204-205	To introduce chapter 8	social studies-map skills	measurement: time
Telling Time: Minutes	206-207	8-1 To tell time to the minute, past the hour, and to the next hour	science-science films	estimation
A.M. and P.M./Reading the Calendar	208-209	8-2 To identify a.m. or p.m.; to read a calendar	fine arts-music club	number
Mental Math: Elapsed Time	210-211	8-3 To calculate ending times and elapsed time	social studies-Frontier Days	calculators
Problem Solving: Problems with More than One Answer	212-213	8-4 To solve problems with more than one answer	health/fitness-playground activities	computation
Estimating and Measuring Length: Nonstandard Units	214-215	8-5 To estimate and measure length, using nonstandard units	language arts-writing	mathematical reasoning
Inch, Foot, and Yard	216-217	8-6 To measure length using inch, foot, and yard	health/fitness-sports equipment	problem solving
Problem Solving: Deciding When to Estimate	218-219	8-7 To decide if an actual or estimated measurement is needed	health/fitness-recipes	measurement
Miles/Midchapter Review/Quiz	220-221	8-8 To estimate lengths in miles	social studies-map skills	problem solving
Perimeter/Estimating Length, Width, and Perimeter: Using a Benchmark	222-223	8-9 To find perimeter; to use a benchmark	health/fitness-dog walking	computatation
Problem Solving: Data from a Chart	224-225	8-10 To solve problems using data from a chart	social studies-buildings	calculators
Estimating and Measuring Capacity	226-227	8-11 To estimate, measure, and compare capacity	health/fitness-recipes	problem solving
Estimating and Measuring Weight/Temperature: Degrees Fahrenheit	228-229	8-12 To compare pounds and ounces; to measure temperature	health/fitness-foods	measurement
Data Collection and Analysis: Group Decision Making	230-231	8-13 To collect, organize, and present data	social studies-group skills	graphing

MATHEMATICAL BACKGROUND

Time
Students learn to tell time to the minute, past the hour, and to the hour. They learn to identify times as a.m. or p.m. hours.

Mental Math
Students use mental math to find ending and elapsed times.

Length, Capacity, Weight, and Temperature
Units of measurement presented in the chapter are: inch, foot, yard, mile, cup, pint, quart, gallon, pound, ounce, and degrees Fahrenheit. Students also learn to find the perimeter of an object and to estimate by using a benchmark.

Problem Solving
Students solve problems that have more than one answer. They also decide when to estimate and use data from a chart.

TIPS FROM TEACHERS

Have students find the distance from your classroom to another place in the school in ''people'' units. Measure the height of each student, then cut an oaktag strip to equal that length. Each student uses the oaktag strip to measure the designated distance in his or her own ''people'' units. Compare individual results.

Donna Bibbins
Knickerbocker School
Watertown, NY

48"
Janet's "people" unit

ASSESSMENT

Pretest — Chapter 8, page 1

Multiple-Choice Format

Name

1. Give the time.
   a. 17 minutes to 4
   b. three-twenty-seven
   c. three-thirty
   d. 17 minutes past 4
   1. d
2. How would the time look on a digital clock?
   a. 7:30 b. 6:30 c. 7:26 d. 8:26
   2. d
3. Lamont eats supper at 6:30 ?. Choose a.m. or p.m.
   a. a.m. b. p.m.
   3. b
4. Name the 6th month.
   a. June b. July c. August d. May
   4. a
5. Give the amount of elapsed time from 6:30 p.m. to 1:30 a.m.
   a. 5 hours b. 8 hours c. 7 hours d. 6 hours
   5. c
6. Norm wants to put 12 chairs into equal rows. He could put 6 chairs into each of 2 rows. Is there another solution?
   a. Yes b. No
   6. a
7. Choose the best estimate for the length of this line.
   a. 1 thumb unit b. 1 arm span
   c. 1 hand span d. 1 step
   7. c

MCT 4 29

Pretest — Chapter 8, page 2

Multiple-Choice Format

Name

8. Tell which measurement is longer.
   a. 3 yd b. 4 ft
   8. a
9. Decide whether you need an estimate or an actual measurement. You are planting some flower bulbs. How deep should you plant each bulb?
   a. Estimate b. Actual Measurement
   9. a
10. Estimate the distance in miles from Taft to Plano using your thumb width.
    Taft — 10 mi. — Plano
    a. 10 miles b. 15 miles
    c. 21 miles d. 30 miles
    10. d
11. Find the perimeter.
    16 ft, 10 ft, 10 ft, 16 ft
    a. 26 ft b. 32 ft
    c. 20 ft d. 52 ft
    11. d
12. How many more points did Hawkins score than Hayward?

Player	Team	Points
Hawkins	Bradley	1,125
Hayward	Loyola	756

    a. 369 points b. 479 points
    c. 379 points d. 459 points
    12. a
13. Multiply to find the missing number: 3 pt = ■ c.
    a. 6 b. 12 c. 24 d. 5
    13. a
14. Tell which weighs more.
    a. Math book: 2 lb b. Paperback book: 9 oz
    14. a
15. Choose the correct temperature.
    Degrees Fahrenheit
    a. 38°F b. 42°F c. 40°F
    15. c

30 MCT 4

Posttest — Chapter 8, page 1

Multiple-Choice Format

Name

1. Give the time.
   a. 26 minutes past 3
   b. 26 minutes to 3
   c. three-thirty
   d. three-sixteen
   1. a
2. How would the time look on a digital clock?
   a. 12:11 b. 11:12 c. 11:15 d. 12:15
   2. b
3. Jeff goes to school at 8:30 ? . Choose a.m. or p.m.
   a. a.m. b. p.m.
   3. a
4. Name the 9th month.
   a. October b. July c. September d. May
   4. c
5. Give the amount of elapsed time from 8:45 a.m. to 1:45 p.m.
   a. 5 hours b. 4 hours c. 7 hours d. 6 hours
   5. a
6. Alice wants to put her 30 stickers onto pages so each page has the same number. She could put 10 stickers on each of 3 pages. Is there another solution?
   a. Yes b. No
   6. a
7. Choose the best estimate for the length of this line.
   a. 1 thumb unit b. 1 arm span
   c. 1 hand span d. 1 step
   7. a

MCT 4 31

Posttest — Chapter 8, page 2

Multiple-Choice Format

Name

8. Tell which measurement is longer.
   a. 57 in. b. 2 yd
   8. b
9. Decide whether you need an estimate or an actual measurement. You are making yeast bread. How much flour should you use?
   a. Estimate b. Actual measurement
   9. b
10. Estimate the distance in miles from Berea to Page using your thumb width.
    Berea — 20 mi — Page
    a. 10 miles b. 15 miles
    c. 40 miles d. 60 miles
    10. d
11. Find the perimeter.
    24 ft, 12 ft, 12 ft, 24 ft
    a. 36 ft b. 72 ft
    c. 24 ft d. 48 ft
    11. b
12. How many more rebounds did Miller get than Lane?

Player	Team	Rebounds
Lane	Pittsburgh	378
Miller	Loyola	395

    a. 23 rebounds b. 773 rebounds
    c. 17 rebounds d. 27 rebounds
    12. c
13. Multiply to find the missing number: 5 half gal = ■ qt.
    a. 20 b. 10 c. 40 d. 7
    13. b
14. Tell which weighs more.
    a. Loaf of bread: 1 lb b. Box of crackers: 10 oz
    14. a
15. Choose the correct temperature.
    Degrees Fahrenheit
    a. 38°F b. 35°F c. 32°F
    15. b

32 MCT 4

ITEM ANALYSIS

Items	Objectives
1, 2	8-1
3, 4	8-2
5	8-3
6	8-4
7	8-5
8	8-6
9	8-7
10	8-8
11	8-9
12	8-10
13	8-11
14, 15	8-12

Note: The item analysis is the same for all pretests and posttests for this chapter.

ALSO AVAILABLE

- **Free Response Tests**
- **Alternative Tests**
- **Thinking Strategies**
- **Concrete Materials**

Optional Chapter Activities

PROJECT AND BULLETIN BOARD

After students complete Lesson 6, have them make a class chart showing how far each student can jump. Pair students, then have one jump as far as he or she can. The partner measures how far that student jumped in yards, feet, and inches. After the jumping distances of all students have been measured, help students to construct a chart showing how far each student jumped in order from the greatest to the smallest distance. Students should use the chart illustrated as a model.

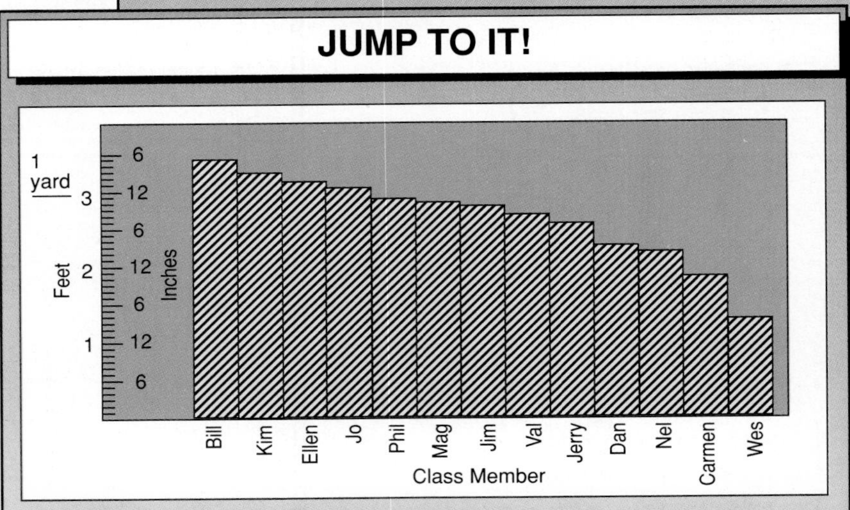

At another time, have students estimate and then measure distance. For example, they could toss a bean bag, estimate how far it landed from the starting point, then measure and chart the distance. They can compare their beginning estimates with later ones and chart their improvements.

COOPERATIVE LEARNING

Divide the class into groups of four. Identify the group skills: listen to others. Provide a kitchen scale and a postal scale for the groups to use. Have each group choose three objects from the classroom and, if suitable, from outdoors. The objects should obviously be of different weights, such as a sheet of paper, a pencil, and a book. Have one person weigh each item on the appropriate scale and tell the group how much each item weighs. Then have the groups exchange objects. Everyone in each group should look carefully at the new objects, lift them, and think about how much they weigh. Then have the group estimate the weight of each object as they listen carefully to each others' opinions.

Have one student in each group write the name of the object and its estimated weight. Then have the student weigh each item and compare the actual weight with the estimate. The group should discuss how the weight of these objects compared with the weight of the original objects they were given. Ask, *Did knowing the weight of the original objects help to make a more accurate estimate of the new objects?*

You will find grouping suggestions and cooperative learning activities in most lessons throughout this chapter.

LITERATURE

Breiter, Herta S. *Time and Clocks.* Milwaukee, Wisconsin: Raintree Publications, 1978.

This carefully planned and well organized book will help children better understand the concepts of telling time. Children could create their own time stories. Then they could write them using a.m. and p.m.

Adler, Irving & Ruth. *The Calendar.* New York: The John Day Company, 1967.

Eager, Edward. *The Time Garden.* New York: A Voyager/HBJ Book, 1958.

Russell, Solveig Paulson. *Size, Distance, Weight.* New York: Henry Z. Walck, 1968.

English as a Second Language

A common problem ESL students have with measurement is understanding the role of units. Show children a need for measurement by discussing familiar measurement subjects. For example, you might inquire how far a child's house is from the school. Units of measurement may be blocks, miles, or minutes. Then ask, *Are all blocks the same size? Can we see miles? What can we use to measure miles?*

Have students participate in measuring perimeter using non-standard units. Use an area in your school or classroom and tell the class they are going to measure its perimeter in ''child'' units. Ask them to stand fingertip to fingertip around the perimeter of the shape. Count the number of children, noting any fractional remainder. Ask, *Is the measurement exact? Why?* They may indicate that the measurement is not exact because the students are of various sizes.

Gifted

Ask your students to imagine that they have hired a company called ''Timely Tips,'' which is going to help them better organize their time. To do this, the students need to show the company exactly how they spend their day now. The organization has asked them to create a chart with four columns showing the name of the day's activity, a clock picturing the beginning time, a clock picturing the ending time, and, in the last column, the amount of time needed for each activity. Remind students to indicate *a.m.* or *p.m.* under each clock.

Suggest that students think of ways to group some of the activities on the chart into categories such as eating, playing sports, or doing homework. Encourage them to draw a circle or pie and to break down their day into accurately sized wedges or slices. Ask them to write the category's name on each wedge.

Have students look at each others' charts and pies. Have them look for similarities and differences. Ask if any of the activities are on all of the charts, and have them consider what the differences might be between weekday and weekend charts. Display their work.

Students at Risk

The essential life skills of telling time and understanding time concepts can be difficult for students with learning disabilities or emotional problems. Reading an analog clock involves sequential and recognitive skills. Understanding elapsed time requires the development of a particular kind of real-life number sense. The following strategies may help.

Clock Cues

Help students verbally cue themselves to tell time. They first ask, ''What hour does the small hand point to?'' Then they ask, ''How many minutes past that hour does the big hand show?'' Provide a model clock with only an hour hand (or a real clock with the minute hand removed), and let students move the hour hand in a clockwise direction to notice its position as it moves.

A kitchen timer can help students develop a sense of elapsed time. Set the timer to ring every 5 minutes for one hour. Have students develop individual lists of activities that take about 5 minutes. Use the same strategy on different days to highlight other intervals, such as 1, 10, 15, or 30 minutes.

You may also use the Reteaching Supplements and the specific Reteaching Tips from each lesson in this chapter.

INTRODUCING THE CHAPTER

SUBJECT INTEGRATION The clock in the tower of the Parliament Building in London is commonly called Big Ben, although Big Ben actually names the huge bell whose famous chimes ring each quarter hour. The photograph suggests the chapter theme of social studies. Some lessons relate the theme to time and measurement situations.

USING DATA The Social Studies Data Bank on page 474 of the Student Edition shows the major time zones of the continental United States. A clock in each zone shows the standard time relationships among zones.

QUESTION 1 ▶ **Locate your state on the map and name its time zone.** (Answers will vary.)
▶ **Identify the sample time given for your time zone.** (Answers will vary.) Student Edition answers: 3:00 Pacific time; 4:00 Mountain time; 5:00 Central time; 6:00 Eastern time

8 TIME AND CUSTOMARY MEASUREMENT

MATH AND SOCIAL STUDIES

DATA BANK

Use the Social Studies Data Bank on page 474 to answer the questions. See teaching notes.

1 What time is shown on each clock on the map of time zones?

TEACHING OPTIONS

LANGUAGE DEVELOPMENT
Write the phrase **time zone** on the chalkboard and ask students what they know about its meaning. Explain that the earth is divided into 24 time zones, 1 for each hour of the day. Places in the same time zone follow the same time. Have students name their time zone.

2 In which time zone is the time one hour later than in the Pacific time zone? 2 hours later? 3 hours later?

3 Do you lose or gain time when you travel from New York to California?

4 **Use Critical Thinking** The time difference from Alaska to Hawaii is 1 hour. Hawaii is farther west, so is the time there earlier or later?

205

QUESTION 2 ► **Determine the order of time zones you would pass through on a trip from Pennsylvania to Nevada.** (You start in the Eastern time zone, then you pass through the Central and Mountain time zones to the Pacific time zone, which contains Nevada.)
Student Edition answers: Mountain; Central; Eastern

QUESTION 3 ► **Use the information on the clocks to analyze the relationship between time and east/west travel.** (Possible answer: As you travel west, the time gets earlier; as you travel east, the time gets later.)
Student Edition answer: gain

QUESTION 4 ► **Explain why Alaska and Hawaii are not shown on the time-zone map.** (They are not in the time zones shown because neither is connected to the other 48 states.)
► **Suppose that there is a 1-hour time difference between Pacific and Alaska time. If it is noon in Alaska, what time is it in Oregon?** (1:00 p.m.)
Student Edition answer: earlier

SUBJECT INTEGRATION PROJECT Have students gather data on time zones by brainstorming a list of places in the world in which they have a friend or a relative or a place anyone they know has lived or visited. Identify locations on a world map with pushpins or stickers placed on or near the spot. Conclude by listing all the different time zones represented on the map and challenging students to formulate and answer questions about making phone calls or travelling between different time zones.

Telling Time: Minutes

OBJECTIVE 8-1 To tell time to the minute, past the hour, and to the next hour

PREBOOK ACTIVITIES

QUICK REVIEW

Find the differences mentally.

1. 60 − 30 (30)	**2.** 60 − 10 (50)	**3.** 60 − 5 (55)
4. 60 − 40 (20)	**5.** 60 − 20 (40)	**6.** 60 − 15 (45)
7. 60 − 25 (35)	**8.** 60 − 7 (53)	**9.** 60 − 13 (47)

PRIOR KNOWLEDGE

Have students visualize the clocks or watches they read in a normal day. List the variety of timepieces students describe. Then classify them by categories, such as Arabic versus Roman numerals, mechanical versus electronic movement, or digital versus analog display. Discuss unusual ways to tell time, such as using sundials or sand timers. Have students draw conclusions about the importance of telling time. (Possible answers: to observe schedules or appointments; to have ways to describe *how long*.)

COMMUNICATION

Discussing Math Generate a list of different uses of the word **time.** (Samples: lunchtime; the time is 5:27; time and time again; mark time; spare time; tell time) Compare uses that mean a specific measurement with ones that indicate a general period. Remind students that certain measures of time can be stated in several ways. Have students share how they would read the time 1:15 and 1:45. (Possible answers: one-fifteen, quarter after one, quarter past one; one-forty-five; quarter to two, quarter of, fifteen to two.)

EXPLORE AND CONNECT

Materials: TA 16 (Clock Face), TA 13 (Spinners 1-4 and 5-8), brads

Grouping Suggestion: cooperative learning pairs

Pairs play a clock game to practice telling **time** to the minute. Each student needs a clock face and a minute hand attached with a brad. All play begins with the minute hand at 12, which is equivalent to 0 min. A player spins for numbers 1-4 or 5-8, then moves the clock hand ahead that number of minutes. The student reads the *time* (such as "4 min after the hour") and earns a point when the partner verifies the *time*. The player begins from that location on his or her next turn. Then the partner takes a turn with his or her clock. After each player has had a turn, he or she can choose to move ahead or back to land on 15, 30, or 45 min and earn 3 points. A player whose minute hand makes it around the clock and lands exactly on 12 earns 12 points. When *time* is up, pairs total their points.

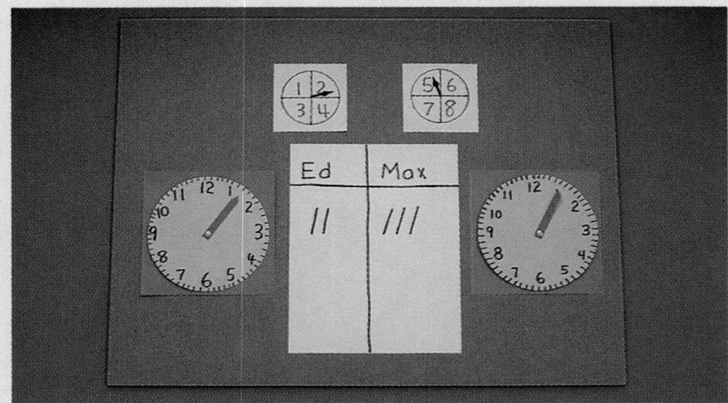

CONNECTIONS Use these anytime.

Problem of the Day

Digit Range List the range of digits that can appear in each place on a digital clock to show all possible times in a 12-h period.

☐ ☐ : ☐ ☐
(0-1 0-9 : 0-5 0-9)

Life Skills

Phone Bill Roger pays 17¢/min to talk long distance to his brother Roy in Chatterly. If Roger calls Roy at 7:52 and talks until 8:09, how much does the call cost? ($2.89)

Creative Thinking

Mirror Image Otto's clock reflects in a mirror. Naturally, the face and hands are backward. At what times are the mirror-image clock hands in the same position as the actual time? (12:00 and 6:00)

Classwork and Homework Supplements

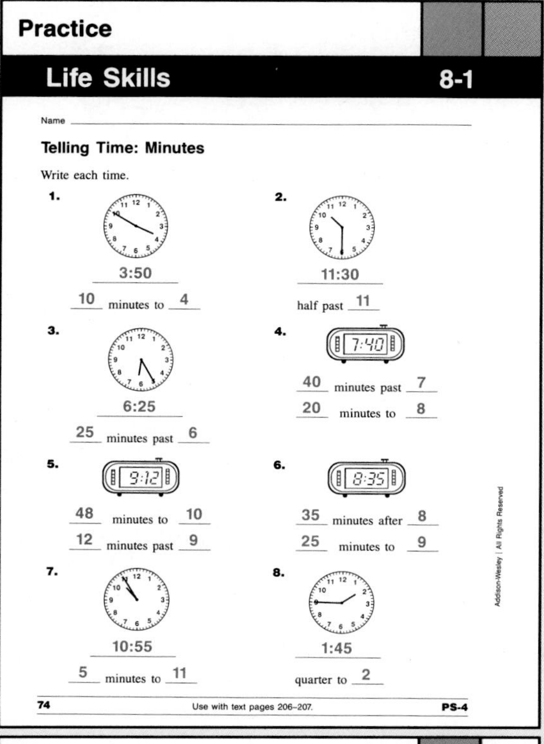
Practice

Life Skills 8-1

Name

Telling Time: Minutes

Write each time.

1. 3:50 — 10 minutes to 4
2. 11:30 — half past 11
3. 6:25 — 25 minutes past 6
4. 7:40 — 40 minutes past 7; 20 minutes to 8
5. 9:12 — 48 minutes to 10; 12 minutes past 9
6. 8:35 — 35 minutes after 8; 25 minutes to 9
7. 10:55 — 5 minutes to 11
8. 1:45 — quarter to 2

Addison-Wesley | All Rights Reserved

74 Use with text pages 206–207. PS-4

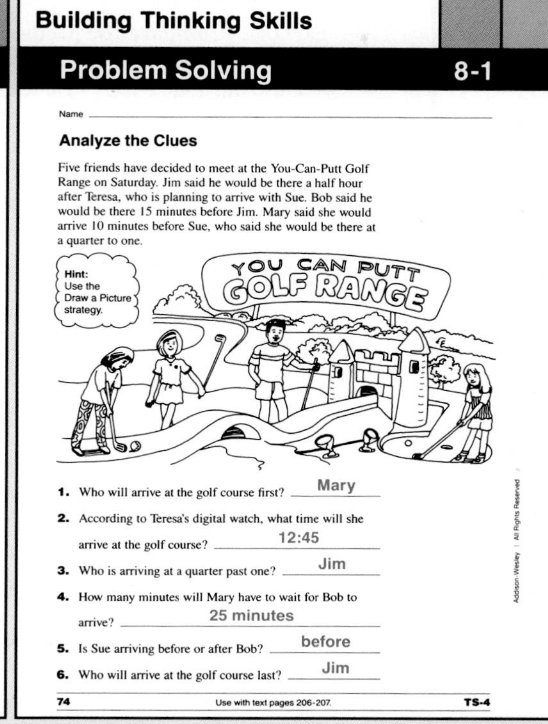
Building Thinking Skills

Problem Solving 8-1

Name

Analyze the Clues

Five friends have decided to meet at the You-Can-Putt Golf Range on Saturday. Jim said he would be there a half hour after Teresa, who is planning to arrive with Sue. Bob said he would be there 15 minutes before Jim. Mary said she would arrive 10 minutes before Sue, who said she would be there at a quarter to one.

Hint: Use the Draw a Picture strategy.
YOU CAN PUTT GOLF RANGE

1. Who will arrive at the golf course first? Mary
2. According to Teresa's digital watch, what time will she arrive at the golf course? 12:45
3. Who is arriving at a quarter past one? Jim
4. How many minutes will Mary have to wait for Bob to arrive? 25 minutes
5. Is Sue arriving before or after Bob? before
6. Who will arrive at the golf course last? Jim

Addison-Wesley | All Rights Reserved

74 Use with text pages 206–207. TS-4

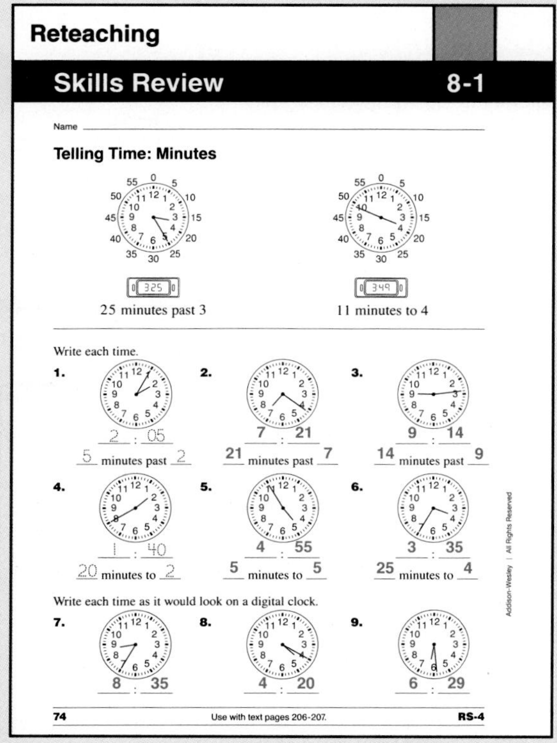
Reteaching

Skills Review 8-1

Name

Telling Time: Minutes

3:25 — 25 minutes past 3

3:49 — 11 minutes to 4

Write each time.

1. 2 : 05 — 5 minutes past 2
2. 7 : 21 — 21 minutes past 7
3. 9 : 14 — 14 minutes past 9
4. 1 : 40 — 20 minutes to 2
5. 4 : 55 — 5 minutes to 5
6. 3 : 35 — 25 minutes to 4

Write each time as it would look on a digital clock.

7. 8 : 35
8. 4 : 20
9. 6 : 29

Addison-Wesley | All Rights Reserved

74 Use with text pages 206–207. RS-4

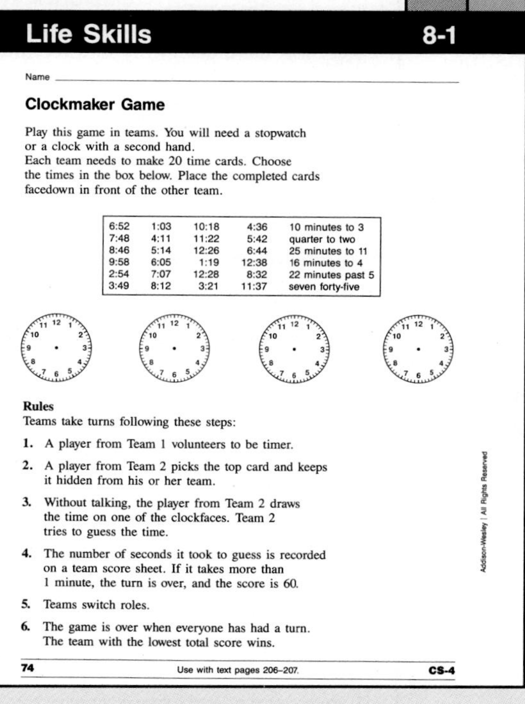
Challenges

Life Skills 8-1

Name

Clockmaker Game

Play this game in teams. You will need a stopwatch or a clock with a second hand.
Each team needs to make 20 time cards. Choose the times in the box below. Place the completed cards facedown in front of the other team.

6:52	1:03	10:18	4:36	10 minutes to 3
7:48	4:11	11:22	5:42	quarter to two
8:46	5:14	12:26	6:44	25 minutes to 11
9:58	6:05	1:19	12:38	16 minutes to 4
2:54	7:07	12:28	8:32	22 minutes past 5
3:49	8:12	3:21	11:37	seven forty-five

Rules

Teams take turns following these steps:

1. A player from Team 1 volunteers to be timer.
2. A player from Team 2 picks the top card and keeps it hidden from his or her team.
3. Without talking, the player from Team 2 draws the time on one of the clockfaces. Team 2 tries to guess the time.
4. The number of seconds it took to guess is recorded on a team score sheet. If it takes more than 1 minute, the turn is over, and the score is 60.
5. Teams switch roles.
6. The game is over when everyone has had a turn. The team with the lowest total score wins.

Addison-Wesley | All Rights Reserved

74 Use with text pages 206–207. CS-4

Options for Individual Needs

Basic

Exercises 1-5, 9-14
Data Bank, p. 474
More Practice, p. 517, set C

Supplements
Reteaching 74 or
Practice 74

Average

Exercises 1-14
Data Bank, p. 474
More Practice, p. 517, set C

Supplements
Practice 74
Challenges 74 or
Thinking Skills 74

Extended

Exercises 3-14
Data Bank, p. 474

Supplements
Challenges 74
Thinking Skills 74

Other Resources:
Problem-Solving Experiences in Mathematics, Grade 4, Problems 54-56
Make It Simpler, A Practical Guide to Problem Solving in Mathematics, p. 281
Kids Are Consumers, Too!, pp. 174, 175

LESSON PLAN 8-1

OBJECTIVE 8-1
To tell time to the minute, past the hour, and to the next hour

Materials: clocks with movable hands

Alternative Materials: toy clocks, TA 16 (Clock Face)

1. MOTIVATE AND TEACH

LEARN ABOUT IT

EXPLORE ▶ **Explain how the hands move around a clock face.** (They start at 12 and move in a circle from the least to the greater digits.)
▶ **Describe the location of the hour hand in relation to the 3 and 4.** (It is past the 3 and approaching the 4.)
▶ **Explain how its position would change if the time were 3:10.** (The hour hand would be between 3 and 4 but closer to 3.)

TALK ABOUT IT ▶ **Why were Linda and Russ confused?** (There are different ways to express the same time.)
▶ **Analyze the ways they chose to express the time.** (Linda said minutes *to* the next hour; Russ said minutes *past* the hour.)
▶ **Explain why 15 min is an important part of an hour.** (Possible answer: 60 min can be divided into 4 equal parts, or *quarters*, each with 15 min.)
Student Edition answers: **1.** Russ, Linda **2.** Possible answer: 15 is one fourth of 60; *quarter* also means one fourth.

2. CHECK UNDERSTANDING

TRY IT OUT

ERROR ALERT Using the hour beyond the position of the hour hand when counting minutes after the hour. Counting wrong for times to the next hour.

Telling Time
Minutes

LEARN ABOUT IT

EXPLORE Compare the Methods
Linda and Russ planned to meet at the science museum. Linda said, "I'll leave my house at 15 minutes to 4." Russ looked at his clock and said, "I thought I'd leave my house at 45 minutes past 3. Does that mean we'll leave at the same time?" "I think so," said Linda, "but let's count on our clocks to check."

Linda's clock

Russ's clock

TALK ABOUT IT See teaching notes.

1. Who counted from the 12 on the clock to find the time? Who counted from the 9?
2. Linda said another way to think about the time was to say "quarter to four." Explain why that works.

Here are some ways to read and write times.

You read five-fifteen, 15 minutes past 5, or quarter past five.

You read ten-thirty, 30 minutes past 10, or half past ten.

You read seven-forty-two, 42 minutes past 7, or 18 minutes to 8.

TRY IT OUT See Additional Answers.

Give each time in three different ways.

1. 

TEACHING OPTIONS

RETEACHING TIPS Students move the clock hands on a real analog clock to observe how the hour hand moves between consecutive numbers. The smaller number is the hour already passed. The greater one will be reached at the next hour. Assign Reteaching Supplement 74.

ENRICHMENT Students use a clock or watch with hands. They find at least 5 times when the hour hand and the minute hand divide the clock face exactly in half. (Answers will vary. Students should find 5 of the following times—12:33, 1:38, 2:44, 3:49, 4:55, 6:00, 7:06, 8:11, 9:16, 10:22, 11:28)

PRACTICE

Write each time as it would look on a digital clock.

1.  2:15
2.  3:48
3.  8:20
4.  11:30
5.  1:55
6.  10:45
7. 7:07
8. 10:19

APPLY

MATH REASONING

9. Which film starts at a quarter past six? Badger Buddies
10. Which film starts at half past 6? Raccoon Runaway
11. Which film starts at a quarter to 6? Animals of the Deep

Science Film Schedule	
Animals of the Deep	5:45
Badger Buddies	6:15
Raccoon Runaway	6:30

PROBLEM SOLVING

12. Where is the hour hand at 14 minutes to 6? Where is the minute hand? hour hand—between 5 and 6; minute hand—one past 9

13. **Social Studies Data Bank** When it is 5:00 in Arkansas (AR), what time is it in New York (NY)? See page 474. 6:00

DATA BANK

► **ESTIMATION**

14. The minute hand is missing from this clock. Choose the best estimate for the time.

a. close to 8:00 (b.) close to 9:00

More Practice, page 517, set C

3. PRACTICE AND APPLY

Basic	1-5, 9-14
Average	1-14
Extended	3-14

Additional Answers: See p. T79.

PRACTICE

How many digits must you use to show minutes on a digital clock? (2)

APPLY

MATH REASONING ► Explain how imagining a clock cut into quarters could help you answer Exercises 9-11. (Possible answer: If you see that each 15-min section is one quarter, you could imagine which quarter would be the 15 min *before* the next hour, which is also 45 min *after* the previous hour, and so on.)

PROBLEM SOLVING ► What strategy could you use to help solve Problem 12? (Possible answer: Draw a picture of a clock, then draw in the time to find the positioning of the hands.)

ESTIMATION ► Explain how you would solve Problem 14. (Think about the positioning of the hour hand. If it is past the halfway point between 8 and 9, it is closer to 9:00.)

CLOSE AND ASSESS

SHOW WHAT YOU KNOW

Have students use a clock or watch with hands to show the following times (they may also draw the times on clock faces): 1:11, 2:22, 3:33, 4:44, 5:55, 6:06. (Check students' clocks or drawings.)

QUICK QUIZ

Write each time in digital form.

1. three-thirty (3:30)
2. quarter past eight (8:15)
3. quarter to one (12:45)
4. twelve minutes to twelve (11:48)

LESSON OPTIONS 8-2

A.M. and P.M./Reading the Calendar

OBJECTIVE 8-2 To identify a given time as a.m. or p.m.; to read a calendar

PREBOOK ACTIVITIES

QUICK REVIEW

Write the time as it would appear on a digital clock.

1. six twenty-five (6:25) **2.** five minutes after three (3:05)
3. eleven o'clock (11:00) **4.** quarter after ten (10:15)
5. half past seven (7:30) **6.** ten minutes to one (12:50)
7. four of four (3:56) **8.** twenty-five of five (4:35)

PRIOR KNOWLEDGE

Have students suggest situations when they might describe a time by saying something such as 2:30 *in the morning* or 2:30 *at night* to avoid confusion. (Answers will vary.) Ask students if they know a way to get around this problem. (Use a.m. or p.m. after the time.) Have students share some observations about 1-yr calendars. (Possible answers: They have at least 12 pages, one for each month; pages always appear in the same order; some months always have 30 days, others have 31; February is the shortest month.)

COMMUNICATION

Discussing Math Explain that a.m. and p.m. are abbreviations of the Latin words *ante meridiem* and *post meridiem*. Tell students that *meridiem* means ''noon,'' then ask them to infer what *ante* and *post* mean. (''before,'' ''after'') Write the word **ordinal** on the chalkboard and ask students what common word sounds like it. (Possible answer: *order*) Have students compare ordinal numbers such as first, second, third, or fourth to their related counting numbers. (Possible answer: Ordinal numbers end in *th*, *st*, *nd*, or *rd*, while most counting numbers have no special endings.)

EXPLORE AND CONNECT

Materials: red and blue pens, time number line (see below)
Grouping Suggestion: cooperative learning pairs
Students generate and classify typical a.m. and p.m. activities. Display a 24-hour number line that starts and ends at midnight, with 12:00 noon clearly marked. Partners imagine an activity that might occur at each hour and then list each. Have them use blue for activities that take place from midnight to noon and red for activities that happen from noon to midnight. Call out each hour as students share the activities they listed. Discuss any relationship that arises between certain times and activities. (Possible answers: There are many hours of sleep from midnight to 6 in the morning; school hours appear before and after noon.) Indicate on the number line the a.m. and p.m. hours. Have students conclude how to express a difference when times repeat. (Possible answer: Say 9:00 in the morning or 9:00 at night; use 9:00 a.m. or 9:00 p.m.)

CONNECTIONS Use these anytime.

Problem of the Day

Sleep Schedule Theresa went to sleep at 10:00 on Friday night. She slept a total of 10 hours. What time on Saturday did she awaken? Give the time as it appeared on Theresa's digital clock. Then write it as a phrase that Theresa might have used when telling a friend the time she woke up. (8:00; eight o'clock in the morning)

Life Skills

Date Writing Joe visited his grandparents in Italy from March 10 to March 20. They wrote the dates of his visit as 10/3/90 to 20/3/90. Joe thought that was a mistake. ''No, we use a different date-writing system,'' they said. Analyze and explain their date-writing system. (They first write the day of the month, then the month and year.)

Math Connection

Measurement Sort the 12 months of the year by how many days they have. Plan the categories, then group the months accordingly. (31 days: January, March, May, July, August, October, December; 30 days: April, June, September, November; 28 [or 29] days: February)

Classwork and Homework Supplements

Practice

Life Skills 8-2

Name ______

A.M. and P.M./Reading the Calendar

Write **a.m.** or **p.m.** to complete each sentence.

1. The sun came up at 6:10 a.m.
2. The sun set at 7:17 p.m.
3. Wendy leaves for school at 7:45 a.m.
4. Sandy's violin lesson is at 3:00 p.m.
5. Sandy's dog takes his afternoon nap at 2:30 p.m.
6. Jane gets up for school at 7:15 a.m.
7. Bill goes to bed at 9:00 p.m.

Use the calendar to show the dates.

8. Tao goes to the orthodontist on the second Saturday of each month. Draw a line under the date she will go.
9. Josh gets a haircut on the fourth Tuesday of each month. Circle the date he will go.

DECEMBER						
Sun.	Mon.	Tues.	Wed.	Thurs.	Fri.	Sat.
				1	2	3
4	5	6	7	8	9	10
11	12	13	14	15	16	17
18	19	20	21	22	23	24
25	26	(27)	28	29	30	31

Write the name of the month.

10. the 8th month August
11. the 2nd month February

Write each date another way.

12. 10/15/91 October 15, 1991
13. April 1, 1990 4/1/90

Building Thinking Skills

Life Skills 8-2

Name ______

Making Sense of a Busy Summer

Rachel's teacher has asked her to write a brief summary of her summer plans. In her summary, Rachel forgot to fill in some of the information. Use the calendar and your knowledge of **a.m.** and **p.m.** to help Rachel complete her assignment.

My Summer Plans

This should be an exciting summer. School lets out on June 15th this year, which is the third Friday of the month. One week after that, on June 22, I am flying with my mom and dad to Japan to visit my older sister!

We return from Japan on the second Monday of July, the 9th day of the month. Eight days later, on the 17th, I am going to a country music concert with my friend Jessie. She told me that it starts at 6—I hope she means 6:00 p.m.!

My busy vacation continues in August. Three weeks and four days after the country music concert, on August 11th, I am going to a music camp. I hope to improve my flute-playing, which I began last year.

My final fun summer event is my family's annual back-to-school party, which is always held on the first Saturday of September. It always starts at 5:30 p.m., and continues until 10:00 p.m.. When everybody leaves, I know that my summer is over!

JUNE						
S	M	T	W	T	F	S
					1	2
3	4	5	6	7	8	9
10	11	12	13	14	15	16
17	18	19	20	21	22	23
24	25	26	27	28	29	30

JULY						
S	M	T	W	T	F	S
1	2	3	4	5	6	7
8	9	10	11	12	13	14
15	16	17	18	19	20	21
22	23	24	25	26	27	28
29	30	31				

AUGUST						
S	M	T	W	T	F	S
			1	2	3	4
5	6	7	8	9	10	11
12	13	14	15	16	17	18
19	20	21	22	23	24	25
26	27	28	29	30	31	

Reteaching

Life Skills 8-2

Name ______

A.M. and P.M./Reading the Calendar

The hours between midnight and noon are the **a.m.** hours. The hours between noon and midnight are the **p.m.** hours.

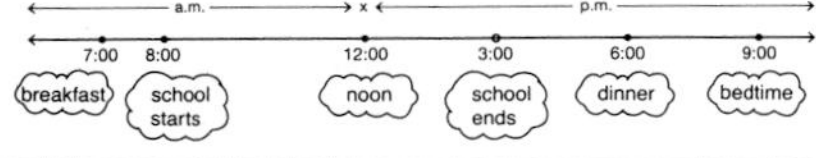

Write each time as **a.m.** or **p.m.**

1. Kao eats breakfast at 7:00 a.m.
2. Holly goes to school at 7:50 a.m.
3. Laurie gets home from school at 3:50 p.m.
4. Mr. Perez cooks his supper at 5:30 p.m.

June is the **sixth** month of the year. Miranda has circled the 14th because it is Flag Day. It is on the second Thursday. To write dates:

JUNE 1990						
S	M	T	W	T	F	S
					1	2
3	4	5	6	7	8	9
10	11	12	13	(14)	15	16
17	18	19	20	21	22	23
24	25	26	27	28	29	30

Write the month. → Write the day. → Write the year.

June 14, 1990 or 6/14/90

(June is the **6th** month)

Use the calendar to name these dates.

5. Miranda's brother's birthday is the second Saturday. Write the date two ways. June 9, 1990 / 6/9/90
6. The second Tuesday falls on what date? Write the date two ways. June 12, 1990 / 6/12/90

Challenges

Family Math 8-2

Name ______

24-Hour Time

Dear Family,
We have been learning about a.m. and p.m. Help your child fill in the schedule below.

A 24-hour watch displays the a.m. hours from 1 to 12, and the p.m. hours according to this time line:

1 p.m.	2 p.m.	3 p.m.	4 p.m.	5 p.m.	6 p.m.	7 p.m.	8 p.m.	9 p.m.	10 p.m.	11 p.m.	midnight
13:00	14:00	15:00	16:00	17:00	18:00	19:00	20:00	21:00	22:00	23:00	00:00

Complete this schedule of your typical week using 24-hour time. Answers will vary.

(Include meals, snacks, wake up, bedtime, homework, TV, start and end of school, sports, lessons, and so on.)

Monday	Tuesday	Wednesday	Thursday	Friday

Options for Individual Needs

Basic

Exercises 1-6; 1-9
More Practice, p. 517, set D, p. 518, set A

Supplements
Reteaching 75 or
Practice 75
Challenges 75

Average

Exercises 1-8; 1-9
More Practice, p. 517, set D, p. 518, set A

Supplements
Practice 75
Challenges 75 or
Thinking Skills 75

Extended

Exercises 1-8; 1-9

Supplements
Challenges 75
Thinking Skills 75

Other Resources:
Problem-Solving Experiences in Mathematics, Grade 4, Problem 58
Make It Simpler, A Practical Guide to Problem Solving in Mathematics, p. 279

LESSON PLAN 8-2

OBJECTIVE 8-2
To identify a given time as a.m. or p.m.

1. MOTIVATE AND TEACH

LEARN ABOUT IT

EXPLORE ► **Explain why the hour hand goes around a clock twice a day.** (The clock face shows 12 hours, but a day has 24 hours.)
► **If a clock says 4:00, how can you tell whether it is night or day?** (Possible answers: Check whether it is dark or light outside; judge by the activities around you.)

TALK ABOUT IT Student Edition answers: **1.** 12, 24 **2.** Each time appears twice a day, but different activities mark a.m. and p.m.

2. CHECK UNDERSTANDING

ERROR ALERT Confusing a.m. and p.m.

3. PRACTICE AND APPLY

Basic	1-6
Average	1-8
Extended	1-8

PRACTICE

Look at Exercises 3 and 4. Give a method you could use to answer each exercise. (Possible answer: Add a.m. and p.m. hours for each activity, then compare the totals.) *Look at Exercises 5-8. Identify clues that can confirm your answers.* (Sample clues: Ex. 5—the middle of the night is also very early morning or a.m. hours; Ex. 6—afternoon hours are p.m. hours; Ex. 7—school is dismissed in the afternoon; Ex. 8—breakfast is served in the morning.)

A.M. and P.M.

a.m.

LEARN ABOUT IT

EXPLORE Study the Information
The hour hand goes around the clock twice each day. It goes around once for the **a.m.** hours, which are before noon. It also goes around once for the **p.m.** hours, which are after noon.

p.m.

TALK ABOUT IT **See teaching notes.**

1. How many hours does it take for the hour hand to go around the clock once? twice?
2. Explain why it is important to know if a given time is in the a.m. hours or p.m. hours.

Thinking of a time line like this can help you decide if a given time is in the a.m. or p.m. hours.

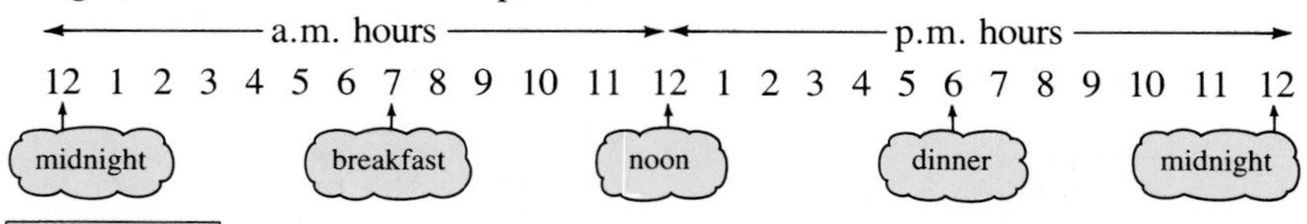

PRACTICE

Use the time line to help answer these questions.
Answers will vary. Sample answers given.

1. What are three things you do in the a.m. hours? **sleep, eat breakfast, go to school**
2. What are three things you do in the p.m. hours? **go home from school, eat dinner, go to bed**
3. Are you in school more a.m. hours or p.m. hours? **a.m.**
4. Do you sleep more a.m. hours or p.m. hours? **a.m.**

Write a.m. or p.m. to complete each sentence.

5. Pernell woke up at 1:00 __?__ in the middle of the night. **a.m.**
6. Tessa napped at 2:45 __?__ in the afternoon. **p.m.**
7. Carla got home from school at 3:20 __?__. **p.m.**
8. Ho cooked his breakfast at 7:30 __?__. **a.m.**

More Practice, page 517, set D

TEACHING OPTIONS

RETEACHING TIPS Have students make a 12-month time line and add a holiday or an event that falls during each month. Students can use the associations to help recall the order of the months. Assign Reteaching Supplement 75.

ENRICHMENT Tell students that on a digital clock that names hours from 0-23, midnight is 00:00, 5:15 a.m. is 05:15, noon is 12:00, 6:07 p.m. is 18:07, and so on. Have students give the following times in standard form: 00:30, 04:25, 23:59. (12:30 a.m., 4:25 a.m., 11:59 p.m.)

Reading the Calendar

LEARN ABOUT IT

EXPLORE **Study the Calendar**

It is important to know the order of the days and weeks so you can talk about dates on the calendar.

August 8 is on Tuesday. It is the second Tuesday in the month.

TALK ABOUT IT See teaching notes.

1. Tell which Thursday is the 24th of August.
2. What is the date of the fifth Wednesday in August?

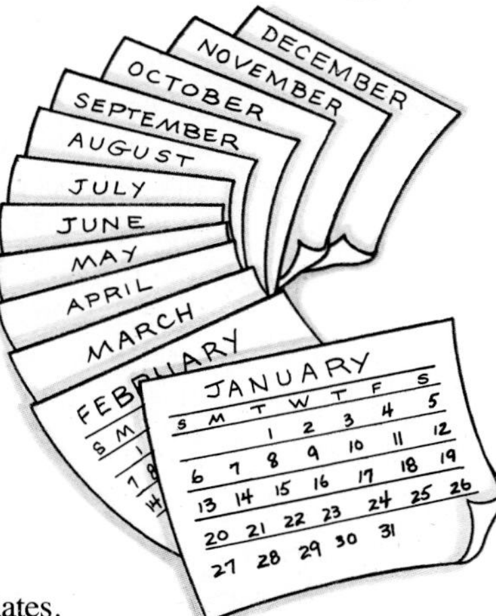

There are 12 months in a year. You can use **ordinal numbers** to describe the months. August is the 8th month.

You can write dates two ways.

August 5, 1989 8/5/89

PRACTICE

Use the August calendar to name these dates.

1. The Camera Club meets on the third Monday of each month. When will it meet in August? on the 21st
2. The Music Club meets on the second Friday of each month. When will it meet in August? on the 11th

Name the month.

3. the 12th month December
4. the 7th month July
5. the 5th month May

Write each date another way.

6. 9/11/88 September 11, 1988
7. June 29, 1985 6/29/85
8. 2/13/87 February 13, 1987
9. November 7, 1989 11/7/89

More Practice, page 518, set A

OBJECTIVE 8-2 To read a calendar

Materials: current calendar

1. Motivate and Teach

LEARN ABOUT IT

EXPLORE ► **Analyze the organization of a calendar page.** (Each day is a date in a box; each week is a row of boxes that goes from Sunday through Saturday.)

TALK ABOUT IT Student Edition answers: **1.** fourth **2.** August 30

2. Check Understanding

ERROR ALERT Confusing month order when writing dates.

3. Practice and Apply

Basic	1-9
Average	1-9
Extended	1-9

PRACTICE

Look at Exercises 1 and 2. Explain how to find all dates that fall on a particular day in August. (Look down the column headed by a particular day.)

Close and Assess

WRITE WHAT YOU THINK

Have students write their birth date in two ways, then use a current calendar to describe exactly when their birthday falls. Last, have them describe two special activities they would like to do on their birthday—one in an a.m. hour and one in a p.m. hour. (Answers will vary.)

QUICK QUIZ

1. Name the fourth and tenth months.
2. Write tomorrow's date in two ways.
3. The sun rose at 5:30 ______. (**1.** April, October **2.** Check students' answers. **3.** a.m.)

LESSON OPTIONS 8-3

Mental Math: Elapsed Time

OBJECTIVE 8-3 To use mental math to calculate ending times and elapsed times

PREBOOK ACTIVITIES

QUICK REVIEW

Add or subtract mentally.

1. 30 + 25 (55) **2.** 5 + 37 (42)
3. 45 + 30 (75) **4.** 60 − 33 (27)
5. 60 − 25 (35) **6.** 45 − 7 (38)
7. 15 + 15 (30) **8.** 44 − 19 (25)

PRIOR KNOWLEDGE

Have students think of occasions when they wanted to know when an event would end or how long it would last. (Possible answers: when a movie lets out; how long gym class lasts) Ask students to explain what facts they need to know in order to figure out such information. (starting and ending times) Have students suggest how they might determine how much time passes. (Answers will vary. Possible responses: subtracting, counting on, estimating, looking at a clock face)

COMMUNICATION

Discussing and Reading Math Write this sentence on the chalkboard: (Use a reasonable number) hours have **elapsed** since I woke up this morning. Have students read the sentence to infer the meaning of *elapsed*. Ask for synonyms. (*passed, gone by*) Ask students to explain what it means to calculate elapsed time. (Possible answer: to figure out how many hours and minutes go by between two given times) Finally, ask students why it is important to be able to calculate elapsed time. (Possible answer: You need to know how long certain activities last to schedule your day or to work around other people's schedules.)

EXPLORE AND CONNECT

Materials: blank index cards, clocks with movable hands, number lines divided to show 24 hours in hourly increments
Alternative Materials: TA 16 (Clock Face)
Grouping Suggestion: small cooperative learning groups
Students explore ways to find **elapsed** time with data they generate. Each student picks two times—one to the hour, one to the half hour—and writes them on separate index cards, noting a.m. or p.m. Members' cards are mixed together and stacked face down. One student turns over two cards and reads the times aloud. Another decides, with the group's help, how to order the times to create the least amount of *elapsed* time. For example, 15 and a half hours **elapse** counting from 3:30 a.m. to 7:00 p.m., while only 8 and a half hours *elapse* counting from 7:00 p.m. to 3:30 a.m. Groups may use clocks with movable hands and 24-hour number lines to help count and verify *elapsed* time. Members should try each task.

CONNECTIONS Use these anytime.

Problem of the Day

The Show Must Go On . . . and On! In 1984, a play called "The Acting Life" was performed in Australia. It lasted 21 hours, including intermissions. If it began at 1:00 p.m. on Friday, when did it end? (10:00 a.m. Saturday)

Subject Integration

Science One day in Seattle, Washington, the sun rose at 5:23 a.m., and Seattle had 13 hours and 9 minutes of daylight. James went to bed 3 hours after the sun set that day. What time was it when he went to bed? (9:32 p.m.)

Life Skills

Train Schedules Pete's watch says 4:53, so his train leaves in 4 minutes. Lori says, "Your watch is 5 minutes fast." What time is it really? When will the train leave? How long must Pete wait? (4:48; 4:57; 9 minutes)

Classwork and Homework Supplements

Practice

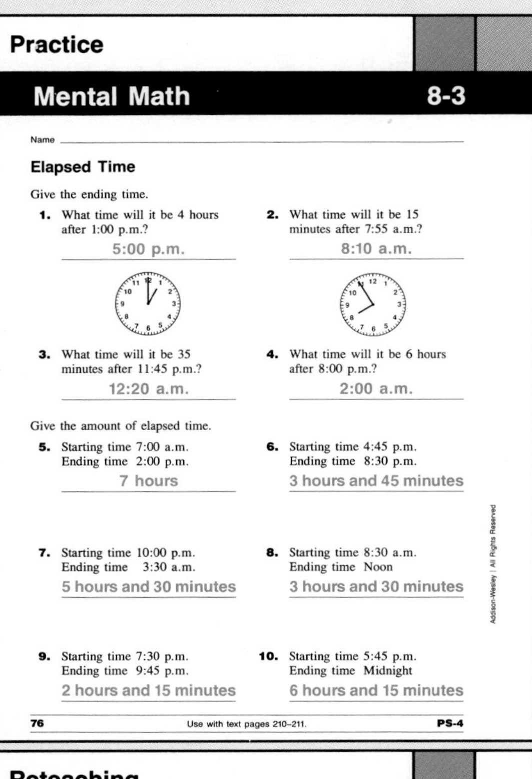

Mental Math 8-3

Name ______

Elapsed Time

Give the ending time.

1. What time will it be 4 hours after 1:00 p.m.? 5:00 p.m.
2. What time will it be 15 minutes after 7:55 a.m.? 8:10 a.m.
3. What time will it be 35 minutes after 11:45 p.m.? 12:20 a.m.
4. What time will it be 6 hours after 8:00 p.m.? 2:00 a.m.

Give the amount of elapsed time.

5. Starting time 7:00 a.m. Ending time 2:00 p.m. 7 hours
6. Starting time 4:45 p.m. Ending time 8:30 p.m. 3 hours and 45 minutes
7. Starting time 10:00 p.m. Ending time 3:30 a.m. 5 hours and 30 minutes
8. Starting time 8:30 a.m. Ending time Noon 3 hours and 30 minutes
9. Starting time 7:30 p.m. Ending time 9:45 p.m. 2 hours and 15 minutes
10. Starting time 5:45 p.m. Ending time Midnight 6 hours and 15 minutes

Addison-Wesley | All Rights Reserved

76 Use with text pages 210-211. PS-4

Building Thinking Skills

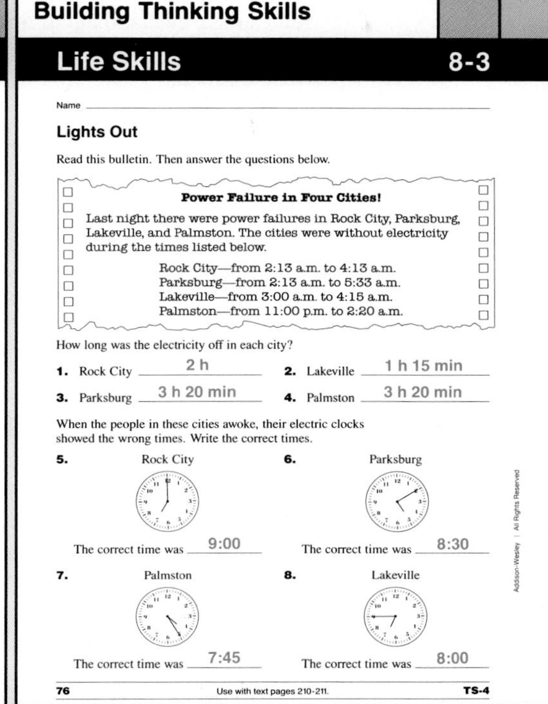

Life Skills 8-3

Name ______

Lights Out

Read this bulletin. Then answer the questions below.

Power Failure in Four Cities!

Last night there were power failures in Rock City, Parksburg, Lakeville, and Palmston. The cities were without electricity during the times listed below.

Rock City—from 2:13 a.m. to 4:13 a.m.
Parksburg—from 2:13 a.m. to 5:33 a.m.
Lakeville—from 3:00 a.m. to 4:15 a.m.
Palmston—from 11:00 p.m. to 2:20 a.m.

How long was the electricity off in each city?

1. Rock City 2 h
2. Lakeville 1 h 15 min
3. Parksburg 3 h 20 min
4. Palmston 3 h 20 min

When the people in these cities awoke, their electric clocks showed the wrong times. Write the correct times.

5. Rock City — The correct time was 9:00
6. Parksburg — The correct time was 8:30
7. Palmston — The correct time was 7:45
8. Lakeville — The correct time was 8:00

Addison-Wesley | All Rights Reserved

76 Use with text pages 210-211. TS-4

Reteaching

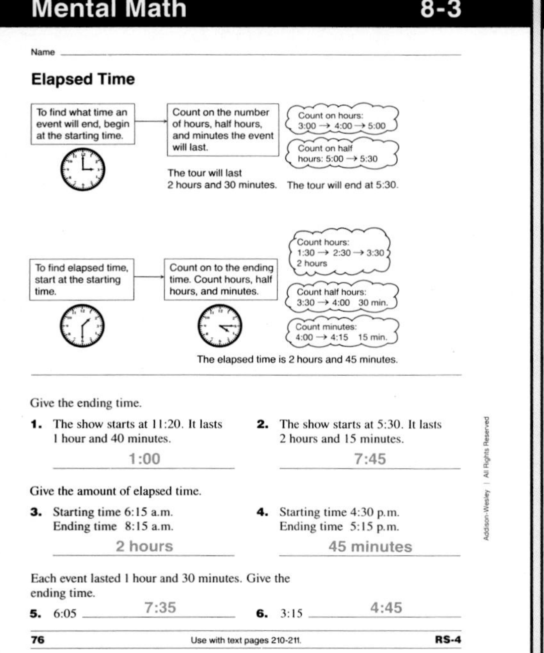

Mental Math 8-3

Name ______

Elapsed Time

To find what time an event will end, begin at the starting time. → Count on the number of hours, half hours, and minutes the event will last. → Count on hours: 3:00 → 4:00 → 5:00. Count on half hours: 5:00 → 5:30

The tour will last 2 hours and 30 minutes. The tour will end at 5:30.

To find elapsed time, start at the starting time. → Count on to the ending time. Count hours, half hours, and minutes. → Count hours: 1:30 → 2:30 → 3:30 2 hours. Count half hours: 3:30 → 4:00 30 min. Count minutes: 4:00 → 4:15 15 min.

The elapsed time is 2 hours and 45 minutes.

Give the ending time.

1. The show starts at 11:20. It lasts 1 hour and 40 minutes. 1:00
2. The show starts at 5:30. It lasts 2 hours and 15 minutes. 7:45

Give the amount of elapsed time.

3. Starting time 6:15 a.m. Ending time 8:15 a.m. 2 hours
4. Starting time 4:30 p.m. Ending time 5:15 p.m. 45 minutes

Each event lasted 1 hour and 30 minutes. Give the ending time.

5. 6:05 7:35
6. 3:15 4:45

Addison-Wesley | All Rights Reserved

76 Use with text pages 210-211. RS-4

Challenges

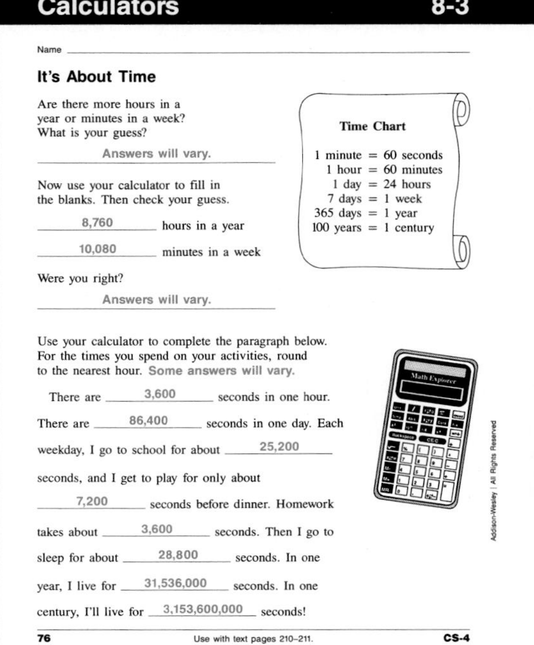

Calculators 8-3

Name ______

It's About Time

Are there more hours in a year or minutes in a week? What is your guess? Answers will vary.

Now use your calculator to fill in the blanks. Then check your guess.

8,760 hours in a year

10,080 minutes in a week

Were you right? Answers will vary.

Time Chart

1 minute = 60 seconds
1 hour = 60 minutes
1 day = 24 hours
7 days = 1 week
365 days = 1 year
100 years = 1 century

Use your calculator to complete the paragraph below. For the times you spend on your activities, round to the nearest hour. Some answers will vary.

There are 3,600 seconds in one hour. There are 86,400 seconds in one day. Each weekday, I go to school for about 25,200 seconds, and I get to play for only about 7,200 seconds before dinner. Homework takes about 3,600 seconds. Then I go to sleep for about 28,800 seconds. In one year, I live for 31,536,000 seconds. In one century, I'll live for 3,153,600,000 seconds!

Addison-Wesley | All Rights Reserved

76 Use with text pages 210-211. CS-4

Options for Individual Needs

Basic

Exercises 1-9
Data Bank, p. 474
Calculator Bank, p. 485
More Practice, p. 518, set B

Supplements
Reteaching 76 or
Practice 76

Average

Exercises 1-9
Data Bank, p. 474
Calculator Bank, p. 485
More Practice, p. 518, set B

Supplements
Practice 76
Challenges 76 or
Thinking Skills 76

Extended

Exercises 1-9
Data Bank, p. 474
Calculator Bank, p. 485

Supplements
Challenges 76
Thinking Skills 76

Other Resources:
Problem-Solving Experiences in Mathematics, Grade 4, Problem 57
Make It Simpler, A Practical Guide to Problem Solving in Mathematics, p. 173
Kids Are Consumers, Too!, pp. 16, 17
Using The Math Explorer Calculator: A Sourcebook for Teachers, Chapter 14

LESSON PLAN 8-3

OBJECTIVE 8-3
To use mental math to calculate ending times and elapsed times

Materials: clocks with movable hands, number line marked in a.m. and p.m. hours, calculators

Alternative Materials: TA 16 (Clock Face)

1. MOTIVATE AND TEACH

LEARN ABOUT IT

EXPLORE ► **Are the times a.m. or p.m.? Explain.** (Probably p.m., or the fair would be in the middle of the night)
► **Explain how to estimate the length of the program.** (Possible answer: Think of 4:15 as 4:30; count on from 1:30 to 4:30; about 3 hours long.)

TALK ABOUT IT ► **Analyze Charnelle's counting.** (She counted on 2 hours from 1:30 to 3:30, 30 minutes to 4:00, then 15 minutes to 4:15.)
► **Explain another way to count on.** (1:30 to 2:15 is 45 minutes; 2:15 to 4:15 is 2 hours.)
► **Explain how you might use compensation to find the elapsed time.** (Possible answer: Add 15 minutes to 4:15 to make 4:30; 1:30 to 4:30 is 3 hours; subtract 15 minutes.)
► **If you know the elapsed time, explain how to find a starting or ending time.** (Count ahead from a starting time; count back from an ending time.)
Student Edition answers: **1.** 2 hours and 45 minutes **2.** Explanations will vary.

2. CHECK UNDERSTANDING

TRY IT OUT

ERROR ALERT Difficulty counting on in increments other than hours. Not noticing the change from a.m. to p.m.

Mental Math
Elapsed Time

I'll count on to find how long the program lasted. 1:30, 2:30, 3:30, 4:00, 4:15

LEARN ABOUT IT

You can use mental math to find out how long an event lasts or when an event will end.

A B

EXPLORE **Study the Clocks**
Charnelle and her family watched the square dancing program at the Frontier Days Fair. Clock A shows the starting time for the program. Clock B shows the ending time.

TALK ABOUT IT See teaching notes.

1. How long did the square dancing program last?
2. Explain how you found out how long the program lasted.

To find what time an event will end, begin at the starting time. Count on the number of hours, half hours, and minutes the event will last.

The rodeo starts at 8:30 p.m. It will last 1 hour and 40 minutes.

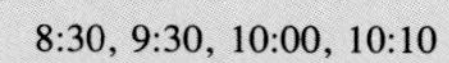

The rodeo will end at 10:10 p.m.

Give the ending time.

1. The cattle show starts at 1:15. It lasts 4 hours and 20 minutes **5:35**
2. The horse show starts at 9:45. It lasts 2 hours and 30 minutes. **12:15**

Give the amount of elapsed time.

3. Starting time 8:00 a.m.
   Ending time 11:00 p.m.
   15 hours
4. Starting time 7:30 p.m.
   Ending time Midnight
   4 hours and 30 minutes
5. Starting time 6:15 p.m.
   Ending time 11:30 p.m.
   5 hours and 15 minutes
6. Starting time 5:45 a.m.
   Ending time 9:15 a.m.
   3 hours and 30 minutes

210

TEACHING OPTIONS

RETEACHING TIPS Clocks with movable hands and hour number lines starting at midnight will help with both errors. Students use the clocks and number lines to find starting and ending times, to visualize elapsed time, and to verbalize counting on. Assign Reteaching Supplement 76.

ENRICHMENT Have students solve: *Dr. Yank schedules 35-minute dental appointments with 5 minutes in between. Her first appointment is at 8:45 a.m. How many appointments can she schedule before noon? When does each appointment begin?* (5; 8:45; 9:25, 10:05, 10:45, 11:25)

PRACTICE

Use the schedule to tell how long each event lasted.

1. The candlemaking show ended at 4:30 p.m. **1 hour and 15 minutes**
2. The soapmaking show lasted until 5:35 p.m. **2 hours and 5 minutes**
3. The weaving show closed at 1:30 p.m. **3 hours**

Use the schedule to give the ending time.

4. The quilting show lasted 3 hours. **12:30 p.m.**
5. The whittling show lasted 55 minutes **12:10 p.m.**

Frontier Days Schedule	
Quilting	9:30 a.m.
Weaving	10:30 a.m.
Whittling	11:15 a.m.
Candlemaking	3:15 p.m.
Soapmaking	3:30 p.m.

MATH REASONING

6. Which is a better estimate for the amount of time? **a**

Starting time 2:15 p.m. Ending time 3:58 p.m.

a. about 2 hours
b. about 3 hours

PROBLEM SOLVING

7. Charnelle left the fair at 6:05. She arrived home 1 hour and 35 minutes later. What time was it? **7:40**

8. **Social Studies Data Bank** Charnelle called from Texas (TX) at 11:35 a.m. to tell her grandma in Florida (FL) about the fair. What time was it in Florida? See page 474. **12:35 a.m.**

► **CALCULATOR**

9. This list shows how long these children rode their horses in the riding contest. The contest began at 3:00. What time did it end? **5:00**

Paco	23 minutes
Lisa	9 minutes
Reggie	19 minutes
Belva	24 minutes
Al	28 minutes
Yvonne	17 minutes

More Practice, page 518, set B

3. Practice and Apply

Basic	1-9
Average	1-9
Extended	1-9

PRACTICE

Look at Exercises 1-3 and Exercises 4 and 5. How are the two sets of exercises different? (In Exercises 1-3, you count on from starting times to find elapsed times. In Exercises 4 and 5, you use starting times and elapsed times to find ending times.)

APPLY

MATH REASONING ► **Explain how you would estimate the elapsed time.** (Possible answer: Adjust 2:15 to 2:00, then 3:58 to 4:00 for an estimate of about 2 hours.)

PROBLEM SOLVING ► **Decide how to solve Problem 7.** (Possible answer: Count on 1 hour to 7:05, then count on 35 more minutes.)

CALCULATOR ► **Explain how to use the calculator to answer Problem 9.** (Add to find the total number of minutes in the program, which must be changed to hours. Then count on that many hours from 3:00.)

Close and Assess

SHOW WHAT YOU KNOW

Have students find the elapsed times from 7:25 a.m. to 10:00 a.m. and from 11:30 a.m. to 1:40 p.m. Ask each to use a clock with movable hands to verify his or her findings. (2 hours and 35 minutes; 2 hours and 10 minutes)

QUICK QUIZ

1. Starting at 1:45, a movie theater is open for $2\frac{3}{4}$ hours. When does the theater close? (4:30)
2. How long is a movie that goes from 2:25 to 4:05? (1 h 40 min)

LESSON OPTIONS 8-4

Problem Solving: Problems with More than One Answer

OBJECTIVE 8-4 To solve problems with more than 1 answer

PREBOOK ACTIVITIES

QUICK REVIEW

Multiply, then add.

1. (5 × 9) + (3 × 9) (72)
2. (4 × 8) + (7 × 4) (60)
3. (2 × 7) + (3 × 2) (20)
4. (9 × 6) + (3 × 9) (81)
5. (4 × 2) + (4 × 4) (24)
6. (5 × 5) + (8 × 5) (65)

PRIOR KNOWLEDGE

Have students pose questions to which there is more than 1 correct answer. [Sample questions: *What does* lead *mean?* (As a noun, it is a heavy metal; as a verb, it means to show the way); *What factors have a product of 12?* (3 × 4, 6 × 2, 1 × 12)]

COMMUNICATION

Discussing Math Have students interpret the meaning of the expression *to consider all possibilities*. (Possible answers: Do not give up after finding 1 answer; try to discover other answers that also fit the same situation.) Discuss why it makes sense to look for more than 1 answer. (Possible answer: Although several answers may be correct, 1 might make more sense than another in a particular situation.)

EXPLORE AND CONNECT

COOPERATIVE ACTIVITY

Grouping Suggestion: small groups
Kara has 5 coins that total 50¢. What are the coins?

TEACHING ACTIONS

Have students work together to discuss possibilities and to plan and verify solutions.

► **Summarize the given data.** (Kara has 5 coins that add up to 50¢.)
► **What relationship among the coins can you identify?** (None is given.)

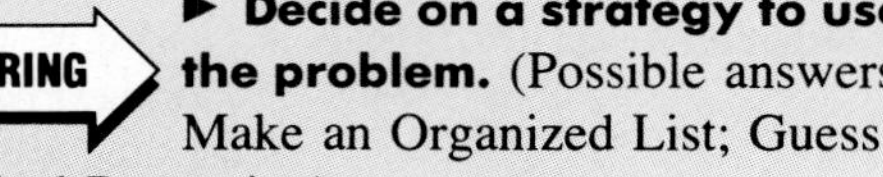

DURING

► **Decide on a strategy to use to begin solving the problem.** (Possible answers: Use Objects; Make an Organized List; Guess and Check; Use Logical Reasoning)
► **Explain how you will know if your solution is reasonable.** (if it fits the situation)

► **Explain the solution you found.** (2 possible solutions: 5 dimes or 1 quarter, 1 dime, 3 nickels)
► **Explain how you knew there might be more than 1 solution.** (Possible answer: You can combine coins in many ways to get a certain total.)
► **Explain why you might need to know both solutions.** (Possible answer: 1 combination might be more useful than the other in some situations.)

CONNECTIONS Use these anytime.

Problem of the Day

Name Those Bugs Spiders have 8 legs and ants have 6 legs. If Mandy saw 24 legs crawl past her tent, what insects could she have seen? (3 spiders or 4 ants)

Subject Integration

Language Arts In a word game, Randy picked the letters *L, P, A,* and *E*. How many different words can you think of that Randy could make using all the letters? (4 possible words: *leap, pale, peal, plea*)

Math Connection

Calculator Use a calculator to create 5 different pairs of 3-digit odd addends whose sum is 1,234. Never use 0. (Answers will vary. Samples: 877 + 357; 345 + 889; 747 + 487; 621 + 613; 567 + 667)

Classwork and Homework Supplements

Practice

Problem Solving 8-4

Name

Problems with More than One Answer

Find as many answers as you can for each problem.
Answers will vary. Sample answers are given.

1. The County Fair opens on June 12. Admission is $4 for adults and $2 for children. How many people can enter for $12?
   3 adults; 1 adult, 4 children; 2 adults, 2 children; 6 children
2. Brian has $2 for refreshments. Drinks cost $0.50. Sandwiches are $1.50. Popcorn is $1. What can Brian buy?
   1 drink, 1 sandwich; 2 drinks, popcorn; 2 popcorns; 4 drinks
3. Visitors at the fair pay $0.25 for each ride ticket. The Ferris wheel costs 2 tickets. A ride on the carousel is 1 ticket. With 6 tickets, how many rides can Cam go on?
   3 Ferris wheel; 6 carousel; 1 Ferris wheel; 4 carousel; 2 Ferris wheel, 2 carousel
4. Pony rides are $0.25 for 1 walk around the ring. Jill and Will together have $1 to spend. How many rides can they take?
   Will 2, Jill 2; Will 1, Jill 3; Will 3, Jill 1; Jill 4, Will 0; Jill 0, Will 4
5. Lauren won 8 prize coupons. A yo-yo is 4 coupons. Jacks are 2. Pencils are 1. What prizes can Lauren win?
   1 yo-yo, 2 jacks; 1 yo-yo, 4 pencils; 1 yo-yo, 1 jacks, 2 pencils; 2 jacks, 2 pencils; 4 jacks, 8 pencils; 2 yo-yos
6. Some pigs and some judges are in the judging ring in front of the grandstand. A boy counts 22 legs. How many judges and pigs are in the ring?
   5 pigs, 1 judge; 4 pigs, 3 judges; 3 pigs, 5 judges; 2 pigs, 7 judges; 1 pig, 9 judges

PS-4 Use with text page 212. 77

Building Thinking Skills

Math Reasoning 8-4

Name

Identifying More Than One Answer

Ellie and Shi-ling signed up for the Phillips Street Elementary School Book-Reading Contest. Contestants have been given eight weeks to read as many books as they can. Prizes are as follows:

Number of pages read	Prize
1,000	automatic camera
800	one month of free videos
600	pen-and-pencil set
400	digital stopwatch
200	T-shirt

Contestants have a choice of 10 books from which to do their reading: three 50-page books, one 75-page book, one 125-page book, three 150-page books, and two 200-page books. All books must be read from beginning to end.

1. Which combination of books would give Ellie the exact number of pages needed for a T-shirt?
   1 × 150, 1 × 50; 1 × 125, 1 × 75; 1 × 200
2. Which combination of books would give Shi-ling the exact number of pages needed for a pen-and-pencil set?
   2 × 200, 1 × 150, 1 × 50; 3 × 150, 3 × 50; 2 × 150, 1 × 200, 2 × 50
3. How could Ellie get the exact number of pages needed for one month of free videos without reading all of the 150-page books?
   2 × 200, 2 × 150, 2 × 50
4. If Shi-ling decided to read 500 pages *without* reading more than one 150-page book, which books would he read?
   2 × 200, 2 × 50; 1 × 75, 1 × 125, 1 × 200, 2 × 50; 1 × 75, 1 × 125, 3 × 50, 1 × 150

TS-4 Use with text page 212. 77

Reteaching

Problem Solving 8-4

Name

Problems with More than One Answer

When solving problems, make sure that you find all the answers. Some problems have more than one answer.

Larry bought 20 pounds of potatoes. They come in 5-pound and 10-pound bags. How many bags of each size did he buy?

List number of sentences with sums of 20. → Try combinations of 5s and 10s. → Count how many of each.

10 + 10 = 20 — 2 10-pound bags (That works.)
10 + 5 + 5 = 20 — 1 10-pound bags and 2 5-pound bags (That works.)
5 + 5 + 5 + 10 = 25 — (That doesn't work.)
5 + 5 + 5 + 5 = 20 — 4 5-pound bags (That works.)

There are three possible answers to this problem.

Find as many answers as you can for each problem.

1. Marika bought 10 pounds of carrots. They come in 2-pound and 5-pound bags. How many bags of each size did she buy?
   List ways. → Number of bags
   5 + 5 = 10 — 2 5-pound bags
   2 + 2 + 2 + 2 + 2 = 10 — 5 2-pound bags
2. Linsay counted 18 wheels on the motorcycles and cars in the parking lot. How many motorcycles and how many cars were there?
   List ways.
   1 motorcycle, 4 cars
   3 motorcycles, 3 cars
   5 motorcycles, 2 cars
   7 motorcycles, 1 car
3. Baker bought 24 feet of ribbon. It came in 3-foot and 4-foot sections. How many of each size did he buy?
   List ways.
   4 (3 ft), 3 (4 ft)
   8 (3 ft), 0 (4 ft)
   0 (3 ft), 6 (4 ft)

RS-4 Use with text page 212. 77

Challenges

Algebra 8-4

Name

Mind-Boggling Balloon Problems

Each problem below has more than one answer. Find all the possible answers

1. Jerry spent less than $29 on giant metallic balloons. The balloons cost $5 each. How many balloons did he buy?
   $5 × ☐ < $29.
   All possible answers: 5, 4, 3, 2, 1
2. Tina spent less than 20 minutes blowing up balloons into dog shapes. It took her 3 minutes to make each dog. How many dogs did she make?
   3 × ☐ < 20.
   All possible answers: 6, 5, 4, 3, 2, 1
3. Hiroko spent between $20 and $35 on helium balloons. The balloons cost $3 each. How many balloons did she buy?
   $3 × ☐ is between $20 and $35.
   All possible answers: 7, 8, 9, 10, 11
4. Jeff spent less than $10 on a get-well balloon and a card. He spent $5 on the balloon. How much did he spend on the card? (He only used bills.)
   $5 + ☐ < $10.
   All possible answers: $4, $3, $2, $1
5. Mark spent between 25 and 45 minutes decorating helium balloons. He spent 4 minutes on each balloon. How many balloons did he decorate?
   4 × ☐ is between 25 and 35.
   All possible answers: 7, 8
6. Ro spent less than 60 seconds filling up helium balloons. He spent 9 seconds on each balloon. How many balloons did he fill up?
   9 × ☐ < 60.
   All possible answers: 6, 5, 4, 3, 2, 1

CS-4 Use with text page 212. 77

Options for Individual Needs

Basic

Exercises 1-8
Skills Bank, p. 465
Calculator Bank, pp. 486, 488
More Practice, p. 518, set C

Supplements
Reteaching 77 or
Practice 77

Average

Exercises 1-8
Skills Bank, p. 465
Calculator Bank, pp. 486, 488
More Practice, p. 518, set C

Supplements
Practice 77
Challenges 77 or
Thinking Skills 77

Extended

Exercises 1-7
Calculator Bank, pp. 486, 488

Supplements
Challenges 77
Thinking Skills 77

Other Resources:
Problem-Solving Experiences in Mathematics, Grade 4, Problems 29, 30
Kids Are Consumers, Too!, pp. 118, 119
Make It Simpler, A Practical Guide to Problem Solving in Mathematics, p. 282
Using the Math Explorer Calculator: A Sourcebook for Teachers, Chapter 14

LESSON PLAN 8-4

OBJECTIVE 8-4
To solve problems with more than 1 answer

Materials: counters, TA 9 (Play Money—Coins and Dollars), blank index cards

1. MOTIVATE AND TEACH

LEARN ABOUT IT

► **Analyze the problem for extra data.** (The parents were building 2 playground structures.)
► **Explain what general fact you must know to understand the situation.** (Children have 2 legs; dogs have 4.)

► **Justify using the Guess and Check method to begin.** (There are no other data that relate or compare the 2- and 4-legged creatures, so start with a reasonable guess, then adjust as needed.)
► **Explain how the table organizes the guesses.** (It shows the number of children and dogs and how many legs each number would mean as a way to account for the possible combinations.)

► **Explain how to verify the answers.** (Possible answers: Use Objects; Draw a Picture)
► **Explain how you could eliminate 1 of the answers by adding an extra fact.** (Possible clue: There were more children than dogs.)

2. CHECK UNDERSTANDING

TRY IT OUT

ERROR ALERT Failing to find more than 1 answer.

Problem Solving
Problems with More than One Answer

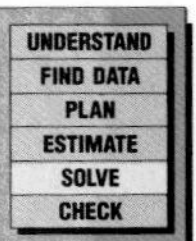

LEARN ABOUT IT

The parents at Hayes School were building two playground structures. While working under the slide, Mrs. Kuang could see only the legs of those walking by. She counted 10 legs in one group. What combination of dogs and children could have been in that group?

Some problems have more than one answer. When you find an answer to a problem, don't stop there. Ask yourself if there might be other answers.

Try 3 children and 2 dogs.
6 legs + 8 legs = 14 legs

I can use guess and check. That's too many legs.

Try 3 children and 1 dog.
6 legs + 4 legs = 10 legs.

Correct! Mrs. Kuang saw 10 legs.

I can check for other answers. I'll organize my work in a table.

Children	Legs	Dogs	Legs	Total
1	2	2	8	10 That works.
2	4	2	8	12 That doesn't work.
3	6	1	4	10 That works.
4	8	1	4	12 That doesn't work.

There are two possible answers: 1 child and 2 dogs, or 3 children and 1 dog.

TRY IT OUT

Find as many answers as you can for each problem. **See Additional Answers.**

1. Brian counted 21 wheels on the bicycles and tricycles on the playground. How many tricycles and how many bicycles were there?
2. Bob's dad bought 100 pounds of sand to put under the structures. The sand came in 25-pound and 50-pound bags. How many bags of each size did he buy?

TEACHING OPTIONS

RETEACHING TIPS Exercise 1: Have students manipulate counters into various combinations of groups of 2 and 3. Exercise 2: Have students write *25 pounds* on 4 index cards and *50 pounds* on 2 index cards. They manipulate the cards into groupings that total 100 pounds. Assign Reteaching Supplement 77.

COMPUTER **Problem-Solving Strategies, MECC, Copyright 1983** For all students (best in pairs). ''Diagonals'' uses 3 strategies: Guess and Check, exhaustive listing, and simplifying the problem. Determine the number of diagonals in a 12-sided figure. The lesson requires 20 to 25 min.

MIXED PRACTICE

Choose a strategy from the list or use other strategies you know to solve these problems.

Some Strategies
Act It Out
Use Objects
Choose an Operation
Draw a Picture
Make an Organized List
Guess and Check
Make a Table
Look for a Pattern
Use Logical Reasoning

1. Redwood posts for the structure cost $6.88 apiece. They are 8 feet long. How much did 9 posts cost? $61.92
2. Paolo's mother laid the 24 monkey bars into rows. There were the same number of bars in each row. How many were in each row? How many rows were there? See Additional Answers.
3. Mr. Chan arrived at 1:45 p.m. He worked until 4:20 p.m. How long did he work? 2 hours and 35 minutes
4. 25 parents volunteered to build the structure. 14 worked on the morning shift and 17 worked on the afternoon shift. How many worked both shifts? 6 parents
5. Kara's father needs 17 feet of lumber for railings. He has some boards that are 5 feet long and some that are 6 feet long. How many 5-foot and 6-foot boards does he need? See Additional Answers.
6. How many more students will be using the large structure than the small structure? 32 students

Grade	Students	Structure
K	59	small
1–3	196	small
4–6	287	large

7. It took Mrs. Whitecloud 1 hour and 25 minutes to make the balance beams. She started at 2:45. When did she finish? 4:10
8. Jane's grandfather carried in 12 bags of sand. Each bag weighed 25 pounds. How heavy were the bags of sand all together? 300 pounds

More Practice, page 518, set C

213

3. Practice and Apply

Basic	1-8
Average	1-8
Extended	1-7

Additional Answers and Sample Solutions: See p. T79.

MIXED PRACTICE

► **Contrast Problems 3 and 7.** (In Problem 3, you must find elapsed time; in Problem 7, you use the elapsed time given to find the ending time.)

► **Identify problems that will have more than 1 answer.** (Problems 2 and 5)

► **Compare Problems 1 and 8.** (Both can be solved by multiplying.)

► **Analyze Problem 4 to choose a strategy to solve it.** (Use Logical Reasoning)

► **Explain how to solve Problem 6.** (Use the table to find how many students use each size structure, then compare the quantities.)

Close and Assess

PROVE WHAT YOU KNOW

Have students use counters to demonstrate that this problem has more than 1 answer:
Angela picked some 3-leaf and some 4-leaf clovers. If she counted 22 leaves in all, how many of each kind of clover did she find? (one 4-leaf and six 3-leaf clovers; four 4-leaf and two 3-leaf clovers)

Quick Quiz

Roy saw 20 feet under the barn door. Some belonged to hens, others to goats. How many of each animal did he see? (1 goat, 8 hens; 2 goats, 6 hens; 3 goats, 4 hens; 4 goats, 2 hens)

LESSON OPTIONS 8-5

Estimating and Measuring Length: Nonstandard Units

OBJECTIVE 8-5 To estimate and measure length, using nonstandard units

PREBOOK ACTIVITIES

QUICK REVIEW

Choose the greater value or measure.
1. 1 year or 11 months (1 year)
2. 48 dimes or 48 nickels (48 dimes)
3. 14 days or 3 weeks (3 weeks)
4. your math book's height or its thickness (height)

PRIOR KNOWLEDGE

Have students generate a list of measurements they know or have used to tell how long something is. (Answers may vary. Possible answers: inch, foot, mile, meter) Have students tell why different units are used to describe distances or objects. (Possible answer: Some units, such as a mile, make sense for long distances—for example, how far it is from Ohio to Maine. Others, such as an inch, make sense for small objects.)

COMMUNICATION

Discussing and Reading Math Write these two sentences on the chalkboard and draw a line under each word in dark type: A **cubit** is a very old **unit** of measure. **Cubits** were **nonstandard units** because they depended on how long someone's arm was from elbow to fingertip. Ask students to use context clues to determine the meaning of each underlined word. (*cubit:* distance from elbow to fingertip; *unit:* size used to measure; *nonstandard:* not always the same) Discuss why nonstandard measurement units could be confusing to use. (Possible answer: People could not be sure what a size description really means.)

EXPLORE AND CONNECT

Materials: early measurement chart (see activity below)
Grouping Suggestion: cooperative learning groups of 4
Students use historical measures to explore **nonstandard units.** Make a chart displaying these terms and descriptions: **cubit** (distance from elbow to fingertip); **span** (distance between outstretched thumb and pinky); **palm** (side-to-side distance across a flat hand); **pace** (two walking steps). Discuss the units as volunteers demonstrate each. Then challenge groups to match classroom objects or distances to 1 of each *nonstandard unit*, based on their own bodies, assigning one *unit* to each member. For example, the pencil sharpener might be 1 *palm* high; the length of a table, 1 *pace* long; a new pencil, 1 *span* long; and a file drawer, 1 *cubit* high. When groups have had time to explore, ask volunteers to demonstrate what they found. Conclude by finding who has the longest and shortest *cubit, span, palm,* and *pace*.

CONNECTIONS Use these anytime.

Problem of the Day

Fathoms Another early unit is the *fathom*, or the distance across the outstretched arms. Imagine your classroom tipped on end so that the length becomes the depth from ceiling to floor. Estimate this depth in fathoms. Check by using your own arm lengths. (Answers will vary.)

Subject Integration

Literature *20,000 Leagues Under the Sea* is a science-fiction story by Jules Verne. Find out the size of a league. About how far under the sea does the story take place? (about 3 mi; about 60,000 mi)

Number Sense

Estimation In early days, the *foot* was based on the size of someone's foot. Use your own foot as the nonstandard unit. About how long is your classroom? (Answers will vary. Check for reasonableness.)

Classwork and Homework Supplements

Practice

Estimation 8-5

Name

Estimating and Measuring Length: Nonstandard Units

Estimate and measure using your body units.
Answers will vary.

1. Item: Width of door
   Unit: Hand span
2. Item: Length of room
   Unit: Step
3. Item: Height of desk
   Unit: Cubit
4. Item: Length of math book
   Unit: Hand span
5. Estimate the length of your foot in thumb units.
   Check by measuring.
6. Estimate the length of your step in cubits.
   Check by measuring.

Building Thinking Skills

Estimation 8-5

Name

Examining a Measurement Problem

Howdy! My name is Jed, and I live on a cattle ranch in Wyoming. Tomorrow I am leaving by train for the New Jersey coast, where I will be spending the summer with my aunt. Since I need to pack enough things for 3 months, I am going to take my big trunk.

4 handspans
2 steps

Jed's body units:
1 step = 2 cubits
1 cubit = 2 handspans

1. Which is the greater measure, the height of the trunk or the length? length Why?
   2 steps = 8 handspans, which is greater than 4 handspans.
2. Jed has a radio that is 2 cubits long and 1 cubit high. Will it fit in the trunk? yes Why or why not?
   2 cubits is less than 2 steps; 1 cubit is less than 4 handspans.
3. Jed would like to take a gift for his aunt that is 3 cubits long and 3 cubits high. Can he pack it? no Why?
   It is too high; 3 cubits is more than 4 handspans.
4. Would your body units have the same measurement as Jed's? No Explain. Different people have different body unit measurements.

Reteaching

Skills Review 8-5

Name

Estimating and Measuring Length: Nonstandard Units

You can estimate and measure using nonstandard units.

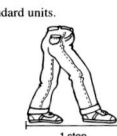

1 span 1 cubit 1 step

Write the body unit you would use to measure each object. Answers will vary. Possible answers given.

1. The length of your classroom — steps
2. The width of a bookcase — spans or steps
3. The height of a chalkboard — cubits or spans
4. The length of a ruler — spans
5. The distance between two desks — steps
6. The length of a school bus — steps

Choose the body unit you would use to measure. Estimate and then measure the length of each item. Answers will vary.

	Estimate	Measurement
7. your desktop		
8. a closet door		
9. a large textbook		
10. your classroom		

Challenges

Cooperative Activities 8-5

Name

Are You Square?

Work in a small group. You will need a long piece of string.

1. Fill in the chart for each person in your group. An example has been done for you.

Name	Which is longer? Height or arm span?	What "shape" is this person?
Example: Teresa	arm span	Rectangle 1

Rectangle 1 Rectangle 2 Square

2. Now use your string to fill in the blanks below with whole numbers. You can wrap the string around different parts of your body or place it along their lengths. Help other group members to measure themselves. Answers will vary. Samples given.

My height is about 3 times the distance around my face.
My arm is about 2 times the length of my foot.
My waist is about 4 times the distance around my wrist.
My height is about 3 times the distance from my knee to the floor.

Discuss everyone's results. What generalizations can you make about different body measurements?

Options for Individual Needs

Basic

Exercises 1-8
Computer Bank, p. 493
More Practice, p. 518, set D

Supplements
Reteaching 78 or
Practice 78
Thinking Skills 78

Average

Exercises 1-8
Computer Bank, p. 493
More Practice, p. 518, set D

Supplements
Practice 78
Challenges 78 or
Thinking Skills 78

Extended

Exercises 1-8
Computer Bank, p. 493

Supplements
Challenges 78
Thinking Skills 78

Other Resources:
Problem-Solving Experiences in Mathematics, Grade 4, Problem 62
Make It Simpler, A Practical Guide to Problem Solving in Mathematics, p. 333
Kids Are Consumers, Too!, p. 23

LESSON PLAN 8-5

OBJECTIVE 8-5
To estimate and measure length, using nonstandard units

Materials: toothpicks

Grouping Suggestion: small groups

1. MOTIVATE AND TEACH

LEARN ABOUT IT

► **Explain which body units may change as you measure.** (Possible answer: The step and the span, because you can move or adjust them.)

EXPLORE ► **Order body units from longest to shortest. Would this order be the same for most people? Explain.** (step, cubit, span, thumb; yes, because of body proportions; Most people's step is longer than the length of their cubit.)

► **Decide how to use partial measures.** (Possible answers: Round to the nearest measure; use half-units.)

TALK ABOUT IT ► **Predict what may happen if two people measure an item with the same unit.** (They may get different measures because of differences in body size.)

► **Which of your estimates were closest? Analyze why.** (Answers may vary. Students may have a sense of the size of their step or hand span but no experience with a cubit.)

Student Edition answers: **1.** Answers will vary. **2.** No, hands are different sizes.

2. CHECK UNDERSTANDING

TRY IT OUT

ERROR ALERT Allowing too much space between thumb units while measuring. Not starting at the edge when beginning to measure.

Estimating and Measuring Length
Nonstandard Units

LEARN ABOUT IT

EXPLORE Use Body Units
Work in groups. Choose six items in your classroom. Estimate and measure the length of each item using one of your body units. Make a table like the one started below. Record your data in the table.

Item	Unit	Estimate	Measure

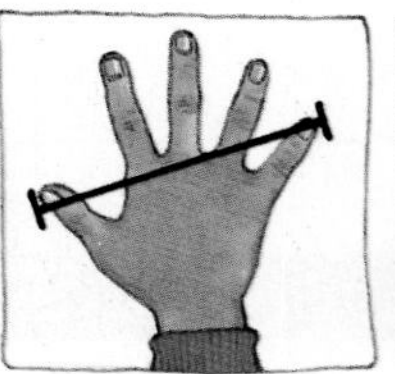
1 span

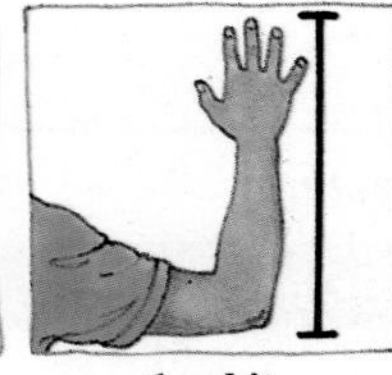
1 cubit

1 step

TALK ABOUT IT See teaching notes.

1. How did you decide which unit to use with each item?
2. If everyone in your group used their hand span to measure a table, would the measures all be the same? Explain.

To measure the length of an object, choose a unit. Then count how many times you can lay that unit along the length of the object.

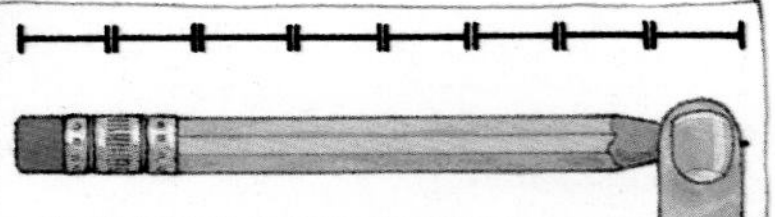
The length of the pencil is close to 7 thumb units.

TRY IT OUT Answers will vary.

Estimate and measure the lengths of these pencils. Use your thumb as the unit of measurement.

1. 

2. 

214

TEACHING OPTIONS

RETEACHING TIPS Have students use toothpicks as thumb guides. They lay the thumb down for the first unit, then put a toothpick against its side to mark where to lay the second thumb unit. Toothpicks and thumbs are moved alternately. Assign Reteaching Supplement 78.

ENRICHMENT Family Math
At home, students use a nonstandard unit, such as the hand span, to measure the height of each family member. They estimate each height, then measure with their hand span. If possible, an adult should do the same. Then students compare their results to the adult's.

PRACTICE Answers will vary.

Estimate and measure using your body units.

1. 

Item: chalkboard
Unit: step

2. 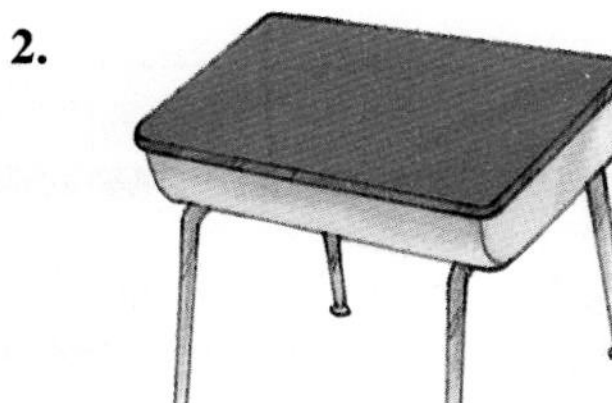

Item: your desk
Unit: hand span

3. Estimate the length of your hand span in thumb units. Check by measuring.

4. Estimate the length of your cubit in hand span units. Check by measuring.

APPLY

MATH REASONING

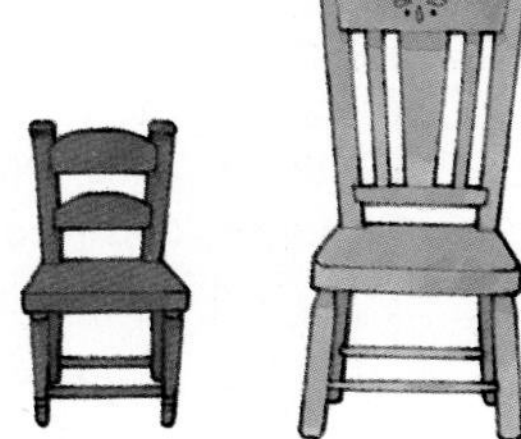

5. One chair is 10 cubits high. The other is 10 hand spans high. Which is higher? Explain how you know. **the chair that is 10 cubits; a cubit is longer than a hand span**

PROBLEM SOLVING

6. Which of the body units would give the largest measure for the width of your classroom? Why? **thumbs, because it is the smallest unit**

7. Bill's hand span is 9 thumbs long. Bill found that the length of his desk is 5 hand spans. How many thumbs long is the desk? **45 thumbs long**

▶ **COMMUNICATION Write About It** Answers will vary.

8. Body units are not used to measure things in everyday life. Write a paragraph to explain why you think they are not used.

More Practice, page 518, set D

3. Practice and Apply

Basic	1-8
Average	1-8
Extended	1-8

PRACTICE

Look at Exercises 1-4. Which might be the most difficult to do? (Answers will vary. Students might find Exercise 3 the most awkward.)

APPLY

MATH REASONING ▶ **How does comparing 1 cubit and 1 hand span help you solve Exercise 5? Explain.** (If you know that 1 cubit is larger than 1 hand span, then 10 cubits must be larger than 10 hand spans.)

PROBLEM SOLVING ▶ **What operation is needed to solve Problem 7? Explain.** (Multiplication, because there is a same-size group: 9 thumbs = 1 hand span, so 9 thumbs × 5 hand spans = 45 thumbs.)

COMMUNICATION ▶ **What difficulty may arise when using nonstandard units?** (Possible answer: People would always have to measure everything for themselves.)

Close and Assess

SAY WHAT YOU THINK Ask students to give reasons why people in past centuries probably used body measures such as the cubit, span, and step. Then ask them to give reasons why they think measuring changed in more modern times. (Answers will vary. Check explanations for reasonableness.)

Quick Quiz

Estimate, then measure the length of your foot using thumb units. (Answers will vary. Check each student's answer by measuring his or her foot.)

LESSON OPTIONS 8-6

Inch, Foot, and Yard

OBJECTIVE 8-6 To measure length in inch, foot, yard and to relate inch, foot, yard

PREBOOK ACTIVITIES

QUICK REVIEW

Find the products.

1. 4 × 12 (48)	. 36 × 7 (252)	**3.** 3 × 25 (75)
4. 12 × 8 (96)	**5.** 58 × 3 (174)	**6.** 36 × 6 (216)
7. 36 × 12 (432)	**8.** 12 × 50 (600)	**9.** 67 × 3 (201)

PRIOR KNOWLEDGE

Write these measurement units on the chalkboard: inch, foot, yard. Have students suggest real-life situations in which they have used these units to measure objects or distances. (Answers will vary. Possible responses: I am 4 feet 7 inches tall; a football field is 100 yards long.) Have students order the units from least to greatest (inch, foot, yard) and give any equivalencies they know. (Possible responses: 1 ft = 12 in.; 1 yd = 3 ft; 1 yd = 36 in.)

COMMUNICATION

Discussing Math Ask students to contrast the inch, foot, and yard with units such as the cubit, step, and hand span. (Possible answer: Inch, foot, and yard are units with sizes that never change, while cubits, steps, and hand spans are nonstandard units with sizes that vary with the person who is measuring.) Have students suggest reasons why the inch, foot, and yard are more convenient to use. (Possible answers: There are rulers, divided into inch, foot,. or yard units, that can be used for measuring; you can more easily picture a measurement given by another person because everyone's inch, for example, is the same size.)

EXPLORE AND CONNECT

Materials: long oaktag strips, scissors

Grouping Suggestion: cooperative learning pairs

Students use a standard measure that the class creates and the nonstandard cubit to find and compare measurements. Ask the class to create their own standard unit that everyone could use. For example, it might be the length of their math book. Each pair uses that measure to make a ''ruler'' by cutting an oaktag strip the length of the math book. Then give all pairs the same list of classroom objects to measure in math-book units and in cubits. Pairs should round all measurements to the nearest book unit or cubit. When all pairs are finished measuring, bring everyone together to compare results. Ask students to tell which measurements were consistently similar among the pairs, those made with the standard book unit or those made with cubits and to explain why. (A standard unit does not change in size.)

CONNECTIONS Use these anytime.

Problem of the Day

Snail Home Run The distance between each of four bases at major league ball parks is 90 feet. Suppose a snail hit a home run and it crawled from one base to the next at a rate of about 3 feet per minute. How long would the snail take to crawl all around the bases? (about 2 hours)

Life Skills

Comparison Shopping Sue needs a roll of tape. For the same price, she can buy either a 50-yard or a 175-foot roll. Which should Sue buy? (50 yard = 150 feet; The 175-foot roll gives more tape for the money.)

Math Connection

Money A hardware store sells chain at 69¢ per foot. Drew needs 6 yards of chain to make a swing. Is $10.00 enough money for him to buy the amount of chain he needs? Explain. (No, 6 yards of chain will cost $12.42.)

Classwork and Homework Supplements

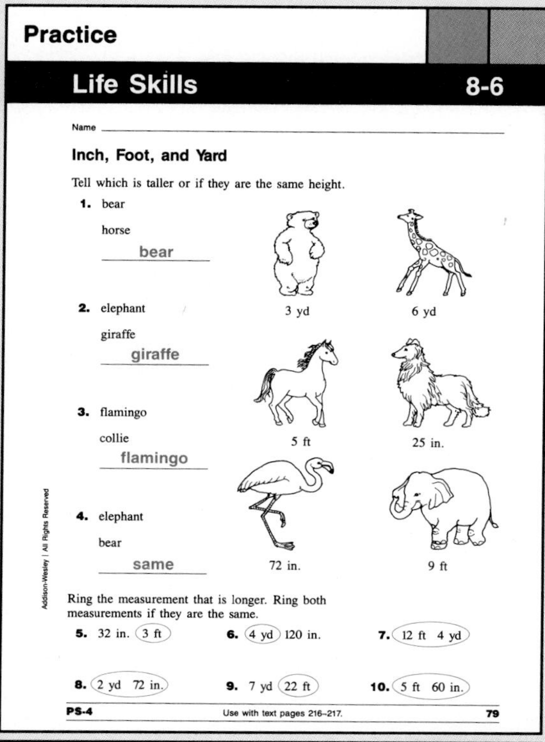

Practice

Life Skills 8-6

Name ______

Inch, Foot, and Yard

Tell which is taller or if they are the same height.

1. bear / horse — bear — 3 yd, 6 yd
2. elephant / giraffe — giraffe — 5 ft, 25 in.
3. flamingo / collie — flamingo — 72 in., 9 ft
4. elephant / bear — same

Ring the measurement that is longer. Ring both measurements if they are the same.

5. 32 in. (3 ft)
6. (4 yd) 120 in.
7. (12 ft) (4 yd)
8. (2 yd) (72 in.)
9. 7 yd (22 ft)
10. (5 ft) (60 in.)

Addison-Wesley | All Rights Reserved

PS-4 Use with text pages 216–217. 79

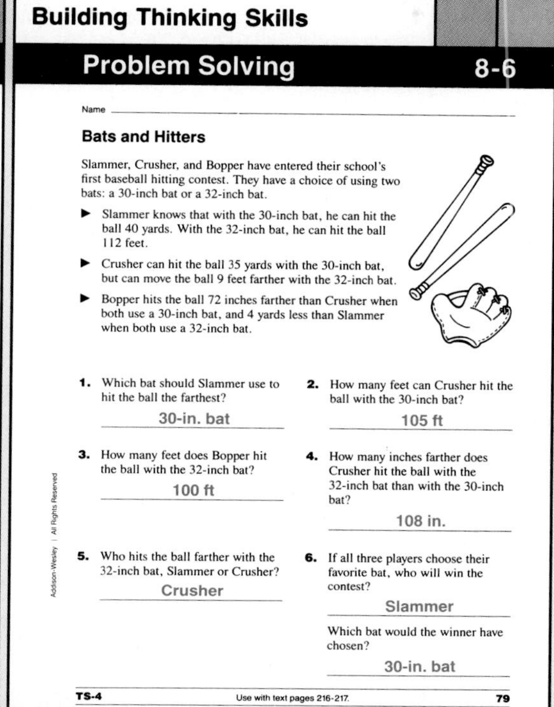

Building Thinking Skills

Problem Solving 8-6

Name ______

Bats and Hitters

Slammer, Crusher, and Bopper have entered their school's first baseball hitting contest. They have a choice of using two bats: a 30-inch bat or a 32-inch bat.

- Slammer knows that with the 30-inch bat, he can hit the ball 40 yards. With the 32-inch bat, he can hit the ball 112 feet.
- Crusher can hit the ball 35 yards with the 30-inch bat, but can move the ball 9 feet farther with the 32-inch bat.
- Bopper hits the ball 72 inches farther than Crusher when both use a 30-inch bat, and 4 yards less than Slammer when both use a 32-inch bat.

1. Which bat should Slammer use to hit the ball the farthest? 30-in. bat
2. How many feet can Crusher hit the ball with the 30-inch bat? 105 ft
3. How many feet does Bopper hit the ball with the 32-inch bat? 100 ft
4. How many inches farther does Crusher hit the ball with the 32-inch bat than with the 30-inch bat? 108 in.
5. Who hits the ball farther with the 32-inch bat, Slammer or Crusher? Crusher
6. If all three players choose their favorite bat, who will win the contest? Slammer

   Which bat would the winner have chosen? 30-in. bat

Addison-Wesley | All Rights Reserved

TS-4 Use with text pages 216-217. 79

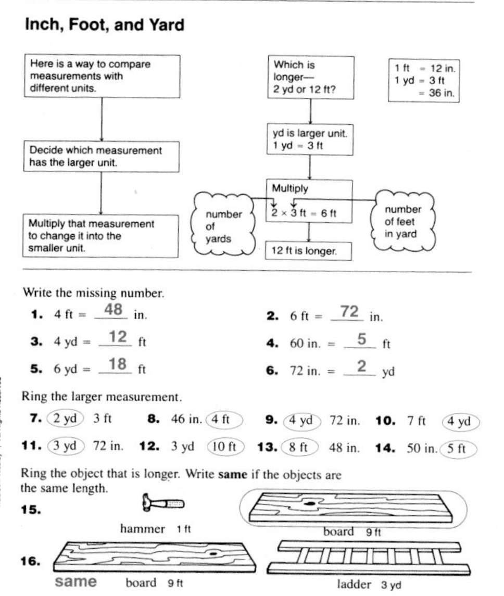

Reteaching

Skills Review 8-6

Name ______

Inch, Foot, and Yard

Here is a way to compare measurements with different units. → Decide which measurement has the larger unit. → Multiply that measurement to change it into the smaller unit.

Which is longer— 2 yd or 12 ft? → yd is larger unit. 1 yd = 3 ft → Multiply (number of yards) 2 × 3 ft = 6 ft (number of feet in yard) → 12 ft is longer.

1 ft = 12 in.
1 yd = 3 ft
= 36 in.

Write the missing number.

1. 4 ft = 48 in.
2. 6 ft = 72 in.
3. 4 yd = 12 ft
4. 60 in. = 5 ft
5. 6 yd = 18 ft
6. 72 in. = 2 yd

Ring the larger measurement.

7. (2 yd) 3 ft
8. 46 in. (4 ft)
9. (4 yd) 72 in.
10. 7 ft (4 yd)
11. (3 yd) 72 in.
12. 3 yd (10 ft)
13. (8 ft) 48 in.
14. 50 in. (5 ft)

Ring the object that is longer. Write **same** if the objects are the same length.

15. hammer 1 ft; (board 9 ft)
16. same — board 9 ft; ladder 3 yd

Addison-Wesley | All Rights Reserved

RS-4 Use with text pages 216-217. 79

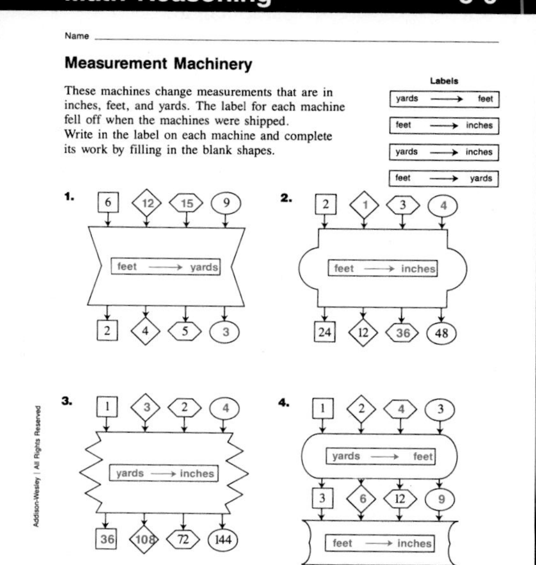

Challenges

Math Reasoning 8-6

Name ______

Measurement Machinery

These machines change measurements that are in inches, feet, and yards. The label for each machine fell off when the machines were shipped. Write in the label on each machine and complete its work by filling in the blank shapes.

Labels: yards → feet; feet → inches; yards → inches; feet → yards

1. In: 6, 12, 15, 9 — feet → yards — Out: 2, 4, 5, 3
2. In: 2, 1, 3, 4 — feet → inches — Out: 24, 12, 36, 48
3. In: 1, 3, 2, 4 — yards → inches — Out: 36, 108, 72, 144
4. In: 1, 2, 4, 3 — yards → feet — 3, 6, 12, 9 — feet → inches — Out: 36, 72, 144, 108

Addison-Wesley | All Rights Reserved

CS-4 Use with text pages 216–217. 79

Options for Individual Needs

Basic

Exercises 1-18
Skills Bank, p. 465
Computer Bank, p. 493
More Practice, p. 518, set E

Supplements
Reteaching 79 or
Practice 79
Challenges 79

Average

Exercises 1-22
Skills Bank, p. 465
Computer Bank, p. 493
More Practice, p. 518, set E

Supplements
Practice 79
Challenges 79 or
Thinking Skills 79

Extended

Exercises 1-20
Computer Bank, p. 493

Supplements
Challenges 79
Thinking Skills 79

Other Resources:
Problem-Solving Experiences in Mathematics, Grade 4, Problem 144
Make It Simpler, A Practical Guide to Problem Solving In Mathematics, p. 144
Kids Are Consumers, Too!, pp.28, 29

LESSON PLAN 8-6

OBJECTIVE 8-6
To measure length in inch, foot, yard and to relate inch, foot, yard

Materials: yardstick, ruler, 1-inch oaktag square, string

Alternative Materials: TA 17 (Rulers)

Grouping Suggestion: pairs

1. MOTIVATE AND TEACH

LEARN ABOUT IT

EXPLORE ► **What problems do you predict in trying to find the distance around your open hand?** (Possible answers: It is hard to measure your own hand; it is hard to measure curves with a ruler.)
► **Explain a way to measure curves.** (Possible answer: First measure with string, then find the length of the string.)

TALK ABOUT IT ► **How can length be compared if it is given in different units?** (Change one of the lengths to the other length's unit of measure so both are expressed in a common unit.)
► **Explain why you multiply 4 × 3 in the ribbon and rope example.** (Multiply 4 yards by 3 because every yard has 3 feet.)
Student Edition answers: **1.** Answers may vary. **2.** If a measurement exceeds 12 inches, change to feet; if it exceeds 36 inches, change to yards.

2. CHECK UNDERSTANDING

TRY IT OUT

ERROR ALERT Multiplying by the wrong factor when attempting to change units. Making multiplication errors when changing from one unit to another.

Inch, Foot, and Yard

LEARN ABOUT IT

The **inch**, the **foot**, and the **yard** are customary units of length that are often compared. To compare measurements made with different units, you may need to change those units.

inch (in.) ├──────┤
1 foot (ft) = 12 inches
1 yard (yd) = 3 feet, or 36 inches

EXPLORE Create a Method
Do you think the distance around your open hand is closer to 6 inches, 12 inches, or 36 inches? Create a way to measure this distance to the nearest inch. Then decide if you can change your measurement into feet or yards.

TALK ABOUT IT See teaching notes.
1. How did you measure the distance?
2. How did you decide if your measurement could be changed into feet or yards?

Here is a way to compare measurements with different units. First decide which measurement has the larger unit. Then multiply that measurement to change it into the smaller unit.

Which is longer—10 feet of ribbon or 4 yards of rope?

Yards is the larger unit, so I multiply 4 × 3 ft.

The rope is 12 feet long.

The rope is longer, since 12 feet is longer than 10 feet.

TRY IT OUT

Tell which measurement is longer or if they are the same length.

1. 5 yd 15 ft — same length
2. <u>56 in.</u> 2 ft
3. 2 yd 72 in. — same length
4. <u>6 yd</u> 12 ft
5. 3 yd 108 in. — same length
6. 6 ft <u>3 yd</u>
7. 4 ft 48 in. — same length
8. <u>50 in.</u> 4 ft

216

TEACHING OPTIONS

RETEACHING TIPS Give students a yardstick, a 12-inch ruler, and a 1-inch oaktag square. For a comparison, students hold the larger unit near the smaller unit and state a relationship. They multiply the larger unit by the number of smaller units. Assign Reteaching Supplement 79.

ENRICHMENT Have students use a calculator to solve this problem: *Amy uses videocassettes that contain 200 feet of blank tape. Her VCR moves the tape at 40 inches per minute. Figure out how long of a show Amy can record on one tape at that rate.* (60 minutes, or 1 hour)

PRACTICE

Tell which is longer or if they are the same length.

1. Water ski
   Bow **water ski**
2. Bow
   Arrow **bow**
3. Fishing pole
   Water ski **same length**
4. Arrow
   Fishing pole **fishing pole**

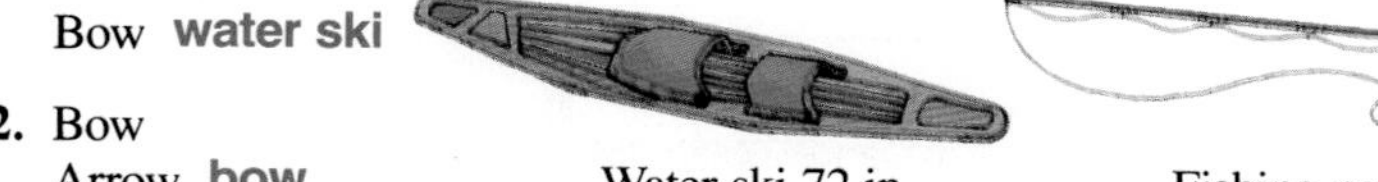

Water ski 72 in.

Fishing pole 2 yd

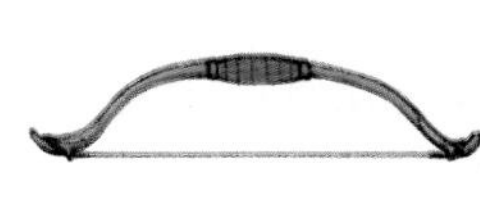

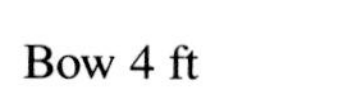

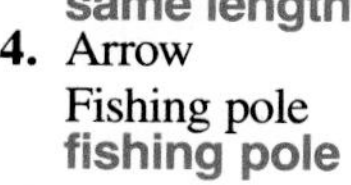

Bow 4 ft

Arrow 36 in.

APPLY

MATH REASONING Which is the better estimate for the length?

5. A garden hose is 25 ft long. **(a.)** about 8 yd **b.** about 9 yd

PROBLEM SOLVING

6. Margo is making a super-long balance beam. She laid 5 boards in a row, with the ends touching. Each board is 47 in. long. How long will her balance beam be? **235 in. long**

7. **Developing a Plan** Spencer bought 4 rolls of twine. Each roll was 15 yd long. How many feet is that? Tell which steps you could use to solve this problem. **180 ft; Multiply 15 and 3. Then multiply by 4.**

MIXED REVIEW

Find the products.

8. 475×7 = **3,325**
9. 219×6 = **1,314**
10. 937×2 = **1,874**
11. 730×5 = **3,650**
12. 555×5 = **2,775**
13. 264×8 **2,112**
14. 827×3 **2,481**
15. 601×4 **2,404**
16. 967×6 **5,802**
17. 82×40 = **3,280**
18. 57×90 = **5,130**
19. 34×60 = **2,040**
20. 69×50 = **3,450**
21. 99×20 = **1,980**
22. 21×70 = **1,470**

More Practice, page 518, set E

3. PRACTICE AND APPLY

Basic	1-18
Average	1-22
Extended	1-20

PRACTICE

Look at Exercises 1-4. What must you do first before you can compare each pair of objects? (Make sure the unit of measurement is the same for both.) *What if you were comparing the water ski and the arrow?* (no need to change either because both are in inches)

APPLY

MATH REASONING ► Explain how to solve Problem 5. (1 yard = 3 feet, so 8 × 3 feet = 24 feet and 9 × 3 feet = 27 feet. Decide if 25 feet is closer to 24 feet or to 27 feet.)

PROBLEM SOLVING ► Is there more than one way to solve Problem 7? Explain. (two ways; Change to feet, then find total footage; find total yardage, then change to feet.)

MIXED REVIEW ► Predict how many digits products will have. Explain your reasoning. (Probably 4 digits; the factors are 3-digit by 1-digit or 2-digit by 2-digit.)

CLOSE AND ASSESS

WRITE WHAT YOU THINK Ask each student to write an explanation of how to compare 5 feet to 64 inches and 16 feet to 5 yards. (Possible answer: Change amounts to the same unit; multiply the larger unit by the number of smaller units that equal it; 5 feet is less than 64 inches; 16 feet is greater than 5 yards.)

QUICK QUIZ

Write <, =, or >.

1. 72 in. ○ 3 yd (<)
2. 7 ft ○ 70 in. (>)
3. 60 in. ○ 3 yd (<)
4. 6 yd ○ 18 ft (=)

LESSON OPTIONS 8-7

Problem Solving: Deciding When to Estimate

OBJECTIVE 8-7 To decide whether an actual measurement is needed or whether an estimate is sufficient

PREBOOK ACTIVITIES

QUICK REVIEW

Is the length greater than, less than, or equal to 1 yd?

1. 36 ft (greater than) **2.** 24 in. (less than)
3. 2 ft (less than) **4.** 2 ft 5 in. (less than)
5. 36 in. (equal to) **6.** 50 in. (greater than)

PRIOR KNOWLEDGE

Have students share experiences in which they have estimated a measurement rather than found an exact answer. (Sample answers: estimating rather than measuring distances to place the bases for a kickball game; feeling your forehead rather than using a thermometer to see whether you have a fever.)

COMMUNICATION

Writing Math In their Math Journals, have students write a paragraph explaining how to draw a floor plan of the classroom. They should decide how they would use both exact measurements and estimates. (Sample answer: Measure the exact length and width of the room to make a scale representation of it, but estimate placement and sizes of features such as furniture, doors, and windows.)

EXPLORE AND CONNECT

COOPERATIVE ACTIVITY

Grouping Suggestion: small groups

You are about to fill your new 20-gal fish tank. Should you measure or estimate the amount of water to use?

TEACHING ACTIONS

Have students discuss the situation to reach a group decision.

► **Analyze the problem to find an exact measurement.** (The tank holds 20 gal of water.)
► **Explain what you must decide.** (As you prepare to fill the tank with water, you must decide whether to measure exactly or to estimate the amount to use.)

► **Explain the action and the outcome.** (Add water to the tank until it is near to the top, but not all the way to the edge.)
► **Decide how much water the tank ought to get.** (less than 20 gal)
► **Analyze how important it is to fill the tank with an exact measure of water.** (The exact amount does not matter, as long as there is enough water for the fish to be healthy.)

► **Justify your decision.** (An exact measurement is not needed, and an estimate is easier to do.)

CONNECTIONS Use these anytime.

Problem of the Day

Weather Clues Mr. Chilly stays inside when the temperature is below freezing. One day he looks out his window and sees 2 things: a broken thermometer and a melted snowman. How can Mr. Chilly decide if he can go out today? (He can estimate that the temperature is above freezing because of the melted snowman.)

Life Skills

Sewing Eleanor must shorten her new skirt because it is too long for her. Should she measure or estimate as she turns up the hem? Give your reasoning. (Measure to be sure the hem is turned up the same amount all around the skirt.)

Number Sense

Estimation Rocco needs 5 ft of rope to make a bell pull for his clubhouse. How can he estimate the right amount of rope without measuring? (Sample answers: Use his height as a non-standard unit and take more or less rope as needed; use a nonstandart measure that is near 1 ft, such as the length of his actual foot.)

Classwork and Homework Supplements

Practice

Problem Solving 8-7

Name

Deciding When to Estimate

Decide whether an estimate or an actual measurement is needed. Explain why.

1. You need to take 1 teaspoon of medicine every 4 hour for 5 days. How much do you need?
   Measurement; the exact amount of medicine should be taken.
2. You are trying a new kind of shampoo. How much shampoo should you use when you wash your hair?
   Estimate; the amount of shampoo does not have to be exact.
3. You want to string beads to make a necklace. How long should the necklace be?
   Estimate; the necklace does not have to be a certain length.
4. You are making tomato sauce with your father. How many tomatoes and green peppers should you add?
   Measurement if you want it to taste the intended way; estimate if done to your taste.
5. You are shipping a box to Japan. Postage is charged per pound. How much will it cost?
   Measurement; the cost will be exact according to the weight.
6. You are making lemonade using a package of powdered mix. How many quarts of water should you add?
   Measurement; the exact amount needs to be added.

Building Thinking Skills

Estimation 8-7

Name

A Zoo-ful of Decisions

Valerie's uncle is one of the zookeepers at the Baker Memorial Zoo. Last Saturday he gave Valerie a chance to help him out on his rounds. She wrote about her day in her journal. Following certain sentences are the words: **(estimate/measure).** Ring the one you think Valerie should do in the situation described in each sentence.

When I arrived at the zoo, my first duty for Uncle Seth was to feed the tropical birds. "Throw them a handful of birdseed," he told me. How much should I feed them, I asked myself?
(estimate / measure)

Next we had to clean the lion cages! Uncle Seth said, "Use 1 cup of cleaning detergent for every 10 cups of water." What now, I wondered?
(estimate / measure)

At the walrus pond, eight huge walruses seemed quite hungry! "Give them 20 pounds of clams and 15 pounds of oysters," my uncle yelled to me. "O.K.," I replied, thinking I will have to **(estimate / measure).**

Our biggest project of the afternoon was to paint the jungle gym in the monkey cage. "Guess we're going to have to get a few cans of paint from the warehouse," Uncle Seth said, "and I want you to decide how many."
(estimate / measure)

The jungle gym looks great with a new coat of paint, but I doubt if the monkeys can tell the difference!

Reteaching

Estimation 8-7

Name

Problem Solving: Deciding When to Estimate

Sometimes you can estimate measurements when solving problems. Knowing how the measurement will be used can help you decide whether to estimate or get an exact answer.

Laurie is having a party. She wants to make salad for 25 friends. Should Laurie estimate or weigh the amount?

Read the problem. → Is an exact answer needed? → YES → Measure.
NO → Estimate.
Laurie can estimate the amount.

Decide whether you need to estimate or measure in each problem. Explain why. Answers will vary.

1. You want to buy roller skates. What size should you buy?
   Measure; your feet will hurt if the skates are not the correct size.
2. You want to put paper on your kite frame. How big is the kite frame?
   Measure; the paper should fit exactly over it.
3. You are making a cushion for your chair. How much stuffing do you need?
   Estimate; you can guess.
4. You are making cheese dip for 4 friends. How much should you make?
   Estimate; you can guess.
5. You want to make a quilt for your bed. How big is the bed?
   Measure; the quilt must be the correct size.
6. You are making a fence around your yard. How many feet of fence do you need?
   Measure; you must fit it exactly.

Challenges

Cooperative Activities 8-7

Name

Brainstorming time

Work in a small group. Think about each situation. Discuss times when you would need an exact measurement and times when an estimate would be enough. Brainstorm ideas with your group members. The first one has been started for you. Answers will vary. Sample answers given.

1. You are making a birthday cake.
   Exact measurement: *Measuring 3 cups of flour according to the recipe.*
   Estimate: deciding how much icing you want to put on the cake
2. You are planting a garden.
   Exact measurement: planting plants 2 feet apart according to the directions
   Estimate: deciding how much fertilizer to buy
3. You are decorating a clubhouse.
   Exact measurement: measuring the window to see how much fabric you need for curtains
   Estimate: deciding where to hang 3 posters in a row
4. You are getting new furniture for your bedroom.
   Exact measurement: deciding if a 36-inch desk will fit in a certain space
   Estimate: deciding how many bookshelves you will need to hold all your books

Options for Individual Needs

Basic

Exercises 1-9
Computer Bank, p. 492

Supplements
Reteaching 80 or
Practice 80

Average

Exercises 1-9
Computer Bank, p. 492

Supplements
Practice 80
Challenges 80 or
Thinking Skills 80

Extended

Exercises 1-9
Computer Bank, p. 492

Supplements
Challenges 80
Thinking Skills 80

Other Resources:
Problem-Solving Experiences in Mathematics, Grade 4, Problem 149
Kids Are Consumers, Too!, pp. 24, 25

LESSON PLAN 8-7

OBJECTIVE 8-7
To decide whether an actual measurement is needed or whether an estimate is sufficient

1. MOTIVATE AND TEACH

LEARN ABOUT IT

▶ **Explain how a real measurement can be used as an estimate.** (Possible answer: *About* 1 c of milk uses a measurement to help you visualize an amount without actually measuring.)

▶ **Contrast the situations involving Cora and Josh.** (Possible answer: Cora is cooking for friends: Josh cooks in a restaurant.)

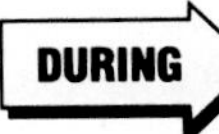

▶ **Explain how Cora could make burgers without measuring.** She could visually estimate making equal portions.)

▶ **Explain how Josh should make his hamburgers.** (He should weigh the meat on a scale.)

▶ **Analyze the decisions to see if they make sense.** (It makes sense for Cora to estimate in her informal situation, since exactly identical hamburgers are unnecessary; Josh should measure exactly in his more strict situation, or else customers could complain of different-sized or skimpy hamburgers.)

2. CHECK UNDERSTANDING

TRY IT OUT

ERROR ALERT Misinterpreting how a measurement is to be used and consequently making an inappropriate decision.

Problem Solving
Deciding When to Estimate

LEARN ABOUT IT

When you solve a problem where a measurement is needed, you must decide whether to actually measure or just estimate. Knowing how the measurement will be used can help you decide.

Cora wants to grill hamburgers for 16 friends. Does she need to make a hamburger and weigh it to decide if she can buy the hamburger for $16?

Josh cooks in a restaurant that sells quarter-pound hamburgers. He has 20 pounds of meat to fill an order for 80 hamburgers. Is that enough meat? Does Josh need to weigh each hamburger patty?

The hamburgers Cora is making do not need to weigh exactly the same.

Cora can estimate that one pound will serve 4 people and so she will need 4 pounds. 4 × $2.98 per pound is about $12.

The hamburgers Josh is making each need to weigh exactly a quarter pound, as they are advertised.

Josh should weigh each amount of meat.

TRY IT OUT See Additional Answers.

Decide whether an estimate or an actual measurement is needed. Explain why.

1. Your dog is on a special diet. You were told to feed her only 1 pound of food each day. How much food should you give her today?
2. You are sick and your doctor wants to know how much your body temperature has risen in the last hour. What is your temperature?

218

TEACHING OPTIONS

RETEACHING TIPS Have students discuss both an estimate and an exact measurement in each problem to consider the effects of each choice. This should help them be able to choose the more appropriate method for each situation. Assign Reteaching Supplement 80.

ENRICHMENT **Family Math** Have students try this activity at home. They find 2 real-life situations around the home related to measurement: 1 that requires an exact measurement and 1 that can be estimated. Students should give reasonable answers, then have a family member check their answers.

MIXED PRACTICE

See Additional Answers.

Decide whether you need to estimate or measure in each problem. Explain why. Then solve problems 1, 4, 8, and 9.

1. You are making a place mat that will cover the entire top of your desk. How long should the mat be? How wide should it be?
2. You want to hang a picture at your eye level. Where should you put the nail?
3. The Box It Up shop wraps packages for mailing. They charge \$0.25 per pound to wrap a package. How much will it cost for them to wrap your package?
4. You are cutting gold yarn to fit exactly across the width of a bulletin board in your classroom. How many inches of yarn will you need?

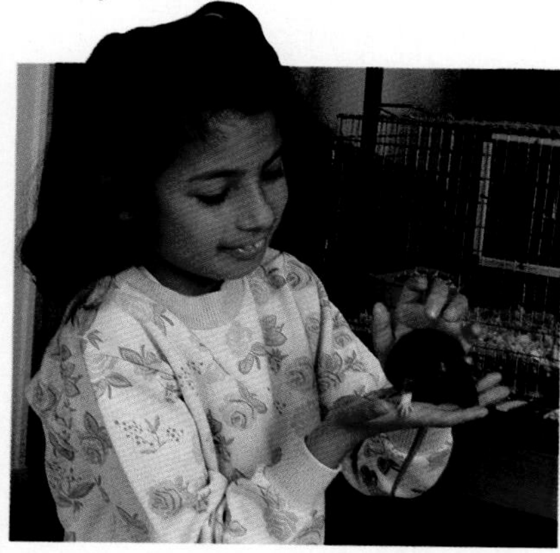

5. You are cutting ribbon to wrap around a present. How long should the ribbon be?
6. You are making cupcakes for a goodbye party. The recipe says to bake the cupcakes for 12 minutes. How long have the cupcakes been baking in the oven?
7. You want to make enough punch for 6 friends. How much punch will you make?
8. Your teacher wants your class to make a height bar graph. The labels under the bars on the graph increase 1 inch at a time. Where will you record your height?
9. **Missing Data** Make up the missing data and solve the problem. You are making a ladder for your pet mouse, Cheesy. Cheesy's cage is 14 inches wide. How long and wide will you make the ladder?

3. Practice and Apply

Basic	1-9
Average	1-9
Extended	1-9

Additional Answers and Sample Solutions: See p. T79.

MIXED PRACTICE

▶ **Explain how Problems 1 and 4 are alike.** (Both require making something to fit exactly.)

▶ **Summarize the situation in Problem 2.** (You plan to hang a picture at an approximate height.)

▶ **Explain what measurement you must consider in Problem 6.** (time; You must find how long the cupcakes have baked.)

▶ **Justify using both exact and estimated measurements in Problem 7.** (You might use exact measurements to make the punch, but estimate how much to make.)

▶ **Analyze Problem 9 to decide what data is missing.** (the height of the cage)

Close and Assess

WRITE WHAT YOU THINK

Have students create 2 story problems about the length of a piece of wood. They should make 1 situation need an exact measurement and the other need an estimate. Have students provide reasonable answers to each problem. (Check students' writing.)

Quick Quiz

Amy is making a leather belt for her father's birthday. Should Amy estimate the length of the belt or measure exactly? Explain why. (Measure exactly to be sure it fits.)

LESSON OPTIONS 8-8

Miles/Midchapter Review/Quiz

OBJECTIVE 8-8 To estimate lengths in miles

PREBOOK ACTIVITIES

QUICK REVIEW

Complete each statement with inch, foot, or yard.

1. A beetle is 1 (inch) long.
2. A work table is 1 (yard) high.
3. A dog collar is 1 (foot) long.

PRIOR KNOWLEDGE

Generate a list of destinations of long trips students may have made. (Answers will vary.) Have students explain how to describe the distance between home and these destinations, using a reasonable unit of measurement. (Answers will vary. Use miles.)

COMMUNICATION

Discussing Math Have students use the word **mile** in an original sentence. (Answers will vary. Sample sentences: Dustin ran in a 1-mile race. The traveling circus covered 1,000 miles in October.) Have students share any comparisons they know to visualize how far 1 mi is. (Answers will vary. Samples: 4 times around a running track; 20 city blocks; the distance from school to the post office)

EXPLORE AND CONNECT

Materials: copies of road maps, TA 17 (Rulers)
Grouping Suggestion: cooperative learning pairs
Students use road maps to determine approximate distances in **miles**. Have partners state their map-scale relationship as an equation, such as 1 in. = 37 miles. Partners locate any 2 cities that are 3 in. apart on the map. After they find 2 such cities, they discuss and plan a method for determining the mileage between the cities, using the scale relationship they identified. For example, if 2 cities are 3 in. apart and the scale relationship is 1 in. = 275 miles, the cities are 3 × 275, or 825, miles apart. Have students repeat the activity with other cities. Conclude by having students summarize the methods and operations they used to find the distance in *miles* between their cities. (Methods may vary; multiply) Discuss why different maps may use different scale relationships. (because they represent different amounts of land)

CONNECTIONS Use these anytime.

Problem of the Day

Backtracking Tom left home and drove 35 mi on the highway before he realized he had left his wallet behind. He returned home, grabbed his wallet, and got back on the highway. He stopped for lunch 40 mi past where he first realized that his wallet was at home. How far had Tom traveled so far that day? (145 mi)

Number Sense

Estimation Nan knows it takes her 20 min to walk a mile. She starts walking the lake loop trail at 1:30 p.m. If she finishes at 2:50 p.m., about how many miles has she walked? (about 4 mi)

Patterns

Calculator Use a calculator to discover the pattern, then continue it 3 more times: 5,280, 10,560, 15,840, 21,120, (26,400), (31,680), (36,960). (Pattern: Add 5,280 each time.)

Classwork and Homework Supplements

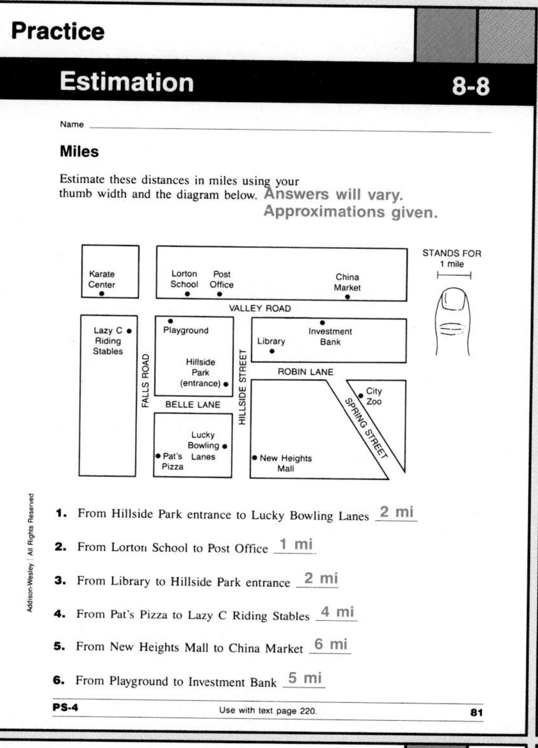
Practice

Estimation 8-8

Name ____________

Miles

Estimate these distances in miles using your thumb width and the diagram below. Answers will vary. Approximations given.

1. From Hillside Park entrance to Lucky Bowling Lanes 2 mi
2. From Lorton School to Post Office 1 mi
3. From Library to Hillside Park entrance 2 mi
4. From Pat's Pizza to Lazy C Riding Stables 4 mi
5. From New Heights Mall to China Market 6 mi
6. From Playground to Investment Bank 5 mi

PS-4 Use with text page 220. 81

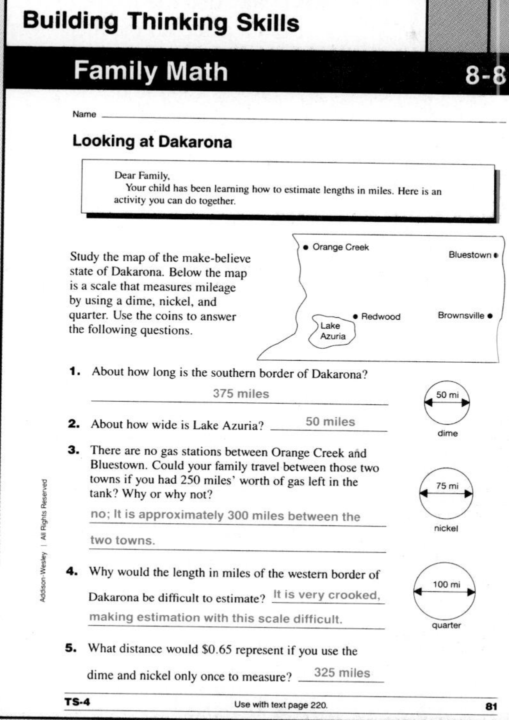
Building Thinking Skills

Family Math 8-8

Name ____________

Looking at Dakarona

Dear Family,
Your child has been learning how to estimate lengths in miles. Here is an activity you can do together.

Study the map of the make-believe state of Dakarona. Below the map is a scale that measures mileage by using a dime, nickel, and quarter. Use the coins to answer the following questions.

1. About how long is the southern border of Dakarona? 375 miles
2. About how wide is Lake Azuria? 50 miles
3. There are no gas stations between Orange Creek and Bluestown. Could your family travel between those two towns if you had 250 miles' worth of gas left in the tank? Why or why not? no; It is approximately 300 miles between the two towns.
4. Why would the length in miles of the western border of Dakarona be difficult to estimate? It is very crooked, making estimation with this scale difficult.
5. What distance would $0.65 represent if you use the dime and nickel only once to measure? 325 miles

TS-4 Use with text page 220. 81

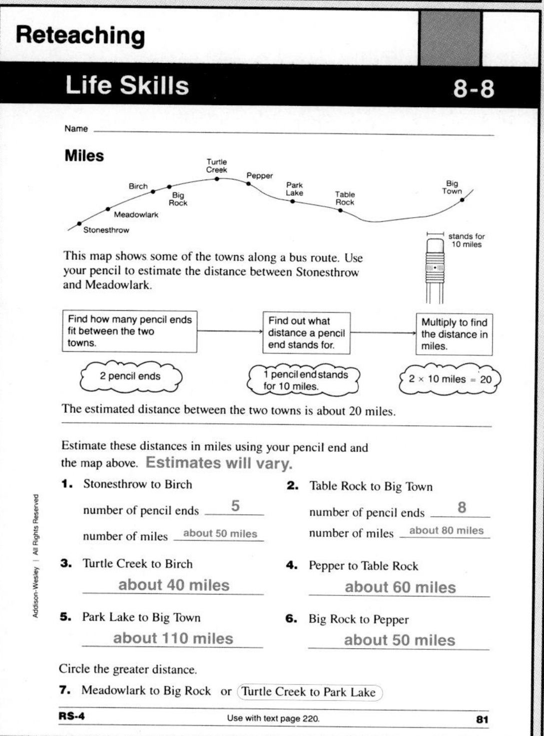
Reteaching

Life Skills 8-8

Name ____________

Miles

This map shows some of the towns along a bus route. Use your pencil to estimate the distance between Stonesthrow and Meadowlark.

Find how many pencil ends fit between the two towns. → Find out what distance a pencil end stands for. → Multiply to find the distance in miles.

2 pencil ends | 1 pencil end stands for 10 miles. | 2 × 10 miles = 20

The estimated distance between the two towns is about 20 miles.

Estimate these distances in miles using your pencil end and the map above. Estimates will vary.

1. Stonesthrow to Birch
   number of pencil ends 5
   number of miles about 50 miles
2. Table Rock to Big Town
   number of pencil ends 8
   number of miles about 80 miles
3. Turtle Creek to Birch about 40 miles
4. Pepper to Table Rock about 60 miles
5. Park Lake to Big Town about 110 miles
6. Big Rock to Pepper about 50 miles

Circle the greater distance.

7. Meadowlark to Big Rock or (Turtle Creek to Park Lake)

RS-4 Use with text page 220. 81

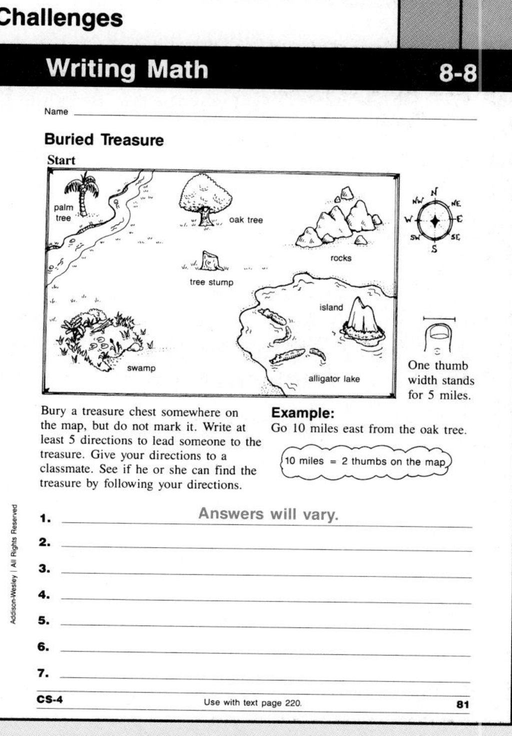
Challenges

Writing Math 8-8

Name ____________

Buried Treasure

Start

Bury a treasure chest somewhere on the map, but do not mark it. Write at least 5 directions to lead someone to the treasure. Give your directions to a classmate. See if he or she can find the treasure by following your directions.

Example:
Go 10 miles east from the oak tree.
10 miles = 2 thumbs on the map

1. Answers will vary.
2.
3.
4.
5.
6.
7.

CS-4 Use with text page 220. 81

Options for Individual Needs

Basic

Exercises 1-6; 1-17
More Practice, p. 519, set A

Supplements
Reteaching 81 or
Practice 81

Average

Exercises 1-6; 1-17
More Practice, p. 519, set A

Supplements
Practice 81
Challenges 81 or
Thinking Skills 81

Extended

Exercises 1-6; 1-17

Supplements
Challenges 81
Thinking Skills 81

Other Resources:
Problem-Solving Experiences in Mathematics, Grade 4, Problem 145
Make It Simpler, A Practical Guide to Problem Solving in Mathematics, p. 125
Kids Are Consumers, Too!, pp. 185-189

8-8

LESSON PLAN 8-8

OBJECTIVE 8-8
To estimate lengths in miles

Grouping Suggestion: pairs

1. MOTIVATE AND TEACH

LEARN ABOUT IT

▶ **Based on the picture, decide how many miles a thumb width represents.** (50 mi)

EXPLORE ▶ **Analyze the map.** (It shows nine cities or towns in Oklahoma.)
▶ **Justify the operation to use to figure a distance of 5 thumb widths.** (Multiply because you can put together same-size groups.)

TALK ABOUT IT ▶ **Explain how to use a thumb width as a nonstandard unit.** (Possible answer: Compare your thumb to the measurement scale to see how much of it equals 50 mi; measure how many thumb units are between 2 cities on the map; multiply that amount times 50 to estimate the number of miles between the 2 cities.)
▶ **Explain the relationship between miles and feet.** (1 mi has 5,280 ft.)
▶ **If a football field is 100 yd long, decide how many football fields equal 1 mi.** (between 17 and 18)
Student Edition answers: **1.** Make it a nonstandard unit related to the number of miles in the map scale. **2.** Answers vary because the unit is nonstandard.

2. CHECK UNDERSTANDING

TRY IT OUT

ERROR ALERT Not accounting for distances that are fractions of a thumb width.

Miles

LEARN ABOUT IT

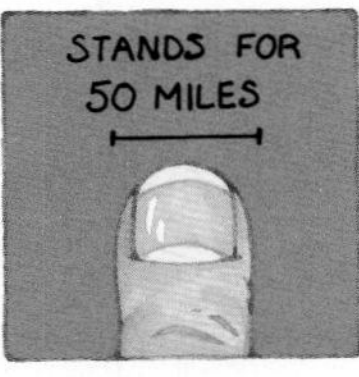

EXPLORE Use the Map
Find a place on the map where your thumb width is about the same as the distance between two towns. About how many miles is it between those towns?

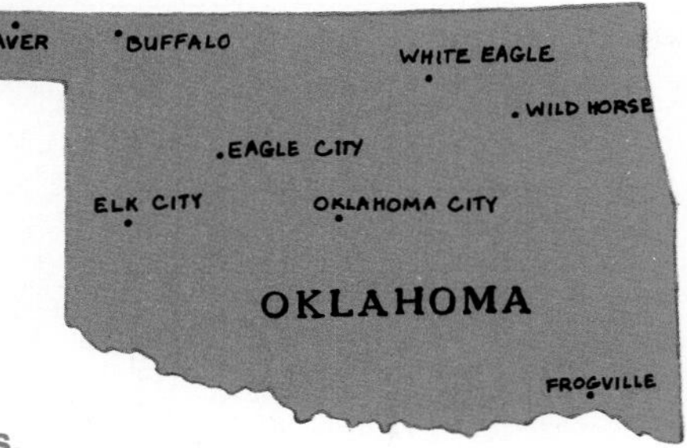

TALK ABOUT IT See teaching notes.

1. Explain how you can use your thumb width to estimate distances on the map.
2. About how many miles is it from White Eagle to Frogville?

The **mile** is another customary unit used to measure length. The relationships between miles, feet, and yards can help you understand how long a mile is.

1 mile (mi) = 5,280 ft = 1,760 yd
You can walk a mile in about 20 min.

PRACTICE

Estimate these distances in miles using your thumb width and the map above. Answers will vary.

1. from Buffalo to White Eagle
2. from Frogville to Wild Horse
3. from Elk City to Buffalo
4. from Wild Horse to Beaver
5. from Beaver to Eagle City
6. from Elk City to Wild Horse

More Practice, page 519, set A

TEACHING OPTIONS

RETEACHING TIPS Have students work in pairs. When partners find distances less than a whole thumb width, have them decide whether to round up or down to the nearest thumb unit or how to adjust an estimate to compensate for partial thumb widths. Assign Reteaching Supplement 81.

ENRICHMENT Have students use a road map to find the distance in miles between your city or town and the state capital. If you live in the state capital, have students find the distance from your city to the capital of the nearest state. (Answers will vary.)

Midchapter Review/Quiz

Write each time. Use a.m. and p.m.

1. Breakfast

7:09 a.m.

2. Bedtime

8:20 p.m.

3. Lunch

12:15 p.m.

4. School ends

3:45 p.m.

Answer these questions. You will need to use the calendar for some of them.

5. What is the fourth Saturday in April? **the 22nd**
6. What day of the week is April 26? **Wednesday**
7. What is another way to write April 3, 1990? **4/3/90**

Estimate and measure the lengths of these things using body units. Then estimate their lengths in inches, and measure their lengths with a ruler. **Answers will vary.**

8. Your leg
9. Your shoe
10. Your pencil

Tell if the distance is more than, less than, or the same as 1 mile.

11. 5,280 ft **the same**
12. 1,000 yd **less than**
13. 5,670 ft **more than**

PROBLEM SOLVING

14. The movie *Watchful Eyes* lasts 100 minutes. If the movie starts at 12:45, what time will it end? **2:25**
15. The movie *Movin' On* begins at 6:30 and ends at 8:55. How long does this movie last? **2 hours and 25 minutes**
16. Mr. Reed wants to buy fencing to put around his garden. Should he estimate or measure the distance around the garden? **measure**
17. Mrs. Reed is planting 28 tomato plants. She wants to put the same number in each row. How many plants can she put in each row? How many rows will she make? **See Additional Answers.**

221

Close and Assess

SHOW WHAT YOU KNOW

Have students use the map on page 220. Explain that Oklahoma's "panhandle" is the narrow rectangular part of the state in which the town of Beaver is found. Then have students use their thumbs to estimate the width of the panhandle in miles. (Answers will vary.)

Quick Quiz

Use the map on page 220 to estimate these distances in miles.

1. from Buffalo to Oklahoma City
2. from Beaver to White Eagle

(Answers will vary.)

3. Practice and Apply

Basic	1-6; 1-17
Average	1-6; 1-17
Extended	1-6; 1-17

Additional Answers: See p. T79.

PRACTICE

Explain the meaning of the calendar box with the diagonal line. (There are 5 Sundays in April, including the last day of the month; the box shows the fourth and fifth Sundays together to save a row.) *For Exercise 8, what body unit could you use to measure your leg?* (Possible answer: your hand) *What would you do first to solve Problem 14?* (Figure out how many hours and minutes are equal to 100 min.)

ITEM ANALYSIS The following table correlates the Midchapter Review/Quiz items with the lesson objectives.

Items	Objectives
1-4	8-1
(1-4), 5-7	8-2
8-10	8-5
11-13	8-8
14, 15	8-3
16	8-7
17	8-4

8-8

LESSON OPTIONS 8-9

Perimeter

OBJECTIVE 8-9 To measure perimeter and to add to find perimeter

PREBOOK ACTIVITIES

QUICK REVIEW

Add.

1. 40 + 60 + 40 + 60 (200)
2. 123 + 123 + 123 (369)
3. 35 + 67 + 35 (137)
4. 35 + 57 + 79 + 24 + 46 (241)
5. 22 + 77 + 77 (176)

PRIOR KNOWLEDGE

Have students think of reasons to know the distance around a shape. (Possible answers: to build a fence; to make a picture frame; to determine how far it is around a park) Then ask students if they have ever estimated length by using the known size of another object as a guide. Have them explain what they did. (Possible answers: used a thumb as about 1 in; used one foot to pace off a game boundary)

COMMUNICATION

Discussing Math Draw an equilateral triangle on the chalkboard and label each side 10 ft. Then write this sentence on the chalkboard: The **perimeter** of the triangle is 30 ft. Have students examine the drawing to determine the meaning of *perimeter*. (''the distance around a figure'') Then have students generalize how to find the perimeter of any figure. (Add the lengths of all sides.) Next, write the word **benchmark** on the chalkboard. Tell students that they used a thumb width as a benchmark to estimate map distances. Challenge students to explain what a benchmark is. (Possible answer: a known reference point or guide for making measurement estimates)

EXPLORE AND CONNECT

Materials: TA 12 (Centimeter Graph Paper), scissors
Grouping Suggestion: cooperative learning groups of 3

Students explore **perimeters** of rectangles. Each student in a group cuts out 2 different-sized graph-paper rectangles, taking care to cut along the lines. The group then spreads out the 6 rectangles in the center of the work space. Students imagine having to make frames for the rectangles, so they need to know the *perimeter*, or distance around the outside of each. Group members work together first to estimate the *perimeters*, then to order the rectangles from least to greatest *perimeter*, based on the estimates. When the group has agreed on an estimated order, members count the units along the sides to find the actual *perimeters* to verify their estimates. Have students summarize how to find *perimeter*, sharing any shortcuts they found. (Possible responses: Add all sides; for rectangles, double the length, then add it to the doubled width.)

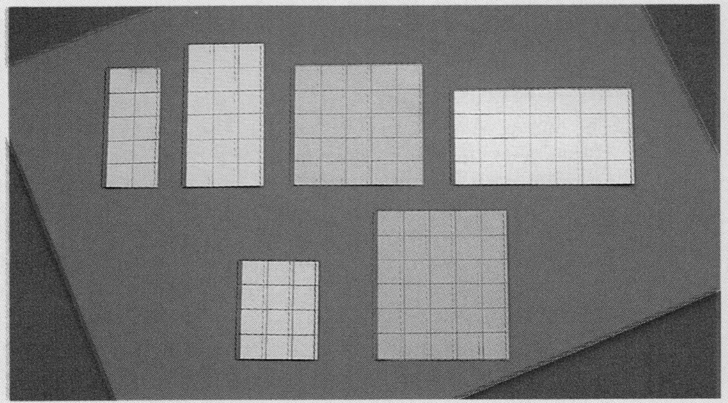

CONNECTIONS Use these anytime.

Problem of the Day

Home Run There is a distance of 90 ft between bases on a regulation baseball diamond. Sluggo McCrash hit 4 home runs in a game. Figure out how far he traveled when he ran the bases for those hits. (90 × 4 × 4 = 1,440 ft)

Life Skills

Wallpaper Woes Martha wants to measure the height of her bedroom wall to buy new wallpaper. But she cannot find her tape measure. She knows the bedroom window is about 5 ft long. How can Martha estimate the height of the walls and make sure she will have enough wallpaper? (Use the window as a benchmark, then overestimate.)

Subject Integration

Fine Arts Kenji plans to glue 36 sea shells around the 4 outside edges of a piece of wood to make a picture frame. Determine all reasonable layouts for Kenji's picture frame. (Possible answers: 12 by 8, 10 by 10, 6 by 14)

Estimating Length, Width, and Perimeter: Using a Benchmark

To estimate length, width, and perimeter using a benchmark

CLASSWORK AND HOMEWORK SUPPLEMENTS

Practice

Calculators 8-9

Name ____________

Perimeter: Using a Benchmark

Use a calculator to find the perimeters.

1. Rectangle: 12 yd, 20 yd, 20 yd, 12 yd — 64 yd
2. Triangle: 40 ft, 50 ft, 30 ft — 120 ft
3. Square: 15 in., 15 in., 15 in., 15 in. — 60 in.

4. Jeffrey has a sandbox in the shape of a square. Each side is 65 in. long. What is the perimeter of the sandbox? 260 in.

Estimate the length, width, and perimeter of these objects in feet. Use a benchmark. Check your estimates by measuring with a ruler. Answers will vary.

5. Bulletin Board
6. Desk Top
7. Classroom Floor

estimate ______ estimate ______ estimate ______
check ______ check ______ check ______

82 Use with text pages 222-223. PS-4

Building Thinking Skills

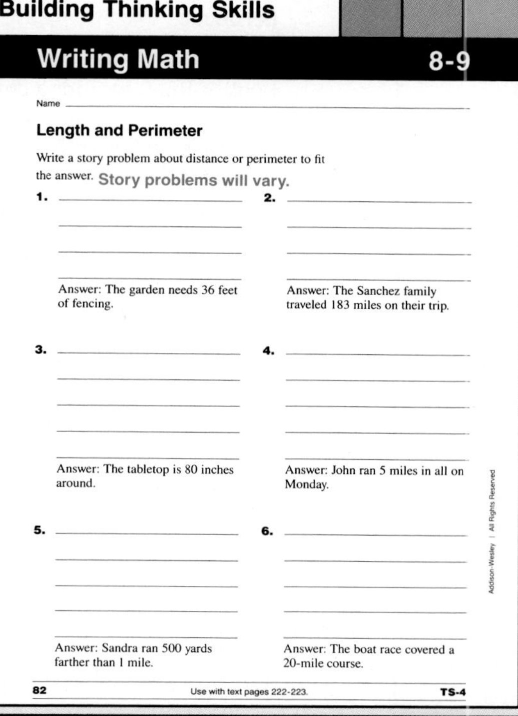

Writing Math 8-9

Name ____________

Length and Perimeter

Write a story problem about distance or perimeter to fit the answer. Story problems will vary.

1. Answer: The garden needs 36 feet of fencing.
2. Answer: The Sanchez family traveled 183 miles on their trip.
3. Answer: The tabletop is 80 inches around.
4. Answer: John ran 5 miles in all on Monday.
5. Answer: Sandra ran 500 yards farther than 1 mile.
6. Answer: The boat race covered a 20-mile course.

82 Use with text pages 222-223. TS-4

Reteaching

Estimation 8-9

Name ____________

Perimeter/Using a Benchmark

Perimeter means the distance around a figure. One way to find the perimeter of a figure is to add the lengths of the sides.

10 + 4 + 10 + 4 = **28 ft** (rectangle 10 ft by 4 ft)

The perimeter is 28 ft.

Find the perimeter.

1. 8 ft, 3 ft, 3 ft, 8 ft — 22 ft
2. 12 in., 20 in., 20 in., 12 in. — 64 in.

Look for an object that is about 1 inch in length. Using that length as a **benchmark**, you can estimate length and width.

3. length 1 in.; width 1 in.; perimeter 4 in.

Use your own benchmark to estimate the length, width, and perimeter of these objects. Check your estimates by measuring with a ruler.

4. your math textbook — Answers will vary.
5. a sheet of paper
6. an envelope

82 Use with text pages 222-223. RS-4

Challenges

Life Skills 8-9

Name ____________

Gardening Puzzle

Julie and Sosuke have 100 m of wire fencing. They have made several plans for a vegetable garden. Ring the plans that have perimeters small enough to use the fencing. (You may need to write in the lengths of some sides.)

Plan A — Perimeter: 120 m
Plan B — Perimeter: 120 m
Plan C — Perimeter: 100 m
Plan D — Perimeter: 120 m
Plan E — Perimeter: 100 m
Plan F — Perimeter: 120 m
Plan G — Perimeter: 100 m
Plan H — Perimeter: 110 m
Plan I — Perimeter: 120 m

82 Use with text page 222. CS-4

OPTIONS FOR INDIVIDUAL NEEDS

Basic

Exercises 1-3; 1-3
Skills Bank, pp. 461, 462
More Practice, p. 519, sets B, C

Supplements
Reteaching 82 or
Practice 82
Thinking Skills 82

Average

Exercises 1-3; 1-3
Skills Bank, p. 462
More Practice, p. 519, sets B, C

Supplements
Practice 82
Challenges 82 or
Thinking Skills 82

Extended

Exercises 1-3; 1-3

Supplements
Challenges 82
Thinking Skills 82

Other Resources:

Problem-Solving Experiences in Mathematics, Grade 4, Problem 61
Kids Are Consumers, Too!, p. 27
Make It Simpler, A Practical Guide to Problem Solving in Mathematics, p. 225
Using the Math Explorer Calculator: A Sourcebook for Teachers, Chapter 14

LESSON PLAN 8-9

OBJECTIVE 8-9
To measure perimeter and to add to find perimeter

Materials: calculators, TA 12 (Centimeter Graph Paper)

1. MOTIVATE AND TEACH

LEARN ABOUT IT

EXPLORE ► **Link addition to finding shapes with a perimeter of 18.** (Possible response: Find combinations of addends with a sum of 18.)

TALK ABOUT IT ► **Decide whether a square and a triangle could both have the same perimeter.** (Yes, as long as the sum of the lengths is the same.)
Student Edition answers: **1.** Not if you can use only whole numbers. Yes, if each side is $4\frac{1}{2}$ yd. **2.** not always; The same perimeter can enclose different shapes.

2. CHECK UNDERSTANDING

ERROR ALERT Failing to add all sides when finding the perimeter of a polygon.

3. PRACTICE AND APPLY

Basic	1-3
Average	1-3
Extended	1-3

PRACTICE

Explain how you could use multiplication to find the perimeter of the park in Problem 3. (Multiply 155 × 4, because all 4 sides of a square are equal.)

Perimeter

LEARN ABOUT IT

The distance around a figure or an object is its **perimeter**.

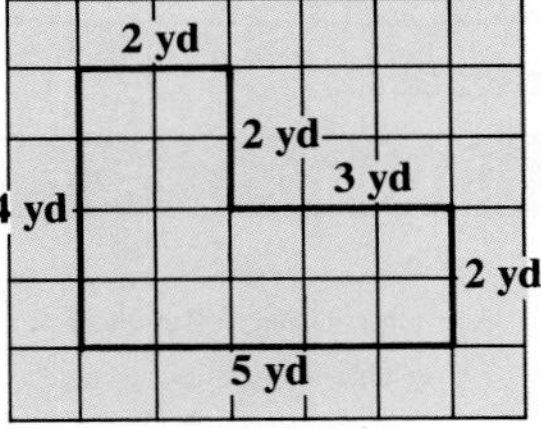

EXPLORE Use Graph Paper
Look at Rita's plan for a dog pen. The perimeter is 18 yd. Use graph paper to draw other plans for a dog pen with this perimeter. Use whole numbers for each side.

TALK ABOUT IT See teaching notes.

1. Can you make a square dog pen with a perimeter of 18 yd? If so, tell the length of each side.
2. Do figures with the same perimeter have the same shape? Explain why or why not.

One way to find the perimeter of a figure or an object is to add the lengths of the sides.

48 ft / 17 ft / 17 ft / 48 ft

48 + 17 + 48 + 17 = 130 ft.
The perimeter is 130 ft.

To find the perimeter on the calculator, use this key code.
[ON/AC] side length [+] side length [+] side length [+] side length [=]

PRACTICE

1. Choose one of these nonstandard units and measure the perimeter of your classroom.
   a. your step b. string as long as your armspan

Use a calculator to find the perimeters. Answers will vary.

2. 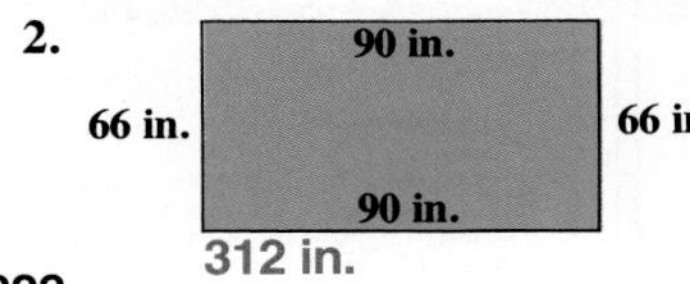

312 in.

3. Rita walks her dog around a square park. Each side of the park is 155 ft long. What is the perimeter of the park? 620 ft

More Practice, page 519, set B

TEACHING OPTIONS

RETEACHING TIPS Students who have difficulty making reasonable estimates should physically measure objects by holding apart their arms to represent 1 ft or 1 yd. This can help students internalize measurements and sharpen their estimation skills. Assign Reteaching Supplement 82.

ENRICHMENT Have students work in pairs. Each partner draws 3 unusual polygons along the lines of centimeter graph paper (TA 12), pretending that each graph-paper square represents 1 ft. Partners exchange papers and find the perimeters of each other's polygons. (Answers will vary.)

Estimating Length, Width, and Perimeter
Using a Benchmark

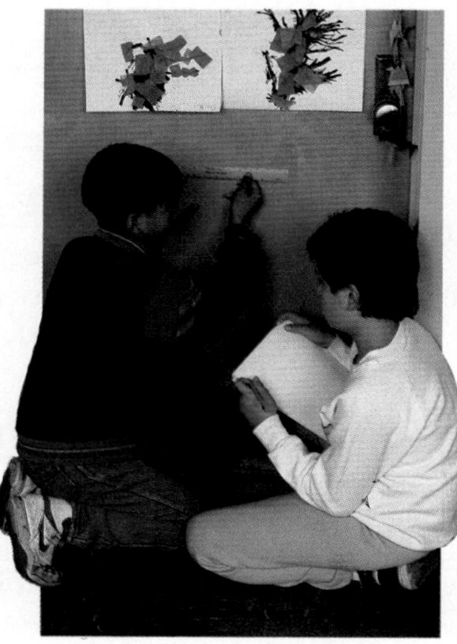

LEARN ABOUT IT

EXPLORE **Use Classroom Objects**
Work in groups. Without leaving your chairs, look for an object about 1 ft or 1 yd long. Thinking of that object, estimate the room's length and width. Check your estimates by measuring with a tape measure.

TALK ABOUT IT See teaching notes.

1. How did you make your estimates? What object did you use?
2. How could you use your estimates to estimate the perimeter of the classroom?
3. What other objects could help you estimate lengths in feet and yards?
4. Would the length of a paperclip or a pencil be a good unit to use as a benchmark for estimating feet and yards? Explain your reasoning.

If you know that the length of an object is close to a given unit, you can use it as a **benchmark**. Then you imagine using that object as the unit and count about how many times it is used.

PRACTICE Answers will vary.

Estimate the length, width, and perimeter of these objects in feet. Use a benchmark. Check your estimates by measuring with a tape measure.

1. Chalkboard
2. Window
3. Door

More Practice, page 519, set C

OBJECTIVE 8-9 To estimate length, width, and perimeter using a benchmark

Materials: TA 17 (Rulers)
Grouping Suggestion: small groups

1. Motivate and Teach

LEARN ABOUT IT

EXPLORE ▶ **Identify classroom objects that are about 1 ft or 1 yd long.** (Answers will vary.)

TALK ABOUT IT Student Edition answers: **1.** Answers will vary. **2.** Find the total of the estimated lengths and widths. **3.** Answers will vary.

2. Check Understanding

ERROR ALERT Greatly overestimating or underestimating.

3. Practice and Apply

Basic	1-3
Average	1-3
Extended	1-3

PRACTICE

Explain how to choose a benchmark. (Find something that is about 1 ft long, then visually measure with that object.)

Close and Assess

WRITE WHAT YOU THINK
Have students write a step-by-step explanation of how to find the perimeter of a triangle whose sides all measure 7 in. Then have them explain how to estimate the perimeter of an art table using a paintbrush for a benchmark. (21 in; answers may vary.)

QUICK QUIZ

1. Find the perimeter of a square garden 215 ft long on each side.
2. Estimate your desk's perimeter in inches, then find the exact perimeter.
(**1.** 860 ft **2.** Answers will vary.)

LESSON OPTIONS 8-10

Problem Solving: Data from a Chart

OBJECTIVE 8-10 To solve problems using data from a chart

PREBOOK ACTIVITIES

QUICK REVIEW

Add or subtract.

1. 421 − 188 (233)
2. 1,729 + 3,752 (5,481)
3. 354,280 + 70,946 (425,226)
4. 1,877 − 1,648 (229)
5. 1,580 + 165 (1,745)
6. 20,000 − 4,923 (15,077)

PRIOR KNOWLEDGE

Have students recall where they have seen data displayed in charts. (Answers will vary. Samples: sports statistics, population charts, price lists) Have students summarize parts that all charts contain, regardless of the kind of information they display. (titles, headings, facts)

COMMUNICATION

Writing Math Have each student create a chart that contains these elements: title, headings, and the name and age of each person in the student's immediate family. When students finish, have them explain how they organized the information on their charts. (Methods may vary.)

EXPLORE AND CONNECT

COOPERATIVE ACTIVITY

Grouping Suggestion: small groups

Find the difference in diameter between the largest planet and the smallest planet. Use the Science Data Bank chart on page 470.

TEACHING ACTIONS

Have groups discuss how to use the chart to find the necessary data and to choose a reasonable solution method.

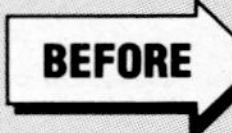

▶ **Explain what you need to do to find the answer.** (Compare the diameters of the biggest planet and the smallest planet.)

▶ **Analyze the chart to locate the data you need.** (Use the column headed *Diameter in km* to find the greatest and smallest numbers; read across the rows for the names of the 2 planets that match the numbers.)

▶ **Explain a strategy for solving the problem.** (Find the data, then subtract to compare.)

▶ **Identify the exact data you need.** (Jupiter, the largest planet, has a diameter of 143,000 km; Pluto, the smallest planet, has a diameter of 3,000 km.)

▶ **Decide on a reasonable calculation method.** (Methods may vary. Mental math makes sense.)

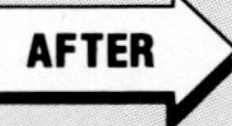

▶ **Evaluate your solution to see if it makes sense.** (143,000 - 3,000 is 140,000; add 140,000 + 3,000 to check.)

CONNECTIONS Use these anytime.

Problem of the Day

Satellites Use the Science Data Bank chart on page 470 to find the total number of satellites of all the planets in our solar system. (60)

Subject Integration

Social Studies Use an almanac to find the population of your state in 1970 and in 1980. Determine how much the population changed during that time. (Answers will vary.)

Number Sense

Mental Math Risa began with 12,345 and added a number to get 23,456. Then she added the same number to that sum to get 34,567. Find a number pattern, find the missing addend, then predict how much longer Risa can continue the pattern. (Each new sum consists of consecutive digits; 11, 111; she can continue only with 45,678 and 56,789.)

Classwork and Homework Supplements

Practice

Problem Solving 8-10

Name

Data from a Chart

Facts About 10 States

State	Order Admitted to the Union	Length	Width
New Mexico	47	395 mi	355 mi
New York	11	320 mi	310 mi
North Carolina	12	503 mi	188 mi
North Dakota	39	350 mi	210 mi
Ohio	17	255 mi	215 mi
Oklahoma	46	470 mi	205 mi
Oregon	33	395 mi	295 mi
Pennsylvania	2	304 mi	174 mi
Rhode Island	13	48 mi	37 mi
South Carolina	8	250 mi	200 mi

Solve using data from the chart.

1. According to the order of admission, how many states earlier was New York admitted than Ohio? 6 states
2. What is the difference in miles between the greatest width and the smallest width of the states shown in the chart? 318 mi
3. How much longer is North Dakota than Pennsylvania? 46 mi
4. Which 2 states have the same length? New Mexico, Oregon
5. How many states were admitted between South Carolina and North Carolina? 3 states
6. Which state has the biggest difference between its length and its width? North Carolina

PS-4 Use with text pages 224-225. 83

Building Thinking Skills

Data Analysis 8-10

Name

Categorizing the Lanigan Lions

The Lanigan Lions Basketball Team

Name	Age	Height	Weight	Points Per Game
Marcy	9	4 ft 1 in.	61 pounds	12
Barney	10	4 ft 5 in.	75 pounds	8
Kelly	9	4 ft 6 in.	73 pounds	13
José	8	4 ft 2 in.	66 pounds	16
Charles	9	4 ft 2 in.	71 pounds	11

Solve these problems. Use the data from the chart.

1. Who is the tallest player on the team? Kelly
   How much taller is that player than the shortest player? 5 inches
2. Which player is 49 inches tall? Marcy
   Which player is 54 inches tall? Kelly
3. The difference in weight between the lightest player and the heaviest player is twice as much as the difference in weight between which two players? Kelly and José
4. Who scores more points per game, the oldest boy or the shorter of the two girls? Name the player. Marcy
5. Who is the leading scorer on the team? José
   Does that player score twice as many points as anybody? yes If so, who? Barney

TS-4 Use with text pages 224-225. 83

Reteaching

Skills Review 8-10

Name

Problem Solving: Data from a Chart

A chart is a way to organize data. The chart below describes 4 passenger ocean liners.

Ship	Length	Width	Passengers
Queen Elizabeth II	963 ft	105 ft	2,025
Canberra	818 ft	102 ft	2,400
Oriana	804 ft	97 ft	2,216
United States	990 ft	102 ft	1,930

What is the difference between the length of the *Canberra* and the length of the *Oriana?*

Find *Canberra* in the chart. Go across to the length column. → Find *Oriana* in the chart. Go across to the length column. → Subtract to find the difference.

818 ft | 804 ft | 818 − 804 = 14 ft

The *Canberra* is 14 feet longer.

Solve using data from the chart above.

1. How much wider is the widest ship than the narrowest?
   widest ship 105 ft
   narrowest ship 97 ft
   difference 8 ft
2. The length of the *Rotterdam* is 848 ft. How much longer is this than the *Canberra?* 30 ft
3. Does the widest ship carry the most passengers? no
4. What is the total passenger capacity for the *Canberra* and the *United States?* 4,330

RS-4 Use with text pages 224-225. 83

Challenges

Data Analysis 8-10

Name

Give Me a Sign

Look at the price tables posted at Rosita's sign shop. Use the tables to solve each problem below.

Banners and Signs

Type	Material	5 ft long	10 ft long	20 ft long	Lettering
Regular Banner	vinyl	$42.50	$60.25	$89.95	See chart below
Fancy Banner	vinyl	$99.99	$117.74	$147.44	
Temporary Sign	paper	$4.29 per ft			FREE

Lettering

Height of Letter	Cost per Letter
1 inch	$0.65
3 inches	$1.35
6 inches	$2.20
10 inches	$4.81

How much would each cost?

1. 10 ft — WELCOME HOME — 10-in. letters
   a regular banner $113.16
   a temporary sign $42.90
2. 5 ft — GRAND OPENING SALE — 6-in. letters
   a fancy banner $135.19
   a temporary sign $21.45
3. You need a 20-foot banner to announce the School Fair on May 15. Decide what the banner will look like and then calculate the cost. (Include material, length, height of letters, and price.) Answers will vary.

CS-4 Use with text pages 224-225. 83

Options for Individual Needs

Basic

Exercises 1-4, 6-9
Skills Bank, pp. 462, 463, 464
Calculator Bank, pp. 485, 486
Computer Bank, p. 492
More Practice, p. 519, set D

Supplements
Reteaching 83 or
Practice 83

Average

Exercises 1-9
Skills Bank, pp. 462, 464
Calculator Bank, pp. 485, 486
Computer Bank, p. 492
More Practice, p. 519, set D

Supplements
Practice 83
Challenges 83 or
Thinking Skills 83

Extended

Exercises 1-9
Calculator Bank, pp. 485, 486
Computer Bank, p. 492

Supplements
Challenges 83
Thinking Skills 83

Other Resources:
Problem-Solving Experiences in Mathematics, Grade 4, Problem 148
Kids Are Consumers, Too!, pp. 35, 37, 38
Make It Simpler, A Practical Guide to Problem Solving in Mathematics, p. 326
Using the Math Explorer Calculator: A Sourcebook for Teachers

LESSON PLAN 8-10

OBJECTIVE 8-10
To solve problems using data from a chart

Materials: index cards, calculators

Grouping Suggestion: pairs

1. MOTIVATE AND TEACH

LEARN ABOUT IT

BEFORE

► **Explain what the question asks you to do.** (Find the heights of the tallest buildings in Houston and Dallas, then compare them.)

► **Explain how the chart is organized.** (It gives the 6 largest cities in Texas in population order, with facts about each city's total rainfall per year and, for most, the city's tallest building.)

► **Decide which part of the chart has the data you need.** (*Tallest Building* column)

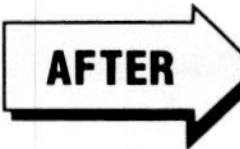
DURING

► **Once you locate the data, decide how to use it.** (Subtract 939 ft from 1,002 ft.)

► **Justify the operation.** (Subtract to compare the heights.)

AFTER

► **Evaluate your solution to see if it makes sense.** (The Texas Commerce Tower is just over 1,000 ft high; First Republic Bank Plaza is slightly under 1,000 ft, so a difference of 63 ft makes sense.)

2. CHECK UNDERSTANDING

TRY IT OUT

ERROR ALERT Selecting the wrong data from the chart.

Problem Solving
Data from a Chart

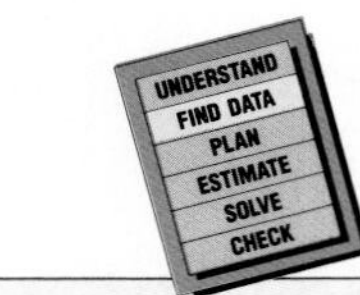

To solve some problems, you need to sort through numbers in a chart to find the data you need.

How much higher is the tallest building in Houston than the tallest building in Dallas?

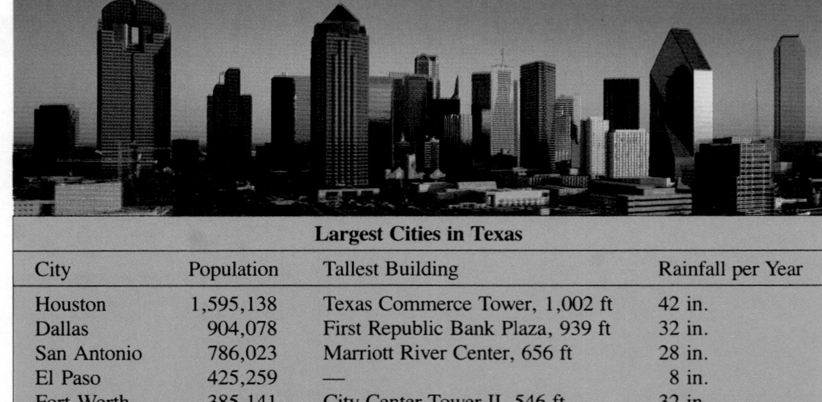

Largest Cities in Texas

City	Population	Tallest Building	Rainfall per Year
Houston	1,595,138	Texas Commerce Tower, 1,002 ft	42 in.
Dallas	904,078	First Republic Bank Plaza, 939 ft	32 in.
San Antonio	786,023	Marriott River Center, 656 ft	28 in.
El Paso	425,259	—	8 in.
Fort Worth	385,141	City Center Tower II, 546 ft	32 in.
Austin	345,890	One American Center, 395 ft	42 in.

I'll find the data I need in the chart.

The Texas Commerce Tower is 1,002 ft high. The First Republic Bank Plaza is 939 ft high.

Now I'll solve the problem.

$1,002 - 939 = 63$

The tallest building in Houston is 63 feet taller than the tallest building in Dallas.

TRY IT OUT

Solve using data from the chart.

1. What is the total height of the Marriott River Center and the City Center Tower II? **1,202 ft**
2. Which cities get 4 times the amount of rainfall per year that El Paso gets? **Dallas and Fort Worth**

224

TEACHING OPTIONS

RETEACHING TIPS Have students use index cards as place markers to highlight 1 row or column at a time. This should help them focus on finding the correct data. Assign Reteaching Supplement 83.

COMPUTER **Zandar III & IV, SVE, Copyright 1984** For all, but begin with the tutorial. Students find 2 unknown objects of the magic key to catch Wargo in the Dragon's Maze, testing to determine the rule of the unknown object. Game takes 20 min, tutorial takes 5 min.

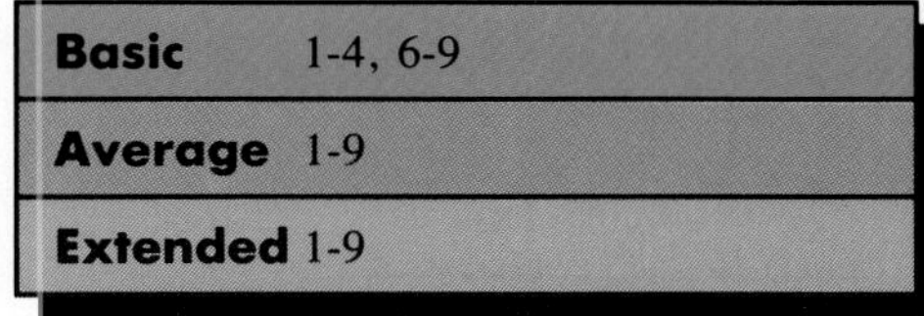

MIXED PRACTICE

Solve these problems. Use the data from the chart.

1. Which building is 183 feet shorter than 3 times the height of One American Center in Austin? **Texas Commerce Tower**
2. What is the difference between the rainfall in the wettest and the driest cities in the chart? **34 in.**
3. The tallest building in the United States is the Sears Tower in Chicago at 1,454 feet. How much taller is this than the Texas Commerce Tower? **452 ft**
4. Houston and Dallas have a total of 64 universities and colleges. Dallas has 10 more than Houston. How many universities and colleges does Houston have? **27 universities and colleges**
5. How much higher is the tallest building in the table than the shortest? **607 ft**
6. Alonso Alvarez de Pineda of Spain mapped the Texas coast in 1519. The Texas Revolution against Mexico began 316 years later. In 1845 Texas became a state. What year did the Texas Revolution begin? **1835**
7. The highest point in Texas is 8,751 feet at Guadalupe Peak. The highest point in the United States is Mt. McKinley. Mt. McKinley is 11,569 feet higher than Guadalupe Peak. How high is Mt. McKinley? **20,320 ft**
8. What is the total amount of rainfall for Austin, Houston, and San Antonio? **112 in.**
9. **Using a Calculator** What is the total population of the three largest cities in Texas? **3,285,239**

More Practice, page 519, set D

3. Practice and Apply

Basic	1-4, 6-9
Average	1-9
Extended	1-9

Sample Solutions: See p. T79.

MIXED PRACTICE

► **Analyze why Problem 1 is a multiple-step problem.** (First you multiply, then you subtract.)

► **Compare and contrast Problems 2 and 8.** (Both need data from the *Rainfall per Year* column of the chart, but they require opposite operations to solve.)

► **Justify the operation to use in Problem 3.** (Subtract to make a comparison.)

► **Explain how Problems 4 and 6 are related.** (None requires data from the chart; all the necessary data are given in each problem.)

Close and Assess

SHOW WHAT YOU KNOW

Have students work in pairs. Each partner uses these facts about past Texas state populations to make a chart. Then each poses a question for the other partner to solve. 1850: 212,592 1860: 604,215 1870: 818,579 1880: 1,591,749 (Check charts. Answers will vary.)

Quick Quiz

Using the chart on page 224, work with a calculator to find the combined population of Dallas and Fort Worth. Then compare it to Houston's population. (1,289,219; It is less.)

Estimating and Measuring Capacity

OBJECTIVE 8-11 To estimate, measure, and compare capacity using nonstandard units and gallon, half gallon,

PREBOOK ACTIVITIES

QUICK REVIEW

Find the products.

1. 4 × 8 (32) **2.** 8 × 12 (96) **3.** 2 × 32 (64)
4. 7 × 4 (28) **5.** 16 × 2 (32) **6.** 2 × 2 × 2 (8)
7. 4 × 3 × 2 (24) **8.** 2 × 4 × 2 (16) **9.** 2 × 4 × 8 (64)

PRIOR KNOWLEDGE

Tell students that certain customary units refer to how much liquid a container can hold. Generate with them a list of any liquid measurement units they know. (Possible answers: fluid ounce, cup, pint, quart, gallon) Have students associate units with familiar containers they see at home or at school. (Answers may vary; samples include half-gallon milk cartons, gallon cider jugs, cup milk cartons in the lunchroom.) Tell students that in this lesson they will explore some ways these standard units relate to one another.

COMMUNICATION

Discussing, Reading, and Writing Math Write **fl oz, c, pt, qt, half gal,** and **gal** on the chalkboard. Ask students to explain what they have in common. (All are liquid measure abbreviations.) Have students copy the abbreviations into their Math Journals, along with the full name of each unit. (**fluid ounce, cup, pint, quart, half gallon, gallon**) Ask students why it would be important to include *fl* when measuring liquids in *fluid* ounces. (Possible answer: It is important to show the difference between fluid ounces and ounces that measure parts of a pound.)

EXPLORE AND CONNECT

Materials: containers for standard liquid measure (measuring cup set, c, pt, qt, half gal, gal); extra gallon containers as pitchers; water; TA 2 (Number Cubes with 2, 2, 4, 4, 8, 8)
Grouping Suggestion: small cooperative learning groups
Students explore equivalent relationships among units of liquid capacity. A student chooses the **pint, quart, half gallon,** or **gallon** as the goal container. Another student rolls a number. He or she selects a container to use as a standard unit, then measures water in the unit the number of times rolled in an attempt to fill the container. For example, suppose the goal is *half gallon*. If Maria rolls 8, she may try to measure 8 *pints* of water to fill the *half gallon*. (8 *pints* will be too much.) If she misjudges, the next student looks for a better unit to use 8 of, to fill the *half gallon*. Members should have a turn at each task. Conclude by having groups share any equivalencies they discovered, such as 2 *c* = 1 *pt*.

CONNECTIONS Use these anytime.

Problem of the Day

Soup Cans Leah pours the contents of a can of soup into a cooking pot. Then she adds 1 can of water to the soup to make four 8-oz servings. What is the capacity of the soup can? (16 fl oz or 1 pt)

Patterns

Times What? Find and continue the pattern: 1, 2, 4, 8, 16, ______, ______, ______, ______, ______. (Each successive number doubles; 32, 64, 128, 256, 512)

Math Connection

Problem Solving A pancake mix uses 3 fl oz of oil for every 2 c of milk. How many batches of pancakes can be made with a half gal of milk? How much oil will be needed? (4 batches; 12 fl oz of oil)

quart, pint, cup, fluid ounce.

Classwork and Homework Supplements

Practice

Life Skills 8-11

Name ______

Capacity

Multiply to write these amounts another way.

1. Soup — 2 gal = 8 qt
2. Lemonade — 3 c = 24 fl oz
3. Maple Syrup — 3 qt = 6 pt
4. Orange Juice — 2 half gal = 4 qt
5. Cream — 6 pt = 12 c
6. Motor Oil — 1 qt = 4 c

84 Use with text pages 226–227. PS-4

Building Thinking Skills

Math Reasoning 8-11

Name ______

Analyzing a Capacity Problem

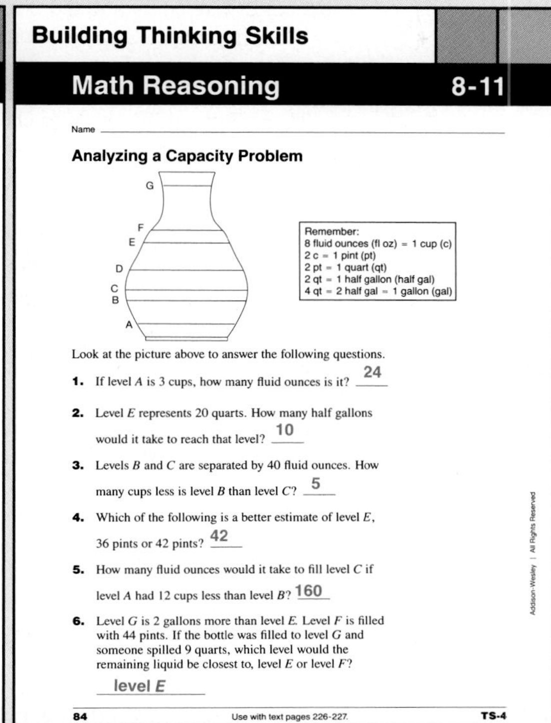

Look at the picture above to answer the following questions.

1. If level *A* is 3 cups, how many fluid ounces is it? 24
2. Level *E* represents 20 quarts. How many half gallons would it take to reach that level? 10
3. Levels *B* and *C* are separated by 40 fluid ounces. How many cups less is level *B* than level *C*? 5
4. Which of the following is a better estimate of level *E*, 36 pints or 42 pints? 42
5. How many fluid ounces would it take to fill level *C* if level *A* had 12 cups less than level *B*? 160
6. Level *G* is 2 gallons more than level *E*. Level *F* is filled with 44 pints. If the bottle was filled to level *G* and someone spilled 9 quarts, which level would the remaining liquid be closest to, level *E* or level *F*? level *E*

84 Use with text pages 226–227. TS-4

Reteaching

Skills Review 8-11

Name ______

Estimating and Measuring Capacity

1 pint = 2 cups

1 quart = 2 pints

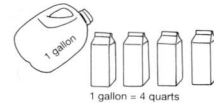

1 quart = 4 cups

1 gallon = 4 quarts

Multiply to find the relationships.

1. 1 gallon = 4 quarts, so (2 times as many) 2 gallons = 8 quarts
2. 1 quart = 4 cups, so (3 times as many) 3 quarts = 12 cups
3. 1 quart = 2 pints, so (2 times as many) 2 quarts = 4 pints
4. 1 pint = 2 cups, so 3 pints = 6 cups
5. 1 quart = 4 cups, so 2 quarts = 8 cups
6. 1 quart = 2 pints, so 3 quarts = 6 pints

Ring the better estimate.

7. water in a sink — 5 pints or (5 gallons)
8. water in an aquarium — 10 cups or (10 gallons)
9. full glass of milk — (2 cups) or 2 pints
10. juice in a pitcher — 2 cups or (2 quarts)

84 Use with text pages 226–227. RS-4

Challenges

Math Reasoning 8-11

Name ______

Make Them Equal

You want an equal amount of juice in each pitcher. Ring the letter of the directions that tell how to do this.

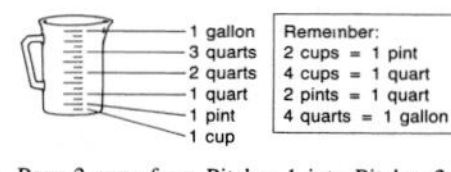

1. Pitcher 1: 8 cups; Pitcher 2: 6 cups
   - A Pour 2 cups from Pitcher 1 into Pitcher 2.
   - B Pour 1 cup from Pitcher 2 into Pitcher 1.
   - (C) Pour 1 cup from Pitcher 1 into Pitcher 2.
2. Pitcher 1: 5 pints; Pitcher 2: 3 quarts
   - (A) Pour 1 cup from Pitcher 2 into Pitcher 1.
   - B Pour 1 pint from Pitcher 2 into Pitcher 1.
   - C Pour 2 pints from Pitcher 1 into Pitcher 2.
3. Pitcher 1: 2 quarts; Pitcher 2: 3 quarts; Pitcher 3: 1 quart
   - A Pour 2 quarts from Pitcher 2 into Pitcher 3.
   - B Pour 1 quart from Pitcher 2 into Pitcher 3. and 1 quart from Pitcher 1 into Pitcher 3.
   - (C) Pour 1 quart from Pitcher 2 into Pitcher 3.
4. Pitcher 1: 3 quarts; Pitcher 2: 3 pints; Pitcher 3: 3 quarts
   - A Pour 1 quart from Pitcher 1 into Pitcher 2.
   - (B) Pour 1 pint from Pitcher 1 into Pitcher 2 and 1 pint from Pitcher 3 into Pitcher 2.
   - C Pour 1 cup from Pitcher 1 into Pitcher 2 and 1 cup from Pitcher 3 into Pitcher 2.
5. Pitcher 1: 1 pint; Pitcher 2: 7 pints; Pitcher 3: 7 pints

   Fill in the missing amounts so that the water in these pitchers will be equal.

   Pour 2 pints from Pitcher 2 into Pitcher 1 and pour 2 pints from Pitcher 3 into Pitcher 1.

84 Use with text pages 226–227. CS-4

Options for Individual Needs

Basic

Exercises 1-12, 15-17
Skills Bank, p. 465
Computer Bank, p. 494
More Practice, p. 519, set E

Supplements
Reteaching 84 or
Practice 84

Average

Exercises 1-18
Skills Bank, p. 465
Computer Bank, p. 494
More Practice, p. 519, set E

Supplements
Practice 84
Challenges 84 or
Thinking Skills 84

Extended

Exercises 1-12, 15-18
Computer Bank, p. 494

Supplements
Challenges 84
Thinking Skills 84

Other Resources:

Problem-Solving Experiences in Mathematics, Grade 4, Problem 68
Kids Are Consumers, Too!, p. 26
Make It Simpler, A Practical Guide to Problem Solving in Mathematics, p. 231
Using the Math Explorer Calculator: A Sourcebook for Teachers, Chapter 14

LESSON PLAN 8-11

OBJECTIVE 8-11
To estimate, measure, and compare capacity using nonstandard units and gallon, half gallon, quart, pint, cup, fluid ounce

Materials: nonstandard containers and measuring cups; standard c, pt, qt, and gal containers; empty half-gal cartons

Grouping Suggestion: small groups

1. MOTIVATE AND TEACH

LEARN ABOUT IT

EXPLORE ► **Which containers allowed you to make more accurate estimates?** (Possible response: the ones with shapes more like the milk carton)
► **From which containers was it most difficult to make estimates?** (Possible response: the ones with irregular shapes)

TALK ABOUT IT ► **Generalize about how many larger or smaller containers fill any large container.** (You need more smaller or fewer larger containers to fill any large container.)
► **Explain why you might want to change units.** (To compare amounts, the units need to be the same.)
► **Explain how to find a factor by which to multiply the larger unit when you want to know the number of smaller units.** (Use the number of smaller units contained in one of the larger units.)
Student Edition answer: Answers will vary based on containers used.

2. CHECK UNDERSTANDING

TRY IT OUT

ERROR ALERT Multiplying by the wrong factor when attempting to change units. Making multiplication errors.

Estimating and Measuring Capacity

LEARN ABOUT IT

EXPLORE Use Nonstandard Units
Work in groups. Choose a container to use as a nonstandard unit. Estimate how many times you could pour that filled container into a milk carton. Then fill the milk carton to check your estimate. Do this again with the other nonstandard units.

TALK ABOUT IT See teaching notes.

Which of the units gave the largest measure for the milk carton? Which gave the smallest? Explain.

These containers have the customary units of capacity.

Cup

Pint

Quart

Half gallon

Gallon

Here are some relationships between these units.

8 fluid ounces (fl oz) = 1 cup (c)
2 c = 1 pint (pt)
2 pt = 1 quart (qt)
2 qt = 1 half gallon (half gal)
4 qt = 2 half gal = 1 gallon (gal)

You can find more relationships between the units. Multiply the larger unit to change it into the smaller unit.

3 gallons = ||||| quarts

Gallons is the larger unit, so I multiply 3 × 4 qt.

3 gallons = 12 quarts

TRY IT OUT

Multiply to find the relationships.

1. 3 gal = ||||| qt 12 **2.** 4 pt = ||||| c 8 **3.** 5 c = ||||| fl oz 40

226

TEACHING OPTIONS

RETEACHING TIPS Have students physically count and compare units. Some may need only to handle related containers to grasp their relationship. Others may need to pour water from one container to another to understand how they relate. Assign Reteaching Supplement 84.

ENRICHMENT Have students use a calculator to solve this problem: *Dr. R. Oma has created a 5-gallon batch of his latest perfume. He plans to give away 1-fl oz samples to attract new customers. How many samples can he prepare from this batch of perfume?* (640 samples)

PRACTICE

Multiply to write these amounts another way.

1. Sour cream

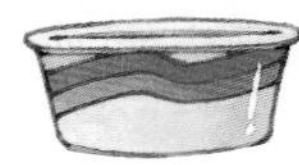

2 pt = |||| c **4**

2. Milk

3 half gal = |||| qt **6**

3. Juice

8 c = |||| fl oz **64**

APPLY

MATH REASONING What is the better estimate for the amount?

4. Detergent **20 fl oz**

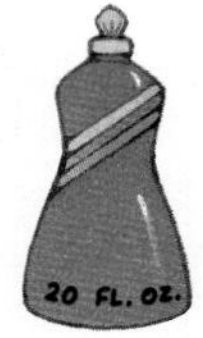

(a) about 2 cups
b about 1 cup

5. Cider **9 qts**

9 QTS.

(a) about 2 gallons
b about 3 gallons

6. Cottage cheese

1 pt each

a about 3 qt
b about 4 qt
equally good estimates

PROBLEM SOLVING

7. Ted needs 9 cups of yogurt. The container of yogurt has 5 pints in it. Does he have enough yogurt? **yes**

8. **Extra Data** Your recipe calls for 7 c of apple juice and 9 c of orange juice. How many fluid ounces of apple juice do you need? **56 fluid ounces**

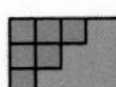
MIXED REVIEW

Find the product.

9. 36×29 = **1,044**
10. 47×81 = **3,807**
11. 70×64 = **4,480**
12. 598×27 = **16,146**
13. 246×33 = **8,118**
14. 805×69 = **55,545**

Round to the highest place or nearest dollar. Then estimate the product.

15. 5×47 **250**
16. $6 \times \$7.81$ **$48**
17. 9×412 **3,600**
18. 7×387 **2,800**

More Practice, page 519, set E

3. Practice and Apply

Basic	1-12, 15-17
Average	1-18
Extended	1-12, 15-18

PRACTICE

Look at Exercises 1-3. Which unit is larger in each exercise? (pt; half gal; c)

APPLY

MATH REASONING ► **Justify whether to round up or down in Exercise 4.** (20 fl oz = 2½ cups; round halfway amounts up, so round to 3 cups.)

PROBLEM SOLVING ► **Explain whether to change the unit in Problem 7 to pints or cups.** (cups, because it is the smaller unit and the unit with which Ted needs to work)
► **Analyze Problem 8 to find unnecessary data. Explain your reasoning.** (9 c of orange juice; The problem is asking for a unit change of apple juice only.)

MIXED REVIEW ► **Explain how Exercises 9-14 differ from Exercises 15-18.** (Exercises 9-14 require exact products; Exercises 15-18 only require estimated products.)

Close and Assess

WRITE WHAT YOU THINK Ask each student to write an explanation of how to compare 3 c to 2 pt and 6 qt to 2 half gal. (Possible answer: Change to the same unit; multiply the number of larger units by the number of smaller units it contains; 3 c is less than 2 pt; 6 qt is greater than 2 half gal.)

QUICK QUIZ

Give the measurement another way.

1. 3 pt = ______ c (6)
2. 8 half gal = ______ qt (16)
3. 9 c = ______ fl oz (72)
4. 3 qt = ______ pt (6)

LESSON OPTIONS 8-12

Estimating and Measuring Weight

OBJECTIVE 8-12 To estimate, measure, and compare weights in pounds and ounces

PREBOOK ACTIVITIES

QUICK REVIEW

Find the products.

1. 4 × 16 (64) **2.** 16 × 12 (192)
3. 16 × 16 (256) **4.** 3 × 16 (48)
5. 0 × 16 (0) **6.** 100 × 16 (1,600)

PRIOR KNOWLEDGE

Have students generate a list of things whose weights they know, including the unit of measurement. (Possible answers: a fast-food sandwich such as a $\frac{1}{4}$-lb hamburger; bags of potatoes or flour in pounds; lunch carton of milk in ounces; shampoo in ounces) Then have them suggest some common temperatures they may know, including measurement units if possible. (Sample answers: average body temperature of 98.6°F; freezing point of water at 32°F)

COMMUNICATION

Discussing and Reading Math Write these measurement units and their abbreviations on the chalkboard: **pound, ounce, degree Fahrenheit, lb, oz, °F.** Have students read the measurement words aloud, then try to match each with its abbreviation. (pound/lb; ounce/oz; degree Fahrenheit/°F) Tell students that the abbreviation lb comes from the Latin word *libra,* which means "pound". The term *Fahrenheit* comes from the name of a German scientist, Gabriel Fahrenheit (1686-1736), who first organized and used this temperature scale.

EXPLORE AND CONNECT

Materials: assorted classroom objects of various weights, 1-lb and 1-oz weights or food packages, scale (optional)
Grouping Suggestion: cooperative learning pairs
Students compare and estimate weights in **pounds** and **ounces.** Pairs of students collect any 5 classroom objects of various weights. By lifting and comparing, partners estimate to determine an order by which to rank the objects from heaviest to lightest. At any point in the activity, encourage students to use the 1-**lb** and 1-**oz** weights to help them estimate and decide how an object's weight compares with 1 *pound* or 1 *ounce*. After the objects are in the chosen order, partners ask another pair to check their work. If a standard or balance scale is available, have students find the actual weights of the objects to confirm the estimated order. Conclude by having students summarize how they determined relative weight. (Methods may vary. Sample method: Hold an object in each hand.)

CONNECTIONS Use these anytime.

Problem of the Day

Heat Wave An automatic thermostat turns the air conditioner on as soon as the temperature reaches 80°F. It is 57°F now, but the weather report promises a scorcher today. How much must the temperature increase to make the air conditioner go on? (23°F)

Life Skills

Cooking Mr. Wixted's secret family recipe for "Meatloaf Delight" calls for 12 oz of chopped meat to serve 4. How much chopped meat should Mr. Wixted buy to serve 16 people? (48 oz)

Subject Integration

Fine Arts Mr. Potter buys modeling clay in 25-lb blocks. If each of his 150 art students may use 1 lb of clay per project, how many blocks of clay should he order? (6)

Temperature: Degrees Farenheit

To measure temperature in degrees Fahrenheit.

Classwork and Homework Supplements

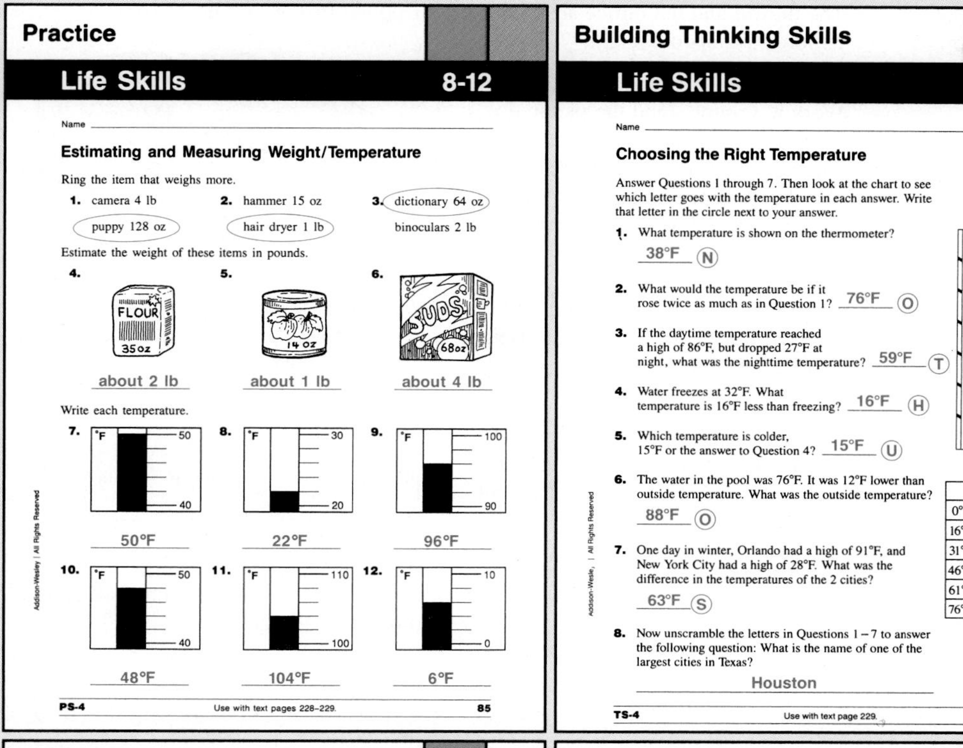

Practice

Life Skills 8-12

Name ______________________

Estimating and Measuring Weight/Temperature

Ring the item that weighs more.

1. camera 4 lb / (puppy 128 oz)
2. hammer 15 oz / (hair dryer 1 lb)
3. (dictionary 64 oz) / binoculars 2 lb

Estimate the weight of these items in pounds.

4. FLOUR 35 oz — about 2 lb
5. 14 oz — about 1 lb
6. SUDS 68 oz — about 4 lb

Write each temperature.

7. 50°F
8. 22°F
9. 96°F
10. 48°F
11. 104°F
12. 6°F

PS-4 Use with text pages 228–229. 85

Building Thinking Skills

Life Skills 8-12

Name ______________________

Choosing the Right Temperature

Answer Questions 1 through 7. Then look at the chart to see which letter goes with the temperature in each answer. Write that letter in the circle next to your answer.

1. What temperature is shown on the thermometer? 38°F (N)
2. What would the temperature be if it rose twice as much as in Question 1? 76°F (O)
3. If the daytime temperature reached a high of 86°F, but dropped 27°F at night, what was the nighttime temperature? 59°F (T)
4. Water freezes at 32°F. What temperature is 16°F less than freezing? 16°F (H)
5. Which temperature is colder, 15°F or the answer to Question 4? 15°F (U)
6. The water in the pool was 76°F. It was 12°F lower than outside temperature. What was the outside temperature? 88°F (O)
7. One day in winter, Orlando had a high of 91°F, and New York City had a high of 28°F. What was the difference in the temperatures of the 2 cities? 63°F (S)
8. Now unscramble the letters in Questions 1 – 7 to answer the following question: What is the name of one of the largest cities in Texas? Houston

°F	Letter
0° – 15°	U
16° – 30°	H
31° – 45°	N
46° – 60°	T
61° – 75°	S
76° – 90°	O

TS-4 Use with text page 229. 85

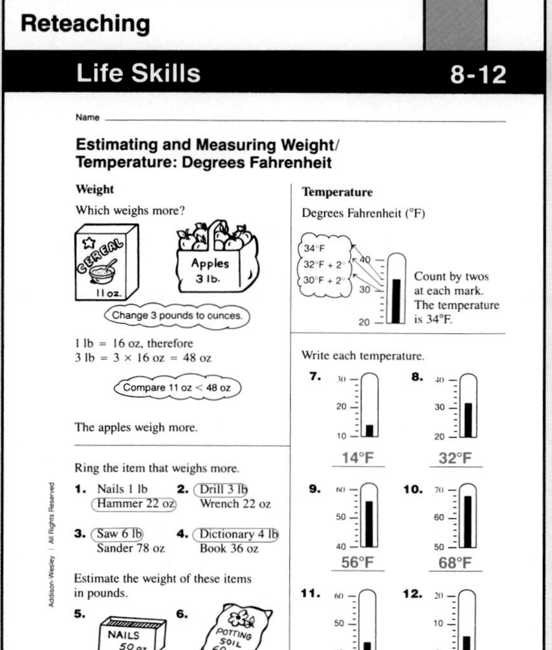

Reteaching

Life Skills 8-12

Name ______________________

Estimating and Measuring Weight/ Temperature: Degrees Fahrenheit

Weight

Which weighs more?

Change 3 pounds to ounces.

1 lb = 16 oz, therefore
3 lb = 3 × 16 oz = 48 oz

Compare 11 oz < 48 oz

The apples weigh more.

Temperature

Degrees Fahrenheit (°F)

34°F
32°F + 2°
30°F + 2°

Count by twos at each mark. The temperature is 34°F.

Write each temperature.

7. 14°F
8. 32°F
9. 56°F
10. 68°F
11. 44°F
12. 6°F

Ring the item that weighs more.

1. Nails 1 lb / (Hammer 22 oz)
2. (Drill 3 lb) / Wrench 22 oz
3. (Saw 6 lb) / Sander 78 oz
4. (Dictionary 4 lb) / Book 36 oz

Estimate the weight of these items in pounds.

5. NAILS 50 oz. — about 3 lb
6. POTTING SOIL 60 oz. — about 4 lb

RS-4 Use with text pages 228–229. 85

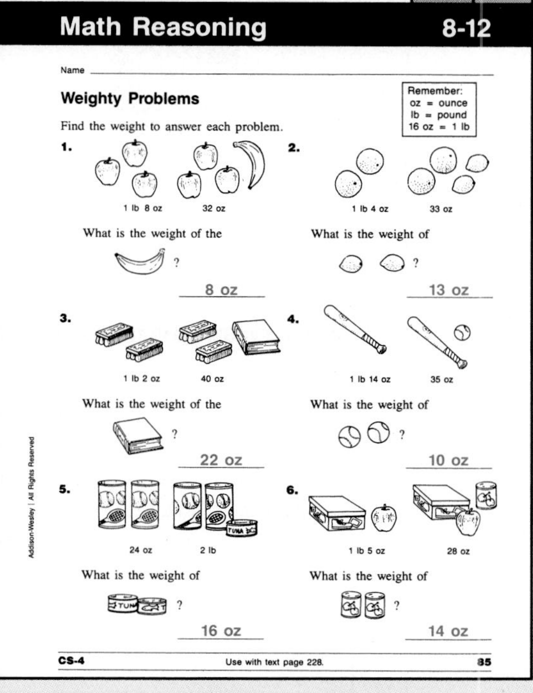

Challenges

Math Reasoning 8-12

Name ______________________

Weighty Problems

Remember:
oz = ounce
lb = pound
16 oz = 1 lb

Find the weight to answer each problem.

1. 1 lb 8 oz; 32 oz. What is the weight of the banana? 8 oz
2. 1 lb 4 oz; 33 oz. What is the weight of ? 13 oz
3. 1 lb 2 oz; 40 oz. What is the weight of the book? 22 oz
4. 1 lb 14 oz; 35 oz. What is the weight of ? 10 oz
5. 24 oz; 2 lb. What is the weight of ? 16 oz
6. 1 lb 5 oz; 28 oz. What is the weight of ? 14 oz

CS-4 Use with text page 228. 85

Options for Individual Needs

Basic

Exercises 1-6; 1-6
Skills Bank, p. 465
Calculator Bank, p. 486
More Practice, p. 520, sets A, B

Supplements
Reteaching 85 or
Practice 85

Average

Exercises 1-6; 1-6
Skills Bank, p. 465
Calculator Bank, p. 486
More Practice, p. 520, sets A, B

Supplements
Practice 85
Challenges 85 or
Thinking Skills 85

Extended

Exercises 1-6; 1-6
Calculator Bank, p. 486

Supplements
Challenges 85
Thinking Skills 85

Other Resources:
Problem-Solving Experiences in Mathematics, Grade 4, Problems 64, 65, 114
Kids Are Consumers, Too!, p. 173
Make It Simpler, A Practical Guide to Problem Solving in Mathematics, p. 222
Using the Math Explorer Calculator: A Sourcebook for Teachers, Chapter 14

LESSON PLAN 8-12

OBJECTIVE 8-12
To estimate, measure, and compare weights in pounds and ounces

Materials: scale

Grouping Suggestion: small groups

1. MOTIVATE AND TEACH

LEARN ABOUT IT

EXPLORE ► **Decide which object is likely to weigh the most.** (probably the book)

TALK ABOUT IT ► **Explain how pounds and ounces relate.** 1 lb is equal to 16 oz)
Student Edition answers: **1.** Use a known weight as a benchmark for comparing to other objects. **2.** 32 erasers

2. CHECK UNDERSTANDING

ERROR ALERT Failing to convert to like units or converting incorrectly.

3. PRACTICE AND APPLY

Basic	1-6
Average	1-6
Extended	1-6

PRACTICE

How would you begin to compare the amounts in Exercise 1 to 3? (Change pounds to ounces so you can compare like units.) *What relationship do you use to change pounds to ounces?* (1 lb = 16 oz)

Estimating and Measuring Weight

LEARN ABOUT IT

The **pound** and the **ounce** are the customary units of weight.

1 pound (lb) = 16 ounces (oz)

EXPLORE Use a Scale
Work in groups. Find the pictured objects in your classroom. Estimate whether the weight of each object is closer to 1 ounce or closer to 1 pound. Check by weighing each object on a scale.

TALK ABOUT IT See teaching notes.

1. How can you use the weight of these objects to estimate the weight of other objects?
2. Two erasers weigh 1 oz. About how many erasers would it take to weigh 1 lb?

To compare measurements of weight, you must often change the units. One way to do that is to multiply the larger unit to change it into the smaller unit.

Which is heavier—3 lb of spaghetti or 40 oz of noodles?

Pounds is the larger unit, so I multiply 3 × 16 oz.

The spaghetti weighs 48 oz.

The spaghetti is heavier, since 48 oz is more than 40 oz.

PRACTICE

Tell which weighs the most.

1. biscuits 2 lb; rolls 30 oz
2. cookies 4 lb; crackers 24 oz
3. plums 5 lb; grapefruit 64 oz

Estimate the weight of these items in pounds.

4. 

about 3 lb

5. 

about 4 lb

6. Carrots 28 oz.
about 2 lb

228

More Practice, page 520, set A

TEACHING OPTIONS

RETEACHING TIPS Have students who make errors reading thermometers touch each mark of the scale in the picture with a pencil tip, starting at the lower multiple of 10 and counting by twos until they reach the mark where the mercury stops. Assign Reteaching Supplement 85.

ENRICHMENT Tell students that pencils, erasers, and chalk are often sold by the *gross,* or 12 dozen. Have students use the weights they found earlier for these classroom objects to determine the weight of a gross of each. They may use their calculators if they prefer. (Answers will vary.)

Temperature
Degrees Fahrenheit

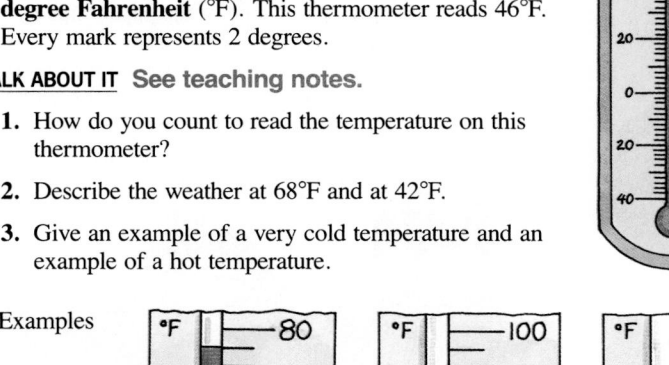

LEARN ABOUT IT

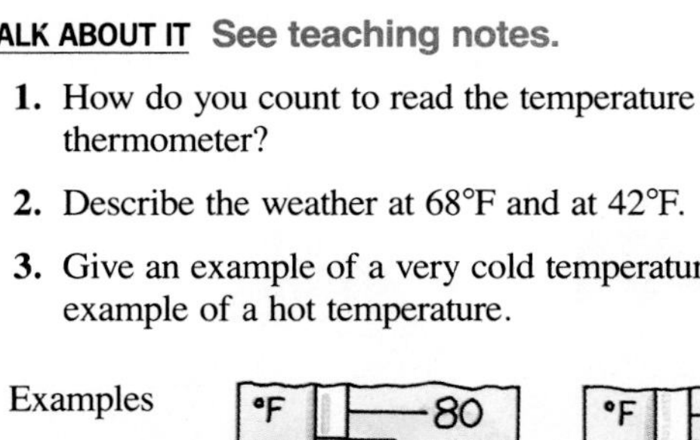

EXPLORE **Study the Thermometer**

A customary unit for measuring temperature is the **degree Fahrenheit** (°F). This thermometer reads 46°F. Every mark represents 2 degrees.

TALK ABOUT IT See teaching notes.

1. How do you count to read the temperature on this thermometer?
2. Describe the weather at 68°F and at 42°F.
3. Give an example of a very cold temperature and an example of a hot temperature.

Examples

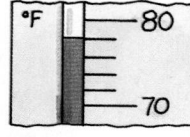

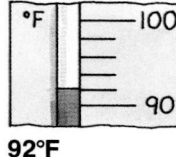

78°F 92°F

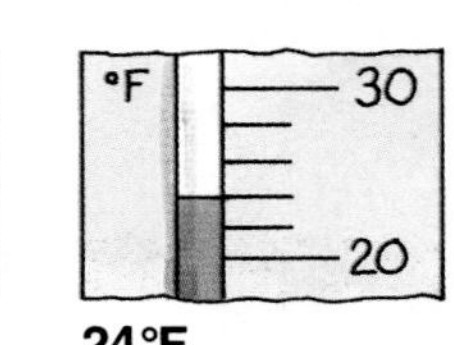

24°F

PRACTICE

Write each temperature.

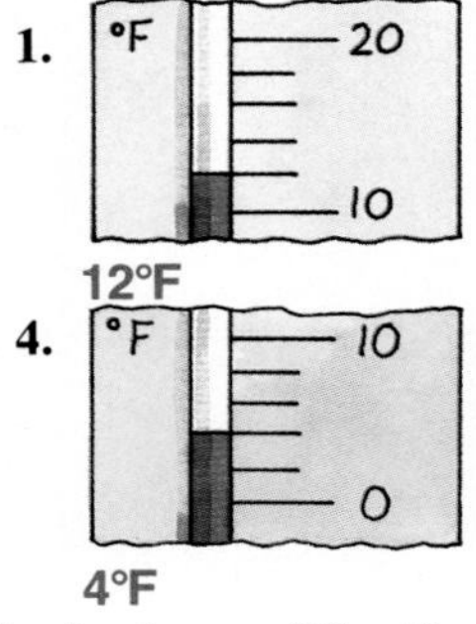

1. 12°F
4. 4°F

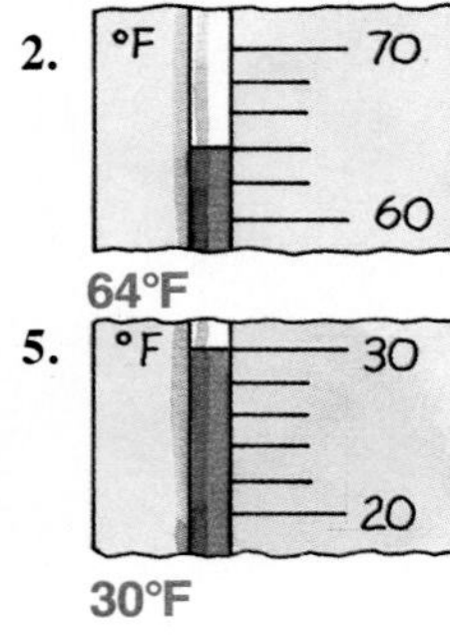

2. 64°F
5. 30°F

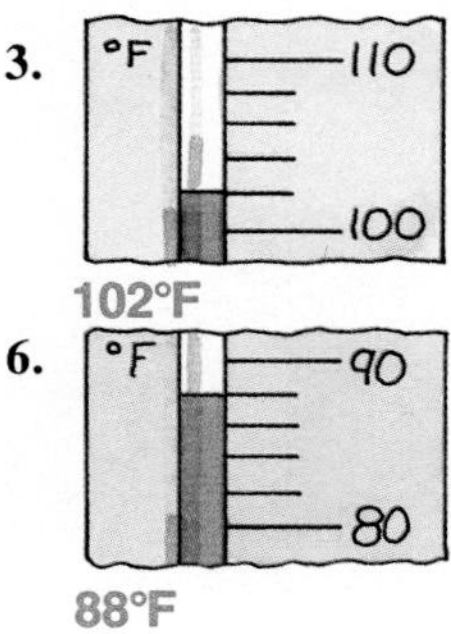

3. 102°F
6. 88°F

More Practice, page 520, set B

OBJECTIVE 8-12 To measure temperature in degrees Fahrenheit

Materials: a Fahrenheit thermometer

1. Motivate and Teach

LEARN ABOUT IT

EXPLORE **Explain how to read a thermometer like the one shown.** (Read the mark on the number scale at the top of the mercury column to find the temperature.)

TALK ABOUT IT Student Edition answers: **1.** by twos **2.** Possible answer: At 68°F, you could wear light clothing, but it would not be warm enough to swim. At 42°F, you would need a heavy jacket, but it would not be cold enough to have snow. **3.** Sample answers: 0°F and 100°F

2. Check Understanding

ERROR ALERT Misreading the number scale on the thermometers.

3. Practice and Apply

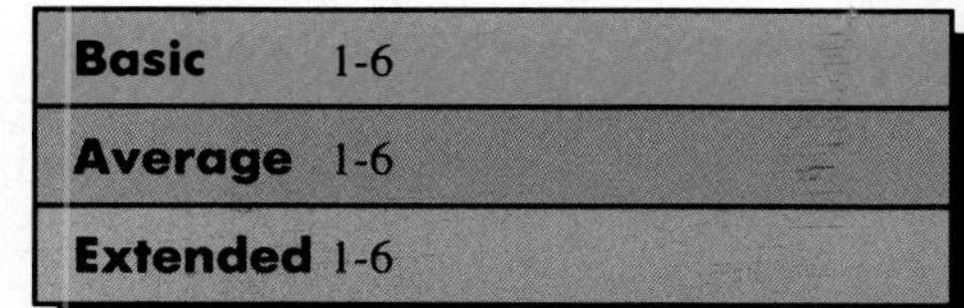

Basic	1-6
Average	1-6
Extended	1-6

Close and Assess

WRITE WHAT YOU THINK

Have students write a paragraph to explain how to compare a 3-lb jar and a 36-oz box of popcorn kernels. Then have them draw a section of a thermometer that shows 56°F and explain how to read that temperature. (Change 3 lb to 48 oz, then compare; other answers will vary.)

QUICK QUIZ

1. Which weighs more—1 lb or 24 oz of cherries? (24 oz)
2. Give a temperature on a day you might ice-skate on a pond. (Accept a reasonable answer below 32°F.)

CHAPTER 8

DATA COLLECTION AND ANALYSIS

GROUP DECISION MAKING

OBJECTIVE To collect, organize, and present data

Provide paper clips and inch rulers. Allow students several practice paper-clip flips before groups actually begin to collect data for the activity.

COLLECTING DATA

▶ **Decide on a general rule for measuring how far a paper clip jumps.** (Rules may vary. One method might use a piece of tape as a starting line; put 1 end of the clip on the line, then flip. Measure from the line to the nearest part of the clip, rounding to the nearest inch.)

▶ **Justify having 3 trials per person.** (Possible answer: You need more than 1 try to determine if there is any improvement; 3 trials is a reasonable number.)

▶ **Decide on a method for finding the sum.** (Answers may vary. Use mental math if the numbers are easy or use column addition.)

Group Decision Making

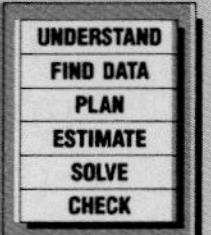

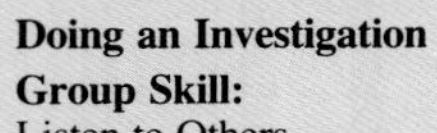

Group Skill:
Listen to Others

For this investigation your group will need two paper clips of any size. You can "flip" one of the paper clips by laying it on your desktop, then pushing down on the end of it with the end of the other clip. The bottom clip will jump like a tiddly wink. Try it! Do you think you can make the paper clip jump farther if you practice?

230

TEACHING OPTIONS

COOPERATIVE LEARNING

Grouping Suggestion:
cooperative learning groups of 4 to 6.

Discuss how groups can cover the following tasks for this activity: setting up a jump area, determining a plan for taking turns, measuring and recording jumps, finding trial sums, designing and making a graph, and analyzing the results to share with the class. Emphasize the importance of listening to each other. Encourage students to analyze their practice jumps to try to anticipate problems that may develop during the actual trials.

Collecting Data

1. Have each student in your group flip a paper clip and measure the distance it jumps in inches. Keep a record like the one below. There should be three trials for each student. Find the sum of your group's distances for each trial.

Trial 1	**Distance**
Dan	6 in.
Suzie	13 in.
Judy	9 in.
Jose	10 in.
Total	38 in.
Trial 2	
Dan	9 in.
Suzie	15 in.
Judy	12 in.
Jose	10 in.
Total	. . . .
Trial 3	
Dan	. . . .
Suzie	. . . .
Judy	. . . .
Jose	. . . .
Total	. . . .

Organizing Data

2. Make a bar graph to show your group's total distance for each trial. Adjust the scale so that the largest and smallest total distances will fit on the graph.
3. Check back. Did you title your graph? Did you label all of its parts?

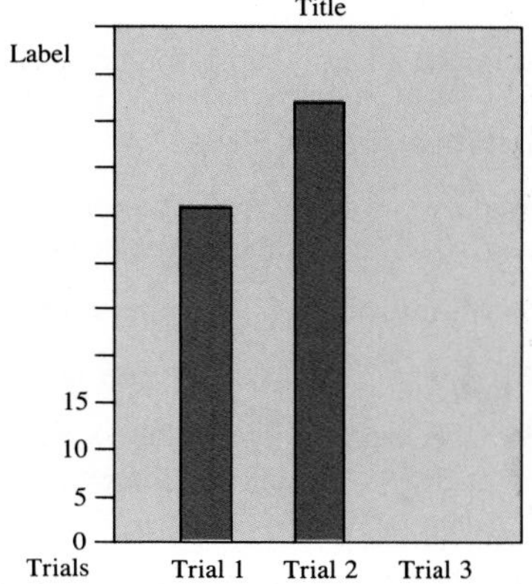

Presenting Your Analysis

4. Did your group get better with practice? Explain how your graph shows whether or not it did.
5. Prepare to share at least three things about your graph with your classmates.

EXTENSION Have students make individual bar graphs showing their own results of the clip-flip activity, using an appropriate number scale. Display individual graphs with the group graph.

ORGANIZING DATA

► **Explain how the range of trial totals affects the number scale you use.** (Possible answer: If totals are quite different, the scale may need larger intervals; if totals are similar, the scale can use smaller intervals.)

► **Decide on a title for the graph.** (Answers will vary.)

PRESENTING YOUR ANALYSIS

► **Summarize the outcome of the experiment.** (Answers will vary. Sample answer: Since the totals increased with each trial, it proves that our group improved with practice.)

► **Analyze how individual scores affected the total in each trial.** (Answers will vary. Sample answer: In trial 2, each student improved, therefore the total score was higher.)

► **Analyze your graph for information it gives about the activity.** (Answers will vary. Sample answer: Our graph shows that the improvement was greater from Trial 1 to Trial 2 than from Trial 2 to Trial 3.) Have each group display its graph so that the class can make comparisons.

CHAPTER 8

WRAP UP

INTRODUCTION The Wrap Up provides activities emphasizing math language and thinking skills for the chapter and a project that integrates those skills with other math strands.

USING PAGE 232

How Do You Measure Up? Have students complete this section independently. Then have them share their answers in small groups, justifying their decisions.

Sometimes, Always, Never

► **Explain a way to evaluate Exercises 7 and 8.** (Exercise 7: Write the given times in numerals to compare them, then think about times during a day when it can be 12:30. Exercise 8: Make a time line for 1 day, then compare the number of a.m. hours to the number of p.m. hours.)

► **Decide a way to prove your decision in Exercise 10.** (Draw figures with the same shape on graph paper to compare their perimeters.)

Project Have students work in pairs to complete the project. Partners can use TA 18 (Calendar) to plan a schedule for recording the growth of their plant.

► **Predict what you think will happen.** (Answers will vary.)

► **Explain how to measure the plant's height.** (Possible answer: Place an inch ruler at the level of the soil, then find the height to the nearest quarter inch.) Have partners keep a log in which they record observations about their plant's growth. When the plants have sprouted, have each pair display its plant, bar graph, and log for classmates to review.

WRAP UP

How Do You Measure Up?

Complete each sentence with a sensible unit of measure.

1. Many airplanes fly at an altitude of 30,000 _?_. feet
2. The new kitten weighed only 12 _?_. ounces
3. Sally's curtain is two _?_ too long. inches
4. Mom's favorite bowl holds about a half _?_ of soup pint
5. Since our family drinks lots of milk, we buy it by the _?_. gallon
6. I need about 3 cups of juice, so I will buy a _?_. quart

Sometimes, Always, Never

Which word should go in the blank, sometimes, always, or never? Explain your choices.

7. Twelve-thirty is _?_ the same as half past noon. sometimes
8. A day _?_ has more a.m. hours than p.m. hours. never
9. A Fahrenheit temperature written with a minus sign _?_ means that the temperature is colder than zero. always
10. Figures with the same shape will _?_ have the same perimeter. sometimes

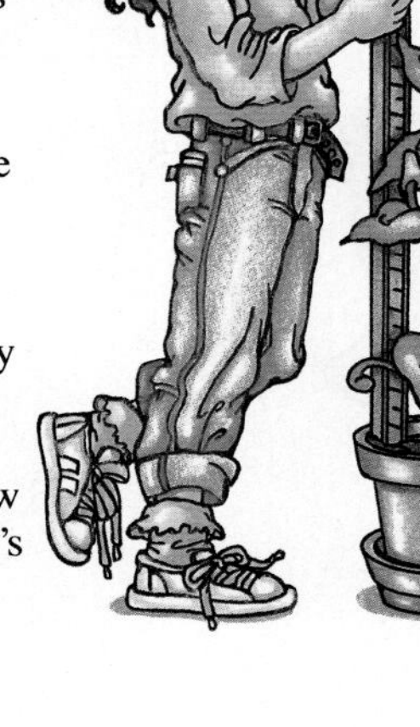

Project Check students' work.

Plant a seed in a small pot and care for it every day. Once it breaks through the soil, measure it once a week for a month. Record the measurements. Then make a bar graph to show the results. Can you find a pattern in the plant's growth? Explain what happened to make the pattern form as it did.

232

TEACHING OPTIONS

ENRICHMENT Provide a balance scale or postage scale. Have students formulate 5 weight comparisons that relate to common classroom items, then verify them with the scale. For example, students might estimate that 8 pencils equal 1 cassette or 3 erasers equal 1 marker.

CHAPTER REVIEW/TEST

Part 1 Understanding

1. Tell two possible ways to find the perimeter of a triangle that has 3 equal sides, each 9 in. long. **3 × 9 or 9 + 9 + 9 = 27 in.**
2. List two activities you might do at 7:45 a.m. List two activities you might do at 7:45 p.m. **Answers will vary.**
3. Find the date that came one month before 1/9/89. Write it in the other form for writing dates. **December 9, 1988**
4. Draw a clock face that shows 5:49.

Part 2 Skills

5. Estimate and then measure the flute in thumb units. **Answers will vary.**
6. Estimate and then measure the flute in inches. **Estimates may vary; 4 in.**

In problems 7–13, tell which is the greater amount.

7. 7 yd or 20 ft
8. 5,000 ft or 1 mi
9. 50 fl oz or 5 c
10. 5 pt or 2 qt
11. 3 lb or 24 oz
12. 50 oz or 3 lb
13. the width of a chalkboard or its perimeter
14. Which room measurement is just under 4 feet? **door width**
15. To buy a window shade, would you estimate or measure its exact width? **measure exactly**

Room Measurements	
window height	41 in.
window width	30 in.
door height	80 in.
door width	46 in.

Part 3 Applications

16. A soccer game began at 1:15 p.m. and ended after 1 hour and 55 minutes. At what time was the game over? **3:10 p.m.**
17. Pens come in packets of 3 or 5. Find 2 different combinations of packets that total 60 pens. **See Additional Answers.**
18. **Challenge** How would you measure 1 gallon of punch with a 1-pint measuring cup? **Measure 8 pt to give 1 gal.**

233

INFORMAL ASSESSMENT

Using Manipulatives Have students use rulers (TA 17) to measure the length and the width of their Student Editions to the nearest whole inch, then to find each book's perimeter. Then have them find the perimeter of a larger book and of a smaller book. (Answers may vary. Check students' work.)

Communication *Tell what a benchmark is and explain how to use a benchmark to help estimate length.* (A benchmark is a length you know, which you can use to compare with an object whose length you want to estimate.)

Critical Thinking *Explain a general method for comparing measurements given in different units, such as 9 yd or 30 ft.* (Decide which measurement uses the larger unit, find a relationship between the units, then multiply to change to the smaller unit.)

CHAPTER REVIEW/TEST

INTRODUCTION The Review/Test is provided to review and evaluate the skills and concepts presented in Chapter 8.

USING PAGE 233 If you prefer to use this page for review, you may want to use the **Multiple-Choice Posttest** (pages 31-32) or the **Free-Response Posttest** (pages 31-32) to evaluate mastery of Chapter objectives.

ITEM ANALYSIS The table below correlates the Chapter Review/Test items with the lesson objectives for the chapter.

Items	Objectives
1	8-9
2, 3	8-2
4	8-1
5	8-5
6, 7	8-6
8	8-8
9, 10	8-11
11, 12	8-12
13	8-9
(14)	8-6
14, 15	8-10
16	8-3
17	8-4
18	8-11

Additional Answers: See p. T79.

CHAPTER 8

ENRICHMENT

INTRODUCTION Students use number sense and logical reasoning to interpret the meaning of negative numbers on a Fahrenheit scale.

USING PAGE 234
This Enrichment page is provided for all students. You may wish to use it after they have completed the Chapter Review/test on page 233.

▶ **Explain what the weather is like on a day when the temperature is 10°F.** (Possible answer: It is very cold, and water would freeze.)

▶ **Explain why ⁻2°F is colder than ⁻1°F.** (Possible answer: ⁻1°F is 1 degree colder than 0°F, but ⁻2°F is 1 degree colder than that.)

▶ **Explain how to compare 2 negative temperatures.** (Possible answer: Of 2 negative numbers, the 1 that is a larger number represents a colder temperature.)

▶ **Summarize a relationship between negative numbers and temperatures below 0°F.** (Possible answer: As the temperature falls farther below 0°F, the negative numbers get larger.)

EXTENSION Have students look in an almanac to find the coldest Fahrenheit temperature ever recorded in your state, in any 10 of the 50 states, and in the world. Have them determine how much colder than freezing each temperature is. (Answers will vary.)

Additional Answers: See p. T79.

ENRICHMENT
Temperatures Below Zero

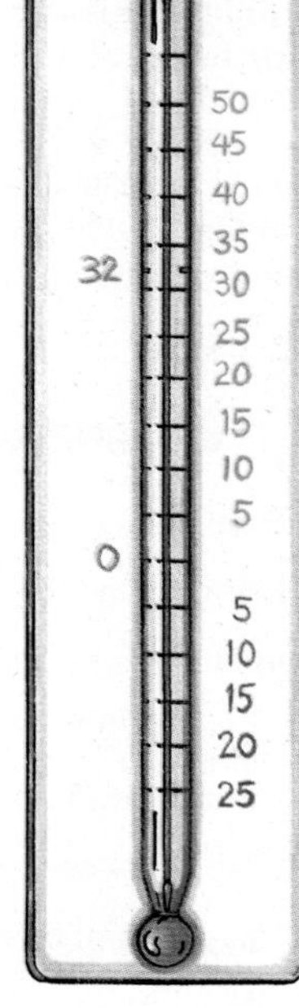

When the temperature is 32° Fahrenheit we say it is at freezing, because water will freeze at 32° F. When the temperature falls lower than 0° Fahrenheit, we say it is **below zero**. We write such very low temperatures as **negative numbers**.

Look at the thermometer as a vertical number line. On this thermometer the numbers below zero are blue. You write these numbers with a minus sign, for example, −2°F or −8°F. The red numbers are above zero. You write these without the minus sign, as 2° F and 8° F.

Look at the thermometer and answer these questions.

1. What number on a thermometer expresses a temperature 8 degrees colder than the point at which water freezes? **24°F**
2. What temperature is 8 degrees above the freezing point? **40°F**
3. How many degrees below the freezing point will the temperature fall before it reaches 0°F? **32°F**
4. Write the Fahrenheit temperatures for 1 degree below zero and 5 degrees below zero. Explain which is colder. **See Additional Answers.**

Solve each weather problem.

5. At midnight it was −3°F in Billings, Montana. Three hours later the temperature was 10 degrees colder. How cold was it at 3 a.m.? **−13°F**
7. At dawn Ingrid's thermometer read −8°F. By noon the temperature had risen 12 degrees. What was the new temperature? **4°F**

234

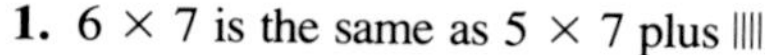

CUMULATIVE REVIEW

1. 6 × 7 is the same as 5 × 7 plus ||||.

Ⓐ 1 × 7 B 7 × 7
C 7 × 5 D 1 × 6

2. 4, 8, 12, and 16 are some of the multiples of ||||.

A 32 B 5
C 12 Ⓓ 4

3. □ + △ = 7 and △ × △ = 16
□ must be

A 5 B 4
Ⓒ 3 D 2

4. Round in order to estimate the product of 6 × 314. The product is a little more than ||||.

A 6,300 B 1,500
Ⓒ 1,800 D 2,400

5. 34 × 6

Ⓐ 204 B 1,104
C 222 D 1,824

6. 6 × 5,000

A 3,000 B 11,000
C 5,600 Ⓓ 30,000

7. 3 × 8 × 2

A 24 Ⓑ 48
C 40 D 30

8. 70 × 80

A 560 B 56,000
Ⓒ 5,600 D 70,800

9. 98 × 40

A 392 B 3,620
Ⓒ 3,920 D 4,820

10. 43 × 79

A 688 B 3,387
C 5,600 Ⓓ 3,397

11. Students sold 957 tickets to a play at $3 each. By how much did ticket sales go over the goal of $2,500?

Ⓐ $371 B $1,540
C $5,371 D $2,871

12. 68 customers ate at a snack bar. 49 ate salad and 35 ate corn on the cob. How many ate both?

A 84 Ⓑ 16
C 19 D 14

235

CUMULATIVE REVIEW

INTRODUCTION The purpose of this Cumulative Review is to maintain previously taught skills and concepts. The emphasis in this Cumulative Review is on multiplication concepts and basic facts. Chapter 5; on multiplication of 2-, 3-, and 4-digit factors by 1-digit factors, Chapter 6; and on multiplication by 2-digit factors, Chapter 7.

ITEM ANALYSIS The table below correlates the Cumulative Review items with the lesson objectives.

Items	Objectives
1	5-8
2	5-10
3	5-6
4	6-2
5	6-5
6	6-1
7	6-9
8	7-1
9	7-3
10	7-4
11	7-10
(11)	7-8
12	7-7

CHAPTER 9 DIVISION CONCEPTS AND FACTS

Chapter Management

OVERVIEW

Lesson	Pages	Objectives	Subject Integration	Strand Integration
Chapter Opener	236-237	To introduce chapter 9	fine arts-puppets	measurement
Problem Solving: Understanding Division	238-239	9-1 To understand the operation of division	fine arts-puppets	problem solving
Relating Multiplication and Division	240-241	9-2 To use multiplication to find quotients	science-trees	mathematical reasoning
Dividing by 2 and 3	242-243	9-3 To use missing factors to divide by 2 and 3	science-flowers	critical thinking
Dividing by 4 and 5	244-245	9-4 To use missing factors to divide by 4 and 5	fine arts-puppets	algebra
Problem Solving: Estimate the Answer	246-247	9-5 To determine by estimation whether answers to a problem are reasonable	fine arts-musical instruments	consumer math
0 and 1 in Division/ Midchapter Review/Quiz	248-249	9-6 To understand 0 and 1 in division	health/fitness-gym class	problem solving
Dividing by 6 and 7	250-251	9-7 To use missing factors to divide by 6 and 7	fine arts-Bunraku puppets	calculators
Dividing by 8 and 9	252-253	9-8 To use missing factors to divide by 8 and 9	fine arts-puppet shows	mathematical reasoning
Using Critical Thinking	254-255	9-9 To use critical thinking to discover function rules	science-function machine	computation
Problem Solving: Work Backward	256-257	9-10 To solve problems using the strategy Work Backward	health/fitness-bowling	consumer math
Applied Problem Solving: Group Decision Making	258-259	9-11 To analyze, organize, and make decisions using relevant data	science-recycling	consumer math

MATHEMATICAL BACKGROUND

Division
In Lesson 9-1, students use counters to practice two actions associated with division. Separate same–size groups and share equally in groups. They learn four division rules in the chapter: 0 divided by any number is 0; never divide by 0; any number divided by itself is 1; and any number divided by 1 is that number.

Multiplication
In Lesson 9-2, students are helped to understand how division and multiplication are related. In multiplication, you know two factors and find a product. In division, you know the product and one factor and you find the missing factor.

Problem Solving
Students learn to use the strategy Work Backward.

TIPS FROM TEACHERS

Use this mnemonic device to help students remember the steps in division:

Divide — Does
Multiply — Max
Subtract — Sell
Compare — Cheesy
Bring down — Burgers?

Donna Martinez
Zavala School
McAllen, TX

ASSESSMENT

Pretest — Chapter 9, page 1

Multiple-Choice Format

Name

1. Each canoe has 2 paddles. The Canoe Club has 10 paddles. How many canoes do they have? Think: ●● ●● ●● ●● ●●
   a. 12 canoes b. 8 canoes c. 5 canoes d. 20 canoes — 1. c

2. Choose an equation to complete this fact family. [2 × 4 = 8, 8 ÷ 2 = 4, 4 × 2 = 8]
   a. 8 ÷ 4 = 2 b. 4 ÷ 2 = 2 c. 2 ÷ 2 = 1 d. 2 × 8 = 16 — 2. a

3. Find 15 ÷ 3. Then choose a multiplication fact you could use to check your answer.
   a. 3 × 4 b. 3 × 5 c. 3 × 6 d. 3 × 7 — 3. b

4. Find 18 ÷ 2.
   a. 7 b. 8 c. 9 d. 10 — 4. c

5. Find 36 ÷ 4. Then choose a multiplication fact you could use to check your answer.
   a. 4 × 9 b. 4 × 8 c. 4 × 7 d. 4 × 6 — 5. a

6. Find 35 ÷ 5.
   a. 6 b. 7 c. 8 d. 9 — 6. b

7. First estimate the answer. Then choose the answer that seems reasonable. Janet rides 28 miles on the bus each day. How many miles does she ride in 22 days?
   a. 616 miles b. 308 miles c. 946 miles d. 112 miles — 7. a

Pretest — Chapter 9, page 2

Multiple-Choice Format

Name

8. Which of these rules would you use to find 0 ÷ 8?
   a. The quotient of a number divided by 1 is that number.
   b. The quotient of a number divided by itself is 1.
   c. Zero divided by any number is 0.
   d. Never divide by 0. — 8. c

9. Find 56 ÷ 7. Then choose a multiplication fact you could use to check your answer.
   a. 7 × 8 b. 7 × 9 c. 7 × 6 d. 8 × 8 — 9. a

10. Find 49 ÷ 7.
   a. 6 b. 7 c. 8 d. 9 — 10. b

11. Find 48 ÷ 8. Then choose a multiplication fact you could use to check your answer.
   a. 8 × 9 b. 8 × 8 c. 8 × 7 d. 8 × 6 — 11. d

12. Find 36 ÷ 9.
   a. 45 b. 5 c. 27 d. 4 — 12. d

13. Use 16 as the input number. What is the output number? [16 → IN → Divide by 2. Subtract 1. → OUT]
   a. 5 b. 7 c. 9 d. 3 — 13. b

14. Laura had some baseball cards. She gave 6 cards to each of 4 friends. She gave another friend the remaining 7 cards. How many baseball cards did she start with?
   a. 17 cards b. 24 cards c. 31 cards d. 14 cards — 14. c

Posttest — Chapter 9, page 1

Multiple-Choice Format

Name

1. Ann puts 3 beads on each chain. She has 12 beads. How many chains does she need? Think: ●●● ●●● ●●● ●●●
   a. 4 chains b. 15 chains c. 36 chains d. 9 chains — 1. a

2. Choose an equation to complete this fact family. [3 × 6 = 18, 6 × 3 = 18, 18 ÷ 3 = 6]
   a. 6 ÷ 3 = 2 b. 3 ÷ 3 = 1 c. 18 ÷ 6 = 3 d. 3 × 18 = 54 — 2. c

3. Find 16 ÷ 2. Then choose a multiplication fact you could use to check your answer.
   a. 2 × 6 b. 2 × 9 c. 2 × 7 d. 2 × 8 — 3. d

4. Find 24 ÷ 3.
   a. 6 b. 7 c. 8 d. 9 — 4. c

5. Find 32 ÷ 4. Then choose a multiplication fact you could use to check your answer.
   a. 4 × 9 b. 4 × 8 c. 4 × 7 d. 4 × 6 — 5. b

6. Find 45 ÷ 5.
   a. 6 b. 7 c. 8 d. 9 — 6. d

7. First estimate the answer. Then choose the answer that seems reasonable. Dion spent $26 on clothing, $19 on food and $32 on entertainment. How much did he spend in all?
   a. $67 b. $57 c. $87 d. $77 — 7. d

Posttest — Chapter 9, page 2

Multiple-Choice Format

Name

8. Which of these rules would you use to find 6 ÷ 6?
   a. The quotient of a number divided by 1 is that number.
   b. The quotient of a number divided by itself is 1.
   c. Zero divided by any number is 0.
   d. Never divide by 0. — 8. b

9. Find 28 ÷ 7. Then choose a multiplication fact you could use to check your answer.
   a. 7 × 3 b. 7 × 4 c. 7 × 6 d. 8 × 7 — 9. b

10. Find 42 ÷ 6.
   a. 9 b. 8 c. 7 d. 6 — 10. c

11. Find 63 ÷ 9. Then choose a multiplication fact you could use to check your answer.
   a. 8 × 9 b. 7 × 9 c. 8 × 8 d. 9 × 9 — 11. b

12. Find 54 ÷ 9.
   a. 6 b. 7 c. 8 d. 9 — 12. a

13. Use 12 as the input number. What is the output number? [12 → IN → Divide by 2. Subtract 1. → OUT]
   a. 3 b. 5 c. 7 d. 9 — 13. b

14. Tom bought 9 books. Each book cost $4. Then he spent $7 for a tape. How much money did Tom start with if he had no money left?
   a. $11 b. $43 c. $35 d. $20 — 14. b

ITEM ANALYSIS

Items	Objectives
1	9-1
2	9-2
3, 4	9-3
5, 6	9-4
7	9-5
8	9-6
9, 10	9-7
11, 12	9-8
13	9-9
14	9-10

Note: The item analysis is the same for all pretests and posttests for this chapter.

ALSO AVAILABLE

- Free Response Tests
- Alternative Tests
- Thinking Strategies
- Concrete Materials

Optional Chapter Activities

PROJECT AND BULLETIN BOARD

As students learn this chapter, have them work in groups to make ''dividend ribbons'' that help show division facts. Post the ribbons on a bulletin board labeled *Division Facts*, such as the one pictured. The ribbons can be made from different colored paper. Preceding each ribbon is the number that is the divisor. The ribbons show the dividends in ascending order. Above the ribbons are the quotients. Have students align the ribbons under the quotients as shown in the diagram. Students can then refer to the bulletin board to help them recall division facts. Once students have completed the bulletin board, challenge them to identify patterns by finding differences in vertical, horizontal, or diagonal columns.

DIVISION FACTS

Divisors \ Quotients	0	1	2	3	4	5	6	7	8	9
1	0	1	2	3	4	5	6	7	8	9
2	0	2	4	6	8	10	12	14	16	18
3	0	3	6	9	12	15	18	21	24	27
4	0	4	8	12	16	20	24	28	32	36
5	0	5	10	15	20	25	30	35	40	45
6	0	6	12	18	24	30	36	42	48	54
7	0	7	14	21	28	35	42	49	56	63
8	0	8	16	24	32	40	48	56	64	72
9	0	9	18	27	36	45	54	63	72	81

COOPERATIVE LEARNING

Divide the class into groups of three or four. Identify the group skill: encourage and respect others. Give each group three or four numbers that have several factors each. Assign a clearly competent student as group leader. The leader should explain the task to the others. The members of the group should decide on how they will approach the task. One way is to divide the given number by those numbers that are thought to be factors of the given number. Have each member of the group choose a number they think is a factor of the given number. Then have them divide to verify. If there is no remainder, two factors have been found, the divisor and the quotient. Have the students pool their results. The leader should encourage the other members of the group to look for as many factors as they can and to respect each other as they attempt to do so. Another student in each group should write all the factors the group finds. Once the task is completed for each given number, have a spokesperson from each group share the results with the rest of the class.

You will find grouping suggestions and cooperative learning activities in most lessons throughout this chapter.

LITERATURE

James, Elizabeth & Carol Barkin. *How to Grow 100 Dollars.* New York: Lothrop, Lee & Shepard, 1979.

Amy wants to go on a camping trip at the end of the Summer. The trip will cost $100. She comes up with a plan to make and sell terrariums. She must figure out how much money she needs to begin and what she can get for the finished product.

Children could use real-world situations as motivation to figure out how to earn money and how much they could make at the different jobs. Then they could write number stories about how much money they need to buy something they want and how long it will take to earn the desired sum.

Froman, Robert. *The Greatest Guessing Game: A Book About Dividing.* New York: Harper & Row, 1978.

Shotwell, Louisa R. *Roosevelt Grady.* New York: Dell Publishing, 1977.

English as a Second Language

For the ESL child, it is particularly important to solve concrete problems that occur in everyday situations.

Have students solve a classroom organizational problem involving division concepts. For example, suppose a group of three students needed to share a box of six crayons. Have students physically demonstrate how to distribute the crayons so that each of the three students has the same number of crayons. On the chalkboard, write $6 \div 3 = 2$. Then ask if any crayons would be left over. Explain that a left-over amount is called a **remainder** in a division problem.

Children should work in groups to solve additional concrete problems. Include students of various language abilities in each group. If possible, mix bilingual students with non-English speakers. Encourage all children to present solutions to the class and to explain results.

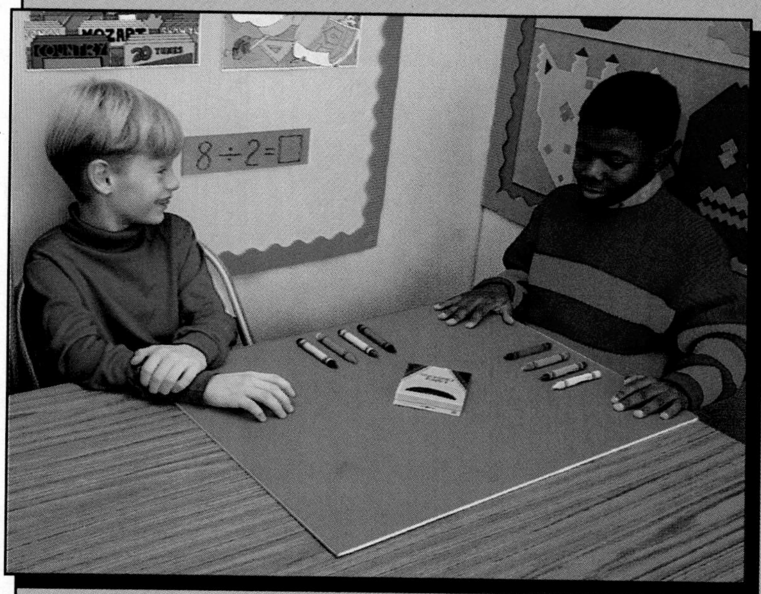

Gifted

Arrange students into groups of four and ask each group to pretend they have been invited to appear as guests on the game show "Math Memory." This week's topic is division. Instruct each group to create a different division problem on each of 16 index cards, dividing any 2-digit number evenly by any number from 2 to 9. On 16 more cards, they list a quotient for each of those problems. Remind them that Mr. Zero, the game show host, will turn all cards face down in front of the audience and the two contestants on the show.

Rotating turns, each contestant will turn over one card from the problem cards and attempt to turn over its match from the solution cards. The player making the match will score one point and the match will be removed by him or her. If that player can correctly name all three of the other equations for the fact family for those three numbers, he or she may score one additional point. If no match is made, both cards are again turned face down and the next player takes a turn.

When all of the cards in the pile are gone, the player with the most points wins "Math Memory."

Students at Risk

Although many students will demonstrate an understanding of the basic concept of division as separating or partitioning equal groups, those who have reversal tendencies, memory problems, or reasoning deficiencies often have difficulty dividing equations that are presented with the algorithm symbol $\overline{)}$.

Unlike the other operations, which are read from left to right or from top to bottom, students must learn to read a division problem by first identifying the dividend "inside" the symbol, then dividing it by the "outside" divisor. Thus, $2\overline{)6}$ is read "six divided by two," rather than in left-to-right order. Some students view the $\overline{)}$ symbol as a "container" or "garage" that holds an amount to be divided into equal groups. Provide frequent opportunities for students to read, explain, and model division problems expressed with the $\overline{)}$ symbol to reinforce this unusual sequence.

You may also use the Reteaching Supplements and the specific Reteaching Tips from each lesson in this chapter.

CHAPTER 9

INTRODUCING THE CHAPTER

SUBJECT INTEGRATION The photograph shows marionettes in the Mad Hatter's tea party scene from *Alice in Wonderland* to represent the chapter theme of fine arts. Several lessons include facts about puppetmaking and puppet show performances to provide students with situations that apply division concepts and basic facts.

USING DATA The Fine Arts Data Bank on page 479 of the Student Edition shows a diagram of part of the "double airplane" controller for a 9-string marionette accompanied by a paragraph of additional information. The Data Bank also includes several sentences about the Japanese Bunraku Puppet Theater.

QUESTION 1 ► **Explain how you found the necessary data to solve the problem.** (The paragraph about the "Double Airplane" controller gives the size of each of the 4 wood strips that form its 2 *T* bars.)
► **Justify the operation you used.** (Add to join groups; or multiply same-size groups, then add.)
Student Edition answer: 34 inches.

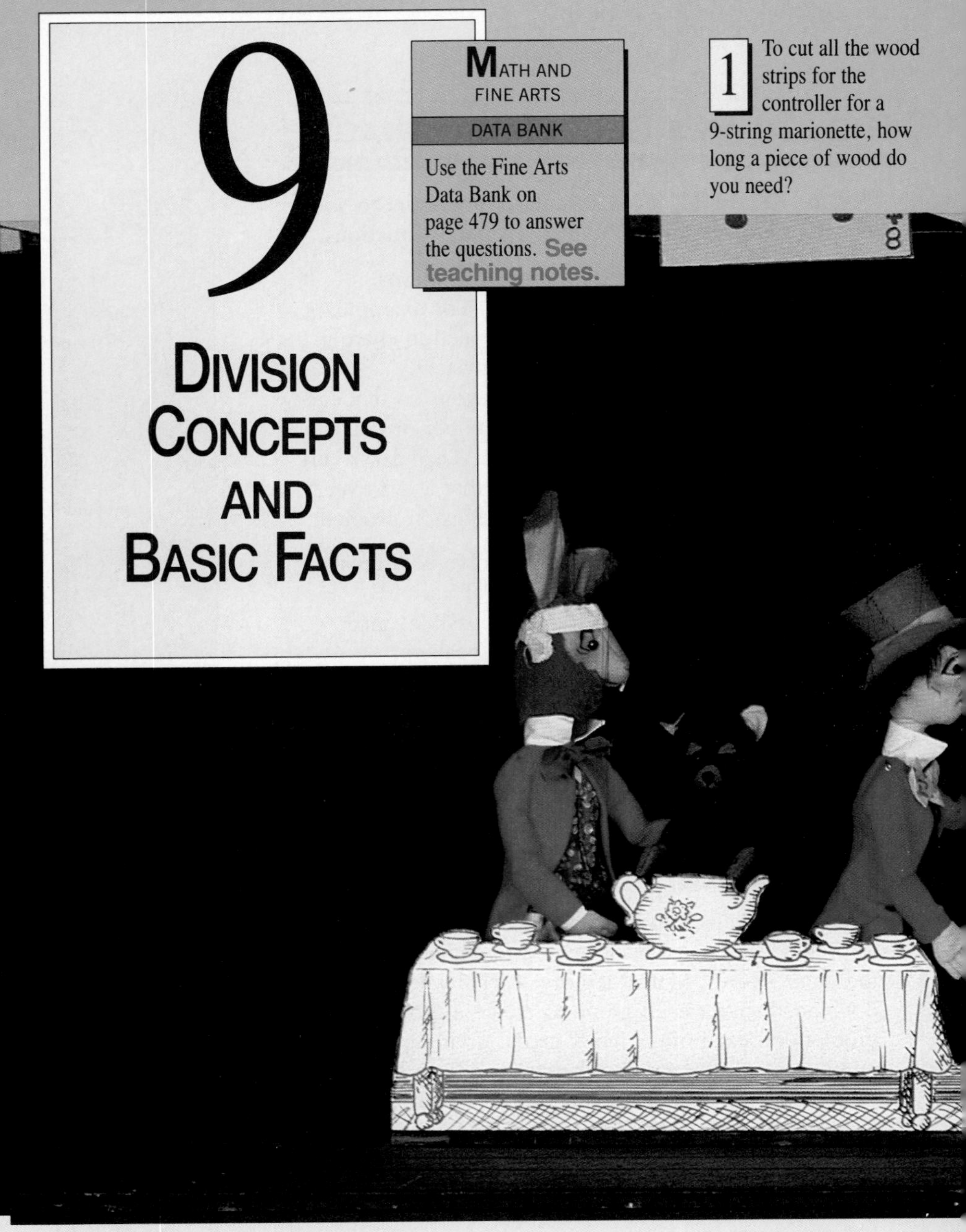

9
DIVISION CONCEPTS AND BASIC FACTS
MATH AND FINE ARTS
DATA BANK
Use the Fine Arts Data Bank on page 479 to answer the questions. See teaching notes.
1 To cut all the wood strips for the controller for a 9-string marionette, how long a piece of wood do you need?

TEACHING OPTIONS

LANGUAGE DEVELOPMENT
Write the words **all** and **each** on the chalkboard, and challenge students to use them in a sentence related to multiplication. (Sample answer: *Each* of 5 teams has 4 players for 20 players in *all*.) Then ask volunteers to use the same 2 words in a question about division. (Possible answer: If you divide *all* class members into 6 teams, can *each* team have the same number of people?)

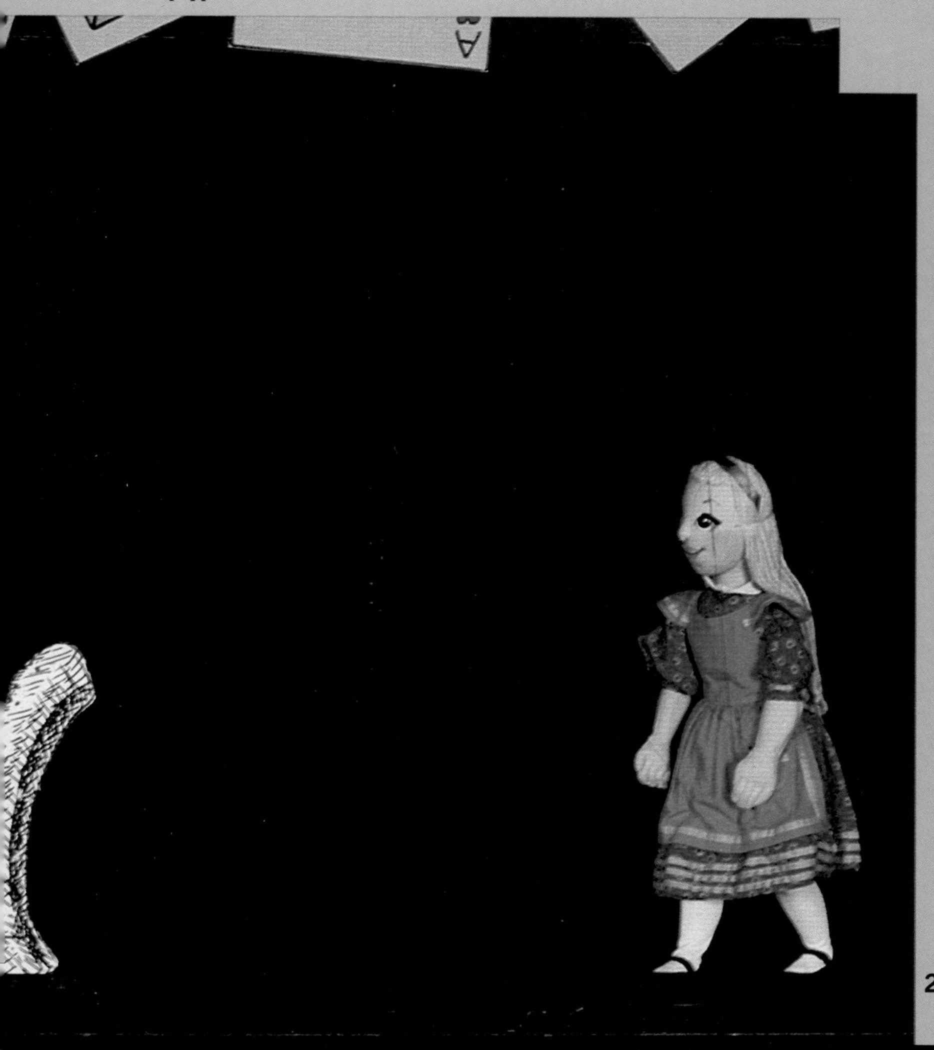

2 The Japanese art of Bunraku uses large, complex puppets. How many people would you see on stage operating 5 male Bunraku puppets?

3 How many people would you see on stage operating 3 female Japanese Bunraku puppets?

4 **Use Critical Thinking** How many feet of wood will you need to make the controller for one marionette?

237

QUESTION 2 ► **Justify an operation to use to answer the question.** (Multiply the number of operators for 1 male puppet by 5 to put together same-size groups.)
Student Edition answer: 20

QUESTION 3 ► **Contrast the number of puppeteers needed to work male and female Bunraku puppets.** (It takes 1 more person to work a male than a female puppet.)
► **Identify the fewest male and female Bunraku puppets that use equal numbers of puppeteers.** (3 male and 4 female puppets need 12 people for each group.)
Student Edition answer: 9

QUESTION 4 ► **Decide on a plan to solve the problem.** (Use the answer to Question 1, which told the number of inches of wood needed for a controller, then decide how many feet are equivalent to that many inches.)
► **Identify a measurement relationship that will help you solve the problem.** (1 ft = 12 in.)
► **Analyze whether the wood measurement in feet will be exactly what is needed.** (1 ft = 12 in. and 3 ft = 36 in., so if 3 ft are used 2 in. will be left over; 36 in. − 34 in. = 2 in.)
Student Edition answer: 3 ft

SUBJECT INTEGRATION PROJECT Have small groups research the various kinds of puppets used to entertain around the world. Begin by brainstorming a list of different kinds of puppets students may have seen or have used. (Samples: finger, rod, sock, hand, and shadow puppets) Each group selects a puppet type. As they work through Chapter 9, groups can use library resources to learn more about their chosen puppet. Conclude with a "parade" of models or drawings of the puppets students researched.

LESSON OPTIONS 9-1

Problem Solving: Understanding Division

OBJECTIVE 9-1 To understand the operation of division

PREBOOK ACTIVITIES

QUICK REVIEW

Multiply.

1. 3 × 4 (12) **2.** 9 × 2 (18)
3. 4 × 6 (24) **4.** 3 × 5 (15)
5. 7 × 3 (21) **6.** 2 × 8 (16)
7. 4 × 9 (36) **8.** 1 × 5 (5)

PRIOR KNOWLEDGE

Have students recall real-life situations when they have divided or shared an amount equally among a number of people. (Possible answers: dealing out cards for a game; splitting money among friends; serving equal portions at a meal)

COMMUNICATION

Discussing and Writing Math Write the words **division** and **divide** on the chalkboard. Ask volunteers to use each word in a sentence that highlights its part of speech. (Sample answers: Division means sharing or making equal groups. Let's divide the tapes between us.) Have students write a sentence in their Math Journals that uses both words. Encourage volunteers to read their sentences aloud. (Sample sentence: In division, you divide a large group into equal parts.)

EXPLORE AND CONNECT

COOPERATIVE ACTIVITY

Grouping Suggestion: small groups

3 friends collect 6 pine cones for a crafts project. If they share the pine cones equally, how many does each get?

TEACHING ACTIONS

Have students work in small groups to act out the situation, plan a solution, and discuss the results.

▶ **Summarize the situation in your own words.** (There are 6 pine cones to be shared among 3 people.)

▶ **Analyze the question.** (You must find how many pine cones each person gets.)

▶ **Identify an important rule for sharing the pine cones equally.** (Each person must get the same number of pine cones.)

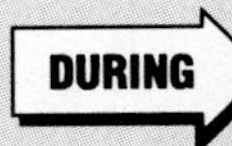

▶ **Decide on a solution method.** (Methods may vary. Possible methods: Act It Out; Use Objects; Draw a Picture; Choose an Operation.)

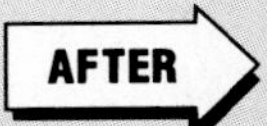

▶ **Explain your solution.** (If each friend gets 2 pine cones, all 6 cones will be shared equally.)

▶ **Evaluate the answer to see if it makes sense.** (Possible answer: 3 × 2 = 6, so you can divide 6 by 3 to get 2.)

CONNECTIONS Use these anytime.

Problem of the Day

Balloons Maureen buys 20 balloons to decorate her house for a party. If she uses the same number of balloons in the living room and in the dining room, how many balloons can she use per room? (10)

Subject Integration

Health and Fitness A class is divided into 4 teams for a relay race. Each team has 7 students. How many students are in the class? (28)

Patterns

Countdowns Find the rule in each pattern, then continue each 3 more times.

27, 24, 21, (18), (15), (12)
72, 63, 54, (45), (36), (27)
90, 75, 60, (45), (30), (15)

(The first decreases by 3 each time; the second decreases by 9 each time; the third decreases by 15 each time.)

Classwork and Homework Supplements

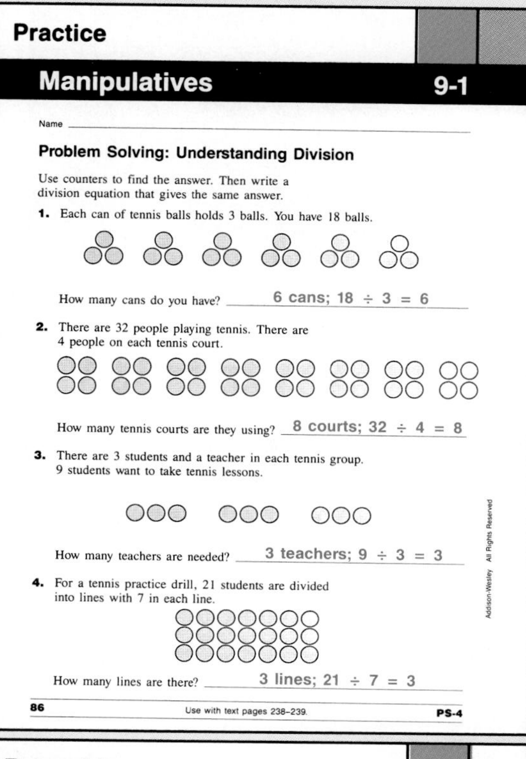

Practice

Manipulatives 9-1

Name ______

Problem Solving: Understanding Division

Use counters to find the answer. Then write a division equation that gives the same answer.

1. Each can of tennis balls holds 3 balls. You have 18 balls.

How many cans do you have? 6 cans; 18 ÷ 3 = 6

2. There are 32 people playing tennis. There are 4 people on each tennis court.

How many tennis courts are they using? 8 courts; 32 ÷ 4 = 8

3. There are 3 students and a teacher in each tennis group. 9 students want to take tennis lessons.

How many teachers are needed? 3 teachers; 9 ÷ 3 = 3

4. For a tennis practice drill, 21 students are divided into lines with 7 in each line.

How many lines are there? 3 lines; 21 ÷ 7 = 3

Addison-Wesley | All Rights Reserved

86 Use with text pages 238–239. PS-4

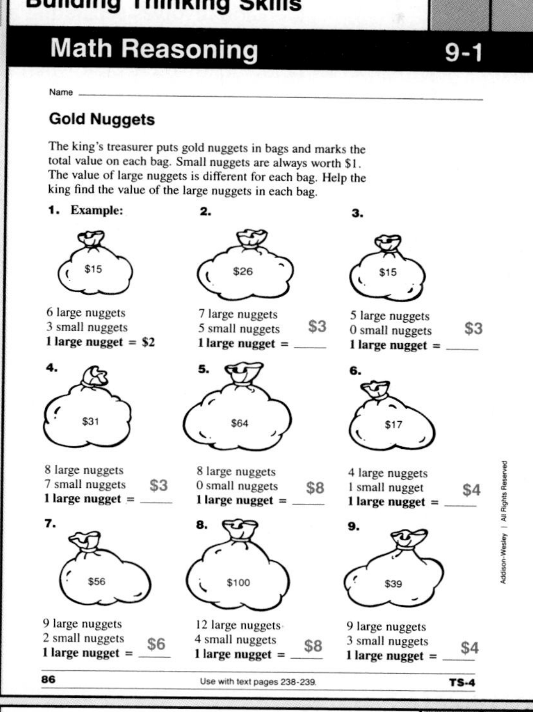

Building Thinking Skills

Math Reasoning 9-1

Name ______

Gold Nuggets

The king's treasurer puts gold nuggets in bags and marks the total value on each bag. Small nuggets are always worth $1. The value of large nuggets is different for each bag. Help the king find the value of the large nuggets in each bag.

1. Example: $15 — 6 large nuggets, 3 small nuggets, 1 large nugget = $2
2. $26 — 7 large nuggets, 5 small nuggets, 1 large nugget = $3
3. $15 — 5 large nuggets, 0 small nuggets, 1 large nugget = $3
4. $31 — 8 large nuggets, 7 small nuggets, 1 large nugget = $3
5. $64 — 8 large nuggets, 0 small nuggets, 1 large nugget = $8
6. $17 — 4 large nuggets, 1 small nugget, 1 large nugget = $4
7. $56 — 9 large nuggets, 2 small nuggets, 1 large nugget = $6
8. $100 — 12 large nuggets, 4 small nuggets, 1 large nugget = $8
9. $39 — 9 large nuggets, 3 small nuggets, 1 large nugget = $4

Addison-Wesley | All Rights Reserved

86 Use with text pages 238–239. TS-4

Reteaching

Problem Solving 9-1

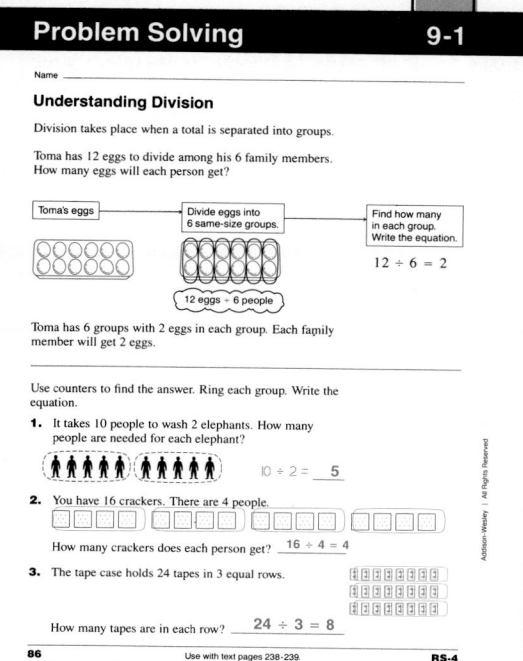

Name ______

Understanding Division

Division takes place when a total is separated into groups.

Toma has 12 eggs to divide among his 6 family members. How many eggs will each person get?

Toma's eggs → Divide eggs into 6 same-size groups. → Find how many in each group. Write the equation.

12 eggs ÷ 6 people

12 ÷ 6 = 2

Toma has 6 groups with 2 eggs in each group. Each family member will get 2 eggs.

Use counters to find the answer. Ring each group. Write the equation.

1. It takes 10 people to wash 2 elephants. How many people are needed for each elephant?

10 ÷ 2 = 5

2. You have 16 crackers. There are 4 people.

How many crackers does each person get? 16 ÷ 4 = 4

3. The tape case holds 24 tapes in 3 equal rows.

How many tapes are in each row? 24 ÷ 3 = 8

Addison-Wesley | All Rights Reserved

86 Use with text pages 238–239. RS-4

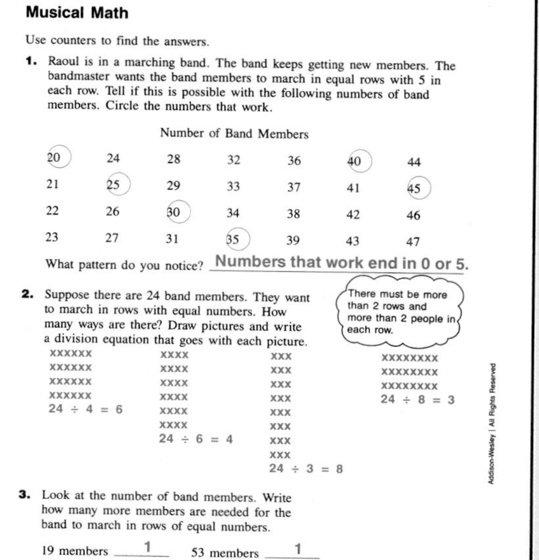

Challenges

Manipulatives 9-1

Name ______

Musical Math

Use counters to find the answers.

1. Raoul is in a marching band. The band keeps getting new members. The bandmaster wants the band members to march in equal rows with 5 in each row. Tell if this is possible with the following numbers of band members. Circle the numbers that work.

Number of Band Members

(20)	24	28	32	36	(40)	44
21	(25)	29	33	37	41	(45)
22	26	(30)	34	38	42	46
23	27	31	(35)	39	43	47

What pattern do you notice? Numbers that work end in 0 or 5.

2. Suppose there are 24 band members. They want to march in rows with equal numbers. How many ways are there? Draw pictures and write a division equation that goes with each picture.

There must be more than 2 rows and more than 2 people in each row.

24 ÷ 4 = 6   24 ÷ 6 = 4   24 ÷ 3 = 8   24 ÷ 8 = 3

3. Look at the number of band members. Write how many more members are needed for the band to march in rows of equal numbers.

19 members 1   53 members 1

Addison-Wesley | All Rights Reserved

86 Use with text pages 238–239. CS-4

Options for Individual Needs

Basic

Exercises 1-5
More Practice, p. 506, set B

Supplements
Reteaching 86 or
Practice 86

Average

Exercises 1-5
More Practice, p. 506, set B

Supplements
Practice 86
Challenges 86 or
Thinking Skills 86

Extended

Exercises 1-5

Supplements
Challenges 86
Thinking Skills 86

Other Resources:
Problem-Solving Experiences in Mathematics, Grade 4, Problem 45
Mathematics, Book A, Teacher's Edition, pp. 47, 48
Math In Stride, Grade 4, p. 55

LESSON PLAN 9-1

OBJECTIVE 9-1
To understand the operation of division

Materials: counters

1. MOTIVATE AND TEACH

LEARN ABOUT IT

BEFORE ▶ **Compare the 2 division actions.** (Both give an amount to be divided into groups; the first action gives the group size, and you find how many groups; the second action gives the number of groups, and you find how many per group.)

▶ **Explain how the equations relate to each situation.** (12 ÷ 3 means 12 puppets, 3 per box; 12 ÷ 4 means 12 people to operate 4 puppets.)

▶ **Explain how the multiplication words relate to the division equation for the first problem.** (12, the product of all groups, is divided by 3, which is 1 of its factors, to give the other factor.)

DURING ▶ **Decide how to finish both division equations.** (Find the missing factors; 4 and 3.)

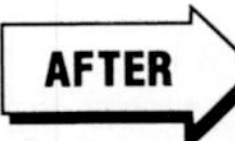

AFTER ▶ **Explain how to check your answer.** (Methods may vary; Use Objects; Act It Out; Draw a Picture.)

▶ **Explain how each answer fits its problem.** (You need 4 boxes; you need 3 people per puppet.)

2. CHECK UNDERSTANDING

TRY IT OUT

ERROR ALERT Confusing the numbers in the equations.

Problem Solving
Understanding Division

LEARN ABOUT IT

Division involves separating a total into same-size groups. The actions below help you decide when to use division. Show the actions with counters. Complete the equations.

Problem	Action	
	Separate Same-Size Groups	
A puppeteer put 12 puppets in boxes, 3 in each box. How many boxes did he need?	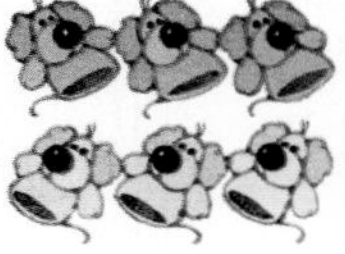 	**Divide** **12 ÷ 3 = ?** **product factor factor**
	Share Equally in Groups	
It takes 12 people to operate 4 large puppets. How many people are needed for each puppet?	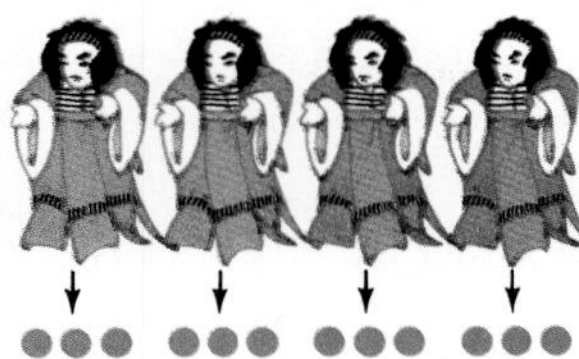	**Divide** **12 ÷ 4 = ?**

TRY IT OUT

Use counters to find the answer. Write an equation.

1. Four wood strips are used to make the controllers for each marionette puppet. How many controllers can you make with 20 wood strips?
5 controllers, 20 ÷ 4 = 5

2. It takes 15 people to operate 5 large female puppets. How many people are needed for each puppet?
3 people, 15 ÷ 5 = 3

TEACHING OPTIONS

RETEACHING TIPS Students write equations in the order they show the problems with counters. They write the amount to be divided, followed by the division sign, then the number of groups or objects per group they are showing. The answer follows the equal sign. Assign Reteaching Supplement 86.

ENRICHMENT Students create 2 division problems relating to the class. In 1 situation, they use the action of sharing equally in a given number of groups. In the other situation, they separate the class into same-size groups. Then they solve each other's problems.

PRACTICE

Use counters to find the answer. Write an equation.

1. Each marionette puppet takes 9 strings. You have 18 strings.

How many puppets can you make?
2 puppets; 18 ÷ 9 = 2

2. The 24 chairs at the puppet show were in rows of 6. How many rows were there?
4 rows; 24 ÷ 6 = 4

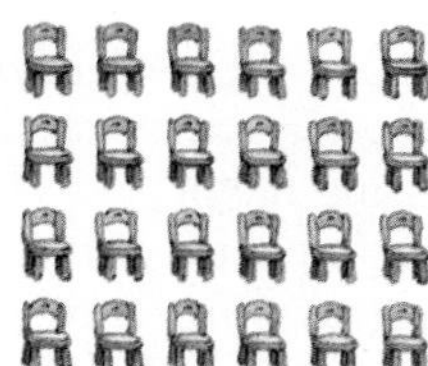

3. 15 puppets were stored in 3 boxes.

How many puppets were put in each box?
5 puppets; 15 ÷ 3 = 5

4. Bill had 20 strips of wood, just enough for 5 puppet controllers.

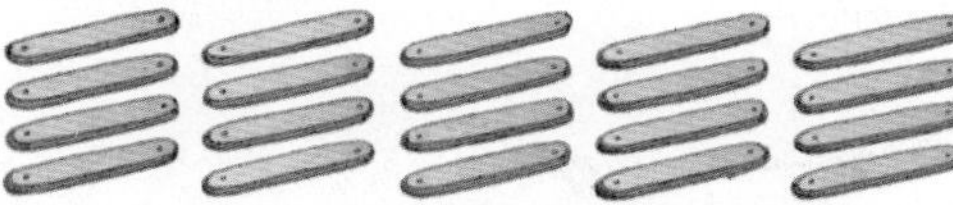

How many strips were needed for each controller?
4 strips; 20 ÷ 5 = 4

▶ **WRITE YOUR OWN PROBLEM**

5. Write two story problems that can be solved by dividing. Use a different action in each.
Answers will vary.

More Practice, page 506, set B

3. Practice and Apply

Basic	1-5
Average	1-5
Extended	1-5

9-1

PRACTICE

Restate the situation in Problem 1 in your own words. (Possible answer: There are 18 strings, and a puppet needs 9 strings.) *Explain how you would begin to solve Problem 1.* (Take 18 counters, make groups of 9.) *Explain how to recognize the answer to Problem 1.* (The answer is how many same-size groups you could make.) *Identify a same-size group in Problem 2.* (6 chairs per row) *What division action do Problems 3 and 4 use?* (sharing equally in groups)

WRITE YOUR OWN PROBLEM

▶ **Generalize about when to divide.** (to share equally or to separate into same-size groups)

▶ **Explain how to select reasonable numbers to use in your story problems.** (Possible answer: Think of a product and its 2 factors. Use the product as the number to divide, then use 1 of the factors as the number to divide by; the other factor will be the answer.)

Close and Assess

SHOW WHAT YOU KNOW

Have students use counters to show 18 ÷ 6 and 21 ÷ 3. Then have them justify the actions and explain the meaning of the answers. (3, 7; Explanations will vary.)

Quick Quiz

Use counters and write an equation to find the answer: 20 children sat in 4 equal rows to watch a puppet show. How many children were in each row? (20 ÷ 4 = 5)

LESSON OPTIONS 9-2

Relating Multiplication and Division

OBJECTIVE 9-2 To use multiplication to find quotients

PREBOOK ACTIVITIES

QUICK REVIEW

Find the products.

1. 4×2 (8)	**2.** 3×8 (24)	**3.** 6×2 (12)
4. 5×7 (35)	**5.** 6×6 (36)	**6.** 4×9 (36)
7. 1×6 (6)	**8.** 7×4 (28)	**9.** 6×8 (48)
10. 4×8 (32)	**11.** 3×7 (21)	**12.** 8×9 (72)

PRIOR KNOWLEDGE

Have students describe a fact family, giving an example of a fact family using addition and subtraction. (Possible answer: A fact family is a set of equations with 2 addends and their sum that can be rearranged to form 2 addition and 2 subtraction facts, such as $4 + 5 = 9$, $5 + 4 = 9$, $9 - 5 = 4$, and $9 - 4 = 5$.) Have students hypothesize about fact families for other operations. (Possible answer: You can make a fact family with related multiplication and division facts.)

COMMUNICATION

Writing and Listening in Math In their Math Journals, have students use 5 and 2 to write 2 multiplication facts, including the answer, and label each number as a factor or a product. ($5 \times 2 = 10$, $2 \times 5 = 10$; 5 and 2 are factors, 10 is the product.) Challenge them to rearrange the same 3 numbers to form 2 division equations. ($10 \div 2 = 5$, $10 \div 5 = 2$) Have students label the numbers in their equations by listening as you read the following sentences aloud: *The* ***dividend*** *is the amount you separate. The number you divide by is the* ***divisor****. The* ***quotient*** *is the answer in division.* (The dividend is 10; the divisor and quotient are 5 or 2, based on order.)

EXPLORE AND CONNECT

Materials: counters

Grouping Suggestion: cooperative learning pairs

Students explore the link between multiplication and division. Write these equations on the chalkboard: $4 \times \square = 12$, $3 \times \square = 15$, $2 \times \square = 14$, $6 \times \square = 18$. One student copies the first equation. A partner arranges 12 counters into 4 equal groups to find the missing factor. (3) That student completes the multiplication equation and writes a related division equation to record the action of separating the 12 counters into the 4 equal groups. ($12 \div 4 = 3$) Trading tasks, partners repeat for the remaining equations. Have students relate multiplication and division by linking factors and products to **dividends**, **divisors**, and **quotients**. (Possible answer: When you multiply, you know 2 factors and you find their product. When you divide, you know the product, or *dividend,* and 1 factor, or *divisor;* you find the other factor, or *quotient*.)

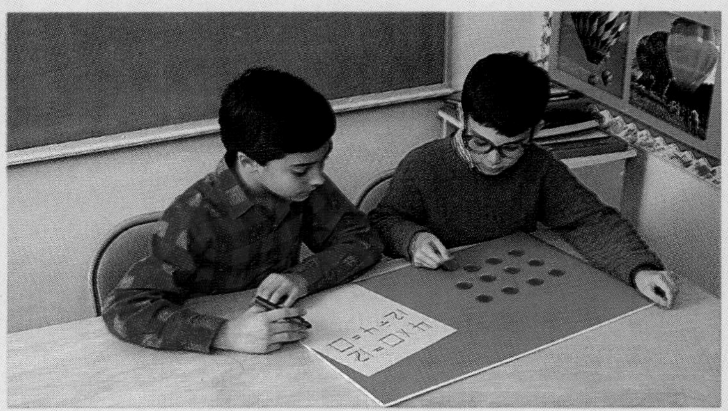

CONNECTIONS Use these anytime.

Problem of the Day

What is the Rule? Discover the rules for the 2 function machines.

In	*Out*
25	5
40	8
15	3

(Divide by 5.)

In	*Out*
4	2
14	7
10	5

(Divide by 2.)

Math Connection

Money Kurt found a $5 bill in his pants pocket and he wants to share the money with his 3 brothers. How many equal groups must Kurt make? How can he divide the money equally? (4; trade the $5 bill for four $1 bills and four quarters; each person gets $1.25.)

Subject Integration

Health and Fitness 24 students joined the after-school sports club. Now they want to make teams that have even numbers of players. Determine all the possible ways to form teams with all 24 players. (1 team of 24; 2 teams of 12; 3 teams of 8; 4 teams of 6; 6 teams of 4; 8 teams of 3; 12 teams of 2)

Classwork and Homework Supplements

Practice

Math Reasoning 9-2

Name ______

Relating Multiplication and Division

Write two multiplication and two division equations for each situation.

1. $3 \times 6 = 18$, $6 \times 3 = 18$;
   $18 \div 3 = 6$, $18 \div 6 = 3$

2. $5 \times 2 = 10$, $2 \times 5 = 10$;
   $10 \div 2 = 5$, $10 \div 5 = 2$

Give three more equations in the same fact family.

3. $7 \times 2 = 14$	4. $8 \times 4 = 32$	5. $9 \times 2 = 18$
$2 \times 7 = 14$	$4 \times 8 = 32$	$2 \times 9 = 18$
$14 \div 7 = 2$	$32 \div 8 = 4$	$18 \div 9 = 2$
$14 \div 2 = 7$	$32 \div 4 = 8$	$18 \div 2 = 9$

6. $30 \div 6 = 5$	7. $24 \div 4 = 6$	8. $35 \div 5 = 7$
$30 \div 5 = 6$	$24 \div 6 = 4$	$35 \div 7 = 5$
$6 \times 5 = 30$	$4 \times 6 = 24$	$7 \times 5 = 35$
$5 \times 6 = 30$	$6 \times 4 = 24$	$5 \times 7 = 35$

PS-4 Use with text pages 240–241. 87

Building Thinking Skills

Math Reasoning 9-2

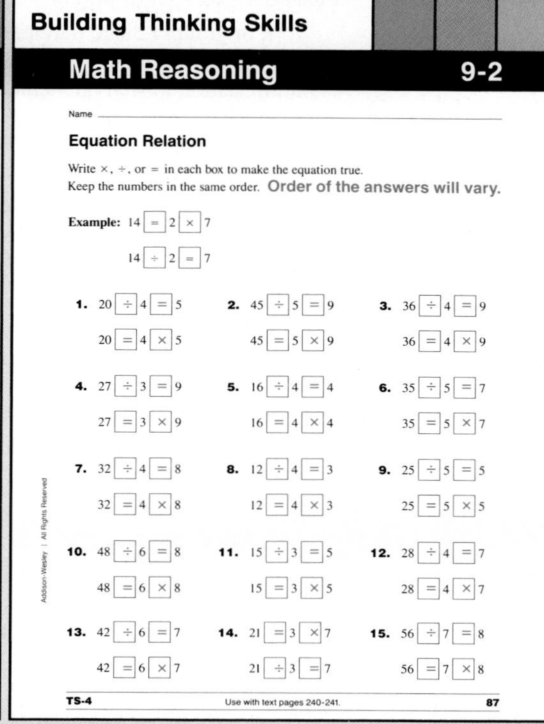

Name ______

Equation Relation

Write ×, ÷, or = in each box to make the equation true. Keep the numbers in the same order. Order of the answers will vary.

Example: 14 = 2 × 7
14 ÷ 2 = 7

1. 20 ÷ 4 = 5	2. 45 ÷ 5 = 9	3. 36 ÷ 4 = 9
20 = 4 × 5	45 = 5 × 9	36 = 4 × 9
4. 27 ÷ 3 = 9	5. 16 ÷ 4 = 4	6. 35 ÷ 5 = 7
27 = 3 × 9	16 = 4 × 4	35 = 5 × 7
7. 32 ÷ 4 = 8	8. 12 ÷ 4 = 3	9. 25 ÷ 5 = 5
32 = 4 × 8	12 = 4 × 3	25 = 5 × 5
10. 48 ÷ 6 = 8	11. 15 ÷ 3 = 5	12. 28 ÷ 4 = 7
48 = 6 × 8	15 = 3 × 5	28 = 4 × 7
13. 42 ÷ 6 = 7	14. 21 = 3 × 7	15. 56 ÷ 7 = 8
42 = 6 × 7	21 ÷ 3 = 7	56 = 7 × 8

TS-4 Use with text pages 240-241. 87

Reteaching

Skills Review 9-2

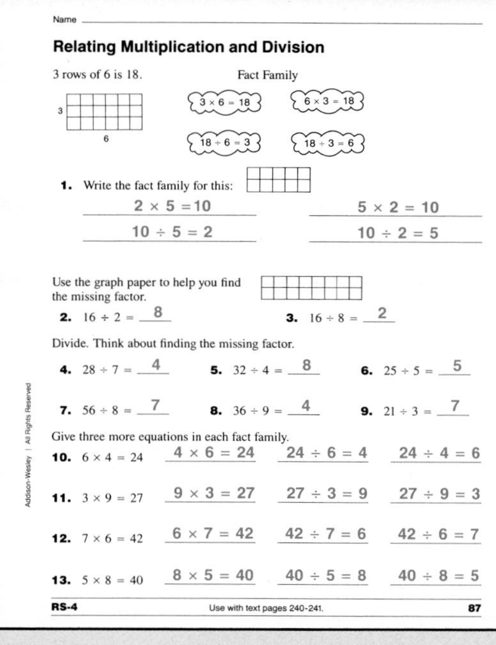

Name ______

Relating Multiplication and Division

3 rows of 6 is 18.

Fact Family: $3 \times 6 = 18$, $6 \times 3 = 18$, $18 \div 6 = 3$, $18 \div 3 = 6$

1. Write the fact family for this:
   $2 \times 5 = 10$ $5 \times 2 = 10$
   $10 \div 5 = 2$ $10 \div 2 = 5$

Use the graph paper to help you find the missing factor.

2. $16 \div 2 =$ 8
3. $16 \div 8 =$ 2

Divide. Think about finding the missing factor.

4. $28 \div 7 =$ 4
5. $32 \div 4 =$ 8
6. $25 \div 5 =$ 5
7. $56 \div 8 =$ 7
8. $36 \div 9 =$ 4
9. $21 \div 3 =$ 7

Give three more equations in each fact family.

10. $6 \times 4 = 24$	$4 \times 6 = 24$	$24 \div 6 = 4$	$24 \div 4 = 6$
11. $3 \times 9 = 27$	$9 \times 3 = 27$	$27 \div 3 = 9$	$27 \div 9 = 3$
12. $7 \times 6 = 42$	$6 \times 7 = 42$	$42 \div 7 = 6$	$42 \div 6 = 7$
13. $5 \times 8 = 40$	$8 \times 5 = 40$	$40 \div 5 = 8$	$40 \div 8 = 5$

RS-4 Use with text pages 240-241. 87

Challenges

Critical Thinking 9-2

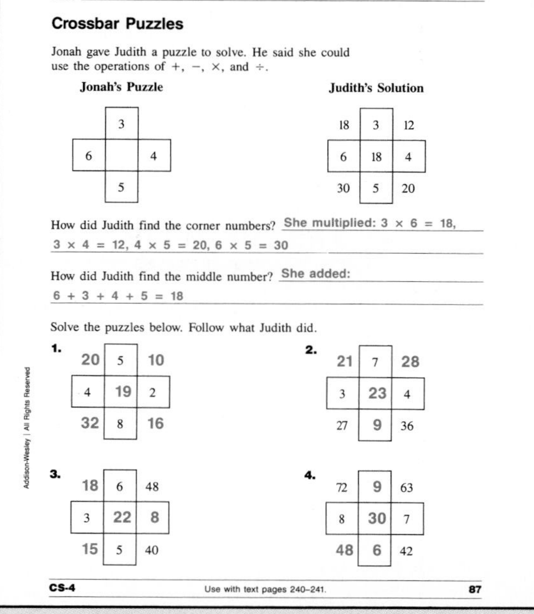

Name ______

Crossbar Puzzles

Jonah gave Judith a puzzle to solve. He said she could use the operations of +, −, ×, and ÷.

Jonah's Puzzle

	3	
6		4
	5	

Judith's Solution

18	3	12
6	18	4
30	5	20

How did Judith find the corner numbers? She multiplied: $3 \times 6 = 18$, $3 \times 4 = 12$, $4 \times 5 = 20$, $6 \times 5 = 30$

How did Judith find the middle number? She added: $6 + 3 + 4 + 5 = 18$

Solve the puzzles below. Follow what Judith did.

1.

20	5	10
4	19	2
32	8	16

2.

21	7	28
3	23	4
27	9	36

3.

18	6	48
3	22	8
15	5	40

4.

72	9	63
8	30	7
48	6	42

CS-4 Use with text pages 240-241. 87

Options for Individual Needs

Basic

Exercises 1-9, 12-22, 27-31
More Practice, p. 520, set C

Supplements
Reteaching 87 or
Practice 87
Thinking Skills 87

Average

Exercises 1-31
More Practice, p. 520, set C

Supplements
Practice 87
Challenges 87 or
Thinking Skills 87

Extended

Exercises 3-29

Supplements
Challenges 87
Thinking Skills 87

Other Resources:
Problem-Solving Experiences in Mathematics, Grade 4, Problem 47
Math In Stride, Grade 4, pp. 117, 118
Mathematics, Book A, Teacher's Edition, pp. 49, 50

LESSON PLAN 9-2

OBJECTIVE 9-2
To use multiplication to find quotients

Materials: TA 12 (Centimeter Graph Paper), scissors, counters

Grouping Suggestion: small groups

1. MOTIVATE AND TEACH

LEARN ABOUT IT

EXPLORE ▶ **Analyze the factors in the rectangle with 12 boxes.** (3 rows of 4 boxes each is 12 boxes.)
▶ **Explain how a fact family relates multiplication and division.** (All the equations use the same 3 numbers.)
▶ **Compare Examples A, B, C, and D.** (Both factors are given in A; the others all have a missing factor.)

TALK ABOUT IT ▶ **Explain how the product in multiplication relates to part of the division equation.** (The product is a total and the dividend is that total.)
▶ **Explain how the quotient relates to multiplication.** (It is always the missing factor.)
Student Edition answers: **1.** 4 × 2 **2.** 4 × 2 = 8, 2 × 4 = 8, 8 ÷ 4 = 2, 8 ÷ 2 = 4; 8 × 3 = 24, 3 × 8 = 24, 24 ÷ 8 = 3, 24 ÷ 3 = 8; 3 × 7 = 21, 7 × 3 = 21, 21 ÷ 3 = 7, 21 ÷ 7 = 3; 6 × 6 = 36, 36 ÷ 6 = 6; You multiply 2 factors to find a product; you divide the product (dividend) by 1 factor (divisor) to find the other factor (quotient).

2. CHECK UNDERSTANDING

TRY IT OUT

ERROR ALERT Using the wrong operation. Finding the wrong quotient.

Relating Multiplication and Division

LEARN ABOUT IT

EXPLORE **Use Graph Paper**
Work in groups. Since multiplication and division are related, you can use multiplication to find quotients. Cut out graph paper rectangles to show that you have found the missing numbers in these examples.

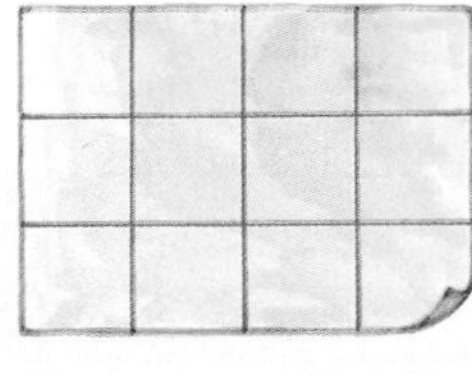

3 rows of 4 is 12

Fact Family

4 × 3 = 12	3 × 4 = 12
12 ÷ 4 = 3	12 ÷ 3 = 4

A
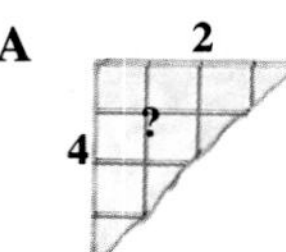

B
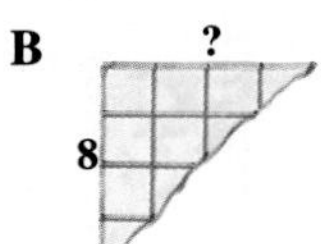

C
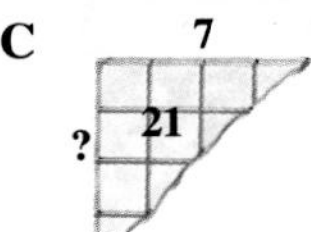

D
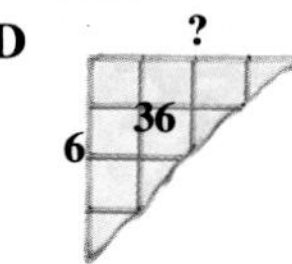

TALK ABOUT IT See teaching notes.

1. In example A, how can you easily find the number that goes with 4 and 2?
2. Give a fact family for each example. Explain how multiplication and division are related.

In multiplication you know two factors and find the product. In division you know the product and one factor. You find the other factor.

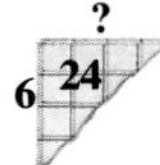

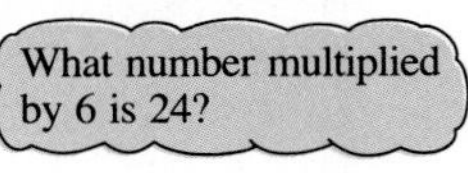

What number multiplied by 6 is 24?

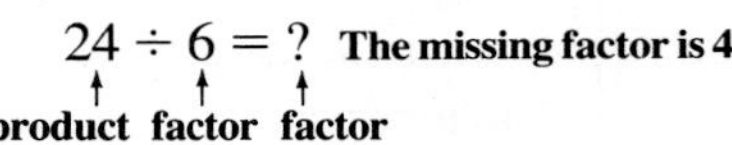

?
4
24
What number multiplied by 4 is 24?

24 ÷ 6 = ? **The missing factor is 4.**
product factor factor

24 ÷ 4 = ? **The missing factor is 6.**
product factor factor

TRY IT OUT

Divide. Think about finding the missing factor.

1. 15 ÷ 3 = |||| 5 **2.** 28 ÷ 4 = |||| 7 **3.** 20 ÷ 5 = |||| 4 **4.** 14 ÷ 2 = |||| 7

TEACHING OPTIONS

RETEACHING TIPS Have students use counters to represent the dividend. They divide the counters into groups based on the size of the divisor. The quotient will be the number of groups that can be made. Assign Reteaching Supplement 87.

ENRICHMENT Have students form a multiplication and division fact family with 2 equations that use the same 3 digits. (1 × 1 = 1; 1 ÷ 1 = 1)

PRACTICE

1. Write two multiplication and two division equations for this situation.
4 × 5 = 20, 5 × 4 = 20
20 ÷ 4 = 5; 20 ÷ 5 = 4

5 | 4 | 20

Give three or more equations in the same fact family.

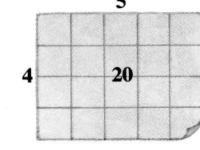

2. 3 × 2 = 6 **3.** 2 × 8 = 16 **4.** 18 ÷ 3 = 6
See Additional Answers.

APPLY

MATH REASONING Give the fact family for each set of factors. Which is different from the others? Why?
See Additional Answers.

5. 2, 5 **6.** 3, 6 **7.** 2, 9 **8.** 4, 3

9. 3, 3 **10.** 2, 6 **11.** 3, 7 **12.** 4, 8

PROBLEM SOLVING

13. Kristy pasted 8 stamps in each row in her stamp book. She filled 4 rows. How many stamps did she put in the book? 32 stamps

14. Rob planted 6 rows with 5 trees in each row. He had 3 extra trees. How many trees were there? 33 trees

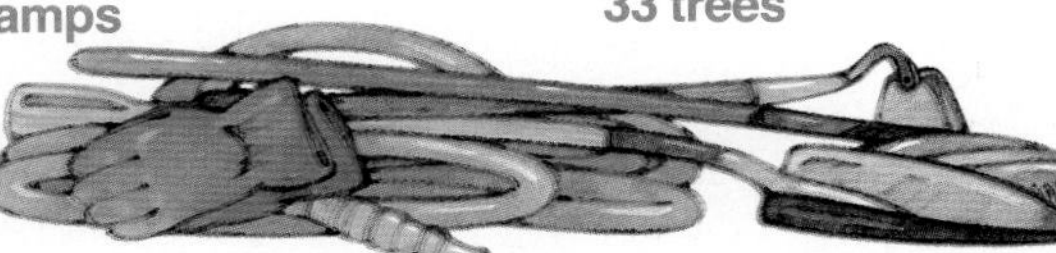

MIXED REVIEW

Find the product.

15. 3,798 × 5 18,990	**16.** 7,654 × 9 68,886	**17.** 2,639 × 7 18,473	**18.** 8,022 × 6 48,132
19. 9,606 × 8 76,848	**20.** 4,394 × 4 17,576	**21.** $22.99 × 3 $68.97	**22.** $6.52 × 2 $13.04
23. 4,526 × 6 27,156	**24.** 1,896 × 5 9,480	**25.** 2,004 × 8 16,032	**26.** 9,420 × 7 65,940

Write the correct time as you would see it on a digital clock.

27. quarter past five 5:15 **28.** twelve minutes past eleven 11:12

29. seven-thirty 7:30 **30.** half past two 2:15 **31.** six-forty-five 6:45

More Practice, page 520, set C

3. Practice and Apply

Basic	1-9, 12-22, 27-31
Average	1-31
Extended	3-29

9-2

Additional Answers: See p. T79.

PRACTICE

Which number must come first when you write a division equation using the ÷ sign? (the number that is the product when you multiply)

APPLY

MATH REASONING ► **Analyze the exercises to decide what you need to know to write a fact family.** (the product of the given factors)

PROBLEM SOLVING ► **Justify the operation to use in Problem 13.** (multiplication to put together same-size groups)
► **Explain the order of operations to solve Problem 14.** (Multiply 6 × 5, then add 3.)

MIXED REVIEW ► **Generalize about how to write digital times.** (Write the hour first, then a colon, then any minutes past the hour.)

Close and Assess

WRITE WHAT YOU THINK
Have students write a fact family for an even multiple of 7. They should label the factors and product in the multiplication equations, then label the dividend, divisor, and quotient in the division equations. (Answers may vary. Check students' writing.)

Quick Quiz

Complete each fact family.
1. 4 × 9 = 36 **2.** 3 × 2 = 6
3. 16 ÷ 4 = 4 (**1.** 9 × 4 = 36, 36 ÷ 9 = 4, 36 ÷ 4 = 9 **2.** 2 × 3 = 6, 6 ÷ 3 = 2, 6 ÷ 2 = 3 **3.** 4 × 4 = 16)

LESSON OPTIONS 9-3

Dividing by 2 and 3

OBJECTIVE 9-3 To use missing factors to divide by 2 and 3

PREBOOK ACTIVITIES

QUICK REVIEW

Find the missing factors.

1. 5 × □ = 15 (3) **2.** 3 × □ = 18 (6)
3. □ × 4 = 8 (2) **4.** 3 × □ = 27 (9)
5. 6 × □ = 12 (2) **6.** □ × 7 = 21 (3)
7. □ × 8 = 16 (2) **8.** 3 × □ = 24 (8)
9. 2 × □ = 14 (7) **10.** 5 × □ = 10 (2)

PRIOR KNOWLEDGE

Have students suggest real-life situations when an amount might be divided by 2. (Possible answers: to find half; to share something between 2 people; to see how many pairs of people can be made) Then have them suggest cases in which amounts might be divided by 3. (Possible answers: to make teams of 3; to share something equally among 3 people)

COMMUNICATION

Discussing Math Have students offer synonyms for the verb **check.** (Possible answers: *test, verify, examine*) Have them suggest a paper-and-pencil way to check addition. (Possible answer: Combine addends in a different order.) Have students tell how to check subtraction. (Add the difference and 1 addend to get the other addend.) Ask them how to check multiplication. (Use another factor order, or go back over your original steps.) Then challenge students to apply their understanding of fact families to suggest a way to check division. (Multiply the quotient by the divisor to get the dividend.)

EXPLORE AND CONNECT

Materials: counters
Grouping Suggestion: cooperative learning pairs
Students explore division by 2 and by 3. Write the numbers 12 to 21 on the chalkboard. Partners use counters to divide each number by 2 and by 3. They record a division equation *only* if all counters can be divided into equal groups. (12 ÷ 2 = 6, 12 ÷ 3 = 4, 14 ÷ 2 = 7, 15 ÷ 3 = 5, 16 ÷ 2 = 8, 18 ÷ 2 = 9, 18 ÷ 3 = 6, 20 ÷ 2 = 10, 21 ÷ 3 = 7; 13, 17, and 19 are not divisible by 2 or by 3.) Partners **check** by writing a related multiplication fact to show that the division is correct. (2 × 6 = 12, 4 × 3 = 12, 2 × 7 = 14, 3 × 5 = 15, 2 × 8 = 16, 2 × 9 = 18, 3 × 6 = 18, 2 × 10 = 20, 3 × 7 = 21) Have students generalize about dividing by 2 or by 3. (Possible answers: You can divide any even number by 2; some odd numbers can be divided by 3, others cannot, but none can be divided by 2; some numbers can be divided by 2 and by 3.)

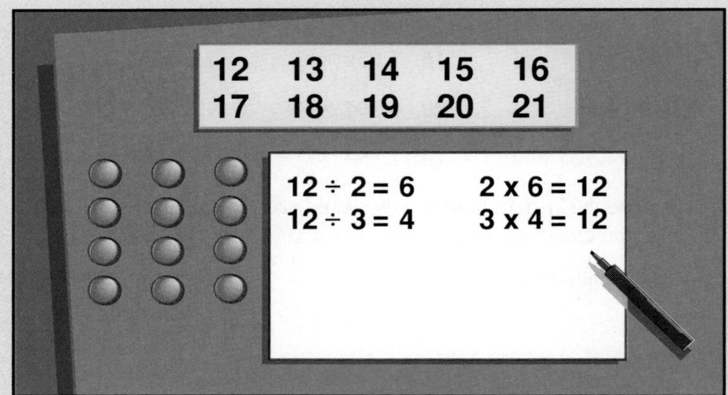

CONNECTIONS Use these anytime.

Problem of the Day

Number Fun Pick a number from 1 to 9, then follow the steps: **1.** Multiply by 3. **2.** Subtract 2. **3.** Add 5. **4.** Subtract 3. **5.** Divide by 3. Give the result, and explain why. (You get the original number because you used opposite operations.)

Math Connection

Math Language Translate these sentences into numbers and symbols.
1. A dividend of 15 and a divisor of 3 give a quotient of 5. (15 ÷ 3 = 5)
2. The quotient is 8 when the divisor is 2 and the dividend is 16. (16 ÷ 2 = 8)

Life Skills

Money Jasmine bought a bracelet and got in change 4 coins that totaled $0.85. If 1 coin was a dime, what were the other 3 coins? (quarters)

Classwork and Homework Supplements

Practice

Skills Maintenance 9-3

Name ____________

Dividing by 2 and 3

Find the quotients.

1. 10 ÷ 2 = 5
2. 9 ÷ 3 = 3
3. 15 ÷ 3 = 5
4. 12 ÷ 2 = 6
5. 27 ÷ 3 = 9
6. 6 ÷ 3 = 2
7. 8 ÷ 2 = 4
8. 14 ÷ 2 = 7
9. 6 ÷ 2 = 3
10. 12 ÷ 3 = 4
11. 18 ÷ 3 = 6
12. 16 ÷ 2 = 8

13. $2\overline{)4}$ 2
14. $3\overline{)24}$ 8
15. $2\overline{)2}$ 1
16. $2\overline{)18}$ 9
17. $3\overline{)27}$ 9
18. $2\overline{)12}$ 6
19. $3\overline{)12}$ 4
20. $2\overline{)16}$ 8
21. $2\overline{)14}$ 7
22. $3\overline{)18}$ 6
23. $3\overline{)3}$ 1
24. $3\overline{)21}$ 7
25. $3\overline{)27}$ 9
26. $2\overline{)16}$ 8
27. $3\overline{)6}$ 2
28. $2\overline{)10}$ 5
29. $3\overline{)15}$ 5
30. $2\overline{)14}$ 7
31. $2\overline{)8}$ 4
32. $3\overline{)27}$ 9
33. Find the quotient of 18 and 3. 6
34. Divide 24 by 3. 8

88 Use with text pages 242-243. PS-4

Building Thinking Skills

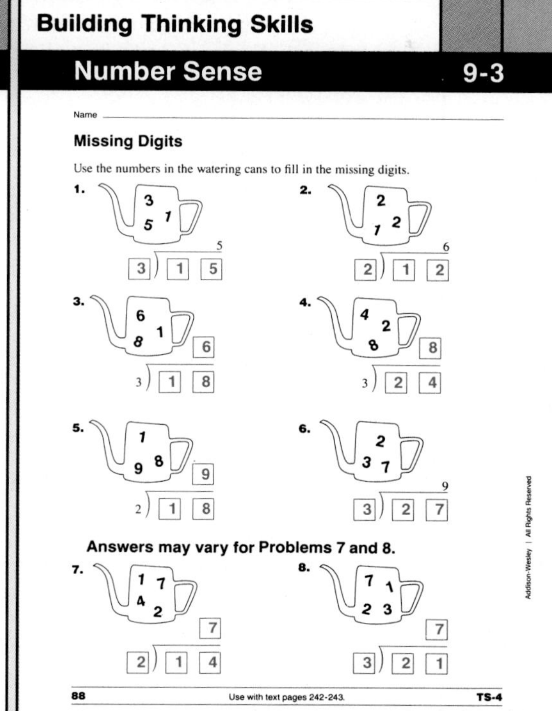

Number Sense 9-3

Name ____________

Missing Digits

Use the numbers in the watering cans to fill in the missing digits.

1. 3, 5, 1 — $3\overline{)15}$ = 5
2. 2, 7, 2 — $2\overline{)12}$ = 6
3. 6, 8, 1 — $3\overline{)18}$ = 6
4. 4, 2, 8 — $3\overline{)24}$ = 8
5. 1, 9, 8 — $2\overline{)18}$ = 9
6. 2, 3, 7 — $3\overline{)27}$ = 9

Answers may vary for Problems 7 and 8.

7. 1, 7, 4, 2 — $2\overline{)14}$ = 7
8. 7, 1, 2, 3 — $3\overline{)21}$ = 7

88 Use with text pages 242-243. TS-4

Reteaching

Skills Review 9-3

Name ____________

Dividing by 2 and 3

Use a multiplication equation to find a quotient.

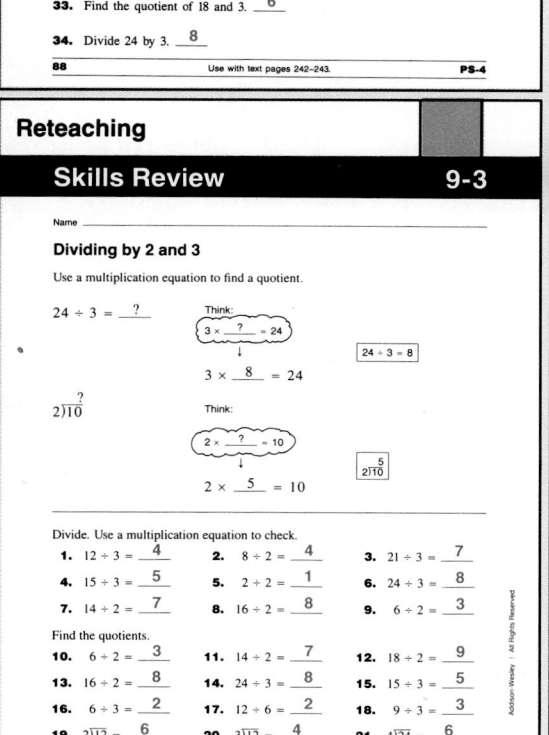

24 ÷ 3 = ? Think: 3 × ? = 24 → 3 × 8 = 24 [24 ÷ 3 = 8]

$2\overline{)10}$? Think: 2 × ? = 10 → 2 × 5 = 10 [$2\overline{)10}$ 5]

Divide. Use a multiplication equation to check.

1. 12 ÷ 3 = 4
2. 8 ÷ 2 = 4
3. 21 ÷ 3 = 7
4. 15 ÷ 3 = 5
5. 2 ÷ 2 = 1
6. 24 ÷ 3 = 8
7. 14 ÷ 2 = 7
8. 16 ÷ 2 = 8
9. 6 ÷ 2 = 3

Find the quotients.

10. 6 ÷ 2 = 3
11. 14 ÷ 2 = 7
12. 18 ÷ 2 = 9
13. 16 ÷ 2 = 8
14. 24 ÷ 3 = 8
15. 15 ÷ 3 = 5
16. 6 ÷ 3 = 2
17. 12 ÷ 6 = 2
18. 9 ÷ 3 = 3
19. $2\overline{)12}$ = 6
20. $3\overline{)12}$ = 4
21. $4\overline{)24}$ = 6
22. $2\overline{)8}$ = 4
23. $3\overline{)21}$ = 7
24. $2\overline{)18}$ = 9
25. $3\overline{)27}$ = 9
26. $3\overline{)15}$ = 5
27. $3\overline{)12}$ = 4

88 Use with text pages 242-243. RS-4

Challenges

Writing Math 9-3

Name ____________

The 3-Tester

Work with a small group to solve this challenge.

Mr. Li wanted to divide the students in his school into 3 equal teams. He invented the 3-Tester. If you tell the 3-Tester a certain number of students, it will tell you if the number can be divided into 3 equal teams.

Start → Pick a number. → Add the digits of the number. → Keep adding the digits until you get only one digit. → Is your digit a 3, 6, or 9?
- NO → This number of students cannot be divided into 3 equal teams. → Stop
- YES → This number of students can be divided into 3 equal teams. → Stop

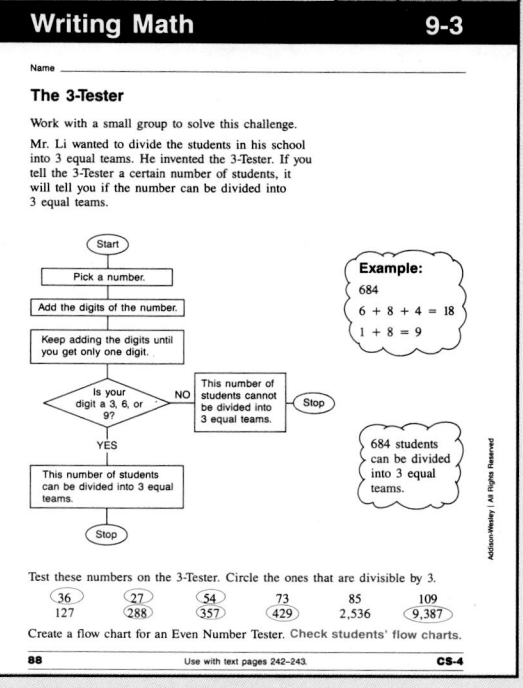

Example: 684; 6 + 8 + 4 = 18; 1 + 8 = 9

684 students can be divided into 3 equal teams.

Test these numbers on the 3-Tester. Circle the ones that are divisible by 3.

(36) (27) (54) 73 85 109
127 (288) (357) (429) 2,536 (9,387)

Create a flow chart for an Even Number Tester. Check students' flow charts.

88 Use with text pages 242-243. CS-4

Options for Individual Needs

9-3

Basic

Exercises 5-22, 29-37
More Practice, p. 506, set C

Supplements
Reteaching 88 or
Practice 88
Challenges 88

Average

Exercises 1-37
More Practice, p. 506, set C

Supplements
Practice 88
Challenges 88 or
Thinking Skills 88

Extended

Exercises 9-20, 29-37

Supplements
Challenges 88
Thinking Skills 88

Other Resources:
Problem-Solving Experiences in Mathematics, Grade 4, Problem 46
Math In Stride, Grade 4, p. 56
Mathematics: A Way of Thinking, Lessons 6-1, 6-2

LESSON PLAN 9-3

OBJECTIVE 9-3

To use missing factors to divide by 2 and 3

Materials: TA 15 (Dot Paper)

Grouping Suggestion: pairs

1. MOTIVATE AND TEACH

LEARN ABOUT IT

EXPLORE ▶ **Explain the given and the missing data in the chart.** (It lists 4 kinds of flower bulbs packed 2 or 3 per package and the total number of bulbs needed; missing is how many packages give the total for 3 types of bulbs.)

TALK ABOUT IT ▶ **Explain how the tulip data relate to a multiplication fact.** (2 bulbs per package multiplied by 6 packages equals 12 bulbs.)
▶ **Explain how the tulip data relate to a division fact.** (12 bulbs divided by 2 bulbs per package equals 6 packages.)
▶ **Explain how division can help you find the number of packages for the total.** (Use the total as the dividend and divide by how many bulbs per package. The quotient is how many packages are needed.)
▶ **Explain how fact families can help with the division.** (Think of the number of packages as a missing factor.)
▶ **Explain why multiplication can check division.** (It uses the fact-family relationship.)
Student Edition answers: **1.** 3 × 5 = 15 **2.** 8, 8, 2 × 8 = 16, 3 × 8 = 24

2. CHECK UNDERSTANDING

TRY IT OUT

ERROR ALERT Finding the wrong quotient. Forgetting to multiply to check quotients.

Dividing by 2 and 3

LEARN ABOUT IT

EXPLORE Discover a Relationship
Knowing the multiplication facts for 2 and 3 can help you divide by 2 and 3.

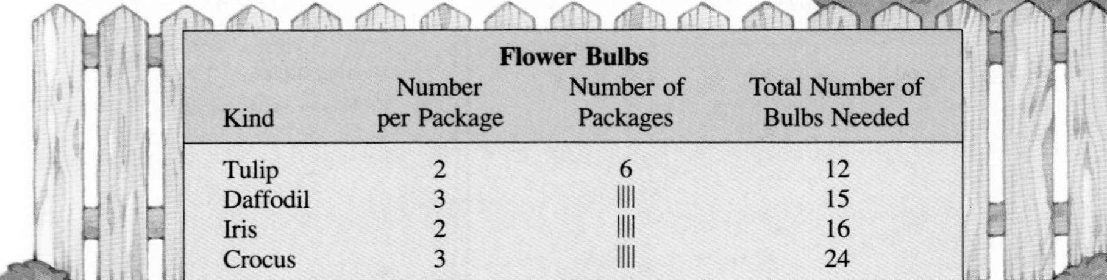

Flower Bulbs

Kind	Number per Package	Number of Packages	Total Number of Bulbs Needed
Tulip	2	6	12
Daffodil	3	▯	15
Iris	2	▯	16
Crocus	3	▯	24

TALK ABOUT IT See teaching notes.

1. To find the number of packages of 3 daffodil bulbs it takes to have 15 bulbs, you find the missing factor when 15 is divided by 3. What multiplication fact would help you?
2. What missing factor would give the number of packages to buy to get 16 iris bulbs? 24 crocus bulbs? What multiplication facts would help you?

Here is how you can use multiplication to find a quotient. The division equation is shown in two ways.

2 times what number is 18?

$18 \div 2 = 9$

Check: $2 \times 9 = 18$

3 times what number is 27?

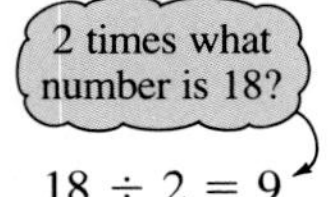

$3\overline{)27}$ with quotient 9

Check: $3 \times 9 = 27$

Here are some special terms used in division.

$2\overline{)12}$ with quotient 6; $12 \div 2 = 6$ — quotient (6), dividend (12), divisor (2)

TRY IT OUT

Divide. Use a multiplication equation to check.

1. 12 ÷ 3 4, 3 × 4 = 12
2. 16 ÷ 2 8, 2 × 8 = 16
3. 21 ÷ 3 7, 3 × 7 = 21
4. 18 ÷ 3 6, 3 × 6 = 18
5. 10 ÷ 2 5, 2 × 5 = 10

242

TEACHING OPTIONS

RETEACHING TIPS On dot paper, students box the number of dots in the dividend. Within that box, they circle groups of 2 or 3, based on the divisor. The quotient is how many groups were made. They check by multiplying the number of groups by the dots per group. Assign Reteaching Supplement 88.

ENRICHMENT Family Math Have students try this activity at home: Count the total number of individual socks you have. Divide that number by 2 to see how many pairs of socks you have. Try the same thing with the shoes belonging to several family members. Have a family member check your answers.

PRACTICE

Find the quotients.

1. 12 ÷ 2 6
2. 9 ÷ 3 3
3. 14 ÷ 2 7
4. 4 ÷ 2 2
5. 15 ÷ 3 5
6. 21 ÷ 3 7
7. 8 ÷ 2 4
8. 27 ÷ 3 9
9. 10 ÷ 2 5
10. 6 ÷ 3 2
11. 24 ÷ 3 8
12. 6 ÷ 2 3
13. 16 ÷ 2 8
14. 18 ÷ 3 6
15. 18 ÷ 2 9
16. 12 ÷ 3 4
17. 3)15 5
18. 2)18 9
19. 3)27 9
20. 2)16 8
21. 3)24 8
22. 2)10 5
23. 3)12 4
24. 2)8 4
25. 2)12 6
26. 3)9 3
27. 2)4 2
28. 3)18 6
29. Find the quotient of 14 and 2. 7
30. Divide 21 by 3. 7

APPLY

MATH REASONING Use the equations in the box to find these quotients.

2 × 243 = 486	2 × 173 = 346
3 × 109 = 327	3 × 152 = 456

31. 346 ÷ 2 173
32. 327 ÷ 3 109
33. 456 ÷ 3 152
34. 486 ÷ 2 243

PROBLEM SOLVING

35. Tim bought 6 packages with 2 bulbs in each and 4 packages with 3 bulbs in each. How many bulbs did he buy? 24 bulbs

36. **Unfinished Problem** Jessica needed 18 bulbs. There were 3 bulbs in each package. Write a question to finish the problem. Answers will vary. Sample answer: How many packages did Jessica need? 6 packages

▶ USING CRITICAL THINKING Logical Reasoning

37. Can you find the secret number? Here are some clues.
    - It is odd and has just one digit.
    - It is not the number of days in a week.
    - It can be divided by 3, but its quotient is not 3. 3

More Practice, page 506, set C

3. PRACTICE AND APPLY

Basic	5-22, 29-37
Average	1-37
Extended	9-20, 29-37

9-3

PRACTICE

In Exercises 1 to 16, which number is the divisor? (the second number) *Which is the divisor in Exercises 17 to 28?* (the number in front of the division symbol)

APPLY

MATH REASONING ▶ **Analyze how fact families can help in Exercises 31 to 34.** (Rewrite the multiplication facts in the table as division facts, then match to the equations.)

PROBLEM SOLVING ▶ **Explain why Problem 35 takes several steps to solve.** (First multiply 6 × 2, then multiply 4 × 3, then add the 2 products.)

USING CRITICAL THINKING

▶ **Develop a plan based on the first clue.** (Possible answer: List all odd 1-digit numbers.)

▶ **How can the next clue narrow the list?** (Cross out 7.)

CLOSE AND ASSESS

SAY WHAT YOU THINK Have students work in pairs. The first student says a division fact with a divisor that is 2 and that can be divided evenly. The second student responds with a multiplication fact that checks the division. Partners switch tasks and repeat, using a divisor of 3. (Answers will vary.)

QUICK QUIZ

Find the quotients.

1. 18 ÷ 2 (9)
2. 24 ÷ 3 (8)
3. 15 ÷ 3 (5)
4. 12 ÷ 2 (6)
5. 6 ÷ 2 (3)
6. 21 ÷ 3 (7)
7. 27 ÷ 3 (9)
8. 14 ÷ 2 (7)

LESSON OPTIONS 9-4

Dividing by 4 and 5

OBJECTIVE 9-4 To use missing factors to divide by 4 and 5

PREBOOK ACTIVITIES

QUICK REVIEW

Find the missing factors.

1.	$5 \times \square = 20$ (4)	**2.**	$3 \times \square = 12$ (4)
3.	$\square \times 4 = 8$ (2)	**4.**	$7 \times \square = 35$ (5)
5.	$6 \times \square = 24$ (4)	**6.**	$\square \times 7 = 28$ (4)
7.	$\square \times 8 = 40$ (5)	**8.**	$3 \times \square = 15$ (5)
9.	$8 \times \square = 32$ (4)	**10.**	$5 \times \square = 30$ (6)

PRIOR KNOWLEDGE

Have students recall how multiplication and division relate. (Possible answer: When you divide, you think of the dividend and the divisor as the product and 1 factor of a multiplication fact. You divide to find the other factor, which is the quotient.)

COMMUNICATION

Discussing Math Have students skip count by fives, then summarize a pattern in the multiples. (All products end in 0 or 5.) Ask students to explain how recognizing multiples of 5 could help in division. (Possible answer: If a dividend ends in 0 or 5, you know you can divide it by 5.)

EXPLORE AND CONNECT

Materials: TA 12 (Centimeter Graph Paper), TA 3 (Number Cards 1-9)

Grouping Suggestion: cooperative learning pairs

Students show the relationship between multiplication and division. Students set aside the 4 and 5 number cards. From the remaining number cards, the first student picks a card and multiplies its number by the 4 card, recording the fact, such as $7 \times 4 = 28$. His or her partner verifies the product, then shows division by 4 on graph paper and records it, such as $28 \div 4 = 7$. Then partners replace the 4 card with the 5 card and repeat the steps with the other factor. When the factor has been multiplied by 4 and by 5 and that product has been divided by 4 and by 5, partners trade tasks and repeat the activity. Have students discuss any patterns they noticed. (Possible answers: 4 is always divided into even numbers; products of 5 and another factor always end in 0 or 5.)

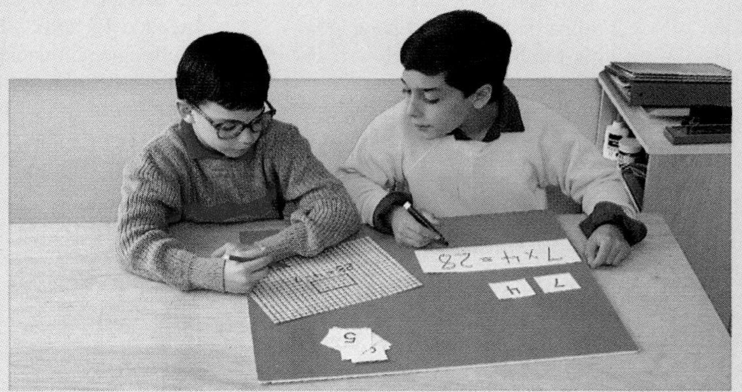

CONNECTIONS Use these anytime.

Problem of the Day

Money Exchange Randy has 43 pennies in his penny bank. He must trade them in for nickels to use for the bus, which does not accept pennies. Explain the trade Randy can make. (He can trade 40 pennies for 8 nickels, but he will have 3 pennies left over.)

Life Skills

Unit Prices A farm stand sells apples at 2 for 18¢, apricots at 5 for 45¢, and plums at 3 for 15¢. If Sasha wants a piece of each fruit, is a quarter enough money? Explain. (yes; An apple is 9¢, an apricot is 9¢, and a plum is 5¢, which comes to 23¢ in all.)

Math Connection

Measurement A recipe for party punch calls for 16 qt of lemonade. Lynne knows that lemonade costs less if she buys it by the gallon. How many gallons of lemonade should she buy? (4 gal)

Classwork and Homework Supplements

Practice

Skills Maintenance 9-4

Name

Dividing by 4 and 5

Find the quotients.

1. 8 ÷ 4 = 2
2. 30 ÷ 5 = 6
3. 15 ÷ 5 = 3
4. 12 ÷ 4 = 3
5. 28 ÷ 4 = 7
6. 25 ÷ 5 = 5
7. 32 ÷ 4 = 8
8. 10 ÷ 5 = 2
9. 35 ÷ 5 = 7
10. 16 ÷ 4 = 4
11. 36 ÷ 4 = 9
12. 20 ÷ 5 = 4

13. 4)20 = 5
14. 5)25 = 5
15. 4)8 = 2
16. 5)35 = 7
17. 5)10 = 2
18. 4)4 = 1
19. 4)28 = 7
20. 5)15 = 3
21. 4)32 = 8
22. 5)30 = 6
23. 5)5 = 1
24. 4)12 = 3
25. 5)45 = 9
26. 4)36 = 9
27. 5)5 = 1
28. 5)40 = 8
29. 4)24 = 6
30. 5)40 = 8
31. 5)20 = 4
32. 4)16 = 4

33. Find the quotient of 30 and 5. 6
34. Divide 28 by 4. 7

PS-4 Use with text pages 244-245. 89

Building Thinking Skills

Math Reasoning 9-4

Name

Organizing a Fishing Trip

Colleen and Randall are going on a fishing trip with their Uncle Jack and Aunt Ginny. Here is the list of things they have to take with them.

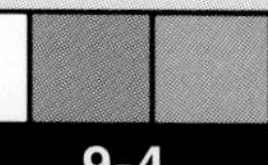

Bait	
Worms	45 worms
Shrimps	5 cans
Food	
Sandwiches	16 sandwiches
Apples	20 apples
Carrots	5 bags
Other	
Lures	5 packs
Hooks	16 hooks
Sinkers	4 packs

1. If they bought 5 cans of worms, and each can had the same number of worms, how many were in each can? 9 worms
2. Aunt Ginny said that 1 can of shrimps is usually needed to catch 5 fish. They want to catch about 20 fish using shrimps as bait. Are they bringing enough shrimp? Yes; only 4 cans are needed.
3. There were 4 sandwiches left at the end of the trip. How many sandwiches did each person eat? 3 sandwiches
4. The carrots came in bags of 6 each. They bought 4 bags of apples. Were there more apples per bag or more carrots per bag? more carrots per bag
5. If they each ended up with 15 lures, how many lures came in each pack? 12 lures
6. They bought 4 packs of hooks and 24 sinkers. How many more sinkers were in each pack than hooks? 2

TS-4 Use with text pages 244-245. 89

Reteaching

Skills Review 9-4

Name

Dividing by 4 and 5

A fact family has four facts. Each fact uses the same three numbers.

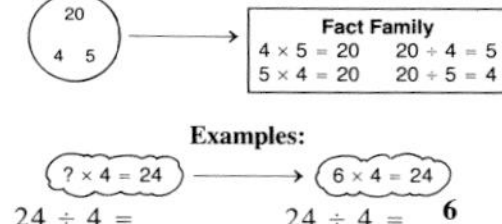

Fact Family	
4 × 5 = 20	20 ÷ 4 = 5
5 × 4 = 20	20 ÷ 5 = 4

Use fact families or missing factors to help find a quotient.

Examples:

? × 4 = 24 → 6 × 4 = 24

24 ÷ 4 = ___ 24 ÷ 4 = 6

Solve.

1. 3 × 4 = 12 12 ÷ 4 = 3; 4 × 3 = 12 12 ÷ 3 = 4
2. 3 × 5 = 15 15 ÷ 5 = 3; 5 × 3 = 15 15 ÷ 3 = 5

Divide.

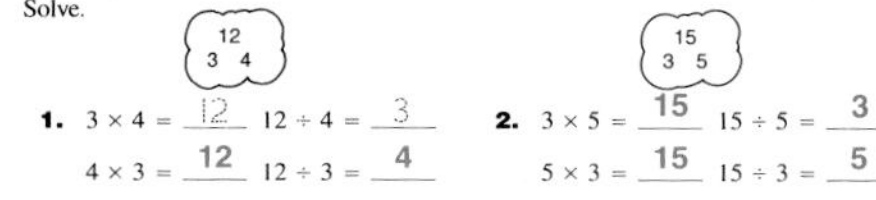

3. 8 ÷ 4 = 2 (? × 4 = 8)
4. 10 ÷ 5 = 2 (? × 5 = 10)
5. 20 ÷ 4 = 5 (? × 4 = 20)

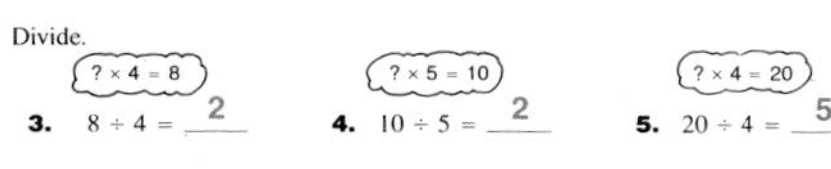

6. 36 ÷ 4 = 9
7. 35 ÷ 5 = 7
8. 16 ÷ 4 = 4
9. 40 ÷ 5 = 8
10. 32 ÷ 4 = 8
11. 24 ÷ 4 = 6
12. 45 ÷ 5 = 9
13. 4 ÷ 4 = 1
14. 20 ÷ 5 = 4
15. 4)16 = 4
16. 5)35 = 7
17. 4)12 = 3
18. 4)28 = 7
19. 4)36 = 9
20. 5)5 = 1
21. 4)4 = 1
22. 4)32 = 8

RS-4 Use with text pages 244-245. 89

Challenges

Creative Thinking 9-4

Name

Division Toss Game

Play this game with a partner or in a small group. You will need 2 number cubes. Each player needs 25 pieces of paper cut small enough to fit in the squares at the bottom of the page.

Rules

Take turns following these steps:

1. Roll 2 number cubes.
2. Write the two numbers on 2 separate pieces of paper **or** write the sum of the two numbers on 1 piece of paper.
3. As you take turns, collect pieces of paper until you have enough numbers to make an equation. When you do, arrange the numbers for the division equation in the squares.

Example: You roll: You write: 1 2 or 3

Example: You roll: Now you can make: 1 2 ÷ 3 = 4

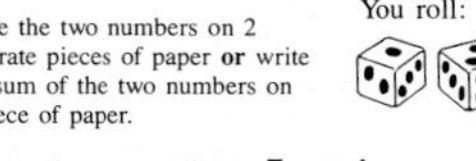

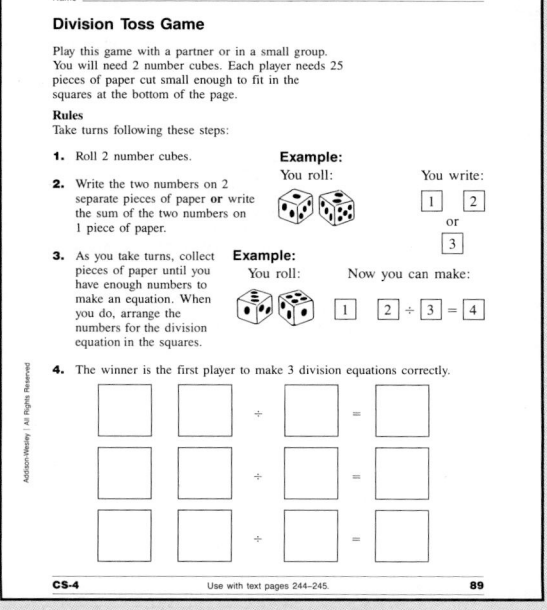

4. The winner is the first player to make 3 division equations correctly.

☐ ☐ ÷ ☐ = ☐

☐ ☐ ÷ ☐ = ☐

☐ ☐ ÷ ☐ = ☐

CS-4 Use with text pages 244-245. 89

Options for Individual Needs

9-4

Basic

Exercises 1-8, 19-36
Data Bank, p. 479
More Practice, p. 506, set D

Supplements
Reteaching 89 or
Practice 89

Average

Exercises 1-38
Data Bank, p. 479
More Practice, p. 506, set D

Supplements
Practice 89
Challenges 89 or
Thinking Skills 89

Extended

Exercises 5-18, 25-38
Data Bank, p. 479

Supplements
Challenges 89
Thinking Skills 89

Other Resources:
Problem-Solving Experiences in Mathematics, Grade 4, Problem 52
Math In Stride, Grade 4, p. 57
Mathematics: A Way of Thinking, Lessons 6-3, 6-11

LESSON PLAN 9-4

OBJECTIVE 9-4
To use missing factors to divide by 4 and 5

Materials: TA 12 (Centimeter Graph Paper)

1. MOTIVATE AND TEACH

LEARN ABOUT IT

EXPLORE ► **Explain the data given in the chart and decide what is not given.** (The chart lists 4 kinds of puppets that use 4 or 5 strings each and the total number of strings needed; the number of puppets that would give the listed totals is not given for 3 of the puppets.)

TALK ABOUT IT ► **Explain why multiplication fact families can help when you divide.** (Multiplication and division are opposite operations. If you know a multiplication fact, you can rearrange the factors and product to form a related division fact.)
► **Explain how the data about horse-puppet strings relates to a multiplication fact.** (4 strings per puppet multiplied by 6 puppets equals 24 strings in all.)
► **Explain how this same data relates to a division fact.** (24 strings divided by 4 strings per puppet equals 6 puppets.)
► **Explain how to find the number of girl puppets it takes to use up 30 strings.** (Find 30 ÷ 5; think 5 × ? = 30, which is 6)
Student Edition answers: **1.** 6, 5 × 6 = 30 **2.** 8, 9

2. CHECK UNDERSTANDING

TRY IT OUT

ERROR ALERT Finding the wrong quotient.

Dividing by 4 and 5

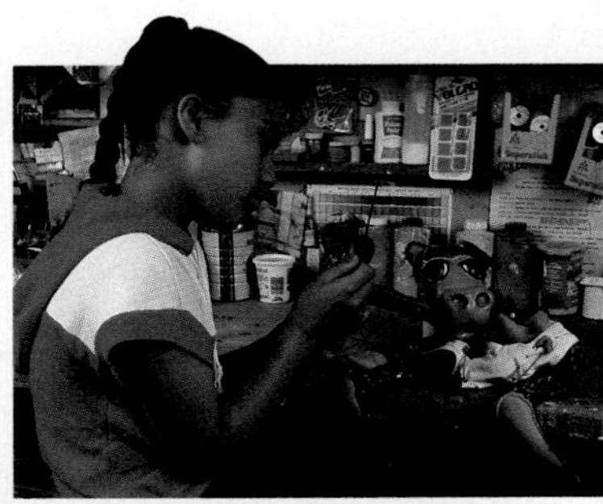

LEARN ABOUT IT

EXPLORE **Study the Chart**
Knowing the multiplication facts for 4 and 5 can help you divide by 4 and 5.

Marionette Strings

Kind of Puppet	Strings per Puppet	Number of Puppets	Total Number of Strings
Horse Puppet	4	6	24
Girl Puppet	5	▒	30
Dragon Puppet	4	▒	32
Boy Puppet	5	▒	45

TALK ABOUT IT See teaching notes.

1. How many girl puppets could be strung with 30 lengths of string? What multiplication fact would help you find this quotient?
2. What quotient would give the number of dragon puppets that can be strung with 32 lengths of string? the number of boy puppets that can be strung with 45 lengths of string?

When you divide, it helps to use multiplication.

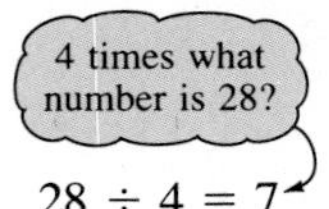

4 times what number is 28?
5 times what number is 40?

28 ÷ 4 = 7 — $5\overline{)40}$ = 8

Check: 4 × 7 = 28 — Check: 5 × 8 = 40

TRY IT OUT

Divide. Use a multiplication equation to check.

1. 25 ÷ 5 — 5, 5 × 5 = 25
2. 24 ÷ 4 — 6, 6 × 4 = 24
3. 30 ÷ 5 — 6, 6 × 5 = 30
4. 28 ÷ 4 — 7, 7 × 4 = 28
5. 36 ÷ 4 — 4, 9 × 4 = 36
6. 16 ÷ 4 — 4, 4 × 4
7. 10 ÷ 5 — 2, 5 × 2
8. 5 ÷ 5 — 1, 1 × 5
9. 20 ÷ 4 — 5, 5 × 4

244

TEACHING OPTIONS

RETEACHING TIPS Have students use centimeter graph paper to divide. They show the dividend as a rectangle with the number of rows equal to the divisor. The quotient is the number of boxes per row. Assign Reteaching Supplement 89.

ENRICHMENT Have students use number sense and mental math to find the missing dividends.
1. ☐ ÷ 5 = 25 (125)
2. ☐ ÷ 4 = 16 (64)
3. ☐ ÷ 4 = 20 (80)
4. ☐ ÷ 5 = 15 (75)
5. ☐ ÷ 5 = 30 (150)
6. ☐ ÷ 4 = 40 (160)

PRACTICE

Find the quotients.

1. 12 ÷ 4 **3**	**2.** 25 ÷ 5 **5**	**3.** 32 ÷ 4 **8**	**4.** 20 ÷ 4 **5**
5. 10 ÷ 5 **2**	**6.** 18 ÷ 3 **6**	**7.** 35 ÷ 5 **7**	**8.** 24 ÷ 3 **8**
9. 16 ÷ 4 **4**	**10.** 15 ÷ 5 **3**	**11.** 18 ÷ 2 **9**	**12.** 12 ÷ 3 **4**

13. 5)20 **4** **14.** 2)10 **5** **15.** 3)15 **5** **16.** 3)21 **7** **17.** 5)30 **6** **18.** 2)12 **6**

19. 2)16 **8** **20.** 3)27 **9** **21.** 4)8 **2** **22.** 2)14 **7** **23.** 4)28 **7** **24.** 5)20 **4**

25. Find the quotient of 24 and 4. **6** **26.** Divide 35 by 5. **7**

APPLY

MATH REASONING Use the equations in the table to find these quotients.

27. 325 ÷ 5 **65** **28.** 248 ÷ 4 **62**

29. 456 ÷ 4 **114** **30.** 490 ÷ 5 **98**

4 × 114	= 456
5 × 65	= 325
5 × 98	= 490
4 × 62	= 248

PROBLEM SOLVING

31. The art teacher cut 20 pieces of string for dragon puppets. How many dragon puppets will they make? **5 puppets**

32. Fine Arts Data Bank

How much string would you need to string a puppet with a 9-string double airplane controller? See page 479. **270 inches**

▶ **ALGEBRA**

Choose a number from the basket that can be written in the □ to make a true sentence.

20 18 24 25 35 14 21

33. □ ÷ 2 = 7 **14** **34.** □ ÷ 3 = 7 **21**

35. □ ÷ 4 = 5 **20** **36.** □ ÷ 5 = 5 **25**

37. □ ÷ 5 = 7 **35** **38.** □ ÷ 3 = 8 **24**

More Practice, page 506, set D

245

3. Practice and Apply

Basic	1-8, 19-36
Average	1-38
Extended	5-18, 25-38

9-4

PRACTICE

In Exercises 1-12, which number is the dividend? (the first number) *Which is the dividend in Exercises 13-24?* (the number inside the division symbol)

APPLY

MATH REASONING ▶ **Analyze how fact families can help in Exercises 27-30.** (Rearrange the multiplication facts in the table as division facts, then match to the equations.)

PROBLEM SOLVING ▶ **Explain what data you need to solve Problem 31.** (how many strings a dragon puppet uses)

▶ **Predict the kind of data you will find in the Fine Arts Data Bank.** (the length of the 9 strings)

ALGEBRA ▶ **Explain how to use fact families to help you solve Exercises 33-38.** (Think of the quotient and divisor as multiplication factors, then find the product.)

Close and Assess

WRITE WHAT YOU THINK

Have students write a fact family for 5, 4, and 20. Then have them multiply the factors 2 and 4 and write that fact family. (5 × 4 = 20, 4 × 5 = 20, 20 ÷ 4 = 5, 20 ÷ 5 = 4; 2 × 4 = 8, 4 × 2 = 8, 8 ÷ 4 = 2, 8 ÷ 2 = 4)

QUICK QUIZ

Find the quotients.

1. 4)32 (8)	**2.** 5)25 (5)
3. 4)16 (4)	**4.** 5)40 (8)
5. 5)15 (3)	**6.** 4)24 (6)
7. 30 ÷ 5 (6)	**8.** 36 ÷ 4 (9)

LESSON OPTIONS 9-5

Problem Solving: Estimate the Answer

OBJECTIVE 9-5 To determine by estimation whether answers to problems are reasonable

PREBOOK ACTIVITIES

QUICK REVIEW

Multiply.

1. 300 × 7 (2,100) **2.** 60 × 30 (1,800)
3. 20 × 40 (800) **4.** 600 × 20 (12,000)
5. 25 × 30 (750) **6.** 12 × 20 (240)

PRIOR KNOWLEDGE

Have students explain how an estimate might point to an error on a calculator. (Possible answer: If the estimate differs from the displayed answer, it might mean that you entered a wrong number or operation key.) Have students tell how estimation can help in problem solving. (Possible answer: to predict a sensible answer; to check if answers make sense)

COMMUNICATION

Discussing Math Have students justify a relationship between rounding and estimation. (Possible answer: You can use rounded numbers to make reasonable estimates.) Have students explain how to use rounding to estimate in addition, subtraction, or multiplication. (Round to the nearest place that suits the numbers, then find special sums, differences, or products.)

EXPLORE AND CONNECT

COOPERATIVE ACTIVITY

Grouping Suggestion: small groups
Emma spends $8.50 to go canoeing each month with the Adventure Club. How much does Emma spend on canoe trips in a year?

TEACHING ACTIONS

Have groups discuss the situation, plan an estimation method, solve the problem, and compare estimated and exact answers.

BEFORE
▶ **Explain the situation in your own words.** (Emma pays $8.50 a month to go on canoe trips.)
▶ **Identify a hidden fact you need to know.** (1 year = 12 months)

▶ **Decide on an operation to solve the problem.** (Multiply $8.50 by 12 to find the total cost.)
▶ **Explain how to make a reasonable estimate of the total cost.** (Possible answer: Round 12 months down to 10, round $8.50 up to $10, find the special product 10 × $10, which is $100.)
▶ **Decide what the exact answer is.** ($102.00)

AFTER
▶ **Use the estimate to evaluate the exact answer.** (The estimate of $100 is close to the exact answer of $102.00, so the exact answer makes sense.)

CONNECTIONS Use these anytime.

Problem of the Day

The Kayak Feldis has saved $32 each month for a year. Explain whether he has enough money to buy a kayak that costs $335. (Round and multiply $30 × 12 = $360; the underestimate is more than the price, so Feldis has enough; the exact amount he has saved is $384.)

Number Sense

Estimation The house Kwan lives in was built in 1799. Is it over or under 200 years old? (under)

Math Connection

Calculator Estimate the product of the greatest 2-digit number and the greatest 3-digit number. Compare your estimate to the exact answer on a calculator. (Round: 100 × 1,000 = 100,000; compare to 99 × 999 = 98,901)

Classwork and Homework Supplements

Practice

Problem Solving 9-5

Name

Estimate the Answer

Estimate the answer. Then solve the problem and decide if your answer is reasonable. Estimates will vary. Samples given.

1. It is 122 miles from Pitville to Brighton. Mr. Sanchez has already driven 63 miles. How far does he have to go? 60 mi; 59 mi
2. Ms. Hafiz drives 592 miles each month. How many miles does she drive each week? 150 mi; 148 mi
3. It costs Ms. Walsh $76 a month to fill her car with gas. How much does Ms. Walsh spend on gas each week? $20; $19
4. Mr. Rice drives 32 miles roundtrip to work each day. How many miles does he drive during a 5-day work week? 150 mi; 160 mi
5. It is 58 miles from Cara's house to the beach. It is 32 miles to the amusement park. How many miles closer is the amusement park than the beach? 30 mi; 26 mi
6. Mrs. Chuen's car is 6 months old. She has already driven 4,789 miles. At this rate, how many miles will she drive in 1 year? 10,000 mi; 9,578 mi
7. Once a month Miss Melrod takes a taxi from her office to the museum. It costs $4.15. How much is this per year? $48; $49.80
8. Tammy's big brother Kyle saved $4,080 from summer jobs. He wants to buy a $5,500 used car. How much more money does he need? $1,500; $1,400

90 Use with text pages 246-247. PS-4

Building Thinking Skills

Estimation 9-5

Name

The Art Supplies

Allyson's Art Supplies

Supply	Price
Paintbrushes	$12.29 per set
Paints	$17.69 per set
Charcoal pencils	$ 1.89 each
Drawing pads	$ 6.20 each
Erasers	$ 0.89 each

Ring the best answer.

1. Wendy bought 5 sets of paintbrushes for her and her friends. Which is the best estimate of the price she paid? ($60) $50 $55
2. The Art Club has raised $150 to buy 10 drawing pads, 30 erasers, and 45 charcoal pencils. Which is the best estimate of the amount of money the club members still need to raise to make their purchase? ($30) $40 $20

Before solving each of the following problems, estimate the answer. Then solve and decide if your answer is reasonable. Estimates will vary. Sample estimates given.

3. How many drawing pads can Shareen buy with the $20 she has saved? 3 How much money would she have left over? about $2; $1.40
4. Marnie has saved $150 over the year. She plans to keep $110 in the bank and use the rest to buy a set of paintbrushes, a set of paints, and as many charcoal pencils as she can. How many pencils can she buy? 5 How much change will she get back? $0; $0.57

90 Use with text pages 246-247. TS-4

Reteaching

Problem Solving 9-5

Name

Estimate the Answer

The bear weighs 377 pounds and the tiger weighs 283 pounds. How much more does the bear weigh?

Round the data in the problem. → Subtract rounded numbers to find the estimated answer. → Solve using the data in the problem.

377 → **400**
283 → **300**

400 − 300 = **100**

377 − 283 = **94**

94 is a reasonable solution because it is close to the estimated answer, 100.

Use estimation to decide which answer is most reasonable. Ring that answer.

1. Min sold drinks at the fair. He sold 775 cups Saturday and 515 cups Sunday. How many cups did he sell?
   A. 1,190 cups
   B. (1,290 cups) (800 + 500 = 1,300)
   C. 1,390 cups
2. Sally bought 24 cans of juice. Each can cost $0.98. How much money did the cans cost?
   A. ($23.52)
   B. $25.52
   C. $26.52

Estimate the answer. Then solve the problem. Decide if your answer is reasonable. Estimates will vary. Sample estimates given.

3. A new chair costs $199.84. Ramon has saved $54.36. How much more money does he need? $150; $145.48
4. Ana pays $14 a month for her stereo. How much is this per year? $160; $168
5. Hilo buys tapes in packages of 4. Each package cost $18. How much would 20 tapes cost? $100; $90
6. Johana was born was born in 1982. When she was 8, she received a new bike. What year was that? 1992; 1990

90 Use with text pages 246-247. RS-4

Challenges

Estimation 9-5

Name

Nice Numbers

Here are some handy estimation techniques to add to your "estimation toolbox."

- It is easy to estimate a sum or difference if you replace the numbers with "nice numbers" from the table.

Some Nice Numbers		
$0.25	$1.00	$1.75
$0.50	$1.25	$2.00
$0.75	$1.50	$2.25

Example: $2.09 + $2.22
(Replace with $2.00 + $2.25.)
Sum is about $4.25.

- It is easy to estimate a quotient if you replace one of the numbers with a "nice number" that makes a division fact you already know.

Example: 37 ÷ 4
(Replace with 36.)
about 9

Use the "nice numbers" to solve each problem. Answers may vary.

1. Josie spent $2.78 on wood and $1.29 on nails for her birdhouse. How much did she spend? about $4
2. Sherry bought 3 packages of embroidery thread to make a friendship bracelet. She paid 28¢. How much did each package cost? about 9¢
3. Rodriguez had $14.58. He bought some cloth for a superhero costume for $7.10. How much money did he have left? about $7.50
4. Nathan bought 4 pegs for his stilts for 27¢. How much did each peg cost? about 7¢
5. Miyoko paid 41¢ for 5 jewelry beads. How much did each bead cost? about 8¢
6. Billy Joe spent his money on supplies for a skateboard ramp. He spent $3.62 on plywood and 1.37 on nails. How much did he spend in all? about $5

90 Use with text pages 246-247. CS-4

Options for Individual Needs

9-5

Basic

Exercises 1-8
Skills Bank, pp. 462, 464, 465
Calculator Bank, pp. 485, 487
Computer Bank, p. 492
More Practice, p. 520, set D

Supplements
Reteaching 90 or
Practice 90

Average

Exercises 1-8
Skills Bank, pp. 464, 465
Calculator Bank, pp. 485, 487
Computer Bank, p. 492
More Practice, p. 520, set D

Supplements
Practice 90
Challenges 90 or
Thinking Skills 90

Extended

Exercises 1-8
Calculator Bank, pp. 485, 487
Computer Bank, p. 492

Supplements
Challenges 90
Thinking Skills 90

Other Resources:

Problem-Solving Experiences in Mathematics, Grade 4, Problem 54
Mathematics, Book A, Teacher's Edition, pp. 50, 51, 54, 55
Math In Stride, Grade 4, p. 105
Using the Math Explorer Calculator: A Sourcebook for Teachers, Chapter 14

LESSON PLAN 9-5

OBJECTIVE 9-5
To determine by estimation whether answers to problems are reasonable

1. MOTIVATE AND TEACH

LEARN ABOUT IT

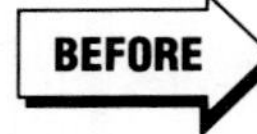

▶ Explain Karen's situation in your own words. (She takes 52 guitar lessons a year at a cost of $9.98 per lesson.)

▶ **Decide *about* how much 1 lesson costs.** (about $10)

▶ **Explain a reasonable way to estimate the cost of the lessons.** (Round both numbers so you can use special products; $10 × 50)

▶ **Justify multiplication as the correct operation.** (A lesson costs the same each week, so multiply to combine same-size groups.)

▶ **What calculation method would you use to find the exact answer? Justify your choice.** (paper and pencil or calculator; the numbers are too difficult for mental math.)

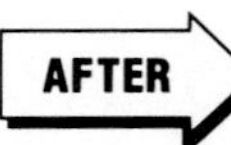

▶ **Compare exact and estimated answers.** ($500 is near $518.96.)

▶ **Explain why this comparison is useful.** (Since the exact answer is so close to the estimate, you can conclude that it is reasonable.)

2. CHECK UNDERSTANDING

TRY IT OUT

ERROR ALERT Choosing the wrong operation. Failing to estimate *and* find exact answers.

Problem Solving
Estimate the Answer

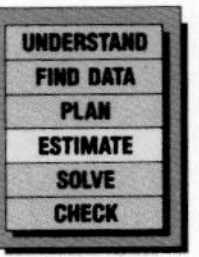

LEARN ABOUT IT

Karen takes guitar lessons. She takes 52 lessons a year. Each lesson costs $9.98. How much do her lessons cost for one year?

Before solving a problem, it is important to decide what would be a reasonable answer. To decide, you will need to **Estimate the Answer**.

I'll begin by rounding the data in the problem. 52 → 50, $9.98 → 10

I'll use the rounded numbers to get an estimate of the cost. 50 × $10 = $500

Now I'll solve the problem. $9.98 × 52 = $518.96

$518.96 is a reasonable answer because it is close to $500.

TRY IT OUT

Before solving each problem, estimate the answer. Then solve the problem and decide if your answer is reasonable.

1. Cliff had $142.50 saved from baby-sitting. He bought a guitar for $119.95. How much money does he have left? **$22.55**
2. It costs Betty $18 a month to rent a saxophone. How much is this per year? **$216**
3. Marlo practiced the piano 22 days this month. She practiced 35 minutes a day. How long did she practice in all? **770 minutes**
4. It took Hyun 5 months to learn 25 piano pieces. He learned the same number each month. How many pieces did he learn a month? **5 pieces**

TEACHING OPTIONS

RETEACHING TIPS Before students estimate, have them analyze each situation to choose the correct operation and justify their decision. Then they can estimate, solve, and evaluate their answers. Assign Reteaching Supplement 90.

COMPUTER **Math Strategies: Estimation, SRA, Copyright 1985** For use with all levels of students. In Lessons 3 to 5, students estimate 10 addition and subtraction problems. In Lessons 6 to 8, they estimate 10 multiplication problems. The recommended lessons take 10 min.

MIXED PRACTICE

Estimate the answer. Then solve the problem and decide if your answer is reasonable. **Estimates will vary. Sample estimates given.**

1. Beethoven was born in 1770. When he was 49, he became totally deaf. What year was that? **1820; 1819**
2. The 37 band members sold greeting cards to raise money for 20 new uniforms. Each member needed to raise $24. How much money did they need to raise in all? **$1,000; $888**

Use this chart to solve 3 and 4.

Drayer's Music Store	new	used
Saxophone	$750.00	$375.50
Clarinet	$450.00	$275.98
Electric Guitar	$169.99	$120.98

3. Bev has saved $87.75 for a brand new electric guitar. About how much more money does she need? **$80; $82.24**
4. Joseph rented a saxophone at $16 a month for 12 months. How much more does it cost to buy a used saxophone than to rent one for a year? **$240; $183.50**

5. There are 27 students in Jerry's flute class at school. Mr. Note divided the students into 3 equal groups for testing. How many are in each group? **9; 9**
6. Betsy buys reeds for her clarinet in packages. Use the price list to find how much 45 reeds would cost. **$40; $40**

Reeds	
Single reed	$1
Package of 9	$8

7. The 18 elementary school students in Newtown's Junior Orchestra come from 6 different schools. There are the same number of students from each school. How many students come from each school? **3 students; 3 students**
8. **Understanding the Question** Tell what operation you would use. Then solve the problem. At the age of 15, Bill came in first in a piano competition. Bill was 3 times as old as Mozart was when the composer wrote his first short pieces. At what age did Mozart write his first short pieces? **division; 5 years old**

More Practice, page 520, set D

3. Practice and Apply

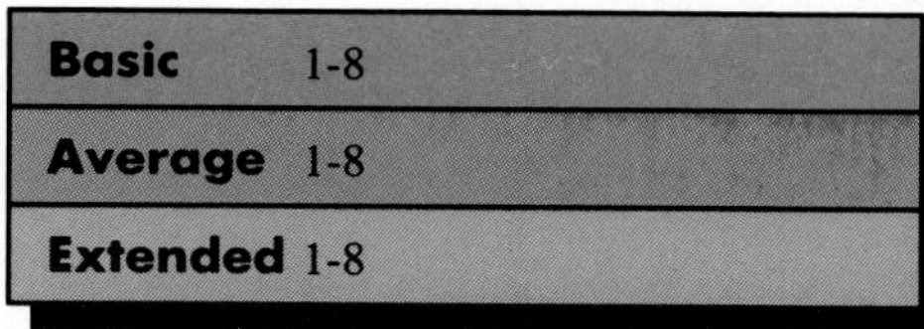

Basic	1-8
Average	1-8
Extended	1-8

9-5

Sample Solutions: See p. T79.

MIXED PRACTICE

► **Analyze Problem 2 to determine which fact is not needed.** (20 uniforms)

► **Explain why Problems 4 and 6 are similar.** (Both require multiplying money amounts.)

► **Explain how Problems 5 and 7 are alike.** (Both use division.)

► **Explain what the question in Problem 8 asks you to do.** (Possible answer: Compare Mozart's age when he first began to write music to Bill's age of 15.)

Close and Assess

WRITE WHAT YOU THINK

Have students write a generalization explaining how an estimate can help them evaluate an exact answer they find to a problem. (Answers will vary. Check students' writing.)

Quick Quiz

Estimate, then solve.
45 students went on a canoeing trip. They rode in vans that held 9 people and their gear. How many vans were needed? (5; 5)

LESSON OPTIONS 9-6

0 and 1 in Division/Midchapter Review/Quiz

OBJECTIVE 9-6 To understand 0 and 1 in division

PREBOOK ACTIVITIES

QUICK REVIEW

Find the products.

1. 4×1 (4)	**2.** 7×0 (0)	**3.** 0×24 (0)
4. 0×11 (0)	**5.** 1×97 (97)	**6.** 17×0 (0)
7. 1×0 (0)	**8.** 45×0 (0)	**9.** 63×1 (63)

PRIOR KNOWLEDGE

Have students suggest real-life situations when people share an amount so that each person gets 1 item. (Possible answers: a 6-slice pizza shared by 6 friends; 5 plates for 5 people in a family) Then have them think of real-life situations when an amount is used by just 1 person. (Possible answers: 8 oz of milk that 1 person drinks; 15 peanuts that 1 person eats)

COMMUNICATION

Discussing Math Have students review the meaning of multiplying by 1 and 0 by giving examples of each case. (A number multiplied by 1 is that number; a number multiplied by 0 is 0.) Have students use fact families to relate multiplication by 1 to division by 1. (If you divide a number by 1, the quotient is that number.)

EXPLORE AND CONNECT

Materials: counters

Grouping Suggestion: cooperative learning groups of 3

Students explore division by 0 and by 1. The first student takes a random number of counters. The second student divides them into groups of 1 counter per group as the third student records an equation, such as $7 \div 1 = 7$. Students repeat with a different number of counters to generalize a rule for dividing by 1. (The quotient of any number divided by 1 is that number.) Have students discuss how to show dividing 0 counters into 3, 4, or 5 equal groups and generalize a rule when 0 is the dividend. (There will always be 0 counters per group if you begin with 0 counters.) Challenge students to divide some counters into 0 groups and tell how many groups there are. (If you divide into 0 groups you will have no groups at all, no matter what the dividend is.) Explain that mathematicians agree that it is meaningless to divide by 0.

CONNECTIONS Use these anytime.

Problem of the Day

Desks The janitor ordered 375 new desks for grades 1 through 6 for the fall. Explain how he probably chose that number. *Hint:* Think about the number of desks per student. (Sample answer: If each student needs one desk, he found out how many students there would be and ordered 1 desk for each.)

Number Sense

Mental Math Explain how many answers there are to the equation $n \times 0 = 0$. (An endless number, because any number you can think of multiplied by 0 is 0.)

Life Skills

Profits When Lucy and Chuck set up their lemonade stand, they agreed to split all the money they would earn. At the end of an unlucky day, they had not sold any lemonade at all. Explain how much money Chuck and Lucy got. (None, because there was no money to share.)

CLASSWORK AND HOMEWORK SUPPLEMENTS

Practice

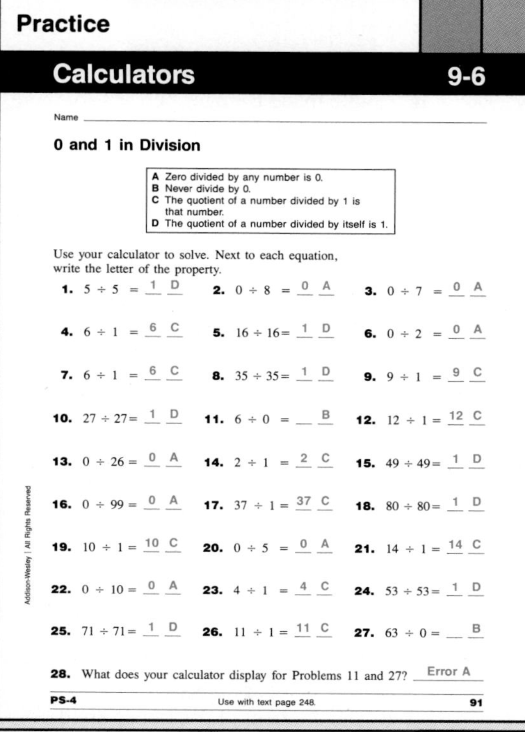

Calculators 9-6

Name ____________

0 and 1 in Division

A Zero divided by any number is 0.
B Never divide by 0.
C The quotient of a number divided by 1 is that number.
D The quotient of a number divided by itself is 1.

Use your calculator to solve. Next to each equation, write the letter of the property.

1. 5 ÷ 5 = 1 D	**2.** 0 ÷ 8 = 0 A	**3.** 0 ÷ 7 = 0 A
4. 6 ÷ 1 = 6 C	**5.** 16 ÷ 16 = 1 D	**6.** 0 ÷ 2 = 0 A
7. 6 ÷ 1 = 6 C	**8.** 35 ÷ 35 = 1 D	**9.** 9 ÷ 1 = 9 C
10. 27 ÷ 27 = 1 D	**11.** 6 ÷ 0 = __ B	**12.** 12 ÷ 1 = 12 C
13. 0 ÷ 26 = 0 A	**14.** 2 ÷ 1 = 2 C	**15.** 49 ÷ 49 = 1 D
16. 0 ÷ 99 = 0 A	**17.** 37 ÷ 1 = 37 C	**18.** 80 ÷ 80 = 1 D
19. 10 ÷ 1 = 10 C	**20.** 0 ÷ 5 = 0 A	**21.** 14 ÷ 1 = 14 C
22. 0 ÷ 10 = 0 A	**23.** 4 ÷ 1 = 4 C	**24.** 53 ÷ 53 = 1 D
25. 71 ÷ 71 = 1 D	**26.** 11 ÷ 1 = 11 C	**27.** 63 ÷ 0 = __ B

28. What does your calculator display for Problems 11 and 27? Error A

PS-4 Use with text page 248. 91

Building Thinking Skills

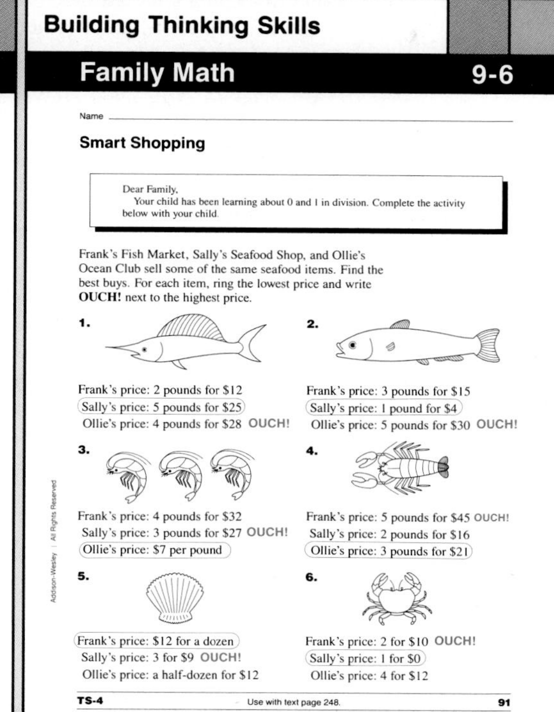

Family Math 9-6

Name ____________

Smart Shopping

Dear Family,
Your child has been learning about 0 and 1 in division. Complete the activity below with your child.

Frank's Fish Market, Sally's Seafood Shop, and Ollie's Ocean Club sell some of the same seafood items. Find the best buys. For each item, ring the lowest price and write **OUCH!** next to the highest price.

1.
Frank's price: 2 pounds for $12
Sally's price: 5 pounds for $25 (ringed)
Ollie's price: 4 pounds for $28 OUCH!

2.
Frank's price: 3 pounds for $15
Sally's price: 1 pound for $4 (ringed)
Ollie's price: 5 pounds for $30 OUCH!

3.
Frank's price: 4 pounds for $32
Sally's price: 3 pounds for $27 OUCH!
Ollie's price: $7 per pound (ringed)

4.
Frank's price: 5 pounds for $45 OUCH!
Sally's price: 2 pounds for $16
Ollie's price: 3 pounds for $21 (ringed)

5.
Frank's price: $12 for a dozen (ringed)
Sally's price: 3 for $9 OUCH!
Ollie's price: a half-dozen for $12

6.
Frank's price: 2 for $10 OUCH!
Sally's price: 1 for $0 (ringed)
Ollie's price: 4 for $12

TS-4 Use with text page 248. 91

Reteaching

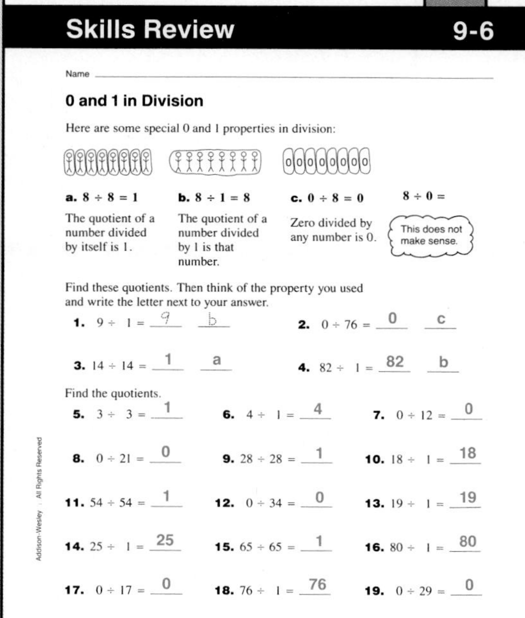

Skills Review 9-6

Name ____________

0 and 1 in Division

Here are some special 0 and 1 properties in division:

a. 8 ÷ 8 = 1 — The quotient of a number divided by itself is 1.

b. 8 ÷ 1 = 8 — The quotient of a number divided by 1 is that number.

c. 0 ÷ 8 = 0 — Zero divided by any number is 0.

8 ÷ 0 = — This does not make sense.

Find these quotients. Then think of the property you used and write the letter next to your answer.

1. 9 ÷ 1 = 9 b
2. 0 ÷ 76 = 0 c
3. 14 ÷ 14 = 1 a
4. 82 ÷ 1 = 82 b

Find the quotients.

5. 3 ÷ 3 = 1	**6.** 4 ÷ 1 = 4	**7.** 0 ÷ 12 = 0
8. 0 ÷ 21 = 0	**9.** 28 ÷ 28 = 1	**10.** 18 ÷ 1 = 18
11. 54 ÷ 54 = 1	**12.** 0 ÷ 34 = 0	**13.** 19 ÷ 1 = 19
14. 25 ÷ 1 = 25	**15.** 65 ÷ 65 = 1	**16.** 80 ÷ 1 = 80
17. 0 ÷ 17 = 0	**18.** 76 ÷ 1 = 76	**19.** 0 ÷ 29 = 0
20. 79 ÷ 79 = 1	**21.** 0 ÷ 62 = 0	**22.** 42 ÷ 42 = 1

RS-4 Use with text page 248. 91

Challenges

Calculators 9-6

Name ____________

Calculator Capers

You will need a calculator for this game. Use one 1-digit number along with the +, −, ×, and ÷ keys to get another 1-digit number.

Example:

Use 2 and the +, −, ×, and ÷ keys to get to 5.

Possible Answers:

2 ÷ 2 = + 2 = + 2 =

2 × 2 = × 2 = + 2 = ÷ 2 =

Answers may vary. Sample answers given.

1. Use 3 and the +, −, ×, and ÷ keys to get to 8.

3 × 3 = × 3 = − 3 = ÷ 3 =

2. Use 2 and the +, −, ×, and ÷ keys to get to 9.

2 × 2 = × 2 = × 2 = + 2 = ÷ 2 =

3. Use 4 and the +, −, ×, and ÷ keys to get to 7.

4 + 4 = + 4 = ÷ 4 = + 4 =

CS-4 Use with text page 248. 91

OPTIONS FOR INDIVIDUAL NEEDS

9-6

Basic

Exercises 1-8; 1-25, 27
More Practice, p. 506, set E

Supplements
Reteaching 91 or
Practice 91

Average

Exercises 1-8; 1-27
More Practice, p. 506, set E

Supplements
Practice 91
Challenges 91 or
Thinking Skills 91

Extended

Exercises 1-8; 2-19, 25-27

Supplements
Challenges 91
Thinking Skills 91

Other Resources:

Problem-Solving Experiences in Mathematics, Grade 4, Problem 48
Math In Stride, Grade 4, p. 107
Mathematics, A Way of Thinking, Lessons 6-4, 6-7
Using the Math Explorer Calculator: A Sourcebook for Teachers, Chapter 14

LESSON PLAN 9-6

OBJECTIVE 9-6
To understand 0 and 1 in division

Materials: calculators, counters

1. MOTIVATE AND TEACH

LEARN ABOUT IT

EXPLORE ▶ **Explain how the situation in Problem A relates to the key code.** (6 puppets divided by 6 friends, to share the puppets equally)
▶ **Contrast Problems A and B.** (In Problem B, all 6 puppets are given to 1 person instead of to 6 people.)
▶ **Explain the meaning of 0 in Problems C and D.** (C: Terri has 0 puppets to share because her dog ate them; D: The divisor, 0, indicates the number of puppets per group.)

TALK ABOUT IT ▶ **Explain how division with 0 relates to a multiplication rule.** (Any number multiplied by 0 equals 0.)
▶ **Explain why dividing by 0 makes no sense.** (Possible answer: You can divide 0 objects among any number of groups, so there is no one answer to give meaning to the action.)
Student Edition answers: **1.** 0 **2.** Yes, but it does not make sense to think about groups with 0 in each, because you could have any number of empty groups. **3.** C, D, B, A

2. CHECK UNDERSTANDING

TRY IT OUT

ERROR ALERT Giving the same number as the quotient when a number is divided by itself. Giving 1 as the quotient when 1 is the divisor.

0 and 1 in Division

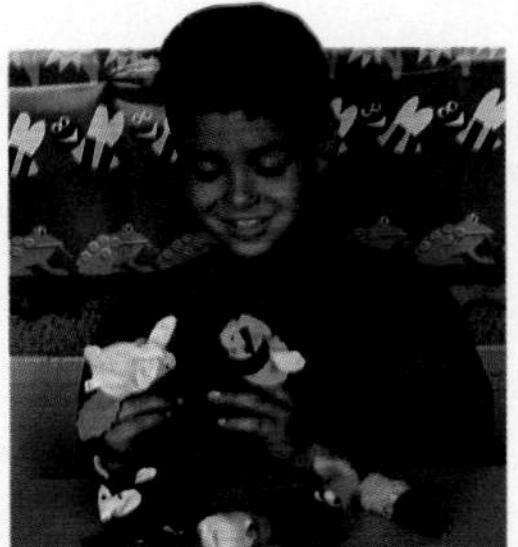

LEARN ABOUT IT

EXPLORE **Use a Calculator**
You can use a calculator to help you understand 0 and 1 in division.

A The art class spent several weeks making finger puppets. Lewis made 6 finger puppets to share among 6 friends. How many will each friend get?

key code: [ON/AC] 6 [÷] 6 [=]

B Julie made 6 finger puppets for 1 friend. How many puppets will the friend get?

key code: [ON/AC] 6 [÷] 1 [=]

C Terri planned to share her finger puppets with 3 friends, but her dog chewed them all up. How many puppets did each friend get?

key code: [ON/AC] 0 [÷] 3 [=]

D Miguel made 3 finger puppets, but he did not want to give any away. To how many friends could he give 0 puppets?

key code: [ON/AC] 3 [÷] 0 [=]

This does not make sense.

TALK ABOUT IT See teaching notes.

1. What did the calculator display show when you pressed 3 [÷] 0 [=]?
2. Could Miguel give 0 puppets to 20 friends? 500 friends? Explain why it does not make sense to divide by zero.
3. Which of the examples above match each of these division rules?
   - Zero divided by any number is 0.
   - Never divide by 0.
   - The quotient of a number divided by 1 is that number.
   - The quotient of a number divided by itself is 1.

TRY IT OUT

Use your calculator to solve.

1. 6 ÷ 6 1
2. 0 ÷ 8 0
3. 5 ÷ 1 5
4. 0 ÷ 4 0
5. 37 ÷ 37 1
6. 0 ÷ 75 0
7. 86 ÷ 1 86
8. 78 ÷ 78 1

More Practice, page 506, set E

TEACHING OPTIONS

RETEACHING TIPS Have students who give 1 as the quotient when 1 is the divisor use counters to show division by 1. They "deal out" counters, 1 per group, to show that the number of groups equals the number in the dividend. Assign Reteaching Supplement 91.

ENRICHMENT Have students use mental math and number sense to solve the following equations.
1. (4 × 5) × (2 + 2) ÷ 1 = (80)
2. (12 + 12) ÷ (3 × 8) = (1)
3. (24 × 0) ÷ (8 × 7) = (0)
4. (28 ÷ 7) × (4 + 6) ÷ (8 × 5) = (1)

Midchapter Review/Quiz

Tell which division action is needed in each problem, share equally or separate same-size groups. Then draw a picture to solve the problem. See Additional Answers.

1. There are 24 students in Jack's gym class. The coach wants 8 teams for a tournament. He assigns one student to each team until all students are assigned. What is the size of each team?

2. In Jill's gym class there are also 24 students. Her coach needs teams with 4 members each. How many teams will there be?

Write four fact family equations for each set of numbers. See Additional Answers.

3. 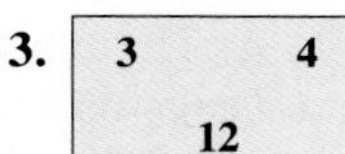

4. 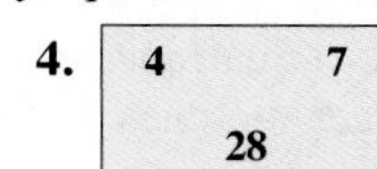

5. 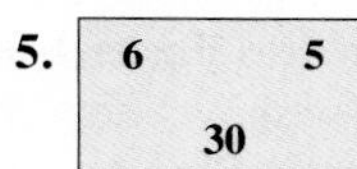

6. 1 2 / 2

Give three more equations in the same family. See Additional Answers.

7. $8 \times 5 = 40$ **8.** $5 \times 2 = 10$ **9.** $27 \div 3 = 9$ **10.** $8 \div 4 = 2$

Divide. Use multiplication to check the division.

11. $18 \div 2$ 9, $2 \times 9 = 18$
12. $24 \div 3$ 8, $8 \times 3 = 24$
13. $20 \div 5$ 4, $4 \times 5 = 20$
14. $36 \div 4$ 9, $9 \times 4 = 36$
15. $5\overline{)15}$ 3, $3 \times 5 = 15$
16. $3\overline{)18}$ 6, $6 \times 3 = 18$
17. $2\overline{)12}$ 6, $6 \times 2 = 12$
18. $4\overline{)32}$ 8, $8 \times 4 = 32$
19. $3\overline{)9}$ 3, $3 \times 3 = 9$
20. $3\overline{)27}$ 9, $9 \times 3 = 27$
21. $2\overline{)10}$ 5, $5 \times 2 = 10$
22. $4\overline{)4}$ 1, $1 \times 4 = 4$
23. $5\overline{)45}$ 9, $9 \times 5 = 45$
24. $2\overline{)8}$ 4, $4 \times 2 = 8$

PROBLEM SOLVING See Additional Answers.

25. Lance has 24 photos to put in his scrapbook. Find 3 different ways he could put the same number of photos on each page. For each way, tell how many pages he would need.

26. Show two ways 21 students can split into teams so that each team has 3 or 4 players.

27. Find three ways Vera can throw 3 darts and score 20 points. Darts that miss the target score 0 points.

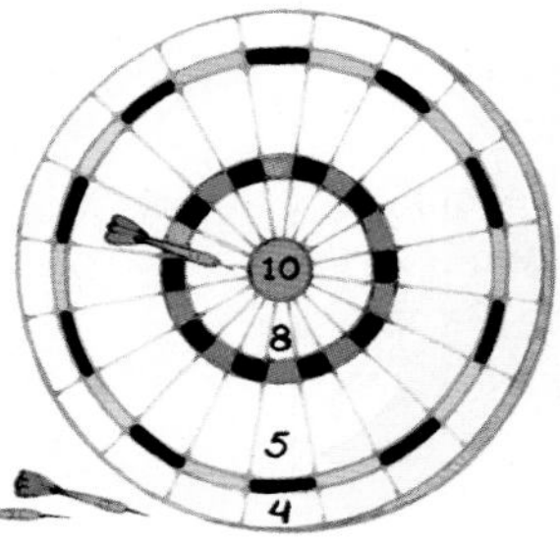

249

3. Practice and Apply

Basic	1-8; 1-25, 27
Average	1-8; 1-27
Extended	1-8; 2-19, 25-27

9-6

Additional Answers: See p. T79

PRACTICE

How are Exercises 3 to 10 related? (All use multiplication/division fact families.) *How would you begin to solve Problem 25?* (Think of factor pairs whose product is 24.) *Which operation makes sense to use in solving Problem 27?* (addition)

ITEM ANALYSIS The following table correlates the Midchapter Review/Quiz items with the lesson objectives.

Items	Objectives
1, 2 (25, 26)	9-1
3-10	9-2
11, 12	9-3
13-15	9-4
16, 17	9-3
18	9-4
19-21	9-3
(6), 22	9-6
23	9-4
24	9-3
25-27	9-5

Close and Assess

SHOW WHAT YOU KNOW

Have students use counters to show how to find the quotients of $8 \div 8$ and $8 \div 1$. Then have them explain what would happen if they tried to divide 8 by 0. (1, 8; It does not make sense to divide by 0.)

Quick Quiz

Divide.

1. $3 \div 3$ (1) **2.** $4 \div 1$ (4)
3. $0 \div 3$ (0) **4.** $1 \div 1$ (1)
5. $13 \div 13$ (1) **6.** $0 \div 13$ (0)

LESSON OPTIONS 9-7

Dividing by 6 and 7

OBJECTIVE 9-7 To use missing factors to divide by 6 and 7

PREBOOK ACTIVITIES

QUICK REVIEW

Find each product.

1. 7 × 6 (42)	**2.** 6 × 4 (24)	**3.** 7 × 3 (21)
4. 5 × 6 (30)	**5.** 6 × 8 (48)	**6.** 7 × 7 (49)
7. 9 × 6 (54)	**8.** 7 × 8 (56)	**9.** 7 × 2 (14)
10. 6 × 6 (36)	**11.** 9 × 7 (63)	**12.** 4 × 7 (28)
13. 5 × 7 (35)	**14.** 3 × 6 (18)	**15.** 7 × 0 (0)

PRIOR KNOWLEDGE

Have students identify things that are customarily grouped by 6 or 7. (Possible answers: 6—beverage 6-packs, seating capacity of large cars, insect legs; 7—days per week, football scores for touchdown and extra point) Have students explain how the multiplication facts for 6 or 7 can help them divide by 6 or 7. (Use fact families or missing factors.)

COMMUNICATION

Discussing Math Have students review the relationship between multiplication and division using the basic fact 5 × 7 = 35. (Multiplication and division are related through fact families. Other members of the family 5 × 7 = 35 are 7 × 5 = 35, 35 ÷ 7 = 5, and 35 ÷ 5 = 7.) Ask students to identify the numbers in the division equations as dividends, divisors, and quotients and to relate them to factors and products. (35 is the dividend and product; factors 5 and 7 alternate as divisor and quotient.)

EXPLORE AND CONNECT

Materials: old calendars, multiplication fact cards for 7
Alternative Materials: TA 18 (Calendar)
Grouping Suggestion: cooperative learning pairs
Partners explore the relationship between multiplication and division with 7. One partner picks a multiplication fact card and writes the fact-family equations related to it. The other partner shows how the fact matches days and weeks on the calendar. For example, suppose a partner picks 6 × 7. That partner writes 6 × 7 = 42, 7 × 6 = 42, 42 ÷ 6 = 7, and 42 ÷ 7 = 6. The other partner counts off 6 wk, at 7 d per wk, starting at any date and ending 42 d later. That student then writes 42 d = 6 wk from (starting date) to (ending date), such as June 1 to July 13. Then partners repeat the task with a new fact card, trading roles. Conclude by having students determine how many calendar pages are needed to show all the basic facts for 7. (3 for 9 wk or 63 d)

CONNECTIONS Use these anytime.

Problem of the Day

Calculator Figure out 2 different methods to find how many groups of 6 are in 48 without ever pressing the ÷ key. (Possible methods: Repeatedly subtract 6 from 48 until you reach 0, or start with 0 and add until you reach 48, keeping track of how many subtractions or additions you make; try to find the missing factor, 8)

Subject Integration

Dance A dancer leaps across a stage that is 40 ft wide. He wants to make 6 leaps to fit the music. If he covers 6 ft with each leap, will he cross the entire stage? Explain. (No, he will cross only 36 ft, leaving 4 ft to go.)

Patterns

6s and 7s Find the pattern, then continue it 7 more times: 63, 54, 56, 48, 49, _____, _____, _____, _____, _____, _____, _____. (Alternate decreasing multiples of 7 and 6; 42, 42, 36, 35, 30, 28, 24.)

Classwork and Homework Supplements

Practice

Skills Maintenance 9-7

Name ______________________

Dividing by 6 and 7

Divide.

1. 30 ÷ 6 = 5
2. 14 ÷ 7 = 2
3. 56 ÷ 7 = 8
4. 42 ÷ 6 = 7
5. 48 ÷ 6 = 8
6. 0 ÷ 6 = 0
7. 21 ÷ 7 = 3
8. 24 ÷ 6 = 4
9. 42 ÷ 7 = 6
10. 35 ÷ 7 = 5
11. 6 ÷ 6 = 1
12. 49 ÷ 7 = 7
13. 28 ÷ 7 = 4
14. 54 ÷ 6 = 9
15. $3\overline{)18}$ 6
16. $6\overline{)12}$ 2
17. $7\overline{)7}$ 1
18. $7\overline{)0}$ 0
19. $6\overline{)48}$ 8
20. $7\overline{)63}$ 9
21. $7\overline{)42}$ 6
22. $6\overline{)36}$ 6
23. $4\overline{)28}$ 7
24. $7\overline{)21}$ 3
25. $3\overline{)21}$ 7
26. $6\overline{)54}$ 9
27. Find the quotient of 42 and 6. 7
28. Divide 54 by 6. 9

Building Thinking Skills

Critical Thinking 9-7

Name ______________________

Find the Fact

Here are some hints about division facts. E's stand for **even** numbers and O's stand for **odd** numbers.

E ÷ E = E or E ÷ E = O
E ÷ O = E
O ÷ O = O

Use the hints above to write division facts that match the clues.

1. My quotient is 4 and my divisor is even. My dividend is either 20 or 24. 24 ÷ 6 = 4
2. My divisor is odd and my quotient is 5. My dividend is either 30 or 35. 35 ÷ 7 = 5
3. My divisor is 6 and my quotient is even. My dividend is either 48 or 49. 48 ÷ 6 = 8
4. My dividend is 36. My quotient and divisor are even. 36 ÷ 6 = 6
5. My divisor is 7 and my quotient is even. My dividend is either 49 or 56. 56 ÷ 7 = 8
6. My quotient is 4 and my divisor is odd. My dividend is either 24 or 28. 28 ÷ 7 = 4
7. My quotient is 9 and my divisor is even. My dividend is either 54 or 27. 54 ÷ 6 = 9
8. My divisor is 5 and my quotient is even. My dividend is either 30 or 35. 30 ÷ 5 = 6

Reteaching

Skills Review 9-7

Name ______________________

Dividing by 6 and 7

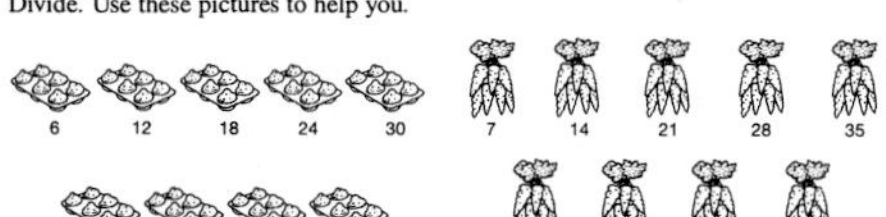

How many 6s are in 18?
How many 7s are in 28?

18 ÷ 6 = 3 $6\overline{)18}$ 3 28 ÷ 7 = 4 $7\overline{)28}$ 4

Divide. Use these pictures to help you.

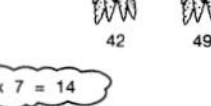
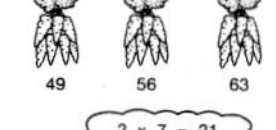

? × 6 = 12 ? × 7 = 14 ? × 7 = 21

1. 12 ÷ 6 = 2
2. 14 ÷ 7 = 2
3. 21 ÷ 7 = 3
4. 48 ÷ 6 = 8
5. 35 ÷ 7 = 5
6. 6 ÷ 6 = 1
7. 36 ÷ 6 = 6
8. 56 ÷ 7 = 8
9. 30 ÷ 6 = 5
10. $7\overline{)21}$ 3
11. $6\overline{)24}$ 4
12. $7\overline{)28}$ 4
13. $7\overline{)14}$ 2
14. $7\overline{)49}$ 7
15. $6\overline{)42}$ 7
16. $6\overline{)36}$ 6
17. $7\overline{)56}$ 8

Challenges

Cooperative Activities 9-7

Name ______________________

Undercover Numbers Game

Play this game with 2 or 3 teams. You will need 3 number cubes and a set of about 15 markers for each team.

Rules

Take turns following these steps:

1. Roll 3 number cubes.
2. Use the numbers you rolled along with the operations of +, −, ×, and ÷ to create a number on the game board.

Example: (6 + 4) ÷ 2 = 5

3. Cover the number you created with a marker.
4. You get 1 point for every number you cover. If the number you cover is touching any other covered number, you get 1 point for each of those numbers too.
5. If you cannot create an uncovered number on the game board, your turn is over.
6. Continue playing until all the numbers are covered.
7. The player with the highest number of points wins.

Game Board

0	1	2	3	4	5	6	7
8	9	10	11	12	13	14	15
16	17	18	19	20	21	22	23
24	25	26	27	28	29	30	31
32	33	34	35	36	37	38	39

Options for Individual Needs

Basic

Exercises 1-8, 13-31
Data Bank, p. 479
Calculator Bank, p. 486
More Practice, p. 506, set F

Supplements

Reteaching 92 or
Practice 92

Average

Exercises 1-31
Data Bank, p. 479
Calculator Bank, p. 486
More Practice, p. 506, set F

Supplements

Practice 92
Challenges 92 or
Thinking Skills 92

Extended

Exercises 7-16, 19-31
Data Bank, p. 479
Calculator Bank, p. 486

Supplements

Challenges 92
Thinking Skills 92

Other Resources:

Problem-Solving Experiences in Mathematics, Grade 4, Problem 49
Math In Stride, Grade 4, p. 109
Mathematics, A Way of Thinking, Lesson 6-5
Using the Math Explorer Calculator: A Sourcebook for Teachers, Chapter 14

LESSON PLAN 9-7

OBJECTIVE 9-7
To use missing factors to divide by 6 and 7

Materials: TA 14 (Practice Table), counters, calculators

1. MOTIVATE AND TEACH

LEARN ABOUT IT

EXPLORE ▶ **Analyze the chart to decide how it organizes data about the Bunraku puppet group.** (It gives four tours of 6 or 7 shows a week and the total number of shows per tour.)
▶ **Analyze the difference in shows per week in the first 2 tours compared with the last 2 tours.** (Possible answer: Perhaps the first 2 tours had 1 show a day and the last 2 tours had 1 day off a week.)

TALK ABOUT IT ▶ **Explain how you would relate the numbers across the first row of the chart.** (6 × 7 are factors that equal the product 42)
▶ **How can you use a fact family to link division to multiplication?** (If 6 × 7 = 42, then you know that 42 ÷ 6 = 7 and 42 ÷ 7 = 6.)
▶ **At 6 shows a week, figure how many weeks it took to do 30 shows. With no more than 1 show per day, can you tell how many days off there were in that time?** (5; 5, because 5 × 1 = 5)
Student Edition answers: **1.** 8; 8 × 7 = 56 **2.** 5; 9; 6 × 5 = 30; 6 × 9 = 54

2. CHECK UNDERSTANDING

TRY IT OUT

ERROR ALERT Making division mistakes. Giving 2 as the quotient in cases of square products like 49 ÷ 7 or 36 ÷ 6.

Dividing by 6 and 7

Bunraku Puppet Shows		
Number of Weeks	Shows per Week	Total Number of Shows
6	7	42
||||	7	56
||||	6	30
||||	6	54

LEARN ABOUT IT

EXPLORE Think About the Relationship
You can use the multiplication facts for 6 and 7 to help you divide by 6 and 7. A Bunraku puppet group did four tours in a year. Use the chart to figure out how many weeks were in each tour.

TALK ABOUT IT See teaching notes.

1. What quotient would you find to decide how many weeks it took for 56 shows? What multiplication fact would help you find this quotient?
2. What quotient would give the number of weeks for 30 shows? for 54 shows? What multiplication facts would help you find these quotients?

You divide by finding a missing factor.

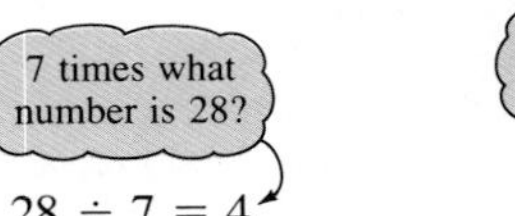

7 times what number is 28?

28 ÷ 7 = 4

Check: 7 × 4 = 28

6 times what number is 54?

$5\overline{)54}$ 9

Check: 6 × 9 = 54

TRY IT OUT

Divide. Multiply to check.

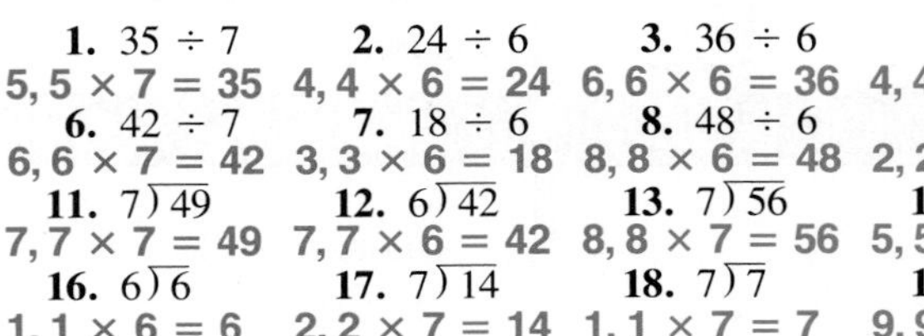

1. 35 ÷ 7 — 5, 5 × 7 = 35
2. 24 ÷ 6 — 4, 4 × 6 = 24
3. 36 ÷ 6 — 6, 6 × 6 = 36
4. 28 ÷ 7 — 4, 4 × 7 = 28
5. 63 ÷ 7 — 9, 9 × 7 = 63
6. 42 ÷ 7 — 6, 6 × 7 = 42
7. 18 ÷ 6 — 3, 3 × 6 = 18
8. 48 ÷ 6 — 8, 8 × 6 = 48
9. 12 ÷ 6 — 2, 2 × 6 = 12
10. 54 ÷ 6 — 9, 9 × 6 = 54
11. $7\overline{)49}$ — 7, 7 × 7 = 49
12. $6\overline{)42}$ — 7, 7 × 6 = 42
13. $7\overline{)56}$ — 8, 8 × 7 = 56
14. $6\overline{)30}$ — 5, 5 × 6 = 30
15. $7\overline{)21}$ — 3, 3 × 7 = 21
16. $6\overline{)6}$ — 1, 1 × 6 = 6
17. $7\overline{)14}$ — 2, 2 × 7 = 14
18. $7\overline{)7}$ — 1, 1 × 7 = 7
19. $7\overline{)63}$ — 9, 9 × 7 = 63
20. $6\overline{)24}$ — 4, 4 × 6 = 24

250

TEACHING OPTIONS

RETEACHING TIPS Allow students to work backward from a completed multiplication table to verify quotients. For instance, to find $6\overline{)36}$ students look across the 6s row to find 36, then up the column in which it appears to find the other factor, which is also 6. Assign Reteaching Supplement 92.

ENRICHMENT Family Math
With a family member, have students draw a *heptel,* an imaginary coin worth 7¢. Then they find some canned foods with the prices still marked and make a chart showing how many heptels would be needed to buy each item.

PRACTICE

Divide.

1. 12 ÷ 6 **2**
2. 49 ÷ 7 **7**
3. 48 ÷ 6 **8**
4. 14 ÷ 7 **2**
5. 36 ÷ 6 **6**
6. 32 ÷ 4 **8**
7. 63 ÷ 7 **9**
8. 9 ÷ 3 **3**
9. 18 ÷ 2 **9**
10. 30 ÷ 6 **5**
11. 25 ÷ 5 **5**
12. 56 ÷ 7 **8**
13. $7\overline{)49}$ **7**
14. $6\overline{)48}$ **8**
15. $4\overline{)28}$ **7**
16. $3\overline{)21}$ **7**
17. $7\overline{)7}$ **1**
18. $3\overline{)24}$ **8**
19. Find the quotient of 42 and 7. **6**
20. Divide 56 by 7. **8**
21. Write multiplication equations to check exercises 5, 10, 15, and 20. **See Additional Answers.**

APPLY

MATH REASONING Sort these into even quotients and odd quotients. Is an even number divided by an even number always even? Explain.

22. 35 ÷ 7 **5**
23. 54 ÷ 6 **9**
24. 48 ÷ 6 **8**
25. 21 ÷ 7 **3**
26. 42 ÷ 7 **6**
27. 30 ÷ 6 **5**

even: 8, 6; odd: 5, 9, 3, 5

PROBLEM SOLVING

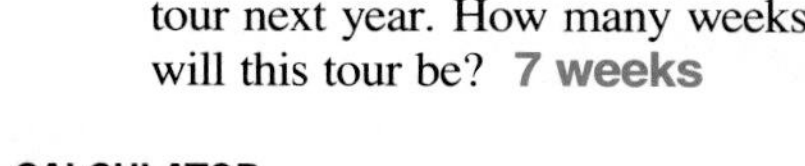

28. The puppet group plans a 49-day tour next year. How many weeks will this tour be? **7 weeks**

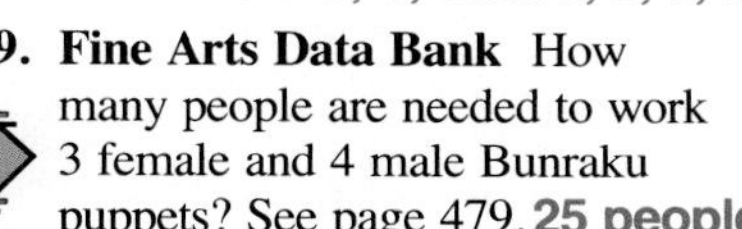

29. **Fine Arts Data Bank** How many people are needed to work 3 female and 4 male Bunraku puppets? See page 479. **25 people**

▶ **CALCULATOR**

Use a calculator and work backward to find the starting number.

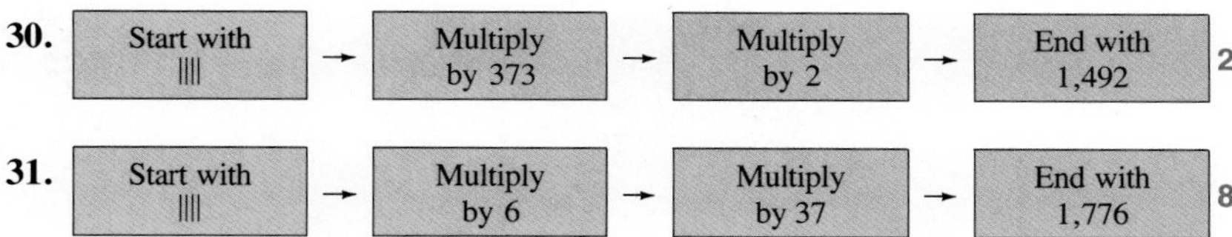

30. Start with ||||| → Multiply by 373 → Multiply by 2 → End with 1,492 **2**

31. Start with ||||| → Multiply by 6 → Multiply by 37 → End with 1,776 **8**

More Practice, page 506, set F

3. Practice and Apply

Basic	1-8, 13-31
Average	1-31
Extended	7-16, 19-31

9-7

Additional Answers: See p. T79.

PRACTICE

Look at Exercises 1-20. What do all the exercises have in common? (All are basic division facts.) *Explain how Exercises 2, 5, 8, and 11 are related.* (Each uses a square fact.)

APPLY

MATH REASONING ▶ Explain how to predict some odd or even quotients without dividing. (Possible answer: If a dividend and a divisor are both odd, the quotient will be odd. If both are even, the quotient will be even.)

PROBLEM SOLVING ▶ What is the divisor in Problem 28? Explain how you know. (The divisor is 7 because a week has 7 d.)

CALCULATOR ▶ Explain another way you could solve Exercise 30 instead of working backward. (Possible answer: You could multiply 373 × 2 to get 746. Then divide 1,492 by 746 to find the starting amount.)

Close and Assess

SHOW WHAT YOU KNOW Give each student 42 counters. Ask students to use their counters to show how many groups of 6 can be made from 42, then to write an equation to record what they find. Then students should show how many groups of 7 can be made and write an equation for that finding. (42 ÷ 6 = 7; 42 ÷ 7 = 6)

Quick Quiz

Find the quotients.

1. 48 ÷ 6 (8)
2. 28 ÷ 7 (4)
3. 0 ÷ 6 (0)
4. $7\overline{)56}$ (8)
5. $6\overline{)30}$ (5)
6. $7\overline{)21}$ (3)
7. $7\overline{)49}$ (7)
8. $6\overline{)36}$ (6)

LESSON OPTIONS 9-8

Dividing by 8 and 9

OBJECTIVE 9-8 To use missing factors to divide by 8 and 9

PREBOOK ACTIVITIES

QUICK REVIEW

Find the products.

1. 8 × 3 (24)	**2.** 4 × 9 (36)	**3.** 9 × 7 (63)
4. 8 × 9 (72)	**5.** 4 × 8 (32)	**6.** 2 × 9 (18)
7. 8 × 5 (40)	**8.** 6 × 9 (54)	**9.** 1 × 8 (8)
10. 9 × 0 (0)	**11.** 7 × 8 (56)	**12.** 6 × 8 (48)
13. 2 × 8 (16)	**14.** 3 × 9 (27)	**15.** 9 × 5 (45)

PRIOR KNOWLEDGE

Help students recall a pattern in the digit sums of products of facts for 9. For example, the product of 9 × 2 is 18. The sum of the digits of the product 18 is 9 (1 + 8 = 9). Have students identify a clue to relate a product of 9, such as 63, to its other factor. (Possible answer: The tens digit of the product is 1 less than the other factor; 7 × 9 = 63.) Have students recall any strategies they may have used to learn facts for 8. (Possible answers: All products are even; break apart factors or use doubles.) Tell students that recognizing products of 8 and 9 will help them divide by 8 and 9.

COMMUNICATION

Writing in Math Have students write a paragraph explaining how multiplication and division are linked. Have them draw a picture of a fact family to illustrate their paragraph. (Answers may vary. Check students' writing.)

EXPLORE AND CONNECT

Materials: product cards (see picture below), paper, markers
Grouping Suggestion: small cooperative learning groups
Students make pictographs to apply multiplication/division relationships for products of 8 and 9. Write these numbers on separate index cards, repeating numbers as necessary to have 2 cards for each group: 81, 72, 64, 63, 56, 54, 48, 45, 40. Give each group 2 cards related to the same factor, 8 or 9. The groups use the cards to formulate a situation for which a pictograph can represent data. Members try missing factors to decide whether to use 8 or 9 as the key amount. For example, given 64 and 48, students determine that 8 is a suitable factor. They might make a pictograph about sled dogs grouped 8 to a sled. The key would show 1 sled = 8 dogs, and the pictograph would have a row of 8 sleds and another row of 6 sleds. To conclude, students compare pictographs, write questions pertaining to them, and discuss the relationships they see.

CONNECTIONS Use these anytime.

Problem of the Day

Number Sense A science class has 9 experiments to do that take about 5 min each. Is there enough time in a 45-min class to do all 9 experiments? Explain your reasoning. (Maybe; 9 × 5 = 45, but that does not allow any time to gather equipment, ask questions, or clean up.)

Math Connection

Measurement 1 c = 8 fl oz. A carton of apple juice contains 64 fl oz. How many 1-c servings does it provide? (8) How many cartons would you need to serve a cup of juice to everyone in your class? (Answers will vary.)

Life Skills

Sports Teams 72 boys and girls want to play in the round-robin softball tournament at the local sports center. How can the coaches form equal-size teams? (8 teams of 9 players or 9 teams of 8 players)

Classwork and Homework Supplements

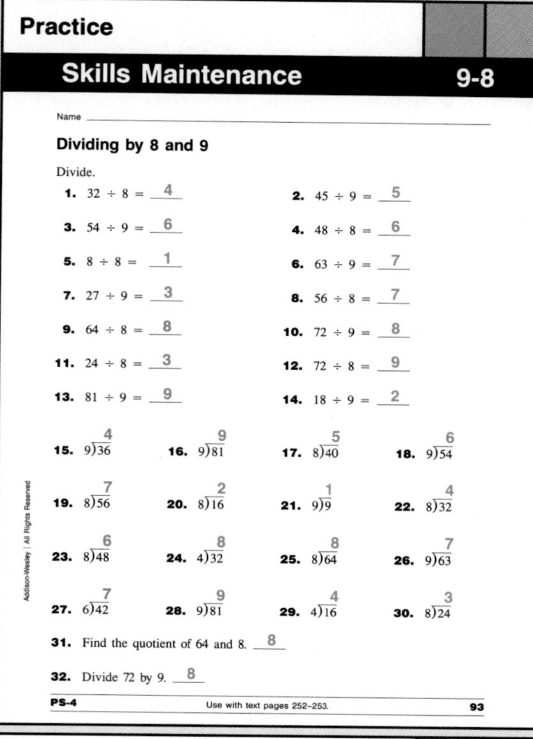

Practice

Skills Maintenance 9-8

Name ______

Dividing by 8 and 9

Divide.

1. 32 ÷ 8 = 4
2. 45 ÷ 9 = 5
3. 54 ÷ 9 = 6
4. 48 ÷ 8 = 6
5. 8 ÷ 8 = 1
6. 63 ÷ 9 = 7
7. 27 ÷ 9 = 3
8. 56 ÷ 8 = 7
9. 64 ÷ 8 = 8
10. 72 ÷ 9 = 8
11. 24 ÷ 8 = 3
12. 72 ÷ 8 = 9
13. 81 ÷ 9 = 9
14. 18 ÷ 9 = 2
15. 9)36 = 4
16. 9)81 = 9
17. 8)40 = 5
18. 9)54 = 6
19. 8)56 = 7
20. 8)16 = 2
21. 9)9 = 1
22. 8)32 = 4
23. 8)48 = 6
24. 4)32 = 8
25. 8)64 = 8
26. 9)63 = 7
27. 6)42 = 7
28. 9)81 = 9
29. 4)16 = 4
30. 8)24 = 3
31. Find the quotient of 64 and 8. 8
32. Divide 72 by 9. 8

Addison-Wesley | All Rights Reserved

PS-4 Use with text pages 252-253. 93

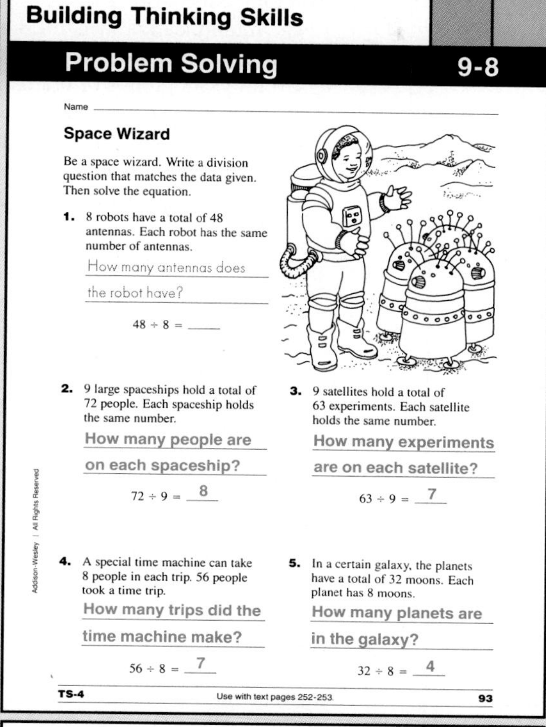

Building Thinking Skills

Problem Solving 9-8

Name ______

Space Wizard

Be a space wizard. Write a division question that matches the data given. Then solve the equation.

1. 8 robots have a total of 48 antennas. Each robot has the same number of antennas.
   How many antennas does the robot have?
   48 ÷ 8 = ____
2. 9 large spaceships hold a total of 72 people. Each spaceship holds the same number.
   How many people are on each spaceship?
   72 ÷ 9 = 8
3. 9 satellites hold a total of 63 experiments. Each satellite holds the same number.
   How many experiments are on each satellite?
   63 ÷ 9 = 7
4. A special time machine can take 8 people in each trip. 56 people took a time trip.
   How many trips did the time machine make?
   56 ÷ 8 = 7
5. In a certain galaxy, the planets have a total of 32 moons. Each planet has 8 moons.
   How many planets are in the galaxy?
   32 ÷ 8 = 4

Addison-Wesley | All Rights Reserved

TS-4 Use with text pages 252-253. 93

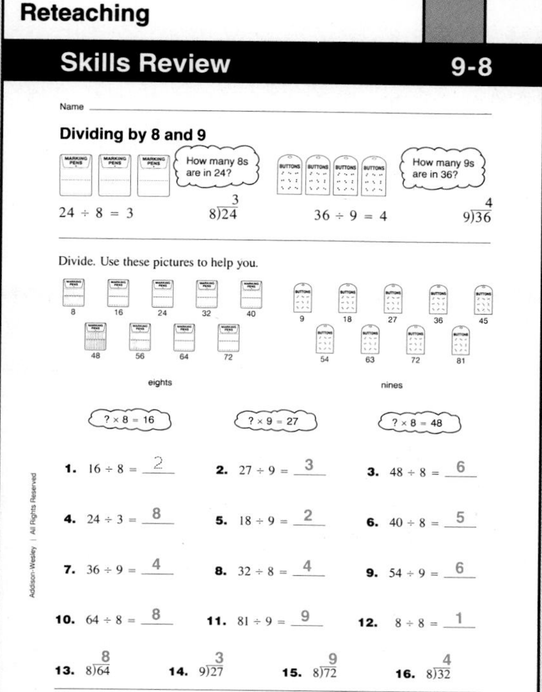

Reteaching

Skills Review 9-8

Name ______

Dividing by 8 and 9

How many 8s are in 24?

24 ÷ 8 = 3 8)24 = 3

How many 9s are in 36?

36 ÷ 9 = 4 9)36 = 4

Divide. Use these pictures to help you.

eights: 8, 16, 24, 32, 40, 48, 56, 64, 72

nines: 9, 18, 27, 36, 45, 54, 63, 72, 81

? × 8 = 16 ? × 9 = 27 ? × 8 = 48

1. 16 ÷ 8 = 2
2. 27 ÷ 9 = 3
3. 48 ÷ 8 = 6
4. 24 ÷ 3 = 8
5. 18 ÷ 9 = 2
6. 40 ÷ 8 = 5
7. 36 ÷ 9 = 4
8. 32 ÷ 8 = 4
9. 54 ÷ 9 = 6
10. 64 ÷ 8 = 8
11. 81 ÷ 9 = 9
12. 8 ÷ 8 = 1
13. 8)64 = 8
14. 9)27 = 3
15. 8)72 = 9
16. 8)32 = 4

Addison-Wesley | All Rights Reserved

RS-4 Use with text pages 252-253. 93

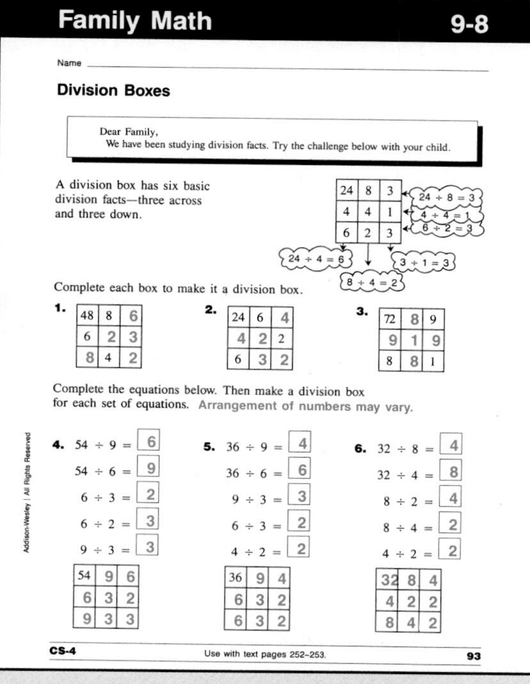

Challenges

Family Math 9-8

Name ______

Division Boxes

Dear Family,
We have been studying division facts. Try the challenge below with your child.

A division box has six basic division facts—three across and three down.

24	8	3
4	4	1
6	2	3

24 ÷ 8 = 3; 4 ÷ 4 = 1; 6 ÷ 2 = 3; 24 ÷ 4 = 6; 8 ÷ 4 = 2; 3 ÷ 1 = 3

Complete each box to make it a division box.

1.

48	8	6
6	2	3
8	4	2

2.

24	6	4
4	2	2
6	3	2

3.

72	8	9
9	1	9
8	8	1

Complete the equations below. Then make a division box for each set of equations. Arrangement of numbers may vary.

4. 54 ÷ 9 = 6; 54 ÷ 6 = 9; 6 ÷ 3 = 2; 6 ÷ 2 = 3; 9 ÷ 3 = 3

54	9	6
6	3	2
9	3	3

5. 36 ÷ 9 = 4; 36 ÷ 6 = 6; 9 ÷ 3 = 3; 6 ÷ 3 = 2; 4 ÷ 2 = 2

36	9	4
6	3	2
6	3	2

6. 32 ÷ 8 = 4; 32 ÷ 4 = 8; 8 ÷ 2 = 4; 8 ÷ 4 = 2; 4 ÷ 2 = 2

32	8	4
4	2	2
8	4	2

Addison-Wesley | All Rights Reserved

CS-4 Use with text pages 252-253. 93

Options for Individual Needs

9-8

Basic

Exercises 1-14, 21-23, 26-30
Calculator Bank, p. 487
More Practice, p. 507, set A

Supplements
Reteaching 93 or
Practice 93

Average

Exercises 1-30
Calculator Bank, p. 487
More Practice, p. 507, set A

Supplements
Practice 93
Challenges 93 or
Thinking Skills 93

Extended

Exercises 5-23, 26-30
Calculator Bank, p. 487

Supplements
Challenges 93
Thinking Skills 93

Other Resources:
Problem-Solving Experiences in Mathematics, Grade 4, Problem 51
Math In Stride, Grade 4, p. 111
Mathematics, A Way of Thinking, Lessons 6-6, 6-8
Using the Math Explorer Calculator: A Sourcebook for Teachers, Chapter 14

LESSON PLAN 9-8

OBJECTIVE 9-8

To use missing factors to divide by 8 and 9

Materials: TA 12 (Centimeter Graph Paper), division fact cards, TA 15 (Dot Paper)

1. MOTIVATE AND TEACH

LEARN ABOUT IT

EXPLORE ► Explain how you could use the numbers on the table to find how many groups performed. (Possible answer: Divide the total number of students by the number in each group.)

TALK ABOUT IT ► Explain how to link the numbers across the first row of the chart. (Multiply or divide: 5 × 8 or 8 × 5 = 40; 40 ÷ 8 = 5 or 40 ÷ 5 = 8.)

► Explain how to use missing factors to help you complete the table. (Possible answer: Think of a factor to multiply by the known factor to give the product.)

► Justify why 48 students make more groups of 8 than 40 students. (Possible answer: If a dividend increases but a divisor stays the same, the quotient must be greater.)

► Identify a row that uses a square fact. Explain. (the third row, because 8 × 8 = 64)

Student Edition answers: **1.** 6; 6 × 8 = 48 **2.** 6, 8, 6; 6 × 8 = 48; 8 × 8 = 64; 6 × 9 = 54

2. CHECK UNDERSTANDING

TRY IT OUT

ERROR ALERT Confusing square facts with multiples of 2. Failing to recall division facts.

Dividing by 8 and 9

LEARN ABOUT IT

EXPLORE Study the Tables

The multiplication facts for 8 and 9 help you divide by 8 and 9. For several years groups of drama club members have performed in a city-wide puppet show contest. Use the chart to tell how many groups performed each year.

Puppet Show Contest

Number of Groups	Number in Each Group	Total Number of Students
5	8	40
	8	48
	8	64
5	9	45
	9	54

TALK ABOUT IT See teaching notes.

1. What quotient would you find to decide how many groups performed if there were 48 students? What multiplication fact would help you find this quotient?
2. Give a quotient suggested by each row in the table. What multiplication facts would help you find these quotients?

Use multiplication to help you divide and check.

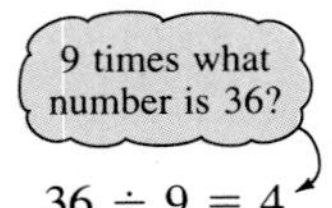

9 times what number is 36?

36 ÷ 9 = 4

Check: 9 × 4 = 36

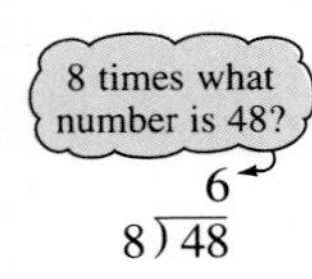

8 times what number is 48?

$8\overline{)48}$ = 6

Check: 8 × 6 = 48

TRY IT OUT

Divide. Multiply to check.

1. 45 ÷ 9 5, 5 × 9 = 45
2. 32 ÷ 8 4, 4 × 8 = 32
3. 81 ÷ 9 9, 9 × 9 = 81
4. 72 ÷ 8 9, 9 × 8 = 72
5. 63 ÷ 9 7, 7 × 9 = 63
6. 56 ÷ 8 7, 7 × 8 = 56
7. 54 ÷ 9 6, 6 × 9 = 54
8. 16 ÷ 8 2, 2 × 8 = 16
9. 27 ÷ 9 3, 3 × 9 = 27
10. 36 ÷ 9 4, 4 × 9 = 36
11. $8\overline{)64}$ 8, 8 × 8 = 64
12. $9\overline{)72}$ 9, 8 × 9 = 72
13. $9\overline{)18}$ 2, 2 × 9 = 18
14. $8\overline{)48}$ 6, 6 × 8 = 48
15. $9\overline{)63}$ 7, 7 × 9 = 63

252

TEACHING OPTIONS

RETEACHING TIPS Have students draw representative pictures of division on graph paper. They make rectangles in which the dividend is comprised of rows the size of the divisor. For example, 18 has 2 rows of 9; 81 has 9 rows of 9. Assign Reteaching Supplement 93.

ENRICHMENT Partners play Division Concentration with fact cards for division by 6-9. Players mix and deal cards face down, then turn over 2 cards at a time to find a pair that belong to the same fact family, such as 48 ÷ 6 = 8 and 48 ÷ 8 = 6. The player who makes the most matches wins.

PRACTICE

1. 18 ÷ 9 2
2. 72 ÷ 8 9
3. 40 ÷ 8 5
4. 63 ÷ 9 7
5. 0 ÷ 8 0
6. 45 ÷ 9 5
7. 72 ÷ 9 8
8. 48 ÷ 8 6
9. 9)0 0
10. 8)32 4
11. 6)48 8
12. 8)64 8
13. 8)24 3
14. 9)72 8
15. 9)63 7
16. 8)72 9
17. 9)9 1
18. 6)54 9
19. 8)48 6
20. 6)24 4

APPLY

MATH REASONING

21. Read this statement. Then write a sentence telling how to correct it.
When you multiply, you know two factors and you find the product. When you divide, you know the product and you find the two factors. **When you divide, you know the product and one factor, and you find the other factor.**

PROBLEM SOLVING

22. In the "Math Is Everywhere" puppet show, the queen, Delila Divide, gives each of her loyal subjects a bag of gold coins. She uses 36 coins. If she puts 9 in each bag, how many loyal subjects does she have? **4 loyal subjects**

23. Queen Delila gives each disloyal subject a bag of pebbles. She has 50 pebbles. How many more does she need to fill 7 bags with 9 pebbles in each? **13 pebbles**

MIXED REVIEW

Write the correct time as it would appear on a digital clock.

24. quarter past five **5:15**
25. six-forty-five **6:45**
26. seven-thirty **7:30**

Are these measures the same amount? Write yes or no.

27. 128 ounces 8 pounds **yes**
28. 6 pints 4 quarts **no**
29. 3 gallons 12 quarts **yes**
30. 4 cups 1 quart **yes**

More Practice, page 507, set A

3. PRACTICE AND APPLY

Basic	1-14, 21-23, 26-30
Average	1-30
Extended	5-23, 26-30

9-8

PRACTICE

Look at Exercises 1-20. Find an exercise with a quotient of 1. (Exercise 17) *For which exercise would it help to look for a double?* (Exercise 12)

APPLY

MATH REASONING ▶ **How can a number fact help you correct the statement?** (Possible answer: Write a fact family; identify the parts of multiplication and division to correct the statement.)

PROBLEM SOLVING ▶ **Restate Problem 22.** (Possible answer: If the queen divides 36 coins into bags with 9 coins per bag, how many bags does she need?)

▶ **What two operations would you use to solve Problem 23? Explain why.** (Multiply to combine same-size groups, subtract to find the difference.)

MIXED REVIEW ▶ **Explain how to write times in number form.** (hour : minutes)

CLOSE AND ASSESS

SHOW WHAT YOU KNOW

Have students use dot paper to show how to find the quotients of 8)72 and 9)63. Ask them to write an equation beside each drawing they make. (72 ÷ 8 = 9; 63 ÷ 9 = 7; Check students' pictures.)

QUICK QUIZ

Find the quotients.

1. 64 ÷ 8 (8)
2. 81 ÷ 9 (9)
3. 9 ÷ 9 (1)
4. 8)56 (7)
5. 9)45 (5)
6. 8)0 (0)
7. 8)40 (5)
8. 9)54 (6)

LESSON OPTIONS 9-9

Using Critical Thinking

OBJECTIVE 9-9 To use critical thinking to discover function rules

PREBOOK ACTIVITIES

QUICK REVIEW

Solve. Watch the operation signs.

1. 5 × 0 (0)	**2.** 5 + 0 (5)	**3.** 0 ÷ 5 (0)
4. 5 ÷ 0 (5)	**5.** 9 × 1 (9)	**6.** 9 + 1 (10)
7. 9 ÷ 1 (9)	**8.** 9 − 1 (8)	**9.** 7 × 0 (0)
10. 7 + 0 (7)	**11.** 0 ÷ 7 (0)	**12.** 7 − 0 (7)

PRIOR KNOWLEDGE

Have students suggest some number rules or relationships they have used that always stay the same, such as: Multiply hours by 60 to find how many minutes. (Possible answers: Divide by 2 to find half of an amount; multiply by 8 to find how many ounces in a cup.)

COMMUNICATION

Discussing Math Write the word **function** on the chalkboard and read it aloud to students. Then have students listen to determine its meaning in the context of these sentences: *The function of the eye is to allow you to see.* (''normal purpose,'' ''expected use'') *Seeing-Eye dogs function as eyes for blind people.* (''work'') Challenge students to use logical reasoning to imagine what a math function machine might be. (Possible answer: something that always works on numbers in an expected way)

EXPLORE AND CONNECT

Materials: TA 3 (Number/Operation Cards)
Grouping Suggestion: cooperative learning groups of 3 or 4
Students investigate number patterns, relationships, and operations to explore **function** rules. The first student in each group picks any 2 number cards, then secretly determines 1 or 2 operations that can connect the numbers in an equation. For example, students might link 4 and 9 by thinking **4** × *2* = 8 and 8 + *1* = **9**; the 2-operation *function* rule is multiply by 2, then add 1. Following his or her *function* rule, the student then gives 2 or 3 other numbers that relate the same way, such as 3 and 7 or 10 and 21. The other group members work together to analyze the numbers, trying to discover the *function* rule used. Once the rule has been found and verified, group members exchange roles and repeat the activity until each has created and illustrated a rule. Have students summarize how they found *function* rules. (Methods may vary.)

CONNECTIONS Use these anytime.

Problem of the Day

Operations Find at least 5 different ways to make this equation work with any 1-digit numbers. (□ × □) + □ = 9 [Answers may vary. Samples: (3 × 3) + 0; (2 × 4) + 1; (1 × 9) + 0; (2 × 2) + 5; (5 × 1) + 4; (3 × 2) + 3; (2 × 1) + 7; (1 × 1) + 8]

Patterns

Number Sense Discover the pattern, then continue it 4 more times:
1,600, 800, 400, (200), (100), (50), (25)
(Pattern: The number decreases by half each time.)

Life Skills

Sales Tax The cash register at Robin's store automatically adds sales tax to a customer's bill. It costs a penny for every $0.25 spent. Determine the sales tax for a purchase of $2.25. (9¢)

Classwork and Homework Supplements

Practice

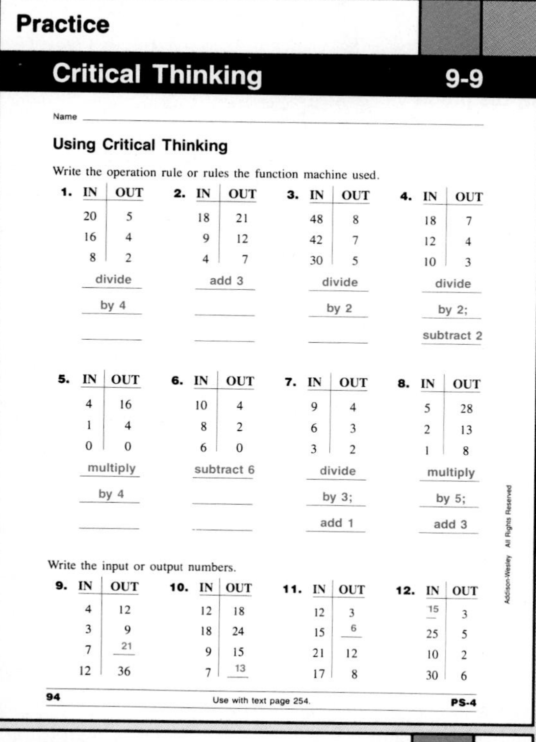

Critical Thinking 9-9

Name ______

Using Critical Thinking

Write the operation rule or rules the function machine used.

1.

IN	OUT
20	5
16	4
8	2

divide by 4

2.

IN	OUT
18	21
9	12
4	7

add 3

3.

IN	OUT
48	8
42	7
30	5

divide by 2

4.

IN	OUT
18	7
12	4
10	3

divide by 2; subtract 2

5.

IN	OUT
4	16
1	4
0	0

multiply by 4

6.

IN	OUT
10	4
8	2
6	0

subtract 6

7.

IN	OUT
9	4
6	3
3	2

divide by 3; add 1

8.

IN	OUT
5	28
2	13
1	8

multiply by 5; add 3

Write the input or output numbers.

9.

IN	OUT
4	12
3	9
7	21
12	36

10.

IN	OUT
12	18
18	24
9	15
7	13

11.

IN	OUT
12	3
15	6
21	12
17	8

12.

IN	OUT
15	3
25	5
10	2
30	6

94 Use with text page 254. PS-4

Building Thinking Skills

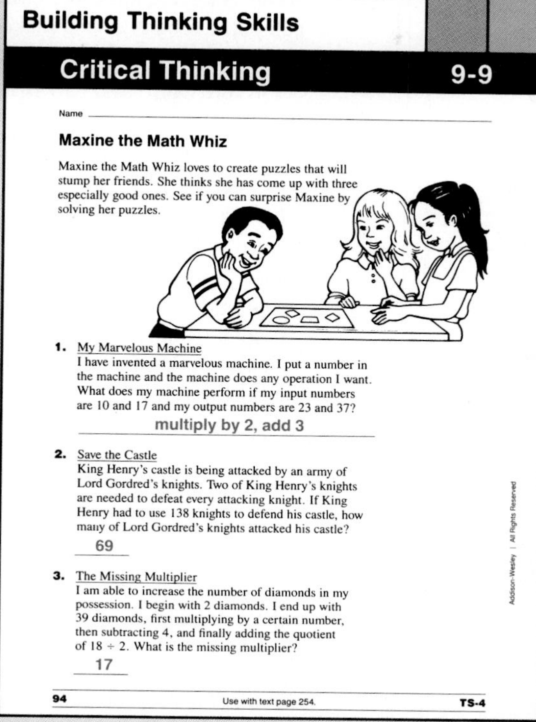

Critical Thinking 9-9

Name ______

Maxine the Math Whiz

Maxine the Math Whiz loves to create puzzles that will stump her friends. She thinks she has come up with three especially good ones. See if you can surprise Maxine by solving her puzzles.

1. My Marvelous Machine
I have invented a marvelous machine. I put a number in the machine and the machine does any operation I want. What does my machine perform if my input numbers are 10 and 17 and my output numbers are 23 and 37?
multiply by 2, add 3

2. Save the Castle
King Henry's castle is being attacked by an army of Lord Gordred's knights. Two of King Henry's knights are needed to defeat every attacking knight. If King Henry had to use 138 knights to defend his castle, how many of Lord Gordred's knights attacked his castle?
69

3. The Missing Multiplier
I am able to increase the number of diamonds in my possession. I begin with 2 diamonds. I end up with 39 diamonds, first multiplying by a certain number, then subtracting 4, and finally adding the quotient of 18 ÷ 2. What is the missing multiplier?
17

94 Use with text page 254. TS-4

Reteaching

Critical Thinking 9-9

Name ______

Using Critical Thinking

When the number 12 is put in the Function Machine, the machine adds 2 to it, and 14 (12 + 2) comes out.

If 16 is put in the machine, what number will come out?
18 will come out.

Function Machine — Operation: Add 2 (IN 12, OUT 14)

Add 2	
IN	OUT
16	18

16 + 2 = 18

Write the numbers that come out of the machine.

1. Add 6

IN	OUT
4	10
12	18
26	32

2. Subtract 7

IN	OUT
9	2
15	8
18	11

3. Multiply by 3

IN	OUT
4	12
7	21
12	36

Write the correct number in the box.

4. Divide by 4

IN	OUT
16	4
12	3
8	2

5. Multiply by 6

IN	OUT
3	18
2	12
1	6

6. Subtract 9

IN	OUT
12	3
18	9
21	12

Write the operation rule in the box.

7. Divide by 3

IN	OUT
21	7
15	5
9	3

8. Add 5

IN	OUT
5	10
9	14
10	15

9. Multiply by 4

IN	OUT
3	12
5	20
9	36

94 Use with text page 254. RS-4

Challenges

Number Sense 9-9

Name ______

Hi-Tech Machines

The machines below perform two different operations on any number placed in them. Find the pattern and complete each machine's work.

1. divides by 2 and adds 1

IN	OUT
4	3
8	5
12	7
14	8
16	9
18	10

2. multiplies by 3 and adds 1

IN	OUT
3	10
7	22
9	28
10	31
20	61
100	301

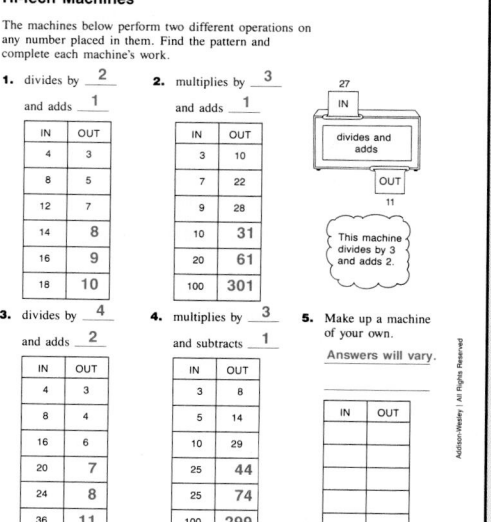

27 IN — divides and adds — OUT 11

This machine divides by 3 and adds 2.

3. divides by 4 and adds 2

IN	OUT
4	3
8	4
16	6
20	7
24	8
36	11

4. multiplies by 3 and subtracts 1

IN	OUT
3	8
5	14
10	29
25	44
25	74
100	299

5. Make up a machine of your own.
Answers will vary.

IN	OUT

94 Use with text pages 254–255. CS-4

Options for Individual Needs

9-9

Basic

Exercises 1-19
Skills Bank, pp. 461, 463
Calculator Bank, p. 486
Computer Bank, p. 495

Supplements
Reteaching 94 or
Practice 94

Average

Exercises 1-21
Skills Bank, pp. 461, 463
Calculator Bank, p. 486
Computer Bank, p. 495

Supplements
Practice 94
Challenges 94 or
Thinking Skills 94

Extended

Exercises 2-21
Calculator Bank, p. 486
Computer Bank, p. 495

Supplements
Challenges 94
Thinking Skills 94

Other Resources:
Problem-Solving Experiences in Mathematics, Grade 4, Problem 55
Math In Stride, Grade 4, p.95
Mathematics, A Way of Thinking, Lesson 6-9
Mathematics, Book A, Teacher's Edition, pp. 52, 53
Using the Math Explorer Calculator: A Sourcebook for Teachers, Chapter 14

LESSON PLAN 9-9

OBJECTIVE 9-9
To use critical thinking to discover function rules

1. MOTIVATE AND TEACH

LEARN ABOUT IT

▶ **Identify the number going in the function machine.** (24)
▶ **Identify the number that comes out.** (6)
▶ **Explain what happens in between.** (The machine does 1 or more operations on 24 that result in 6.)
▶ **Explain how the IN/OUT chart relates to the function machine.** (IN went 24, OUT came 6.)

TALK ABOUT IT ▶ **Explain what rule might link 24 to 6.** (Divide by 4.)
▶ **Explain another link between 24 and 6.** (Sample answer: Divide by 3, then subtract 2.)
▶ **Explain how other data might help you discover the function rule.** (More numbers in the IN/OUT table would help you recognize a pattern.)
Student Edition answers: **1.** It applies its rule to any number you input. **2.** $24 \div 4 = 6$ **3.** division, subtraction **4.** more examples in the IN/OUT chart **5.** Answers may vary. Sample: subtract 18, then divide by 1. **6.** Answers will vary. Check students' work.

2. CHECK UNDERSTANDING

TRY IT OUT

ERROR ALERT Misunderstanding that a rule must fit all input numbers in the same function machine. Failing to apply the function rule correctly.

Using Critical Thinking

LEARN ABOUT IT

"This is a great machine," said Carl, "You can put in a number and make it do any operation you want!"

"You sure can," said Mr. Bright, the proud inventor of the function machine.

"It's easy to see that it's dividing by 4," said Carl, perfectly sure of himself.

"It's not that easy for me to see," said Ginger, who often comes up with interesting ideas. "I'm thinking of two operations it could do to put out 6."

"I wouldn't draw any conclusion too quickly," said Mr. Bright. "Sometimes your first conjectures aren't correct!"

IN
24
Function Machine
Operation A
6
OUT

TALK ABOUT IT See teaching notes.

1. What does a function machine do?
2. Why did Carl think the machine was dividing by 4?
3. What other operations might the machine be doing?
4. What additional information might help you decide what rule the machine is using?
5. As Ginger suggested, the rule for the function machine can involve more than one operation. Can you think of two operations she might be thinking about that would produce the output 6 when the input number is 24?
6. Make up a rule for a function machine. Give some "in" and "out" numbers and ask a partner to discover the rule.

IN	OUT
24	6

TEACHING OPTIONS

RETEACHING TIPS Students who have trouble applying the function rule consistently can write an equation for each input number that links it with the rule in symbolic form, such as $5 \times 6 = 30$ for Exercise 10. Assign Reteaching Supplement 94.

ENRICHMENT Students make a function chart. They write 180, 210, 300, and 600 in the IN column, then 65 and 75 in the OUT column. They find the rule, then write the missing numbers that belong in the OUT column across from 300 and 600 in the IN column. (Rule: Divide by 3, add 5; 105 and 205.)

TRY IT OUT

1. Matt pretended to be a function machine.
   When Jorie said 24, Matt said 4.
   When Jorie said 12, Matt said 2.
   When Jorie said 18, Matt said 3.
   What rule do you think Matt was using? **Divide by 6.**

Give the output number for each of these input numbers.

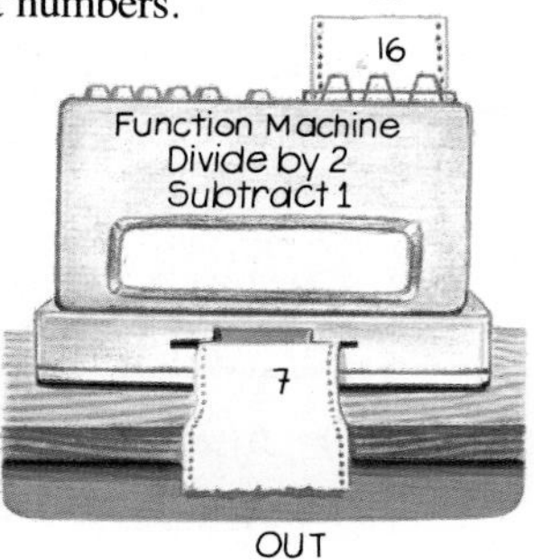

2. 8 **3** **3.** 10 **4**
4. 14 **6** **5.** 40 **19**
6. 20 **9** **7.** 24 **11**
8. 16 **7** **9.** 100 **49**

Think about what rule the function machine could be using. What do you think should go in each gray space? **See Additional Answers.**

	RULE	
	Multiply by 6.	
	IN	OUT
	3	18
10.	5	☐
11.	9	☐
12.	7	☐
13.	0	☐

	RULE	
14.	☐	
	IN	OUT
	6	2
	12	4
	3	1
	9	3
15.	24	☐

	RULE	
	Divide by 4. Add 3.	
	IN	OUT
	16	7
16.	12	☐
17.	8	☐
18.	24	☐
19.	36	☐

	RULE	
20.	☐	
	IN	OUT
	2	5
	3	7
	4	9
	5	11
21.	10	☐

3. Practice and Apply

Basic	1-19
Average	1-21
Extended	2-21

9-9

Additional Answers: See p. T79.

PRACTICE

What is the rule to use on the input numbers in Exercises 2 to 9? (Divide by 2, then subtract 1.) *How do you use a function rule once you know what it is?* (Start with the input number, then perform the operation(s) given in the function rule to get the output number,)

APPLY

► **Explain why it is easier to recognize a function rule when it involves only 1 operation.** (Possible answer: You may recognize a number relationship more easily.)

► **Generalize about the relationship between operations and input and output numbers.** (Possible answer: If the output number is greater than the input number, the rule is probably multiply or add; if the output number is less than the input number, the rule is probably divide or subtract.)

Close and Assess

SHOW WHAT YOU KNOW

Have students make a function machine that shows this rule: Divide by 5, then add 2. Ask them to give 5 rows of input numbers with the resulting output numbers. (Answers may vary. Check students' charts.)

Quick Quiz

Rule: Multiply by 9, then add 2. Give the output number for each input number.

1. 6 (56) **2.** 0 (2)
3. 3 (29) **4.** 9 (83)

LESSON OPTIONS 9-10

Problem Solving: Work Backward

OBJECTIVE 9-10 To solve problems using the strategy Work Backward

PREBOOK ACTIVITIES

QUICK REVIEW

Find each missing number.

1. 45 + (33) = 78
2. 48 ÷ (6) = 8
3. (100) − 27 = 73
4. 52 × (10) = 520
5. 75 − (30) = 45
6. (9) × 7 = 63
7. (617) + 383 = 1,000
8. (36) ÷ 4 = 9

PRIOR KNOWLEDGE

Have students recall stories, films, or television shows they have seen to explain how detectives use clues to help solve mysteries. (They use logical reasoning to piece together what happened.) Have students explain how the clues relate to what happened, in terms of order. (The clues are found after an event took place, so detectives must work backward to imagine the situation.)

COMMUNICATION

Discussing Math Have students use number sense to explain how to undo an operation, such as subtraction. (Do the opposite operation, which would be addition.) Have students match each operation with the opposite operation that could undo it. (subtract/add, add/subtract; divide/multiply, multiply/divide)

EXPLORE AND CONNECT

COOPERATIVE ACTIVITY

Grouping Suggestion: small groups

3 runners waited their turns while three 4-runner teams ran relay races. How many runners in all came to race?

TEACHING ACTIONS

Have students work together to discuss the situation and plan a strategy for solving the problem.

▶ **Analyze the data to understand the situation.** (Three 4-runner teams were racing while three other runners had to wait.)

▶ **Analyze the question to answer.** (You want to know how many runners there were all together.)

▶ **Explain a solution method.** (Possible answer: Multiply to find how many runners on the relay teams, then add back the runners who are waiting their turns.)

▶ **Decide on operations that make sense.** (Multiply, then add.)

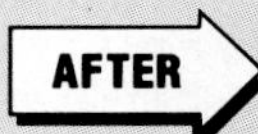

▶ **Analyze how you worked backward.** (You knew how many runners were waiting, so when you found how many were racing, you could add to find the total.)

▶ **Justify your solution.** (3 × 4 = 12 team racers, 12 + 3 = 15, so 15 racers were at the meet.)

CONNECTIONS Use these anytime.

Problem of the Day

The Forgetful 4 After her class was dismissed, Ms. Kelly found 4 lunchboxes in the rack and 22 empty spots. If everyone in the class had been in school that day and the lunchbox rack had been completely filled, how many students were in Ms. Kelly's class? (26)

Life Skills

Checking Account After Mr. Torrance wrote his rent check, he had $150 left in his checking account. If his rent is $375, how much money was in his account just before he wrote the check? ($525)

Subject Integration

Fine Arts Ms. Mavlios held a show of student paintings. She hung 4 display panels with 6 paintings on each, then she placed 5 smaller paintings on a separate easel. Determine the total number of paintings in the show. (29)

Classwork and Homework Supplements

Practice

Problem Solving 9-10

Name

Work Backward

Work backward to solve these problems.

1. Mr. Silber bought 5 small pine trees. Each cost $30. He also bought 1 bush for $16. He had $34 left in his garden budget. How much money did he have in his budget in the beginning? $200

2. It began to rain when the Lovely Lawn Company had 30 trees still on its truck. Before the rain each of the 4 workers had planted 5 trees. How many trees had been on the truck when they started work that day? 50 trees

3. After a big storm, the workers of the Bunyan Tree Company removed fallen trees. They had removed 3 dead trees from each yard of 4 different homes, and a total of 4 trees from other homes. They had 16 trees left. How many trees had they been hired to remove altogether? 32 trees

4. Mr. and Mrs. Kealoha bought market packs of pansies. There are 6 pansies in each pack. They planted 24 pansies by the front steps and 34 pansies in their backyard. They had 2 pansies left. How many market packs did they buy? 10 packs

6. Yoko bought plants at the Garden Center on Saturday and Sunday. Each day she spent $7. On Monday she got daisies for $3. She had $3 left. How much money did she have Saturday morning? $20

6. Lance bought some coleus plants. He planted 3 rows of plants with 8 plants in each row. He had 12 left. How many plants did he buy? 36 plants

Building Thinking Skills

Problem Solving 9-10

Name

Making Sense of Problems—Backward!

Solve the following problems.

1. Isabella was selling raffle tickets at her school fair. She was in a contest with her friends Craig and Nina to see who could sell the most tickets in 3 days. At the end of the first day, she had sold 5 fewer than Craig. She did sell 11 more than Nina. On the second day, she sold twice as many as she did on the first day. Craig sold 95, and Nina outsold him by 12. On the third day, both Craig and Nina sold 50 tickets, outselling Isabella by 9 tickets each. Craig sold a total of 212 tickets over the 3 days. How many tickets did Isabella sell in the 3 days? 227 tickets

How many tickets did Nina sell in 3 days? 208 tickets

2. Ramapo summer camp holds a big swimming meet every year. The races are held on Cayuga Pond, which is divided into 8 lanes. In the second race of the day, which was an individual event, all the lanes but two were filled. In the third race, a long-distance event, only 2 swimmers entered. The fourth race was a relay race, with 4 swimmers per team. Five teams entered that race. The fifth race was also a 4-person relay race, but 7 teams entered. The last race was an individual event. Three times as many swimmers entered as in the third race. By day's end, 69 swimmers had competed in the meet. How many swimmers swam in the first race? 7 swimmers

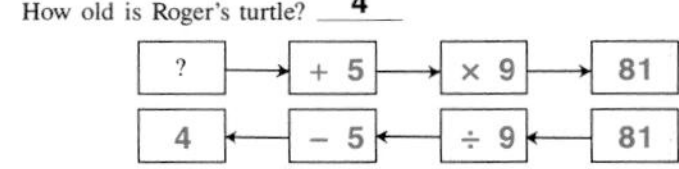

Reteaching

Problem Solving 9-10

Name

Work Backward

To solve a problem, you may have to start at the end of the problem and work backward.

Jamal was given his allowance on Friday. On Saturday, he spent $3. On Monday, Laura paid Jamal the $5 she owed him. If Jamal now has $6, how much is his allowance?

Subtract to find how much Jamal had before Laura paid him.

$6 − $5 = $1

Add back what he spent to the $1 to find his allowance.

$1 + $3 = $4

Jamal's allowance is $4.

Work backward to solve these problems.

1. Pedro bought 5 records. Each record cost $6. Then he spent $7 for a tape. He had $2 left. How much money did Pedro have in the beginning?

   How much does Pedro have left? 2

   Add back what he spent on the tape. $ 2 + $7 = $9

   How much did he spend on the records? $ 5 × 6 = $ $30

   How much did he have in the beginning? $ 30 + $ 9 = $ 39

2. Larry took all the books out of the bookcase. He put 14 books on one table. Then he put the rest on another table in 6 stacks of 7. How many books were in the bookcase when he started? 56 books

3. Geena put 15 stamps on one page. She put the rest on 4 pages of 9 each. How many stamps are in her stamp book? 51 stamps

Challenges

Problem Solving 9-10

Name

Age Riddles

You can use a "backward" machine to solve these problems.

Example: Tom said, "If I multiply my age by 3 and add 10, I get 37." How old is Tom?

The "backward" machine changes all the operations: + becomes −. − becomes +. × becomes ÷. ÷ becomes ×.

? → × 3 → + 10 → 37

9 ← ÷ 3 ← − 10 ← 37

Tom is 9 years old.

1. Becky said, "If I divide my cat's age by 4 and add 14, I get 17."

   How old is Becky's cat? 12

   ? → ÷ 4 → + 14 → 17

   12 ← × 4 ← − 14 ← 17

2. Roger said, "If I add 5 to my turtle's age and multiply by 9, I get 81."

   How old is Roger's turtle? 4

   ? → + 5 → × 9 → 81

   4 ← − 5 ← ÷ 9 ← 81

3. Grampa Dan said, "If I divide my age by 2 and subtract 9, I get 40."

   How old is Grampa? 98

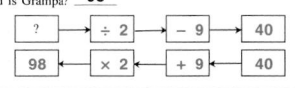

   ? → ÷ 2 → − 9 → 40

   98 ← × 2 ← + 9 ← 40

Options for Individual Needs

9-10

Basic

Exercises 1-6
Skills Bank, pp. 461, 463
Calculator Bank, p. 488
More Practice, p. 520, set E

Supplements
Reteaching 95 or
Practice 95

Average

Exercises 1-6
Skills Bank, pp. 461, 463
Calculator Bank, p. 488
More Practice, p. 520, set E

Supplements
Practice 95
Challenges 95 or
Thinking Skills 95

Extended

Exercises 1-6
Calculator Bank, p. 488

Supplements
Challenges 95
Thinking Skills 95

Other Resources:
Problem-Solving Experiences in Mathematics, Grade 4, Problem 64
Math In Stride, Grade 4, p. 160
Mathematics, A Way of Thinking, Lesson 6-10
Mathematics, Book A, Teacher's Edition, pp. 53, 54

LESSON PLAN 9-10

OBJECTIVE 9-10
To solve problems using the strategy Work Backward

Materials: TA 9 (Play Money—Coins and Dollars)

1. MOTIVATE AND TEACH

LEARN ABOUT IT

► **Explain the situation in your own words.** (Of all bowlers, 14 waited as others got to start bowling, 4 at a time, on 6 available lanes.)
► **Analyze the question.** (You must find how many junior bowlers in all.)

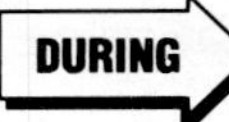

► **Justify using multiplication as a first step.** (It will tell how many bowlers got started right away; 6 × 4 = 24)
► **Explain how to use that product to solve the problem.** (add it to the 14 bowlers who are still waiting; 24 + 14 = 38)

► **Explain how to verify your solution.** (Start with 38, subtract the 14 bowlers who waited, see if there are 24 bowlers for 6 lanes, 4 per lane; it works.)

2. CHECK UNDERSTANDING

TRY IT OUT

► **Decide which data you can start with.** (Possible answer: Andy has $2.)
► **Analyze the problem to choose the operations to use to work backward.** (Possible answer: add, multiply, add)

ERROR ALERT Misinterpreting data.

Problem Solving
Work Backward

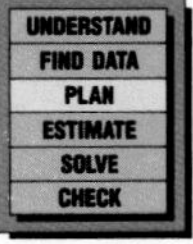

LEARN ABOUT IT

To solve some problems, you may need to undo the key actions in the problem. This strategy is called **Work Backward**.

The junior bowling teams came to Lucky Lanes. 14 bowlers had to wait for lanes to open up. The rest of the bowlers were assigned to the 6 open lanes. 4 bowlers were assigned to each lane. How many junior bowlers came to Lucky Lanes?

First, I'll multiply to find out how many bowlers were assigned to lanes. 6 × 4 = 24

Now, I'll add back the number of bowlers waiting for lanes to see how many bowlers there were all together. 24 + 14 = 38

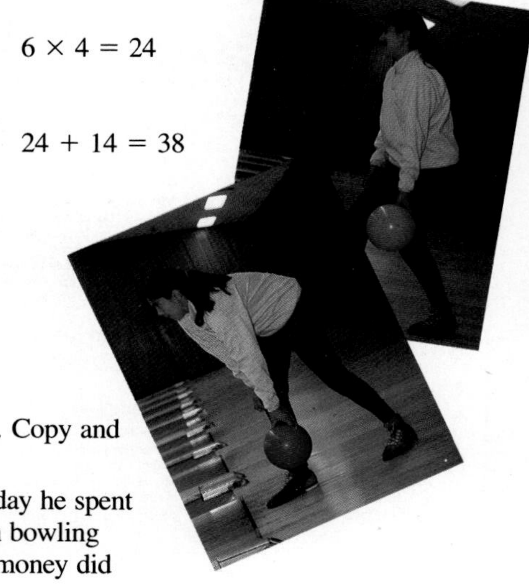

There were 38 bowlers all together.

TRY IT OUT

Work backward to solve this problem. Copy and complete the steps.

Andy went bowling on 3 days. Each day he spent $4. The last day, he also spent $13 on bowling shoes. Andy had $2 left. How much money did he have in the beginning? $27

- How much money does Andy have left? $2
- How much money did he spend on shoes? $13
- How much money did he spend each day at the bowling alley? $4
- How much did he have in the beginning? $27

Start with the $2 Andy has left.
Add back the $13.
$2 + $13 = $15
He spent 3 × $4 bowling.
3 × $4 = ||||
|||| + |||| = $||||

TEACHING OPTIONS

RETEACHING TIPS Some students may interpret data more clearly if they work through the situation from the beginning. They might first find the total cost of 3 days of bowling, then add $13 for shoes, then add the $2 Andy has left to reach the total of $27. Assign Reteaching Supplement 95.

COMPUTER **Teasers by Tobbs, Sunburst Communications, Copyright 1985** For all student levels (best in pairs). Choose multiplication and level two. A 2-by-2 table is given with empty squares to fill. Emphasize working backward. Game time: 10 to 15 min.

PRACTICE

Work backward to solve these problems.

1. Raul came in first in raising money for the Scout-A-Rama. He got a book of free bowling tickets as a prize. He gave away 5 tickets each to 4 friends. Then he gave 7 to his brother. Raul kept 13. How many bowling tickets did he win? **40 tickets**

2. Alexa's grandmother gave her some birthday money. Alexa spent $5 on bowling. Then her sister gave her the $4 she owed her. Alexa now had $9. How much money did she get for her birthday? **$10**

MIXED PRACTICE

Choose a strategy from the list or use other strategies you know.

Some Strategies
Act It Out
Use Objects
Choose an Operation
Draw a Picture
Make an Organized List
Guess and Check
Make a Table
Look for a Pattern
Use Logical Reasoning
Work Backward

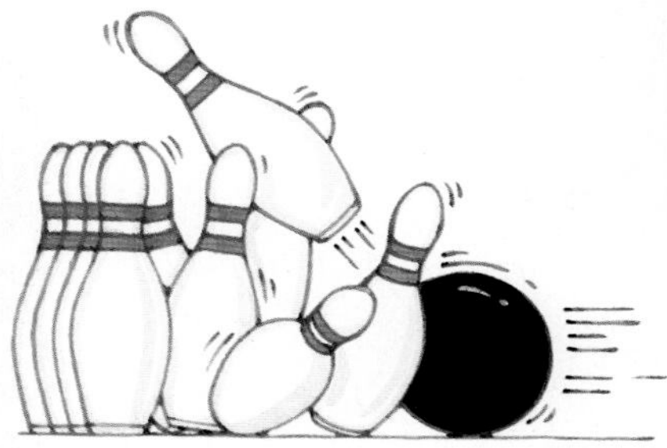

3. There are 9 junior bowling teams and 45 bowlers in all. Each team has the same number of bowlers. How large is each team? **5 bowlers**

4. Marco bowled his first frame. In the second frame he knocked down 4 pins. In the third frame he knocked down twice as many as in the second. His score so far is 21. How many pins did he knock down in the first frame? **9 pins**

5. In the girl's league, Lia had the top score for the season with 2,954 points. Her highest game was 234. Kim came in second with 2,527. Rhonda was third with 2,489. What was the difference between the first and the third place scores for the season? **465 points**

6. The Brighton Bowling Alley has a package deal for birthday parties. It costs $3.50 for each person. Joe would like to invite 17 people. His mother says 7 is plenty. How much more would Joe's plan cost than his mother's? **$35**

More Practice, page 520, set E

3. PRACTICE AND APPLY

Basic	1-6
Average	1-6
Extended	1-6

9-10

Sample Solutions: See p. T79.

PRACTICE

In Problem 1, what number does Raul have at the end? (13) *Which data should be multiplied?* (5 × 4) *In Problem 2, what might help you understand the situation?* (Possible answers: Act It Out, use play money, Guess and Check)

MIXED PRACTICE

► **Identify the problem that can be solved using the Work Backward strategy.** (Problem 4)

► **Analyze Problem 3 to decide which strategy to use.** (Choose an Operation)

► **Analyze Problem 5 for extra data.** (You do not need to know that Lia's highest score was 234 and that Kim's second-place score was 2,527.)

► **Explain how to use logical reasoning to solve Problem 6 mentally.** (Joe wants 10 more people, so his plan costs 10 × $3.50 more than his mother's plan; use special products to multiply.)

CLOSE AND ASSESS

SHOW WHAT YOU KNOW

Have students use play money to solve this problem. When Kayla got her allowance, she spent $3 of it right away. The next day, Tim paid Kayla the $2 he owed her. If Kayla now has $4, what is her allowance? ($5)

QUICK QUIZ

Len had some toy cars. He gave 6 friends 5 cars each. He gave his sister 9 cars and kept his 7 favorite toy cars for himself. How many toy cars did Len start with? (46)

CHAPTER 9

APPLIED PROBLEM SOLVING
GROUP DECISION MAKING

OBJECTIVE To analyze, organize, and make decisions using relevant data

Discuss with students what it means to recycle and help them understand the ecological benefits of recycling. (to reuse; less waste or depletion of our natural resources)

FACTS TO CONSIDER

► **Explain why you need to know the size of the class.** (to determine the cost of the farm trip; to estimate how much any 1 student can contribute to the recycling totals)
► **Analyze the data shown in the 3 columns of the chart to find a relationship.** (Rate per Pound × Pounds Collected = Amount Earned)
► **Explain how to complete the chart.** (Multiply rate by the number of pounds to find amount earned; divide amount earned by the number of pounds or by the rate to find the missing data.)
► **Decide on a calculation method.** (calculator or mental math, depending on the numbers)

Applied Problem Solving
Group Decision Making

UNDERSTAND
FIND DATA
PLAN
ESTIMATE
SOLVE
CHECK

Group Skill:
Encourage and Respect Others

To help clean up the neighborhood and save natural resources, your class is taking part in a neighborhood recycling program. Recycling is also a way to earn money for your class's outdoor education program.

A recycling company will buy items at the rates shown in the chart. Your class has decided to spend the money you earn to go and work for three days at a special farm school. The farm charges $30 for each student. Decide how long you will need to earn the necessary funds.

TEACHING OPTIONS

COOPERATIVE LEARNING

Grouping Suggestion: cooperative learning groups of 4 to 6
Have students plan and divide tasks related to the decision making, such as completing and verifying data in the chart, finding totals, comparing data, predicting long-range totals, listing possible concerns, and summarizing the final decision.
Have partners discuss each part of the task, verify each other's work, and contribute ideas to consider the problem from various points of view. One student may take notes on the pros and cons discussed to help the group reach a consensus.

Facts to Consider

1. There are 25 students in the class.
2. The chart, when completed, will tell you how much the class collected and earned the first day of the program.

Some Questions to Answer

1. What was the total amount earned the first day?
2. Which item collected earned the most money?

Items for Recycling	Rate per Pound	Pounds Collected	Amount Earned
Aluminum cans	$.59	16	$9.44
Glass bottles/jars	.04	78	IIII
Plastic	.01	12	IIII
Newspapers	.01	IIII	.94
Cardboard	.02	IIII	.38

3. Which item seems easiest to collect?
4. Can the class expect to earn this amount each day?
5. How much will the farm trip cost all together?

What Is Your Decision?

How long do you think it will take to earn the money the class needs? Support your conclusions.

259

EXTENSION Contact a recycling center or scrap dealer in your area to learn the actual rates per pound for recycling each type of item in the chart. Find out how to begin a recycling program in your class or school and discuss possible ways to spend whatever money you would earn.

SOME QUESTIONS TO ANSWER

► **Decide on a plan for answering Question 1.** (Find all amounts earned, then add the 5 amounts in the last column.)
► **Explain how to interpret Question 3.** (The item with the greatest number of pounds collected is probably the easiest to collect.)
► **Analyze factors that may affect how much the class could collect on any given day.** (Possible answers: other obligations students may have; different family habits about separating or saving items for recycling; transportation; storage; weather; illness)

WHAT IS YOUR DECISION?

► **List things to consider when predicting how long the class should plan to continue recycling.** (Answers may vary. Some considerations: Students will probably not be able to collect items daily; rates may change; enthusiasm may decline.)
► **Predict a reasonable amount of time in which to earn the money.** (Answers will vary. Suggested time: a minimum of at least 2 mo.)

CHAPTER 9

WRAP UP

INTRODUCTION The Wrap Up provides activities emphasizing math language and thinking skills for the chapter and a project that integrates those skills with other math strands.

USING PAGE 260

Operations Match Have students complete this section independently. Have them illustrate their responses with an example of each operation, including the answer.

Sometimes, Always, Never

▶ **Identify the operations in which order does not affect the answer.** (addition, multiplication)

▶ **Explain how to verify your decision for Exercise 8.** (Divide a number by several smaller divisors and observe the outcomes.)

Project Have students work in small groups to discuss and solve Problems a and b.

▶ **Analyze the situations to decide which operations to use.** (Possible answers: divide; divide and add; multiply and add)

▶ **Decide which strategies you could use to solve the problems.** (Answers will vary. Sample answers: Use Objects; Draw a Picture; Act It Out; Make an Organized List; Guess and Check) Have students display their drawings of the table arrangements for Problem b on a bulletin board. Encourage volunteers to explain their arrangement schemes.

Additional Answers: See p. T79.

WRAP UP

Operations Match

Match each operation with its answer.

1. multiplication **d**
2. division **a**
3. subtraction **c**
4. addition **b**

a. quotient
b. sum
c. difference
d. product

Sometimes, Always, Never

Which word should go in the blank, sometimes, always, or never? Explain your choices. **Explanations will vary.**

5. You can __?__ check division with multiplication. **always**
6. $15 \div 3$ and $3 \div 15$ __?__ give the same quotient. **never**
7. Dividing by 2 __?__ tells you half of an amount. **always**
8. Dividing by a smaller number __?__ gives a smaller quotient. **never**
9. There are __?__ 4 equations in a fact family for multiplication or division. **sometimes**

Project **See Additional Answers.**

There are 28 students in art class. Small tables hold 3 students. Large tables hold 4 students.

a. If everybody wanted to sit at a full table, how many different ways could students be arranged? Explain each arrangement.

b. How many students would sit at large tables of 4 and how many at small tables of 3 to have the same number of each size table filled? Draw a picture of the arrangement.

260

TEACHING OPTIONS

ENRICHMENT Have students apply the strategy they used successfully in the project to a similar situation. A popular carnival ride has 8 each of different-sized cars that hold 4, 5, or 6 riders. Find the total number of people who can ride at once. Then figure out how 75 people can ride at one time in the *same* number of each size car. (120; 5 cars of each size is $5 \times 4 = 20$, $5 \times 5 = 25$, $6 \times 5 = 30$, $20 + 25 + 30 = 75$)

CHAPTER REVIEW/TEST

Part 1 Understanding

Draw a picture, then write a division equation for the answer. **See Additional Answers.**

1. A store sells boxes of juice in packs of 3. How many packs can you make with 18 boxes?
2. 15 bananas will make 5 batches of banana bread. How many bananas go in each batch?
3. In multiplication, you have __?__ and you find the __?__. In division, you know the __?__ and one __?__. You use that information to find the other __?__. **factors product; product factor factor**
4. Give the fact family for the factors 6 and 7. **See Additional Answers.**

Part 2 Skills

Find the quotients.

5. 14 ÷ 2 **7**
6. 40 ÷ 5 **8**
7. 49 ÷ 7 **7**
8. 27 ÷ 3 **9**
9. $4\overline{)16}$ **4**
10. $9\overline{)63}$ **9**
11. $5\overline{)0}$ **0**
12. $6\overline{)24}$ **4**
13. 32 divided by 8 **4**
14. 42 divided by 7 **6**
15. |||| ÷ 1 = 6 **6**

Part 3 Applications

16. Jan traded 13 baseball cards to Dan for 4 new packs of 6 cards each. Jan lost 3 cards so now she has 75. How many did she have at the start? **67 cards**

Give an estimate and then find the exact solution.

17. Toy Town sells baseball cards at $0.49 a pack. How much money will Elise, the clerk, collect if she sells 82 packs? **$40; $40.18**
18. **Challenge** A display rack holds 21 sports cards in each of 9 rows. Figure out the total number of cards on two display racks. **400 racks; 378 racks**

261

CHAPTER REVIEW/TEST

INTRODUCTION The Review/Test is provided to review and evaluate the skills and concepts presented in Chapter 9.

USING PAGE 261
If you prefer to use this page for review, you may want to use the **Multiple-Choice Posttest** (pages 35-36) or the **Free-Response Posttest** (pages 35-36) to evaluate mastery of Chapter objectives.

ITEM ANALYSIS The table below correlates the Chapter Review/Test items with the lesson objectives for the chapter.

Items	Objectives
1, 2	9-1
3, 4	9-2
5	9-3
6	9-4
(4), 7	9-7
8	9-3
9	9-4
10	9-8
11	9-6
12	9-7
13	9-8
14	9-7
15	9-6
16	9-10
17, 18	9-5

Additional Answers: See p. T79.

INFORMAL ASSESSMENT

Using Manipulatives Have students use counters to find the quotients of 24 ÷ 3 and 24 ÷ 6. Then have them state a fact family related to each division. (24 ÷ 3 = 8, 24 ÷ 8 = 3, 3 × 8 = 24, 8 × 3 = 24; 24 ÷ 6 = 4, 24 ÷ 4 = 6, 4 × 6 = 24, 6 × 4 = 24)

Communication *Describe 2 kinds of actions that suggest division. Create an example of a situation that fits each action.* (Possible answer: Separate same-size groups: *If juice cans come in 3-packs, how many 3-packs can 15 juice cans make?* Share equally in groups: *If 4 children share 20 grapes, how many can each child have?*)

Critical Thinking *Analyze how the fact 5 × 184 = 920 could help in a division situation.* (Because of fact family relationships, you know that 920 ÷ 5 = 184 and 920 ÷ 184 = 5.)

ENRICHMENT

INTRODUCTION Students are challenged to use the link between multiplication and division to find and evaluate factors.

USING PAGE 262
This Enrichment page is provided for all students. You may wish to use it after they have completed the Chapter Review/Test on page 261.

▶ **Explain how to verify that you have found all factor pairs for 24.** (Possible answer: Test numbers from 1 to 24 to see if each is part of a factor pair that gives 24.)

▶ **Identify 2 factors that are always in a list of factors for any number.** (The number itself and 1.)

▶ **Explain which number is also the product in each set of factors.** (the greatest number; the factor paired with 1)

▶ **Generalize a rule for evaluating factor sets.** (Add all factors less than the factor that is also the product.

▶ **Compare the 3 kinds of numbers.** (Without including the product as a factor, the sum of ''too full'' factors is greater than the product; the sum of ''hungry'' factors is less than the product; the sum of ''just right'' factors is equal to the product.)

EXTENSION Have students write a paragraph to summarize what they found when they analyzed factor sets. Have them draw conclusions based on their tables. (Possible conclusions: There are more ''hungry'' numbers than any other; all ''too full'' numbers are even.)

Additional Answers: See p. T79.

ENRICHMENT
Factor Pair Fun

Here is one way you can cut a rectangle with 24 squares from a piece of graph paper. There are 4 rows of 6 squares, so 4 and 6 are a **factor pair** for 24.

You can use graph paper in this way to find factor pairs and list all the factors of a number. See Additional Answers.

1. How many different ways can you find to cut a rectangle with 24 squares from graph paper? Show each way and list the factor pairs.
2. Copy and complete this factor pair table to show all of the factors of 24.
3. Cut graph paper squares and make a factor pair table to show all of the factors of 16. Make a list of the factors in numerical order. See Additional Answers.

Factor Pair Table

Factors of 24			
1	×		24
2	×		12
3	×		8
4	×	6	

Just for fun, we could say that some numbers are *too full*, some are *hungry*, and some are *just right*! In these examples, add all the factors that are less than the number itself. Then tell why you think the numbers could have these names.

Factors: (1, 2, 3, 4, 6,) 12

Factors: (1, 2, 4,) 8

6 Just Right

Factors: (1, 2, 3,) 6

4. Find all the factors of each number up to 20. Make a table that shows the factors and tells which numbers are *too full*, which are *hungry*, and which are *just right*. See Additional Answers.

262

CUMULATIVE REVIEW

1. 803 × 6

   A 4,808 B 4,868

   (C) 4,818 D 4,809

2. (4 × 40) + 4

   A 444 (B) 164

   C 4,404 D 640

3. $62.48 × 7

   (A) $437.36 B $440.25

   C $455.36 D $476.36

4. 819 × 76

   A 10,647 B 62,234

   C 66,094 (D) 62,244

5. Which calculation method is probably best to find (76 × 68) + 47?

   A pencil, paper B estimation

   C mental math (D) calculator

6. What is another way to write the date October 19, 1991?

   A 19/10/91 B 9/19/91

   (C) 10/19/91 D 10/91/19

7. The play started at 2:30 p.m. It lasted until 5:10 p.m. How long did it last?

   A 3 h 20 min B 2 h 10 min

   (C) 2 h 40 min D 7 h 40 min

8. Intermission began 1 hour and 23 minutes after the 2:30 p.m. start of the play. What time was that?

   A 4:03 p.m. (B) 3:53 p.m.

   C 3:48 p.m. D 3:57 p.m.

9. Which is less than 3 yards?

   (A) 90 in. B 12 ft

   C 9 ft D 300 in.

10. 4 gal = |||| qt

    A 64 B 1

    C 32 (D) 16

11. One side of a square patio measures 27 feet. Find the patio's perimeter.

    A 31 ft (B) 108 ft

    C 54 ft D 729 ft

12. Estimate the product of 49 × 80.

    A 3,920 (B) 4,000

    C 3,200 D 4,500

263

CUMULATIVE REVIEW

INTRODUCTION The purpose of this Cumulative Review is to maintain previously taught skills and concepts. The emphasis in this Cumulative Review is on multiplication of 2-, 3-, and 4-digit factors by 1-digit factors, Chapter 6; on multiplication by 2-digit factors, Chapter 7; and on time and customary measurement, Chapter 8.

ITEM ANALYSIS The table below correlates the Cumulative Review items with the lesson objectives.

Items	Objectives
1	6-6
2	6-3
3	6-11
4	7-5
5	7-9
6	8-2
7, 8	8-3
9	8-6
10	8-11
11	8-9
12	7-2
(12)	7-1

Chapter Management

OVERVIEW

Lesson	Pages	Objectives	Subject Integration	Strand Integration
Chapter Opener	264-265	To introduce chapter 10	social studies-historical ships	measurement
Finding and Checking Quotients and Remainders	266-267	10-1 To find and check quotients and remainders	science-boats	critical thinking
Mental Math: Special Quotients	268-269	10-2 To find the quotient of a multiple and a 1-digit number	language arts-writing	mathematical reasoning
Estimating Quotients	270-271	10-3 To round and to use compatible numbers	social studies-historical ships	calculators
Dividing Whole Numbers: Making the Connection	272-273	10-4 To divide a 2-digit number by a 1-digit number	social studies-group skills	numeration
Dividing Whole Numbers: 2-Digit Quotients	274-275	10-5 To find 2-digit quotients	health/fitness-baseball	estimation
Problem Solving: Interpreting Remainders	276-277	10-6 To solve problems by interpreting the remainder	health/fitness-lifesaving	consumer math
3-Digit Quotients	278-279	10-7 To find 3-digit quotients	social studies-historical ships	mathematical reasoning
Finding Averages/Midchapter Review/Quiz	280-281	10-8 To find the average of 3 or more numbers	language arts-mystery book	problem solving
Deciding Where to Start	282-283	10-9 To decide where to start in division	science-car speeds	mental math
Zero in the Quotient	284-285	10-10 To divide 3-digit numbers when there is a 0 in the quotient	social studies-plane transportation	algebra
Problem Solving: Choosing A Calculation Method	286-287	10-11 To choose an appropriate calculation method	social studies-ships	measurement
Dividing with Money	288-289	10-12 To divide an amount of money less than $10	fine arts-photography	critical thinking
Data Collection and Analysis: Group Decision Making	290-291	10-13 To collect, organize, and present data	social studies-daily chores	statistics

MATHEMATICAL BACKGROUND

Division
This chapter introduces division with larger numbers and with remainders. Students learn where to start when dividing a 1-digit number into a 2- or 3-digit number.

Multiplication
In Lesson 10-1, students learn that the division check is based on the inverse relationship between multiplication and division. To check, multiply the quotient by the divisor, then add the remainder. The answer should be the dividend.

Mental Math
Students learn to mentally find quotients of multiples of 10.

Problem Solving
Students solve problems that involve interpreting remainders.

TIPS FROM TEACHERS

Use this handy and quiet activity to assess each student's comprehension of math facts. Read a problem aloud and give a correct or an incorrect answer. Students solve the problem mentally, then show thumbs up if your answer was correct or thumbs down if your answer was incorrect.

Jerry Stenson
Monte Verde School
San Francisco, CA

ASSESSMENT

Pretest — Chapter 10, page 1

Multiple-Choice Format

Name ____________

1. Find the quotient and remainder. 8)74
   a. 8 R1 **b.** 9 R1 **c.** 9 R2 **d.** 8 R2 — 1. c
2. Use mental math to find 630 ÷ 9.
   a. 80 **b.** 70 **c.** 90 **d.** 7 — 2. b
3. Estimate: 820 ÷ 9.
   a. 9 **b.** 90 **c.** 900 **d.** 80 — 3. b
4. Find 28 ÷ 2. Think:
   Set 1 Set 2
   a. 14 **b.** 5 **c.** 28 **d.** 30 — 4. a
5. Find the quotient and remainder. 5)79
   a. 11 R4 **b.** 15 R4 **c.** 16 R1 **d.** 12 R4 — 5. b
6. Find 95 ÷ 4.
   a. 2 R5 **b.** 21 R1 **c.** 23 R3 **d.** 22 R1 — 6. c
7. 68 students are going on a field trip. Only 6 students can go in each car. How many cars do they need?
   a. 12 cars **b.** 2 cars **c.** 10 cars **d.** 11 cars — 7. a
8. Janie has 68 beads. She uses 9 beads on each purse she makes. How many purses can she make?
   a. 9 purses **b.** 5 purses **c.** 8 purses **d.** 7 purses — 8. d

Pretest — Chapter 10, page 2

Multiple-Choice Format

Name ____________

9. Find the quotient and remainder. 2)763
   a. 321 R1 **b.** 381 R1 **c.** 331 R1 **d.** 382 R1 — 9. b
10. Find 337 ÷ 2.
    a. 118 R1 **b.** 113 R1 **c.** 163 R1 **d.** 168 R1 — 10. d
11. Find the average of these numbers: 16, 39, 47, 22.
    a. 124 **b.** 26 **c.** 31 **d.** 104 — 11. c
12. Find 512 ÷ 6. Do you start dividing by tens or by dividing by hundreds?
    a. tens **b.** hundreds — 12. a
13. Divide. 9)185
    a. 2 R5 **b.** 20 R5 **c.** 21 R5 **d.** 21 R4 — 13. b
14. Divide. 4)835
    a. 208 R3 **b.** 28 R3 **c.** 29 R1 **d.** 201 R1 — 14. a
15. Think of the most useful calculation method. Then solve. How many 8-inch ribbons can you cut from a 40-inch piece of ribbon?
    a. 8 ribbons **b.** 32 ribbons **c.** 5 ribbons **d.** 320 ribbons — 15. c
16. Divide. 3)$4.86
    a. $1.22 **b.** $1.62 **c.** $0.22 **d.** $0.12 — 16. b

Posttest — Chapter 10, page 1

Multiple-Choice Format

Name ____________

1. Find the quotient and remainder. 8)59
   a. 6 R1 **b.** 9 R1 **c.** 7 R5 **d.** 7 R3 — 1. d
2. Use mental math to find 350 ÷ 5.
   a. 7 **b.** 700 **c.** 70 **d.** 17 — 2. c
3. Estimate: $55 ÷ 7.
   a. $9 **b.** $6 **c.** $7 **d.** $8 — 3. d
4. Find 26 ÷ 2. Think:
   Set 1 Set 2
   a. 14 **b.** 28 **c.** 13 **d.** 4 — 4. c
5. Find the quotient and remainder. 5)64
   a. 10 R4 **b.** 11 R1 **c.** 12 R1 **d.** 12 R4 — 5. d
6. Find 37 ÷ 3.
   a. 12 R1 **b.** 18 R1 **c.** 11 R2 **d.** 1 R7 — 6. a
7. Andy cut as many 7-inch ribbons from a 50-inch length as he could. How many inches of ribbon were left over?
   a. 1 in. **b.** 43 in. **c.** 57 in. **d.** 7 in. — 7. a
8. 38 students are going on a field trip. Only 6 students can go in each car. How many full cars will there be?
   a. 5 cars **b.** 6 cars **c.** 7 cars **d.** 32 cars — 8. b

Posttest — Chapter 10, page 2

Multiple-Choice Format

Name ____________

9. Find the quotient and remainder. 4)965
   a. 211 R1 **b.** 216 R1 **c.** 241 R1 **d.** 240 R1 — 9. c
10. Find 648 ÷ 5.
    a. 129 R3 **b.** 128 R3 **c.** 12 R8 **d.** 101 R3 — 10. a
11. Find the average of these numbers: 36, 94, 75, 27.
    a. 53 **b.** 212 **c.** 232 **d.** 58 — 11. d
12. Find 729 ÷ 3. Do you start dividing by tens or by dividing by hundreds?
    a. tens **b.** hundreds — 12. b
13. Divide. 8)163
    a. 2 R3 **b.** 20 R3 **c.** 21 R3 **d.** 20 R8 — 13. b
14. Divide. 6)617
    a. 102 R5 **b.** 12 R5 **c.** 112 R1 **d.** 113 R1 — 14. a
15. Think of the most useful calculation method. Then solve. How many 8-inch pieces of twine can you cut from a 48-inch roll?
    a. 8 pieces **b.** 6 pieces **c.** 140 pieces **d.** 56 pieces — 15. b
16. Divide. 5)$6.45
    a. $1.25 **b.** $1.31 **c.** $1.01 **d.** $1.29 — 16. d

ITEM ANALYSIS

Items	Objectives
1	10-1
2	10-2
3	10-3
4	10-4
5, 6	10-5
7, 8	10-6
9, 10	10-7
11	10-8
12	10-9
13, 14	10-10
15	10-11
16	10-12

Note: The item analysis is the same for all pretests and posttests for this chapter.

ALSO AVAILABLE

- **Free Response Tests**
- **Alternative Tests**
- **Thinking Strategies**
- **Concrete Materials**

Optional Chapter Activities

PROJECT AND BULLETIN BOARD

After students have completed Lesson 8, have them work individually or in pairs to make a bulletin board display showing the average scores of their favorite sports teams. They should post the scores for three or four games together with the average for those games.

At subsequent sessions, have students display individual and average figures for such things as temperature, student heights, distances, or prices of certain items or services.

WHAT'S THE SCORE?

Team	Scores	Average Scores
Kats	10 16 22	16
Colts	8 15 7	10

COOPERATIVE LEARNING

Divide the class into groups of three or four. Identify the group skill: check for understanding. Give each group two word problems such as the following:

Carol bought 3 tapes at the record store. The total cost of the tapes was $7.83. If the tapes were the same price, how much did each tape cost? ($2.61)

Have the group work together to solve each problem. Tell them to make sure that everyone in the group understands what operation (division) the group should perform to solve each problem and why. Someone in the group should carry out the division and someone else should check it with a calculator. Have one member of the group read the problems to the class, tell what operation or operations were used to solve the problems and why, and give the answers.

You will find grouping suggestions and cooperative learning activities in most lessons throughout this chapter.

LITERATURE

James, Elizabeth & Carol Barkin. *What Do You Mean by 'Average'? Means, Medians, and Modes.* New York: Lothrop, Lee & Shepard, 1978.

Jill is running for class president. She decides to prove she is the most average person in the school and would therefore be the best person to represent everyone. A great idea. But how do you find out what's average? Children could use the story to discuss averages. Then they could use information about their classmates to find averages.

Barnstone, Aliki. "Numbers." from: ***Zero Makes Me Hungry: A Collection of Poems for Today***. Compiled by Lueders & St. John. New York: Lothrop, Lee & Shepard, 1976.

Srivastava, Jane Jonas. *Averages.* New York: Thomas Y. Crowell, 1975.

Whitney, David C. *The Easy Book of Division.* New York: Franklin Watts, 1970.

English as a Second Language

There are many applications of averages to daily life which the ESL child will understand and which will reinforce the concepts of quotient and remainder. Try this activity for averages.

Arrange children in groups of four or five. Assign one person from each group to record the number of family members living at home for each group member. Each group adds all the family members together for a total sum, then divides that sum by the number of group members to find a quotient and remainder. Discuss each group's results with the whole class. First consider cases where there is no remainder. Then discuss cases where there is a remainder and the average is between two whole numbers. In such cases, ask to which whole number the average is closest.

Finish the project by adding the sums from each group and dividing by the total number of children to compute the average number of family members per student in the class.

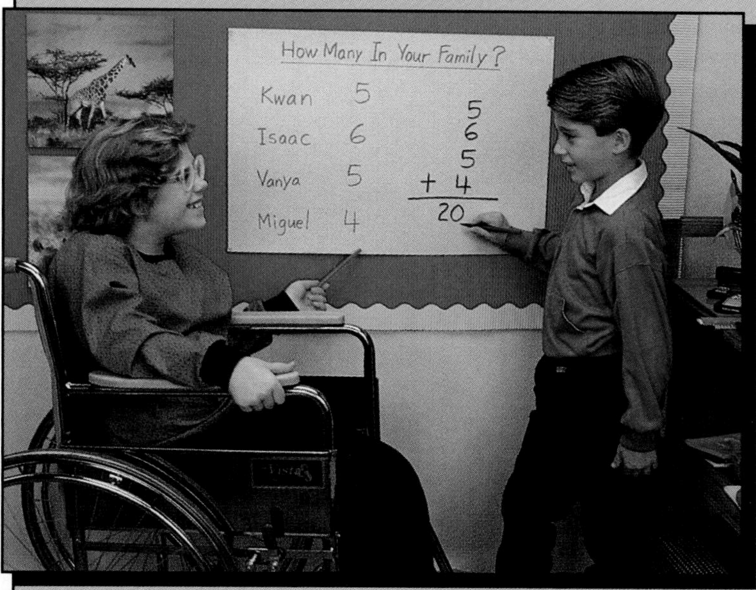

Gifted

Tell students they have been invited to apply for membership in an imaginary club called "Astounding Averages." This club gathers information and uses it to determine averages that are of interest to students. To qualify for admission, each potential member must compute averages for 5 items relevant to fourth graders. Remind them to choose their items carefully and to compute the averages accurately.

Ask volunteers for suggestions for including such items as their average age in years and months, the average number of people in their immediate family, or their average height in feet and inches. Encourage them to be creative in choosing their items and to have fun. Have them determine whether they will be collecting information from only their group or from the entire class.

Ask students to discuss various methods for obtaining the information. Invite them to record their averages in chart form. Have them present their findings orally to the class and display their charts on the class bulletin board. Challenge them to analyze the information, and to look for patterns or conclusions that can be inferred from their averages.

Students at Risk

Because the algorithm involves so many steps, long division presents a host of problems for students who have problems with retention, sequence, and organization. Inadequate mastery of number facts, confusion over the use of three operations, and difficulty with spatial alignment may occur as single or multiple errors. Students may benefit from a simple mnemonic device and a visual organizer.

Did My Sister Call Back? Students who have trouble recalling the order of steps in the division algorithm can ask Did my sister call back? as a mnemonic device. Initial consonants in the question match the steps in the division process: divide, multiply, subtract, compare, bring down.

Grid Division Have students divide on grid paper, writing one digit per box. Students align and organize their work with horizontal and vertical lines. Using grid paper with the mnemonic may help students master the algorithm.

You may also use the Reteaching Supplements and the specific Reteaching Tips from each lesson in this chapter.

INTRODUCING THE CHAPTER

SUBJECT INTEGRATION The photograph of a tall sailing ship in the Virgin Islands represents the chapter theme of social studies. Various lessons incorporate data about historical ships to provide situations involving division by 1-digit divisors.

USING DATA The Social Studies Data Bank on page 475 of the Student Edition provides 2 tables relating to historical ships. The first table compares the lengths of 6 early ships. The second table presents data about the number of crew members required to work some of the same early ships.

QUESTION 1 ► **Describe a mental math method you could use to subtract without pencil and paper.** (compensation; Adjust 150 *up* 4 to subtract 154 − 54, which is 100, then compensate by adjusting 100 *down* 4, leaving 96.)
Student Edition answer: 96 ft

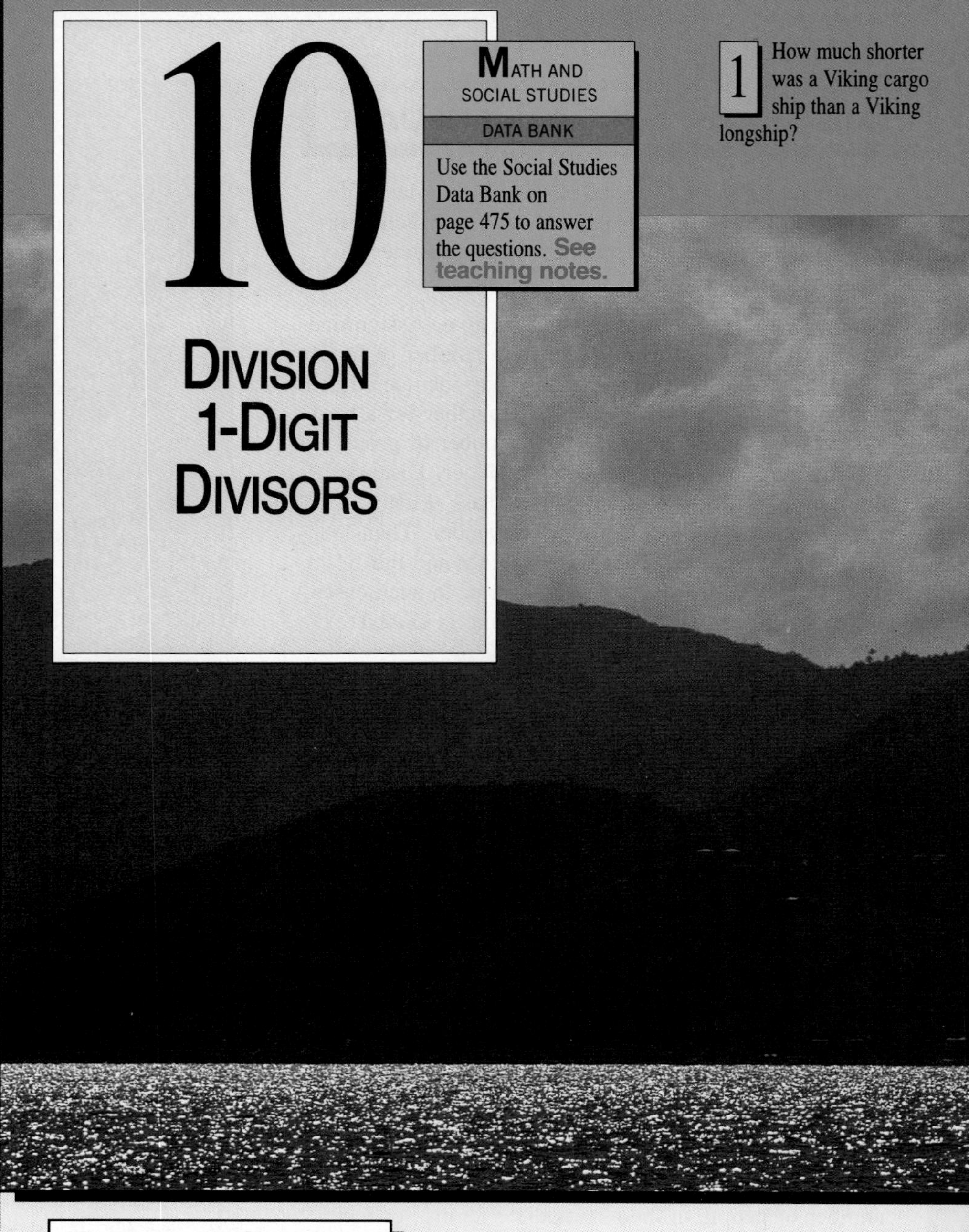

10 DIVISION 1-DIGIT DIVISORS

MATH AND SOCIAL STUDIES

DATA BANK

Use the Social Studies Data Bank on page 475 to answer the questions. See teaching notes.

1 How much shorter was a Viking cargo ship than a Viking longship?

TEACHING OPTIONS

LANGUAGE DEVELOPMENT
Write the word **crew** on the chalkboard and ask students to give its meaning. (a group of people who work on a ship) Ask them for a synonym for crew members. (Possible answer: sailors) Have students relate the idea of a crew to a division action. (Possible answer: You might separate a large group of sailors into equal crews to work on several ships.)

2 The crew of the *Niña,* Columbus' smallest ship, was 4 times the size of a small Viking ship crew. How many were in the *Niña's* crew?

3 If an equal number of rowers sat at the oars on each side of a small Viking ship, how many rowers would be on each side?

4 **Use Critical Thinking** Longer boats usually go faster than shorter boats. Would you predict that the *Pinta* or the longship would be faster?

265

QUESTION 2 ► **Justify the operation you used to answer the question.** (A small Viking ship had a crew of 6, so multiply 6 × 4 to find the size of the *Nina's* crew.)
► **Analyze the length data to make an inference about the length of the *Nina* and give your reasoning.** (If the *Nina* was the smallest ship, it must have been under 75 ft since that was the length of *Pinta*, his second smallest ship.)
Student Edition answer: 24 sailors

QUESTION 3 ► **Visualize the situation.** (6 Vikings work the oars of a ship, half on 1 side and half on the other side.)
► **Explain how to solve the problem.** (Possible answer: Divide 6 by 2 to form 2 equal groups.)
Student Edition answer: 3

QUESTION 4 ► **Identify the data you need to solve the problem.** (The *Pinta* was 75 ft long, the longship was 150 ft long.)
► **Describe a relationship between the lengths of the 2 ships to predict a possible speed relationship.** (The longship was twice as long as the *Pinta* because 75 × 2 = 150, so the longship might have gone twice as fast.)
Student Edition answer: longship

SUBJECT INTEGRATION PROJECT Have small groups work together to design, plan, and build a simple model of an old sailing ship. They can refer to illustrations in the chapter, in history books, or in encyclopedias for ideas. Have them sketch a plan, then construct the ship from common materials such as empty milk cartons, string, and straws. Groups should choose a name for their ship, label its length and height, and give a typical crew size, using the Social Studies Data Bank on page 475 for a reasonable range.

Finding and Checking Quotients and Remainders

OBJECTIVE 10-1 To find and check quotients and remainders

PREBOOK ACTIVITIES

QUICK REVIEW

Give each quotient.

1. 36 ÷ 9 (4)	**2.** 18 ÷ 6 (3)	**3.** 6 ÷ 6 (1)
4. 24 ÷ 4 (6)	**5.** 27 ÷ 3 (9)	**6.** 30 ÷ 5 (6)
7. 28 ÷ 7 (4)	**8.** 56 ÷ 8 (7)	**9.** 0 ÷ 5 (0)
10. 42 ÷ 7 (6)	**11.** 32 ÷ 8 (4)	**12.** 7 ÷ 1 (7)

PRIOR KNOWLEDGE

Have students review the actions that relate to division. (separating same-size groups; sharing equally in groups) Ask students to suggest real-life situations in which they tried to share or divide things into equal groups, but the quantity did not divide equally. (Possible answers: making teams in gym class; sharing snacks) Have students recall the math word that refers to an amount left over when a number cannot be divided into equal groups. *(remainder)*

COMMUNICATION

Discussing and Reading Math Write these sentences on the chalkboard: *She* ***remains*** *at school until 6 p.m. Only 4* ***remaining*** *apartments need painting. The* ***remainder*** *of the meal will be served later*. Discuss each word as it is used in each sentence. (*remains*—stays, continues; *remaining*—still left; *remainder*—left-over part, the rest) Discuss how these forms of the verb *remain* relate to the math noun *remainder*. (Possible response: A remainder is an amount left over after as many equal groups as possible have been made; it is the rest of the original amount that does not fit into one of the same-size groups.)

EXPLORE AND CONNECT

Materials: TA 3 (Number Cards 0-9), calculators
Grouping Suggestion: cooperative learning groups of 5
Teams take turns with different roles to predict **remainders.** One student picks any 3 number cards to form a division problem. The highest number is the divisor, but the other two digits can form two different dividends. For example: Using the digits 1, 4, and 6, 6 is the divisor. Two more team members divide to find 6)14 and 6)41. (2 R2; 6 R5) A fourth student verifies both quotients and **remainders** and records the equation that has the greater **remainder.** A fifth student adds the value of the greater **remainder** to a running score being kept on a calculator. After 5 rounds, all teams compare their scores to see who scored the highest. Last, students generalize about possible **remainder** size and divisors. (Possible answer: A greater divisor can give a greater **remainder**, but **remainders** cannot equal or exceed the size of the divisor.)

CONNECTIONS Use these anytime.

Problem of the Day

Number Sense Find a digit for each symbol to make the division work. (12 ÷ 5 = 2 R2; 24 ÷ 5 = 4 R4; 35 ÷ 6 = 5 R5; or 45 ÷ 8 = 5 R5)

```
      ★ R★
  △)✿ ★
   −✿ ♡
   ─────
      ★
```

Patterns

Finding Remainders Finish the table for divisors to 10.

Divisor	*Possible Remainders*
1	0
2	0, 1
3	0, 1, 2

(For any divisor n, possible remainders always range from 0 to $n - 1$.)

Creative Thinking

Penny Design Arrange 12 pennies in 3 same-size rows and 3 same-size columns. *Hint:* Some pennies can be stacked. (Possible answers: see below)

```
⊗○○    ○○⊗    ○○○
○⊗○    ○⊗○    ○○○
○○⊗    ⊗○○    ⊗⊗⊗
```

[⊗ = 2 pennies stacked
○ = 1 penny]

Classwork and Homework Supplements

Practice

Skills Maintenance 10-1

Name ____________

Finding and Checking Quotients and Remainders

Check these division problems. Correct those with errors.

1. 7)40 = 5 R5; 35, 5 — correct
2. 6)26 = 4 R4; 22, 4 — 4 R2
3. 8)75 = 9 R3; 72, 3 — correct
4. 4)25 = 6 R1; 24, 1 — correct
5. 7)24 = 3 R2; 22, 2 — 3 R3
6. 9)56 = 6 R4; 52, 4 — 6 R2

Finds the quotients and remainders. Check.

7. 6)37 — 6 R1; 6 × 6 = 36, + 1 = 37
8. 7)56 — 8; 8 × 7 = 56
9. 8)63 — 7 R7; 7 × 8 = 56, + 7 = 63
10. 5)42 — 8 R2; 8 × 5 = 40, + 2 = 42
11. 5)29 — 5 R4; 5 × 5 = 25, + 4 = 29
12. 9)47 — 5 R2; 5 × 9 = 45, + 2 = 47
13. 6)48 — 8; 8 × 6 = 48
14. 8)35 — 4 R3; 4 × 8 = 32, + 3 = 35
15. 7)50 — 7 R1; 7 × 7 = 49, + 1 = 50

Building Thinking Skills

Problem Solving 10-1

Name ____________

Divide and Ship

A bicycle factory has shipping boxes of 2, 4, 5, or 8 bicycles. The factory shipped 21 bicycles. It used 2 boxes that hold 8 bicycles and 1 box that holds 5 bicycles.

1. Show 5 other combinations for shipping 21 bicycles.
Answers will vary. Some possible answers are given.

Number Shipped	Number of Bicycles per Box: 2	4	5	8
21			1	2
21	8		1	
21		4	1	
21		2	1	1
21	4		1	1
21	2	3	1	

2. Find 6 different ways they could ship 28 bicycles. Record them on the chart. Answers will vary. Some possible answers are given.

Number Shipped	Number of Bicycles per Box: 2	4	5	8
28	4		4	
28			4	1
28		2	4	
28	14			
28		7		
28	2	6		

Reteaching

Manipulatives 10-1

Name ____________

Quotients and Remainders

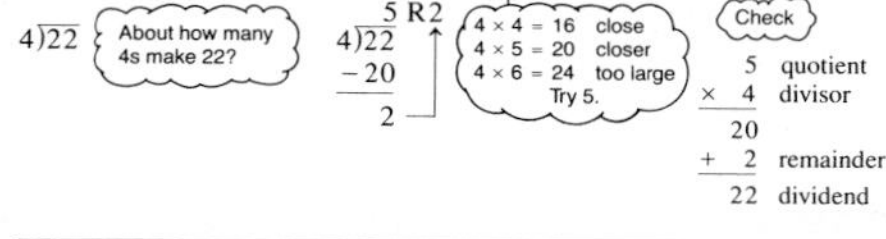

An artist donated 25 books to Ray School. It has not been decided how many classes will share the books. Complete the chart. You may use counters.

	Number of Classes Sharing the Books	Number of Books for Each Class	Number of Books Left Over
1.	3	8	1
2.	4	6	1
3.	5	5	0
4.	6	4	1
5.	7	3	4
6.	8	3	1
7.	9	2	7

Use the chart above to help you find each quotient and remainder. Multiply and add to check.

8. 4)25 — 6 R1
9. 5)25 — 5
10. 8)25 — 3 R1
11. 6)25 — 4 R1
12. 9)25 — 2 R7
13. 7)25 — 3 R4

Challenges

Mental Math 10-1

Name ____________

Remainder Game

Play this game with a partner or in 2 teams. Each player or team will need different markers.

Rules

Take turns following these steps:

1. Pick one number from the number pool. Then cross it out.
2. Divide that number by 1, 2, 3, 4, 5, 6, 7, 8, or 9 and note the remainder.
3. Place a marker on the basketball court on one of the numbers that is the same as your remainder.
4. The winner is the first player (or team) to dribble across the court from △ to △ or from 🏀 to 🏀.

Basketball Court

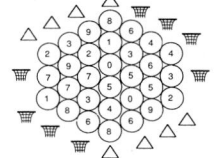

Number Pool

60, 71, 72, 80, 61, 63, 73, 82, 84, 64, 75, 76, 86, 66, 67, 78, 87, 89, 20, 30, 31, 41, 51, 52, 26, 35, 36, 45, 55, 57, 34, 43, 44, 54

Describe the strategy you used for picking numbers from the number pool.

Wording will vary. Pick a number that is near a multiple of a number. Then you can figure out the remainder using mental math.

Options for Individual Needs

10-1

Basic

Exercises 1-14, 20-27
More Practice, p. 507, set B

Supplements
Reteaching 96 or
Practice 96

Average

Exercises 1-27
More Practice, p. 507, set B

Supplements
Practice 96
Challenges 96 or
Thinking Skills 96

Extended

Exercises 1-4, 12-27

Supplements
Challenges 96
Thinking Skills 96

Other Resources:
Problem-Solving Experiences in Mathematics, Grade 4, Problem 79
Math In Stride, Grade 4, p. 203
Mathematics, A Way of Thinking, Lesson 6-9
Using the Math Explorer Calculator: A Sourcebook for Teachers, Chapter 14

LESSON PLAN 10-1

OBJECTIVE 10-1
To find and check quotients and remainders

Materials: oaktag strips, place value blocks

Alternative Materials: TA 6 (Place Value Models)

1. MOTIVATE AND TEACH

LEARN ABOUT IT

EXPLORE ▶ **How do you know same-size groups are needed?** (Pam wanted 6 pictures on each page.)
▶ **Explain how the quotient helps you answer the question.** (The 7 tells you Pam needs at least 7 pages.)
▶ **Why is there a remainder?** (There are more than 7 × 6 pictures.)

TALK ABOUT IT ▶ **Why does it make sense to multiply to check division?** (Multiplication and division are opposite operations; the quotient and the divisor are factors that give the dividend.)
▶ **Explain why you multiply, then add the remainder.** (Multiply to find the number of equal groups, then add the extras to find the total.)
Student Edition answers: **1.** 43, 6, 7, 1 **2.** Multiply the quotient by the divisor, then add any remainder. **3.** Answers may vary. **4.** Sample answer: Pam can fill 7 pages, but she needs 8 pages for all the pictures.

2. CHECK UNDERSTANDING

TRY IT OUT

ERROR ALERT Adding the remainder to the quotient first when checking quotients and remainders. Overestimating or underestimating quotients.

Finding and Checking Quotients and Remainders

LEARN ABOUT IT

EXPLORE Think About the Process
Pam made a picture book about different kinds of famous boats. She had 43 pictures and wanted to put 6 pictures on each page. How many pages would she need?

Since you must separate the pictures into equal groups, you divide to find the answer.

Here is how to find the correct quotient.

Estimate the quotient.	Multiply and subtract.	Compare. Write the remainder beside the quotient.	Check.
(6)42) 6)43 ↑ divisor	7 ← quotient; 6)43 ← dividend; (7 × 6) → − 42; 1 ← remainder	7 R1; 6)43; − 42; (1 < 6) → 1	7 quotient; × 6 divisor; 42; + 1 remainder; 43 dividend

TALK ABOUT IT See teaching notes.

1. Which number in the third step shows the number of pictures? the number of pictures per page? the number of pages filled? the number of pictures left over?
2. Explain how to check the answer.
3. How would you have estimated the answer?
4. Use a complete sentence to give a reasonable answer to the story problem.

TRY IT OUT

Find the quotients and remainders. Check your answers.

1. 4)30 7 R2 **2.** 6)38 6 R2 **3.** 4)26 6 R2 **4.** 2)13 6 R1 **5.** 7)54 7 R5 **6.** 9)57 6 R3

266

TEACHING OPTIONS

RETEACHING TIPS Review how to check division: multiply, then add. Help students recognize that this is the order used in any multiplication. Have them make and use an oaktag template to recall the division check: *quotient* × *divisor* + *remainder* = *dividend*. Assign Reteaching Supplement 96.

ENRICHMENT Have students use each digit from 3 to 7 once to make the division true:
____ ____ ÷ ____ = ____ R____
(45 ÷ 6 = 7 R3)

PRACTICE

Check these division problems. Correct those with errors.

1. $4\overline{)29}$ = 7 R1; 28; 1 correct
2. $6\overline{)60}$ = 9 R4; 56; 4 wrong; 10
3. $8\overline{)37}$ = 4 R5; 32; 5 correct
4. $9\overline{)58}$ = 6 R2; 56; 2 wrong; 6 R4

Find the quotients and remainders. Check.

5. $6\overline{)46}$ 7 R4
6. $4\overline{)39}$ 9 R3
7. 48 ÷ 5 9 R3
8. 16 ÷ 3 5 R1
9. 64 ÷ 8 8
10. $7\overline{)51}$ 7 R2
11. $8\overline{)75}$ 9 R3
12. $9\overline{)80}$ 8 R8
13. $5\overline{)29}$ 5 R4
14. 15 ÷ 2 7 R1
15. 41 ÷ 6 6 R5
16. 24 ÷ 7 3 R3
17. 54 ÷ 4 13 R2
18. $3\overline{)27}$ 9
19. 62 ÷ 9 6 R8
20. What is 66 divided by 9? 7 R3
21. What is 32 divided by 5? 6 R2

APPLY

MATH REASONING Use the basic fact and mental math to give each quotient and remainder.

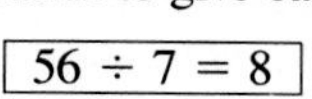
56 ÷ 7 = 8

22. $7\overline{)57}$ 8 R1
23. $7\overline{)58}$ 8 R2
24. $7\overline{)60}$ 8 R4
25. $7\overline{)62}$ 8 R6

PROBLEM SOLVING

26. **Data Hunt** What is the largest number of each of these size pictures you could paste, without overlapping, on a sheet of your tablet paper?

a. $2\frac{1}{2}$ in. by 3 in.
b. 3 in. × 6 in.
c. 7 in. × 8 in.

How many tablet sheets would you need for 81 of the $2\frac{1}{2}$ in. by 3 in. pictures? Can you find a pattern and decide, without dividing, how many sheets you will need for 81 of the other size pictures? See Additional Answers.

► **USING CRITICAL THINKING** Analyze the Situation

27. All the digits are hidden except the answer. The divisor is a 1-digit number and the dividend is a 2-digit number. Write as many problems as you can for which this answer would be correct.

6 R6
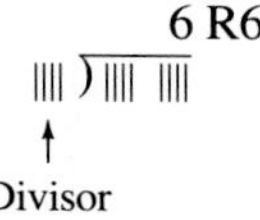
Divisor

$7\overline{)48}$ $8\overline{)54}$ $9\overline{)60}$

More Practice, page 507, set B

3. PRACTICE AND APPLY

Basic	1-14, 20-27
Average	1-27
Extended	1-4, 12-27

Additional Answers: See p. T79.

PRACTICE

Look at Exercises 1-4. Predict the steps in the division process where errors might be likely to occur. (wrong estimates, basic fact or subtracting errors)

APPLY

MATH REASONING ► **Compare the quotients in this series of exercises.** (Each has a remainder equal to its dividend minus 56.)

PROBLEM SOLVING ► **Explain what you need to know before you can start to solve the problem.** (Possible answer: the dimensions of the tablet paper)

USING CRITICAL THINKING ► **Why must the divisor be greater than 6?** (A remainder of 6 says you cannot divide by 6 or less.)

CLOSE AND ASSESS

SHOW WHAT YOU KNOW

Have students draw a picture to show 27 divided by 6. When students have finished, have them write an equation to go with their picture. (Students should show 4 groups of 6, or 6 groups of 4, with 3 left over; or 27 ÷ 6 = 4 R3) $6\overline{)27}$ 4 R3

QUICK QUIZ

Divide and check.
1. $6\overline{)40}$ (6 R4) 2. $7\overline{)10}$ (1 R3)
3. 50 ÷ 8 (6 R2)
4. What is 44 divided by 5? (8 R4)
5. What is 44 divided by 8? (5 R4)

LESSON OPTIONS 10-2

Mental Math: Special Quotients

OBJECTIVE 10-2 To use mental math to find the quotient of a multiple divided by a 1-digit number

PREBOOK ACTIVITIES

QUICK REVIEW

Find the products using mental math.

1. 30×9 (270)	**2.** 8×60 (480)	**3.** 4×60 (240)
4. 20×6 (120)	**5.** 30×3 (90)	**6.** 4×80 (320)
7. 80×0 (0)	**8.** 70×6 (420)	**9.** 70×9 (630)

PRIOR KNOWLEDGE

Have students review the meaning of special sums, differences, and products and give examples for each operation. (Possible answer: Special sums, differences, or products link basic facts and multiples of 10; 100; or 1,000 to let you use mental math. Examples may vary. Samples: 400 + 500, 140 − 90, 500 × 7.) Have students name another special answer they could learn to find. (special quotients) Have them suggest a division example that might give a special quotient. (Answers may vary. Samples: 80 ÷ 2 or 320 ÷ 4.)

COMMUNICATION

Discussing Math Have students analyze and then generalize how number facts in an arithmetic operation relate to mental math in that operation. (Possible answer: If you know basic number facts, you can use them to find special answers mentally or to make good estimates.) Have students predict situations in which finding special quotients might be useful. (Possible answers: estimating same-size groups; performing quick exact calculations if the numbers are related by a basic fact)

EXPLORE AND CONNECT

Materials: TA 10 (Play Money—Larger Bills), calculators
Alternative Materials: index cards
Grouping Suggestion: small cooperative learning groups
Groups show special quotient division with play money and a calculator. One student gives a basic division fact, such as 12 ÷ 4. Another student counts out 12 play $10 bills (or index cards) and shows the division. Groups decide how to record the process ($120 ÷ 4 = $30; 12 tens ÷ 4 = 3 tens) and how to enter the division on a calculator. (Enter 120 ÷ 4 = .) Groups repeat the activity for 5 other division facts, trading tasks. Conclude by having students describe a relationship between a basic fact, a multiple of 10 represented by the $10 bill, and the quotient. (When dividends are multiples of 10, quotients are also multiples of 10.) Students may predict how to find special quotients with $100 bills. (If dividends are multiples of 100, quotients will be multiples of 10 or 100.)

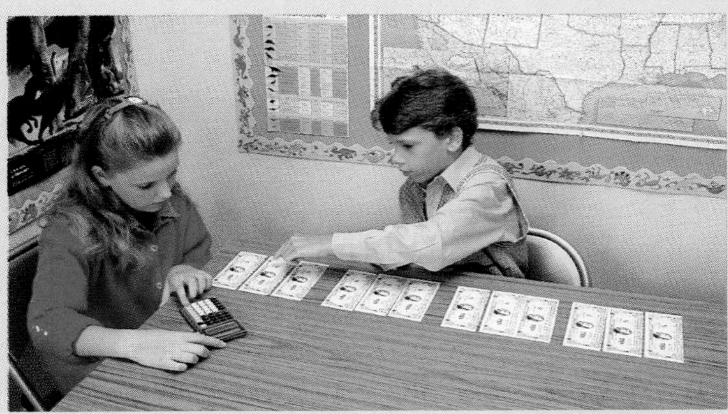

CONNECTIONS Use these anytime.

Problem of the Day

Number Sense Create 5 different division equations with a special quotient of 40. (Answers will vary. Samples: 160 ÷ 4, 120 ÷ 3, 200 ÷ 5, 280 ÷ 7, and 320 ÷ 8.)

Patterns

Divide by 5 Discover the pattern. Predict the equation in the tenth row.
30 ÷ 5 = 6
300 ÷ 5 = 60
3,000 ÷ 5 = 600
(Look at the pattern of zeros and predict 30,000,000,000 ÷ 5 = 6,000,000,000.)

Life Skills

Travel Time The Millers are taking a 300-mi car trip. How long will the trip take if they drive 60 mi/h? (5 h) If they decide to take a train instead of driving and they arrive at their destination in 3 h, how fast did the train go? (100 mi/h)

Classwork and Homework Supplements

Practice

Mental Math 10-2

Name ______

Special Quotients

Use mental math to find the quotients. Check your answers by multiplying.

1. 60 ÷ 3 = 20	**2.** 80 ÷ 4 = 20
3. 40 ÷ 2 = 20	**4.** 80 ÷ 2 = 40
5. 90 ÷ 3 = 30	**6.** 60 ÷ 6 = 10
7. 640 ÷ 8 = 80	**8.** 180 ÷ 2 = 90
9. 720 ÷ 9 = 80	**10.** 270 ÷ 3 = 90
11. 560 ÷ 8 = 70	**12.** 120 ÷ 2 = 60
13. 490 ÷ 7 = 70	**14.** 540 ÷ 6 = 90
15. 140 ÷ 7 = 20	**16.** 810 ÷ 9 = 90
17. 320 ÷ 4 = 80	**18.** 250 ÷ 5 = 50
19. 480 ÷ 6 = 80	**20.** 420 ÷ 6 = 70
21. 630 ÷ 9 = 70	**22.** 210 ÷ 7 = 30
23. 180 ÷ 9 = 20	**24.** 300 ÷ 5 = 60
25. 150 ÷ 5 = 30	**26.** 720 ÷ 8 = 90
27. 280 ÷ 7 = 70	**28.** 450 ÷ 9 = 50
29. 160 ÷ 4 = 40	**30.** 100 ÷ 2 = 50
31. 630 ÷ 7 = 90	**32.** 280 ÷ 7 = 40
33. 270 ÷ 9 = 30	**34.** 480 ÷ 8 = 60

PS-4 Use with text pages 268–269. 97

Building Thinking Skills

Mental Math 10-2

Name ______

Dolls and Trucks

Use mental math to decide how many of each toy were manufactured each day at the Tootsie Toy Factory.

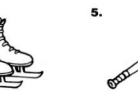

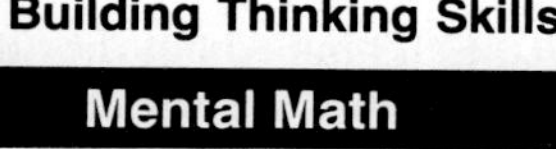

1. Total: 300 trucks
Number of days: 5
Trucks per day: 60

2. Total: 250 minicars
Number of days: 5
Minicars per day: 50

3. Total: 720 masks
Number of days: 9
Masks per day: 80

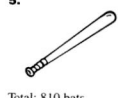

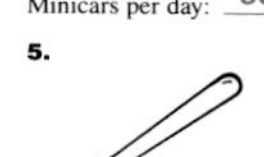

4. Total: 280 ice skates
Number of days: 7
Ice skates per day: 40

5. Total: 810 bats
Number of days: 9
Bats per day: 90

6. Total: 420 dolls
Number of days: 6
Dolls per day: 70

7. The president of Tootsie Toys wants to lower the production of trucks. If the factory makes 200 trucks in 5 days, how many fewer trucks are being made each day? 20

8. The president of Tootsie Toys wants to increase the production of dolls. If the same number of dolls are made in 3 days, how many more dolls are made in one day? 70

TS-4 Use with text pages 268-269. 97

Reteaching

Mental Math 10-2

Name ______

Special Quotients

To find 240 ÷ 6 → find 24 ÷ 6 → then multiply by 10.

4 → 4 × 10 = 40 → 240 ÷ 6 = 40

Check: 6 × 40 = 240

Find the quotients. Check your answers by multiplying.

1. 60 ÷ 3 = 20 Check: 3 × 20 = 60
2. 40 ÷ 4 = 10 Check: 4 × 10 = 40
3. 120 ÷ 6 = 20 Check: 6 × 20 = 120
4. 240 ÷ 8 = 30 Check: 8 × 30 = 240
5. 150 ÷ 3 = 50 Check: 3 × 50 = 150
6. 720 ÷ 9 = 80 Check: 9 × 80 = 720
7. 90 ÷ 3 = 30 Check: 3 × 30 = 90
8. 80 ÷ 8 = 10 Check: 8 × 10 = 80
9. 140 ÷ 7 = 20 Check: 7 × 20 = 140
10. 350 ÷ 5 = 70 Check: 5 × 70 = 350
11. 450 ÷ 9 = 50 Check: 9 × 50 = 450
12. 640 ÷ 8 = 80 Check: 8 × 80 = 640

RS-4 Use with text pages 268-269. 97

Challenges

Family Math 10-2

Name ______

Who Am I?

Dear Family,
In our math class we have been learning how to use mental math to find special quotients. The following riddles give your child an opportunity to share the skill with you.

If a number is divided by another number and the remainder is zero, then the first number is **divisible** by the second. 720 is divisible by 8.

All the mystery numbers below have a zero in the ones place. Analyze the clues to identify the numbers.

1. I am less than 40. I am divisible by 5 and 4. Who am I? 20

2. I am between 10 and 80. I am divisible by 2, 3, and 6. Who am I? 30 or 60

3. I am greater than 60 and less than 100. I am divisible by 2 and 4. Who am I? 80

4. I am between 100 and 200. I am divisible by 3 and 5. I am **not** divisible by 4. Who am I? 150

5. I am less than 100. When you divide my by 2, you get 10 move than when you divide me by 4. Who am I? 40

6. I am between 100 and 500. Two of my digits are zeros. I am divisible by 3, 5, and 6. Who am I? 300

CS-4 Use with text pages 269–269. 97

Options for Individual Needs

10-2

Basic

Exercises 1-11, 17-20, 23-26
Calculator Bank, p. 487
More Practice, p. 507, set C

Supplements
Reteaching 97 or
Practice 97

Average

Exercises 1-28
Calculator Bank, p. 487
More Practice, p. 507, set C

Supplements
Practice 97
Challenges 97 or
Thinking Skills 97

Extended

Exercises 13-28
Calculator Bank, p. 487

Supplements
Challenges 97
Thinking Skills 97

Other Resources:
Problem-Solving Experiences in Mathematics, Grade 4, Problem 77
Math In Stride, Grade 4, p. 105
Using the Math Explorer Calculator: A Sourcebook for Teachers, Chapter 14

LESSON PLAN 10-2

OBJECTIVE 10-2
To use mental math to find the quotient of a multiple divided by a 1-digit number

Materials: colored markers

1. MOTIVATE AND TEACH

LEARN ABOUT IT

EXPLORE ► **Formulate a question about the clown college.** (Possible answer: How many students were in each class?)

TALK ABOUT IT ► **What facts must you know to understand the situation? Why?** (the number of months in a year; there was a new class every other month)
► **Do you need to know *which* months classes were held? Explain.** (No, holding a class every other month means classes will be held for 6 mo, no matter when you start.)
► **What relationship do you notice between 240 and 6? Explain.** (6 is a factor of 24, so it must also be a factor of 240.)
► **Create a rule to find special quotients.** (Possible answer: If a dividend is a multiple of 10 and you see a basic fact, find the basic-fact quotient; multiply it by 10.)
Student Edition answers: **1.** 6; *Every other* means only half of the 12 months had classes. **2.** 40 **3.** 4, 4 is ten times less than 40.

2. CHECK UNDERSTANDING

TRY IT OUT

ERROR ALERT Forgetting to multiply the basic-fact quotient by 10. Failing to notice basic facts to use.

Mental Math
Special Quotients

LEARN ABOUT IT

EXPLORE **Think About the Situation**
A circus runs a clown college. During one year 240 people attended the college. There was a new class every other month and each class was the same size.

TALK ABOUT IT See teaching notes.

1. How many different classes were there in one year? Explain.
2. How many people were in each class? It may be helpful to use the guess and check strategy.
3. Suppose 24 people had attended the college and there were 6 classes. How many would be in each class? How does this number compare with the number you found in question 2?

The mental math method below gives a quick way to find quotients like 320 ÷ 4.

To find 320 ÷ 4, find 32 ÷ 4 and then multiply by 10.

32 tens ÷ 4 = 8 tens

320 ÷ 4 = 80

Examples

60 ÷ 3 = 20 400 ÷ 5 = 80 360 ÷ 4 = 90

TRY IT OUT

Use mental math to find the quotients.

1. 80 ÷ 4 **20**
2. 320 ÷ 8 **40**
3. 280 ÷ 4 **70**
4. 640 ÷ 8 **80**
5. 250 ÷ 5 **50**
6. 420 ÷ 7 **60**
7. 360 ÷ 9 **40**
8. 300 ÷ 6 **50**

268

TEACHING OPTIONS

RETEACHING TIPS Have students circle the divisor and the part of the dividend that makes a basic fact in one color, then underline the extra zero in a second color. After they find the basic-fact quotient, students affix the extra zero to the *right* of the quotient. Assign Reteaching Supplement 97.

ENRICHMENT Tell students 1 ton (T) = 2,000 lb. They use mental math to solve: *Ken's mine produces 1 T of coal in 4 min. Len's mine produces 1 T in 5 min. How much coal does each mine produce per minute? Compare the difference over an h.* (Ken's = 500 lb/min; Len's = 400 lb/min; 3 T difference/h)

PRACTICE

Find the quotients. Check your answers by multiplying.

1. 80 ÷ 4 **20** **2.** 90 ÷ 9 **10** **3.** 180 ÷ 3 **60** **4.** 280 ÷ 7 **40**

5. 180 ÷ 2 **90** **6.** 420 ÷ 7 **60** **7.** 250 ÷ 5 **50** **8.** 360 ÷ 6 **60**

9. 640 ÷ 8 **80** **10.** 120 ÷ 4 **30** **11.** 320 ÷ 8 **40** **12.** 450 ÷ 9 **50**

13. 490 ÷ 7 **70** **14.** 240 ÷ 3 **80** **15.** 810 ÷ 9 **90** **16.** 720 ÷ 8 **90**

APPLY

MATH REASONING Tell which quotient is larger.

17. 342 ÷ 5 or 322 ÷ 5 **18.** 483 ÷ 9 or 481 ÷ 8

PROBLEM SOLVING

19. How many people were enrolled per month in the trapeze artist school? **20 people**

20. Write Your Own Problem Use the data in the graph to write a division problem. **Answers will vary.**

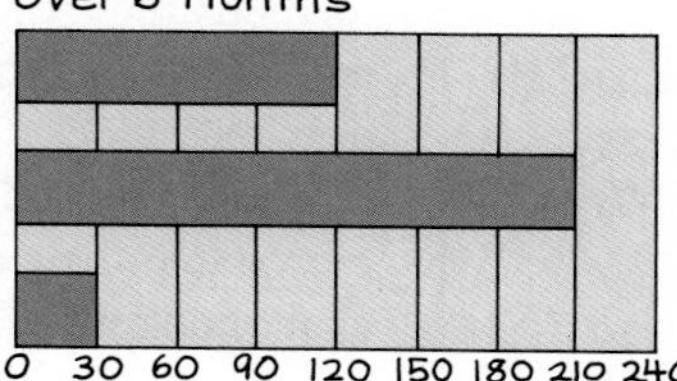

MIXED REVIEW

Tell which weighs the most.

21. corn chips 1 lb / onion dip 18 oz

22. laundry detergent 3 lb / bleach 32 oz.

23. potatoes 5 lb / asparagus 64 oz

24. flour 36 oz / corn meal 2 lb

Write four fact family equations for these factors and products. The order of the equations may vary. **See Additional Answers.**

25. 18 3 6

26. 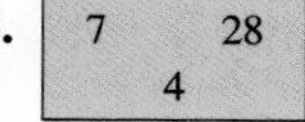

27. 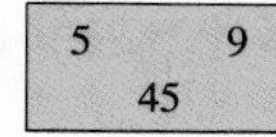

28. 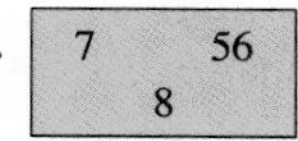

More Practice, page 507, set C 269

3. PRACTICE AND APPLY

Basic	1-11, 17-20, 23-26
Average	1-28
Extended	13-28

Additional Answers: See p. T79.

PRACTICE

Look at Exercises 1-16. Predict how many digits the special quotients will have. (2)

APPLY

MATH REASONING ► **Analyze the division pairs to find a way to pick the larger quotient.** (For equal divisors, a larger dividend gives a larger quotient; the same dividend divided into fewer groups gives a larger quotient.)

PROBLEM SOLVING ► **Explain how the graph title helps solve Problem 19.** (It tells the data is for 6 mo; divide to find number per month.)

MIXED REVIEW ► **Explain what measurement is needed to solve Exercises 21-24.** (1 lb = 16 oz, so you can convert amounts to the same measurement.)

► **How can you identify the product in Exercises 25-28?** (It is always the greatest number.)

10-2

CLOSE AND ASSESS

SHOW WHAT YOU KNOW

Have students create 3 division examples for finding special quotients. One example should have a divisor of 7, one a dividend of 480, and one a quotient of 50. Have students explain how to use basic facts and mental math to find each quotient. (Sample answers: 140 ÷ 7 = 20; 480 ÷ 8 = 60; 250 ÷ 5 = 50.)

QUICK QUIZ

Find the quotients. Check by multiplying.

1. 300 ÷ 6 (50) **2.** 160 ÷ 4 (40)
3. 90 ÷ 3 (30) **4.** 270 ÷ 9 (30)
5. 50 ÷ 5 (10) **6.** 360 ÷ 4 (90)

LESSON OPTIONS 10-3

Estimating Quotients

OBJECTIVE 10-3 To use the estimation technique of rounding and substituting compatible numbers

PREBOOK ACTIVITIES

QUICK REVIEW

Find the special quotients using mental math.

1. 150 ÷ 5 (30)	**2.** 180 ÷ 6 (30)	**3.** 240 ÷ 8 (30)
4. 300 ÷ 6 (50)	**5.** 360 ÷ 4 (90)	**6.** 560 ÷ 7 (80)
7. 400 ÷ 5 (80)	**8.** 540 ÷ 9 (60)	**9.** 490 ÷ 7 (70)

PRIOR KNOWLEDGE

Review the meaning of using compatible numbers to estimate a sum such as 76 + 82. (Possible answer: Round to make easy numbers to add mentally, such as the doubles 80 + 80.) Write 203 and 7 on the chalkboard. Have students explain the methods they might use to estimate the sum, difference, and product of these numbers. (Possible answers: Break apart 203 to add; compensate to subtract; round to multiply.) Have students describe a method they might use to estimate a quotient. (Answers may vary: Sample answers: Round, then divide; find a missing factor; find compatible numbers.)

COMMUNICATION

Discussing and Reading Math Write the word **substitute** on the chalkboard. Have students read the word aloud and tell what a substitute teacher and a substitute player on a team have in common. (Possible answer: Both replace or stand in for the usual person.) Ask students what it means to substitute a digit for the n in an equation such as $5 + n = 9$. (Possible answer: Use a number for n that makes the equation work.) Tell students they will estimate quotients by **substituting** compatible numbers to make mental computation easier.

EXPLORE AND CONNECT

Materials: division cards (see activity below), place value blocks, calculators
Alternative Materials: TA 6 (Place Value Models)
Grouping Suggestion: small cooperative learning groups
Groups explore ways to estimate quotients, then they divide with a calculator to evaluate estimates. Make enough division cards so there are 3 per group. Choose problems such as 234 ÷ 8, 175 ÷ 6, and 441 ÷ 7. Groups estimate, using any methods they know, to find a reasonable quotient. When they agree on a method, one member records the steps. Another uses tens blocks to show the estimated division. A third uses a calculator to find the exact answer. Members then analyze how reasonable their estimate was and how it compares with the exact quotient. They trade tasks to complete 2 more division problems. Groups discuss their most helpful method and how over- and underestimates occurred.

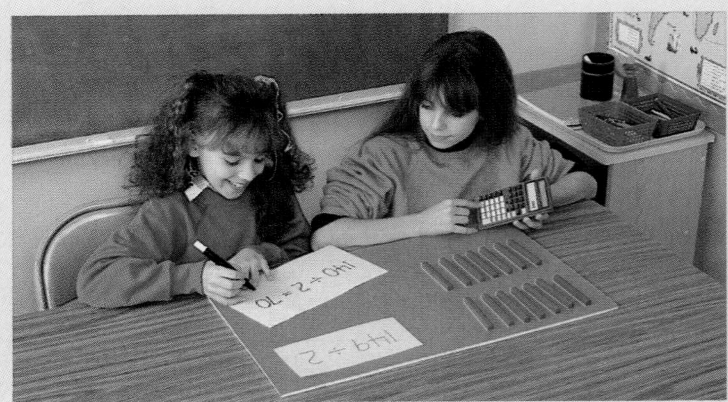

CONNECTIONS Use these anytime.

Problem of the Day

Number Riddle A 3-digit and a 1-digit number have a sum of 147, a difference of 133, and a product of 980. Find the numbers and then give their quotient. (140, 7; 20)

Life Skills

Party Tables The Cooking Club is having a big lunch party for 153 people. If tables can seat 8 people, how many tables should be set to make sure everyone will have a seat? (20)

Math Connection

Time During one 6-h school day, a very busy teacher checked 287 workbook pages. Is that closer to 40 or 50 pages per hour? Explain. (50; 300 ÷ 6 gives a closer estimate than 240 ÷ 6.)

to estimate quotients.

Classwork and Homework Supplements

Practice

Estimation 10-3

Name ______

Estimating Quotients

Use rounding to estimate the quotients. Substitute if necessary.

1. 52 ÷ 5 10
2. 83 ÷ 4 20
3. $8.84 ÷ 3 $3
4. 419 ÷ 7 60
5. 316 ÷ 8 40
6. 139 ÷ 3 50
7. 632 ÷ 9 70
8. 209 ÷ 3 70
9. 477 ÷ 8 60
10. 719 ÷ 9 80
11. 8)244 30
12. 4)$23.55 $6
13. 5)396 80
14. 9)358 40

Estimate each quotient. Write whether the estimate is **over** or **under** the exact quotient.

15. 59 ÷ 2 30; over
16. 62 ÷ 6 10; under
17. 362 ÷ 6 60; under
18. 276 ÷ 7 40; over
19. $9.62 ÷ 5 12; over
20. $8.21 ÷ 4 $2; under
21. 7)558 80; over
22. 6)295 50; over
23. 3)212 70; under
24. 8)$31.66 $4; over
25. 734 ÷ 9 80; under
26. 629 ÷ 8 80; over

Building Thinking Skills

Estimation 10-3

Name ______

Test Your Estimation Skills

Estimate each quotient to the nearest ten. Then find the exact quotient. Subtract to find the difference between your estimate and the exact quotient. Estimates may vary.

1. 4)164 = 41 (− 16, 04, − 4, 0) Estimate: ___ Exact: 41 Difference: ___
2. 5)395 = 79 (− 35, 45, − 45, 0) Estimate: ___ Exact: 79 Difference: ___
3. 3)153 = 51 (− 15, 03, − 3, 0) Estimate: ___ Exact: 51 Difference: ___
4. 4)324 = 81 (− 32, 04, − 4, 0) Estimate: ___ Exact: 81 Difference: ___
5. 5)145 = 29 (− 10, 45, − 45, 0) Estimate: ___ Exact: 29 Difference: ___
6. 2)184 = 92 (− 18, 04, − 4, 0) Estimate: ___ Exact: 92 Difference: ___
7. 3)267 = 89 (− 24, 27, − 27, 0) Estimate: ___ Exact: 89 Difference: ___
8. 2)136 = 68 (− 12, 16, − 16, 0) Estimate: ___ Exact: 68 Difference: ___

Reteaching

Estimation 10-3

Name ______

Estimating Quotients

You can estimate a quotient by rounding and dividing.

Estimate to the nearest ten.	Estimate to the nearest ten.	Estimate to the nearest dollar.
46 ÷ 5	322 ÷ 4	$11.75 ÷ 6
46 is close to 50. 50 ÷ 5 = 10	320 ÷ 4 = 80	$12 ÷ 6 = $2
About 10	About 80	About $2

Round to the nearest ten and divide.

(Round 77 to 80.) (Round 123 to 120.)

1. 77 ÷ 2 → 80 ÷ 2 = 40
2. 123 ÷ 3 → 120 ÷ 3 = 40
3. 57 ÷ 2 → 60 ÷ 2 = 30
4. 89 ÷ 3 → 90 ÷ 3 = 30
5. 78 ÷ 4 → 80 ÷ 4 = 20
6. 43 ÷ 4 → 40 ÷ 4 = 10
7. 147 ÷ 5 → 150 ÷ 5 = 30
8. 241 ÷ 6 → 240 ÷ 6 = 40
9. 634 ÷ 7 → 630 ÷ 7 = 90
10. 110 ÷ 4 → 120 ÷ 4 = 30

Round to the nearest dollar and divide. Write whether the estimate is **over** or **under** the exact quotient.

(Round to $6.)

11. $5.75 ÷ 3 → $6 ÷ 3 = $2 over
12. $14.10 ÷ 2 → $14 ÷ 2 = $7 under
13. $29.95 ÷ 6 → $30 ÷ 6 = $5 over

Challenges

Calculators 10-3

Name ______

Over and Under Game

Play this game with a partner. You will need a calculator.

Rules

Take turns following these steps:

1. Choose a division problem below that you estimate will have a quotient that is greater than 20 and less than 30. Cross off the problem.
2. Use your calculator to find the exact quotient.
3. You score a point if the quotient is greater than 20 and less than 30.
4. Continue until neither player can find a quotient that will score a point.
5. The player with the most points wins.

7)147 = 21	8)600 = 75	3)72 = 24	9)261 = 29
5)125 = 25	4)364 = 91	7)189 = 27	3)66 = 22
2)114 = 57	8)616 = 77	9)288 = 32	3)114 = 38
3)132 = 44	4)104 = 26	7)175 = 25	9)207 = 23
4)112 = 28	8)256 = 32	4)256 = 64	3)237 = 79

Options for Individual Needs

10-3

Basic

Exercises 5-20, 25-28
Data Bank, p. 475
More Practice, p. 507, set D

Supplements
Reteaching 98 or
Practice 98

Average

Exercises 1-28
Data Bank, p. 475
More Practice, p. 507, set D

Supplements
Practice 98
Challenges 98 or
Thinking Skills 98

Extended

Exercises 7-20, 25-28
Data Bank, p. 475

Supplements
Challenges 98
Thinking Skills 98

Other Resources:
Problem-Solving Experiences in Mathematics, Grade 4, Problem 86
Math In Stride, Grade 4, p. 106

LESSON PLAN 10-3

OBJECTIVE 10-3
To use the estimation technique of rounding and substituting compatible numbers to estimate quotients

Materials: calculators

1. MOTIVATE AND TEACH

LEARN ABOUT IT

EXPLORE ► **Find an unnecessary fact in the problem. Explain why it is not needed.** (the date, 1010; The problem is about the number of people on each of 3 ships.)
► **Justify division as the appropriate operation.** (Division separates same-size groups.)

TALK ABOUT IT ► **Explain how rounding 162 to the nearest hundred affects the estimated quotient.** (200 ÷ 3 would give a large overestimate.)
► **Justify substituting a different dividend after rounding to the nearest ten.** (It makes sense to substitute numbers that divide easily.
► **Generalize about estimated quotients compared with the exact answers, based on how you adjust the dividends.** (When the divisor stays the same, then increased dividends give overestimates; reduced dividends give underestimates.)
Student Edition answers: **1.** 162 ÷ 3 **2.** No, 160 cannot be divided by 3 without a remainder. **3.** Round 162 to 150 to use the basic fact 15 ÷ 3; divide 150 by 3.

2. CHECK UNDERSTANDING

TRY IT OUT

ERROR ALERT Not knowing if estimates are over or under the exact answers. Not substituting compatible numbers to create easy estimates.

Estimating Quotients

LEARN ABOUT IT

EXPLORE Solve to Understand
In the year 1010, a Viking named Thorfinn sailed for Vinland. His 3 ships carried 162 people. If each ship carried the same number of people, how many were on each?

TALK ABOUT IT See teaching notes.

1. What numbers do you need to divide to get the answer?
2. If you round the number of people to the nearest ten, will you be able to estimate the answer easily? Explain.
3. How can you change the rounded number to make the problem into a basic fact?

When you estimate a quotient, sometimes rounding is not enough. You may need to substitute a compatible number that makes the computation easier.

To estimate 162 ÷ 3, round the dividend to the nearest ten.

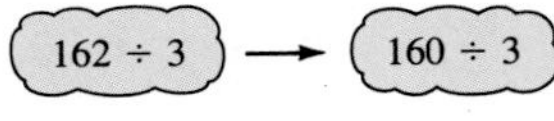

Then substitute a close number so you can estimate using a basic fact.

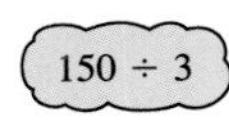

Each ship carried about 50 people. Since you reduced the dividend to find the estimate, the answer is an underestimate.

TRY IT OUT

Use rounding to estimate. Substitute if necessary. Tell if the estimate is over or under the exact answer.

1. 43 ÷ 4 10; under
2. 67 ÷ 3 20; under
3. 118 ÷ 6 20; over
4. 157 ÷ 5 30; under

TEACHING OPTIONS

RETEACHING TIPS Have students compare each rounded or substituted dividend with the actual dividend. For instance, if they round $4\overline{)318}$ to $4\overline{)320}$, they write 320 > 318. The estimated quotient has the same relationship (is greater than) to the exact quotient. Assign Reteaching Supplement 98.

ENRICHMENT Family Math Have students do this activity at home with a family member. They use a shopping bill or grocery receipt to estimate the quotient if each family member shared food costs. Then they tell if the estimate is over or under the exact quotient.

PRACTICE

Use rounding to estimate the quotients. Substitute if necessary.

1. 66 ÷ 7 10
2. $8.90 ÷ 5 $2
3. 348 ÷ 4 80
4. 461 ÷ 9 50
5. 355 ÷ 6 60
6. 712 ÷ 8 90
7. 3)117 40
8. 164 ÷ 2 80
9. 5)242 50
10. $48.66 ÷ 7 $7
11. 9)269 30
12. 153 ÷ 4 40

Estimate each quotient. Tell whether the estimate is over or under the exact quotient.

13. 397 ÷ 5 80; over
14. 106 ÷ 6 20; over
15. 218 ÷ 3 70; under
16. 233 ÷ 8 30; over
17. 4)$19.79 $5; over
18. 7)294 40; under
19. 471 ÷ 5 90; under
20. 534 ÷ 9 60; over
21. 193 ÷ 2 100; over
22. 486 ÷ 8 60; under
23. 4)256 60; under
24. 542 ÷ 6 90; under

APPLY

MATH REASONING

25. The closer the divisor is to 1, the closer the dividend comes to equaling the _?_. quotient

PROBLEM SOLVING

26. A copy of a Viking ship crossed the Atlantic Ocean in 28 days. The ship's length of 76 ft was about 4 times its width. About how wide was it? 20 ft

27. **Social Studies Data Bank** DATA BANK In 1970 a Norwegian explorer crossed the Atlantic Ocean in a reed boat he had made, called Ra II. 4 boats the length of Ra II would equal the length of a Viking longship. About how long was Ra II? See page 475. 40 ft

▶ **CALCULATOR**

28. Start with 510. Guess how many times you can subtract 34. Then try it with a calculator. 15 times

Begin your calculator steps like this.

[ON/AC] [−] 34 [Cons] 510 [−] 34 [=] 476   1 time ⟶ [=] 442   2 times

More Practice, page 507, set D

3. PRACTICE AND APPLY

Basic	5-20, 25-28
Average	1-28
Extended	7-20, 25-28

PRACTICE

For Exercises 13-24, tell how to decide if an estimated quotient is over or under the exact quotient. (Increased dividends give overestimates. Decreased dividends give underestimates.)

10-3

APPLY

MATH REASONING ▶ **Explain what it means to have a divisor of 1.** (You divide by 1 or make 1 group.) ▶ **Explain a rule that relates to division by 1.** (When you divide a number by 1, the quotient is that number.)

PROBLEM SOLVING ▶ **Analyze Problem 26 to find the data you need to solve it.** (Ship's length = 76 ft; its length is 4 times its width; 28 days is extra data.)

CALCULATOR ▶ **Analyze how subtracting the same amount over and over relates to division.** (You separate same-size groups each time you subtract the same number.)

CLOSE AND ASSESS

WRITE WHAT YOU THINK

Have students write letters to you, their teacher. In the letters, they explain how and why they might substitute numbers to estimate the quotients of 444 ÷ 9 and 6)555. Have them explain how to know if an estimate is *over* or *under* the exact answer. (450 ÷ 9 = 50; over; 540 ÷ 6 = 90; under; check students' writing.)

QUICK QUIZ

Estimate quotients. Tell if the estimate is *over* or *under* the exact quotient.

1. 88 ÷ 3 (30; over)
2. 5)262 (50; under)
3. $18.95 ÷ 9 ($2; under)

LESSON OPTIONS 10-4

Dividing Whole Numbers: Making the Connection

OBJECTIVE 10-4 To use objects to develop an understanding of dividing a 2-digit number by a 1-digit number

PREBOOK ACTIVITIES

QUICK REVIEW

Find the quotients.

1. 32 ÷ 5 (6 R2) **2.** 34 ÷ 7 (4 R6)
3. 19 ÷ 2 (9 R1) **4.** 35 ÷ 8 (4 R3)
5. 25 ÷ 6 (4 R1) **6.** 70 ÷ 9 (7 R7)
7. 9 ÷ 4 (2 R1) **8.** 23 ÷ 3 (7 R2)

PRIOR KNOWLEDGE

Have students explain a connection between showing an action, such as subtracting with trading, and recording the action. (Possible answer: If the problem requires trading 1 ten for 10 ones, you cross out the ten you trade, show how many tens remain, then show the new amount of ones.)

COMMUNICATION

Discussing Math Have students visualize adding, subtracting, and multiplying to generalize where each process begins in terms of place value. (ones place) Then write $2\overline{)33}$ on the chalkboard and ask students how they might show dividing 3 tens and 3 ones into 2 equal groups. (Put 1 ten in each of the 2 groups, which uses 2 tens; trade the last ten for 10 ones, add the 10 ones to the 3 ones, then divide the 13 ones.) Have students compare how that process differs from the other operations. (To divide, you begin with tens instead of with ones.)

EXPLORE AND CONNECT

Materials: TA 6 (Place Value Models), TA 2 (Number Cubes numbered 1-6)

Grouping Suggestion: cooperative learning groups of 5

Students explore dividing and recording their actions. Write the dividend 83 on the chalkboard. The first student takes 8 tens and 3 ones as the second student rolls the number cube to get a divisor. The third student divides as many tens as possible as the fourth student makes any necessary trades to continue dividing. The fifth student records the quotient and any remainder. (16 R3) Have students formulate a way to record each step of the division action. Trading tasks, groups repeat the division with a new divisor. Have groups share their quotients for each divisor and generalize how they divided. (Divide tens first, trade any extra tens for ones, then divide as far as you can.) Have volunteers show how they recorded the actions by writing their methods on the chalkboard.

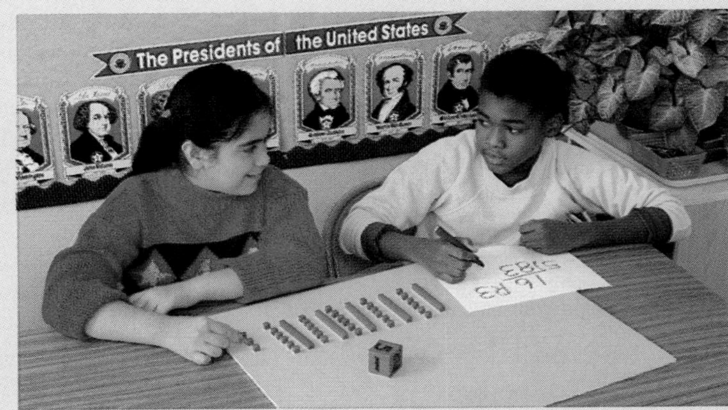

CONNECTIONS Use these anytime.

Problem of the Day

Number Riddle Write the digits 1, 2, 3, and 5 to show a completed division problem. (54 ÷ 4 = 13 R2)

□□ R □
4)□ 4

Subject Integration

Fine Arts On Talent Night, 77 students will put on original skits. If each skit has 7 characters, how many skits will be performed? If every skit lasts 5 min and there will be 2 min between skits, how long will the show be if it stays on schedule? [11 skits; 55 + 20 (no 2 min after the last skit) = 75 min or $1\frac{1}{4}$ h]

Life Skills

Travel An airplane has seats in groups of 3, with 3 groups per row. If 45 people are traveling on a tour and they want to sit together, how many rows of seats do they need? (5)

Classwork and Homework Supplements

Practice

Manipulatives 10-4

Name ______

Dividing Whole Numbers: Making the Connection

Use blocks to find answers to the following.
Trade when necessary. Record what you do.

1. 96 ÷ 3 — 32; 3)96; 9; 06; 6; 0
2. 84 ÷ 8 — 10 R4; 8)84; 8; 04; 0; 4
3. 82 ÷ 7 — 11 R5; 7)82; 7; 12; 7; 5
4. 77 ÷ 2 — 38 R1; 2)77; 6; 17; 16; 1
5. 53 ÷ 4 — 13 R1; 4)53; 4; 13; 12; 1
6. 95 ÷ 3 — 31 R2; 3)95; 9; 05; 3; 2
7. 73 ÷ 5 — 14 R3; 5)73; 5; 23; 20; 3
8. 95 ÷ 9 — 10 R5; 9)95; 9; 05; 0; 5
9. 43 ÷ 3 — 14 R1; 3)43; 3; 13; 12; 1
10. 68 ÷ 5 — 13 R3; 5)68; 5; 18; 15; 3
11. 93 ÷ 7 — 13 R2; 7)93; 7; 23; 21; 2
12. 69 ÷ 4 — 17 R1; 4)69; 4; 29; 28; 1
13. 82 ÷ 5 — 16 R2; 5)82; 5; 32; 30; 2
14. 75 ÷ 4 — 18 R3; 4)75; 4; 35; 32; 3
15. 99 ÷ 8 — 12 R3; 8)99; 8; 19; 16; 3
16. 82 ÷ 3 — 27 R1; 3)82; 6; 22; 21; 1

PS-4 Use with text pages 272–273. 99

Building Thinking Skills

Number Sense 10-4

Name ______

Animal Division

Write a division problem that uses the information in each group of data cards. Then write the equation. The first one has been done for you. Problems will vary.

1. 2 monkeys / 34 bananas / 17 bananas — There are 34 bananas. Each monkey gets the same number of bananas. How many bananas does each monkey get? 34 ÷ 2 = 17
2. 87 crackers / 29 crackers / 3 parrots
3. 3 horses / 19 apples / 57 apples
4. 30 carrots / 6 carrots / 5 rabbits
5. 45 fish / 5 seals / 9 fish

TS-4 Use with text pages 272–273. 99

Reteaching

Manipulatives 10-4

Name ______

Dividing Whole Numbers: Making the Connection

Divide 57 into 4 groups.

Total Number — Change 1 ten to ones. — 4 groups, with 14 in each group — 1 left over

Use blocks to help you complete the chart.

	Total Number	Groups	Number in Each Group	Number Left Over
1.	57	4	14	1
2.	12	4	3	0
3.	33	5	6	3
4.	19	2	9	1
5.	25	5	5	0
6.	37	7	6	1
7.	49	6	7	0
8.	24	4	6	0
9.	66	6	11	0

RS-4 Use with text pages 272–273. 99

Challenges

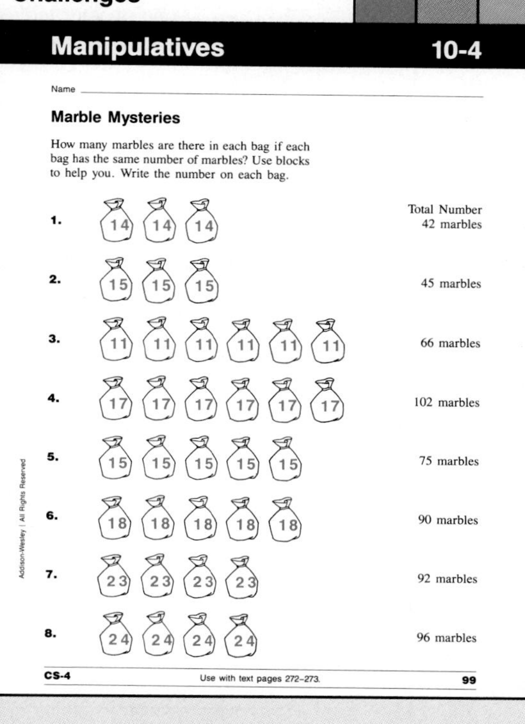

Manipulatives 10-4

Name ______

Marble Mysteries

How many marbles are there in each bag if each bag has the same number of marbles? Use blocks to help you. Write the number on each bag.

	Bags	Total Number
1.	14, 14, 14	42 marbles
2.	15, 15, 15	45 marbles
3.	11, 11, 11, 11, 11, 11	66 marbles
4.	17, 17, 17, 17, 17, 17	102 marbles
5.	15, 15, 15, 15, 15	75 marbles
6.	18, 18, 18, 18, 18	90 marbles
7.	23, 23, 23, 23	92 marbles
8.	24, 24, 24, 24	96 marbles

CS-4 Use with text pages 272–273. 99

Options for Individual Needs

10-4

Basic

Exercises 2-5
Skills Bank, p. 460

Supplements
Reteaching 99 or
Practice 99
Challenges 99

Average

Exercises 1-5
Skills Bank, p. 460

Supplements
Practice 99
Challenges 99 or
Thinking Skills 99

Extended

Exercises 3-5

Supplements
Challenges 99
Thinking Skills 99

Other Resources:
Problem-Solving Experiences in Mathematics, Grade 4, Problem 78
Math In Stride, Grade 4, pp. 107, 108
Mathematics, A Way of Thinking, Lessons 10-1, 10-2
Using the Math Explorer Calculator: A Sourcebook for Teachers, Chapter 14

LESSON PLAN 10-4

OBJECTIVE 10-4
To use objects to develop an understanding of dividing a 2-digit number by a 1-digit number

Materials: TA 11 (Blank Spinners), place value blocks, TA 8 (3-Digit Place Value Charts)

Alternative Materials: TA 6 (Place Value Models)

Grouping Suggestion: groups, pairs

1. MOTIVATE AND TEACH

LEARN ABOUT IT

EXPLORE ▶ **Summarize the rule for choosing a divisor.** (Divide by 2 if your third spin is an even number; divide by 3 if you spin an odd number.)
▶ **Explain the meaning of "extras" in the table.** (any blocks left over that cannot be divided equally; remainder)
▶ **Justify trading 1 ten for 10 ones to divide the blocks completely.** (You might need to break a ten into ones to split it into 2 or 3 groups.)

TALK ABOUT IT Student Edition answers: **1.** To divide by 2, students may trade 1 ten for 10 ones; to divide by 3, they may trade 1 or 2 tens for 10 or 20 ones. **2.** Possible answer: Trade tens first to see how many must be traded for ones, then divide all the ones at once. Opinions may vary. **3.** There are always extras when you divide an odd number by 2 and when you divide some even or odd numbers by 3.

2. CHECK UNDERSTANDING

ERROR ALERT Dividing ones before dividing tens.

Dividing Whole Numbers
Making the Connection

LEARN ABOUT IT

EXPLORE Use a Place Value Model
Work in groups. Use a spinner with digits 1–9 and make piles of blocks.

- Spin two times to give the number of tens and ones blocks for a pile. Record the numbers in a table like the first one shown.
- Spin the spinner again. If you land on an even number, write 2 on the blank line next to "equal sets." Then divide the pile into 2 equal piles. If you land on an odd number, write 3 and divide the pile into 3 equal piles. Trade a tens block for 10 ones blocks if necessary.
- Record any extras in the extra box.
- Do this several times. Make a separate table each time.

Divide. Record results.

Tens	Ones	Tens (in each equal set)	Ones (in each equal set)	Extras
7	4	3	7	0

into 2 equal sets.

Separate into same-size piles to share the blocks equally.

TALK ABOUT IT See teaching notes.

1. Look at one of your tables and tell what trades, if any, you made to divide up the pile.
2. Did you divide the tens or ones first? Which seems easier? Why?
3. When are there extras? Do you see a pattern?

272

TEACHING OPTIONS

RETEACHING TIPS Have students use 3-digit place value charts to organize the blocks. Guide them to divide tens first to clarify how many tens will be left to trade for ones. After making any necessary trades, students can divide all available ones in 1 step. Assign Reteaching Supplement 99.

COMPUTER Number Munchers, MECC, Copyright 1986 For use with all levels of students. In "Factors," students move the "Number Muncher" around the grid to eat expressions that are factors of the target number before "Toggle Monster" eats "Number Muncher."

You have used your blocks to divide numbers into 2 and 3 equal sets. Now you will see another way to record what you have done. This process can help you find quotients such as 74 ÷ 2.

What You Do | **What You Record**

1. Lay out 74 with your blocks. Show the sets into which the blocks are to be divided.

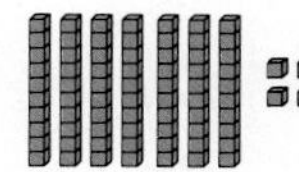
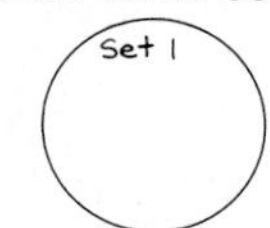

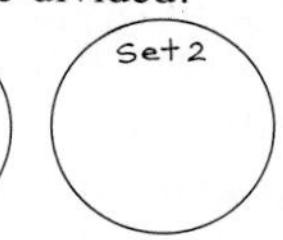

2)74

2. Divide the tens. Show how many tens you used and how many are left over.

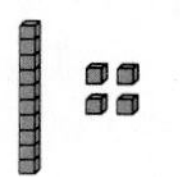
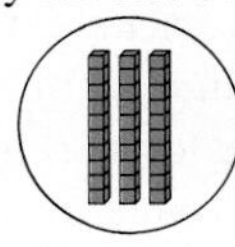
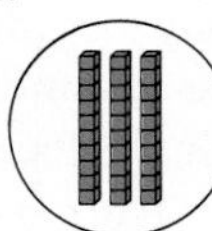

```
   3     Three tens
2)74     in each set.
  6      Six tens used.
  1      One ten left over.
```

3. Trade left over tens for ones.

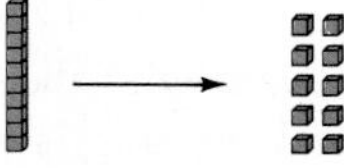

4. Divide the ones. Show how many ones you used and how many are left over.

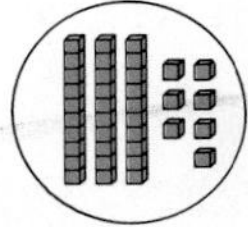
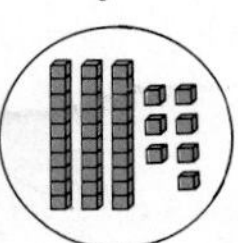
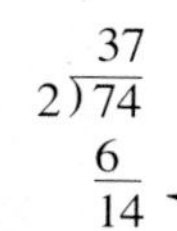

```
   37
2)74
  6
  14
```

After the trade, there are fourteen ones.

```
   37    Seven ones
2)74     in each set.
  6
  14
  14     All fourteen ones
   0     used. No remainder.
```

TRY IT OUT

Use blocks to find answers to the following. Trade when necessary. Record what you do.

1. 46 ÷ 2 **23** **2.** 52 ÷ 3 **17 R1** **3.** 27 ÷ 2 **13 R1** **4.** 35 ÷ 3 **11 R2**

5. Use blocks to solve a division problem of your choice. **Answers will vary.**

 273

3. Practice and Apply

Basic	2-5
Average	1-5
Extended	3-5

PRACTICE

Have students look at each step of the division example on page 273. *Explain the connection between What You Do and What You Record in Step 1.* (Show 74 as 7 tens and 4 ones; write a dividend of 74 with a divisor of 2.) *In Step 2, how many tens were divided? How is this recorded?* (6 tens, 3 per group; show 3 in the quotient; show 6 of the 7 tens used, leaving 1 ten to trade.) *Explain how to record the traded ten in Step 4.* (Combine the 4 ones with the 1 ten as 14 ones to divide into 2 groups.) *Explain how the quotient shows division of ones.* (7 ones in each group) Have students continue working in groups to complete the Try It Out exercises.

10-4

Close and Assess

WRITE WHAT YOU THINK

Have students list the steps to follow to divide 77 by 3 using place value materials. Then have partners exchange papers and follow each other's steps to verify the answer and to check that the steps are in a sensible order. (25 R2; Check students' writing.)

QUICK QUIZ

Find the quotient of 53 divided by 2. Use place value materials and record what you do. (26 R1)

LESSON OPTIONS 10-5

Dividing Whole Numbers: 2-Digit Quotients

OBJECTIVE 10-5 To find 2-digit quotients by dividing 1-digit divisors into 2-digit dividends

PREBOOK ACTIVITIES

QUICK REVIEW

Find each difference.

1. 13 − 5 (8)	**2.** 11 − 6 (5)	**3.** 9 − 8 (1)
4. 10 − 7 (3)	**5.** 15 − 8 (7)	**6.** 13 − 6 (7)
7. 12 − 4 (8)	**8.** 4 − 4 (0)	**9.** 9 − 4 (5)
10. 16 − 9 (7)	**11.** 14 − 7 (7)	**12.** 17 − 8 (9)

PRIOR KNOWLEDGE

Review the trading rules for addition and multiplication. (When necessary, trade 10 of a place for 1 of the next higher place.) Have students compare this with a trade in subtraction. (When necessary, trade 1 of a place for 10 of the next lower place.) Tell students that they may have to make trades when dividing larger numbers. Have them guess the kind of trading they will do and give their reason. (Trade 1 of a larger place for 10 of the next lower place; division relates to subtraction.)

COMMUNICATION

Discussing Math Have students explain how to make comparisons. (Possible answer: Evaluate two things to see how they are alike or different.) Have them suggest some math words used to make comparisons. (Possible answers: *greater than; less than; equal to*) Ask students to use people or objects in the classroom and comparing words to make number comparisons. For example, they could compare the number of boys to girls or the number of desks to chairs. (Answers will vary.) Tell students that when they divide, they will use a comparing step as they find quotients.

EXPLORE AND CONNECT

Materials: place value blocks
Alternative Materials: TA 6 (Place Value Models)
Grouping Suggestion: cooperative learning pairs
Partners explore division with 2-digit dividends and 1-digit divisors. They generate a division problem together: One picks a 2-digit dividend, the other picks a 1-digit divisor. Partners discuss and agree on an estimated quotient. Then one student divides using place value materials and the other divides using pencil and paper. Partners compare the two quotients to determine if their answers agree. If the answers are not the same, they review each other's work to find the point of error. They also compare the exact quotient with their estimate to see if it was reasonable. Then partners generate a new problem, trade methods, and repeat the activity. Each student should divide by each method twice. Conclude by asking students which method they prefer and why. (Answers will vary.)

CONNECTIONS Use these anytime.

Problem of the Day

Number Sense Divide by a certain odd number and the quotient will be the same as the dividend. What odd number is the divisor? (1)

Math Connection

Calculator Figure out how to find the quotient and remainder of $4\overline{)91}$ on a calculator without pressing the ÷ key. (22 R3; Solution methods may vary; you could repeatedly subtract 4 or guess and test missing factors.)

Subject Integration

Music Waltz music has 3 beats to a measure. Fritz is a composer. He is writing a new piece of waltz music. So far, he has composed 72 beats of music. How many measures has Fritz written? (24)

Classwork and Homework Supplements

Practice

Skills Maintenance 10-5

Name ____________________

Dividing Whole Numbers: 2-Digit Quotients

Find the quotients and remainders.

Exercise	Problem	Quotient	Work
1.	$8\overline{)84}$	10 R4	8, 04, 0, 4
2.	$7\overline{)82}$	11 R5	7, 12, 7, 5
3.	$3\overline{)95}$	31 R2	9, 05, 3, 2
4.	$5\overline{)82}$	16 R2	5, 32, 30, 2
5.	$2\overline{)77}$	38 R1	6, 17, 16, 1
6.	$4\overline{)53}$	13 R1	4, 13, 12, 1
7.	$6\overline{)88}$	14 R4	6, 28, 24, 4
8.	$5\overline{)73}$	14 R3	5, 23, 20, 3
9.	$9\overline{)95}$	10 R5	9, 05, 0, 5
10.	$3\overline{)43}$	14 R1	3, 13, 12, 1
11.	$5\overline{)68}$	13 R3	5, 18, 15, 3
12.	$4\overline{)75}$	18 R3	4, 35, 32, 3
13.	$7\overline{)93}$	13 R2	7, 23, 21, 2
14.	$6\overline{)92}$	15 R2	6, 32, 30, 2
15.	$4\overline{)69}$	17 R1	4, 29, 28, 1
16.	$72 \div 5$	14 R2	5, 22, 20, 2
17.	$55 \div 4$	13 R3	4, 15, 12, 3
18.	$82 \div 3$	27 R1	6, 22, 21, 1
19.	$94 \div 6$	15 R4	6, 34, 30, 4

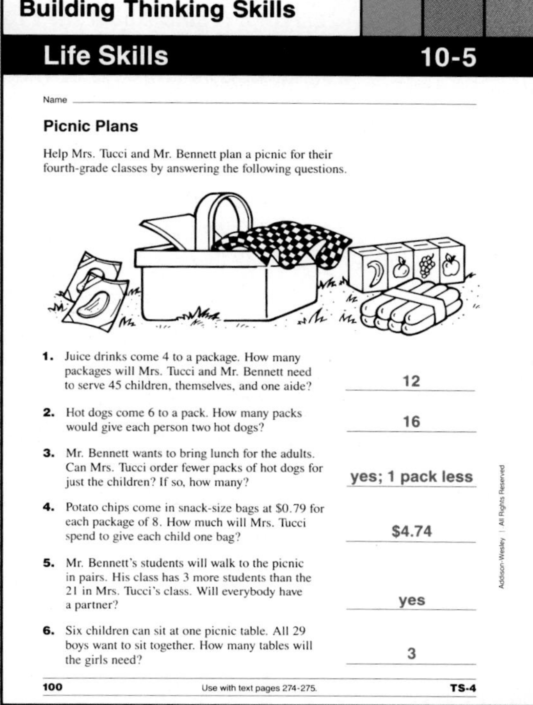

Building Thinking Skills

Life Skills 10-5

Name ____________________

Picnic Plans

Help Mrs. Tucci and Mr. Bennett plan a picnic for their fourth-grade classes by answering the following questions.

1. Juice drinks come 4 to a package. How many packages will Mrs. Tucci and Mr. Bennett need to serve 45 children, themselves, and one aide? **12**
2. Hot dogs come 6 to a pack. How many packs would give each person two hot dogs? **16**
3. Mr. Bennett wants to bring lunch for the adults. Can Mrs. Tucci order fewer packs of hot dogs for just the children? If so, how many? **yes; 1 pack less**
4. Potato chips come in snack-size bags at $0.79 for each package of 8. How much will Mrs. Tucci spend to give each child one bag? **$4.74**
5. Mr. Bennett's students will walk to the picnic in pairs. His class has 3 more students than the 21 in Mrs. Tucci's class. Will everybody have a partner? **yes**
6. Six children can sit at one picnic table. All 29 boys want to sit together. How many tables will the girls need? **3**

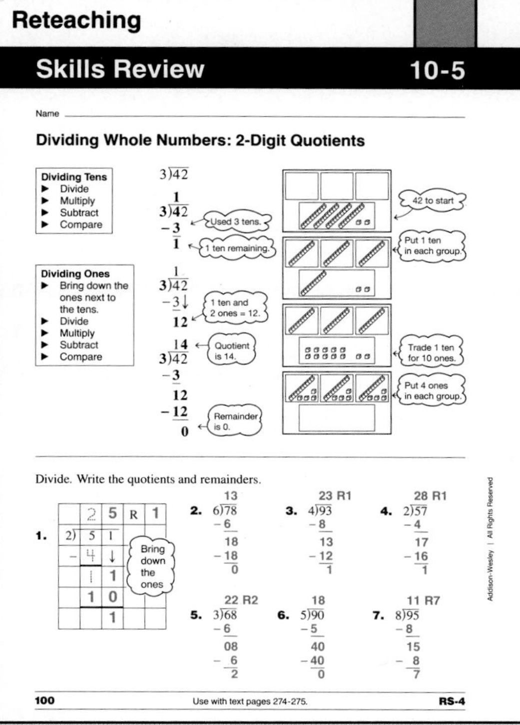

Reteaching

Skills Review 10-5

Name ____________________

Dividing Whole Numbers: 2-Digit Quotients

Dividing Tens
- Divide
- Multiply
- Subtract
- Compare

Dividing Ones
- Bring down the ones next to the tens.
- Divide
- Multiply
- Subtract
- Compare

3)42
42 to start
Used 3 tens.
1 ten remaining.
Put 1 ten in each group.
1 ten and 2 ones = 12.
Quotient is 14.
Trade 1 ten for 10 ones.
Put 4 ones in each group.
Remainder is 0.

Divide. Write the quotients and remainders.

1. $2\overline{)51}$ = 25 R1 (−4, 11, −10, 1) Bring down the ones
2. $6\overline{)78}$ = 13 (−6, 18, −18, 0)
3. $4\overline{)93}$ = 23 R1 (−8, 13, −12, 1)
4. $2\overline{)57}$ = 28 R1 (−4, 17, −16, 1)
5. $3\overline{)68}$ = 22 R2 (−6, 08, −6, 2)
6. $5\overline{)90}$ = 18 (−5, 40, −40, 0)
7. $8\overline{)95}$ = 11 R7 (−8, 15, −8, 7)

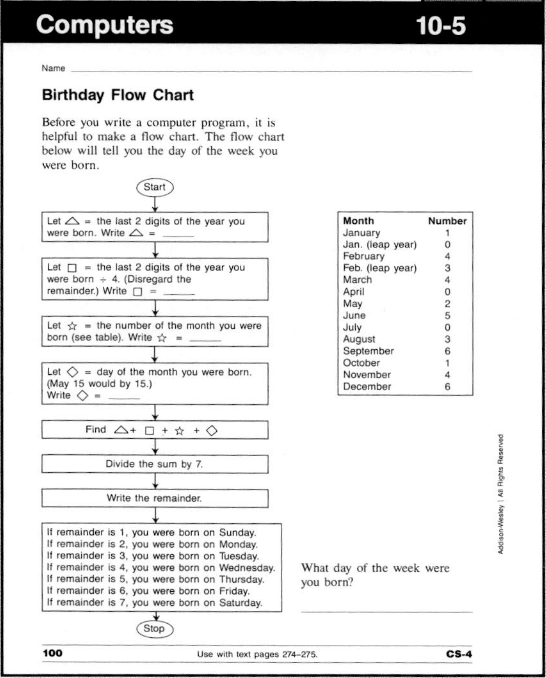

Challenges

Computers 10-5

Name ____________________

Birthday Flow Chart

Before you write a computer program, it is helpful to make a flow chart. The flow chart below will tell you the day of the week you were born.

Start
Let △ = the last 2 digits of the year you were born. Write △ = ____
Let □ = the last 2 digits of the year you were born ÷ 4. (Disregard the remainder.) Write □ = ____
Let ☆ = the number of the month you were born (see table). Write ☆ = ____
Let ◇ = day of the month you were born. (May 15 would be 15.) Write ◇ = ____
Find △ + □ + ☆ + ◇
Divide the sum by 7.
Write the remainder.
If remainder is 1, you were born on Sunday.
If remainder is 2, you were born on Monday.
If remainder is 3, you were born on Tuesday.
If remainder is 4, you were born on Wednesday.
If remainder is 5, you were born on Thursday.
If remainder is 6, you were born on Friday.
If remainder is 7, you were born on Saturday.
Stop

Month	Number
January	1
Jan. (leap year)	0
February	4
Feb. (leap year)	3
March	4
April	0
May	2
June	5
July	0
August	3
September	6
October	1
November	4
December	6

What day of the week were you born? ____________

Options for Individual Needs

Basic

Exercises 3-16, 19-23
More Practice, p. 507, set E

Supplements
Reteaching 100 or
Practice 100
Thinking Skills 100

Average

Exercises 1-23
More Practice, p. 507, set E

Supplements
Practice 100
Challenges 100 or
Thinking Skills 100

Extended

Exercises 5-15, 19-23

Supplements
Challenges 100
Thinking Skills 100

Other Resources:
Problem-Solving Experiences in Mathematics, Grade 4, Problem 80
Math In Stride, Grade 4, p. 115
Mathematics, A Way of Thinking, Lesson 10-3
Using the Math Explorer Calculator: A Sourcebook for Teachers, Chapter 14

LESSON PLAN 10-5

OBJECTIVE 10-5
To find 2-digit quotients by dividing 1-digit divisors into 2-digit dividends

Materials: calculators, place value blocks

Alternative Materials: TA 6 (Place Value Models)

Grouping Suggestion: pairs

1. MOTIVATE AND TEACH

LEARN ABOUT IT

EXPLORE ▶ **Explain the 2 in the quotient.** (8 tens divided into 3 groups gives 2 tens per group.)
▶ **Explain why you subtract 6 tens.** (3 × 2 tens—6 tens—have been divided equally.)
▶ **Justify the compare step.** (After subtracting, the difference should be less than the divisor, or else another group could be made.)
▶ **Explain how the 2 remaining tens divide into 3 groups.** (If you trade 2 tens for 20 ones, the number is greater than 3.)
▶ **Explain why you bring down the 7.** (to divide those 7 ones along with the leftover tens)
▶ **Explain how you know when you are finished dividing.** (when all numbers have been brought down)

TALK ABOUT IT ▶ **What does it mean that the remainder is zero?** (Each child pays the same amount.)
Student Edition answers: **1.** 2, 2
2. Answers may vary; 90 ÷ 3 = 30.
3. Each child will pay $29.

2. CHECK UNDERSTANDING

TRY IT OUT

ERROR ALERT Stopping after dividing the tens. Losing track of the steps in the division process.

Dividing Whole Numbers
2-Digit Quotients

LEARN ABOUT IT

EXPLORE Think About the Process
Jonathan and his two friends were playing catch and by accident broke the neighbor's window. Repairing the window will cost $87. What is each child's fair share of the cost?

Since an amount of money is to be separated into equal groups, you divide to find the answer.

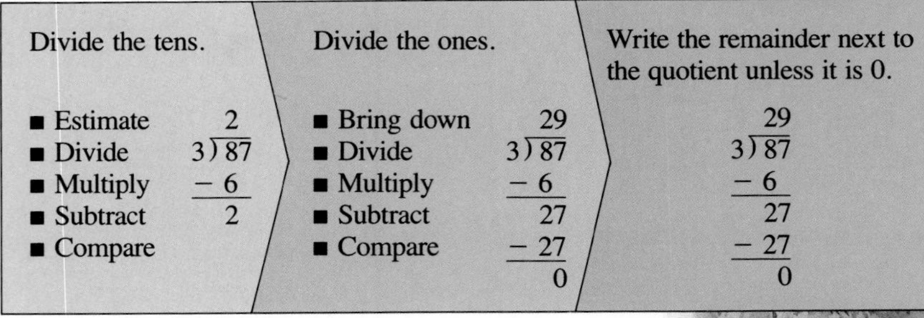

Divide the tens.	Divide the ones.	Write the remainder next to the quotient unless it is 0.
■ Estimate ■ Divide ■ Multiply ■ Subtract ■ Compare	■ Bring down ■ Divide ■ Multiply ■ Subtract ■ Compare	
2 3)87 − 6 2	29 3)87 − 6 27 − 27 0	29 3)87 − 6 27 − 27 0

TALK ABOUT IT See teaching notes.

1. In step 1, 8 was divided into 3 groups. How many tens were in each group? How many tens were left over?
2. How would you have estimated the answer?
3. Give the answer in a complete sentence.

TRY IT OUT

1. 6)74 12 R2
2. 8)93 11 R5
3. 3)60 20
4. 4)94 23 R2
5. 5)86 17 R1

TEACHING OPTIONS

RETEACHING TIPS Students use place value blocks to show the dividend, then separate it into the given number of groups, using tens first. When they cannot divide any more tens equally, they trade for ones and divide all ones. The group size is the quotient. Assign Reteaching Supplement 100.

ENRICHMENT Students use the digits 1, 2, 3, 4 and 5 to make the division work. (51 ÷ 4 = 12 R3)

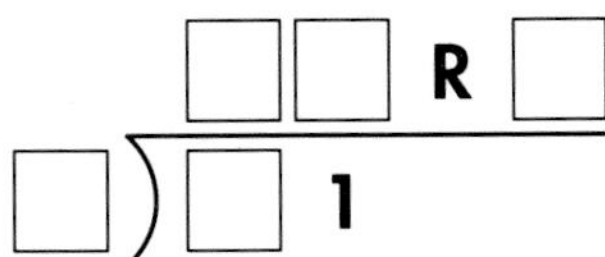

PRACTICE

Find the quotients and remainders.

1. 73 ÷ 4 18 R1
2. 98 ÷ 9 10 R8
3. 65 ÷ 3 21 R2
4. 70 ÷ 6 11 R4
5. 55 ÷ 4 13 R3
6. 7)86 12 R2
7. 5)58 11 R3
8. 2)69 34 R1
9. 8)47 5 R7
10. 9)46 5 R1
11. Divide 84 by 6. 14
12. Divide 93 by 4. 23 R1
13. Divide 78 by 7. 11 R1

Estimate each quotient.

14. 85 ÷ 2 40
15. 71 ÷ 3 20
16. 89 ÷ 8 10
17. 95 ÷ 5 20
18. 23 ÷ 4 5

APPLY

MATH REASONING For each exercise, make up and complete 3 division problems to help you give the number for the blank. See Additional Answers.

19. When an even number is divided by 2, the remainder is _?_.
20. When an odd number is divided by 2, the remainder is _?_.

PROBLEM SOLVING

21. **Developing a Plan** Choose the steps you could follow to solve this problem. Jack had 32 marbles. He found 4 more. Then he decided to give all of his marbles to 3 of his friends. How many marbles did each friend get?
    a. Divide 32 by 3. Then add 4.
    b. Add 32 and 4. Then divide by 3.
    c. Add 32 and 4. Then multiply by 3.
    b
22. Maria's mother bought tickets and lunch for Maria and 3 friends at the Oakland A's and Houston Astros game. The total cost was $52. How much was this per person? $13

► **ESTIMATION** Estimates will vary.

23. Suppose there are 817 people in the whole picture. Estimate the number of people in one section.

More Practice, page 507, set E

3. PRACTICE AND APPLY

Basic	3-16, 19-23
Average	1-23
Extended	5-15, 19-23

Additional Answers: See p. T79.

PRACTICE

Look at Exercises 1-13. Find two exercises with 1-digit quotients. (Exercises 9, 10)

APPLY

MATH REASONING ► **Explain how you will choose the dividends for the problems you make up.** (According to the directions, they need to be even numbers in Exercise 19 and odd numbers in Exercise 20.)

PROBLEM SOLVING ► **What is the best way to solve Problem 21?** (Possible answer: It makes the most sense to add first, then to divide.)

► **Analyze Problem 22 to find how many had lunch at the game.** (4; Maria + 3 others)

ESTIMATION ► **How does the picture help you estimate? Explain.** (Answers vary. Check for reasonableness.)

CLOSE AND ASSESS

SAY WHAT YOU THINK Have partners divide 95 by 3 and 82 by 4. One student verbalizes each step his or her partner must follow to complete the division process. Students do as their partners dictate, then they both do the division on a calculator before changing roles to complete the second problem. (31 R2; 20 R2)

QUICK QUIZ

Find the quotients and any remainders.

1. 5)83 (16 R3)
2. 60 ÷ 4 (15)
3. 6)91 (15 R1)
4. 79 ÷ 3 (26 R1)
5. Divide 87 by 7. (12 R3)
6. What is 89 divided by 8? (11 R1)

LESSON OPTIONS 10-6

Problem Solving: Interpreting Remainders

OBJECTIVE 10-6 To solve problems by interpreting the remainder

PREBOOK ACTIVITIES

QUICK REVIEW

Divide.

1. $5\overline{)93}$	(18 R3)	**2.** $6\overline{)89}$	(14 R 5)
3. $3\overline{)77}$	(25 R 2)	**4.** $8\overline{)89}$	(11 R 1)
5. $4\overline{)91}$	(22 R 3)	**6.** $2\overline{)97}$	(48 R 1)
7. $9\overline{)94}$	(10 R4)	**8.** $7\overline{)96}$	(13 R 5)

PRIOR KNOWLEDGE

Have students recall the meaning of a remainder in division. (Possible answer: an amount left over that cannot be divided into another same-size group) Have students suggest real-life situations that may involve remainders. (Possible answers: serving food; making teams; sharing money)

COMMUNICATION

Discussing and Writing Math In their Math Journals, have students write synonyms for the word *remainder*. (Sample synonyms: *rest, leftover, extra, odd amount*) Then have students write possible wordings for typical questions at the end of division story problems. (Possible answers: *How many groups can be made? How many in each group? How many are left over?*) Discuss students' entries.

EXPLORE AND CONNECT

COOPERATIVE ACTIVITY

Grouping Suggestion: small groups

A page in Pam's album holds 6 photos. If she has 20 photos from camp, how many pages does she need to mount them all?

TEACHING ACTIONS

Have students work together to discuss the situation, plan a solution, and evaluate their answer.

► **Explain the situation in your own words.** (Pam wants to put 20 photos in an album, 6 per page.)

► **Decide what you need to find out.** (how many pages it will take to hold all 20 photos)

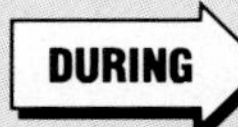

► **Decide on a solution method.** (Answers may vary; divide or model the situation with objects.)

► **Predict whether every album page Pam uses will be filled.** (no, because 20 is not a multiple of 6)

► **Analyze the answer to the division to solve the problem.** ($20 \div 6 = 3$ R2, which means that Pam can fill 3 pages completely, with 2 photos left over. But since the 2 leftover photos must go in the album, Pam must start a fourth page; she will need 4 pages.)

CONNECTIONS Use these anytime.

Problem of the Day

Sunglasses Grant collects sunglasses. He sees 4 new pairs of sunglasses that cost $7 per pair. If he has $25, how many pairs can he afford to add to his collection? How much money, if any, will he have left? (3 pairs; $4 left)

Math Connection

Money Toni had $5 left after she bought 6 tubes of sunscreen to use during her summer at the beach. Each tube cost $4.50. How much money did Toni begin with? ($32)

Creative Thinking

Beach Balls Mr. Lattif bought 32 beach balls at an end-of-season sale. He plans to pack them in beach bags to donate to various day camps in his area. Determine how many different ways he can share the beach balls with none left over. (1 each to 32 or 32 to 1 camp; 2 each to 16 or 16 each to 2 camps; 4 each to 8 or 8 each to 4 camps)

Classwork and Homework Supplements

Practice

Life Skills 10-6

Name

Problem Solving: Interpreting Remainders

Solve each problem.

1. Socks are $4 a pair. Ben has $14 to buy socks. How many pairs can he buy? **3 pairs**
2. 416 people are going on a tour. If there are 9 people in each tour group, how many groups are there? **47 groups**
3. 365 glasses are to be put in boxes. If there are 8 glasses in a box, now many boxes are needed? **46 boxes**
4. 3 bananas are needed for each loaf of banana bread. How many loaves can be made from 124 bananas? **41 loaves**
5. 123 people want to be on baseball teams. There are 9 people on a team. How many teams can they make? **13 teams**
6. Linda has $26. Tapes cost $8 each. How many tapes can Linda buy? **3 tapes**
7. How many cars are needed to take the 75 members of the ski club on a trip? Each car can carry 6 people. **13 cars**
8. Juice is being served to 20 people. If it comes in packages of 6, how many packages are needed? **4 packages**

PS-4 Use with text page 276. 101

Building Thinking Skills

Writing Math 10-6

Name

Division Story Problems

Write a division story problem to match the given data and answer. Then solve the problem.

Example: $95 to spend on softballs
$7 for each softball
Answer: $4 left

$$\begin{array}{r} 13\ R4 \\ 7\overline{)95} \\ -7 \\ 25 \\ -21 \\ 4 \end{array}$$

Answer: $4

The team has $95 to spend on softballs. Each ball costs $7. The team buys as many balls as they can. How much money do they have left?

Story problems may vary.

1. 109 children
   9 players on a team
   Answer: 12 teams
2. 135 people at the game
   7 people on a bench
   Answer: 20 benches
3. 145 hot dogs needed
   8 hot dogs in each package
   Answer: 19 packages
4. $105 to spend on mitts
   $9 for each mitt
   Answer: $6 left

TS-4 Use with text page 276. 101

Reteaching

Problem Solving 10-6

Name

Interpreting Remainders

Jane bought 50 apples. A bag holds 8 apples.

Questions:

- How many bags can Jane fill completely?
- How many bags does Jane need to get all 50 apples home?
- How many apples are in the bag that is not full?

$$\begin{array}{r} 6\ R2 \\ 8\overline{)50} \\ -48 \\ 2 \end{array}$$

(2 apples remain.)

Answers:

- Jane can completely fill 6 bags.
- Jane needs 7 bags.
- There are 2 apples in the bag that is not full.

All three problems use the same division, but they have different answers.

Ring the correct answer.

1. John bought 64 pear trees. His truck can hold 6 trees. How many trips will the truck have to make to get all the trees home?
   A 10 trips **B** (11 trips) **C** 4 trips
   (6)64 = 10 R4. 10 trips are not enough.)
2. Peg has $15 to spend on strawberry plants. Each plant costs $2. How much money will Peg have after she buys the plants?
   A $7 **B** $8 **C** ($1)
   (2)15 = 7 R1. She can buy 7 plants. That leaves $1.)
3. Patrick is making peach pies. He has 35 peaches and needs 8 for each pie. How many pies can he make?
   A (4 pies) **B** 5 pies **C** 3 pies
4. Jack has 58 melons to take to market. He can fit 5 melons in a box. How many boxes will he need to get all the melons to market?
   A 11 boxes **B** (12 boxes) **C** 3 boxes

RS-4 Use with text page 276. 101

Challenges

Cooperative Activities 10-6

Name

Camp Counselor Headaches

Work in a small group. Use the charts to solve each problem. **Answers may vary.**

Headache 1
There are 27 campers. Grape drink comes in 6-packs and orange drink comes in 4-packs. How many 6-packs and how many 4-packs should you buy to have the fewest drinks left over?

(You want some of each kind of drink.)

Number of 6-packs	Number of 4-packs	Total Number of drinks	Number of drinks left over
3	3	30	3
2	4	28	1

Headache 2
There are 29 campers. Joe needs groups of exactly 6 campers for his activity. Sherry needs groups of exactly 7 for hers. How can you group them so that there are the fewest campers left over?

(Both counselors must have at least 1 group.)

Number of groups of 6	Number of groups of 7	Total Number of campers in groups	Number of campers left over
1	3	27	2

CS-4 Use with text page 276. 101

Options for Individual Needs

10-6

Basic

Exercises 1-8
More Practice, p. 521, set A

Supplements
Reteaching 101 or
Practice 101

Average

Exercises 1-8
More Practice, p. 521, set A

Supplements
Practice 101
Challenges 101 or
Thinking Skills 101

Extended

Exercises 1-8

Supplements
Challenges 101
Thinking Skills 101

Other Resources:
Problem-Solving Experiences in Mathematics, Grade 4, Problem 83
Math In Stride, Grade 4, p. 204
Mathematics, A Way of Thinking, Lesson 10-4
Using the Math Explorer Calculator: A Sourcebook for Teachers, Chapter 14

LESSON PLAN 10-6

OBJECTIVE 10-6
To solve problems by interpreting the remainder

1. MOTIVATE AND TEACH

LEARN ABOUT IT

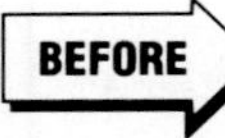

► **Explain why the 2 sample problems use division.** (Both have an amount to be separated into same-size groups.)

► **Analyze each question.** (The first problem asks how many complete 7-person teams can be formed; the second asks how many 6-bar boxes are needed.)

► **Explain how to use the data and division to solve the problems.** (Divide 88 by 7; divide 86 by 6.)

► **Evaluate how each remainder applies to the situation.** (R4 means 4 campers are not on teams, even though 12 full teams are possible; R2 means that 2 campers would not get juice bars if 14 boxes were bought.)

► **Explain why a 15th box of juice bars is needed.** (to have enough for the other 2 campers)

2. CHECK UNDERSTANDING

TRY IT OUT

ERROR ALERT Misinterpreting the remainder.

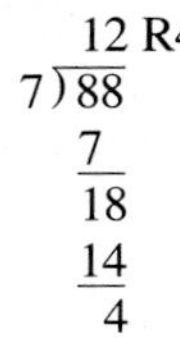

Problem Solving
Interpreting Remainders

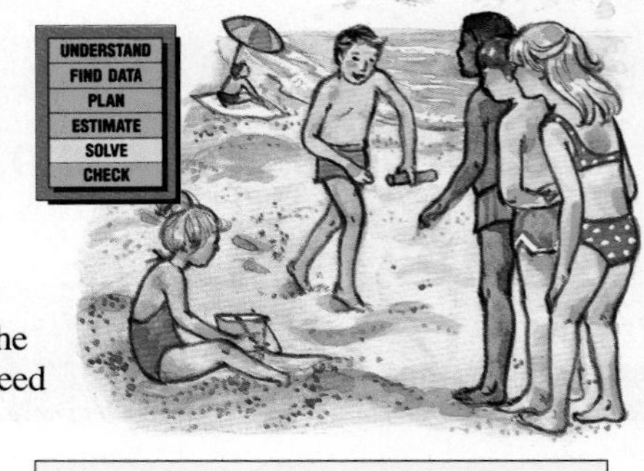

LEARN ABOUT IT

Sometimes division does not give you the complete answer to the problem. You need to understand the remainder.

At junior lifesaving camp at the beach, the counselors divided 88 campers into teams of 7 for the freestyle relay race. How many complete teams could they make?

$$\begin{array}{r} 12\text{ R4} \\ 7\overline{)88} \\ \underline{7} \\ 18 \\ \underline{14} \\ 4 \end{array}$$

They could make 12 teams.

There aren't enough campers in the last group to make a team.

The camp counselors bought juice bars for the 86 campers who came on Tuesday. The bars come in boxes of 6. How many boxes should they buy?

$$\begin{array}{r} 14\text{ R2} \\ 6\overline{)86} \\ \underline{6} \\ 26 \\ \underline{24} \\ 2 \end{array}$$

They should buy 15 boxes.

They need 14 full boxes. A 15th box is needed to have some for the 2 remaining campers.

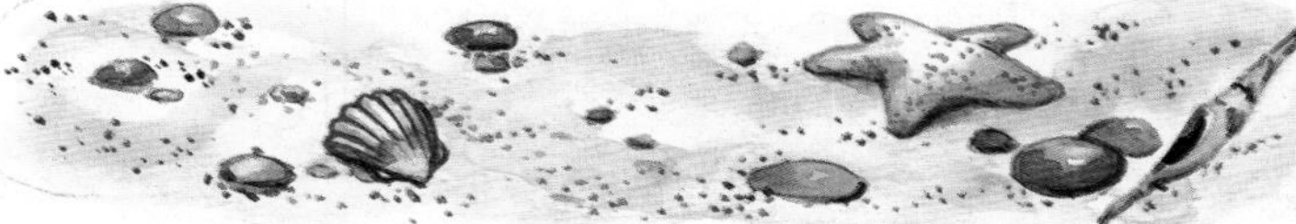

TRY IT OUT

Read and then solve each problem.

1. One Saturday, 98 passengers rented paddleboats. A boat can hold 4 people. How many boat rides were needed for everyone to get a ride? **25 boat rides**

2. There were 53 people waiting to play in the White Sands Beach volleyball competition. They divided into teams of 5. How many complete teams could they form? **10 teams**

276

TEACHING OPTIONS

RETEACHING TIPS Have students verbalize how each part of the division fits the situation. In Problem 1, the dividend is how many riders in all, the divisor is how many per boat, the quotient is how many full boats, the remainder is how many riders were left. Assign Reteaching Supplement 101.

ENRICHMENT Have students formulate 2 division story problems. Ask them to structure 1 problem to ask about only the remainder. The solution to the other problem should require interpreting the remainder to make an extra group. (Answers will vary. Check students' problems and solutions.)

MIXED PRACTICE

Solve the problems. Use any problem solving strategy.

Some Strategies
Act It Out
Use Objects
Choose an Operation
Draw a Picture
Make an Organized List
Guess and Check
Make a Table
Look for a Pattern
Use Logical Reasoning
Work Backward

1. There were 95 campers on the beach. They formed teams of 7 for volleyball. How many campers were left over? **4 campers**
2. The Beach Store had a window display of 18 flying disks in different colors. Each disk was worth $6.99. How much were all the disks in the window worth? **$125.82**

The Outdoor Store		
Complete Windsurfing Boards	Regular	On Sale
Fantastic 304	$769	$599
Fantastic Seaviper	$1,499	$999
Fantastic Seaboa	$1,524	$1,199
Fantastic Cat	$1,894	$1,549

Use the table above to solve problems 3–6.

3. How much money would you save by buying a Fantastic Seaboa on sale? **$325**
4. A used windsurfing board is $399. Which new board on sale is almost 4 times as much as a used board? **Fantastic Seaboa**
5. Yang wants to start a windsurfing rental service at the beach. How much money would he save by buying 4 Fantastic 304s on sale rather than at the regular price? **$680**
6. How much would Yang pay for 3 Fantastic Seavipers on sale? **$2,997**
7. Mario spent $36 on a skin board. Then he bought 3 T-shirts at $11 each. He had $3 left. How much money did he start with? **$72**
8. Jon and his friends are renting wetsuits for surfing. They rent for $9 each. How many suits could they rent with $39? **4 suits**

More Practice, page 521, set A

3. Practice and Apply

Basic	1-8
Average	1-8
Extended	1-8

Sample Solutions: See p. T79.

MIXED PRACTICE

▶ **Decide which problems require division.** (Problems 1 and 8)
▶ **Interpret the question in Problem 1 to decide how to use the remainder.** (It asks how many campers were left over, so the remainder will tell you how many.)
▶ **Justify the operation to use to solve Problem 2.** (Multiply to put together same-size groups.)
▶ **Explain how Problems 4 to 6 are similar.** (All can be solved using multiplication as 1 step or as the only step.)
▶ **Analyze Problem 7 to choose a strategy to solve it.** (Work Backward)

Close and Assess

SAY WHAT YOU THINK Have students solve the problem, then explain how they interpreted the remainder to answer the question. *A ferry can take 8 cars at a time across a river to an island. How many trips are needed to take 58 cars?* (8; 7 fully loaded trips; 2 cars in the last trip)

Quick Quiz

A log cabin at Camp Muckabout has room for 6 campers. How many cabins must there be for 175 campers? (30)

LESSON OPTIONS 10-7

3-Digit Quotients

OBJECTIVE 10-7 To find 3-digit quotients by dividing 3-digit dividends by 1-digit divisors

PREBOOK ACTIVITIES

QUICK REVIEW

Find the quotients and remainders.

1. 3)75 (25)	**2.** 2)87 (43 R1)	**3.** 4)86 (21 R2)
4. 5)68 (13 R3)	**5.** 6)77 (12 R5)	**6.** 7)95 (13 R4)
7. 9)99 (11)	**8.** 1)53 (53)	**9.** 8)97 (12 R1)

PRIOR KNOWLEDGE

Have students review the steps in the division process. (Estimate, divide, multiply, subtract, compare, bring down.) Have students find the quotient of 333 ÷ 3 mentally and tell how they did so. (111; Methods may vary.) Have them suggest a situation to suit the numbers. (Answers will vary. Sample: 3 planes took 333 people to Ohio. If each plane had the same number of people, how many people were on each plane?) Tell students that in this lesson they will use the steps of the division process to find other 3-digit quotients.

COMMUNICATION

Writing in Math In their Math Journals, have students write a paragraph to explain the purpose of each step in the division process. They should include a sentence for each key action: estimate, divide, multiply, subtract, compare, and bring down. (Answers may vary. Check students' writing.)

EXPLORE AND CONNECT

Materials: multiplication cards (see below), colored markers
Grouping Suggestion: cooperative learning pairs
Partners work to find the link between the multiplication and the division of larger numbers. Make enough multiplication cards so each pair has 2. Cards have equations that can relate to 3-digit division, such as (213 × 4) = □ or (123 × 3) + 2 = □. Pairs solve the equation, then decide how to arrange the same numbers to form a division problem. Have students use colored markers to highlight the factors, product, and extra addend as they appear in the division. (Factors become the divisor and quotient, product is the dividend, extra addend is the remainder.) Students should find a way to work through the division problem they have created, using the division process steps they already know. Conclude by having students summarize the relationships they found and tell how they applied the division steps to the new division problem.

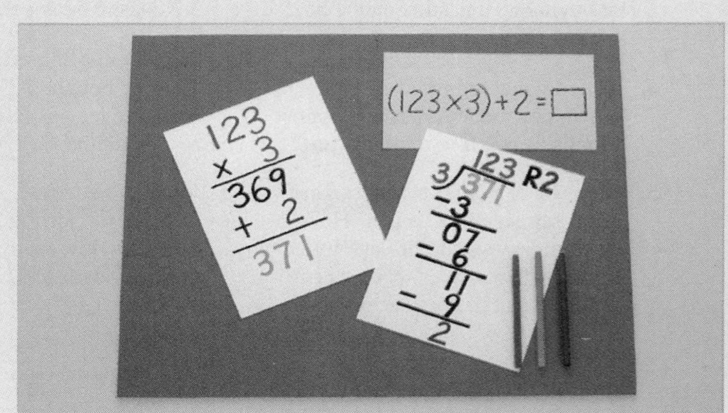

CONNECTIONS Use these anytime.

Problem of the Day

Number Sense Create 2 different division problems in this format: __ __ __ ÷ __ = __ __ __. In one problem, use all *even* numbers. In the other, use all *odd* numbers. (Answers may vary. Samples: 484 ÷ 2 = 242; 957 ÷ 3 = 319.)

Subject Integration

Physical Education In the 1988 Olympics, an athlete from Bulgaria did a triple jump that totaled 57 ft 9 in. What was the distance for each part of the jump if each part was the same length? (231 in. = 19 ft 3 in.)

Life Skills

Nutrition A recipe for cream of potato soup serves 4 and has a total of 656 calories. If 4 people share the soup equally, how many calories does each person consume? (164)

Classwork and Homework Supplements

Practice

Skills Maintenance 10-7

Name ______

3-Digit Quotients

Find the quotients and remainders.

1. 5)712 = **142 R2** (5, 21, 20, 12, 10, 2)
2. 2)586 = **293** (4, 18, 18, 06, 6, 0)
3. 7)822 = **117 R3** (7, 12, 7, 52, 49, 3)
4. 4)915 = **228 R3** (8, 11, 8, 35, 32, 3)
5. 3)858 = **286** (6, 25, 24, 18, 18, 0)
6. 6)733 = **122 R1** (6, 13, 12, 13, 12, 1)
7. 5)846 = **169 R1** (5, 34, 30, 46, 45, 1)
8. 9)999 = **111** (9, 09, 9, 09, 9, 0)
9. 8)945 = **118 R1** (8, 14, 8, 65, 64, 1)
10. 4)635 = **158 R3** (4, 23, 20, 35, 32, 3)
11. 2)793 = **396 R1** (6, 19, 18, 13, 12, 1)
12. 7)786 = **112 R2** (7, 08, 7, 16, 14, 2)
13. 3)764 = **254 R2** (6, 16, 15, 14, 12, 2)
14. 2)671 = **335 R1** (6, 07, 6, 11, 10, 1)
15. 6)911 = **151 R5** (6, 31, 30, 11, 6, 5)
16. 8)889 = **111 R1** (8, 08, 8, 09, 8, 1)

Building Thinking Skills

Family Math 10-7

Name ______

Winning with Small Quotients

Dear Family,
We have been learning how to find 3-digit quotients. You may wish to play the game below with your child to help reinforce our work in math class.

You will need scratch paper and a pencil. Using a separate piece of paper, make and cut out the 20 number pieces as shown below. Put them in a box or cup.

Rules

1. Each player uses a division game board.
2. Take turns choosing a number piece and placing it in one of the 4 spaces.
3. After each player has filled all 4 spaces, find the answers (quotients and remainders).
4. The player with the smallest 3-digit quotient wins.
5. Check the quotients by using multiplication.

Game Board Player A

Game Board Player B

Number Pieces

0	1	2	3	4	5	6	7	8	9
0	1	2	3	4	5	6	7	8	9

Reteaching

Skills Review 10-7

Name ______

3-Digit Quotients

Dividing Hundreds	Dividing Tens	Dividing Ones
► Divide ► Multiply ► Subtract ► Compare	► Bring down the tens ► Divide ► Multiply ► Subtract ► Compare	► Bring down the ones ► Divide ► Multiply ► Subtract ► Compare
4)735 = 1; −4; 3	4)735 = 18; −4↓; 33; −32; 1	4)735 = 183 R3; −4; 33; −32↓; 15; −12; 3

Divide.

1. 3)853 = **284 R1** (−6, 25, −24, 13, −12, 1) Divide ones.
2. 2)975 = **487 R1** (−8, 17, −16, 15, −14, 1)
3. 4)563 = **140 R3** (−4, 16, −16, 03, −00, 3)
4. 3)986 = **328 R2** (−9, 08, −6, 26, −24, 2)
5. 2)735 = **367 R1** (−6, 13, −12, 15, −14, 1)

Challenges

Math Reasoning 10-7

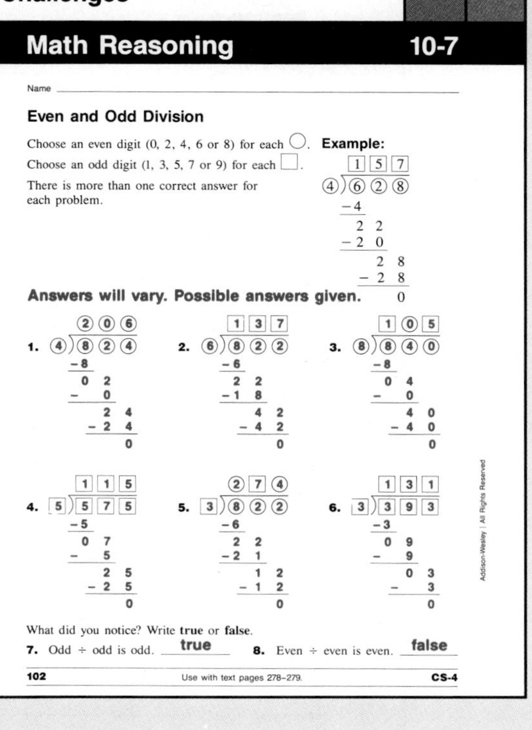

Name ______

Even and Odd Division

Choose an even digit (0, 2, 4, 6 or 8) for each ○.
Choose an odd digit (1, 3, 5, 7 or 9) for each □.
There is more than one correct answer for each problem.

Example: ④)⑥②⑧ = [1][5][7] (−4, 22, −20, 28, −28, 0)

Answers will vary. Possible answers given.

1. ④)⑧②④ = ②⓪⑥ (−8, 02, −0, 24, −24, 0)
2. ⑥)⑧②② = [1][3][7] (−6, 22, −18, 42, −42, 0)
3. ⑧)⑧④⓪ = [1]⓪[5] (−8, 04, −0, 40, −40, 0)
4. [5])[5][7][5] = [1][1][5] (−5, 07, −5, 25, −25, 0)
5. [3])⑧②② = ②[7]④ (−6, 22, −21, 12, −12, 0)
6. [3])[3][9][3] = [1][3][1] (−3, 09, −9, 03, −3, 0)

What did you notice? Write **true** or **false**.

7. Odd ÷ odd is odd. **true**
8. Even ÷ even is even. **false**

Options for Individual Needs

10-7

Basic

Exercises 1-12, 13-30
Data Bank, p. 475
Calculator Bank, p. 487
More Practice, p. 508, set A

Supplements
Reteaching 102 or
Practice 102

Average

Exercises 1-35
Data Bank, p. 475
Calculator Bank, p. 487
More Practice, p. 508, set A

Supplements
Practice 102
Challenges 102 or
Thinking Skills 102

Extended

Exercises 7-30
Data Bank, p. 475
Calculator Bank, p. 487

Supplements
Challenges 102
Thinking Skills 102

Other Resources:
Problem-Solving Experiences in Mathematics, Grade 4, Problem 82
Math In Stride, Grade 4, p. 116
Mathematics, A Way of Thinking, Lesson 10-12
Using the Math Explorer Calculator: A Sourcebook for Teachers, Chapter 14

LESSON PLAN 10-7

OBJECTIVE 10-7
To find 3-digit quotients by dividing 3-digit dividends by 1-digit divisors

Materials: colored pens

1. MOTIVATE AND TEACH

LEARN ABOUT IT

EXPLORE ► **Compare and contrast this problem with dividing a 2-digit dividend.** (Possible answer: The steps are the same; you repeat them more often to complete the division.)
► **Explain how you show a remainder of zero.** (You do not need to write a remainder of zero at all.)

TALK ABOUT IT ► **Why do you begin dividing hundreds first?** (Possible answer: because it is the greatest place)
► **Explain which factors you multiply.** (The divisor and each digit you write in the quotient.)
► **Why do you compare before you bring down?** (to be sure another group cannot be made)
► **What happens to the extra hundred?** (Trade it for 10 tens; divide it with the 4 tens you bring down.)
► **Explain why you "bring down" twice.** (You bring down once for tens and once for ones.)
Student Edition answers: **1.** divisor and difference **2.** Estimates may vary. **3.** 944 mi is 236 Portuguese leagues.

2. CHECK UNDERSTANDING

TRY IT OUT

ERROR ALERT Losing track of the steps in the division process. Accidentally bringing down the same number twice.

3-Digit Quotients

LEARN ABOUT IT

EXPLORE Think About the Process
Columbus measured the distance he sailed in a unit called the Portuguese league, which is equal to 4 miles. A two-weeks' journey was about 944 miles. How many Portuguese leagues is 944 miles?

Since you want to separate a total number of miles into equal parts, you divide.

Divide the hundreds.		Divide the tens.		Divide the ones.	
■ Estimate ■ Divide ■ Multiply ■ Subtract ■ Compare	2 4)944 8 1	■ Bring down ■ Divide ■ Multiply ■ Subtract ■ Compare	23 4)944 8 14 12 2	■ Bring down ■ Divide ■ Multiply ■ Subtract ■ Compare	236 4)944 8 14 12 24 24 0

TALK ABOUT IT See teaching notes.

1. In each step, what did you compare?
2. How would you have estimated the answer?
3. Give the answer in a complete sentence.

TRY IT OUT

1. 3)646 **215 R1**
2. 5)933 **186 R3**
3. 2)974 **487**
4. 4)870 **217 R2**
5. 8)962 **120 R2**
6. 7)892 **124 R4**
7. 4)575 **143 R3**
8. 5)907 **181 R2**
9. 2)685 **342 R1**

TEACHING OPTIONS

RETEACHING TIPS Students write each dividend digit in a different color. After students divide hundreds, they bring down the tens, drawing an arrow of that color. They continue to divide. The new color signals them to bring down the next digit to divide ones. Assign Reteaching Supplement 102.

ENRICHMENT Students divide 785 by 3 and check their answer. Then they write 2 different story problems that suit the numbers. They create situations that will require interpreting the remainders in different ways. (261 R2; Story problems will vary; check students' writing.)

PRACTICE

Find the quotients and remainders.

1. 6)692 115 R2	**2.** 3)424 141 R1	**3.** 8)985 123 R1	**4.** 7)801 114 R3
5. 2)783 391 R1	**6.** 9)999 111	**7.** 4)569 142 R1	**8.** 5)790 158
9. 815 ÷ 3 271 R2	**10.** 779 ÷ 7 111 R2	**11.** 838 ÷ 5 167 R3	**12.** 925 ÷ 2 462 R1

13. What is 642 divided by 5? 128 R2 **14.** What is 814 divided by 3? 271 R1

Estimate these quotients.

15. 3)950 300 **16.** 8)843 100 **17.** 4)834 200 **18.** 2)550 300

APPLY

MATH REASONING

19. In these problems, what pattern do the remainders make? They increase by 1.

145 ÷ 9, 146 ÷ 9, 147 ÷ 9, 148 ÷ 9, 149 ÷ 9, 150 ÷ 9, 151 ÷ 9, 152 ÷ 9

PROBLEM SOLVING

20. A league in English-speaking countries is equal to 3 miles. How many more English leagues than Portuguese leagues is a distance of 600 miles? Remember a Portuguese league is equal to 4 miles. 50 leagues

21. Social Studies Data Bank The length of a carrack was about 3 times the width. About how much wider was a man-of-war carrack than a merchant carrack? See page 475. about 7 ft

DATA BANK

MIXED REVIEW

Tell if the object is closer to an ounce or a pound.

22. a feather oz **23.** a brick lb **24.** 2 pencils oz **25.** a watermelon lb

Find the quotients.

26. 18 ÷ 2 9	**27.** 18 ÷ 3 6	**28.** 27 ÷ 3 9	**29.** 16 ÷ 2 8	**30.** 12 ÷ 3 4
31. 8 ÷ 2 4	**32.** 20 ÷ 2 10	**33.** 24 ÷ 3 8	**34.** 21 ÷ 3 7	**35.** 14 ÷ 2 7

More Practice, page 508, set A

3. PRACTICE AND APPLY

Basic	1-12, 13-30
Average	1-35
Extended	7-30

PRACTICE

Look at Exercise 6. Try dividing this exercise mentally, then explain the method you followed. (111; Explanations will vary.)

10-7

APPLY

MATH REASONING ► Analyze the change in each division problem. (Dividends increase by 1.)

PROBLEM SOLVING ► Explain why 600 mi is equal to more English than Portuguese leagues. (Dividing by a smaller division gives a greater quotient.)
► Before using the Data Bank, explain what you know about a man-of-war carrack. (It was wider than a merchant carrack; its length was about 3 times its width.)

MIXED REVIEW ► Explain how to do Exercises 22-25 without a scale. (Use common sense to make reasonable estimates.)

CLOSE AND ASSESS

SHOW WHAT YOU KNOW

Write the adjacent division problem on the chalkboard. Ask students to find the errors in the division, to explain what is wrong, and to correct it. (159 R3; 2 overestimates, 9 used twice)

```
  164 R1
5)798
  5
  29
  30
   19
   20
    1
```

QUICK QUIZ

Find the quotients and remainders.

1. 989 ÷ 8 (123 R5)
2. 3)790 (263 R1)
3. Divide 808 by 5. (161 R3)
4. Divide 808 by 6. (134 R4)

LESSON OPTIONS 10-8

Finding Averages/Midchapter Review/Quiz

OBJECTIVE 10-8 To find the average of 3 or more numbers

PREBOOK ACTIVITIES

QUICK REVIEW

Find the sums.

1. 88 + 77 + 66 (231)
2. 182 + 168 + 173 (523)
3. 79 + 92 + 81 + 96 (348)
4. 146 + 324 + 209 + 277 (956)
5. 646 + 575 + 484 (1,705)

PRIOR KNOWLEDGE

Ask students if they think they get the exact same amount of sleep every night. (probably not) Then ask if they know how much sleep they usually get most nights. (Answers will vary.) Tell students that this estimated amount can be called their average amount of sleep.

COMMUNICATION

Discussing Math Have students share expressions they have heard that include the term **average**. (Possible answers: *batting average; average speed; average temperature; average gas mileage*) Have a volunteer suggest what an average amount of sleep means. (Possible answer: the amount of sleep you usually get, even though it may vary on different nights) Explain that an average is a special kind of estimate based on usual expectations or measurements.

EXPLORE AND CONNECT

Materials: counters, TA 3 (Number Cards 1-9)
Grouping Suggestion: cooperative learning pairs
Students explore **average** (mean) by manipulating assorted-sized groups. The first student picks 4 number cards and spreads them. The second student forms 4 piles of counters, 1 for each value shown. Partners discuss how to rearrange the groups to form 4 *average*-size groups. Students show how this can be done and record the size of the *average* group size. When equal groups cannot be formed, students record the nearest whole number for *average* group size. Pairs trade tasks and repeat. Have students share their strategies for making same-size groups from various-size piles. (Possible answers: Combine all counters, then divide by 4; rearrange the groups counter by counter until all are equal.) Challenge them to generalize how to find an *average* of greater numbers. (Find the sum; divide by the number of addends.)

CONNECTIONS Use these anytime.

Problem of the Day

A Messy Dresser Sal has 3 shirts in his bottom drawer, 7 shirts jammed into the next drawer, 5 rumpled shirts in the third drawer, and 1 shirt in the top drawer of his dresser. He decides to rearrange the drawers so that each has the same number of shirts. What should he do? (Put 4 shirts per drawer.)

Life Skills

Gas Mileage Jacey's car gets an average of 24 mpg of gas. If the gas tank holds 18 gal, determine whether she can make a 400-mi trip on a full tank of gas. (yes; 18 × 24 = 432, so a tank of gas should be enough.)

Number Sense

Mental Math When Lorna reads fiction, she can average 45 pages per hour. At that rate, how many hours will it take her to finish a 450-page novel? (10 hours)

Classwork and Homework Supplements

Practice

Skills Maintenance 10-8

Name ______

Finding Averages

Find the average of these numbers.

1. 9, 7, 2 Average 6

9
7
+ 2
18

3)18 = 6; 18; 0

2. 1, 3, 5, 2, 4 Average 3

1
3
5
2
+ 4
15

5)15 = 3; 15; 0

3. 39, 44, 84, 33 Average 50

39
44
84
+ 33
200

4)200 = 50; 20; 00; 0; 0

4. 369, 461, 168, 654 Average 413

369
461
168
+ 654
1,652

4)1652 = 413; 16; 05; 4; 12; 12; 0

5. 68, 44, 38, 50, 45, 25 Average 45

68
44
38
50
45
+ 25
270

6)270 = 45; 24; 30; 0

6. 293, 279, 111, 109 Average 198

293
279
111
+ 109
792

4)792 = 198; 4; 39; 36; 32; 0

PS-4 Use with text page 280. 103

Building Thinking Skills

Calculators 10-8

Name ______

It Is All on Record

Joy made a table to record her test scores this semester. Use a calculator to help you answer the questions about her scores.

Spelling	85	78	99	100	82	72
Math	100	100	98	69	89	96
Reading	78	91	85	81	79	
Science	100	79	88	88		

1. If Joy's average score in spelling was 84.2 last semester, did she do better this semester? yes

2. Joy's teacher does not count every score in math. Find the scores counted to give Joy an average score of 96.6. 100, 100, 98, 89, 96

3. Joy forgot to record one score in reading. What score will give her an average score of 84? 90

4. Write the subject in which Joy had the highest average score. math

5. The teacher found a mistake on Joy's record. She received an 86 on her last science test. By how much will this increase or decrease Joy's science average score? decrease by 0.5

TS-4 Use with text page 280. 103

Reteaching

Skills Review 10-8

Name ______

Finding Averages

Tina exercised 14 minutes on Monday, 18 minutes on Tuesday, and 31 minutes on Wednesday. Suppose Tina exercised the same total number of minutes by exercising an equal number of minutes every day. How many minutes would Tina exercise each day?

The number of minutes Tina would be exercising each day is called the **average**.

To find the average:

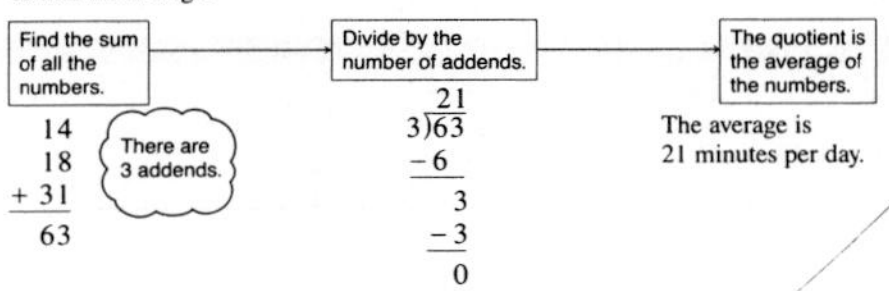

Find the sum of all the numbers.
Divide by the number of addends.
The quotient is the average of the numbers.
14
18
+ 31
63
There are 3 addends.
3)63 = 21
− 6
3
− 3
0

The average is 21 minutes per day.

Find the average of these numbers. Show your work.

1. 47, 23, 38 36 — 47 + 23 + 38 = 108; 3)108 = 36; 9; 18; 18; 0

2. 62, 41, 77 60 — 62 + 41 + 77 = 180; 3)180 = 60; 18; 0; 0; 0

3. 36, 10, 45, 33 31 — 36 + 10 + 45 + 33 = 124; 4)124 = 31; 12; 4; 4; 0

4. 21, 36, 14, 13 21 — 21 + 36 + 14 + 13 = 84; 4)84 = 21; 8; 4; 4; 0

5. 121, 116, 132 123 — 121 + 116 + 132 = 369; 3)369 = 123; 3; 6; 6; 9; 9; 0

6. 214, 376, 148 246 — 214 + 376 + 148 = 738; 3)738 = 246; 6; 13; 12; 18; 18; 0

RS-4 Use with text page 280. 103

Challenges

Cooperative Activities 10-8

Name ______

Averages Game

Play this game with 3 to 6 players. Each person will need paper and a pencil, and the group will need at least one calculator. (Cover the answers at the bottom of the page with a piece of paper.)

Rules

1. Each player copies on a separate piece of paper a different question from the chart.
2. Each player asks 5 classmates to estimate the answer to his or her question and writes down the answers.
3. When everyone is finished, each player uses a calculator to find the average answer.
4. Each player reads out loud his or her question and the average answer.

Uncover the answers at the bottom of the page and compare them with the average answers.

Example: Just use the whole number on the calculator display. 16.525 Answer is 16.

1. About how many times does the average human heart beat in 1 minute?	**2.** About how many bones are there in the human body?
3. At about what age are your muscles the strongest?	**4.** About how many sweat glands are there in the back of your hand?
5. How many bones are there in the human spine?	**6.** About how many nerve endings are there in the back of your hand?

Answers: 1. 72 2. 206 3. 25 4. 300 5. 26 6. 9,000

CS-4 Use with text page 280. 103

Options for Individual Needs

10-8

Basic

Exercises 1-5; 1-17, 23-39
Calculator Bank, p. 485
More Practice, p. 521, set B

Supplements
Reteaching 103 or
Practice 103

Average

Exercises 1-6; 1-39
Calculator Bank, p. 485
More Practice, p. 521, set B

Supplements
Practice 103
Challenges 103 or
Thinking Skills 103

Extended

Exercises 1-5; 5-15, 28-39
Calculator Bank, p. 485

Supplements
Challenges 103
Thinking Skills 103

Other Resources:
Problem-Solving Experiences in Mathematics, Grade 4, Problem 86
Math In Stride, Grade 4, pp. 109, 110
Mathematics, A Way of Thinking, Lesson 10-6
Using the Math Explorer Calculator: A Sourcebook for Teachers, Chapter 14

LESSON PLAN 10-8

OBJECTIVE 10-8
To find the average of 3 or more numbers

Materials: calculators

Grouping Suggestion: pairs

1. MOTIVATE AND TEACH

LEARN ABOUT IT

EXPLORE ► **Explain why Jay read different numbers of pages each day.** (Possible answer: He did not always have the same amount of time for reading.)

TALK ABOUT IT ► **Explain how to determine the length of the book Jay read.** (Find the sum of all the pages he read, day by day.)
► **Explain how to use that data to estimate how many pages you would read per day in equal sections.** (Divide the total by 6.)
► **Look at the example for finding the average of 243, 259, and 275 to justify the steps involved.** (First add the 3 numbers to find the total; then divide by 3 to make 3 equal groups, since you want an average of 3 amounts.)
► **Summarize how to find an average of any group of numbers.** (Find the sum, then divide by the number of addends.)
Student Edition answers: **1.** 564 **2.** more; less

2. CHECK UNDERSTANDING

TRY IT OUT

ERROR ALERT Giving the addend sum as the average. Choosing the wrong divisor.

Finding Averages

LEARN ABOUT IT

EXPLORE Think About the Process
Jay read a mystery book in 6 days. He read 55 pages the first day, 62 the second, 109 the third, 78 the fourth, 123 the fifth, and 137 the last. Suppose you read the same book in 6 days by reading an equal number of pages every day. How many pages would you read per day?

TALK ABOUT IT See teaching notes.

1. How many pages are in the book?
2. Do you think you would read more or less than 50 pages a day? more or less than 100 a day?

The number of pages you would be reading each day is called the average. To find the average of a set of numbers, add the numbers and divide by the number of addends.

Find the average of 243, 259, and 275.

Add: 243 + 259 + 275 = 777

Divide: $777 \div 3 = 259$

The average is 259.

You can use this key code to find the average on the calculator.

[ON/AC] 243 [+] 259 [+] 275 [=] |||| [÷] 3 [=] ||||

PRACTICE

Find the average of these numbers.

1. 36, 32, 43 **37**
2. 17, 24, 19, 16 **19**
3. 65, 59, 38, 47, 56 **53**
4. 138, 175, 143 **152**
5. 164, 196, 132, 128 **155**
6. 321, 339, 306 **322**

More Practice, page 521, set B

TEACHING OPTIONS

RETEACHING TIPS Have students who make the first error write this simple guide to the steps they follow to find averages: (1) Find the sum of all addends. (2) Divide by the number of addends and write the quotient as the average. Assign Reteaching Supplement 103.

ENRICHMENT Have students solve: *The figures tell how many books the new library loaned since June. June: 4,307; July: 3,333; August: 4,910; September: 5,723; October: 6,007; November: 5,191; December: 2,764. What is the average monthly circulation?* (4,605 books per month)

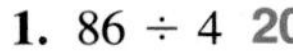

MIDCHAPTER REVIEW/QUIZ

Use rounding and substitution to estimate each quotient. Circle your estimate if it is over the actual quotient.

1. 86 ÷ 4 **20** **2.** 267 ÷ 3 **(90)** **3.** 95 ÷ 2 **50** **4.** 188 ÷ 6 **30**

5. 335 ÷ 8 **40** **6.** 344 ÷ 5 **(70)** **7.** 410 ÷ 7 **60** **8.** 801 ÷ 9 **(90)**

Check these division problems. Correct those with errors.

9. 8)56 = 7 R2; 54; 2 **wrong; 7**

10. 7)40 = 6 R2; 42; 2 **wrong; 5 R5**

11. 4)17 = 31 R1; 12; 5; 4; 1 **wrong; 4 R1**

12. 6)56 = 9 R0; 56; 0 **wrong; 9 R2**

Suppose you use blocks to show each problem. Write T if you would trade tens for ones. Write R if there will be ones remaining.

13. 4)89 **R** **14.** 5)64 **T, R** **15.** 3)27 **T** **16.** 2)80 **17.** 7)90 **T, R**

Find the quotients and remainders.

18. 6)8 **1 R2** **19.** 2)11 **5 R1** **20.** 5)72 **14 R2** **21.** 3)87 **29** **22.** 3)456 **152**

23. 8)96 **12** **24.** 4)79 **19 R3** **25.** 7)783 **111 R6** **26.** 6)784 **130 R4** **27.** 6)62 **10 R2**

28. 7)87 **12 R3** **29.** 2)42 **21** **30.** 4)27 **6 R3** **31.** 8)907 **113 R3** **32.** 5)85 **17**

33. 5)903 **180 R3** **34.** 3)29 **9 R2** **35.** 9)999 **111** **36.** 4)60 **15** **37.** 7)40 **5 R5**

38. Use multiplication to check. Explain what is wrong with this problem. **The remainder is larger than the divisor. Correct answer: 9 R1**

6)55 = 8 R7; 48; 7

PROBLEM SOLVING

39. When Gretchen and some friends shared $17, they had $2 left over. How many friends might there have been? Can you find another way? **4 friends or 2 friends**

281

3. PRACTICE AND APPLY

Basic	1-5; 1-17, 23-39
Average	1-6; 1-39
Extended	1-5; 5-15, 28-39

PRACTICE

How can multiplication help you to solve division problems? (Possible answers: Use it to check division; think of the divisor as 1 factor and the quotient as the missing factor.)

10-8

ITEM ANALYSIS The following table correlates the Midchapter Review/Quiz items with the lesson objectives.

Items	Objectives
1-8	10-3
9-12, 18, 19, 30, 34, 37, 38	10-1
13-17	10-4
20, 21, 23, 24, 27-29, 32, 36	10-5
22, 25, 26, 31, 33, 35	10-7
39	10-6

CLOSE AND ASSESS

SAY WHAT YOU THINK Have students work in pairs. The first student shows the second how to find an average by explaining the steps to follow using these numbers: 171, 167, 184, 178. Then the second student explains how to find the average of 214, 223, 209, and 230. (Check explanations; 175, 219)

QUICK QUIZ

Find the average of these numbers.

1. 114, 123, 106, 117 (115)
2. 90, 81, 77, 88, 79, 89 (84)
3. 270, 311, 304, 294, 286 (293)

LESSON OPTIONS 10-9

Deciding Where to Start

OBJECTIVE 10-9 To develop skill in deciding where to start in division

PREBOOK ACTIVITIES

QUICK REVIEW

Estimate the quotients. (Answers may vary.)

1. 814 ÷ 2 (400)	**2.** 654 ÷ 3 (220)	**3.** 437 ÷ 4 (110)
4. 292 ÷ 4 (70)	**5.** 142 ÷ 7 (20)	**6.** 306 ÷ 6 (50)
7. 558 ÷ 8 (70)	**8.** 716 ÷ 9 (80)	**9.** 131 ÷ 3 (40)

PRIOR KNOWLEDGE

Ask students to imagine dividing $150 among 3 people. Have a student write an equation for this situation. ($150 ÷ 3 = ?) Have students find the quotient mentally. ($50) Then ask them to explain how many hundreds each person got. (none; There were not enough hundreds for everyone.) Tell students that they will be using the division process to divide other 3-digit numbers in which there may not be enough hundreds to divide.

COMMUNICATION

Discussing Math Write the problems $5\overline{)615}$ and $5\overline{)165}$ on the chalkboard. Have students compare the two problems for differences as well as for similarities. Challenge them to predict the size of the quotient in each problem. (Possible answers: Both problems have a divisor of 5; neither has a remainder; $5\overline{)615}$ has a 3-digit quotient, $5\overline{)165}$ has a 2-digit quotient.)

EXPLORE AND CONNECT

Materials: TA 3 (Number Cards), place value blocks
Alternative Materials: TA 6 (Place Value Models)
Grouping Suggestion: small cooperative learning groups
A student thinks of a multiple of 10 as a target quotient. Another picks 4 number cards. The group members work together to form a division problem (3-digit dividend, 1-digit divisor) with an estimated quotient that is near the target. A third student uses place value materials to do the division. For example: With digits 2, 4, 5, 7, and a target of 50, $5\overline{)247}$ gives a quotient of 49 R2. If the group cannot create a problem with a quotient near the target, the first student picks another target quotient or new number cards. Repeat until each member has had a turn at each task. Then have students summarize what links they noticed between dividend and divisor. (If a dividend's hundreds place is less than the divisor, the quotient has no hundreds.)

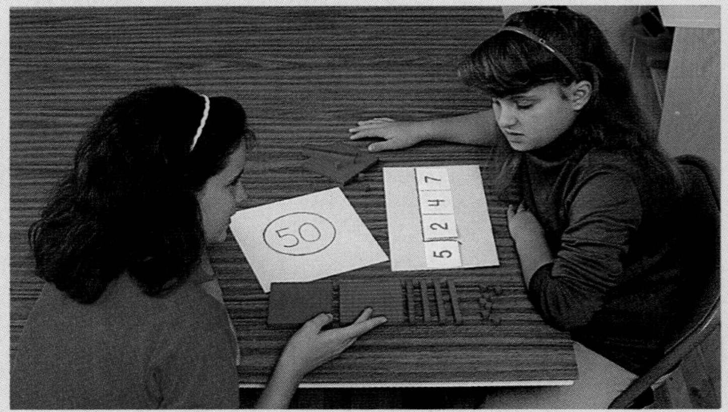

CONNECTIONS Use these anytime.

Problem of the Day

Geometry Each patch on a quilt has a design made of 6 triangles. If the quilt contains 588 triangles, how many patches does it have? (98) As an extra challenge, figure out how many patches form the length and the width of the quilt if it is twice as long as it is wide. (14 patches long by 7 patches wide)

Number Sense

Estimation Use these directions to form 3 division problems in this format: ____)____ ____ ____. Create one problem with a quotient between 20 and 30, another with a quotient between 60 and 70, and a third with any 3-digit odd quotient. (Answers will vary; samples: $6\overline{)156}$; $9\overline{)585}$; $5\overline{)555}$.)

Subject Integration

Reading A book of 8 short stories has 216 pages. Each story has the same number of pages. If Dan read 2 stories last evening, how many pages did he read? Explain your answer. (54 pages; 216 ÷ 8 = 27; 27 × 2 = 54.)

Classwork and Homework Supplements

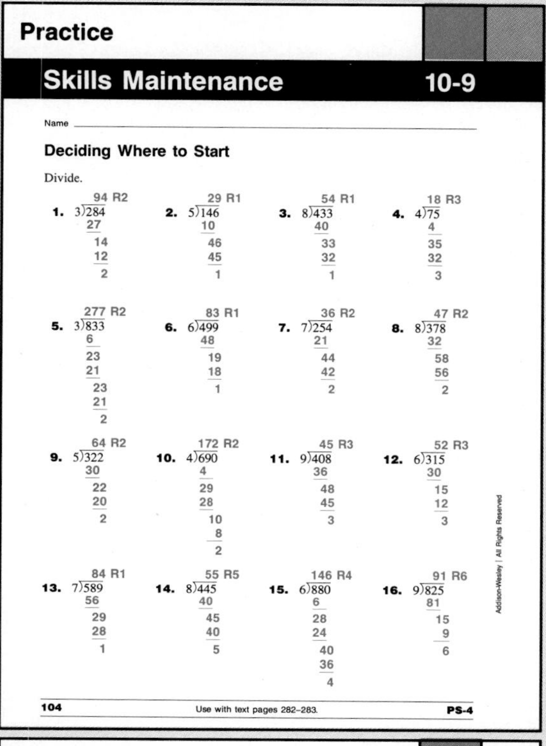

Practice

Skills Maintenance 10-9

Name

Deciding Where to Start

Divide.

1. 3)284 — 94 R2; 27, 14, 12, 2
2. 5)146 — 29 R1; 10, 46, 45, 1
3. 8)433 — 54 R1; 40, 33, 32, 1
4. 4)75 — 18 R3; 4, 35, 32, 3
5. 3)833 — 277 R2; 6, 23, 21, 23, 21, 2
6. 6)499 — 83 R1; 48, 19, 18, 1
7. 7)254 — 36 R2; 21, 44, 42, 2
8. 8)378 — 47 R2; 32, 58, 56, 2
9. 5)322 — 64 R2; 30, 22, 20, 2
10. 4)690 — 172 R2; 4, 29, 28, 10, 8, 2
11. 9)408 — 45 R3; 36, 48, 45, 3
12. 6)315 — 52 R3; 30, 15, 12, 3
13. 7)589 — 84 R1; 56, 29, 28, 1
14. 8)445 — 55 R5; 40, 45, 40, 5
15. 6)880 — 146 R4; 6, 28, 24, 40, 36, 4
16. 9)825 — 91 R6; 81, 15, 9, 6

104 Use with text pages 282-283. PS-4

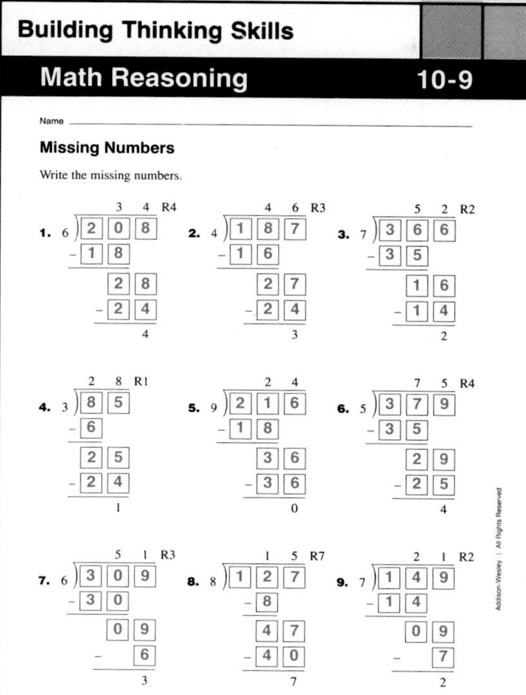

Building Thinking Skills

Math Reasoning 10-9

Name

Missing Numbers

Write the missing numbers.

1. 6)208 = 34 R4; − 18, 28, − 24, 4
2. 4)187 = 46 R3; − 16, 27, − 24, 3
3. 7)366 = 52 R2; − 35, 16, − 14, 2
4. 3)85 = 28 R1; − 6, 25, − 24, 1
5. 9)216 = 24; − 18, 36, − 36, 0
6. 5)379 = 75 R4; − 35, 29, − 25, 4
7. 6)309 = 51 R3; − 30, 09, − 6, 3
8. 8)127 = 15 R7; − 8, 47, − 40, 7
9. 7)149 = 21 R2; − 14, 09, − 7, 2

104 Use with text pages 282-283. TS-4

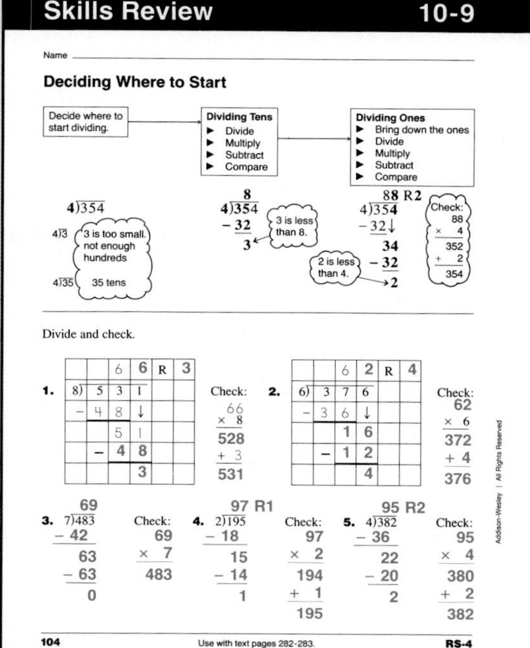

Reteaching

Skills Review 10-9

Name

Deciding Where to Start

Decide where to start dividing. → Dividing Tens: Divide, Multiply, Subtract, Compare → Dividing Ones: Bring down the ones, Divide, Multiply, Subtract, Compare

4)354 — 4)3 (3 is too small, not enough hundreds); 4)35 (35 tens)

4)354 = 8, − 32, 3 (3 is less than 8.)

4)354 = 88 R2, − 32↓, 34, − 32, 2 (2 is less than 4.) Check: 88 × 4 = 352, + 2 = 354

Divide and check.

1. 8)531 = 66 R3; − 48, 51, − 48, 3. Check: 66 × 8 = 528, + 3 = 531
2. 6)376 = 62 R4; − 36, 16, − 12, 4. Check: 62 × 6 = 372, + 4 = 376
3. 7)483 = 69; − 42, 63, − 63, 0. Check: 69 × 7 = 483
4. 2)195 = 97 R1; − 18, 15, − 14, 1. Check: 97 × 2 = 194, + 1 = 195
5. 4)382 = 95 R2; − 36, 22, − 20, 2. Check: 95 × 4 = 380, + 2 = 382

104 Use with text pages 282-283. RS-4

Challenges

Cooperative Activities 10-9

Name

Are You in Range?

Work in a small group. Make sure everyone understands all solutions.

Create a true equation by filling in the box with a 1-digit number. Formulate and write answers to fill in the blanks to the right of each problem.

1. 193 ÷ ☐ = a number between 20 and 30 (30–20)
   Highest number: 9
   Lowest number: 7
   All possible numbers: 7, 8, 9
2. 375 ÷ ☐ = a number between 60 and 90 (90–60)
   Highest number: 6
   Lowest number: 5
   All possible numbers: 5, 6
3. 413 ÷ ☐ = a number between 35 and 40 (40–35)
   Highest number: none
   Lowest number: none
   All possible numbers: none
4. 275 ÷ ☐ = a number between 20 and 100 (100–20)
   Highest number: 9
   Lowest number: 3
   All possible numbers: 3, 4, 5, 6, 7, 8, 9

104 Use with text pages 282-283. CS-4

Options for Individual Needs

10-9

Basic

Exercises 1-28
More Practice, p. 508, set B

Supplements
Reteaching 104 or
Practice 104

Average

Exercises 1-31
More Practice, p. 508, set B

Supplements
Practice 104
Challenges 104 or
Thinking Skills 104

Extended

Exercises 5-31

Supplements
Challenges 104
Thinking Skills 104

Other Resources:
Problem-Solving Experiences in Mathematics, Grade 4, Problem 69
Math In Stride, Grade 4, p. 114
Mathematics, A Way of Thinking, Lesson 10-5
Using the Math Explorer Calculator: A Sourcebook for Teachers, Chapter 14

LESSON PLAN 10-9

OBJECTIVE 10-9
To develop skill in deciding where to start division

Grouping Suggestion: pairs

1. MOTIVATE AND TEACH

LEARN ABOUT IT

EXPLORE ► **Estimate the speed for 1 h. Explain.** (about 100 mi/h; round 485 to 500, 500 ÷ 5 = 100)
► **Explain if your estimate is over or under the exact quotient.** (over, because the dividend was increased)
► **Explain what that tells you about the exact quotient.** (Since 100 is an overestimate, the exact quotient must be a 2-digit number.)

TALK ABOUT IT ► **Explain how you can divide the hundreds when 4 is less than 5.** (Imagine trading 4 hundreds for 40 tens; group with the 8 tens, then divide the 48 tens.)
► **Relate the size of a divisor to the first digit of a dividend and link both with quotient size.** (If a divisor is equal to or is less than the first digit of a dividend, the quotient and dividend have an equal number of digits; if not, the quotient has one digit less than the dividend.)
Student Edition answers: **1.** too few hundreds to make 5 groups **2.** 48 tens **3.** Estimates may vary. **4.** Sample answer: The car went 97 mi/h.

2. CHECK UNDERSTANDING

TRY IT OUT

ERROR ALERT Misjudging where to start dividing. Writing quotient digits in the wrong places.

Deciding Where to Start

LEARN ABOUT IT

EXPLORE Think About the Process
A test driver in a compact car took 5 hours to drive 485 miles. At what speed was the car traveling?

Decide where to start. Divide the hundreds if possible.	Divide the tens.	Divide the ones.
5)485 $5 > 4$ Not enough hundreds. Divide the tens.	9 5)485 45 3	97 5)485 45 35 35 0

TALK ABOUT IT See teaching notes.

1. Why can't you divide the hundreds in step 1?
2. How many tens do you divide in step 2?
3. How would you have estimated the answer?
4. Give the answer in a complete sentence.

Other Examples

A	B	C
33 R3 4)135 12 15 12 3	71 R1 8)569 56 09 8 1	68 3)204 18 24 24 0

TRY IT OUT

1. 5)637 **127 R2**
2. 7)568 **81 R1**
3. 4)239 **59 R3**
4. 3)342 **114**

282

TEACHING OPTIONS

RETEACHING TIPS Help students predict how many digits a quotient will have. If they can divide hundreds, make a box over each dividend place. If not, they circle hundreds and tens together to indicate a grouping, then make 2 boxes for the quotient. Assign Reteaching Supplement 104.

ENRICHMENT Family Math With a family member, students find the total age of everyone in their immediate family. Then they find their family's average age. Students tell whose age is *over* the average; whose age is *under* the average; and whose age, if anyone's, is exactly the average.

PRACTICE

Write whether you start by dividing tens or by dividing hundreds.

1. 6)432 tens
2. 9)926 hundreds
3. 2)634 hundreds
4. 8)309 tens

Divide and check.

5. 644 ÷ 4 161
6. 826 ÷ 7 118
7. 245 ÷ 5 49
8. 773 ÷ 9 85 R8
9. Divide 381 by 6. 63 R3
10. Divide 925 by 8. 115 R5
11. Divide 507 by 3. 169
12. Divide 659 by 7. 94 R1

Estimate these quotients.

13. 2)683 300
14. 7)146 20
15. 9)873 90
16. 6)452 70

APPLY

MATH REASONING

17. If a, b, and c represent numbers, how would you check the answer to this problem? a × c = b

$$a\overline{)b}\ \text{with quotient } c$$

PROBLEM SOLVING

18. **Missing Data** Tell what data is missing in this problem. In a famous auto race, a car finished in about 3 hours. The purse for the race was over $1,500,000. How fast did the car go? How many miles long was the race?

19. Last year the speed record in an auto race was 147 miles per hour. This year the record was 162 miles per hour. How much faster is this year's record? 15 miles per hour

▶ MENTAL MATH

Use mental math and break apart the dividends to find the quotients.

20. 728 ÷ 7 104
21. 812 ÷ 4 203
22. 428 ÷ 4 107
23. 614 ÷ 2 307
24. 636 ÷ 6 106
25. 921 ÷ 3 307
26. 545 ÷ 5 109
27. 832 ÷ 8 104
28. 2)450 225
29. 3)618 309
30. 9)963 107
31. 3)627 209

More Practice, page 508, set B

3. PRACTICE AND APPLY

Basic	1-28
Average	1-31
Extended	5-31

10-9

PRACTICE

Look at Exercises 1-12. Identify exercises that have 3-digit quotients and ones that have 2-digit quotients. (Exercises 2, 3, 5, 6, 10, 11; 1, 4, 7-9, 12)

MATH REASONING ▶ Explain how the method of checking would change if you substituted numbers for letters. (It would not change; you would still multiply the divisor by the quotient to give the dividend.)

PROBLEM SOLVING ▶ Analyze Problem 18 to identify an extra fact. (The purse was over $1,500,000.)
▶ Explain the operation you would use to solve Problem 19. (Subtract to compare speeds.)

MENTAL MATH ▶ Explain a helpful way to break apart the dividend in Exercise 20. (700 + 28, so each divides easily by 7; 100 + 4 = 104.)

CLOSE AND ASSESS

WRITE WHAT YOU THINK

Have each student write a rule to use to judge where to start dividing. Then have students exchange papers with a partner while you write a division problem on the chalkboard. Partners follow each other's rules to divide the problem. Discuss the results. (Check each student's rule and division.)

QUICK QUIZ

Divide and check.

1. 654 ÷ 9 (72 R6)
2. 5)273 (54 R3)
3. Divide 400 by 6. (66 R4)
4. Divide 400 by 7. (57 R1)

LESSON OPTIONS 10-10

Zero in the Quotient

OBJECTIVE 10-10 To divide 3-digit numbers when there is a 0 in the quotient

PREBOOK ACTIVITIES

QUICK REVIEW

Divide mentally.

1. 240 ÷ 3 (80)	**2.** 400 ÷ 8 (50)	**3.** 180 ÷ 9 (20)
4. 900 ÷ 9 (100)	**5.** 800 ÷ 2 (400)	**6.** 600 ÷ 3 (200)
7. 350 ÷ 7 (50)	**8.** 150 ÷ 1 (150)	**9.** 500 ÷ 2 (250)

PRIOR KNOWLEDGE

Have students explain the meaning of 0 in numbers such as 30 and 203. (Possible answer: 30 means 3 tens but no ones; 203 means 2 hundreds, no tens, and 3 ones.) Have them review 0 in division. (Possible answers: Never divide by 0; 0 divided by any number is 0; a 0 remainder means the entire dividend was equally divided.) Have students give a situation in which a quotient is 0. (Sample answer: 4 books divided equally among 7 students; you cannot make same-size groups, so the quotient is 0.) Tell students that they will be dividing numbers in which the quotient contains one or more zeros.

COMMUNICATION

Discussing Math Ask students to evaluate the importance of the estimate step at the beginning of the division process. (Possible answers: to make a reasonable guess about quotient size or range; to decide where to start dividing; to predict how many places a quotient has) Have students analyze how to use the estimate step to check division. (Possible answer: to quickly determine if a quotient is reasonable)

EXPLORE AND CONNECT

Materials: division cards, place value blocks, calculators
Alternative Materials: TA 6 (Place Value Models)
Grouping Suggestion: cooperative learning groups of 3
Groups explore division in which quotients have a zero. Make enough division cards with problems such as the following for each group to have 3 to do: 3)212, 4)123, 5)104, 6)123, 3)922, 4)822, 5)531, 3)326, 4)811. (70 R2; 30 R3; 20 R4; 20 R3; 307 R1; 205 R2; 106 R1; 108 R2; 202 R3) Groups solve each problem 3 ways: estimate, use place value materials, and use a calculator. Members trade tasks for each new problem, comparing results to verify accuracy. Have students explain how quotients reflect possible trades. (A middle 0 shows a trade in the tens place.) Ask them to draw conclusions about quotients with 0. (A 0 means a place does not have enough to make same-size groups.) Have students tell how to check quotients mentally. (Answers will vary.)

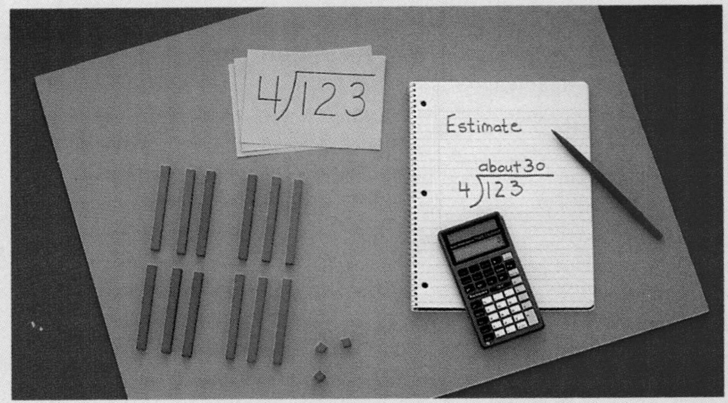

CONNECTIONS Use these anytime.

Problem of the Day

Number Sense Create a division problem that fits all the requirements:
—The dividend uses 3 odd digits.
—The divisor and remainder are odd.
—The quotient is a 2-digit number that is an odd multiple of 10. (Answers will vary. Samples: 355 ÷ 7 = 50 R5; 153 ÷ 5 = 30 R3; 351 ÷ 5 = 70 R1.)

Math Connection

Money 4 friends collected $4.32 for recycling cans and bottles. Of that amount, 12¢ was in pennies and the rest was in nickels. The friends shared the money equally. Exactly what coins did each person get? (21 nickels and 3 pennies)

Life Skills

Flower Arranging A decoration committee was given 23 dozen tulips for a party. They must decide whether to put 8 or 9 tulips in each vase. Which arrangement will result in fewer unused flowers? Explain. (8; 12 × 23 = 276; 276 ÷ 8 = 34 and 4 extra; 276 ÷ 9 = 30 and 6 extra.)

Classwork and Homework Supplements

Practice

Skills Maintenance 10-10

Name ______

Zero in the Quotient

Divide.

1. 5)152 — 30 R2 (15, 02, 0, 2)
2. 2)61 — 30 R1 (6, 01, 0, 1)
3. 7)724 — 103 R3 (7, 02, 0, 24, 21, 3)
4. 4)817 — 204 R1 (8, 01, 0, 17, 16, 1)
5. 3)272 — 90 R2 (27, 02, 0, 2)
6. 6)618 — 103 (6, 01, 0, 18, 18, 0)
7. 9)635 — 70 R5 (63, 05, 0, 5)
8. 8)816 — 102 (8, 01, 0, 16, 16, 0)
9. 2)411 — 205 R1 (4, 01, 0, 11, 10, 1)
10. 7)564 — 80 R4 (56, 04, 0, 4)
11. 2)812 — 406 (8, 01, 0, 12, 12, 0)
12. 3)922 — 307 R1 (9, 02, 0, 22, 21, 1)
13. 615 ÷ 3 — 3)615 = 205 (6, 01, 0, 15, 15, 0)
14. 53 ÷ 5 — 5)53 = 10 R3 (5, 03, 0, 3)

Building Thinking Skills

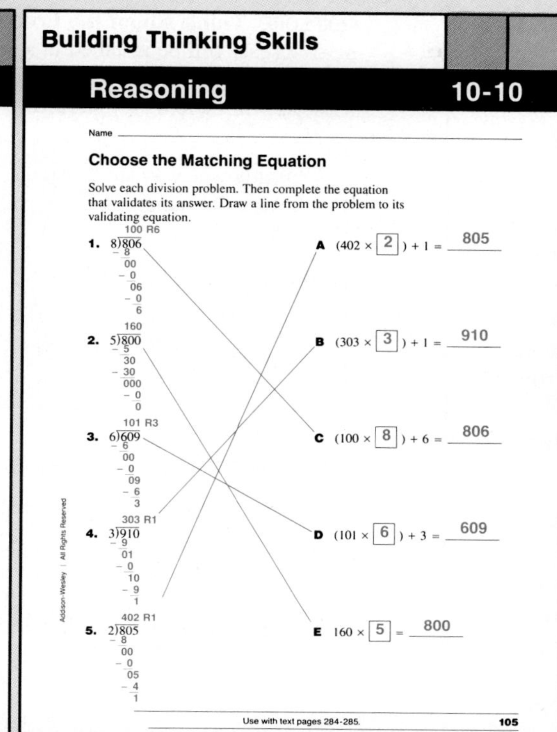

Reasoning 10-10

Name ______

Choose the Matching Equation

Solve each division problem. Then complete the equation that validates its answer. Draw a line from the problem to its validating equation.

1. 8)806 — 100 R6
2. 5)800 — 160
3. 6)609 — 101 R3
4. 3)910 — 303 R1
5. 2)805 — 402 R1

A (402 × [2]) + 1 = 805

B (303 × [3]) + 1 = 910

C (100 × [8]) + 6 = 806

D (101 × [6]) + 3 = 609

E 160 × [5] = 800

Reteaching

Skills Review 10-10

Name ______

Zero in the Quotient

Decide where to start. → **Dividing Hundreds**: Divide, Multiply, Subtract, Compare → **Dividing Tens**: Bring down the tens, Divide, Multiply, Subtract, Compare → **Dividing Ones**: Bring down the ones, Divide, Multiply, Subtract, Compare

3)614 — 3 < 6 Divide the hundreds.

3)614 = 2 (−6, 0)

3)1 = 0 (−0, 1)

3)614 = 20 (−6, 01, −0, 1)

3)614 = 204 R2 (−6, 01, −0, 14, −12, 2)

Divide and check.

1. 5)403 — 80 R3 (−40, 03, −00, 3) Divide ones.
2. 4)413 — 103 R1 (−4, 01, −00, 13, −12, 1) Divide tens.
3. 6)784 — 130 R4 (−6, 18, −18, 04, −00, 4)
4. 3)320 — 106 R2 (−3, 02, −0, 20, −18, 2)
5. 9)450 — 50 (−45, 00, −00, 0)
6. 4)483 — 120 R3 (−4, 08, −08, 03, −00, 3)

Challenges

Number Sense 10-10

Name ______

Bigger Is Better Game

Play the game with 2 to 4 players. You will need a spinner with the digits 0 to 9 on it.

Rules

1. Take turns spinning the spinner.
2. Each player should write the number that is spun in one of the blank boxes in his or her division problem. A number cannot be changed once it has been written down.
3. The goal is to create the division problem with the largest quotient.
4. When all 4 boxes have been filled, compute the answer to discover the winning player.

Game 1

☐) ☐ ☐ ☐

Describe the strategy you used for determining the numbers to fill in the boxes.

Put the highest numbers in the dividend; put the highest number in the hundreds place; put the lowest number in the divisor.

Game 2

☐) ☐ ☐ ☐

Game 3

☐) ☐ ☐ ☐

Options for Individual Needs

10-10

Basic

Exercises 5-14, 17-20
Calculator Bank, p. 488
More Practice, p. 508, set C

Supplements
Reteaching 105 or
Practice 105

Average

Exercises 1-20
Calculator Bank, p. 488
More Practice, p. 508, set C

Supplements
Practice 105
Challenges 105 or
Thinking Skills 105

Extended

Exercises 7-14, 17-20
Calculator Bank, p. 488

Supplements
Challenges 105
Thinking Skills 105

Other Resources:

Problem-Solving Experiences in Mathematics, Grade 4, Problem 84

Math In Stride, Grade 4, p. 112

Mathematics, A Way of Thinking, Lesson 10-13

Using the Math Explorer Calculator: A Sourcebook for Teachers, Chapter 14

LESSON PLAN 10-10

OBJECTIVE 10-10

To divide 3-digit numbers when there is a 0 in the quotient

Materials: place value blocks

Alternative Materials: TA 6 (Place Value Models)

1. MOTIVATE AND TEACH

LEARN ABOUT IT

EXPLORE ► **Explain what suggests making same-size groups.** (9 seats in each row)
► **How can you predict that there is a remainder?** (The question implies that there will be extra seats for another row.)
► **Predict how many digits the quotient will have. Explain.** (2; There are not enough hundreds to divide.)

TALK ABOUT IT ► **Analyze the division of the tens.** (All the tens divided evenly; there is none to regroup.)
► **Explain why the quotient has a zero in the ones place.** (not enough ones to divide)
► **Compare the remainder with the ones that were not divided.** (They are equal.)
► **Explain how to verify the division by checking it mentally.** ($60 \times 9 + 8 = 548$)

Student Edition answers: **1.** Answers may vary. **2.** Sample sentence: The jet can have 60 rows of 9 seats and another row with 8 seats.

2. CHECK UNDERSTANDING

TRY IT OUT

ERROR ALERT Forgetting to write the 0 in 2-digit quotients. Omitting a middle 0 in 3-digit quotients.

Zero in the Quotient

LEARN ABOUT IT

EXPLORE **Think About the Process**

548 seats will be installed in a new Boeing 747 jet. How many rows of 9 can be put in? How many extra seats will there be for another row?

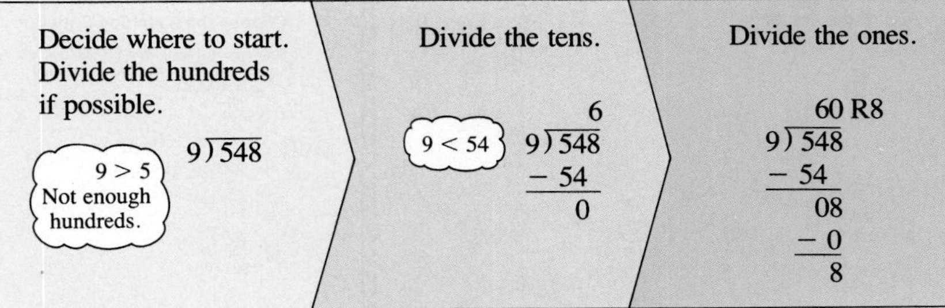

Decide where to start.
Divide the hundreds if possible.
9 > 5
Not enough hundreds.
9)548
Divide the tens.
9 < 54
6
9)548
− 54
0
Divide the ones.
60 R8
9)548
− 54
08
− 0
8

TALK ABOUT IT See teaching notes.

1. How would you have estimated the answer?
2. Give the answer in a complete sentence.

Other Examples

A 6)65 = 10 R5
− 6, 05, − 0, 5

B 2)813 = 406 R1
− 8, 01, − 0, 13, − 12, 1

C 3)602 = 200 R2
− 6, 00, − 0, 02, − 0, 2

TRY IT OUT

1. 6)65 **10 R5**
2. 6)638 **106 R2**
3. 4)201 **50 R1**
4. 5)904 **180 R4**
5. 2)615 **307 R1**
6. 8)165 **20 R5**
7. 2)813 **406 R1**
8. 3)602 **200 R2**

284

TEACHING OPTIONS

RETEACHING TIPS Help students predict how many digits a quotient has *before* they divide, then indicate a space for each digit above the division line. Have them check that their completed quotients have as many digits as predicted, including any possible 0s. Assign Reteaching Supplement 105.

ENRICHMENT Have students use a calculator to solve this riddle: *I am a 3-digit number. The sum of my digits is 4. If you divide me by 7, I have a remainder of 0. But if you divide me by 2, 3, 4, 5, or 6, my remainder is always 1. What number am I?* (301)

PRACTICE

Divide.

1. 75 ÷ 7 10 R5
2. 640 ÷ 4 160
3. 907 ÷ 9 100 R7
4. 252 ÷ 5 50 R2
5. 815 ÷ 2 407 R1
6. 803 ÷ 8 100 R3
7. 120 ÷ 6 20
8. 928 ÷ 3 309 R1
9. $7\overline{)751}$ 107 R2
10. $5\overline{)508}$ 101 R3
11. $3\overline{)625}$ 208 R1
12. $8\overline{)483}$ 60 R3

Use mental math to find these quotients.

13. $3\overline{)363}$ 121
14. $6\overline{)642}$ 107
15. $4\overline{)164}$ 41
16. $9\overline{)909}$ 101

APPLY

MATH REASONING Use the first equation to find the missing numbers in the second.

17. 45 × 7 + 3 = 318   318 ÷ 7 = |||| R|||| 45 R3

PROBLEM SOLVING

18. A Boeing 727 holds 189 people. How many rows of 8 can there be? How many seats are left over? 23 rows of 8, 5 seats left over

19. The O'Neals paid $744 for three plane tickets to Disneyland. How much was each ticket if all fares were the same? $248

▶ **ALGEBRA**

20. The output of function machine A is the input for function machine B. Study the example. Then figure out the two function rules and complete the table. rule: divide by 8, add 2

Input A	Output B	
24	5	
72	11	
8	3	
32						6
40						7
48						8

More Practice, page 508, set C

3. PRACTICE AND APPLY

Basic	5-14, 17-20
Average	1-20
Extended	7-14, 17-20

PRACTICE

Look at Exercise 5. Tell whether it will have a remainder and explain why or why not. (Yes; any odd number divided by 2 has a remainder of 1.)

10-10

APPLY

MATH REASONING ▶ **How do you know which operation to do first in Exercise 17?** (The order of operations says to multiply, then to add.)
▶ **Explain how these two equations are related.** (Possible answers: 318 and 7 appear in both; the first equation is like a division check.)

PROBLEM SOLVING ▶ **Explain how you know that Problem 18 has a remainder.** (Leftover seats suggests a remainder.)

ALGEBRA ▶ **Predict one operation used by one function machine and explain your reasoning.** (Possible answer: Division, because the output numbers are smaller than the input ones.)

CLOSE AND ASSESS

SHOW WHAT YOU KNOW Ask students to use place value blocks to demonstrate these two divisions: $5\overline{)153}$ and $3\overline{)311}$. Have them record the process they follow to complete each division. (30 R3; 103 R2; Check students' models and recordings.)

QUICK QUIZ

Divide.
1. 912 ÷ 3 (304)
2. 504 ÷ 5 (100 R4)
3. 285 ÷ 7 (40 R5)
4. 483 ÷ 6 (80 R3)

LESSON OPTIONS 10-11

Problem Solving: Choosing a Calculation Method

OBJECTIVE 10-11 To choose an appropriate method of calculation

PREBOOK ACTIVITIES

QUICK REVIEW

Solve using any suitable mental math method.

1. 199 + 345 (544) **2.** 720 ÷ 8 (90)
3. 31 × 5 (155) **4.** 402 + 398 + 397 + 403 (1,600)
5. 999 ÷ 3 (333) **6.** 500 − 98 (402)

PRIOR KNOWLEDGE

Have students recall the different calculation methods they have used to perform any of the 4 operations. (paper and pencil; mental math; calculator) Ask students to explain which method they prefer and why. (Answers will vary.)

COMMUNICATION

Discussing and Writing Math List these 3 calculation methods on the chalkboard: mental math, paper and pencil, calculator. Have the class discuss the differences among the methods in terms of ease, speed, accuracy, and any other factors they might consider. Then have students write in their Math Journals a sentence that summarizes why or when they might select each method. Volunteers may share their sentences with the class.

EXPLORE AND CONNECT

COOPERATIVE ACTIVITY

Grouping Suggestion: small groups

If a double-decker bus has room for 72 passengers, how many can ride in 5 double-decker buses?

TEACHING ACTIONS

Have students work together to discuss the situation and determine a sensible calculation method.

▶ **Summarize the problem in your own words.** (You must find how many people can ride in 5 double-decker buses if each bus can hold 72 passengers.)

▶ **Analyze the situation to determine the operation you need to solve the problem.** (Multiply to put together same-size groups.)

▶ **Decide on a sensible calculation method.** [Answers may vary. You could multiply mentally by breaking apart 72 as 70 + 2 and use the grouping property to find (70 × 5) ÷ (2 × 5); you could use paper and pencil or a calculator.]

▶ **Explain how to estimate the answer.** (70 × 5 = 350)

▶ **Evaluate your answer to see if it makes sense.** (72 × 5 = 360, which is close to the estimate.)

▶ **Evaluate your calculation method.** (Answers will vary.)

CONNECTIONS Use these anytime.

Problem of the Day

Math Average Elliot got the following scores on math quizzes during March: 91, 100, 86, 76, 89, 87, 94. What is his math-quiz average for that month? Which is the most sensible calculation method to use to find the answer? Why? (89; calculator because there are many numbers and more than one operation to do)

Life Skills

Checking Account At the start of the day, Mr. Gray has $429.18 in his checking account at Tenth National Bank. After he writes a check for $76 to pay for a car repair and a check for $15.72 to the telephone company, how much does he have left in his checking account? ($337.46)

Number Sense

Mental Math When Mimi practices her juggling, she counts how many times she catches the red ball in her right hand until she drops a ball. At her last juggling practice, she counted 49, 88, and 51 times. Use mental math to find the total number of times she caught the red ball during that practice. (188)

Classwork and Homework Supplements

Practice

Problem Solving 10-11

Name ______________________

Choosing a Calculation Method

Write which calculation method you choose. Then solve. Methods will vary.

• Mental Math • Paper and Pencil • Calculator

1. 22 × 8 = 176
2. 93 − 50 = 43
3. 476 ÷ 7 = 68
4. $6.54 × 11 = $71.94
5. 845 + 90 = 935
6. 427 × 86 = 36,722
7. 27 + 68 + 56 + 37 = 188

Solve. Choose the most useful calculation method.

8. A long-haired dog called a Maltese is 5 inches high. An American foxhound is 25 inches high. How many Maltese would it take to match the height of a foxhound? 5 Maltese
9. A boxer weighs 75 pounds, a collie weighs 50 pounds, a whippet weighs 20 pounds, and a dachsund weighs 15 pounds. Which 3 dogs' weights equal that of a 140-pound Irish wolfhound? boxer, collie, dachshund
10. A Great Dane may weigh 150 pounds. That is 10 times the weight of a Welsh corgi. How much does a Welsh corgi weigh? 15 pounds
11. Kenny was hiding under a bed. He saw 12 legs enter the room. If the family dogs had come in, how many dogs were there? 3 dogs

106 Use with text pages 286–287. PS-4

Building Thinking Skills

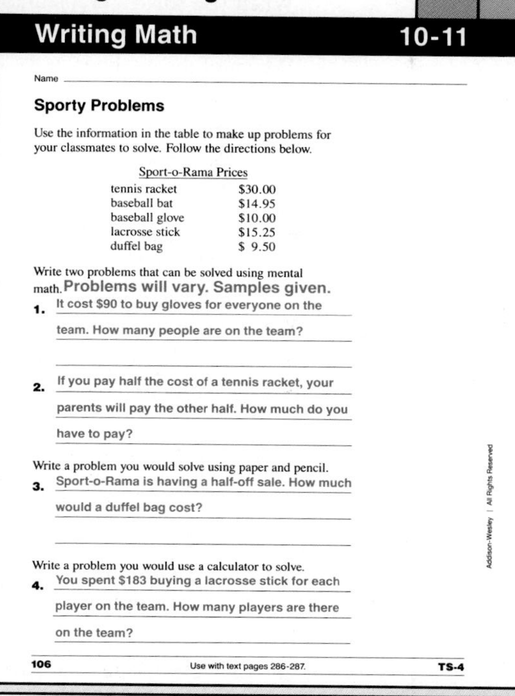
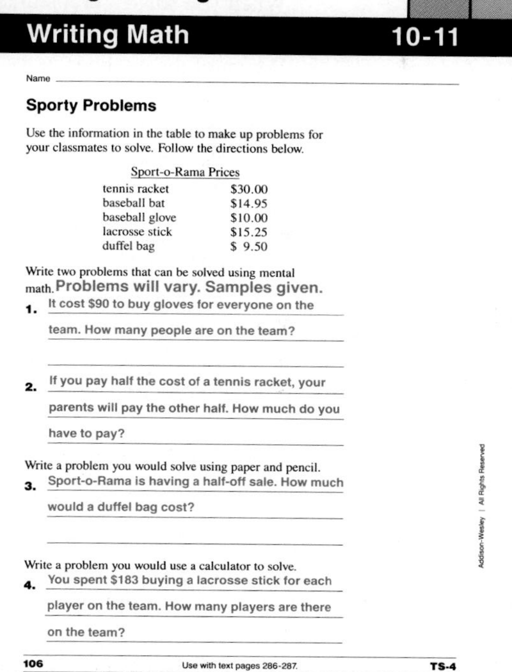

Writing Math 10-11

Name ______________________

Sporty Problems

Use the information in the table to make up problems for your classmates to solve. Follow the directions below.

Sport-o-Rama Prices	
tennis racket	$30.00
baseball bat	$14.95
baseball glove	$10.00
lacrosse stick	$15.25
duffel bag	$ 9.50

Write two problems that can be solved using mental math. Problems will vary. Samples given.

1. It cost $90 to buy gloves for everyone on the team. How many people are on the team?
2. If you pay half the cost of a tennis racket, your parents will pay the other half. How much do you have to pay?

Write a problem you would solve using paper and pencil.

3. Sport-o-Rama is having a half-off sale. How much would a duffel bag cost?

Write a problem you would use a calculator to solve.

4. You spent $183 buying a lacrosse stick for each player on the team. How many players are there on the team?

106 Use with text pages 286–287. TS-4

Reteaching

Problem Solving 10-11

Name ______________________

Choosing a Calculation Method

To help you solve problems you can choose from 3 calculation methods.

Mental Math	Paper and Pencil	Calculator
Use with easy computations.	Use with few-step computations.	Use with many-step computations.

Tell which calculation method you choose and why. Then solve. Methods will vary.

1. 36 + 14 = 50 (easy computation) Use mental math
2. 381 ÷ 3 = 127 (few steps) Use paper and pencil
3. 76 × 24 = 1,824 (many steps) Use calculator
4. 7 × 23 = 161 paper and pencil; few steps
5. 427 × 641 = 273,707 calculator; many steps
6. $73 − $24.76 = $48.24 paper and pencil; few steps
7. 25 + 76 = 101 mental math; easy computation
8. 128 − 48 = 80 mental math; easy computation
9. 756 ÷ 21 = 36 calculator; many steps

Solve. Choose the most useful calculation method. Methods will vary.

10. It took Sidney 54 minutes one day to deliver papers and 47 minutes the second day. How much longer did it take him the first day? 7 minutes
11. Juanita has 75 papers to deliver each day. How many papers does she deliver in 31 days? 2,325

106 Use with text pages 286-287. RS-4

Challenges

Writing Math 10-11

Name ______________________

Change the Numbers

Change the data in each problem so that the problem can be solved using a different calculation method. Then solve the problem using the method. The first one has been started for you. Answers will vary. Samples given.

1. Change from pencil and paper to mental math.

Original	Changed
Pam delivers 56 papers a day. How many does she deliver in 28 days?	Pam delivers 60 papers a day. How many does she deliver in 30 days? Answer: 1,800

2. Change from calculator to pencil and paper.

Original	Changed
Sari baby-sits for $5.75 per hour. How much does she make in 72 hours?	Sari baby-sits for $5 per hour. How much does she make in 72 hours? Answer: $360

3. Change from calculator to mental math.

Original	Changed
Lee delivers 1,127 newspapers in 19 days. He delivers the same number of papers every day. How many does he deliver per day?	Lee delivers 1,000 newspapers in 20 days. He delivers the same number of papers every day. How many does he deliver per day? Answer: 50

CS-4 Use with text pages 286-287. 106

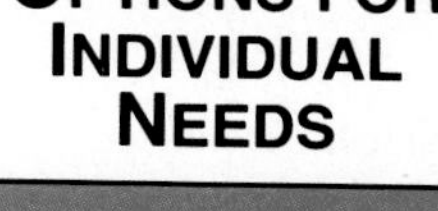

Options for Individual Needs

10-11

Basic

Exercises 1-9, 13-22
More Practice, p. 521, set C

Supplements
Reteaching 106 or
Practice 106

Average

Exercises 1-22
More Practice, p. 521, set C

Supplements
Practice 106
Challenges 106 or
Thinking Skills 106

Extended

Exercises 4-22

Supplements
Challenges 106
Thinking Skills 106

Other Resources:
Problem-Solving Experiences in Mathematics, Grade 4, Problems 70, 74
Math In Stride, Grade 4, p. 95
Mathematics, A Way of Thinking, Lessons 10-15, 10-16
Using the Math Explorer Calculator: A Sourcebook for Teachers, Chapter 14

LESSON PLAN 10-11

OBJECTIVE 10-11
To choose an appropriate calculation method

Materials: calculators

1. MOTIVATE AND TEACH

LEARN ABOUT IT

► **Explain what Jack wants to know.** (how many 12-ft sailboats would match the length of 2 old ships)
► **Justify division as the correct operation.** (Divide to find how many 12s in 120 and in 216.)

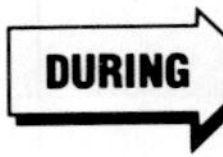

► **Analyze 12 and 120 to identify a relationship between the numbers.** ($12 \times 10 = 120$)
► **Explain why it helps to recognize that relationship.** (to realize that you can use mental math to solve the problem)
► **Evaluate the division in the second situation to justify using a calculator.** (You would have to divide by a 2-digit number, which is a new skill, but a calculator can do it easily.)

► **Summarize how to choose a sensible calculation method.** (Possible answer: Try to use mental math if possible; if you do not see helpful number relationships, then use paper and pencil or calculator.)

2. CHECK UNDERSTANDING

TRY IT OUT

ERROR ALERT Failing to notice number relationships that suggest mental math.

Problem Solving
Choosing a Calculation Method

UNDERSTAND
FIND DATA
PLAN
ESTIMATE
SOLVE
CHECK

LEARN ABOUT IT

When you solve a problem, you must choose the calculation method that is best to use.

Which of the methods in the box would you use for this problem?

Calculation Methods
- Mental Math
- Paper and Pencil
- Calculator

Jack's sailboat was 12 ft long. He wanted to find how many boats like his, put end to end, would reach the length of these two historical ships.

Baltimore Clipper Ship	120 ft long
California Clipper Ship	216 ft long

How many of my boats will match the Baltimore Clipper?

$120 \div 12$ This is easy to do in my head. I'll use mental math.

How many of my boats will match the California Clipper?

$216 \div 12$ I could try paper and pencil, but I've never divided by a 2-digit number, so I'll use a calculator.

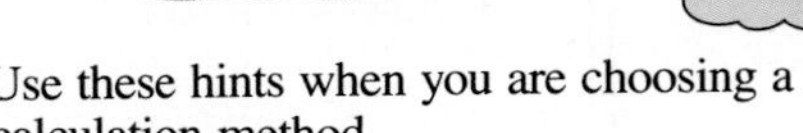

Use these hints when you are choosing a calculation method.

- **First try mental math.** Look for computations you can do easily in your head.
- **Then choose paper and pencil or a calculator.** It is often better to use a calculator when many steps or trades are needed.

TRY IT OUT

Tell which calculation method you choose and why. Then solve. **Methods will vary.**

1. $54 - 40$ **14**
2. $278 + 99$ **377**
3. 56×28 **1,568**
4. $\$69.58 + \$98.79$ **$168.37**
5. $576 \div 9$ **64**

TEACHING OPTIONS

RETEACHING TIPS Encourage students to examine each exercise to attempt to recognize any number relationships and to verbalize what they see. If they do not notice any helpful patterns, they should feel free to choose paper and pencil or a calculator over mental math. Assign Reteaching Supplement 106.

COMPUTER Safari Search, Sunburst Communications, Copyright 1985 All may compare problem-solving methods. In "Catch the Kittens," students search to find 2 kittens in a 5-by-5 grid. In "Round Up the Rhinos," they find 2 rhinos in the same grid. Each game takes 10 to 15 min.

MIXED PRACTICE

Methods will vary.

Tell which calculation method you choose and why. Then solve.

1. 5 × 18 × 2 **180**
2. 200 − 99 **101**
3. 678 × 563 **381,714**
4. 160 ÷ 4 **40**
5. 137 − 67 **70**
6. 49 + 50 + 51 **150**
7. 158 × 5 **790**
8. $72 − $16.67 **$55.33**
9. 192 ÷ 8 **24**
10. 8 × 21 **168**
11. 57 + 5 **62**
12. 666 ÷ 2 **333**

Solve. Choose the most useful calculation method. **Methods will vary.**

13. How many 15 ft sailboats end to end would match a 150 ft Egyptian galley ship? **10 sailboats**
14. A whaling ship was 107 ft long. How much less was this length than the length of a 207 ft English warship? **100 ft**
15. A giant clipper ship was 8 times as long as it was wide. It was 432 feet long. How wide was it? **54 ft**
16. The largest clipper ship had 5 masts with 12 sails on each mast. It had another sail in front and in back. How many sails did it have? **62 sails**
17. A historical ship collection in a museum contained models of 29 sailing ships and 47 engine-driven ships. How many ships were in the collection? **76 ships**
18. A modern ocean liner might travel 38 miles per hour. A clipper ship could travel 22 miles per hour. How much faster is the ocean liner's speed? **16 miles per hour**
19. The average amount of cloth per sail was 968 square feet. Use your answer to problem 16 to find how many square feet of cloth were needed to make all the sails on the ship. **60,016 square feet**

▶ **WRITE YOUR OWN PROBLEM**

Write a problem using each of these methods. **Answers will vary.**

20. mental math
21. paper and pencil
22. a calculator

More Practice, page 521, set C

3. PRACTICE AND APPLY

Basic	1-9, 13-22
Average	1-22
Extended	4-22

Sample Solutions: See p. T79.

MIXED PRACTICE

For which of Exercises 1 to 12 would you want a calculator? (Answers may vary; Exercise 3) *Which of Exercises 1 to 12 seem easy enough to solve using mental math?* (Answers may vary; Exercises 1, 2, 4 to 6, 10 to 12)

▶ **Explain which problems can be solved by division.** (Problems 13 and 15, because you are finding how many equal sets in each)

▶ **Explain which calculation method to use in Problem 17.** (Possible answers: mental math or paper and pencil, because the numbers are small)

WRITE YOUR OWN PROBLEM

▶ **Explain how you will choose numbers to use in Problems 20 to 22.** (Possible answers: easy ones for Problem 20, more difficult ones for Problem 21, and complicated ones for Problem 22)

10-11

CLOSE AND ASSESS

SAY WHAT YOU THINK Have students choose a calculation method for each problem and justify their decision. They do not need to solve the problem. (Answers will vary.)

1. 693 × 482 (calculator)
2. 87 + 11 (mental math)
3. 5)317 (paper and pencil)

QUICK QUIZ

Solve by any calculation method that makes sense.

1. 7 × 34 (238)
2. 14,504 ÷ 37 (392)
3. 884 ÷ 4 (221)

LESSON OPTIONS 10-12

Dividing with Money

OBJECTIVE 10-12 To divide an amount of money less than $10 by a 1-digit divisor

PREBOOK ACTIVITIES

QUICK REVIEW

Write the money amounts.
1. five dollars and seventy-two cents ($5.72)
2. seven dollars and twenty-eight cents ($7.28)
3. three dollars ($3.00) **4.** nine dollars ($9.00)
5. one dollar and sixteen cents ($1.16) **6.** a dime ($0.10)
7. two dollars and five cents ($2.05) **8.** a quarter ($0.25)

PRIOR KNOWLEDGE

Have students suggest real-life situations in which they might divide money amounts. (Possible answers: divide a total bill to find equal costs per item; divide to share money equally among several people) Have students tell how they might divide a money amount, such as $5.25 ÷ 5. (Possible answer: Divide dollars, then divide cents—$1.05.)

COMMUNICATION

Discussing and Writing Math Have 3 volunteers write the money amounts $4.29, $5.00, and $0.75 on the chalkboard. Ask one to explain the correct way to write a money amount. (Write the dollar sign, then the number of dollars, then a decimal point, then the two places for cents, even if there are fewer than 10 cents.) Discuss what a remainder means in real-life money transactions. For example, have students determine how much they would pay for 1 yogurt if the price is 2 for $0.99. (Possible answer: You cannot pay $0.49 plus half a penny, so the store often rounds the price up to the next penny. One yogurt would cost $0.50.)

EXPLORE AND CONNECT

Materials: play money, grocery store ads, calculators
Alternative Materials: TA 9 (Play Money, Coins and Dollars), TA 10 (Play Money, Larger Bills)
Grouping Suggestion: small cooperative learning groups
Students divide money amounts in a shopping simulation. Groups use grocery ads to find prices given in the form "3 for $0.79." The group's goal is to spend as close to $5.00 as possible without going over the amount. Students may buy just 1 of any item that is sold in multiples. Members use play money or mental math to find each unit cost and mental math to check their answers. One member records the chosen purchases and uses a calculator to keep a running total. Last, students discuss how they handled the division of money amounts and any remainders they encountered. (Divide money amounts the same way you divide whole numbers; round remainders up to the next penny.)

CONNECTIONS Use these anytime.

Problem of the Day

Mental Math 24 people are going to a holiday party. Each one needs a silly hat and a noisemaker. If silly hats cost $2.40 a dozen and noisemakers cost $1.20 a dozen, how much will the 2 items cost per person? ($0.30) What is the cost for all these supplies? ($7.20)

Life Skills

School Lunch A school spends $3.40 a week on hot lunches for each fourth grader. What is the daily cost of lunch? ($0.68) If there are 28 fourth graders, is their weekly lunch bill over or under $100? ($95.20—under)

Subject Integration

Social Studies You can compare the value of the money other countries use to the value of the American dollar. If 1 U.S. dollar is worth about 8 Hong Kong dollars and an item costs $9.36 in Hong Kong dollars, how much would it cost in U.S. dollars? ($1.17)

Classwork and Homework Supplements

Practice

Life Skills 10-12

Name ______________________________

Dividing with Money

Divide. Show dollars and cents.

1. 5)$6.15 = $1.23 (5, 11, 10, 15, 15, 0)
2. 2)$7.32 = $3.66 (6, 13, 12, 12, 12, 0)
3. 7)$4.20 = $0.60 (0, 42, 42, 00, 0, 0)
4. 3)$8.16 = $2.72 (6, 21, 21, 06, 6, 0)
5. 4)$3.40 = $0.85 (32, 20, 20, 0)
6. 8)$0.72 = $0.09 (72, 0)
7. 6)$1.80 = $0.30 (18, 00, 0, 0)
8. 9)$9.27 = $1.03 (9, 02, 0, 27, 27, 0)
9. 3)$9.42 = $3.14 (9, 04, 3, 12, 12, 0)
10. 5)$8.40 = $1.68 (5, 34, 30, 40, 40, 0)
11. 2)$1.16 = $0.58 (10, 16, 16, 0)
12. 7)$9.24 = $1.32 (7, 22, 21, 14, 14, 0)
13. $9.00 ÷ 3 — 3)$9.00 = $3.00 (9, 00, 0, 00, 0, 0)
14. $0.05 ÷ 5 — 5)$0.95 = $0.19 (5, 45, 45, 0)

Building Thinking Skills

Life Skills 10-12

Name ______________________________

Better Bargains

Birthday items are sold at Sal's toy store and the ABC Market. Ring the better bargain for each item. Use a calculator if needed.

	Items	Sal's	ABC Market
1.		**6 for $2.15**	4 for $1.59
2.		**30 for $0.79**	10 for $0.29
3.		25 for $0.88	**36 for $1.15**
4.		6 for $2.69	**2 for $0.79**
5.		**8 for $0.65**	6 for $0.55
6.		100 for $1.69	**50 for $0.79**

7. Carlo is having a birthday party. He invited 11 friends. Where should he buy whistles? Why?
   ABC Market; He needs 2 bags; 2 bags at Sal's cost more than 2 bags at ABC Market.

8. Help Carlo shop for his party. Make a list of items he should buy at ABC Market and another list of items he should buy at Sal's. Be sure that he buys every item and spends the least amount of money. Answers will vary.

Items to buy at Sal's ____________ Items to buy at ABC Market ____________

Reteaching

Life Skills 10-12

Name ______________________________

Dividing with Money

You can divide with money in the same way you divide with whole numbers.

9)$7.20 — Think cents. Divide as with whole numbers. Think: 9)720 = 80 — Write $ and . in the quotient. 9)$7.20 = $0.80 — If there are no dollars, write 0.

Divide. Show dollars and cents.

1. 4)$6.40 = $1.60 (4, 24, 24, 00, 00, 0)
2. 8)$8.08 = $1.01 (8, 0, 0, 08, 8, 0)
3. 7)$5.67 = $0.81 (56, 07, 7, 0)
4. 8)$3.68 = $0.46 (32, 48, 48, 0)
5. 6)$7.26 = $1.21 (6, 12, 12, 6, 6, 0)
6. 3)$9.99 = $3.33 (9, 9, 9, 9, 9, 0)
7. 5)$5.25 = $1.05 (5, 02, 0, 25, 25, 0)
8. 2)$7.50 = $3.75 (6, 15, 14, 10, 10, 0)
9. 7)$0.56 = $0.08 (0, 56, 56, 0)

Challenges

Math Reasoning 10-12

Name ______________________________

Division Crossnumber Puzzle

Solve the crossnumber puzzle. Be sure to do the work in parentheses first.

[1] 5					[2] 1	0			[3] 9
[4] 5	[5] 2		[6] $2	.0	8		[7] $3	.5	0
	[8] 1	0	7				2		9
[9] 4			[10] 9	[11] 9		[12] 2	0	[13] 4	
[14] 2	[15] 1			[16] 2	[17] 3	0		0	
	0		[18] $8	0	0			[19] 8	[20] 6
	[21] 3	[22] 1	0		[23] 6	[24] 4			0
		0				[25] 8	0	[26] 8	
	[27] 3	4		[28] $7	.2	0		[29] 1	[30] 2
[31] 5	0		[32] 4	0					7

Across

2. 60 ÷ 6
4. 156 ÷ 3
6. 4)$8.32
7. (2)$8.24) − $0.62
8. 7 × □□□ = 749
10. 9)891
12. 408 ÷ 2
14. (735 ÷ 7) ÷ 5
16. 4)920
18. 2)$□.□□ = $4.00
19. (8)640) + 6
21. 620 ÷ 2
23. □□ × 5 = 320
25. 4)□□□ = 202
27. 272 ÷ 8
28. $□.□□ ÷ 8 = $0.90
29. (4)480) − 108
31. 7 × □□ = 350
32. (364 − 44) ÷ 8

Down

1. 4 × □□ = 220
2. 6)108
3. 9)□□□ = 101
5. 7)147
6. 9)$□□□ = $ 3 1
7. 2)$□□□ = $1 6 0
9. 7)294
11. □□□ ÷ 5 = 184
12. 8)160
13. 816 ÷ 2
15. 9 × □□□ = 927
17. 3)918
18. $240 ÷ 3
20. (2 × 4) × □□ = 480
22. 624 ÷ 6
24. 8)□□□ = 6 0
26. 4)324
27. 270 ÷ (3 × 3)
28. 6)$□□ = $1 1 R4
30. 243 ÷ 9

Options for Individual Needs

10-12

Basic

Exercises 5-22
Calculator Bank, pp. 487, 489
More Practice, p. 508, set D

Supplements
Reteaching 107 or
Practice 107

Average

Exercises 1-22
Calculator Bank, pp. 487, 489
More Practice, p. 508, set D

Supplements
Practice 107
Challenges 107 or
Thinking Skills 107

Extended

Exercises 9-22
Calculator Bank, pp. 487, 489

Supplements
Challenges 107
Thinking Skills 107

Other Resources:

Problem-Solving Experiences in Mathematics, Grade 4, Problem 85
Mathematics, A Way of Thinking, Lessons 10-18, 10-19
Mathematics, Book A, Teacher's Edition, pp. 52, 53
Using the Math Explorer Calculator: A Sourcebook for Teachers, Chapter 14

LESSON PLAN 10-12

OBJECTIVE 10-12

To divide an amount of money less than $10 by a 1-digit factor

Materials: play money, colored pens

Alternative Materials: TA 9 (Play Money, Coins and Dollars)

1. MOTIVATE AND TEACH

LEARN ABOUT IT

EXPLORE ► **Use play money to show how to divide the money total by the number of photos to find the cost of each. Explain what you did.** (Answers may vary. Possible answer: Trade 3 $1 bills for 30 dimes, group with the 9 dimes to make 8 groups of 4. Then trade the 7 remaining dimes for 70 pennies and group with the 2 pennies to make 8 groups of 9—$0.49.)

TALK ABOUT IT ► **Explain the similarities and the differences between dividing money and dividing other numbers.** (Possible answer: You follow all the same division steps. The difference is that quotients must include a dollar sign and a decimal point.)

► **Decide where to place the dollar sign and decimal point.** (in the quotient above where they are in the dividend)

Student Edition answers: **1.** You must separate money into same-size groups. **2.** less

2. CHECK UNDERSTANDING

TRY IT OUT

ERROR ALERT Omitting dollar signs or decimal points in quotients. Forgetting to write a zero in the dollar place when amounts are under one dollar.

Dividing with Money

LEARN ABOUT IT

EXPLORE Think About the Situation

Tina and her best friend made silly photos of themselves in the mall photo booth. They paid $3.92 for 8 photos. How much did each photo cost?

TALK ABOUT IT See teaching notes.

1. How do you know to divide in this problem?
2. Will the photos cost more or less than $0.50 each?

Think cents.	Think dollars and cents.
Divide as with whole numbers.	Show dollars and cents in the quotient.

```
     49                    $0.49
8)$3.92  (392 cents)   8)$3.92
 - 3 2                  - 3 2
    72                     72
  - 72                   - 72
     0                      0
```

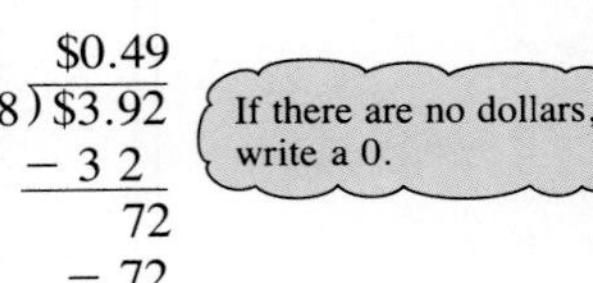
If there are no dollars, write a 0.

Other Examples

```
  $0.91       $1.04       $0.05
5)4.55     8)$8.32     9)$0.45
  0          - 8         -  0
  4 5         0 3          45
- 4 5          0         - 45
   05          32           0
    5        - 32
    0           0
```

If there are no tens, write a 0.

TRY IT OUT

1. 4)$8.20 **$2.05**
2. 7)$9.45 **$1.35**
3. 6)$1.38 **$0.23**
4. 9)$0.72 **$0.08**

TEACHING OPTIONS

RETEACHING TIPS Have students write a dollar sign and decimal point above the division bar *before* they divide. Ask students to identify how many digits money quotients need and draw a colored box for each. (3: 1 for dollars, 2 for cents) Assign Reteaching Supplement 107.

ENRICHMENT Have students write 3 division story problems based on the price list: one with no remainder, one with a remainder, and one that is their choice. (Answers will vary.)

Blank cassettes *SALE* 6 for $9.99
Wooden cassette rack $15.75
Tape grab bag $16.95

PRACTICE

1. 3)$4.38 $1.46
2. 6)$9.72 $1.62
3. 4)$1.36 $0.34
4. 8)$0.96 $0.12
5. 7)$0.63 $0.09
6. 5)$8.80 $1.76
7. 3)$6.09 $2.03
8. 9)$8.46 $0.994
9. 4)$9.00 $2.25
10. 8)$5.52 $0.69
11. 2)$7.06 $3.53
12. 6)$8.28 $1.38

Estimate these quotients.

13. 8)$2.50 $0.30
14. 7)$7.65 $1.00
15. 4)$9.28 $2.00
16. 3)$10.00 $3.00

APPLY

MATH REASONING Use number sense to complete the following.

17. If there are three 35s in 105, how many 35s will be in 210? six
18. If there are four 52s in 208, how many 52s will be in 416? eight

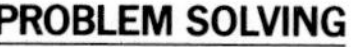

PROBLEM SOLVING

19. Rita had a roll of film developed for $8.64. Her flash was not working so only 9 prints turned out. What did each print cost? $0.96
20. Rita had 5 reprints made of one photo and 3 reprints made of another photo. The total cost was $6.16. How much did the store charge per reprint? $0.77
21. At a photo shop it cost $0.50 per picture to develop a roll of 24 pictures. What was the total cost? $12

▶ **USING CRITICAL THINKING** Careful Reasoning

22. You have savings accounts at 3 banks. You want to make 2 money transfers so that all accounts have the same amount. Tell what transfers you could make. $15 from Tight Wad to Last National, $15 from Tight Wad to Savers' National; all accounts have $50.

Last National Bank	Tight Wad Bank	Savers' National Bank
$35	$80	$35

More Practice, page 508, set D

3. Practice and Apply

Basic	5-22
Average	1-22
Extended	9-22

PRACTICE

In Exercises 1-16, which quotients will be less than $1.00? Why? (Exercises 3-5, 8, 10, 13; Exercises 4 and 5 divide less than $1.00 to start with; the divisors in the other exercises are greater than the amount in the dollars place.)

APPLY

MATH REASONING ▶ **Relate 105 and 210, then explain how to apply the relationship to Exercise 17.** (210 is twice 105, so 210 should have twice as many 35s.)

PROBLEM SOLVING ▶ **Explain which operations are needed in Problem 20.** (addition of 5 + 3, division of $6.16 by 8)

USING CRITICAL THINKING

▶ **Explain how you could solve the problem by finding an average.** (Possible answer: You could find the average of the accounts, use it as the goal, then adjust each account until it meets the goal amount.)

Close and Assess

WRITE WHAT YOU THINK

Have each student write an explanation of how to divide $3.68 by 4. Ask students to include in their paragraphs a comparison of the steps they use to divide money with the process of dividing whole numbers. ($0.92; Check students' writing.)

Quick Quiz

Divide. Show dollars and cents.

1. 6)$8.16 ($1.36)
2. 7)$4.27 ($0.61)
3. 2)$9.04 ($4.52)

CHAPTER 10

DATA COLLECTION AND ANALYSIS

GROUP DECISION MAKING

OBJECTIVE To collect, organize, and present data

COLLECTING DATA

▶ **Decide ways to classify the chores you list.** (Possible answers: indoor vs. outdoor; in my room vs. in rooms the whole family uses; daily vs. weekly chores)
▶ **Analyze the chores to determine the 3 most common to place on the questionnaire.** (Answers will vary.)
▶ **Identify a word in each sample question that makes it easier for someone to answer *yes* or *no*.** (*usually; often*)
▶ **Explain why it is important that questions be answered with *yes* or *no*.** (It would be too hard to tally other kinds of responses.)
▶ **Explain why the same number of boys and girls should answer your questionnaire.** (to compare even groups of results)

Data Collection and Analysis
Group Decision Making

UNDERSTAND
FIND DATA
PLAN
ESTIMATE
SOLVE
CHECK

Doing a Questionnaire
Group Skill:
Check for Understanding

Do you think boys and girls do the same kinds of chores or different chores at home? Make a prediction and then make a questionnaire to help you find out.

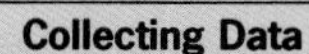

1. Work with your group to make a list of chores that children often do at home. Then choose the three chores that you think are the most common.
2. Write a question about each of the three chores for your questionnaire. The questions should have a yes or no answer. Make sure you find out if the person answering the questionnaire is a boy or a girl.

290

TEACHING OPTIONS

COOPERATIVE LEARNING

Grouping Suggestion: cooperative learning groups of 4 to 8
Discuss the tasks required to complete the Group Decision Making activity. These may include listing chores, choosing the 3 most common ones, formulating questions, editing, revising, typing or word processing and duplicating the questionnaire, tallying the responses, making the bar graph, and planning how to present an analysis. Allow groups time to discuss their plans and to evaluate the results before they present their final analysis.

CHAPTER REVIEW/TEST

Part 1 Understanding

1. Explain how to find the quotient and remainder for 38 ÷ 5. Tell how to check the answer. See Additional Answers.
2. Since 36 ÷ 4 = ▮▮▮▮, then 360 ÷ 4 = ▮▮▮▮. 9, 90
3. Tell why substituting a number can make estimation easier. Use 413 ÷ 6 as an example. See Additional Answers.

Estimate each quotient. Tell whether your estimate is over or under the exact quotient.

4. 217 ÷ 5 40, under
5. $7.75 ÷ 8 $1.00, over

Part 2 Skills

Decide where to start dividing. Do not solve. Just write hundreds or tens.

6. 4)131 tens
7. 6)849 hundreds
8. 3)305 hundreds

Divide and check.

9. 63 ÷ 5 12 R3
10. 4)948 237
11. 8)825 103 R1
12. 6)$3.24 $0.54
13. 80 ÷ 7 11 R3
14. 552 ÷ 3 184
15. 9)987 109 R6
16. 8)$0.88 $0.11
17. Divide 85 by 6 14 R1
18. What is 670 divided by 4? 167 R2

Use mental math to find the quotients.

19. 2)416 208
20. 7)$7.49 $1.07
21. 3)124 41 R1
22. 160 ÷ 4 40

Part 3 Applications

23. A model truck is 4 times longer than its height. If it is 35 in. high, find its length. Tell the calculation method you used. 140″ Calculation methods may vary.
24. 114 cars used a parking garage near the auto show. They were parked in full rows of 8. How many cars were in the last row? 2 cars
25. **Challenge** A bus driver drove 185 miles each day Monday through Thursday and 220 miles on Friday. What was her weekly average? 192 mi

293

CHAPTER REVIEW/TEST

INTRODUCTION The Review Test is provided to review and evaluate the skills and concepts presented in Chapter 10.

USING PAGE 293
If you prefer to use this page for review, you may want to use the **Multiple-Choice Posttest** (pages 39-40) or the **Free-Response Posttest** (pages 39-40) to evaluate mastery of Chapter objectives.

ITEM ANALYSIS The table below correlates the Chapter Review/Test items with the lesson objectives for the chapter.

Items	Objectives
1	10-1
2	10-2
3-5	10-3
6-8, 21	10-9
9, 13, 17	10-5
10, 14, 18	10-7
11, 15, 19, 20, 22	10-10
12, 16, (20)	10-12
23	10-11
24	10-6
25	10-8

Additional Answers: See p. T79.

INFORMAL ASSESSMENT

Using Manipulatives Students use place value blocks or place value models (TA 6) to do the following division problems and record their actions in standard division notation: 4)93, 3)412, 5)110. (23 R1, 137 R1, 22; check students' written algorithms.)

Communication *Explain the meaning of* average *and give the steps you use to find the average of a set of numbers.* (The average is a way to determine an equal number based on a set of unequal numbers; find the sum of all numbers in the set, then divide by the number of addends.)

Critical Thinking *Determine the possible divisors in a division problem whose remainder is 6.* (The divisor can be any number over 6; if the divisor were 6 or less, you could make another group.)

ENRICHMENT

INTRODUCTION Using their knowledge of multiplication, students will be able to identify factors and sort products according to new criteria.

USING PAGE 294
This Enrichment page is provided for all students. You may wish to use it after they have completed the Chapter Review/Test on page 293.

► **Analyze the factor pair tables to determine how they organize data.** (A table has factor pairs that give its identifying number as a product; each factor pair list begins with 1 times the number, then adds other possible factor pairs.)

► **Analyze factor tables for 2, 3, 5, and 7 to decide what a prime number is.** (a number with only 1 and itself for its factors)

► **Contrast composite and prime numbers.** (Composite numbers have more than 2 factors.)

► **Explain how odd and even numbers relate to prime numbers.** (Except for 2, all prime numbers are odd, but all odd numbers are not prime.)

EXTENSION Provide students with hundred charts (TA 4) for a simplified version of the *sieve* of Eratosthenes, who was a Greek mathematician responsible for developing a method for finding prime numbers. Have students circle the numbers 2, 3, 5, and 7, then cross out every multiple of 2, of 3, of 5, then of 7. All remaining numbers, except for 1, will be prime.

Additional Answers: See p. T79.

ENRICHMENT
Discovering Prime Numbers

Here are the factor pair tables for the numbers up to 10. What patterns do you see?

Factors of 1
1 × 1

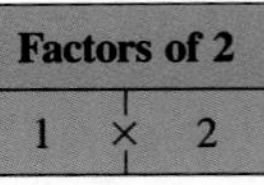

Factors of 2
1 × 2

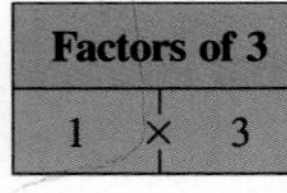

Factors of 3
1 × 3

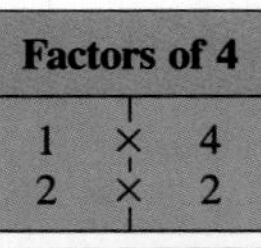

Factors of 4
1 × 4
2 × 2

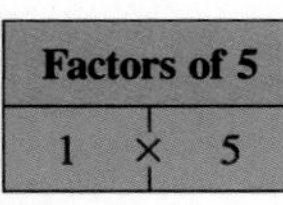

Factors of 5
1 × 5

Factors of 6
1 × 6
2 × 3

Factors of 7
1 × 7

Factors of 8
1 × 8
2 × 4

Factors of 9
1 × 9
3 × 3

Factors of 10
1 × 10
2 × 5

1. Which number has just one factor? 1
2. Which numbers have three factors? 4, 9
3. Study the factor tables above to discover how the numbers called **prime numbers** in the pattern below were chosen. Give the next 5 numbers in the pattern and their factor pair tables. See Additional Answers.
   2, 3, 5, 7, ___, ___, ___, ___, ___.
4. Copy and complete this definition of prime numbers. A **prime number** is a number with exactly ▯ factors. 2
5. Study the factor pair tables above to discover how the numbers called **composite numbers** in the pattern below were chosen. Give the next 5 numbers in the pattern and their factor pair tables.
   4, 6, 8, 9, ___, ___, ___, ___, ___.
   See Additional Answers.
6. Copy and complete this definition of composite numbers. A **composite number** is a number, other than 1, that is not a ▯ number. prime
7. Give all the prime numbers between 20 and 30. 23, 29
8. Give all the composite numbers between 20 and 30.
   21, 22, 24, 25, 26, 27, 28

CUMULATIVE REVIEW

1. Estimate the product of 83 and 683.
   - A 48,000
   - B 5,600
   - (C) 56,000
   - D 54,000
2. Find the product of $7.08 and 29.
   - (A) $205.32
   - B $211.92
   - C $203.32
   - D $204.32
3. A reasonable time to have a midmorning snack is ▯.
   - A 6:15 p.m.
   - B 6:15 a.m.
   - C 10:45 p.m.
   - (D) 10:45 a.m.
4. A nonstandard unit you might use to measure the length of a pen is a ▯.
   - A span
   - (B) thumb
   - C step
   - D cubit
5. Which distance is greater than a mile?
   - A 5,280 ft
   - (B) 2,000 yd
   - C 1,760 yd
   - D 60,000 in.
6. △ × ○ = □
   Which division equation is in the same fact family?
   - A △ ÷ ○ = □
   - B △ ÷ □ = ○
   - (C) □ ÷ △ = ○
7. Which amount of rice weighs less than 3 pounds?
   - (A) 45 oz
   - B 48 oz
   - C 60 oz
   - D 72 oz
8. What is the quotient of 21 divided by 7?
   - A 28
   - B 14
   - (C) 3
   - D 147
9. 48 ÷ 6
   - (A) 8
   - B 9
   - C 7
   - D 10
10. $4\overline{)28}$
    - A 4
    - B 9
    - C 6
    - (D) 7
11. Vito rents a car for 10 days at a total cost of $248.80. About how much does the car cost per day?
    - A $2.48
    - B $20
    - C $48
    - (D) $25
12. After shopping, Ella had $4. She got a $7 belt, 3 books at $3 each, and a $14 skirt. How much did she start with?
    - A $28
    - (B) $34
    - C $31
    - D $30

295

CUMULATIVE REVIEW

INTRODUCTION The purpose of this Cumulative Review is to maintain previously taught skills and concepts. The emphasis in this Cumulative Review is on multiplication by 2-digit factors, Chapter 7; on time and customary measurement, Chapter 8; and on division concepts and basic facts, Chapter 9.

ITEM ANALYSIS The table below correlates the Cumulative Review items with the lesson objectives.

Items	Objectives
1	7-2
2	7-8
3	8-2
4	8-5
5	8-8
6	9-2
7	8-12
8, 9	9-7
10	9-4
11	9-5
12	9-10

CHAPTER 11 GEOMETRY

Chapter Management

OVERVIEW

Lesson	Pages	Objectives	Subject Integration	Strand Integration
Chapter Opener	296-297	To introduce chapter 11	fine arts-sun mask	critical thinking
Space Figures and Plane Figures	298-299	11-1 To identify space figures and plane figures	fine arts-masks	critical thinking
Polygons and Angles	300-301	11-2 To name polygon plane figures and to compare their angles to 90°	health/fitness-walking	problem solving
Analyzing Polygons: Parallel and Perpendicular Lines	302-303	11-3 To identify parallel and perpendicular lines	health/fitness-bicycle riding	measurement: time
Symmetric Figures	304-305	11-4 To make symmetric figures and identify lines of symmetry	fine arts-masks	mathematical reasoning
Classifying Angles and Triangles	306-307	11-5 To classify triangles and angles	science-rabbits	estimation
Classifying Quadrilaterals	308-309	11-6 To classify quadrilaterals as squares, rectangles, parallelograms, or trapezoids	social studies-household chores	measurement
Congruent Figures	310-311	11-7 To find congruent figures	fine arts-mask patterns	critical thinking
Curves and Circles/Midchapter Review/Quiz	312-313	11-8 To identify and draw simple closed curves and circles	fine arts-drawing	problem solving
Coordinate Geometry	314-315	11-9 To use number pairs to make coordinate graphs	social studies-plane travel	algebra
Similar Figures	316-317	11-10 To identify and graph similar figures	fine arts-masks	calculators
Problem Solving: Data from a Diagram	318-319	11-11 To solve problems using data from a diagram	health/fitness-basketball	graphing
Applied Problem Solving: Group Decision Making	320-321	11-12 To analyze, organize, and make decisions using relevant data	social studies-group skills	measurement

MATHEMATICAL BACKGROUND

Space and Plane Figures
In Lesson 11-1, students are introduced to 6 space figures and to their flat faces, called plane figures.

Segments and Angles
In Lesson 11-2, students learn to use a right angle protractor to measure angles. They learn the number of sides and the angles in a hexagon, octagon, and pentagon.

Coordinate Geometry
In Lesson 11-9, students learn to identify coordinates on a graph. They learn to graph points and to graph a figure by drawing lines from point to point.

Problem Solving
Students solve problems using data from a diagram.

TIPS FROM TEACHERS

Have each student fold a sheet of paper in half, then cut out a favorite shape. Open shapes to show symmetry. Staple the open shapes to sheets of colored construction paper. Tape to a sunny window, with the shapes facing the window. After a week or more, remove the shapes and observe the symmetrical patterns on the papers.

Frank Hall, Jr.
North Elementary School
Watertown, NY

ASSESSMENT

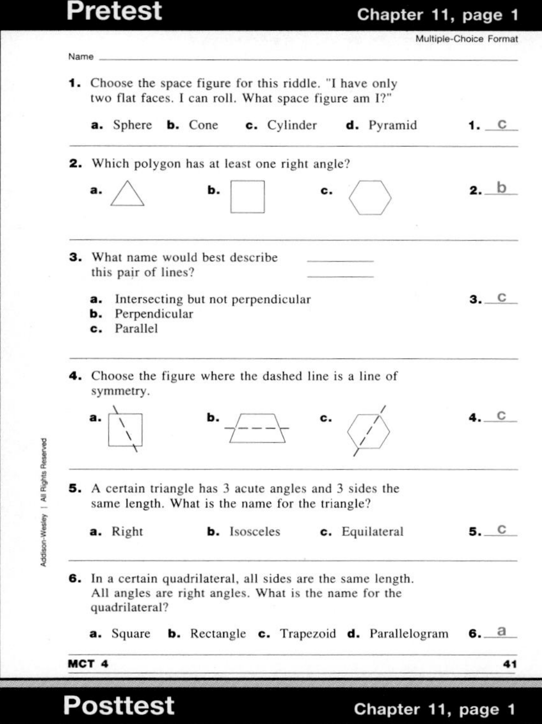

Pretest — Chapter 11, page 1

Multiple-Choice Format

Name ____________

1. Choose the space figure for this riddle. "I have only two flat faces. I can roll. What space figure am I?"
   a. Sphere b. Cone c. Cylinder d. Pyramid — 1. c

2. Which polygon has at least one right angle?
   a. b. c. — 2. b

3. What name would best describe this pair of lines?
   a. Intersecting but not perpendicular
   b. Perpendicular
   c. Parallel — 3. c

4. Choose the figure where the dashed line is a line of symmetry.
   a. b. c. — 4. c

5. A certain triangle has 3 acute angles and 3 sides the same length. What is the name for the triangle?
   a. Right b. Isosceles c. Equilateral — 5. c

6. In a certain quadrilateral, all sides are the same length. All angles are right angles. What is the name for the quadrilateral?
   a. Square b. Rectangle c. Trapezoid d. Parallelogram — 6. a

Pretest — Chapter 11, page 2

Multiple-Choice Format

Name ____________

7. Which pair of figures are congruent?
   a. b. c. — 7. b

8. Which choice best describes this curve?
   a. Simple closed curve
   b. A curve that is not closed
   c. A curve that is not simple — 8. a

9. Which coordinates locate the point for letter M?
   a. (3, 4) b. (4, 2) c. (2, 4) d. (4, 3) — 9. d

10. Which figure is similar to the one at the right?
    a. b. c. — 10. a

11. How long is Side A? (25 ft, 17 ft, 25 ft, A)
    a. 25 ft b. 50 ft c. 17 ft d. 42 ft — 11. d

Posttest — Chapter 11, page 1

Multiple-Choice Format

Name ____________

1. Choose the space figure for this riddle. "I have no flat faces, no corners, and no edges. What figure am I?"
   a. Cone b. Sphere c. Cylinder d. Cube — 1. b

2. Which polygon has at least one right angle?
   a. b. c. — 2. a

3. What name would best describe this pair of lines?
   a. Intersecting but not perpendicular
   b. Perpendicular
   c. Parallel — 3. b

4. Choose the figure where the dashed line is a line of symmetry.
   a. b. c. — 4. a

5. A certain triangle has a right angle and all sides different lengths. What is the name for the triangle?
   a. Right b. Isosceles c. Equilateral — 5. a

6. In a certain quadrilateral, there are two pairs of parallel sides. There are no right angles. What is the name for the quadrilateral?
   a. Square b. Rectangle c. Trapezoid d. Parallelogram — 6. d

Posttest — Chapter 11, page 2

Multiple-Choice Format

Name ____________

7. Which pair of figures are congruent?
   a. b. c. — 7. a

8. Which choice best describes this curve?
   a. Simple closed curve
   b. A curve that is not closed
   c. A curve that is not simple — 8. b

9. Which coordinates locate the point for letter G?
   a. (3, 4) b. (4, 2) c. (2, 4) d. (4, 3) — 9. a

10. Which figure is similar to the one at the right?
    a. b. c. — 10. c

11. How long is Side A? (50 ft, 25 ft, 25 ft, A)
    a. 75 ft b. 50 ft c. 125 ft d. 25 ft — 11. a

ITEM ANALYSIS

Items	Objectives
1	11-1
2	11-2
3	11-3
4	11-4
5	11-5
6	11-6
7	11-7
8	11-8
9	11-9
10	11-10
11	11-11

Note: The item analysis is the same for all pretests and posttests for this chapter.

ALSO AVAILABLE

- **Free Response Tests**
- **Alternative Tests**
- **Thinking Strategies**
- **Concrete Materials**

CHAPTER 11 GEOMETRY

Optional Chapter Activities

PROJECT AND BULLETIN BOARD

Divide a bulletin board into four sections with these headings: Space Figures, Quadrilaterals, Triangles, and Other Polygons. Use one color of edging for the horizontal borders, another for the vertical borders, and a third for the diagonals that form the sections. This will be helpful when discussing parallel and perpendicular lines and symmetry. As students work through Chapter 11, have them find pictures of realistic examples in old magazines, catalogs, or newspapers that can be added to each classification. From time to time during the chapter, have students play a guessing game based on the figures posted by giving hints such as this one: *I am thinking of an equilateral triangle designed for safety.* (a *yield* sign) Students can also add separated pairs of congruent or symmetric figures to the appropriate section of the bulletin board and challenge classmates to find the pairs.

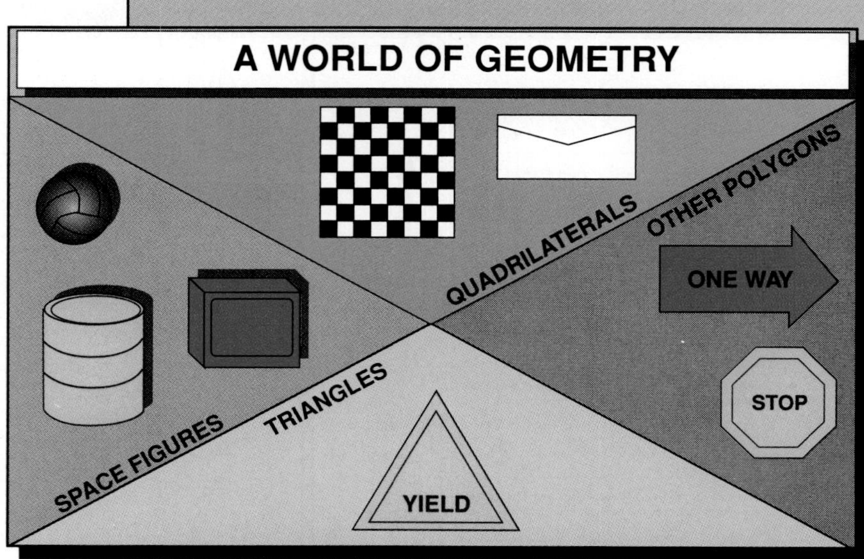

COOPERATIVE LEARNING

Divide the class into groups of three or four. Identify the group skill: disagree in an agreeable way. Have one member of each group look through the student textbook and list some of the geometric concepts. Have each member choose a concept or shape and make up a riddle. For example, *You can never come to the end of me; you'll just keep going around and around. What am I?* (a circle) Group members should test their riddles on each other and, if anyone disagrees, he or she should politely suggest a way to improve the riddle. Have each group ask the rest of the class to figure out the answers to its riddles. Riddles may be bound into a class riddle book.

You will find grouping suggestions and cooperative learning activities in most lessons throughout this chapter.

LITERATURE

Phillips, Jo. *Exploring Triangles: Paper Folding Geometry.* New York: Harper & Row, 1975.

Children learn the properties of triangles by using these paper folding exercises.
Children will enjoy making their own paper triangles and discussing them with their classmates.

Froman, Robert. *Rubber Bands, Baseballs, and Doughnuts: A Book About Topology.* New York: Young Math Book Series, Thomas Y. Crowell, 1972.

Sitomer, Mindel and Harry. *What Is Symmetry?* New York: Young Math Book Series, Thomas Y. Crowell, 1970.

Srivastava, Jane Jonas. *Spaces, Shapes, and Sizes.* New York: Thomas Y. Crowell, 1980.

English as a Second Language

The following activity is designed to help ESL students identify polygons and angles and find them in their environment as students progress through this chapter.

Explain that a polygon is a closed shape with straight sides. Draw different kinds of shapes on the chalkboard and ask the class to identify which are polygons and to explain why. Show the class familiar polygons; squares, rectangles, and triangles. Ask students how they can tell what the shapes are. Have the class make a data sheet that names different polygons in the classroom and that lists the number of sides and angles in each. Students may use the data sheet for reference throughout the chapter.

Gifted

Have students choose partners. Instruct each set of partners to create 26 pairs of index cards. Each pair of cards will have a plane-figure item cut out from a magazine, newspaper, or catalogue, and should be matched with the word that denotes it. Remind students to include items and words such as rectangle, triangle, circle, square, hexagon, pentagon, quadrilateral, or octagon.

Ask partners to shuffle cards thoroughly and to deal the entire deck so that each partner has a pile face down. Have them each simultaneously turn over one card and look to see if an item and its matching word have been displayed. The first player to notice a match and to announce the word denoting the correct plane figure collects both cards. If the player announces the wrong word or makes an incorrect match, the other player then claims both cards. If no match is apparent, each player returns his or her card to approximately the center of his or her deck. The first player to collect 10 matches wins.

Students at Risk

The geometry strand requires mastery of new vocabulary, the spatial skill of visualizing figures in various orientations and dimensions, and an ability to organize and classify. Students with weaknesses in language, spatial, visual, or memory skills need frequent opportunities to relate geometric concepts to real-life objects and situations.

Geometry Station Set up a work station to give students tactile, visual, and kinesthetic experiences with geometric figures. Materials might include space figure solids, dowels, holiday ornaments, cans, boxes, templates, graph paper, pattern blocks, rulers, geoboards, and compasses.

Math Art Have students use modeling clay to create their own space figures, identifying the features they must include to represent particular figures. Students can use templates to trace, cut, and paste plane figures collages. They can make symmetrical designs by coloring boxes on graph paper. You can use these art projects as bases for review or discussion of key geometric concepts.

You may also use the Reteaching Supplements and the specific Reteaching Tips from each lesson in this chapter.

CHAPTER 11

INTRODUCING THE CHAPTER

SUBJECT INTEGRATION The photograph of ceremonial masks from Ghana and the Ivory Coast represents the chapter theme of fine arts. Several lessons involve situations about masks to provide students with fine-arts applications of geometry concepts.

USING DATA The Fine Arts Data Bank on page 480 of the Student Edition shows a symmetrical pattern for a sun mask superimposed on a coordinate grid. Various polygons form the facial features of the mask: square, octagon, triangle, rectangle, trapezoid.

QUESTION 1 ► **Explain a rule for recognizing squares.** (Possible rule: A square always has 4 equal sides and 4 corners)
Student Edition answer: eyes

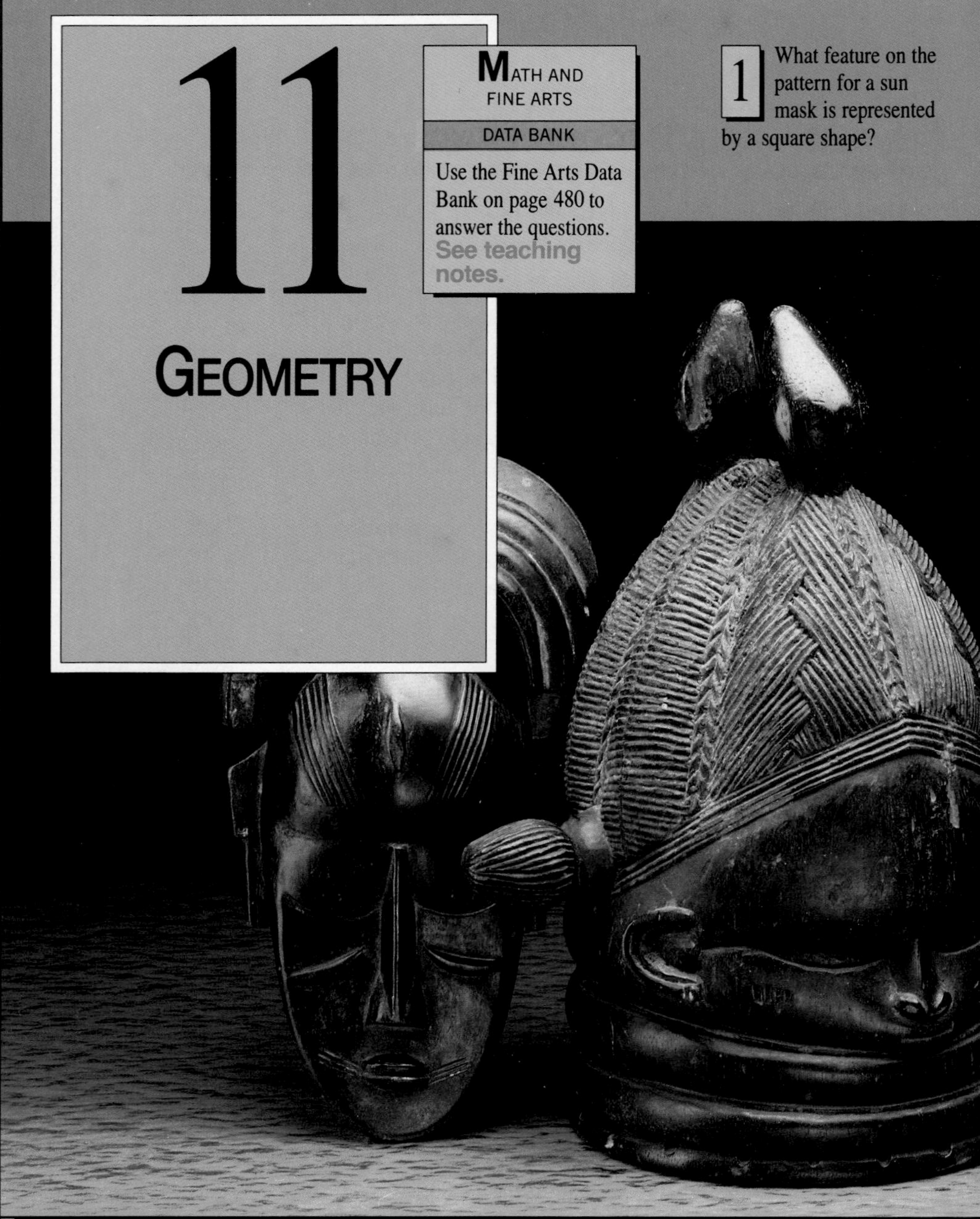

11 GEOMETRY

MATH AND FINE ARTS

DATA BANK

Use the Fine Arts Data Bank on page 480 to answer the questions. See teaching notes.

1 What feature on the pattern for a sun mask is represented by a square shape?

TEACHING OPTIONS

LANGUAGE DEVELOPMENT
Write on the chalkboard a list of every shape students can identify as they look around the classroom. Discuss similarities in the construction of the words that name certain shapes, such as tri*angle* and rect*angle* or hexa*gon* and octa*gon*, and ask students to attempt to explain the link. (Explanations may vary.)

2 How many triangles can you find on the sun mask pattern?

3 What feature on the pattern for a sun mask is represented by a rectangle shape?

4 **Use Critical Thinking** What two shapes on the pattern for a sun mask could you put together to make a rectangle?

297

QUESTION 2 ► **Explain a rule for recognizing triangles.** (Possible rule: A triangle always has 3 sides and 3 angles.)
► **Explain how triangles can look different.** (Possible answer: Triangles can be tall and thin, short and wide; they can have equal sides or sides of different lengths.)
► **Analyze the triangles in the sun mask.** (Both eyebrows are the same kind of triangle, but they are different from triangles that form the rays, which all have equal sides.)
► **Analyze whether the nose is a triangle.** (It is not because it has 4 sides, not 3.)
Student Edition answer: 10

QUESTION 3 ► **Compare and contrast a square and a rectangle.** (Both shapes have 4 sides and 4 corners, but a square is a special rectangle because all 4 of its sides are the same length. Other rectangles may have sides of 2 different lengths.)
Student Edition answer: The mouth is a rectangle and the eyes are squares, which are special rectangles.

QUESTION 4 ► **Explain a way to answer the question.** (Possible answer: Imagine sliding or turning shapes to fit them together until you form a rectangle.)
Student Edition answer: eyebrows or eyes

SUBJECT INTEGRATION PROJECT Encourage students to design original collage masks comprised *only* of geometric shapes cut from paper or tagboard. Begin by brainstorming a list of all the shapes students can recognize around the classroom, sorting them into categories by number of sides. Allow students to work on their masks as they progress through the chapter. To spark their ideas, provide for students to look through materials that show different kinds of masks. Conclude by having students hang the masks around the classroom or display them for another class.

LESSON OPTIONS 11-1

Space Figures and Plane Figures

OBJECTIVE 11-1 To identify space figures and plane figures

PREBOOK ACTIVITIES

QUICK REVIEW

Find the perimeter of each figure.

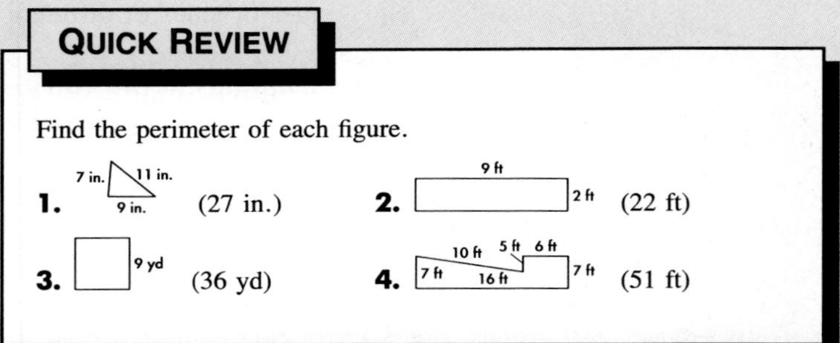

1. (27 in.)
2. (22 ft)
3. (36 yd)
4. (51 ft)

PRIOR KNOWLEDGE

Draw a square, circle, and triangle on the chalkboard. Display models of a cube, sphere, and triangular prism. Have students generalize similarities and differences in each set of figures and among the sets. (Possible answer: All figures on the board are flat; all models are 3-dimensional.) Review the term **space figure** as another way to describe solid shapes, as contrasted with **plane figure**, as a way to classify flat shapes. Students may use *3-dimensional* as an adjective for space figure, so help them name the 3 dimensions of space figures: height, width, and depth or thickness. Help students notice that plane figures have only 2 dimensions: height and width.

COMMUNICATION

Discussing and Reading Math Have students read the following illustrative sentences as they examine cubes to find examples of each term: *You can classify space figures by describing their* ***plane faces. Edges*** *are where* ***faces*** *meet. A* ***vertex*** *(plural:* ***vertices****) is a point where edges meet.* Discuss how the general meanings of *edge* and *face* are similar to their math meanings (table edge; clock face).

EXPLORE AND CONNECT

Materials: space-figure models, tables (see below)
Grouping Suggestion: small cooperative learning groups
Groups examine **space figures** to gather data on **faces, edges,** and **vertices**. Each group uses the table below:

Space Figure	*Faces?*	*Vertices?*	*Straight Edges?*	*Curved Edges?*

Groups explore each element of a sphere, cone, cylinder, cube, rectangular prism, triangular prism, and pyramid, recording data on the chart. They may consult page 298 of their Student Edition to help them identify and spell each *space figure*. Discuss ways to count *faces, edges,* and *vertices* accurately. (Possible strategy: Keep a finger on each *face* until all are counted.) Group members share their findings for each *space figure,* as others verify the data. Discuss similarities and differences among *space figures*. (Answers may vary.)

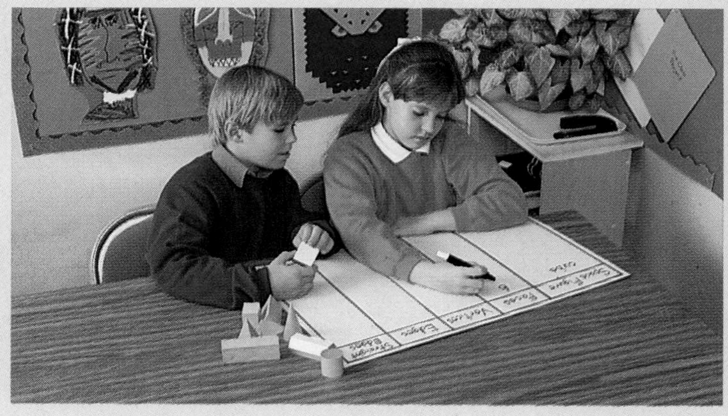

CONNECTIONS Use these anytime.

Problem of the Day

Creative Thinking Jim used 6 white cubes as pictured to make a rectangular prism. Then he painted the whole outside blue. If Jim separates the cubes, how many will have more blue faces than white? How many will have an equal number of blue and white faces? (4; 2)

Subject Integration

Social Studies Thousands of years ago, when a king died in Egypt, he was buried in a tomb the shape of a space figure with 4 triangular sides. What is that space figure called? What shape is at the bottom of that figure? (a pyramid; a square)

Life Skills

Sports Equipment Name at least 5 sports that are played with spheres. Then give some properties of spheres that would help explain why they are used in so many sports. (Answers will vary. Samples: basketball, baseball, golf, tennis, soccer. Sample reasons: a sphere has no points or edges, so it can roll and bounce easily and be hit predictably.)

Classwork and Homework Supplements

Practice

Life Skills 11-1

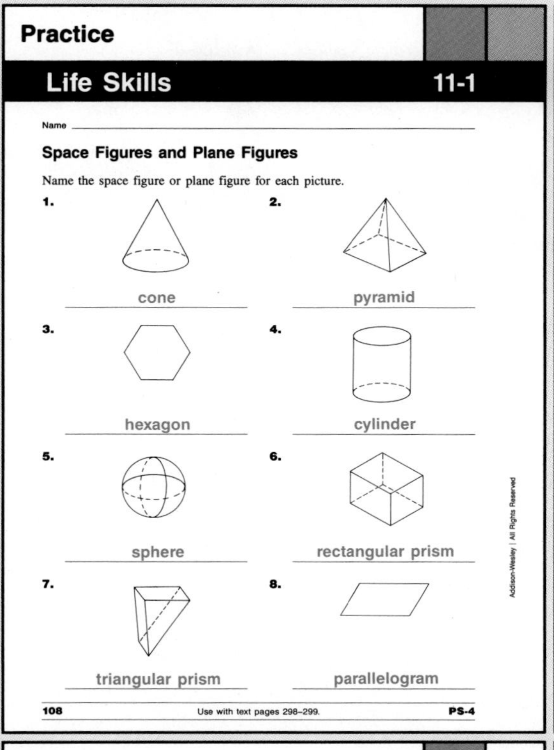

Name ______

Space Figures and Plane Figures

Name the space figure or plane figure for each picture.

1. cone
2. pyramid
3. hexagon
4. cylinder
5. sphere
6. rectangular prism
7. triangular prism
8. parallelogram

Addison-Wesley | All Rights Reserved

108 Use with text pages 298–299. PS-4

Building Thinking Skills

Creative Thinking 11-1

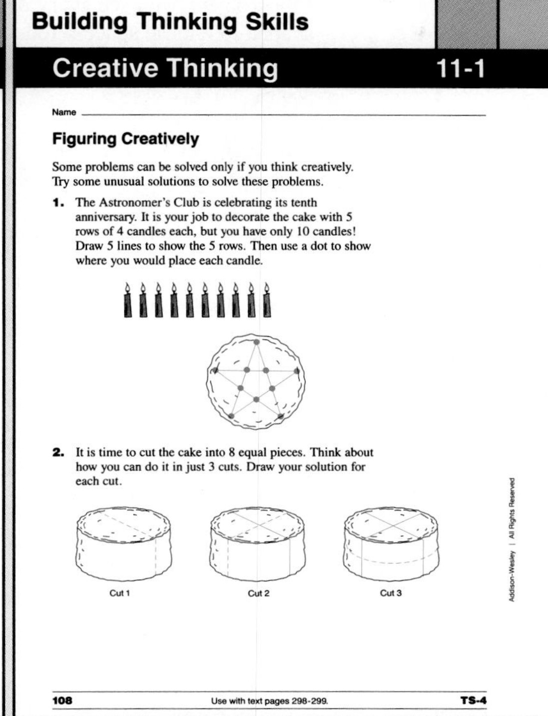

Name ______

Figuring Creatively

Some problems can be solved only if you think creatively. Try some unusual solutions to solve these problems.

1. The Astronomer's Club is celebrating its tenth anniversary. It is your job to decorate the cake with 5 rows of 4 candles each, but you have only 10 candles! Draw 5 lines to show the 5 rows. Then use a dot to show where you would place each candle.
2. It is time to cut the cake into 8 equal pieces. Think about how you can do it in just 3 cuts. Draw your solution for each cut.

Cut 1 Cut 2 Cut 3

Addison-Wesley | All Rights Reserved

108 Use with text pages 298–299. TS-4

Reteaching

Life Skills 11-1

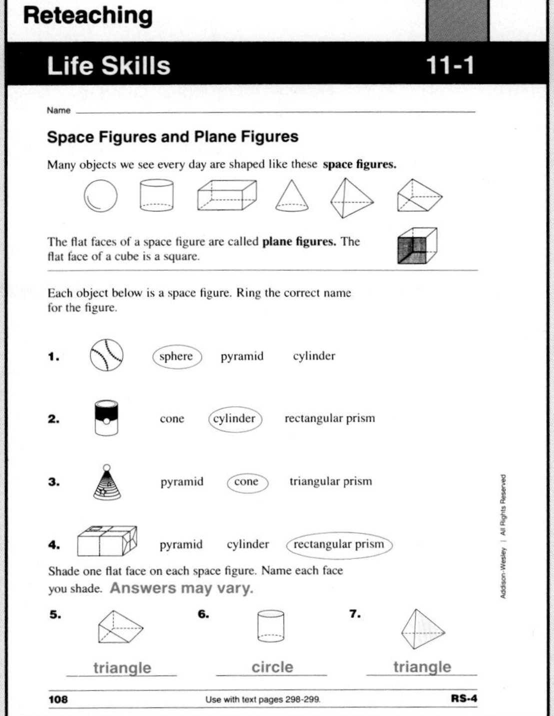

Name ______

Space Figures and Plane Figures

Many objects we see every day are shaped like these **space figures.**

The flat faces of a space figure are called **plane figures.** The flat face of a cube is a square.

Each object below is a space figure. Ring the correct name for the figure.

1. (sphere) pyramid cylinder
2. cone (cylinder) rectangular prism
3. pyramid (cone) triangular prism
4. pyramid cylinder (rectangular prism)

Shade one flat face on each space figure. Name each face you shade. Answers may vary.

5. triangle
6. circle
7. triangle

Addison-Wesley | All Rights Reserved

108 Use with text pages 298–299. RS-4

Challenges

Manipulatives 11-1

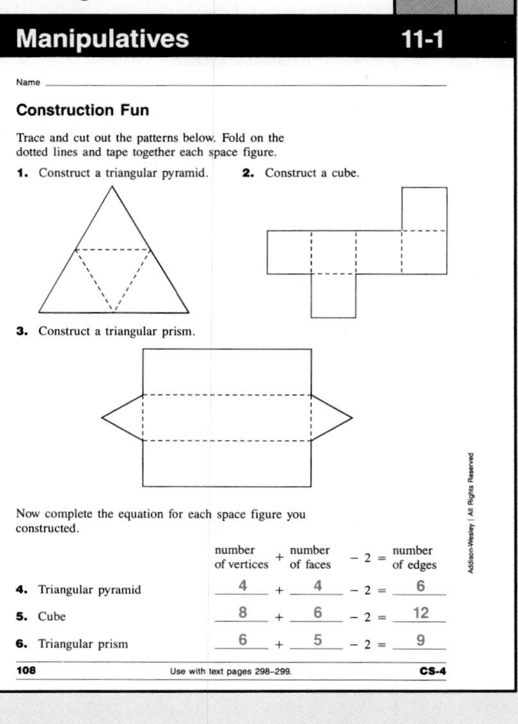

Name ______

Construction Fun

Trace and cut out the patterns below. Fold on the dotted lines and tape together each space figure.

1. Construct a triangular pyramid.
2. Construct a cube.
3. Construct a triangular prism.

Now complete the equation for each space figure you constructed.

	number of vertices	+	number of faces	− 2 =	number of edges
4. Triangular pyramid	4	+	4	− 2 =	6
5. Cube	8	+	6	− 2 =	12
6. Triangular prism	6	+	5	− 2 =	9

Addison-Wesley | All Rights Reserved

108 Use with text pages 298–299. CS-4

Options for Individual Needs

Basic

Exercises 1-13
More Practice, p. 521, set D

Supplements
Reteaching 108 or
Practice 108

Average

Exercises 1-15
More Practice, p. 521, set D

Supplements
Practice 108
Challenges 108 or
Thinking Skills 108

Extended

Exercises 1-15

Supplements
Challenges 108
Thinking Skills 108

Other Resources:
Math In Stride, Grade 4, pp. 67, 68
Mathematics, Book A, Teacher's Edition, pp. 45, 46
Mathematics, A Way of Thinking, Lessons 13-8—13-11

11-1

LESSON PLAN 11-1

OBJECTIVE 11-1
To identify space figures and plane figures

Materials: space-figure models

Grouping Suggestion: pairs

1. MOTIVATE AND TEACH

LEARN ABOUT IT

EXPLORE ► **How is the sphere different from the other figures?** (Possible answer: It has no flat faces.)
► **Explain how to tell a triangular prism from a pyramid.** (A pyramid has at least 3 triangular faces, while a triangular prism has more edges.)
► **Analyze how the prisms differ.** (A rectangular prism has faces that are rectangles or squares; a triangular prism has faces that are rectangles or triangles.)

TALK ABOUT IT ► **If you were making up a riddle about a cylinder, what information would you include? Explain your reasoning.** (Possible answer: It is curved and has 2 flat faces. You need to include the flat faces to differentiate it from a sphere.)
► **Explain why a circle is not a polygon.** (A polygon does not have any curved sides.)
Student Edition answers: **1.** Answers will vary. **2.** sphere: no flat faces; cylinder, cone: circle; rectangular prism: square, rectangle; triangular prism: triangle, rectangle; pyramid: square, triangle

2. CHECK UNDERSTANDING

TRY IT OUT

ERROR ALERT Confusing faces, edges, and vertices.

Space Figures and Plane Figures

LEARN ABOUT IT

Many objects you see every day are shaped like these space figures.

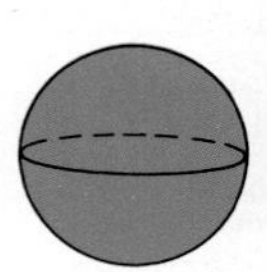
Sphere

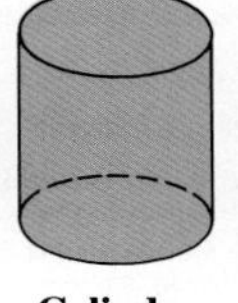
Cylinder

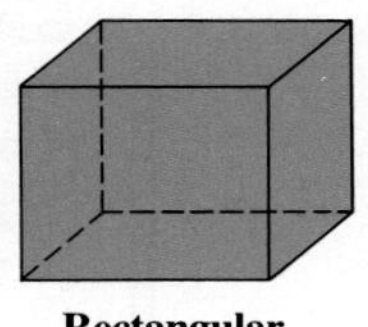
Rectangular Prism

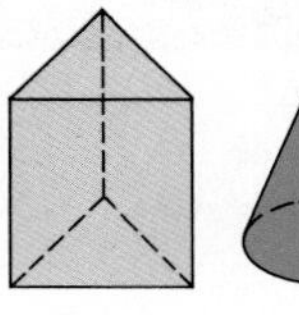
Triangular Prism

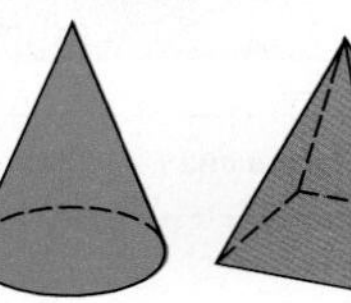
Cone

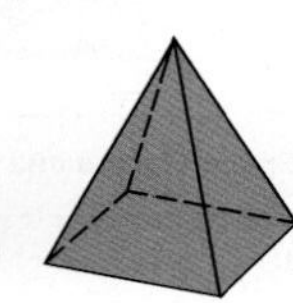
Pyramid

EXPLORE **Use Space Figure Models**
Work in groups. Find the space figure for each riddle.

I am flat everywhere. I have some rectangle faces. Who am I?

I have no vertices. I have no flat faces. Who am I?

TALK ABOUT IT See teaching notes.

1. Make up a riddle and give it to another group to solve.
2. Name the shapes of the faces on each space figure above.

The flat faces of a **space figure** are called **plane figures**. If all sides of a plane figure are straight and connected, it is a **polygon**.

A cube is a space figure with square faces. Each face is a plane figure and a polygon.

TRY IT OUT

1. How many faces, edges, and vertices does a rectangular prism have? a triangular prism? a pyramid? See Additional Answers.

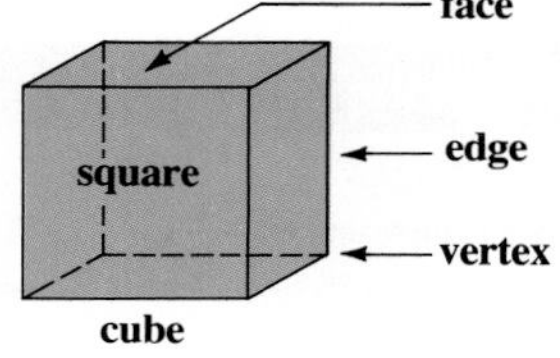

TEACHING OPTIONS

RETEACHING TIPS Students use models to list space figures, featuring the mathematical name and a common object that looks like each one. Let them refer to their lists and to models to become more familiar with space figures and to distinguish among them. Assign Reteaching Supplement 108.

ENRICHMENT **Family Math**
At home, students ask a family member to help them try to find in their home as many objects as possible that are the shape of a sphere, cone, cube, cylinder, rectangular prism, triangular prism, and pyramid. Together, they list each object and its shape.

PRACTICE

Name the space figure for each riddle.

1. I have only two flat faces. I can roll. cylinder
2. I have just one flat face. I roll, but not straight. cone
3. I am flat all over. My faces are squares. cube
4. My faces are triangles. On top I have a point. pyramid
5. I have no flat faces, no corners and no edges. sphere
6. My faces are two triangles and three rectangles. triangular prism

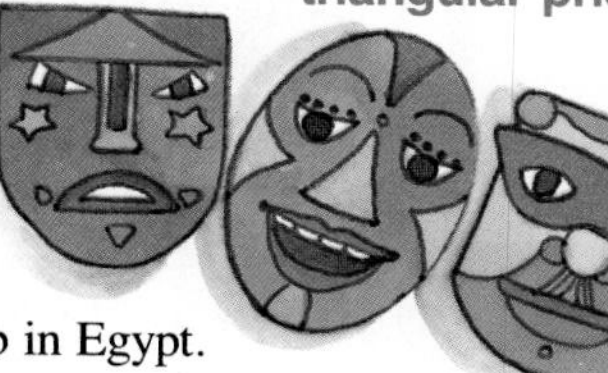

APPLY

MATH REASONING Think about the object. What space figure is it like?

7. It holds ice cream. cone
8. It is a tomb in Egypt. pyramid
9. You bounce it or throw it. sphere
10. It can hold crayons or cereal. rectangular prism

PROBLEM SOLVING

11. With her eyes closed Maria guessed what she held in her hands. It felt like a cylinder with one end open. It had a handle on the side. What was it? a cup
12. Tomas used geometric shapes to decorate the mask he had made. He painted 17 triangles across the top and put 2 circles under each. Then he used circles for eyes, a rectangle for a nose, and another circle for a mouth. How many plane figures did he use? 55 plane figures

▶ **USING CRITICAL THINKING Take a Look**

Pretend you cut some clay space figure models down the middle. Each cut made two new identical faces. Imagine what each shape looked like and draw a picture of it. Check students' drawings.

13. 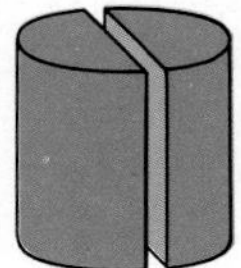
14. 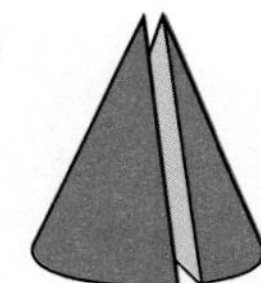
15. 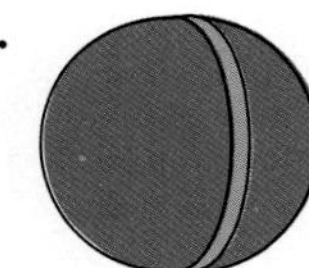

More Practice, page 521, set D 299

3. PRACTICE AND APPLY

Basic	1-13
Average	1-15
Extended	1-15

Additional Answers: See p. T79.

PRACTICE

Look at Exercises 1-6. *What strategies could you use to solve the space-figure riddles?* (Answers may vary, possible strategy: Eliminate models that do not work.)

APPLY

MATH REASONING ▶ **Explain a strategy you could use to solve Exercises 7-10.** (Picture the real object; compare it with space-figure models.)

PROBLEM SOLVING ▶ **What strategy would help you organize the data in Problem 12? Explain your reasoning.** (Possible answer: Draw a Picture, because there is a lot of information to visualize.)

USE CRITICAL THINKING ▶ **Why is it important to visualize straight cuts?** (Possible answer: Slanted cuts may give different shapes and then the 2 faces would not be identical.)

11-1

CLOSE AND ASSESS

SAY WHAT YOU THINK Have students work with a partner to identify space-figure models. The first partner gives clues about 1 space figure while the second partner tries to identify it. Then partners trade roles to identify another space figure. Pairs continue to take turns until together they have named all the space figures in this lesson.

QUICK QUIZ

Name a space figure that each object suggests.

1. shoe box (rectangular prism)
2. globe (sphere)
3. funnel (cone)

LESSON OPTIONS 11-2

Polygons and Angles

OBJECTIVE 11-1 To name polygon plane figures and compare their angles to 90°

PREBOOK ACTIVITIES

QUICK REVIEW

Match the space figure with an object it is like.

1. sphere	**a.** ones block	(1-d)
2. rectangular prism	**b.** wizard's hat	(2-c)
3. cylinder	**c.** VCR	(3-e)
4. cube	**d.** beach ball	(4-a)
5. cone	**e.** soup can	(5-b)

PRIOR KNOWLEDGE

Draw a right angle on the chalkboard and have students describe it. (Possible answers: a square; a corner) Have them locate objects or places in the classroom with right angles. (Possible answers: table corners; the letters, *T, L, E, H*) Have students explain what a polygon is. (''a plane figure whose sides are all straight and connected'') Draw a rectangle on the board. Ask students if they can tell the size of the angles in the rectangle. (all right angles) Explain that angles in polygons are described by comparing their size to a right angle.

COMMUNICATION

Discussing Math Have students suggest common meanings of the word **right**. (''correct''; ''opposite of left'') Ask whether they think either meaning applies to the math term **right angle** and to explain why. (Neither, because you are not saying a ''correct'' angle and right angles can face directions other than right.) Have students name some common measurement tools. (Possible answers: ruler; thermometer) Hold up a **protractor** and ask whether anyone is familiar with it. (Answers will vary.) Explain that it is marked in units called degrees that measure angle size, not temperature.

EXPLORE AND CONNECT

Materials: oaktag strips (approximately 1 in. by 5 in.), paper fasteners, tangrams, pattern blocks
Alternative Materials: TA 19 (Tangram), TA 20 (Plane Shapes)
Grouping Suggestion: partners
Partners make informal **protractors** from 2 oaktag strips held together with a paper fastener. Students fasten the strips at a **right angle** corner. The *protractor* may adjust, but when it opens to a *right angle,* it should have the shape of an *L*. Have partners use the protractor to measure the angles on pattern blocks, tangrams, or pictures of plane shapes. Partners take turns recording the findings by classifying angles as greater than, less than, or equal to a *right angle*. Conclude by having students tell how to use a protractor to compare angles to a right angle. (Open the protractor wider to measure greater angles; close it some to measure smaller angles.)

CONNECTIONS Use these anytime.

Problem of the Day

Calculator Most calculator displays show each of the digits 0-9 as straight lines connected by right angles. Draw each digit as a calculator would display it. If you need help, enter the digits in a calculator to study the connections. (Check students' drawings.)

Math Connection

Geometry Trace and cut out a circle. Fold it in half, then in half again. When you unfold the circle, how many right angles do you see? Describe how they relate. If each right angle has 90°, explain how you know how many degrees a circle has. (4; all meet in the middle of the circle at the center point; 360° because $4 \times 90° = 360°$)

Creative Thinking

Visual Problem Solving How many squares do you see? How many right angles do you see? (10; 36)

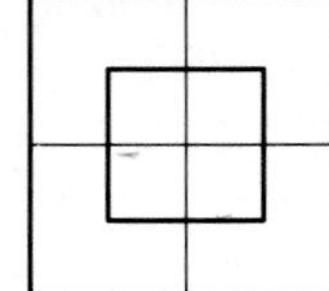

Classwork and Homework Supplements

Practice

Skills Maintenance 11-2

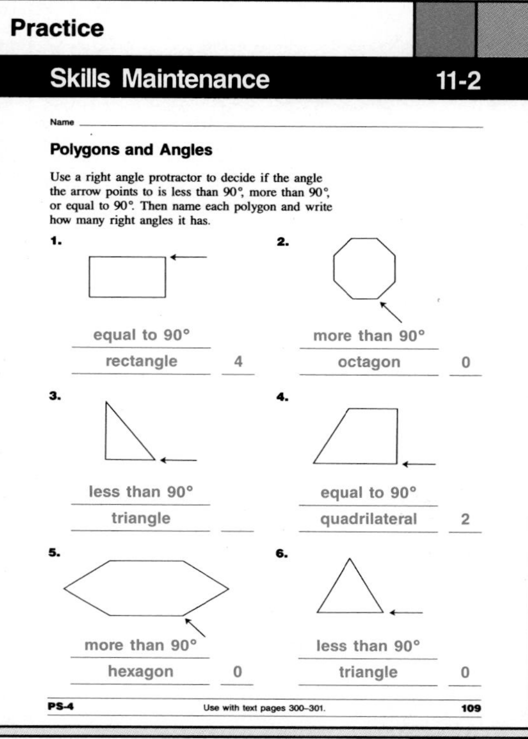

Name

Polygons and Angles

Use a right angle protractor to decide if the angle the arrow points to is less than 90°, more than 90°, or equal to 90°. Then name each polygon and write how many right angles it has.

1. equal to 90° — rectangle — 4
2. more than 90° — octagon — 0
3. less than 90° — triangle
4. equal to 90° — quadrilateral — 2
5. more than 90° — hexagon — 0
6. less than 90° — triangle — 0

PS-4 Use with text pages 300-301. 109

Building Thinking Skills

Problem Solving 11-2

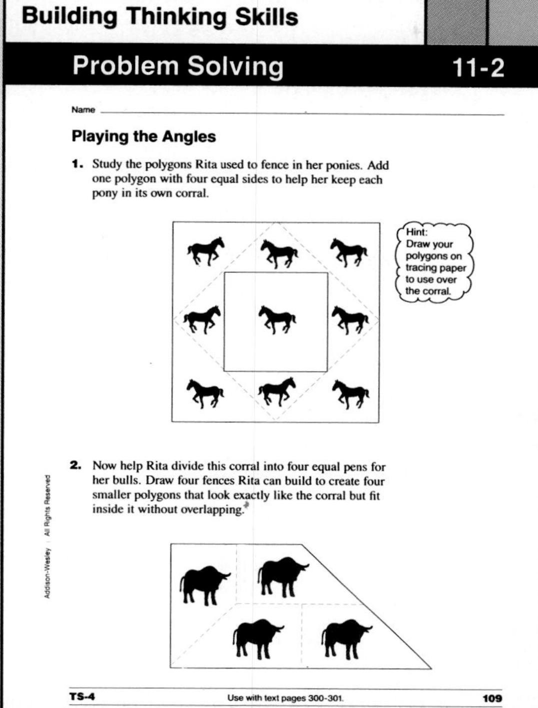

Name

Playing the Angles

1. Study the polygons Rita used to fence in her ponies. Add one polygon with four equal sides to help her keep each pony in its own corral.

Hint: Draw your polygons on tracing paper to use over the corral.

2. Now help Rita divide this corral into four equal pens for her bulls. Draw four fences Rita can build to create four smaller polygons that look exactly like the corral but fit inside it without overlapping.

Addison-Wesley | All Rights Reserved

TS-4 Use with text pages 300-301. 109

Reteaching

Skills Review 11-2

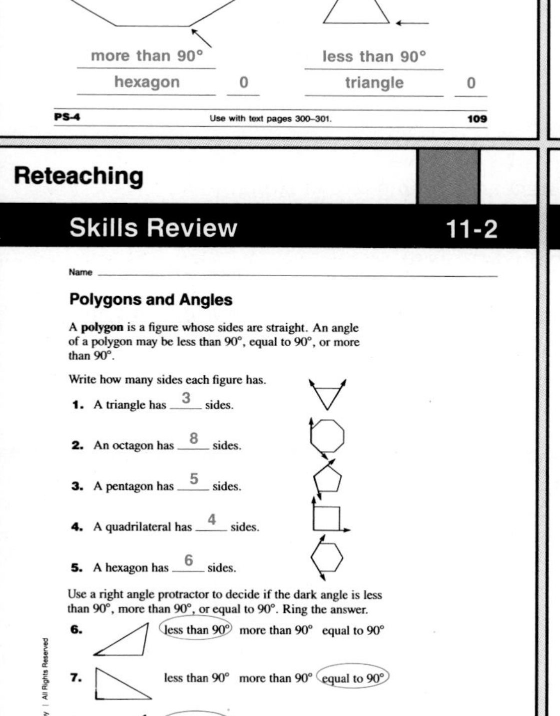

Name

Polygons and Angles

A **polygon** is a figure whose sides are straight. An angle of a polygon may be less than 90°, equal to 90°, or more than 90°.

Write how many sides each figure has.

1. A triangle has 3 sides.
2. An octagon has 8 sides.
3. A pentagon has 5 sides.
4. A quadrilateral has 4 sides.
5. A hexagon has 6 sides.

Use a right angle protractor to decide if the dark angle is less than 90°, more than 90°, or equal to 90°. Ring the answer.

6. (less than 90°) more than 90° equal to 90°
7. less than 90° more than 90° (equal to 90°)
8. (less than 90°) more than 90° equal to 90°
9. less than 90° (more than 90°) equal to 90°
10. less than 90° (more than 90°) equal to 90°

Addison-Wesley | All Rights Reserved

RS-4 Use with text pages 300-301. 109

Challenges

Data Analysis 11-2

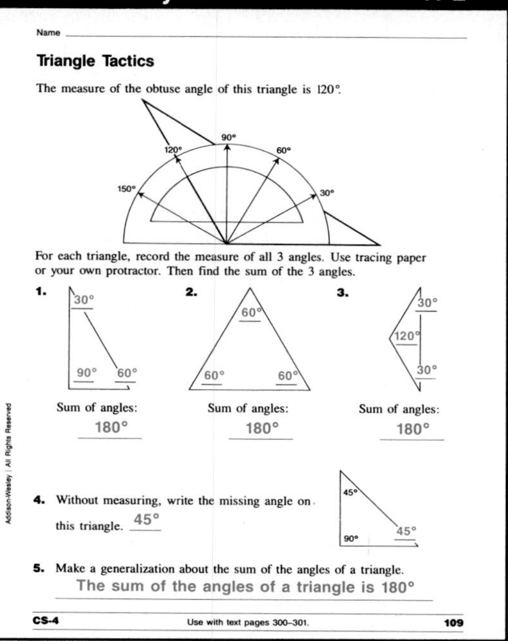

Name

Triangle Tactics

The measure of the obtuse angle of this triangle is 120°.

For each triangle, record the measure of all 3 angles. Use tracing paper or your own protractor. Then find the sum of the 3 angles.

1. 30°, 90°, 60° — Sum of angles: 180°
2. 60°, 60°, 60° — Sum of angles: 180°
3. 30°, 120°, 30° — Sum of angles: 180°

4. Without measuring, write the missing angle on this triangle. 45°

5. Make a generalization about the sum of the angles of a triangle.
The sum of the angles of a triangle is 180°

Addison-Wesley | All Rights Reserved

CS-4 Use with text pages 300-301. 109

Options for Individual Needs

11-2

Basic

Exercises 1-14
More Practice, p. 521, set E

Supplements
Reteaching 109 or
Practice 109
Challenges 109

Average

Exercises 1-20
More Practice, p. 521, set E

Supplements
Practice 109
Challenges 109 or
Thinking Skills 109

Extended

Exercises 1-17

Supplements
Challenges 109
Thinking Skills 109

Other Resources:
Math In Stride, Grade 4, pp. 120, 121
Mathematics, A Way of Thinking, Lesson 20-2
Challenge E, A Program for the Mathematically Talented, Teacher's Edition, Activity 36

LESSON PLAN 11-2

OBJECTIVE 11-2
To name polygon plane figures and compare their angles to 90°

1. MOTIVATE AND TEACH

LEARN ABOUT IT

Materials: tracing paper, inch graph paper, right angle protractors

EXPLORE ► **Explain why a square is used as a symbol for a right angle.** (Squares have four 90° angles.)
► **Describe angles greater or less than 90°.** (Possible answer: Angles greater than 90° open wider than right-angle corners; angles less than 90° are more closed than right angles.)

TALK ABOUT IT ► **Explain what defines a triangle if it can be different shapes.** (Possible answer: It always has 3 sides.)
► **Identify quadrilaterals by other names.** (Possible answers: diamond; square; rectangle; box)
► **Must all quadrilaterals have right angles? Explain.** (No, a quadrilateral must have 4 sides, but the sides could be slanted so that the angles would not be 90°)
► **What associations can help you recall the names of other polygons?** (Possible answer: U.S. *Pentagon*; the *x* in *six*; *octo*pus)
Student Edition answers: **1.** Stop sign (largest), yield sign (smallest) **2.** Possible answer: Angles more closed than a right angle are less than 90°; angles more open are greater.

2. CHECK UNDERSTANDING

TRY IT OUT

ERROR ALERT **Exercise 1** Incorrectly comparing angles to 90°. **Exercise 2** Incorrectly measuring angles.

Polygons and Angles

LEARN ABOUT IT

EXPLORE **Use a Right Angle Protractor**
Use tracing paper to make a right angle protractor like the one shown here. Find some objects with different size angles and use your protractor to decide if the angles are more, less, or equal to 90°. Make a table to record your conclusions.

Right Angle Protractor

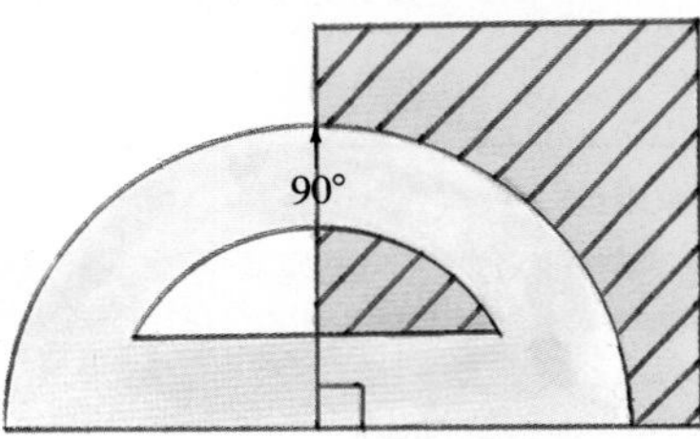

The corner of a square is a **right angle**. It measures 90 degrees (90°).

TALK ABOUT IT See teaching notes.

1. Which object has the largest angle? the smallest?
2. How would you explain to someone how to use the protractor to compare an angle to 90°?

Here are some special polygons with an angle of each shown in red.

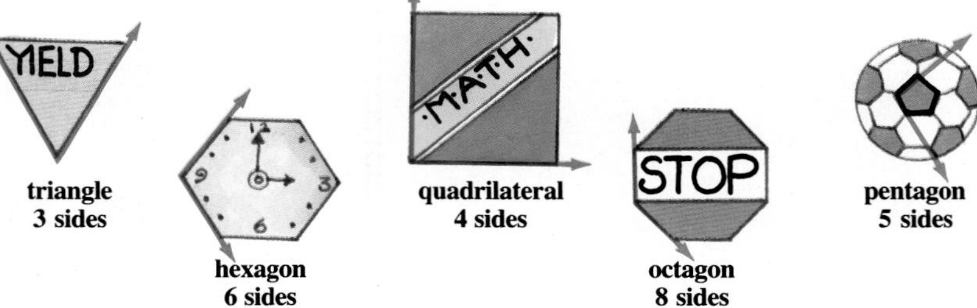

TRY IT OUT

1. Try to make a model of a right angle with pieces of string, strips of cardboard, or by folding paper. Check students' models.
2. Use a right angle protractor to draw these.
   a. a triangle with one angle greater than 90°
   b. a quadrilateral with 2 angles less than 90° Check students' drawings.

TEACHING OPTIONS

RETEACHING TIPS Have students draw a right angle along graph-paper squares. Then they "close" 1 side of the angle to form an adjusted angle less than 90°. Once this angle is prepared, have students draw another angle less than 90°. Assign Reteaching Supplement 109.

ENRICHMENT On dot paper (TA 15), have students draw 2 different polygons of their own design, then highlight all right angles in red, all angles less than 90° in blue, and all angles greater than 90° in green. Have them name each polygon based on the number of sides or kind of angles it has.

PRACTICE

Use a right angle protractor to decide if the red angle is less than 90°, more than 90°, or equal to 90°.

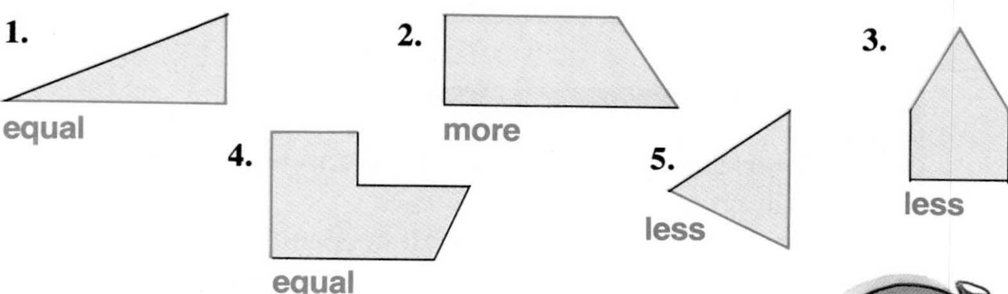

3. less

5. less

6. Name each polygon in exercises 1–5 and tell how many sides it has. See Additional Answers.
7. Tell how many right angles each polygon has in exercises 1–5. See Additional Answers.

APPLY

MATH REASONING Check students' drawings.

8. Draw a polygon that looks like this.

4 sides	1 angle more than a right angle
2 right angles	1 angle less than a right angle

PROBLEM SOLVING

9. Cathy made a square pen for her baby ducks. She used 24 feet of fence. How long was each side of the pen? 6 ft
10. Tim took 120 steps to walk around a rectangular field. He took 20 steps to walk along the width of the field. How long is the field? 40 steps

MIXED REVIEW

Divide.

11. $2\overline{)13}$ 6 R1
12. $6\overline{)45}$ 7 R3
13. $5\overline{)150}$ 30
14. $8\overline{)\$8.00}$ \$1.00
15. $9\overline{)75}$ 8 R3
16. $6\overline{)360}$ 60
17. $2\overline{)\$4.20}$ \$2.10
18. $8\overline{)240}$ 30
19. $5\overline{)\$3.00}$ \$0.60
20. $4\overline{)\$8.64}$ \$2.16

More Practice, page 521, set E

3. PRACTICE AND APPLY

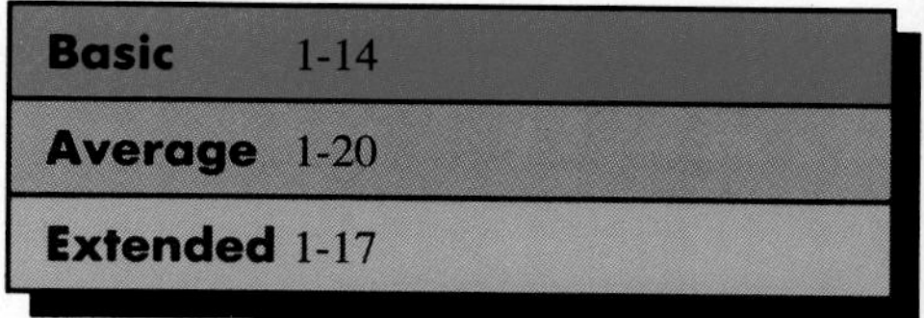

Basic	1-14
Average	1-20
Extended	1-17

Additional Answers: See p. T79.

PRACTICE

Look at Exercises 1-5. Estimate just by looking at the red angles which polygons have red angles that are right angles. Explain your reasoning. (Exercises 1 and 4; possible explanation: In Exercises 1 and 4, the red angles look like the right angles in a square or rectangle.)

APPLY

MATH REASONING ► To what group of polygons will the drawing belong? Explain your reasoning. (quadrilaterals; It will have 4 sides.)

PROBLEM SOLVING ► What fact about the pen will help you solve Problem 9? Explain. (the fact that it is a square; All sides will be equal.)

MIXED REVIEW ► Why will the answers to Exercises 14, 17, 19, and 20 be different? (They will be money amounts with dollar signs and decimal points.)

CLOSE AND ASSESS

PROVE WHAT YOU KNOW

Have each student use a right-angle protractor to prove this statement to be true or false: Any polygon can include at least 1 right angle. Then ask each student to try drawing a right angle as part of a triangle, a quadrilateral, a pentagon, a hexagon, and an octagon. (true; Check students' drawings.)

QUICK QUIZ

Match.

1. hexagon	**a.** 4 sides	(1-c)
2. pentagon	**b.** 5 sides	(2-b)
3. octagon	**c.** 6 sides	(3-d)
4. quadrilateral	**d.** 8 sides	(4-a)

LESSON OPTIONS 11-3

Analyzing Polygons: Parallel and Perpendicular Lines

OBJECTIVE 11-3 To identify parallel and perpendicular lines

PREBOOK ACTIVITIES

QUICK REVIEW

Match.

1. rectangle **a.** 4 sides (2 long and 2 short)
2. triangle **b.** 4 equal sides
3. pentagon **c.** 3 sides
4. hexagon **d.** 5 sides
5. square **e.** 6 sides (**1.** a **2.** c **3.** d **4.** e **5.** b)

PRIOR KNOWLEDGE

Draw 2 perpendicular lines on the chalkboard. Have students find a relationship between the lines. (Possible answer: Right angles form where they meet.) Then draw 2 parallel lines and have students notice their relationship. (Possible answer: They are side by side; they do not meet.) Ask students to identify geometric figures or real-life objects that have parallel lines (rectangles, window blinds, bookshelves) or perpendicular lines (T-square, the letter *L,* table legs.)

COMMUNICATION

Discussing and Reading Math Write the words **parallel** and **perpendicular** on the chalkboard. Have students pronounce them after you. Ask them to identify a clue in the spelling of *parallel* that might help them remember its meaning. (The *ll* resembles parallel lines.) Have students explain how the terms relate to each other. (Possible answer: Perpendicular lines meet at a right angle, but parallel lines never meet at any angle.) Challenge students to tell how 2 lines could cross, or **intersect,** without being perpendicular. (Possible answer: They could meet at angles greater or less than 90°.)

EXPLORE AND CONNECT

Materials: craft sticks, TA 12 (Centimeter Graph Paper), right angle protractors
Grouping Suggestion: small cooperative learning groups
Groups explore **parallel, intersecting,** and **perpendicular** lines. Members arrange 2 craft sticks on graph paper any way they wish to represent lines. Other group members test whether the lines are *parallel, perpendicular,* or *intersecting* at nonright angles. (Possible strategies: Check whether equal numbers of graph paper boxes separate *parallel* lines; use protractors to measure whether *intersecting* lines meet at right angles.) Groups plan strategies to test lines that do not touch yet appear not to be *parallel.* (Possible strategy: Extend the lines with extra sticks until they meet.) Have students generalize about *parallel, perpendicular,* and *intersecting* lines. (Possible answers: *Parallel* lines never meet; *perpendicular* lines make a right-angle *intersection.*)

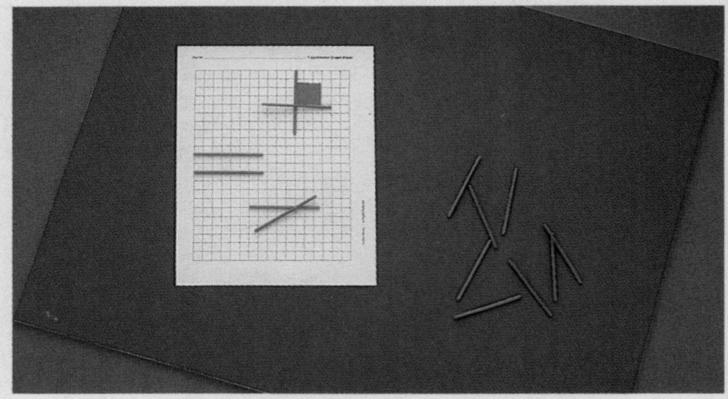

CONNECTIONS Use these anytime.

Problem of the Day

Data Analysis Classify any 10 of the uppercase letters of the alphabet by those formed with parallel lines, perpendicular lines, intersecting lines that do not form a right angle, no pairs of lines, or some combination. Summarize your findings. (Answers may vary.)

Subject Integration

Fine Arts Examine a song in a music book. Locate as many perpendicular and parallel lines as you can that help notate the music. (Samples: parallel—5 ledger lines, successive bar lines; perpendicular—note stems to ledger lines, bar lines to ledger lines)

Creative Thinking

Math Art Use dot paper, colored markers or pencils, and a straightedge to create designs with intersecting lines. (Students' designs will vary.)

Classwork and Homework Supplements

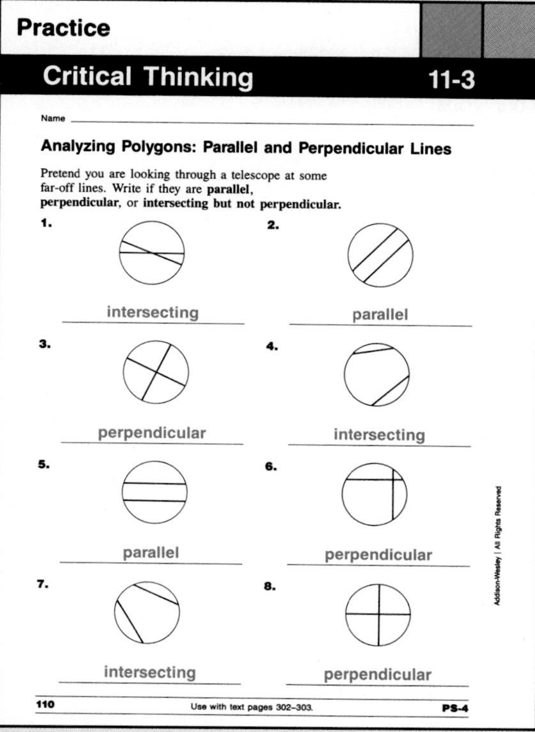

Practice

Critical Thinking 11-3

Name

Analyzing Polygons: Parallel and Perpendicular Lines

Pretend you are looking through a telescope at some far-off lines. Write if they are **parallel**, **perpendicular**, or **intersecting but not perpendicular.**

1. intersecting
2. parallel
3. perpendicular
4. intersecting
5. parallel
6. perpendicular
7. intersecting
8. perpendicular

Addison-Wesley | All Rights Reserved

110 Use with text pages 302–303. PS-4

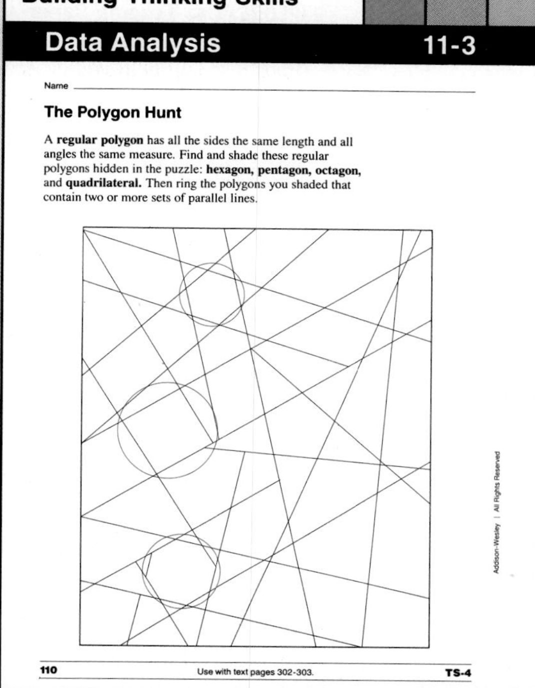

Building Thinking Skills

Data Analysis 11-3

Name

The Polygon Hunt

A **regular polygon** has all the sides the same length and all angles the same measure. Find and shade these regular polygons hidden in the puzzle: **hexagon, pentagon, octagon,** and **quadrilateral.** Then ring the polygons you shaded that contain two or more sets of parallel lines.

Addison-Wesley | All Rights Reserved

110 Use with text pages 302–303. TS-4

Reteaching

Skills Review 11-3

Name

Analyzing Polygons: Parallel and Perpendicular Lines

Two lines that never meet are called **parallel** lines.

Two lines that meet in a right angle are called **perpendicular** lines.

A C E B D

Write the letter of the figure described.

1. a polygon with 1 pair of parallel sides A
2. a quadrilateral with no parallel or perpendicular sides C
3. a polygon with 1 pair of perpendicular sides B
4. a polygon with 2 pairs of parallel sides E
5. Ring the quadrilateral with 2 pairs of parallel sides.
6. Ring the triangle with a pair of perpendicular sides.
7. Ring the quadrilateral with 2 pairs of perpendicular sides.

Challenges

Cooperative Activities 11-3

Name

Create a Town

Work in a small group of 3 or 4. Follow these steps:

1. Let each member of your group pick a row of clues.
2. Cover the other rows as you copy your clues onto small sheets of paper.
3. Work together. Read your clues to one another, but do not show them to other group members.
4. The goal is to label the streets and buildings.

Clues

Birch Rd. is south of Oak Rd. and west of Washington Ave.	Pine Ave. is perpendicular to Jefferson Rd.	The railroad tracks are south of Birch Rd. and parallel to Oak Rd.
Washington Ave. is between Buckeye Ave. and Pine Ave.	Jefferson Rd. is north of Lincoln Rd. and parallel to Oak Rd.	Fire station is on the S.E. corner of Lincoln and Washington.
Police station is on the S.W. corner of Pine and Jefferson.	Birch Road is perpendicular to Pine Ave.	Lincoln Rd. is between Jefferson Rd. and Oak Rd.

Jefferson Road
Police Station
Lincoln Road
Fire Station
Oak Road
Birch Road
Buckeye Ave.
Washington Ave.
Pine Ave.
N W E S

Options for Individual Needs

11-3

Basic

Exercises 1-10
More Practice, p. 522, set A

Supplements
Reteaching 110 or
Practice 110
Thinking Skills 110

Average

Exercises 1-10
More Practice, p. 522, set A

Supplements
Practice 110
Challenges 110 or
Thinking Skills 110

Extended

Exercises 1-10

Supplements
Challenges 110
Thinking Skills 110

Other Resources:
Problem-Solving Experiences in Mathematics, Grade 4, Problem 108
Math In Stride, Grade 4, pp. 217

LESSON PLAN 11-3

OBJECTIVE 11-3
To identify parallel and perpendicular lines

Materials: tracing paper, oaktag

Grouping Suggestion: pairs

1. MOTIVATE AND TEACH

LEARN ABOUT IT

EXPLORE ▶ **Are there any perpendicular parts of railroad tracks? Explain.** (Yes, the rails are perpendicular to the ties.)
▶ **Explain how to prove that the intersection is really perpendicular.** (Use a protractor to check for a right angle where lines meet.)
▶ **Explain how to prove that lines are parallel.** (Measure to check that they are always the same distance apart.)

TALK ABOUT IT ▶ **Explain how a square can have both perpendicular and parallel sides.** (Every side has 1 side parallel to it and 2 sides perpendicular to it.)
▶ **Compare the lines of a square and the l es of a triangle.** (A square has parallel and perpendicular lines; a triangle has perpendicular or intersecting lines but never parallel lines.)
Student Edition answers: **1.** A square has 2 pairs of parallel and 2 pairs of perpendicular sides. **2.** No, because at least 2 additional sides are needed to close a figure with 2 parallel sides, and a triangle has a total of only 3 sides, not 4 sides.

2. CHECK UNDERSTANDING

TRY IT OUT

ERROR ALERT Confusing the meanings of parallel and perpendicular. Classifying all intersecting lines as perpendicular.

Analyzing Polygons
Parallel and Perpendicular Lines

LEARN ABOUT IT

EXPLORE Use Tracing Paper
These pictures show some special types of lines that will help you describe polygons.

railroad tracks → **parallel lines**

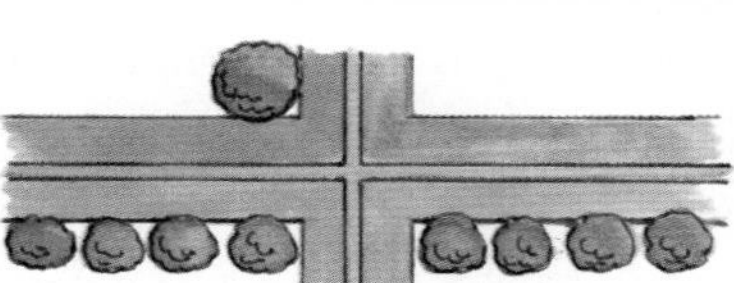

intersection → **perpendicular lines**

Look for these polygons in the picture. Find one example of each and use tracing paper to copy them.

- a polygon with a pair of parallel sides
- a triangle with a pair of perpendicular sides
- a polygon with no parallel or perpendicular sides

TALK ABOUT IT See teaching notes.

1. How would you use the words parallel and perpendicular to tell about the sides of a square?
2. Can a triangle have a pair of parallel sides? Explain.

Intersecting lines meet in a point. **Parallel** lines do not meet. **Perpendicular** lines meet to form a right angle.

TRY IT OUT Answers will vary.

1. Find some other objects around you that suggest parallel, perpendicular, or intersecting lines.
2. Find some ways to make models of intersecting, parallel, and perpendicular lines. You may want to fold paper or use pieces of string.

TEACHING OPTIONS

RETEACHING TIPS Have students make oaktag cards like those pictured below to help them recall the difference between perpendicular and parallel lines.

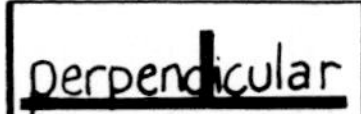

Assign Reteaching Supplement 110.

ENRICHMENT Have partners use a map from an atlas, a travel guide, or a social studies book to make up questions with the terms *parallel, perpendicular,* and *intersecting*. Students create questions that ask their partner to interpret the map, such as: *What street is perpendicular to Pine?*

PRACTICE

Do you think the lines in these circles are parallel, perpendicular, or intersecting but not perpendicular? See Additional Answers.

1. 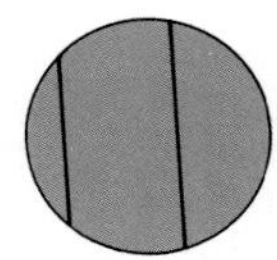

2. 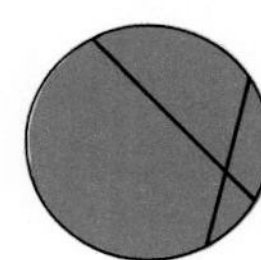

3. 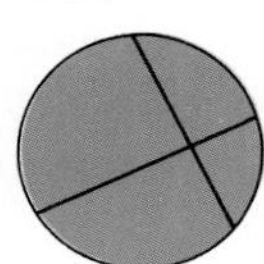

4. Make a pattern of squares like this. Then color pairs of lines that you think will be parallel, intersecting, or perpendicular when the pattern is folded to make a cube. Fold and tape to make the cube, then check your colored lines. Check students' models.

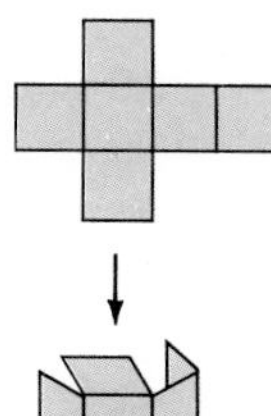

APPLY

MATH REASONING

5. At what times each day are the hands of a clock perpendicular with the minute hand pointing to 12? 3:00 and 9:00

6. At about what time would the clock hands be perpendicular when the hour hand is between 2 and 3? about 2:25

PROBLEM SOLVING

7. Doli rode her bicycle up First Street to where it intersected Hill Street. Her plan was to make a perpendicular right turn and go one block, repeating this until she got back to First Street. If the blocks are rectangular, how many turns would she have to make? 3 turns

8. Carl thought he would try and make a triangle with 2 parallel lines and 1 acute angle. Is this possible? Explain. No; the figure would not be closed.

▶ **COMMUNICATION Write to Learn**

Copy and complete each sentence. See Additional Answers.

9. If bookshelves were not parallel to the floor, __?__.

10. If playground slides were perpendicular to the ground, __?__.

More Practice, page 522, set A

3. Practice and Apply

Basic	1-10
Average	1-10
Extended	1-10

Additional Answers: See p. T79.

PRACTICE

Look at Exercises 1-3. Explain how to test whether lines are perpendicular, parallel, or intersecting but not at right angles. (Possible answers: Use a protractor; visually estimate.)

APPLY

MATH REASONING ▶ **What strategy would you use to solve Exercises 5 and 6? Explain.** (Possible answer: Draw a picture of a clock face to test where lines are perpendicular.)

PROBLEM SOLVING ▶ **Can it help to draw Carl's triangle? Explain why.** (Yes, then you can see whether the figure is possible to draw.)

COMMUNICATION ▶ **Explain how to use cause and effect to complete the sentences.** (Possible answer: The sentences each give a cause; use common sense to visualize a result of each.)

11-3

Close and Assess

WRITE WHAT YOU THINK

Have students identify streets in the area or sidewalks near the school that they think are parallel, perpendicular, or neither. Ask students to write a sentence to explain each choice. (Answers will vary. Check students' writing.)

Quick Quiz

Draw each situation. (Answers vary.)

1. a number with digits suggesting parallel lines (11)

2. an operation symbol with perpendicular lines (+)

LESSON OPTIONS 11-4

Symmetric Figures

OBJECTIVE 11-4 To make symmetric figures and identify lines of symmetry

PREBOOK ACTIVITIES

QUICK REVIEW

How many flat faces are in each space figure?

1. triangular prism (5)
2. cone (1)
3. cube (6)
4. rectangular prism (6)
5. sphere (0)
6. cylinder (2)
7. square pyramid (5)
8. triangular pyramid (4)

PRIOR KNOWLEDGE

Cut a half of a heart on folded paper as students watch. Before you open it, have students tell why the open shape will look like a heart if you cut only a half. (Possible answer: You cut along a fold, so when you unfold it, you see a heart of 2 equal, attached parts.) Have students relate the parts of the heart to the fold. (The fold separates 2 same-sized parts.) Explain that the fold is along a line of symmetry that separates equal parts. Have students name some real objects that are symmetrical, meaning that they can be divided into 2 parts that are identical. (Possible answers: a bicycle wheel; a butterfly)

COMMUNICATION

Discussing Math Compare the math terms **line of symmetry** and **symmetric**. (Possible answer: *Line of symmetry* is a noun phrase that names the line or fold that separates identical parts of a figure; *symmetric* is an adjective that describes the figure.) Have students describe the direction of the heart's line of symmetry. (vertical) Ask if students think lines of symmetry must be vertical; if they do not think so, have them offer a counterexample. (no; For instance, a square can have a vertical, horizontal, or diagonal line of symmetry.)

EXPLORE AND CONNECT

Materials: pattern blocks, TA 19 (Tangram), colored cubes or rods
Alternative Materials: TA 12 (Centimeter Graph Paper), crayons
Grouping Suggestion: cooperative learning pairs
Partners explore **symmetry** by making mirror-image designs with manipulative materials. A student places a pattern block, tangram piece, or a cube or rod on a table (or colors a graph-paper box). His or her partner responds by adding a piece identical to it across an imaginary **line of symmetry.** Partners expand their cooperative designs, piece by piece in turn, always observing the *line of symmetry*. When time is up, each pair studies another pair's design to locate its *line of symmetry*. Conclude by having students define *lines of symmetry* and *symmetric* figures. (Possible answer: *Lines of symmetry* separate the identical parts of *symmetric* figures.)

CONNECTIONS Use these anytime.

Problem of the Day

Logical Thinking Dawn's great-great grandfather was born in the 1800s in a year that has both a vertical and a horizontal line of symmetry. What year is it? (1881)

Creative Thinking

Frustrating Flurries Tony was making symmetric snowflakes from folded paper. When he finished cutting, the snowflake halves fell apart. Explain what you think happened. (Tony cut away the folds, so the parts were not attached anymore.)

Patterns

Counting Parts Identify and complete the pattern:
1 line of symmetry = 2 identical parts
2 lines of symmetry = (4) identical parts
4 lines of symmetry = (8) identical parts
8 lines of symmetry = (16) identical parts

Classwork and Homework Supplements

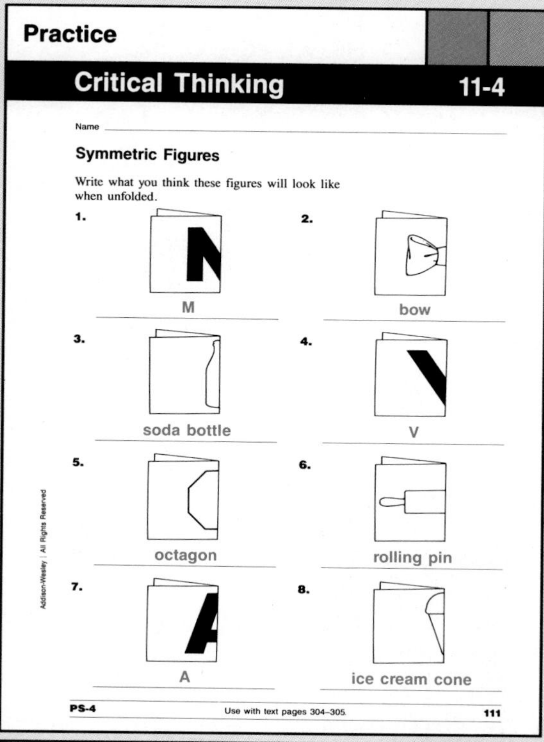

Practice
Critical Thinking 11-4
Name
Symmetric Figures
Write what you think these figures will look like when unfolded.
1. M
2. bow
3. soda bottle
4. V
5. octagon
6. rolling pin
7. A
8. ice cream cone
Addison-Wesley | All Rights Reserved
PS-4 Use with text pages 304-305. 111

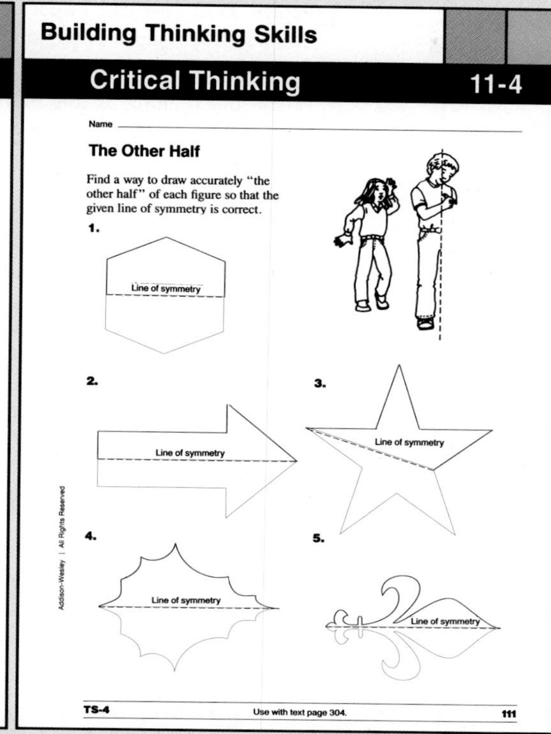

Building Thinking Skills
Critical Thinking 11-4
Name
The Other Half
Find a way to draw accurately "the other half" of each figure so that the given line of symmetry is correct.
1. Line of symmetry
2. Line of symmetry
3. Line of symmetry
4. Line of symmetry
5. Line of symmetry
Addison-Wesley | All Rights Reserved
TS-4 Use with text page 304. 111

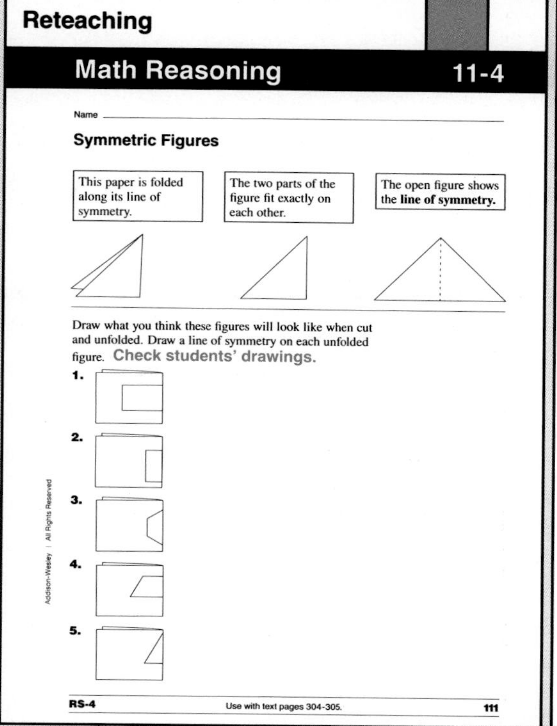

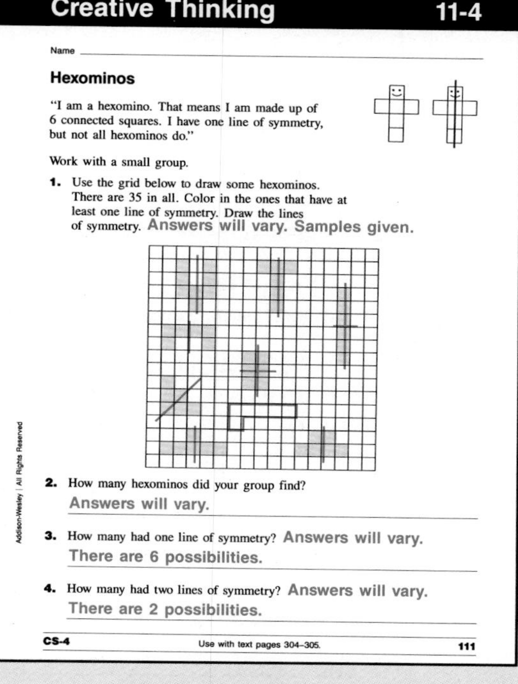

Challenges
Creative Thinking 11-4
Name
Hexominos
"I am a hexomino. That means I am made up of 6 connected squares. I have one line of symmetry, but not all hexominos do."
Work with a small group.
1. Use the grid below to draw some hexominos. There are 35 in all. Color in the ones that have at least one line of symmetry. Draw the lines of symmetry. Answers will vary. Samples given.
2. How many hexominos did your group find? Answers will vary.
3. How many had one line of symmetry? Answers will vary. There are 6 possibilities.
4. How many had two lines of symmetry? Answers will vary. There are 2 possibilities.
Addison-Wesley | All Rights Reserved
CS-4 Use with text pages 304-305. 111

Options for Individual Needs

Basic

Exercises 2-10

Supplements
Reteaching 111 or
Practice 111

Average

Exercises 1-10

Supplements
Practice 111
Challenges 111 or
Thinking Skills 111

Extended

Exercises 3-10

Supplements
Challenges 111
Thinking Skills 111

Other Resources:
Problem-Solving Experiences in Mathematics, Grade 4, Problem 111
Math In Stride, Grade 4, p. 87
Mathematics, A Way of Thinking, Lesson 20-1

LESSON PLAN 11-4

OBJECTIVE 11-4
To make symmetric figures and identify lines of symmetry

Materials: tracing paper, scissors

1. MOTIVATE AND TEACH

LEARN ABOUT IT

EXPLORE ▶ **Explain why the apple can be called a symmetric figure.** (It has a line of symmetry with 2 parts that fit exactly on each other.)
▶ **Could you cut symmetric figures without folded paper? Explain.** (Possibly, but it would be harder to make sure that both sides are exactly alike.)

TALK ABOUT IT ▶ **If a figure is cut from paper folded exactly in half, explain what must be true about the 2 parts.** (They must have the exact same size and shape because the fold creates the line of symmetry.)
▶ **Visualize how many lines of symmetry a circle has. Explain your thinking.** (It has many; you could fold it in half through its center an infinite number of places to show 2 identical parts.)
▶ **Compare the size of the full design to the size of the part you see in Examples A-C.** (Each design is double the size of the part that is shown because the fold is the line of symmetry.)
Student Edition answers: **1.** Possible answer: It is a line that separates 2 parts of equal size and shape. **2.** yes; circle, square.

2. CHECK UNDERSTANDING

TRY IT OUT

ERROR ALERT Incorrectly cutting the given shape. Failing to use the fold as the line of symmetry.

Symmetric Figures

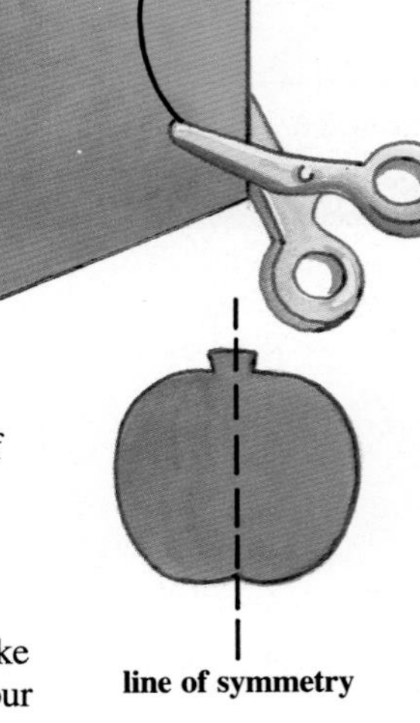

LEARN ABOUT IT

EXPLORE Fold and Cut Paper
You can fold a piece of paper and cut out a figure that has **symmetry**.
When folded along its **line of symmetry**, the two parts of the figure fit exactly upon each other.

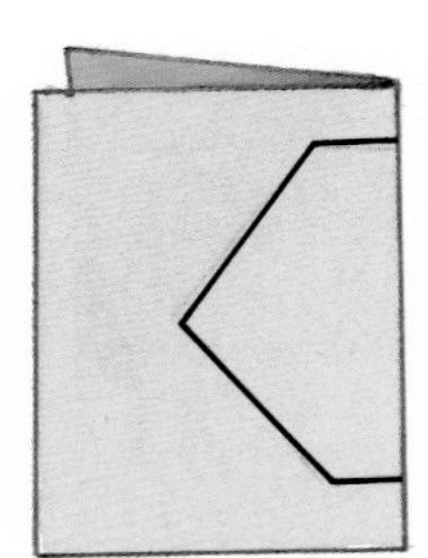

TALK ABOUT IT See teaching notes.

1. How would you describe the line of symmetry of a figure?
2. Could a figure have more than one line of symmetry? Give an example.

■ What symmetric figure would you make with cuts like these? First predict and draw the figure. Then test your prediction.

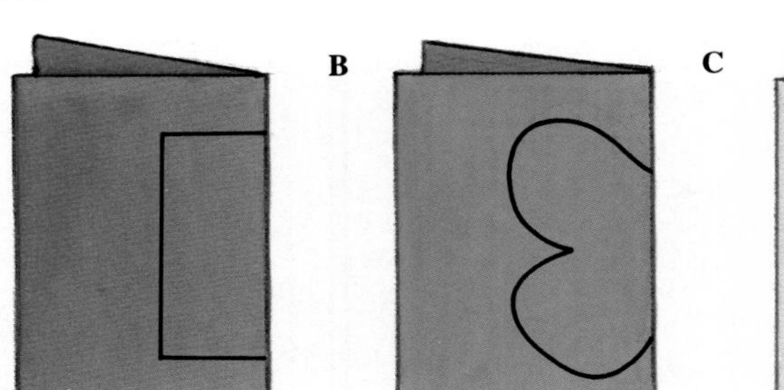

TRY IT OUT

Fold pieces of paper and cut out pieces that will make these symmetric figures when unfolded. Check students' work.

1. rectangle 2. tall thin pumpkin 3. triangle 4. ball

TEACHING OPTIONS

RETEACHING TIPS First have students quickly sketch a completed figure to help them visualize the identical halves across imaginary lines of symmetry. Then they can attempt to cut the appropriate half-figure along the fold to form each symmetric figure. Assign Reteaching Supplement 111.

COMPUTER **Logo Works, Terrapin, Copyright 1985** For students with some Logo experience. The student will use Chapter 4 (with 7 activities) to generate symmetrical geometric figures through guided activities. Each activity requires 35 to 50 min.

PRACTICE

Draw what you think these figures will look like when cut and unfolded. Check by folding and cutting. Check students' drawings.

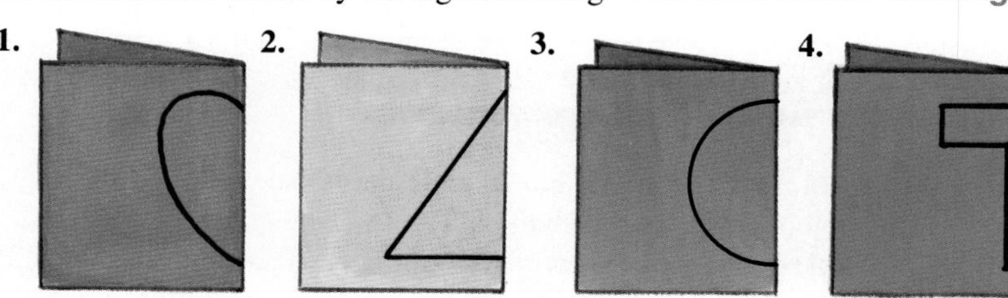

APPLY

MATH REASONING Does the dashed line appear to be a line of symmetry? Find a way to check to be sure.

5. yes 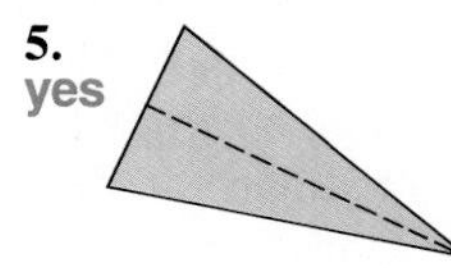

6. no 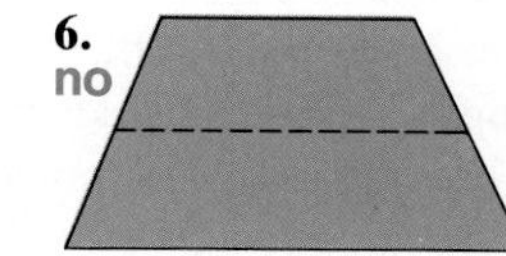

7. no 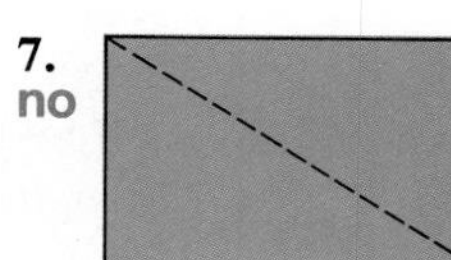

PROBLEM SOLVING

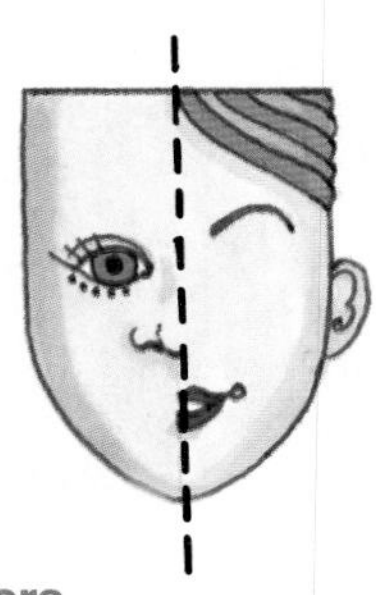

8. Tonya wanted the mask she was making to be symmetrical. It is pictured here, with some parts missing. Can you draw the mask and show the missing parts? Check students' drawings.
9. Nicolo wanted to draw a line of symmetry on the red cross sign on his first aid kit. Can you show 2 different ways he could do this? Draw pictures to show your answer. Check students' drawings.

▶ **COMMUNICATION Find Some Words** See Additional Answers.

10. The word HIDE is a "symmetric word." How many other symmetric words can you find?

    Hint: Which capital letters in the alphabet are symmetric?

 305

3. Practice and Apply

Basic	2-10
Average	1-10
Extended	3-10

Additional Answers: See p. T79.

PRACTICE

Look at Exercises 1-4. Explain how to use tracing paper to confirm what each figure will look like when it is cut and unfolded. (Trace the half shown, then reverse the tracing over the line of symmetry to see the complete figure.)

11-4

APPLY

MATH REASONING ▶ **Compare horizontal, vertical, or diagonal lines of symmetry.** (Direction makes no difference as long as the parts formed by each line are identical halves.)

PROBLEM SOLVING ▶ **Explain how to finish Problem 8.** (Trace what is given; give each part a match across the line of symmetry.)

COMMUNICATION ▶ **Can the line of symmetry in *HIDE* be horizontal and vertical? Explain.** (No, only horizontal because a vertical line between *I* and *D* would not give identical halves.)

Close and Assess

SHOW WHAT YOU KNOW

Have each student make a symmetric letter *H* by cutting a folded piece of paper. Tell students that the line of symmetry they use may be horizontal or vertical. (Check students' letters.)

Quick Quiz

Write *yes* or *no* to tell if each line is a line of symmetry. (**1.** no **2.** yes)

1. **2.**

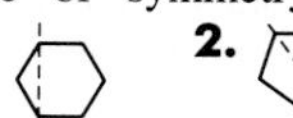

LESSON OPTIONS 11-5

Classifying Angles and Triangles

OBJECTIVE 11-5 To classify triangles and angles

PREBOOK ACTIVITIES

QUICK REVIEW

Visually estimate if the angles are greater than 90°, less than 90°, or equal to 90°.

1. ∠ (less) **2.** ⌞ (greater) **3.** ⌟ (equal)
4. V (less) **5.** ∟ (equal) **6.** ︿ (greater)

PRIOR KNOWLEDGE

Draw a right angle on the chalkboard as students identify it. Ask a volunteer to add a segment to make a triangle. (Connect a point on 1 ray to a point on the other.) Ask volunteers to draw some angles greater than 90° and less than 90°. Then have others form triangles by connecting points on the rays. Tell students they will classify angles and triangles in this lesson, some based on comparisons with right angles.

COMMUNICATION

Listening and Writing in Math Have students copy these terms in their Math Journals: **isosceles, equilateral, obtuse, acute.** Ask them to guess which word means "equal sides" and to give their reasoning. (*equilateral*; It starts with letters that sound like *equal*.) Draw 2 tall isosceles triangles. Pronounce the word *isosceles* and have students use the drawings to deduce the meaning of the term. ("2 equal sides") Then have students listen to this sentence to find the meanings of the remaining terms: A right angle is smaller than an obtuse angle but greater than an acute angle. (*Obtuse* means greater than 90°; *acute* means less than 90°.) Ask students to define the terms in their Math Journals using their own words.

EXPLORE AND CONNECT

Materials: angle and triangle cards (see activity below), geoboards, rubber bands, TA 15 (Dot Paper)
Grouping Suggestion: cooperative learning groups of 3
Students explore angle and triangle relationships. Each group needs 3 angle and 3 triangle cards. (angle cards: **acute** $< 90°$; right $= 90°$; **obtuse** $> 90°$; triangle cards: no equal sides; **isosceles**—2 equal sides; **equilateral**—3 equal sides) One student picks an angle card and forms the angle on the geoboard. The next student picks a triangle card then, based on the first angle, adjusts the rubber band to try to make the pictured triangle. The third student sketches the completed triangle and describes it, then notes if no triangle can be formed with the given angle and sides. Students trade tasks to repeat the activity. Have students summarize their findings. (Possible conclusions: No triangle has a right angle and 3 equal sides; no triangle has an *obtuse* angle and 3 equal sides.)

CONNECTIONS Use these anytime.

Problem of the Day

Creative Problem Solving Count all the triangles you can find in this figure. (28)

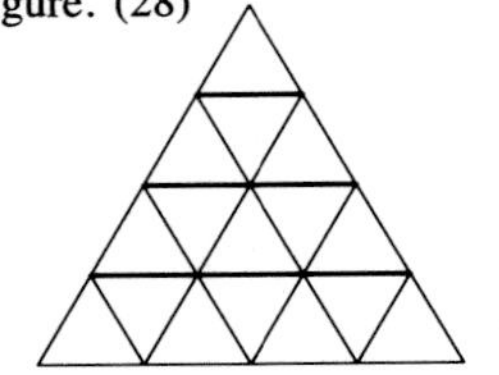

Math Connection

Measurement On centimeter graph paper, draw a triangle with a right angle. Make each side of the right angle 6 cm long. How many square centimeters are inside the triangle? (18 square cm)

Life Skills

Classification Identify these real-life triangles and explain how they relate to each other. An ordinary envelope flap and a team pennant; a doorstop and a bookend. (Envelope flap and team pennant are usually isosceles triangles; doorstop and bookend can both be right triangles.)

Classwork and Homework Supplements

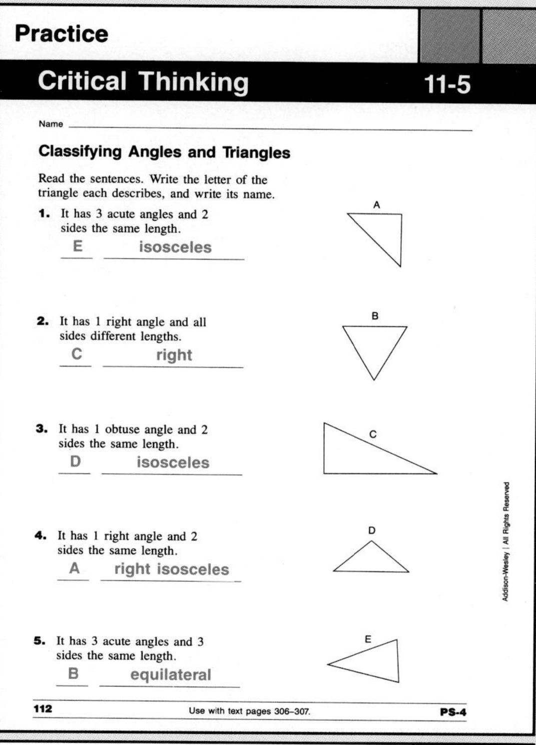

Practice

Critical Thinking 11-5

Name ______________________

Classifying Angles and Triangles

Read the sentences. Write the letter of the triangle each describes, and write its name.

1. It has 3 acute angles and 2 sides the same length. E isosceles
2. It has 1 right angle and all sides different lengths. C right
3. It has 1 obtuse angle and 2 sides the same length. D isosceles
4. It has 1 right angle and 2 sides the same length. A right isosceles
5. It has 3 acute angles and 3 sides the same length. B equilateral

112 Use with text pages 306-307. PS-4

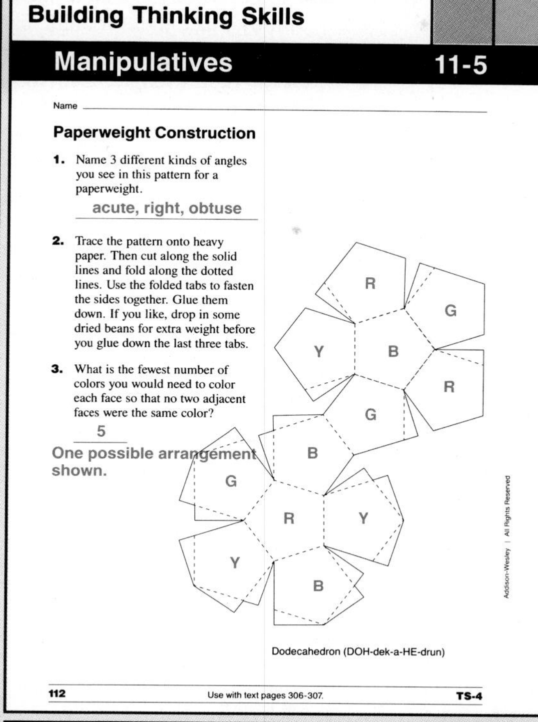

Building Thinking Skills

Manipulatives 11-5

Name ______________________

Paperweight Construction

1. Name 3 different kinds of angles you see in this pattern for a paperweight.
   acute, right, obtuse
2. Trace the pattern onto heavy paper. Then cut along the solid lines and fold along the dotted lines. Use the folded tabs to fasten the sides together. Glue them down. If you like, drop in some dried beans for extra weight before you glue down the last three tabs.
3. What is the fewest number of colors you would need to color each face so that no two adjacent faces were the same color?
   5
   One possible arrangement shown.

Dodecahedron (DOH-dek-a-HE-drun)

112 Use with text pages 306-307. TS-4

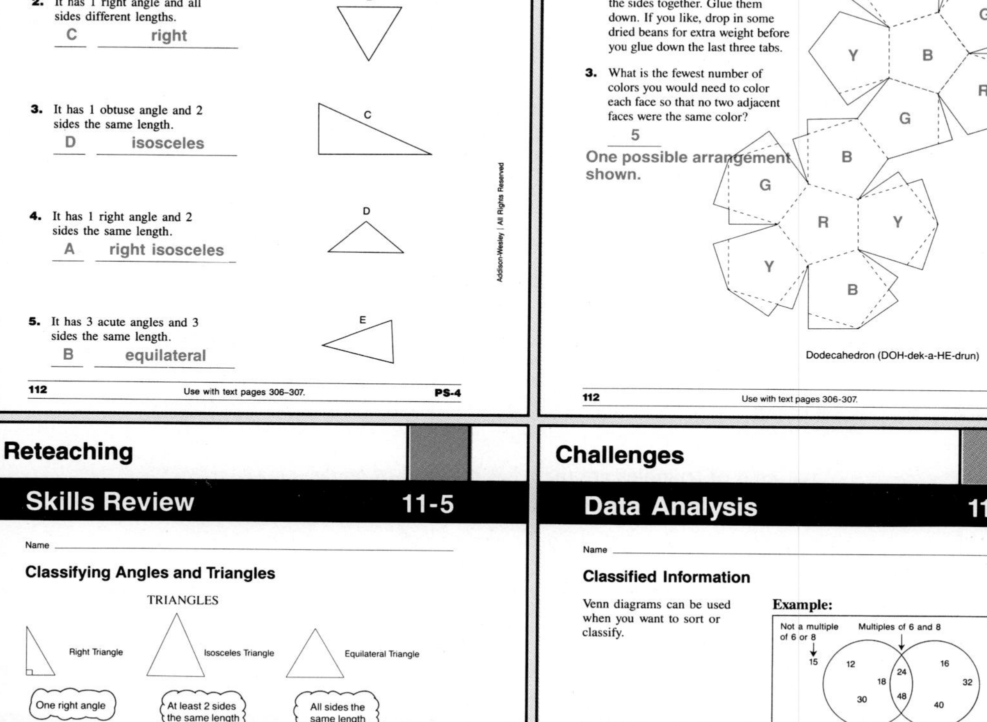

Reteaching

Skills Review 11-5

Name ______________________

Classifying Angles and Triangles

Write the name for each triangle. Then color each acute angle red and each obtuse angle blue.

1. A. isosceles triangle
2. B. equilateral triangle
3. C. right triangle

Write the letter of triangle that matches the description.

4. C has a right angle.
5. A has an obtuse angle and two sides the same length.
6. B has 3 acute angles and 3 sides the same length.

112 Use with text pages 306-307. RS-4

Challenges

Data Analysis 11-5

Name ______________________

Classified Information

Venn diagrams can be used when you want to sort or classify.

Example:

1. Analyze and label the parts of the Venn diagram.

2. Decide where these polygons would go on the Venn diagram above. Draw them in.

112 Use with text pages 306-307. CS-4

Options for Individual Needs

Basic

Exercises 1-7
More Practice, p. 522, set B

Supplements
Reteaching 112 or
Practice 112

Average

Exercises 1-7
More Practice, p. 522, set B

Supplements
Practice 112
Challenges 112 or
Thinking Skills 112

Extended

Exercises 1-7

Supplements
Challenges 112
Thinking Skills 112

Other Resources:
Math In Stride, Grade 4, p. 82
Mathematics, A Way of Thinking, Lessons 13-13—13-15

11-5

LESSON PLAN 11-5

OBJECTIVE 11-5
To classify triangles and angles

Materials: tracing paper, scissors, right-angle protractors

1. MOTIVATE AND TEACH

LEARN ABOUT IT

EXPLORE ► **Compare an isosceles and an equilateral triangle.** (All sides are equal in an equilateral triangle; only 2 are equal in an isosceles triangle.)
► **Could you create an isosceles triangle with a shape different from the picture? Explain.** (It could be short and wide, as long as 2 sides are equal.)
► **Explain how the angles of an equilateral triangle are related.** (They are the same because the sides are all the same.)

TALK ABOUT IT ► **Analyze the triangles to decide what kind of angles they have.** (There are only acute angles and a right angle; no angle is greater than 90°, so none is an obtuse angle.)
► **Could a triangle have an obtuse and a right angle? Explain.** (No, such a figure would need 4 sides to be closed.)
Student Edition answers: **1.** All 3 have acute angles; none has an obtuse angle. **2.** Yes, the right angle's sides can be equal to form an isosceles right triangle. **3.** No, the side opposite the right angle must be longer than the other sides to close the figure.

2. CHECK UNDERSTANDING

TRY IT OUT

ERROR ALERT Difficulty visualizing angles greater or less than 90°.

Classifying Angles and Triangles

LEARN ABOUT IT

EXPLORE Discover a Relationship
Jimmy made these triangle cards to show three types of triangles. Trace and cut out two copies of the right triangle. Can you put the copies together to form an equilateral triangle? an isosceles triangle that is not equilateral? a figure that is not a triangle?

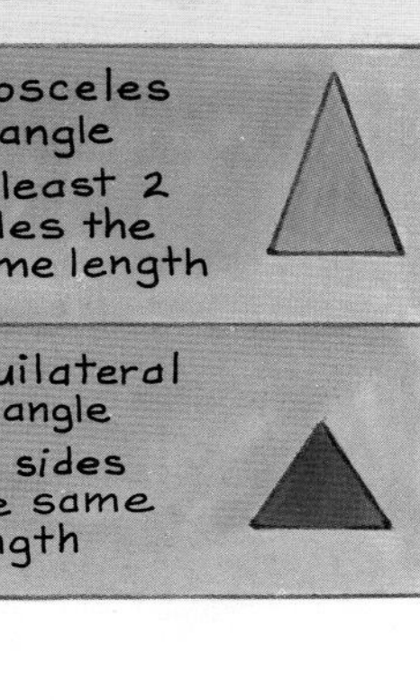

TALK ABOUT IT See teaching notes.

1. Which of the triangles Jimmy made have an angle that measures less than 90°? more than 90°?
2. Is it possible to draw a right triangle that is also isosceles? Explain.
3. Is it possible to draw a right triangle that is also equilateral? Explain.

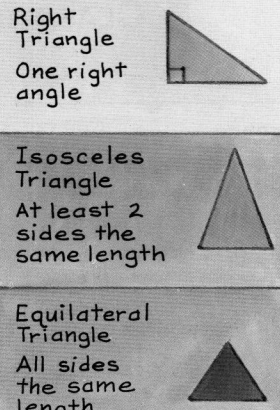

The angles in these triangles all have names.

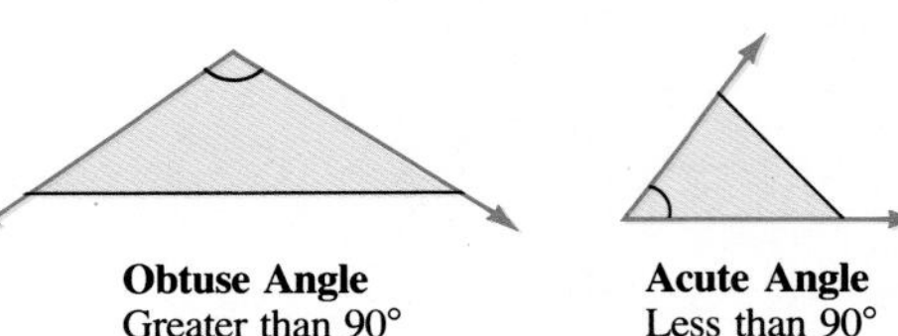

Obtuse Angle
Greater than 90°

Acute Angle
Less than 90°

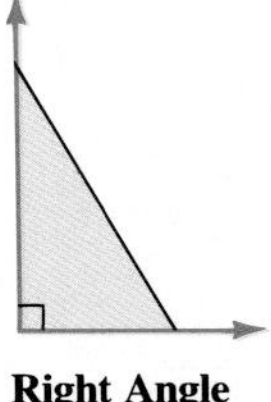

Right Angle
90°

TRY IT OUT

What kind of triangles are these? What kind of angle is the red angle?

1. right triangle, right angle

2. 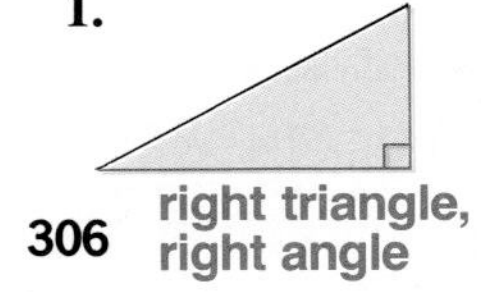 equilateral triangle, acute angle

3. 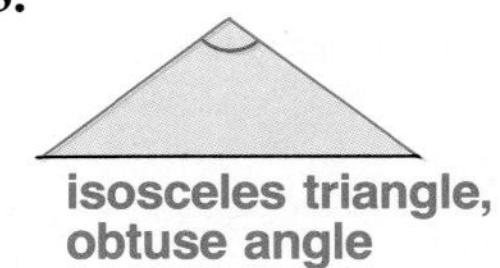 isosceles triangle, obtuse angle

306

TEACHING OPTIONS

RETEACHING TIPS Remind students to focus on the red angle in each figure. Have students measure angles with the simple oaktag protractors they made to use in Lesson 11-2. Students may also use this memory trick: *o*btuse angles *o*pen wide. Assign Reteaching Supplement 112.

ENRICHMENT Students use visual estimation to draw each angle.
1. an acute angle that equals half of a right angle
2. an acute angle that equals a third of a right angle
3. an obtuse angle that equals double a right angle
(**1.** 45°∠ **2.** 30°∠ **3.** 180°∠)

PRACTICE

Read the sentences. Tell which triangle each describes and give its name.

A 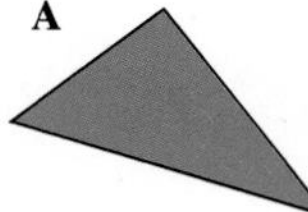 B 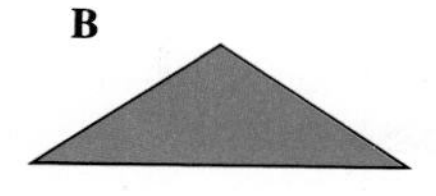 C 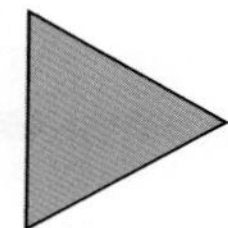 D 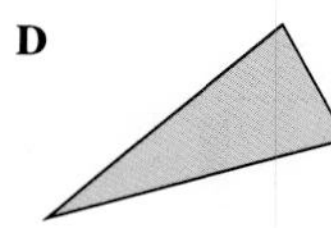

1. It has an obtuse angle and 2 sides the same length. **B, isosceles triangle**
2. It has 3 acute angles and 3 sides the same length. **C, equilateral triangle**
3. It has 3 acute angles and two sides the same length. **D, isosceles triangle**
4. It has a right angle and all sides different lengths. **A, right triangle**

APPLY

MATH REASONING

5. Two isosceles triangles have the same perimeter. Find the missing numbers. What is the perimeter of each triangle? **30**

   8 + |||| + 11 = 12 + |||| + 6
   11 **12**

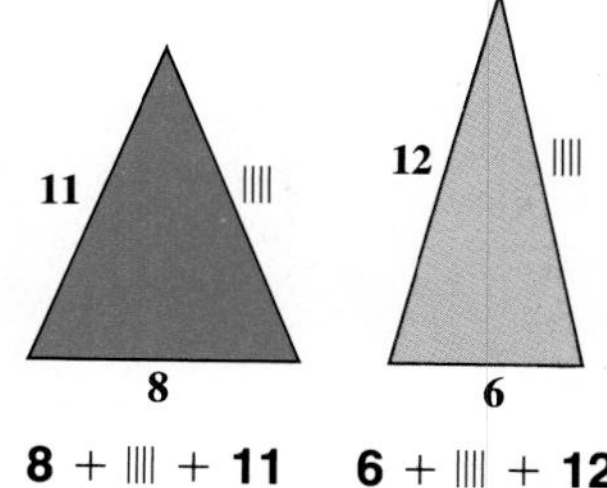

8 + |||| + 11 6 + |||| + 12

PROBLEM SOLVING

6. Linnea had 22 ft of fencing to make a pen for her rabbits. She wanted the pen to be in the shape of a triangle and to have equal sides. She needed an extra foot to fasten the gate. How long should she make each side? **7 ft**

▶ **ESTIMATION**

7. If you cut off the corners of a triangle will they fill half a circle? more than half a circle? less than half a circle? Cut out a triangle and check your estimate.
   equals half a circle

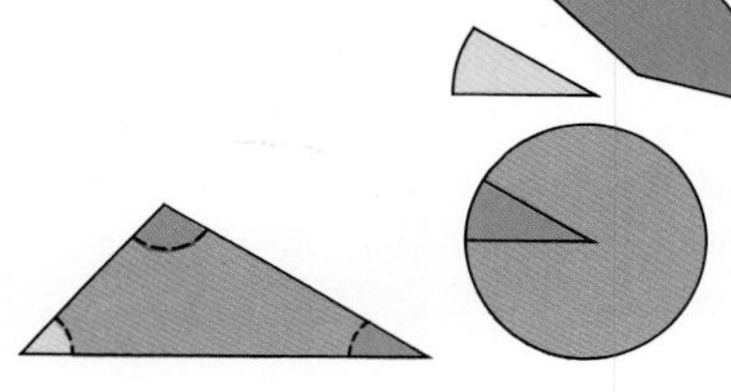

More Practice, page 522, set B

3. Practice and Apply

Basic	1-7
Average	1-7
Extended	1-7

PRACTICE

Look at Exercises 1-4. How could you sort these triangles into groups? (Possible answer: Identify all right triangles, all obtuse angles, or all triangles with equal sides.)

APPLY

MATH REASONING ▶ **What must be true in each set of 3 numbers? Explain why.** (There must be 2 numbers that are the same because an isosceles triangle has 2 equal sides.)

PROBLEM SOLVING ▶ **Explain what operations to use to solve Problem 6.** (Subtract 1 because she took away 1 foot; divide by 3 to get equal groups from 21.)

ESTIMATION ▶ **Analyze the illustration to see how to test your estimate. Explain what to do.** (Possible answer: Put the angle vertices at the center of the circle.)

Close and Assess

SHOW WHAT YOU KNOW

Have students draw and label each figure: an acute angle, a right angle, an obtuse angle, a right triangle, an isosceles triangle, and an equilateral triangle. (Answers may vary slightly. Check students' drawings.)

QUICK QUIZ

Draw the figures.
1. isosceles triangle
2. triangle with an obtuse angle
3. triangle with no equal sides

(Check students' drawings.)

LESSON OPTIONS 11-6

Classifying Quadrilaterals

OBJECTIVE 11-6 To classsify quadrilaterals as squares, rectangles, parallelograms, or trapezoids

PREBOOK ACTIVITIES

QUICK REVIEW

Identify each angle as acute, right, or obtuse.

1. 90° **2.** 30° **3.** 150°

4. 115° **5.** 65° **6.** 45°

(**1.** right **2.** acute **3.** obtuse **4.** obtuse **5.** acute **6.** acute)

PRIOR KNOWLEDGE

Have students recall the general math term for a 4-sided polygon. (*quadrilateral*) List more specific names students may know for quadrilaterals, such as a *square* or *rectangle,* and have a volunteer draw an example of each. (Answers may vary.) Have students verbalize any rules they know for the specific quadrilaterals. (Possible answer: Squares have 4 equal sides and 4 right angles.) Tell students that in this lesson they determine ways to classify other quadrilaterals, based on angles and parallel sides.

COMMUNICATION

Discussing Math Write **trapezoid** and **parallelogram** on the chalkboard and draw an unidentified example of each. Tell students that each term names a special kind of quadrilateral. Have students use their understanding of the term *parallel* to guess which is the parallelogram, and why. (Both pairs of opposite sides are parallel.) Point out that although a trapezoid does have 2 parallel sides, the other 2 sides are not parallel.

EXPLORE AND CONNECT

Materials: 4-, 6-, and 8-in. oaktag strips, paper fasteners
Grouping Suggestion: cooperative learning pairs
Students explore quadrilaterals by experimenting with various lengths of oaktag strips. Partners use assorted strips and paper fasteners to make as many different quadrilaterals as they can. They record each combination on a chart like this:

Quadrilateral	*Strips Used*	*Number of Right Angles*

Encourage students to try transforming 1 quadrilateral into another by shifting the sides to adjust the angles. When pairs have made as many different quadrilaterals as they can, discuss as a group relationships students discovered. For instance, they can convert a **parallelogram** into a rectangle or a square into a **parallelogram**. They may have noticed that a **trapezoid** can have no more than 2 right angles.

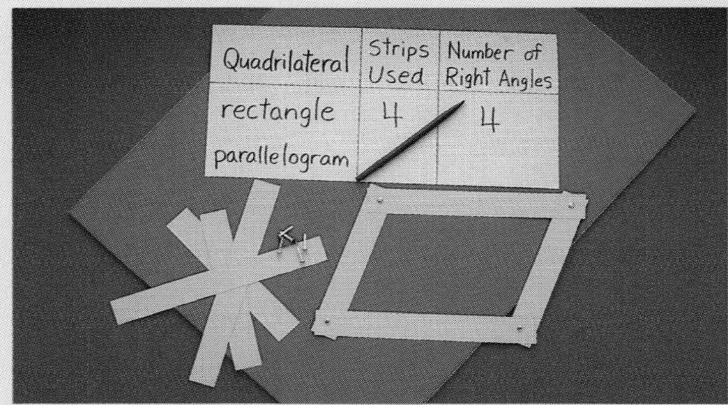

CONNECTIONS Use these anytime.

Problem of the Day

Creative Problem Solving Use all 7 tangram pieces to make a rectangle that is not a square.

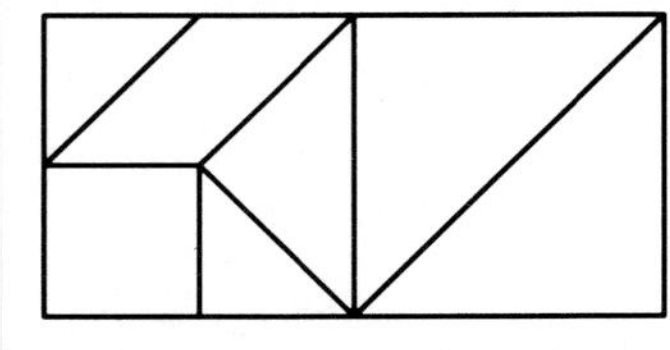

Math Connection

Logical Reasoning You know what an isosceles triangle is. Use logical reasoning to determine how to draw an isosceles trapezoid.

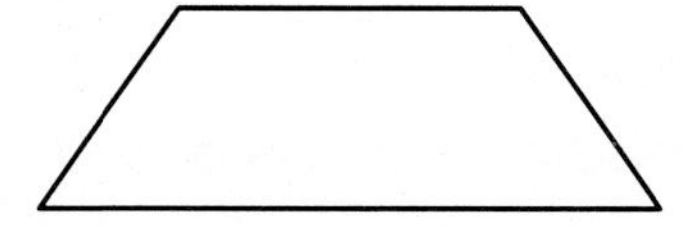

Subject Integration

Social Studies The flags of most countries are shaped like rectangles. Use an encyclopedia or almanac to find flags whose designs are made of 3 smaller rectangles. (Answers may vary; countries include Barbados, Chad, Peru, France, Italy, Guatemala, and Yemen.)

Classwork and Homework Supplements

Practice

Critical Thinking 11-6

Name

Classifying Quadrilaterals

Draw and name the quadrilateral. Drawings will vary.

1. It has two pairs of parallel sides of the same length and no right angle. parallelogram
2. All four of the sides are the same length. All of its angles are right angles. square
3. It has only one pair of parallel sides that are not the same length. trapezoid
4. It has two pairs of same-length sides. All of its angles are right angles. rectangle

PS-4 Use with text pages 308–309. 113

Building Thinking Skills

Family Math 11-6

Name

Matching Geometric Shapes

Dear Family,
We have been learning about quadrilaterals. Here is an activity you can do together with your child.

Trace the figures at the right onto a piece of paper and cut them out. Mark an **F** on the front and a **B** on the back of each cutout figure. See how many different ways you can place each figure on its matching figure in the box. The dots will help you count.

1. 2. 3. 4. 5. 6. 7.

TS-4 Use with text pages 308–309. 113

Reteaching

Skills Review 11-6

Name

Classifying Quadrilaterals

Square
All sides the same length
All angles right angles

Rectangle
Two pairs of same-length sides
All angles right angles

Trapezoid
Exactly one pair of parallel sides

Parallelogram
Two pairs of same-length sides
Two pairs of parallel sides

Find the quadrilaterals in the puzzle. Answers will vary.

1. Color one square red.
2. Color one parallelogram blue.
3. Color one rectangle green.
4. Color one trapezoid yellow.

Complete the drawing of each quadrilateral.

5. Square
6. Trapezoid
7. Parallelogram
8. Rectangle

RS-4 Use with text pages 308–309. 113

Challenges

Manipulatives 11-6

Name

Tangram Puzzles

Use a tangram puzzle to create the shapes below. Make a drawing of your solution. Answers will vary.

A B C D E F G

1. Use C, E, and F to create a rectangle, a triangle, and a parallelogram.
2. Use C, D, E, and F to create a parallelogram.
3. Use C, E, F, and G to create a rectangle, a parallelogram, and a trapezoid.
4. Use A, B, C, E, and G to create as many shapes as you can.

CS-4 Use with text pages 308–309. 113

Options for Individual Needs

11-6

Basic

Exercises 1-16, 20, 21
More Practice, p. 522, set C

Supplements
Reteaching 113 or
Practice 113

Average

Exercises 1-21
More Practice, p. 522, set C

Supplements
Practice 113
Challenges 113 or
Thinking Skills 113

Extended

Exercises 1-9, 16-21

Supplements
Challenges 113
Thinking Skills 113

Other Resources:
Math In Stride, Grade 4, p. 84
Mathematics, A Way of Thinking, Lesson 13-1
Spatial Visualization, p. 34

LESSON PLAN 11-6

OBJECTIVE 11-6
To classify quadrilaterals as squares, rectangles, parallelograms, or trapezoids

Materials: TA 12 (Centimeter Graph Paper), TA 19 (Tangrams), tracing paper

1. MOTIVATE AND TEACH

LEARN ABOUT IT

EXPLORE ► **Classify triangles A, B, C, E, and G. Explain your reasoning.** (They are all isosceles right triangles because each has a right angle and 2 equal sides.)
► **What shapes can you make using only triangles A and B? Explain why.** (A square because the long sides adjacent to each other leave 4 equal sides around the perimeter; a parallelogram, because if you put together 2 of the shorter sides, you are left with 2 sets of equal sides.)

TALK ABOUT IT ► **A rectangle is a special parallelogram. Explain what makes the figures different from each other.** (A parallelogram does not have any right angles; a rectangle has 4.)
► **A square is a special rectangle. Explain their relationship.** (A rectangle does not have to have 4 same-length sides.)
► **Explain why a trapezoid cannot be a kind of parallelogram.** (A trapezoid has only 1 pair of parallel sides.)
Student Edition answers: **1.** square, rectangle **2.** trapezoid **3.** rectangle, square, parallelogram **4.** square

2. CHECK UNDERSTANDING

TRY IT OUT

ERROR ALERT Classifying quadrilaterals incorrectly after they have been turned.

Classifying Quadrilaterals

LEARN ABOUT IT

EXPLORE **Use a Tangram Puzzle**

- How many quadrilaterals of different shapes can you make using any combination of pieces A and B? Draw each one.
- How many different quadrilaterals can you make with pieces C, D, and E? Draw each one.

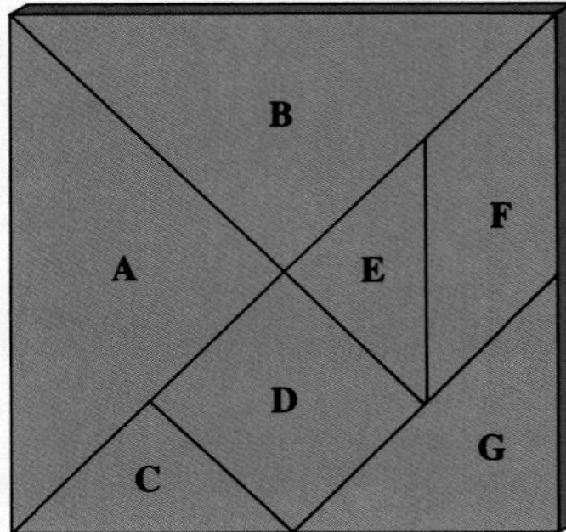

Tangram Puzzle

TALK ABOUT IT See teaching notes.

1. Which of your quadrilaterals have at least one right angle?
2. Which have one pair of parallel sides?
3. Which have two pairs of sides that are the same length?
4. Which have all sides the same length?

Here are some types of quadrilaterals.

Square

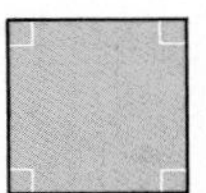

All sides the same length
All angles right angles

Rectangle

Two pairs of same-length sides
All angles right angles

Trapezoid

Exactly one pair of parallel sides

Parallelogram

Two pairs of same-length sides
Two pairs of parallel sides

TRY IT OUT Check students' drawings.

1. Draw a picture of each type of quadrilateral turned to a different position than in the picture above. Write the names under your drawings.

TEACHING OPTIONS

RETEACHING TIPS First have students draw each figure. To verify that each was turned and drawn correctly, have students trace each quadrilateral in the book and fit the tracing over their drawing. If they must turn tracings to make a fit, it means they turned the figures, too. Assign Reteaching Supplement 113.

ENRICHMENT Tell students that a *rhombus* is another quadrilateral. Have them use the clues and logical reasoning to determine what a rhombus looks like, then draw one.
1. It has 2 pairs of parallel sides.
2. All of its sides are equal.
3. None of its angles is a right angle.

PRACTICE Check students' drawings.

Draw and name the quadrilateral.

1. All of its sides are the same length. All of its angles are right angles. square
2. It has two pairs of parallel sides. It has no right angles. parallelogram
3. It has four right angles. Not all of its sides are the same length. rectangle
4. It has just one pair of parallel sides. trapezoid

APPLY

MATH REASONING Which color of strips would you use to make the quadrilateral?

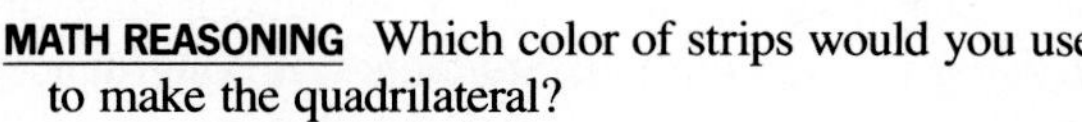

5. square red
6. rectangle yellow and red
7. trapezoid yellow, red, and blue
8. parallelogram yellow and red

PROBLEM SOLVING

9. The Rivera's tool shed is shaped like a cube. Mrs. Rivera used half a can of paint to paint one inside wall. How many cans will she use to paint all the surfaces except the floor? $2\frac{1}{2}$ cans

MIXED REVIEW

Check these quotients. Correct the answer if it is wrong.

10. $2\overline{)16}$ = 8
11. $4\overline{)35}$ = 8 R3
12. $5\overline{)75}$ = 15
13. $3\overline{)25}$ = 8 — 8 R1
14. $9\overline{)80}$ = 8 R8

Write the unit of measure you would use to find each amount.

15. the weight of one mushroom
    ounces or pounds
16. the amount in a large container of milk
    pints or gallons

More Practice, page 522, set C

3. Practice and Apply

Basic	1-16, 20, 21
Average	1-21
Extended	1-9, 16-21

PRACTICE

Look at Exercises 1-4. Describe a strategy you could use to decide which quadrilateral matches each statement. (Possible answer: Follow the directions to draw each figure, then decide what quadrilateral it looks like.)

APPLY

MATH REASONING ► **What quadrilateral can you make with red strips? Explain.** (They are the same size, so they must make a square.)

► **Explain why the blue strip can work only in 1 possible quadrilateral.** (It is the only 1 of its size, and only the trapezoid has 1 pair of unequal sides.)

PROBLEM SOLVING ► **Analyze how many surfaces Mrs. Rivera paints.** (4 walls plus 1 ceiling make 5 surfaces.)

MIXED REVIEW ► **Explain how to check division.** (Multiply the quotient by the divisor; add the remainder.)

11-6

Close and Assess

SHOW WHAT YOU KNOW

Have students use graph paper to draw and label each quadrilateral: a rectangle, a trapezoid, a parallelogram, and a square. Then ask students to draw a quadrilateral that is unlike any of those. (Check students' drawings.)

Quick Quiz

Name both quadrilaterals.

1. all equal sides and angles (square)
2. one pair of parallel sides (trapezoid)

LESSON OPTIONS 11-7

Congruent Figures

OBJECTIVE 11-7 To decide if two figures are congruent

PREBOOK ACTIVITIES

QUICK REVIEW

Draw each figure.

right triangle	rectangle	trapezoid
parellelogram	obtuse angle	hexagon
acute angle	isosceles triangle	square

PRIOR KNOWLEDGE

Have students review symmetric figures, relating them to a line of symmetry. (Symmetric figures have the same shape and size, separated by a line of symmetry.) Show the 2 large tangram triangles at different orientations and ask students how to prove whether they are the same size and shape. (See if they fit exactly on top of each other.) Have a volunteer try it, verbalizing any actions used. (Possible answer: Turn or flip the triangles until they match.) Have students name classroom figures that would fit exactly on top of each other if they could be moved. (Possible answers: floor tiles; desktops; sheets of notebook paper; window panes)

COMMUNICATION

Discussing Math Write the word **congruent** on the chalkboard. Have students infer its meaning based on the statement that the 2 large tangram triangles are congruent. (having exactly the same shape and size) Have students use the term *congruent* to describe some figures around the classroom. (Sample answer: The classroom door is congruent to the closet door.)

EXPLORE AND CONNECT

Materials: TA 19 (Tangram), unlined paper
Grouping Suggestion: individuals, pairs
Students explore congruence by creating polygons with 1 or more tangram pieces, then challenging partners to build polygons **congruent** to them. Independently, students create 5 different polygons, tracing just the outside edges on unlined paper. Partners swap papers, then attempt to build a tangram polygon *congruent* to each outline. Students test congruence by fitting pieces inside the outline. Conclude by having students tell how they manipulated tangram pieces to form *congruent* figures. List any verbs students may use, such as *flip, turn, move, slide,* and *rotate*. Have students conclude how movements affect congruence. (Movement does not affect congruence. You may need to move objects around to line them up, but moving them does not change their shape or size.)

CONNECTIONS Use these anytime.

Problem of the Day

Visual Problem Solving Without tracing, use centimeter graph paper to draw a polygon that is the same size and shape as this one. When you finish, test to make sure they match exactly.

Subject Integration

Fine Arts A *rubbing* is made by placing paper over a small object, then rubbing the paper with pencil, crayon, or chalk until the outline of the object appears. The rubbing will be the exact same size and shape as the object. Try it with coins or other small, textured objects. Compare the rubbings with the objects to make sure they are congruent.

Life Skills

Vision Chart The *E Chart* is a vision chart. It is made up of various sizes of captial *E*s shown facing in different directions. Find a copy of the chart in an encyclopedia or health book. Then identify the *E*s on the chart that are the exact same size. (*E*s appear in 4 positions; congruent *E*s are of equal size, despite their orientation.)

Classwork and Homework Supplements

Practice

Math Reasoning 11-7

Name ____________________

Congruent Figures

Use tracing paper to decide if the figures in each pair are congruent. Write **yes** or **no**. You may need to slide, turn, or flip your tracing paper.

1. yes
2. no
3. yes
4. no
5. no
6. no
7. yes
8. no

114 Use with text pages 310-311. PS-4

Building Thinking Skills

Critical Thinking 11-7

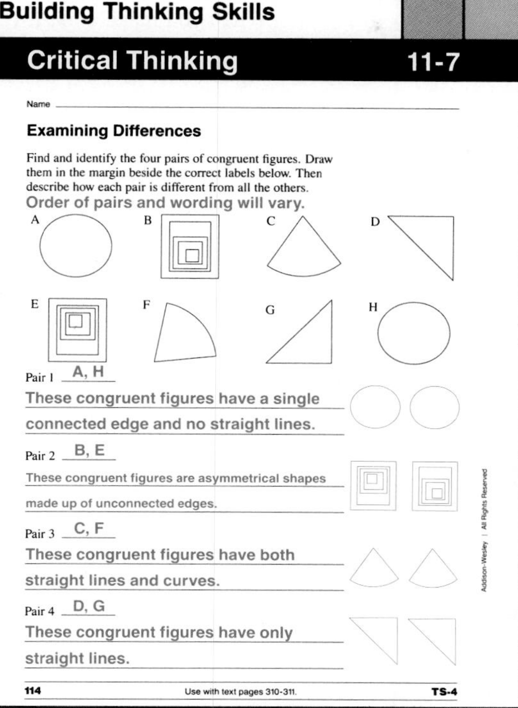

Name ____________________

Examining Differences

Find and identify the four pairs of congruent figures. Draw them in the margin beside the correct labels below. Then describe how each pair is different from all the others.
Order of pairs and wording will vary.

A B C D E F G H

Pair 1 A, H
These congruent figures have a single connected edge and no straight lines.

Pair 2 B, E
These congruent figures are asymmetrical shapes made up of unconnected edges.

Pair 3 C, F
These congruent figures have both straight lines and curves.

Pair 4 D, G
These congruent figures have only straight lines.

Addison-Wesley | All Rights Reserved

114 Use with text pages 310-311. TS-4

Reteaching

Critical Thinking 11-7

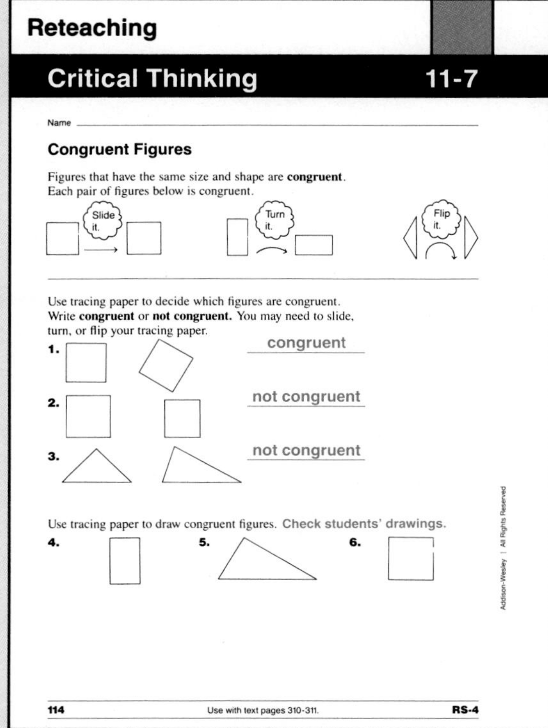

Name ____________________

Congruent Figures

Figures that have the same size and shape are **congruent**. Each pair of figures below is congruent.

Slide it. Turn it. Flip it.

Use tracing paper to decide which figures are congruent. Write **congruent** or **not congruent.** You may need to slide, turn, or flip your tracing paper.

1. congruent
2. not congruent
3. not congruent

Use tracing paper to draw congruent figures. Check students' drawings.

4. 5. 6.

Addison-Wesley | All Rights Reserved

114 Use with text pages 310-311. RS-4

Challenges

Family Math 11-7

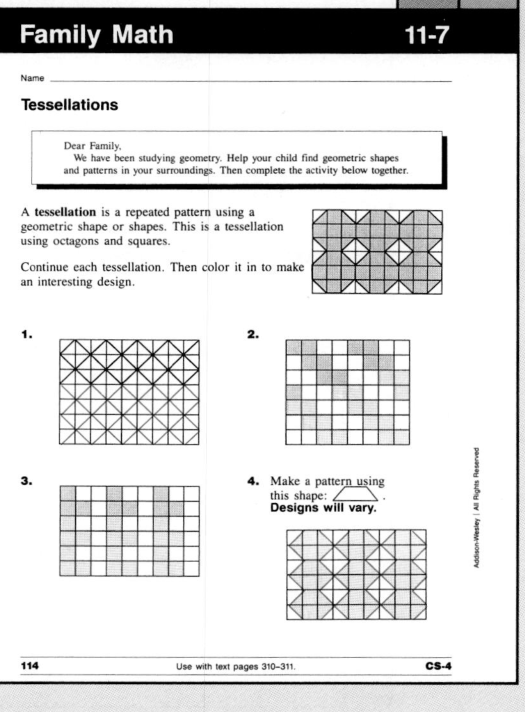

Name ____________________

Tessellations

Dear Family,
We have been studying geometry. Help your child find geometric shapes and patterns in your surroundings. Then complete the activity below together.

A **tessellation** is a repeated pattern using a geometric shape or shapes. This is a tessellation using octagons and squares.

Continue each tessellation. Then color it in to make an interesting design.

1. 2. 3.

4. Make a pattern using this shape:
Designs will vary.

Addison-Wesley | All Rights Reserved

114 Use with text pages 310-311. CS-4

Options for Individual Needs

Basic

Exercises 1-7
Data Bank, p. 480
More Practice, p. 522, set D

Supplements
Reteaching 114 or
Practice 114

Average

Exercises 1-7
Data Bank, p. 480
More Practice, p. 522, set D

Supplements
Practice 114
Challenges 114 or
Thinking Skills 114

Extended

Exercises 1-7
Data Bank, p. 480

Supplements
Challenges 114
Thinking Skills 114

Other Resources:
Problem-Solving Experiences in Mathematics, Grade 4, Problem 109
Math In Stride, Grade 4, pp. 122, 123
Spatial Visualization, p. 33

LESSON PLAN 11-7

OBJECTIVE 11-7
To decide if two figures are congruent

Materials: tracing paper

Grouping Suggestion: pairs

1. MOTIVATE AND TEACH

LEARN ABOUT IT

EXPLORE ▶ **Explain why a tracing will always be congruent to the figure traced.** (Possible answer: You trace by drawing along the sides of a figure; you are reproducing it exactly.)
▶ **Explain how to use graph or dot paper to draw congruent polygons.** (Count the boxes or dots to make figures with sides of equal numbers.)

TALK ABOUT IT ▶ **If objects are the same shape but different sizes, are they still congruent? Explain.** (No, congruent means they must match exactly—size and shape.)
▶ **Can you tell that 2 shapes are congruent just by looking at them? Explain.** (Possible answer: You may be able to tell if the shapes face the same direction.)
▶ **Explain why it helps to move figures to test if they are congruent.** (Possible answer: By moving figures and placing them on top of each other, you can be sure they are exactly the same size and shape.)
Student Edition answers: **1.** They are congruent if they match exactly. **2.** Move them to see if they fit on top exactly.

2. CHECK UNDERSTANDING

TRY IT OUT

ERROR ALERT Not finding both congruent figures. Failing to flip, turn, or slide to test congruence.

Congruent Figures

LEARN ABOUT IT

EXPLORE Use Tracing Paper
When you make a mask you may need to make two figures exactly alike. Figures that have the same size and shape are **congruent**.

- Draw a triangle. Then use tracing paper to draw another triangle that is the same size and shape.
- Do the same for a quadrilateral.

TALK ABOUT IT See teaching notes.

1. How do you know that the two shapes you drew are congruent?
2. How can you check to see if two cut-out shapes are congruent?

Here are some ways you can move triangle A to see if it will fit exactly on another triangle. If it will, the triangles are congruent.

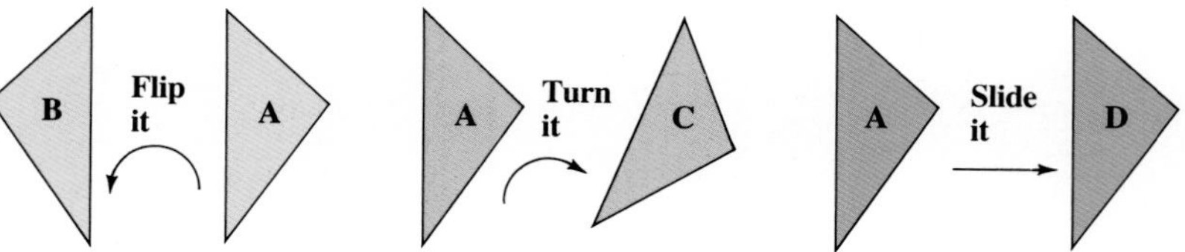

TRY IT OUT

Use tracing paper to decide which triangles are congruent to triangle A. B and D

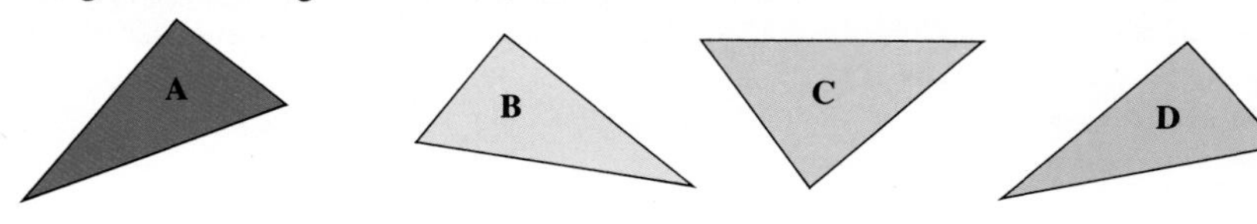

TEACHING OPTIONS

RETEACHING TIPS Students test each triangle, B-E, with their tracing of triangle A to be certain to find all possible triangles congruent to A. Have them record their findings in order. Ask students to verbalize actions they used to make the comparisons. (flip, turn, slide) Assign Reteaching Supplement 114.

COMPUTER Geometric preSupposer: Points and Lines, Sunburst Communications, Copyright 1986 For use with students of all levels. They can construct perpendicular, parallel, and intersecting lines, right angles, and 2- and 3-dimensional figures. Angles can be measured.

PRACTICE

Use tracing paper to decide which figures are congruent. You may need to slide, turn, or flip your tracing.

1.

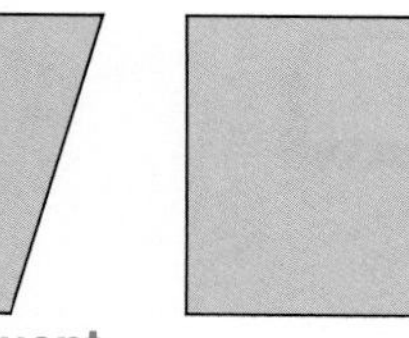

not congruent

2.

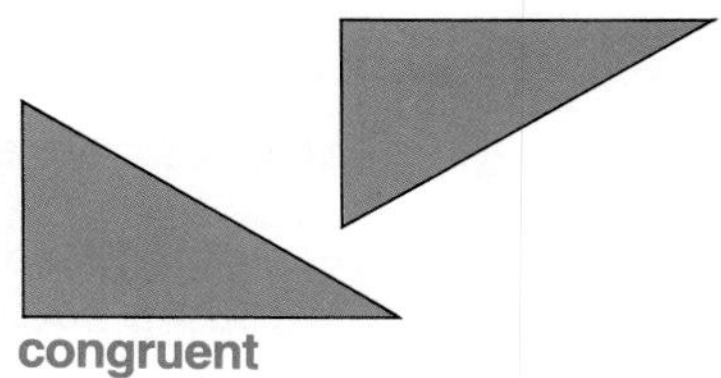

congruent

3. Draw 3 points. Then draw 3 segments to connect the points. What kind of polygon did you draw? Use tracing paper to make a congruent figure. Check students' drawings.

APPLY

MATH REASONING

4. Name these two quadrilaterals. How are they alike? How are they different? See Additional Answers.

PROBLEM SOLVING

5. A new downtown office building has two identical wings. One wing is divided into 32 dental offices and 43 medical offices. How many offices are in the building? 150 offices

6. **Fine Arts Data Bank** Name congruent polygons on the mask pattern in the Data Bank. See page 480. eyebrows, eyes, and rays

DATA BANK

▶ USING CRITICAL THINKING Comparing Polygons

7. Describe one of these figures to a partner. Have your partner try to draw a figure congruent to it, without looking at the book. Talk about the results. Answers will vary.

A

B

C

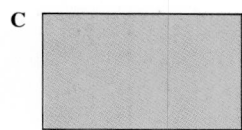

More Practice, page 522, set D

CLOSE AND ASSESS

WRITE WHAT YOU THINK

Have students write letters to you, their math teacher. Tell students that in the letters they should expain what it means when figures are congruent and give 2 possible methods to use to prove congruence. (Possible proofs: Trace; measure; fit figures over each other.)

QUICK QUIZ

Decide if the figures are congruent.

1. 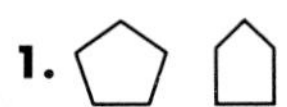 **2.** 

(**1.** not congruent; **2.** congruent)

3. PRACTICE AND APPLY

Basic	1-7
Average	1-7
Extended	1-7

Additional Answers: See p. T79.

PRACTICE

Look at Exercises 1 and 2. Can you predict just by looking if any of the pairs of figures are congruent or not congruent? (Answers may vary.)

APPLY

MATH REASONING ▶ **What parts of the quadrilaterals would you compare? Explain.** (Sides and angles will show similarities and differences.)

PROBLEM SOLVING ▶ **Explain how to solve Problem 5?** (add to find the number of offices in a wing; then multiply, because the 2 wings are exactly alike)

USING CRITICAL THINKING ▶ **Explain what math or position words can help describe the figures to a partner.** (Possible answers: *in, on, left, right, parallel, perpendicular, right angle, length, width, isosceles triangle*; are terms that help in visualizing.)

LESSON OPTIONS 11-8

Curves and Circles/Midchapter Review/Quiz

OBJECTIVE 11-8 To identify and draw simple closed curves and circles

PREBOOK ACTIVITIES

QUICK REVIEW

Draw the figures.

1. an obtuse angle
2. 2 parallel lines
3. 2 congruent triangles
4. a trapezoid
5. a hexagon
6. a right triangle
7. intersecting lines that are not perpendicular

(Check students' drawings.)

PRIOR KNOWLEDGE

Have students give examples of circles in the classroom. (Possible answers: clock; roll of tape; bottom of a pencil cup) Then have students look around to find examples of things that can form curves or that have curves. (Possible answers: curtains; string; keyhole)

COMMUNICATION

Discussing Math Write the word **simple** on the chalkboard and have students give synonyms for it. (Possible answers: *not hard; easy; uncomplicated*) Then draw an oval and an 8 and tell students that in mathematical terms, one is a simple curve and the other is not simple. Challenge them to guess which is which, giving their reasons. (Answers will vary.) Explain that a simple curve encloses 1 area, like the oval, while a curve that is not simple encloses more than 1 area, like the 8.

EXPLORE AND CONNECT

Materials: yarn or string
Grouping Suggestion: cooperative learning pairs
Students compare **simple** and not **simple** curves by forming numerals using lengths of yarn. Challenge partners to form the digits 0, 5, and 8 by shaping yarn to form recognizable numerals. Remind students not to use scissors to cut pieces; each numeral should be formed with 1 length of yarn. For each numeral they form, students should record whether they joined the ends of the yarn, whether they closed any space inside the yarn, and whether the yarn crossed over itself. Then have students classify their numerals as **simple closed** if the yarn ends were joined and the yarn never crossed over itself, *not closed* if the ends did not come together, and *not* **simple** if more than 1 section of inside space was formed. (*simple closed*—0; *not closed*—5; *not simple*—8) Conclude by having students demonstrate forming and classifying numerals.

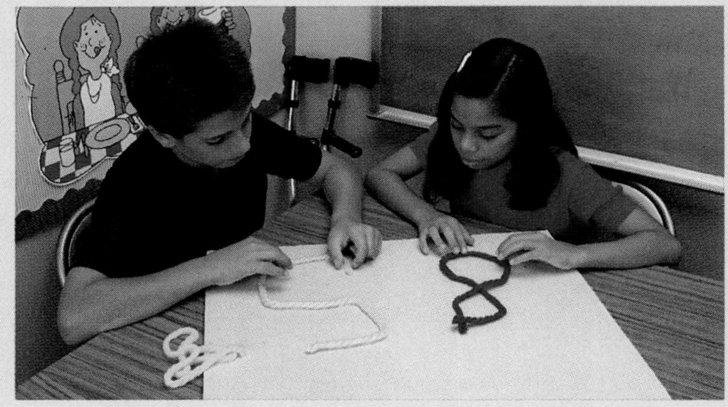

CONNECTIONS Use these anytime.

Problem of the Day

The Treasure Map Jessica is following a treasure map her cousin made. Starting at the signal rock, she walks 5 meters west, then 6 meters north, then 6 meters east, then 3 meters south, then 1 meter west. How far is Jessica from where she started? Draw a picture if it will help. (3 meters north of the rock)

Math Connection

Logical Reasoning One of the following letters does not belong. Decide which it is and tell why.

E H Z U K

(*U* is formed by curves; the others are formed by straight lines.)

Creative Thinking

Dog Run Steve ties his beagle, Corky, to a chain hitched to a stake buried in the ground. Corky can run safely because a special hinge prevents the chain from getting tangled. Visualize the shape Corky makes as he runs if he pulls the chain out as far as it can go in all directions. (a circle)

Classwork and Homework Supplements

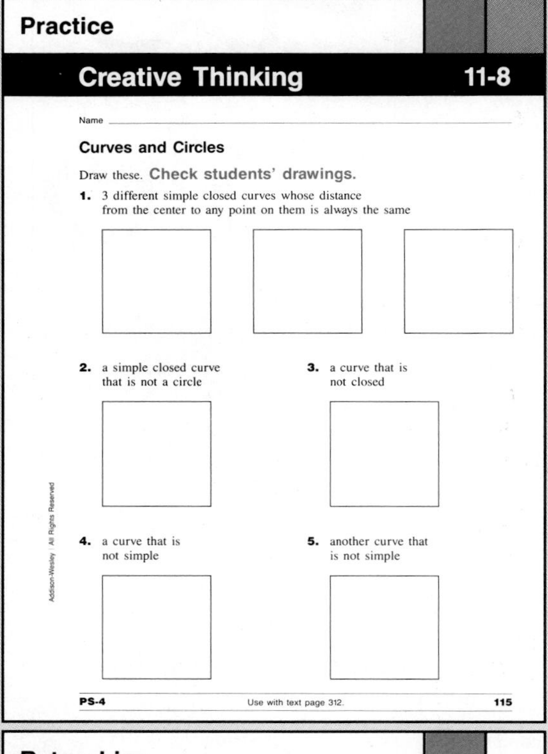

Practice

Creative Thinking 11-8

Name ______

Curves and Circles

Draw these. Check students' drawings.

1. 3 different simple closed curves whose distance from the center to any point on them is always the same
2. a simple closed curve that is not a circle
3. a curve that is not closed
4. a curve that is not simple
5. another curve that is not simple

PS-4 Use with text page 312. 115

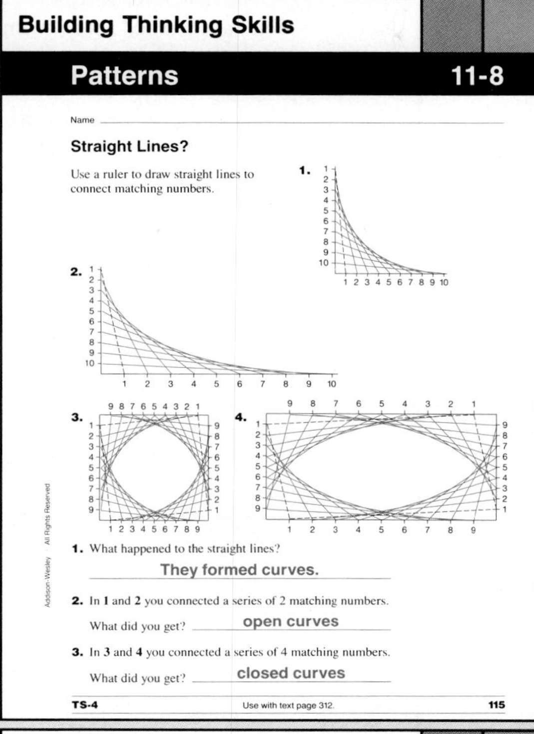

Building Thinking Skills

Patterns 11-8

Name ______

Straight Lines?

Use a ruler to draw straight lines to connect matching numbers.

1. What happened to the straight lines? They formed curves.
2. In 1 and 2 you connected a series of 2 matching numbers. What did you get? open curves
3. In 3 and 4 you connected a series of 4 matching numbers. What did you get? closed curves

TS-4 Use with text page 312. 115

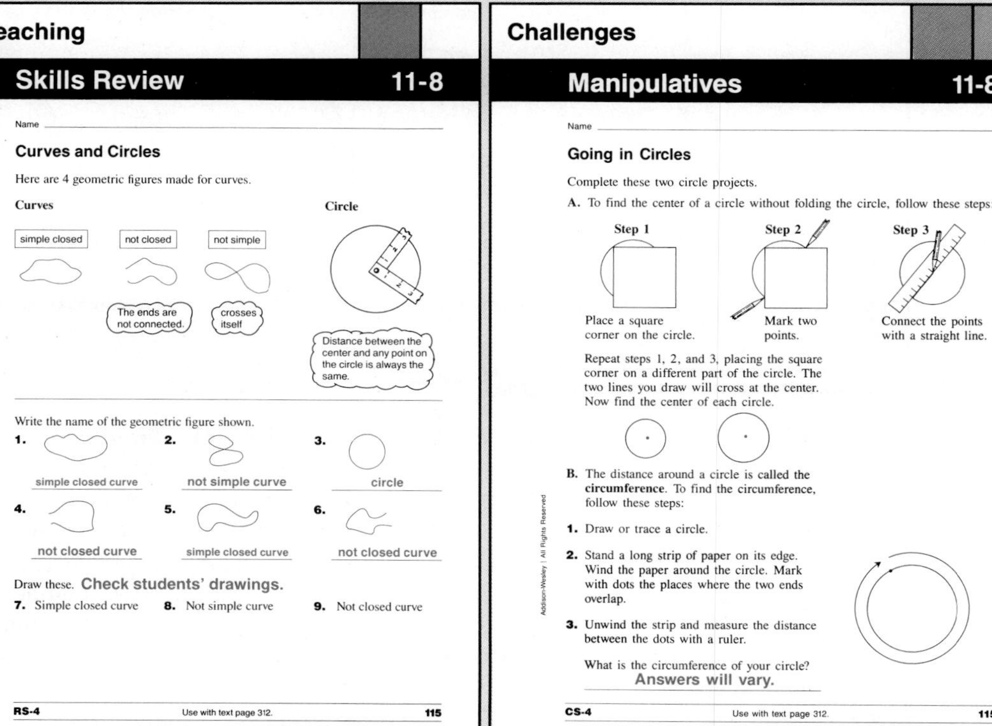

Reteaching

Skills Review 11-8

Name ______

Curves and Circles

Here are 4 geometric figures made for curves.

Curves

simple closed
not closed
not simple
The ends are not connected.
crosses itself

Circle

Distance between the center and any point on the circle is always the same.

Write the name of the geometric figure shown.

1. simple closed curve
2. not simple curve
3. circle
4. not closed curve
5. simple closed curve
6. not closed curve

Draw these. Check students' drawings.

7. Simple closed curve
8. Not simple curve
9. Not closed curve

RS-4 Use with text page 312. 115

Challenges

Manipulatives 11-8

Name ______

Going in Circles

Complete these two circle projects.

A. To find the center of a circle without folding the circle, follow these steps:

Step 1: Place a square corner on the circle.
Step 2: Mark two points.
Step 3: Connect the points with a straight line.

Repeat steps 1, 2, and 3, placing the square corner on a different part of the circle. The two lines you draw will cross at the center. Now find the center of each circle.

B. The distance around a circle is called the **circumference**. To find the circumference, follow these steps:

1. Draw or trace a circle.
2. Stand a long strip of paper on its edge. Wind the paper around the circle. Mark with dots the places where the two ends overlap.
3. Unwind the strip and measure the distance between the dots with a ruler.

What is the circumference of your circle? Answers will vary.

CS-4 Use with text page 312. 115

Options for Individual Needs

11-8

Basic

Exercises 1-4; 1-11
More Practice, p. 523, set A

Supplements
Reteaching 115 or
Practice 115

Average

Exercises 1-4; 1-12
More Practice, p. 523, set A

Supplements
Practice 115
Challenges 115 or
Thinking Skills 115

Extended

Exercises 1-4; 1-12

Supplements
Challenges 115
Thinking Skills 115

Other Resources:
Math In Stride, Grade 4, p. 83
Mathematics, A Way of Thinking, Lesson 13-12

LESSON PLAN 11-8

OBJECTIVE 11-8
To identify and draw simple closed curves and circles

Materials: rubber bands

Grouping Suggestion: pairs

1. MOTIVATE AND TEACH

LEARN ABOUT IT

EXPLORE ▶ **Contrast straight sides and curves.** (Possible answer: Curves are like wavy lines; curves do not make sharp corners.)

TALK ABOUT IT ▶ **Explain why A is a closed curve.** (There is no open place along it.)
▶ **Contrast curves A and B.** (B has a break in its curve.)
▶ **Explain how to draw curve C without lifting your pencil.** (You would draw part of the curve crossing over itself.)
▶ **Summarize a mathematical rule to describe a circle.**
(A circle is a simple closed curve whose edge is always the same distance from its center at any point around it.)
▶ **Explain how a compass helps you draw a circle.** (The compass point marks the center; the pencil makes the simple closed curve at an equal distance from the center.)
Student Edition answers: **1.** It is not closed because the ends are not connected. **2.** C **3.** not necessarily; You can go out through the opening.

2. CHECK UNDERSTANDING

TRY IT OUT

ERROR ALERT Misunderstanding the meaning of a curve that is not simple.

Curves and Circles

CURVES

Simple Closed Curve

A

Not Closed

B

Not Simple

C

LEARN ABOUT IT

EXPLORE Discover a Rule
You have learned about geometric figures that have straight sides. Now you will learn about geometric figures that have **curves**.

Jenny glued yarn on a poster to show some things about curves.

TALK ABOUT IT See teaching notes.

1. Why is curve B called "not closed"?
2. Which curve crosses itself?
3. You must cross a simple, closed curve to go from the inside to the outside. Is this true of curve B? Explain.

A **circle** is a special type of simple closed curve. The distance between the center of a circle and any point on the circle is always the same.

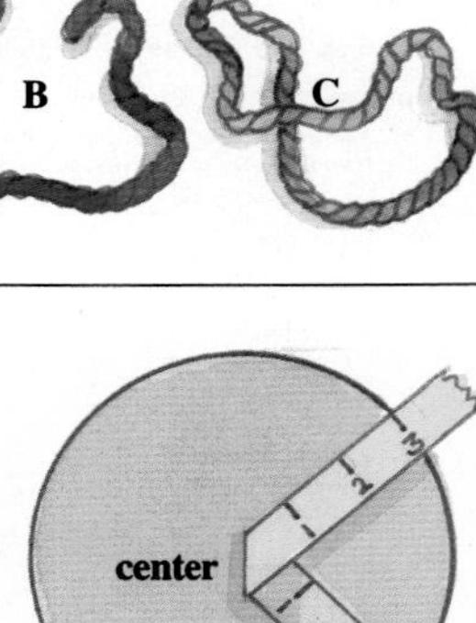

circle

TRY IT OUT Check students' drawings.

Draw these.

1. a simple closed curve
2. a curve that is not closed
3. a curve that is not simple
4. Choose one of these methods to draw some different-sized circles.

Compass

Round Object

String

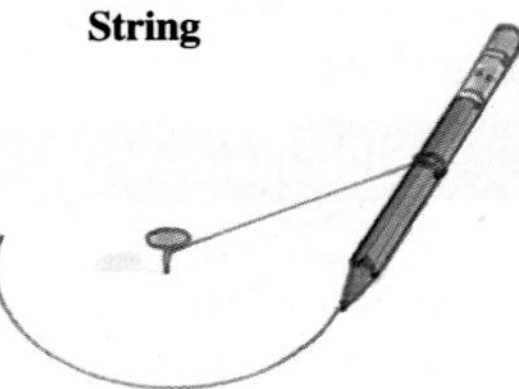

More Practice, page 523, set A

TEACHING OPTIONS

RETEACHING TIPS Students use rubber bands to show the difference between a simple closed curve and a not simple curve. As they twist the rubber bands to form a "figure 8," tell them a curve that is not simple crosses itself to form 2 or more sections. Assign Reteaching Supplement 115.

ENRICHMENT Family Math
Have students look around their homes for examples of simple closed curves, not simple curves, not closed curves, and circles. Encourage them to try to find at least 2 of each kind. They should have a family member check their list.

Midchapter Review/Quiz

A B C D E F

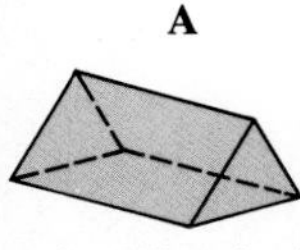 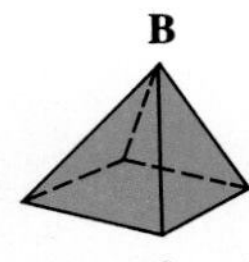 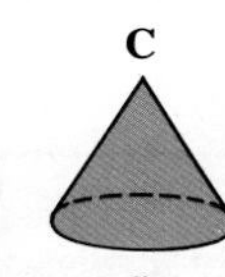 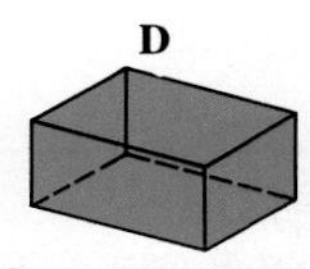 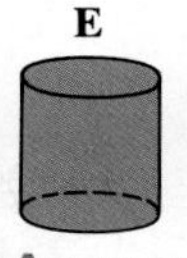 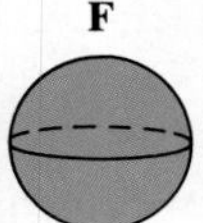

1. What is the name of each space figure? **See Additional Answers.**
2. Tell which of the figures' faces you could trace to make
   - a circle **C and E**
   - a triangle **A and B**
   - two different rectangles **D**
   - a rectangle and a triangle **A**
3. Which figures have curved edges? Which have straight edges? **rounded—C, E, F; straight—A, B, D**
4. Choose two figures. Tell how they are alike and different. **Answers will vary.**

Use these polygons.

A  B 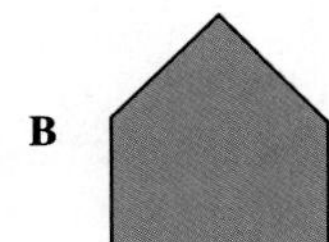 C 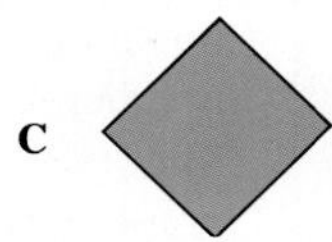

5. Name each polygon and tell how many sides it has. **See Additional Answers.**
6. Tell how many right angles each polygon has. **A 1, B 3, C 4**
7. Which polygons have an angle that is less than 90°? **A, C**

Draw the polygon that is described. **Check students' drawings.**

8. "I am a quadrilateral. Two of my sides are parallel. My other two sides are not parallel."
9. "I am a hexagon. Two of my sides are perpendicular and all have different lengths."

PROBLEM SOLVING

10. Ray tried to make a triangle with two perpendicular lines and one angle more than 90°. Is that possible? Tell how you know. **No, the sides won't connect.**

Liz has 5 sticks, one of each of these sizes: 2 in., 3 in., 3 in., 4 in., and 6 in.

11. How many different triangles can she make with a perimeter of 12 in.? **2 triangles**
12. Name the polygon, other than a triangle, Liz could make with a perimeter of 12 in. Which sticks would she use? **trapezoid; 2″, 3″, 3″, 4″**

313

Close and Assess

SHOW WHAT YOU KNOW

Have students work in pairs. Each partner draws a simple closed curve, a curve that is not simple, a curve that is not closed, and a circle. Then partners exchange drawings and try to label each other's figures. (Check students' drawings.)

Quick Quiz

Explain how a circle is a very special simple closed curve. (The distance between any point on the circle and its center point is always the same.)

3. Practice and Apply

Basic	1-4; 1-11
Average	1-4; 1-12
Extended	1-4; 1-12

Additional Answers: See p. T79.

PRACTICE

How are space figures and polygons related? (Space figures often have faces made of polygons.) *How is a right angle special?* (It always has exactly 90°.) *Compare parallel and perpendicular lines.* (Perpendicular lines meet at a right angle; parallel lines never meet.)

ITEM ANALYSIS The following table correlates the Midchapter Review/Quiz items with the lesson objectives.

Items	Objectives
1-4	11-1
5-7	11-2
8	11-6
9, 10	11-3
(7), 11	11-5
12	11-6

11-8

LESSON OPTIONS 11-9

Coordinate Geometry

OBJECTIVE 11-9 To use number pairs to make coordinate graphs

PREBOOK ACTIVITIES

QUICK REVIEW

Use graph paper to draw each of the following figures.

1. right triangle **2.** rectangle
3. square **4.** perpendicular lines
5. trapezoid **6.** hexagon
7. isosceles triangle **8.** pentagon

PRIOR KNOWLEDGE

Have students share real-life situations involving a set of directions to follow, in which the order of the directions is especially important. (Answers will vary. Samples: recipe steps; map routes; model building) Have students recall math situations in which order is important. (Possible answers: multiply, then add; trade before subtracting)

COMMUNICATION

Discussing Math Have students explain the meaning of the verb *coordinate,* as in this sentence: The team must coordinate a plan. (Possible answer: The team must find a sensible order for the steps of its plan.) Write the term **coordinates** on the chalkboard. Tell students that 4 and 3 are coordinates in the number pair (4, 3), which can describe an exact point on a graph. Challenge students to relate the verb *coordinate* to the math meaning of coordinate. (Possible answer: The coordinates work together in a certain order to describe a point on a graph.)

EXPLORE AND CONNECT

Materials: TA 12 (Centimeter Graph Paper), red and blue markers

Grouping Suggestion: cooperative learning pairs

On the chalkboard, write: *RIGHT* 1, 2, 3; *UP* 2, 3, 4. Pairs prepare a 6-by-6 grid as shown below, with red numbers along the bottom and blue numbers up the side. Challenge partners to make an organized list of all possible number pairs that use one number from each list. [(1, 2) (1, 3) (1, 4) (2, 2) (2, 3) (2, 4) (3, 2) (3, 3) (3, 4)] Partners then try to locate the points on the graph according to 2 rules: (1) Start at zero. (2) Go right first, then up. Have students tell how many number pairs they made, how they found the points using those **coordinates,** and what arrangement the points form. (The 9 points form a 3-by-3 array.) Have students analyze why it takes 2 *coordinates* to describe a point on a graph. (One tells how far to the right to count, the other tells how far up to count.)

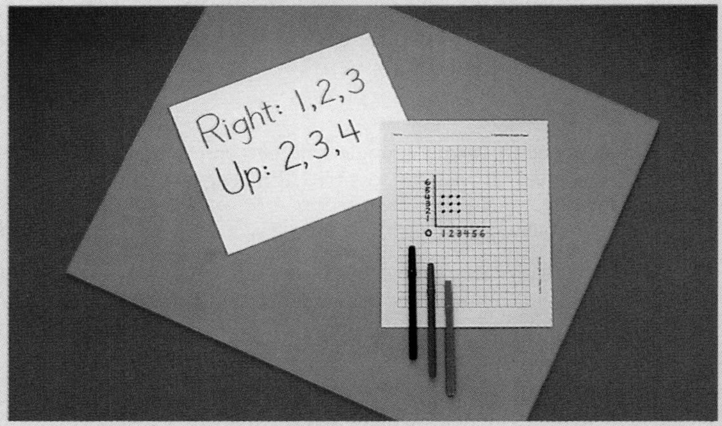

CONNECTIONS Use these anytime.

Problem of the Day

Where Is the Center? A rectangular floor is covered with tiles. There are 30 tiles in each of 40 rows. Describe the center point of the room in terms of the tiles. (The center is 15 tiles across and 20 tiles up.)

Creative Thinking

Make a Map The distance between each consecutive point on a graph-paper map equals 1 km. Use graph paper to make a map of the following towns, then tell what shape the lines connecting them form on the map: Eames is located at (0, 0). Davenport is 2 km east and 4 km north of Eames. Wassily is 4 km south and 2 km east of Davenport. (triangle)

Subject Integration

Social Studies You can describe exact map locations in terms of latitude and longitude. Use an almanac, an atlas, or a geography book to find the latitude and longitude of your city or another important spot in your state. (Answers will vary.)

Classwork and Homework Supplements

Practice

Skills Maintenance 11-9

Name

Coordinate Geometry

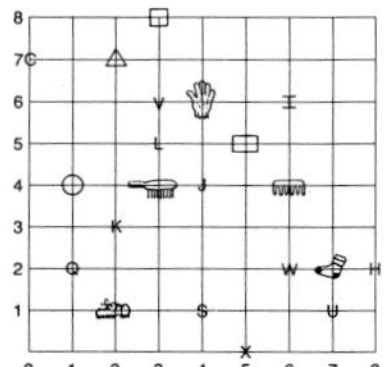

Give the coordinates for the point that locates each object in the above graph.

1. circle 1,4
2. rectangle 5,5
3. shoe 2,1
4. triangle 2,7
5. glove 4,6
6. sock 7,2
7. square 3,8
8. hairbrush 3,4
9. comb 6,4

Give the letter that is at the location given by these coordinates in the above graph.

10. (4,1) S
11. (0,7) C
12. (8,2) H
13. (2,3) K
14. (3,5) L
15. (6,6) I
16. (1,2) Q
17. (6,2) W
18. (3,6) V
19. (4,4) J
20. (5,0) X
21. (7,1) U

116 Use with text pages 314–315. PS-4

Building Thinking Skills

Critical Thinking 11-9

Name

Hidden Triangles

Mark the points located by the following coordinates on the grid. Label each point with a letter. The first one has been done for you.

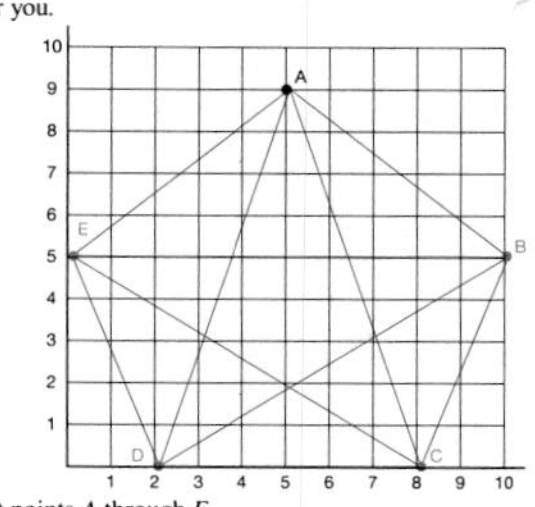

A (5, 9)
B (10, 5)
C (8, 0)
D (2, 0)
E (0, 5)

Connect points *A* through *E*.

What shape do you get? pentagon

Draw as many triangles as you can by connecting any three points in the shape. Identify each triangle by three letters. The first one has been done for you. Order may vary.

1. A, E, B
2. A, D, C
3. B, A, C
4. B, E, D
5. C, B, D
6. C, A, E (There are 10 in all.)
7. D, C, E
8. D, B, A
9. E, D, A
10. E, C, B

Now, what shape do you see inside the first shape? star

116 Use with text pages 314–315. TS-4

Reteaching

Skills Review 11-9

Name

Coordinate Geometry

A pair of numbers describes the location of a point. The numbers in the pair are called **coordinates.** Find the point located by the coordinates (4, 3).

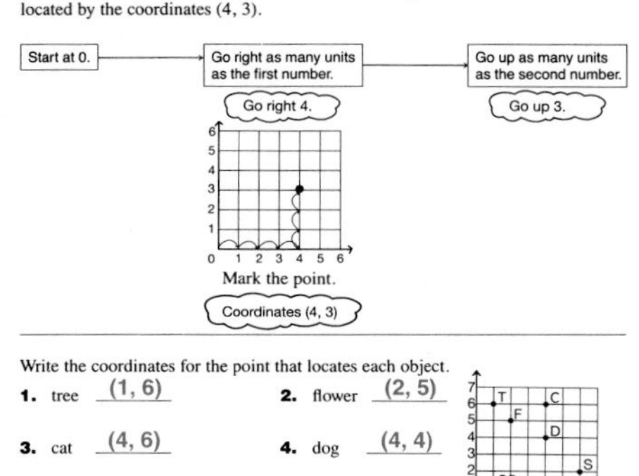

Start at 0.
Go right as many units as the first number.
Go right 4.
Go up as many units as the second number.
Go up 3.
Mark the point.
Coordinates (4, 3)

Write the coordinates for the point that locates each object.

1. tree (1, 6)
2. flower (2, 5)
3. cat (4, 6)
4. dog (4, 4)
5. slide (6, 2)
6. seesaw (1, 1)

Graph these coordinates. Then connect them in order.

(3, 2) → (2, 3) → (2, 4) → (3, 5) → (4, 5) → (5, 4) → (5, 3) → (4, 2) → (3, 2)

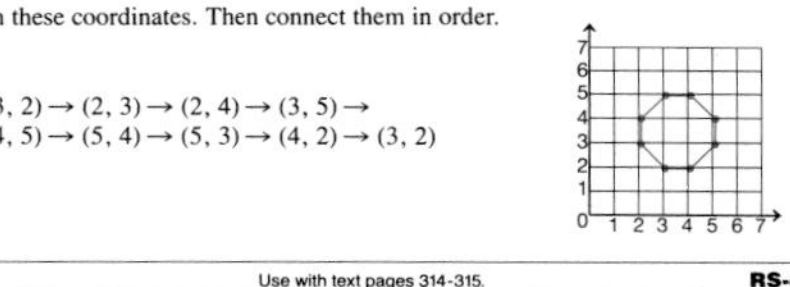

116 Use with text pages 314–315. RS-4

Challenges

Critical Thinking 11-9

Name

Invisible Trolls

Play this game with a partner.

Rules

1. Draw a small troll face on any point on Board 2. Cover the face with a small piece of paper.
2. Use Board 1 to try to guess the coordinates of your partner's hidden troll. Take turns guessing coordinates. **Example:** "Is your troll on (2,4)?" Mark your guesses on Board 1.
3. Every time you guess a pair of coordinates, your partner gives you a hint by saying, "To find my troll, go (a direction) from the point you just guessed." Use arrows to mark these hints on Board 1.
4. The winner is the first player to find the hidden troll and give its coordinates.

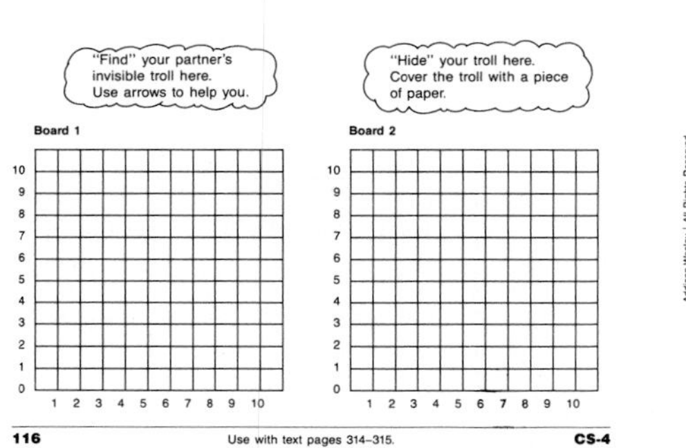

"Find" your partner's invisible troll here. Use arrows to help you.
"Hide" your troll here. Cover the troll with a piece of paper.
Board 1
Board 2

116 Use with text pages 314–315. CS-4

Options for Individual Needs

Basic

Exercises 1-12

Supplements
Reteaching 116 or
Practice 116

Average

Exercises 1-12

Supplements
Practice 116
Challenges 116 or
Thinking Skills 116

Extended

Exercises 1-12

Supplements
Challenges 116
Thinking Skills 116

Other Resources:
Mathematics, A Way of Thinking, Lessons 18-5—18-8
Spatial Visualization, p. 35

LESSON PLAN 11-9

OBJECTIVE 11-9
To use number pairs to make coordinate graphs

Materials: TA 12 (Centimeter Graph Paper), index cards

1. MOTIVATE AND TEACH

LEARN ABOUT IT

EXPLORE ▶ **Analyze the arrangement of the number pairs.** (2 numbers in parentheses, separated by a comma)
▶ **Explain how a number pair describes a point.** (After you count to the right, you count up from that spot to specifically identify a point horizontally and vertically.)
▶ **Explain where to start counting.** [Always start at (0, 0); it is the first point on the graph.]

TALK ABOUT IT ▶ **Analyze how a number pair reflects order.** (The first coordinate tells how many units to count to the right; the second number tells how many units to count up from there.)
▶ **Compare opposite number pairs, such as (2, 1) and (1, 2).** [(2, 1) means to go right 2, up 1; (1, 2) means to go right 1, up 2.]
Student Edition answers: **1.** Yes, (2, 1) is right 1 more and up 1 less unit than (1, 2). **2.** Count the number of units the point is to the right of 0, then count the number of units it is up from 0.

2. CHECK UNDERSTANDING

TRY IT OUT

ERROR ALERT Giving coordinates in the wrong order.

Coordinate Geometry

LEARN ABOUT IT

EXPLORE **Use Graph Paper**
You can use a pair of numbers to describe the location of a point. The numbers in the pair are called **coordinates**.

Here is how to graph the point for (3, 2).

1. Start at 0. Go **right** as many units as the first number. Go **up** as many units as the second number.
2. Mark the point.

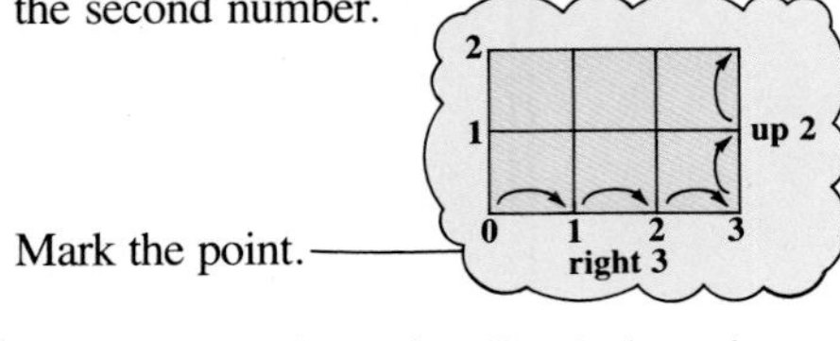

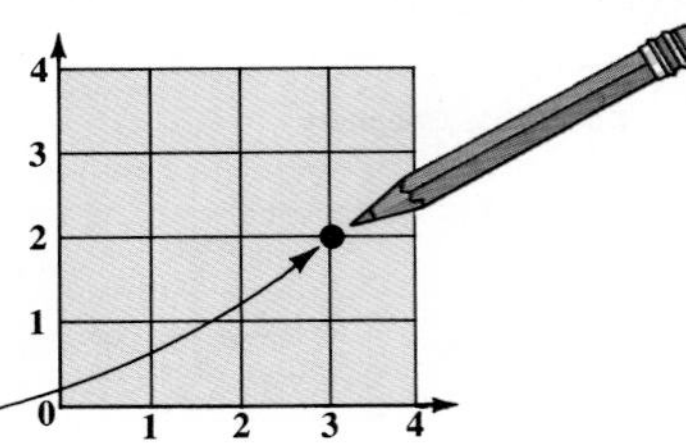

Choose some number pairs. Graph the points.

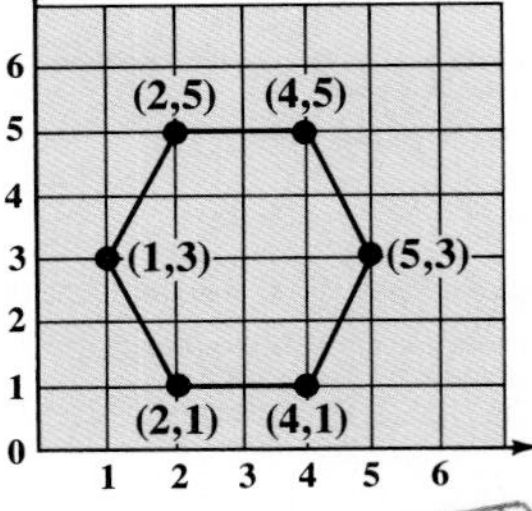

TALK ABOUT IT See teaching notes.

1. Are (2, 1) and (1, 2) pairs for different points? Explain.
2. Tell how to find the number pair for a point on the grid.

You can graph a figure by graphing points and connecting them in order. The graph of these points is a hexagon.

(2, 5) → (1, 3) → (2, 1) → (4, 1) → (5, 3) → (4, 5) → (2, 5)

TRY IT OUT Check students' drawings.

Draw a pentagon shaped like a house by connecting points on graph paper. Give number pairs for the points and ask a classmate to draw the house.

TEACHING OPTIONS

RETEACHING TIPS On a blank index card, have each student show parentheses with arrows in place of coordinates: (→, ↑) This guide can help cue students to remember which coordinate to give first. Assign Reteaching Supplement 116.

ENRICHMENT Pair students. Each pair prepares a 7-by-7 graph with each letter of the alphabet written at a different point on it. Each partner thinks of 3 secret words, then lists the number pairs for the letters that spell those words. Partners exchange coordinates to figure out each other's secret words.

PRACTICE

Give the coordinates for the point that locates each object.

1. drum 1, 0 **2.** car 3, 4
3. whistle 3, 1 **4.** key 1, 3

Give the letter that is at the location given by these coordinates.

5. (1, 4) E **6.** (3, 2) C
7. 2, 1 M **8.** (4, 4) B

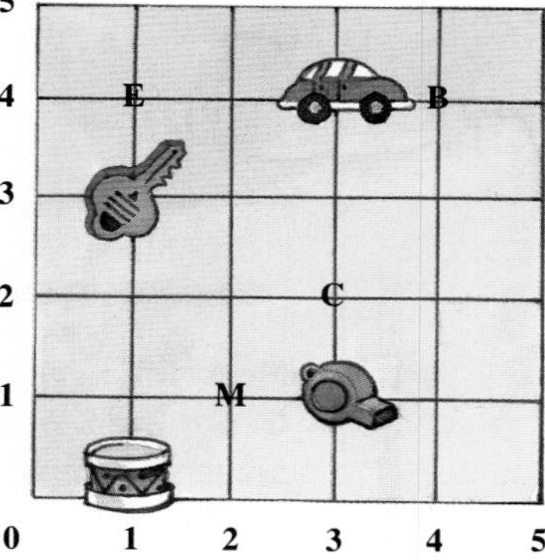

APPLY

MATH REASONING

9. Give the coordinates that could be graphed and connected to form these polygons. Answers will vary.

a rectangle a square a triangle

PROBLEM SOLVING

10. An airport was at a location given on a map by the coordinates (0,0). A plane flying from the airport radioed back when it was at the location (1,2). It later radioed back at the locations (2,4), (3,6), and (4,8). Show all the plane's locations on a graph, find a pattern, and decide at what locations the plane will be when it radios back the next two times. See Additional Answers.

ALGEBRA

- Pick a number less than 10, say 4. Make it the first number of a pair.
- Subtract 1 from the first number. Make the answer the second number of the pair.

11. How many different number pairs can you make like this? List them. 9 pairs; 9, 8; 8, 7; 7, 6; 6, 5; 5, 4; 4, 3; 3, 2; 2, 1; 1, 0

12. Graph the pairs you found. What do you discover?
Check students' graphs.
The number pairs form a straight line.

315

3. Practice and Apply

Basic	1-12
Average	1-12
Extended	1-12

Additional Answers: See p. T79.

PRACTICE

Which comes first in a number pair, the number of units to the right of 0 or up from 0? (number of units to the right)

APPLY

MATH REASONING ► **Explain how many points you must locate for each figure.** (Each point will form an angle when connected by lines, so you need 4 for the rectangle and square and 3 for the triangle.)

PROBLEM SOLVING ► **Analyze what to do first to solve Problem 10.** (Plot the coordinates in the given order.)

ALGEBRA ► **Explain what would be the greatest and least possible numbers in the number pairs.** [Following the rules of numbers less than 10 and the second number 1 less than the first, you cannot go higher than (9, 8) or lower than (1, 0)].

11-9

Close and Assess

WRITE WHAT YOU THINK

Have students write the rules for using number pairs to identify points on a graph. Have them compare the coordinates (3, 5) and (5, 3) to help explain the importance of order. (Answers will vary. Check students' writing.)

Quick Quiz

Graph the points and connect them in order. What do you see?
(2, 0) → (4, 4) → (3, 4) → (1, 4)
(the number 7)

LESSON OPTIONS 11-10

Similar Figures

OBJECTIVE 11-10 To identify and graph similar figures

PREBOOK ACTIVITIES

QUICK REVIEW

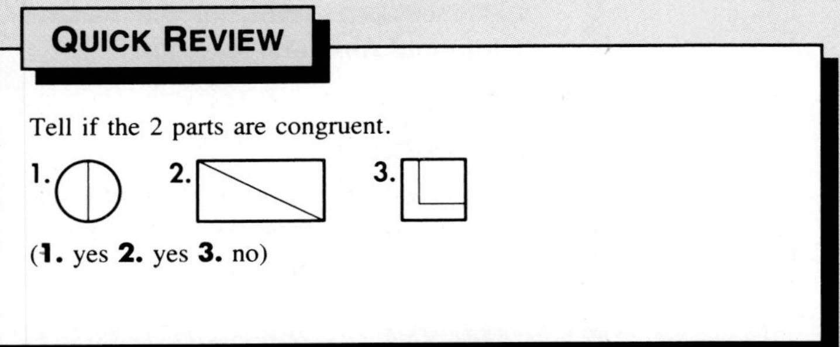

Tell if the 2 parts are congruent.

1. 2. 3.

(**1.** yes **2.** yes **3.** no)

PRIOR KNOWLEDGE

Have students review the meaning of **congruent polygons.** (''polygons with the exact same size and shape'') Then have students suggest pairs of real objects that are the same in every way *except* for size. (Possible answers: sizes 6 and 14 of the same shirt; wallet size and 8-by-10 enlargements of the same photo; large and small square tiles)

COMMUNICATION

Discussing and Writing Math Discuss the general meaning of the word **similar.** (''alike in some ways'') Have students use the word to make some real-life comparisons. (Sample answers: Zebras and horses are similar animals; turkey and chicken have a similar taste.) Then draw a large and a small square on the chalkboard. Have students write the headings *Similar* and *Not Similar* in their Math Journals, then write under each heading a statement about the 2 squares. (Similar: Both have 4 equal sides and 4 right angles; Not Similar: The size of the sides is different.)

EXPLORE AND CONNECT

Materials: geoboards, TA 12 (Centimeter Graph Paper)
Grouping Suggestion: cooperative learning groups of 3
Students compare congruent and **similar** figures. The first student makes a polygon on a geoboard. The second student makes a congruent polygon on another geoboard. The third student makes a *similar* polygon on graph paper. Students compare geoboard polygons first to verify congruence. Then they determine how to verify that the graph-paper polygon is *similar* to the geoboard polygon. (Possible method: Count the number of geoboard pins per side, compare to graph paper points per side, even if the pins and points are not the same distance apart.) Have students trade tasks and repeat the activity twice. Conclude by having students contrast congruent and *similar* figures. (Congruent figures are exactly the same size and shape; *similar* figures have the same shape but not necessarily the same size.)

CONNECTIONS Use these anytime.

Problem of the Day

The New Playground Lincoln School is expanding its playground to make it twice as big as the old one, which was a square 35 yd on a side. Describe the size and shape of the new playground and tell how much fencing is needed to enclose it. (a square 70 yd per side; 280 yd of fencing needed)

Subject Integration

Fine Arts Dawn designed a logo for the art club on 1-in. graph paper. The club members loved the design, but the teacher said it was too big to fit on art club folders. How can Dawn keep the design the same but make it smaller? (Possible answer: Copy it onto smaller graph paper, box by box.)

Life Skills

Understanding Maps The scale on a map of Webb County is 1 in. = 18 mi. If Drake and Mallard are 4 in. apart on the map, how far apart are they in real life? (72 mi)

Classwork and Homework Supplements

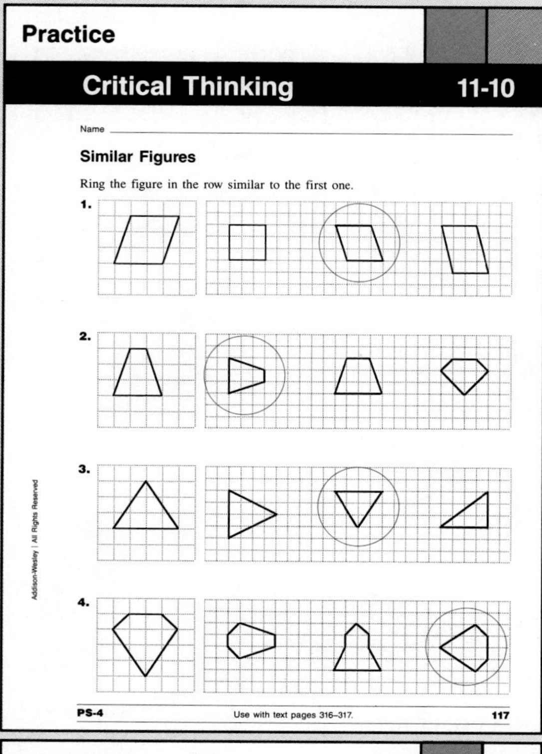

Practice

Critical Thinking 11-10

Name ______

Similar Figures

Ring the figure in the row similar to the first one.

1.

2.

3.

4.

Addison-Wesley | All Rights Reserved

PS-4 Use with text pages 316-317. 117

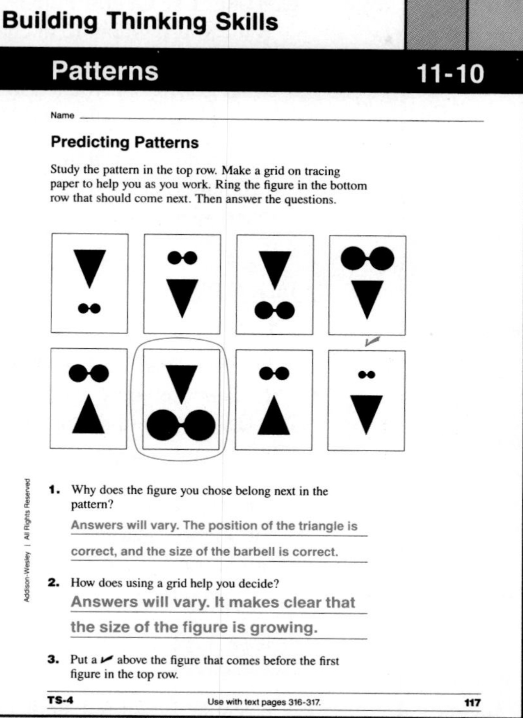

Building Thinking Skills

Patterns 11-10

Name ______

Predicting Patterns

Study the pattern in the top row. Make a grid on tracing paper to help you as you work. Ring the figure in the bottom row that should come next. Then answer the questions.

1. Why does the figure you chose belong next in the pattern?
Answers will vary. The position of the triangle is correct, and the size of the barbell is correct.

2. How does using a grid help you decide?
Answers will vary. It makes clear that the size of the figure is growing.

3. Put a ✔ above the figure that comes before the first figure in the top row.

Addison-Wesley | All Rights Reserved

TS-4 Use with text pages 316-317. 117

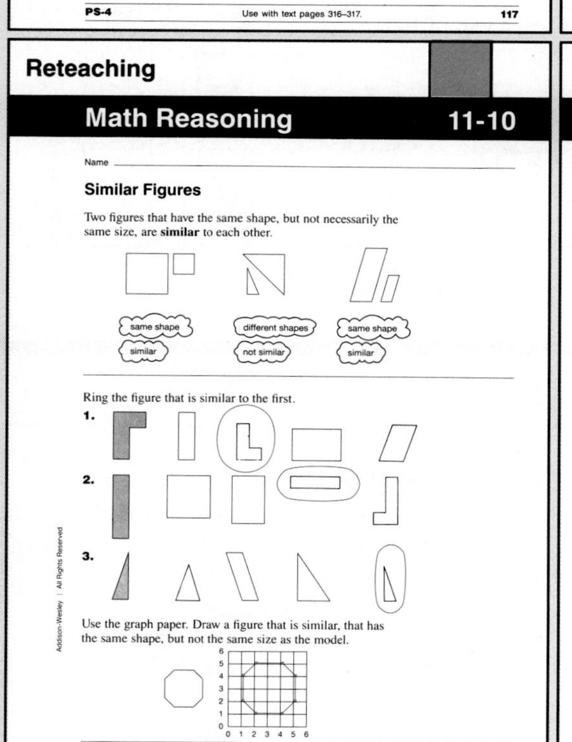

Reteaching

Math Reasoning 11-10

Name ______

Similar Figures

Two figures that have the same shape, but not necessarily the same size, are **similar** to each other.

Ring the figure that is similar to the first.

1.

2.

3.

Use the graph paper. Draw a figure that is similar, that has the same shape, but not the same size as the model.

Addison-Wesley | All Rights Reserved

RS-4 Use with text pages 316-317. 117

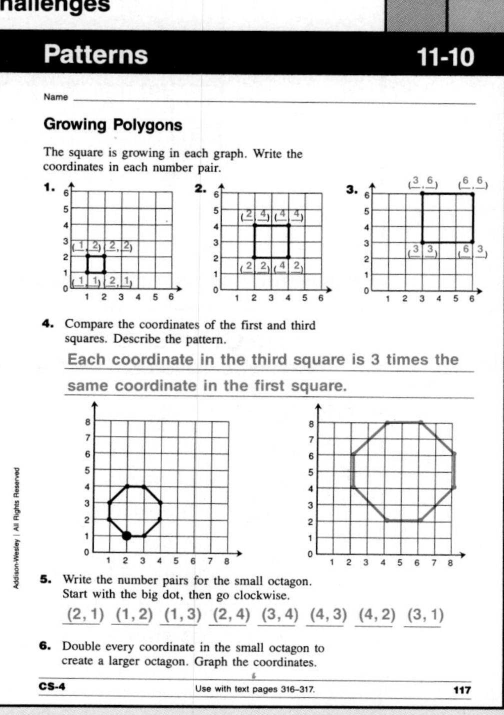

Challenges

Patterns 11-10

Name ______

Growing Polygons

The square is growing in each graph. Write the coordinates in each number pair.

1. (1, 2) (2, 2) (1, 1) (2, 1)

2. (2, 4) (4, 4) (2, 2) (4, 2)

3. (3, 6) (6, 6) (3, 3) (6, 3)

4. Compare the coordinates of the first and third squares. Describe the pattern.
Each coordinate in the third square is 3 times the same coordinate in the first square.

5. Write the number pairs for the small octagon. Start with the big dot, then go clockwise.
(2, 1) (1, 2) (1, 3) (2, 4) (3, 4) (4, 3) (4, 2) (3, 1)

6. Double every coordinate in the small octagon to create a larger octagon. Graph the coordinates.

Addison-Wesley | All Rights Reserved

CS-4 Use with text pages 316-317. 117

Options for Individual Needs

Basic

Exercises 1-6
Data Bank, p. 480
Calculator Bank, p. 486
More Practice, p. 523, set B

Supplements
Reteaching 117 or
Practice 117

Average

Exercises 1-6
Data Bank, p. 480
Calculator Bank, p. 486
More Practice, p. 523, set B

Supplements
Practice 117
Challenges 117 or
Thinking Skills 117

Extended

Exercises 1-6
Data Bank, p. 480
Calculator Bank, p. 486

Supplements
Challenges 117
Thinking Skills 117

Other Resources:
Problem-Solving Experiences in Mathematics, Grade 4, Problem 110
Math In Stride, Grade 4, pp. 124, 125

11-10

LESSON PLAN 11-10

OBJECTIVE 11-10
To identify and graph similar figures

Materials: TA 12 (Centimeter Graph Paper), calculators

Grouping Suggestion: groups of three

1. MOTIVATE AND TEACH

LEARN ABOUT IT

EXPLORE ▶ **Compare and contrast the 2 grids.** (Both are square graphs, 8 boxes per side; box size is different.)
▶ **Summarize a relationship between the 2 face masks.** (same shape, different sizes)

TALK ABOUT IT ▶ **Explain how to make the cat mask bigger without changing its design.** (Copy it onto graph paper with larger boxes; double the size of the mask on the same-size grid.)
▶ **Explain how to make the cat mask smaller.** (Copy it onto graph paper with smaller boxes.)
▶ **If you copy the cat mask onto the same-size grid but with a square face instead of a rectangle, will the masks be similar? Explain.** (No, shape and size will be different.)
Student Edition answers: **1.** Use graph paper with a larger grid; use graph paper with a smaller grid. **2.** Pick graph paper with a grid twice as large.

2. CHECK UNDERSTANDING

TRY IT OUT

ERROR ALERT Miscounting sides or boxes when trying to determine similarity. Confusing similarity and congruence.

Similar Figures

LEARN ABOUT IT

EXPLORE Use Graph Paper
You can use graphing to change the size of a figure. A mask pattern in a book was on a small grid. Chen wanted to make it larger, so he graphed the pattern on a larger grid.

Use graph paper with a different-sized grid to make a larger cat mask.

Cat Mask Pattern

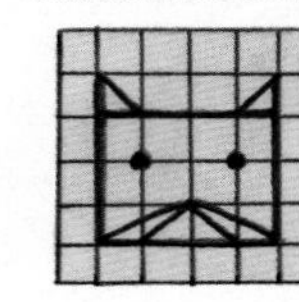

TALK ABOUT IT See teaching notes.

1. What would you do to make the cat mask larger? to make it smaller?
2. Suppose you want a cat mask that is twice as large as the one in the picture. How would you choose the graph paper?

Two figures that have the same shape, but not necessarily the same size, are similar to each other.

TRY IT OUT

Write similar or not similar for each pair of figures.

1. 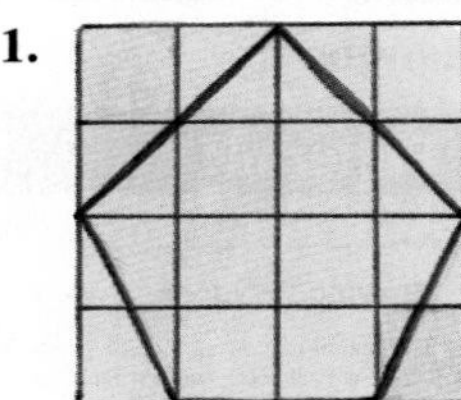 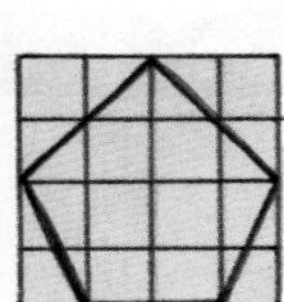
similar

2. 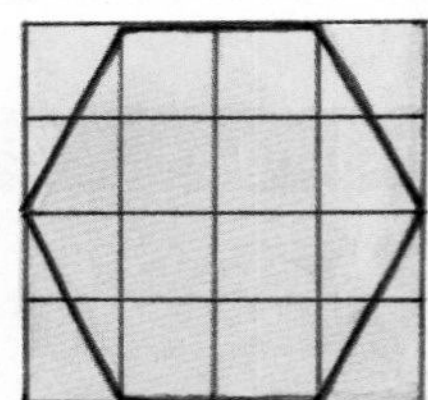
not similar

TEACHING OPTIONS

RETEACHING TIPS Students mask the top figure except for 1 side, count boxes on that side, then compare the measurement to the side in the same position in the bottom figure. They repeat for all sides. If lengths are equivalent, figures are similar. Assign Reteaching Supplement 117.

ENRICHMENT Each student chooses a small cartoon from a newspaper or magazine. Students draw a grid on their cartoons, using centimeter graph paper (TA 12) as a guide. Then students double the size of their cartoons by making a similar copy on another piece of centimeter graph paper.

PRACTICE

Which figure in the row is similar to the first?

1. b

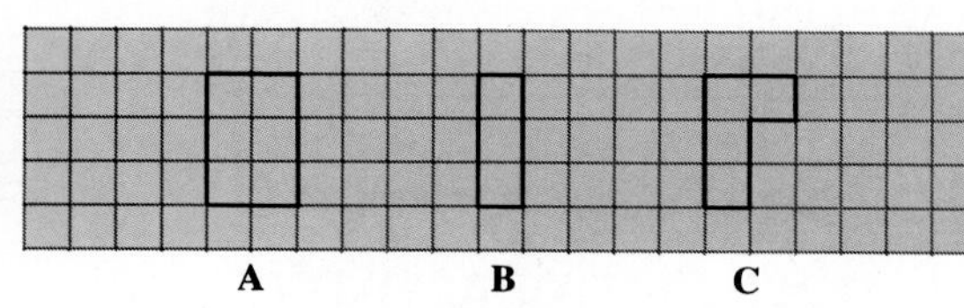

A B C

2. c

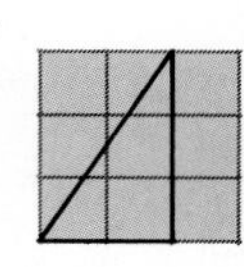

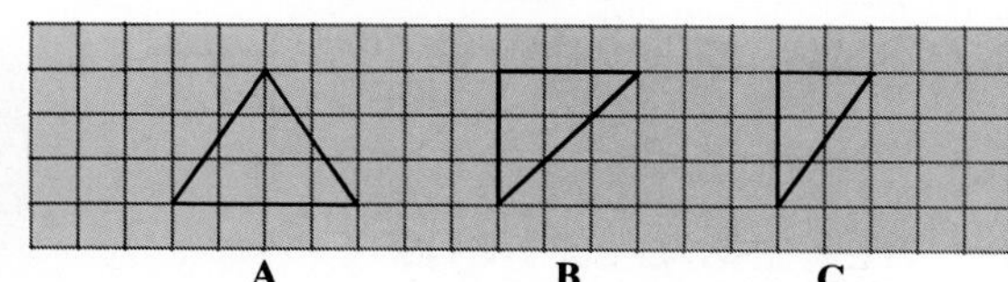

A B C

APPLY

MATH REASONING

3. Complete this sentence in 2 different ways. Use a single word each time. Any two ___?___ that I draw will be similar to each other. See Additional Answers.

PROBLEM SOLVING

4. **Fine Arts Data Bank** Use different-sized graph paper to draw a sun mask similar to the one on page 480. Check students' drawings.

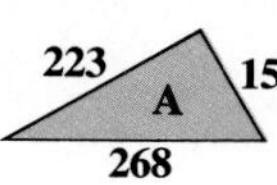

5. Look for a pattern to solve this problem. Here are the first, second, third, and fourth "similar dot triangles." How many dots does the sixth one have? 21 dots

► CALCULATOR

6. Figure B is similar to A. The sides of B are twice as long as the sides of A. Use a calculator to find the perimeters of both figures.
A = 647 B = 1,294

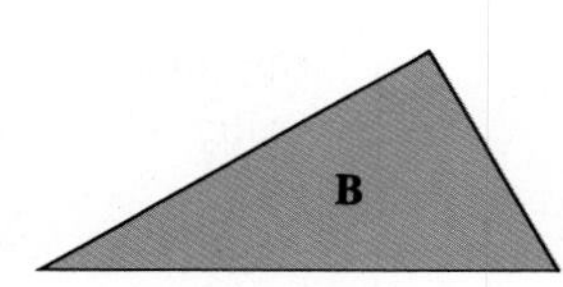

More Practice, page 523, set B

3. Practice and Apply

Basic	1-6
Average	1-6
Extended	1-6

Additional Answers: See p. T79.

PRACTICE

Can figures still be similar if they are flipped or turned? Explain. (yes, as long as they have the same shape) *Are all triangles similar? Explain.* (No, triangles have different shapes, such as isosceles, right, and equilateral.)

APPLY

MATH REASONING ► How can you verify that your sentence is true? (Possible answer: See if a partner can find an exception by drawing 2 figures you named that are not similar.)

PROBLEM SOLVING ► Explain how to make a similar sun mask. (Possible method: Count boxes; draw the simplest shape first, then add details, using boxes to maintain similarity.)

CALCULATOR ► Justify the operation to use to find perimeter. (addition, because you need to find the total of all three sides)

11-10

Close and Assess

SHOW WHAT YOU KNOW

Have students work in groups of 3. The first student draws a triangle on centimeter graph paper. The paper is passed to the second student, who draws a larger similar triangle; then it is passed to the third student, who draws a smaller similar triangle. Trios repeat the task so each student draws each step.

Quick Quiz

Use centimeter graph paper to make a face similar to, but larger than, the one on page 316. (Check students' drawings.)

LESSON OPTIONS 11-11

Problem Solving: Data from a Diagram

OBJECTIVE 11-11 To solve problems using data from a diagram

PREBOOK ACTIVITIES

QUICK REVIEW

Find each perimeter.

1. square, 8 yd on a side (32 yd)
2. equilateral triangle, 11 in. on a side (33 in.)
3. quadrilateral with 4-ft, 3-ft, 6-ft, and 5-ft sides (18 ft)

PRIOR KNOWLEDGE

Have students suggest real-life uses for diagrams. (Possible answers: instructions for building or repairing; floor plans) Ask students what kinds of data are usually included on a diagram. (dimensions such as length, width, angle size)

COMMUNICATION

Discussing Math Copy the following diagram on the chalkboard, giving dimensions as shown. Have students suggest who might use such a diagram. (architect; builder; painter) Have them name the shape of the room (rectangle), locate the window and door, and tell how lengths are given. (Arrows show how far measurements extend.) Have students determine the width of the doorway. (Since the room is a rectangle, 14 − 10 = 4 ft.)

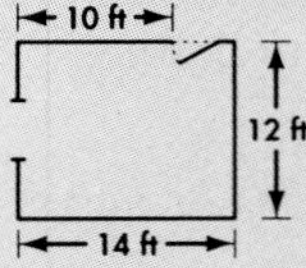

EXPLORE AND CONNECT

COOPERATIVE ACTIVITY

Grouping Suggestion: small groups

Joe's window and the wall sections touching it are the same size. How wide is each wall section and the window?

TEACHING ACTIONS

Have students work with the floor plan in the Communication section to find and use the necessary data.

▶ **Explain the situation in your own words.** (Each of 2 wall sections and a window are of equal width.)

▶ **Analyze how to approach the problem.** (Find the length of the whole wall, then divide by 3 to find the size of each of the 3 equal sections.)

▶ **Decide what data you need from the diagram.** (The opposite wall is 12 ft; since the room is a rectangle, the total width of the window wall is also 12 ft.)

▶ **Justify dividing by 3.** (2 wall sections and a window make 3 equal parts, so divide 12 by 3.)

▶ **Evaluate your solution to verify that it makes sense.** (If the window is 4 ft wide and the wall sections on either side of it are also 4 ft each, the total wall width is 12 ft; this equals the size of the opposite wall, so the solution makes sense.)

CONNECTIONS Use these anytime.

Problem of the Day

Parallel Bars Alice forgot to label her diagram of parallel bars. Label the diagram for her based on these facts: The bars are 160 cm high, 350 cm long, and 42 cm apart. (Check students' drawings.)

Subject Integration

Health and Fitness An official balance beam is 5 m long and 10 cm wide. The top of the beam must be 120 cm from the floor. Draw and label a picture of such a balance beam.

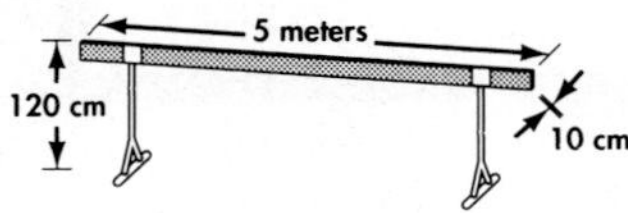

Math Connection

Money Bobby plans to replace the blade pads on a dozen hockey sticks. He knows the right material costs $1.25 per foot. How much will the repair cost? ($15.00)

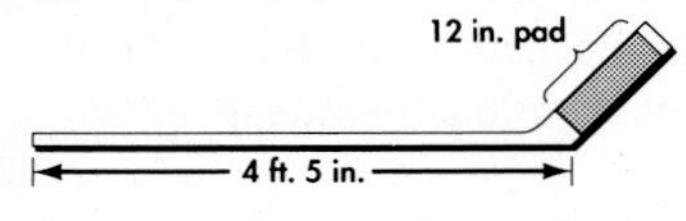

Classwork and Homework Supplements

Practice

Problem Solving 11-11

Name

Data from a Diagram

Left Field — Right Field — Grass Line — Second Base — Foul Line — Shortstop Position — 90 ft — 127 ft — 90 ft — 95 ft — Pitcher's Plate — Third Base — 60 ft — First Base — 90 ft — 90 ft — Home Plate

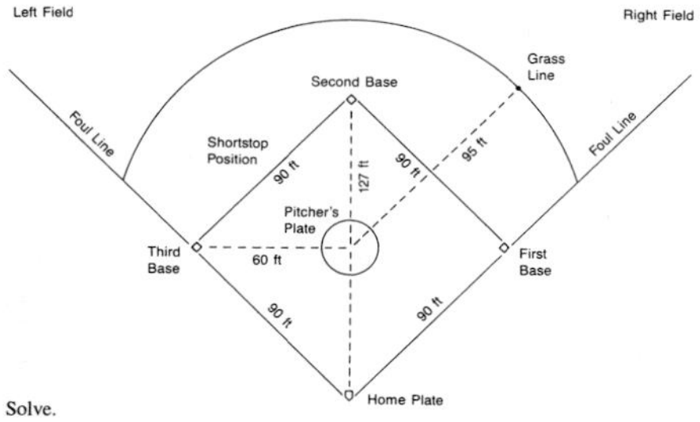

Solve.

1. A baseball player hits a home run. How far is it to run around the perimeter of the baseball diamond? 360 feet
2. How far does a ball travel if it is thrown from the pitcher to third base and then to home plate? 150 feet
3. A player hits a triple. What is the distance he runs from home to third? 270 feet
4. What is the perimeter of the triangle formed by first base, second base, and home plate? 307 feet
5. How far does a baseball travel if it is thrown from the grass line to the pitcher and then to third base? 155 feet
6. Two parallel lines on the field have the same length. The sum of their lengths is 180 feet. Which lines are they? home to first and 2nd to 3rd or home to 3rd and 1st to 2nd

118 Use with text page 318. PS-4

Building Thinking Skills

Critical Thinking 11-11

Name

Figure It Out

On the grid below, 1 unit represents 1 inch. Follow the directions to draw the figure. Then answer the questions that follow.

- Draw a rectangle that is 20 inches long and 10 inches wide. In each corner make a 1-inch square.
- Draw a horizontal line that divides your rectangle into two symmetrical rectangles.
- Draw a rectangle within your rectangle so that its corners meet the innermost corners of the small squares. This rectangle should be 18 inches long and 8 inches wide.

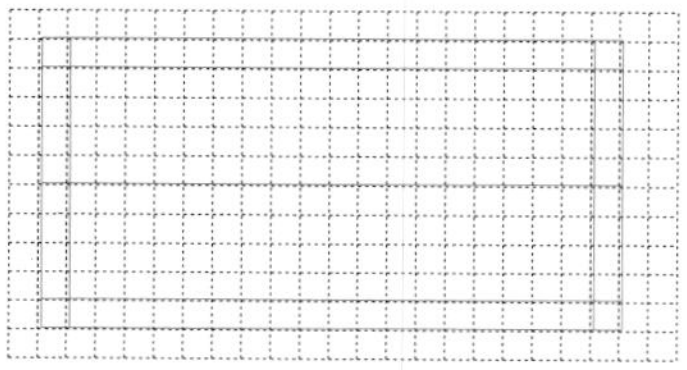

1. How many lines are perpendicular to the line of symmetry? 4
2. Ray says there are fewer than 10 rectangles in the figure. Rita says there are more than 15. Who is right? Rita

118 Use with text pages 318-319. TS-4

Reteaching

Problem Solving 11-11

Name

Data from a Diagram

To solve some problems you must first locate the needed data in a diagram.

Here is a diagram that shows the floor plan for Nan's bedroom. What is the total length of the two longest walls?

12 ft. — 4 ft — 10 ft. — door — 9 ft.

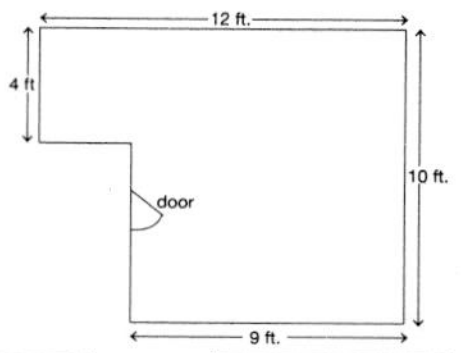

Read the question. Decide what data are needed. → Locate the data in the diagram. → Decide which operation would help you solve the problem.

I need to find out which two walls are the longest. — The lengths of the walls are 12 feet and 10 feet. — Add the two lengths. 12 ft + 10 ft = 22 ft

The total length of the two longest walls in Nan's bedroom is 22 ft.

Solve using the floor plan.

1. What is the length of the shortest wall? 3 ft
2. What is the length of the wall with the door? 6 ft
3. Nan's uncle is building a shelf the full length of the second longest wall for all Nan's stuffed animals. How long will the shelf be? 10 ft
4. Nan wants to put a wallpaper border around the top of the room. How many feet of wallpaper border is needed? 44 ft

118 Use with text page 318. RS-4

Challenges

Writing Math 11-11

Name

Batter Up!

Use the diagram to write facts about a baseball diamond.

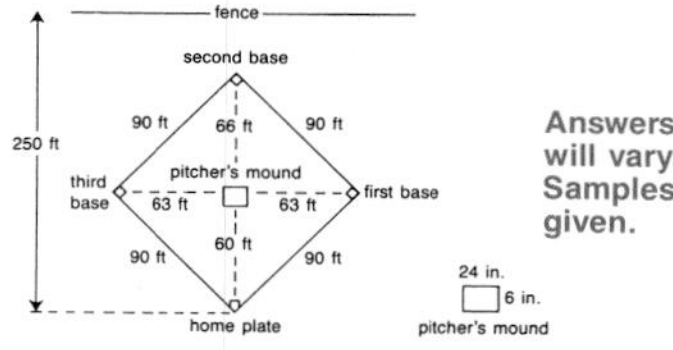

Answers will vary. Samples given.

1. Write a fact you get when you add. It is 126 feet from home plate to second base.
2. Write a fact about perpendicular lines. The line from first to third base is perpendicular to the line from home plate to second base.
3. Write a fact you get when you multiply. The distance around the bases is 360 feet.
4. Write a fact about a perimeter. The perimeter of the pitcher's mound is 60 inches.
5. Write a fact about a triangle. The perimeter of the triangle formed by first base, second base, and the pitcher's mound is 306 feet.
6. Write a fact you get when you subtract. It is 27 feet farther from home plate to first base than from first base to the pitcher's mound.

118 Use with text page 318. CS-4

Options for Individual Needs

11-11

Basic

Exercises 1-7
Computer Bank, p. 499
More Practice, p. 523, set C

Supplements
Reteaching 118 or
Practice 118

Average

Exercises 1-7
Computer Bank, p. 499
More Practice, p. 523, set C

Supplements
Practice 118
Challenges 118 or
Thinking Skills 118

Extended

Exercises 1-7
Computer Bank, p. 499

Supplements
Challenges 118
Thinking Skills 118

Other Resources:
Problem-Solving Experiences in Mathematics, Grade 4, Problems 112, 113
Math In Stride, Grade 4, pp. 73-75

LESSON PLAN 11-11

OBJECTIVE 11-11
To solve problems using data from a diagram

1. MOTIVATE AND TEACH

LEARN ABOUT IT

▶ **Analyze what Rosita did.** (She began at an end line and dribbled to the center line, parallel to the sideline.)
▶ **Decide which places on the diagram represent where Rosita started and stopped.** (the end line; the center line)
▶ **Analyze the diagram to determine the length of the center line.** (42 ft, just like the end line)

▶ **Decide which measurements will help you plan a solution strategy.** (The full length of the court is 74 ft; Rosita dribbled half as far.)
▶ **Justify the operation to use to solve the problem.** (Divide 74 by 2 to find the length of 2 equal parts.)
▶ **Explain how to estimate a solution.** (Half of 70 is 35, so she dribbled about 35 ft.)

▶ **Evaluate the answer to see if it makes sense.** (74 ÷ 2 = 37, which is near the estimate; 37 + 37 fits the diagram.)

2. CHECK UNDERSTANDING

TRY IT OUT

ERROR ALERT Choosing the wrong measurements from the diagram. Choosing the wrong operation.

Problem Solving
Data from a Diagram

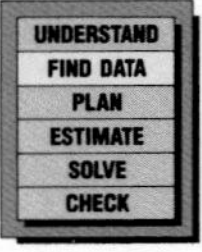

LEARN ABOUT IT

To solve some problems you must first locate the needed data in a diagram.

Rosita dribbled from the end line to the center line. She dribbled parallel to the sideline. How far did she dribble?

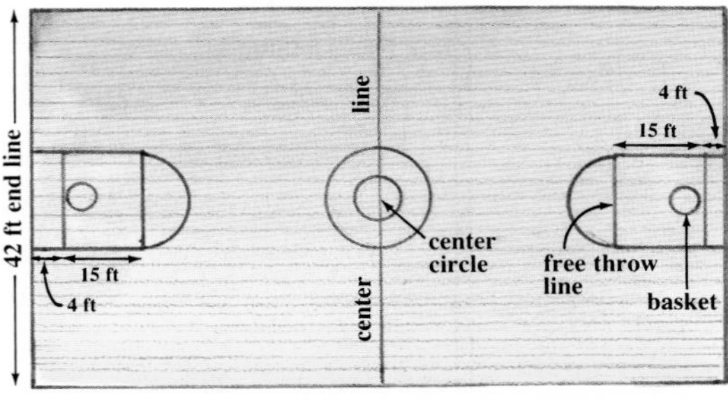

First I'll find where Rosita started and stopped.

end line
center line
sideline 74 ft

The side line is 74 feet long. I'll divide that distance by 2.

$$2\overline{)74}\quad 37$$

Rosita dribbled 37 feet.

TRY IT OUT

Solve.

1. Pablo's coach had the team jog around the perimeter of the court 12 times. How far did they jog? **2,784 ft**
2. Two parallel lines on the court have the same length. The sum of their lengths is 148 feet. Which lines are they? **side lines**
3. What is the length of the court from basket to basket? **66 ft**

318

TEACHING OPTIONS

RETEACHING TIPS Have students identify the necessary measurements before trying to solve a problem. For Exercise 1, they write 74 + 42 + 74 + 42 to find the perimeter. For Exercise 2, they list 74, 42, 12, 15, and 4 as lengths of possible parallel lines. Assign Reteaching Supplement 118.

ENRICHMENT Have students use this data to draw a diagram of a Ping-Pong table. The rectangular table has 9-ft side lines and 5-ft end lines. A 6-in.-high net divides the table into playing sides. The height of a leg equals half the width of the end line. (Leg height is $2\frac{1}{2}$ ft; check students' drawings.)

MIXED PRACTICE

Solve. Use any problem solving strategy.

1. Manny dribbled the ball the length of the court 15 times. How far did he go? **1,110 ft**
2. Each quarter in Ben's game lasts 8 minutes. How many seconds is this? **480 seconds**
3. There are two pairs of congruent rectangles in the basketball court diagram. What is the perimeter of each of the smaller rectangles? **32 ft**
4. The Heroines played 4 games. Use the graph and find their average score. **42 points**
5. 47 fourth graders signed up for basketball. There are 5 more girls than boys. How many boys signed up? **21 boys**
6. After school Jayal practiced his hook shot. He threw the ball 47 times and sunk all but 16. How many baskets did he make? **31 baskets**
7. **Talk About Your Solution**
   Solve. Georgia passed the ball from the middle of the center circle to the middle of the free throw line. How far was her pass? Explain your solution to a classmate. Compare your solutions. **18 ft**

Some Strategies

Act It Out
Use Objects
Choose an Operation
Draw a Picture
Make an Organized List
Guess and Check
Make a Table
Look for a Pattern
Use Logical Reasoning
Work Backward

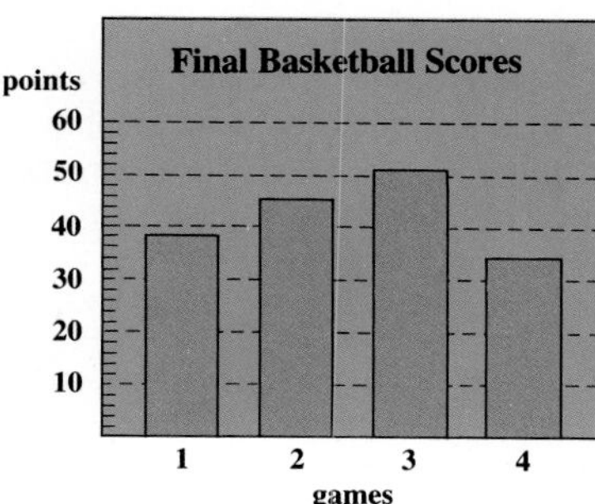

More Practice, page 523, set C

3. PRACTICE AND APPLY

Basic	1-7
Average	1-7
Extended	1-7

Sample Solutions: See p. T79.

MIXED PRACTICE

▶ **Identify problems that use data from the diagram.** (Problems 1, 3, and 7)

▶ **Explain how Problems 1 and 2 are related.** (Both can be solved by multiplying.)

▶ **Explain the steps you would follow to solve Problem 4.** (Read the graph to find the score for each game; add the scores; divide by 4.)

▶ **Analyze Problem 5 to choose a strategy to use to solve it.** (Use Logical Reasoning or Guess and Check.)

▶ **Justify the operation to use in Problem 6.** (Subtract to find a difference.)

CLOSE AND ASSESS

SAY WHAT YOU THINK Have students use the diagram on page 318 to determine the distance from the end line behind the basket to the free throw line. Have them give their reasoning. (19 ft; add 4 ft + 15 ft)

QUICK QUIZ

Rosita's team symbol is painted in the exact center of the court. Find the distance from the center of the symbol to the side line. (21 ft)

CHAPTER 11

APPLIED PROBLEM SOLVING
GROUP DECISION MAKING

OBJECTIVE To analyze, organize, and make decisions using relevant data

Have students recall restaurants in which they have eaten. Ask them to think about how the tables and chairs were arranged; about how a counter was set up, if there was one; and about other features of the physical setup that may help them in drawing their restaurant plans.

FACTS TO CONSIDER

▶ **Decide which facts are fixed and cannot change and which are flexible.** (fixed: size of diner, furniture, fixtures; amount of space to leave between tables; flexible: where things may go; how much space to leave by the door, cash register, and behind the counter; how many of each kind of table to use)

▶ **Explain why you must know the size of the diner.** (It makes a boundary for the plan.)

▶ **Explain how to use the furniture patterns.** (Possible answer: Try various plans by modeling them with the patterns to see if they work.)

▶ **Explain a way to determine a reasonable amount of space to leave behind the counter for the cooks.** (Answers will vary.)

Applied Problem Solving
Group Decision Making

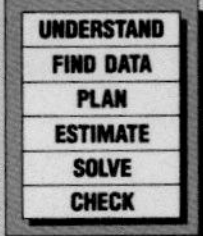

Group Skill:
Disagree in an Agreeable Way

The uncle of one of your classmates is opening a new diner. He has asked you to draw up a plan for arranging the tables, counter, and stools so that the largest number of customers can be seated at one time. Use graph paper to figure out a plan that you can show the owner.

Facts to Consider

1. 6 people can sit at a round table.
2. 4 people can sit at a square table.
3. You need to leave at least 3 squares between tables.

320

TEACHING OPTIONS

COOPERATIVE LEARNING

Grouping Suggestions: cooperative learning groups of 4

Have students work in pairs within groups to share and evaluate ideas leading to the best possible plan. Since there is not 1 correct plan, students should discuss ideas, possibly combining strategies.

Provide enough graph paper for students to cut out multiple copies of each kind of table. They should not trace a plan until they are sure they have found the best possible arrangement. Groups should examine their plan based on each of the 7 facts given.

4. Customers can sit on stools on 1 side of the counter.
5. You need at least 1 square between each stool.
6. You need to leave some space at the door for the cash register.

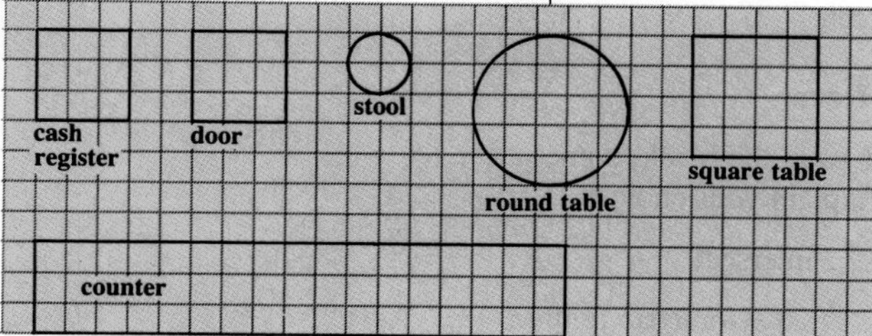

7. The diner is 24 squares wide and 31 squares long.
8. Here are the sizes of the furniture. Cut out copies of the patterns and trace around them on the graph paper to show your plan.

Some Questions to Answer

1. How many round tables can you fit in a row?
2. How many square tables can you fit in a row?
3. How many stools can you fit at the counter?
4. If a square table is against a wall, how many people can sit at it?
5. Did you leave enough room for the customers to get to their tables and to the cash register?

What Is Your Decision?

Use the furniture patterns and graph paper to show a plan that allows the most people to eat at the diner at the same time. Label the diagram so the owner understands your ideas.

321

SOME QUESTIONS TO ANSWER

► **Decide on a plan for finding how many of each size table would fit across the room.** (Possible answer: Add 3 squares to each table width to allow for the space between tables, then divide the 31 squares by each number; Guess and Check various arrangements.)

► **Explain whether it is necessary to have rows of the same kind of table.** (not necessarily; Rows could use a combination of tables if that would provide a greater seating capacity.)

► **Justify putting a table against the wall even though you might lose some seats.** (Possible answer: A table against the wall might use space that would otherwise be lost.)

► **Visualize the counter to explain where stools would go.** (along its length: Possibly a stool could go at each end if the counter is not against a wall.)

► **Explain why the cash register would go by the door.** (It makes sense to have people pay as they leave.)

WHAT IS YOUR DECISION?

Have groups present their diagrams with an oral summary of how many seats the plan provides. Since plans are likely to differ, provide time for a question-and-answer session among groups.

CHAPTER 11

WRAP UP

INTRODUCTION The Wrap Up provides activities emphasizing math language and thinking skills for the chapter and a project that integrates those skills with other math strands.

USING PAGE 322

Number Prefixes Have students complete the section independently, then share their sentences with a partner to discuss how they chose their answers.

Sometimes, Always, Never

▶ **Explain how a picture can help determine the best choice for Exercises 6 and 7.** (Exercise 6: Draw parallel lines to see whether they intersect. Exercise 7: Try drawing symmetric and nonsymmetric trapezoids to see which are possible.)

▶ **Explain the meanings of *congruent* and *similar* to help answer Exercises 8 and 9.** (Congruent figures are the same size and shape; similar figures are the same shape but not always the same size; congruent figures must be similar, but similar figures may not always be congruent.)

Project Have students work in pairs, using centimeter graph paper (TA 12) to create their coordinate codes.

▶ **Explain how to name points on a coordinate grid.** (Beginning at 0, tell how many spaces to count to the right, then how many spaces to count up. Write the numbers in parentheses, separated by a comma.)

▶ **Decide how to separate words in your message.** (Methods may vary.) Display completed projects where students can try decoding classmates' messages.

WRAP UP

Number Prefixes

Complete each sentence.

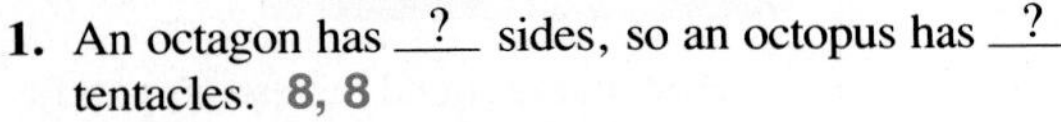

1. An octagon has __?__ sides, so an octopus has __?__ tentacles. 8, 8

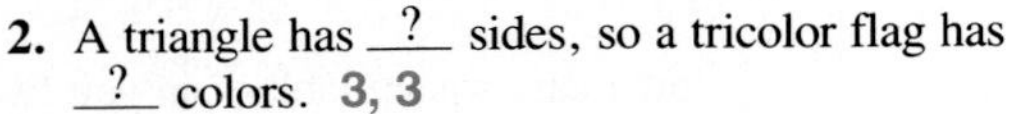

2. A triangle has __?__ sides, so a tricolor flag has __?__ colors. 3, 3

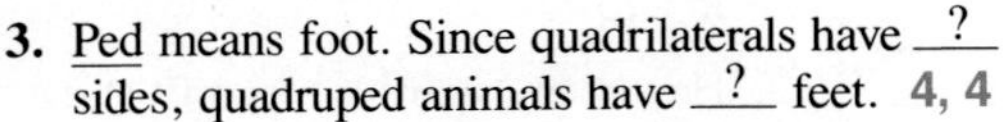

3. Ped means foot. Since quadrilaterals have __?__ sides, quadruped animals have __?__ feet. 4, 4
4. A pentagon has __?__ sides. At the Olympics, the pentathlon involves __?__ events. 5, 5
5. Pod also means foot. Insects are hexapods because they have __?__ feet. 6

Sometimes, Always, Never

Which word should go in the blank, sometimes, always, or never? Explain your choices. Explanations may vary.

6. Parallel lines __?__ intersect. never
7. A trapezoid is __?__ a symmetric figure. sometimes
8. Congruent figures are __?__ similar as well. always
9. Similar figures are __?__ congruent as well. sometimes
10. To plot the coordinates (5,7) on a graph, you __?__ go up 5 and over 7. never

Project Answers will vary.

Make a code with number pairs. First make a key by plotting alphabet letters at different points on a coordinate grid. Then think of a secret message. "Spell" the words in your message by giving the number pairs for each letter. Trade keys and codes with a friend. Read each other's messages.

322

TEACHING OPTIONS

ENRICHMENT Have partners play a coordinate geometry game on 6-by-6 grids. Without letting his or her partner see, each player writes the word *GRID* vertically, horizontally, or diagonally on 4 adjacent coordinates. In turn, players name number pairs. If Player A names a point on which a letter is written, Player B identifies which letter was found, and Player A takes an extra turn to try to name all 4 points that contain the hidden word. The first player to "find" all 4 letters in *GRID* wins. Players may vary the game by not revealing which letter was found or by using a larger grid.

CHAPTER REVIEW/TEST

Part 1 Understanding

1. Name an intersection in your town that suggests perpendicular lines. **Answers will vary.**
2. What would happen if railroad tracks were not parallel? **Answers will vary.**
3. Compare a square and a rectangle. **See Additional Answers.**
4. Compare a parallelogram and a trapezoid. **See Additional Answers.**
5. Draw these curves.
   a. simple b. not simple c. closed d. not closed
   Check students' drawings.

Part 2 Skills

Name an object shaped like each space figure. **Answers will vary.**

6. sphere
7. cone
8. cylinder
9. pyramid
10. cube
11. rectangular prism

Name the polygon that has these features.

12. 5 sides **pentagon**
13. 8 sides **octagon**
14. 6 sides **hexagon**
15. Trace this figure. Draw its line of symmetry.

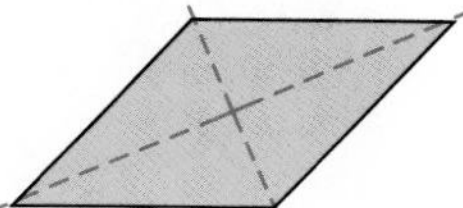

16. Which figure is congruent to this triangle? **a**

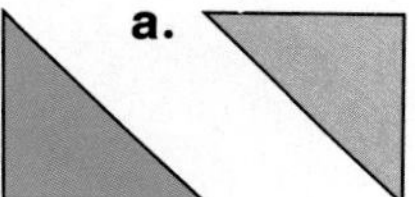

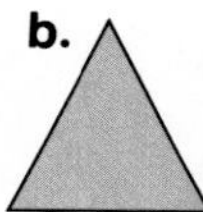

a. b.

Part 3 Applications

17. A swim club built a pool shaped like a regular hexagon. One side is 43 ft long. What is the perimeter of the pool? **258 ft**
18. Randy is designing a patio in the shape of an isosceles triangle. Its perimeter must be 30 ft. Draw and label two possible patio diagrams. **See Additional Answers.**
19. **Challenge** A square fits along the two numbered edges of a grid. The coordinates (4,0) name its lower right-hand corner. Give the other coordinates. **(0,0) (4,4) (0,4)**

323

CHAPTER REVIEW/TEST

INTRODUCTION The Review/Test is provided to review and evaluate the skills and concepts presented in Chapter 11.

USING PAGE 323
If you prefer to use this page for review, you may want to use the **Multiple-Choice Posttest** (pages 43-44) or the **Free-Response Posttest** (pages 43-44) to evaluate mastery of Chapter objectives.

ITEM ANALYSIS The table below correlates the Chapter Review/Test items with the lesson objectives for the chapter.

Items	Objectives
1, 2	11-3
3, 4	11-6
5	11-8
6-11	11-1
12-14	11-2
15	11-4
16	11-7
17	11-2
18	11-5
(18)	11-11
19	11-9

Additional Answers: See p. T79.

INFORMAL ASSESSMENT

Using Manipulatives Have students use centimeter graph paper (TA 12) to draw and label these figures: parallel lines, perpendicular lines, pentagon, right triangle, parallelogram, octagon, and hexagon. Then have them draw a line of symmetry for each of the figures. (Check students' drawings.)

Communication *Relate a vertex to edges in a space figure.* (A vertex is a point where 2 or more edges meet, like a corner.)

Critical Thinking *Imagine a hexagon with all equal sides. If you folded it into 2 congruent parts, visualize the shape each part would have.* (trapezoid or pentagon, depending on the position of the line of symmetry)

CHAPTER 11

ENRICHMENT

INTRODUCTION Students will sharpen their visual-problem-solving ability by combining the ideas of flips, turns, and slides with tangram geometry.

USING PAGE 324
This Enrichment page is provided for all students. You may wish to use it after they have completed the Chapter Review/Test on page 323. Provide each student with a set of tangrams, or have them create their own set by cutting out TA 19 (Tangram).

► **Decide on a plan for trying each new shape with tangram pieces.** (Possible strategy: Build a tangram square as shown, remove pieces A and B, try to visualize how the remaining pieces would form part of each new shape to determine where and how to replace triangles A and B.)

EXTENSION Challenge students to scramble the 7 tangram pieces, then use all 7 to construct a rectangle, a parallelogram, a square, an isosceles right triangle, and an isosceles trapezoid.

ENRICHMENT
Modeling Changes in Geometric Figures

How can you flip, turn, or slide the pieces to change the tangram puzzle square into the figures shown? Use tangram pieces to show your solutions.

Start with a tangram puzzle square. Move only pieces A and B to make each figure below.

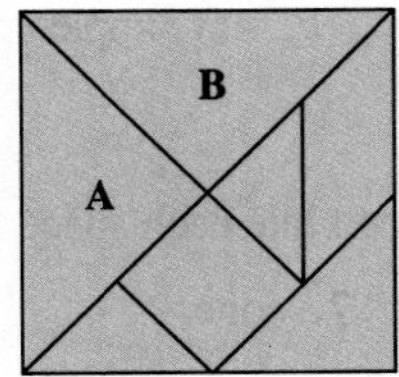

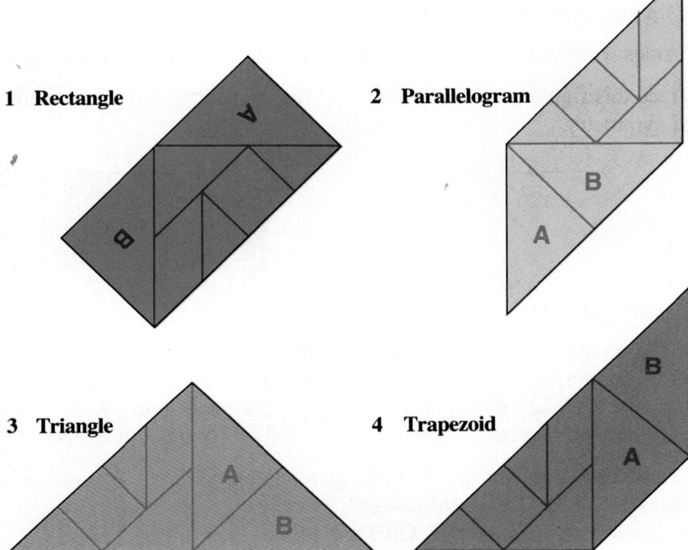

3 Triangle

A

B

4 Trapezoid

B

A

324

CUMULATIVE REVIEW

1. A passenger elevator can carry 900 pounds safely. How many adults weighing an average of 150 pounds each can safely ride in the elevator at the same time?

   (A) 6 B 8
   C 7 D 10

2. 11 yards = |||| feet

   A 22 B 44
   (C) 33 D 396

3. A good outdoor activity when it is 30°F is ||||.

   A raking leaves (B) sledding
   C swimming D gardening

4. $5\overline{)0}$

   A 5 B 1
   C 50 (D) 0

5. 64 ÷ 8

   A 6 (B) 8
   C 7 D 9

6. |||| × 9 = 45

   A 6 B 4
   (C) 5 D 3

7. If a function rule is divide by 9, what number should go in so that 8 comes out?

   (A) 72 B 81
   C 7 D 64

8. $6\overline{)23}$

   A 3 R3 B 4 R1
   C 4 (D) 3 R5

9. 240 ÷ 8

   A 3,000 (B) 30
   C 300 D 3

10. If you estimate these quotients using compatible numbers, which estimate will be an underestimate?

    A 396 ÷ 5 (B) 216 ÷ 3
    C 415 ÷ 7 D 114 ÷ 6

11. Find the average of 135, 153, 140, and 136.

    A 4 B 139
    (C) 141 D 564

12. $5\overline{)529}$

    (A) 105 R4 B 150 R4
    C 106 R1 D 104 R9

CUMULATIVE REVIEW

INTRODUCTION The purpose of this Cumulative Review is to maintain previously taught skills and concepts. The emphasis in this Cumulative Review in on time and customary measurement, Chapter 8; on division concepts and basic facts, Chapter 9; and on division using 1-digit divisors, Chapter 10.

ITEM ANALYSIS The table below correlates the Cumulative Review items with the lesson objectives.

Items	Objectives
1	9-2
2	8-6
3	8-12
4	9-6
5, 6	9-8
7	9-9
8	9-7
9	10-2
10	10-3
11	10-8
12	10-10

CHAPTER 12 FRACTION CONCEPTS

Chapter Management

OVERVIEW

Lesson	Pages	Objectives	Subject Integration	Strand Integration
Chapter Opener	326-327	To introduce chapter 12	language arts-Laura Ingalls Wilder	computation
Understanding Fractions: Regions	328-329	12-1 To understand the region interpretation of a fraction	social studies-group skills	critical thinking
Understanding Fractions: Sets	330-331	12-2 To understand the set interpretation of a fraction	language arts-Laura Ingalls Wilder	problem solving
Estimating Fractional Parts/Problem Solving	332-333	12-3 To estimate parts of a whole as fractions; to practice problem solving	social studies-guide dog schools	computation
Equivalent Fractions	334-335	12-4 To understand the concept of equivalent fractions	science-computers	critical thinking
More About Equivalent Fractions	336-337	12-5 To find equivalent fractions by multiplying	social studies-cooking	calculators
Lowest-Terms Fractions	338-339	12-6 To reduce fractions to lowest terms	science-fish	algebra
Comparing Fractions	340-341	12-7 To compare fractions	health/fitness-pizza	mental math
Exploring Algebra/Midchapter Review/Quiz	342-343	12-8 To explore algebra by finding and graphing ordered pairs that make true equations	health/fitness-pizza	number
Mental Math: Finding a Fraction of a Number	344-345	12-9 To use mental math to find a fraction of a number	social studies-stamp collection	calculators
Mixed Numbers	346-347	12-10 To understand a mixed number	fine arts-quilting	mathematical reasoning
Problem Solving: Measuring to a Fractional Part of an Inch	348-349	12-11 To solve problems by measuring to a fractional part of an inch	fine arts-bracelets	consumer math
Data Collection and Analysis: Group Decision Making	350-351	12-12 To collect, organize, and present data	health/fitness-bicycles	statistics

MATHEMATICAL BACKGROUND

Fractions
Students learn that fractions describe parts of a whole. The denominator names the total number of parts in the whole and the numerator gives the number of parts of that whole. Concepts covered in the chapter include equivalent fractions, lowest-terms fractions, comparing fractions with unlike denominators by finding a common denominator, and mixed numbers.

Estimation
In Lesson 12-3, students practice visually estimating a fractional part of an object or region.

Problem Solving
In this chapter, students solve problems by measuring to a fractional part of an inch.

TIPS FROM TEACHERS

Help students make their own fraction kits. Students cut five 12-inch strips, each strip from a different color of construction paper. They label one strip as one whole: $\frac{1}{1}$. They divide the next strip into two equal parts and label each part $\frac{1}{2}$. Then they divide the other strips into fourths, eighths, and sixteenths.

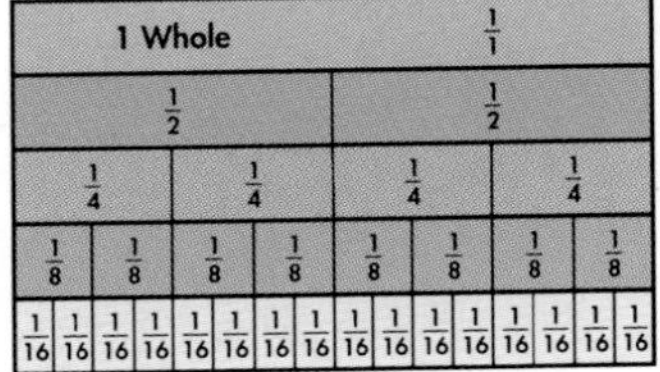

Pat Wiemann
Martin Sortun School
Kent, WA

ASSESSMENT

Pretest — Chapter 12, page 1

Multiple-Choice Format

Name

1. Choose the fraction that tells what part is shaded.
a. $\frac{2}{5}$ b. $\frac{2}{3}$ c. $\frac{3}{4}$ d. $\frac{3}{5}$ 1. d

2. Choose the fraction that tells what part of the letters are x's. x o o x x o o
a. $\frac{3}{7}$ b. $\frac{4}{7}$ c. $\frac{3}{4}$ d. $\frac{4}{3}$ 2. a

3. Choose the best fractional estimate for the shaded part of this figure.
a. $\frac{2}{3}$ b. $\frac{9}{10}$ c. $\frac{1}{3}$ d. $\frac{3}{4}$ 3. d

4. In a relay race, Ben finished in front of Jack and behind Mark. Craig finished last. Who won the race?
a. Ben b. Jack c. Mark d. Craig 4. c

5. Which choice shows the completed equation? $\frac{1}{5} = \frac{■}{10}$
a. $\frac{1}{5} = \frac{8}{10}$ b. $\frac{1}{5} = \frac{5}{10}$ c. $\frac{1}{5} = \frac{2}{10}$ d. $\frac{1}{5} = \frac{1}{10}$ 5. c

6. Choose the equivalent fraction. Think: $\frac{3}{4}$ ×2/×2 = ■
a. $\frac{5}{8}$ b. $\frac{7}{8}$ c. $\frac{4}{8}$ d. $\frac{6}{8}$ 6. d

Pretest — Chapter 12, page 2

Multiple-Choice Format

Name

7. Choose the lowest terms fraction for $\frac{4}{8}$.
a. $\frac{2}{4}$ b. $\frac{1}{2}$ c. $\frac{4}{8}$ d. $\frac{1}{12}$ 7. b

8. Compare: $\frac{7}{8}$ ● $\frac{3}{4}$. Use <, >, or =.
a. < b. > c. = 8. b

9. Jeff used the data in the table to make these ordered pairs: 1,1 2,2 3,3. Then he graphed the ordered pairs. Which line shows Jeff's graph?

▲	1	2	3
■	1	2	3

a. Line A
b. Line B
9. a

10. Find: $\frac{3}{4}$ of 8. Think:
a. 24 b. 12 c. 6 d. 8 10. c

11. Choose the mixed number for $\frac{7}{3}$.
a. $1\frac{1}{3}$ b. $2\frac{1}{3}$ c. $1\frac{1}{4}$ d. $2\frac{1}{7}$ 11. b

12. Find the length of the line.
a. 3 in b. $3\frac{1}{4}$ in c. $3\frac{1}{2}$ in d. $3\frac{3}{4}$ in 12. d

Posttest — Chapter 12, page 1

Multiple-Choice Format

Name

1. Choose the fraction that tells what part is shaded.
a. $\frac{5}{8}$ b. $\frac{3}{5}$ c. $\frac{1}{8}$ d. $\frac{2}{5}$ 1. c

2. Choose the fraction that tells what part of the letters are x's. x o o o x o o o o
a. $\frac{7}{9}$ b. $\frac{2}{7}$ c. $\frac{2}{9}$ d. $\frac{7}{2}$ 2. c

3. Choose the best fractional estimate for the shaded part of this figure.
a. $\frac{1}{2}$ b. $\frac{1}{4}$ c. $\frac{1}{3}$ d. $\frac{2}{3}$ 3. a

4. In a relay race, Jan finished in front of Amy and behind Ellie. Barbara won the race. Who was second?
a. Jan b. Amy c. Ellie d. Barbara 4. c

5. Which choice shows the completed equation? $\frac{3}{9} = \frac{■}{3}$
a. $\frac{3}{9} = \frac{1}{3}$ b. $\frac{3}{9} = \frac{1}{9}$ c. $\frac{3}{9} = \frac{2}{3}$ d. $\frac{3}{9} = \frac{3}{3}$ 5. a

6. Choose the equivalent fraction. Think: $\frac{1}{6}$ ×5/×5 = ■
a. $\frac{5}{30}$ b. $\frac{6}{11}$ c. $\frac{5}{6}$ d. $\frac{6}{30}$ 6. a

Posttest — Chapter 12, page 2

Multiple-Choice Format

Name

7. Choose the lowest terms fraction for $\frac{3}{9}$.
a. $\frac{2}{6}$ b. $\frac{3}{9}$ c. $\frac{1}{3}$ d. $\frac{1}{12}$ 7. c

8. Compare: $\frac{3}{5}$ ● $\frac{3}{4}$. Use <, >, or =.
a. < b. > c. = 8. a

9. Ann used the data in the table to make these ordered pairs: 1,2 2,4 3,6. Then she graphed the ordered pairs. Which line shows Ann's graph?

▲	1	2	3
■	2	4	6

a. Line A
b. Line B
9. a

10. Find: $\frac{2}{3}$ of 6. Think:
a. $\frac{2}{9}$ b. 6 c. 2 d. 4 10. d

11. Choose the mixed number for $\frac{5}{2}$.
a. $2\frac{1}{5}$ b. $1\frac{3}{5}$ c. $3\frac{1}{2}$ d. $2\frac{1}{2}$ 11. d

12. Find the length of the line.
a. $\frac{2}{3}$ in b. $3\frac{1}{4}$ in. c. $3\frac{1}{2}$ in. d. $3\frac{3}{4}$ in. 12. b

ITEM ANALYSIS

Items	Objectives
1	12-1
2	12-2
3, 4	12-3
5	12-4
6	12-5
7	12-6
8	12-7
9	12-8
10	12-9
11	12-10
12	12-11

Note: The item analysis is the same for all pretests and posttests for this chapter.

ALSO AVAILABLE

- **Free Response Tests**
- **Alternative Tests**
- **Thinking Strategies**
- **Concrete Materials**

Chapter 12 Fraction Concepts

Optional Chapter Activities

Project and Bulletin Board

After students have completed Lesson 4, have them construct a table of equivalent fractions to display on the bulletin board. First, give students a list of fractions in lowest terms that will appear in the left–hand column of the table as shown. Have students order the fractions from greatest to least, beginning at the bottom of the table. Write the fractions on the chart, then arrange students into four cooperative learning groups. Assign one fraction to each group and have them write equivalent fractions on index cards to be posted on the chart in the appropriate row. Students should order their equivalent fractions so that the size of the numerators increases from least to greatest. Encourage students to explain what procedure they followed to find equivalent fractions, then challenge them to find patterns to invent games that involve removing, mixing, and replacing the fraction cards.

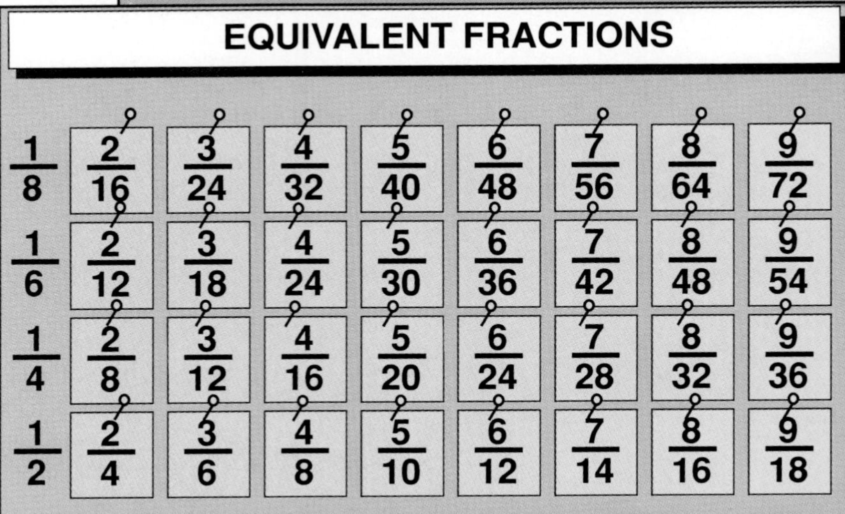

EQUIVALENT FRACTIONS
1/8 2/16 3/24 4/32 5/40 6/48 7/56 8/64 9/72
1/6 2/12 3/18 4/24 5/30 6/36 7/42 8/48 9/54
1/4 2/8 3/12 4/16 5/20 6/24 7/28 8/32 9/36
1/2 2/4 3/6 4/8 5/10 6/12 7/14 8/16 9/18

Cooperative Learning

Divide the class into groups of three or four. Identify the group skill: listen to others. Tell students they are going to find fractional parts of an hour. Remind students that there are 60 minutes in an hour. Around the edge of a clock face (TA 16), have groups mark the fraction of an hour represented by each of the following: 5 minutes, 6 minutes, 10 minutes, 12 minutes, 15 minutes, 18 minutes, 20 minutes, 30 minutes, 40 minutes, and 45 minutes. Have them first write each fraction with a denominator of 60 and then reduce it to its lowest terms. Students may want to divide the tasks so that, for example, one student writes the original fraction, another reduces the fraction to lowest terms, and a third checks the work. Tell students they should listen to one another's ideas about how to proceed.

You will find grouping suggestions and cooperative learning activities in most lessons throughout this chapter.

Literature

Stallworth, Lyn. *Wond'rous Fare: A Classic Childrens Cookbook.* Chicago, Illinois: A Calico Book, Contemporary Books, 1988.

Many classic children's stories have wonderful descriptions of luscious lunches, delicious dinners, and much more. Children will enjoy a ''Mad Hatter Tea Party.'' Cooking is an enjoyable way for children to learn about fractions.
Children could discuss food from stories they remember. Then children could bring in their own favorite recipes, discuss them with the class and use multiplication and division to make larger or smaller amounts.

Weiss, Malcolm E. *666 Jelly Beans! All That?* New York: Young Math Book Series, Thomas Y. Crowell, 1976.

Wyler, Rose and Eva-Lee Baird. *Nutty Number Riddles.* New York: Doubleday, 1977.

English as a Second Language

ESL children who do not understand equivalent fractions can use the following activity for review.

First check to make sure students can identify the *denominator,* or the number of parts into which the whole is divided, and the *numerator,* or the number of parts available. Write $\frac{2}{6}$ on the chalkboard, then carefully enunciate *two sixths* as you point to each part of the fraction. Have students copy the fraction and say "two sixths" as they point to each part just as you did.

Next, arrange students into small groups and provide each group with fraction strips (TA 21). Students cut the strips apart according to the number of pieces into which each strip is divided. Then students manipulate the pieces to try combinations that equal other pieces. Students should write each discovery as an equality.

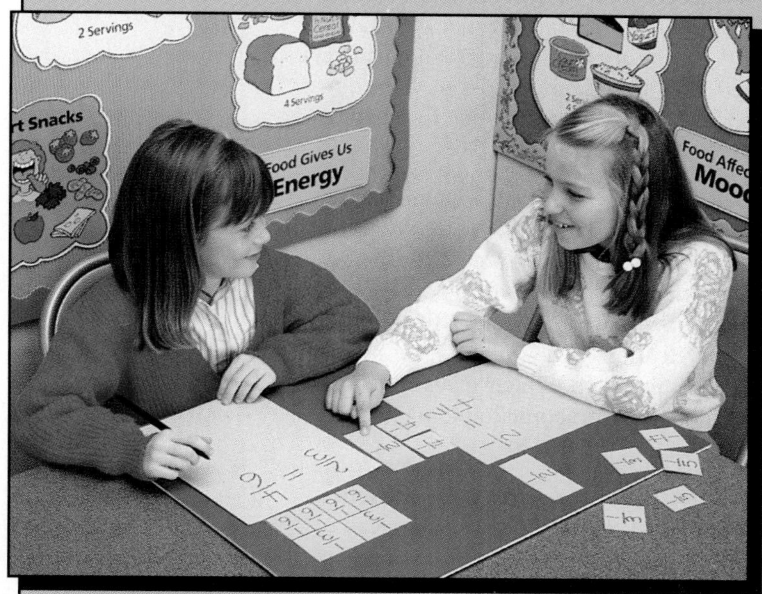

Gifted

Introduce your students to the Fraction Family. This family consists of Mr. and Mrs. Equivalent Fraction, their children, Numerator and Denominator, and their dog, Lowest Term. Ask students to create several paragraphs describing a Saturday spent with the Fraction Family. Anything a Fraction–Family member does relates to his or her name. Encourage students to use fractions creatively in identifying family members and in describing their activities.

Remind them that when using fractions with regard to the mother and the father, the fractions must always be equivalent. Ask them to use only fractions in their lowest terms when referring to the family's dog. Have them consider that the children may have different interests and activities and may need different fractions in their descriptions.

Instruct students to use at least 10 fractions in their creative writing. Ask students to share their day with the Fraction Family with other class members by reading their paragraphs aloud. Encourage brainstorming and discussion as to the use of fractions in daily living.

Students at Risk

Fractions are used to represent parts of a set, regions of a whole, or segments of a measurement. Comparing fractions and recognizing equivalent fractions are skills fundamental to the understanding of many basic fraction concepts. Both are used in fraction computations. Some students may have done little prior work with fractions, or may have developed misconceptions about fractions. Frequent experience with fraction models may improve their grasp of basic concepts and vocabulary.

Comparing Fractions Write these fractions on separate cards: $\frac{1}{2}$, $\frac{1}{3}$, $\frac{2}{3}$, $\frac{1}{4}$, $\frac{2}{4}$, $\frac{3}{4}$, $\frac{1}{5}$, $\frac{2}{5}$, $\frac{3}{5}$, $\frac{4}{5}$, $\frac{1}{6}$, $\frac{2}{6}$, $\frac{3}{6}$, $\frac{4}{6}$, $\frac{5}{6}$, $\frac{1}{8}$, $\frac{2}{8}$, $\frac{3}{8}$, $\frac{4}{8}$, $\frac{5}{8}$, $\frac{6}{8}$, $\frac{7}{8}$, $\frac{1}{10}$, $\frac{2}{10}$, $\frac{3}{10}$, $\frac{4}{10}$, $\frac{5}{10}$, $\frac{6}{10}$, $\frac{7}{10}$, $\frac{8}{10}$, $\frac{9}{10}$. Provide fraction strips (TA 21), fraction bars, or any manipulative fraction pieces. Students shuffle the cards, then pick any two and place them face up on the table. They use models to compare the two fractions, deciding which is the larger fraction or proving that they are equivalent. Allow students to play this game frequently to help them build a stronger understanding of these essential fraction concepts.

You may also use the Reteaching Supplements and the specific Reteaching Tips from each lesson in this chapter.

INTRODUCING THE CHAPTER

SUBJECT INTEGRATION The photograph of the birch forest suggests a scene from *Little House in the Big Woods* by Laura Ingalls Wilder, which represents the chapter theme of language arts. Some lessons incorporate characters and situations from Wilder's well-known books to offer opportunities for students to explore fractions.

USING DATA The Language Arts Data Bank on page 477 of the Student Edition has a table entitled "Books by Laura Ingalls Wilder" that lists each book in chronological order of the year of publication. It also provides a recipe for Johnny Cake, which gives most ingredients in fractional amounts.

QUESTION 1 ► **Analyze the table of books to determine how they are organized.** (in order of the year each was published, starting with the earliest book)
Student Edition answers: 9, 3, 6

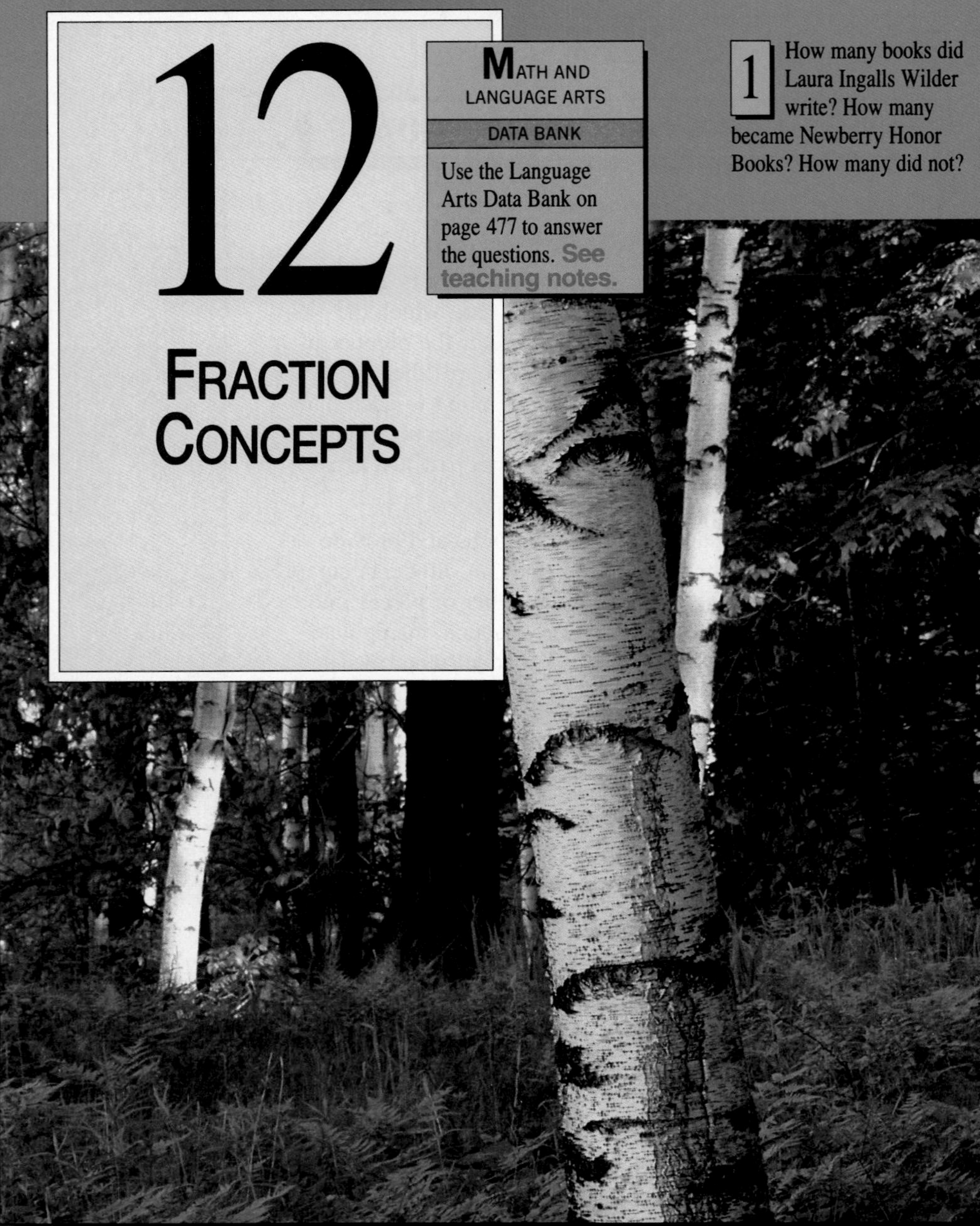

12 FRACTION CONCEPTS

MATH AND LANGUAGE ARTS

DATA BANK

Use the Language Arts Data Bank on page 477 to answer the questions. See teaching notes.

1 How many books did Laura Ingalls Wilder write? How many became Newberry Honor Books? How many did not?

TEACHING OPTIONS

LANGUAGE DEVELOPMENT
Write the word **half** on the chalkboard and ask students to recall its meaning. ("1 of 2 equal parts") Have students suggest realistic situations in which they might describe half of something. (Sample answers: half an hour; half a sandwich; half of the room; half the class; half a cup)

2 How many servings of Johnny Cake would you get if you were to double the recipe?

3 In *Little House in the Big Woods,* Laura Ingalls Wilder writes that the story she is telling took place 60 years earlier. What year would that be?

4 **Use Critical Thinking** Laura and Mary get two cookies. Each nibbles half her cookie and saves the other half for Baby Carrie. Is this fair?

QUESTION 2 ► **Analyze the recipe to identify the kinds of data included in it.** (Possible answers: quantities of ingredients; oven temperature; baking time; number of servings; steps to follow; capacity of the baking dish you need)
Student Edition answer: 12

QUESTION 3 ► **Explain how to answer the question.** (Find the date when *Little House in the Big Woods* was published, then subtract 60 to determine a date 60 years earlier than that.)
► **Decide how many years have passed since *Little House in the Big Woods* was first published.** (Answers may vary.)
Student Edition answer: 1872

QUESTION 4 ► **Explain the meaning of *half.*** (Possible answer: "1 part of something that has been divided into 2 equal parts")
► **Explain how much cookie Baby Carrie would get in the situation.** ($\frac{1}{2}$ from Laura, $\frac{1}{2}$ from Mary, which equals a whole cookie.)
► **Compare the amount of cookie Laura and Mary each get with the amount Baby Carrie would get to decide if the situation is fair for all 3 girls.** (No, because the baby would get more cookie than either sister.)
Student Edition answer: Baby Carrie would get 2 halves, while Laura and Mary would each get $\frac{1}{2}$, so it seems unfair to Mary and Laura.

SUBJECT INTEGRATION PROJECT Have students share any information they may know about Laura Ingalls Wilder from her books that they have read or from the television series based on them. Have students select 1 of her books to read independently, or you may prefer to read excerpts aloud to the class during the time allotted for Chapter 12. Challenge students to construct a diorama to represent a favorite scene and have them share their projects at the conclusion of the chapter.

LESSON OPTIONS 12-1

Understanding Fractions: Regions

OBJECTIVE 12-1 To understand the region interpretation of a fraction

PREBOOK ACTIVITIES

QUICK REVIEW

Answer these questions about the word *rectangle*.

1. How many letters are in the whole word? (9)
2. How many vowels are in the whole word? (3)
3. What letter is third? (c)
4. What letter is fifth? (a)
5. What position is the *l* in? (eighth)

PRIOR KNOWLEDGE

Have students explain in their own words what a fraction is. (Possible answer: a name for part of something) Have students name some familiar fractions and tell how they could use them to describe part of something. (Answers may vary. Sample: $\frac{1}{2}$, as in $9\frac{1}{2}$ years old; $\frac{1}{2}$ h) Have students look around the room for things to describe with a fraction. (Possible answers: windows with panes, file cabinet with drawers)

COMMUNICATION

Reading and Writing Math Write **fraction, numerator,** and **denominator** on the chalkboard. Have students read each word after you. Ask volunteers to share what they may recall about the meanings of these math terms and their relationship to each other. (Possible answer: Write a fraction with a numerator on top and a denominator on the bottom.) Have volunteers write sample fractions on the board while other students identify each numerator and denominator. Then have students summarize the terms in their Math Journals by writing a sentence that uses all three terms. (Check students' writing.)

EXPLORE AND CONNECT

Materials: TA 12 (Centimeter Graph Paper), TA 13 (Spinners 1-4, 5-8), crayons, 4 fraction guides per group (see below)
Grouping Suggestion: cooperative learning groups of 4
Students generate **numerators** and **denominators** to explore **fractions.** A student spins a 5-8 spinner and writes that number in a **fraction** guide for *How many in all*. The second student draws a rectangle of that many boxes on graph paper. The third student spins a 1-4 spinner and writes that number on the same fraction guide for *How many shaded parts,* as the fourth student shades that many parts of the rectangle. Groups repeat the activity 4 times, trading jobs. Conclude by asking students to relate *fraction* numbers to the *fraction* pictures. (The top number, or **numerator,** is the number of shaded parts in the rectangle; the bottom number, or **denominator,** is the total number of parts.) Have students generalize about the fractional parts of any figure. (They are the same size.)

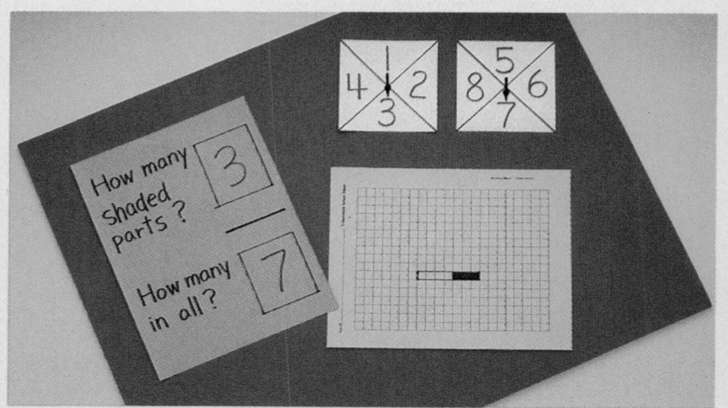

CONNECTIONS Use these anytime.

Problem of the Day

Board Cutting Ann must saw a long board into 5 equal pieces for a bird feeder. How many cuts must she make? Draw the cuts. (4)

Life Skills

Logic Half the windshield of Mr. Egan's car got cracked by a stone kicked up by a truck on a highway. Explain why he must replace the whole windshield. (The whole windshield must be replaced because a windshield is not a whole made up of parts, like a window with panes. It is one solid piece.)

Math Connection

Graphing A circle graph shows a whole amount as a circle, then divides it into parts for each fact. Draw a 4-h circle graph that shows 1 h for reading, 1 h for math, and 2 h for all other subjects.

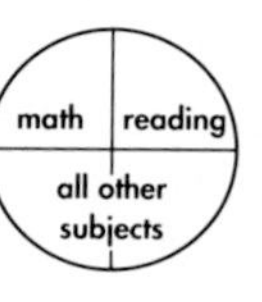

Classwork and Homework Supplements

Practice

Skills Maintenance 12-1

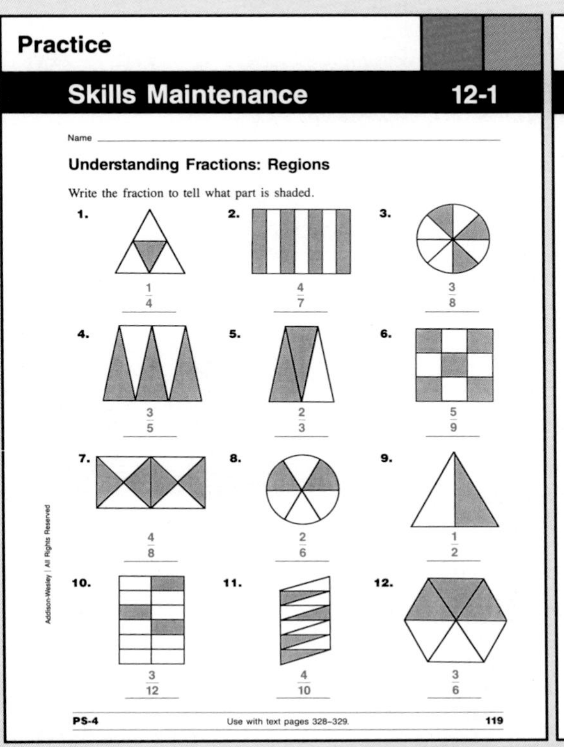
Name

Understanding Fractions: Regions

Write the fraction to tell what part is shaded.

1. $\frac{1}{4}$
2. $\frac{4}{7}$
3. $\frac{3}{8}$
4. $\frac{3}{5}$
5. $\frac{2}{3}$
6. $\frac{5}{9}$
7. $\frac{4}{8}$
8. $\frac{2}{6}$
9. $\frac{1}{2}$
10. $\frac{3}{12}$
11. $\frac{4}{10}$
12. $\frac{3}{6}$

PS-4 Use with text pages 328–329. 119

Building Thinking Skills

Math Reasoning 12-1

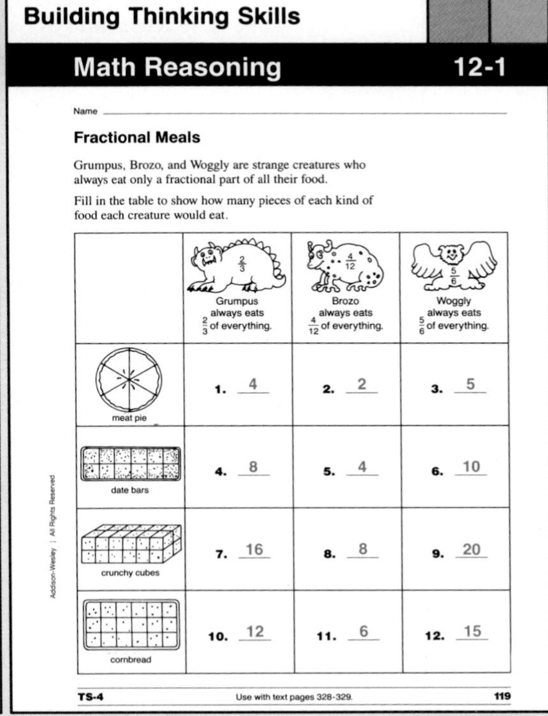
Name

Fractional Meals

Grumpus, Brozo, and Woggly are strange creatures who always eat only a fractional part of all their food.

Fill in the table to show how many pieces of each kind of food each creature would eat.

	Grumpus always eats $\frac{2}{3}$ of everything.	Brozo always eats $\frac{4}{12}$ of everything.	Woggly always eats $\frac{5}{6}$ of everything.
meat pie	1. 4	2. 2	3. 5
date bars	4. 8	5. 4	6. 10
crunchy cubes	7. 16	8. 8	9. 20
cornbread	10. 12	11. 6	12. 15

TS-4 Use with text pages 328-329. 119

Reteaching

Skills Review 12-1

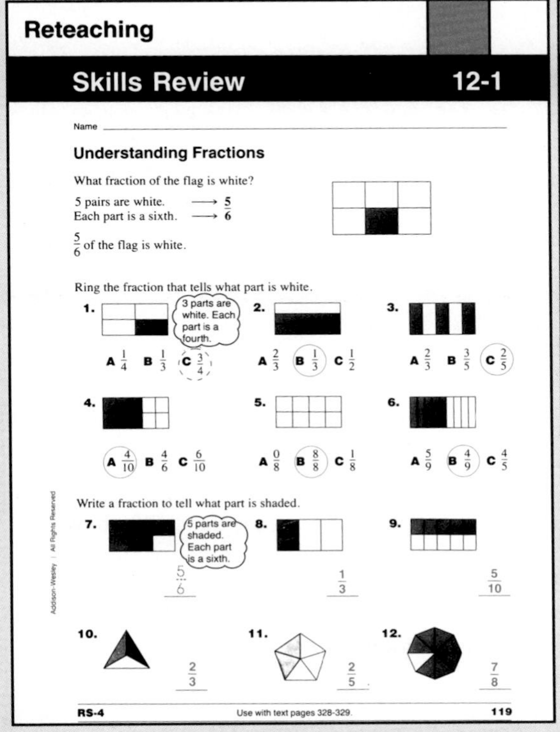
Name

Understanding Fractions

What fraction of the flag is white?

5 parts are white. ⟶ 5
Each part is a sixth. ⟶ 6

$\frac{5}{6}$ of the flag is white.

Ring the fraction that tells what part is white.

1. A $\frac{1}{4}$ B $\frac{1}{3}$ C $\frac{3}{4}$ (3 parts are white. Each part is a fourth.)
2. A $\frac{2}{3}$ B $\frac{1}{3}$ C $\frac{1}{2}$
3. A $\frac{2}{3}$ B $\frac{3}{5}$ C $\frac{2}{5}$
4. A $\frac{4}{10}$ B $\frac{4}{6}$ C $\frac{6}{10}$
5. A $\frac{0}{8}$ B $\frac{8}{8}$ C $\frac{1}{8}$
6. A $\frac{5}{9}$ B $\frac{4}{9}$ C $\frac{4}{5}$

Write a fraction to tell what part is shaded.

7. $\frac{5}{6}$ (5 parts are shaded. Each part is a sixth.)
8. $\frac{1}{3}$
9. $\frac{5}{10}$
10. $\frac{2}{3}$
11. $\frac{2}{5}$
12. $\frac{7}{8}$

RS-4 Use with text pages 328-329. 119

Challenges

Number Sense 12-1

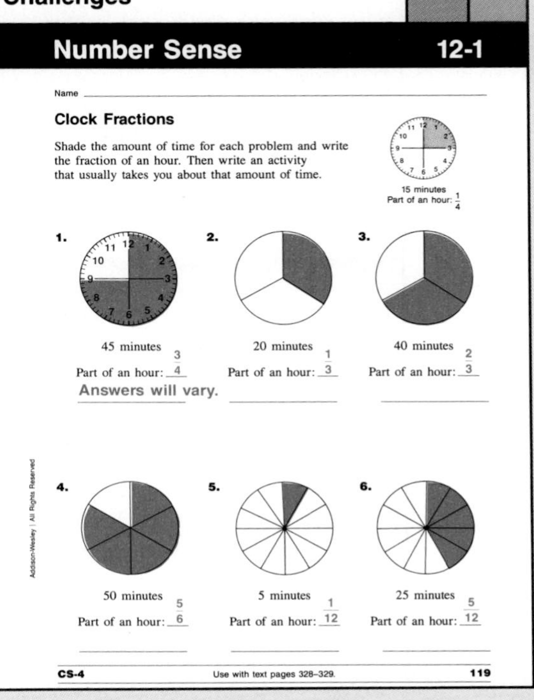
Name

Clock Fractions

Shade the amount of time for each problem and write the fraction of an hour. Then write an activity that usually takes you about that amount of time.

15 minutes
Part of an hour: $\frac{1}{4}$

1. 45 minutes
Part of an hour: $\frac{3}{4}$
Answers will vary.
2. 20 minutes
Part of an hour: $\frac{1}{3}$
3. 40 minutes
Part of an hour: $\frac{2}{3}$
4. 50 minutes
Part of an hour: $\frac{5}{6}$
5. 5 minutes
Part of an hour: $\frac{1}{12}$
6. 25 minutes
Part of an hour: $\frac{5}{12}$

CS-4 Use with text pages 328–329. 119

Options for Individual Needs

Basic

Exercises 2-7, 9-12
More Practice, p. 523, set D

Supplements
Reteaching 119 or
Practice 119

Average

Exercises 1-12
More Practice, p. 523, set D

Supplements
Practice 119
Challenges 119 or
Thinking Skills 119

Extended

Exercises 3-6, 8-12

Supplements
Challenges 119
Thinking Skills 119

Other Resources:
Problem-Solving Experiences in Mathematics, Grade 4, Problem 87
Mathematics, A Way of Thinking, Lesson 11-1
Mathematics, Book A, Teacher's Edition, p. 65

12-1

LESSON PLAN 12-1

OBJECTIVE 12-1
To understand the region interpretation of a fraction

Materials: unlined paper, scissors, TA 17 (Rulers), TA 12 (Centimeter Graph Paper)

Grouping Suggestion: small groups

1. MOTIVATE AND TEACH

LEARN ABOUT IT

EXPLORE ► **Relate fourths to four parts.** (Fourths means there are four parts of equal size.)
► **Explain another way to test the three drawings.** (Possible answer: Use tracing paper to trace each part, then see if the four parts are congruent.)

TALK ABOUT IT ► **Link congruent parts to fractions.** (If a figure is divided into equal parts, all parts must be congruent.)
► **Why must fractions have numerators and denominators?** (Possible answer: The numerator tells how many parts to consider of the total number of parts given in the denominator.)
Student Edition answers: **1.** All four parts will be congruent. **2.** Yes, if whole rectangles are equal, all fourths are equal, too.

2. CHECK UNDERSTANDING

TRY IT OUT

ERROR ALERT Shading the wrong fractional part.

Understanding Fractions
Regions

LEARN ABOUT IT

EXPLORE Use Ruler and Scissors
Work in groups. The teacher gave some fourth graders each a sheet of typing paper and asked them to divide it into fourths or four equal parts. These drawings show some of the ways they found.

Use paper, scissors, and a ruler to decide whether or not each of these methods shows fourths. Find other ways to show fourths.

TALK ABOUT IT See teaching notes.

1. How do you know you have divided the paper into fourths?
2. Are the fourths equal to each other even though they have different shapes? Explain.

You can write fractions to describe a part or parts of something.

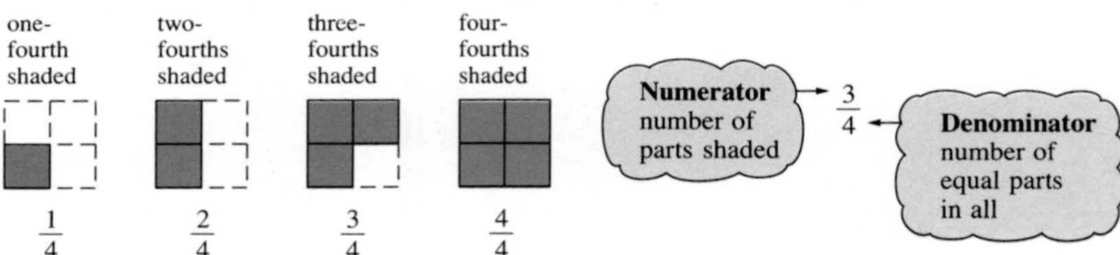

TRY IT OUT

Draw 4 circles and divide each into 8 parts. Do this by hand and make the parts as equal as you can.

Color $\frac{1}{8}$, $\frac{3}{8}$, $\frac{5}{8}$, and $\frac{7}{8}$.
Check students' drawings.

TEACHING OPTIONS

RETEACHING TIPS Have students say *out of* at a fraction bar to read fractions. So, $\frac{1}{8}$ is "1 out of 8," $\frac{3}{8}$ is "3 out of 8," and so on. Students label each circle with the fraction and verbalize it with the "out of" method to verify that they colored the right number of parts. Assign Reteaching Supplement 119.

ENRICHMENT Have students make a quilt design by coloring solid-color squares on centimeter graph paper. Using the quilt, they formulate and answer 3 fraction questions, such as "What fraction of the quilt is blue?" and "What fraction of the quilt is corner squares?" (Answers will vary.)

PRACTICE

Write the fraction.

1. What part of the fruit pie is eaten? $\frac{1}{3}$

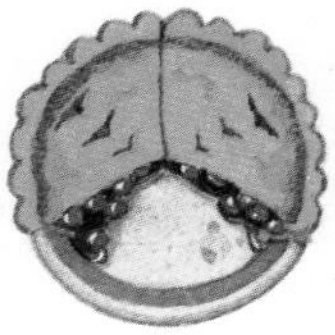

2. What part of the window is broken? $\frac{1}{4}$

3. What part of the garden is planted? $\frac{5}{6}$

Write fractions to tell what part is shaded and what part is not shaded.

4. 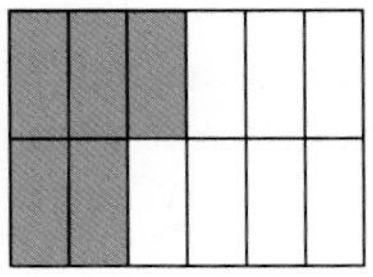

5. 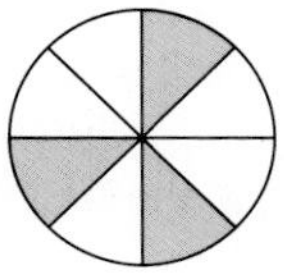

6. 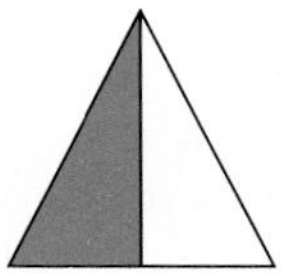

7. 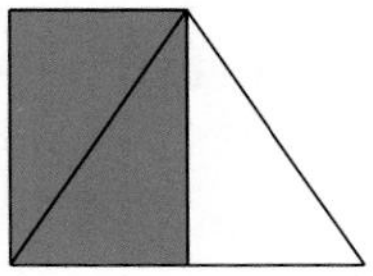

See Additional Answers.

APPLY

MATH REASONING

8. Is the shaded part more or less than $\frac{1}{2}$?

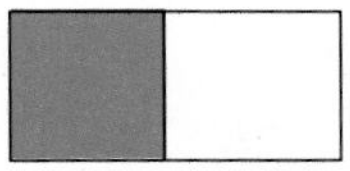

less

9. Is the shaded part more or less than $\frac{1}{4}$?

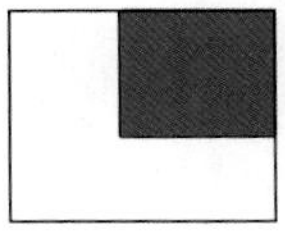

more

10. Is the shaded part more or less than $\frac{1}{3}$?

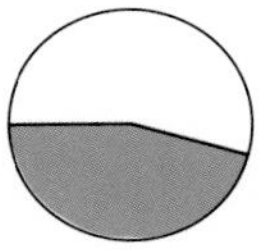

more

PROBLEM SOLVING

11. Miguel washed the living room window. It had 8 panes of glass. After he had washed 7 of them, what fractional part did he have left to wash? $\frac{1}{8}$

▶ USING CRITICAL THINKING Evaluate the Assumptions

12. "You got the bigger half of the granola bar!" Linette said to her sister. How would you answer this protest?
If Linette's part is "half," then both parts are equal.

More Practice, page 523, set D

3. Practice and Apply

Basic	2-7, 9-12
Average	1-12
Extended	3-6, 8-12

Additional Answers: See p. T79.

PRACTICE

How do Exercises 4-7 and 1-3 differ? (Exercises 4-7 require fractions for both shaded *and* unshaded parts.)

APPLY

MATH REASONING ▶ **Analyze how to answer the questions.** (Possible answers: Use visual estimation or trace the figures, divide into the given fractional part, then compare with the shaded part.)

PROBLEM SOLVING ▶ **Analyze the given data to determine a reasonable numerator and denominator. Explain your thinking.** (8 is the denominator because it is the total number of windows being washed; 1 is the numerator because it is the one part of the whole not completed.)

USING CRITICAL THINKING ▶ **Identify and explain a math word in the statement that has an exact meaning.** (half; It means 2 equal parts.)

12-1

Close and Assess

SHOW WHAT YOU KNOW

Have each student draw a 1-by-10 rectangle on centimeter graph paper. Tell each to make *X*s in three tenths of the rectangle and *O*s in a different four tenths of it. Then have students write a fraction for the plain part of their rectangles. (Check students' drawings; $\frac{3}{10}$ is the plain part.)

QUICK QUIZ

Write fractions for the shaded part and for the white part. (**1.** $\frac{1}{4}$, $\frac{3}{4}$ **2.** $\frac{4}{7}$, $\frac{3}{7}$)

1. 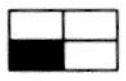

2. 

LESSON OPTIONS 12-2

Understanding Fractions: Sets

OBJECTIVE 12-2 To understand the set interpretation of a fraction

PREBOOK ACTIVITIES

QUICK REVIEW

Find each difference mentally.

1. 6 − 4 (2)	**2.** 5 − 5 (0)	**3.** 7 − 4 (3)
4. 13 − 6 (7)	**5.** 8 − 3 (5)	**6.** 6 − 6 (0)
7. 9 − 7 (2)	**8.** 12 − 5 (7)	**9.** 5 − 4 (1)

PRIOR KNOWLEDGE

Have students recall the meaning of a fraction, including how the numerator and the denominator organize information. (Possible answer: A fraction names part of a whole; the numerator tells how many special parts, the denominator tells how many parts in all.) Have students write some fractions on the chalkboard as others draw pictures to illustrate them. Review how fractional parts of the same object compare. (They are the same size.) Discuss cases when students might describe parts of a group rather than of an object. (Possible answers: *What part of the class is green-eyed boys? What fraction of our shoes have Velcro closings?*)

COMMUNICATION

Discussing Math Discuss how a fraction can refer to parts of a group of objects. (The total number of objects is like the whole; some of the objects are like the fractional parts.) Have students apply the rules about numerators and denominators to name a fraction to describe the vowels in *grape*, then justify their answer. ($\frac{2}{5}$; 5 letters in all, 2 out of 5 are vowels)

EXPLORE AND CONNECT

Materials: colored snap cubes, TA 13 (Spinner 5-8)
Alternative Materials: colored counters
Grouping Suggestion: cooperative learning pairs
Partners explore fractions of sets by describing subsets. One student spins a number and takes that many snap cubes, all of one color. The other student spins and takes that many snap cubes of a different color. Partners connect their cubes to form a track. Then they determine how to write fractions to describe how much of the track is the first color and how much is the second color. For instance, a track of 5 blue and 6 red cubes is $\frac{5}{11}$ blue and $\frac{6}{11}$ red. Students write the 2 fractions, then repeat the activity to generate 4 pairs of fractions. Conclude by having students explain how they derived the fractions and what the numerator and denominator represent in each case. (Numerators tell how many of each color cube; denominators give the total number of cubes.)

CONNECTIONS Use these anytime.

Problem of the Day

Math Connection Write a fraction for the number of quadrilaterals that are squares. ($\frac{2}{3}$)

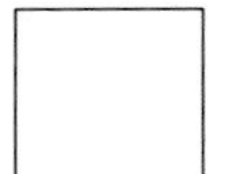

Subject Integration

Handwriting Write a fraction for the number of manuscript alphabet letters with uppercases and lowercases that look alike—except for size—such as *S* and *s*. (Answers may vary based on penmanship styles used. Possible answer: $\frac{10}{26}$ includes *C, O, P, S, U, V, W, X, Y,* and *Z*.)

Life Skills

Advertising A television commercial says, "4 out of 5 dentists recommend fluoride gel toothpaste." In your own words, explain what the statement means. Then write a fraction for the number of dentists who recommend the toothpaste. (Explanations may vary; $\frac{4}{5}$)

CLASSWORK AND HOMEWORK SUPPLEMENTS

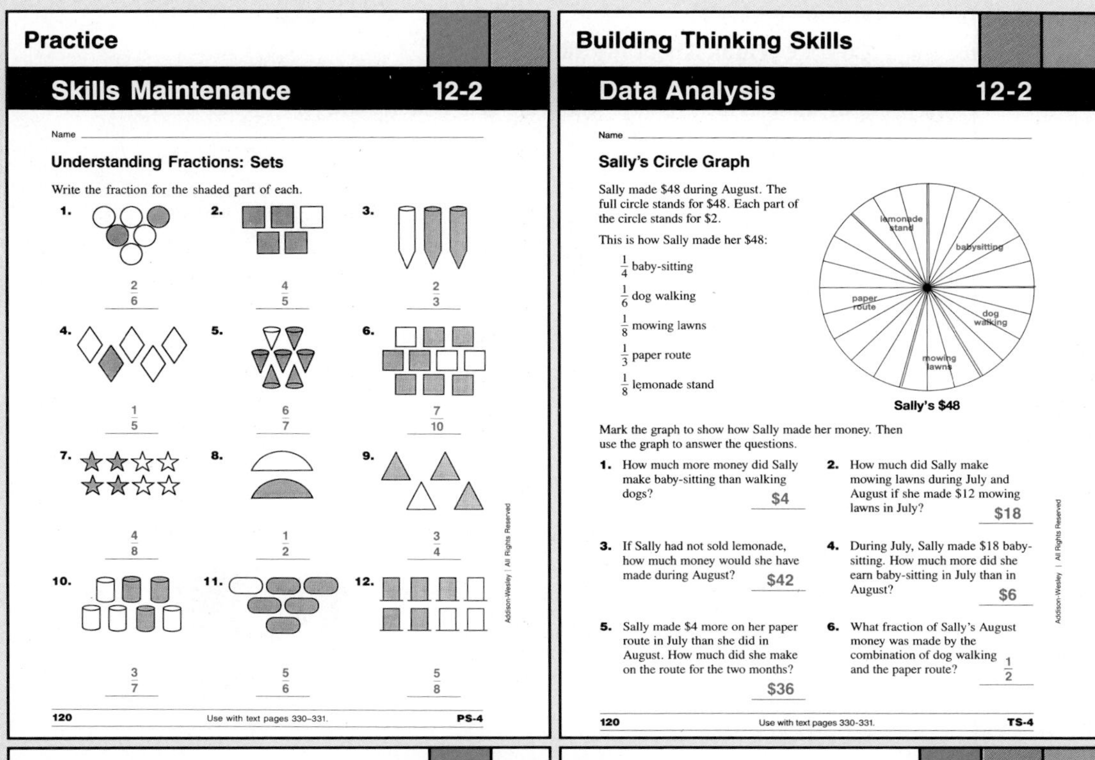

Practice

Skills Maintenance 12-2

Name ______

Understanding Fractions: Sets

Write the fraction for the shaded part of each.

1. $\frac{2}{6}$
2. $\frac{4}{5}$
3. $\frac{2}{3}$
4. $\frac{1}{5}$
5. $\frac{6}{7}$
6. $\frac{7}{10}$
7. $\frac{4}{8}$
8. $\frac{1}{2}$
9. $\frac{3}{4}$
10. $\frac{3}{7}$
11. $\frac{5}{6}$
12. $\frac{5}{8}$

120 Use with text pages 330-331. PS-4

Building Thinking Skills

Data Analysis 12-2

Name ______

Sally's Circle Graph

Sally made $48 during August. The full circle stands for $48. Each part of the circle stands for $2.

This is how Sally made her $48:

$\frac{1}{4}$ baby-sitting

$\frac{1}{6}$ dog walking

$\frac{1}{8}$ mowing lawns

$\frac{1}{3}$ paper route

$\frac{1}{8}$ lemonade stand

Mark the graph to show how Sally made her money. Then use the graph to answer the questions.

1. How much more money did Sally make baby-sitting than walking dogs? $4
2. How much did Sally make mowing lawns during July and August if she made $12 mowing lawns in July? $18
3. If Sally had not sold lemonade, how much money would she have made during August? $42
4. During July, Sally made $18 baby-sitting. How much more did she earn baby-sitting in July than in August? $6
5. Sally made $4 more on her paper route in July than she did in August. How much did she make on the route for the two months? $36
6. What fraction of Sally's August money was made by the combination of dog walking and the paper route? $\frac{1}{2}$

120 Use with text pages 330-331. TS-4

Reteaching

Skills Review 12-2

Name ______

More About Fractions

What fraction of the stamps shows birds?

3 stamps show birds. ⟶ 3
8 stamps in all ⟶ 8

$\frac{3}{8}$ of the stamps show birds.

Write the fraction of each stamp set that shows birds.

1. $\frac{5}{8}$ (5 bird stamps out of 8 stamps)
2. $\frac{3}{6}$
3. $\frac{3}{5}$

Write the fraction that makes each sentence true.

4. $\frac{1}{5}$ of the bowls have fish. (1 of the 5 bowls has fish.)
5. $\frac{4}{7}$ of the bowls have fish.
6. $\frac{5}{8}$ of the bowls have fish.
7. $\frac{2}{3}$ of the set are soccer balls.
8. $\frac{4}{5}$ of the set are baseballs.
9. $\frac{2}{6}$ of the set are footballs.

120 Use with text pages 330-331. RS-4

Challenges

Family Math 12-2

Name ______

Block Party

Dear Family,
Your child has been studying fractions. Here is an activity you can do with your child.

Write the fraction that makes each sentence true.

1. $\frac{5}{8}$ of the animals are dogs.
2. $\frac{4}{8}$ of the animals are white.
3. $\frac{2}{3}$ of the cats are white.
4. $\frac{1}{5}$ of the dogs are spotted.
5. $\frac{3}{8}$ of the animals are on leashes.
6. $\frac{1}{8}$ of the animals are white with short tails.
7. $\frac{5}{9}$ of the people are children.
8. $\frac{3}{5}$ of the dogs are on leashes.
9. $\frac{4}{9}$ of the people have jackets.
10. $\frac{2}{5}$ of the children have hats.
11. $\frac{1}{4}$ of the adults have plaid jackets.
12. $\frac{2}{9}$ of the people are children with dogs on leashes.

120 Use with text pages 330-331. CS-4

OPTIONS FOR INDIVIDUAL NEEDS

12-2

Basic

Exercises 1-9, 12, 13
Data Bank, p. 477
More Practice, p. 524, set A

Supplements
Reteaching 120 or
Practice 120
Challenges 120

Average

Exercises 1-13
Data Bank, p. 477
More Practice, p. 524, set A

Supplements
Practice 120
Challenges 120 or
Thinking Skills 120

Extended

Exercises 2-13
Data Bank, p. 477

Supplements
Challenges 120
Thinking Skills 120

Other Resources:
Problem-Solving Experiences in Mathematics, Grade 4, Problem 88
Mathematics, A Way of Thinking, Lesson 11-2
Mathematics, Book A, Teacher's Edition pp. 66, 67

LESSON PLAN 12-2

OBJECTIVE 12-2
To understand the set interpretation of a fraction

Materials: counters

1. MOTIVATE AND TEACH

LEARN ABOUT IT

EXPLORE ► **Explain how many hats each member of the family could have.** (2 each for Ma and Pa because together they had 4; 1 each for Laura and Mary because they had 2.)

TALK ABOUT IT ► **Explain the difference between half the hats and half of one hat.** (Possible answer: Half the hats means half of the whole group of hats; half of one hat means cutting the hat into two equal pieces.)
► **Justify describing some of the hats with a fraction.** (Possible answer: Consider all the hats as one whole group, then talk about certain ones as part of that group.)
► **Identify a denominator to use for all the straw hats. Explain.** (6, because that is the total number of hats Ma made)
► **Identify a numerator to use to describe only the big hats. Explain.** (4, because it is the number of big hats in the set)
► **Explain how the fractions describe the red bonnets and green top hats.** (3 of the 4 bonnets are red; 2 of the 3 top hats are green)
Student Edition answers: **1.** 6 **2.** 2 **3.** 4

2. CHECK UNDERSTANDING

TRY IT OUT

ERROR ALERT Switching numerators and denominators. Writing a fraction for the wrong subset.

Understanding Fractions
Sets

LEARN ABOUT IT

EXPLORE **Think About the Situation**
In *Little House in the Big Woods,* Ma braided pieces of straw to make 6 hats. The 4 big hats were for Ma and Pa. The 2 small hats were for Laura and Mary.

TALK ABOUT IT See teaching notes.

1. How many hats did Ma make?
2. How many of the hats were small?
3. How many of the hats were big?

You can use a fraction to tell what part of the hats were small.

$$\frac{\text{number of small hats}}{\text{total number of hats}} \quad \frac{2}{6}$$

We say **two-sixths** of the hats are small or $\frac{2}{6}$ of the hats are small.

Other Examples $\frac{3}{4}$ of the bonnets are red. $\frac{2}{3}$ of the top hats are green.

TRY IT OUT

1. What fraction of the lockets are on ribbons? $\frac{1}{6}$

2. What fraction of the parasols are yellow? $\frac{2}{5}$

330

TEACHING OPTIONS

RETEACHING TIPS Have students build fractions from the bottom up. First they write the total number of objects *below* the fraction bar. Then they count specific objects, such as how many open fans, and write that number *above* the fraction bar. Assign Reteaching Supplement 120.

ENRICHMENT **Family Math** Students interview family members to write 4 facts about their family that can be described with fractions. For example: *What part of your family likes to swim? What part of your family picks blue as their favorite color?* A family member checks their work.

PRACTICE

Write the fraction for each ||||.

1. |||| of the toys are cornhusk dolls.

2. |||| of the fiddles have bows.

APPLY

MATH REASONING Give the fraction for each ||||.

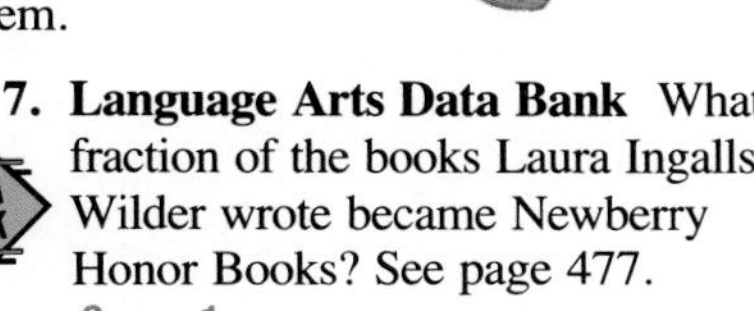

3. |||| of the aprons have **some** red. $\frac{4}{5}$
4. |||| of the aprons have **no** red. $\frac{1}{5}$
5. |||| of the aprons have **all** red. $\frac{2}{5}$

PROBLEM SOLVING

Draw a picture to help you solve the problem.

6. One Spring the Ingalls had 9 baby animals. $\frac{2}{9}$ of the animals were calves. The rest were piglets. How many were piglets? 7 piglets

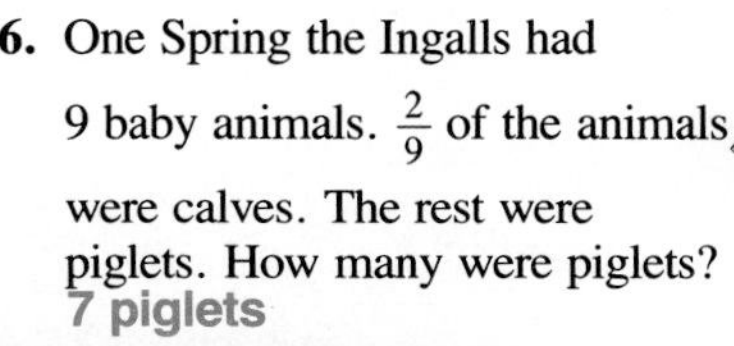

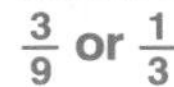

7. **Language Arts Data Bank** What fraction of the books Laura Ingalls Wilder wrote became Newberry Honor Books? See page 477. $\frac{3}{9}$ or $\frac{1}{3}$

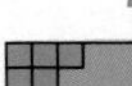

MIXED REVIEW

Divide. Show dollars and cents

8. \$3.45 ÷ 5 \$0.69
9. \$2.04 ÷ 4 \$0.51
10. \$0.70 ÷ 7 \$0.10
11. \$6.36 ÷ 6 \$1.06

Tell what the geometric shape is.

12. I have 4 sides. Each pair of sides is parallel. All my sides are equal. square
13. I have three sides. No two sides are the same size. triangle

More Practice, page 524, set A

CLOSE AND ASSESS

SHOW WHAT YOU KNOW

Have students use counters to show one set that is $\frac{2}{7}$ red and another set that is $\frac{3}{5}$ red. (Check students' models: 7 counters, of which 2 are red; 5 counters, of which 3 are red)

QUICK QUIZ

Write a fraction for how many are open. ($\frac{3}{4}$)

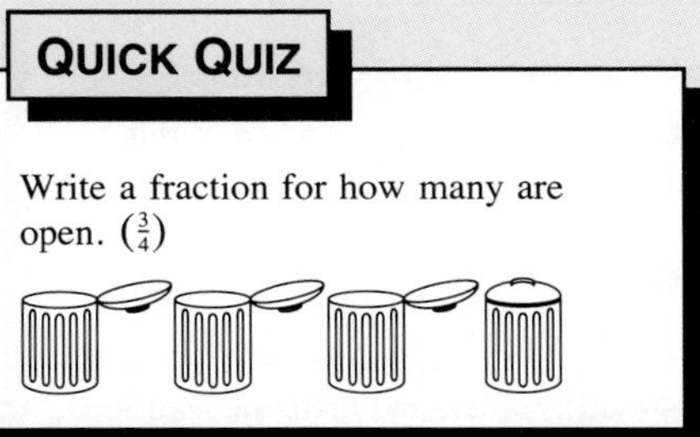

3. PRACTICE AND APPLY

Basic	1-9, 12,13
Average	1-13
Extended	2-13

PRACTICE

Look at Exercises 1 and 2. Describe a strategy you could use to write fractions of sets of objects. (Possible answer: Count all the objects for the denominator, then count the ones specially described for the numerator.)

APPLY

MATH REASONING ► **What denominator makes sense to use to describe any part of the aprons? Explain.** (5, because that is the total number of aprons pictured)

PROBLEM SOLVING ► **Justify describing fractions of a group for different kinds of animals.** (Possible answer: It gives you a mental picture of which group of animals has the greater number.)

MIXED REVIEW ► **Why are there two places following each decimal point in Exercises 8-11?** (They show parts of a dollar, or cents.)

LESSON OPTIONS 12-3

Estimating Fractional Parts/Problem Solving

OBJECTIVE 12-3 To estimate parts of a whole as fractions; to practice problem solving

PREBOOK ACTIVITIES

QUICK REVIEW

Tell the fractional part of each word that is vowels.

1. fig ($\frac{1}{3}$)
2. onion ($\frac{3}{5}$)
3. peach ($\frac{2}{5}$)
4. cabbage ($\frac{3}{7}$)
5. zucchini ($\frac{3}{8}$)
6. pineapple ($\frac{4}{9}$)
7. tomato ($\frac{3}{6}$ or $\frac{1}{2}$)
8. watermelon ($\frac{4}{10}$ or $\frac{2}{5}$)

PRIOR KNOWLEDGE

Have students suggest real-life situations when they might need to estimate fractional amounts. (Possible answers: about how much milk is left in the carton; about what part of a book has been read; about what part of a room has been painted)

COMMUNICATION

Discussing Math Draw a circle on the chalkboard and have students explain how to estimate half of it. (Possible answer: Imagine a line dividing the circle into 2 equal parts: focus on 1 part.) Then ask them to explain how to visualize $\frac{1}{4}$ of the circle. (Possible answer: Imagine cutting each half in half to make 4 equal parts: focus on 1 part.) Now draw a rectangle and shade about $\frac{5}{6}$ of it without showing the individual sixths. Challenge students to explain how they would name that fractional amount without knowing the denominator. (Possible answer: Visualize dividing the whole into equal parts that include the shaded and unshaded areas to determine the denominator, then give the shaded amount a sensible numerator.)

EXPLORE AND CONNECT

Materials: TA 21 (Fraction Strips), plain paper strips equal to the length of 1 whole Fraction Strip, scissors
Grouping Suggestion: cooperative learning pairs
Partners explore estimating fractional parts. The first student looks away as his or her partner cuts a plain paper strip equal to any fractional amount less than 1 whole, using 1 of the fraction strips as a guide. The first student then tries to estimate the size of the cut strip. If the student names the fractional part correctly, partners confirm it by comparing the cut strip to the fraction strip it matches. If the guess is wrong, the student may try to match the cut strip to the other fraction strips until the correct fraction is found. Trading tasks, partners repeat the activity several times. Conclude by having students explain successful methods they used to estimate fractional size. (Answers may vary.)

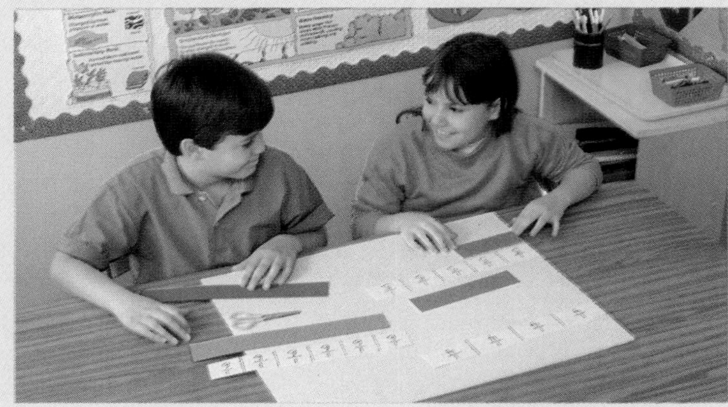

CONNECTIONS Use these anytime.

Problem of the Day

Creative Thinking Find at least 4 times of the day when the hands of a clock suggest $\frac{1}{4}$ of the clock face. (Answers may vary. Sample times: 3:00; 9:00; 6:16; 2:28)

Math Connection

Measurement Hank looked at this 1-gal container of milk. Estimate if he saw 1 c, 1 pt, or 1 qt of milk left.

(1 qt because there is about $\frac{1}{4}$ left and there are 4 qt in 1 gal.)

Number Sense

Estimation Look around to estimate a fractional amount of the class wearing plain-colored tops. (Answers will vary.)

Classwork and Homework Supplements

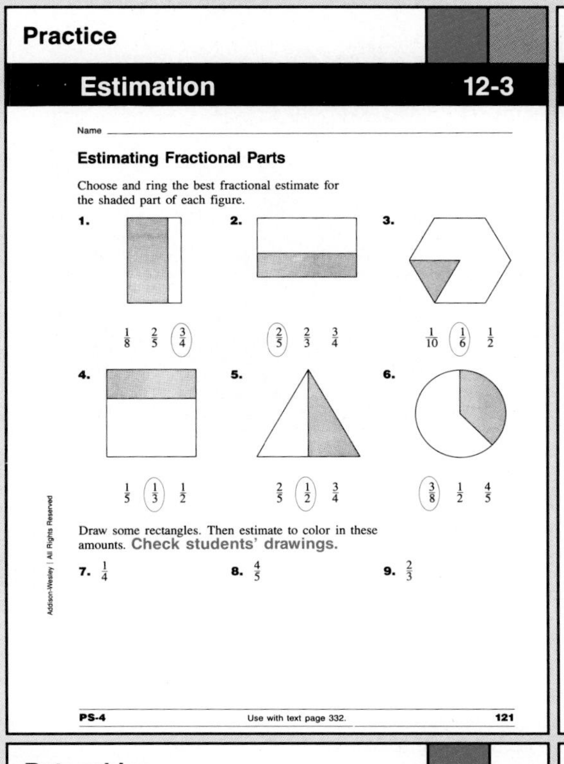

Practice

Estimation 12-3

Name

Estimating Fractional Parts

Choose and ring the best fractional estimate for the shaded part of each figure.

1. $\frac{1}{8}$ $\frac{2}{5}$ ($\frac{3}{4}$)
2. ($\frac{2}{5}$) $\frac{2}{3}$ $\frac{3}{4}$
3. $\frac{1}{10}$ ($\frac{1}{6}$) $\frac{1}{2}$
4. $\frac{1}{5}$ ($\frac{1}{3}$) $\frac{1}{2}$
5. $\frac{2}{5}$ ($\frac{1}{2}$) $\frac{3}{4}$
6. ($\frac{3}{8}$) $\frac{1}{2}$ $\frac{4}{5}$

Draw some rectangles. Then estimate to color in these amounts. Check students' drawings.

7. $\frac{1}{4}$ 8. $\frac{4}{5}$ 9. $\frac{2}{3}$

Addison-Wesley | All Rights Reserved

PS-4 Use with text page 332. 121

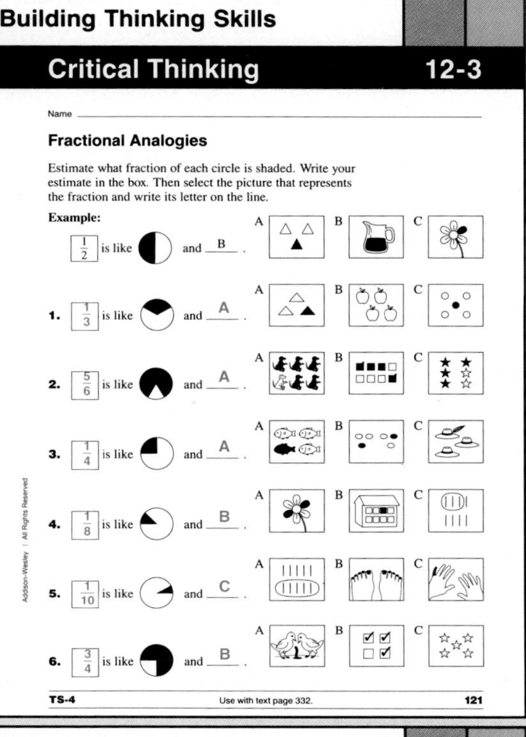

Building Thinking Skills

Critical Thinking 12-3

Name

Fractional Analogies

Estimate what fraction of each circle is shaded. Write your estimate in the box. Then select the picture that represents the fraction and write its letter on the line.

Example: $\frac{1}{2}$ is like [circle] and B.

1. $\frac{1}{3}$ is like [circle] and A.
2. $\frac{5}{6}$ is like [circle] and A.
3. $\frac{1}{4}$ is like [circle] and A.
4. $\frac{1}{8}$ is like [circle] and B.
5. $\frac{1}{10}$ is like [circle] and C.
6. $\frac{3}{4}$ is like [circle] and B.

Addison-Wesley | All Rights Reserved

TS-4 Use with text page 332. 121

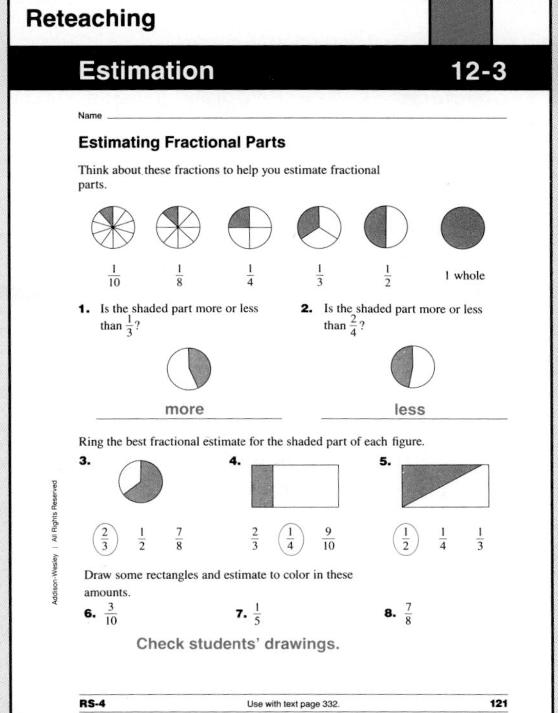

Reteaching

Estimation 12-3

Name

Estimating Fractional Parts

Think about these fractions to help you estimate fractional parts.

$\frac{1}{10}$ $\frac{1}{8}$ $\frac{1}{4}$ $\frac{1}{3}$ $\frac{1}{2}$ 1 whole

1. Is the shaded part more or less than $\frac{1}{3}$? more
2. Is the shaded part more or less than $\frac{2}{4}$? less

Ring the best fractional estimate for the shaded part of each figure.

3. ($\frac{2}{3}$) $\frac{1}{2}$ $\frac{7}{8}$
4. $\frac{2}{3}$ ($\frac{1}{4}$) $\frac{9}{10}$
5. ($\frac{1}{2}$) $\frac{1}{4}$ $\frac{1}{3}$

Draw some rectangles and estimate to color in these amounts.

6. $\frac{3}{10}$ 7. $\frac{1}{5}$ 8. $\frac{7}{8}$

Check students' drawings.

Addison-Wesley | All Rights Reserved

RS-4 Use with text page 332. 121

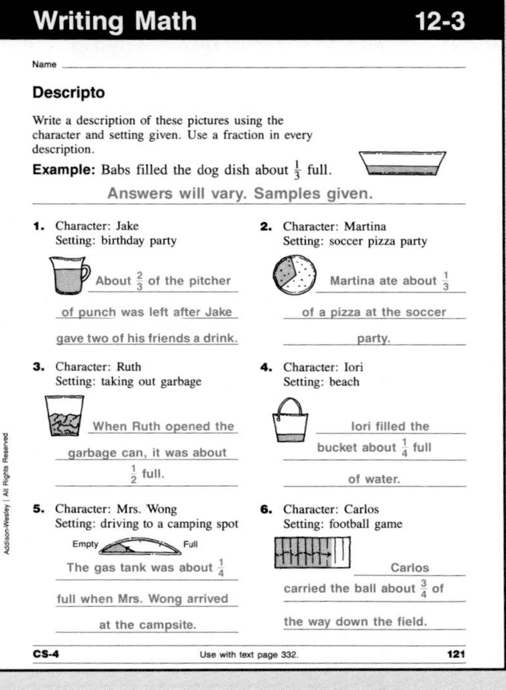

Challenges

Writing Math 12-3

Name

Descripto

Write a description of these pictures using the character and setting given. Use a fraction in every description.

Example: Babs filled the dog dish about $\frac{1}{3}$ full.

Answers will vary. Samples given.

1. Character: Jake
Setting: birthday party
About $\frac{2}{3}$ of the pitcher of punch was left after Jake gave two of his friends a drink.

2. Character: Martina
Setting: soccer pizza party
Martina ate about $\frac{1}{3}$ of a pizza at the soccer party.

3. Character: Ruth
Setting: taking out garbage
When Ruth opened the garbage can, it was about $\frac{1}{2}$ full.

4. Character: Iori
Setting: beach
Iori filled the bucket about $\frac{1}{4}$ full of water.

5. Character: Mrs. Wong
Setting: driving to a camping spot
Empty Full
The gas tank was about $\frac{1}{4}$ full when Mrs. Wong arrived at the campsite.

6. Character: Carlos
Setting: football game
Carlos carried the ball about $\frac{3}{4}$ of the way down the field.

Addison-Wesley | All Rights Reserved

CS-4 Use with text page 332. 121

Options for Individual Needs

Basic

Exercises 1-8
Computer Bank, p. 494
More Practice, p. 524, sets B, C

Supplements
Reteaching 121 or
Practice 121

Average

Exercises 1-8
Computer Bank, p. 494
More Practice, p. 524, sets B, C

Supplements
Practice 121
Challenges 121 or
Thinking Skills 121

Extended

Exercises 1-8
Computer Bank, p. 494

Supplements
Challenges 121
Thinking Skills 121

Other Resources:
Problem-Solving Experiences in Mathematics, Grade 4, Problem 93
Mathematics, A Way of Thinking, Lesson 11-9
Using The Math Explorer Calculator: A Sourcebook for Teachers, Chapter 14

LESSON PLAN 12-3

OBJECTIVE 12-3
To estimate parts of a whole as fractions; to practice problem solving

Materials: inch rulers, tracing paper, scissors

Alternative Materials: TA 17 (Rulers)

Grouping Suggestion: pairs

1. MOTIVATE AND TEACH

LEARN ABOUT IT

EXPLORE ▶ **Explain what Laura meant when she said she weeded about $\frac{3}{4}$ of the garden.** (Possible answer: Visualize a garden in 4 equal parts: Laura weeded about 3 of them.)

TALK ABOUT IT ▶ **Explain how you might divide the garden into fourths to verify Laura's estimate.** (Methods may vary, but by any method the weeded part is much less than $\frac{3}{4}$.)
▶ **Explain how to use $\frac{1}{2}$ as a visual guide to help you estimate the size of the weeded part.** (Possible answer: It is easy to imagine $\frac{1}{2}$, so compare it with $\frac{3}{4}$, which is more than $\frac{1}{2}$.)
▶ **Decide on a plan that could help you estimate fractional parts.** (Answers may vary.)
Student Edition answers: **1.** Mary **2.** $\frac{1}{4}$; $\frac{7}{8}$ and $\frac{6}{10}$ are too much.

2. CHECK UNDERSTANDING

TRY IT OUT

ERROR ALERT Choosing the wrong fraction for the shaded part.

Estimating Fractional Parts

LEARN ABOUT IT

EXPLORE **Make a Decision**
Laura told Ma at lunch that she had weeded about $\frac{3}{4}$ of the garden that morning. When Mary went to help finish the job she did not agree with Laura's estimate. What do you think?

Weeded Part

TALK ABOUT IT See teaching notes.

1. Do you agree with Laura or Mary? Use an inch ruler to help you decide.
2. Which of these estimates do you think is best? Why?

   $\frac{1}{4}$ $\frac{7}{8}$ $\frac{6}{10}$

Think about these fractions to help you estimate fractional parts.

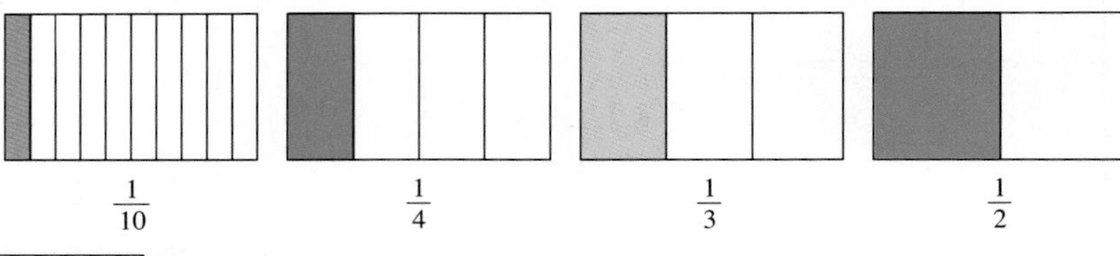

TRY IT OUT

Choose the best fractional estimate for the shaded part of each figure.

1. 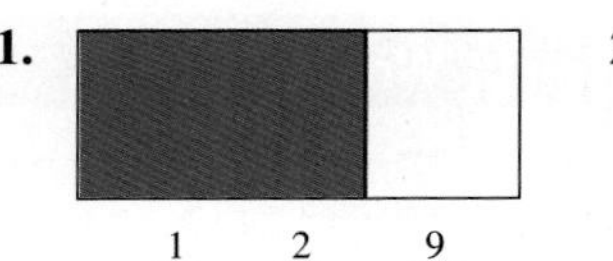
$\frac{1}{2}$ $\frac{2}{3}$ $\frac{9}{10}$

2.
$\frac{2}{3}$ $\frac{3}{4}$ $\frac{9}{10}$

3. 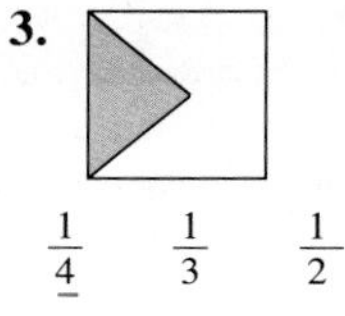
$\frac{1}{4}$ $\frac{1}{3}$ $\frac{1}{2}$

More Practice, page 524, set B

TEACHING OPTIONS

RETEACHING TIPS Students trace and cut out 1 unshaded part in each figure, then use it to verify the fractional estimates. For example, the unshaded part in Exercise 1 is $\frac{1}{3}$ and, when placed side by side, will fit twice on top of the shaded portion to show $\frac{2}{3}$. Assign Reteaching Supplement 121.

COMPUTER **Trading Post, Sunburst Communications, Copyright 1985** For all students (best used in pairs). Use lowest difficulty level. Begin with items, then add, exchange, or take an item. The first player to match the goal items wins. The game takes 10 to 15 min.

Problem Solving

MIXED PRACTICE

Solve. Use any problem solving strategy.

1. Guide dog schools train dogs for the blind. A school has been training 3 different kinds of dogs for 38 years. About 95 dogs are trained each year. How many dogs have been trained all together at the school? **3,610 dogs**

2. The guide dog school had the same number of golden retrievers, Labrador retrievers, and German shepherds. There were 105 dogs in all. How many of each type of dog were there? **35 dogs**

3. 5 out of every 10 dogs at the school pass the guide dog test. How many would pass out of 50 dogs? **25 dogs**

4. For a 4-H project, Mary kept one of the dogs at her home until he was ready for guide dog training. She got him when he was 3 months old and kept him until he was 15 months old. How many days did she have the dog in all? Use 30 days for 1 month. **360 days**

5. Carl is blind. He jogs 36 miles a week by holding onto his friend Kirk's shoulder. How many miles does he jog in a year? **1,872 miles**

6. Walter is 1 of 25 volunteers who records books on tape for the blind. 13 volunteers record science books. 17 record math books. Some record both kinds. How many record both kinds of books? **5 volunteers**

7. At the recording center, Jane reads books onto tape. She recorded these books.

Book	Number of Pages
Law	1,636
Math	356
Science	427
History	275

How many pages did she record in all? **2,694 pages**

8. A special machine can read a printed page out loud for visually handicapped people. It reads 900 words in 5 minutes. How many words does it read each minute? **180 words**

More Practice, page 524, set C

3. Practice and Apply

Basic	1-8
Average	1-8
Extended	1-8

Sample Solutions: See p. T79.

MIXED PRACTICE ► **Explain how Problems 2 and 8 are alike.** (Both require division.)
► **Explain how Problems 4 and 5 are alike.** (Both require multiplying measurement amounts.)
► **Analyze Problem 3 to choose a solution strategy.** (Make a Table)
► **Explain which strategy makes sense with Problem 6.** (Use Logical Reasoning, because you have to interpret results after completing an operation.)

12-3

Close and Assess

SHOW WHAT YOU KNOW
Have students work in pairs. Each partner draws a picture showing 3 shapes with these fractional amounts shaded: $\frac{1}{2}$; $\frac{3}{4}$; $\frac{9}{10}$. Then partners exchange pictures to see if they can identify each other's fractional amounts. (Check students' drawings.)

QUICK QUIZ

Estimate the shaded part. (about $\frac{1}{3}$)

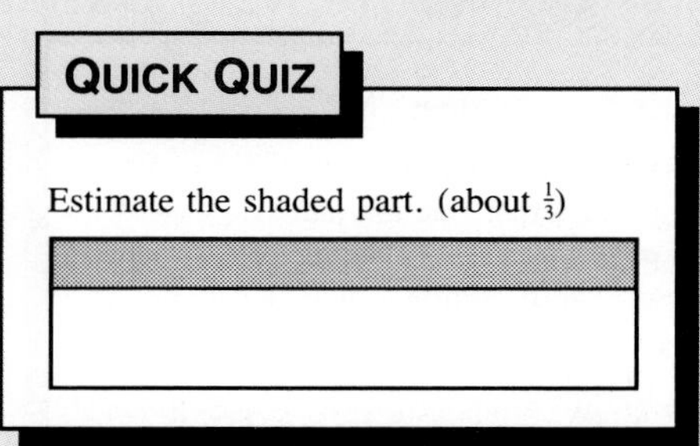

LESSON OPTIONS 12-4

Equivalent Fractions

OBJECTIVE 12-4 To understand the concept of equivalent fractions

PREBOOK ACTIVITIES

QUICK REVIEW

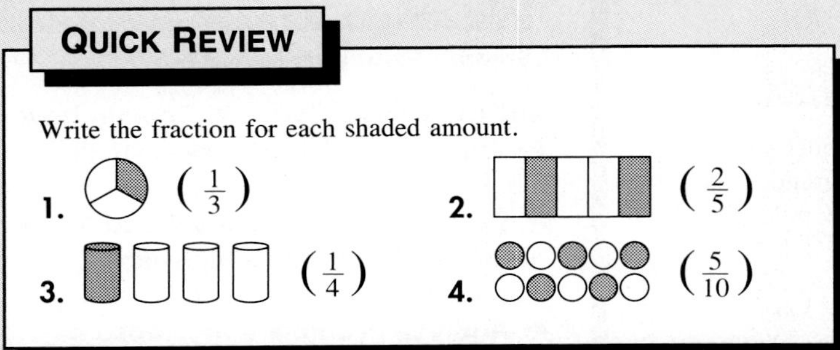

Write the fraction for each shaded amount.

1. $(\frac{1}{3})$
2. $(\frac{2}{5})$
3. $(\frac{1}{4})$
4. $(\frac{5}{10})$

PRIOR KNOWLEDGE

Have students define *half*. (''One of two equal parts of an object or amount.'') Then have them suggest real-life situations in which they might consider half of an amount that has more than two parts, such as half of a class, half of a book, or half of a dozen. Tell students that they will learn about fractions that name the same amount in different ways.

COMMUNICATION

Discussing and Reading Math Write **equivalent** on the chalkboard. Have students read the word aloud, then suggest related math words. (*equal, value*) Discuss that equivalent amounts have the same value, even though they may not seem exactly equal at first. Have students infer the meaning of equivalent chores or equivalent players on a team. (Possible answers: The exact chores may differ, but they take the same amount of time or effort, or have similar importance; different athletes have similar skills or abilities, so they can play the same position with similar results.) Equivalent fractions name the same amount but in different ways.

EXPLORE AND CONNECT

Materials: egg cartons, counters, fraction cards for $\frac{1}{2}$, $\frac{1}{3}$, $\frac{1}{4}$ and $\frac{1}{6}$
Grouping Suggestion: cooperative learning groups of 3
Students explore **equivalent** fractions with egg cartons. The first student picks a fraction card and fills the egg carton with the number of counters representing that fractional amount. For example, if $\frac{1}{3}$ is picked, the student must find a way to fill $\frac{1}{3}$ of the egg carton. The next student records the fraction $\frac{1}{3}$ as a third student writes a fraction *equivalent* to it in 12ths by counting the counters. $(\frac{4}{12})$ Together, students should discuss the *equivalent* fractions to verify that they name the same amount of the egg carton. Repeat the activity for each fraction card. Each time students use counters to model the *equivalent* fraction in 12ths and then record it along with the original fraction. Conclude by having students summarize what they noticed about *equivalent* fractions. (Answers may vary.)

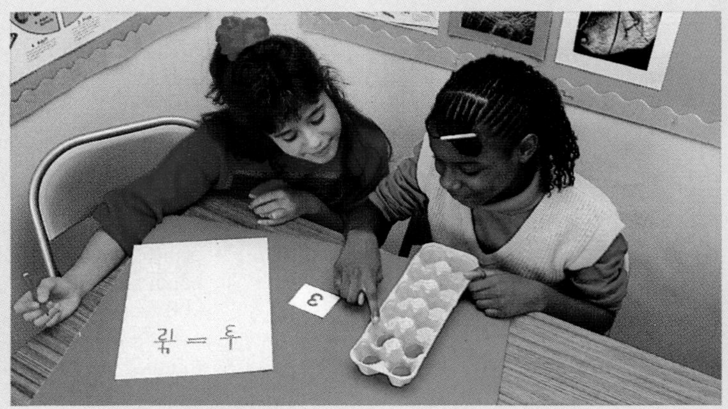

CONNECTIONS Use these anytime.

Problem of the Day

Patterns Figure out the pattern, then continue it 3 more times.
$\frac{1}{3}$ $\frac{3}{9}$ $\frac{5}{15}$ $\frac{7}{21}$ $\frac{9}{27}$ $\frac{11}{\square}$ $\frac{13}{\square}$ $\frac{15}{\square}$
(33, 39, 45)

Math Connection

Money Describe the value of a nickel using 3 different fraction names. Compare a nickel to a dollar, to a quarter, and to a dime. (A nickel is $\frac{5}{100}$, or $\frac{1}{20}$, of a dollar; $\frac{5}{25}$, or $\frac{1}{5}$, of a quarter; $\frac{5}{10}$, or $\frac{1}{2}$, of a dime.)

Subject Integration

Health and Fitness In gym class, 24 students played kickball. $\frac{12}{24}$ of the students were on the red team and $\frac{1}{2}$ of them were on the blue team. Which team had more players? Explain. (neither; Both teams had 12 players.)

Classwork and Homework Supplements

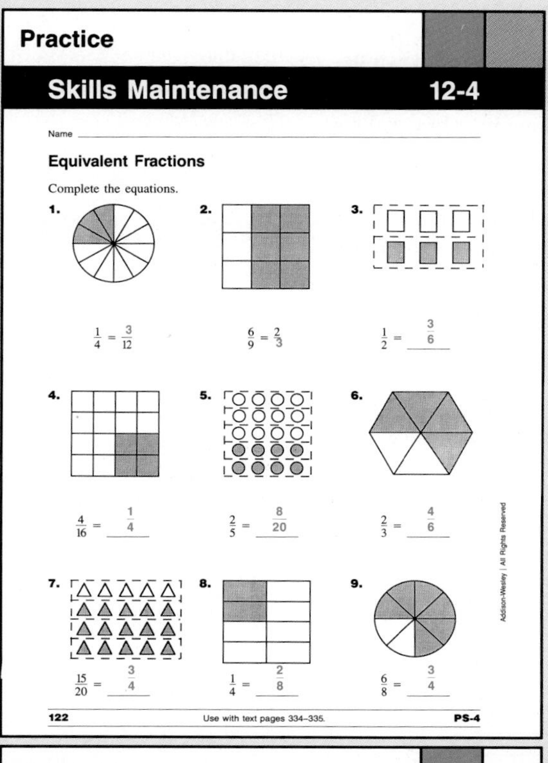

Practice

Skills Maintenance 12-4

Name ______

Equivalent Fractions

Complete the equations.

1. $\frac{1}{4} = \frac{3}{12}$
2. $\frac{6}{9} = \frac{2}{3}$
3. $\frac{1}{2} = \frac{3}{6}$
4. $\frac{4}{16} = \frac{1}{4}$
5. $\frac{2}{5} = \frac{8}{20}$
6. $\frac{2}{3} = \frac{4}{6}$
7. $\frac{15}{20} = \frac{3}{4}$
8. $\frac{1}{4} = \frac{2}{8}$
9. $\frac{6}{8} = \frac{3}{4}$

122 Use with text pages 334-335. PS-4

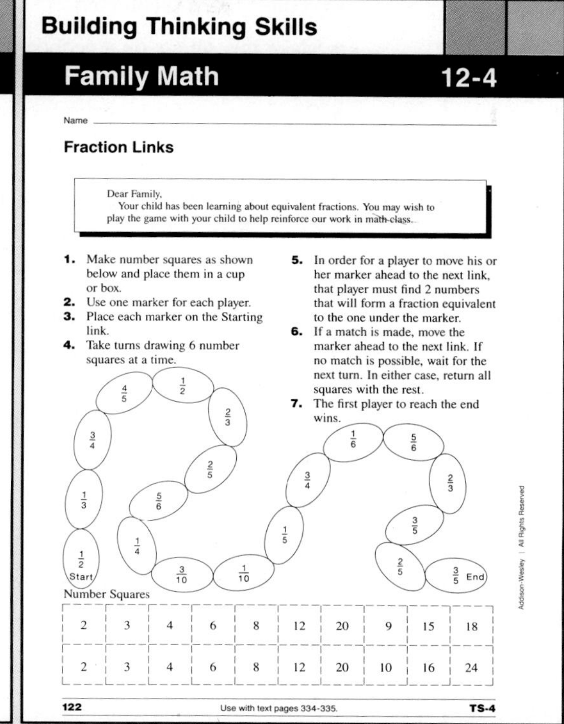

Building Thinking Skills

Family Math 12-4

Name ______

Fraction Links

Dear Family,
Your child has been learning about equivalent fractions. You may wish to play the game with your child to help reinforce our work in math class.

1. Make number squares as shown below and place them in a cup or box.
2. Use one marker for each player.
3. Place each marker on the Starting link.
4. Take turns drawing 6 number squares at a time.
5. In order for a player to move his or her marker ahead to the next link, that player must find 2 numbers that will form a fraction equivalent to the one under the marker.
6. If a match is made, move the marker ahead to the next link. If no match is possible, wait for the next turn. In either case, return all squares with the rest.
7. The first player to reach the end wins.

Number Squares

2	3	4	6	8	12	20	9	15	18
2	3	4	6	8	12	20	10	16	24

122 Use with text pages 334-335. TS-4

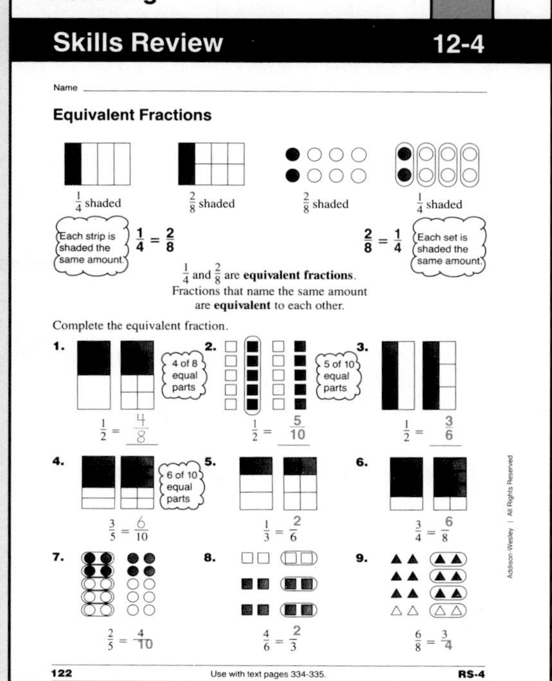

Reteaching

Skills Review 12-4

Name ______

Equivalent Fractions

$\frac{1}{4}$ shaded $\frac{2}{8}$ shaded $\frac{2}{8}$ shaded $\frac{1}{4}$ shaded

Each strip is shaded the same amount. $\frac{1}{4} = \frac{2}{8}$

$\frac{2}{8} = \frac{1}{4}$ Each set is shaded the same amount.

$\frac{1}{4}$ and $\frac{2}{8}$ are **equivalent fractions**.
Fractions that name the same amount are **equivalent** to each other.

Complete the equivalent fraction.

1. 4 of 8 equal parts. $\frac{1}{2} = \frac{4}{8}$
2. 5 of 10 equal parts. $\frac{1}{2} = \frac{5}{10}$
3. $\frac{1}{2} = \frac{3}{6}$
4. 6 of 10 equal parts. $\frac{3}{5} = \frac{6}{10}$
5. $\frac{1}{3} = \frac{2}{6}$
6. $\frac{3}{4} = \frac{6}{8}$
7. $\frac{2}{5} = \frac{4}{10}$
8. $\frac{4}{6} = \frac{2}{3}$
9. $\frac{6}{8} = \frac{3}{4}$

122 Use with text pages 334-335. RS-4

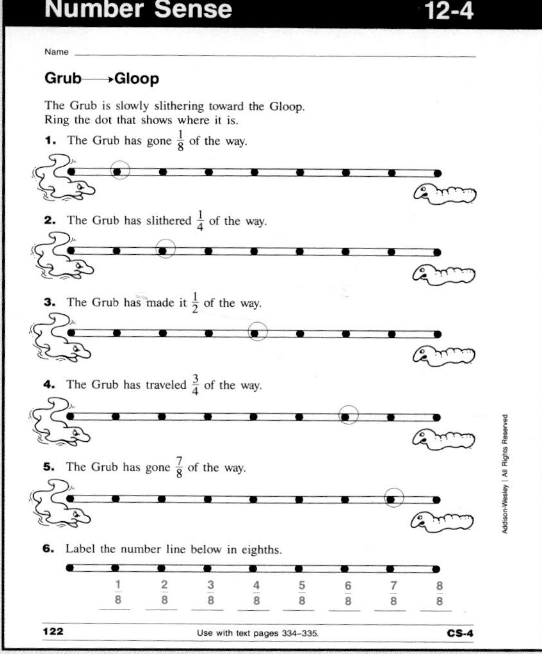

Challenges

Number Sense 12-4

Name ______

Grub → Gloop

The Grub is slowly slithering toward the Gloop.
Ring the dot that shows where it is.

1. The Grub has gone $\frac{1}{8}$ of the way.
2. The Grub has slithered $\frac{1}{4}$ of the way.
3. The Grub has made it $\frac{1}{2}$ of the way.
4. The Grub has traveled $\frac{3}{4}$ of the way.
5. The Grub has gone $\frac{7}{8}$ of the way.
6. Label the number line below in eighths.

$\frac{1}{8}$ $\frac{2}{8}$ $\frac{3}{8}$ $\frac{4}{8}$ $\frac{5}{8}$ $\frac{6}{8}$ $\frac{7}{8}$ $\frac{8}{8}$

122 Use with text pages 334-335. CS-4

Options for Individual Needs

Basic

Exercises 1-8
Skills Bank, p. 466
More Practice, p. 508, set E

Supplements
Reteaching 122 or
Practice 122

Average

Exercises 1-8
Skills Bank, p. 466
More Practice, p. 508, set E

Supplements
Practice 122
Challenges 122 or
Thinking Skills 122

Extended

Exercises 1-8

Supplements
Challenges 122
Thinking Skills 122

Other Resources:
Problem-Solving Experiences in Mathematics, Grade 4, Problem 89
Mathematics, A Way of Thinking, Lessons 11-4, 11-20
Mathematics, Book A, Teacher's Edition, pp. 67, 68

12-4

LESSON PLAN 12-4

OBJECTIVE 12-4
To understand the concept of equivalent fractions

Materials: geoboards, rubber bands, TA 15 (Dot Paper), counters

1. MOTIVATE AND TEACH

LEARN ABOUT IT

EXPLORE ► **Explain how you can confirm that you made a square.** (Count the pegs on each side to ensure all four sides are equal, then visually check for four right angles.)
► **Into how many equal parts can you divide the half? Explain how you know.** (Answers may vary depending on the number of pegs in the geoboard.)
► **What must be true about the parts? Why?** (They are the same size; fractional parts are equal.)

TALK ABOUT IT ► **Relate the larger and smaller parts in equivalent fractions.** (Possible answer: You can divide a larger part into as many equal smaller parts as you want, as long as the smaller parts together equal the larger.)
► **Describe the relationship between the numerator and the denominator in fractions equivalent to $\frac{1}{2}$.** (Possible answer: The denominator is always double the numerator.)
► **Explain why $\frac{2}{3}$ and $\frac{6}{9}$ are equivalent.** (Possible answer: They name the same amount on the geoboard.)
Student Edition answers: **1.** Possible answers: $\frac{2}{4}$, $\frac{3}{6}$, $\frac{4}{8}$, $\frac{8}{16}$ **2.** Answers will vary.

2. CHECK UNDERSTANDING

TRY IT OUT

ERROR ALERT Naming equivalent fractions incorrectly.

Equivalent Fractions

LEARN ABOUT IT

EXPLORE Use a Geoboard

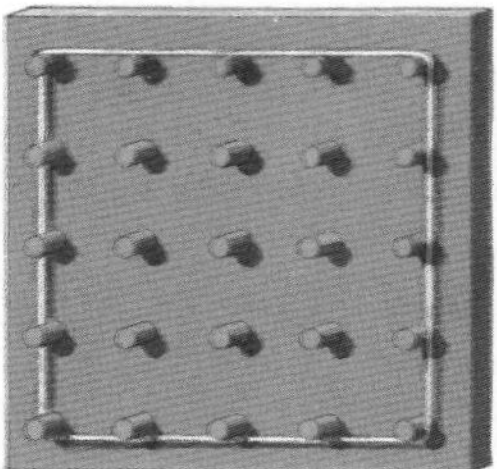

- Make this square on a geoboard. Divide it down the middle to show halves.
- Divide each of the halves into a number of equal parts in exactly the same way.
- Record the different ways to do this on dot paper. Think about how to use your dot paper pictures to write different fractions to describe half of the square.

TALK ABOUT IT See teaching notes.

1. Pick out one of your squares. What fraction shows $\frac{1}{2}$ of the square?
2. Use your dot paper drawings to make a list of different fractions that show $\frac{1}{2}$ of the square.

Fractions that name the same amount are called equivalent fractions.

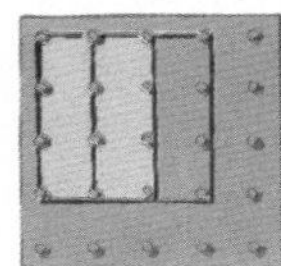

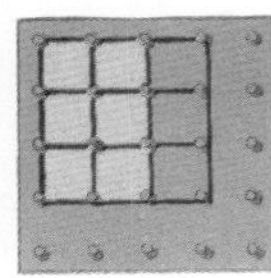

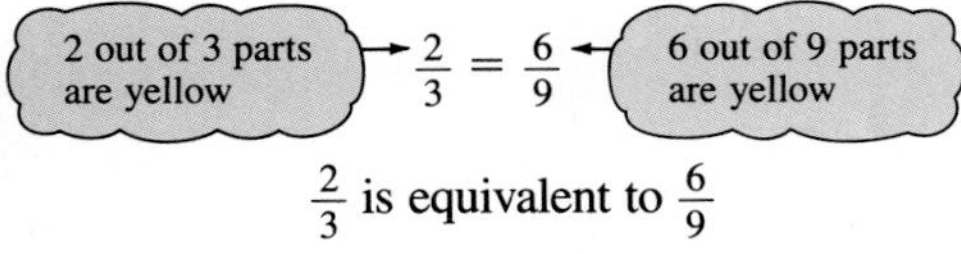

$\frac{2}{3}$ is equivalent to $\frac{6}{9}$

TRY IT OUT

Copy and complete the equations.

1. $\frac{5}{10} = \frac{|||}{|||}$ $\frac{1}{2}$

2. 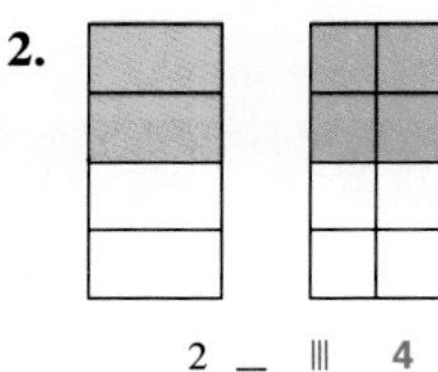

$\frac{2}{4} = \frac{|||}{|||}$ $\frac{4}{8}$

TEACHING OPTIONS

RETEACHING TIPS Have students use counters to represent the first fractional amount (such as 8 counters, of which 6 are red). Then have them rearrange the counters to show the equivalent grouping (such as moving counters closer to show 4 pairs instead of 8 separate counters). Assign Reteaching Supplement 122.

ENRICHMENT Have students solve: *Marie cut cornbread into 12 pieces. Steve ate $\frac{1}{3}$ of the pieces. Phil ate only $\frac{1}{12}$. Kelly ate $\frac{1}{4}$ of the pieces. Tell how many pieces each person had. Then tell how many pieces were left for Marie.* (Steve ate 4, Phil ate 1, and Kelly ate 3, leaving 4 pieces for Marie.)

PRACTICE

Copy and complete the equations.

1. 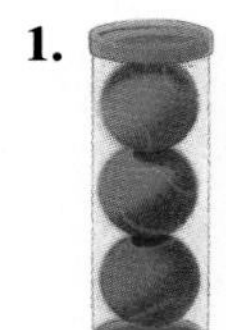   $\frac{2}{3} = \frac{\square}{9}$ **6**

2. 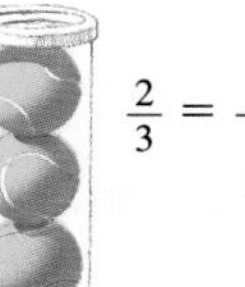   $\frac{1}{4} = \frac{2}{\square}$ **8**

3. 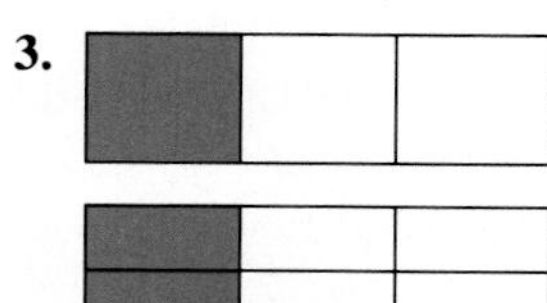 $\frac{2}{6} = \frac{\square}{\square}$ $\frac{1}{3}$

4. 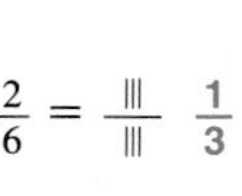 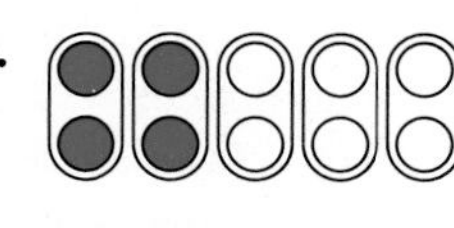 $\frac{4}{10} = \frac{\square}{\square}$ $\frac{2}{5}$

APPLY

MATH REASONING Write the fraction that does not belong. Use the pictures to help you.

5. $\frac{1}{2}$ $\frac{3}{4}$ $\frac{4}{8}$  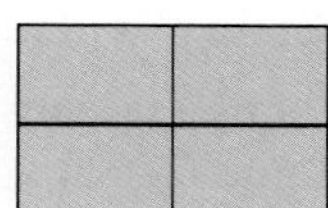 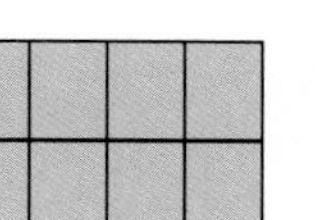 $\frac{3}{4}$

PROBLEM SOLVING

6. One of every 3 members of Jo's club had a computer. How many of the 12 members had a computer? **4**

► **USING CRITICAL THINKING Give a Counterexample**

Find an exception to the rule, if possible.

7. For any 2 equivalent fractions, the denominators are both even or both odd. **Answers will vary. Sample answer: $\frac{2}{6} = \frac{1}{3}$**

8. All fractions equivalent to $\frac{1}{3}$ have odd denominators. **Answers will vary. Sample answer: $\frac{1}{3} = \frac{4}{12}$**

More Practice, page 508, set E

3. PRACTICE AND APPLY

Basic	1-8
Average	1-8
Extended	1-8

PRACTICE

Look at Exercise 1. Before you complete the equation, relate the picture to the fraction $\frac{2}{3}$. (Possible answer: $\frac{2}{3}$ means 2 of the 3 cans of tennis balls are shaded.) *Now describe the other grouping in ninths.* (Possible answer: Each ball is $\frac{1}{9}$, so $\frac{6}{9}$ are shaded; $\frac{2}{3} = \frac{6}{9}$.)

APPLY

MATH REASONING ► **Explain a reasonable first step to use to solve Exercise 5.** (Possible answer: Match the fractions with the pictures.)

USING CRITICAL THINKING

► **Explain in your own words what to do to solve Problems 7 and 8.** (Possible answer: For each problem, try to find a case to show that the rule is not always true.)

► **How could you begin?** (Possible answer: Be sure you understand the rule as given, then try to create a situation in which it will not be true.)

12-4

CLOSE AND ASSESS

PROVE WHAT YOU KNOW

Have students use counters to prove that $\frac{4}{5}$ is equivalent to $\frac{8}{10}$ and that $\frac{5}{6}$ is equivalent to $\frac{10}{12}$. (Check students' models.)

QUICK QUIZ

Give the equivalent fractions.

1. $\left(\frac{2}{10} = \frac{1}{5}\right)$
2. $\left(\frac{3}{4} = \frac{9}{12}\right)$

Lesson Options 12-5

More About Equivalent Fractions

OBJECTIVE 12-5 To find equivalent fractions by multiplying

Prebook Activities

Quick Review

Give the equivalent fraction.

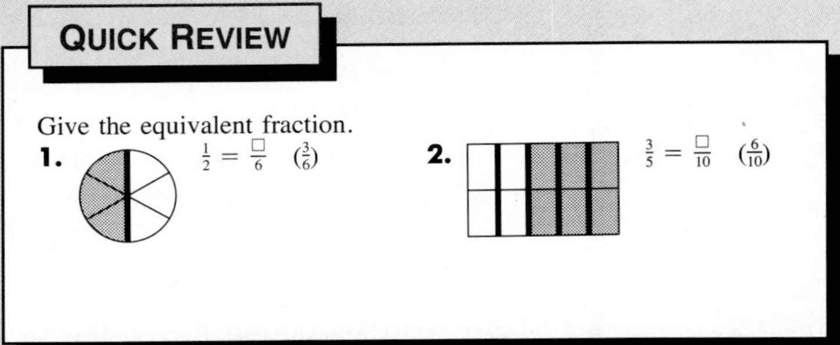

PRIOR KNOWLEDGE

Have students express the meaning of equivalent fractions in their own words. (Possible answer: Equivalent fractions describe the same amount.) Have students give two equivalent fractions that describe the part of the word *banana* that is *A*s. ($\frac{3}{6}$, $\frac{1}{2}$) Tell students that they will learn a multiplication method that will enable them to find equivalent fractions without needing a model or a drawing.

COMMUNICATION

Discussing Math Have students review the terms used to identify numbers above and below the fraction bar. (**numerator, denominator**) Have them relate each term to a fraction it would describe. (A denominator tells how many parts in all; a numerator tells how many specific parts.) Have them apply these rules to equivalent fractions. (The two denominators show different ways to divide the whole amount or object; the numerators refer to the specific parts using related numbers.)

Explore and Connect

Materials: TA 12 (Centimeter Graph Paper), markers
Grouping Suggestion: cooperative learning pairs
Partners investigate equivalent fractions and number relationships between numerators and denominators. Using a marker, one student draws along the lines of a 6-by-6 graph-paper square to form a fractional part that can be named with a 1-digit denominator that is a multiple of 36—2, 3, 4, 6, or 9. The partner writes an equivalent fraction by describing the same part in 36ths. Partners record a pair of equivalent fractions as an equation: $\frac{1}{3} = \frac{12}{36}$ or $\frac{5}{6} = \frac{30}{36}$. Then they look for a number relationship between the numerators and the denominators. Pairs repeat the activity several times, trading roles. Conclude by having students share patterns they found and generalize about equivalent fractions. (Possible answer: If you multiply the numerator and the denominator of a fraction by the same factor, you will get an equivalent fraction.)

Connections Use these anytime.

Problem of the Day

Creative Problem Solving Use 4 different odd numbers to write a pair of equivalent fractions. Draw a picture if it will help. (Answers may vary. Samples: $\frac{1}{3} = \frac{5}{15}$, $\frac{3}{5} = \frac{9}{15}$.)

Math Connection

Measurement Sonni was absent from school $\frac{1}{3}$ of the month of April because of a bad case of chicken pox. Write an equivalent fraction for the amount of school she missed that month that relates to the 30 d in April. ($\frac{10}{30}$)

Life Skills

Television Commercials Will's favorite television show lasts 1 h. One night, Will noticed that only $\frac{3}{4}$ of the time was spent on the program. The rest of the time had commercials. Write a fraction to tell how many minutes is equivalent to $\frac{3}{4}$ of an h. Hint: First think about the best denominator to use. ($\frac{45}{60}$)

Classwork and Homework Supplements

Practice

Skills Maintenance 12-5

Name ______

More About Equivalent Fractions

Find these equivalent fractions.

1. $\frac{1}{3} = \frac{2}{6}$ (×2)
2. $\frac{1}{3} = \frac{3}{9}$ (×3)
3. $\frac{1}{3} = \frac{4}{12}$ (×4)
4. $\frac{3}{7} = \frac{6}{14}$ (×2)
5. $\frac{3}{7} = \frac{9}{21}$ (×3)
6. $\frac{3}{7} = \frac{12}{28}$ (×4)
7. $\frac{2}{5} = \frac{4}{10}$ (×2)
8. $\frac{2}{5} = \frac{6}{15}$ (×3)
9. $\frac{2}{5} = \frac{8}{20}$ (×4)

Multiply the numerator and denominator by 2, 3, and 4 to find the equivalent fractions.

10. $\frac{2}{3} = \frac{4}{6} = \frac{6}{9} = \frac{8}{12}$
11. $\frac{3}{5} = \frac{6}{10} = \frac{9}{15} = \frac{12}{20}$
12. $\frac{1}{4} = \frac{2}{8} = \frac{3}{12} = \frac{4}{16}$
13. $\frac{1}{6} = \frac{2}{12} = \frac{3}{18} = \frac{4}{24}$
14. $\frac{3}{8} = \frac{6}{16} = \frac{9}{24} = \frac{12}{32}$
15. $\frac{4}{5} = \frac{8}{10} = \frac{12}{15} = \frac{16}{20}$

PS-4 Use with text pages 336–337. 123

Building Thinking Skills

Math Reasoning 12-5

Name ______

Where Is the Cup?

Messy Marty is making her favorite muffins, but she can find only her $\frac{1}{8}$-cup measure. Help her figure out alternative measures by answering the questions.

Messy Muffins
Makes 12 muffins

1 egg	2 cups sifted flour
$\frac{3}{4}$ cup milk	$\frac{1}{2}$ cup sugar
$\frac{1}{2}$ cup oil	3 teaspoons baking powder
1 teaspoon salt	

1. For which ingredients should Marty fill her $\frac{1}{8}$-cup measure 4 times? **oil, sugar**
2. Messy Marty found a $\frac{1}{2}$-cup measure in her sock drawer. If she fills it 4 times for flour, is she correct? **yes**
3. For which ingredient should Marty fill her $\frac{1}{8}$-cup measure 6 times? **milk**
4. Marty uses her $\frac{1}{8}$-cup measure to measure flour. How many times should she fill it? **16 times**
5. Greedy Glenda ate 3 muffins before she said hello. Was that more than $\frac{1}{4}$ of the total? **no**
6. Then Marty ate $\frac{1}{3}$ of the remaining muffins and her dog ate $\frac{3}{9}$. Who ate more? **Both ate the same amount.**
7. Marty finds her $\frac{1}{4}$-cup measure. How many times does she have to fill it for milk? **3** Oil? **2** Flour? **8** Sugar? **2**

TS-4 Use with text pages 336–337. 123

Reteaching

Skills Review 12-5

Name ______

More About Equivalent Fractions

You can find equivalent fractions by multiplying the numerator and denominator by the same number.

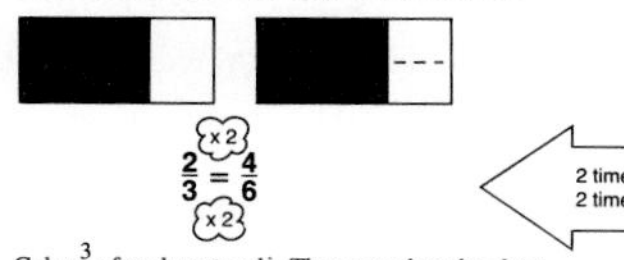

$\frac{2}{3} = \frac{4}{6}$ (×2)

2 times as many shaded parts
2 times as many total parts

Color $\frac{3}{4}$ of each rectangle. Then complete the chart.

	Rectangle	Number of Colored Parts	Total Number of Parts	Fraction
1.		3	4	$\frac{3}{4}$
2.		9	12	$\frac{9}{12}$
3.		6	8	$\frac{6}{8}$
4.		12	16	$\frac{12}{16}$

Use your chart to find equivalent fractions. Write the number by which you would multiply the numerator and denominator.

5. $\frac{3}{4} = \frac{6}{8}$ **2**
6. $\frac{3}{4} = \frac{9}{12}$ **3**
7. $\frac{3}{4} = \frac{12}{16}$ **4**

Now find these equivalent fractions.

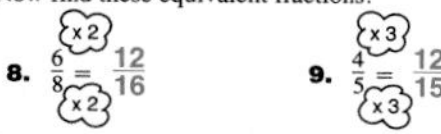

8. $\frac{6}{8} = \frac{12}{16}$ (×2)
9. $\frac{4}{5} = \frac{12}{15}$ (×3)
10. $\frac{5}{6} = \frac{20}{24}$ (×4)

RS-4 Use with text pages 336–337. 123

Challenges

Calculators 12-5

Name ______

Crisscross Products

While experimenting with her calculator, Rosita discovered what she called "crisscross products."

Example:
Rosita multiplies the crisscross products of 2 fractions to decide if they are equivalent.

$2 \times 6 = 12$
$4 \times 3 = 12$

If the crisscross products are equal, the fractions are equivalent. $\frac{2}{4} = \frac{3}{6}$

Write = or ≠ between the fractions. Use your calculator to find the crisscross products.

1. $\frac{8}{17} = \frac{16}{34}$; $8 \times 34 = 272$, $17 \times 16 = 272$
2. $\frac{4}{6} = \frac{10}{15}$; $4 \times 15 = 60$, $6 \times 10 = 60$
3. $\frac{8}{19} \neq \frac{12}{30}$; $8 \times 30 = 240$, $19 \times 12 = 228$
4. $\frac{12}{50} = \frac{36}{150}$; $12 \times 150 = 1{,}800$, $50 \times 36 = 1{,}800$
5. $\frac{8}{11} = \frac{24}{33}$; $8 \times 33 = 264$, $11 \times 24 = 264$
6. $\frac{12}{24} = \frac{50}{100}$; $12 \times 100 = 1{,}200$, $24 \times 50 = 1{,}200$
7. $\frac{9}{27} = \frac{3}{9}$; $9 \times 9 = 81$, $27 \times 3 = 81$
8. $\frac{17}{40} \neq \frac{21}{120}$; $17 \times 120 = 2{,}040$, $40 \times 21 = 840$
9. $\frac{64}{128} = \frac{75}{150}$; $64 \times 150 = 9{,}600$, $128 \times 75 = 9{,}600$

CS-4 Use with text pages 336–337. 123

Options for Individual Needs

Basic

Exercises 1-6, 9-13
Data Bank, p. 477
Skills Bank, pp. 465, 466
Calculator Bank, p. 486
More Practice, p. 508, set F

Supplements
Reteaching 123 or
Practice 123

Average

Exercises 1-14
Data Bank, p. 477
Skills Bank, pp. 465, 466
Calculator Bank, p. 486
More Practice, p. 508, set F

Supplements
Practice 123
Challenges 123 or
Thinking Skills 123

Extended

Exercises 3-14
Data Bank, p. 477
Calculator Bank, p. 486

Supplements
Challenges 123
Thinking Skills 123

Other Resources:

Problem-Solving Experiences in Mathematics, Grade 4, Problem 90
Mathematics, A Way of Thinking, Lesson 11-21
Using The Math Explorer Calculator: A Sourcebook for Teachers, Chapter 14

LESSON PLAN 12-5

OBJECTIVE 12-5
To find equivalent fractions by multiplying

Materials: calculators

Grouping Suggestion: pairs

1. MOTIVATE AND TEACH

LEARN ABOUT IT

EXPLORE ▶ **Analyze the picture.** (4 black horses in teams of 2 and 4 white horses in teams of 2)

TALK ABOUT IT ▶ **Explain a way to classify the horses and the teams.** (by color—4 black and 4 white horses; 2 all-black and 2 all-white teams)
▶ **What denominator makes sense to describe all horses? Explain.** (8, because it is the total number of horses)
▶ **What denominator can describe all teams? Explain.** (4; It is the total number of teams.)
▶ **What fraction would describe one team out of all the teams? What equivalent fraction would compare those same horses to all the horses? Explain.** ($\frac{1}{4}$; $\frac{2}{8}$; 1 team out of 4 teams, 2 horses out of 8 horses)
▶ **Do you see a connection between the two denominators and the two numerators? Explain.** (yes; $4 \times \underline{2} = 8$ and $1 \times \underline{2} = 2$; $\frac{1}{4} \times$ the same factor $= \frac{2}{8}$)
Student Edition answers: **1.** 2, $\frac{2}{4}$ or $\frac{1}{2}$ **2.** $\frac{4}{8}$

2. CHECK UNDERSTANDING

TRY IT OUT

ERROR ALERT Failing to multiply both the numerator and the denominator by the same factor.

More About Equivalent Fractions

LEARN ABOUT IT

EXPLORE Think About the Situation
At harvest time in *The Little House in the Big Woods,* teams, or pairs, of horses were hitched to a horsepower machine to run a machine called a separator.

TALK ABOUT IT See teaching notes.

1. How many of the 4 teams are black? What fraction tells the part of the teams that are black?
2. Multiply the number of teams by 2. Multiply the number of black teams by 2. With these new numbers how can you write a fraction equivalent to the one in question 1?

To find equivalent fractions, multiply the numerator and the denominator by the same number.

Two-thirds and four-sixths are equivalent fractions.

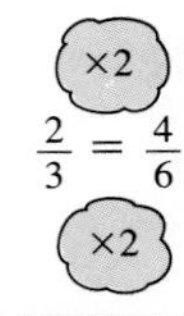

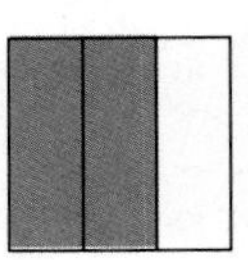

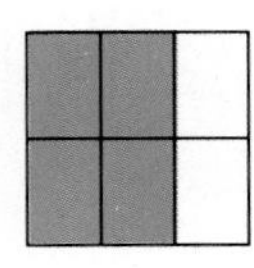

Other fractions equivalent to two-thirds.

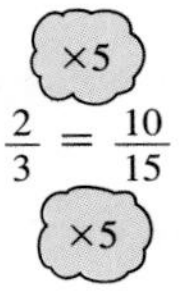

TRY IT OUT

Multiply to find equivalent fractions.

1. (×2) $\frac{1}{4} = \frac{|||}{|||}$ $\frac{2}{8}$ (×2)
2. (×3) $\frac{1}{4} = \frac{|||}{|||}$ $\frac{3}{12}$ (×3)
3. (×2) $\frac{3}{5} = \frac{|||}{|||}$ $\frac{6}{10}$ (×2)
4. (×3) $\frac{3}{5} = \frac{|||}{|||}$ $\frac{9}{15}$ (×3)

TEACHING OPTIONS

RETEACHING TIPS Have students record the steps in the process of multiplying the numerator and the denominator. Suggest a record such as this:

$\frac{1}{4} = \frac{1 \times 2}{4 \times 2} = \frac{2}{8}$ $\quad \frac{1}{4} = \frac{1 \times 3}{4 \times 3} = \frac{3}{12}$

Assign Reteaching Supplement 123.

ENRICHMENT Have students use mental math to complete the equivalent fractions.

1. $\frac{8}{11} = \frac{\triangle}{99}$ (72) **2.** $\frac{4}{7} = \frac{160}{\triangle}$ (280)
3. $\frac{5}{6} = \frac{505}{\triangle}$ (606) **4.** $\frac{2}{3} = \frac{\triangle}{606}$ (404)

PRACTICE

Multiply to find these equivalent fractions. Check with fraction pieces.

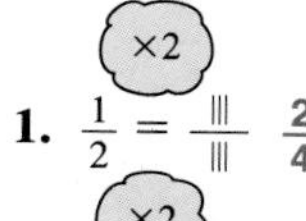

1. $\frac{1}{2} = \frac{\|}{\|}$ (×2) **2/4** 2. $\frac{1}{2} = \frac{\|}{\|}$ (×3) **3/6** 3. $\frac{5}{6} = \frac{\|}{\|}$ (×2) **10/12** 4. $\frac{5}{6} = \frac{\|}{\|}$ (×4) **20/24**

Multiply the numerator and denominator by 2, 3, and 4 to find the equivalent fractions.

5. $\frac{3}{4} = \frac{\|}{\|} = \frac{\|}{\|} = \frac{\|}{\|}$ **6/8, 9/12, 12/16** 6. $\frac{2}{5} = \frac{\|}{\|} = \frac{\|}{\|} = \frac{\|}{\|}$ **4/10, 6/15, 8/20** 7. $\frac{1}{8} = \frac{\|}{\|} = \frac{\|}{\|} = \frac{\|}{\|}$ **2/16, 3/24, 4/32**

APPLY

MATH REASONING

8. If □ = 15, what is △? **24**
$\frac{5}{8} = \frac{□}{△}$

9. If □ = 10, what is △? **16**
$\frac{5}{8} = \frac{□}{△}$

PROBLEM SOLVING

10. **Language Arts Data Bank** How can you measure the cornmeal to make Johnny Cake if you have only a tablespoon measure? Hint: 4 tablespoons equal $\frac{1}{4}$ cup. See page 477. **12 tablespoons**

DATA BANK

▶ CALCULATOR

You can use a calculator to tell if 2 fractions are equivalent. Divide the numerator by the denominator. Are the calculator displays the same?

To see if $\frac{3}{5} = \frac{75}{100}$ is an equivalent fraction, do this.

[ON/AC] 3 [÷] 5 [=] 0.6

[ON/AC] 75 [÷] 125 [=] 0.6

11. $\frac{2}{5} = \frac{32}{80}$ **yes** 12. $\frac{3}{4} = \frac{164}{224}$ **no** 13. $\frac{3}{8} = \frac{126}{336}$ **yes** 14. $\frac{5}{6} = \frac{240}{288}$ **yes**

More Practice, page 508, set F

337

3. PRACTICE AND APPLY

Basic	1-6, 9-13
Average	1-14
Extended	3-14

PRACTICE

Look at Exercises 1-4. Identify factors you would use to multiply the given fractions to form equivalent fractions. (2, 3 and 4) *In Exercises 5-7, why are four fractions linked by equal signs in each exercise?* (Fractions equivalent to one fraction equal each other.)

APPLY

MATH REASONING ▶ Explain what you must find to fill the triangle. (a relationship between numerators in order to find a factor by which to multiply the denominator)

PROBLEM SOLVING ▶ Explain steps to follow to solve Problem 10. (Find the amount of cornmeal in the recipe; multiply to find the number of tablespoons in $\frac{3}{4}$.)

CALCULATOR ▶ State a rule for using a calculator to test if fractions are equivalent. (Possible rule: Fractions are equivalent if quotients of numerators divided by denominators are equal.)

12-5

CLOSE AND ASSESS

SAY WHAT YOU THINK Pair students. One partner writes any fraction with a 1-digit numerator and denominator. The other gives another fraction that is equivalent to it. Partners check for accuracy, then switch tasks. Have pairs repeat the activity so that each partner makes two equivalent fractions.

QUICK QUIZ

Multiply the numerator and denominator by 3 and 5 to make two equivalent fractions.

1. $\frac{1}{3}$ ($\frac{3}{9}$, $\frac{5}{15}$) 2. $\frac{5}{6}$ ($\frac{15}{18}$, $\frac{25}{30}$)
3. $\frac{2}{4}$ ($\frac{6}{12}$, $\frac{10}{20}$) 4. $\frac{7}{8}$ ($\frac{21}{24}$, $\frac{35}{40}$)

LESSON OPTIONS 12-6

Lowest-Terms Fractions

OBJECTIVE 12-6 To reduce fractions to lowest terms

PREBOOK ACTIVITIES

QUICK REVIEW

Write *yes* or *no* to tell whether the fractions are equivalent.

1. $\frac{1}{2} = \frac{1}{3}$ (no) **2.** $\frac{2}{5} = \frac{4}{10}$ (yes) **3.** $\frac{3}{4} = \frac{9}{12}$ (yes)
4. $\frac{4}{7} = \frac{7}{4}$ (no) **5.** $\frac{5}{6} = \frac{10}{12}$ (yes) **6.** $\frac{1}{3} = \frac{3}{6}$ (no)

PRIOR KNOWLEDGE

Have students recall previous experiences in which the same amount was described by more than 1 fraction. (Possible answers: $\frac{5}{10}$ of a dollar equals $\frac{1}{2}$ dollar; $\frac{1}{3}$ or $\frac{3}{9}$ of a team.) Have students choose which of the fraction pairs that follow are easier to imagine and tell why: $\frac{4}{8}$ or $\frac{1}{2}$, $\frac{9}{12}$ or $\frac{3}{4}$, $\frac{10}{15}$ or $\frac{2}{3}$. (Answers may vary. Students will probably choose lowest-terms fractions because those fractions require less pieces to imagine.) Tell students that they will find ways to rename fractions in simpler form to make them easier to visualize.

COMMUNICATION

Discussing Math Write **simple** and **reduce** on the chalkboard and ask students to give synonyms for each. (Possible answers: *easy, uncomplicated; make smaller*) Explain that some fractions are considered *simple* if they are easier to imagine than others and use **lower terms,** or smaller numbers. For instance, $\frac{1}{2}$ is easier to visualize than $\frac{9}{18}$, although these fractions are equivalent. You **simplify,** or reduce, a fraction by finding an equivalent fraction in *lowest terms*.

EXPLORE AND CONNECT

Materials: fraction list (see activity below), counters
Grouping Suggestion: cooperative learning pairs
Partners explore how to **simplify** or **reduce** fractions to **lowest terms.** List these fractions on the chalkboard so that all pairs can see them: $\frac{10}{15}$, $\frac{15}{20}$, $\frac{14}{21}$, $\frac{18}{27}$, $\frac{21}{28}$, $\frac{27}{36}$. Students show each fraction with counters, then try to find an equivalent fraction for each amount that uses **simpler** numbers. Partners take turns modeling the fraction, verifying the model, recording the given fraction, and listing equivalent fractions in *lower terms* on a table or chart. Conclude by having students share the equivalent fractions they found and explain how they found them. (Methods may vary. All fractions *reduce* to $\frac{2}{3}$ or $\frac{3}{4}$. Accept intermediary reductions.) Have students identify *lowest-terms* fractions and group fractions that go together. ($\frac{10}{15}$, $\frac{14}{21}$, and $\frac{18}{27}$ *reduce* to $\frac{2}{3}$; $\frac{15}{20}$, $\frac{21}{28}$, and $\frac{27}{36}$ *reduce* to $\frac{3}{4}$)

CONNECTIONS Use these anytime.

Problem of the Day

Fraction Riddle Find 3 different fractions that fit all the clues.
1. The denominator is a multiple of 8.
2. The numerator is a multiple of 4.
3. It is equivalent to $\frac{1}{2}$.
(Answers may vary. Possible answers: $\frac{8}{16}$, $\frac{16}{32}$, $\frac{24}{48}$, $\frac{32}{64}$, $\frac{40}{80}$.)

Subject Integration

Science Russell is doing a science experiment with moths. $\frac{6}{9}$ of his moths are yellow, and $\frac{3}{9}$ are white. Find an equivalent fraction in simpler form for each amount. Draw a picture if it will help you. ($\frac{2}{3}$, $\frac{1}{3}$)

Number Sense

Mental Math $\frac{25}{100}$ of Janey's coin collection are nickels and the rest are pennies. Use your knowledge of money and equivalent fractions to find a fraction to describe the amount of the collection that is pennies. Then give an equivalent fraction in simpler form for each amount. ($\frac{75}{100}$; $\frac{1}{4}$ are nickels, $\frac{3}{4}$ are pennies)

Classwork and Homework Supplements

Practice

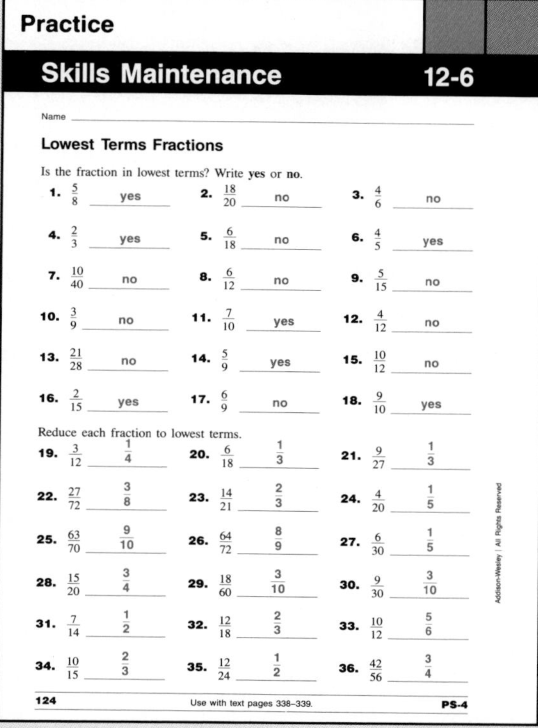

Skills Maintenance 12-6

Name

Lowest Terms Fractions

Is the fraction in lowest terms? Write **yes** or **no**.

1. $\frac{5}{8}$	yes	**2.** $\frac{18}{20}$	no	**3.** $\frac{4}{6}$	no
4. $\frac{2}{3}$	yes	**5.** $\frac{6}{18}$	no	**6.** $\frac{4}{5}$	yes
7. $\frac{10}{40}$	no	**8.** $\frac{6}{12}$	no	**9.** $\frac{5}{15}$	no
10. $\frac{3}{9}$	no	**11.** $\frac{7}{10}$	yes	**12.** $\frac{4}{12}$	no
13. $\frac{21}{28}$	no	**14.** $\frac{5}{9}$	yes	**15.** $\frac{10}{12}$	no
16. $\frac{2}{15}$	yes	**17.** $\frac{6}{9}$	no	**18.** $\frac{9}{10}$	yes

Reduce each fraction to lowest terms.

19. $\frac{3}{12}$	$\frac{1}{4}$	**20.** $\frac{6}{18}$	$\frac{1}{3}$	**21.** $\frac{9}{27}$	$\frac{1}{3}$
22. $\frac{27}{72}$	$\frac{3}{8}$	**23.** $\frac{14}{21}$	$\frac{2}{3}$	**24.** $\frac{4}{20}$	$\frac{1}{5}$
25. $\frac{63}{70}$	$\frac{9}{10}$	**26.** $\frac{64}{72}$	$\frac{8}{9}$	**27.** $\frac{6}{30}$	$\frac{1}{5}$
28. $\frac{15}{20}$	$\frac{3}{4}$	**29.** $\frac{18}{60}$	$\frac{3}{10}$	**30.** $\frac{9}{30}$	$\frac{3}{10}$
31. $\frac{7}{14}$	$\frac{1}{2}$	**32.** $\frac{12}{18}$	$\frac{2}{3}$	**33.** $\frac{10}{12}$	$\frac{5}{6}$
34. $\frac{10}{15}$	$\frac{2}{3}$	**35.** $\frac{12}{24}$	$\frac{1}{2}$	**36.** $\frac{42}{56}$	$\frac{3}{4}$

124 Use with text pages 338-339. PS-4

Building Thinking Skills

Math Reasoning 12-6

Name

Find the Missing Fraction

Write the missing fraction on each blank tag.

1. $\frac{2}{3}$; $\frac{18}{27}$; $\frac{14}{21}$ — lowest terms
2. $\frac{25}{100}$; $\frac{1}{4}$; $\frac{2}{8}$ — hundredths
3. $\frac{8}{10}$; $\frac{32}{40}$; $\frac{16}{20}$ — tenths
4. $\frac{3}{4}$; $\frac{75}{100}$; $\frac{27}{36}$ — lowest terms
5. $\frac{2}{10}$; $\frac{8}{40}$; $\frac{1}{5}$ — tenths
6. $\frac{15}{100}$; $\frac{30}{200}$; $\frac{45}{300}$ — hundredths
7. $\frac{1}{10}$; $\frac{7}{70}$; $\frac{8}{80}$ — lowest terms
8. $\frac{3}{8}$; $\frac{30}{80}$; $\frac{6}{16}$ — lowest terms
9. $\frac{4}{10}$; $\frac{2}{5}$; $\frac{40}{100}$ — tenths
10. $\frac{1}{4}$; $\frac{25}{100}$; $\frac{3}{12}$ — lowest terms
11. $\frac{3}{10}$; $\frac{6}{20}$; $\frac{21}{70}$ — lowest terms

124 Use with text pages 338-339. TS-4

Reteaching

Skills Review 12-6

Name

Lowest Terms Fractions

To reduce a fraction to lowest terms, use division to find an equivalent fraction that cannot be reduced.

$\frac{8}{16}$ of the socks have stripes.

$\frac{8}{16} = \frac{4}{8} \rightarrow \frac{4}{8}$ of the pairs have stripes. (÷2)

$\frac{4}{8} = \frac{1}{2} \rightarrow \frac{1}{2}$ of the socks have stripes. (÷4)

Is the fraction in lowest terms? Ring **yes** or **no**.

1. $\frac{4}{6}$ yes (no) — I can still divide both 4 and 6 by 2.
2. $\frac{2}{3}$ (yes) no — I cannot divide both 2 and 3 by the same number.
3. $\frac{6}{8}$ yes (no) — I can still divide both 6 and 8 by 2.
4. $\frac{8}{10}$ yes (no)
5. $\frac{3}{9}$ yes (no)
6. $\frac{3}{5}$ (yes) no

Reduce each fraction to lowest terms. Divide the numerator and denominator by the same number.

7. $\frac{6}{10} = \frac{3}{5}$ (÷2)
8. $\frac{6}{8} = \frac{3}{4}$ (÷2)
9. $\frac{6}{9} = \frac{2}{3}$ (÷3)
10. $\frac{6}{12} = \frac{1}{2}$ (÷6)
11. $\frac{8}{10} = \frac{4}{5}$
12. $\frac{3}{12} = \frac{1}{4}$
13. $\frac{5}{15} = \frac{1}{3}$
14. $\frac{2}{6} = \frac{1}{3}$

124 Use with text pages 338-339. RS-4

Challenges

Cooperative Activities 12-6

Name

Fraction Reducer Game

Play this game in 2 teams. You will need a spinner with the numerals 0 through 9 on it. Each team should cut out 20 pieces of paper small enough to fit in the boxes below.

Rules

1. Take turns spinning 1 number at a time. Write each number on a piece of paper.
2. The goal is to cover the boxes below to make true equations using the numbers on the pieces of paper. Each equation should show a fraction reduced to its lowest terms.
3. The winner is the first team to complete the two equations correctly.

Examples: $\frac{6}{8} = \frac{3}{4}$ $\frac{2}{10} = \frac{1}{5}$

You can complete the equations in any order.

124 Use with text pages 338-339. CS-4

Options for Individual Needs

Basic

Exercises 2-10, 13-16
Calculator Bank, p. 487
More Practice, p. 508, set G

Supplements
Reteaching 124 or
Practice 124

Average

Exercises 1-17
Calculator Bank, p. 487
More Practice, p. 508, set G

Supplements
Practice 124
Challenges 124 or
Thinking Skills 124

Extended

Exercises 3-9, 13-17
Calculator Bank, p. 487

Supplements
Challenges 124
Thinking Skills 124

Other Resources:

Problem-Solving Experiences in Mathematics, Grade 4, Problem 91
Mathematics, A Way of Thinking, Lesson 11-22
Mathematics, Book A, Teacher's Edition, pp. 68, 69
Using The Math Explorer Calculator: A Sourcebook for Teachers, Chapter 14

12-6

LESSON PLAN 12-6

OBJECTIVE 12-6
To reduce fractions to lowest terms

Materials: TA 3 (Number Cards 2-4)

1. MOTIVATE AND TEACH

LEARN ABOUT IT

EXPLORE ▶ **Why must you count the fish to check the fractions?** (You must know the fish total to judge whether the denominators make sense.)
▶ **How can you test for equivalent fractions?** (Fractions are equivalent if you can multiply the numerator and the denominator of one by the same factor and get the other.)

TALK ABOUT IT ▶ **Justify Tom's fractional description of the fish.** (Possible answer: *Half* means 2 equal groups; there are 6 striped and 6 nonstriped fish.)
▶ **Justify Mary's fractional description of the fish.** (Of the 12 fish in all, 6 are striped.)
▶ **Are both correct? Explain.** (Yes, because $\frac{1}{2}$ and $\frac{6}{12}$ are equivalent fractions.)
▶ **Explain why you divide the numerator and denominator by the same number.** (to keep the fractions equivalent)
▶ **Could $\frac{6}{12}$ be reduced to $\frac{1}{2}$ in one step? Explain.** (Yes, divide both the numerator and the denominator by 6 to get $\frac{1}{2}$.)
Student Edition answers: **1.** 12, 6 **2.** Since the fractions are equivalent, both are correct. **3.** $\frac{1}{2}$; reasons will vary.

2. CHECK UNDERSTANDING

TRY IT OUT

ERROR ALERT Using 2 different divisors. Failing to reduce completely.

Lowest-Terms Fractions

LEARN ABOUT IT

EXPLORE Think About the Situation

Tom says that $\frac{1}{2}$ of the fish in the aquarium are striped. Mary says that $\frac{6}{12}$ are striped.

TALK ABOUT IT See teaching notes.

1. How many fish are there? How many are striped?
2. Who do you think is correct and why?
3. Which do you think is a simpler fraction, $\frac{1}{2}$ or $\frac{6}{12}$? Why?

A fraction is in lowest terms when no number except 1 will divide evenly into its numerator and denominator.

Find a number that will divide evenly into the numerator and denominator.

Keep dividing until you cannot divide by any number except 1. The fraction is in lowest terms.

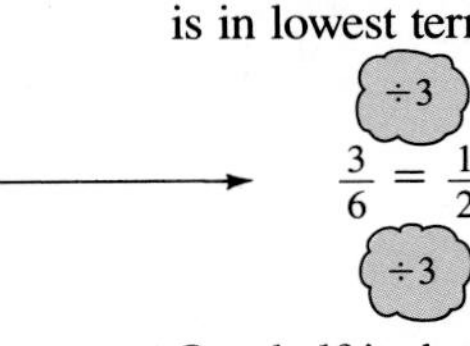

2 divides evenly. You could also have started dividing by 3 or 6.

One-half is the lowest-terms fraction for six-twelfths.

TRY IT OUT

Reduce each fraction to lowest terms.

1. $\frac{6}{8} = \frac{\square}{\square}$ (÷2) $\frac{3}{4}$
2. $\frac{12}{20} = \frac{\square}{\square}$ (÷4) $\frac{3}{5}$
3. $\frac{6}{15} = \frac{\square}{\square}$ (÷3) $\frac{2}{5}$
4. $\frac{3}{9}$ $\frac{1}{3}$
5. $\frac{9}{12}$ $\frac{3}{4}$

338

TEACHING OPTIONS

RETEACHING TIPS For students using 2 different divisors, provide number cards 2-4. Have students use 1 number card at a time as the divisor by which to reduce *both* terms of the fraction. If both terms do not divide evenly, students try the next number. Assign Reteaching Supplement 124.

ENRICHMENT Family Math Students play "Fraction Concentration" with a family member. They write these fractions on blank index cards: $\frac{1}{2}, \frac{2}{3}, \frac{3}{4}, \frac{4}{5}, \frac{5}{6}, \frac{6}{7}, \frac{7}{8}, \frac{7}{10}, \frac{4}{8}, \frac{8}{12}, \frac{15}{20}, \frac{8}{10}, \frac{25}{30}, \frac{12}{14}, \frac{21}{24}, \frac{14}{20}$. They shuffle the cards, line them up face down in rows, and turn over 2 at a time. If equivalent, they keep the pair.

PRACTICE

Is the fraction in lowest terms? Answer yes or no.

1. $\frac{2}{4}$ no **2.** $\frac{1}{8}$ yes **3.** $\frac{3}{15}$ no **4.** $\frac{4}{5}$ yes **5.** $\frac{3}{9}$ no

If possible, reduce to lowest terms.

6. $\frac{10}{12}$ $\frac{5}{6}$ **7.** $\frac{6}{9}$ $\frac{2}{3}$ **8.** $\frac{2}{16}$ $\frac{1}{8}$ **9.** $\frac{4}{8}$ $\frac{1}{2}$ **10.** $\frac{1}{6}$ **11.** $\frac{18}{24}$ $\frac{3}{4}$

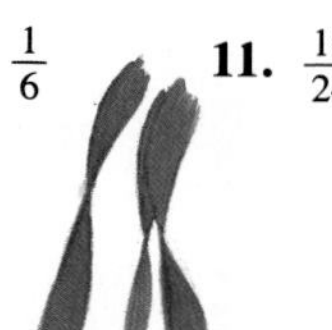

APPLY

MATH REASONING

For each pair, use mental math to reduce each fraction to lowest terms. Are they equivalent fractions?

12. $\frac{3}{6}, \frac{4}{8}$ yes **13.** $\frac{9}{12}, \frac{4}{6}$ no **14.** $\frac{10}{15}, \frac{4}{6}$ yes

PROBLEM SOLVING

15. Developing a Plan Tell which steps you could follow to solve this problem. Find all the correct choices. Jan has 12 tropical fish. Three are half-beaks, 2 are neons, and the rest are algae eaters. What fraction of the fish are algae eaters? $3 + 2 = 5, 12 - 5 = 7$

► **ALGEBRA**

$\frac{7}{12}$ are algae eaters.

When a fraction in the IN row is put into a machine, the fraction in the OUT row comes out. Tell what rule the machine is using. Give the missing fraction.

16. Math Machine A

IN $\frac{1}{3}$ $\frac{4}{5}$ $\frac{2}{3}$ OUT $\frac{2}{6}$ $\frac{8}{10}$ $\frac{4}{6}$

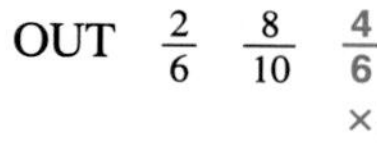

×2

17. Math Machine B

IN $\frac{2}{5}$ $\frac{1}{2}$ $\frac{3}{4}$ OUT $\frac{8}{20}$ $\frac{4}{8}$ $\frac{12}{16}$

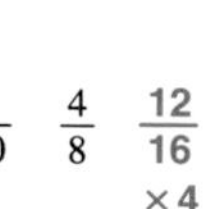

×4

More Practice, page 508, set G

3. Practice and Apply

Basic	2-10, 13-16
Average	1-17
Extended	3-9, 13-17

PRACTICE

Look at Exercises 1-5. Find a fraction already in lowest terms and tell how you know. (Exercise 2; $\frac{1}{8}$ must be in lowest terms because its numerator is 1.)

APPLY

MATH REASONING ► Explain how to relate equivalent fractions to reduced fractions. (Equivalent fractions should reduce to the same lowest-terms fraction.)

PROBLEM SOLVING ► Identify the operations to use to solve Problem 15. Explain your reasoning. (First add 3 + 2 to find the fish that are not algae eaters, then subtract 5 from 12 to find the number that are.)

ALGEBRA ► Explain the relationship between IN and OUT fractions. (They are equivalent; when both parts of an IN fraction are multiplied by the same factor, they equal the OUT fraction.)

Close and Assess

WRITE WHAT YOU THINK

Have students list all the steps they would follow to reduce $\frac{12}{15}$ to lowest terms. Ask them to write the steps in order and to give the lowest-terms fraction. ($\frac{4}{5}$; check students' writing.)

Quick Quiz

If possible, reduce to lowest terms.

1. $\frac{5}{15}$ ($\frac{1}{3}$) **2.** $\frac{5}{7}$ (already reduced)
3. $\frac{8}{12}$ ($\frac{2}{3}$) **4.** $\frac{12}{18}$ ($\frac{2}{3}$)
5. $\frac{10}{16}$ ($\frac{5}{8}$) **6.** $\frac{1}{6}$ (already reduced)

LESSON OPTIONS 12-7

Comparing Fractions

OBJECTIVE 12-7 To compare fractions

PREBOOK ACTIVITIES

QUICK REVIEW

Write an equivalent fraction whose denominator is between 10 and 20. (Answers may vary. Samples are given.)

1. $\frac{4}{5}$ $(\frac{12}{15})$	**2.** $\frac{2}{3}$ $(\frac{8}{12})$	**3.** $\frac{3}{7}$ $(\frac{6}{14})$
4. $\frac{1}{2}$ $(\frac{9}{18})$	**5.** $\frac{3}{4}$ $(\frac{12}{16})$	**6.** $\frac{5}{8}$ $(\frac{10}{16})$
5. $\frac{1}{3}$ $(\frac{6}{18})$	**8.** $\frac{7}{10}$ $(\frac{14}{20})$	**9.** $\frac{5}{6}$ $(\frac{15}{18})$

PRIOR KNOWLEDGE

Write the symbols $<$ and $>$ on the chalkboard. Have students give the meanings of the symbols. ($<$ means "is less than"; $>$ means "is greater than.") Ask students to explain how they have used these symbols before. (Possible answer: to compare numbers, such as $4 > 3$; in math expressions, such as $3 \times 3 < 2 \times 5$; in units of measurement, such as 1 pint $<$ 1 quart)

COMMUNICATION

Discussing and Writing in Math On the chalkboard, draw a fraction number line marked in fifths from $\frac{0}{5}$ to $\frac{5}{5}$. Have students apply their knowledge of other number lines to generalize about comparing fractions on a fraction number line. (Fractions increase from left to right.) In their Math Journals, have students write 2 fraction comparisons with $<$ and two with $>$, using the number line. (Answers may vary. Samples: $\frac{1}{5} < \frac{2}{5}$, $\frac{2}{5} < \frac{4}{5}$, $\frac{4}{5} > \frac{3}{5}$, $\frac{3}{5} > \frac{1}{5}$)

EXPLORE AND CONNECT

Materials: fraction pieces for halves, fifths, and tenths; TA 3 (Operation Cards)
Alternative Materials: TA 21 (Fraction Strips)
Grouping Suggestion: cooperative learning groups of 3
Students use the $<$, $>$, and $=$ symbols to compare fractions with unlike denominators of 2, 5, or 10. The first student uses $<$ to compare 2 fractions, such as $\frac{2}{5} < \frac{7}{10}$. The second student records the comparison, and the third student uses the fraction pieces to verify it. Students trade tasks. Then a student uses $>$ to compare 2 fractions, such as $\frac{4}{5} > \frac{1}{2}$, as the next student records it and the third student verifies it. Last, a student uses the $=$ symbol to compare 2 fractions, such as $\frac{2}{5} = \frac{4}{10}$. Conclude by having students generalize how to compare fractions with unlike denominators without using fraction pieces. (Rewrite them as equivalent fractions with like denominators.)

CONNECTIONS Use these anytime.

Problem of the Day

Money Fractions Find the coins equal to each fraction of a dollar. Then choose the greater amount of money.

1. $\frac{3}{4}$ or $\frac{6}{10}$ of a dollar?
2. $\frac{1}{20}$ or $\frac{4}{100}$ of a dollar?
3. $\frac{1}{2}$ or $\frac{11}{20}$ of a dollar?

(**1.** $\frac{3}{4}$, 75¢ > 60¢ **2.** $\frac{1}{20}$, 5¢ > 4¢ **3.** $\frac{11}{20}$, 55¢ > 50¢)

Number Sense

Estimation Visualize fraction pieces for $\frac{1}{17}$, $\frac{1}{24}$, $\frac{1}{86}$, $\frac{1}{13}$, $\frac{1}{41}$, $\frac{1}{5}$, and $\frac{1}{39}$. Put them in order from the smallest to the largest piece. ($\frac{1}{86}$, $\frac{1}{41}$, $\frac{1}{39}$, $\frac{1}{24}$, $\frac{1}{17}$, $\frac{1}{13}$, $\frac{1}{5}$)

Life Skills

Cooking The recipe Matt is making calls for $\frac{3}{4}$ c of flour, but his only measuring cup measures thirds. What can Matthew do to measure about the right amount of flour? (Possible answer: Since $\frac{3}{4} = \frac{9}{12}$ and $\frac{1}{3} = \frac{4}{12}$, Matt can measure a tiny bit more than $\frac{2}{3}$ c of flour.)

Classwork and Homework Supplements

Practice

Math Reasoning 12-7

Name ______________________

Comparing Fractions

Write <, >, or = for each ◯.

1. $\frac{3}{8}$ (<) $\frac{1}{2}$	2. $\frac{1}{2}$ (>) $\frac{1}{4}$	3. $\frac{3}{9}$ (=) $\frac{6}{18}$
4. $\frac{2}{3}$ (<) $\frac{4}{5}$	5. $\frac{1}{4}$ (=) $\frac{2}{8}$	6. $\frac{3}{4}$ (>) $\frac{5}{12}$
7. $\frac{1}{5}$ (<) $\frac{1}{4}$	8. $\frac{5}{8}$ (<) $\frac{2}{3}$	9. $\frac{3}{8}$ (>) $\frac{1}{4}$
10. $\frac{1}{10}$ (<) $\frac{1}{5}$	11. $\frac{3}{4}$ (>) $\frac{2}{3}$	12. $\frac{1}{3}$ (<) $\frac{4}{6}$
13. $\frac{2}{3}$ (>) $\frac{3}{8}$	14. $\frac{2}{10}$ (=) $\frac{1}{5}$	15. $\frac{2}{9}$ (<) $\frac{3}{4}$
16. $\frac{1}{2}$ (>) $\frac{1}{3}$	17. $\frac{3}{10}$ (>) $\frac{1}{4}$	18. $\frac{2}{5}$ (>) $\frac{3}{10}$
19. $\frac{2}{5}$ (<) $\frac{3}{4}$	20. $\frac{3}{4}$ (>) $\frac{5}{8}$	21. $\frac{1}{4}$ (>) $\frac{1}{10}$
22. $\frac{3}{10}$ (>) $\frac{1}{5}$	23. $\frac{3}{8}$ (<) $\frac{2}{5}$	24. $\frac{3}{5}$ (<) $\frac{3}{4}$
25. $\frac{2}{5}$ (=) $\frac{4}{10}$	26. $\frac{5}{8}$ (>) $\frac{3}{10}$	27. $\frac{5}{8}$ (>) $\frac{3}{5}$
28. $\frac{1}{4}$ (<) $\frac{1}{3}$	29. $\frac{1}{5}$ (>) $\frac{1}{8}$	30. $\frac{2}{3}$ (<) $\frac{5}{6}$

PS-4 Use with text pages 340-341. 125

Building Thinking Skills

Math Reasoning 12-7

Name ______________________

It's About Time

You are about to make some decisions. Use what you know about equivalent fractions to help you decide.

1. You want to stop cleaning your room and play with your new puppy instead. Would you rather have 15 minutes of cleaning left, or $\frac{1}{3}$ of an hour still remaining? **15 min**

2. Your best friend is coming over to play. Would you rather have 3 hours or $\frac{1}{6}$ of a day of playing time? **$\frac{1}{6}$ day**

3. You talked on the phone for $\frac{3}{4}$ of an hour today. Your sister talked for 40 minutes. Who should your parents be more annoyed with for talking on the phone too long, you or your sister? **you**

4. You have put it off long enough. Now it is time to practice the violin. Your brother says to practice for $\frac{2}{3}$ of an hour. So you ask your mother. She says 40 minutes is time enough. Whom will you listen to? Why? **Either, the two times are equivalent.**

5. Your friends Clark and Chuck had to spend Saturday doing homework and chores. Clark said he worked like a horse for $\frac{1}{4}$ of the day. Chuck complained that he was busy as a beaver for 5 hours. Who should you feel most sorry for, Clark or Chuck? **Clark**

TS-4 Use with text pages 340-341. 125

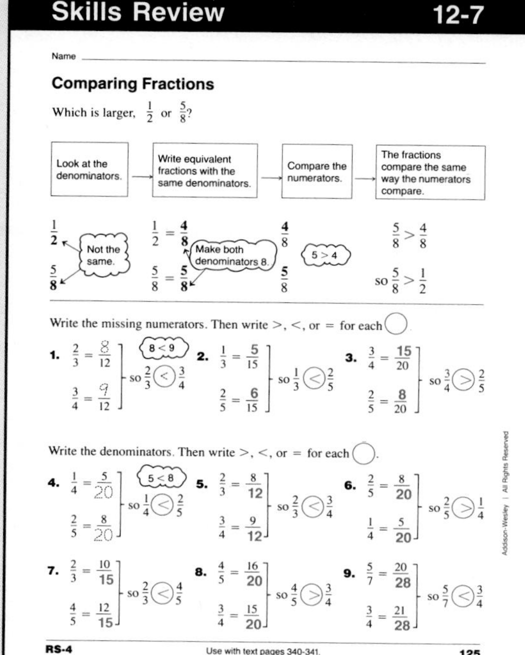

Reteaching

Skills Review 12-7

Name ______________________

Comparing Fractions

Which is larger, $\frac{1}{2}$ or $\frac{5}{8}$?

Look at the denominators. → Write equivalent fractions with the same denominators. → Compare the numerators. → The fractions compare the same way the numerators compare.

$\frac{1}{2}$, $\frac{5}{8}$ (Not the same.) — $\frac{1}{2} = \frac{4}{8}$, $\frac{5}{8} = \frac{5}{8}$ (Make both denominators 8.) — $\frac{4}{8}$, $\frac{5}{8}$ (5 > 4) — $\frac{5}{8} > \frac{4}{8}$ so $\frac{5}{8} > \frac{1}{2}$

Write the missing numerators. Then write >, <, or = for each ◯.

1. $\frac{2}{3} = \frac{8}{12}$, $\frac{3}{4} = \frac{9}{12}$ (8 < 9) so $\frac{2}{3}$ (<) $\frac{3}{4}$
2. $\frac{1}{3} = \frac{5}{15}$, $\frac{2}{5} = \frac{6}{15}$ so $\frac{1}{3}$ (<) $\frac{2}{5}$
3. $\frac{3}{4} = \frac{15}{20}$, $\frac{2}{5} = \frac{8}{20}$ so $\frac{3}{4}$ (>) $\frac{2}{5}$

Write the denominators. Then write >, <, or = for each ◯.

4. $\frac{1}{4} = \frac{5}{20}$, $\frac{2}{5} = \frac{8}{20}$ (5 < 8) so $\frac{1}{4}$ (<) $\frac{2}{5}$
5. $\frac{2}{3} = \frac{8}{12}$, $\frac{3}{4} = \frac{9}{12}$ so $\frac{2}{3}$ (<) $\frac{3}{4}$
6. $\frac{2}{5} = \frac{8}{20}$, $\frac{1}{4} = \frac{5}{20}$ so $\frac{2}{5}$ (>) $\frac{1}{4}$
7. $\frac{2}{3} = \frac{10}{15}$, $\frac{4}{5} = \frac{12}{15}$ so $\frac{2}{3}$ (<) $\frac{4}{5}$
8. $\frac{4}{5} = \frac{16}{20}$, $\frac{3}{4} = \frac{15}{20}$ so $\frac{4}{5}$ (>) $\frac{3}{4}$
9. $\frac{5}{7} = \frac{20}{28}$, $\frac{3}{4} = \frac{21}{28}$ so $\frac{5}{7}$ (<) $\frac{3}{4}$

RS-4 Use with text pages 340-341. 125

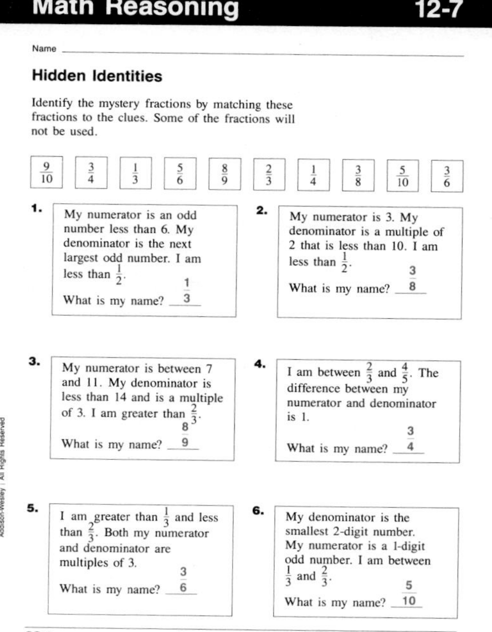

Challenges

Math Reasoning 12-7

Name ______________________

Hidden Identities

Identify the mystery fractions by matching these fractions to the clues. Some of the fractions will not be used.

$\frac{9}{10}$ $\frac{3}{4}$ $\frac{1}{3}$ $\frac{5}{6}$ $\frac{8}{9}$ $\frac{2}{3}$ $\frac{1}{4}$ $\frac{3}{8}$ $\frac{5}{10}$ $\frac{3}{6}$

1. My numerator is an odd number less than 6. My denominator is the next largest odd number. I am less than $\frac{1}{2}$. What is my name? $\frac{1}{3}$

2. My numerator is 3. My denominator is a multiple of 2 that is less than 10. I am less than $\frac{1}{2}$. What is my name? $\frac{3}{8}$

3. My numerator is between 7 and 11. My denominator is less than 14 and is a multiple of 3. I am greater than $\frac{2}{3}$. What is my name? $\frac{8}{9}$

4. I am between $\frac{2}{3}$ and $\frac{4}{5}$. The difference between my numerator and denominator is 1. What is my name? $\frac{3}{4}$

5. I am greater than $\frac{1}{3}$ and less than $\frac{2}{3}$. Both my numerator and denominator are multiples of 3. What is my name? $\frac{3}{6}$

6. My denominator is the smallest 2-digit number. My numerator is a 1-digit odd number. I am between $\frac{1}{3}$ and $\frac{2}{3}$. What is my name? $\frac{5}{10}$

CS-4 Use with text pages 340-341. 125

Options for Individual Needs

Basic

Exercises 1-14
More Practice, p. 509, set A

Supplements
Reteaching 125 or
Practice 125
Thinking Skills 125

Average

Exercises 1-16
More Practice, p. 509, set A

Supplements
Practice 125
Challenges 125 or
Thinking Skills 125

Extended

Exercises 1-15

Supplements
Challenges 125
Thinking Skills 125

Other Resources:
Problem-Solving Experiences in Mathematics, Grade 4, Problem 92
Mathematics, A Way of Thinking, Lesson 11-3
Mathematics, Book A, Teacher's Edition, pp. 69-71

12-7

LESSON PLAN 12-7

OBJECTIVE 12-7
To compare fractions

Materials: TA 12 (Centimeter Graph Paper), fraction pieces

Alternative Materials: TA 21 (Fraction Strips)

1. MOTIVATE AND TEACH

LEARN ABOUT IT

EXPLORE ► **Justify coloring 6 units to show $\frac{1}{2}$.** (There are 12 units in the strip, so 6 units are half.)
► **Explain how to construct a fraction strip for $\frac{1}{3}$.** ($\frac{1}{3}$ means 3 equal parts, so divide 12 by 3, which is 4 units per part.)
► **Analyze how this can help you make a strip for $\frac{2}{3}$.** ($\frac{1}{3}$ is 4 units, so $\frac{2}{3}$ is 8 units.)
► **Decide how you can make strips for $\frac{1}{4}$ and $\frac{3}{4}$.** ($\frac{1}{4}$ means 4 equal parts; $12 \div 4 = 3$, so $\frac{1}{4}$ of 12 units is 3 units per part; $\frac{3}{4}$ of 12 is three 3s, or 9 units.)

TALK ABOUT IT ► **Explain how to use the fraction strips to compare fractions.** (Lay strips side by side; the one with more colored parts represents the greater fraction.)
► **Justify writing equivalent fractions for $\frac{2}{3}$ and $\frac{3}{4}$ to compare them.** (Fractions with like denominators are easier to compare.)
Student Edition answers: **1.** Compare lengths. **2.** $\frac{2}{3} = \frac{8}{12}, \frac{3}{4} = \frac{9}{12}; \frac{9}{12} > \frac{8}{12}$

2. CHECK UNDERSTANDING

TRY IT OUT

ERROR ALERT Making incorrect comparisons. Confusing the < and > symbols.

Comparing Fractions

LEARN ABOUT IT

$\frac{1}{2}$

EXPLORE **Use Graph Paper**

- Cut some 12-unit strips from graph paper.
- Color a strip for each of these fractions.

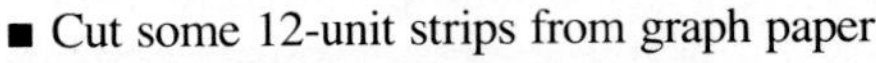

$\frac{1}{2}, \frac{1}{3}, \frac{1}{4}, \frac{1}{6}, \frac{1}{12}, \frac{2}{3}, \frac{3}{4}, \frac{5}{6}, \frac{5}{12}, \frac{7}{12}, \frac{11}{12}$

- Use your strips to help you complete some statements like these. $\frac{1}{2} < \frac{3}{4}$ $\frac{1}{2} > \frac{1}{3}$

TALK ABOUT IT See teaching notes.

1. How can you use the strips to show that $\frac{2}{3} < \frac{3}{4}$?
2. How can you look at your strips and easily write fractions with denominator 12 that are equivalent to $\frac{2}{3}$ and $\frac{3}{4}$? How can you use these fractions to show that $\frac{3}{4} > \frac{2}{3}$?

Three-sixths is less than five-sixths.

Fractions with the same denominator are easily compared on the number line.

0, $\frac{1}{6}$, $\frac{2}{6}$, $\frac{3}{6}$, $\frac{4}{6}$, $\frac{5}{6}$, 1

Fractions with unlike denominators can be compared by changing them to equivalent fractions with like denominators.

$\frac{1}{2} = \frac{3}{6}$ $\frac{1}{3} = \frac{2}{6}$

Since $\frac{3}{6} > \frac{2}{6}$, we know that $\frac{1}{2} > \frac{1}{3}$

TRY IT OUT

Write <, >, or = for each ▥. Use graph paper strips or write equivalent fractions to help you.

1. $\frac{1}{4}$ ▥ $\frac{1}{3}$ <
2. $\frac{2}{3}$ ▥ $\frac{1}{4}$ >
3. $\frac{5}{6}$ ▥ $\frac{7}{8}$ <

TEACHING OPTIONS

RETEACHING TIPS Have students use fraction pieces (or fraction strips) to compare fractions. The larger piece is always the greater fraction. Assign Reteaching Supplement 125.

ENRICHMENT Have students use their number sense to try to arrange these 3 unusual fractions from smallest to largest: $\frac{69}{115}, \frac{248}{310}, \frac{94}{235}$. To verify their chosen order, have students use a calculator to divide the numerator of each fraction by the denominator. ($\frac{94}{235} = 0.4$, $\frac{69}{115} = 0.6$, $\frac{248}{310} = 0.8$)

PRACTICE

Write $<$, $>$, or $=$ for each ▥.

1. $\frac{1}{3}$ ▥ $\frac{1}{2}$ $<$	**2.** $\frac{2}{5}$ ▥ $\frac{1}{2}$ $<$	**3.** $\frac{2}{6}$ ▥ $\frac{3}{9}$ $=$	**4.** $\frac{1}{4}$ ▥ $\frac{1}{5}$ $>$
5. $\frac{7}{8}$ ▥ $\frac{3}{4}$ $>$	**6.** $\frac{2}{8}$ ▥ $\frac{2}{3}$ $<$	**7.** $\frac{4}{20}$ ▥ $\frac{1}{4}$ $<$	**8.** $\frac{5}{8}$ ▥ $\frac{5}{6}$ $<$

APPLY

MATH REASONING

9. Which of these fractions are more than $\frac{1}{4}$ but less than $\frac{1}{2}$? $\frac{1}{6}, \frac{1}{5}, \frac{1}{3}, \frac{2}{3}, \frac{3}{8}$ $\frac{1}{3}$

PROBLEM SOLVING

10. Determining Reasonable Answers
Tell which of the answers seems reasonable. Sarah ate more than $\frac{1}{3}$ of a pizza and less than $\frac{2}{3}$ of it. The pizza was cut into sixths. How much could she have eaten?

a. $\frac{1}{4}$ pizza b. $\frac{5}{6}$ pizza c. $\frac{1}{2}$ pizza

d. none, there is no fraction between $\frac{1}{3}$ and $\frac{2}{3}$

MENTAL MATH

Think about pictures to help you discover a way to compare special fractions.

Which is bigger, $\frac{7}{8}$ or $\frac{5}{6}$? $\frac{7}{8}$

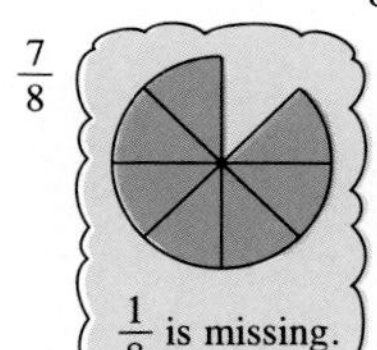

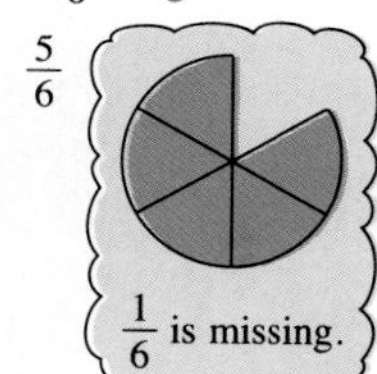

$\frac{1}{8}$ is smaller, so $\frac{7}{8}$ is greater than $\frac{5}{6}$.

Which is greater?

11. $\frac{3}{4}$ or $\frac{2}{3}$	**12.** $\frac{5}{6}$ or $\frac{8}{9}$
13. $\frac{9}{10}$ or $\frac{7}{8}$	**14.** $\frac{2}{3}$ or $\frac{5}{6}$
15. $\frac{4}{5}$ or $\frac{7}{8}$	**16.** $\frac{5}{7}$ or $\frac{3}{4}$

More Practice, page 509, set A

3. Practice and Apply

Basic	1-14
Average	1-16
Extended	1-15

PRACTICE

What do you notice about the denominators of the fractions you must compare? (They are not alike.)

APPLY

MATH REASONING ▶ **Decide what strategy would help you solve Exercise 9. Explain why.** (Possible answers: Draw a Picture, Use Models, Find Equivalent Fractions; any of these will help you compare the fractions to $\frac{1}{4}$ and $\frac{1}{2}$.)

PROBLEM SOLVING ▶ **Explain how you would analyze the situation in Problem 10.** (Possible answer: Draw a pizza cut in sixths; show how many pieces equal $\frac{1}{3}$ and $\frac{2}{3}$, then compare your picture with the choices given.)

MENTAL MATH ▶ **Explain how all the fractions in Exercises 11 to 16 are alike.** (Each fraction is one part less than 1 whole.)

12-7

Close and Assess

SHOW WHAT YOU KNOW

Have students use 2 methods to demonstrate how to compare $\frac{3}{4}$ to $\frac{2}{5}$ and $\frac{1}{4}$ to $\frac{2}{3}$. ($\frac{3}{4} > \frac{2}{5}$, $\frac{1}{4} < \frac{2}{3}$; Students may use fraction models or write equivalent fractions to show comparisons.)

QUICK QUIZ

Write $<$, $>$, or $=$.

1. $\frac{1}{2}$ ○ $\frac{4}{8}$ $(=)$	**2.** $\frac{1}{3}$ ○ $\frac{1}{5}$ $(>)$
3. $\frac{2}{3}$ ○ $\frac{1}{4}$ $(>)$	**4.** $\frac{1}{5}$ ○ $\frac{3}{10}$ $(<)$
5. $\frac{3}{4}$ ○ $\frac{7}{8}$ $(<)$	**6.** $\frac{3}{4}$ ○ $\frac{12}{16}$ $(=)$

Exploring Algebra/Midchapter Review Quiz

OBJECTIVE 12-8 To explore algebra by finding and graphing ordered pairs that make true equations

PREBOOK ACTIVITIES

QUICK REVIEW

Write two fractions equivalent to the given fraction. (Answers may vary; sample answers given.)

1. $\frac{1}{4}$ ($\frac{2}{8}$, $\frac{3}{12}$) **2.** $\frac{3}{8}$ ($\frac{6}{16}$, $\frac{9}{24}$)
3. $\frac{7}{10}$ ($\frac{14}{20}$, $\frac{21}{30}$) **4.** $\frac{5}{6}$ ($\frac{10}{12}$, $\frac{15}{18}$)
5. $\frac{11}{12}$ ($\frac{22}{24}$, $\frac{33}{36}$) **6.** $\frac{2}{9}$ ($\frac{4}{18}$, $\frac{6}{27}$)

PRIOR KNOWLEDGE

Have students recall how to read a number pair, such as (3, 5), and explain how to locate that point on a coordinate grid. [Start at (0, 0), count 3 spaces to the right. From there, count 5 spaces up to the point named (3, 5)]. Have students generalize a rule about the order used to locate points based on number pairs. (right, then up)

COMMUNICATION

Discussing Math Have students recall another mathematical term for number pairs. (coordinates) Tell students that still another term for number pair is *ordered pair*. Have students justify using that term for a number pair. (Possible answer: You plot or name points always using the order *right, then up;* so to call a number pair an ordered pair reminds you that order is very important.)

EXPLORE AND CONNECT

Materials: TA 3 (Number Cards 2, 4, 6, 8), TA 12 (Centimeter Graph Paper)
Grouping Suggestion: cooperative learning pairs
Students plot number pairs based on fractions equivalent to $\frac{1}{2}$. The first student picks a number card, which becomes the denominator of a fraction equivalent to $\frac{1}{2}$. The other student writes the appropriate numerator to complete the fraction. Partners then convert the fraction into a number pair, using the numerator as the first coordinate and the denominator as the second coordinate. They plot that point on a coordinate grid. Trading tasks, partners repeat the activity until four equivalent fractions have been found and plotted. [fractions: $\frac{1}{2}$, $\frac{2}{4}$, $\frac{3}{6}$, $\frac{4}{8}$; coordinates: (1, 2), (2, 4), (3, 6), (4, 8)] Conclude by having students describe a pattern the points make. (They make a straight line that rises diagonally to the right.)

CONNECTIONS Use these anytime.

Problem of the Day

Name Graphs Number the alphabet letters 1 to 26. Write the numbers for the letters in your first and last names. Then, starting with your first name, group 2 numbers at a time to form ordered pairs. If your name has an odd amount of letters, leave off the last letter. Use the pairs to plot and connect the points in your name. How does it look?

Patterns

Fraction Table Find a pattern to complete the table of numerators and denominators of equivalent fractions.

4	8	(12)	(16)	20	(24)
(7)	(14)	21	28	(35)	42

(Pattern: top row: multiples of 4; bottom row: multiples of 7)

Math Connection

Money Emily has 6 coins in her pocket. $\frac{1}{2}$ are nickels, $\frac{1}{3}$ are dimes, and $\frac{1}{6}$ are quarters. How much money does Emily have? (60 cents)

Classwork and Homework Supplements

Practice

Algebra 12-8

Name ______________________

Exploring Algebra

Write the numerators and denominators of a set of equivalent fractions as number pairs. Then graph them.

1. Fill in the table below. Replace □ and ○ with numbers to make fractions equivalent to $\frac{1}{3}$.

$\frac{1}{3} = \frac{□}{○}$

□	1	2	3	4	5	6	7
○	3	6	9	12	15	18	21

2. Write each of the pairs of numbers from the table as an ordered pair. Use the order (□, ○).

1,3 2,6
3,9 4,12
5,15 6,18
7,21

3. Graph the ordered pairs on the graph.

4. Connect the points on the graph. What do you notice?
They make a straight line.

126 Use with text page 342. PS-4

Building Thinking Skills

Algebra 12-8

Name ______________________

Connect the Dots

Use the graph to complete the following.

1. Ring the number pairs that could be written as part of a set of fractions equivalent to $\frac{1}{2}$.
(2, 6) (6, 12) (4, 8) — (6, 12) and (4, 8) ringed

2. Ring the fractions that can be written as number pairs that are graphed as points *B* and *C*.
$\frac{1}{6}$ $\frac{2}{4}$ $\frac{2}{12}$ — $\frac{1}{6}$ and $\frac{2}{12}$ ringed

3. Graph the number pair (4, 8). Label the point *I*.

4. Graph the number pair (6, 12). Label the point *K*.

5. Connect points *A, G, H, I, J,* and *K*. What fraction does the line show? $\frac{1}{2}$

6. Think of $\frac{1}{4}$ and a fraction equivalent to $\frac{1}{4}$, written as number pairs. Put 2 points on the graph for the number pairs and label them *E* and *F*. Connect the two points.

7. Look at the 2 lines you drew on the graph. Which is steeper, one for $\frac{1}{2}$ or $\frac{1}{4}$? $\frac{1}{4}$

126 Use with text page 342. TS-4

Reteaching

Algebra 12-8

Name ______________________

Exploring Algebra

You can graph fractions. Use the numerator and denominator as the ordered pair. $\frac{1}{3}$ can be written (1, 3).

1. Complete the table below. Replace △ and □ with numbers to make fractions equivalent to $\frac{1}{3}$.

$\frac{1}{3} = \frac{△}{□}$ Answers will vary. Possible answers given.

△	1	2	3	4
□	3	6	9	12

2. Write the pairs of numbers as an ordered pair. Use the order (△, □).
$\frac{1}{3}$ → (1, 3) $\frac{2}{6}$ → (2, 6)
$\frac{3}{9}$ → (3, 9) $\frac{4}{12}$ → (4, 12)

3. Graph the ordered pairs on the graph.

4. Connect the points on the graph. What do you notice?
The points form a straight line.

126 Use with text page 342. RS-4

Challenges

Algebra 12-8

Name ______________________

Which Is Steeper?

Tony graphed two sets of equivalent fractions. Look at the example.

Example:

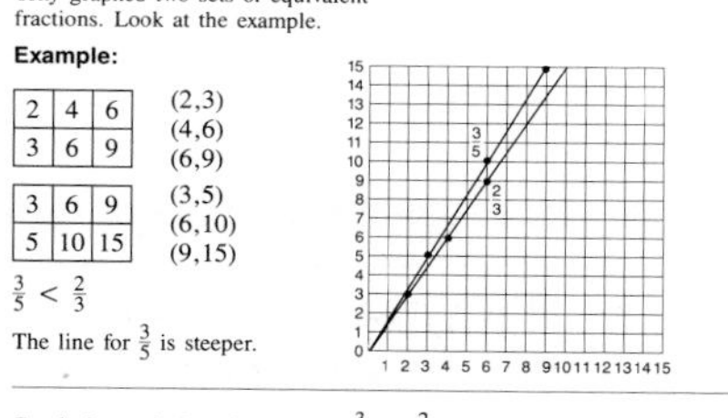

2	4	6
3	6	9

(2,3) (4,6) (6,9)

3	6	9
5	10	15

(3,5) (6,10) (9,15)

$\frac{3}{5} < \frac{2}{3}$

The line for $\frac{3}{5}$ is steeper.

Graph the equivalent fractions for $\frac{3}{4}$ and $\frac{2}{5}$. Write < or > in the circle next to the graph.

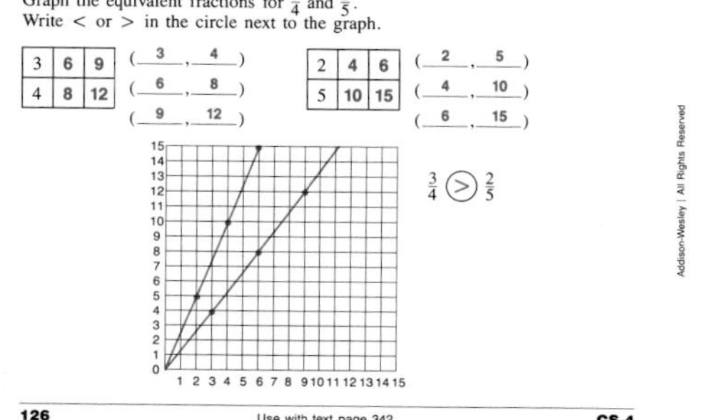

3	6	9
4	8	12

(3, 4) (6, 8) (9, 12)

2	4	6
5	10	15

(2, 5) (4, 10) (6, 15)

$\frac{3}{4} > \frac{2}{5}$

126 Use with text page 342. CS-4

Options for Individual Needs

Basic

Exercises 1-4; 1-12, 15-19

Supplements
Reteaching 126 or
Practice 126

Average

Exercises 1-4; 1-19

Supplements
Practice 126
Challenges 126 or
Thinking Skills 126

Extended

Exercises 1-4; 3-12, 15-19

Supplements
Challenges 126
Thinking Skills 126

Other Resources:
Problem-Solving Experiences in Mathematics, Grade 4, Problems 74, 75, 89, 99
Mathematics, A Way of Thinking, Lesson 11-7
Mathematics, Book A, Teacher's Edition, p. 75

LESSON PLAN 12-8

OBJECTIVE 12-8
To explore algebra by finding and graphing ordered pairs that make true equations

Materials: TA 12 (Centimeter Graph Paper), straight edge

1. MOTIVATE AND TEACH

LEARN ABOUT IT

▶ **Analyze the pattern in each row of the table.** (△ row has multiples of 2, □ row has multiples of 3.)
▶ **Explain the relationship between the table and the number pairs.** (The first number in the pair is a multiple of 2, the second number is the corresponding multiple of 3.)
▶ **Decide what the second number in a pair would be if the first number is 20.** (30)
▶ **Explain how to graph coordinates such as (2, 3).** (Start at 0, go to the right 2 spaces, then up 3 spaces; make a dot at that point on the graph.)
Student Edition answers: **1.** △: 2, 4, 6, 8, 10, 12, 14; □: 3, 6, 9, 12, 15, 18, 21 **2.** Check students' graphs; the points make a straight line rising diagonally to the right.

2. CHECK UNDERSTANDING

ERROR ALERT Plotting points incorrectly.

Exploring Algebra

LEARN ABOUT IT

Suppose you write the numerators and denominators of a set of equivalent fractions as number pairs. Then you graph them. What do you notice about the points?

1. Copy the table below. Write numbers for △ and □.

$$\frac{2}{3} = \frac{\triangle}{\square}$$

△	2	4	6				
□	3	6	9				

2. Graph the number pairs (△, □) from the table above on a graph like this.
3. Connect the points on the graph. What do you notice? **The points make a straight line.**
4. Repeat using the fraction $\frac{2}{5}$. What do you notice about this graph? **The points make a straight line.**

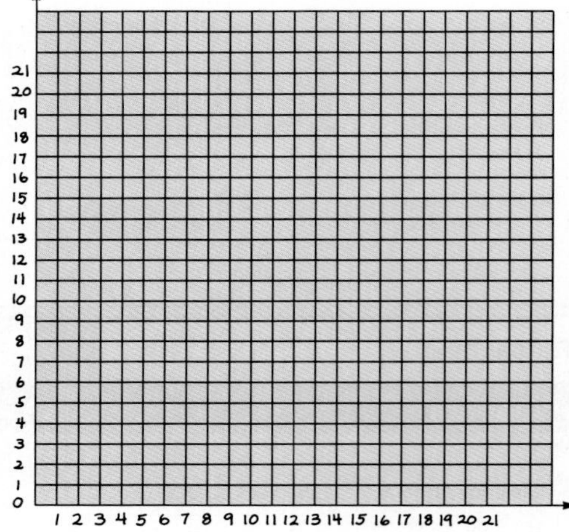

TEACHING OPTIONS

RETEACHING TIPS Students verbalize the rule for plotting number pairs: First right, then up. First they find the number in the △ row of the table to count *right* along the △ row of the graph. Then they count *up* the corresponding number in the □ row of the table. Assign Reteaching Supplement 126.

ENRICHMENT Have students make two graphs based on fractions as number pairs. For one, they use *unit* fractions: $\frac{1}{2}$, $\frac{1}{3}$, $\frac{1}{4}$, $\frac{1}{5}$, $\frac{1}{6}$, $\frac{1}{7}$, $\frac{1}{8}$. For the other, they use eighths: $\frac{1}{8}$ to $\frac{8}{8}$. Have them predict how the graphs will look before they begin. (Units make a vertical line; eighths make a horizontal line.)

Midchapter Review/Quiz

Write fractions to tell what part is red and what part is blue. **See Additional Answers.**

1. 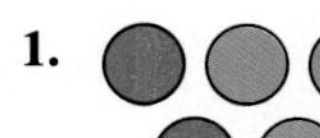

2. 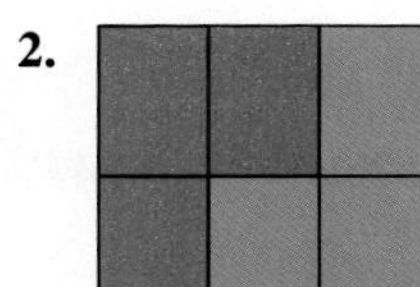

3. 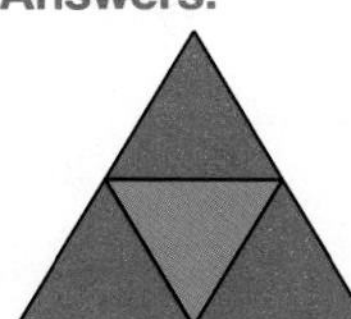

Copy and complete the equations.

4.  $\frac{1}{2} = \frac{\square}{8}$ 4

5. 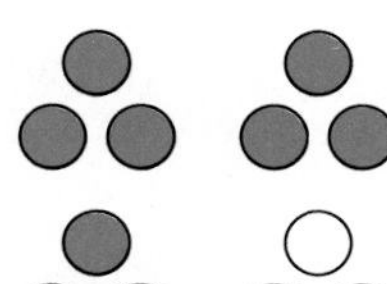 $\frac{3}{4} = \frac{\square}{12}$ 9

Find equivalent fractions.

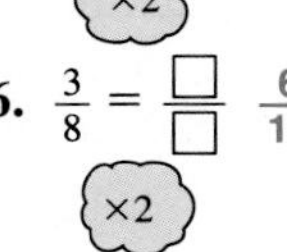

6. $\frac{3}{8} = \frac{\square}{\square}$ (×2) $\frac{6}{16}$
7. $\frac{1}{6} = \frac{\square}{\square}$ (×3) $\frac{3}{18}$
8. $\frac{1}{2} = \frac{\square}{\square}$ (×5) $\frac{5}{10}$
9. $\frac{3}{10} = \frac{\square}{\square}$ (×4) $\frac{12}{40}$

Reduce each fraction to lowest terms.

10. $\frac{6}{20}$ $\frac{3}{10}$
11. $\frac{12}{32}$ $\frac{3}{8}$
12. $\frac{5}{30}$ $\frac{1}{6}$
13. $\frac{15}{18}$ $\frac{5}{6}$
14. $\frac{16}{24}$ $\frac{2}{3}$

Write < or > for each ▥.

15. $\frac{1}{3}$ ▥ $\frac{1}{4}$ >
16. $\frac{2}{3}$ ▥ $\frac{3}{4}$ <
17. $\frac{2}{5}$ ▥ $\frac{2}{3}$ <
18. $\frac{3}{5}$ ▥ $\frac{2}{3}$ <

PROBLEM SOLVING

19. Nicholas ate $\frac{1}{3}$ of the pizza, Sebastian ate $\frac{3}{8}$, and Christine ate $\frac{7}{24}$. Did Sebastian eat the most? Tell how you know.
yes. $\frac{3}{8} > \frac{1}{3}$ **and** $\frac{3}{8} > \frac{7}{24}$

343

3. Practice and Apply

Basic	1-4; 1-12, 15-19
Average	1-4; 1-19
Extended	1-4; 3-12, 15-19

Additional Answers: See p. T79.

PRACTICE

How would you begin to solve Exercises 1 to 3? (Find the denominator for each fraction.) *How do you use the numbers in clouds in Exercises 6 to 9?* (Multiply numerators and denominators by them to form equivalent fractions.) *How are Exercises 15 to 18 like Problem 19?* (For all of them, you must make equivalent fractions to compare fractions with unlike denominators.)

ITEM ANALYSIS The following table correlates the Midchapter Review/Quiz items with the lesson objectives.

Items	Objectives
1	12-2
2	12-1
3	12-2
4, 5	12-4
6-9	12-5
10-14	12-6
15-19	12-7

12-8

Close and Assess

SHOW WHAT YOU KNOW

Have students find three equivalent fractions based on this graph. ($\frac{1}{3}$, $\frac{2}{6}$, $\frac{3}{9}$)

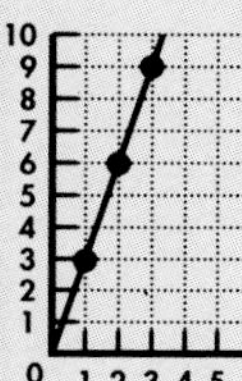

Quick Quiz

Graph the number pairs for 5 fractions equivalent to $\frac{3}{4}$. Then connect the points and describe the graph. (Graphs may vary; the points form a straight line rising diagonally to the right.)

LESSON OPTIONS 12-9

Mental Math: Finding a Fraction of a Number

OBJECTIVE 12-9 To use mental math to find a fraction of a number

PREBOOK ACTIVITIES

QUICK REVIEW

Divide:

1. 18 ÷ 6	(3)	**2.** 24 ÷ 8	(3)
3. 25 ÷ 5	(5)	**4.** 36 ÷ 4	(9)
5. 27 ÷ 9	(3)	**6.** 16 ÷ 2	(8)
7. 28 ÷ 4	(7)	**8.** 14 ÷ 2	(7)
9. 20 ÷ 4	(5)	**10.** 32 ÷ 8	(4)

PRIOR KNOWLEDGE

Have students give real-life examples of fractions used to describe amounts of a group. (Sample answer: $\frac{1}{2}$ of the class sits facing the window.) Ask students to explain how to determine the number of students in $\frac{1}{2}$ of the class and to give their reasoning. (Divide the number of students by 2, since *half* means "2 equal parts.")

COMMUNICATION

Discussing Math Have students relate fractions to division. (Possible answer: Fractions describe something divided into equal parts, which is the same action as division.) Have students apply their understanding of fractions to reason how to find $\frac{1}{3}$ of a number and to explain the result. (If you divide by 3, the quotient will be $\frac{1}{3}$ of the original number.)

EXPLORE AND CONNECT

Materials: counters

Grouping Suggestion: cooperative learning pairs

Students explore finding fractions of a set of objects. Each pair needs 24 counters. Write these fractions on the chalkboard: $\frac{1}{2}$, $\frac{1}{3}$, $\frac{1}{4}$, $\frac{1}{6}$, $\frac{1}{8}$, $\frac{1}{12}$. Partners work to find each fraction of 24. For instance, to find $\frac{1}{3}$ of 24, students may discuss that $\frac{1}{3}$ means "1 out of 3 equal parts." They show the 24 counters arranged in 3 equal groups, or thirds, then count the number in each group. (8) After pairs model $\frac{1}{3}$ of 24, they record an equation, such as $\frac{1}{3}$ of 24 = 8. Pairs repeat the task for each fraction on the list, taking turns using the counters and recording the results. Conclude by having students share the results, relating fractions and division. (To find a fraction of a set of objects, divide by the denominator.) Challenge the class to use logical reasoning to find $\frac{2}{3}$ of 24. (If $\frac{1}{3}$ of 24 = 8, then $\frac{2}{3}$ of 24 would mean 2 of the 3 equal parts, or 2 × 8 = 16.)

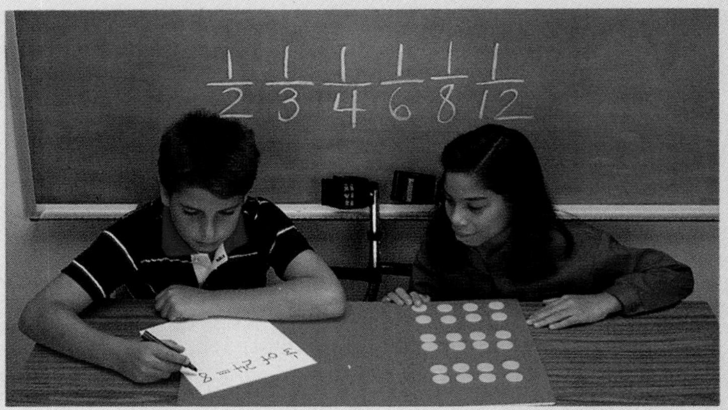

CONNECTIONS Use these anytime.

Problem of the Day

Creative Thinking Jerry had 80 comics. He donated $\frac{1}{2}$ to the school fair. Then he gave $\frac{1}{2}$ of what was left to his cousin, Judy. Then he traded $\frac{1}{2}$ of what was left to his neighbor for a Frisbee and kept the rest for himself. How many comics did Jerry keep? (10)

Subject Interpretation

Health and Fitness Every day, Pete and Nan do sit-ups before breakfast. Nan does 50 sit-ups, and Pete does 60. One day, Nan did only $\frac{1}{2}$ of her routine, and Pete did just $\frac{1}{3}$ of his routine. Who did more sit-ups? How many more? (Nan did 25, and Pete did 20, so Nan did 5 more.)

Math Connection

Measurement Which is more, $\frac{1}{2}$ of 1 year or 180 days? Explain your reasoning.
($\frac{1}{2}$ of 1 year; 1 year has 365 days and 365 ÷ 2 = 182 R1.)

CLASSWORK AND HOMEWORK SUPPLEMENTS

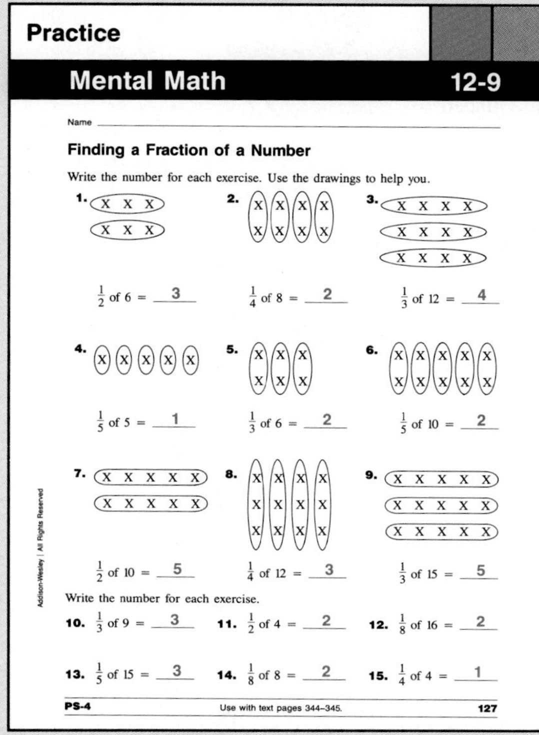

Practice

Mental Math 12-9

Name

Finding a Fraction of a Number

Write the number for each exercise. Use the drawings to help you.

1. $\frac{1}{2}$ of 6 = 3
2. $\frac{1}{4}$ of 8 = 2
3. $\frac{1}{3}$ of 12 = 4
4. $\frac{1}{5}$ of 5 = 1
5. $\frac{1}{3}$ of 6 = 2
6. $\frac{1}{5}$ of 10 = 2
7. $\frac{1}{2}$ of 10 = 5
8. $\frac{1}{4}$ of 12 = 3
9. $\frac{1}{3}$ of 15 = 5

Write the number for each exercise.

10. $\frac{1}{3}$ of 9 = 3
11. $\frac{1}{2}$ of 4 = 2
12. $\frac{1}{8}$ of 16 = 2
13. $\frac{1}{5}$ of 15 = 3
14. $\frac{1}{4}$ of 8 = 2
15. $\frac{1}{4}$ of 4 = 1

Addison-Wesley | All Rights Reserved

PS-4 Use with text pages 344-345. 127

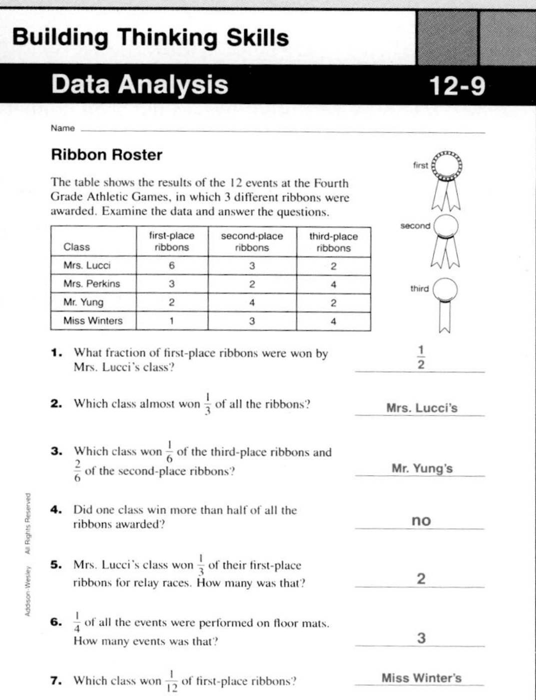

Building Thinking Skills

Data Analysis 12-9

Name

Ribbon Roster

The table shows the results of the 12 events at the Fourth Grade Athletic Games, in which 3 different ribbons were awarded. Examine the data and answer the questions.

Class	first-place ribbons	second-place ribbons	third-place ribbons
Mrs. Lucci	6	3	2
Mrs. Perkins	3	2	4
Mr. Yung	2	4	2
Miss Winters	1	3	4

1. What fraction of first-place ribbons were won by Mrs. Lucci's class? $\frac{1}{2}$
2. Which class almost won $\frac{1}{3}$ of all the ribbons? Mrs. Lucci's
3. Which class won $\frac{1}{6}$ of the third-place ribbons and $\frac{2}{6}$ of the second-place ribbons? Mr. Yung's
4. Did one class win more than half of all the ribbons awarded? no
5. Mrs. Lucci's class won $\frac{1}{3}$ of their first-place ribbons for relay races. How many was that? 2
6. $\frac{1}{4}$ of all the events were performed on floor mats. How many events was that? 3
7. Which class won $\frac{1}{12}$ of first-place ribbons? Miss Winter's

Addison-Wesley | All Rights Reserved

TS-4 Use with text pages 344-345. 127

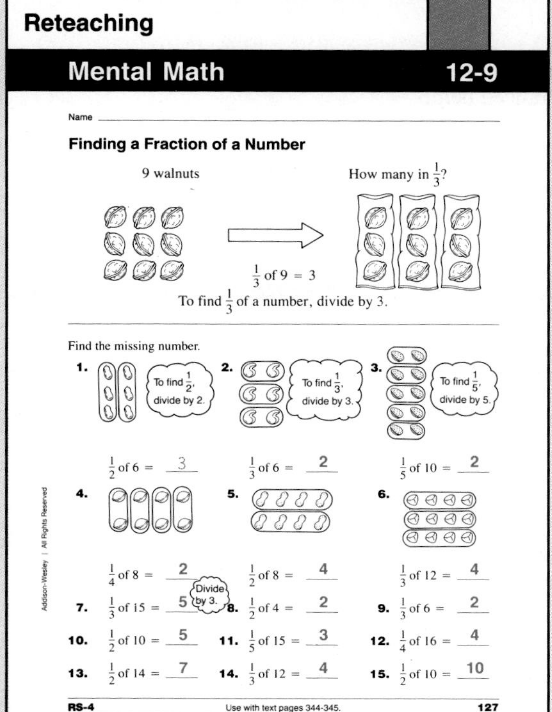

Reteaching

Mental Math 12-9

Name

Finding a Fraction of a Number

To find $\frac{1}{3}$ of a number, divide by 3.

Find the missing number.

1. $\frac{1}{2}$ of 6 = 3
2. $\frac{1}{3}$ of 6 = 2
3. $\frac{1}{5}$ of 10 = 2
4. $\frac{1}{4}$ of 8 = 2
5. $\frac{1}{2}$ of 8 = 4
6. $\frac{1}{3}$ of 12 = 4
7. $\frac{1}{3}$ of 15 = 5
8. $\frac{1}{2}$ of 4 = 2
9. $\frac{1}{3}$ of 6 = 2
10. $\frac{1}{2}$ of 10 = 5
11. $\frac{1}{5}$ of 15 = 3
12. $\frac{1}{4}$ of 16 = 4
13. $\frac{1}{2}$ of 14 = 7
14. $\frac{1}{3}$ of 12 = 4
15. $\frac{1}{2}$ of 10 = 10

Addison-Wesley | All Rights Reserved

RS-4 Use with text pages 344-345. 127

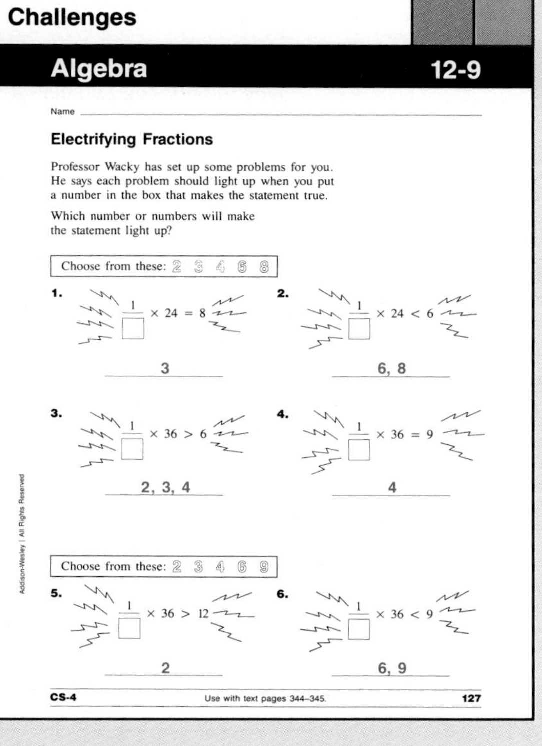

Challenges

Algebra 12-9

Name

Electrifying Fractions

Professor Wacky has set up some problems for you. He says each problem should light up when you put a number in the box that makes the statement true.

Which number or numbers will make the statement light up?

Choose from these: 2 3 4 6 8

1. $\frac{1}{\square} \times 24 = 8$ — 3
2. $\frac{1}{\square} \times 24 < 6$ — 6, 8
3. $\frac{1}{\square} \times 36 > 6$ — 2, 3, 4
4. $\frac{1}{\square} \times 36 = 9$ — 4

Choose from these: 2 3 4 6 9

5. $\frac{1}{\square} \times 36 > 12$ — 2
6. $\frac{1}{\square} \times 36 < 9$ — 6, 9

Addison-Wesley | All Rights Reserved

CS-4 Use with text pages 344-345. 127

OPTIONS FOR INDIVIDUAL NEEDS

Basic

Exercises 1-10
Skills Bank, p. 465
Calculator Bank, p. 487
Computer Bank, p. 497
More Practice, p. 509, set B

Supplements
Reteaching 127 or
Practice 127

Average

Exercises 1-11
Skills Bank, p. 465
Calculator Bank, p. 487
Computer Bank, p. 497
More Practice, p. 509, set B

Supplements
Practice 127
Challenges 127 or
Thinking Skills 127

Extended

Exercises 2-11
Calculator Bank, p. 487
Computer Bank, p. 497

Supplements
Challenges 127
Thinking Skills 127

Other Resources:
Problem-Solving Experiences in Mathematics, Grade 4, Problem 94
Mathematics, A Way of Thinking, Lesson 11-13
Using The Math Explorer Calculator: A Sourcebook for Teachers, Chapter 14

12-9

LESSON PLAN 12-9

OBJECTIVE 12-9
To use mental math to find a fraction of a number

Materials: calculators, counters

1. MOTIVATE AND TEACH

LEARN ABOUT IT

EXPLORE ► **Compare $\frac{1}{4}$ of all the walnut shell animals to $\frac{1}{4}$ of 1 animal.** ($\frac{1}{4}$ of 1 animal would mean cutting it into 4 pieces; $\frac{1}{4}$ of all the animals means dividing the set into 4 parts and discussing the number of animals in 1 part.)

TALK ABOUT IT ► **Analyze how finding $\frac{1}{4}$ of 8 relates to a division fact.** ($8 \div 4 = 2$)
► **Explain how many walnut shell animals are in each fourth.** (2, because 2 per part multiplied by 4 parts equals the total of 8 animals.)
► **How many animals would be in $\frac{2}{4}$? in $\frac{3}{4}$? Explain your reasoning.** (4; 6; Each $\frac{1}{4}$ has 2 animals, so $\frac{2}{4}$ is 2×2, or 4, and $\frac{3}{4}$ is 3×2, or 6.)
► **Generalize about how to find a fraction about a number of objects.** (Sample answer: Divide by the denominator to make equal parts, then multiply by the numerator.)
Student Edition answers: **1.** 4 **2.** 2; $\frac{1}{4}$ of 8 = 2.

2. CHECK UNDERSTANDING

TRY IT OUT

ERROR ALERT Forgetting to multiply by the numerator with non-unit fractions. Using the wrong operation.

Mental Math
Finding a Fraction of a Number

LEARN ABOUT IT

EXPLORE Think About the Situation
Annie decided to give her friend Samantha $\frac{1}{4}$ of her walnut shell animals. She placed them in these four groups.

TALK ABOUT IT See teaching notes.

1. Into how many equal parts did Annie divide her walnut shell animals?
2. How many animals will Annie give Samantha? Explain how you decided.

You can find $\frac{1}{2}$ of a number by dividing the number by 2.

To find $\frac{1}{3}$ of the number, divide it by 3.

To find $\frac{1}{4}$, divide by 4.

Here is how to find $\frac{3}{4}$ of a number.

■ First find $\frac{1}{4}$ of the number

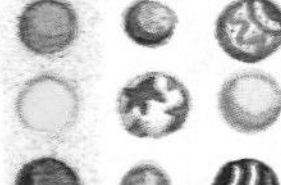
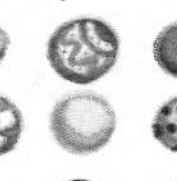
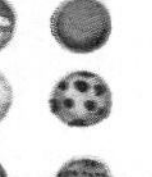
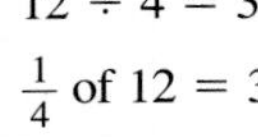

$12 \div 4 = 3$

$\frac{1}{4}$ of 12 = 3

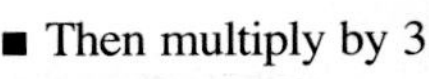

■ Then multiply by 3.

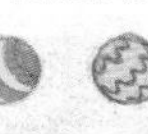
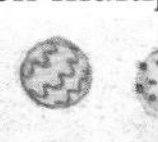
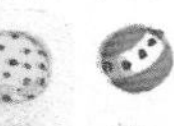
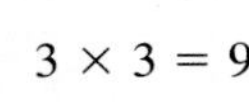
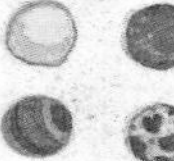
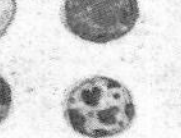
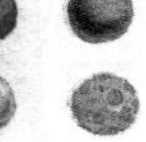
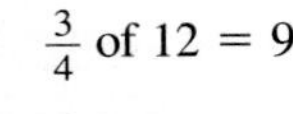

$3 \times 3 = 9$

$\frac{3}{4}$ of 12 = 9

TRY IT OUT

Find the missing number. If you need help, draw or use objects.

1. $\frac{1}{3}$ of 9 = |||| **3** $\frac{2}{3}$ of 9 = |||| **6**
2. $\frac{1}{4}$ of 12 = |||| **3** $\frac{3}{4}$ of 12 = |||| **9**

TEACHING OPTIONS

RETEACHING TIPS For Exercise 1, have students show $\frac{1}{3}$ of 9 with counters by dividing 9 into 3 parts, as the denominator indicates. Then have them verbalize that since $\frac{2}{3}$ means 2 of the 3 parts, they must find the total value of 2 of the thirds, or $2 \times 3 = 6$. Assign Reteaching Supplement 127.

ENRICHMENT Give students the following problem to solve: *Sean has 8 coins. $\frac{1}{8}$ of the coins are quarters, $\frac{3}{8}$ are nickels, $\frac{1}{4}$ are pennies, and $\frac{1}{4}$ are dimes. Determine the amount of money he has.* Hint: *Draw a picture if it will help.* (62¢)

PRACTICE

Give the number for each ▥. Use the drawings or objects to help you.

1. $\frac{1}{4}$ of 8 = ▥ 2 $\frac{3}{4}$ of 8 = ▥ 6   **2.** $\frac{1}{5}$ of 10 = ▥ 2 $\frac{3}{5}$ of 10 = ▥ 6

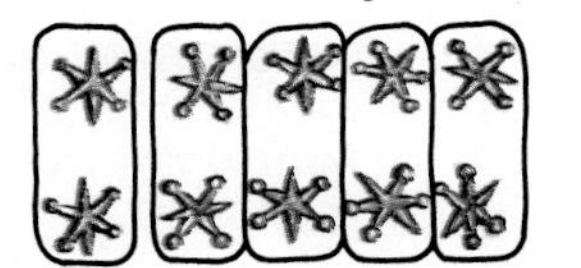

Give the number for each exercise.

3. $\frac{1}{2}$ of 14 7   **4.** $\frac{1}{8}$ of 32 4   **5.** $\frac{2}{5}$ of 20 8   **6.** $\frac{5}{6}$ of 36 30

APPLY

MATH REASONING

7. If this is $\frac{1}{3}$ of Carla's elf doll collection, how many elf dolls does she have in all? 12

PROBLEM SOLVING

8. Missing Data Tell what information you need to be able to solve this problem. Troy has 4 stamps with presidents on them, 8 space stamps, and the rest are stamps of inventors. What fraction of the stamps are space stamps? total number of stamps

► **CALCULATOR**

You can use your calculator to find a fraction of a number.

To find $\frac{2}{3}$ of 126

Divide by the denominator. Enter: [ON/AC] 126 [÷] 3 [=] 42

Multiply by the numerator. Enter: [ON/AC] 42 [×] 2 [=] 84

9. $\frac{3}{4}$ of 312 234   **10.** $\frac{7}{8}$ of 3,648 3,192   **11.** $\frac{2}{5}$ of 755 302

More Practice, page 509, set B

3. Practice and Apply

Basic	1-10
Average	1-11
Extended	2-11

PRACTICE

Contrast Exercises 3 and 4 with Exercises 5 and 6. (The fractions in Exercises 3 and 4 have numerators of 1; the numerators in Exercises 5 and 6 are 2 and 5.)

APPLY

MATH REASONING ► **Analyze the situation.** (The picture shows only a part of Carla's collection.)

PROBLEM SOLVING ► **Explain why you need more data.** (You must know how many stamps of inventors Troy has to find the total number of stamps. Then you can find a fraction of that total.)

CALCULATOR ► **Explain how the calculator steps relate to the mental math you use to find fractions of a number.** (They are exactly the same—divide first by the denominator, then multiply by the numerator.)

12-9

Close and Assess

WRITE WHAT YOU THINK

Have students write the steps to follow to find $\frac{1}{3}$ of 15 and $\frac{3}{4}$ of 20. Have them draw a picture to go with each example. (Check students' writing; 5, 15)

QUICK QUIZ

Give the number for each exercise.

1. $\frac{1}{2}$ of 18 (9)   **2.** $\frac{1}{4}$ of 20 (5)
3. $\frac{1}{4}$ of 28 (7)   **4.** $\frac{1}{5}$ of 35 (7)
5. $\frac{2}{3}$ of 15 (10)   **6.** $\frac{3}{5}$ of 25 (15)
7. $\frac{5}{6}$ of 24 (20)   **8.** $\frac{3}{4}$ of 36 (27)

LESSON OPTIONS 12-10

Mixed Numbers

OBJECTIVE 12-10 To understand a mixed number

PREBOOK ACTIVITIES

QUICK REVIEW

Use mental math to find each quotient and remainder.

1. $4\overline{)9}$ (2 R1)	**2.** $3\overline{)11}$ (3 R2)	**3.** $5\overline{)16}$ (3 R1)
4. $2\overline{)9}$ (4 R1)	**5.** $6\overline{)27}$ (4 R3)	**6.** $9\overline{)15}$ (1 R6)
7. $5\overline{)32}$ (6 R2)	**8.** $3\overline{)22}$ (7 R1)	**9.** $4\overline{)30}$ (7 R2)
10. $8\overline{)9}$ (1 R1)	**11.** $7\overline{)37}$ (5 R2)	**12.** $6\overline{)37}$ (6 R1)

PRIOR KNOWLEDGE

Generate with students a list of numbers they have heard or used that combine whole numbers and fractions, such as $4\frac{1}{2}$. (Answers may vary. Samples: The exit is $2\frac{1}{2}$ more miles; Ian is $8\frac{1}{2}$ years old; measure $2\frac{3}{4}$ cups of flour.)

COMMUNICATION

Discussing and Reading Math Write these numbers on the chalkboard and ask students to classify them: $\frac{7}{6}$, $2\frac{3}{4}$, $5\frac{1}{2}$, $\frac{8}{5}$. ($2\frac{3}{4}$ and $5\frac{1}{2}$; $\frac{7}{6}$ and $\frac{8}{5}$) Have students give their reasoning. ($2\frac{3}{4}$ and $5\frac{1}{2}$ combine whole numbers and fractions; $\frac{7}{6}$ and $\frac{8}{5}$ are fractions.) Ask students what is unusual about the fractions. (The numerators are greater than the denominators.) Write **improper fraction** and **mixed number** on the chalkboard. Challenge students to use logical reasoning to match each expression with the numbers it describes and to explain their thinking. ($2\frac{3}{4}$ and $5\frac{1}{2}$ are mixed numbers because they mix whole numbers and fractions; $\frac{7}{6}$ and $\frac{8}{5}$ are improper fractions because their numerators are greater than their denominators.)

EXPLORE AND CONNECT

Materials: fraction pieces for fourths, TA 3 (Number Cards 4-9)
Alternative Materials: TA 21 (Fraction Strips)
Grouping Suggestion: cooperative learning groups of 4
Students explore **improper fractions** and **mixed numbers**. The first student picks a number card, such as 7, and takes that many fourths. The second student writes a fraction whose denominator is 4 and whose numerator is the chosen number. ($\frac{7}{4}$) The third student forms the fraction pieces into as many wholes as possible; the fourth student records the number of wholes and the number of fourths left over. ($1\frac{3}{4}$) Trading tasks, students repeat the activity 3 times. Have students relate *improper fractions* and *mixed numbers*. (*Improper fractions* and *mixed numbers* describe amounts more than 1 whole; *improper fractions* give a total amount of *fractional parts*; *mixed numbers* tell how many wholes and how many fractional parts.)

CONNECTIONS Use these anytime.

Problem of the Day

Birthdays Roberto's birthday is 1 month away. He will be 10 years old. Determine his age now in years and months. Then write the number of months as a fraction that follows the number of years old Roberto is. *Hint:* 1 year = 12 months. ($9\frac{11}{12}$)

Life Skills

Meal Planning There are 6 people in the Roth family. Mr. Roth plans to serve $\frac{1}{4}$ of a honeydew melon to each family member for dessert. How many fourths are needed? How many melons should Mr. Roth buy? Describe any leftovers. ($\frac{6}{4}$, 2, $\frac{2}{4}$, or $\frac{1}{2}$ melon left)

Math Connection

Time Joelle roller-skated for $1\frac{1}{2}$ hour. How many minutes did she skate? (90 minutes)

Classwork and Homework Supplements

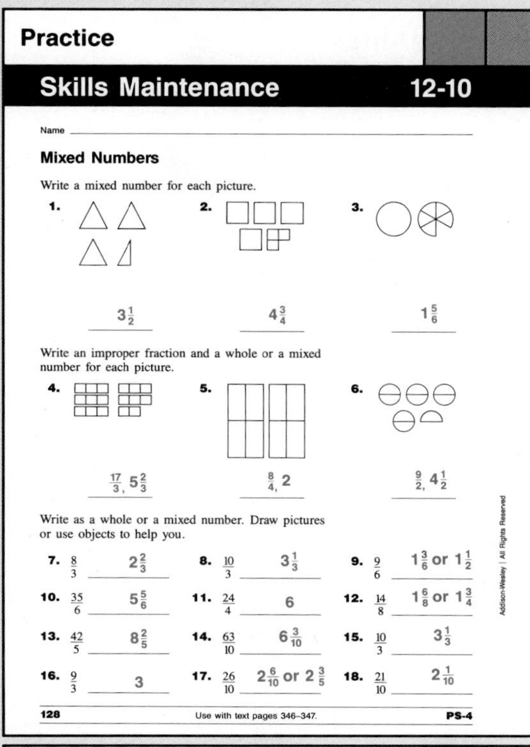

Practice
Skills Maintenance 12-10

Name ____________

Mixed Numbers

Write a mixed number for each picture.

1. $3\frac{1}{2}$ 2. $4\frac{3}{4}$ 3. $1\frac{5}{6}$

Write an improper fraction and a whole or a mixed number for each picture.

4. $\frac{17}{3}$, $5\frac{2}{3}$ 5. $\frac{8}{4}$, 2 6. $\frac{9}{2}$, $4\frac{1}{2}$

Write as a whole or a mixed number. Draw pictures or use objects to help you.

7. $\frac{8}{3}$ $2\frac{2}{3}$ 8. $\frac{10}{3}$ $3\frac{1}{3}$ 9. $\frac{9}{6}$ $1\frac{3}{6}$ or $1\frac{1}{2}$
10. $\frac{35}{6}$ $5\frac{5}{6}$ 11. $\frac{24}{4}$ 6 12. $\frac{14}{8}$ $1\frac{6}{8}$ or $1\frac{3}{4}$
13. $\frac{42}{5}$ $8\frac{2}{5}$ 14. $\frac{63}{10}$ $6\frac{3}{10}$ 15. $\frac{10}{3}$ $3\frac{1}{3}$
16. $\frac{9}{3}$ 3 17. $\frac{26}{10}$ $2\frac{6}{10}$ or $2\frac{3}{5}$ 18. $\frac{21}{10}$ $2\frac{1}{10}$

128 Use with text pages 346-347. PS-4

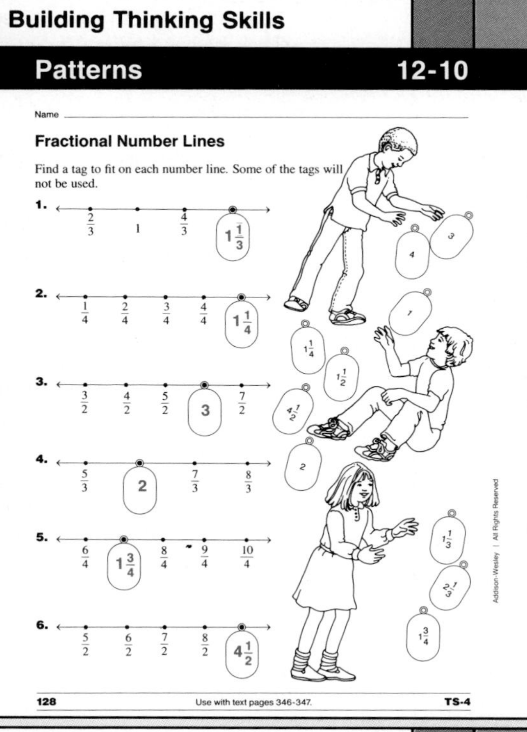

Building Thinking Skills
Patterns 12-10

Name ____________

Fractional Number Lines

Find a tag to fit on each number line. Some of the tags will not be used.

1. $\frac{2}{3}$, 1, $\frac{4}{3}$, $1\frac{1}{3}$
2. $\frac{1}{4}$, $\frac{2}{4}$, $\frac{3}{4}$, $\frac{4}{4}$, $1\frac{1}{4}$
3. $\frac{3}{2}$, $\frac{4}{2}$, $\frac{5}{2}$, 3, $\frac{7}{2}$
4. $\frac{5}{3}$, 2, $\frac{7}{3}$, $\frac{8}{3}$
5. $\frac{6}{4}$, $1\frac{3}{4}$, $\frac{8}{4}$, $\frac{9}{4}$, $\frac{10}{4}$
6. $\frac{5}{2}$, $\frac{6}{2}$, $\frac{7}{2}$, $\frac{8}{2}$, $4\frac{1}{2}$

128 Use with text pages 346-347. TS-4

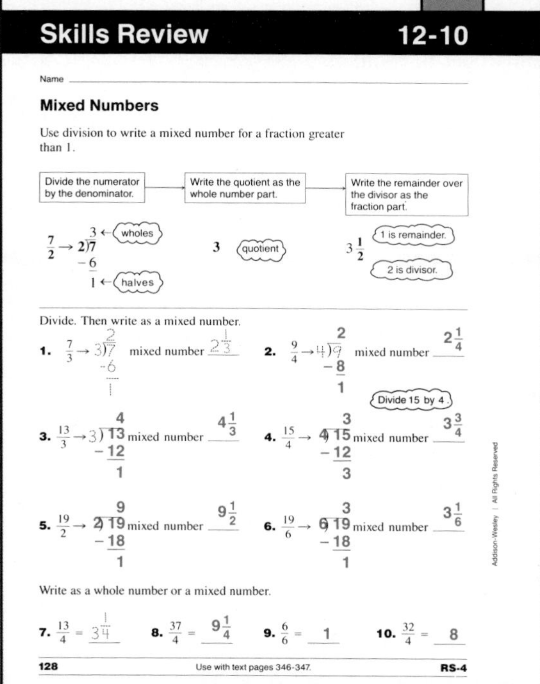

Reteaching
Skills Review 12-10

Name ____________

Mixed Numbers

Use division to write a mixed number for a fraction greater than 1.

Divide the numerator by the denominator. → Write the quotient as the whole number part. → Write the remainder over the divisor as the fraction part.

$\frac{7}{2} \rightarrow 2\overline{)7}$ = 3 (wholes), − 6, 1 (halves) 3 (quotient) $3\frac{1}{2}$ (1 is remainder.) (2 is divisor.)

Divide. Then write as a mixed number.

1. $\frac{7}{3} \rightarrow 3\overline{)7}$ mixed number $2\frac{1}{3}$
2. $\frac{9}{4} \rightarrow 4\overline{)9}$ mixed number $2\frac{1}{4}$
3. $\frac{13}{3} \rightarrow 3\overline{)13}$ mixed number $4\frac{1}{3}$
4. $\frac{15}{4} \rightarrow 4\overline{)15}$ mixed number $3\frac{3}{4}$ (Divide 15 by 4)
5. $\frac{19}{2} \rightarrow 2\overline{)19}$ mixed number $9\frac{1}{2}$
6. $\frac{19}{6} \rightarrow 6\overline{)19}$ mixed number $3\frac{1}{6}$

Write as a whole number or a mixed number.

7. $\frac{13}{4} = 3\frac{1}{4}$ 8. $\frac{37}{4} = 9\frac{1}{4}$ 9. $\frac{6}{6} = 1$ 10. $\frac{32}{4} = 8$

128 Use with text pages 346-347. RS-4

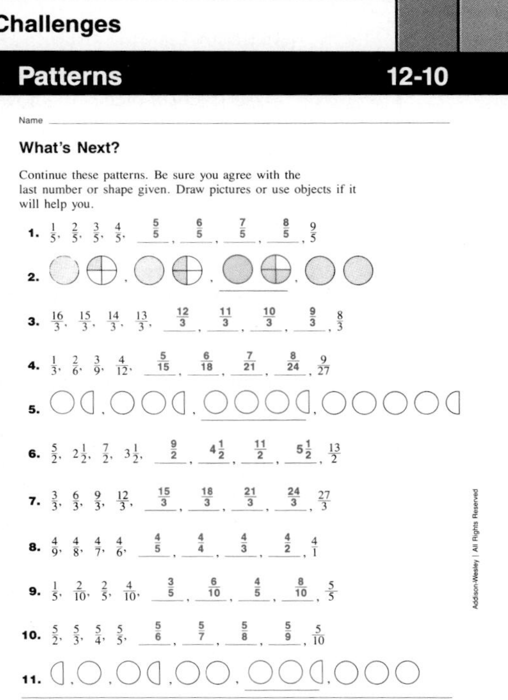

Challenges
Patterns 12-10

Name ____________

What's Next?

Continue these patterns. Be sure you agree with the last number or shape given. Draw pictures or use objects if it will help you.

1. $\frac{1}{5}, \frac{2}{5}, \frac{3}{5}, \frac{4}{5}, \frac{5}{5}, \frac{6}{5}, \frac{7}{5}, \frac{8}{5}, \frac{9}{5}$
2.
3. $\frac{16}{3}, \frac{15}{3}, \frac{14}{3}, \frac{13}{3}, \frac{12}{3}, \frac{11}{3}, \frac{10}{3}, \frac{9}{3}, \frac{8}{3}$
4. $\frac{1}{3}, \frac{2}{6}, \frac{3}{9}, \frac{4}{12}, \frac{5}{15}, \frac{6}{18}, \frac{7}{21}, \frac{8}{24}, \frac{9}{27}$
5.
6. $\frac{5}{2}, 2\frac{1}{2}, \frac{7}{2}, 3\frac{1}{2}, \frac{9}{2}, 4\frac{1}{2}, \frac{11}{2}, 5\frac{1}{2}, \frac{13}{2}$
7. $\frac{3}{3}, \frac{6}{3}, \frac{9}{3}, \frac{12}{3}, \frac{15}{3}, \frac{18}{3}, \frac{21}{3}, \frac{24}{3}, \frac{27}{3}$
8. $\frac{4}{9}, \frac{4}{8}, \frac{4}{7}, \frac{4}{6}, \frac{4}{5}, \frac{4}{4}, \frac{4}{3}, \frac{4}{2}, \frac{4}{1}$
9. $\frac{1}{5}, \frac{2}{10}, \frac{2}{5}, \frac{4}{10}, \frac{3}{5}, \frac{6}{10}, \frac{4}{5}, \frac{8}{10}, \frac{5}{5}$
10. $\frac{5}{2}, \frac{5}{3}, \frac{5}{4}, \frac{5}{5}, \frac{5}{6}, \frac{5}{7}, \frac{5}{8}, \frac{5}{9}, \frac{5}{10}$
11.

128 Use with text pages 346-347. CS-4

Options for Individual Needs

Basic

Exercises 1-20
Calculator Bank, p. 491
More Practice, p. 509, set C

Supplements
Reteaching 128 or
Practice 128

Average

Exercises 1-22
Calculator Bank, p. 491
More Practice, p. 509, set C

Supplements
Practice 128
Challenges 128 or
Thinking Skills 128

Extended

Exercises 3-20
Calculator Bank, p. 491

Supplements
Challenges 128
Thinking Skills 128

Other Resources:
Problem-Solving Experiences in Mathematics, Grade 4, Problem 95
Mathematics, A Way of Thinking, Lesson 11-15
Using The Math Explorer Calculator: A Sourcebook for Teachers, Chapter 14

LESSON PLAN 12-10

OBJECTIVE 12-10
To understand a mixed number

Materials: fraction pieces, TA 12 (Centimeter Graph Paper)

Alternative Materials: TA 21 (Fraction Strips)

1. MOTIVATE AND TEACH

LEARN ABOUT IT

EXPLORE ▶ **Analyze Blocks A and B to determine the number of quilt pieces each uses.** (A uses 4 pieces; B uses 8 pieces.)

TALK ABOUT IT ▶ **If a triangle in Block A is always a fourth, decide how to show two whole Block As as an improper fraction. Explain.** ($\frac{8}{4}$; The numerator shows the total number of parts; the denominator shows the number of parts into which a whole is divided.)
▶ **Explain how to use division to make quilt blocks from 30 pieces.** (Divide 30 by 4 to make Block As; divide by 8 for Block Bs.)
▶ **Explain how the parts of division relate to the parts of a mixed number.** (The quotient is the number of wholes, the remainder is the numerator of the fraction, and the divisor is the denominator.)
Student Edition answers: **1.** $\frac{1}{4}$, $\frac{1}{8}$ **2.** 7, $\frac{1}{2}$; 3, $\frac{3}{4}$

2. CHECK UNDERSTANDING

TRY IT OUT

ERROR ALERT Using the wrong denominator when writing mixed numbers. Exercises 2 and 5: Failing to reduce fractions to lowest terms.

Mixed Numbers

LEARN ABOUT IT

EXPLORE Study the Pictures
Jake cut 30 quilt pieces in the shape of right triangles. Then he tried two different ways of placing them in quilt blocks.

Block A

TALK ABOUT IT See teaching notes.

1. One quilt piece is what fraction of block A? of block B?
2. How many whole quilt blocks like block A could Jake make with 30 quilt pieces? What fraction of a whole block would be left? What about block B?

Block B

An **improper fraction** has a numerator greater than or equal to the denominator. Here's how to write an improper fraction as a **mixed number.**

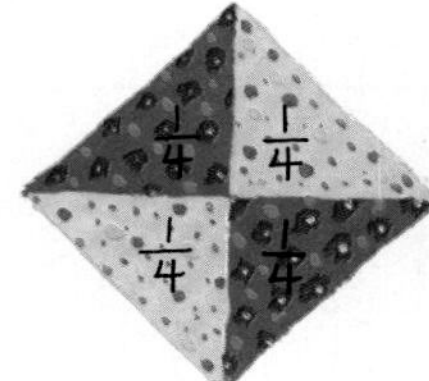

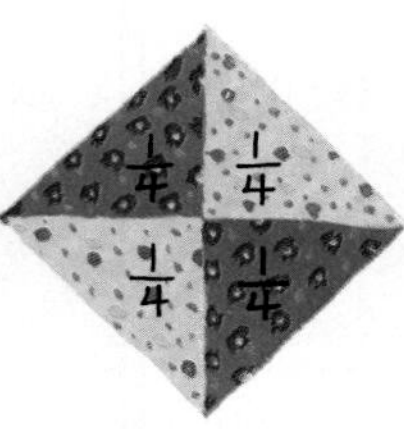

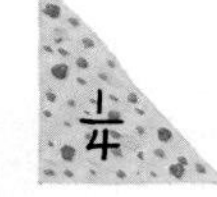

Improper Fraction ↓ $\frac{9}{4} = 2\frac{1}{4}$ **Mixed Number**

You can divide numerator by denominator to write a mixed number for an improper fraction.

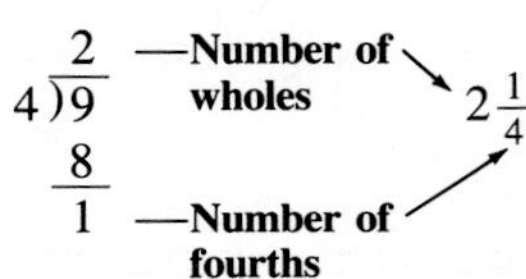

TRY IT OUT

Use fraction pieces to show the improper fraction. Then divide to write a mixed number for each fraction.

1. $\frac{5}{2}$ $2\frac{1}{2}$ **2.** $\frac{6}{4}$ $1\frac{1}{2}$ **3.** $\frac{7}{3}$ $2\frac{1}{3}$ **4.** $\frac{8}{5}$ $1\frac{3}{5}$ **5.** $\frac{12}{9}$ $1\frac{1}{3}$

346

TEACHING OPTIONS

RETEACHING TIPS Students making the second error should use fraction pieces to show improper fractions and the related mixed numbers. After they have made as many wholes as possible, have them try to trade any leftover pieces for equivalent pieces in lower terms. Assign Reteaching Supplement 128.

COMPUTER **Fraction Munchers, MECC, Copyright 1987** For use with all levels of students. In "Fraction Types," move "Number Muncher" to eat expressions of the same type as the target number before "Toggle Monster" eats "Number Muncher." The game requires 10 min.

PRACTICE

Write an improper fraction and a mixed number for each picture.

1. 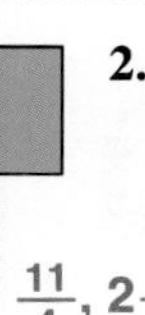 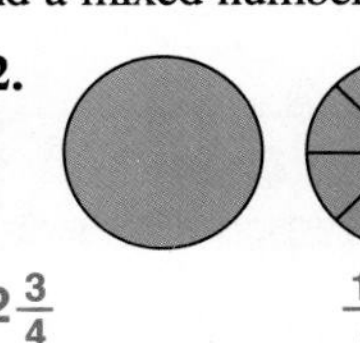 $\frac{11}{4}, 2\frac{3}{4}$

2. 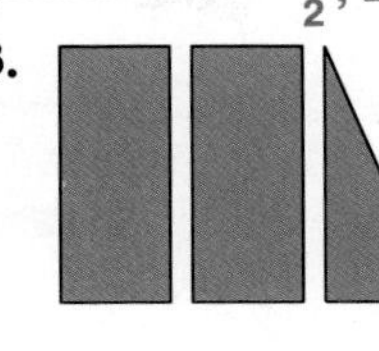 $\frac{15}{8}, 1\frac{7}{8}$

3. $\frac{5}{2}, 2\frac{1}{2}$

Write as a whole or mixed number. Draw pictures or use objects to help you.

4. $\frac{7}{3}$ $2\frac{1}{3}$ 5. $\frac{12}{2}$ 6 6. $\frac{9}{4}$ $2\frac{1}{4}$ 7. $\frac{11}{5}$ $2\frac{1}{5}$ 8. $\frac{8}{6}$ $1\frac{1}{3}$ 9. $\frac{20}{5}$ 4

APPLY

MATH REASONING Match each statement with a reasonable number from the box.

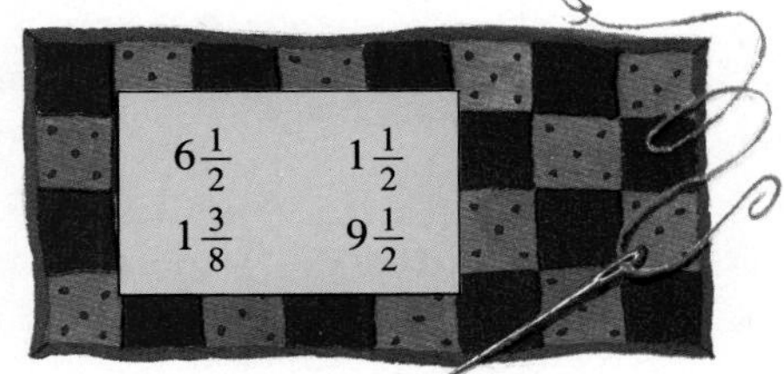

10. hours of school in a day $6\frac{1}{2}$
11. number of orange halves for a baseball team $9\frac{1}{2}$
12. age of a 4th grader $9\frac{1}{2}$

PROBLEM SOLVING

13. Tina used $3\frac{3}{8}$ yards of string to tie her quilt. Joe used $3\frac{1}{2}$ yards of string. Who used more string? Joe

14. Each quilt tie takes $\frac{1}{8}$ yard of string. How many yards of string will Sue use if her quilt needs 36 ties? $4\frac{1}{2}$ yd

MIXED REVIEW

Are these words symmetric? Write yes or no.

15. ALGEBRA no 16. HIDE yes 17. BOOK yes 18. CIDER no

Draw a picture of each of these types of quadrilateral. Check students' drawings.

19. square 20. parallelogram 21. trapezoid 22. rectangle

More Practice, page 509, set C

3. Practice and Apply

Basic	1-20
Average	1-22
Extended	3-20

PRACTICE

In Exercises 1 to 3, what must you count to write a mixed number? (number of wholes and the number of fractional parts)

APPLY

MATH REASONING ► **Analyze Exercise 11 to decide what you need to know to solve it.** (the number of players on a baseball team)

PROBLEM SOLVING ► **How would you compare the mixed numbers in Problem 13?** (Compare the whole numbers, then compare the fractions.)
► **Decide what strategy to use in Problem 14.** (Answers will vary; Draw a Picture, Use Models.)

MIXED REVIEW ► **Explain why the line of symmetry must be horizontal in Exercises 15 to 18.** (If it were vertical, none of the words would be symmetric.)

12-10

Close and Assess

SHOW WHAT YOU KNOW

Have students draw pictures to show $3\frac{1}{4}$ and $2\frac{5}{6}$. Then ask them to write an improper fraction for each picture. (Check students' drawings; $\frac{13}{4}$, $\frac{17}{6}$)

QUICK QUIZ

Write as a whole or mixed number.

1. $\frac{7}{5}$ ($1\frac{2}{5}$) 2. $\frac{9}{8}$ ($1\frac{1}{8}$)
3. $\frac{14}{3}$ ($4\frac{2}{3}$) 4. $\frac{21}{7}$ (3)
5. $\frac{9}{2}$ ($4\frac{1}{2}$) 6. $\frac{10}{4}$ ($2\frac{1}{2}$)

LESSON OPTIONS 12-11

Problem Solving: Measuring to a Fractional Part of an Inch

OBJECTIVE 12-11 To solve problems by measuring to a fractional part of an inch

PREBOOK ACTIVITIES

QUICK REVIEW

Solve.

1. $\frac{1}{6}$ of 24 (4) **2.** $\frac{1}{3}$ of 18 (6)
3. $\frac{1}{5}$ of 20 (4) **4.** $\frac{3}{4}$ of 16 (12)
5. $\frac{3}{7}$ of 35 (15) **6.** $\frac{7}{8}$ of 40 (35)

PRIOR KNOWLEDGE

Have students suggest real-life measurements that may not come out to an exact inch. (Answers will vary.) Ask students how they could describe measurements of less than 1 in. (Use fractions of an inch.) Then ask how they might describe a measurement between 5 and 6 in. (Use a mixed number for the whole inches and the fractional parts of an inch.)

COMMUNICATION

Writing in Math In their Math Journals, have students write an explanation of how mixed numbers can be used to express measurements that fall between inch marks on a ruler. When they finish, invite volunteers to share their writing with the class. (Answers will vary. Check students' writing.)

EXPLORE AND CONNECT

COOPERATIVE ACTIVITY

Grouping Suggestion: small groups
Tisa's bead necklace will be 16 in. long when she finishes it. So far, she has made $7\frac{3}{4}$ in. Is she halfway done?

TEACHING ACTIONS

Have students work together to discuss the situation and plan a solution method.

► **Explain the situation in your own words.** (Tisa has made part of a necklace and wants to know if she has reached the halfway mark yet.)

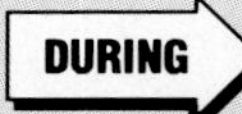

► **Identify the data you need to be able to solve the problem.** (how long the necklace is so far, which is $7\frac{3}{4}$ in., and what length is half of 16 in.)

► **Explain how you could have determined the length of the necklace if the measurement $7\frac{3}{4}$ had not been given to you.** (measure to a fractional part of an inch)

► **Explain how to determine half of 16.** ($\frac{1}{2}$ of 16 is the same as 16 ÷ 2, which is 8.)

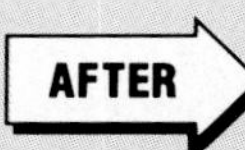

► **Evaluate your solution to see if it makes sense.** (Tisa has made $7\frac{3}{4}$ in. of her necklace, and 8 in. would be half; since $7\frac{3}{4}$ is less than 8, the necklace is not yet halfway done.)

CONNECTIONS Use these anytime.

Problem of the Day

Mixed Number Riddle Use the digits 3, 4, and 5 to create a mixed number that tells a length slightly less than half a foot. ($5\frac{3}{4}$ in.)

Math Connections

Measurement The smallest measure on Bill's ruler is a quarter of an in. But the width of a grain of rice he tries to measure for his art project does not even reach the first $\frac{1}{4}$-in. mark. Give 2 possible fractional measurements for the width of the grain of rice. Hint: Think of other fractional amounts that may appear on a ruler. (Possible answers: $\frac{1}{8}$ in.; $\frac{1}{16}$ in.)

Life Skills

Sewing Daisy used $10\frac{1}{2}$ in. of ribbon to trim a blouse. Did she need more or less than $\frac{1}{4}$ yd of ribbon? (more)

Classwork and Homework Supplements

Practice

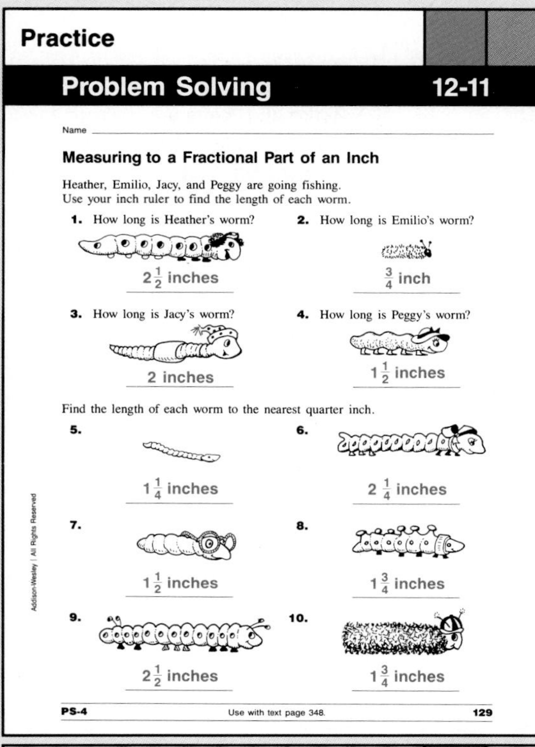

Problem Solving 12-11

Name ______________________

Measuring to a Fractional Part of an Inch

Heather, Emilio, Jacy, and Peggy are going fishing. Use your inch ruler to find the length of each worm.

1. How long is Heather's worm? $2\frac{1}{2}$ inches
2. How long is Emilio's worm? $\frac{3}{4}$ inch
3. How long is Jacy's worm? 2 inches
4. How long is Peggy's worm? $1\frac{1}{2}$ inches

Find the length of each worm to the nearest quarter inch.

5. $1\frac{1}{4}$ inches
6. $2\frac{1}{4}$ inches
7. $1\frac{1}{2}$ inches
8. $1\frac{3}{4}$ inches
9. $2\frac{1}{2}$ inches
10. $1\frac{3}{4}$ inches

PS-4 Use with text page 348. 129

Building Thinking Skills

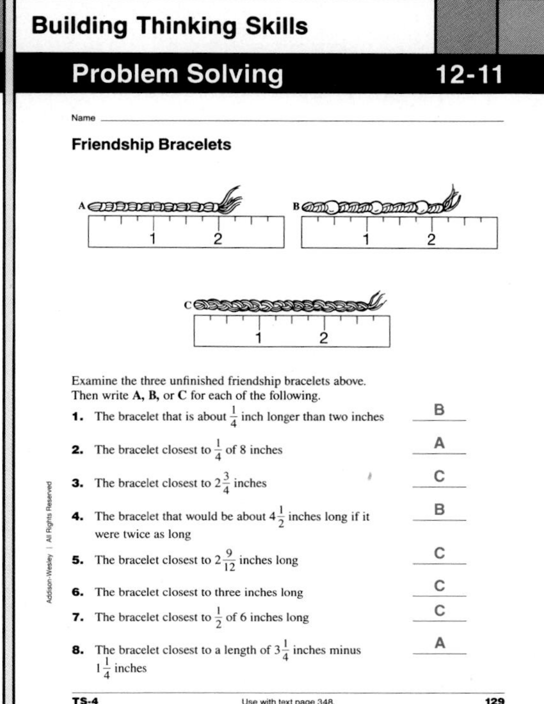

Problem Solving 12-11

Name ______________________

Friendship Bracelets

Examine the three unfinished friendship bracelets above. Then write **A, B,** or **C** for each of the following.

1. The bracelet that is about $\frac{1}{4}$ inch longer than two inches B
2. The bracelet closest to $\frac{1}{4}$ of 8 inches A
3. The bracelet closest to $2\frac{3}{4}$ inches C
4. The bracelet that would be about $4\frac{1}{2}$ inches long if it were twice as long B
5. The bracelet closest to $2\frac{9}{12}$ inches long C
6. The bracelet closest to three inches long C
7. The bracelet closest to $\frac{1}{2}$ of 6 inches long C
8. The bracelet closest to a length of $3\frac{1}{4}$ inches minus $1\frac{1}{4}$ inches A

TS-4 Use with text page 348. 129

Reteaching

Problem Solving 12-11

Name ______________________

Measuring to a Fractional Part of an Inch

This ruler is divided into quarter and half inches. The longest lines show **inch** markings. The shorter lines show **half-inch** markings. The shortest lines show **quarter-inch** markings.

quarter inch | half inch | inch

$\frac{1}{4}$ $\frac{1}{2}$ $\frac{3}{4}$ 1 in. $\frac{1}{4}$ $\frac{1}{2}$ $\frac{3}{4}$ 2 in. $\frac{1}{4}$ $\frac{1}{2}$ $\frac{3}{4}$ 3 in. $\frac{1}{4}$ $\frac{1}{2}$ $\frac{3}{4}$

The length of this nail is between 1 and 2 inches. It is on the $\frac{3}{4}$ inch mark. The length of this nail is $1\frac{3}{4}$ inches.

Use your ruler to find each length.

1. 2 inches
2. 1 inch
3. $2\frac{1}{2}$ inches
4. $1\frac{1}{4}$ inches

Find the length of each nail to the nearest quarter inch.

5. $1\frac{1}{4}$ inches
6. $2\frac{3}{4}$ inches
7. $1\frac{1}{2}$ inches
8. $3\frac{1}{4}$ inches

RS-4 Use with text page 348. 129

Challenges

Estimation 12-11

Name ______________________

Scavenger Hunt

Play this game in 2 teams. You will need rulers.

Rules:

- Find objects whose lengths are as close to the given lengths as possible. (You may not cut or alter objects to fit a given length.)
- After 10 minutes, both teams must stop.
- Measure each team's objects. The team that comes closer to the actual length gets 1 point. The team with the higher score wins. **Answers will vary.**

1. Find a pencil that is about $6\frac{1}{2}$ inches long.
   Measurement
   Team 1 ______
   Team 2 ______
2. Find a piece of chalk that is about $1\frac{1}{4}$ inches long.
   Measurement
   Team 1 ______
   Team 2 ______
3. Find a piece of human hair that is about $5\frac{1}{5}$ inches long.
   Measurement
   Team 1 ______
   Team 2 ______
4. Find a shoe that is about 7 inches long.
   Measurement
   Team 1 ______
   Team 2 ______
5. Find an object that is about $11\frac{1}{2}$ inches long.
   Measurement
   Team 1 ______
   Team 2 ______
6. Find a object that is about $2\frac{1}{4}$ inches long.
   Measurement
   Team 1 ______
   Team 2 ______

To continue playing, make up a new list of lengths and copy it for each team.

CS-4 Use with text page 348. 129

Options for Individual Needs

Basic

Exercises 1-9
Skills Bank, p. 466
Computer Bank, p. 493
More Practice, p. 524, set D

Supplements
Reteaching 129 or
Practice 129

Average

Exercises 1-9
Skills Bank, p. 466
Computer Bank, p. 493
More Practice, p. 524, set D

Supplements
Practice 129
Challenges 129 or
Thinking Skills 129

Extended

Exercises 1-9
Computer Bank, p. 493

Supplements
Challenges 129
Thinking Skills 129

Other Resources:
Problem-Solving Experiences in Mathematics, Grade 4, Problem 146
Mathematics, A Way of Thinking, Lesson 11-14

LESSON PLAN 12-11

OBJECTIVE 12-11
To solve problems by measuring to a fractional part of an inch

Materials: TA 17 (Rulers), red pencil

1. MOTIVATE AND TEACH

LEARN ABOUT IT

▶ **Explain the situation in your own words.** (You must identify the lengths of the string bracelets Reiko and Anita are making.)
▶ **Decide by visually estimating if the bracelets are the same length.** (Reiko's is longer.)

▶ **Explain how to find a measurement for each bracelet.** (Read the mark on the ruler nearest to the end of the bracelet.)
▶ **Decide the approximate length of each bracelet.** (Reiko's bracelet is between 2 and 3 in.; Anita's is a little over 2 in.)
▶ **Decide the length of each bracelet to the nearest half inch.** (Both bracelets are nearest $2\frac{1}{2}$ in. long.)

▶ **Justify how 2 bracelets that are not equal can have the same measure.** (Measurements are rounded, so it is possible for 2 different lengths to round to the same quarter inch.)

2. CHECK UNDERSTANDING

TRY IT OUT

ERROR ALERT Misreading the ruler.

Problem Solving
Measuring to a Fractional Part of an Inch

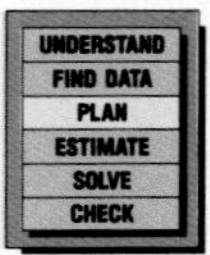

LEARN ABOUT IT

Sometimes you need to record a measurement to the nearest fractional part of an inch to get the data you need to solve a problem.

Reiko and Anita are making string bracelets. How long are their bracelets so far?

The length of Anita's bracelet to the nearest half inch is $2\frac{1}{2}$ inches.

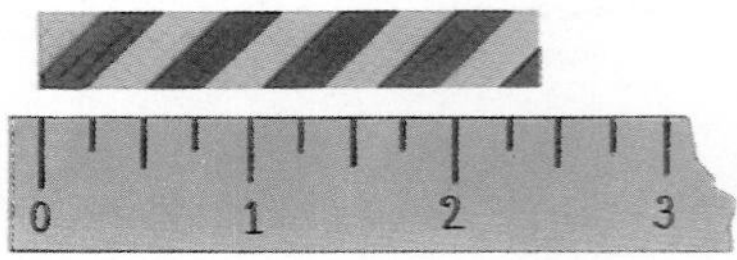

The length of Reiko's bracelet is $2\frac{1}{2}$ inches.

TRY IT OUT

Solve. Measure to the nearest $\frac{1}{2}$ inch to find the data needed.

1. Jane's finished lanyard is 8 inches long. Is Scott's lanyard so far more or less than $\frac{1}{4}$ the length of Jane's lanyard? **Record measurement as $1\frac{1}{2}$ in; less**

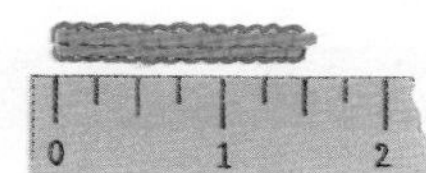

348

TEACHING OPTIONS

RETEACHING TIPS Have students make a red pencil mark to highlight each $\frac{1}{2}$ in. on their rulers to help them read fractional parts more easily. Assign Reteaching Supplement 129.

ENRICHMENT Have students use rulers to measure the lengths of 3 classroom objects to the nearest $\frac{1}{4}$ in. Then have them formulate 2 story problems based on the measurements they found. Have students solve each other's problems. (Check students' work.)

MIXED PRACTICE

Solve these problems. Use any problem solving strategy.

1. Sheryl wants to make a 6-inch long bracelet. Is she more or less than $\frac{1}{3}$ finished? **more**

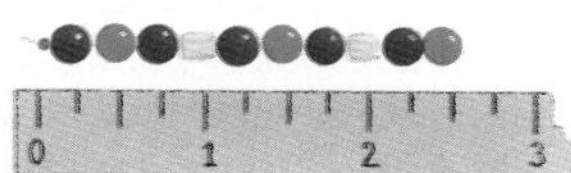

2. How many yellow beads will there be before the seventh red bead? **3**

3. Sam made 24 bookmarks to sell. He's already sold $\frac{1}{3}$ of them. $\frac{3}{4}$ of them are made out of leather. How many did he sell? **8 bookmarks**

4. Jana had some glass beads from the Bead Shop. She gave 13 to her sister Bella. Then she divided the rest into piles of 4 to make earrings. There were 5 piles. How many beads did Jana have in the beginning? **33 beads**

5. At Bob's Craft Supply, there are 23 different colors of yarn. Each ball costs $3.21 with tax. How much would it cost to get 2 balls of each color? **$147.66**

6. Roberto is making lanyard keychains as gifts. He needs 4 pieces of gimp for each keychain. He has cut 66 pieces of gimp. How many keychains can he make? **16 keychains**

The fourth graders were planning what to make for their booth at the school holiday fair. They made a graph to show the results from the year before. Use their graph to answer these questions.

7. How much did the fourth graders earn the year before? **$48**

8. What fraction of their profits came from key chains? $\frac{1}{4}$

9. How much money did they make selling both kinds of bracelets? What fraction of the profits was that? **$30; $\frac{5}{8}$**

Profits from School Fair

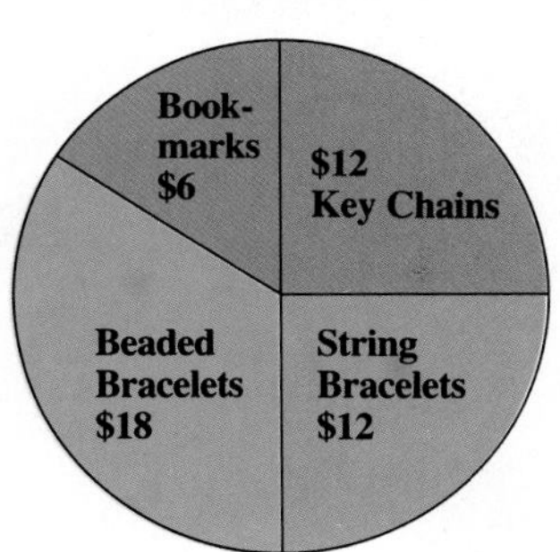

More Practice, page 524, set D

3. Practice and Apply

Basic	1-9
Average	1-9
Extended	1-9

Sample Solutions: See p. T79.

MIXED PRACTICE

▶ **Identify a problem to solve by measuring to a fraction of an inch.** (Problem 1)

▶ **Analyze Problem 3 to identify extra data.** (You do not need to know that $\frac{3}{4}$ were made of leather.)

▶ **Analyze Problem 4 to pick a sensible solution method.** (Work Backward)

▶ **Analyze how Problems 5 and 6 differ.** (Multiply to solve Problem 5; divide to solve Problem 6.)

▶ **Explain how to use the graph to solve Problems 7 to 9.** (7: find the sum of all parts; 8: name the fraction; 9: add money amounts; name a fraction for both sections together.)

12-11

Close and Assess

SHOW WHAT YOU KNOW Give students the following problem to solve:
Suppose that you are making a macramé belt that will eventually be 30 in. long. So far, you have made $\frac{1}{4}$ in. more than $\frac{1}{10}$ of the belt. Name and show the point on a ruler that marks the belt's length right now. ($3\frac{1}{4}$ in.)

Quick Quiz

Measure to the nearest $\frac{1}{4}$ in.

1. ______________ ($1\frac{1}{2}$ in.)
2. ______________ ($1\frac{1}{4}$ in.)
3. ______________ (1 in.)

CHAPTER 12

DATA COLLECTION AND ANALYSIS

GROUP DECISION MAKING

OBJECTIVE To collect, organize, and present data

Have volunteers describe the kind of bike locks they own. Then have groups decide the most popular bike lock among their members. Have each group predict the most popular kind of lock among students in the whole school.

COLLECTING DATA

▶ **Decide how to determine the most popular bike lock among your group.** (Possible answer: Poll members.)
▶ **Analyze different bike locks to list different features to look for.** (Possible features: chain; cable; combination; bar; key; a combination of these)
▶ **Explain how to record an unlocked bike or one with an unexpected kind of lock.** (Possible answer: Add a category called *Unlocked Bikes;* add another category called *Other* for unusual locks.)
▶ **Decide how to create a table to record your findings.** (Tables may vary.)

Data Collection and Analysis
Group Decision Making

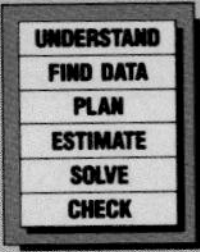

Doing an Investigation
Group Skill:
Listen to Others

There are several different kinds of bike locks. Some open with keys and some have combinations. Some are chains and others are not. Predict what kind of bike lock is the most popular at your school. Conduct an investigation to find out.

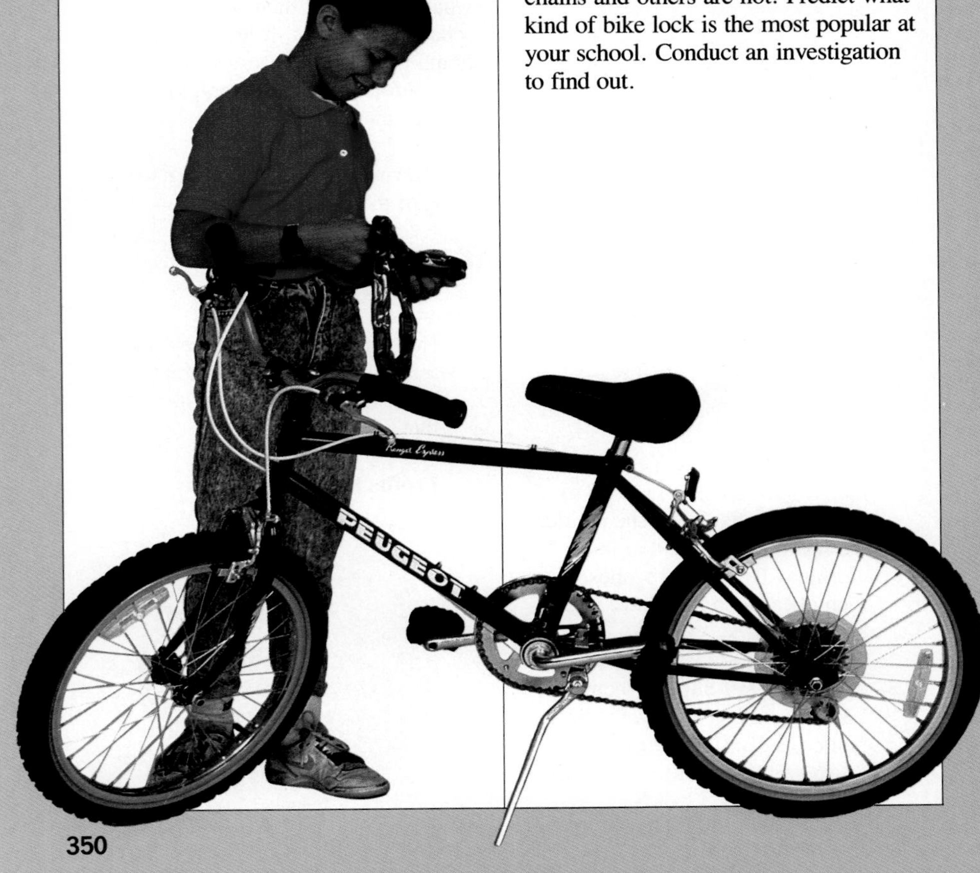

350

TEACHING OPTIONS

COOPERATIVE LEARNING

Grouping Suggestion:
cooperative groups of 4 to 6
Groups consider how to organize the tasks: brainstorm lock features; list most common kinds; plan bike-rack investigation (1 student can count all the bikes, other students can each look for 1 type of lock, 1 can record findings, and 1 can verify totals); design and draw a bar graph; summarize the results in writing; and suggest conclusions. If there is no school bike rack, groups can collect bike-lock data with a questionnaire to distribute to schoolmates.

Collecting Data

1. Discuss the kinds of bike locks students in your group have. Which is the most popular kind for your group?
2. Go to the bike rack at your school to find out what kinds of locks are on the bikes. Make a table to keep track of how many of each kind you find.

	combination lock	key lock
chain type	卌 III	I
not a chain type	卌 I	卌 卌 III

Organizing Data

3. Count how many locks you found in each category. Make a bar graph using this information.

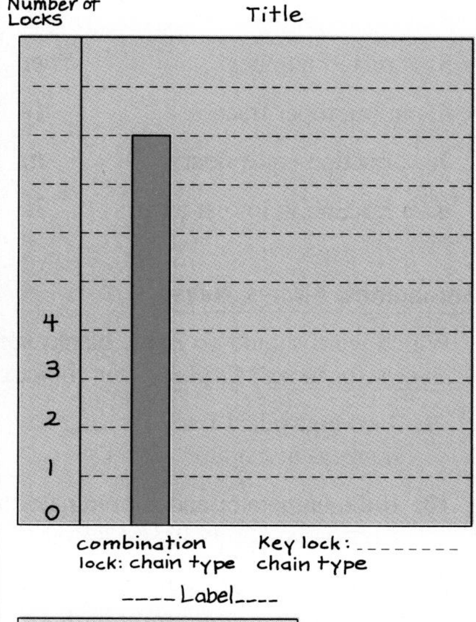

Presenting Your Analysis

4. Write a paragraph to tell what you found out. Were your predictions correct?
5. Give some reasons why you think one bike lock might be more popular than another.

351

ORGANIZING DATA

► **Decide how to label each bar on your graph.** (Answers may vary.)
► **Explain how you selected a reasonable number scale for each graph.** (Answers may vary.)

PRESENTING YOUR ANALYSIS

► **Decide on a way to reach a conclusion with your group.** (Methods may vary.)
► **Compare the results with your original predictions.** (Answers will vary.)
► **Analyze how the results might change on a different day.** (Possible answers: More or fewer bikes might be in the rack: some students may have changed the type of lock they use.)

EXTENSION Have students from each group interview workers at a bike or lock shop to collect different opinions on the best kinds of bike locks, including comparable prices. Groups should then present a summary of these findings to accompany their investigation.

CHAPTER 12

WRAP UP

INTRODUCTION The Wrap Up provides activities emphasizing math language and thinking skills for the chapter and a project that integrates those skills with other math strands.

USING PAGE 352

Fraction Match Have students complete this section independently, then compare answers with a partner to discuss any discrepancies they may find.

Sometimes, Always, Never

▶ **Identify examples for Exercise 9.** (Answers will vary.)

▶ **Contrast the statements in Exercises 10 and 11.** (Exercise 10 considers fractions made up of only odd numbers; Exercise 11 considers fractions made up of only even numbers.)

Project Provide tracing paper so that students can accurately copy the 2 polygons.

▶ **Explain why you need 4 of each shape to complete the puzzles.** (Each shape is $\frac{1}{4}$ of a square, which means that it takes 4 pieces to make a whole.)

▶ **What conclusion can you draw about any piece that is named $\frac{1}{4}$?** (Anything named $\frac{1}{4}$ means that it is 1 of 4 equal pieces that make a whole.) Have students present their finished squares, explaining how they put the pieces together. Display the squares and the shapes from the Enrichment exercise on a bulletin board.

Additional Answers: See p. T79.

WRAP UP

Fraction Match

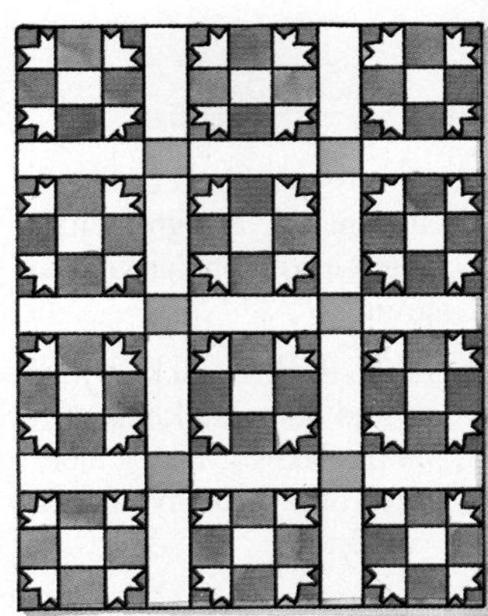

Find a match.

1. two tenths d
2. a numerator of eight h
3. a denominator of eight e
4. a whole number b
5. a mixed number f
6. an improper fraction a
7. a fraction equivalent to $\frac{1}{2}$ c
8. a fraction in lowest terms g

a. $\frac{5}{4}$
b. 12
c. $\frac{7}{14}$
d. $\frac{2}{10}$
e. $\frac{6}{8}$
f. $3\frac{4}{6}$
g. $\frac{9}{13}$
h. $\frac{8}{14}$

Sometimes, Always, Never

Which word should go in the blank, sometimes, always, or never? Explain your choices. Explanations may vary.

9. Two equivalent fractions __?__ have the same nonzero numerator. never
10. If the numerator and denominator are odd, the fraction is __?__ in lowest terms. sometimes
11. If the numerator and denominator are even, the fraction is __?__ in lowest terms. never

Project

Don't let your eyes fool you! Each shape pictured is exactly $\frac{1}{4}$ of a square. Make 4 copies of each shape. Can you fit the pieces together to form a square?
See Additional Answers.

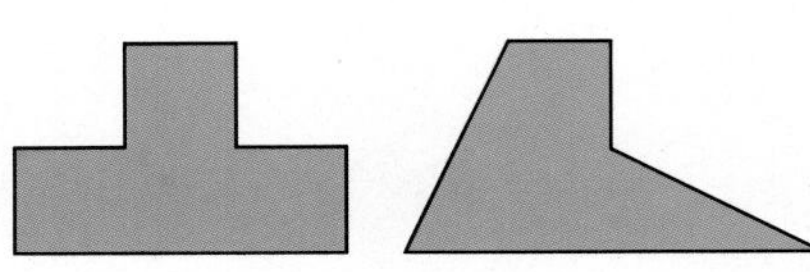

352

TEACHING OPTIONS

ENRICHMENT Challenge students to extend their visual-problem-solving ability by providing 2 more puzzles like the ones in the Project. Have students make 4 of each irregular shape, then put them together to form squares.

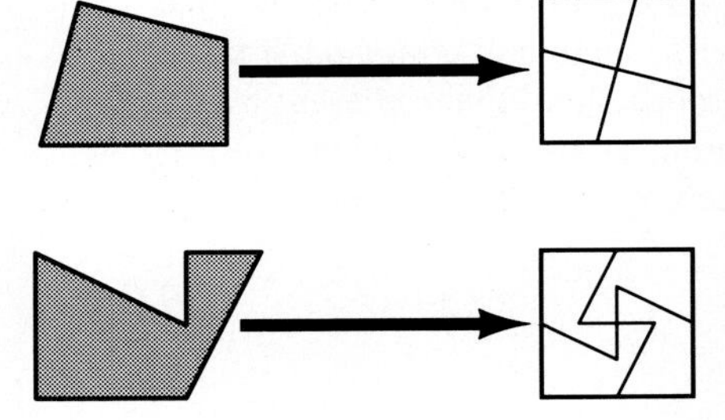

CHAPTER REVIEW/TEST

Part 1 Understanding

1. How much of this strip is red? blue? green? How much is not colored? $\frac{3}{8}, \frac{1}{8}, \frac{1}{8}, \frac{3}{8}$
2. Write a fraction to tell what part of the group of triangles is red. $\frac{3}{4}$

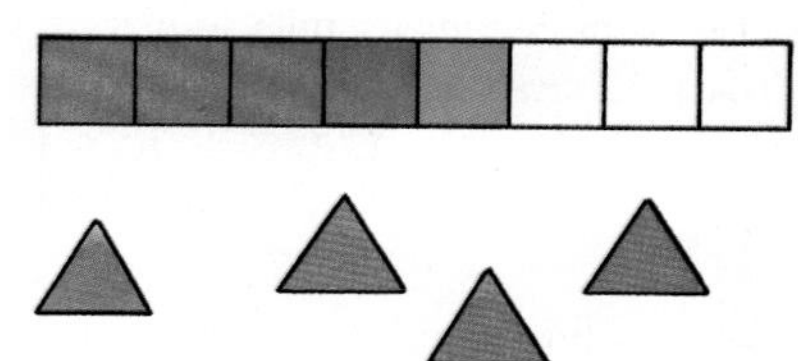

Part 2 Skills

Find the missing numbers for the equivalent fractions.

3. $\frac{1}{5} = \frac{3}{\square}$ 15
4. $\frac{1}{4} = \frac{\square}{8}$ 2
5. $\frac{4}{6} = \frac{\square}{24}$ 16
6. $\frac{1}{2} = \frac{10}{\square}$ 20

If possible, reduce to lowest terms.

7. $\frac{6}{18}$ $\frac{1}{3}$
8. $\frac{21}{24}$ $\frac{7}{8}$
9. $\frac{5}{25}$ $\frac{1}{5}$
10. $\frac{8}{10}$ $\frac{4}{5}$

Write <, > or =.

11. $\frac{1}{3}$ ▥ $\frac{1}{4}$ >
12. $\frac{3}{8}$ ▥ $\frac{1}{2}$ <
13. $\frac{9}{16}$ ▥ $\frac{18}{32}$ =
14. $\frac{5}{6}$ ▥ $\frac{2}{3}$ >

Give the number.

15. $\frac{3}{4}$ of 20 15
16. $\frac{1}{6}$ of 30 5
17. $\frac{3}{8}$ of 24 9
18. $\frac{1}{2}$ of 40 20

Part 3 Applications

19. Sonya served melon quarters to 9 people. Give a mixed number for the amount of melon Sonya served. $2\frac{1}{4}$ melons
20. Paul cut a honeydew into 6 pieces. He ate half the melon and his sister ate a third. How much is left? $\frac{1}{6}$ melon
21. Ray is 9 years and 10 months old. Express his age in years as a mixed number reduced to lowest terms. $9\frac{5}{6}$ years
22. **Challenge** Doug has 8 coins. $\frac{1}{2}$ are quarters, $\frac{1}{4}$ are dimes, $\frac{1}{8}$ are pennies, and the rest are nickels. How much money is this? $1.26

353

CHAPTER REVIEW/TEST

INTRODUCTION The Review/Test is provided to review and evaluate the skills and concepts presented in Chapter 12.

USING PAGE 353
If you prefer to use this page for review, you may want to use the **Multiple-Choice Posttest** (pages 47-48) or the **Free-Response Posttest** (pages 47-48) to evaluate mastery of Chapter objectives.

ITEM ANALYSIS The table below correlates the Chapter Review/Test items with the lesson objectives for the chapter.

Items	Objectives
1	12-1
2	12-2
3-6	12-5
7-10	12-6
11-14	12-7
15-18	12-9
19	12-10
(20)	12-1
20, 21	12-4
(21)	12-6
(21)	12-10
(21), 22	12-2
(22)	12-9

INFORMAL ASSESSMENT

Using Manipulatives Have students use 16 counters to show $\frac{3}{16}$, $\frac{5}{16}$, $\frac{9}{16}$, and $\frac{13}{16}$. Then have them show how many counters are in $\frac{1}{2}$, $\frac{3}{4}$, and $\frac{5}{8}$ of 16 and state an equivalent fraction in sixteenths for each amount. (Check students' work; 8, 12, 10; $\frac{8}{16}$, $\frac{12}{16}$, $\frac{10}{16}$)

Communication *Compare and contrast lowest-terms fractions and equivalent fractions.* (Possible answers: Lowest-terms fractions cannot be reduced any more; equivalent fractions express the same amount with different numerators and denominators, and 1 of the group of equivalent fractions may be in lowest terms.)

Critical Thinking *Explain a relationship between the numerator and denominator in fractions that are equivalent to $\frac{1}{2}$.* (The denominator is always twice the numerator.)

ENRICHMENT

INTRODUCTION Students will explore equivalent fractions by constructing fraction strips.

USING PAGE 354
This Enrichment page is provided for all students. You may wish to use it after they have completed the Chapter Review/Test on page 353.

▶ **Identify the relationship between 12 cm and $\frac{1}{2}$.** ($\frac{1}{2}$ of 12 is 6, so $\frac{1}{2}$ of 12 cm is 6 cm.)

▶ **Identify the number of centimeters in $\frac{1}{3}$, $\frac{1}{4}$, $\frac{1}{6}$, and $\frac{1}{12}$ of 12 cm.** (4 cm; 3 cm; 2 cm; 1 cm)

▶ **Identify in the picture a fraction piece that is not completely covered by the sheet of paper.** ($\frac{1}{3}$)

▶ **Explain why it is important to line up fraction strips to see equivalent fractions.** (Possible answer: If strips are not lined up, you cannot be sure which fractional segments are equivalent.)

Additional Answers: See p. T79.

ENRICHMENT
Patterns of Equivalent Fractions

Use your centimeter ruler to make 6 cardboard strips, each 12 cm long.

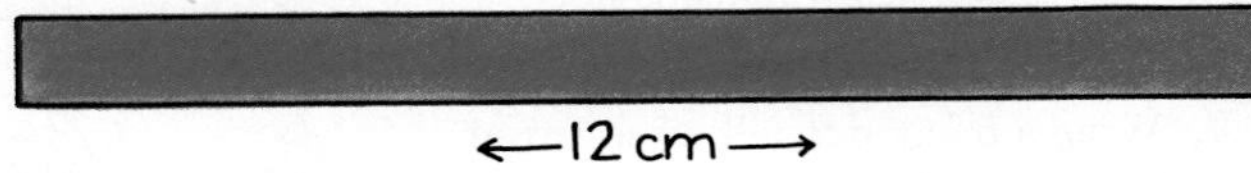

Here is how to use your ruler to make a fraction strip showing halves.

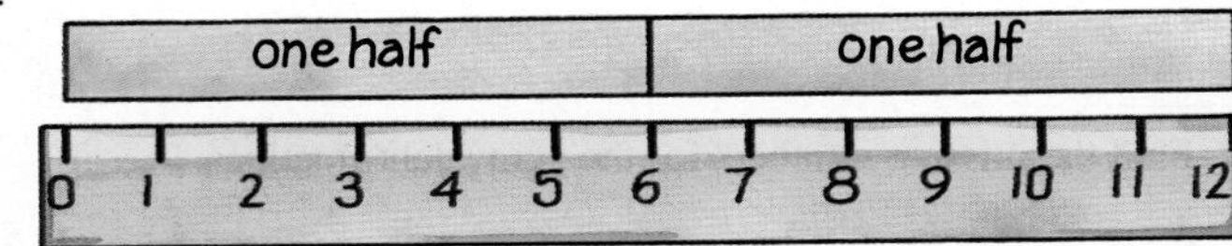

Make fraction strips showing halves, thirds, fourths, sixths, and twelfths.

Now lay strips together and cover part of them with a sheet of paper as shown.

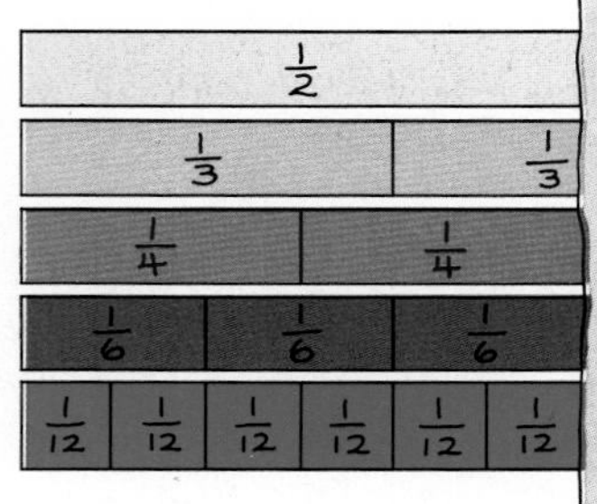

1. What pattern of equivalent fractions do you see in the part of the strips uncovered? Make a list of these fractions. $\frac{1}{2}, \frac{2}{4}, \frac{6}{12}, \frac{3}{6}$
2. Move the paper so that the following parts of the strips are covered. List the patterns of equivalent fractions that are shown.

   a. $\frac{2}{3}$ b. $\frac{1}{4}$ c. $\frac{2}{6}$ **See Additional Answers.**

354

CUMULATIVE REVIEW

1. 4)20

A 6 B 4
(C) 5 D 3

2. 7)56

A 6 (B) 8
C 7 D 9

3. 3)21

A 5 B 6
(C) 7 D 8

4. 4)93

A 20 R3 B 24 R3
C 23 (D) 23 R1

5. What is 860 divided by 3?

A 293 R1 (B) 286 R2
C 287 R1 D 353 R1

6. 5)$7.85

A $1.55 B $157
C $1.59 (D) $1.57

7. Which of these things suggests a triangular prism?

A ball B flag
(C) roof D TV set

8. A space figure with no vertices is the ▯.

A pyramid (B) sphere
C cone D rectangular prism

9. What kind of triangle is this?

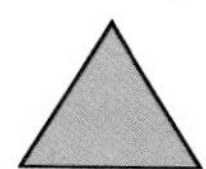

A right (B) equilateral
C isosceles D obtuse

10. These two lines are ▯.

A intersecting B equilateral
C perpendicular (D) parallel

11. How many different lines of symmetry can you draw for one square?

A 0 B 2
C 8 (D) 4

12. A quadrilateral that has exactly one pair of parallel sides is a ▯.

(A) trapezoid B rectangle
C tangram D right angle

355

CUMULATIVE REVIEW

INTRODUCTION The purpose of this Cumulative Review is to maintain previously taught skills and concepts. The emphasis in this Cumulative Review is on division concepts and basic facts, Chapter 9; on division with 1-digit divisors, Chapter 10; and on geometry, Chapter 11.

ITEM ANALYSIS The table below correlates the Cumulative Review items with the lesson objectives.

Items	Objectives
1	9-4
2	9-7
3	9-3
4	10-5
5	10-7
6	10-12
7, 8	11-1
9	11-5
10	11-3
11	11-4
12	11-6

CHAPTER 13 DECIMAL CONCEPTS

Chapter Management

OVERVIEW

Lesson	Pages	Objectives	Subject Integration	Strand Integration
Chapter Opener	356-357	To introduce chapter 13	health/fitness-Winter Olympics	computation
Reading and Writing Decimals: Tenths	358-359	13-1 To read and write decimals with tenths	health/fitness-walking	critical thinking
Reading and Writing Decimals: Hundredths	360-361	13-2 To read and write decimals with hundredths	health/fitness-olympic skiing	calculators
Decimals: Counting and Order/Midchapter Review/Quiz	362-363	13-3 To find the decimal when counting by tenths or hundredths	social studies-house painting	problem solving
Comparing and Ordering Decimals	364-365	13-4 To compare and order decimals	health/fitness-bicycle riding	mental math
Rounding Decimals	366-367	13-5 To round decimals to a whole number	health/fitness-speed skating	problem solving
Decimals and Fractions	368-369	13-6 To relate fractions and decimals	health/fitness-olympic games	problem solving
Problem Solving: Determining Reasonable Answers	370-371	13-7 To determine by estimation whether answers to problems are reasonable	fine arts-movie posters	consumer math
Applied Problem Solving: Group Decision Making	372-373	13-8 To analyze, organize, and make decisions using relevant data	fine arts-photography	consumer math

MATHEMATICAL BACKGROUND

Decimals
Decimal notation is an extension of the place value system for numbers less than one. Students learn to think of decimals as a way to write fractions or mixed numbers using tenths and hundredths.

Comparing and Ordering Decimals
Students learn how to compare two decimals. They learn to order decimals by comparing the numbers two at a time, then listing them from least to greatest or from greatest to least.

Rounding Decimals
In Lesson 13-5, students round to the nearest whole number.

Problem Solving
Students check the reasonableness of answers using estimation.

TIPS FROM TEACHERS

Distribute individual bags of play coins and bills worth different amounts to students. Pass out shopping lists with a price written next to each item. Each student tries to buy as many items as possible with the amount of money in his or her bag. Compare results.

Margaret Bates
Liverpool Elementary School
Liverpool, NY

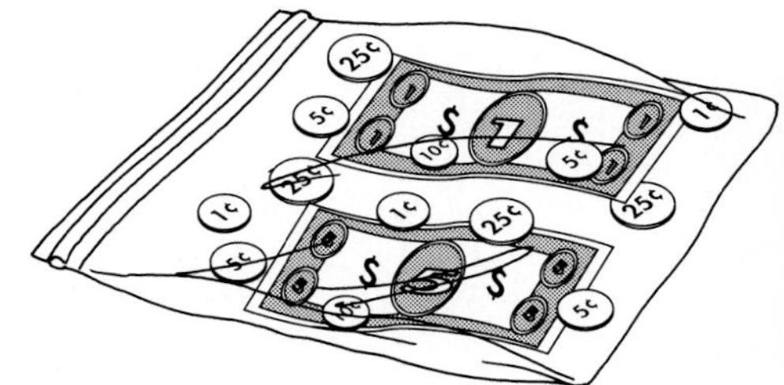

Shopping List

socks	-	$1.50 / pair
T-shirt	-	$5.95
shorts	-	$3.75

ASSESSMENT

Pretest — Chapter 13, page 1

Multiple-Choice Format

Name ____________________

1. Choose a decimal for the shaded part.
   a. 0.7 b. 0.8 c. 0.3 d. 0.4 1. c

2. Choose a decimal for the amount: two and six tenths.
   a. 2.6 b. 26 c. 62 d. 6.2 2. a

3. Choose a decimal for the shaded part.
   a. 1.09 b. 1.90 c. 0.19 d. 1.91 3. a

4. Choose a decimal for the amount: one and forty-five hundredths.
   a. 14.5 b. 1.45 c. 145 d. 45.01 4. b

5. Choose a decimal that comes between 3.09 and 3.11 when you count by hundredths.
   a. 3.01 b. 3.00 c. 3.10 d. 310 5. c

6. Choose a decimal that comes between 4.2 and 4.22 when you count by hundredths.
   a. 4.3 b. 4.20 c. 4.02 d. 4.21 6. d

7. Compare: 7.61 ● 7.59. Use <, >, or =.
   a. < b. > c. = 7. b

MCT 4 49

Pretest — Chapter 13, page 2

Multiple-Choice Format

Name ____________________

8. Order these decimals from least to greatest: 2.90 2.43 2.09 2.41
   a. 2.09, 2.90, 2.41, 2.43 b. 2.41, 2.43, 2.09, 2.90 c. 2.09, 2.41, 2.43, 2.90 d. 2.90, 2.09, 2.43, 2.41 8. c

9. Which number rounds to 35 when rounded to the nearest whole number?
   a. 34.09 b. 3.59 c. 35.91 d. 34.9 9. d

10. Which number rounds to 67 when rounded to the nearest whole number?
    a. 66.51 b. 67.9 c. 6.72 d. 66.09 10. a

11. Count small squares and choose a decimal for $\frac{3}{4}$.
    a. 0.50 b. 0.25 c. 0.45 d. 0.75 11. d

12. Count small squares and choose a decimal for $\frac{1}{2}$.
    a. 0.50 b. 0.30 c. 0.45 d. 0.75 12. a

13. Estimate to decide which answer is reasonable. Marla paid $8.98 for each of 6 cassette tapes. How much did she spend?
    a. $48.26 b. $53.88 c. $47.88 d. $61.88 13. b

50 MCT 4

Posttest — Chapter 13, page 1

Multiple-Choice Format

Name ____________________

1. Choose a decimal for the shaded part.
   a. 0.4 b. 0.6 c. 0.2 d. 0.8 1. b

2. Choose a decimal for the amount: nine and one tenth.
   a. 1.9 b. 19 c. 91 d. 9.1 2. d

3. Choose a decimal for the shaded part.
   a. 5.6 b. 0.44 c. 0.56 d. 4.4 3. c

4. Choose a decimal for the amount: two and five hundredths.
   a. 0.25 b. 2.50 c. 2.05 d. 5.02 4. c

5. Choose a decimal that comes between 7.09 and 7.11 when you count by hundredths.
   a. 7.01 b. 7.10 c. 7.00 d. 710 5. b

6. Choose a decimal that comes between 3.9 and 3.92 when you count by hundredths.
   a. 3.90 b. 3.09 c. 3.91 d. 3.19 6. c

7. Compare: 3.48 ● 3.52. Use <, >, or =.
   a. < b. > c. = 7. a

MCT 4 51

Posttest — Chapter 13, page 2

Multiple-Choice Format

Name ____________________

8. Order these decimals from least to greatest: 5.28 5.04 5.40 5.25
   a. 5.40, 5.04, 5.25, 5.28 b. 5.25, 5.28, 5.40, 5.04 c. 5.04, 5.40, 5.25, 5.28 d. 5.04, 5.25, 5.28, 5.40 8. d

9. Which number rounds to 58 when rounded to the nearest whole number?
   a. 58.07 b. 5.81 c. 58.79 d. 57.4 9. a

10. Which number rounds to 98 when rounded to the nearest whole number?
    a. 97.09 b. 98.9 c. 9.84 d. 98.09 10. d

11. Count small squares and choose a decimal for $\frac{2}{5}$.
    a. 0.25 b. 0.40 c. 0.50 d. 0.75 11. b

12. Count small squares and choose a decimal for $\frac{7}{10}$.
    a. 0.30 b. 0.25 c. 0.50 d. 0.70 12. d

13. Estimate to decide which answer is reasonable. Leigh paid $1.98 for each of 8 magazines. How much did she spend?
    a. $8.24 b. $14.24 c. $7.84 d. $15.84 13. d

52 MCT 4

ITEM ANALYSIS

Items	Objectives
1, 2	13-1
3, 4	13-2
5, 6	13-3
7, 8	13-4
9, 10	13-5
11, 12	13-6
13	13-7

Note: The item analysis is the same for all pretests and posttests for this chapter.

ALSO AVAILABLE

- **Free Response Tests**
- **Alternative Tests**
- **Thinking Strategies**
- **Concrete Materials**

Optional Chapter Activities

Project and Bulletin Board

Remind students that most prices are listed as decimal numbers. Help students make a place value chart on which they can list prices. As they begin this chapter, ask them to notice prices in supermarkets, in newspapers, and on television. Have them write one or two prices, bring them to school, and record them on the place value chart. Next to each price they may write the name of the product or draw a picture. After students complete Lesson 4, have them work in pairs to order the prices from lowest to highest. After Lesson 5, pairs can round each price to the nearest dollar.

HOW MUCH DOES IT COST?

Hundreds	Tens	Ones	Tenths	Hundredths
0	1	0	. 9	8
0	0	2	. 4	9
0	0	0	. 6	9

Cooperative Learning

Divide the class into groups of four. Identify the group skill: disagree in an agreeable way. Have one member of each group choose some decimal numbers in tenths to convert to fractions. Another student should express the decimal number as a fraction, and a third student should reduce the fraction to its lowest terms. A fourth student should check the work. After they have converted several decimals, have students switch roles. Some groups may wish to try decimals in hundredths and/or mixed numbers. Remind students that the person who checks the work should point out any mistakes politely. Each group should present its work to another group, explaining each step in the process.

You will find grouping suggestions and cooperative learning activities in most lessons throughout this chapter.

Literature

Elwood, Ann and Carol Orsag. "Starting Your Own Business." from: Chapter 9 "Money and Work," ***Macmillan Illustrated Almanac for Kids.*** New York: Macmillan, 1981.

Here are some helpful hints for children about how to start making their own money. Included are helpful business tips on what to charge, how to advertise and to figure costs.
Children could discuss their own business ideas and any new money making plans they might have. Then children could write number stories using decimals.

Brooke, Maxey. ***Coin Games and Puzzles.*** New York: Dover Publications, 1973.

Viorst, Judith. ***Alexander Who Used To Be Rich Last Sunday.*** New York: Atheneum, 1978.

Williams, Jay. ***A Box Full of Infinity.*** New York: Grosset & Dunlap, 1970.

English as a Second Language

Use the following activity to help ESL children visualize the position of fractions and decimals in relation to whole numbers on a numberline.

Review the concept of place value by writing a 3-digit number on the chalkboard. In unison, ask children to identify the ones, tens, and hundreds places as you point to each. Then give each child a copy of a numberline numbered from 0 to 2, divided into intervals of ten, with only the whole numbers labeled. Ask children to count the intervals from 0 to 1, beginning with 0 and ending at 1. Point out that each interval is one of ten intervals and count *one out of ten, two out of ten* and so on until you say *ten out of ten*. Then explain that 10 tens equal 1 whole, and that *one out of ten* is the same as *one tenth*. Show how one tenth is written with a decimal point and explain that the decimal point is needed to show where the ones place is. Children can then count from 0 to 1 by tenths stressing the *th* sound. Have them examine the tenths between the whole numbers 1 and 2.

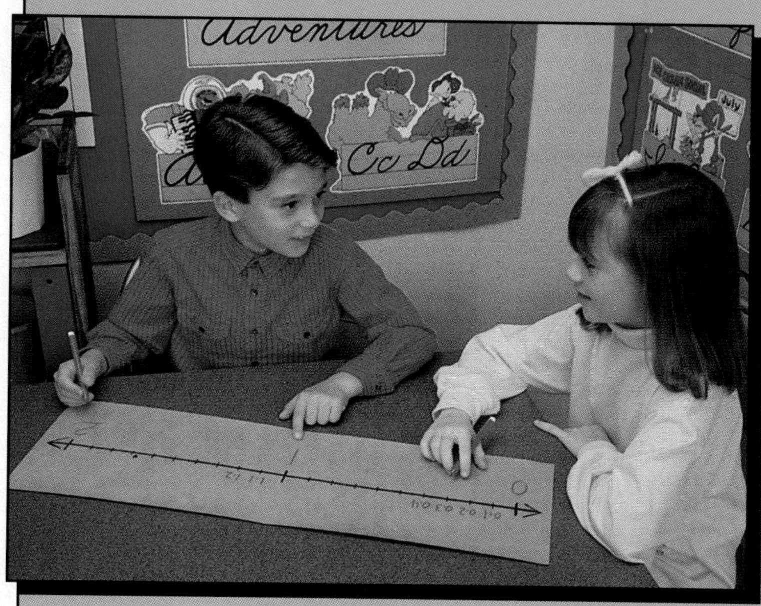

Gifted

Divide students into small groups. Give each group 52 index cards. Tell them to leave four of the cards blank so they can be used as wild cards. The remaining 48 must consist of 12 groups of four cards each. Each of those twelve groups should have three equivalent fractions and their lowest-term decimal representation.

The object of the game is to collect three equivalent fractions and their matching decimal, plus three other cards with either three equivalent fractions or two equivalent fractions and their decimal form. Wild cards may be used as players wish.

Ask groups to shuffle their cards, deal seven to each player, and place the remaining cards face down in a pile, turning the top one face up in another pile. One player begins by choosing either the face up card or the top card in the face down pile. If that player keeps either card, he or she must discard a card into the face up pile. The next player may either pick up the discarded card or take the top card from the face down pile. Players continue taking turns until the face down pile is gone; then they shuffle the face up pile, turn it over, and continue playing. The first player to meet the object of the game wins.

Students at Risk

The key concept students must develop in this chapter is an understanding of decimal place value relationships. This game may help students use place value materials to represent values other than whole numbers.

Race to One The goal is to reach 1 whole, represented by a flat block usually viewed as 1 hundred. Help students think of ones cubes as hundredths and ten sticks as tenths. Players need a number cube numbered 0.01 to 0.06, place value materials, and a decimal place value chart (TA 22). Taking turns, players roll the cube, read the decimal that appears, and take that many hundredths cubes. Whenever a player has 10 hundredths, he or she must trade for 1 tenth. The first player to have 10 tenths to trade will reach 1 whole, which is the goal. Vary the task by using different values on the number cube. To reinforce decimal subtraction skills, have students begin with 1 whole and roll to see how much to take away until they reach 0, making decimal trades as necessary.

You may also use the Reteaching Supplements and the specific Reteaching Tips from each lesson in this chapter.

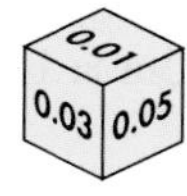

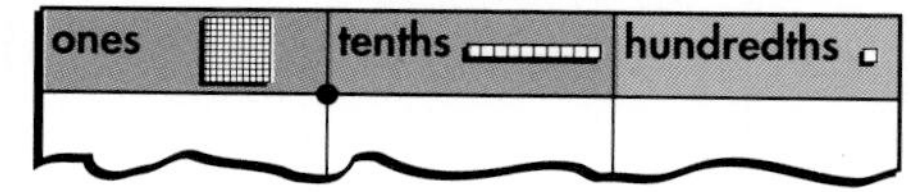

CHAPTER 13

INTRODUCING THE CHAPTER

SUBJECT INTEGRATION The photograph of the Olympic speed skater represents the chapter theme of health and fitness. Several lessons incorporate data about Winter Olympic sports to offer realistic opportunities for students to work with decimals in tenths and in hundredths.

USING DATA The Health and Fitness Data Bank on page 482 of the Student Edition provides facts and data on the Winter Olympic Games. One table lists gold medalists and their winning times in Women's 500-Meter Speed Skating, 1960 to 1988. The other table has the winners and their times in the Men's Alpine Skiing Slalom event, 1980 to 1988.

QUESTION 1 ▶ **Identify the necessary data to solve the problem.** (The first Winter Olympic Games were held in 1924.)
▶ **Decide how to use the data.** (Subtract 1924 from the current year to find how many years have passed, then divide by 10 to determine the number of decades equivalent to that many years.) Student Edition answer: over 6 decades

13 DECIMAL CONCEPTS

MATH AND HEALTH AND FITNESS
DATA BANK
Use the Health and Fitness Data Bank on page 482 to answer the questions. See teaching notes.

1 A decade is 10 years. How many decades have passed since the first Winter Olympic Games were held?

TEACHING OPTIONS

LANGUAGE DEVELOPMENT
Write the word **meter** on the chalkboard. Have students use logical reasoning to determine the kind of measurement unit a meter is, based on the fact that 1 event in the Winter Olympics is a 500-meter speed skating race. (length; the course is 500 m long.)

2 What fraction of the winners of the Men's Slalom medals in 1984 and 1988 were from the United States?

3 What fraction of the winners of the Women's 500-Meter Speed Skating in the last 5 Olympics were from the United States?

4 **Use Critical Thinking** Do you think a course with 58 gates could be used for both a men's and a women's race? Support your conclusion.

QUESTION 2 ▶ **Decide the number of different countries represented by medalists.** (7)
▶ **Identify a pattern in the American medal winners.** [The same person won medals in 1980 and 1984, and the other medalist has the same last name. (They are brothers.)]
Student Edition answer: $\frac{2}{6}$ or $\frac{1}{3}$

QUESTION 3 ▶ **Identify the years of the last 5 Winter Olympics.** (1972, 1976, 1980, 1984, 1988)
▶ **Decide the fraction of female medalists listed whose winning times were under 40 seconds.** ($\frac{1}{8}$)
Student Edition answer: $\frac{3}{5}$

QUESTION 4 ▶ **Evaluate the fairness of Men's and Women's Slalom skiing events if they shared a course with 58 gates.** (Possible answer: The course might feel easier to the men but harder to the women, because the men would be used to more gates and the women would be used to fewer gates.)
Student Edition answer: yes; possible explanation: 58 is in the lower end of the range of gates required for the Men's Slalom event and in the upper end of the range for the Women's Slalom event.

SUBJECT INTEGRATION PROJECT Have students create an Olympic Records display over the duration of their work in Chapter 13. They need almanacs or library books that list Olympic events and winning times. Discuss what students already know about the Winter Olympic Games and specific events or athletes they may have read about or have seen. Students pick an event or an Olympic year to research, then decide how to display the data they find. Group Olympic Record facts by countries, events, years, or decimal order.

LESSON OPTIONS 13-1

Reading and Writing Decimals: Tenths

OBJECTIVE 13-1 To read and write decimals with tenths

PREBOOK ACTIVITIES

QUICK REVIEW

Write each fraction or mixed number.

1. one third $(\frac{1}{3})$
2. two sevenths $(\frac{2}{7})$
3. one half $(\frac{1}{2})$
4. five sixths $(\frac{5}{6})$
5. three tenths $(\frac{3}{10})$
6. five eighths $(\frac{5}{8})$
7. two and three fourths $(2\frac{3}{4})$
8. eleven and two thirds $(11\frac{2}{3})$

PRIOR KNOWLEDGE

Write the decimals 0.5, 9.8, and 98.6 on the chalkboard. Ask students when they have ever seen or used such numbers. (Possible answers: calculator displays, gymnastics scores, fever thermometers, metric measurements) Have volunteers read the numbers aloud, using any method they may know. (Students may say ''point five,'' ''nine point eight,'' or ''ninety-eight point six.'') Tell students that they will learn more about numbers such as these, which are known as decimals.

COMMUNICATION

Discussing and Writing Math Write the word **decimal** on the chalkboard. Tell students that the word comes from a Latin word *decimus,* which means ''ten.'' Write the words *decade, decagon,* and *decathlon* on the board. Have students try to explain why each word uses the same beginning letters as in *decimal.* (A decade is 10 years; a decagon is a 10-sided polygon; a decathlon is a sports contest that includes 10 different events.) In their Math Journals, have students generalize what decimal numbers are. (Possible answer: Decimals are numbers that let us show tenths.)

EXPLORE AND CONNECT

Materials: place value blocks (hundreds and tens), TA 22 (Decimal Place Value Charts), TA 3 (Number Cards 0-4)
Alternative Materials: TA 6 (Place Value Models)
Grouping Suggestion: cooperative learning groups of 4
Students explore **decimals** with place value materials. A hundreds square will be 1 whole; tens stick will be $\frac{1}{10}$ of that whole. A student draws one number card for wholes and one for tenths. A second student takes that many hundreds squares and tens sticks and puts them on a **decimal** place value chart. A third student writes a fraction or mixed number for the amount. A fourth student writes a *decimal* number for it. Groups repeat three times, trading tasks. Students compare fractions and *decimals* and generalize about *decimals*. (Possible answers: You can write a fraction and a decimal for an amount with tenths; *decimals* need a *decimal* point.)

CONNECTIONS Use these anytime.

Problem of the Day

Number Sense Write a decimal that is equivalent to one half. Draw a picture to prove your reasoning. (0.5; Check students' pictures.)

Patterns

Tenths Figure out each decimal pattern, then give the next three decimals.

0.8, 0.7, 0.6, (0.5), (0.4), (0.3)
1.2, 1.4, 1.6, (1.8), (2.0), (2.2)
23.0, 23.5, 24.0, (24.5), (25.0), (25.5)

Math Connection

Money Find the value of each group of dimes. Then express each amount as a decimal for tenths of a dollar.

3 dimes (0.3)
7 dimes (0.7)
2 dimes (0.2)

Classwork and Homework Supplements

Practice

Skills Maintenance 13-1

Name ______________________

Reading and Writing Decimals: Tenths

Write the fraction and the decimal shown by each figure.

1. shaded $\frac{4}{10}$, 0.4 white $\frac{6}{10}$, 0.6
2. shaded $\frac{3}{10}$, 0.3 white $\frac{7}{10}$, 0.7
3. shaded $\frac{8}{10}$, 0.8 white $\frac{2}{10}$, 0.2
4. shaded $\frac{1}{10}$, 0.1 white $\frac{9}{10}$, 0.9
5. shaded $\frac{5}{10}$, 0.5 white $\frac{5}{10}$, 0.5
6. shaded $\frac{9}{10}$, 0.9 white $\frac{1}{10}$, 0.1

Write a decimal for the amount.

7. two and four tenths 2.4
8. sixteen and nine tenths 16.9
9. thirty and two tenths 30.2
10. fourteen and eight tenths 14.8

Building Thinking Skills

Reading Math 13-1

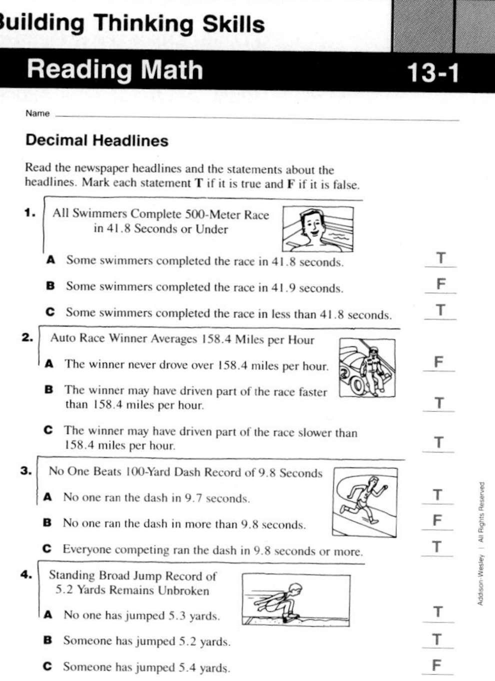

Name ______________________

Decimal Headlines

Read the newspaper headlines and the statements about the headlines. Mark each statement **T** if it is true and **F** if it is false.

1. All Swimmers Complete 500-Meter Race in 41.8 Seconds or Under
   - A Some swimmers completed the race in 41.8 seconds. T
   - B Some swimmers completed the race in 41.9 seconds. F
   - C Some swimmers completed the race in less than 41.8 seconds. T
2. Auto Race Winner Averages 158.4 Miles per Hour
   - A The winner never drove over 158.4 miles per hour. F
   - B The winner may have driven part of the race faster than 158.4 miles per hour. T
   - C The winner may have driven part of the race slower than 158.4 miles per hour. T
3. No One Beats 100-Yard Dash Record of 9.8 Seconds
   - A No one ran the dash in 9.7 seconds. T
   - B No one ran the dash in more than 9.8 seconds. F
   - C Everyone competing ran the dash in 9.8 seconds or more. T
4. Standing Broad Jump Record of 5.2 Yards Remains Unbroken
   - A No one has jumped 5.3 yards. T
   - B Someone has jumped 5.2 yards. T
   - C Someone has jumped 5.4 yards. F

Reteaching

Skills Review 13-1

Name ______________________

Reading and Writing Decimals: Tenths

A fraction or a mixed number that uses tenths can easily be written as a decimal.

	Say	Write: fraction	Write: decimal
shaded part:	"two tenths"	$\frac{2}{10}$	0.2
white part:	"eight tenths"	$\frac{8}{10}$	0.8

$\frac{2}{10}$ $\frac{8}{10}$

mixed number	decimal
$1\frac{5}{10}$	1.5

1 $\frac{5}{10}$

Write the fraction and the decimal to tell how much is shaded.

1. $\frac{3}{10}$, 0.3
2. $\frac{7}{10}$, 0.7
3. $\frac{6}{10}$, 0.6

Write a decimal for the amount.

4. one and four tenths 1.4
5. two and three tenths 2.3
6. sixteen and two tenths 16.2
7. eleven and five tenths 11.5

Challenges

Data Analysis 13-1

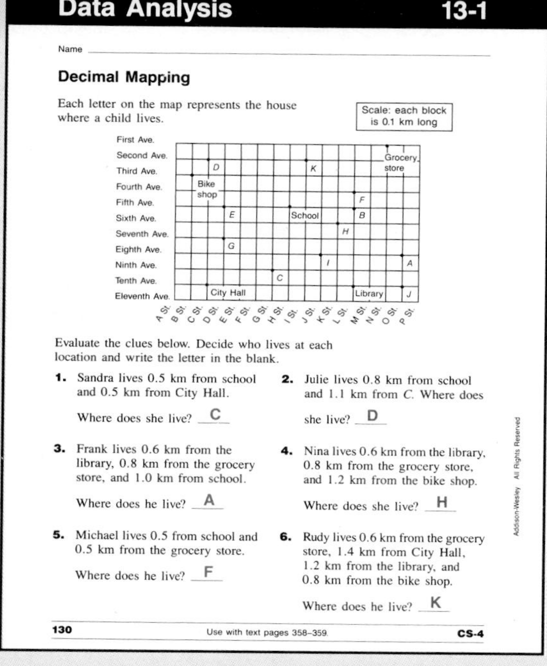

Name ______________________

Decimal Mapping

Each letter on the map represents the house where a child lives.

Scale: each block is 0.1 km long

Evaluate the clues below. Decide who lives at each location and write the letter in the blank.

1. Sandra lives 0.5 km from school and 0.5 km from City Hall. Where does she live? C
2. Julie lives 0.8 km from school and 1.1 km from C. Where does she live? D
3. Frank lives 0.6 km from the library, 0.8 km from the grocery store, and 1.0 km from school. Where does he live? A
4. Nina lives 0.6 km from the library, 0.8 km from the grocery store, and 1.2 km from the bike shop. Where does she live? H
5. Michael lives 0.5 from school and 0.5 km from the grocery store. Where does he live? F
6. Rudy lives 0.6 km from the grocery store, 1.4 km from City Hall, 1.2 km from the library, and 0.8 km from the bike shop. Where does he live? K

Options for Individual Needs

Basic

Exercises 1-13
Calculator Bank, p. 490

Supplements
Reteaching 130 or
Practice 130

Average

Exercise 1-13
Calculator Bank, p. 490

Supplements
Practice 130
Challenges 130 or
Thinking Skills 130

Extended

Exercises 3-13
Calculator Bank, p. 490

Supplements
Challenges 130
Thinking Skills 130

Other Resources:
Problem-Solving Experiences in Mathematics, Grade 4, Problem 136
Mathematics, A Way of Thinking, Lesson 12-1
Math In Stride, Grade 4, pp. 186, 187
Using the Math Explorer Calculator: A Sourcebook for Teachers, Chapter 14

LESSON PLAN 13-1

OBJECTIVE 13-1
To read and write decimals with tenths

Materials: graph paper, crayons, TA 22 (Decimal Place Value Charts)

1. MOTIVATE AND TEACH

LEARN ABOUT IT

EXPLORE ► **Compare the 10 parts of your square.** (all same size)
► **Apply the rules for naming fractions to name each part of the square. Explain your reasoning.** (1 tenth, because 10 equal parts make up the whole and each part is $\frac{1}{10}$ of that whole)

TALK ABOUT IT ► **Explain how you know which fractions can be written as decimals.** (Those that have 10 as the denominator can because decimals show tenths.)
► **Analyze the decimal number 4 tenths.** (0 for no ones; a decimal point; 4 for 4 tenths)
► **Compare how a fraction and a decimal show 4 tenths.** (10 in the denominator of the fraction identifies tenths, and the numerator tells that there are 4 tenths; the decimal shows only the point 4—it means 4 tenths because of decimal place value.)
► **Analyze how the decimal 1.7 shows a mixed number.** (1 means 1 whole; the decimal point signals a fractional part; 7 means 7 tenths.)
Student Edition answers: **1-2.** Answers will vary. **3.** $\frac{10}{10}$, 1

2. CHECK UNDERSTANDING

TRY IT OUT

ERROR ALERT Omitting the 0 in decimals less than 1. Omitting the decimal point.

Reading and Writing Decimals
Tenths

LEARN ABOUT IT

EXPLORE Discover a Relationship
Use graph paper and mark off three 10 by 10 squares. Divide your squares into 10 parts, like the square shown. In each square, color some of the 10 parts.

TALK ABOUT IT See teaching notes.

1. What fraction of each square is colored?
2. What fraction of each square is not colored?
3. If you colored 10 tenths, how would you write it as a fraction? as a whole number?

A fraction or a mixed number that uses tenths can easily be written as a decimal.

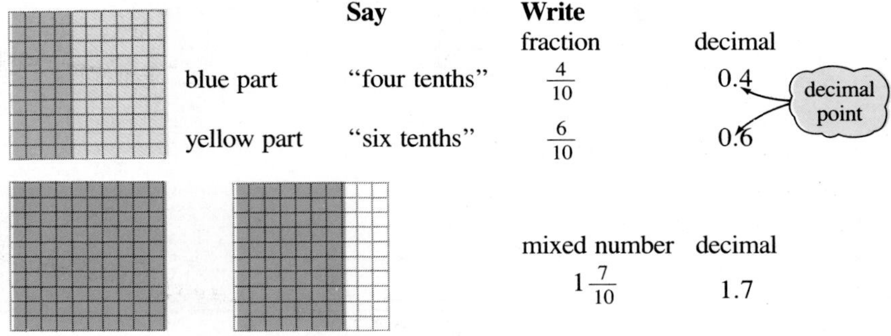

	Say	Write fraction	decimal
blue part	"four tenths"	$\frac{4}{10}$	0.4
yellow part	"six tenths"	$\frac{6}{10}$	0.6

mixed number	decimal
$1\frac{7}{10}$	1.7

TRY IT OUT

Write the fraction for the colored part. Then write the decimal.

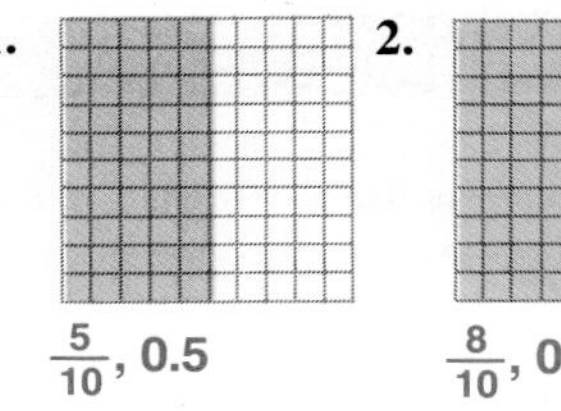

1. $\frac{5}{10}$, 0.5
2. $\frac{8}{10}$, 0.8

TEACHING OPTIONS

RETEACHING TIPS Have students use a decimal place value chart for tenths. Students write the number of whole units to the *left* of the decimal point and the number of tenths to the *right* of it. Assign Reteaching Supplement 130.

ENRICHMENT Have students use place value models (TA 6), to determine how to write a decimal for each amount: 14 tenths, 22 tenths, 31 tenths, 40 tenths. Ask students to explain their reasoning. (1.4, 2.2, 3.1, 4.0; trade 10 tenths for 1 whole.)

PRACTICE

Write the fraction and the decimal for the colored part.

1. green $\frac{7}{10}$, 0.7
2. yellow $\frac{3}{10}$, 0.3
3. orange $\frac{5}{10}$, 0.5
4. white $\frac{5}{10}$, 0.5

Write a decimal for the amount.

5. one and nine tenths 1.9
6. twenty-one and three tenths 21.3

APPLY

MATH REASONING Give the numbers from the list in which the digit 3 has these values.

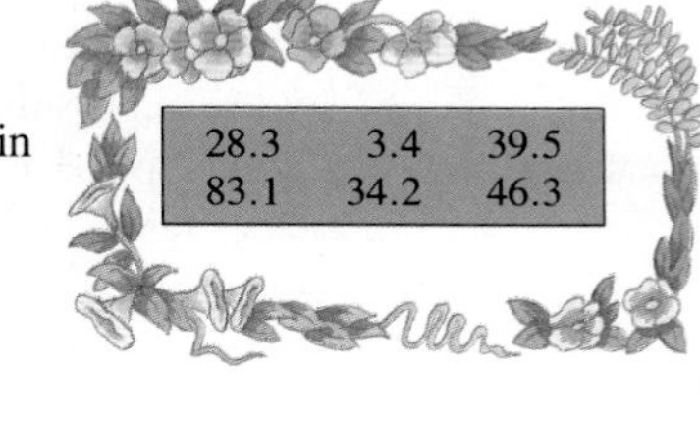

28.3	3.4	39.5
83.1	34.2	46.3

7. 30 34.2, 39.5
8. 3 83.1, 3.4
9. 0.3 46.3, 28.3

PROBLEM SOLVING

10. Louann colored these 3 squares. If she had colored 2 more tenths what decimal would she have shown? if she had colored 2 less tenths? 3.0, 2.6

► **USING CRITICAL THINKING** **Analyze the Data**

Which of the following statements is true about the distance walked by each student?

11. Some students might have walked more than 1.5 miles. true
12. Some students might have walked 1.5 miles. true
13. Some students might have walked less than 1.5 miles. false

MARSHALL SCHOOL WALKATHON A SUCCESS
ALL STUDENTS WALKED AT LEAST 1.5 MILES

359

3. Practice and Apply

Basic	1-13
Average	1-13
Extended	3-13

PRACTICE

Look at Exercises 1-4. Explain how to complete these exercises. (Every two exercises share one picture; write a fraction and a decimal for each color.)

APPLY

MATH REASONING ► **Explain how 30, 3, and 0.3 are different.** (30 means 3 tens, 3 means 3 ones, and 0.3 means 3 tenths.)

PROBLEM SOLVING ► **Explain what you would do first to solve Problem 10.** (Possible answer: Find a decimal that names how much she did color.)

► **Explain how to work backward to name the decimal.** (Subtract 2 tenths from 3 whole things.)

USING CRITICAL THINKING

► **Examine the headline to find an expression that can help you analyze Problems 11-13. Explain your reasoning.** (*at least;* it means ''not less than''—not less than 1.5 mi.)

13-1

Close and Assess

SHOW WHAT YOU KNOW

Have each student use graph paper and crayons to draw a picture that represents $\frac{1}{10}$, $\frac{6}{10}$, and $1\frac{9}{10}$. Then have each student label his or her picture with an equivalent decimal. (Check students' pictures; 0.1, 0.6, 1.9.)

QUICK QUIZ

Write each decimal.

1. two tenths (0.2)
2. seven tenths (0.7)
3. four and five tenths (4.5)
4. sixteen and nine tenths (16.9)

LESSON OPTIONS 13-2

Reading and Writing Decimal Numbers: Hundredths

OBJECTIVE 13-2 To read and write decimals with hundredths

PREBOOK ACTIVITIES

QUICK REVIEW

Write a decimal for each fraction or mixed number.

1. 1/10 (0.1)	**2.** 3/10 (0.3)	**3.** 7/10 (0.7)
4. 9/10 (0.9)	**5.** 1 4/10 (1.4)	**6.** 3 2/10 (3.2)
7. 7 5/10 (7.5)	**8.** 9 (9.0)	**9.** 14 6/10 (14.6)

PRIOR KNOWLEDGE

Have students explain how to write money amounts such as 42¢ or 8¢ using a dollar sign and a decimal point. ($0.42, $0.08) Have them give a rule for the number of places to the right of a decimal point when writing money amounts. (always use two) Have students name the place just to the right of the decimal point (tenths). Have them guess the name of the place to the right of that by thinking of pennies per dollar. (hundredths, because there are 100 pennies in a dollar) Tell students that in this lesson they will learn more about decimal numbers that include tenths and hundredths.

COMMUNICATION

Discussing and Reading Math Write these word pairs on the chalkboard: **tens** and **tenths**, **hundreds** and **hundredths**. Have students read the words, then discuss their similarities and differences. (Possible answers: Words that end in *-ths* express fractional amounts; tens and hundreds mean 10 times and 100 times 1; tenths and hundredths mean 10 parts and 100 parts of 1.)

EXPLORE AND CONNECT

Materials: place value blocks, TA 3 (Number Cards 0-4), TA 22 (Decimal Place Value Charts)
Grouping Suggestion: cooperative learning groups of 4
Students extend the exploration they did in Lesson 13-1 to include decimal numbers with **hundredths**. A **hundreds** square represents 1 whole; a tens stick is 1/10, or 0.1, of the square; and 1 cube is 1/100, or 0.01, of it. Groups use decimal place value charts that show wholes, tenths, and *hundredths*. Students take turns drawing number cards for each of the three places, modeling the number with the appropriate materials, writing a fraction or mixed number for the amount, and writing a decimal for it. Trading tasks, groups repeat the activity 4 times. Conclude by having students generalize about decimal numbers with *hundredths*. (Possible answers: Decimals with *hundredths* show more exact amounts than decimals with tenths; decimals with *hundredths* use 2 decimal places.)

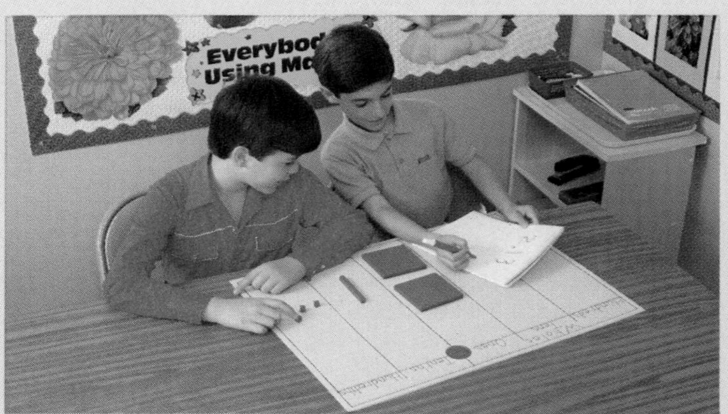

CONNECTIONS Use these anytime.

Problem of the Day

Number Sense Give a decimal number that will make each statement true.

______ is less than 0.60 but more than 0.50.

______ is less than 1.00 but more than 0.90.

(Answers may vary. Samples: 0.55, 0.92.)

Patterns

Hundredths Figure out each pattern, then give the next three decimals.

0.11, 0.22, 0.33, (0.44), (0.55), (0.66)

0.05, 0.10, 0.15, (0.20), (0.25), (0.30)

0.30, 0.40, 0.50, (0.60), (0.70), (0.80)

Math Connection

Logical Reasoning Solve the riddle to identify a mystery decimal number. I use only 3 different odd digits. If I were a money amount, you could add a quarter to me to have an amount equal to 3 twenty-dollar bills. What number am I? (59.75)

Classwork and Homework Supplements

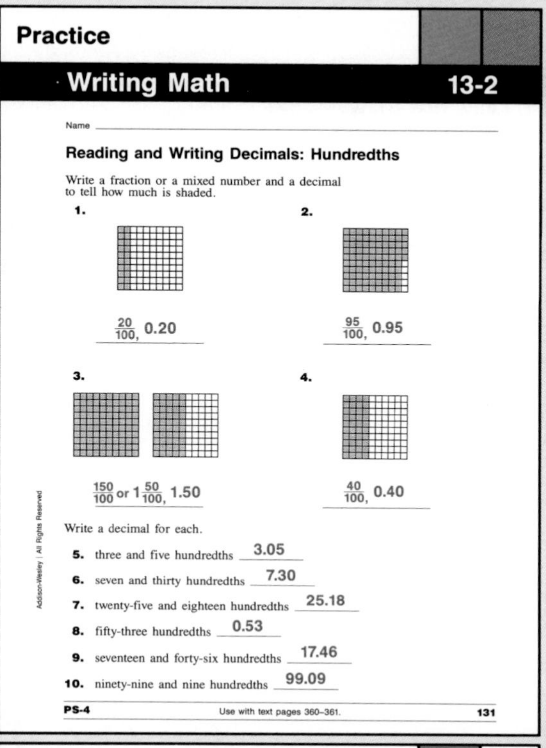

Practice

Writing Math 13-2

Name

Reading and Writing Decimals: Hundredths

Write a fraction or a mixed number and a decimal to tell how much is shaded.

1. $\frac{20}{100}$, 0.20
2. $\frac{95}{100}$, 0.95
3. $\frac{150}{100}$ or $1\frac{50}{100}$, 1.50
4. $\frac{40}{100}$, 0.40

Write a decimal for each.

5. three and five hundredths 3.05
6. seven and thirty hundredths 7.30
7. twenty-five and eighteen hundredths 25.18
8. fifty-three hundredths 0.53
9. seventeen and forty-six hundredths 17.46
10. ninety-nine and nine hundredths 99.09

PS-4 Use with text pages 360–361. 131

Addison-Wesley | All Rights Reserved

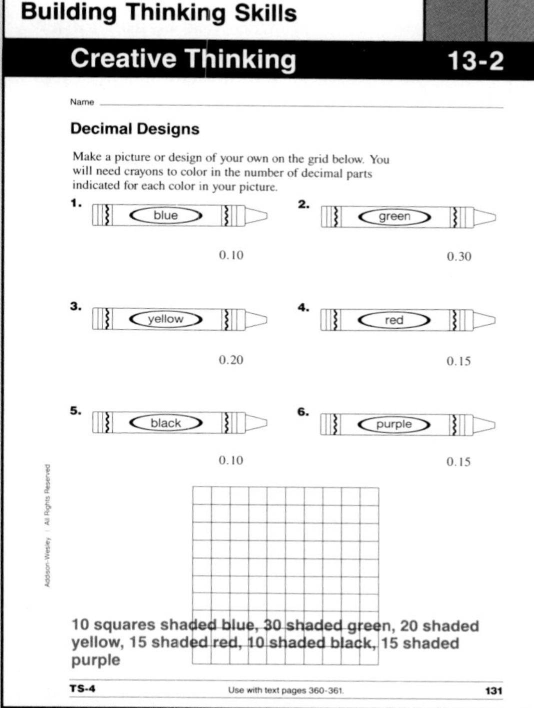

Building Thinking Skills

Creative Thinking 13-2

Name

Decimal Designs

Make a picture or design of your own on the grid below. You will need crayons to color in the number of decimal parts indicated for each color in your picture.

1. blue 0.10
2. green 0.30
3. yellow 0.20
4. red 0.15
5. black 0.10
6. purple 0.15

10 squares shaded blue, 30 shaded green, 20 shaded yellow, 15 shaded red, 10 shaded black, 15 shaded purple

TS-4 Use with text pages 360–361. 131

Addison-Wesley | All Rights Reserved

Reteaching

Skills Review 13-2

Name

Reading and Writing Decimals: Hundredths

Show	Say	Write
	"thirty-nine hundredths"	0.39
	mixed number	decimal
Say "one and six tenths" or "one and sixty hundredths"	$1\frac{6}{10}$ or $1\frac{60}{100}$	1.6 or 1.60

Write a fraction or mixed number and a decimal to tell how much is shaded.

1. $\frac{85}{100}$, 0.85
2. $\frac{25}{100}$, 0.25
3. $1\frac{62}{100}$, 1.62
4. $1\frac{10}{100}$, 1.10

Write a decimal for each.

5. two and six hundredths 2.06
6. fifty-nine hundredths 0.59
7. four and one hundredth 4.01
8. thirty-three hundredths 0.33

RS-4 Use with text pages 360–361. 131

Addison-Wesley | All Rights Reserved

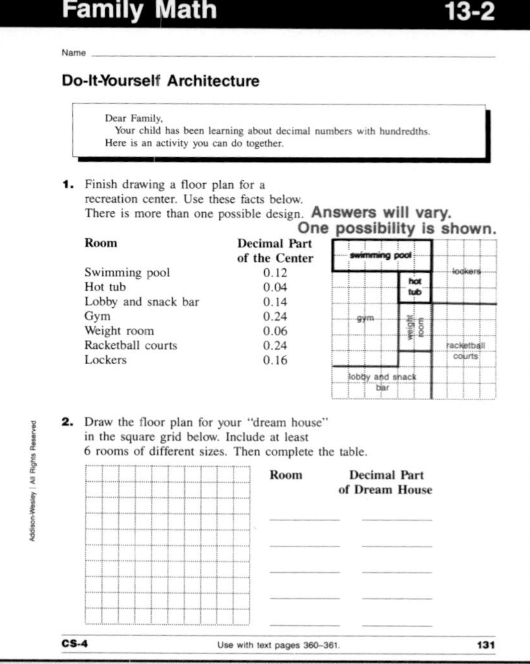

Challenges

Family Math 13-2

Name

Do-It-Yourself Architecture

Dear Family,
Your child has been learning about decimal numbers with hundredths. Here is an activity you can do together.

1. Finish drawing a floor plan for a recreation center. Use these facts below. There is more than one possible design. **Answers will vary. One possibility is shown.**

Room	Decimal Part of the Center
Swimming pool	0.12
Hot tub	0.04
Lobby and snack bar	0.14
Gym	0.24
Weight room	0.06
Racketball courts	0.24
Lockers	0.16

2. Draw the floor plan for your "dream house" in the square grid below. Include at least 6 rooms of different sizes. Then complete the table.

Room	Decimal Part of Dream House

CS-4 Use with text pages 360–361. 131

Addison-Wesley | All Rights Reserved

Options for Individual Needs

Basic

Exercises 1-5, 8-13
Data Bank, p. 482
Calculator Bank, p. 489
More Practice, p. 525, set A

Supplements
Reteaching 131 or
Practice 131
Challenges 131

Average

Exercises 1-17
Data Bank, p. 482
Calculator Bank, p. 489
More Practice, p. 525, set A

Supplements
Practice 131
Challenges 131 or
Thinking Skills 131

Extended

Exercises 2-17
Data Bank, p. 482
Calculator Bank, p. 489

Supplements
Challenges 131
Thinking Skills 131

Other Resources:
Problem-Solving Experiences in Mathematics, Grade 4, Problem 138
Mathematics, A Way of Thinking, Lesson 12-8
Math in Stride, Grade 4, pp. 188, 189
Using the Math Explorer Calculator: A Sourcebook for Teachers, Chapter 14

LESSON PLAN 13-2

OBJECTIVE 13-2
To read and write decimals with hundredths

Materials: graph paper, crayons, TA 22 (Decimal Place Value Charts), calculators

1. MOTIVATE AND TEACH

LEARN ABOUT IT

EXPLORE ► **Compare the size of the small boxes in the 10-by-10 square.** (They are the same size.)

TALK ABOUT IT ► **How many boxes are in each square? Explain how to name each as a fractional part of the whole.** (100; 1 hundredth, because each part is 1/100 of the whole)
► **Explain how the decimal point helps you understand a decimal number.** (Possible answer: It separates the wholes from the tenths and hundredths.)
► **Explain how the colored part of each square relates to the part *not* colored.** (Possible answer: Together, both parts equal the whole square.)
► **Compare the number of decimal places used to show tenths with the number used to show hundredths.** (One for tenths, two for hundredths; tenths is the first place to the right of the decimal point and hundredths is to the right of that.)
Student Edition answers: **1.** 100 **2.** Answers will vary. The two decimals written for each square must total 1.00.

2. CHECK UNDERSTANDING

TRY IT OUT

ERROR ALERT Omitting the whole number part of the decimal.

Reading and Writing Decimals
Hundredths

SKIER BEATS HIS TWIN BY 0.21 SECOND TO WIN GOLD

LEARN ABOUT IT

EXPLORE **Use Graph Paper**
To measure small amounts, you sometimes need to use a unit smaller than one tenth. Draw five 10 by 10 squares on graph paper. In each 10 by 10 square color in a different number of ones units.

TALK ABOUT IT See teaching notes.

1. How many ones units are in each 10 by 10 square?
2. For each of your five squares, how many parts out of 100 are colored? How many are not colored?

Show	Say	Write	
		fraction	decimal
	"twenty-one hundredths"	$\frac{21}{100}$	0.21
		mixed number	decimal
	"one and five tenths" or "one and fifty hundredths"	$1\frac{5}{10}$ $1\frac{50}{100}$	1.5 or 1.50

Tens	Ones	Tenths	Hundredths
3	1	2	8

To find the value of a digit in a decimal number, think about its place. A decimal point always separates the ones place from the tenths place.

TRY IT OUT

Write a fraction or mixed number and a decimal to tell how much is colored.

1. 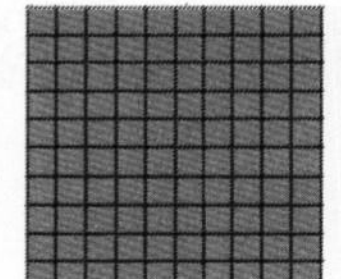 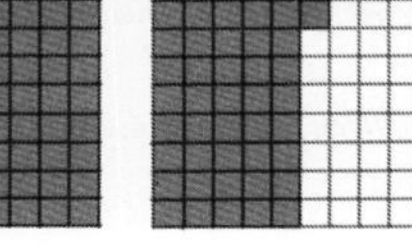

$1\frac{63}{100}$, 1.63

360

TEACHING OPTIONS

RETEACHING TIPS Have students use a decimal place value chart for hundredths to help them write whole units to the *left* of the decimal point. They use the two places to the *right* of the decimal point to show hundredths. Assign Reteaching Supplement 131.

ENRICHMENT Tell students the following: *In 1968, when Olympic skating speeds were timed to the nearest tenth of a second, 3 women tied for second place.* Ask: *Now that speeds are timed to hundredths of a second, explain why there have been no more ties.* (Times to the hundredth are 10 times more exact.)

PRACTICE

Write a fraction or mixed number and a decimal to tell how much is colored.

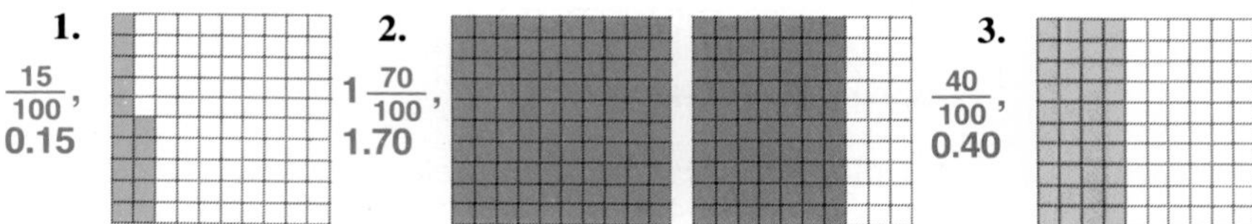

1. $\frac{15}{100}$, 0.15
2. $1\frac{70}{100}$, 1.70
3. $\frac{40}{100}$, 0.40

Write a decimal for each.

4. two and three hundredths 2.03
5. sixty-two hundredths 0.62
6. one and eighteen hundredths 1.18
7. four and fifty hundredths 4.50

APPLY

MATH REASONING Give the numbers from the list in which the digit 7 has these values.

7.32	0.47	1.74
5.7	2.07	3.87

8. 7 7.32
9. 0.7 5.7, 1.74
10. 0.07 0.47, 2.07, 3.87

PROBLEM SOLVING

11. **Health and Fitness Data Bank** In which Olympic times for the 1980 and 1984 Men's Slalom does the digit 6 have a value of 0.6? In which times does the digit 6 have a value of 0.06? See page 482. 39.62; 45.06; 44.26; 44.76

DATA BANK

► CALCULATOR

Change the number by adding or subtracting just once. Only one digit changes. Tell what you did to make each change.

12. Change 2.43 to 2.03. subtract 0.40
13. Change 10.35 to 10.4. add 0.05
14. Change 4.65 to 4.6 subtract 0.05
15. Change 7.10 to 8. add 0.90
16. Change 34.68 to 4.68. subtract 30
17. Change 1.65 to 1.6. subtract .05

More Practice, page 525, set A

3. Practice and Apply

Basic	1-5, 8-13
Average	1-17
Extended	2-17

PRACTICE

What is true for all the decimals in Exercises 1-7? (All include hundredths, so they all need 2 decimal places.)

APPLY

MATH REASONING ► **Explain how 7, 0.7, and 0.07 are different.** (7 means 7 whole ones, 0.7 means 7 of 10 fractional parts, or 7 tenths; and 0.07 means 7 of 100 fractional parts, or 7 hundredths.)

PROBLEM SOLVING ► **Explain how to look for the decimal numbers in the Data Bank.** (Look for decimals with a 6 in the tenths or hundredths place.)

CALCULATOR ► **Explain why you only add or subtract decimal numbers in Exercises 12-15 and 17.** (The change is always less than 1.)
► **Explain how to decide when to add or to subtract.** (Add when the changed number is greater than the original; subtract when it is smaller.)

13-2

Close and Assess

SHOW WHAT YOU KNOW

Have students use graph paper and crayons to draw 3 different pictures that represent 53/100, 8/100, and 1 85/100. Then have them label each of their pictures with an equivalent decimal. (Check students' pictures; 0.53, 0.08, 1.85.)

Quick Quiz

Write each decimal.
1. twenty-two hundredths (0.22)
2. sixty hundredths (0.60)
3. one and nineteen hundredths (1.19)
4. nine and six hundredths (9.06)

LESSON OPTIONS 13-3

Decimals: Counting and Order/Midchapter Review/Quiz

OBJECTIVE 13-3 To find the decimal when counting by tenths or hundredths

PREBOOK ACTIVITIES

QUICK REVIEW

Write a decimal for each fraction or mixed number.

1. $4\frac{3}{10}$ (4.3) **2.** $3\frac{17}{100}$ (3.17)
3. $\frac{87}{100}$ (0.87) **4.** $25\frac{9}{10}$ (25.9)
5. $99\frac{44}{100}$ (99.44) **6.** $6\frac{2}{10}$ (6.2)
7. $8\frac{4}{100}$ (8.04) **8.** $\frac{7}{100}$ (0.07)

PRIOR KNOWLEDGE

Have students explain how to use a calculator to count. (Clear; enter a starting number; press + 1; keep pressing = to make the display show continuous increases of 1.) Ask students how to count by twos or fives on the calculator. (Clear; enter a starting number; press + 2 or + 5; keep pressing = to display increases of 2 or 5.) Have students visualize how to use a calculator to count by tenths or by hundredths. (Clear; enter a starting number; press + 0.1 or + 0.01; keep pressing = to display increases of 0.1 or 0.01.)

COMMUNICATION

Writing in Math In their Math Journals, have students write an explanation of how counting up relates to addition and how counting back relates to another operation. (subtraction) Volunteers may share their writing aloud.

EXPLORE AND CONNECT

Materials: TA 6 (Place Value Models), TA 22 (Decimal Place Value Charts), TA 2 (Number Cubes numbered 0 to 5)
Grouping Suggestion: cooperative learning pairs
Students count by hundredths, using decimal values for place value materials as in the 2 earlier decimal explorations. Partners roll a number cube twice, using the 2 digits and place value materials to form the least possible decimal with ones and tenths. The first student records this decimal as the second adds 1 hundredth (1 ones block) to the model and records the new decimal. The first student keeps adding 1 hundredth at a time, the second keeps recording the new decimal, until they must trade 10 hundredths for 1 tenth. Trading tasks, pairs repeat with a new starting decimal. Have students summarize what they notice about counting by hundredths. (Possible answers: It is like counting by pennies; tenths do not change until you accumulate 10 hundredths to trade for 1 tenth.)

CONNECTIONS Use these anytime.

Problem of the Day

Number Sense Give a decimal to make each statement true. (Answers may vary. Samples are given.)
☐ comes between 0.2 and 0.3. (0.29)
☐ comes between 1.9 and 2. (1.93)
☐ comes between 10 and 10.1. (10.05)

Math Connection

Logical Reasoning Solve the riddle to identify a mystery decimal. The number uses only 2 different digits. It is a palindrome, which means it reads the same forward and backward. It is the smallest possible number with 2 whole number places and 2 decimal places. (10.01)

Creative Thinking

Calculator Dylan's calculator is very worn out. The only keys that work are 0, 1, 2, ., +, and =. How can he add 3.4 + 0.3 on his calculator? (Possible answer: 2.2 + 1.2 + 0.2 + 0.1)

Classwork and Homework Supplements

Practice

Skills Maintenance 13-3

Name ______________________

Decimals: Counting and Order

Give the next four decimals in the counting pattern.

1. 6.2 6.3 6.4 6.5 6.6 6.7 6.8 6.9 7.0 7.1 7.2

Write the decimal that comes after each number when you count by hundredths.

2. 4.62 4.63
3. 7.49 7.50
4. 2.99 3.00
5. 8.5 8.51
6. 6.43 6.44
7. 9.0 9.01
8. 1.59 1.60
9. .04 .05

Write the decimal that comes before each number when you count by hundredths.

10. 8.91 8.90
11. 7.29 7.28
12. 3.3 3.29
13. 0.24 0.23
14. 6.70 6.69
15. 14.11 14.10
16. 2.89 2.88
17. 9.5 9.49

Write the decimal that comes between each pair of number when you count by hundredths.

18. 6.99 and 7.01 7.00
19. 9.9 and 9.92 9.91
20. 0.08 and 0.10 0.09

132 Use with text page 362. PS-4

Building Thinking Skills

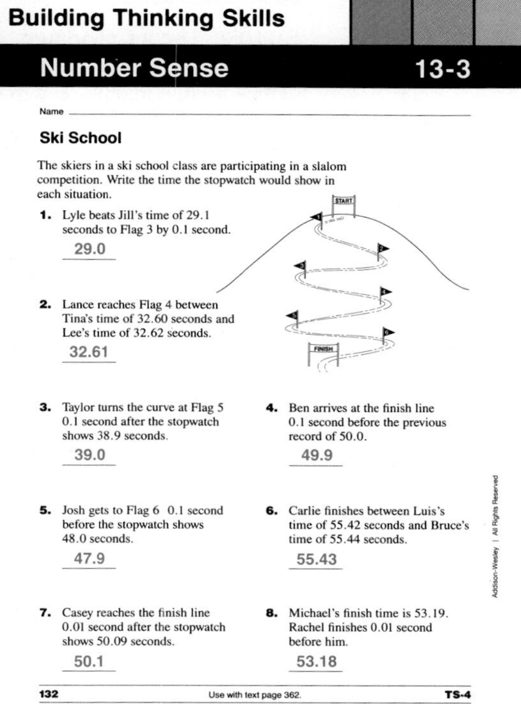

Number Sense 13-3

Name ______________________

Ski School

The skiers in a ski school class are participating in a slalom competition. Write the time the stopwatch would show in each situation.

1. Lyle beats Jill's time of 29.1 seconds to Flag 3 by 0.1 second. 29.0
2. Lance reaches Flag 4 between Tina's time of 32.60 seconds and Lee's time of 32.62 seconds. 32.61
3. Taylor turns the curve at Flag 5 0.1 second after the stopwatch shows 38.9 seconds. 39.0
4. Ben arrives at the finish line 0.1 second before the previous record of 50.0. 49.9
5. Josh gets to Flag 6 0.1 second before the stopwatch shows 48.0 seconds. 47.9
6. Carlie finishes between Luis's time of 55.42 seconds and Bruce's time of 55.44 seconds. 55.43
7. Casey reaches the finish line 0.01 second after the stopwatch shows 50.09 seconds. 50.1
8. Michael's finish time is 53.19. Rachel finishes 0.01 second before him. 53.18

132 Use with text page 362. TS-4

Reteaching

Calculators 13-3

Name ______________________

Decimals: Counting and Order

You can use a calculator to help you count and order by tenths and hundredths. When counting by tenths, what decimals come next?

14.7, 14.8, ______, ______, ______

Press ON/AC	Press 14.7 +	Press 0.1 =	Press =	Press =	Press =
0	14.7	14.8	14.9	15	15.1

14.9, 15.0, 15.1 come next.

When counting by hundredths, press **0.01** instead of **0.1**.

Give the next four decimals in the counting pattern.

1. 15.2 15.3 15.4 15.5 15.6 15.7 15.8 15.9 16.0
2. 1.52 1.53 1.54 1.55 1.56 1.57 1.58 1.59 1.60

Write the decimal that comes before each number when you count by hundredths.

3. 1.52, 1.53
4. 1.46, 1.47
5. 1.70, 1.71

Write the decimal that comes after each number when you count by hundredths.

6. 1.85, 1.86
7. 1.26, 1.27
8. 15.12, 15.13

Write the decimal that comes between each pair of numbers when you count by hundredths.

9. 1.55, 1.56, 1.57
10. 4.50, 4.51, 4.52

132 Use with text page 362. RS-4

Challenges

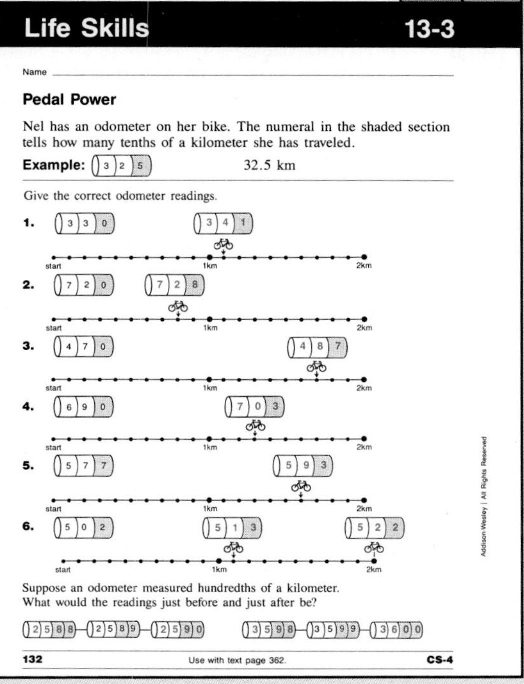

Life Skills 13-3

Name ______________________

Pedal Power

Nel has an odometer on her bike. The numeral in the shaded section tells how many tenths of a kilometer she has traveled.

Example: 3 2 5 32.5 km

Give the correct odometer readings.

Suppose an odometer measured hundredths of a kilometer. What would the readings just before and just after be?

2 5 8 8 — 2 5 8 9 — 2 5 9 0   3 5 9 8 — 3 5 9 9 — 3 6 0 0

132 Use with text page 362. CS-4

Options for Individual Needs

Basic

Exercises 1-4, 9-14; 3-14
Calculator Bank, p. 489
More Practice, p. 525, set B

Supplements
Reteaching 132 or
Practice 132
Thinking Skills 132

Average

Exercises 1-4; 1-14
Calculator Bank, p. 489
More Practice, p. 525, set B

Supplements
Practice 132
Challenges 132 or
Thinking Skills 132

Extended

Exercises 3-13; 3-14
Calculator Bank, p. 489

Supplements
Challenges 132
Thinking Skills 132

Other Resources:
Problem-Solving Experiences in Mathematics, Grade 4, Problem 139
Mathematics, A Way of Thinking, Lesson 12-3
Math In Stride, Grade 4, pp. 190, 191
Using the Math Explorer Calculator: A Sourcebook for Teachers, Chapter 14

LESSON PLAN 13-3

OBJECTIVE 13-3
To find the decimal when counting by tenths or hundredths

Materials: calculators, TA 22 (Decimal Place Value Charts)

Grouping Suggestion: pairs

1. MOTIVATE AND TEACH

LEARN ABOUT IT

EXPLORE ► **Justify the key strokes used to count by tenths and by hundredths on the calculator.** (Begin with 0; use + because counting is repeated adding; enter 0.1 to show counting by tenths or 0.01 to show counting by hundredths; keep pressing = to repeat the addition.)

TALK ABOUT IT ► **Explain how many tenths make 1 whole.** (10 tenths, because you would trade that many for 1 one.)
► **Notice the display for the decimal after 0.9 and explain what the calculator did.** (0.1 more than 0.9 is 10 tenths, which is equivalent to 1 whole; the calculator simply shows 1.)
► **Explain why it takes longer to reach 1 whole when you count by hundredths.** (It takes 10 hundredths just to equal 0.1 and 100 hundredths to equal 1 whole.)
Student Edition answers: **1**. 1.0, 2.0, 3.0; 3.6, 4.1, 4.9 **2.** 0.10, 0.20, 0.30, 1.00; Possible answer: counting by hundredths is like regular counting.

2. CHECK UNDERSTANDING

TRY IT OUT

ERROR ALERT Having trouble counting by hundredths when decimals are given in tenths.

Decimals
Counting and Order

LEARN ABOUT IT

EXPLORE **Use a Calculator**
Use a calculator to count by tenths and then by hundredths. Try to guess the next decimal on the display before you press [=] each time.

[ON/AC] 0 [+] 0.1 [=] [=] [=]
Keep pressing the [=] key.
[ON/AC] 0 [+] 0.01 [=] [=] [=]
Keep pressing the [=] key.

TALK ABOUT IT See teaching notes.

1. When you count by tenths, what decimal comes after 0.9? 1.9? 2.9? What decimal comes before 3.7? 4.2? 5?
2. When you count by hundredths, what decimal comes after 0.09? 0.19? 0.29? 0.99? What pattern do you see?

PRACTICE

Give the next four decimals in the counting pattern.

1. 13.1 13.2 13.3 13.4 13.5 13.6 13.7 ||| ||| ||| ||| **13.8 13.9 14.0 14.1**

Write the decimal that comes after each number when you count by hundredths.

2. 8.34 **8.35** **3.** 9.9 **10.0** **4.** 7.43 **7.44** **5.** 8.89 **8.90** **6.** 8.99 **9.0**

Write the decimal that comes before each number when you count by hundredths.

7. 0.77 **0.76** **8.** 1.5 **1.49** **9.** 17.11 **17.10** **10.** 35.4 **35.3** **11.** 99.91 **99.90**

Write the decimal that comes between each pair of numbers when you count by hundredths.

12. 1.47 and 1.49 **1.48** **13.** 3.4 and 3.42 **3.41** **14.** 5.05 and 5.07 **5.06**

More Practice, page 525, set B

TEACHING OPTIONS

RETEACHING TIPS Have students write the decimal numbers on a decimal place value chart. When they see that a decimal given only in tenths has 0 hundredths, they may be able to count on or back more easily. Assign Reteaching Supplement 132.

COMPUTER **Building Perspective, Sunburst Communications, Copyright 1986** For all students (best in pairs). Students find colored buildings in a 3-by-3 array after seeing 4 side views. Students may first guess, then check their answers. The lesson requires 10 to 15 min.

Midchapter Review/Quiz

Write a fraction and a decimal for the colored part.

1. red $\frac{5}{10}$, 0.5
2. blue $\frac{5}{10}$, 0.5

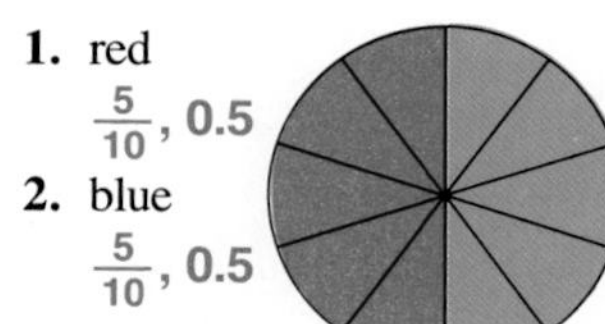

3. green $\frac{8}{10}$, 0.8
4. yellow $\frac{2}{10}$, 0.2

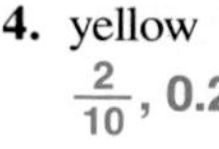

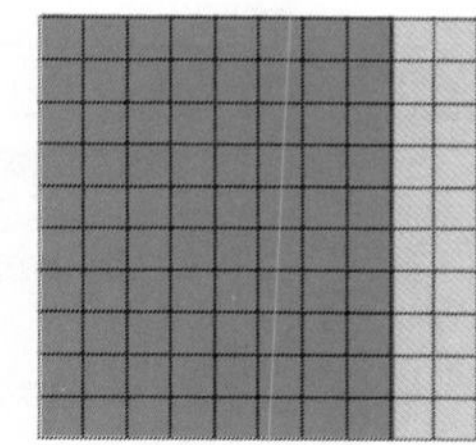

Write a fraction or mixed number and a decimal for the colored part.

5. $\frac{54}{100}$, 0.54

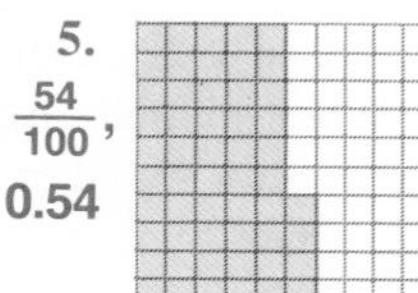

6.

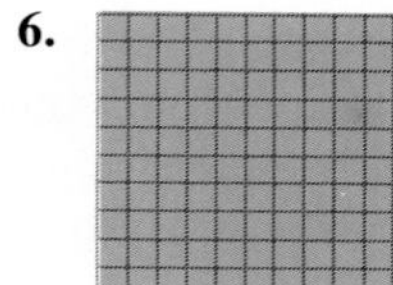

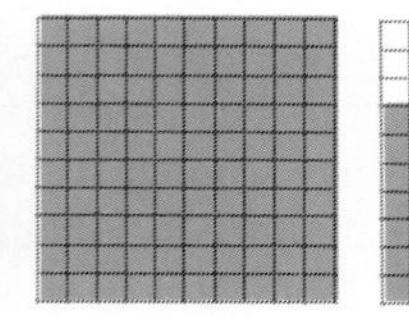

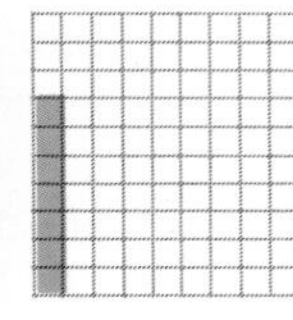

$2\frac{7}{100}$, 2.07

Write a decimal for the amount.

7. fifteen and seven tenths 15.7
8. ten and one tenth 10.1

Find the numbers in the list for which 5 has the value given.

9. 0.5 9.57, 74.5
10. 50 53.41, 256.9
11. 5 65.8, 125
12. 0.05 6.35, 0.95

6.35	53.41	125	74.5
65.8	0.95	9.57	256.9

PROBLEM SOLVING

13. Holly made up this puzzle problem. Can you solve it?
The tenths digit of a 2-digit decimal number is 3 more than twice the ones digit. The ones digit is 2. What is the decimal number? 2.7

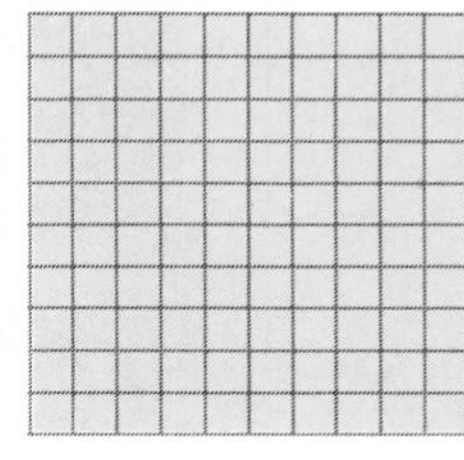

14. Rick painted 0.3 of this wall. Later he painted another 0.4. What decimal shows the amount of the wall Rick painted? 0.7

363

3. Practice and Apply

Basic	1-4, 9-14; 3-14
Average	1-14; 1-14
Extended	3-13; 3-14

PRACTICE

How are Exercises 1 to 4 alike? (Each one asks for a fraction and a decimal number for a certain amount.) *What clue can help you write Exercises 7 and 8 correctly?* (Write a decimal point at the word *and*.) *Which number in the box for Exercises 9-12 is different from all the others? Why?* (125 has no decimal places.)

ITEM ANALYSIS The following table correlates the Midchapter Review/Quiz items with the lesson objectives.

Items	Objectives
1-4	13-1
5, 6	13-2
7-9	13-1
10	13-2
11	13-1
12	13-2
13, 14	13-1

13-3

Close and Assess

SAY WHAT YOU THINK Have students work in pairs. The first student says any decimal in tenths or hundredths. The second gives the decimals in hundredths that come just before and just after the decimal. Then have partners switch roles and repeat the task. (Check students' decimals.)

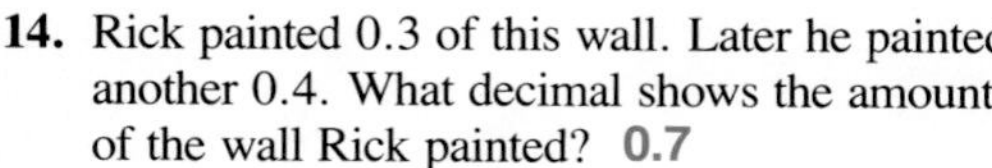

Quick Quiz

Continue each pattern 3 more times.

1. 4.6, 4.7, 4.8, (4.9), (5.0), (5.1)
2. 2.27, 2.28, 2.29, (2.30), (2.31), (2.32)

LESSON OPTIONS 13-4

Comparing and Ordering Decimals

OBJECTIVE 13-4 To compare and order decimals

PREBOOK ACTIVITIES

QUICK REVIEW

What decimal comes *after* each number when you count by hundredths?

1. 5.78 (5.79) **2.** 0.89 (0.90) **3.** 1.6 (1.61)

What decimal comes *before* each number when you count by hundredths?

4. 0.65 (0.64) **5.** 1.5 (1.49) **6.** 8.08 (8.07)

PRIOR KNOWLEDGE

Ask students how a number line is organized. (Possible answer: Numbers are arranged from smallest to largest.) Have students generalize how to compare two numbers on or off a number line. (Possible answer: Starting with the digits on the left, compare numbers digit by digit to find which is larger and which is smaller.)

COMMUNICATION

Writing in Math Write the symbols $<$, $>$, and $=$ on the chalkboard. In their Math Journals, have students describe or identify each symbol and illustrate its proper usage by writing a number sentence for each. (Check students' writing: $<$ means "is less than," $>$ means "is greater than," and $=$ means "is equal to;" possible illustrations: $3 < 4$; $5 > 4$, $4.5 = 4.5$.)

EXPLORE AND CONNECT

Materials: TA 12 (Centimeter Graph Paper), crayons or markers

Grouping Suggestion: cooperative learning pairs

Partners draw models to compare decimals. Write these decimals on the chalkboard for all pairs to use: 0.2, 0.3, 0.4, 0.5, 0.22, 0.33, 0.44, 0.55. Each partner selects 4 different decimals—2 with tenths and 2 with hundredths—to represent by coloring 10-by-10 graph-paper squares. When partners have created models for the 8 given decimals, they work together to put them in size order from least to greatest. Then they record the decimal numbers that match the models. (0.2, 0.22, 0.3, 0.33, 0.4, 0.44, 0.5, 0.55) Conclude by having students create rules for comparing decimal numbers by comparing only the digits, not the models. (Possible answers: First compare tenths, then compare hundredths; the decimal numbers compare the same way the digits compare.)

CONNECTIONS Use these anytime.

Problem of the Day

Number Sense Add a decimal point to each number to make the statements true. (Answers may vary. Samples are given.)

$345 > 345$ $(34.5 > 3.45)$
$402 < 402$ $(4.02 < 40.2)$
$101 = 101$ $(1.01 = 1.01)$

Creative Thinking

Analyzing Data Analyze the Data Bank on page 482 for *Alpine Skiing: Men's Slalom*. What do you notice about the scores? (Possible answer: In 1984, Phil Mahre won a gold medal with the fastest time for the gold medalists listed in all 3 years; in 1980, he won a silver medal with the slowest time listed for all the silver medalists.)

Life Skills

Health One day, Lamar stayed home from school with a fever. That morning, his temperature was 101.4. By noon, his temperature was 102. Did his fever go up or down? Explain. (It went up—102 is a greater number than 101.4.)

Classwork and Homework Supplements

Practice

Number Sense 13-4

Name ______

Comparing and Ordering Decimals

Decide whether each equation is true or false. If it is false, change the <, >, or = sign to make it true.

1. 0.82 < 0.87 __true__
2. 0.90 > 0.9 __false, =__
3. 17 = 17.5 __false, <__
4. 6.2 = 6.20 __true__
5. 5.27 < 5.29 __true__
6. 2.72 > 2.68 __true__
7. 7.16 > 7.2 __false, <__
8. 3.8 < 3.08 __false, >__
9. 0.23 > 0.32 __false, <__
10. 9.67 < 9.7 __true__
11. 6.05 = 6.50 __false, <__
12. 0.80 < 0.08 __false, >__
13. 0.66 > 0.06 __true__
14. 2.91 > 2.8 __true__
15. Order these numbers from greatest to least.
    0.52, 0.25, 0.55 __0.55; 0.52; 0.25__

Use the number list to answer these questions.

8.02
5
3.84
4.9
7.53
7.2
7.8
5.1

16. Which numbers are greater than 7.53? __8.02; 7.8__
17. Which numbers are less than 5.1? __5; 3.84; 4.9__
18. Which numbers are between 3.6 and 5.1? __5; 3.84; 4.9__
19. Order the numbers between 5 and 8 from least to greatest. __5.1; 7.2; 7.53; 7.8__

Building Thinking Skills

Math Reasoning 13-4

Name ______

Creating Decimal Numbers

Write all of the decimal numbers you can create that are greater than 20 and smaller than 100. In each number you can use each of the 4 numerals only once.

1. 0, 2, 4, 5

(54.20)	54.02
52.40	52.04
50.24	50.42
45.20	45.02
42.05	42.50
40.52	40.25
25.40	25.04
24.50	24.05
20.54	<u>20.45</u>

2. 1, 3, 6, 8

(86.31)	86.13
83.61	83.16
81.63	81.36
68.31	68.13
63.81	63.18
61.83	61.38
38.61	38.16
36.81	36.18
31.86	<u>31.68</u>

3. 0, 2, 3, 8

(83.20)	83.02
82.30	82.03
80.32	80.23
38.20	38.02
32.80	32.08
30.82	30.28
28.30	28.03
23.80	23.08
20.83	<u>20.38</u>

4. Ring the largest number in each box. Write the circled numbers in order from least to greatest.
   __54.20, 83.20, 86.31__
5. Underline the smallest number in each box. Write the underlined numbers in order from least to greatest.
   __20.38, 20.45, 31.68__

Reteaching

Number Sense 13-4

Name ______

Comparing and Ordering Decimals

Which number is larger, 6.9 or 6.4? Here is a way to compare decimals.

Line up the decimal points. → Start at the left. Find the first place where the digits are different. → Compare these digits. → The numbers compare the same way the digits compare.

6.9 / 6.4 — 6.9 / 6.4 — ones → same; tenths → different — 9 > 4 — 6.9 > 6.4; 6.9 > 6.4

Write >, <, or = for each ◯.

1. 6.7 (>) 4.8
2. 21.5 (<) 21.9
3. 4.76 (>) 4.67

Write whether each equation is true or false. If it is false, write <, >, or = to make it true.

4. 3.45 < 3.54 __true__
5. 6.54 < 6.65 __true__
6. 0.43 = 4.03 __false; <__
7. 8.8 > 8.79 __true__

Use the numbers in the box to answer these questions.

6.5	4.3
2.1	7.21

8. Write the numbers greater than 4.9. __6.5, 7.21__
9. Write the numbers less than 2.34. __2.1__
10. Write the numbers between 6.44 and 7.61. __6.5, 7.21__
11. Order the numbers from least to greatest. __2.1, 4.3, 6.5, 7.21__

Challenges

Cooperative Activities 13-4

Name ______

Across-the-Ocean Game

Play this game in 2 teams of 3 players each. You will need a chip marked **S** on one side and **L** on the other, 3 red markers, and 3 blue markers. Each team needs to place 3 markers on the starting rafts (the 3 darker hexagons).

Rules

Take turns following these steps:

1. Flip the L and S chip.
2. If you get L, move to an adjacent raft with a larger number.
3. If you get S, move to an adjacent raft with a smaller number.
4. You must move your marker if you can.
5. If you land on a raft with the other team's marker on it, the other team must move the marker back to one of their starting rafts.
6. The first team to move all markers to the other side of the ocean is the winner.

HEXAGON OCEAN

0.33, 0.36, 0.72, 0.4, 0.13, 0.6, 0.47, 0.51, 0.27, 0.57, 0.63, 1.27, 0.37, Team A, 0.32, 0.17, 0.2, 0.72, Team B, 0.21, 2.56, 0.85, 0.25, 2.12, 2.57, 0.64, 1.23, 0.63, 1.45, 0.75, 2.33, 0.45

Hint: 0.4 = 0.40

Options for Individual Needs

Basic

Exercises 1-3, 7-15
Calculator Bank, p. 489
More Practice, p. 509, set D

Supplements
Reteaching 133 or
Practice 133

Average

Exercises 1-17
Calculator Bank, p. 489
More Practice, p. 509, set D

Supplements
Practice 133
Challenges 133 or
Thinking Skills 133

Extended

Exercises 5-17
Calculator Bank, p. 489

Supplements
Challenges 133
Thinking Skills 133

Other Resources:
Problem-Solving Experiences in Mathematics, Grade 4, Problem 140
Mathematics, A Way of Thinking, Lesson 12-4
Math In Stride, Grade 4, p. 193

LESSON PLAN 13-4

OBJECTIVE 13-4
To compare and order decimals

Materials: counters, TA 22 (Decimal Place Value Charts)

1. MOTIVATE AND TEACH

LEARN ABOUT IT

EXPLORE ► **Express the data in the table in your own words.** (Possible answer: To the nearest tenth of a mile, it shows 4 d of Larry's bicycle rides.)
► **Explain how the blocks show Monday's distance.** (If each ones block counts for 1 tenth of a mile, then 10 ones blocks equal 10 tenths, or 1 whole mile. So the 2 groups of 10 ones blocks represent 2 miles. The 8 ones blocks equal 8 tenths, or .8 of a mile. All together, the blocks represent 2.8 miles.)

TALK ABOUT IT ► **Analyze how the decimal point can help you compare decimals.** (Line up decimal points, then compare the numbers digit by digit as you would compare whole numbers.)
► **Explain why 8.2 is less than 8.25.** (Possible answer: 8.2 and 8.25 both have 8 ones and 2 tenths, but 8.25 has 5 hundredths and 8.2 has 0 hundredths, so 8.25 is greater.)
Student Edition answers: **1.** Monday **2.** Thursday, Monday, Wednesday, Tuesday

2. CHECK UNDERSTANDING

TRY IT OUT

ERROR ALERT Failing to line up decimal points before comparing. Confusing inequality symbols.

Comparing and Ordering Decimals

LEARN ABOUT IT

EXPLORE Use Ones Blocks
Larry measured how far he rode his bicycle each day. You can compare the distances by showing them with ones blocks. Each block counts for one tenth of a mile. These blocks show Monday's distance. Use blocks to show the other distances.

Larry's Riding Distances	
Monday	2.8 miles
Tuesday	2.1 miles
Wednesday	2.5 miles
Thursday	3 miles

Monday 2.8 miles

TALK ABOUT IT See teaching notes.

1. Did Larry ride farther on Monday or Tuesday?
2. How can you list the days in order from longest to shortest?

Here is another way to compare decimals.

Line up the decimal points.	Start at the left. Find the first place where the digits are different.	Compare these digits.	The numbers compare the same way the digits compare.
2.8 2.5	2.8 2.5	8 > 5	2.8 > 2.5

To order decimals such as 8.25, 8.2, 8.35, 8.29, compare the numbers two at a time.

List the numbers from least to greatest	8.2	8.25	8.29	8.35
or greatest to least.	8.35	8.29	8.25	8.2

TRY IT OUT

Write >, <, or = for each ▥.

1. 4.6 ▥ 5.3 < **2.** 18.7 ▥ 18.3 > **3.** 6.58 ▥ 6.52 >

4. Order these decimals from least to greatest. 3.45 3.54 3.49 3.52
3.45, 3.49, 3.52, 3.54

364

TEACHING OPTIONS

RETEACHING TIPS Students use counters on decimal place value charts. For Exercise 1, 4 counters are put in the ones place and 6 in the tenths. Under that set, 5 counters are put in the ones place and 3 in the tenths. Students then compare decimals. Assign Reteaching Supplement 133.

ENRICHMENT Family Math
With another family member, students make up 7 rules such as these: Find a decimal with only odd digits and find a decimal with 0 tenths. They set a time limit, then look in newspapers and on grocery receipts for decimals with tenths and hundredths.

PRACTICE

Decide whether each equation is true or false. If it is false, change the <, >, or = sign to make it true.

1. 4.38 < 4.42 **true** **2.** 9.6 > 9.58 **true** **3.** 8.3 = 8.03 **false, >**

4. 7.46 > 7.54 **false, <** **5.** 0.5 > 0.51 **false, <** **6.** 1.8 > 1.73 **true**

7. Order these numbers from greatest to least. 0.37, 0.41, 0.39 **0.41, 0.39, 0.37**

Use the number list to answer these questions.

8.73	3.2
8.49	7
4.9	4.38
7.1	8.05

8. List the numbers greater than 8.5. **8.73**

9. List the numbers less than 4.91. **4.9, 3.2, 4.38**

10. List the numbers between 4.83 and 7.01. **4.9, 7**

11. Order the numbers between 4 and 8 from least to greatest. **4.38, 4.9, 7, 7.1**

APPLY

MATH REASONING

12. Use these digits to fit in the empty boxes. How many different decimals can you make greater than 25? What are they?
See Additional Answers.

□□.□□

PROBLEM SOLVING

13. Larry's sister, Rhonda, also kept a record of her riding distances for the same days. On which days did Rhonda ride a shorter distance than Larry? Use the table on page 364.
Monday and Thursday

Rhonda's Riding Distances	
Monday	2.6 miles
Tuesday	2.5 miles
Wednesday	2.8 miles
Thursday	2.9 miles

► MENTAL MATH Counting On

Use mental math and count on by tenths to find these sums.

14. 1.3 + 0.1 **1.4** **15.** 3.4 + 0.2 **3.6**

16. 5.2 + 0.3 **5.5** **17.** 2.7 + 0.3 **3.0**

More Practice, page 509, Set D

3. Practice and Apply

Basic	1-3, 7-15
Average	1-17
Extended	5-17

Additional Answers: See p. T79.

PRACTICE

How might you begin to decide whether Exercises 1-6 are true or false? (Possible answer: Ignore the given sign and figure out the relationship yourself.)

APPLY

MATH REASONING ► **Explain which digits must appear in which places to meet the conditions of Exercise 12.** (3 or 5 in the tens place; 30 and 50 are greater than 25.)

PROBLEM SOLVING

► **Generalize about Rhonda's riding distances compared with Larry's.** (Possible answer: There is less variation in Rhonda's distances than in Larry's.)

MENTAL MATH ► **Analyze Exercises 14-17 to decide how many tenths to count on for each one.** (14: 1; 15: 2; 16 and 17: 3)

► **Explain how Exercise 17 is different from the others.** (Its sum goes to the next whole number.)

Close and Assess

WRITE WHAT YOU THINK For each pair of decimals below, have students write < or > and name the place that helped them decide which number was greater in each pair.

1. 6.01 ○ 6.02 **2.** 0.74 ○ 0.68
3. 3.84 ○ 4.83 **4.** 6.34 ○ 6.3
(**1.** <, hundredths **2.** >, tenths **3.** <, ones **4.** >, hundredths)

Quick Quiz

Write <, >, or =.
1. 3.7 ○ 3.6 **2.** 0.46 ○ 0.5
Order from least to greatest.
3. 5, 4.8, 4.95, 5.03
(**1.** > **2.** < **3.** 4.8, 4.95, 5, 5.03)

LESSON OPTIONS 13-5

Rounding Decimals

OBJECTIVE 13-5 To round decimals to a whole number

PREBOOK ACTIVITIES

QUICK REVIEW

Round each money amount to the nearest dollar.

1. $4.89 ($5)	**2.** $3.36 ($3)	**3.** $0.56 ($1)
4. $32.23 ($32)	**5.** $3.50 ($4)	**6.** $8.49 ($8)
7. $7.75 ($8)	**8.** $49.61 ($50)	**9.** $84.29 ($84)
10. $30.44 ($30)	**11.** $99.60 ($100)	**12.** $19.04 ($19)

PRIOR KNOWLEDGE

Have students tell how to round 673, 350, and 738 to the nearest hundred. (Possible answer: Look at the digit in the tens place; if it is 5 or more, round up; if it is less than 5, round down; 700, 400, 700.) Have students generalize about rounding to any given place. (Possible answer: Look at the place to the right of the target place; round up if it is 5 or more; round down if it is less than 5.) Have students guess how to apply the same basic rules to round decimals to the nearest whole number. (Possible answer: Look at the tenths place since it is to the right of the decimal point; if it is 5 tenths or more, round up; if it is less than 5 tenths, round down.)

COMMUNICATION

Writing in Math Have students summarize the rounding rules in their Math Journals, illustrating each with a sample rounded number that observes the rule. (Check students' writing.)

EXPLORE AND CONNECT

Materials: TA 12 (Centimeter Graph Paper), crayons, TA 3 (Number Cards 0-9)

Grouping Suggestion: cooperative learning pairs

Partners build decimals with number cards, then draw models to visualize how the decimals round to the nearest whole number. One student chooses 2 number cards that will tell how many ones and tenths a decimal will have. The other student draws a model of the number on graph paper using 10-by-10 squares. Partners record the whole numbers between which the decimal falls, then circle the closer number. They record their decision, checking that the drawing confirms their conclusion. Students repeat the activity 3 times, trading tasks. Have volunteers show some of their models to validate their rounding decision and generalize how to round decimals to the nearest whole number. (If there are 5 or more tenths, round up; if there are less than 5 tenths, round down.)

CONNECTIONS Use these anytime.

Problem of the Day

Number Riddle Use all the clues to find the mystery decimal: When rounded to the nearest ten, I am the number of days in April. When rounded to the nearest whole, I am a multiple of 7. All my digits are even and they add up to 12. (28.2 or 28.02)

Life Skills

Gas Mileage Teddy's car averages 24.8 mi/gal of gas. Sally's car averages 29.5 mi/gal. Round each figure to the nearest mile. Whose car goes farther on a gallon of gas? Whose car would use about 4 gal of gas to go 100 mi? (Sally's; Teddy's)

Math Connection

Measurement 1 m is equivalent to 39.37 in. Compare the length of a meter with the length of a yard. (A meter is about 3 in. longer than a yard, which is 36 in.)

Classwork and Homework Supplements

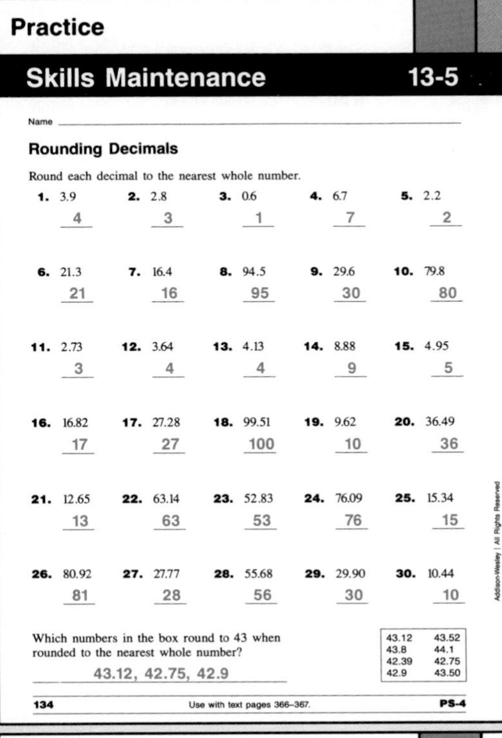

Practice

Skills Maintenance 13-5

Name ________________

Rounding Decimals

Round each decimal to the nearest whole number.

1. 3.9 → 4	**2.** 2.8 → 3	**3.** 0.6 → 1	**4.** 6.7 → 7	**5.** 2.2 → 2
6. 21.3 → 21	**7.** 16.4 → 16	**8.** 94.5 → 95	**9.** 29.6 → 30	**10.** 79.8 → 80
11. 2.73 → 3	**12.** 3.64 → 4	**13.** 4.13 → 4	**14.** 8.88 → 9	**15.** 4.95 → 5
16. 16.82 → 17	**17.** 27.28 → 27	**18.** 99.51 → 100	**19.** 9.62 → 10	**20.** 36.49 → 36
21. 12.65 → 13	**22.** 63.14 → 63	**23.** 52.83 → 53	**24.** 76.09 → 76	**25.** 15.34 → 15
26. 80.92 → 81	**27.** 27.77 → 28	**28.** 55.68 → 56	**29.** 29.90 → 30	**30.** 10.44 → 10

Which numbers in the box round to 43 when rounded to the nearest whole number?

43.12, 42.75, 42.9

43.12	43.52
43.8	44.1
42.39	42.75
42.9	43.50

134 Use with text pages 366–367. PS-4

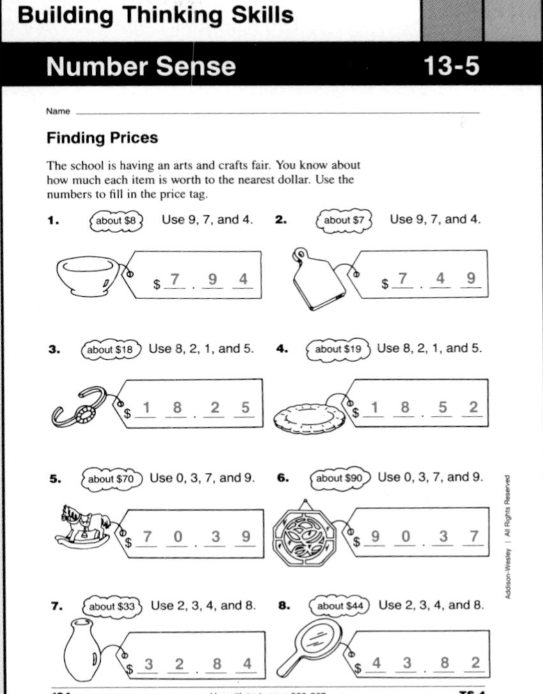

Building Thinking Skills

Number Sense 13-5

Name ________________

Finding Prices

The school is having an arts and crafts fair. You know about how much each item is worth to the nearest dollar. Use the numbers to fill in the price tag.

1. about $8 — Use 9, 7, and 4. — $7.94
2. about $7 — Use 9, 7, and 4. — $7.49
3. about $18 — Use 8, 2, 1, and 5. — $18.25
4. about $19 — Use 8, 2, 1, and 5. — $18.52
5. about $70 — Use 0, 3, 7, and 9. — $70.39
6. about $90 — Use 0, 3, 7, and 9. — $90.37
7. about $33 — Use 2, 3, 4, and 8. — $32.84
8. about $44 — Use 2, 3, 4, and 8. — $43.82

134 Use with text pages 366–367. TS-4

Reteaching

Skills Review 13-5

Name ________________

Rounding Decimals

Here is how you can round a decimal to the nearest whole number.

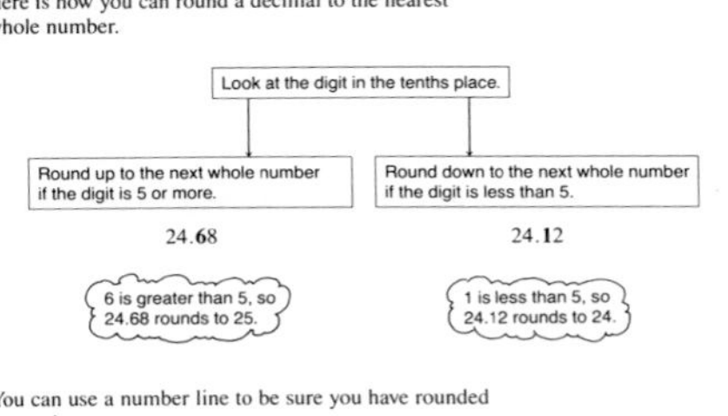

Look at the digit in the tenths place.
Round up to the next whole number if the digit is 5 or more.
Round down to the next whole number if the digit is less than 5.
24.68
24.12
6 is greater than 5, so 24.68 rounds to 25.
1 is less than 5, so 24.12 rounds to 24.

You can use a number line to be sure you have rounded correctly.

24 24.1 24.2 24.3 24.4 24.5 24.6 24.7 24.8 24.9 25
round down — 24.12 rounds to 24
round up — 24.68 rounds to 25

Round each decimal to the nearest whole number. Use the number line to check your answer.

1. 24.11 24 **2.** 24.86 25 **3.** 24.01 24 **4.** 24.98 25

Round each decimal to the nearest whole number.

5. 4.6 5	**6.** 7.2 7	**7.** 0.7 1
8. 5.1 5	**9.** 14.3 14	**10.** 24.9 25
11. 7.38 7	**12.** 4.79 5	**13.** 20.75 21
14. 15.66 16	**15.** 34.34 34	**16.** 61.29 61

134 Use with text pages 366–367. RS-4

Challenges

Number Sense 13-5

Name ________________

Number Builders

Use these cards to build the numbers below. Each card may be used only once in each number.

3
2
9
6
1
4
0

1. 9 6 . 4 3 — largest number
2. 0 1 . 2 3 — smallest number
3. 0 1 . 2 9 — smallest number using the 9 card
4. 6 0 . 1 2 — smallest number between 60 and 90
5. 2 9 . 6 4 — largest number between 10 and 30
6. 1 6 . 9 4 — largest number between 16 and 19
7. 4 9 . 6 3 — largest number that rounds to 50
8. 2 4 . 9 6 — largest number that rounds to 25
9. 6 4 . 9 3 — largest number that rounds to 65
10. 4 0 . 2 1 — number closest to 40 with an odd digit in the hundredths place
11. 2 1 . 4 9 — largest number that rounds to 21
12. 4 6 . 9 3 — largest number that rounds to 50 with a 9 in the tenths place

134 Use with text pages 366–367. CS-4

Options for Individual Needs

Basic

Exercises 1-15, 24-31
Data Bank, p. 482
More Practice, p. 509, set E

Supplements
Reteaching 134 or
Practice 134

Average

Exercises 1-31
Data Bank, p. 482
More Practice, p. 509, set E

Supplements
Practice 134
Challenges 134 or
Thinking Skills 134

Extended

Exercises 4-8, 14-31
Data Bank, p. 482

Supplements
Challenges 134
Thinking Skills 134

Other Resources:
Problem-Solving Experiences in Mathematics, Grade 4, Problem 25
Math In Stride, Grade 4, pp. 194, 199, 200

13-5

LESSON PLAN 13-5

OBJECTIVE 13-5
To round decimals to a whole number

Grouping Suggestion: pairs

1. MOTIVATE AND TEACH

LEARN ABOUT IT

EXPLORE ▶ **Explain how all the skating times are alike.** (Possible answer: All are measured to the hundredth of a second.)

TALK ABOUT IT ▶ **Why might a person give a rounded time?** (Possible answers: It is easier to read; it is easier to understand.)
▶ **Who skated faster, Dana or Seth? Explain.** (Dana; 52.84 is less than 53.49, so Dana took less time to finish the race.)
▶ **Explain why both their times round to 53.** (Dana's time rounds up; Seth's time rounds down.)
▶ **Explain how Seth's rounded time would change if he had skated 0.01 s slower.** (His exact time would be 53.50 s, which would round up to 54 s.)
▶ **Compare decimal rounding with other rounding rules you know.** (Rules are generally the same; examine the tenths place to round decimals to the nearest whole number.)
Student Edition answers: **1.** No, Dana's time was .65s faster than Seth's. **2.** 53 is the closest whole number to both times. **3.** Kim: 52 s; the decimal part is less than 50 hundredths; Scott: 53 s; always round up halfway amounts.

2. CHECK UNDERSTANDING

TRY IT OUT

ERROR ALERT Rounding decimals with hundredths to the nearest tenth. Rounding numbers with tens to the nearest ten rather than to the nearest whole number.

Rounding Decimals

LEARN ABOUT IT

EXPLORE Study the Data
Bill said that Dana and Seth each finished the race in 53 seconds.

Speed Skating Race Results

Dana	52.84 seconds
Scott	52.50 seconds
Seth	53.49 seconds
Kim	52.16 seconds

TALK ABOUT IT See teaching notes.

1. Were Dana's and Seth's race times the same? Explain.
2. Why do you think Bill used 53 seconds to describe their race times?
3. What whole numbers might Bill use to describe Kim's and Scott's finishing times? Explain why.

- Look at the digit in the tenths place. — 52.16
- Round up to the next whole number if the digit is 5 or more. Round down to the next whole number if the digit is less than 5. — 1 is less than 5, so 52.16 rounds to 52.

You can use a number line to be sure you have rounded correctly.

52.1 52.2 52.3 52.4 52.5 52.6 52.7 52.8 52.9 53

52.16 rounds to 52 52.50 rounds to 53 52.84 rounds to 53

TRY IT OUT

Round each number to the nearest whole number.

1. 3.8 4	**2.** 9.2 9	**3.** 75.8 76	**4.** 14.1 14	**5.** 92.5 93	**6.** 0.6 1
7. 25.11 25	**8.** 2.55 3	**9.** 46.35 46	**10.** 39.10 39	**11.** 99.99 100	**12.** 9.49 9

366

TEACHING OPTIONS

RETEACHING TIPS Students circle the tenths place to determine whether to round up or down. They use the same whole number to round down or the next counting number to round up. Remind them that whole numbers need no decimal point or decimal places. Assign Reteaching Supplement 134.

ENRICHMENT Students use an almanac with sports records to locate 10 different decimals in statistics on sporting events. They round each to the nearest whole number, then sort the decimals by those rounded up and those rounded down. They identify any halfway amounts found.

PRACTICE

Round each decimal to the nearest whole number.

1. 2.9 **3** **2.** 4.8 **5** **3.** 7.2 **7** **4.** 3.7 **4** **5.** 0.5 **1**

6. 18.3 **18** **7.** 11.4 **11** **8.** 46.5 **47** **9.** 39.6 **40** **10.** 49.8 **50**

11. 3.72 **4** **12.** 4.88 **5** **13.** 9.14 **9** **14.** 5.63 **6** **15.** 6.97 **7**

16. 17.83 **18** **17.** 26.26 **26** **18.** 81.17 **81** **19.** 49.65 **50** **20.** 99.50 **100**

21. Which numbers in the box round to 24 when rounded to the nearest whole number?
23.75, 24.05, 23.99

24.8	23.75	25.25
23.26	24.50	24.05
25.6	23.49	23.99

APPLY

MATH REASONING **Answers will vary.**

22. Write 3 decimals that round to 5.

23. Write 3 decimals that round to 10.

24. Write 3 decimals that round to 50.

PROBLEM SOLVING

25. The men's World Speed Skating record for 500 meters is 38.00 seconds. The women's record is 41.80 seconds. Round to the nearest whole number to estimate the difference in the records.
4 seconds

26. Health and Fitness Data Bank Round to the nearest whole number to estimate the difference between Karen Enke's and Bonnie Blair's winning times. See page 482. **3 seconds**

MIXED REVIEW

Use the list at the right to identify each figure.

cube
cone
sphere
cylinder
pyramid
rectangular prism

27. fish tank **rectangular prism** **28.** globe **sphere** **29.** roll of paper **cylinder**

30. a volcano **cone or pyramid** **31.** an orange **sphere**

More Practice, page 509, Set E

3. PRACTICE AND APPLY

Basic	1-15, 24-31
Average	1-31
Extended	4-8, 14-31

PRACTICE

How do Exercises 1-5 differ from 6-10? (Exercises 1-5 have ones; Exercises 6-10 have ones and tens.) *How do Exercises 1-10 differ from 11-20?* (Decimals in Exercises 1-10 go to tenths; decimals in Exercises 11-20 go to hundredths.)

APPLY

MATH REASONING ► **Explain how rounding up *and* down can help you complete Exercises 22-24.** (Possible answer: Decimals with 0.5 or greater round *up* to the next whole number; decimals with 0.49 or less round *down*.)

PROBLEM SOLVING ► **What would you do first to solve Problem 25?** (Possible answer: Round 41.80 s to 42.00, then compare to 38.00 s.)

MIXED REVIEW ► **Explain how a rectangular prism and a cube are alike.** (Both have 6 faces, 8 vertices, 12 edges.)

CLOSE AND ASSESS

SHOW WHAT YOU KNOW

Have students make a decimal number line to demonstrate that 5.6 and 5.75 round to 6 and that 5.45 and 5.3 round to 5. (Check students' number lines.)

QUICK QUIZ

Round to the nearest whole number.

1. 0.6 (1) **2.** 1.47 (1)
3. 2.71 (3) **4.** 23.09 (23)
5. 16.61 (17) **6.** 20.3 (20)
7. 41.5 (42) **8.** 77.77 (78)

LESSON OPTIONS 13-6

Decimals and Fractions

OBJECTIVE 13-6 To relate fractions and decimals

PREBOOK ACTIVITIES

QUICK REVIEW

Choose the equivalent fraction.

1. $\frac{3}{6}$ $\frac{1}{3}$ or $\frac{1}{2}$ **2.** $\frac{8}{12}$ $\frac{2}{3}$ or $\frac{3}{4}$

3. $\frac{1}{3}$ $\frac{3}{9}$ or $\frac{9}{12}$ **4.** $\frac{7}{11}$ $\frac{14}{21}$ or $\frac{14}{22}$

5. $\frac{4}{5}$ $\frac{16}{25}$ or $\frac{16}{20}$ **6.** $\frac{5}{8}$ $\frac{15}{24}$ or $\frac{10}{18}$

(**1.** $\frac{1}{2}$ **2.** $\frac{2}{3}$ **3.** $\frac{3}{9}$ **4.** $\frac{14}{22}$ **5.** $\frac{16}{20}$ **6.** $\frac{15}{24}$)

PRIOR KNOWLEDGE

Have students review the meaning of *equivalent fractions*. (Possible answers: Two different fractions are equivalent if they fill the same amount of a whole thing; equivalent fractions reduce to the same lowest-terms fraction.) Ask students if they can visualize any decimal amounts that are equivalent to a common fraction. (Answers may vary. Students may be able to visualize $\frac{1}{2}$ = 0.5 or 0.50.) Tell students that in this lesson they will learn two ways to relate certain fractions and decimals.

COMMUNICATION

Discussing Math Discuss the meaning of *half* and *fourth*. (*Half* means that something is divided into 2 equal parts; *fourth* means that something is divided into 4 equal parts.) Ask students to explain how something divided into 100 parts can also be visualized in halves. (Possible answer: As with equivalent fractions, the same object can be divided more than one way as long as all parts are the same size; half of 100 is 50, so $\frac{50}{100}$ is equivalent to $\frac{1}{2}$.)

EXPLORE AND CONNECT

Materials: calculators, decimal/fraction tables (see below)
Grouping Suggestion: cooperative learning pairs
Students explore equivalent fractions and decimals with calculators. Have students review how to use a calculator to find a decimal based on a given fraction. (Enter the numerator, the divide symbol, the denominator, then the equal sign.) Pairs work together to find equivalent decimals for these unit fractions: $\frac{1}{2}$, $\frac{1}{4}$, $\frac{1}{5}$, $\frac{1}{20}$, $\frac{1}{25}$, $\frac{1}{50}$. Partners take turns using the calculator and recording the results in a table like this:

Fraction	*Equivalent Decimal*	*Fraction Equivalent to Decimal*
$\frac{1}{2}$	0.5	$\frac{5}{10}$

Conclude by having students tell how decimals and fractions can be equivalent. (Possible answer: If a fraction has an equivalent fraction with 10 or 100 as its denominator, you can write a decimal for it.)

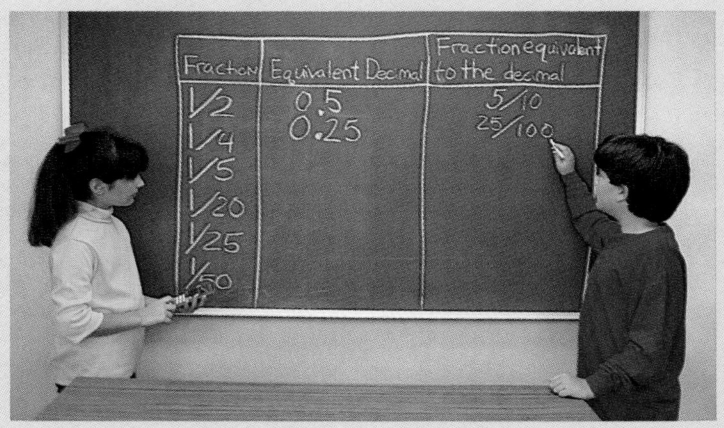

CONNECTIONS Use these anytime.

Problem of the Day

Calculator LaToya says she can find $\frac{1}{4}$ + $\frac{1}{2}$ on her calculator, even though her calculator is unable to show fractions. Explain what LaToya can do. (Change $\frac{1}{4}$ to 0.25, change $\frac{1}{2}$ to 0.50, then add 0.25 + 0.50 = 0.75.)

Math Connection

Metric Measurement Devon's favorite kind of juice comes in 3 different liter sizes: 0.25 L, 0.5 L, and 0.75 L. If he wants to buy 6 containers and have exactly 2 L of juice, what should he buy? (five 0.25-L containers and one 0.75-L container or two 0.5-L containers and four 0.25-L containers.)

Number Sense

Mental Math Willa is 10 years old. For $\frac{1}{2}$ of her life, she lived in Ohio. For $\frac{2}{10}$ of her life, she lived in Iowa. Since then, she has lived in Maine. Express the fractions as decimals, then give a decimal for the part of her life Willa has spent in Maine. (0.5, 0.2, 0.3)

Classwork and Homework Supplements

Practice

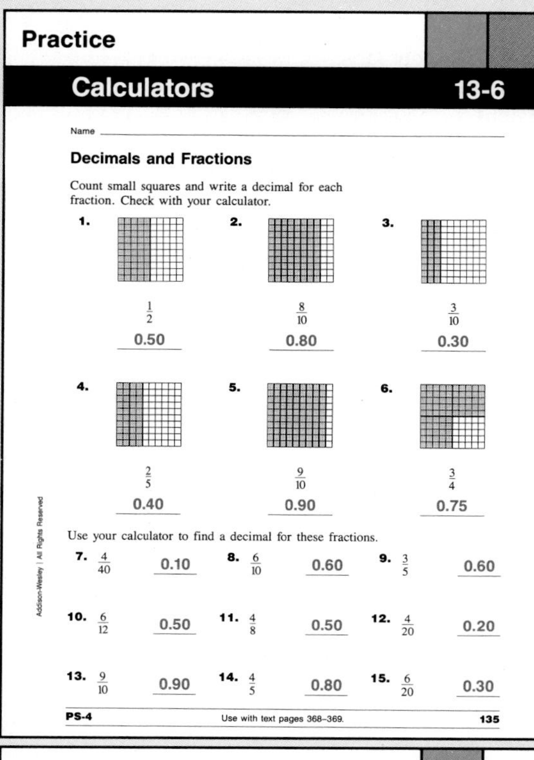

Calculators 13-6

Name

Decimals and Fractions

Count small squares and write a decimal for each fraction. Check with your calculator.

1. $\frac{1}{2}$ 0.50
2. $\frac{8}{10}$ 0.80
3. $\frac{3}{10}$ 0.30
4. $\frac{2}{5}$ 0.40
5. $\frac{9}{10}$ 0.90
6. $\frac{3}{4}$ 0.75

Use your calculator to find a decimal for these fractions.

7. $\frac{4}{40}$ 0.10
8. $\frac{6}{10}$ 0.60
9. $\frac{3}{5}$ 0.60
10. $\frac{6}{12}$ 0.50
11. $\frac{4}{8}$ 0.50
12. $\frac{4}{20}$ 0.20
13. $\frac{9}{10}$ 0.90
14. $\frac{4}{5}$ 0.80
15. $\frac{6}{20}$ 0.30

Addison-Wesley | All Rights Reserved

PS-4 Use with text pages 368-369. 135

Building Thinking Skills

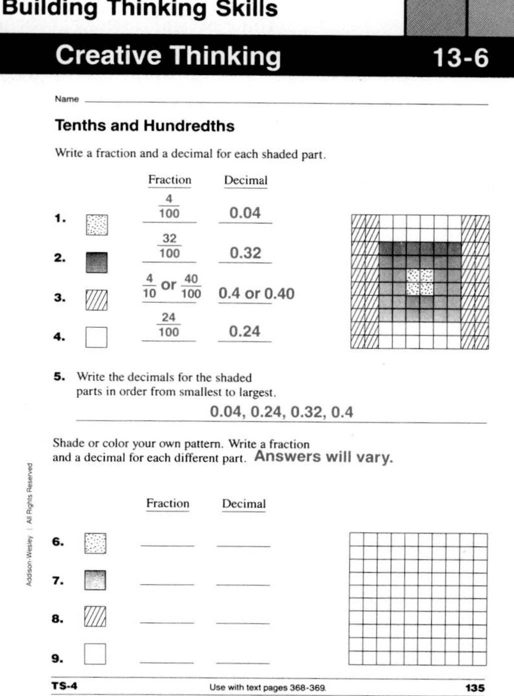

Creative Thinking 13-6

Name

Tenths and Hundredths

Write a fraction and a decimal for each shaded part.

	Fraction	Decimal
1.	$\frac{4}{100}$	0.04
2.	$\frac{32}{100}$	0.32
3.	$\frac{4}{10}$ or $\frac{40}{100}$	0.4 or 0.40
4.	$\frac{24}{100}$	0.24

5. Write the decimals for the shaded parts in order from smallest to largest. 0.04, 0.24, 0.32, 0.4

Shade or color your own pattern. Write a fraction and a decimal for each different part. Answers will vary.

	Fraction	Decimal
6.		
7.		
8.		
9.		

Addison-Wesley | All Rights Reserved

TS-4 Use with text pages 368-369. 135

Reteaching

Calculators 13-6

Name

Decimals and Fractions

You can use graph paper to find the decimal for $\frac{3}{5}$.

Use a 10 × 10 square. → Color the square to show the fraction. → Count the hundredths.

$\frac{3}{5}$ 60 hundredths = 0.60

You can also use a calculator to find the decimal for $\frac{3}{5}$.

AC/ON 3 ÷ 5 = 0.60

Count small squares and write a decimal for each fraction.

1. 0.40
2. 0.75
3. 0.90

Use your calculator to find a decimal for these fractions.

4. $\frac{4}{5}$ 0.80
5. $\frac{2}{4}$ 0.50
6. $\frac{2}{8}$ 0.25
7. $\frac{6}{10}$ 0.60
8. $\frac{1}{5}$ 0.20
9. $\frac{8}{10}$ 0.80
10. $\frac{3}{4}$ 0.75
11. $\frac{3}{15}$ 0.20
12. $\frac{3}{10}$ 0.30

Addison-Wesley | All Rights Reserved

RS-4 Use with text pages 368-369. 135

Challenges

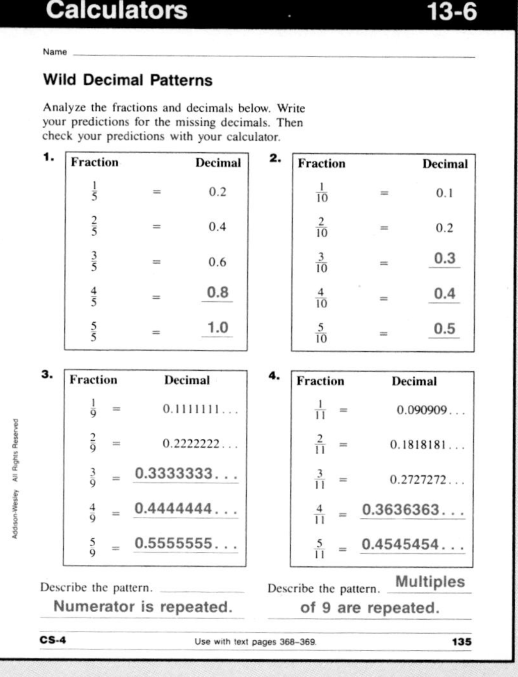

Calculators 13-6

Name

Wild Decimal Patterns

Analyze the fractions and decimals below. Write your predictions for the missing decimals. Then check your predictions with your calculator.

1.

Fraction		Decimal
$\frac{1}{5}$	=	0.2
$\frac{2}{5}$	=	0.4
$\frac{3}{5}$	=	0.6
$\frac{4}{5}$	=	0.8
$\frac{5}{5}$	=	1.0

2.

Fraction		Decimal
$\frac{1}{10}$	=	0.1
$\frac{2}{10}$	=	0.2
$\frac{3}{10}$	=	0.3
$\frac{4}{10}$	=	0.4
$\frac{5}{10}$	=	0.5

3.

Fraction		Decimal
$\frac{1}{9}$	=	0.1111111. . .
$\frac{2}{9}$	=	0.2222222. . .
$\frac{3}{9}$	=	0.3333333. . .
$\frac{4}{9}$	=	0.4444444. . .
$\frac{5}{9}$	=	0.5555555. . .

4.

Fraction		Decimal
$\frac{1}{11}$	=	0.090909. . .
$\frac{2}{11}$	=	0.1818181. . .
$\frac{3}{11}$	=	0.2727272. . .
$\frac{4}{11}$	=	0.3636363. . .
$\frac{5}{11}$	=	0.4545454. . .

Describe the pattern. Numerator is repeated.

Describe the pattern. Multiples of 9 are repeated.

Addison-Wesley | All Rights Reserved

CS-4 Use with text pages 368-369. 135

Options for Individual Needs

Basic

Exercises 2-18
Calculator Bank, p. 490
More Practice, p. 509, set F

Supplements
Reteaching 135 or
Practice 135

Average

Exercises 1-21
Calculator Bank, p. 490
More Practice, p. 509, set F

Supplements
Practice 135
Challenges 135 or
Thinking Skills 135

Extended

Exercises 3-10, 14-21
Calculator Bank, p. 490

Supplements
Challenges 135
Thinking Skills 135

Other Resources:
Problem-Solving Experiences in Mathematics, Grade 4, Problem 137
Mathematics, A Way of Thinking, Lesson 12-2
Math In Stride, Grade 4, pp. 201, 202
Using The Math Explorer Calculator: A Sourcebook for Teachers, Chapter 14

LESSON PLAN 13-6

OBJECTIVE 13-6
To relate fractions and decimals

Materials: TA 12 (Centimeter Graph Paper), crayons, calculators

1. MOTIVATE AND TEACH

LEARN ABOUT IT

EXPLORE ▶ **Explain how to fold the paper to avoid partial boxes in any section.** (Possible answer: Fold on grid lines; show square fourths rather than rectangles or triangles.)

TALK ABOUT IT ▶ **Use equivalent fractions to explain why $\frac{1}{4}$ equals $\frac{25}{100}$.** ($\frac{1}{4}$ and $\frac{25}{100}$ cover the same amount of the whole square.)
▶ **Which fractions are equivalent? Explain why.** ($\frac{1}{2}$ and $\frac{2}{4}$, because multiplying $\frac{1}{2}$ by $\frac{2}{2}$ equals $\frac{2}{4}$)
▶ **What should be true about the decimals for those two fractions? Explain why.** (They should also be equal because equivalent fractions share the same decimal value.)
▶ **Explain how the picture proves that $\frac{1}{5}$ = 0.20.** (Possible answer: The shaded $\frac{1}{5}$ has 20 squares out of 100, or $\frac{20}{100}$, or 0.20.)
▶ **Explain why $\frac{1}{4}$ equals 1 ÷ 4.** (You divide to find how many equal parts in a number; dividing 1 by 4 gives the size of the fractional part that is 1 of the 4 equal parts.)
Student Edition answers: **1.** 25 **2.** 0.25, 0.50, 0.75, 0.50

2. CHECK UNDERSTANDING

TRY IT OUT

ERROR ALERT Writing fractions rather than decimals. Exercise 3: Entering numbers incorrectly on the calculator.

Decimals and Fractions

LEARN ABOUT IT

EXPLORE Use Graph Paper
You can find a decimal for a fraction. Cut four large 10 by 10 squares from graph paper. Fold and color a square to show each of these fractions.

$\frac{1}{4}$ $\frac{2}{4}$ $\frac{3}{4}$ $\frac{1}{2}$

Think about how a decimal could describe each colored part.

Each small square is a hundredth.

TALK ABOUT IT See teaching notes.

1. How many small squares did you color for each fourth?
2. What decimal would you write for
$\frac{1}{4}$? $\frac{2}{4}$? $\frac{3}{4}$? $\frac{1}{2}$?

To use a 10 × 10 square to find a decimal for a fraction, first color the square to show the fraction. To find the decimal, count how many hundredth squares have been colored.

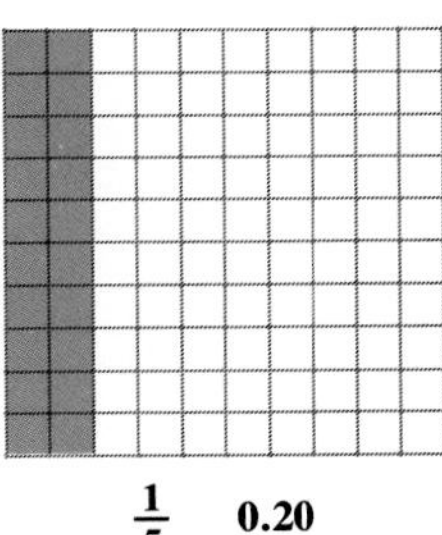
$\frac{1}{5}$ 0.20

You can also use a calculator to find a decimal for a fraction. Since one meaning for $\frac{1}{4}$ is 1 ÷ 4, use this keycode.

[ON/AC] 1 [÷] 4 [=]

TRY IT OUT

Count small squares and write a decimal for each fraction. Check with your calculator.

1. 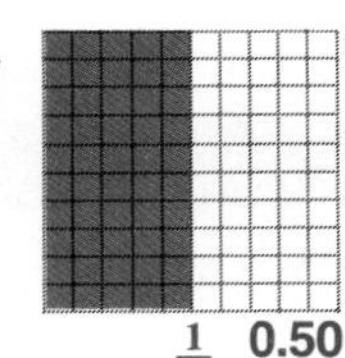
$\frac{1}{2}$ 0.50

2. 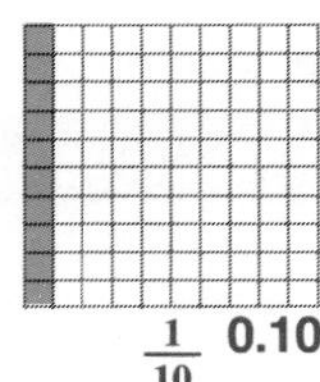
$\frac{1}{10}$ 0.10

3. Use your calculator to find a decimal for $\frac{2}{8}$. 0.25

368

TEACHING OPTIONS

RETEACHING TIPS Have students who use the calculator incorrectly verbalize the correct order of operations. They read the fraction from top to bottom, saying the words *divided by* for the fraction bar, like this: "3 divided by 5." Entry order is top-to-bottom. Assign Reteaching Supplement 135.

ENRICHMENT Have students use a calculator to find decimals for the following mixed numbers after they change them to improper fractions.

1. $5\frac{1}{2}$ (5.5) **2.** $4\frac{37}{100}$ (4.37)
3. $26\frac{7}{10}$ (26.7) **4.** $9\frac{2}{5}$ (9.4)
5. $3\frac{30}{40}$ (3.75) **6.** $6\frac{11}{20}$ (6.55)

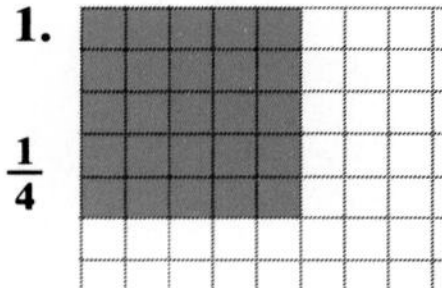

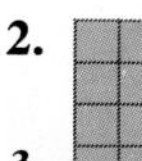

PRACTICE

Count small squares and write a decimal for each fraction. Check with your calculator.

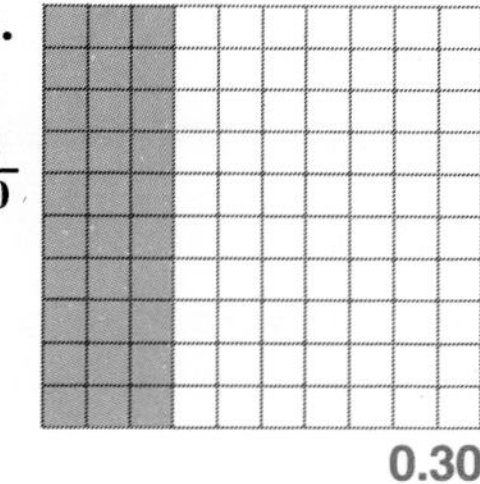

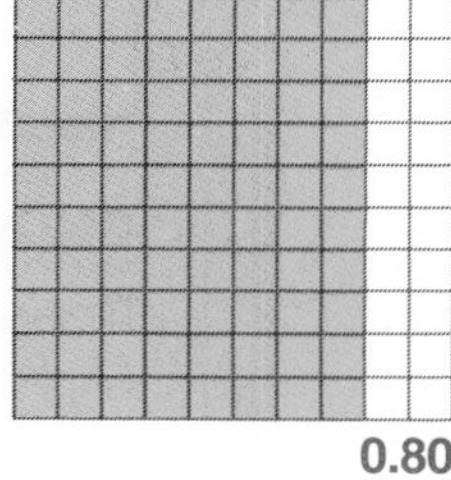

1. $\frac{1}{4}$ 0.25
2. $\frac{3}{10}$ 0.30
3. $\frac{4}{5}$ 0.80

Use your calculator to find a decimal for these fractions.

4. $\frac{3}{5}$ 0.60 5. $\frac{3}{4}$ 0.75 6. $\frac{4}{8}$ 0.50 7. $\frac{9}{10}$ 0.90

APPLY

MATH REASONING Give the missing decimals.

8. If $\frac{2}{5}$ = 0.40, then $\frac{4}{5}$ = ▒. 0.80
9. If $\frac{1}{4}$ = 0.25, then $\frac{2}{4}$ = ▒. 0.50

PROBLEM SOLVING

10. Ten out of 20 students in Jane's class watched the Olympic games. What decimal tells the part of the class that saw the games? .50

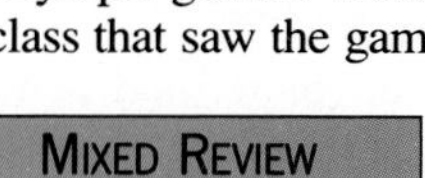

MIXED REVIEW

Tell if the angle is obtuse, acute, or right.

11. more than 90° obtuse 12. 20° acute 13. 134° obtuse 14. 100° obtuse 15. 90° right

Write yes if the fractions are equivalent. Write no if they are not.

16. $\frac{2}{3}$ and $\frac{3}{6}$ no 17. $\frac{4}{5}$ and $\frac{16}{20}$ yes 18. $\frac{4}{8}$ and $\frac{1}{2}$ yes

19. $\frac{3}{10}$ and $\frac{2}{5}$ no 20. $\frac{3}{4}$ and $\frac{9}{12}$ yes 21. $\frac{5}{6}$ and $\frac{4}{5}$ no

More Practice Bank, page 509, set F

3. Practice and Apply

Basic	2-18
Average	1-21
Extended	3-10, 14-21

PRACTICE

How are Exercises 1-3 different from Exercises 4-7? (Exercises 1-3 provide a picture for counting the hundredths; Exercises 4-7 require the use of a calculator to find the equivalent decimals.)

APPLY

MATH REASONING ► **Explain the relationship of the two fractions in each exercise.** (The second fraction is twice as big as the first.)

PROBLEM SOLVING ► **Analyze the information to write a fraction to fit the situation. Explain your reasoning.** ($\frac{10}{20}$; 20 is the total of students, 10 the number who watched.)

MIXED REVIEW ► **Explain how to judge if fractions are equivalent.** (They are equivalent if you can multiply the numerator and the denominator of one by the same factor to give the other.)

13-6

Close and Assess

SHOW WHAT YOU KNOW

Have students use two different ways to demonstrate that $\frac{1}{4}$ is equivalent to 0.25. (Possible responses: Divide 1 by 4 on a calculator; color $\frac{1}{4}$ of 100 squares, which is $\frac{25}{100}$, or 0.25.)

QUICK QUIZ

Write a decimal for each fraction.

1. $\frac{1}{2}$ (0.5 or 0.50)
2. $\frac{9}{10}$ (0.9 or 0.90)
3. $\frac{3}{4}$ (0.75)
4. $\frac{1}{5}$ (0.2 or 0.20)

LESSON OPTIONS 13-7

Problem Solving: Determining Reasonable Answers

OBJECTIVE 13-7 To determine by estimation whether answers to problems are reasonable

PREBOOK ACTIVITIES

QUICK REVIEW

Estimate each answer. (Answers may vary. Samples are given.)

1. 189 + 711 (900)
2. \$7.98 × 5 (\$40)
3. 622 + 597 + 594 + 604 (2,400)
4. 878 − 299 (600)
5. 48 × 12 (500)
6. 315 × 88 (2,700)

PRIOR KNOWLEDGE

Have students think of real-life situations when some aspect of the situation makes no sense. (Sample answers: The clock says 3:00 a.m. when it is the middle of the day; the oven-temperature gauge says 375°, but the oven is cold.) Have students offer reasonable explanations for these situations. (Possible answers: The power went off; the oven is not working.)

COMMUNICATION

Discussing Math Have students suggest synonyms for the word **reasonable**. (*sensible, logical, acceptable, fair*) Ask them to analyze when they might check for reasonableness in a problem-solving situation. (while selecting necessary data; after finding an answer)

EXPLORE AND CONNECT

COOPERATIVE ACTIVITY

Grouping Suggestion: small groups

Liz bought 6 yogurts at \$.49 each. When the clerk asked for \$29.40, Liz refused to pay. Why would Liz be upset?

TEACHING ACTIONS

Have students work together to evaluate the situation.

► **Explain Liz's situation in your own words.** (She bought 6 yogurts at \$.49 apiece, then refused to pay the amount for which the clerk asked.)

► **Develop a plan to analyze what happened.** (Find the cost of the yogurts; compare that amount to the total the clerk arrived at to understand why Liz refused to pay.)

► **Explain how to estimate a reasonable answer.** (\$.49 is about \$.50; 50 × 6 = 300, or about \$3.00)

► **Decide on a calculation method.** (paper and pencil or the mental math strategy of compensation)

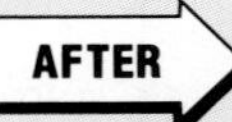

► **Evaluate the solution to see whether it is reasonable.** (6 × \$.49 = \$2.94, which is near the estimate of \$3.00)

► **Analyze what the clerk may have done to get a total of \$29.40.** (Possible answer: Maybe the clerk pressed \$.49 × 60 or \$4.90 × 6, because the clerk's total was 10 times too great.)

CONNECTIONS Use these anytime.

Problem of the Day

What's Going On Here? Nelson turns off his bedroom light. Then he goes to his bed, which is across the room from the switch, and snuggles under the covers. But it is still light in his room. How can this be? (Possible answer: It is dusk outside, so it is not yet completely dark.)

Number Sense

Estimation Sybil plans to spend about \$15 on a birthday gift for her grandmother. She is able to buy a dozen golf balls and a funny card. About how much do you think she spent on each golf ball? (About \$1 each)

Subject Integration

Social Studies A person must be at least 30 years old to be a U.S. senator. If elected, the person serves a 6-year *term*. Janet says her favorite senator has served 12 terms. Evaluate Janet's statement. (12 × 6 = 72, 72 + 30 = 102; it is unlikely for a senator to serve 12 terms, even if the person began at the youngest possible age.)

CLASSWORK AND HOMEWORK SUPPLEMENTS

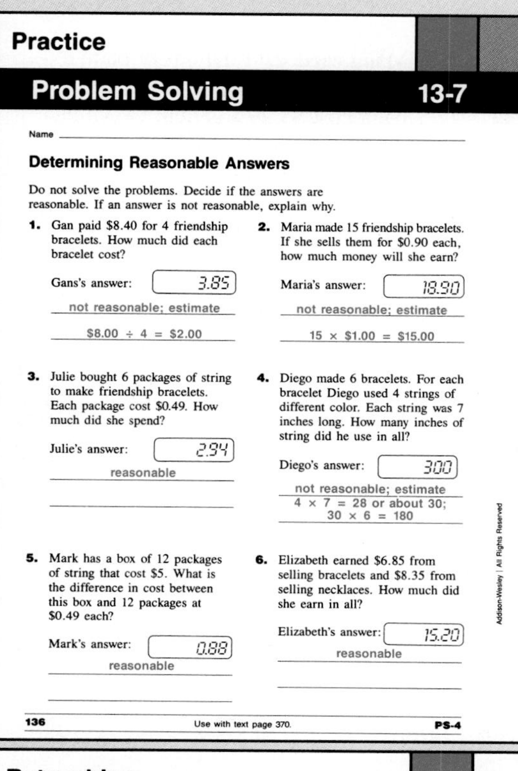

Practice

Problem Solving 13-7

Name ____________

Determining Reasonable Answers

Do not solve the problems. Decide if the answers are reasonable. If an answer is not reasonable, explain why.

1. Gan paid \$8.40 for 4 friendship bracelets. How much did each bracelet cost?
   Gans's answer: 3.85
   not reasonable; estimate
   \$8.00 ÷ 4 = \$2.00

2. Maria made 15 friendship bracelets. If she sells them for \$0.90 each, how much money will she earn?
   Maria's answer: 18.90
   not reasonable; estimate
   15 × \$1.00 = \$15.00

3. Julie bought 6 packages of string to make friendship bracelets. Each package cost \$0.49. How much did she spend?
   Julie's answer: 2.94
   reasonable

4. Diego made 6 bracelets. For each bracelet Diego used 4 strings of different color. Each string was 7 inches long. How many inches of string did he use in all?
   Diego's answer: 300
   not reasonable; estimate
   4 × 7 = 28 or about 30;
   30 × 6 = 180

5. Mark has a box of 12 packages of string that cost \$5. What is the difference in cost between this box and 12 packages at \$0.49 each?
   Mark's answer: 0.88
   reasonable

6. Elizabeth earned \$6.85 from selling bracelets and \$8.35 from selling necklaces. How much did she earn in all?
   Elizabeth's answer: 15.20
   reasonable

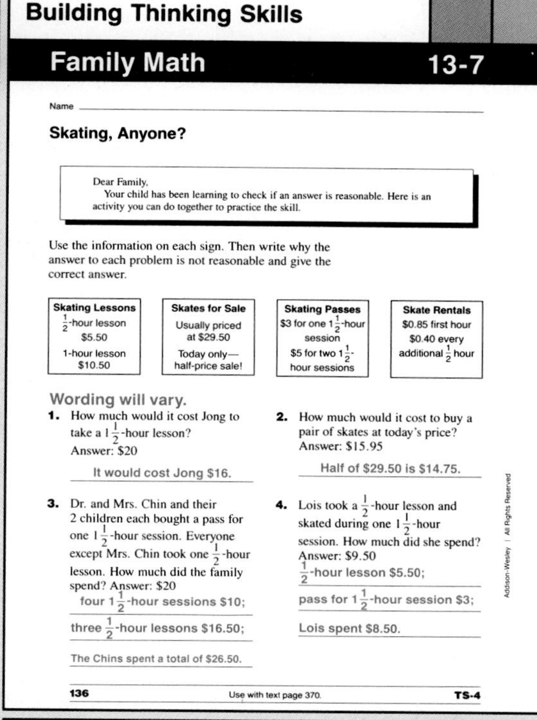

Building Thinking Skills

Family Math 13-7

Name ____________

Skating, Anyone?

Dear Family,
Your child has been learning to check if an answer is reasonable. Here is an activity you can do together to practice the skill.

Use the information on each sign. Then write why the answer to each problem is not reasonable and give the correct answer.

Skating Lessons	Skates for Sale	Skating Passes	Skate Rentals
$\frac{1}{2}$-hour lesson \$5.50 1-hour lesson \$10.50	Usually priced at \$29.50 Today only—half-price sale!	\$3 for one $1\frac{1}{2}$-hour session \$5 for two $1\frac{1}{2}$-hour sessions	\$0.85 first hour \$0.40 every additional $\frac{1}{2}$ hour

Wording will vary.

1. How much would it cost Jong to take a $1\frac{1}{2}$-hour lesson?
   Answer: \$20
   It would cost Jong \$16.

2. How much would it cost to buy a pair of skates at today's price?
   Answer: \$15.95
   Half of \$29.50 is \$14.75.

3. Dr. and Mrs. Chin and their 2 children each bought a pass for one $1\frac{1}{2}$-hour session. Everyone except Mrs. Chin took one $\frac{1}{2}$-hour lesson. How much did the family spend? Answer: \$20
   four $1\frac{1}{2}$-hour sessions \$10;
   three $\frac{1}{2}$-hour lessons \$16.50;
   The Chins spent a total of \$26.50.

4. Lois took a $\frac{1}{2}$-hour lesson and skated during one $1\frac{1}{2}$-hour session. How much did she spend?
   Answer: \$9.50
   $\frac{1}{2}$-hour lesson \$5.50;
   pass for $1\frac{1}{2}$-hour session \$3;
   Lois spent \$8.50.

Reteaching

Problem Solving 13-7

Name ____________

Determining Reasonable Answers

Always check your work to see if your answers are reasonable. Use estimation.

Theo found a desk for \$65.98 at one store and the same type of desk at another store for \$84.25. What is the difference in the prices?
Theo's answer: 8.24.
Is his answer reasonable?

Round each number. → Solve using the rounded numbers. → Compare the answer with your estimate. Decide if the answer is reasonable.

\$65.98 (\$66) \$84 − \$66 = \$18
\$84.25 (\$84)

His answer does not seem reasonable. \$8.24 is too low.

Do not solve the problems. Decide if the answers are reasonable. If an answer is not reasonable, explain why.

1. Maria put a bookshelf in her room. She has 144 books to be placed on 6 shelves. If she puts the same number of books on each shelf, how many books will be on each shelf? Maria's answer: 30.
   unreasonable; too high

2. Theresa ordered new tennis racquets for her team. Each racquet costs \$8.95. How much would 12 racquets cost? Theresa's answer: 107.40.
   reasonable

3. Trevor ordered shirts for 8 team members. The bill came to \$47.60. How much should each team member pay?
   Trevor's answer: 5.95.
   reasonable

4. Leila's team had a book fair. There were 275 bags of books sold. Each bag sold for a quarter. How much money did the team raise?
   Leila's answer: 45.50.
   unreasonable; too low

Challenges

Reading Math 13-7

Name ____________

What Is Wrong Here?

Analyze the ads. Then find six places where what you are told does not seem reasonable. The first one has been done for you.

Windsurfing Lessons
5 lessons normally \$48.98. Now half price at \$28.95.
Boardwalk Tickets
Family of 5 for under \$60.
Adults \$15.95
Children \$11.95
Video Games
\$2.25 per book of tickets.
Special rate:
11 for \$25.95
Boardwalk Menu
Hamburger \$2.68
Drink \$1.19
Salad \$2.58
Save on special meal of hamburger, drink, and salad for only \$7.19.
I'll take 4 specials.
\$20
I'll take 2 of each.
\$50
Rentals/Windsurfing
Boards \$15.65
Masts \$6.25
Sails \$8.45

1. \$28.95 is not half of \$48.98. Half is \$24.49.
2. Boardwalk tickets come to at least \$63.75 (if there are 4 children and one adult).
3. 11 books of video game tickets would cost \$24.75. \$25.95 is not a good deal.
4. The man with the \$50 bill does not have enough for windsurfing equipment, which comes to \$60.70.
5. The woman with the \$20 bill does not have enough for 4 specials which would cost \$28.76.
6. The "special" on the menu is not special. Normally a hamburger, drink, and salad would cost \$6.45.

OPTIONS FOR INDIVIDUAL NEEDS

Basic

Exercises 1, 3-7
Skills Bank, p. 465
Calculator Bank, pp. 485-488
Computer Bank, p. 492
More Practice, p. 525, set C

Supplements
Reteaching 136 or
Practice 136

Average

Exercises 1-7
Skills Bank, p. 465
Calculator Bank, pp. 485-488
Computer Bank, p. 492
More Practice, p. 525, set C

Supplements
Practice 136
Challenges 136 or
Thinking Skills 136

Extended

Exercises 1-7
Calculator Bank, pp. 485-488
Computer Bank, p. 492

Supplements
Challenges 136
Thinking Skills 136

Other Resources:
Problem-Solving Experiences in Mathematics, Grade 4, Problem 36
Math In Stride, Grade 4, pp. 237, 238
The Math Explorer Calculator: A Sourcebook for Teachers, Chapter 14

13-7

LESSON PLAN 13-7

OBJECTIVE 13-7

To determine by estimation whether answers to problems are reasonable

1. MOTIVATE AND TEACH

LEARN ABOUT IT

▶ **Explain Malia's situation in your own words.** (She is buying paint for her room.)

▶ **Decide how to solve the problem.** (Find the total cost of all 11 gal of paint.)

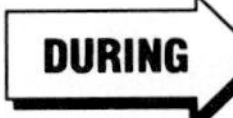

▶ **Explain which operation makes sense to use.** (Multiply to put together same-size groups.)

▶ **Explain how to estimate the product.** (Round \$3.99 to \$4; round 11 to 10; 10 × \$4 = \$40)

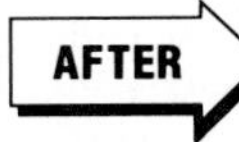

▶ **Evaluate Malia's answer.** (The estimate was about \$40; Malia's answer is \$78.29, which is too high.)

▶ **Explain what Malia may have done.** (She may have entered the wrong numbers in the calculator or used the wrong operation, because her answer does not make sense.)

2. CHECK UNDERSTANDING

TRY IT OUT

ERROR ALERT Estimating answers based on the wrong operation.

Problem Solving
Determining Reasonable Answers

LEARN ABOUT IT

When you solve a problem, the last step is to check your work. You can ask yourself some questions.

- Is my arithmetic correct?
- Did I use the strategy correctly?
- Is my answer reasonable?

Malia needed 11 gallons of paint to paint her room bright pink. The paint cost \$3.99 a gallon. How much did she pay for the paint?
Malia's answer: 78.29

To see if the answer is reasonable, I can use estimation.

I can round numbers and multiply.

\$3.99 is about \$4.
11 gallons is close to 10 gallons.
\$4 × 10 = \$40

Malia's answer doesn't seem reasonable.

\$78.29 is too high.

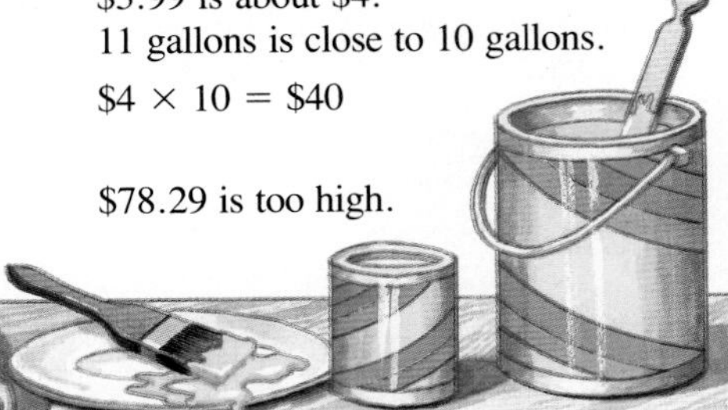

PRACTICE

Do not solve the problems. Decide if the answers are reasonable. If an answer is not reasonable, explain why.

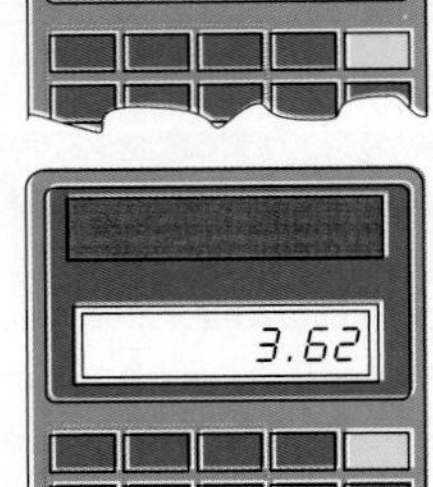

1. Jesse paid \$25.50 for 6 posters of cars. How much did each poster cost? **reasonable**

   Jesse's answer: 4.25

2. Willie is thinking of putting tiles in his room. He will need 125 tiles. Tiles cost a quarter each. How much would it cost to tile his room? **not reasonable; 100 × .25 = \$25.00**

   Willie's answer: 3.62

370

TEACHING OPTIONS

RETEACHING TIPS Have students paraphrase the situation in their own words to help select the operation that makes the most sense to use. Then have them proceed to round, estimate, and compare their estimates with the answers given. Assign Reteaching Supplement 136.

ENRICHMENT **Family Math** Have students try this activity at home. Each student determines how many tiles it would take to replace the bathroom floor if each tile is 1 square ft, then estimates the cost at \$0.25 per tile. A family member finds the exact cost, then they compare solutions.

MIXED PRACTICE

Choose a strategy from the strategies list to solve these problems.

1. Rachel's mom bought Rachel a used TV for her room. It cost $126, and she paid it off in 9 months. How much did she pay each month? **$14**

2. It cost Sang-Ho $31 to mount 2 movie posters on cardboard. Mounting the large adventure poster cost $7 more than the comedy poster. How much did the comedy poster cost to mount? **$12**

3. Juan's aunt bought him a new study set:

desk	$49.49
chair	$69.95
computer table	$115.98
lamp	$46.58

She paid the bill off in 6 months. How much did she pay per month? **$47**

Some Strategies

Act It Out
Use Objects
Choose an Operation
Draw a Picture
Make an Organized List
Guess and Check
Make a Table
Look for a Pattern
Use Logical Reasoning
Work Backward

4. Mrs. Chung bought 12 rolls of wallpaper at $11.95 each. How much did the wallpaper cost? **$143.40**

5. Marla's grandmother made a quilt for her room. How many of this type of square were in the quilt? **25 squares**

6. The temperature in Bob's room in the garage was 50.6°F one night. His dad agreed to use $59.95 of the month's house budget to buy a space heater. Now there is $110.57 left in the budget. How much is the monthly house budget? **$170.52**

7. Masato had saved $25. She bought a wall hanging for her room with half of her money. How much did the wall hanging cost? **$12.50**

More Practice, page 525, set C

3. PRACTICE AND APPLY

Basic	1, 3-7
Average	1-7
Extended	1-7

Sample Solutions: See p. T79.

MIXED PRACTICE

► **Compare and contrast Problems 1 and 3.** (Both require division to find a monthly cost; the total is given in Problem 1, but you must find the total in Problem 3.)

► **Explain how you would solve Problem 5.** (Draw a Picture to complete the pattern, then count the type of square mentioned.)

► **Identify the necessary data in Problem 6.** ($59.95 for a space heater; $110.57 left)

► **Justify the operations you would use for Problems 4 and 7.** (Problem 4: Multiply to put together same-size groups. Problem 7: Divide to separate into same-size groups.)

13-7

CLOSE AND ASSESS

WRITE WHAT YOU THINK

Have students write a paragraph explaining how to use estimation to check the answer to a problem, even if they have solved it with a calculator. (Answers will vary. Check students' writing.)

QUICK QUIZ

A store sells film at $4.29 per roll. Ivan asks for 8 rolls, and the clerk asks for $55.80. Decide whether Ivan is paying a reasonable amount. (No, the total should be closer to $32.00.)

CHAPTER 13

APPLIED PROBLEM SOLVING
GROUP DECISION MAKING

OBJECTIVE To analyze, organize, and make decisions using relevant data

FACTS TO CONSIDER

▶ **Explain why it matters that all cameras produce photos of the same quality.** (Posible answer: You can still count on a cheaper camera to take photos as clear as the most expensive one.)
▶ **Explain the significance of each category.** (Possible answers: Batteries and film are added costs; a built-in flash is important for indoor photos, or you may need a separate flash attachment; automatic rewind is a time-saving feature.)
▶ **Decide how you would rate the categories in order of importance to you.** (Answers will vary.)

Applied Problem Solving
Group Decision Making

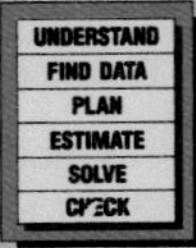

Group Skill:
Disagree in an Agreeable Way

You are a reporter for Children's Choice magazine. You need to look over some information on the four top children's cameras. Your job is to choose the best camera for kids to buy.

Facts to Consider

1. The photos taken with the cameras are of the same quality.
2. Some facts about the cameras are more important than others.
3. The camera you recommend should be the best in the important catagories.
4. This is what you found out about the cameras.

Some Questions to Answer

1. Which is the best buy when you consider only the price? List the cameras from least expensive to most expensive.
2. Which cameras have the best film price?
3. Which cameras use the cheapest batteries?
4. Do you think a lighter or heavier camera would be better? How important is this fact?
5. Can you think of a way to organize your data to make a decision? Hint: you could start by assigning the numbers 1, 2, 3, and 4 in each category to show best to worst.

Name of Camera	Price	Film Price	Battery Price	Weight	Built-in Flash?	Automatic Rewind?
Kidcam	$56	$3.89	$5.00	12 oz	yes	yes
Wonder	$78	$4.39	$4.25	11 oz	yes	yes
Wizard	$58	$4.39	$4.25	9 oz	yes	no
Topper	$50	$3.89	$5.00	10 oz	no	yes

What Is Your Decision?

Which camera did you decide was the best? Explain your decision.

372

TEACHING OPTIONS

COOPERATIVE LEARNING

Grouping Suggestion:
cooperative groups of 4 to 6
If possible, assign to each group at least 1 student who has used a camera to share real-life experiences that may help in the decision-making process. Have groups discuss and evaluate the data in table; clarify any unknown information; devise a method for organizing their decisions; and agree on an entertaining way to present their conclusion, possibly in the form of a role-play.

373

COMPUTER **Magic Cash Register, Avant-Garde, Copyright 1983** For all students (may be used in groups). Read the introduction to the students. Students open the cash register, deal with customers, and close the cash register. Students supply customer information. A cash register session takes 15 min.

CHAPTER 13

SOME QUESTIONS TO ANSWER

► **Explain how you can develop a plan to rank the cameras with so many categories of data.** (Methods may vary.)

► **Analyze how to use the hint to organize data.** (If you rank each category 1 to 4, you can find a total score for each camera, then choose the 1 with the highest score as the best choice.)

WHAT IS YOUR DECISION?

Have groups role-play a commercial for the camera they selected as the best. Each student in a group can give a determining factor or reason that contributed to the group's decision, presented in the form of a sales pitch. Have students recall camera commercials they have watched on television to help them with their presentations.

CHAPTER 13

WRAP UP

INTRODUCTION The Wrap Up provides activities emphasizing math language and thinking skills for the chapter and a project that integrates those skills with other math strands.

USING PAGE 374

Decimal Points Have students complete this section independently, then share answers in a small group. Have students use each unchosen word in a sentence about fractions or decimals.

Sometimes, Always, Never

▶ **Identify cases when a decimal *must* have 2 digits after the decimal point.** (money amounts involving parts of $1.00)

▶ **Identify the place values discussed in Exercise 7.** (hundredths place, hundreds place)

▶ **Identify examples for Exercise 8.** (Answers will vary.)

Project Have students work in pairs to complete the project.

▶ **Decide how to tell when your chosen activity starts and stops.** (Answers will vary.)

▶ **Predict how you think the three trials will compare.** (Answers may vary.)

▶ **Explain the meaning of slower and faster times in terms of decimal size.** (The greater the number, the slower the time.)

Have students share their tasks and trial times with the group. Then display project results so that students who tried the same task can compare results.

WRAP UP

Decimal Points

Choose the word or words that complete each sentence correctly.

1. Fractions in __?__ can be written easily as decimals. **tenths**
2. In a decimal, a __?__ separates the ones and tenths places. **decimal point**
3. The decimal 2.7 is equivalent to the __?__ $2\frac{7}{10}$. **mixed number**
4. In a place value chart, the hundredths place is to the __?__ of the tenths place. **right**
5. The decimal 3.98 is a little __?__ than 4. **less**

Sometimes, Always, Never

Which word should go in the blank, sometimes, always, or never? Explain your choices. **Explanations will vary.**

6. There are __?__ 2 digits written after a decimal point. **sometimes**
7. Two hundredths is __?__ equivalent to two hundred. **never**
8. A number with two decimal places is __?__ greater than a number with only one decimal place. **sometimes**

Project

Use a digital stopwatch that shows tenths or hundredths of a second. Time how long it takes you to do a specific task. It might be to count to 100, climb a flight of stairs, or sharpen your pencil. Do the task 3 times. Record your time after each try. Then order the results from the slowest to the fastest time. Why do you think the times were different? **Answers will vary.**

374

TEACHING OPTIONS

ENRICHMENT Work with students to plan a math "Olympics" of contests that can be done in any classroom. Sample contest tasks: copy a paragraph, write the full name and address of the school, find a word in a dictionary, alphabetize a list of 10 words, complete a multiplication table, measure the perimeter of an irregular shape. Students sign up for different "events" and also take turns timing and recording outcomes. Present the results in a table of times to the nearest tenth or hundredth of a second.

CHAPTER REVIEW/TEST

Part 1 Understanding

1. Use graph paper to draw the following pictures. Label each with a fraction or mixed number and a decimal. **Check students' work.**

   a. three tenths b. 33 hundredths c. one and 2 tenths

2. Give a decimal in tenths and another in hundredths that can round to each number. **Answers will vary.** **Sample answers given.**

   a. 1 **0.7,1.14** b. 5 **4.5,4.77** c. 22 **22.1,21.92** d. 40 **39.6,39.63**

Part 2 Skills

Write the decimal that comes before and after each number when you count by hundredths.

3. 0.43 **0.42,0.44** 4. 1.89 **1.88, 1.90** 5. 11.06 **11.05, 11.07**

Write <, >, or = for each ▥.

6. 5.20 ▥ 5.2 **=** 7. 3.7 ▥ 3.8 **<** 8. 5.9 ▥ 5.85 **>**

9. Order these decimals from least to greatest.

   0.85, 0.91, 0.84, 0.93, 0.89 **0.84, 0.85, 0.89, 0.91, 0.93**

Write a decimal for the fraction.

10. $\frac{1}{2}$ **0.5** 11. $\frac{7}{10}$ **0.7** 12. $\frac{23}{100}$ **0.23** 13. $\frac{1}{4}$ **0.25**

Part 3 Applications

14. 13 team members each gave $5.50 for an end-of-season party. Estimate if this is a reasonable amount for a party that cost $60. **yes**

15. **Challenge** When rounded to the nearest one, I am 1. When rounded to the nearest tenth, I am 0.9. When rounded to the nearest hundredth, I am 0.86. Which am I?

   (a.) 0.862 b. 0.868 c. 0.854

375

INFORMAL ASSESSMENT

Using Manipulatives Have students use centimeter graph paper (TA 12) to draw and label pictures representing the decimals 0.6, 0.44, 1.1, 1.09, and 2.75. Have them write an equivalent fraction or a mixed number for each picture. (Check students' drawings; $\frac{6}{10}$, $\frac{44}{100}$, $1\frac{1}{10}$, $1\frac{9}{100}$, $2\frac{75}{100}$)

Communication *Explain how to write an equivalent fraction for any decimal.* (Use a denominator of 10 or 100, depending on the decimal places; if the decimal has whole number places, write a mixed number.)

Critical Thinking *Tell why world class race times are usually measured to the nearest hundredth of a second rather than to the tenth of a second.* (Times measured to the nearest hundredth are more exact than times measured to the nearest tenth of a second.)

CHAPTER REVIEW/TEST

INTRODUCTION The Review/Test is provided to review and evaluate the skills and concepts presented in Chapter 13.

USING PAGE 375 If you prefer to use this page for review, you may want to use the **Multiple-Choice Posttest** (pages 51-52) or the **Free-Response Posttest** (pages 51-52) to evaluate mastery of Chapter objectives.

ITEM ANALYSIS The table below correlates the Chapter Review/Test items with the lesson objectives for the chapter.

Items	Objectives
1	13-1
(1)	13-2
2	13-5
3-5	13-3
6-9	13-4
10-13	13-6
14	13-7
15	13-5

ENRICHMENT

INTRODUCTION Students will explore patterns in repeating decimals by using calculators to convert fractions to decimals.

USING PAGE 376
This Enrichment page is provided for all students. You may wish to use it after they have completed the Chapter Review/Test on page 375.

► **Justify using division to convert a fraction to a decimal.** (Possible answer: A fraction is a way to represent how a whole object or set has been divided into a certain number of equal parts.)

► **Explain how to predict an equivalent decimal for $\frac{3}{5}$ if you know the equivalent decimal for $\frac{1}{5}$.** ($\frac{3}{5}$ means three pieces that are each $\frac{1}{5}$, so multiply the decimal by 3.)

EXTENSION Mathematicians use a short cut to write repeating decimals by drawing a bar over the digits that repeat. For instance, the decimal 0.1111111 . . . can be written as $0.\overline{1}$; the decimal 0.0404040 . . . can be written as $0.\overline{04}$. Challenge students to rewrite the repeating decimals found in Exercises 3, 4, 6, and 7 using this short cut. (Exercise 3: $0.\overline{1}$, $0.\overline{2}$, $0.\overline{3}$ Exercise 4: $0.\overline{4}$, $0.\overline{7}$, $0.\overline{8}$ Exercise 6: $0.\overline{04}$, $0.\overline{06}$, $0.\overline{08}$, $0.\overline{13}$, $0.\overline{46}$ Exercise 7: Answers will vary. Check students' work.)

Additional Answers: See p. T79.

ENRICHMENT
Fraction and Decimal Patterns

You know that decimals and fractions are related.

$\frac{1}{2} = 0.5$ $\frac{4}{5} = 0.8$ $\frac{3}{4} = 0.75$

1 ÷ 999 = ?

1. How can you use a calculator to convert a fraction to a decimal? Think: A meaning for $\frac{4}{5}$ is 4 divided by 5. **See Additional Answers.**

2. Find the decimal that equals $\frac{1}{5}$ on your calculator. Then use mental math to find the decimal for $\frac{3}{5}$. Check with your calculator. Explain your thinking.
0.2, 0.6, explanations may vary

Here's how to use your calculator to explore other relationships between fractions and decimals. You may find some interesting patterns!

3. Find the decimals that equal $\frac{1}{9}$, $\frac{2}{9}$, and $\frac{3}{9}$. What do you notice? **See Additional Answers.**

4. Predict the decimal equivalents for $\frac{4}{9}$, $\frac{7}{9}$, and $\frac{8}{9}$. Check with your calculator.
0.4444444, 0.777777, 0.888888

5. Imagine that your calculator had a wider display and more digits would fit across the display. How would this affect the decimals you found in problems 3 and 4? **See Additional Answers.**

6. Find the decimals that equal $\frac{4}{99}$ and $\frac{6}{99}$. Then predict the decimal for $\frac{8}{99}$. Explain what will happen in the decimals for $\frac{13}{99}$ or $\frac{46}{99}$. Check with your calculator. **See Additional Answers.**

7. Find a decimal pattern for fractions with a denominator of 999. Make a table to record at least 7 examples. Then describe your findings.
See Additional Answers.

376

CUMULATIVE REVIEW

1. Look at the coordinate grid. Which coordinates name a point inside triangle P?

   (A) (1,2) B (2,2)
   C (2,3) D (4,5)

2. Which triangles on the coordinate grid are congruent?

   A P and R B Q and R
   (C) P and Q D P, Q, and R

3. Which of the triangles on the grid is similar to triangle R?

   A P B T
   (C) S D Q

4. Find the average of these test scores: 85, 92, 100, 90, and 88.

   A 89 B 92
   (C) 91 D 455

5. Choose the best fractional estimate for the shaded part.

   A $\frac{1}{6}$ B $\frac{1}{4}$
   C $\frac{1}{5}$ (D) $\frac{1}{3}$

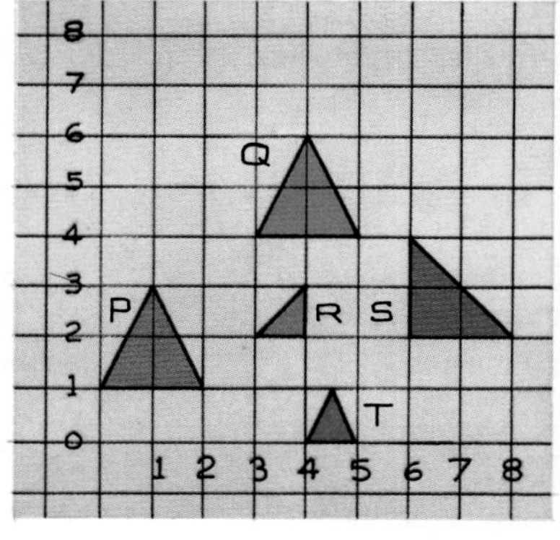

6. What fractional part of the letters in BANANAS are A's?

   A $\frac{1}{2}$ (B) $\frac{3}{7}$
   C $\frac{3}{4}$ D $\frac{4}{7}$

7. Which fraction is equivalent to $\frac{1}{4}$?

   A $\frac{4}{8}$ (B) $\frac{4}{16}$
   C $\frac{4}{12}$ D $\frac{4}{20}$

8. What is 58,620 rounded to the nearest thousand?

   (A) 59,000 B 58,600
   C 58,000 D 60,000

9. $2\overline{)817}$

   A 418 R1 (B) 408 R1
   C 409 R1 D 403 R1

CUMULATIVE REVIEW

INTRODUCTION The purpose of this Cumulative Review is to maintain previously taught skills and concepts. The emphasis in this Cumulative Review is on division with 1-digit divisors, Chapter 10; on geometry, Chapter 11; and on fraction concepts, Chapter 12.

ITEM ANALYSIS The table below correlates the Cumulative Review items with the lesson objectives.

Items	Objectives
1	11-9
2	11-7
3	11-10
4	10-8
5	12-3
6	12-2
7	12-4
8	12-4
9	10-7

CHAPTER 14 METRIC MEASUREMENT

Chapter Management

OVERVIEW

Lesson	Pages	Objectives	Subject Integration	Strand Integration
Chapter Opener	378-379	To introduce chapter 14	science-rainfall	computation
Centimeters, Decimeters, Meters, and Kilometers	380-381	14-1 To measure length in cm, dm, m, and km and to relate these units	science-rain forest	estimation
Estimating Length: Unitizing	382-383	14-2 To estimate length in centimeters by unitizing	social studies-room measurements	mathematical reasoning
Millimeters	384-385	14-3 To measure length in millimeters	science-Florida tree frog	calculators
Problem Solving/Midchapter Review/Quiz	386-387	14-4 To decide whether an actual measurement is needed or whether an estimate is sufficient	science-Florida Everglades	computation
Area	388-389	14-5 To measure area in square centimeters and to multiply to find area	fine arts-drawing	problem solving
Volume	390-391	14-6 To measure volume in cubic centimeters and to multiply to find volume	language arts-creating data	critical thinking
Problem Solving: Finding Related Problems	392-393	14-7 To solve problems by finding related problems	social studies-Florida beaches	computation
Capacity	394-395	14-8 To estimate and measure capacity in mL and L	science-rainfall	mental math
Grams and Kilograms/Temperature: Degrees Celsius	396-397	14-9 To estimate and measure mass in kilograms and grams; to measure temperature in degrees Celsius	science-experiment	graphing
Data Collection and Analysis: Group Decision Making	398-399	14-10 To collect, organize, and present data	science-animals	statistics

MATHEMATICAL BACKGROUND

Metric Units
In Chapter 14, students are taught these metric units: millimeter, centimeter, decimeter, meter, kilometer, liter, milliliter, gram, kilogram, degrees Celsius. Students learn to use these units to find length, capacity, volume, or mass of various objects. They also learn to find the area of an object and to read a thermometer in degrees Celsius.

Estimation
Students learn to unitize to estimate length in Lesson 14-2.

Problem Solving
In this chapter, students solve problems by deciding when to estimate and by finding related problems and using the same strategy for both.

TIPS FROM TEACHERS

Before introducing customary or metric units of measurement, let students practice measuring with non-standard units, such as paper-clip chains, knotted yarn, wooden sticks, and shoe lengths.

Betty Looney
Milam Elementary School
Grand Prairie, TX

Assessment

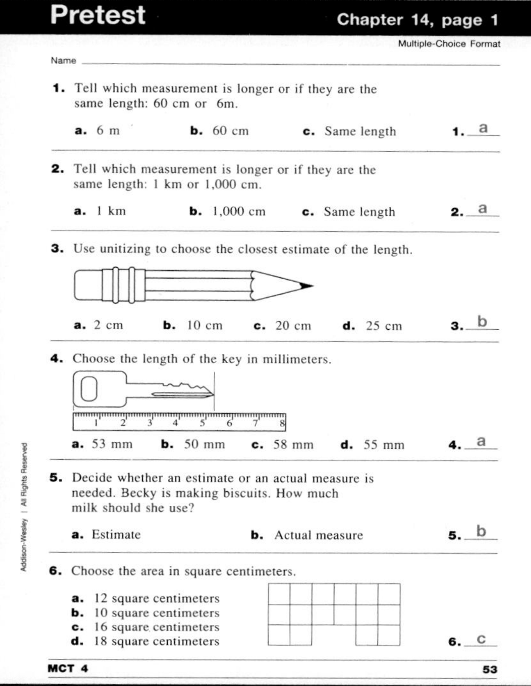

Pretest — Chapter 14, page 1

Multiple-Choice Format

Name ____________

1. Tell which measurement is longer or if they are the same length: 60 cm or 6m.
   a. 6 m b. 60 cm c. Same length 1. a

2. Tell which measurement is longer or if they are the same length: 1 km or 1,000 cm.
   a. 1 km b. 1,000 cm c. Same length 2. a

3. Use unitizing to choose the closest estimate of the length.
   a. 2 cm b. 10 cm c. 20 cm d. 25 cm 3. b

4. Choose the length of the key in millimeters.
   a. 53 mm b. 50 mm c. 58 mm d. 55 mm 4. a

5. Decide whether an estimate or an actual measure is needed. Becky is making biscuits. How much milk should she use?
   a. Estimate b. Actual measure 5. b

6. Choose the area in square centimeters.
   a. 12 square centimeters
   b. 10 square centimeters
   c. 16 square centimeters
   d. 18 square centimeters 6. c

MCT 4 53

Pretest — Chapter 14, page 2

Multiple-Choice Format

Name ____________

7. Choose the volume in cubic centimeters.
   a. 6 cubic centimeters
   b. 16 cubic centimeters
   c. 10 cubic centimeters
   d. 12 cubic centimeters 7. d

8. Could you use the same problem solving strategy to solve these two problems? Choose yes or no. Do not solve the problems.
   Problem 1: I am a number under 100. My digits are the same. The sum of my digits is 16. What number am I?
   Problem 2: I am a number between 80 and 100. The sum of my digits is 15. Their difference is 1. What number am I?
   a. Yes b. No 8. a

9. Which unit would make more sense to use for measuring the capacity of an eyedropper?
   a. mL b. L 9. a

10. Choose the better estimate of capacity for a juice glass.
    a. 150 mL b. 150 L 10. a

11. Choose the better estimate for the mass of two nickels.
    a. 10 g b. 1 kg 11. a

12. What is the temperature shown?
    a. 20° C b. 15° C
    c. -20° C d. -15° C 12. c

Degrees Centigrade

54 MCT 4

Posttest — Chapter 14, page 1

Multiple-Choice Format

Name ____________

1. Tell which measurement is longer or if they are the same length: 6 dm or 600 cm.
   a. 6 dm b. 600 cm c. Same length 1. b

2. Tell which measurement is longer or if they are the same length: 8 km or 8,000 m.
   a. 8 km b. 8,000 m c. Same length 2. c

3. Use unitizing to choose the closest estimate of the length.
   a. 2 cm b. 5 cm c. 15 cm d. 25 cm 3. c

4. Choose the length of the paper clip in millimeters.
   a. 39 mm b. 44 mm c. 34 mm d. 49 mm 4. c

5. Decide whether an estimate or an actual measure is needed. Dan is making a sandwich. How much mayonnaise should he use?
   a. Estimate b. Actual measure 5. a

6. Choose the area in square centimeters.
   a. 10 square centimeters
   b. 12 square centimeters
   c. 8 square centimeters
   d. 14 square centimeters 6. d

MCT 4 55

Posttest — Chapter 14, page 2

Multiple-Choice Format

Name ____________

7. Choose the volume in cubic centimeters.
   a. 24 cubic centimeters
   b. 20 cubic centimeters
   c. 10 cubic centimeters
   d. 14 cubic centimeters 7. b

8. Could you use the same problem solving strategy to solve these two problems? Choose yes or no. Do not solve the problems.
   Problem 1: At night, Jim has $0.56 in his pocket. During the day, he spent $1.85 for lunch and $0.38 for a snack. How much money did he have in the morning?
   Problem 2: Cathy is in line behind Paul and in front of Marsha. Max is first in line. Who is second in line?
   a. Yes b. No 8. b

9. Which unit would make more sense to use for measuring the capacity of a pool?
   a. mL b. L 9. b

10. Choose the better estimate of capacity for a teakettle.
    a. 500 mL b. 500 L 10. a

11. Choose the better estimate for the mass of your math book.
    a. 10 g b. 1 kg 11. b

12. What is the temperature shown?
    a. 40° C b. 48° C
    c. 50° C d. 45° C 12. d

Degrees Centigrade

56 MCT 4

Item Analysis

Items	Objectives
1, 2	14-1
3	14-2
4	14-3
5	14-4
6	14-5
7	14-6
8	14-7
9, 10	14-8
11, 12	14-9

Note: The item analysis is the same for all pretests and posttests for this chapter.

Also Available

- **Free Response Tests**
- **Alternative Tests**
- **Thinking Strategies**
- **Concrete Materials**

Optional Chapter Activities

PROJECT AND BULLETIN BOARD

As students progress through this chapter, have them look for examples of items that are measured by both the U.S. and metric systems. Whenever possible, have them bring to class examples of or labels from these items and display them on the bulletin board or on a table. If students cannot bring to class the item or its label, have them draw a picture of it and post it on the bulletin board. Next to each item, label, or picture, students should list its measurements in the metric and U.S. systems.

When students have completed Lesson 9, ask them to categorize the items displayed as liquid or solid, and by length, weight, capacity, or any other method they choose.

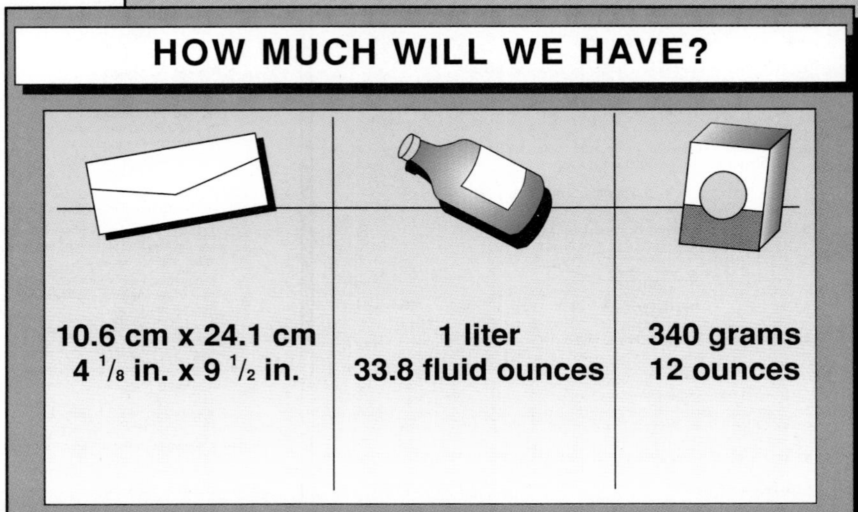

COOPERATIVE LEARNING

Divide the class into groups of three or four. Identify the group skill: explain and summarize. Give each group some string, a ruler measured in feet and inches, and a metric ruler. Have each group determine how to use these materials to measure distances around various circular things, such as round tabletops, balls, and plates. Help students assign tasks. One person should measure the object with string, another should measure the length of string used with both the U.S. and metric rulers, and a third person should record the measurements. Have students measure and record their measurements to the nearest inch and to the nearest centimeter. Have each group compare the measurements they arrived at using both systems and then explain their results in a report written cooperatively.

You will find grouping suggestions and cooperative learning activities in most lessons throughout this chapter.

LITERATURE

Bontemps, Arna and Jack Conroy. *The Fast Sooner Hound.* Boston, MA: Houghton Mifflin, 1969.

The Sooner Hound would rather run than eat. In order not to be separated from his master he runs alongside a train.
Children could use the story to discuss how fast different things can go and how to measure speed and distance using meters and kilometers. Children might also enjoy measuring a distance on the playground. Then each child could measure and run, skip, or hop the distance.

Branley, Franklyn M. *Measure with Meter.* New York: Young Math Book Series, Thomas Y. Crowell, 1975.

O'Connor, Vincent F. *Mathematics on the Playground.* Milwaukee, WI: Raintree, 1978.

Leaf, Munro. *Metric Can Be Fun.* New York: J. B. Lippincott, 1976.

Schneider, Herman and Nina. *How Big Is Big?: From Stars to Atoms.* New York: William R. Scott, 1950.

English as a Second Language

Before beginning Lesson 6, have ESL students try the following activity to become familiar with the concept of volume.

Arrange students into small groups and provide each group with 48 centimeter blocks. Model forming a 6-by-4 rectangle for students to copy with their blocks, then add a second layer and ask students to do the same. Point out the length, width, and height as you say each word and have students repeat after you. Then ask students to count the number of blocks in their prism's length, width, and height and to record those numbers on a chart. Have students count the total number of blocks in their prism and add that information to their chart. Repeat the activity using different-sized prisms or cubes, then have students look for a pattern in the data they recorded and discuss their findings.

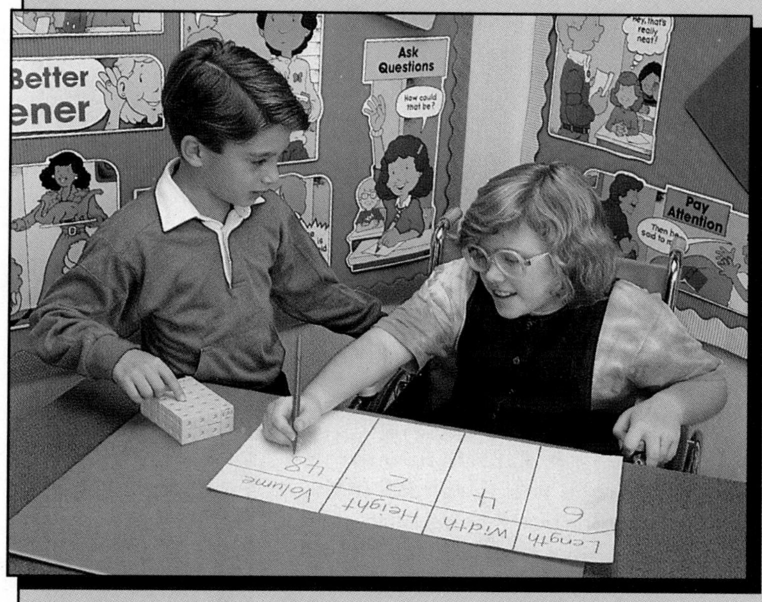

Gifted

Assign students a partner and give each pair a list of 10 items in the classroom or the school. First they estimate an item's length, height, or width using the metric unit of measure they feel is most appropriate; then they actually measure it. For example, they might measure the height of the bulletin board in meters, the length of their math book in centimeters, and the width of their desk in decimeters. Ask them to add five items of their own to the list. Instruct each student to make a chart with three columns to show the name of the object, its estimate, and its actual measurement.

Encourage class discussion, comparing actual measurements of the same item by different partners. Have them resolve any significant differences by remeasuring the items together. Ask them to determine which partner has the closest estimate for each item. Have them determine which estimates were the most accurate.

Have students brainstorm and suggest 5 instances in daily life when actual measurements would be needed and 5 occasions when estimates would suffice. Ask them to justify their examples.

Students at Risk

The concepts, skills, and tasks of metric measurement can present particular challenges to students who have physical or neurological impairments. These students may have difficulty using rulers or measuring cups or manipulating objects to clarify the concepts of area, volume, or mass. You may wish to match some students with a partner who can do the actual measurements. Other students may benefit from using alternate measuring devices, such as trundle wheels or tape measures.

Language disabled students may need help distinguishing between the measurement ideas of perimeter, area, and volume. You may wish to substitute the simpler terms *border* (perimeter), *cover* (area), and *fill* (volume) to help students visualize the action each type of measurement suggests.

You may also use the Reteaching Supplements and the specific Reteaching Tips from each lesson in this chapter.

INTRODUCING THE CHAPTER

SUBJECT INTEGRATION The photograph of a blue heron suggests the chapter theme of natural science. Several lessons include data about rain forests, waterfowl, rainfall, and other features of tropical climates to provide realistic situations involving metric measurement.

USING DATA The Science Data Bank on page 471 of the Student Edition has a bar graph of Average Rainfall Per Year in 4 locations. It also gives a graphic representation of Types of Rain Forest on a Typical Tropical Mountain that are related to height. Layers of Vegetation in a Tropical Rain Forest pictures the 4 classifications of forest growth.

QUESTION 1 ▶ **Explain how to find the average yearly rainfall in the Florida Everglades.** (Find the place on the graph scale that meets the top of the Florida Everglades bar, then compare that number to 2,000 mm, which is the minimum yearly rainfall needed to qualify as a rain forest.)
Student Edition answer: no

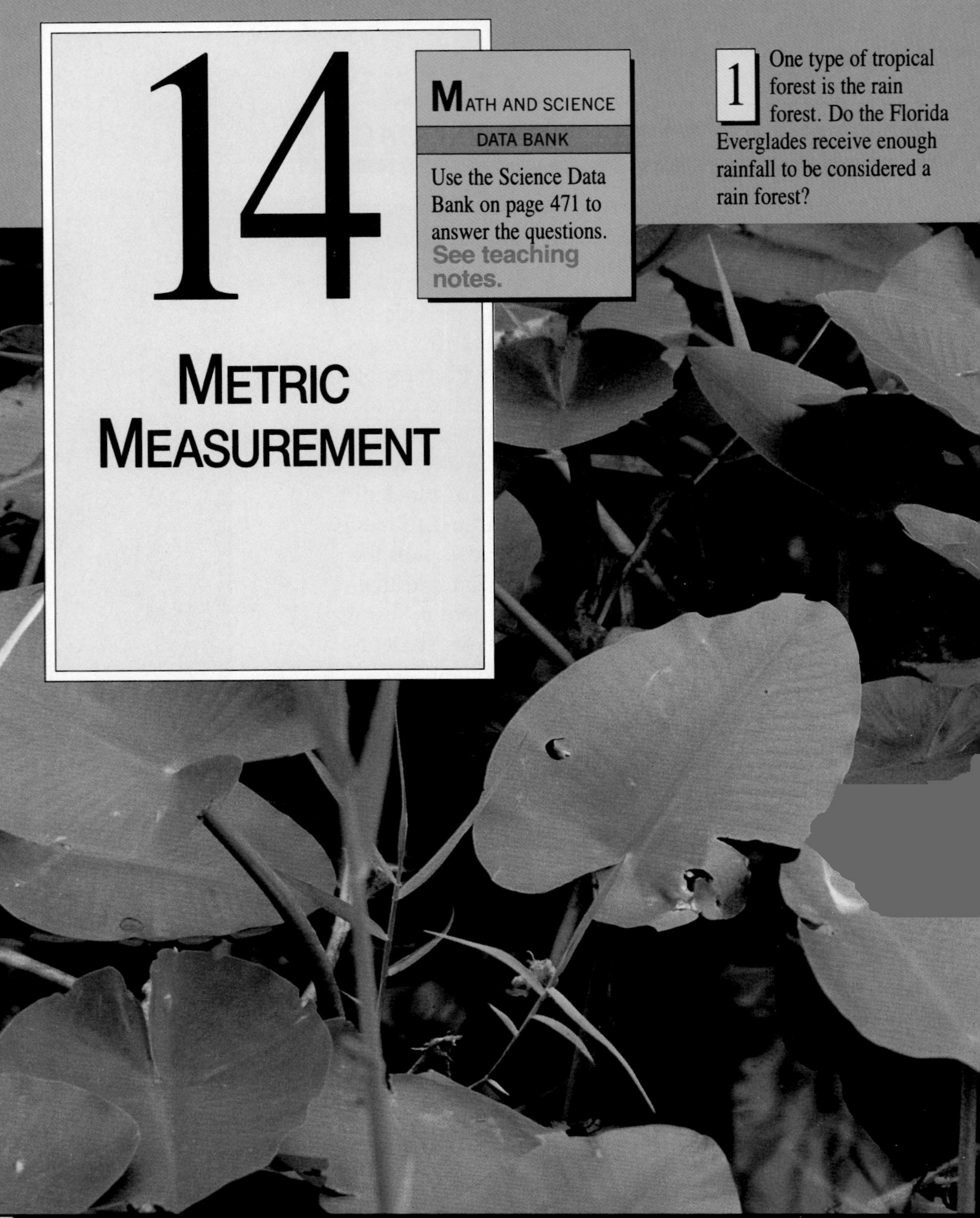

14 METRIC MEASUREMENT

MATH AND SCIENCE DATA BANK

Use the Science Data Bank on page 471 to answer the questions. See teaching notes.

1 One type of tropical forest is the rain forest. Do the Florida Everglades receive enough rainfall to be considered a rain forest?

TEACHING OPTIONS

LANGUAGE DEVELOPMENT
Write **mm** on the chalkboard and tell students that it is an abbreviation for a unit of measure called the **millimeter.** Have students find where mm appears in the Science Data Bank on page 471 and decide what kind of measurement unit it is. (It appears on the Average Rainfall Per Year graph; length) Challenge them to use number sense to classify it as a large or small unit, based on analyzing the number of millimeters of rainfall in Chicago or the Florida Everglades. (small)

2 Would a forest that received 200.9 mm of rainfall per year be a rain forest?

3 What type of rain forest would you find 1,000 m high on a tropical mountain?

4 **Use Critical Thinking** If a tree in the emergent layer of a rain forest is 35 m high, can a tree in the canopy layer be 48 m high? Why?

379

QUESTION 2 ► **Explain how to interpret the number 200.9.** (Answers may vary. Sample: It is more than 200 but not the same as 2,009.)
Student Edition answer: no

QUESTION 3 ► **Identify which graph or picture helps you answer the question.** (Types of Rain Forest on a Typical Tropical Mountain)
► **Explain how to use the graph.** (Find the mark that stands for 1,000 m, then see which section of the mountain it matches.)
Student Edition answer: Lower Montane

QUESTION 4 ► **Compare the heights of the two trees mentioned in the situation.** (The tree in the emergent layer is 35 m tall, the other tree, at 48 m, is taller.)
► **Explain a relationship between the emergent and canopy layers in a tropical rain forest.** (The emergent layer is the highest layer and the canopy layer is the next highest one.)
Student Edition answer: no; the emergent layer is the highest part of a tropical rain forest so trees in the canopy layer must be smaller.

SUBJECT INTEGRATION PROJECT Have students prepare a weather and climate data log for interesting or unusual places in America. Begin by having students name metric units they already know as you write them on the chalkboard. Then brainstorm weather conditions that scientists generally measure, such as snowfall, temperature, or air pressure. Students can follow local weather reports and use almanacs or other science materials to gather metric data they can include in each entry of the log over the days they work on Chapter 14.

LESSON OPTIONS 14-1

Centimeters, Decimeters, Meters, and Kilometers

OBJECTIVE 14-1 To measure length in cm, dm, m, and km and to relate these units

PREBOOK ACTIVITIES

QUICK REVIEW

Multiply mentally.

1. 3 × 10 (30)	**2.** 4 × 100 (400)
3. 7 × 1,000 (7,000)	**4.** 9 × 100 (900)
5. 10 × 46 (460)	**6.** 10 × 100 (1,000)
7. 10 × 25 (250)	**8.** 100 × 14 (1,400)
9. 1,000 × 37 (37,000)	**10.** 100 × 357 (35,700)

PRIOR KNOWLEDGE

Have students name customary measurement units they have used to describe length or distance. (inch, foot, yard, mile) Ask them if they know of other measurement units that also describe length. (Possible answers: meter, centimeter, decimeter, kilometer) Ask students where they have seen metric measurements used. (Possible answers: Olympic races, scientific data, measuring tapes) Tell students that in this lesson they will work with 4 metric units of length—centimeter, decimeter, meter, and kilometer.

COMMUNICATION

Reading and Writing in Math Have students write the following words in their Math Journals, under a heading Metric Measurement: **meter, centimeter, decimeter, kilometer.** Point out that the word *metric* is an adjective that describes measurement units based on the meter. Then list the following abbreviations and have students match each with its appropriate metric unit: **km, m, dm, cm.** Have students find a pattern in the measurement words and abbreviations. (Possible answer: All units have meter in them, as all abbreviations have *m*.)

EXPLORE AND CONNECT

Materials: TA 17 (Centimeter Ruler), meter sticks, metric tape measures

Grouping Suggestion: cooperative learning groups of 4

Students explore the sizes of and relationships among metric units of length. Review **centimeter, decimeter,** and **meter**. Groups work as two pairs: one pair finds classroom objects or distances that are 10 **cm**, 20 *cm*, and 30 *cm* long, while the other pair finds those that are 1 *dm,* 2 *dm,* and 3 *dm* long. Pairs record their results, then compare findings to establish a relationship. (10 *cm* = 1 *dm*, 20 *cm* = 2 *dm*, 30 *cm* = 3 *dm*) Then one pair finds classroom objects or distances that are 10 *dm*, 20 *dm*, and 30 *dm* long, as the other finds ones that are 1 *m*, 2 *m*, and 3 *m* long. Groups compare their findings to establish another relationship. (10 *dm* = 1 *m*, 20 *dm* = 2 *m*, 30 *dm* = 3 *m*) Conclude by having the class give as many metric equivalencies as they can.

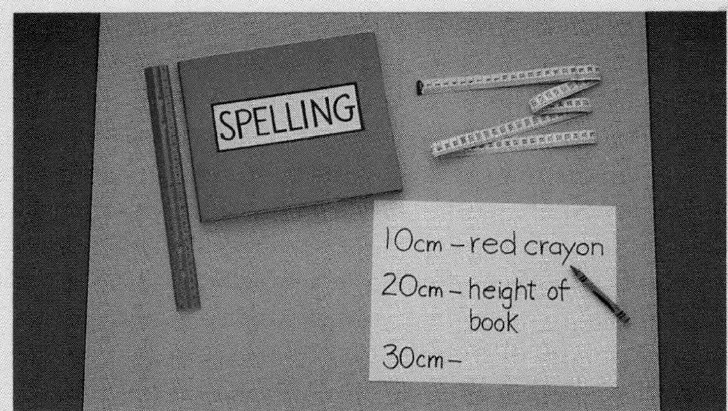

CONNECTIONS Use these anytime.

Problem of the Day

Olympics The shortest foot race in the Olympic Games is the 100-m run. The world's fastest male runners finish the race in about 10 s. Determine the distance they cover per second, then mark off that length in or near your classroom. (about 10 m/s)

Subject Integration

Science Scientists say that the female blue whale is the largest animal that ever lived. She may grow to be 30 m long, which is about as long as a parade of 6 African elephants walking tail to trunk. About how long is one African elephant? (5 m)

Math Connection

Decimal Numeration 1 dm = 10 cm. Find a way to use decimals to give lengths of 1 cm and 5 cm as parts of a decimeter. (1 cm = 0.1 dm; 5 cm = 0.5 dm)

CLASSWORK AND HOMEWORK SUPPLEMENTS

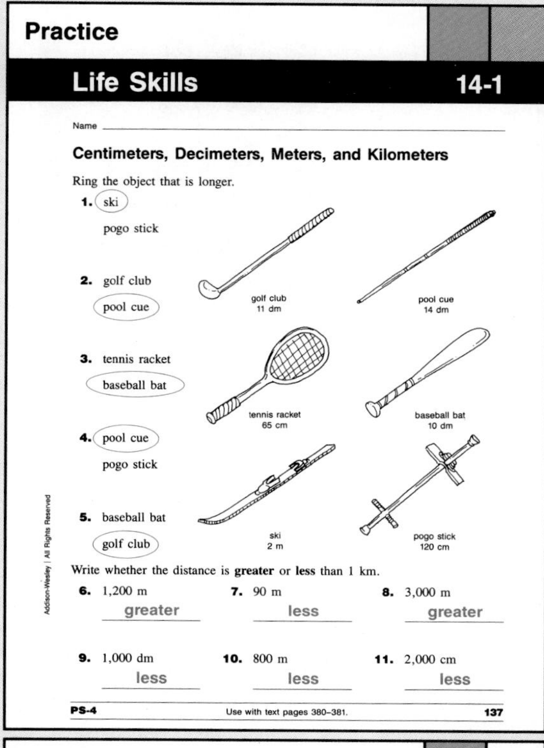

Practice

Life Skills 14-1

Name

Centimeters, Decimeters, Meters, and Kilometers

Ring the object that is longer.

1. (ski) pogo stick
2. golf club (pool cue)
3. tennis racket (baseball bat)
4. (pool cue) pogo stick
5. baseball bat (golf club)

Write whether the distance is **greater** or **less** than 1 km.

6. 1,200 m greater
7. 90 m less
8. 3,000 m greater
9. 1,000 dm less
10. 800 m less
11. 2,000 cm less

PS-4 Use with text pages 380–381. 137

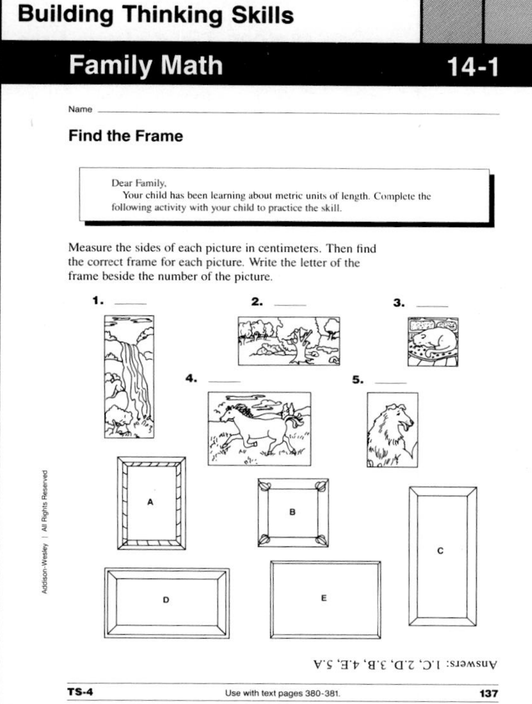

Building Thinking Skills

Family Math 14-1

Name

Find the Frame

Dear Family,
Your child has been learning about metric units of length. Complete the following activity with your child to practice the skill.

Measure the sides of each picture in centimeters. Then find the correct frame for each picture. Write the letter of the frame beside the number of the picture.

1. ____ 2. ____ 3. ____ 4. ____ 5. ____

Answers: 1.C, 2.D, 3.B, 4.E, 5.A

TS-4 Use with text pages 380-381. 137

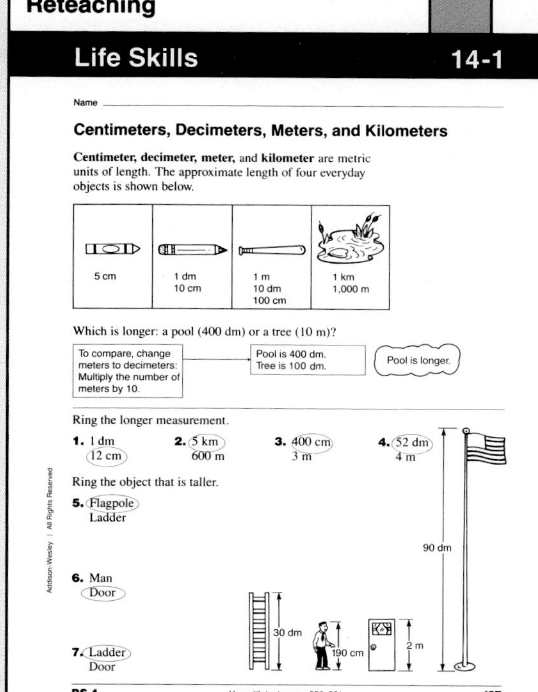

Reteaching

Life Skills 14-1

Name

Centimeters, Decimeters, Meters, and Kilometers

Centimeter, decimeter, meter, and **kilometer** are metric units of length. The approximate length of four everyday objects is shown below.

5 cm	1 dm 10 cm	1 m 10 dm 100 cm	1 km 1,000 m

Which is longer: a pool (400 dm) or a tree (10 m)?

To compare, change meters to decimeters: Multiply the number of meters by 10. → Pool is 400 dm. Tree is 100 dm. → Pool is longer.

Ring the longer measurement.

1. 1 dm (12 cm)
2. (5 km) 600 m
3. (400 cm) 3 m
4. (52 dm) 4 m

Ring the object that is taller.

5. (Flagpole) Ladder
6. Man (Door)
7. (Ladder) Door

RS-4 Use with text pages 380-381. 137

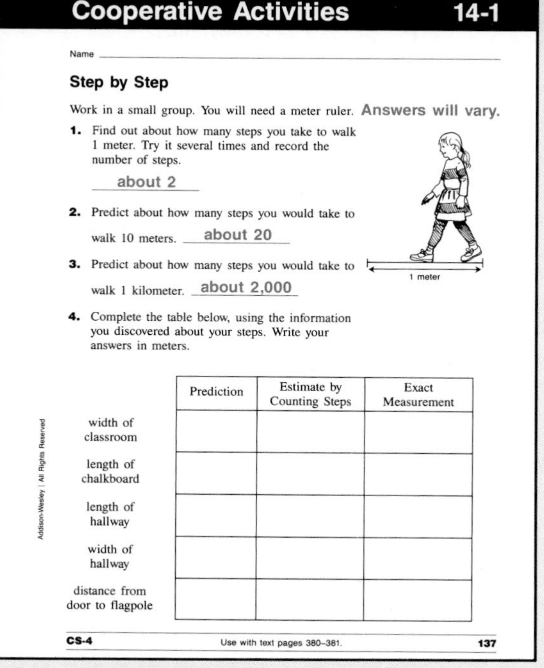

Challenges

Cooperative Activities 14-1

Name

Step by Step

Work in a small group. You will need a meter ruler. Answers will vary.

1. Find out about how many steps you take to walk 1 meter. Try it several times and record the number of steps. about 2
2. Predict about how many steps you would take to walk 10 meters. about 20
3. Predict about how many steps you would take to walk 1 kilometer. about 2,000
4. Complete the table below, using the information you discovered about your steps. Write your answers in meters.

	Prediction	Estimate by Counting Steps	Exact Measurement
width of classroom			
length of chalkboard			
length of hallway			
width of hallway			
distance from door to flagpole			

CS-4 Use with text pages 380-381. 137

OPTIONS FOR INDIVIDUAL NEEDS

Basic

Exercises 1-14
Data Bank, p. 471
More Practice, p. 525, set D

Supplements
Reteaching 137 or
Practice 137

Average

Exercises 1-14
Data Bank, p. 471
More Practice, p. 525, set D

Supplements
Practice 137
Challenges 137 or
Thinking Skills 137

Extended

Exercises 1-14
Data Bank, p. 471

Supplements
Challenges 137
Thinking Skills 137

Other Resources:
Problem-Solving Experiences in Mathematics, Grade 4, Problems 59, 60
Mathematics, A Way of Thinking, Lesson 16-1
Math In Stride, Grade 4, p. 157

14-1

LESSON PLAN 14-1

OBJECTIVE 14-1
To measure length in cm, dm, m, and km and to relate these units

Materials: assorted metric rulers or tapes, stick-on stars or dots

Alternative Materials: TA 17 (Centimeter Ruler)

Grouping Suggestion: pairs

1. MOTIVATE AND TEACH

LEARN ABOUT IT

EXPLORE ► **Explain a way to measure your height in centimeters.** (Possible answer: Have a partner mark your height on the chalkboard, then measure up from the floor to the mark.)

TALK ABOUT IT ► **What relationship can you use to compare your height in centimeters to 1, 2, or 3 m? Explain your reasoning.** (100 cm = 1 m because 10 cm = 1 dm and 10 dm = 1 m, so 10 cm × 10 = 100 cm)
► **Determine which unit gives your height most precisely. Explain your reasoning.** (centimeters; It is the smallest unit so it is most accurate.)
► **What would you measure in kilometers? Explain why.** (long distances; It is a large measure.)
Student Edition answers: **1.** See if your height is closer to 100, 200, or 300 cm. **2.** Answers will vary; divide height in centimeters by 10. **3.** Possible answer: Height in decimeters is better than meters, but best in centimeters.

2. CHECK UNDERSTANDING

TRY IT OUT

ERROR ALERT Exercises 1-3 Confusing decimeters and centimeters. Exercises 4-7 Inaccurately comparing measurement units.

Centimeters, Decimeters, Meters, and Kilometers

LEARN ABOUT IT

1 dm = 10 cm
1 m = 10 dm = 100 cm

EXPLORE **Use a Metric Tape Measure**
The **centimeter** (cm), **decimeter** (dm), and **meter** (m) are metric units of length. Use a metric tape measure to measure your height and the lengths of some objects to the nearest centimeter. Record your measurements.

TALK ABOUT IT See teaching notes.

1. How can you decide whether your height in centimeters is closer to 1, 2, or 3 meters?
2. About how many decimeters tall are you? Tell how you know.
3. Is decimeters a good unit of measure for your height? Explain.

The **kilometer** (km) is another metric unit of length. 1 km is about the same length as 5 city blocks. It takes about 10 minutes to walk a kilometer.

1 km = 1,000 m

TRY IT OUT

Measure the lengths of these objects in centimeters and decimeters. Then measure them to the nearest meter if you can.

1. your math book **2.** a piece of chalk **3.** your teacher's desk
Check students' measurements.

Tell which measurement is longer or if they are the same length.

4. 4 dm	**5.** 7 dm	**6.** 250 cm	**7.** 8,000 m
40 cm	2 m	3 m	8 km
same	(2 m underlined)	(3 m underlined)	same

380

TEACHING OPTIONS

RETEACHING TIPS Have students who are confusing decimeters and centimeters use stick-on stars or dots to highlight every 10 cm on their metric rulers. This will help students more clearly visualize the difference between centimeters and decimeters. Assign Reteaching Supplement 137.

ENRICHMENT Have students use an almanac to find data in meters for the deepest spots in the Pacific, Atlantic, Indian, and Arctic Oceans. They round each measurement to the nearest thousand, then restate the data in kilometers. Have them make a table or chart to display the data.

PRACTICE

Tell which object is wider or if they are the same width.

1. Table / Chalkboard
2. Window / Door
3. Chalkboard / Window
4. Door / Table

85 cm

2m

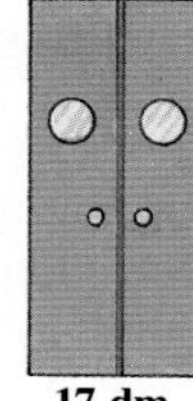

17 dm

30 dm

Tell if the distance is greater than or less than 1 km.

5. 200 m **less**
6. 1,500 m **greater**
7. 400 m **less**
8. 1,000 cm **less**

APPLY

MATH REASONING

9. Would a door 2 m tall fit into an opening 190 cm high? **no**
10. Would a bookcase 250 cm tall fit into a classroom with a ceiling 3 m high? **yes**

PROBLEM SOLVING

11. A strip of rain forest is 600 dm long and 90 dm wide. Is the perimeter of the strip more or less than 100 m? **more**
12. **Science Data Bank** DATA BANK Which type of rain forest is found 2 km high on a tropical mountain? See page 471. **Upper Montane**

► **ESTIMATION**

Estimate the height of these trees.

13. Tree A
14. Tree B

Answers will vary.
Sample answers: A, 18 m
B, 12 m

Tree A

6 m

Tree B

More Practice, page 525, set D

3. Practice and Apply

Basic	1-14
Average	1-14
Extended	1-14

PRACTICE

Of the 4 objects shown, which is the widest? (chalkboard) *Which is the narrowest?* (table) *What do you need to know about meters and kilometers to answer Exercises 5-8?* (1,000 m equal 1 k.)

APPLY

MATH REASONING ► **What relationship do you need to know to solve Exercises 9 and 10? Explain why.** (1 m = 100 cm, so that you can convert all measurements in meters to centimeters to make the comparisons.)

PROBLEM SOLVING ► **After looking at the graph in the Data Bank, what relationship do you need to know to solve Problem 12? Why?** (1 km = 1,000 m, because the heights in the graph are given in meters)

ESTIMATION ► **Explain how to estimate the heights of Trees A and B.** (Estimate how many 6-m sections are in each.)

14-1

Close and Assess

SHOW WHAT YOU KNOW Ask students to find the 3 measurements below. Have them first decide whether to use centimeters, decimeters, or meters and then justify their decisions. (Reasonable units are given.)

1. thickness of a dictionary (centimeters)
2. height of a bookshelf (decimeters)
3. length of the classroom (meters)

QUICK QUIZ

Write <, >, or =.
1. 5 dm ○ 50 cm
2. 60 dm ○ 5 m
3. 3,000 m ○ 4 km
(**1.** = **2.** > **3.** <)

LESSON OPTIONS 14-2

Estimating Length: Unitizing

OBJECTIVE 14-2 To use the estimation technique of unitizing to estimate length in centimeters

PREBOOK ACTIVITIES

QUICK REVIEW

Which is the sensible measure? Write cm, dm, or m.

1. A paper clip is 3 _(cm)_ long.
2. A dog is 5 _(dm)_ tall.
3. A baseball bat is 10 _(dm)_ long.
4. An eyelash is 1 _(cm)_ long.
5. A doorway is 2 _(m)_ high.
6. A stapler is 2 _(dm)_ long.

PRIOR KNOWLEDGE

Have students think of situations when they estimated length or distance. (Answers will vary. Samples: judging how far you are from a goal; measuring something longer than a ruler; estimating the height of something taller than your reach) Have students share methods they have used to estimate lengths. (Answers will vary.) Tell students that in this lesson they will learn a visual estimation method known as unitizing.

COMMUNICATION

Discussing and Reading Math Write the words *alphabetize, legalize,* and **unitize** on the chalkboard. Ask students to read the words and find a pattern among them. (All have *-ize* at the end of a familiar word.) Ask students to explain what it means to alphabetize a list or to legalize voting. (''put a list in ABC order''; ''make voting legal'') Challenge students to use logical reasoning to guess what *unitizing* would mean, offering the clue that the word relates to measurement. (Possible answer: ''make something into a unit of measure'')

EXPLORE AND CONNECT

Materials: TA 12 (Centimeter Graph Paper)
TA 17 (Centimeter Ruler)
Grouping Suggestion: cooperative learning pairs
Students explore **unitizing** to estimate length. Pairs need a 5-cm strip of graph paper. The first student picks any classroom object longer than 5 cm and estimates its length using *only* the 5-cm strip as a guide. Before estimating, partners may plan helpful strategies. After an estimate has been made and recorded, the second student finds the actual measurement with a metric ruler and records it by the estimate. Trading tasks, partners repeat the activity with another object. Conclude by having students explain how they estimated. (Visually divide an object into parts the size of the strip, then multiply by the number of parts.) Have students imagine *unitizing* without a paper strip of known size. (Estimate the size of a small part; visually divide the object; multiply.)

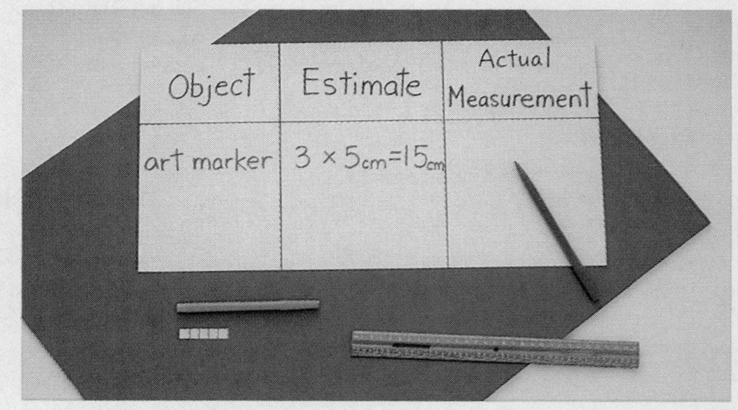

CONNECTIONS Use these anytime.

Problem of the Day

Freight Train At a railroad crossing, Mr. Metzger counts 60 boxcars in a freight train. What data would help him estimate the length of the train? (length of a boxcar) If he guesses that a boxcar is about 18 m long, explain whether the train is longer or shorter than 1 km. (60 × 18 m = 1,080 m; 1,000 m = 1 km, so the train is longer than 1 km.)

Number Sense

Mental Math A nickel is 2 cm wide. Suppose that you place enough nickels side by side to form a row 1 m long. How much is the row worth? Explain your reasoning. (1 m = 100 cm; 100 ÷ 2 = 50, so 50 nickels = 1 m; 50 × $0.05 = $2.50)

Subject Integration

Health and Fitness Adam practices the triple jump in his yard, but he does not have a tape measure long enough to find the total distance. His aunt says that his first jump is the same length as a section of fence. How can Adam estimate the other two parts of his jump to find the total length? (Measure the section of fence; multiply by 3.)

Classwork and Homework Supplements

Practice

Estimation 14-2

Name ______________________________

Estimating Length: Unitizing

Use unitizing to estimate each length in centimeters or meters. Then measure the length to the nearest centimeter or meter. Find the difference between the estimated and the actual measures.

Record your data in the table below. **Answers will vary.**

Object	Estimate (cm or m)	Measure (cm or m)	Difference (cm or m)
1. pencil			
2. science book			
3. door (height)			
4. your arm			
5. your shortest finger			
6. your foot			
7. chair (height)			
8. window (width)			

138 Use with text pages 382-383. PS-4

Building Thinking Skills

Life Skills 14-2

Name ______________________________

How Far?

Lyons, Elm, Beetson, Axton, Gardner, Dry Wells, High Falls, Puddington, Foggy Creek, Morris, Roseburg, N, W, E, S

The distance from Morris to Roseburg is about 20 km.
The distance from Axton to Dry Wells is about 50 km.

Use these two distances to help you decide which of the given estimates is best. Ring the best estimate.

1. The distance from Elm to Gardner is about
   A 10 km **B** 20 km (ringed) **C** 50 km
2. The distance from Roseburg to Foggy Creek is about
   A 30 km **B** 50 km (ringed) **C** 70 km
3. The distance from High Falls to Puddington is about
   A 40 km (ringed) **B** 75 km **C** 100 km
4. The distance from Dry Wells to Foggy Creek is about
   A 40 km **B** 60 km (ringed) **C** 80 km
5. The distance from Lyons to Beetson is about
   A 100 km **B.** 120 km (ringed) **C** 150 km
6. The distance from Lyons to Morris is about
   A 150 km **B** 180 km **C** 220 km (ringed)

138 Use with text pages 382-383. TS-4

Reteaching

Estimation 14-2

Name ______________________________

Estimating Length: Unitizing

Use unitizing to estimate the length of this object.

Divide object into equal parts. → Estimate length of each part. → Multiply estimate by number of parts.

4 equal parts

One part is about 2 cm long.

$2 \text{ cm} \times 4 \text{ parts} = 8 \text{ cm}$
The length of the nail is about 8 cm.

Use unitizing to estimate each length in centimeters. Then measure the length to the nearest centimeter. Find the difference between the estimated and actual measures.

Record your data in the table below.
Estimates and differences may vary.

	Object	Estimate	Measure	Difference
1.	screwdriver		10 cm	
2.	pencil		12 cm	
3.	hammer		15 cm	
4.	screw		3 cm	

138 Use with text pages 382-383. RS-4

Challenges

Estimation 14-2

Name ______________________________

20 cm Game

Play this game with a small group. Take turns being the dealer.
Make 20 cards with one of the line segments below on each.
There should be 2 cards for each segment.

(1 cm) (2 cm) (3 cm) (4 cm) (5 cm) (6 cm) (7 cm) (8 cm) (9 cm) (10 cm)

Rules

1. The object of the game is for a player to accumulate enough cards to reach 20 cm without going over.
2. The dealer deals out 2 cards to each player. Then the dealer asks each player if he or she wants another card. Once a player has said no to a card, he or or she cannot take any more cards. The dealer deals out a card to the next player who says yes.
3. The dealer continues dealing out cards until one player estimates that all of his or her line segments joined together would be close to, but no longer than, 20 cm. The player then calls out **20 cm!** to stop the game.
4. When the game is stopped, each player measures the length of each of his or her line segments and records the added measurements.
5. Here is how points are awarded:

Total line length	Points
20 cm	3
19 cm	2
18 cm	1
less than 18 cm	0
more than 20 cm	0

6. After 10 rounds, the player with the highest total score wins.

138 Use with text pages 382-383. CS-4

Options for Individual Needs

Basic

Exercises 2-14, 17, 18
Computer Bank, p. 493
More Practice, p. 525, set E

Supplements
Reteaching 138 or
Practice 138
Challenges 138

Average

Exercises 1-18
Computer Bank, p. 493
More Practice, p. 525, set E

Supplements
Practice 138
Challenges 138 or
Thinking Skills 138

Extended

Exercises 1-13, 17, 18
Computer Bank, p. 493

Supplements
Challenges 138
Thinking Skills 138

Other Resources:
Problem-Solving Experiences in Mathematics, Grade 4, Problem 62
Mathematics, A Way of Thinking, Lesson 14-1
Math In Stride, Grade 4, p. 158

14-2

LESSON PLAN 14-2

OBJECTIVE 14-2
To use the estimation technique of unitizing to estimate length in centimeters

Materials: scissors, blank paper, TA 17 (Centimeter Ruler), TA 12 (Centimeter Graph Paper)

1. MOTIVATE AND TEACH

LEARN ABOUT IT

EXPLORE ► **Explain how to fold the paper strip into 4 equal parts.** (First fold it in half, then fold it in half again.)

TALK ABOUT IT ► **How is unitizing like division? Explain.** (Division involves finding the number of equal parts in a whole, and so does unitizing.)
► **Explain how the estimate for 1 part of the strip helps you determine the length of the entire strip.** (You can multiply the estimated part by 4 since there are 4 equal parts.)
► **How would you decide on the size of a part when unitizing?** (Possible answer: Use any size you can estimate closely.)
► **Analyze why unitizing can give a closer estimate than an estimate of the entire length of an object.** (Possible answer: It may be easier to pick a familiar size, then multiply.)
Student Edition answers: **1.** Answers will vary. **2.** It helps you total same-size groups.

2. CHECK UNDERSTANDING

TRY IT OUT

ERROR ALERT Being unable to decide how to unitize an object. Giving unreasonable estimates.

Estimating Length
Unitizing

LEARN ABOUT IT

EXPLORE Use Paper Strips
Cut a strip of paper to match the width of one of your textbooks. Fold it into four parts. Estimate the length of one part in centimeters. Use that length to estimate the total width of your book.

TALK ABOUT IT See teaching notes.

1. What is your estimated length for one part of the strip?
2. How can multiplication help you estimate the total width of your book?

You can use **unitizing** to estimate lengths.

- Visually or physically divide an object into equal parts.
- Estimate the length of one part.
- Multiply that estimate by the number of parts.

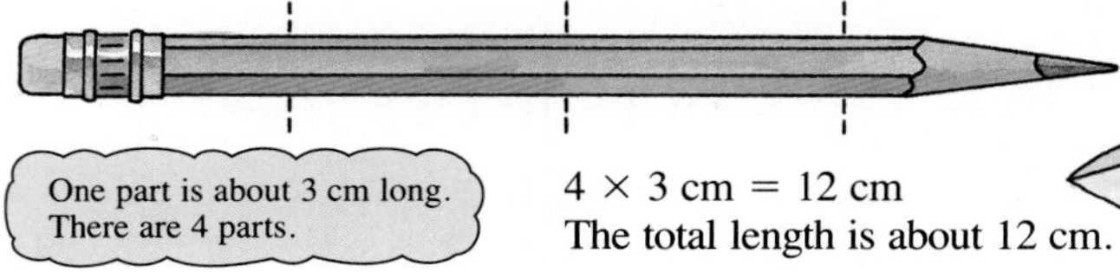

One part is about 3 cm long. There are 4 parts.

4×3 cm = 12 cm
The total length is about 12 cm.

TRY IT OUT

Use unitizing to estimate the lengths of these objects in centimeters.

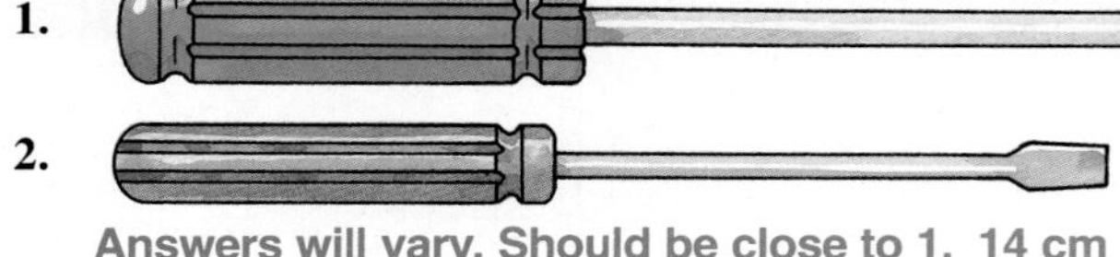

1.

2.

Answers will vary. Should be close to 1. 14 cm 2. 10 cm

382

TEACHING OPTIONS

RETEACHING TIPS Students use small sections of centimeter graph paper to formulate some centimeter "rules of thumb" to unitize. For instance, if students know that their thumb is 2 cm wide, they can use this known size to begin to unitize more accurately. Assign Reteaching Supplement 138.

ENRICHMENT Have each student work with a partner to cut 4 different lengths of string or yarn, without measuring the lengths. Tell them to unitize to estimate the length of each piece, then to measure to verify the estimate. (Answers will vary. Check students' estimates and measurements.)

PRACTICE

Use unitizing to estimate each length. Then measure the length. Find and record the difference between the estimated and actual measures.

Record your data in a table like the one below.
Check students' tables.

Object	Estimate (cm)	Measure (cm)	Difference (cm)
1. Spelling book			

1. Spelling book
2. Desktop
3. Chalkboard
4. Chalkboard eraser
5. Table
6. Scissors

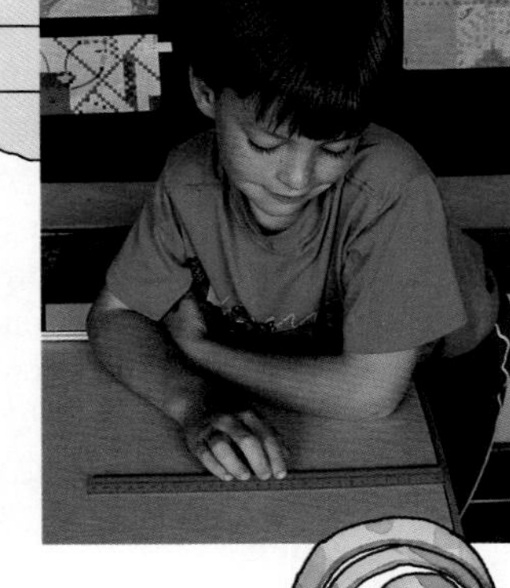

APPLY

MATH REASONING

7. Imagine that you estimated half of your classroom's width. How could you find an estimate for the whole classroom width?
double the estimate

PROBLEM SOLVING

8. Joe divided his bedroom length into 3 equal parts. He estimated that one of these parts is 2 m long. About how long is his bedroom?
6 m

MIXED REVIEW

Write >, <, or = in each ▥.

9. $\frac{1}{5}$ ▥ $\frac{2}{15}$ **>**
10. $\frac{2}{3}$ ▥ $\frac{2}{4}$ **>**
11. $\frac{1}{5}$ ▥ $\frac{1}{4}$ **<**

Write each fraction as a whole or mixed number.

12. $\frac{8}{4}$ **2**
13. $\frac{11}{3}$ **$3\frac{2}{3}$**
14. $\frac{7}{2}$ **$3\frac{1}{2}$**
15. $\frac{15}{5}$ **3**
16. $\frac{10}{3}$ **$3\frac{1}{3}$**

Write the decimals in order from least to greatest.

17. 7.34 7.23 7.38 7.29
7.23, 7.29, 7.34, 7.38

18. 2.10 2.04 2.11 2.01
2.01, 2.04, 2.10, 2.11

More Practice, page 525, set E

3. Practice and Apply

Basic	2-14, 17, 18
Average	1-18
Extended	1-13, 17, 18

PRACTICE

For Exercises 1 to 6, what would a difference of zero mean between an estimate and a measurement? (You estimated correctly.)

APPLY

MATH REASONING ► **Explain what you know about the size of one half of any object.** (Possible answer: You can double that amount to find the size of the whole object.)

PROBLEM SOLVING ► **Explain how to solve Problem 8.** (Multiply 3 × 2 m.)

MIXED REVIEW ► **Explain how to compare the fractions in Exercises 9-11.** (Change each pair to equivalent fractions, then compare.)
► **Explain how you know that all fractions in Exercises 12-16 must be whole or mixed numbers.** (All have larger numerators than denominators.)

Close and Assess

WRITE WHAT YOU THINK
Have each student pick a classroom object and estimate its length by unitizing. Ask students to write down each step they followed to use this estimation method. (Check students' estimates and writing.)

Quick Quiz

Use unitizing to estimate the length of your foot and of your arm in centimeters. (Answers will vary. Check students' estimates for reasonableness.)

LESSON OPTIONS 14-3

Millimeters

OBJECTIVE 14-3 To measure length in millimeters

PREBOOK ACTIVITIES

QUICK REVIEW

Use mental math and the order of operations to finish each equation.

1. $4 \times 10 + 3 =$ (43) **2.** $3 \times 10 + 7 =$ (37)
3. $10 \times 6 + 1 =$ (61) **4.** $10 \times 9 + 9 =$ (99)
5. $10 \times 10 + 8 =$ (108) **6.** $13 \times 10 + 5 =$ (135)
7. $2 \times 10 +$ (6) $= 26$ **8.** (8) $\times 10 + 2 = 82$

PRIOR KNOWLEDGE

Have students recall the metric units of length they have used, giving them in order from greatest to least. (kilometer, meter, decimeter, centimeter) Ask students to evaluate how precise their measuring was when they measured to the nearest centimeter. (Possible answer: Objects were rarely *precisely* a certain centimeter, so you usually had to round up or down.) Ask students how to find a more precise measurement. (Use a smaller unit than a centimeter.) Tell students that in this lesson they will measure using a smaller metric unit called the millimeter.

COMMUNICATION

Discussing and Reading Math Write **millimeter** on the chalkboard. Have students analyze *millimeter* to compare it with other metric measurement words, then guess its abbreviation. (Possible answer: Like *centimeter, decimeter,* or *kilometer, millimeter* has a special prefix before the word *meter;* **mm**)

EXPLORE AND CONNECT

Materials: TA 17 (Centimeter Ruler), magazines, scissors, glue, colored paper

Grouping Suggestion: cooperative learning groups of 5

Students measure small lengths in **millimeters.** Most students have probably noticed the small marks between centimeters on their metric rulers. Tell them that each mark is a **millimeter,** and that 5 **mm** marks are made slightly longer for easy reading. Challenge groups to look through old magazines to find 10 different words from 5 to 50 *mm* long, increasing by multiples of 5 *mm*. Groups may split the task any way that seems reasonable to find and measure words, cut them out, organize them into some kind of chart, and label each with its measurement in *mm*. Conclude by having students tell how they read *millimeters,* and how *millimeters* helped them make more precise measurements than they could have done with centimeters. (Answers will vary.)

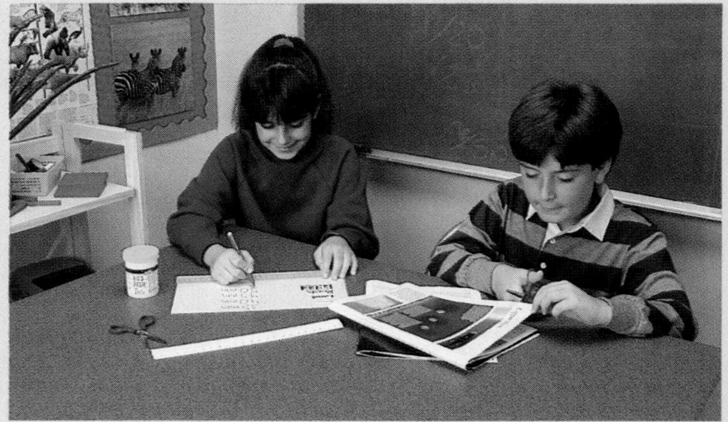

CONNECTIONS Use these anytime.

Problem of the Day

Equivalent Units Dr. DeLuge measures rainfall to the millimeter. So far this month, 93 mm of rain has fallen. If it rains 7 more mm, give the total rainfall in three ways using different units. Hint: 10 millimeters = 1 centimeter = 0.1 decimeter. (100 mm, 10 cm, 1 dm)

Number Sense

Mental Math 1m = 1,000 mm. Determine the number of millimeters in 5 m, then in 5 km. (5,000 mm; 5,000,000 mm)

Creative Thinking

Logic A baby snail slowly climbs a sand hill 40 mm high. Each minute it climbs up 5 mm, then slides back 1 mm. At that rate, how many minutes does it take the baby snail to reach the top of the hill? (10 min)

Classwork and Homework Supplements

Practice

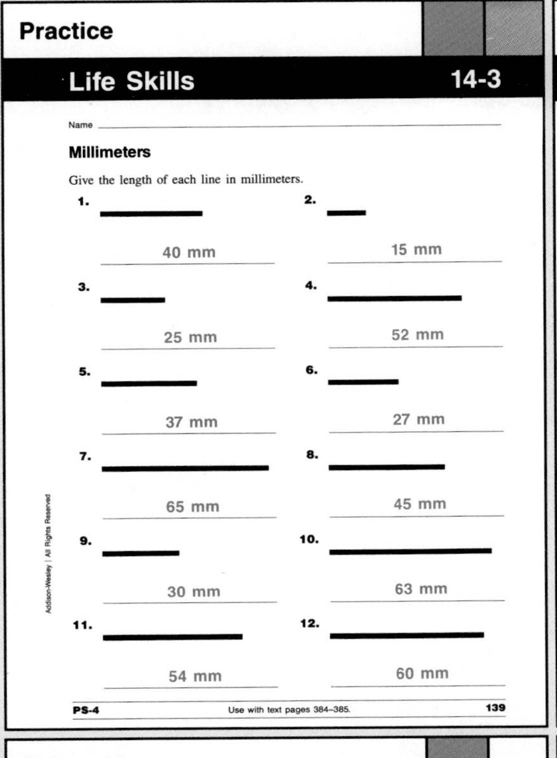

Life Skills 14-3

Name ______

Millimeters

Give the length of each line in millimeters.

1. 40 mm
2. 15 mm
3. 25 mm
4. 52 mm
5. 37 mm
6. 27 mm
7. 65 mm
8. 45 mm
9. 30 mm
10. 63 mm
11. 54 mm
12. 60 mm

Addison-Wesley | All Rights Reserved

PS-4 Use with text pages 384–385. 139

Building Thinking Skills

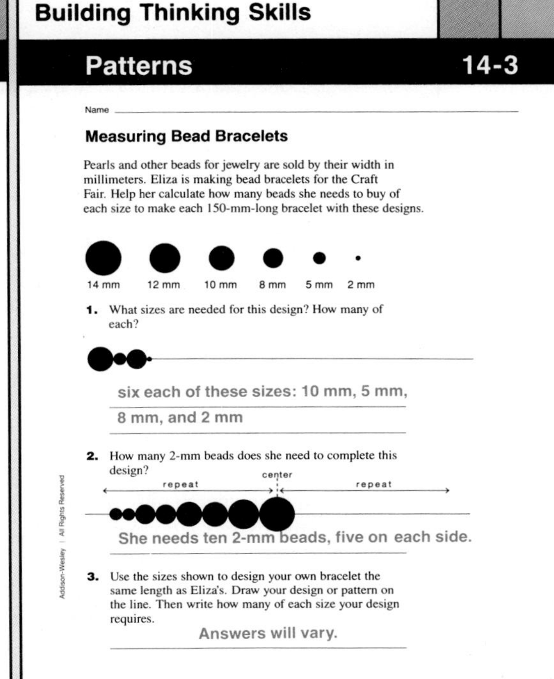

Patterns 14-3

Name ______

Measuring Bead Bracelets

Pearls and other beads for jewelry are sold by their width in millimeters. Eliza is making bead bracelets for the Craft Fair. Help her calculate how many beads she needs to buy of each size to make each 150-mm-long bracelet with these designs.

14 mm 12 mm 10 mm 8 mm 5 mm 2 mm

1. What sizes are needed for this design? How many of each?

six each of these sizes: 10 mm, 5 mm, 8 mm, and 2 mm

2. How many 2-mm beads does she need to complete this design?

repeat center repeat

She needs ten 2-mm beads, five on each side.

3. Use the sizes shown to design your own bracelet the same length as Eliza's. Draw your design or pattern on the line. Then write how many of each size your design requires.

Answers will vary.

Addison-Wesley | All Rights Reserved

TS-4 Use with text pages 384–385. 139

Reteaching

Mental Math 14-3

Name ______

Millimeters

A **millimeter** is a very small metric unit of length. 1 cm = 10 mm

Find the height of this bottle in millimeters.

Find the length in centimeters and extra millimeters. → Use mental math to change **cm** to **mm** and add the extra millimeters.

5 × 10 mm = 50 mm

1 2 3 4 5 6

5 cm + 2 mm = 52 mm
The bottle is 52 mm.

Use a millimeter ruler to write the height of the corn plant for each week.

1. first week: 23 mm
2. second week: 41 mm
3. third week: 66 mm
4. fourth week: 87 mm

Addison-Wesley | All Rights Reserved

RS-4 Use with text pages 384-385. 139

Challenges

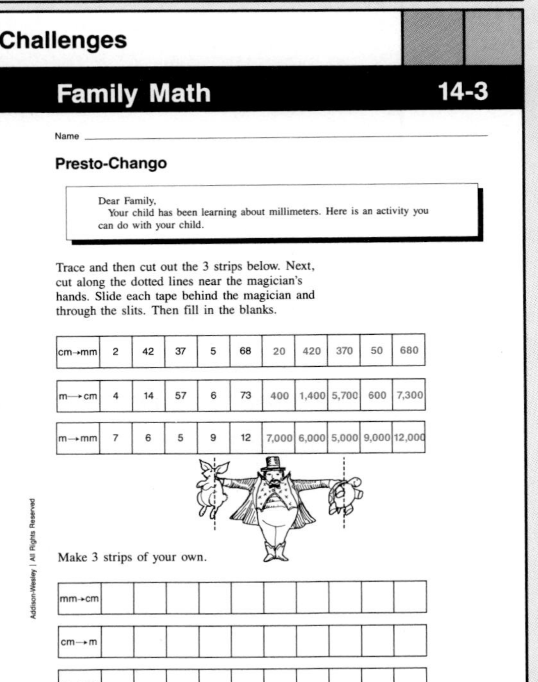

Family Math 14-3

Name ______

Presto-Chango

Dear Family,
Your child has been learning about millimeters. Here is an activity you can do with your child.

Trace and then cut out the 3 strips below. Next, cut along the dotted lines near the magician's hands. Slide each tape behind the magician and through the slits. Then fill in the blanks.

cm→mm	2	42	37	5	68	20	420	370	50	680
m→cm	4	14	57	6	73	400	1,400	5,700	600	7,300
m→mm	7	6	5	9	12	7,000	6,000	5,000	9,000	12,000

Make 3 strips of your own.

mm→cm										
cm→m										
m→mm										

Addison-Wesley | All Rights Reserved

CS-4 Use with text pages 384–385. 139

Options for Individual Needs

Basic

Exercises 1-9
Data Bank, p. 471

Supplements
Reteaching 139 or
Practice 139

Average

Exercises 1-9
Data Bank, p. 471

Supplements
Practice 139
Challenges 139 or
Thinking Skills 139

Extended

Exercises 1-9
Data Bank, p. 471

Supplements
Challenges 139
Thinking Skills 139

Other Resources:
Problem-Solving Experiences in Mathematics, Grade 4, Problem 145
Mathematics, A Way of Thinking, Lesson 14-5

14-3

LESSON PLAN 14-3

OBJECTIVE 14-3
To measure length in millimeters

Materials: metric rulers, calculators

Alternative Materials: TA 17 (Centimeter Ruler)

Grouping Suggestions: pairs

1. MOTIVATE AND TEACH

LEARN ABOUT IT

EXPLORE ► **Explain the relationship between millimeters and centimeters.** (There are 10 mm to 1 cm.)
► **Explain how Dana would find 30 mm on the ruler.** (Since there are 10 mm in every cm, 30 mm is equivalent to 3 cm.)
► **Why is a millimeter a useful measurement unit?** (It allows more precise measurement than a centimeter.)

TALK ABOUT IT ► **What is the halfway point between 3 and 4 cm in millimeters? Explain.** (35 mm; 3 and 4 cm are equivalent to 30 mm and 40 mm.)
► **Justify how Dana would round the length of the tadpole to the nearest centimeter.** (3 cm; 34 mm is less than halfway, so she would round down.)
► **Analyze the equation that explains why the tadpole is 48 mm.** (4 cm = 4 × 10 mm, or 40 mm, plus 8 more millimeters is 48 mm.)
Student Edition answers: **1.** 4 cm; 4 cm 2 mm **2.** 46 mm

2. CHECK UNDERSTANDING

TRY IT OUT

ERROR ALERT Giving measurements in centimeters rather than in millimeters. Misreading the metric ruler.

Millimeters

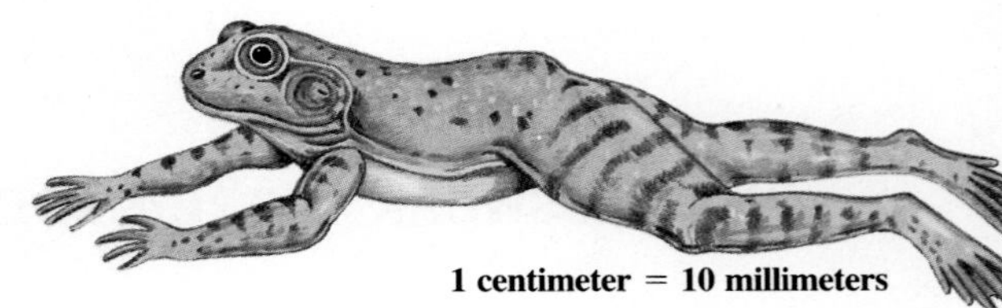

LEARN ABOUT IT

1 centimeter = 10 millimeters

The **millimeter** (mm) is a metric unit used for measuring length.

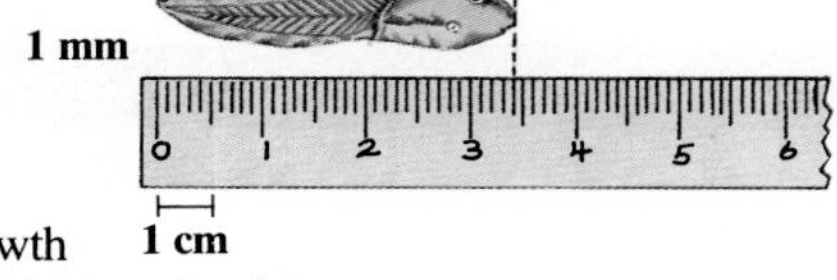

EXPLORE Solve to Understand
Dana had a Florida tree frog that was in the tadpole stage. She measured the tadpole every week and recorded its growth in a table. Read the ruler pictured to get the length of the tadpole the second week. Look for a pattern in the table.

TALK ABOUT IT See teaching notes.

Week	1	2	3	4	5
Length mm	30	34	38	42	?

1. Is the tadpole's length the fourth week closer to 3 cm or 4 cm? The tadpole is __?__ cm __?__ mm long.
2. Using any table patterns you have found, how long would you expect the tadpole to be the fifth week?

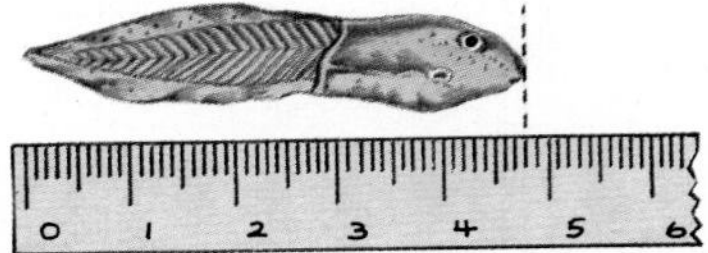

You can use mental math to give a length in millimeters. Think of the object's length in centimeters and extra millimeters. Change the centimeters to millimeters and add the extra.

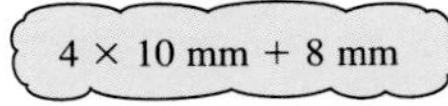

4 cm 8 mm = 48 mm

The tadpole is 48 mm long.

TRY IT OUT

Give the length of each tadpole in millimeters.

1.  41 mm

2. 53 mm

TEACHING OPTIONS

RETEACHING TIPS Have students review the equivalence that 1 cm = 10 mm. Have them skip count by tens for each centimeter of length, then count on by single millimeters for every millimeter beyond the greatest multiple of ten. Assign Reteaching Supplement 139.

ENRICHMENT Family Math Students try this with their family. They use string or yarn and a metric ruler to find the width of each person's smile to the nearest millimeter. (Cut the string to equal the length of the grin, then measure the string.) Rank family members by smile widths.

PRACTICE

Give the length of the tree frog in millimeters for each stage.

1. Egg 8 mm
2. Tadpole 50 mm
3. Adult frog 66 mm

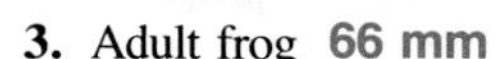
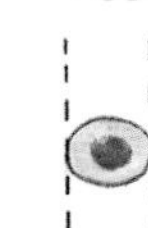

APPLY

MATH REASONING

4. The red numbers show how much the frog's length increased each week. Find the pattern and complete the table.

Frog Length

Week	1	2	3	4	5	6	7	8
Length (mm)	2	4	8	14	22			

32, 44, 58

PROBLEM SOLVING

5. Miami, Florida, receives about 1,280 mm of rain per year. How much rain is that in centimeters? 128 cm

6. **Science Data Bank** The Florida Everglades receive an average of 1,250 mm of rain each year. How much less is this than the wettest rain forest? See page 471. 8,750 mm

► CALCULATOR

Measure your height in centimeters. Use these keystrokes to enter 10 into the calculator's memory: [ON/AC] 10 [M+]. Then try each of the keystroke sequences below. Use the final number displayed and a metric unit (millimeter, centimeter, decimeter, meter, kilometer) to give your height. Answers will vary.

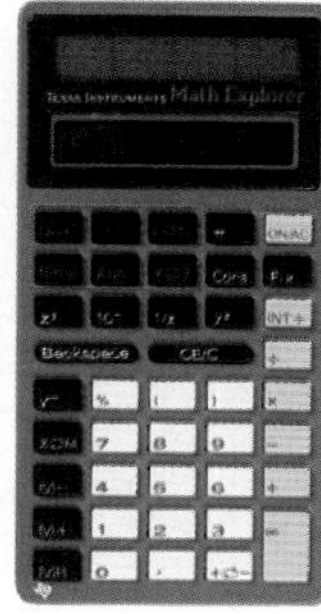

7. [CE/C] your height in cm [×] [MR] [=]
8. [CE/C] your height in cm [÷] [MR] [=]
9. [CE/C] your height in cm [÷] [MR] [=] [=] [=]

385

3. Practice and Apply

Basic	1-9
Average	1-9
Extended	1-9

PRACTICE

Which stage of the tree frog's growth seems nearest to 1 cm? (egg) *How will you measure the lengths?* (Use a centimeter ruler, count 10 mm for every 1 cm, than add on the extra mm.)

APPLY

MATH REASONING ► **Explain a strategy you could use to understand the pattern.** (Study the amount of change in length from week to week to look for a pattern.)

PROBLEM SOLVING ► **Explain how to convert millimeters to centimeters to solve Problem 5.** (Since there are 10 mm for every 1 cm, divide 1,280 mm by 10.)

► **Without looking at the data, justify the operation needed to solve Problem 6.** (Subtract to compare.)

CALCULATOR ► **How can you find your height in centimeters?** (Have a friend measure you with a metric ruler.)

14-3

Close and Assess

SHOW WHAT YOU KNOW

Have students work in pairs. Each pair uses a metric ruler to measure the length of each other's left and right pinkie fingers to the nearest mm. Pairs should estimate before they measure, then see how close their estimates are. (Check pairs' answers for reasonableness.)

Quick Quiz

Complete each equation.

1. 5 cm = (50) mm
2. 80 mm = (8) cm
3. 6 cm 4mm = (64) mm
4. 73 mm = (7) cm (3) mm

LESSON OPTIONS 14-4

Problem Solving: Deciding When to Estimate

OBJECTIVE 14-4 To decide whether an actual measurement is needed or whether an estimate is sufficient

PREBOOK ACTIVITIES

QUICK REVIEW

Complete each statement with mm, cm, dm, m, or km.

1. A garden path is 1 (km) long.
2. A ladder is 2 (m) long.
3. A hammer is 3 (dm) long.
4. A safety pin is 4 (cm) long.
5. A pearl is 5 (mm) wide.

PRIOR KNOWLEDGE

Have students give realistic examples of exact and estimated lengths using each of the 5 metric measurements they know. (Answers will vary. Samples: exact—My doctor says I grew 6 cm; My uncle's farm is 10 km away. estimated—The tree is about 8 m tall; My nails grow about 1 mm per week. This dictionary is about 3 dm long.)

COMMUNICATION

Discussing Math Have students imagine a situation when they might need to know the exact height of a window and a related situation when the estimated height would do. (Possible answer: Use the exact height to know what length shade to get; use an estimate to decide what height ladder you need to install the shade.)

EXPLORE AND CONNECT

COOPERATIVE ACTIVITY

Grouping Suggestion: small groups

To make the track team, you must be able to run a 50-m dash in under 12 seconds. Should you measure or estimate your time?

TEACHING ACTIONS

Have students discuss the situation to reach a group decision.

► **Analyze the situation to identify exact measurements.** (50 m; 12 seconds)

► **Explain what decision you must make.** (whether to estimate or time yourself exactly)

► **Analyze the units used in the situation.** (Seconds are very small units of time, which might be difficult to estimate, especially when you are concentrating on running.)

► **Predict the outcome using an estimate.** (You may not know for sure if you make the team without an exact measurement to verify.)

► **Explain a way to find an exact measure.** (Possible answer: Use a stopwatch.)

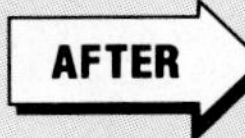

► **Evaluate your decision.** (An exact measurement makes more sense in this situation; an estimate may not be exact enough to let you know whether you can make the team.)

CONNECTIONS Use these anytime.

Problem of the Day

Phone Bill When Brian was at basketball camp, he called home 3 times a week. He knew the calls cost \$0.15/min and that his parents had given him \$15 a week for the long-distance calls. About how long could Brian talk each time and still stay within the weekly budget? (about 30 min per call)

Number Sense

Estimation When you are "It" in Hide and Seek, you are supposed to close your eyes for 1 min while others hide. What methods can you use to estimate how long 1 min is? (Possible answers: Count to 60 at about the rate seconds pass; sing a 1-min song.)

Life Skills

New Carpet Rick is going to put wall-to-wall carpeting in the living room. Explain how he can combine exact measurements and estimates to determine how much carpeting to buy. (Possible answer: Measure the floor space exactly, then overestimate to have a little extra.)

Classwork and Homework Supplements

Practice

Problem Solving 14-4

Name ______________________

Deciding When to Estimate

Decide whether an estimate or an actual measure is needed. Write why. **Answers may vary.**

1. Mrs. Foster needs a frame for a picture that is 48 cm wide and 52 cm long. What is the perimeter of the picture?
   Measure; the frame must fit the picture exactly.
2. On Saturday, Frank ran for 19 minutes. He played tennis for 52 minutes. How long did he exercise on Saturday?
   Estimate; no need to know the exact number of minutes.
3. Jocelyn is reading a book that has 482 pages. She wants to read about the same number of pages each day for 5 days. How many pages does she have to read each day?
   Estimate; the exact number of pages is not needed.
4. Brenda's vegetable garden is 16 m wide and 22 m long. She wants to put a wooden fence around it to protect it from the wild animals. What is the perimeter of the garden?
   Measure; the fence has to fit exactly around the garden.
5. Takeshi needs 500 mL of milk for a recipe to make fish chowder. He has 212 mL of milk. How much more milk does Takeshi need?
   Measure; he needs an exact amount when following a recipe.
6. Larry had 463 m of wood to make some projects. He used 313 m to build a bench. How much wood does Larry have left to make something else?
   Estimate; no need to know exactly how much is left over.

140 Use with text page 386. PS-4

Building Thinking Skills

Critical Thinking 14-4

Name ______________________

Build a Model Statue of Liberty

Look at the diagram of the Statue of Liberty. Use estimation to help you choose the correct pieces to build a model of the statue. Put an X in each of your choices.

1. Body
2. Arm
3. Torch
4. Head and crown together
5. Base

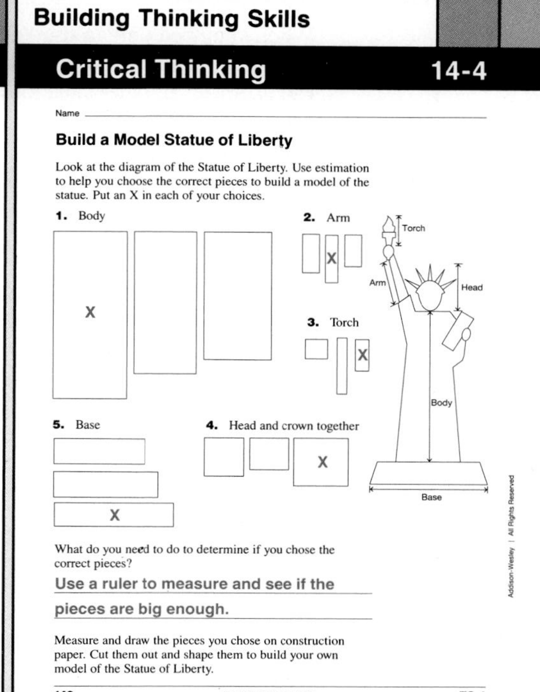

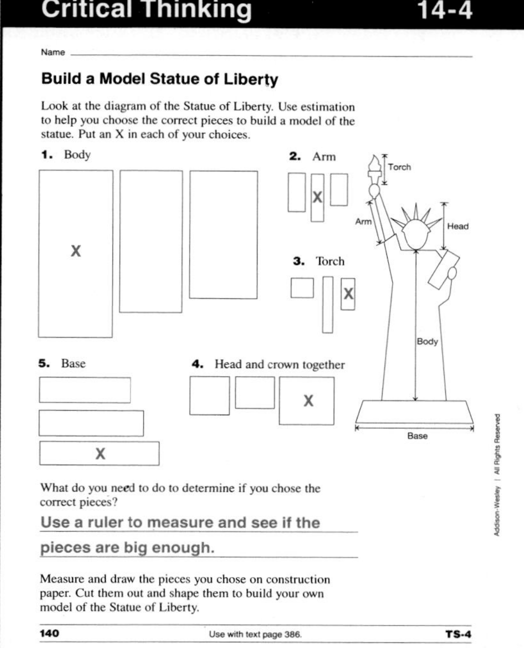

What do you need to do to determine if you chose the correct pieces?

Use a ruler to measure and see if the pieces are big enough.

Measure and draw the pieces you chose on construction paper. Cut them out and shape them to build your own model of the Statue of Liberty.

140 Use with text page 386. TS-4

Reteaching

Problem Solving 14-4

Name ______________________

Deciding When to Estimate

Sometimes to solve a problem, you can estimate a measurement. Other times an exact measure is needed.

Only an estimate is needed
- when you need to know only "about what is the measure."
- when comparing with a reference point.

Actual measure is needed
- when exact measurement is necessary to solve the problem.

Decide whether an estimate or an actual measure is needed. Tell why.

1. Judy is making a dress for the school play. She needs to add trim around the neck. How much trim does she need?
   - Will an estimate work? no
   - Does she need the actual measure? yes
   - Why? The trim needs to go exactly around neck.
2. Pedro is in charge of the props for the play. He must put the tree on the stage after Act I. How far from the edge of the stage should the tree be placed?
   estimate; tree does not have to be in exact spot.
3. Vanessa will provide the refreshments during intermission. How much punch should she make for 150 people?
   estimate; she does not have to serve exact quantities.
4. Bill needs to make a door for the hut in the play. What size plywood should he buy?
   exact; the board has to fit the door opening exactly.
5. Jerry is meeting friends after the play. At what time should he tell his friends the play will be over?
   exact; his friends need to know when to meet him.

140 Use with text page 386. RS-4

Challenges

Estimation 14-4

Name ______________________

High-End Estimation

Sometimes estimates can be misleading, so you need to do a special kind of estimate that is designed to be "high." It is called a **high-end estimate**. In a high-end estimate, you round upward only.

Example: Jane has a piece of lumber 185 cm long. She needs to cut three pieces that are 24 cm, 62 cm, and 100 cm long. Does Jane have enough lumber?

	Length		Enough?
Regular estimate:	180 cm	20 + 60 + 100	yes
High-end estimate:	200 cm	30 + 70 + 100	no
Length needed:	186 cm		no

The regular estimate is misleading since there is not enough lumber.

1. Mark has 225 m of fencing. He wants to fence a rectangular garden that is 84 m by 33 m. Does Mark have enough fencing?

	Length	Enough?
Regular estimate:	220 m	yes
High-end estimate:	260 m	no
Length needed:	234 m	no

2. Rosa had 250 mL of juice. She used 193 mL. She needs 60 mL for a recipe. Does she have enough juice?

	Amount	Enough?
Regular estimate:	60 mL	yes
High-end estimate:	50 mL	no
Amount left:	57 mL	no

3. Sue wants to drive 83 km to Roth, then 44 km to Elton, and then 132 km back home through the mountains. She has enough gas to go 250 km. Can she make it?

	Distance	Enough?
Regular estimate:	250 km	yes
High-end estimate:	280 km	no
Actual distance:	259 km	no

4. Tom wants to make a picture frame. He needs two pieces of wood 64 cm long and two pieces 33 cm long. Will a piece 190 cm long be enough for the four pieces?

	Length	Enough?
Regular estimate:	180 cm	yes
High-end estimate	220 cm	no
Length needed:	194 cm	no

140 Use with text page 386. CS-4

Options for Individual Needs

Basic

Exercises 1-4, 6-11
Skills Bank, pp. 462, 464
Calculator Bank, p. 485

Supplements
Reteaching 140 or
Practice 140

Average

Exercises 1-11
Skills Bank, pp. 462, 464
Calculator Bank, p. 485

Supplements
Practice 140
Challenges 140 or
Thinking Skills 140

Extended

Exercises 1-11
Calculator Bank, p. 485

Supplements
Challenges 140
Thinking Skills 140

Other Resources:
Problem-Solving Experiences in Mathematics, Grade 4, Problem 144
Mathematics, A Way of Thinking, Lesson 14-2
Make It Simpler, A Practical Guide to Problem Solving in Mathematics, p. 275
Using the Math Explorer Calculator: A Sourcebook for Teachers, Chapter 14

LESSON PLAN 14-4

OBJECTIVE 14-4
To decide whether an actual measurement is needed or whether an estimate is sufficient

Materials: TA 17 (Rulers)

1. MOTIVATE AND TEACH

LEARN ABOUT IT

▶ Analyze the situations to identify the exact measurements in each. (10:53; 9 min, 53 seconds)

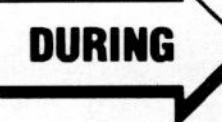

▶ Contrast the 2 situations. (Vicky's friends need to know only *about* when she is due back; Jeff is in a race, when precise times determine a winner.)

▶ Justify using estimation to determine Vicky's return. (She can give her friends an approximate time so they will not worry, but an exact time is not crucial.)

▶ Justify finding an exact measurement in Jeff's case. (He must know if he can beat the course record, which is measured to the nearest second, so he needs an exact time.)

▶ Evaluate the 2 decisions to check that they make sense. (It makes sense for Vicky to estimate in her informal situation; Jeff should measure exactly in his situation because more depends on the outcome.)

2. CHECK UNDERSTANDING

TRY IT OUT

ERROR ALERT Making an inappropriate decision due to misinterpreting a situation.

Problem Solving
Deciding When to Estimate

UNDERSTAND
FIND DATA
PLAN
ESTIMATE
SOLVE
CHECK

LEARN ABOUT IT

When you need only to use "about what is the measure," or to compare with a reference point, you can estimate. In other situations, you may want to actually measure. How the answer will be used often helps you decide.

Vicky is on boat patrol in the Florida Everglades. It is 10:53. She wants to go by boat to a wildlife area. At what time shall she tell her friends she will be back?

Jeff is practicing for an Everglades speedboat race. He wants to know how much greater his trial time is than the course record time of 9 minutes, 56 seconds.

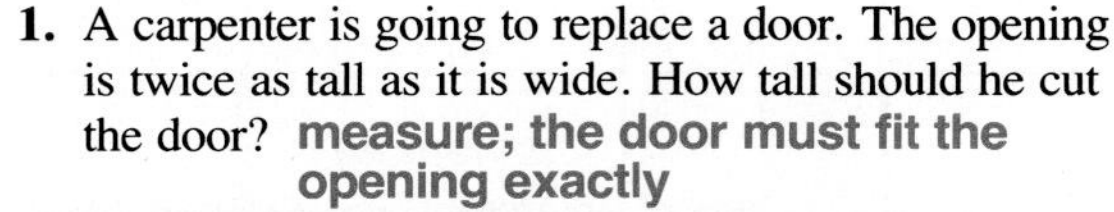

Vicky does not need to be back at an exact time.
Jeff needs to know exactly how many seconds faster he must go to beat the record.

She can estimate the time needed.

Jeff should measure his trial time.

TRY IT OUT

Decide whether an estimate or an actual measure is needed. Tell why.

1. A carpenter is going to replace a door. The opening is twice as tall as it is wide. How tall should he cut the door? **measure; the door must fit the opening exactly**
2. You need to buy garden hoses and connect them together to reach from the faucet to a flower garden. Each hose is 20 m long. How many hoses will you need? **estimate; hose does not need to reach an exact spot**

TEACHING OPTIONS

RETEACHING TIPS Have students discuss *both* an estimate and an actual measure in each problem to consider the effect of each measure on the outcome of the situation. This should help students more clearly evaluate which decision makes sense. Assign Reteaching Supplement 140.

COMPUTER **Metric and Problem Solving, MECC, Copyright 1982** For use with all levels of students. In "Metric Estimate," estimate the lengths of lines using metric measurements. In "Metric 21," estimate lengths of objects using metric measurements. Each lesson requires 10 to 15 min.

MIDCHAPTER REVIEW/QUIZ

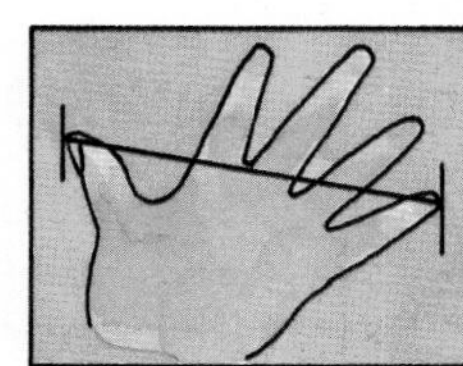

Measure your hand span to the nearest decimeter and the nearest centimeter.
Answers will vary.

1. Is your hand span closer to 1 dm, 2 dm, or 3 dm wide?
2. Is your hand span wider than a 15-cm hand span?
3. Which is wider, a 15-cm hand span or a 2-dm hand span? 2 dm

Use unitizing to estimate these measurements. Then measure in centimeters to check. Answers will vary.

4. length of your hand
5. height of a friend

Measure the height of the water in the rain gauge to the nearest millimeter.

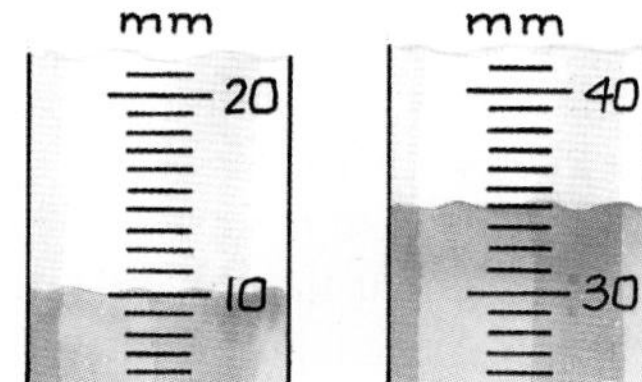

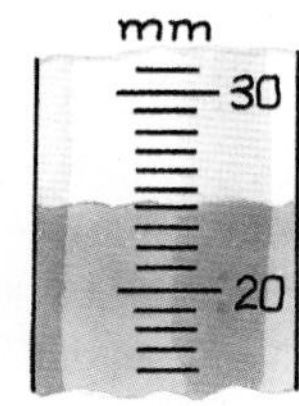

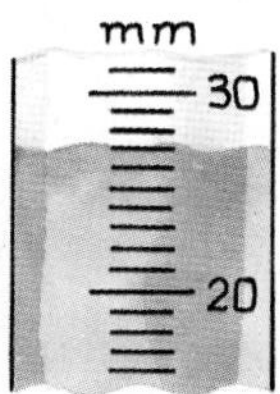

Tuesday | Wednesday | Thursday | Friday

6. How much rain was there each day? Tuesday 10 mm; Wednesday, 34 mm; Thursday 24 mm; Friday 27 mm
7. Which days had about 3 cm of rain? Wednesday and Friday
8. Which days had about the same amount of rain? Thursday and Friday

PROBLEM SOLVING

9. Is the perimeter of this rug more or less than 5 m? more
10. Reneé lives 2 km from Janice. Tia lives 850 m from Reneé. Who lives closer to Renee? How much closer? Tia, 1,150 m closer
11. What can you say about the heights of Tom, Dick, and Harry if Tom is 2 m tall, Dick is 20 dm tall, and Harry is 200 cm tall? All are 2 m tall.

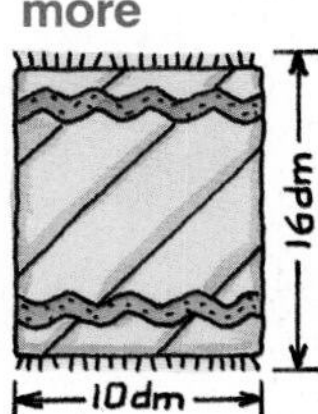

387

CLOSE AND ASSESS

SAY WHAT YOU THINK Have students generalize about how to determine whether to estimate or to find an exact measure when they solve a problem. Have them give an example of 2 different situations to support their ideas. (Check students' explanations.)

QUICK QUIZ

When you make biscuits, should you estimate their baking time or time them exactly? Give your reasons. (Time them exactly so they do not undercook or burn.)

3. PRACTICE AND APPLY

Basic	1-4, 6-11
Average	1-11
Extended	1-11

PRACTICE

What do you need to know to solve Exercises 3 and 7 and Problems 9 to 11? (the size relationships of metric measurements) *Review the meaning of unitizing.* (visually dividing an object into equal parts, estimating the length of one part, then multiplying by the number of parts)

ITEM ANALYSIS The following table correlates the Midchapter Review/Quiz items with the lesson objectives.

Items	Objectives
1-3	14-1
4, 5	14-2
6-8	14-3
(7), 9-11	14-1

14-4

Area

OBJECTIVE 14-5 To measure area in square centimeters and to multiply to find area

PREBOOK ACTIVITIES

QUICK REVIEW

Find the value of n.

1. $4 \times n = 28$ (7) **2.** $n \times 5 = 15$ (3)
3. $3 \times n = 21$ (7) **4.** $7 \times 6 = n$ (42)
5. $n \times 8 = 40$ (5) **6.** $6 \times 6 = n$ (36)
7. $n \times 9 = 63$ (7) **8.** $7 \times n = 35$ (5)
9. $8 \times n = 56$ (7) **10.** $6 \times 4 = n$ (24)

PRIOR KNOWLEDGE

Have students recall the meaning of *perimeter*. (''distance around the outside of a figure'') Have them identify the measurements they need to find perimeter. (lengths of sides) Have students justify using perimeter to find how much fencing to use around a garden. (If you know the perimeter of the garden, you know how much fencing material to get.) Ask students to visualize the amount of space enclosed by a fence. Explain that the inside space, known as the area, can also be measured. Tell students that in this lesson they will find area in square centimeters.

COMMUNICATION

Discussing Math Have students give the meaning of the word **area** as it is used in such phrases as *the art area, the wooded area,* or *the parking area*. (Possible answers: ''region,'' ''spot,'' ''section,'' ''place'') Have students guess the mathematical meaning of the area of a parking lot. (the amount of space inside the boundaries of the parking lot) Explain that *area* means ''the space inside a figure'' and that it is always measured in square units.

EXPLORE AND CONNECT

Materials: TA 12 (Centimeter Graph Paper), rectangular pieces of oaktag in assorted sizes, TA 17 (Centimeter Ruler)
Grouping Suggestion: small cooperative learning groups
Students explore the perimeter and **area** of rectangles. Groups need several oaktag rectangles, centimeter graph paper, and centimeter rulers. Students first find and record the perimeter of each rectangle in centimeters. Then they find the *area* of each rectangle by using any reasonable method to determine how many centimeter squares would fill the inside. They divide tasks and one person verifies each *area* and perimeter. Students summarize how to find perimeter. (Measure sides, then add.) They explain how to find *area*. (Possible answers: Trace rectangles on graph paper, then count the squares; measure length and width, then multiply.) Students identify a relationship between *area* and other measurements of a rectangle. (Its *area* is the product of its length and width.)

CONNECTIONS Use these anytime.

Problem of the Day

Mouse Flooring A mouse gathered 32 lost centimeter-graph-paper squares from a classroom. She used them to cover the floor of her home. If the floor was a rectangle twice as long as it was wide, what were the measurements of its sides? *Hint*: Think about factors of 32. (4 cm wide by 8 cm long)

Math Connection

Geometry A 4-sided figure has a perimeter of 16 cm and an area of 16 square cm. What is the shape? What is the length of each side? (a square; 4 cm)

Life Skills

Playhouse Design Cut out a graph-paper square that is 1 dm long on all sides. Think of it as a dm tile. Now imagine that you are building a playhouse. 4 desktops equal the size of the floor. How can you use the dm tile and your desktop to figure out the number of tiles needed for the floor? (Find the number in 1 desktop × 4.)

Classwork and Homework Supplements

Practice

Math Reasoning 14-5

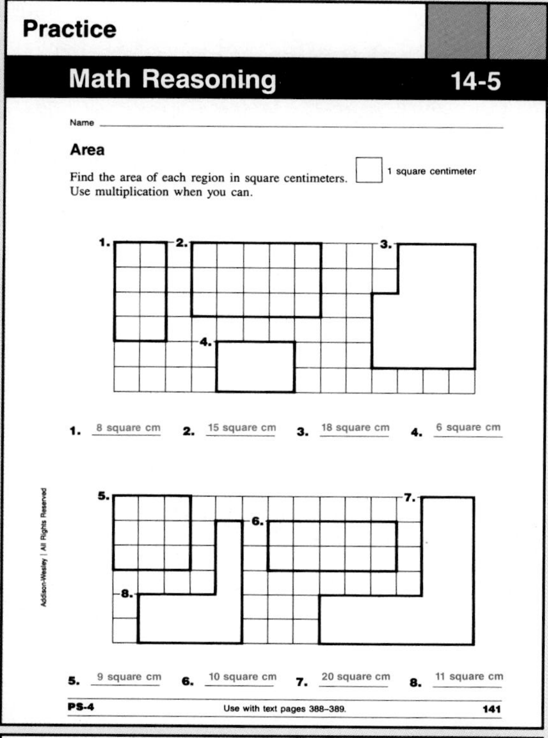

Name

Area

Find the area of each region in square centimeters. Use multiplication when you can.

1 square centimeter

1. 8 square cm 2. 15 square cm 3. 18 square cm 4. 6 square cm

5. 9 square cm 6. 10 square cm 7. 20 square cm 8. 11 square cm

PS-4 Use with text pages 388–389. 141

Building Thinking Skills

Critical Thinking 14-5

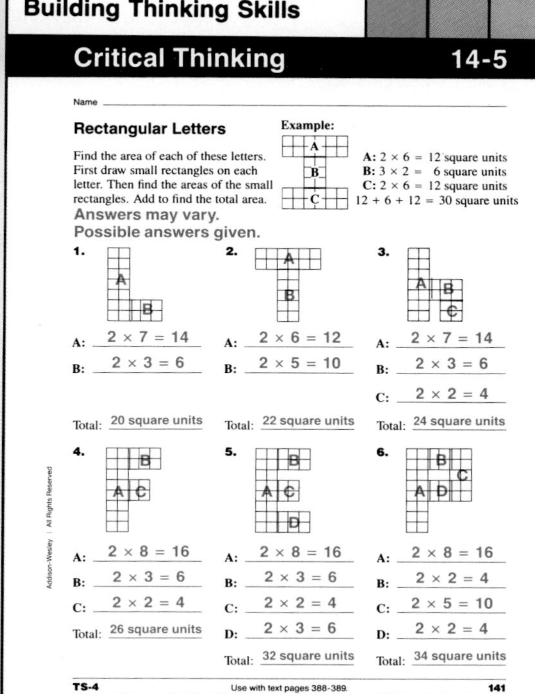

Name

Rectangular Letters

Find the area of each of these letters. First draw small rectangles on each letter. Then find the areas of the small rectangles. Add to find the total area.

Example:

A: 2 × 6 = 12 square units
B: 3 × 2 = 6 square units
C: 2 × 6 = 12 square units
12 + 6 + 12 = 30 square units

Answers may vary. Possible answers given.

1. A: 2 × 7 = 14 B: 2 × 3 = 6 Total: 20 square units

2. A: 2 × 6 = 12 B: 2 × 5 = 10 Total: 22 square units

3. A: 2 × 7 = 14 B: 2 × 3 = 6 C: 2 × 2 = 4 Total: 24 square units

4. A: 2 × 8 = 16 B: 2 × 3 = 6 C: 2 × 2 = 4 Total: 26 square units

5. A: 2 × 8 = 16 B: 2 × 3 = 6 C: 2 × 2 = 4 D: 2 × 3 = 6 Total: 32 square units

6. A: 2 × 8 = 16 B: 2 × 2 = 4 C: 2 × 5 = 10 D: 2 × 2 = 4 Total: 34 square units

TS-4 Use with text pages 388–389. 141

Reteaching

Skills Review 14-5

Name

Area

The **square centimeter** is a metric unit for measuring **area**. You can use multiplication to find the area of rectangular regions.

2 rows

5 in each row

2 rows × 5 in each row
2 × 5 = 10 square centimeters

Write the area of each region in square centimeters. Use multiplication when you can.

1. 2 rows, 6 in each row
2 rows × 6 in each row = 12 square centimeters

2. 6 square cm

3. 3 rows × 7 in each row = 21 square centimeters.

4. 24 square cm

5. 10 square cm

6. 12 square cm

RS-4 Use with text pages 388–389. 141

Challenges

Estimation 14-5

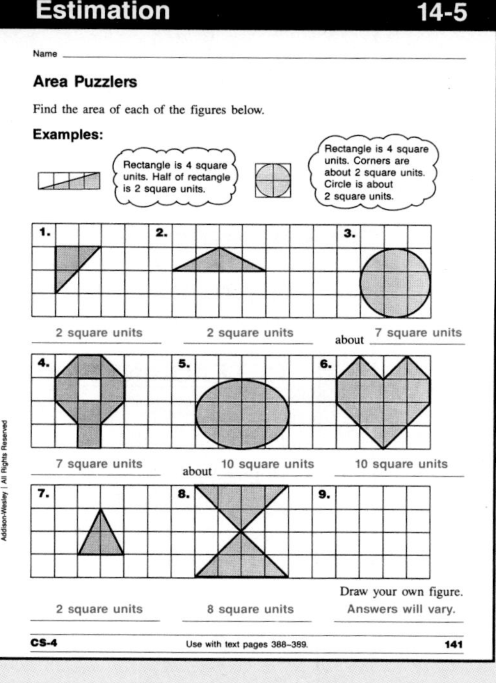

Name

Area Puzzlers

Find the area of each of the figures below.

Examples:

Rectangle is 4 square units. Half of rectangle is 2 square units.

Rectangle is 4 square units. Corners are about 2 square units. Circle is about 2 square units.

1. 2 square units 2. 2 square units 3. about 7 square units

4. 7 square units 5. about 10 square units 6. 10 square units

7. 2 square units 8. 8 square units 9. Draw your own figure. Answers will vary.

CS-4 Use with text pages 388–389. 141

Options for Individual Needs

Basic

Exercises 1-10, 14-16
More Practice, p. 526, set A

Supplements
Reteaching 141 or
Practice 141
Thinking Skills 141

Average

Exercises 1-17
More Practice, p. 526, set A

Supplements
Practice 141
Challenges 141 or
Thinking Skills 141

Extended

Exercises 3-11, 14-17

Supplements
Challenges 141
Thinking Skills 141

Other Resources:
Problem-Solving Experiences in Mathematics, Grade 4, Problem 61
Mathematics, A Way of Thinking, Lesson 14-9
Math In Stride, Grade 4, p. 159
Using the Math Explorer Calculator: A Sourcebook for Teachers, Chapter 14

14-5

LESSON PLAN 14-5

OBJECTIVE 14-5
To measure area in square centimeters and to multiply to find area

Materials: TA 12 (Centimeter Graph Paper)

1. MOTIVATE AND TEACH

LEARN ABOUT IT

EXPLORE ► **Explain a relationship between graph-paper rectangles and multiplication facts.** (Since the rectangles are made up of same-size rows, the number of squares per row is one factor and the number of rows is the other factor.)
► **How can multiplication be used to arrive at a total of 12 squares? Explain.** (You can multiply the number of rows and columns in various arrangements that equal 12, such as 1 × 12, 2 × 6, 3 × 4.)
► **Explain why you can make more than one rectangle with 12 squares.** (More than one pair of factors equal 12.)

TALK ABOUT IT ► **What limits the number of different rectangles that have 12 squares? Explain.** (The number of factors of 12; since there are 6 factors, only 3 different rectangles can be formed with 12 squares.)
Student Edition answers: **1.** 3 **2.** yes; 2-by-6 and 3-by-4 rectangles have equal areas.

2. CHECK UNDERSTANDING

TRY IT OUT

ERROR ALERT Exercise 3: Failing to use square centimeters. Finding perimeter instead of area.

Area

The area of this table top is 12 square units.

LEARN ABOUT IT

EXPLORE **Use Graph Paper**
Draw as many different rectangles as you can that have 12 squares. Use only whole squares.

TALK ABOUT IT See teaching notes.

1. How many different rectangles did you find?
2. Can regions with different numbers of rows have the same area? If so, give an example.

The **square centimeter** is a metric unit for measuring **area**.

You can use multiplication to find the area of a rectangle.

3 rows × 7 in each row

3 × 7 = 21 square centimeters

The area of the rectangle is 21 square centimeters.

TRY IT OUT

Give the area of each region in square centimeters. Use multiplication for the rectangular regions.

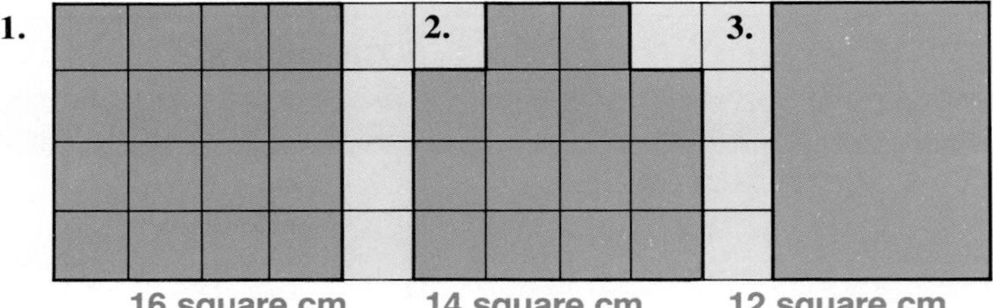

16 square cm 14 square cm 12 square cm

TEACHING OPTIONS

RETEACHING TIPS Have students trace the rectangle in Exercise 3 onto centimeter graph paper or place centimeter graph paper over it. Then have students count or multiply to find the correct number of squares that make up the area of the rectangle. Assign Reteaching Supplement 141.

ENRICHMENT Students find the area of the figures in square cm.

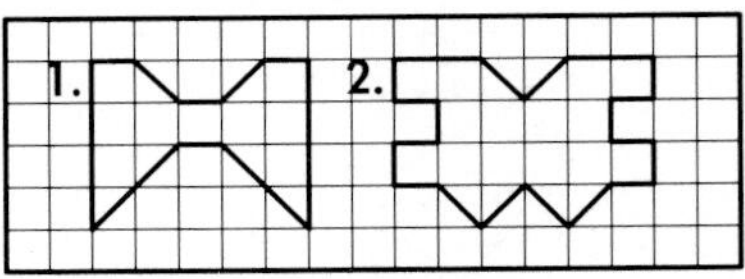

(**1.** 12 square cm **2.** 17 square cm)

PRACTICE

Find the area of each region in square centimeters.
Use multiplication when you can.

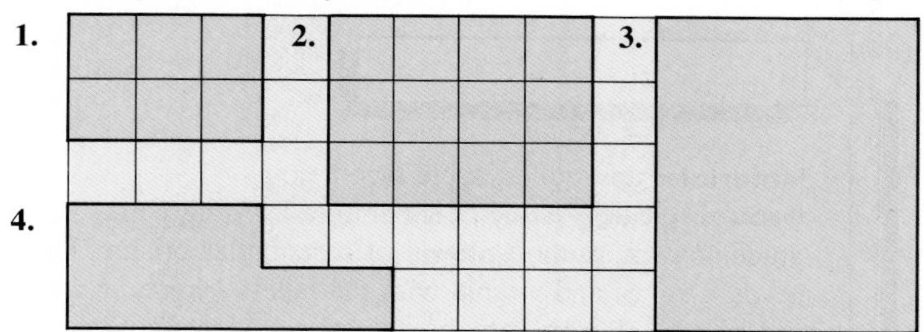

1. 8 square cm 2. 12 square cm 3. 20 square cm 4. 9 square cm

APPLY

MATH REASONING Use the figures below to answer these questions.

5. Which figures have the same areas, but different perimeters? A & B

6. Which figures have the same perimeters, but different areas? B & C

A 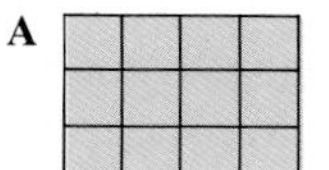 B 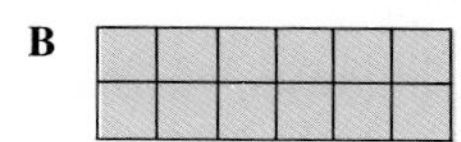 C 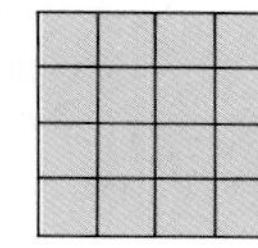

PROBLEM SOLVING

7. Draw a Picture Draw a rectangular region on graph paper. It should have an area of 12 square centimeters and a perimeter of 14 cm. Check students' drawings.

MIXED REVIEW

Round each number to the nearest whole number.

8. 45.1	**9.** 7.9	**10.** 21.6	**11.** 37.5	**12.** 61.3	**13.** 8.6
45	8	22	38	61	9

Tell which measurement is longer.

14. 20 cm	**15.** 6 cm	**16.** 8 dm	**17.** 44,000 m
3 dm	2 m	8 m	4 km

More Practice, page 526, set A

3. PRACTICE AND APPLY

Basic	1-10, 14-16
Average	1-17
Extended	3-11, 14-17

PRACTICE

Why can you find the area of the regions in Exercises 1-3 in the same way? (Since all are rectangles, you can multiply the number of rows by the number of columns.)

APPLY

MATH REASONING ▶ What would you do first to solve Exercises 5 and 6? Explain. (Possible answer: Find perimeter and area of each figure, then compare the perimeters and areas.)

PROBLEM SOLVING ▶ Before you draw anything for Problem 7, explain how an organized list can help. (Find factor combinations equal to 12, then see which give a rectangle with a perimeter of 14 cm.)

MIXED REVIEW ▶ Summarize how to decide whether to round up or down in Exercises 8-13. (Look at the tenths digit; round down if it is less than 5; round up if it is 5 or more.)

CLOSE AND ASSESS

SHOW WHAT YOU KNOW

Have students demonstrate how to find the area of the rectangle below. (Count squares or multiply 3 rows by 6 squares per row; 18 square cm.)

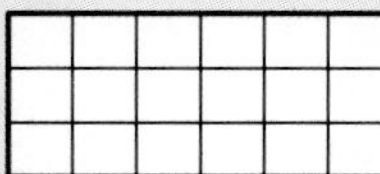

QUICK QUIZ

Find the area in square centimeters.

1. 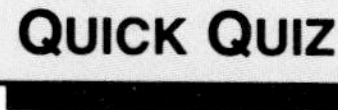 2. 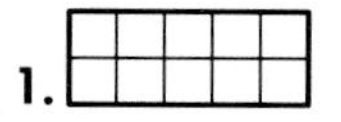

(1. 10 square cm; 2. 14 square cm)

LESSON OPTIONS 14-6

Volume

OBJECTIVE 14-6 To measure volume in cubic centimeters and to multiply to find volume

PREBOOK ACTIVITIES

QUICK REVIEW

Multiply.

1. 3 × 5 × 2 (30) **2.** 2 × 6 × 3 (36)
3. 4 × 5× 7 (140) **4.** 2 × 8 × 4 (64)
5. 4 × 4 × 4 (64) **6.** 3 × 6 × 3 (54)
7. 9 × 2 × 3 (54) **8.** 8 × 5 × 7 (280)

PRIOR KNOWLEDGE

Have students scan the classroom to locate rectangular prisms. (Answers may vary. Possible answers: crayon box, file cabinet, the room itself) Have students identify the shapes of the faces of a rectangular prism. (rectangles or squares) Have students explain how they have found the area of a square or rectangle. (Possible answer: counted squares inside the perimeter) Then have students name a space figure with faces that are all squares. (a cube) Now ask students to use logical reasoning to guess how to calculate the amount of space inside a 3-dimensional rectangular prism. (Possible answer: Count the number of cubes inside the rectangular prism.)

COMMUNICATION

Discussing Math Talk about the meaning of **volume** in the following phrases: *the fourth volume of the encyclopedia; turn down the volume on the television; the volume of a rectangular prism.* (''the fourth book in a set''; ''loudness''; ''amount of space inside'') Explain that *volume* is a measure of the inside of a space figure and that it is always given in cubic units.

EXPLORE AND CONNECT

Materials: unit cubes, table (see below)
Grouping Suggestion: cooperative learning pairs
Students explore the **volume** of rectangular prisms. Each pair needs 8 cubes and a table with the labels *length, width, height,* and *volume*. Before they begin, have students compare the dimensions of length, width, and height in a space figure to help them record data about the figures they will build. One student uses the 8 cubes to build a rectangular prism as his or her partner records in the table data about the figure. Then partners repeat the activity, trading tasks. Each partner will build 2 different rectangular prisms, always with a *volume* of 8 cubes and always recording data in the table. Conclude by asking students why each figure had a *volume* of 8 cubic units. (All figures had 8 cubes.) Have them link length, width, and height to *volume*. (length × width × height = *volume*)

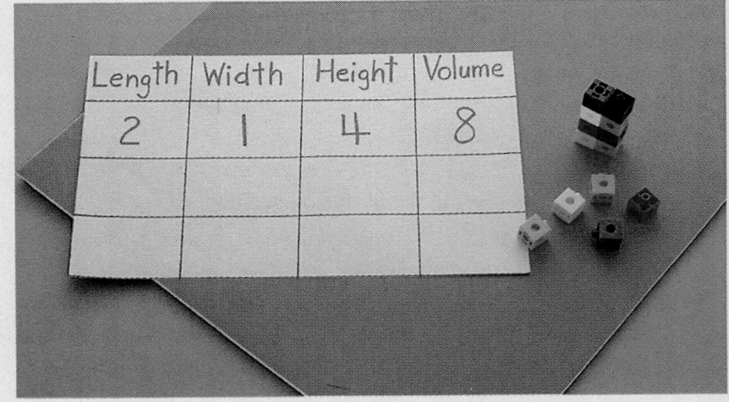

CONNECTIONS Use these anytime.

Problem of the Day

Storage A storage room is 6 m long, 5 m wide, and 3 m high. It is designed to be filled with boxes that are 1-m cubes. How many boxes can fit on the floor of the room? How many can be stacked in a column up to the ceiling? Multiplying the area of the floor by the number of boxes in each column, how many boxes fit in the room in all? (30; 3; 90)

Creative Thinking

Painted Block Lev paints the faces of a cube black, red, blue, brown, and green. If he paints the top and bottom of the cube the darkest color, then does the other faces in colors ordered alphabetically, what color is opposite blue? What color is opposite red? Draw a picture if it will help. (green; brown)

Math Connection

Algebra A small 3 written above a number is a special way to show a square fact multiplied by itself again, or a *cubed* fact. 6^3 is read ''six cubed'' and means 6 × 6 × 6. Read each number aloud, tell the factors, and give the product: 2^3, 3^3, 4^3, 5^3. (2 cubed, 2 × 2 × 2 = 8; 3 cubed, 3 × 3 × 3 = 27; 4 cubed, 4 × 4 × 4 = 64; 5 cubed, 5 × 5 × 5 = 125)

Classwork and Homework Supplements

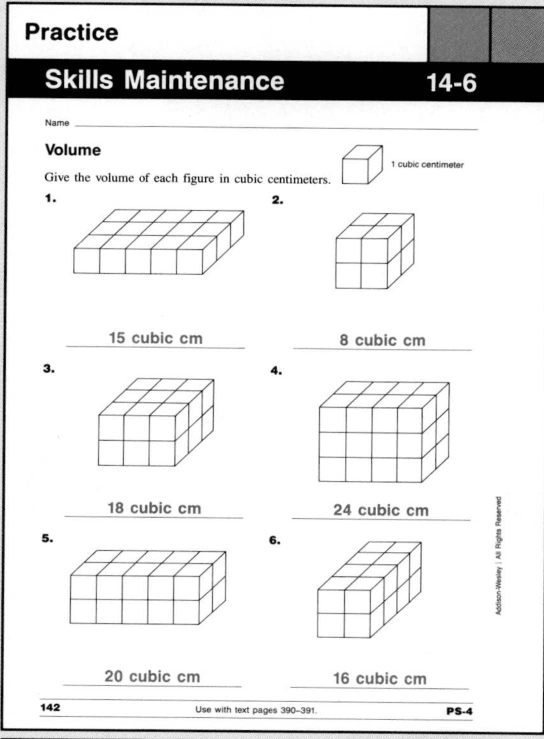

Practice

Skills Maintenance 14-6

Name ____________

Volume

Give the volume of each figure in cubic centimeters. (1 cubic centimeter)

1. 15 cubic cm
2. 8 cubic cm
3. 18 cubic cm
4. 24 cubic cm
5. 20 cubic cm
6. 16 cubic cm

Addison-Wesley | All Rights Reserved

142 Use with text pages 390–391. PS-4

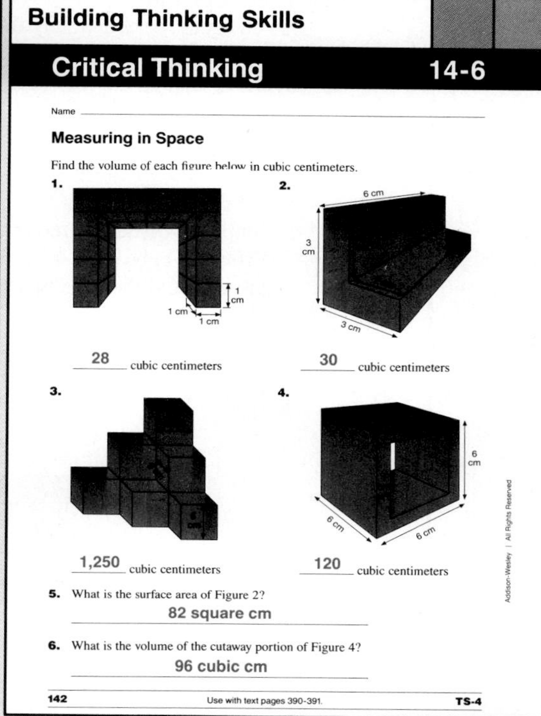

Building Thinking Skills

Critical Thinking 14-6

Name ____________

Measuring in Space

Find the volume of each figure below in cubic centimeters.

1. 28 cubic centimeters
2. 30 cubic centimeters
3. 1,250 cubic centimeters
4. 120 cubic centimeters
5. What is the surface area of Figure 2? 82 square cm
6. What is the volume of the cutaway portion of Figure 4? 96 cubic cm

Addison-Wesley | All Rights Reserved

142 Use with text pages 390–391. TS-4

Reteaching

Skills Review 14-6

Name ____________

Volume

The **cubic centimeter** is a meter unit for measuring **volume.**

Use multiplication to find the volume of a rectangular prism.

Rows × number in each row × layers

1 × 4 × 2 = 8

The volume is 8 cubic centimeters.

1 cm, 1 cm, 1 cm; 2 layers; 1 row; 4 in each row

Write the volume of each figure in cubic centimeters.

1. 1 layer, 3 rows, 7 in each row — 21 cubic cm
2. 2 layers, 3 rows, 3 in each row — 18 cubic cm
3. 20 cubic cm
4. 24 cubic cm
5. 32 cubic cm

Addison-Wesley | All Rights Reserved

142 Use with text pages 390-391. RS-4

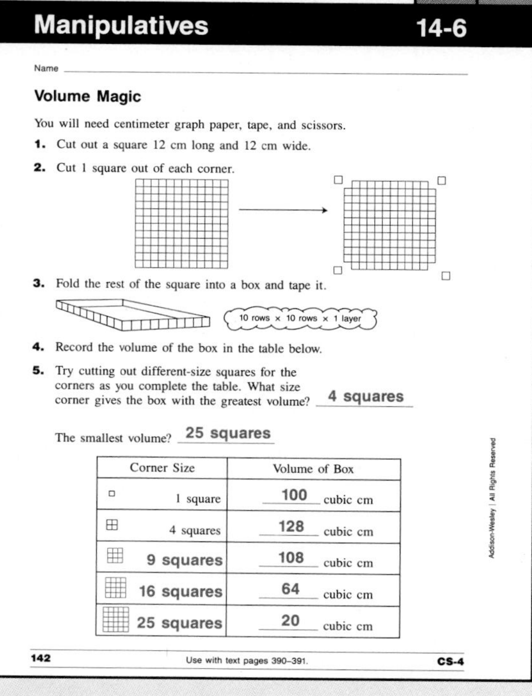

Challenges

Manipulatives 14-6

Name ____________

Volume Magic

You will need centimeter graph paper, tape, and scissors.

1. Cut out a square 12 cm long and 12 cm wide.
2. Cut 1 square out of each corner.
3. Fold the rest of the square into a box and tape it. (10 rows × 10 rows × 1 layer)
4. Record the volume of the box in the table below.
5. Try cutting out different-size squares for the corners as you complete the table. What size corner gives the box with the greatest volume? 4 squares

The smallest volume? 25 squares

Corner Size	Volume of Box
1 square	100 cubic cm
4 squares	128 cubic cm
9 squares	108 cubic cm
16 squares	64 cubic cm
25 squares	20 cubic cm

Addison-Wesley | All Rights Reserved

142 Use with text pages 390–391. CS-4

Options for Individual Needs

Basic

Exercises 1-8
More Practice, p. 526, set B

Supplements
Reteaching 142 or
Practice 142

Average

Exercises 1-8
More Practice, p. 526, set B

Supplements
Practice 142
Challenges 142 or
Thinking Skills 142

Extended

Exercises 1-8

Supplements
Challenges 142
Thinking Skills 142

14-6

Other Resources:

Problem-Solving Experiences in Mathematics, Grade 4, Problem 66
Mathematics, A Way of Thinking, Lesson 14-4
Make It Simpler, A Practical Guide to Problem Solving in Mathematics, p. 180
Using the Math Explorer Calculator: A Sourcebook for Teachers, Chapter 14

LESSON PLAN 14-6

OBJECTIVE 14-6
To measure volume in cubic centimeters and to multiply to find volume

Materials: unit cubes

Grouping Suggestion: pairs

1. MOTIVATE AND TEACH

EXPLORE ▶ **Analyze a rectangular prism to define its key features.** (6 faces are rectangles or squares; opposite faces are congruent)

TALK ABOUT IT ▶ **Explain why you multiply to show how many cubes per layer.** (You are actually finding the area, so you multiply length by width.)
▶ **If your rectangular prism has 1 layer, determine its height. Explain.** (1 cm, because the height is the number of cubes starting from the base and counting up)
▶ **Explain how to find the height of a rectangular prism.** (Count how many layers.)
▶ **Explain why you multiply 3 factors to find volume.** (factors for how many rows, how many cubes per row, and how many layers)
▶ **Explain what a cubic centimeter is.** (a cube of 1-cm square faces)
▶ **Justify using cubic centimeters as units of volume.** (You can count how many centimeter cubes fill a space figure.)
Student Edition answers: **1.** 4 possible rectangular prisms **2.** 12, 24, 36

2. CHECK UNDERSTANDING

TRY IT OUT

ERROR ALERT Having difficulty visualizing a 3-dimensional figure from a flat picture. Counting faces rather than cubes.

Volume

LEARN ABOUT IT

EXPLORE Use Cubes
Use cubes to make as many different rectangular prisms as you can. Each prism should be made with 12 cubes.

TALK ABOUT IT See teaching notes.

1. How many different rectangular prisms were you able to make?
2. Suppose you have a rectangular prism with 3 rows of cubes and 4 in each row. How many cubes would there be in 1 layer? in 2 layers? in 3 layers?

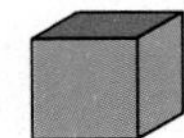

The **cubic centimeter** is a metric unit for **volume**.

You can use multiplication to find the volume of a rectangular prism.

2 rows × 3 in each row × 2 layers

$2 \times 3 \times 2 = 12$ cubic centimeters

The volume is 12 cubic centimeters.

TRY IT OUT

Find the volume of each figure in cubic centimeters.

1. 6 cubic cm
2. 16 cubic cm

390

TEACHING OPTIONS

RETEACHING TIPS Allow students to replicate the figures using unit cubes, then count the number of cubes they needed in the construction to determine the volume of the figure. Assign Reteaching Supplement 142.

ENRICHMENT Students draw a figure that has a volume of 50 cubic cm. The figure can be any shape they choose. When they complete their drawing, they label the figure with the dimensions that reflect that the volume is 50 cubic cm. (Check students' figure and equations.)

PRACTICE

Give the volume of each figure in cubic centimeters.

1. 
24 cubic cm

2. 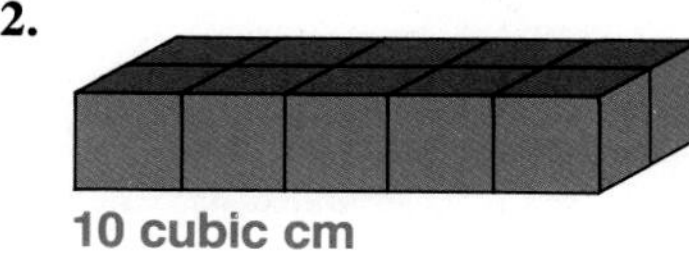
10 cubic cm

APPLY

MATH REASONING Find the volume of each figure in cubic units.

3. 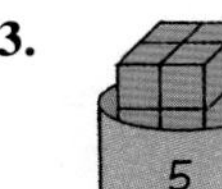

20 cubic units

4. 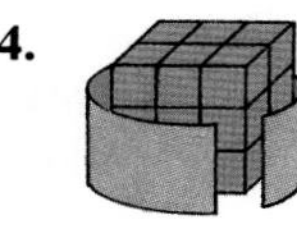
18 cubic units

5. 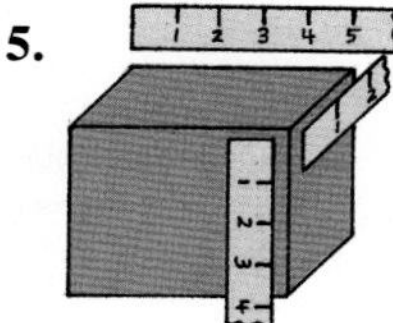
40 cubic units

PROBLEM SOLVING

6. Dan filled a box with 6 layers of centimeter cubes. Each layer had 4 rows with 5 cubes in each row. How many cubes were in the box? 120 cubes

7. **Missing Data** Make up missing data and solve the problem. A box of blocks is 3 blocks long and 4 blocks wide. How many blocks are in the box? Answers will vary.

▶ **USING CRITICAL THINKING Take a Look**

Find the volume in cubic centimeters.

8. 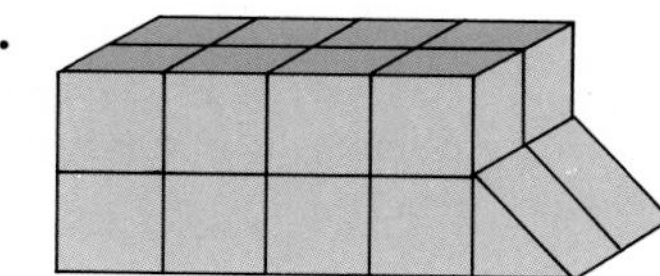
17 cubic cm

More Practice, page 526, set B

3. Practice and Apply

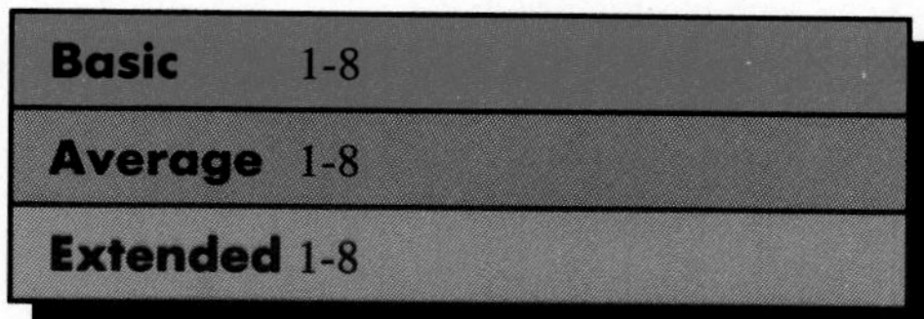

Basic	1-8
Average	1-8
Extended	1-8

PRACTICE

How can you be sure to count all the cubes in each figure? (Possible answers: Visualize each row and layer; use models.)

APPLY

MATH REASONING ▶ **Do you have all the information you need to solve Exercises 3-5? Explain.** (Yes, you can account for the number of cubes in each layer; the number of layers is given or can be counted.)

PROBLEM SOLVING ▶ **What are you solving for in Problem 6? Explain.** (the volume of the box, because you are finding out how many cubes fill it up)

▶ **What else do you need to know in Problem 7? Explain.** (height; to know how many layers of 3 × 4)

USING CRITICAL THINKING

▶ **Explain what to do with the 2 half cubes.** (think of them as one whole)

Close and Assess

SAY WHAT YOU THINK Have students work in pairs. One student explains to the other how to find the volume of a rectangular prism that is 5 cm long, 3 cm wide, and 4 cm high. Then the other partner explains how to find the volume of one that is 6 cm long, 2 cm wide, and 5 cm high. (both 60 cubic cm)

Quick Quiz

Find the volume.
(27 cubic cm)

LESSON OPTIONS 14-7

Problem Solving: Finding Related Problems

OBJECTIVE 14-7 To solve problems by finding related problems

PREBOOK ACTIVITIES

QUICK REVIEW

Write an equation related to the one given but with the opposite operation. (Answers may vary. Samples are given.)

1. 57 × 32 = 1,824 (1,824 ÷ 57 = 32)
2. 1,877 − 1,642 = 235 (1,642 + 235 = 1,877)
3. 3 × 18 = 54 (54 ÷ 3 = 18)
4. 744 ÷ 6 = 124 (124 × 6 = 744)

PRIOR KNOWLEDGE

Have students generate a list of the various problem-solving strategies they have used. (Answers may vary.) Challenge students to analyze the strategies listed to find pairs that are similar in some way. Have them give their reasons. (Possible answer: Make a Table and Look for a Pattern are similar because both involve organizing data; Choose an Operation and Work Backward are similar because both involve deciding which operation to use.)

COMMUNICATION

Discussing Math Have students give synonyms for the word **related**. (Possible answers: *in the same family, similar, equivalent)* Have them suggest what it might mean if 2 problems are related. (Possible answers: They use similar data; you could solve them using the same strategy.) Challenge students to tell how recognizing related problems may help solve them. (Possible answer: Once you decide how to solve one problem, you can use similar thinking to solve the other.)

EXPLORE AND CONNECT

COOPERATIVE ACTIVITY

Grouping Suggestion: small groups

Zoe owns 11 videotapes. She has 3 more blank tapes than movie tapes. How many of each kind does she have?

TEACHING ACTIONS

Have students work together to discuss the situation in order to plan a solution strategy.

▶ **Explain the situation in your own words.** (Zoe has both blank videotapes and movie videotapes.)

▶ **Decide what you must determine.** (how many of each kind of video Zoe has)

▶ **Decide on a useful solution strategy.** (Possible answer: Guess and Check)

▶ **Explain how you will solve the problem.** (Find 2 addends whose sum is 11 but whose difference is 3.)

▶ **Evaluate your solution to see if it makes sense.** (If Zoe has 7 blank tapes and 4 movie tapes, the sum is 11 and the difference is 3, so the solution works.)

▶ **Identify a related problem that you could solve using the same reasoning.** (Answers will vary, but students' related problems should require the Guess and Check strategy to solve.)

CONNECTIONS Use these anytime.

Problem of the Day

Zorbeks Zelda flew 186 zorbeks to the new space museum. Then she flew twice as many zorbeks to see her cousin, Zeke. How many zorbeks did Zelda fly? What is a zorbek? How do you know? (558 zorbeks; from the way it is used in the problem, it must be a measure of distance.)

Creative Thinking

Classification Sort these 7 numbers into 2 groups by discovering a relationship among them: 8, 10, 16, 18, 25, 36, 81. *Hint:* Think of each number as a sum or product, then put 4 numbers in 1 group and 3 in the other. (8, 10, and 18 are sums of doubles; 16, 36, 25, and 81 are products of square factors.)

Patterns

Function Machine Find the rule to complete the missing numbers.

IN	7	3	(8)	4
OUT	77.7	33.3	88.8	(44.4)

(Multiply the IN number by 11.1.)

Classwork and Homework Supplements

Practice

Problem Solving 14-7

Name

Finding Related Problems

Solve. Explain why these pairs of problems are related.

1. There are 22 students in Mr. Wise's class. 16 students took the morning test. 19 took the afternoon test. How many took both tests? 13 students
2. 24 students in Ms. Min's class studied over the weekend for the big spelling test. 19 students studied on Saturday. 12 students studied on Sunday. How many students studied on both days? 7 students

Both use the strategy Use Logical Reasoning.

3. Leslie studied her spelling review words for 3 days. Each day she reviewed 15 words. The third day she also studied 6 bonus words. She has 19 words left to study. How many words did she have in all? 70 words
4. For 5 nights, Tara looked up spelling words in the dictionary. Each night she looked up the meaning of 4 words. One of the nights, she looked up 2 additional words. She had 3 words left to look up. How many words did she have altogether? 25 words

Both use the strategy Work Backward.

5. A palindrome is a word that reads the same backward or forward. The letter *m* is at the beginning and end of one palindrome. The letter *d* is in the middle. The letter *a* is between *m* and *d*. What is the word? madam
6. Near the end of the spelling bee, Rosa was standing to the left of Carl. Lindsey was standing next to Rosa. Jacob was at the far right. Divya was between Carl and Jacob. Who was standing in the center? Carl

Both use the strategy Draw a Picture.

Building Thinking Skills

Writing Math 14-7

Name

Spring Training

Solve each problem below. Write the strategy you used. Then make up a related problem for a classmate to solve using the same strategy. Strategies and problems will vary. Samples given.

1. Four players were in line, waiting for their turn at batting practice. Roger was second in line. Faith was before Rico, who stood between Roger and Soojin. Who was first in line? Faith; Draw a Picture

   Four players are sitting on the bench. Allen is at one end. Dale is between Kevin and Ralph. Kevin sits next to Allen. Who sits on the other end? (Ralph)

2. Twenty years after the stadium was built, an artificial surface was put in. Six years later, in 1990, the artificial surface was removed and natural grass was put back in. In what year was the stadium built? 1964; Work Backward

   Thirty years after the team moved to Florida, its new stadium was built. Eight years later, in 1970, a running track was put in. When did the team move to Florida? (1932)

3. In one spring training game, the Grasshoppers got 28 hits. One fourth of the hits were singles. The rest were either doubles or home runs. If there were twice as many doubles as home runs, how many of each were there? 14 doubles, 7 home runs; Guess and Check

   Thirty players made the team. There were 16 fewer rookies than veterans. How many rookies and how many veterans made the team? (7; 23)

Reteaching

Problem Solving 14-7

Name

Finding Related Problems

Many problems are related. These problems can be solved using the same strategy. Sometimes it helps if you can think about a related problem. At the right are a list of strategies to choose from to solve the following problems.

Some Strategies
- Choose an Operation
- Draw a Picture
- Guess and Check
- Make a Table
- Work Backward

Solve. Then answer the strategy questions to help you understand how the pairs of problems are related.

1. Roberta took a spelling test. There were 25 problems on the test. She got 15 more right answers than wrong answers. How many answers did Roberta get right? 20 answers
2. Jonathan spent $14 for two tapes. One tape cost $2 more than the other. How much did the higher-priced tape cost? $8

What strategy did you use to solve both problems? Answers may vary. Guess and Check.

3. Each coat the tailor makes takes 4 buttons and 2 shoulder pads. When the tailor has used 12 buttons, how many shoulder pads will he have used? 6 pads
4. Mr. Kim gives clarinet lessons to 5 boys and 6 girls a week. When he has taught 20 boys, how many girls has he taught? 24 girls

What strategy did you use to solve both problems? Answers may vary. Make a Table

5. There were 15 crew members for two flights. The early flight had 3 more members than the late flight. How many crew members were on the first flight? 9 members

Is this problem related to Problem 2 or Problem 4? Problem 2

Challenges

Problem Solving 14-7

Name

Twin Problems

For each problem, write another problem that could be solved using the same strategy. Write your problem about the situation given and give it to a classmate to solve. Answers will vary.

1. Rob is shorter than Jenna. Rosita is shorter than Rob. Bill is between Rob and Jenna's height. Who is shortest?
   Solution: Jenna, Bill, Rob, Rosita
   Rosita is shortest.

   Situation: waiting in line for a dolphin show

2. Kerry's soccer team can choose between blue and red tops and black and white shorts. How many possibilities are there?
   Solution:
   blue top—white shorts
   blue top—black shorts
   red top—white shorts
   red top—black shorts
   There are 4 possibilities.

   Situation: deciding what musical instrument to play and whether to play it in fifth or sixth grade

3. Sacha has 15 pets. She has 3 more mammals than birds. How many birds does she have?
   Solution:

	Mammals	Birds	Check
Guess	11	4	11 − 4 = 7
Guess	9	6	9 − 6 = 3

   She has 6 birds.

   Situation: sorting out a coin collection with Spanish and French coins

Options for Individual Needs

Basic

Exercises 1-7
Skills Bank, pp. 462, 464
More Practice, p. 526, set C

Supplements
Reteaching 143 or
Practice 143

Average

Exercises 1-7
Skills Bank, pp. 462, 464
More Practice, p. 526, set C

Supplements
Practice 143
Challenges 143 or
Thinking Skills 143

Extended

Exercises 1-7

Supplements
Challenges 143
Thinking Skills 143

14-7

Other Resources:
Problem-Solving Experiences in Mathematics, Grade 4, Problem 81
Mathematics, A Way of Thinking, Lesson 14-5
Make It Simpler, A Practical Guide to Problem Solving in Mathematics, p. 175
Using the Math Explorer Calculator: A Sourcebook for Teachers, Chapter 14

LESSON PLAN 14-7

OBJECTIVE 14-7
To solve problems by finding related problems

1. MOTIVATE AND TEACH

LEARN ABOUT IT

► **Explain the situation in the first problem.** (You must determine the order of the 4 people in line.)

► **Analyze the situation in the second problem to find similarities.** (You must find the order of beaches Pedro visited.)

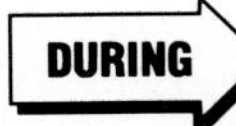

► **Decide on a solution strategy to help determine each order.** (Possible strategies: Draw a Picture; Guess and Check; Use Logical Reasoning; Use Objects)

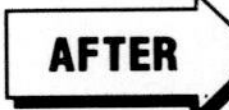

► **Evaluate the 2 solutions to see whether they make sense.** (The pictures show that Ken is last and that Pedro visited Miami Beach last, which fits the data given.)

► **Explain why it made sense to use the same strategy in both problems.** (The problems were related because both required a picture to organize the data to find a reasonable order, so the Draw a Picture strategy made sense to use with both.)

2. CHECK UNDERSTANDING

TRY IT OUT

ERROR ALERT Failing to notice a relationship between the two problems.

Problem Solving
Finding Related Problems

UNDERSTAND
FIND DATA
PLAN
ESTIMATE
SOLVE
CHECK

LEARN ABOUT IT

Many problems are related. That means they can be solved using the same strategy. When you are solving a problem, sometimes it helps if you think about a related problem.

Here are two related problems. They have both been solved by drawing a picture.

Ming, Becky, Tish, and Ken are in line for a tour of the Kennedy Space Center. Ming is ahead of Tish. Tish is between Ken and Ming. Ming is behind Becky. Who is last in line?

Ken — Tish — Ming — Becky

Ken is last in line.

Pedro went to 4 beaches in Florida. He went to Cocoa Beach before Jensen Beach. He went to Miami Beach after Palm Beach. He went to Palm Beach after Jensen Beach. What was the last beach he visited?

Miami — Palm — Jensen — Cocoa

Pedro went to Miami Beach last.

TRY IT OUT

Solve. Explain why these two problems are related. **See Additional Answers.**

1. 22 of the fourth graders have been to Florida. 17 have been to Miami and 13 have been to Daytona Beach. How many have been to both Miami and Daytona Beach?

2. 34 students went on a field trip to Everglades National Park. 15 bought food for lunch at the park. 21 brought their own lunch. How many both brought their own lunch and bought food?

TEACHING OPTIONS

RETEACHING TIPS Allow students to solve the problems using any reasonable strategies. If they do use other methods than the suggested strategy (Use Logical Reasoning), then ask students to justify their decisions and to identify similarities between the problems. Assign Reteaching Supplement 143.

ENRICHMENT Have students select any problem from the Mixed Practice on page 393 and formulate a related problem to be solved by the same strategy. Partners exchange problems, solve them, and identify the related one. (Answers will vary. Check students' work.)

MIXED PRACTICE

Choose a strategy from the list or use other strategies you know to solve these problems.

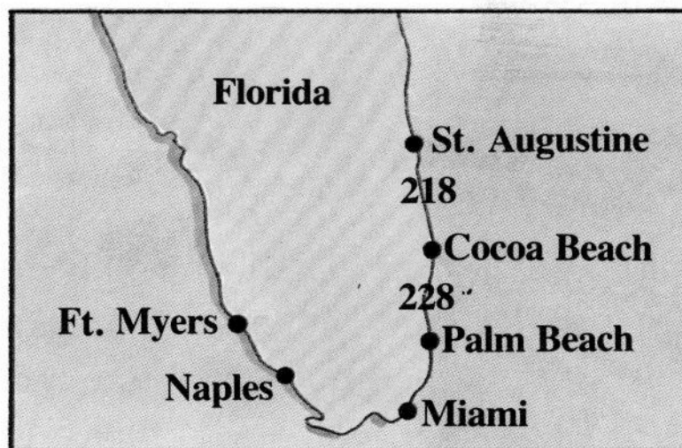

1. In 1513 Ponce de Leon traveled along Florida's coastline from what is now St. Augustine to what is now Fort Myers. How many kilometers did he travel? Use the Florida map shown. **823 km**
2. Georgia and her family drove 160 km to see the Florida Keys. They crossed 42 bridges. It took them 4 hours, and they drove the same distance each hour. How many kilometers did they drive each hour? **40 km**
3. 16 years after Maine became one of the United States, Arkansas became a state. 9 years later, in 1845, Florida became a state. What year did Maine become a state? **1820**
4. The state of Florida is about 723 km long. Its widest part is about $\frac{1}{3}$ of its length. How wide is its widest part? **241 km**

Some Strategies
Act It Out
Use Objects
Choose an Operation
Draw a Picture
Make an Organized List
Guess and Check
Make a Table
Look for a Pattern
Use Logical Reasoning
Work Backward

5. Postcards at Everglades National Park are 6 for $3. How much would 36 postcards cost? **$18.00**
6. Daytona Beach, famous for car racing, is 37 km long. The width of the beach is 4 km longer than 4 times its length. How wide is Daytona Beach? **152 km**
7. **Find a Related Problem** Tell which of the problems on this page is related to this one. Then solve. Abe is 124 cm tall. At National Key Deer Refuge, he photographed a tiny deer that was half as tall as he is. How tall was the deer? **Problem 4 is related (choose the operation division) 62 cm tall**

More Practice, page 526, set C

393

3. Practice and Apply

Basic	1-7
Average	1-7
Extended	1-7

Additional Answers and Sample Solutions: See p. T79.

MIXED PRACTICE

► **Justify the operation to use to solve Problem 1.** (Add to find the total distance.)

► **Explain how Problems 2, 4, and 7 are alike.** (All 3 can be solved by division.)

► **Analyze Problem 5 to choose a solution strategy.** (Make a Table)

► **Identify a strategy to solve Provlem 6.** (Draw a Picture to visualize the dimensions.)

14-7

Close and Assess

WRITE WHAT YOU THINK

Have students write a paragraph to explain how they can use related problems to help them find solutions. (Answers will vary. Check students' writing.)

Quick Quiz

Solve this problem, then identify a related problem on page 393. *Model airplane kits are on sale at 3 for $5. How many kits could you buy for $20?* (12; Problem 5, Make a Table)

LESSON OPTIONS 14-8

Capacity

OBJECTIVE 14-8 To estimate and measure capacity in milliliters and liters

PREBOOK ACTIVITIES

QUICK REVIEW

Solve using mental math.

1. 3 × 1,000 (3,000) **2.** 6 × 1,000 (6,000)
3. 12 × 1,000 (12,000) **4.** 7,000 ÷ 1,000 (7)
5. 2,000 ÷ 1,000 (2) **6.** 9,000 ÷ 1,000 (9)

PRIOR KNOWLEDGE

Have students recall the meaning of *liquid capacity* (''how much liquid a container can hold''), then name some customary units of capacity they have used. (gallon, quart, pint, cup, fluid ounce) Tell students that there are metric units of capacity called liters and milliliters. Ask students what liquids they have heard of or seen measured in these units. (Possible answers: soft drinks, medicine) Tell students that in this lesson they will examine these metric measures of capacity.

COMMUNICATION

Discussing and Reading Math Write **liter** and **milliliter** on the chalkboard, along with their abbreviations, **L** and **mL.** Have students find a relationship between the two words, comparing them to other metric measurements they know. (*Milliliter* has the prefix *milli-* before the word *liter,* just as *millimeter* relates to *meter*.) Based on their knowledge of meters and millimeters, have students use logical reasoning to choose the greater unit of capacity and determine exactly how they relate. (liter; 1 L = 1,000 mL)

EXPLORE AND CONNECT

Materials: liter containers, various smaller containers, water
Grouping Suggestion: volunteers from the full class
Students estimate the capacity of a **liter**. Display empty *liter* containers and a variety of smaller containers, such as paper cups and assorted empty jars. You need not know the capacity of the small containers. For each small container, have students estimate how many times they would fill the container with water to fill a 1-*L* bottle. After students have recorded their estimates, ask volunteers to find the actual number of times you would have to fill each container with water to fill a 1-*L* bottle. Discuss how students' estimates compare with the actual amounts. Conclude by challenging students to describe the capacity of each smaller container based on how many fill a *liter,* using the fact that 1 *L* = 1,000 **mL.** For instance, if it takes 5 paper cups to fill 1 *L,* students can divide 1,000 by 5 to find that the capacity of one paper cup would be 200 *mL*.

CONNECTIONS Use these anytime.

Problem of the Day

Punch Max pours a can of pineapple juice into a 3-L pitcher. Then he adds seltzer and orange juice to make a fruit juice punch. If Max uses equal amounts of all 3 liquids and the pitcher is half-full, what is the capacity of the pineapple juice can? *Hint:* 1 L equals 1,000 mL. ($\frac{1}{2}$ L, or 500 mL)

Life Skills

Consumer Math At Food-O-Rama, the sale price of lemonade is 3 L for $1.98. At Grocery Goodies, the same lemonade costs $0.59/L. Where would you pay less for 1 L of lemonade? How much less? (Grocery Goodies; $0.07 less)

Subject Integration

Health and Fitness When Elyse got sick, she had to take a liquid medicine. The doctor told her to take 5 mL of it 4 times a day for 10 d. Should the doctor give Elyse a 250 mL or 500 mL bottle of the medicine? Explain. (Elyse needs 200 mL of medicine, so 250 mL is enough.)

Classwork and Homework Supplements

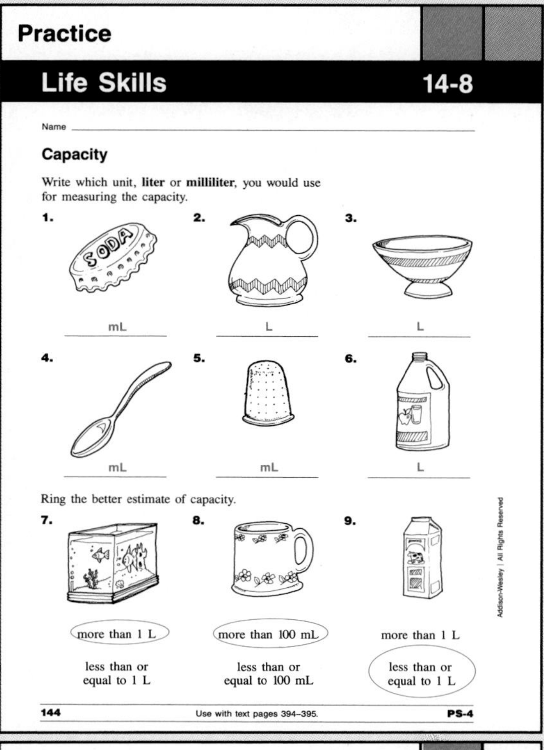

Practice

Life Skills 14-8

Name ______

Capacity

Write which unit, **liter** or **milliliter**, you would use for measuring the capacity.

1. mL
2. L
3. L
4. mL
5. mL
6. L

Ring the better estimate of capacity.

7. (more than 1 L) less than or equal to 1 L
8. (more than 100 mL) less than or equal to 100 mL
9. more than 1 L (less than or equal to 1 L)

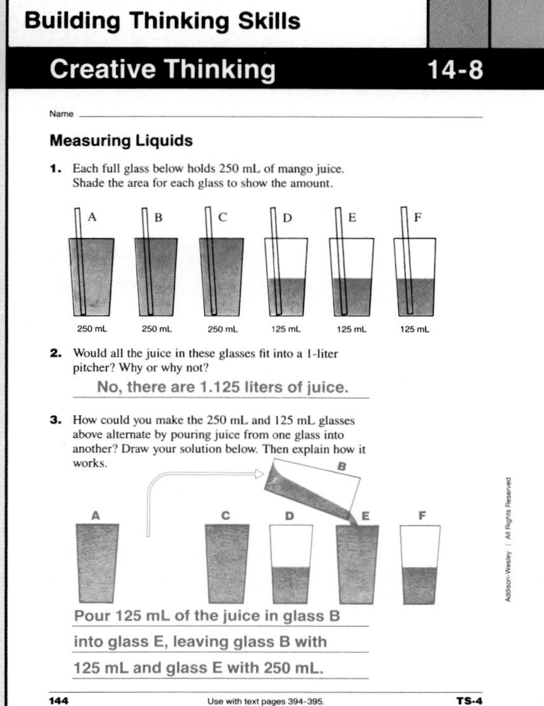

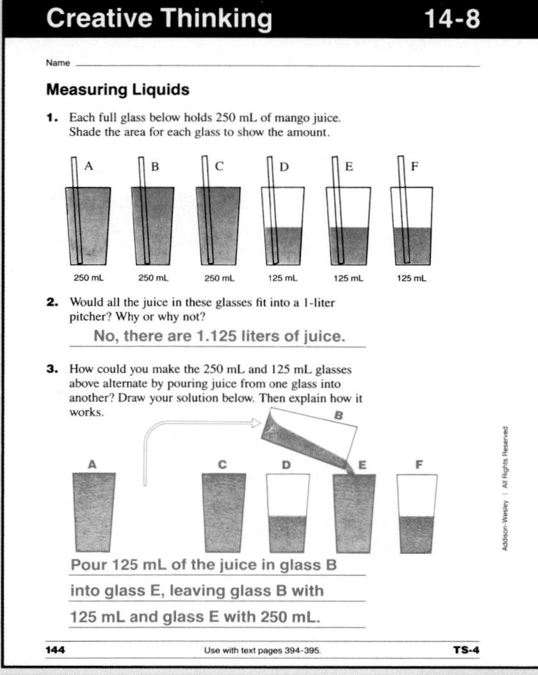

Building Thinking Skills

Creative Thinking 14-8

Name ______

Measuring Liquids

1. Each full glass below holds 250 mL of mango juice. Shade the area for each glass to show the amount.

2. Would all the juice in these glasses fit into a 1-liter pitcher? Why or why not?
No, there are 1.125 liters of juice.

3. How could you make the 250 mL and 125 mL glasses above alternate by pouring juice from one glass into another? Draw your solution below. Then explain how it works.

Pour 125 mL of the juice in glass B into glass E, leaving glass B with 125 mL and glass E with 250 mL.

Reteaching

Life Skills 14-8

Name ______

Capacity

Liter and **milliliter** are metric units for measuring **capacity**.

1 mL 1 L = 1,000 mL

Which unit would you use for measuring the capacity of this can?

Look at the can.

Does the can hold more than the pail? NO → Measure in milliliters.

YES → Measure in liters.

The answer is no.

You would use milliliters to measure the can's capacity.

Write which unit, **liter** or **milliliter**, you would use for measuring the capacity.

1. liter
2. milliliter
3. milliliter

Ring the better estimate of capacity.

4. more than 100 mL (less than or equal to 100 mL)
5. (more than 1 L) less than or equal to 1 L

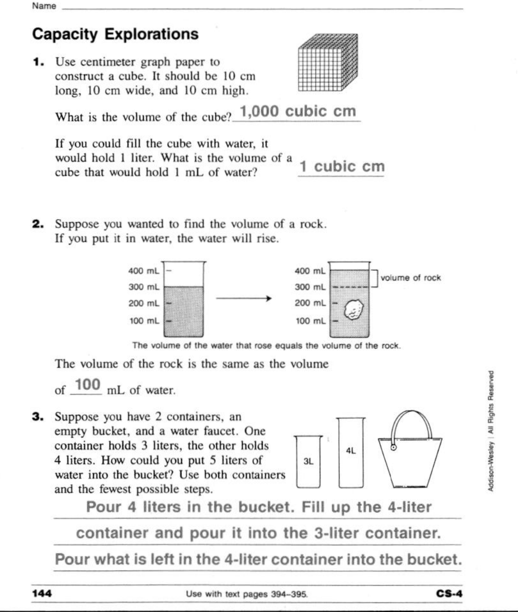

Challenges

Creative Thinking 14-8

Name ______

Capacity Explorations

1. Use centimeter graph paper to construct a cube. It should be 10 cm long, 10 cm wide, and 10 cm high.

What is the volume of the cube? 1,000 cubic cm

If you could fill the cube with water, it would hold 1 liter. What is the volume of a cube that would hold 1 mL of water? 1 cubic cm

2. Suppose you wanted to find the volume of a rock. If you put it in water, the water will rise.

The volume of the water that rose equals the volume of the rock.

The volume of the rock is the same as the volume of 100 mL of water.

3. Suppose you have 2 containers, an empty bucket, and a water faucet. One container holds 3 liters, the other holds 4 liters. How could you put 5 liters of water into the bucket? Use both containers and the fewest possible steps.

Pour 4 liters in the bucket. Fill up the 4-liter container and pour it into the 3-liter container. Pour what is left in the 4-liter container into the bucket.

Options for Individual Needs

Basic

Exercises 1-10
Computer Bank, p. 494
More Practice, p. 526, set D

Supplements
Reteaching 144 or
Practice 144

Average

Exercises 1-10
Computer Bank, p. 494
More Practice, p. 526, set D

Supplements
Practice 144
Challenges 144 or
Thinking Skills 144

Extended

Exercises 1-10
Computer Bank, p. 494

Supplements
Challenges 144
Thinking Skills 144

Other Resources:
Problem-Solving Experiences in Mathematics, Grade 4, Problem 67
Mathematics, A Way of Thinking, Lesson 14-16
Kids Are Consumers, Too!, pp. 35, 37, 38

LESSON PLAN 14-8

OBJECTIVE 14-8
To estimate and measure capacity in milliliters and liters

Materials: 1-L containers, assorted smaller containers, index cards

1. MOTIVATE AND TEACH

LEARN ABOUT IT

EXPLORE ► **Explain the problem of trying to rank containers in capacity order.** (If they have different shapes, it is hard to compare them visually.)

TALK ABOUT IT ► **Explain a method for comparing the capacity of the containers.** (Possible answer: Fill each with water, then pour the water into a measuring cup or other marked container to see which held the most, the next most, to the least.)
► **Is height always an indicator of capacity? Explain.** (No, tall, thin jars may not hold as much as short, wide ones.)
► **Explain the method you used to verify the capacity order.** (Answers may vary.)
► **Explain how to use the teaspoon and juice container as benchmarks.** (Possible answer: Think of them as references against which to judge the capacity of other containers.)
Student Edition answers: **1.** Answers will vary. **2.** No, a short, wide container can hold more than a tall, narrow one. **3.** Answers will vary.

2. CHECK UNDERSTANDING

TRY IT OUT

ERROR ALERT Confusing liters and milliliters.

Capacity

LEARN ABOUT IT

EXPLORE **Use Containers**
You will need a 1-liter container plus several containers of different shapes and sizes. Estimate to put all the containers in order from the one that holds the least to the one that holds the most. Find a way to check your estimates.

TALK ABOUT IT See teaching notes.

1. How did you decide on the order of the containers?
2. Does the tallest container always hold the most? Explain.
3. What method did you use to check your estimates?

You can use what you know about estimating with a benchmark to help you estimate capacity using the metric units **liter** (L) and **milliliter** (mL).

A teaspoon holds about 5 mL.
A tablespoon holds about 3 times as much as a teaspoon, so it holds about 15 mL.

A juice container holds about 1 L.
1 L = 1,000 mL.
A milk carton holds about the same as a juice container, so it holds about 1 L.

TRY IT OUT

Which unit, *liter* or *milliliter*, would make most sense to use when measuring the capacity of the object?

1. a medicine dropper **mL**
2. a large pail **L**
3. a tea cup **mL**

Choose the better estimate of capacity.

4. a pitcher (**a**) 3 L **b** 3 mL
5. a kitchen sink (**a**) 20 L **b** 20 mL
6. a juice glass **a** 150 L (**b**) 150 mL

TEACHING OPTIONS

RETEACHING TIPS Have students use an index card to make a visual reminder of the difference in capacity between liters and milliliters. They can draw and label an eyedropper 1 mL and a tall milk carton 1 L. Allow them to use the cue card to make the comparisons. Assign Reteaching Supplement 144.

ENRICHMENT Have students listen and answer the question: *If you could fill a centimeter cube with water, it would hold 1 mL. What volume, in cubic centimeters, must a container have to hold 1 L of water? (1,000 cubic cm)*

PRACTICE

Which unit, *liter* or *milliliter*, would you use for measuring the capacity?

1. L

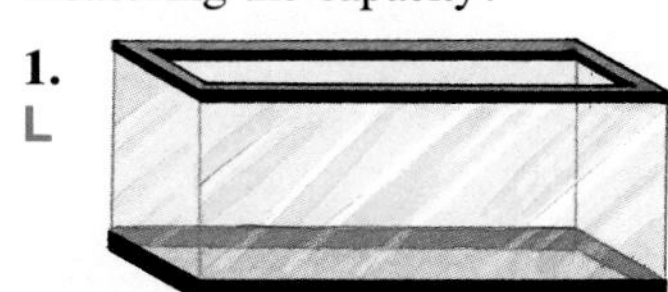

2. mL

Choose the better estimate of capacity.

3.

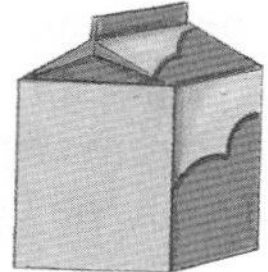

(**a**) more than 1 L
b less than or equal to 1 L

4.

a more than 100 mL
(**b**) less than or equal to 100 mL

APPLY

MATH REASONING Write the missing numbers.

5. If 5 drops of water make 1 mL, then ||||| drops make 1 L.
5,000 drops

6. If a teaspoon of water is 5 mL, then ||||| teaspoons make 1 L.
200 teaspoons

PROBLEM SOLVING

7. A bucket holds 6 L of water. After a rain it was one third full. How many L of water were in the bucket? How many mL?
2 L, 2,000 mL

8. A cup holds 250 mL. How many cupfuls would it take to make 1 L?
4 cupfuls

▶ **MENTAL MATH**

Use mental math to answer the questions.

9. One large glass holds 300 mL. Do 3 glasses hold more or <u>less</u> than 1 L?

10. A small juice can holds 150 mL. Do 5 juice cans hold more or <u>less</u> than 1 L?

More Practice, page 526, set D

3. Practice and Apply

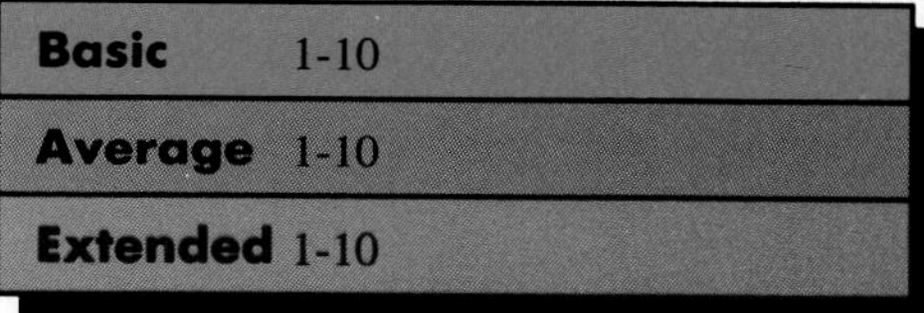

Basic	1-10
Average	1-10
Extended	1-10

PRACTICE

How can you decide whether to measure in liters or milliliters? (Possible answer: Measure small containers in milliliters, large ones in liters.)

APPLY

MATH REASONING ▶ **Explain what you need to know to answer Exercises 5 and 6.** (how many milliliters equal 1 liter)

PROBLEM SOLVING ▶ **Explain the steps you would use to solve Problem 7.** (Find $\frac{1}{3}$ of 6; find how many milliliters in that many liters.)
▶ **Explain how knowing the relationship of liters to milliliters helps you solve Problem 8.** (1 L = 1,000 mL, so you can figure out how many 250s are in 1,000.)

MENTAL MATH ▶ **Justify the operation to use to solve Exercises 9 and 10.** (multiply because you are combining containers of the same size)

Close and Assess

WRITE WHAT YOU THINK
Have students list 3 different containers that hold *less* than 1 L and 3 that hold *more* than 1 L. Then ask students to list 2 containers that hold less than 50 mL. (Answers will vary. Check students' writing.)

Quick Quiz

Tell whether you would measure the capacity in liters or in milliliters.
1. swimming pool (liters)
2. thimble (milliliters)
3. bottle cap (milliliters)

Grams and Kilograms/Temperature: Degrees Celsius

OBJECTIVE 14-9 To estimate and measure mass in kilograms and grams; to measure temperature

PREBOOK ACTIVITIES

QUICK REVIEW

Complete each metric measurement statement.

1. 1,000 mL = (1) L
2. 3 m = 300 (cm)
3. 5 km = (5,000) m
4. 20 mm = 2 (cm)
5. 10 dm = (1) m
6. 4 L = 4,000 (mL)

PRIOR KNOWLEDGE

Have students recall customary units of weight and temperature they have used. (Possible answers: ounce; pound; ton; degree Fahrenheit) Tell students that the metric system also has weight and temperature units. Ask students to recall any such units they have used or have heard used by others. (Possible answers: gram; kilogram; degree Celsius)

COMMUNICATION

Discussing Math Write these metric-measurement units and abbreviations on the chalkboard: **gram (g), kilogram (kg), degree Celsius (°C).** Tell students that the gram is the standard metric unit of **mass,** or weight. Have students relate the word *kilogram* to another metric measurement they know with the same prefix to guess the relationship between grams and kilograms. (Possible answer: 1 km equals 1,000 m, so 1 kg must equal 1,000 g.) Explain to students that Anders Celsius (1701-1744) was a Swedish astronomer who first used the idea of a *centigrade*, or 100-degree, temperature scale. Celsius decided to call the freezing point of water 0° and its boiling point 100°.

EXPLORE AND CONNECT

Materials: assorted classroom objects of various weights, 1-g and 1-kg weights, balance scale
Alternative Materials: large paper clips to equal 1 g
Grouping Suggestion: small groups
Students explore the **mass** of objects in **grams** and **kilograms.** Each group collects 3 classroom objects of different weights. By lifting and comparing the weights, group members work together to rank the objects in order from heaviest to lightest. Then students estimate and record the *mass* of each object in *grams* or *kilograms*. They verify their estimates using a balance scale and the appropriate size and number of weights (or paper clips) to balance the pans. Conclude by having students name benchmark objects they might use to estimate *mass* in *grams* and in *kilograms*. (Answers will vary.)

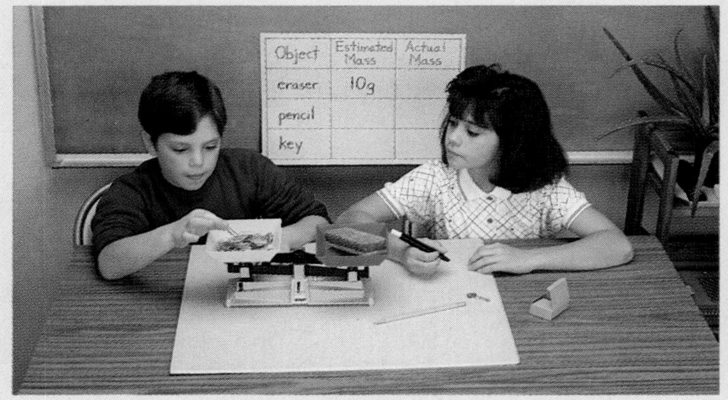

CONNECTIONS Use these anytime.

Problem of the Day

Baby Animal Logic 4 same-size bunnies have a total weight of 936 g, 3 same-size kittens have a total weight of 954 g, and 2 same-size puppies have a total weight of 890 g. Use a calculator to determine the total weight of 1 bunny, 1 kitten, and 1 puppy together. (997 g)

Math Connection

Place Value At the zoo's annual ape weigh-in, 5 chimpanzees weighed 67.9 kg, 70.1 kg, 68.9 kg, 69.8 kg, and 68 kg. Rank the apes in order from the heaviest to the lightest. (70.1 kg; 69.8 kg; 68.9 kg; 68 kg; 67.9 kg)

Subject Integration

Science For a science project, Vanessa recorded the daily high temperature in degrees Celsius for 1 wk. At the end of those 7 days, she had recorded high temperatures of 26°C, 25°C, 22°C, 25°C, 24°C, 19°C, and 20°C. Based on her data, find the average high temperature that week. (23°C)

in degrees Celsius

Classwork and Homework Supplements

Practice

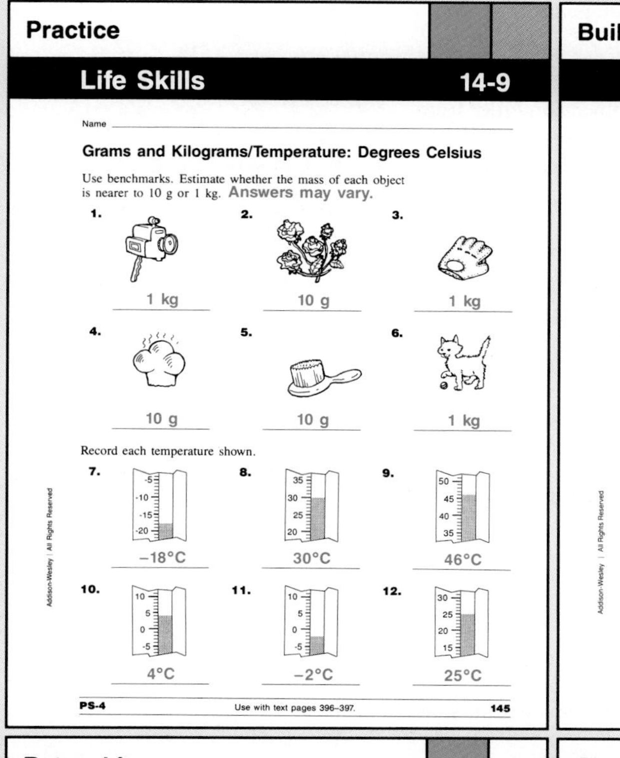
Life Skills 14-9

Name

Grams and Kilograms/Temperature: Degrees Celsius

Use benchmarks. Estimate whether the mass of each object is nearer to 10 g or 1 kg. Answers may vary.

1. 1 kg
2. 10 g
3. 1 kg
4. 10 g
5. 10 g
6. 1 kg

Record each temperature shown.

7. −18°C
8. 30°C
9. 46°C
10. 4°C
11. −2°C
12. 25°C

PS-4 Use with text pages 396–397. 145

Building Thinking Skills

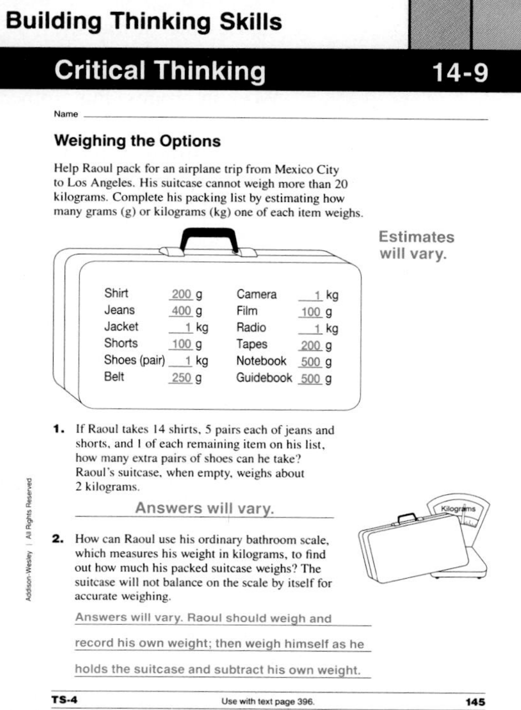
Critical Thinking 14-9

Name

Weighing the Options

Help Raoul pack for an airplane trip from Mexico City to Los Angeles. His suitcase cannot weigh more than 20 kilograms. Complete his packing list by estimating how many grams (g) or kilograms (kg) one of each item weighs.

Estimates will vary.

Shirt	200 g	Camera	1 kg
Jeans	400 g	Film	100 g
Jacket	1 kg	Radio	1 kg
Shorts	100 g	Tapes	200 g
Shoes (pair)	1 kg	Notebook	500 g
Belt	250 g	Guidebook	500 g

1. If Raoul takes 14 shirts, 5 pairs each of jeans and shorts, and 1 of each remaining item on his list, how many extra pairs of shoes can he take? Raoul's suitcase, when empty, weighs about 2 kilograms.

Answers will vary.

2. How can Raoul use his ordinary bathroom scale, which measures his weight in kilograms, to find out how much his packed suitcase weighs? The suitcase will not balance on the scale by itself for accurate weighing.

Answers will vary. Raoul should weigh and record his own weight; then weigh himself as he holds the suitcase and subtract his own weight.

TS-4 Use with text page 396. 145

Reteaching

Life Skills 14-9

Name

Grams and Kilograms/Temperature: Degrees Celsius

Mass

Gram (g) and **kilogram** (kg) are metric units of **mass.**

1 kg = 1,000 g

A nickel weighs about 5 g.

This bat weighs about 1 kg.

You can use benchmarks like these to help you estimate the mass of objects.

Ring the best mass for each item.

1. (A 1 g) B 1 kg C 10 g
2. A 16 g (B 16 kg) C 3 kg

Estimate whether the mass of each object is nearer 5 g or 1 kg.

3. 5 g
4. 1 kg
5. 1 kg
6. 5 g

Temperature
Degrees Celsius (°C)

The temperature is 17°C to the nearest degree.

−10°C is below 0°C. We read this temperature as "negative 10 degrees" or "10 degrees below zero."

Record each temperature shown.

7. 20°C
8. 36°C
9. 14°C
10. −20°C

RS-4 Use with text pages 396-397. 145

Challenges

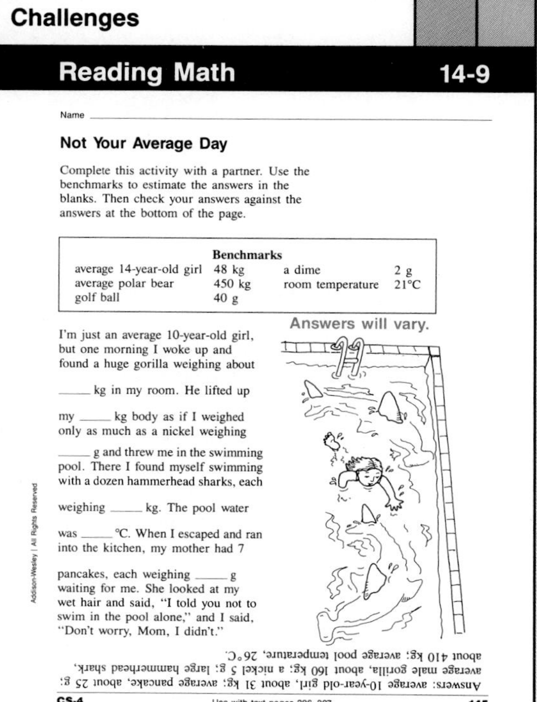
Reading Math 14-9

Name

Not Your Average Day

Complete this activity with a partner. Use the benchmarks to estimate the answers in the blanks. Then check your answers against the answers at the bottom of the page.

Benchmarks			
average 14-year-old girl	48 kg	a dime	2 g
average polar bear	450 kg	room temperature	21°C
golf ball	40 g		

Answers will vary.

I'm just an average 10-year-old girl, but one morning I woke up and found a huge gorilla weighing about _____ kg in my room. He lifted up my _____ kg body as if I weighed only as much as a nickel weighing _____ g and threw me in the swimming pool. There I found myself swimming with a dozen hammerhead sharks, each weighing _____ kg. The pool water was _____ °C. When I escaped and ran into the kitchen, my mother had 7 pancakes, each weighing _____ g waiting for me. She looked at my wet hair and said, "I told you not to swim in the pool alone," and I said, "Don't worry, Mom, I didn't."

Answers: average 10-year-old girl, about 31 kg; average pancake, about 25 g; average male gorilla, about 160 kg; a nickel 5 g; large hammerhead shark, about 410 kg; average pool temperature, 26°C.

CS-4 Use with text pages 396–397. 145

Options for Individual Needs

Basic

Exercises 1-3; 1-4
More Practice, p. 527, set B

Supplements
Reteaching 145 or
Practice 145

Average

Exercises 1-3; 1-4
More Practice, p. 527, set B

Supplements
Practice 145
Challenges 145 or
Thinking Skills 145

Extended

Exercises 1-3; 1-4

Supplements
Challenges 145
Thinking Skills 145

Other Resources:
Problem-Solving Experiences in Mathematics, Grade 4, Problem 68
Mathematics, A Way of Thinking, Lesson 14-3
Kids Are Consumers, Too!, pp. 24, 25, 26

14-9

LESSON PLAN 14-9

OBJECTIVE 14-9
To estimate and measure mass in kilograms and grams

Materials: metric scale, paper clips, 1 kg weight or object

Grouping Suggestion: small groups

1. MOTIVATE AND TEACH

LEARN ABOUT IT

EXPLORE ► **Explain the meaning of *mass* by substituting a synonym for it.** (*weight*)

TALK ABOUT IT ► **Decide on a reasonable metric unit of mass to use for a toy car and for a real car.** (gram; kilogram)
► **Explain how the gram and kilogram relate.** (1,000 g = 1 kg)
Student Edition answers: **1.** Answers may vary. **2.** Possible answer: A big object made of a lightweight material, such as a plastic-foam tray, can have less mass than a small object made of a heavy material, such as a metal stapler.

2. CHECK UNDERSTANDING

ERROR ALERT Choosing an inappropriate measurement.

3. PRACTICE AND APPLY

Basic	1-3
Average	1-3
Extended	1-3

PRACTICE

Which objects are most likely to be the heaviest? (pumpkin) *Which are most likely to be the lightest?* (chalkboard eraser; scissors)

Grams and Kilograms

LEARN ABOUT IT

The **gram** (g) and the **kilogram** (kg) are metric units of **mass**.

EXPLORE Use a Scale
Work in groups. Put 5 objects in order from heaviest to lightest. Check your estimates by measuring each object's mass in grams.

TALK ABOUT IT See teaching notes.

1. How did you compare the objects when you first put them in order?
2. If someone said that the largest object always has the greatest mass, would you agree or disagree? Explain.

Benchmarks like these can help you estimate the mass of objects.

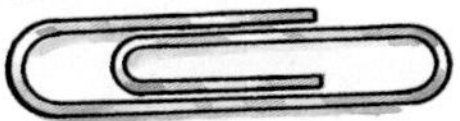

The mass of a large paper clip is about 1 g.

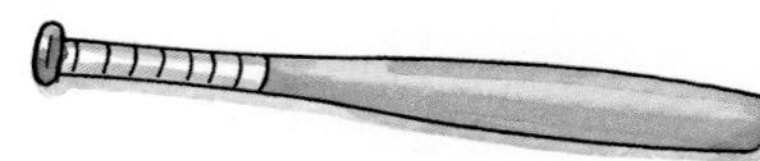

The mass of a baseball bat is about 1 kg. 1 kg = 1,000 g

PRACTICE

Use benchmarks. Estimate whether the mass of each object is 10 g or 1 kg. Answers will vary. Suitable answer given.

1.  10 g

2.  1 kg

3.  10 g

More Practice, page 526, set E

TEACHING OPTIONS

RETEACHING TIPS Students who choose inappropriate mass measurements should feel the weight of 10 paper clips to represent 10 g and a 1-kg weight or 1-kg object to help them make more accurate estimates. Assign Reteaching Supplement 145.

ENRICHMENT Family Math
Have students examine food or household item labels to find 3 whose mass is given in metric units. Have them make a table of the data, listing each item, its metric measure, and the customary equivalent if it is given.

Temperature
Degrees Celsius

LEARN ABOUT IT

The metric unit for temperature is the **degree Celsius** (°C). On the thermometer at the right, the temperature is 27°C to the nearest degree.

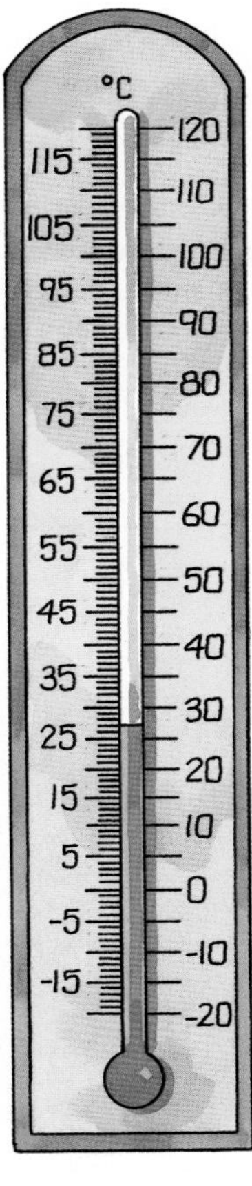

EXPLORE **Try an Experiment**

Does the location of a thermometer make a difference in the temperature reading? To find out, place two thermometers outside in the sunshine, one with a glass over it.

Record each temperature to the nearest degree every 30 minutes for 2 hours. Make a table to show the results.

TALK ABOUT IT See teaching notes.

1. What did you find out in your experiment?
2. What was the greatest temperature? the least?
3. What was the greatest difference in the two temperatures?

PRACTICE

1. Make bar graphs to show the results of your experiment. Check students' graphs.

Record each temperature shown.

2. 40°C

3. 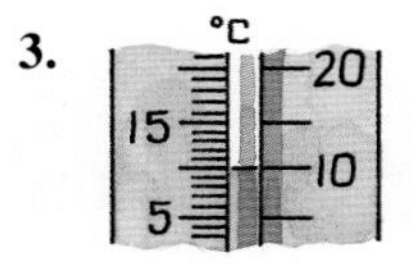

10°C

4. 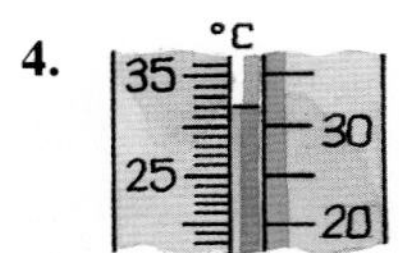

32°C

More Practice, page 527, set A

OBJECTIVE 14-9 To measure temperature in degrees Celsius

Materials: Celsius thermometers, a glass, TA 12 (Centimeter Graph Paper)

1. Motivate and Teach

LEARN ABOUT IT

EXPLORE ► **Predict how the glass may affect the temperature of the thermometer it covers.** (The glass may trap the heat, causing higher temperatures to register.)

TALK ABOUT IT Student Edition answers: **1 to 3**. Answers will vary.

2. Check Understanding

ERROR ALERT Misreading the thermometer scale.

3. Practice and Apply

Basic	1-4
Average	1-4
Extended	1-4

PRACTICE

What number scale will you use for your bar graph? (Answers will vary.)

Close and Assess

WRITE WHAT YOU THINK

Have students fill in each blank with a sensible metric measurement. (Samples are given.)

1. After being out in a winter temperature of (2°C), I drink hot soup with a temperature of (80°C).

2. A stamp may weigh (2 g), but it will take many to mail a (3 kg) book.

Quick Quiz

1. Which weighs more, a 1-kg or 750-g package of cheese? (1 kg)

2. What is a sensible temperature for frozen yogurt? (Accept any negative Celsius temperature.)

CHAPTER 14

DATA COLLECTION AND ANALYSIS

GROUP DECISION MAKING

OBJECTIVE To collect, organize, and present data

COLLECTING DATA

► **Predict which pets will be the most popular before you do the survey.** (Answers will vary.)

► **Explain why it is helpful to plan how many people to survey.** (Possible answer: It helps you organize results and check totals.)

► **Decide on a reasonable list of animals and on reasons to narrow the choices when you conduct your survey.** (Choices may vary; too many choices may confuse respondants and make it hard for them to select one pet.)

► **Decide how to record responses.** (Possible answer: Use tallies.)

► **Explain how you could record an unpredicted response.** (Provide a category called Other.)

Data Collection and Analysis
Group Decision Making

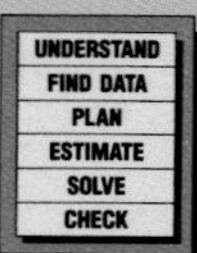

Doing a Survey:
Group Skill:
Explain and Summarize

What animal do people think makes the best pet? Predict what animal you think most people will choose. Then conduct a survey to find out.

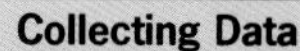

Collecting Data

1. Your group will ask a total of 30 people the survey questions. Decide how many people each student in your group will survey.
2. Write down the questions that you will ask. Make a table to record the answers.

398

TEACHING OPTIONS

COOPERATIVE LEARNING

Grouping Suggestion: cooperative learning groups of 5 Groups should discuss, plan, evaluate, and then assign the tasks involved in conducting the pet survey. These may include making a prediction; formulating a list of possible choices; planning a way to record responses; designing, making, and labeling the bar graph; and writing sentences summarizing the data collected. The group should word process or duplicate the survey they agree to use so that every group member has the identical form for collecting data.

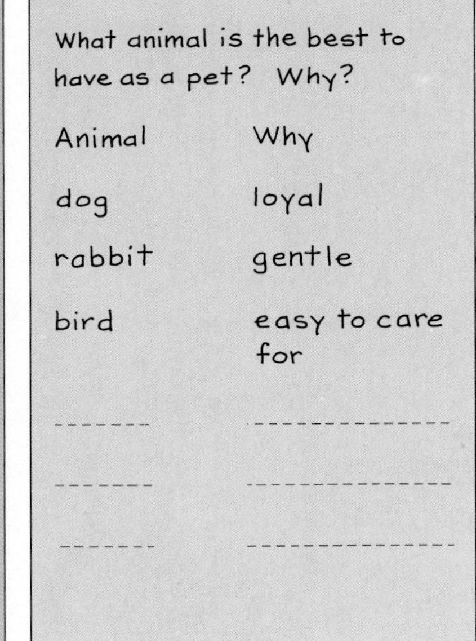

What animal is the best to have as a pet? Why?
Animal
Why
dog
loyal
rabbit
gentle
bird
easy to care for

Organizing Data

3. Count how many times each animal was named. Make a bar graph to show how many people in your survey chose each animal. Adjust the scale to fit your data.

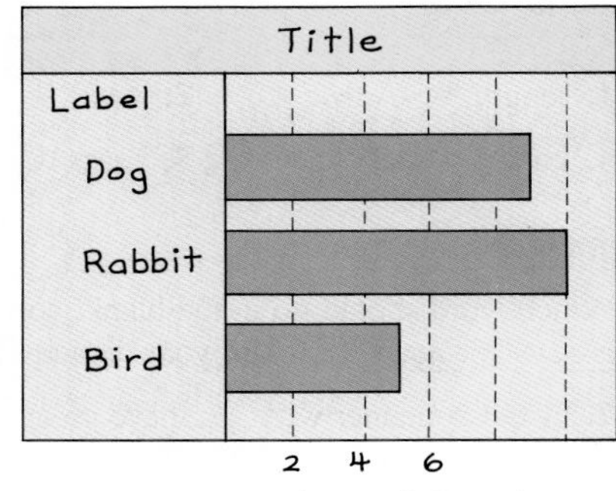

Presenting Your Analysis

4. Which animal was chosen by the most people? How many people named that animal?
5. Explain some of the reasons people chose a certain animal as the best pet.
6. Write at least three true sentences about the information in your graph.

399

ORGANIZING DATA

▶ **Decide on a reasonable order for the categories in your graph.** (Answers may vary.)

▶ **Explain a way to use your original prediction to organize the actual data.** (Possible answer: Order the bars based on the group's predicted order, even if results are different, to build a reminder into the graph.)

PRESENTING YOUR ANALYSIS

Suggest that students make a companion bar graph to compare reasons people gave for naming a certain animal as the best pet. Allow time for groups to discuss their findings and compare the reasons people express for preferring 1 kind of pet to another.

EXTENSION Have students contact pet stores and animal shelters in your area to find out more about the kinds of pets people actually buy or adopt. Have students evaluate this information to see if it supports the results of their survey.

COMPUTER **Explorer Metros: A Metric Adventure, Sunburst Communications, Copyright 1981** For all levels (best in pairs). Students explore an alien planet in a limited amount of time and must return to the ship by estimating metric measurements of mass, capacity, length, and temperature. The simulation requires 20 min.

CHAPTER 14

WRAP UP

INTRODUCTION The Wrap Up provides activities emphasizing math language and thinking skills for the chapter and a project that integrates those skills with other math strands.

USING PAGE 400

Measurement Mix-Up Have students complete this section independently, then share their answers in small groups to discuss any discrepancies.

Sometimes, Always, Never

► **Identify the various shapes a container may have to plan how to compare capacities.** (Possible answers: tall, thin, wide, short, round are possibilities to keep in mind.)

► **Identify a distance you might measure with each of the metric units of length.** (Answers will vary.)

Project Have students work in pairs. Provide metric measuring cups.

► **Identify something whose capacity you know is about 1 L to use as a benchmark.** (Answers will vary.)

► **Compare the capacity of 1 mL to something familiar.** (Answers will vary.)

► **Explain how to test your capacity estimates.** (Fill a model with water, then pour the water into the liter or milliliter measuring cup.)

Have pairs illustrate their results on sheets of posterboard. Have pairs present and then display their results.

WRAP UP

Measurement Mix-Up

Put these measurement cards in the correct categories.

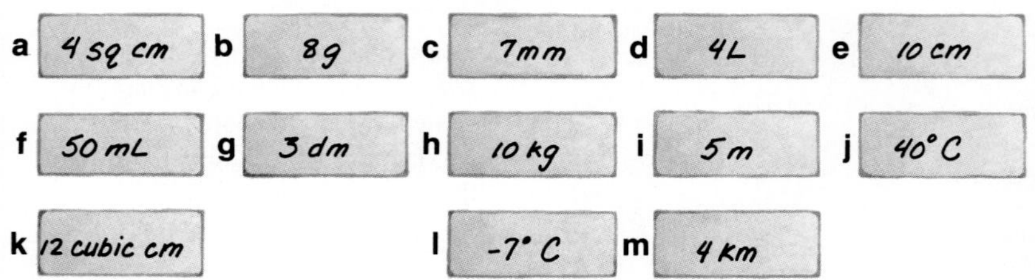

1. length c, e, g, i, m **2.** area a **3.** volume k

4. capacity d, f **5.** mass b, h **6.** temperature j, l

Sometimes, Always, Never

Which word should go in the blank, sometimes, always, or never? Explain your choices. Explanations may vary.

7. A tall container will __?__ have greater capacity than a short container. sometimes

8. The kilometer is __?__ the most useful unit for measuring distance. sometimes

9. You __?__ measure in milligrams to find the perimeter of a very small region. never

Project

Find 2 containers that have the capacity of about 1 liter. Find 2 containers that have the capacity of about 1 milliliter. Then use a liter measure and a milliliter measure to check the capacities of the models you found.

Now look for a container larger than your liter model. Estimate how many liters it will hold. Then do an actual measurement to check. Answers will vary.

400

TEACHING OPTIONS

ENRICHMENT Challenge students to estimate in cubic centimeters the volume of some small containers, such as paper-clip boxes, pencil cases, or cassette boxes. Students test estimates by filling containers with centimeter cubes and then counting them, adjusting totals up or down depending on how the cubes actually fit inside of the containers.

CHAPTER REVIEW/TEST

Part 1 Understanding

1. Use liter or milliliter to answer these problems.
   A large spoon might hold 15 __?__. **milliliters**

   A laundry sink might hold 25 __?__. **liters**

2. Use grams or kilograms to answer these problems.
   The mass of a cement block may be 4 __?__. **kilograms**

   The mass of a pencil may be 4 __?__. **grams**

3. Explain how to unitize to estimate the length of the toy car in centimeters. **Answers may vary.**

4. David is making a window screen and a sand sifter with wire mesh. Explain for which object David needs an actual measure and for which he can use an estimate. **See Additional Answers.**

Part 2 Skills

5. Find the area in square centimeters.

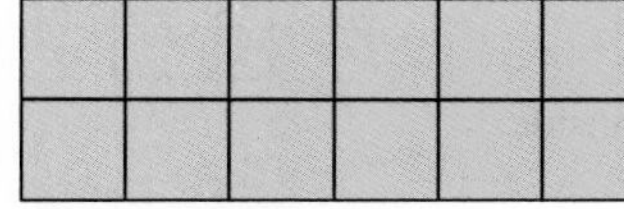

12 square cm

6. Find the volume in cubic centimeters.

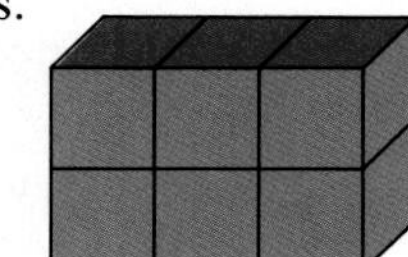

6 cubic cm

Measure to the nearest centimeter and millimeter.

7. 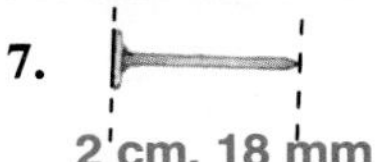

2 cm, 18 mm

8. **3 cm, 31 mm**

Part 3 Applications

9. Sam's castle wall had 5 layers of cm cubes. Each layer had 8 rows of 7 cubes. What is the volume of Sam's castle wall? **280 cubic cm**

10. **Challenge** Draw a figure whose area is an odd square number but whose perimeter is an even number.
    See Additional Answers.

INFORMAL ASSESSMENT

Using Manipulatives Have students use centimeter rulers (TA 17) to draw a rectangle 15 cm by 10 cm, then find its area and perimeter. Have them label the sides of the rectangle in millimeters as well as in centimeters. (area = 150 square cm; perimeter = 50 cm; 150 mm, 100 mm)

Communication *Explain how to use the strategy of unitizing to estimate length.* (Visually divide an object into equal parts, estimate the length of 1 part, then multiply the estimate by the number of parts.)

Critical Thinking *Which has a greater volume, a container that holds 188 cubic cm or one that holds 2 cubic m? Give your reason.* (2 cubic m is a greater volume because 2 m = 200 cm.)

CHAPTER REVIEW/TEST

INTRODUCTION The Review/Test is provided to review and evaluate the skills and concepts presented in Chapter 14.

USING PAGE 401
If you prefer to use this page for review, you may want to use the **Multiple-Choice Posttest** (pages 55-56) or the **Free-Response Posttest** (pages 55-56) to evaluate mastery of Chapter objectives.

ITEM ANALYSIS The table below correlates the Chapter Review/Test items with the lesson objectives for the chapter.

Items	Objectives
1	14-8
2	14-9
3	14-2
4	14-4
5	14-5
6	14-6
7, 8	14-1
(7, 8)	14-3
9	14-6
10	14-5

Additional Answers: See p. T79.

ENRICHMENT

INTRODUCTION Students will sharpen their skills at finding area of a figure by exploring a method for finding the approximate area of a curved figure.

USING PAGE 402
This Enrichment page is provided for all students. You may wish to use it after they have completed the Chapter Review/Test on page 401.

► **Summarize how to find the area of a rectangle.** (Count square units; multiply length times width.)

► **Analyze why this method does not always work with a curved figure.** (Some squares are not completely inside the curve.)

► **Summarize the steps you use to find an average.** (First add, then divide the total by the number of addends.)

EXTENSION Doctors say that most people have 1 foot slightly larger than the other. Have students use the count-and-average method to find the area of their other foot to see if 1 foot is larger.

Additional Answers: See p. T79.

ENRICHMENT
Estimating Area

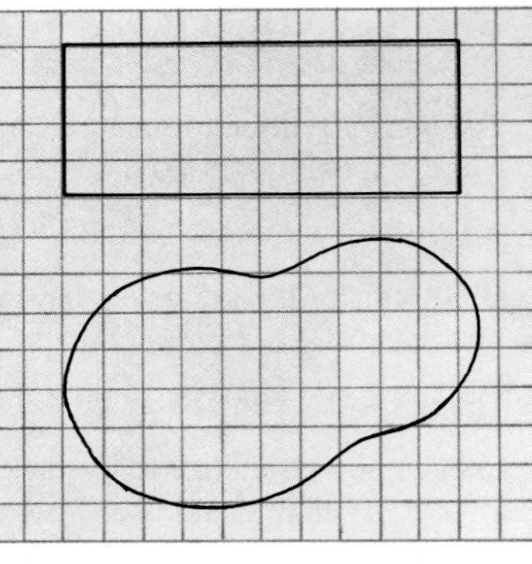

You can find the area of a rectangle by counting square units. But how can you find the area of other figures?

Look at the simple closed curve on this page. Then draw your own simple closed curve on centimeter grid paper.

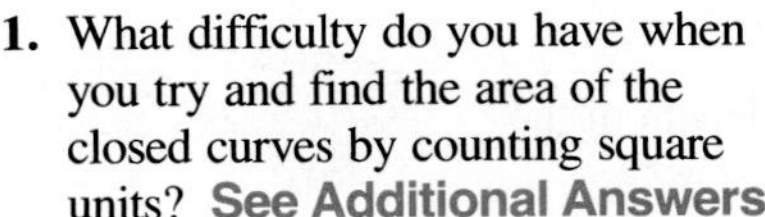

1. What difficulty do you have when you try and find the area of the closed curves by counting square units? **See Additional Answers.**

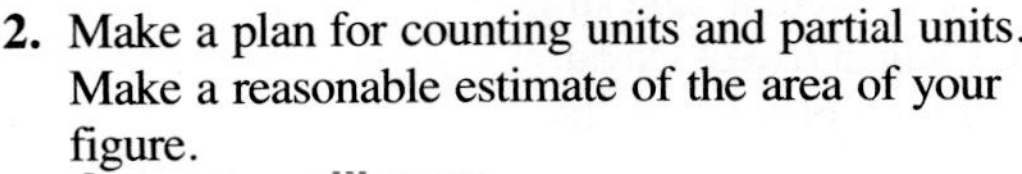

2. Make a plan for counting units and partial units. Make a reasonable estimate of the area of your figure. **Answers will vary.**

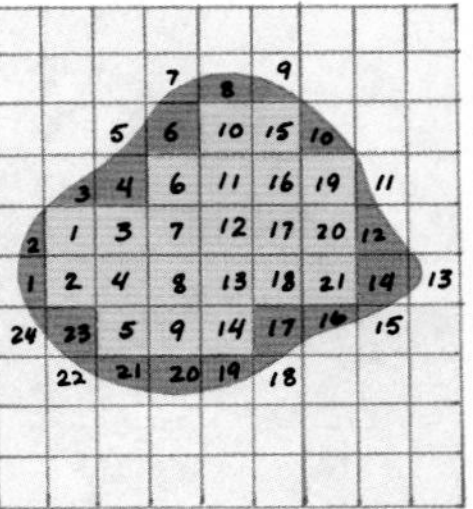

The count-and-average method gives a close estimate of the area of curved shapes. Here is what you do.

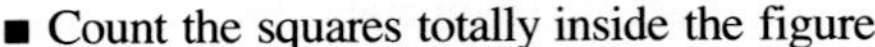

- Count the squares <u>totally</u> inside the figure.
- Look at the partial squares and estimate how many full squares they make.
- Count all the squares totally inside <u>and</u> partly inside the figure.
- Find the average of the two numbers. Compare the average with your estimate.

3. How do you find an average?
4. Find the area of your closed curve with the count-and-average method. Compare this area with your earlier estimate. **Answers will vary.**
5. Trace your foot on centimeter grid paper. First, estimate, then use the count-and-average method to find its area. **Answers will vary.**

402

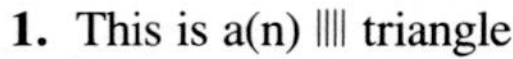

CUMULATIVE REVIEW

1. This is a(n) |||| triangle.

   (A) right   B equilateral
   C obtuse   D isosceles

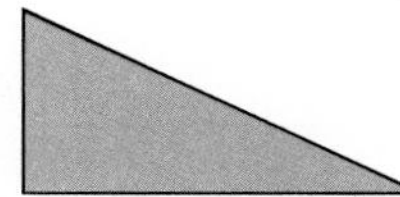

2. A rectangle is a special ||||.

   (A) parallelogram   B square
   C trapezoid   D curve

3. Which space figure is like this road marker?

   A cube   B cylinder
   C sphere   (D) cone

4. Which fraction is reduced to lowest terms?

   A $\frac{6}{9}$ (B) $\frac{6}{7}$
   C $\frac{6}{18}$ D $\frac{6}{21}$

5. Choose the fraction that is greater than $\frac{2}{3}$.

   A $\frac{1}{2}$ (B) $\frac{3}{4}$
   C $\frac{2}{5}$ D $\frac{4}{6}$

6. Find $\frac{3}{7}$ of 28.

   (A) 12   B 9
   C 7   D 21

7. Which decimal is two and seven hundredths?

   (A) 2.07   B 2.70
   C 207.07   D 0.27

8. Choose the decimal in which the 3 equals 3 hundredths.

   A 302.64   B 1.37
   (C) 48.53   D 0.32

9. Which is between 5.7 and 5.78?

   A 5.8   (B) 5.74
   C 5.79   D 5.70

10. Dean won a vocal music prize for holding a note for 44.42 seconds. Find the time to the nearest second.

   A 40   B 50
   (C) 44   D 45

11. A ribbon is 0.25 yd long. Which fraction describes the same part of a yard?

   (A) $\frac{1}{4}$ B $\frac{2}{5}$
   C $\frac{2}{10}$ D $\frac{1}{3}$

403

CUMULATIVE REVIEW

INTRODUCTION The purpose of this Cumulative Review is to maintain previously taught skills and concepts. The emphasis in this Cumulative Review is on geometry, Chapter 11; on fraction concepts, Chapter 12; and on decimal concepts, Chapter 13.

ITEM ANALYSIS The table below correlates the Cumulative Review items with the lesson objectives.

Items	Objectives
1	11-5
2	11-6
3	11-1
4	12-6
5	12-7
6	12-9
7, 8	13-2
9	13-4
10	13-5
11	13-6

CHAPTER 15 ADDITION AND SUBTRACTION:

Chapter Management

OVERVIEW

Lesson	Pages	Objectives	Subject Integration	Strand Integration
Chapter Opener	404-405	To introduce chapter 15	health/fitness-sport balls	measurement
Adding and Subtracting Fractions with Like Denominators: Making the Connection	406-407	15-1 To add and subtract fractions with like denominators using objects	social studies-group skills	number
Adding and Subtracting Fractions: Like Denominators	408-409	15-2 To add and subtract fractions with like denominators	health/fitness-volleyball camp	mathematical reasoning
Problem Solving: Data from a Recipe	410-411	15-3 To solve problems using data from a recipe	health/fitness-cooking	consumer math
Adding Fractions with Models: Unlike Denominators	412-413	15-4 To add fractions with unlike denominators	health/fitness-exercise	mental math
Subtracting Fractions with Models: Unlike Denominators	414-415	15-5 To use objects to subtract fractions with unlike denominators	health/fitness-basketball	estimation
Exploring Algebra/Midchapter Review/Quiz	416-417	15-6 To understand that a variable can represent a range of numbers	health/fitness-recipes	patterns
Adding and Subtracting Decimals: Making the Connection	418-419	15-7 To use objects to understand adding and subtracting decimals	social studies-group skills	numeration
Adding and Subtracting Decimals	420-421	15-8 To add and subtract decimals	health/fitness-sport balls	calculators
More Adding and Subtracting Decimals	422-423	15-9 To annex zeros to add and subtract decimals	science-rainfall	problem solving
Estimating Decimal Sums and Differences	424-425	15-10 To estimate the sum or difference of two decimals	social studies-map skills	problem solving
Using Critical Thinking/Problem Solving	426-427	15-11 To analyze and follow a flow chart	science-penguins	measurement
Applied Problem Solving: Group Decision Making	428-429	15-12 To use relevant data	fine arts-kite making	measurement

MATHEMATICAL BACKGROUND

Addition and Subtraction of Fractions
Students learn to add and subtract fractions that have like denominators. In Lessons 15-4 and 15-5, they use models to add and subtract fractions with unlike denominators.

Addition and Subtraction of Decimals
Lessons 15-7, 15-8, and 15-9 all focus on helping students learn the steps to follow to add and subtract decimals, including making trades when necessary.

Estimation
Students learn how to round decimals to decide whether a sum is close to a reference-point number.

Problem Solving
Students solve problems using data from a recipe.

TIPS FROM TEACHERS

Go ''around the clock'' *to change a mixed number to an improper fraction. Students start at the denominator, move clockwise to multiply the denominator by the whole number, then add the numerator to the product. For example* $5\frac{1}{2} = 2 \times 5 + 1 = \frac{11}{2}$.

Patricia Mingus
Fred Moore Junior High School
Anoka, MI

$5\frac{1}{2} = \frac{11}{2}$

$2 \times 5 = 10$

$10 + 1 = 11$

ASSESSMENT

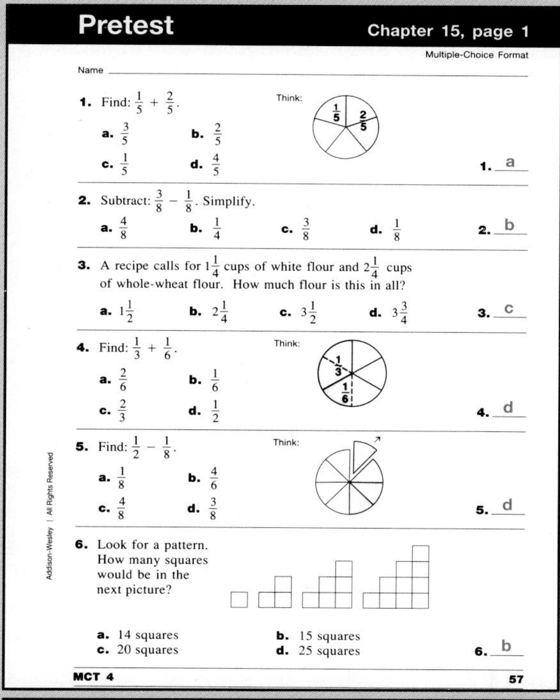

Pretest Chapter 15, page 1

Multiple-Choice Format

Name ______

1. Find: $\frac{1}{5} + \frac{2}{5}$. Think:

a. $\frac{3}{5}$ **b.** $\frac{2}{5}$ **c.** $\frac{1}{5}$ **d.** $\frac{4}{5}$ **1.** a

2. Subtract: $\frac{3}{8} - \frac{1}{8}$. Simplify.

a. $\frac{4}{8}$ **b.** $\frac{1}{4}$ **c.** $\frac{3}{8}$ **d.** $\frac{1}{8}$ **2.** b

3. A recipe calls for $1\frac{1}{4}$ cups of white flour and $2\frac{1}{4}$ cups of whole-wheat flour. How much flour is this in all?

a. $1\frac{1}{2}$ **b.** $2\frac{1}{4}$ **c.** $3\frac{1}{2}$ **d.** $3\frac{3}{4}$ **3.** c

4. Find: $\frac{1}{3} + \frac{1}{6}$. Think:

a. $\frac{2}{6}$ **b.** $\frac{1}{6}$ **c.** $\frac{2}{3}$ **d.** $\frac{1}{2}$ **4.** d

5. Find: $\frac{1}{2} - \frac{1}{8}$. Think:

a. $\frac{1}{8}$ **b.** $\frac{4}{6}$ **c.** $\frac{4}{8}$ **d.** $\frac{3}{8}$ **5.** d

6. Look for a pattern. How many squares would be in the next picture?

a. 14 squares **b.** 15 squares **c.** 20 squares **d.** 25 squares **6.** b

MCT 4 57

Pretest Chapter 15, page 2

Multiple-Choice Format

Name ______

7. Find: 2.4 + 1.8. Think:

Trade

a. 3.2 **b.** 1.4 **c.** 1.6 **d.** 4.2 **7.** d

8. Add. 73.8 + 24.6

a. 9.84 **b.** 98.4 **c.** 97.4 **d.** 9.74 **8.** b

9. Find: 7.25 − 3.6.

a. 6.89 **b.** 7.61 **c.** 10.85 **d.** 3.65 **9.** d

10. Use rounding to estimate 28.42 + 13.92. Decide whether the actual sum will be over or under the reference point 50.

a. Over **b.** Under **10.** b

11. Use the flow chart. How many times do you have to add 1 before you stop?

START → Begin with 0. → Add 1. → Is the sum 4? Yes → STOP; No → Add 1.

a. 1 **b.** 2 **c.** 3 **d.** 4 **11.** d

12. Joy runs the 100-yard dash in 21.6 seconds. Mary runs it in 18.9 seconds. How many seconds faster does Mary run the hundred yards than Joy?

a. 17.3 sec **b.** 3.7 sec **c.** 2.7 sec **d.** 3.3 sec **12.** c

58 MCT 4

Posttest Chapter 15, page 1

Multiple-Choice Format

Name ______

1. Find: $\frac{2}{5} + \frac{2}{5}$. Think:

a. $\frac{1}{5}$ **b.** $\frac{3}{5}$ **c.** $\frac{4}{5}$ **d.** $\frac{2}{5}$ **1.** c

2. Subtract: $\frac{5}{6} - \frac{3}{6}$. Simplify.

a. $\frac{2}{3}$ **b.** $\frac{1}{6}$ **c.** $\frac{1}{2}$ **d.** $\frac{1}{3}$ **2.** d

3. A recipe calls for $2\frac{1}{8}$ cups of flour. Another recipe calls for $1\frac{1}{8}$ cups of flour. How much flour would you need to make both recipes?

a. $3\frac{3}{8}$ **b.** $3\frac{1}{4}$ **c.** $3\frac{1}{8}$ **d.** $3\frac{3}{4}$ **3.** b

4. Find: $\frac{1}{2} + \frac{3}{8}$. Think:

a. $\frac{4}{8}$ **b.** $\frac{7}{8}$ **c.** $\frac{1}{8}$ **d.** $\frac{6}{8}$ **4.** b

5. Find: $\frac{3}{8} - \frac{1}{4}$. Think:

a. $\frac{5}{8}$ **b.** $\frac{1}{4}$ **c.** $\frac{1}{8}$ **d.** $\frac{2}{8}$ **5.** c

6. Look for a pattern. How many squares would be in the next picture?

a. 14 squares **b.** 15 squares **c.** 20 squares **d.** 25 squares **6.** d

MCT 4 59

Posttest Chapter 15, page 2

Multiple-Choice Format

Name ______

7. Find: 3.5 + 1.7. Think:

Trade

a. 1.8 **b.** 4.2 **c.** 5.2 **d.** 2.2 **7.** c

8. Add. 42.7 + 13.9

a. 5.66 **b.** 55.6 **c.** 56.6 **d.** 5.56 **8.** c

9. Find: 9.35 − 5.9.

a. 3.45 **b.** 4.65 **c.** 15.25 **d.** 3.35 **9.** a

10. Use rounding to estimate 18.62 + 29.51. Decide whether the actual sum will be over or under the reference point 50.

a. Over **b.** Under **10.** b

11. Use the flow chart. How many times do you have to subtract 1 before you stop?

START → Begin with 4. → Subtract 1. → Is the difference 0? Yes → STOP; No → Subtract 1.

a. 1 **b.** 2 **c.** 3 **d.** 4 **11.** d

12. Melanie jogged 2.4 miles on Monday and 1.7 miles on Tuesday. How many miles did she jog in all?

a. 0.7 mi **b.** 3.1 mi **c.** 311 mi **d.** 4.1 mi **12.** d

60 MCT 4

ITEM ANALYSIS

Items	Objectives
1	15-1
2	15-2
3	15-3
4	15-4
5	15-5
6	15-6
7	15-7
8	15-8
9	15-9
10	15-10
11	15-11
12	15-12

Note: The item analysis is the same for all pretests and posttests for this chapter.

ALSO AVAILABLE

- Free Response Tests
- Alternative Tests
- Thinking Strategies
- Concrete Materials

Optional Chapter Activities

PROJECT AND BULLETIN BOARD

Prepare a bulletin board called ''What's Cooking With Fractions?'' Post some real recipes for foods most children enjoy, such as muffins, spaghetti, party punch, fruit salad, or pancakes. Include pictures of measuring cups and spoons, kitchen utensils, or pots and pans if possible. After students complete Lesson 15-3, have them bring in favorite family recipes written on index cards or on food-related shapes to add to the display. After Lesson 15-4, encourage students to use the data in the recipes to formulate problems that involve doubling or halving recipes, adding and subtracting fractions and mixed numbers, or other realistic situations that may arise in cooking.

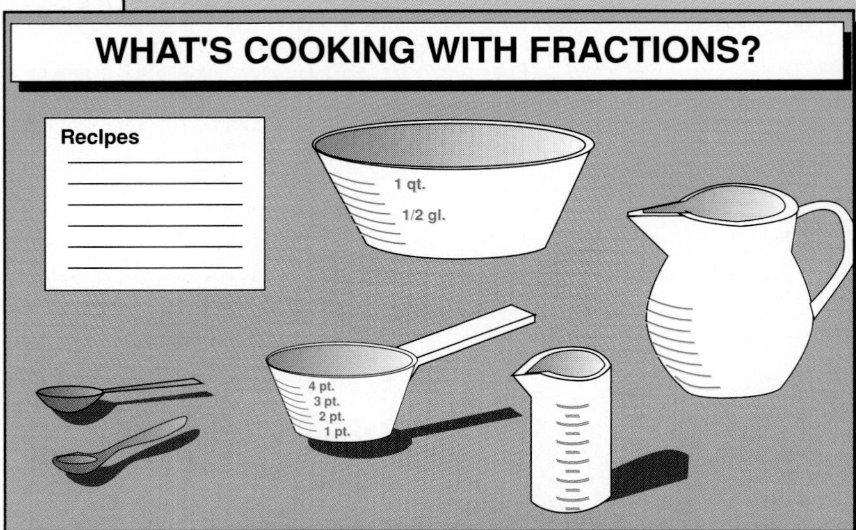

COOPERATIVE LEARNING

Divide the class into groups of three to five students. Identify the group skill: disagree in an agreeable way. Tell groups that gymnastics scores are usually expressed as decimals and are given in the categories of skill, strength, and style. Have groups role play being judges at a gymnastics meet. Each ''judge'' gives a score to an imaginary gymnast in each of the three categories, using decimal scores from a low of 1.0 to a high of 10.0. As they create reasons to justify the scores they give, encourage students to support their opinions clearly and calmly. After the judges discuss all three scores, they should decide how to find individual and group totals. You may allow students to use calculators to verify the results.

You will find grouping suggestions and cooperative learning activities in most lessons throughout this chapter.

LITERATURE

Hooks, William H. *The 17 Gerbils of Class 4A.* New York: Coward, McCann & Geoghegon, 1976.

Their fourth grade teacher has finally had it. All 17 gerbils must go by the end of the week. The difficulty is how to divide the gerbils equally among three friends. They finally do figure it out using fractions. The story lends itself to writing number sentences.

Dennis, Richard J. *Fractions are Parts of Things.* New York: Young Math Book Series, Thomas Y. Crowell, 1971.

Whitney, David C. *The Easy Book of Fractions.* New York: Franklin Watts, 1970.

ENGLISH AS A SECOND LANGUAGE

To help ESL students understand the need to find a common denominator, write $\frac{1}{2} + \frac{1}{4}$ on the chalkboard and ask them to say: "one half plus one quarter." Have students think about how to solve it. To provide a concrete example of how to find a common denominator, have students fold a paper in half and shade in one side. Ask what part of the paper is shaded. ($\frac{1}{2}$) Then have students fold the paper in half the opposite way to create four boxes. Have them count aloud the number of boxes and then write $\frac{1}{4}$ in each box as they say "one fourth" each time. Ask how many boxes of fourths are shaded. (2) This will help students see the equivalency of $\frac{1}{2}$ to $\frac{2}{4}$. Write $\frac{2}{4}$ under the $\frac{1}{2}$ in the example on the chalkboard to show the equivalency. Then ask students how much more still needs to be added. ($\frac{1}{4}$) Have them shade in another fourth on their paper and count aloud the total number of fourths shaded. ($\frac{3}{4}$) Have a volunteer write $= \frac{3}{4}$ to complete the equation on the chalkboard. Then have the class say: *One half plus one fourth equals three fourths.*

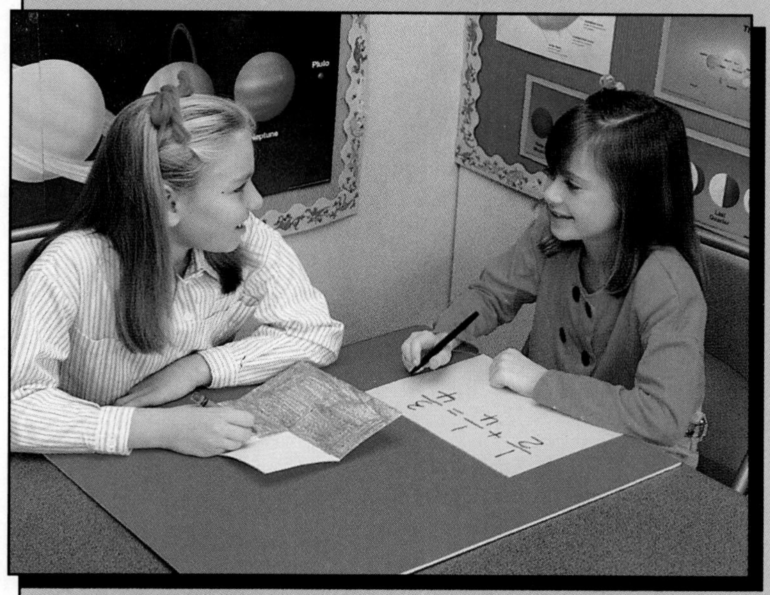

GIFTED

Group your students into pairs. Ask them to create eight index cards, numbering them from 2 to 9. One student begins this game by choosing two cards. These numbers will be the denominators for two fractions. Have the other student select another two cards. These numbers will be the numerators for the two fractions.

Set a specified time period, such as two minutes. Instruct each student to create fractions from the numbers chosen. Encourage students to create fractions that are different from their partner's fractions. Have each student add their fractions and then subtract the smaller fraction from the larger fraction. Remind them to find the least common denominator to do so. Each correct answer receives one point.

When time is up, instruct partners to exchange papers. Remind them that their two original fractions should be different from their partner's. Ask them to check each other's paper for accuracy. Then have them repeat the entire process, once again timing it. The partner with more points after a fixed number of turns wins the game.

STUDENTS AT RISK

The combination of skills and concepts required to add and subtract decimals or fractions may present a sizable challenge for students who have difficulty moving from a conceptual understanding to the written computation algorithms. These students may need to rely on visual and manipulative cues to help them make the transition successfully. Help students resist the inclination to add or subtract both the numerators and denominators. The use of fraction models may help many students. Others may need to verbalize the situation by translating the fraction into words, emphasizing the unit in the denominators as a constant. Some students may need to see 1 fifth + 3 fifths in written form. Others may work best with color-highlighted numerators.

$\frac{1}{5} + \frac{3}{5}$ → 1 fifth + 3 fifths = 4 fifths → $\frac{4}{5}$

$\frac{\boxed{1}}{5} + \frac{\boxed{3}}{5} = \frac{\boxed{4}}{5}$

You may also use the Reteaching Supplements and the specific Reteaching Tips from each lesson in this chapter.

CHAPTER 15

INTRODUCING THE CHAPTER

SUBJECT INTEGRATION The photograph of the volleyball game represents the chapter theme of health and fitness. Several lessons include situations involving sports that use balls to provide opportunities for students to add and subtract fractions and decimals.

USING DATA The Health and Fitness Data Bank on page 483 of the Student Edition provides 2 tables related to sport balls. "Official Weights of Sport Balls" gives maximum and minimum weights in grams of 5 kinds of sport balls. The other table gives comparative bounce heights in fractions of feet of various sport balls that have been dropped from a height of 6 ft.

QUESTION 1 ► **Explain the meaning of the two columns of data in the table called "Official Weights of Sport Balls."** (The first column tells the lowest possible weight an official ball for a sport may have; the second tells the greatest possible weight an official ball for the sport may have.)
Student Edition answer: 58 $\frac{5}{10}$, 58 $\frac{1}{2}$

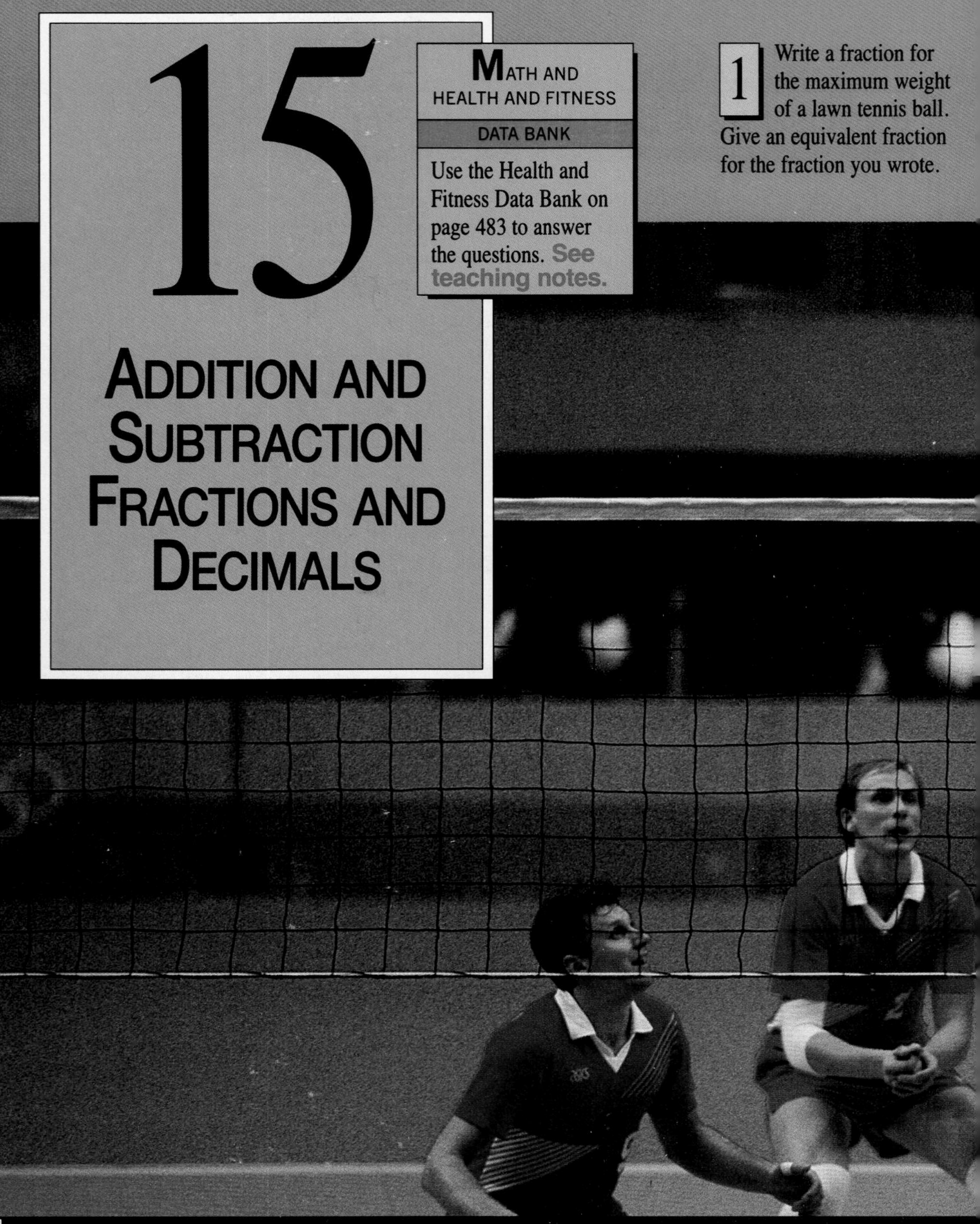

15

ADDITION AND SUBTRACTION FRACTIONS AND DECIMALS

MATH AND HEALTH AND FITNESS

DATA BANK

Use the Health and Fitness Data Bank on page 483 to answer the questions. See teaching notes.

1 Write a fraction for the maximum weight of a lawn tennis ball. Give an equivalent fraction for the fraction you wrote.

TEACHING OPTIONS

LANGUAGE DEVELOPMENT Write the words **maximum** and **minimum** on the chalkboard and have students discuss and compare their meanings. (Possible answer: Maximum and minimum describe greatest and least amounts.) Have students formulate sentences using maximum and minimum. (Samples: 6 is the maximum number of people our car can seat; I spend a minimum of 15 minutes a day walking my dog.)

2 Would a table tennis ball weighing 2.49 grams meet the official weight standard?

3 Which ball bounces higher when dropped from a height of 6 feet, a lawn tennis ball or a soccer ball?

4 **Use Critical Thinking** If a volleyball and a basketball bounced the same height, which was bounced with more force? Explain.

405

SUBJECT INTEGRATION PROJECT Brainstorm a list of as many different sport balls as possible, then challenge students to rank them in size order. During the time you spend on Chapter 15, have small groups collect data on as many varieties of sport balls as possible. Have them use metric tape measures to determine the circumference of each ball (distance around), then have them design a table or graph to display the data. Groups may conduct their own bounce experiments with the balls they collect to augment the Data Bank.

QUESTION 2 ► **Decide which sport balls permit the greatest and least weight range.** (softball; table tennis) ► **Identify a sport ball whose maximum and minimum weights are whole numbers.** (croquet)
Student Edition answer: yes

QUESTION 3 ► **Explain how you would compare mixed numbers to determine the higher bounce.** (Possible answers: Use number sense; find equivalent fractions with like denominators.)
Student Edition answer: lawn tennis ball

QUESTION 4 ► **Analyze the data about bounce heights to tell how to compare the bounces of two balls.** (A basketball bounces higher than a volleyball when dropped, so if both balls bounce the same height, the less bouncy ball must have been dropped with extra force to make it bounce higher than usual.)
Student Edition answer: volleyball; it naturally bounces less than a basketball so it would need more force to reach the same height as a basketball.

LESSON OPTIONS 15-1

Adding and Subtracting Fractions with Like Denominators:

OBJECTIVE 15-1 To use objects to develop an understanding of adding and subtracting fractions

PREBOOK ACTIVITIES

QUICK REVIEW

Choose the greater fraction.

1. $\frac{1}{3}$ or $\frac{1}{2}$ ($\frac{1}{2}$) **2.** $\frac{1}{6}$ or $\frac{1}{4}$ ($\frac{1}{4}$) **3.** $\frac{2}{5}$ or $\frac{4}{5}$ ($\frac{4}{5}$)
4. $\frac{7}{8}$ or $\frac{4}{8}$ ($\frac{7}{8}$) **5.** $\frac{1}{2}$ or $\frac{3}{4}$ ($\frac{3}{4}$) **6.** $\frac{2}{3}$ or $\frac{1}{2}$ ($\frac{2}{3}$)
7. $\frac{1}{3}$ or $\frac{4}{9}$ ($\frac{4}{9}$) **8.** $\frac{5}{6}$ or $\frac{9}{12}$ ($\frac{5}{6}$) **9.** $\frac{3}{5}$ or $\frac{9}{10}$ ($\frac{9}{10}$)

PRIOR KNOWLEDGE

Have students describe the meaning of fractions such as $\frac{1}{3}$, $\frac{2}{5}$, and $\frac{7}{8}$, using the appropriate mathematical language. (Possible answer: Fractions describe the division of a whole object or set of objects into equal parts. The denominator, or bottom number, tells how many parts in all; the numerator, or top number, refers to the number of parts to consider. $\frac{1}{3}$ means 1 out of 3 equal parts; $\frac{2}{5}$ means 2 out of 5 equal parts; $\frac{7}{8}$ means 7 out of 8 equal parts.) Tell students that in this lesson they will add and subtract fractions that have the same denominators.

COMMUNICATION

Discussing Math Write the phrase **like denominators** on the chalkboard and ask students to suggest possible meanings for it. (''denominators that are the same'') Have students relate the word *like* to a familiar word with a similar meaning. (*alike*) Explain that in the phrase *like denominators, like* is an adjective that describes denominators. Have students give examples of fractions with like denominators. (Answers will vary. Samples: $\frac{3}{5}$ and $\frac{1}{5}$, $\frac{3}{10}$ and $\frac{5}{10}$.)

EXPLORE AND CONNECT

Materials: TA 21 (Fraction Strips—Eighths), TA 3 (Number Cards 0-8, Operation Cards + and −)

Grouping Suggestion: cooperative learning pairs

Students explore adding and subtracting fractions with **like denominators**. Each pair needs 24 eighths. The goal is to fill 1 whole. The first partner draws a number card and an operation card. If the minus card is drawn, the player loses the turn. If + 5 is drawn, for example, the student takes 5 eighths and puts them together. On the same student's next turn, if − 3 is drawn, 3 of the 5 eighths are returned. If students collect more than 8 eighths, they put the extra aside. If their cards indicate that they must return more eighths than they have, they draw another card. Partners take turns until 1 player makes exactly 1 whole. Students relate their actions to adding and subtracting fractions with **like denominators.** (You add or subtract just as you would any like objects.)

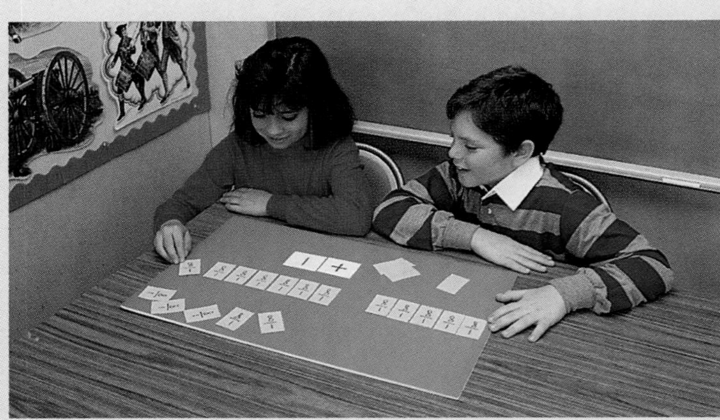

CONNECTIONS Use these anytime.

Problem of the Day

Fraction Doubles Substitute pairs of like fractions to make true statements. HINT: All answers are in lowest terms.

1. ☆ + ☆ = $\frac{1}{2}$ 3. ⬠ + ⬠ = $\frac{1}{4}$
2. △ + △ = $\frac{1}{3}$ 4. ☽ + ☽ = $\frac{1}{5}$

(Possible answers: **1.** $\frac{1}{4}$ **2.** $\frac{1}{8}$ **3.** $\frac{1}{6}$ **4.** $\frac{1}{10}$)

Number Sense

Mental Math Find the missing addends or sums. Change all *sums* only to whole numbers or to lowest-terms fractions.

1. $\frac{4}{7} + \square = \frac{6}{7}$ ($\frac{2}{7}$)
2. $\frac{3}{5} + \frac{2}{5} = \square$ ($\frac{5}{5}$ or 1)
3. $\square + \frac{3}{10} = \frac{7}{10}$ ($\frac{4}{10}$)
4. $\frac{1}{6} + \frac{2}{6} = \square$ ($\frac{3}{6}$ or $\frac{1}{2}$)

Subject Integration

Fine Arts Darnell played a short musical phrase that had 2 eighth notes on C, 2 eighth notes on E, and 3 eighth notes on D. How many eighth notes did Darnell play in that musical phrase? (7)

Classwork and Homework Supplements

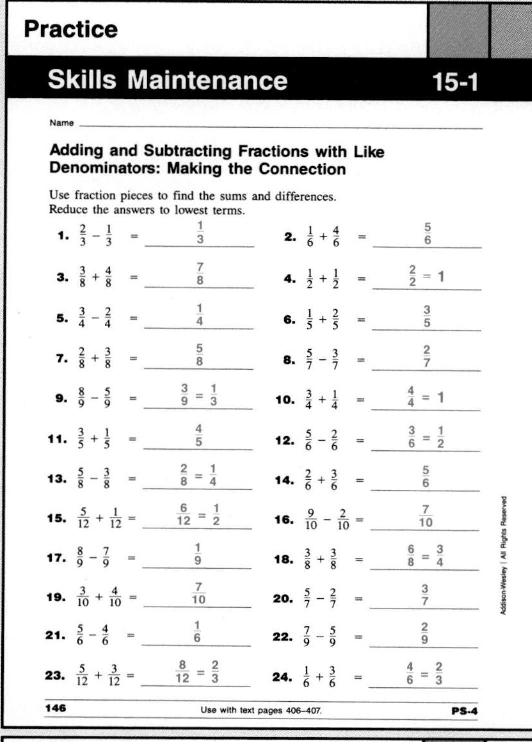

Practice

Skills Maintenance 15-1

Name ______

Adding and Subtracting Fractions with Like Denominators: Making the Connection

Use fraction pieces to find the sums and differences. Reduce the answers to lowest terms.

1. $\frac{2}{3} - \frac{1}{3} = \frac{1}{3}$
2. $\frac{1}{6} + \frac{4}{6} = \frac{5}{6}$
3. $\frac{3}{8} + \frac{4}{8} = \frac{7}{8}$
4. $\frac{1}{2} + \frac{1}{2} = \frac{2}{2} = 1$
5. $\frac{3}{4} - \frac{2}{4} = \frac{1}{4}$
6. $\frac{1}{5} + \frac{2}{5} = \frac{3}{5}$
7. $\frac{2}{8} + \frac{3}{8} = \frac{5}{8}$
8. $\frac{5}{7} - \frac{3}{7} = \frac{2}{7}$
9. $\frac{8}{9} - \frac{5}{9} = \frac{3}{9} = \frac{1}{3}$
10. $\frac{3}{4} + \frac{1}{4} = \frac{4}{4} = 1$
11. $\frac{3}{5} + \frac{1}{5} = \frac{4}{5}$
12. $\frac{5}{6} - \frac{2}{6} = \frac{3}{6} = \frac{1}{2}$
13. $\frac{5}{8} - \frac{3}{8} = \frac{2}{8} = \frac{1}{4}$
14. $\frac{2}{6} + \frac{3}{6} = \frac{5}{6}$
15. $\frac{5}{12} + \frac{1}{12} = \frac{6}{12} = \frac{1}{2}$
16. $\frac{9}{10} - \frac{2}{10} = \frac{7}{10}$
17. $\frac{8}{9} - \frac{7}{9} = \frac{1}{9}$
18. $\frac{3}{8} + \frac{3}{8} = \frac{6}{8} = \frac{3}{4}$
19. $\frac{3}{10} + \frac{4}{10} = \frac{7}{10}$
20. $\frac{5}{7} - \frac{2}{7} = \frac{3}{7}$
21. $\frac{5}{6} - \frac{4}{6} = \frac{1}{6}$
22. $\frac{7}{9} - \frac{5}{9} = \frac{2}{9}$
23. $\frac{5}{12} + \frac{3}{12} = \frac{8}{12} = \frac{2}{3}$
24. $\frac{1}{6} + \frac{3}{6} = \frac{4}{6} = \frac{2}{3}$

146 Use with text pages 406-407. PS-4

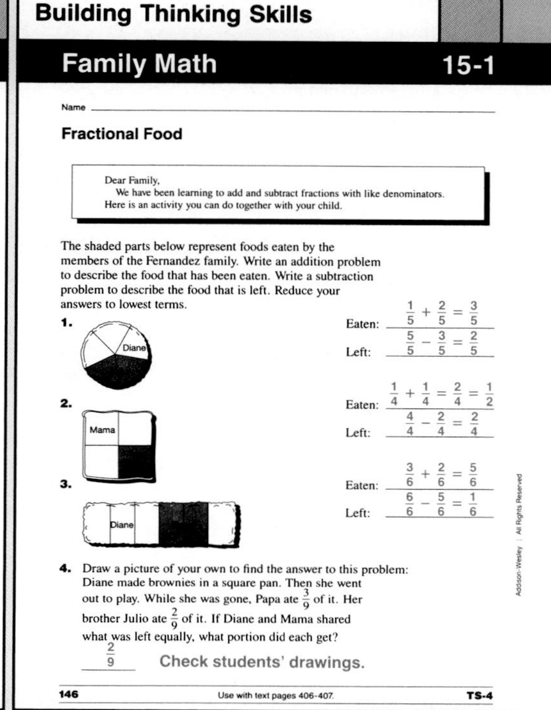

Building Thinking Skills

Family Math 15-1

Name ______

Fractional Food

Dear Family,
We have been learning to add and subtract fractions with like denominators. Here is an activity you can do together with your child.

The shaded parts below represent foods eaten by the members of the Fernandez family. Write an addition problem to describe the food that has been eaten. Write a subtraction problem to describe the food that is left. Reduce your answers to lowest terms.

Diane
Mama
Diane

1. Eaten: $\frac{1}{5} + \frac{2}{5} = \frac{3}{5}$ Left: $\frac{5}{5} - \frac{3}{5} = \frac{2}{5}$
2. Eaten: $\frac{1}{4} + \frac{1}{4} = \frac{2}{4} = \frac{1}{2}$ Left: $\frac{4}{4} - \frac{2}{4} = \frac{2}{4}$
3. Eaten: $\frac{3}{6} + \frac{2}{6} = \frac{5}{6}$ Left: $\frac{6}{6} - \frac{5}{6} = \frac{1}{6}$
4. Draw a picture of your own to find the answer to this problem: Diane made brownies in a square pan. Then she went out to play. While she was gone, Papa ate $\frac{3}{9}$ of it. Her brother Julio ate $\frac{2}{9}$ of it. If Diane and Mama shared what was left equally, what portion did each get?
$\frac{2}{9}$ Check students' drawings.

146 Use with text pages 406-407. TS-4

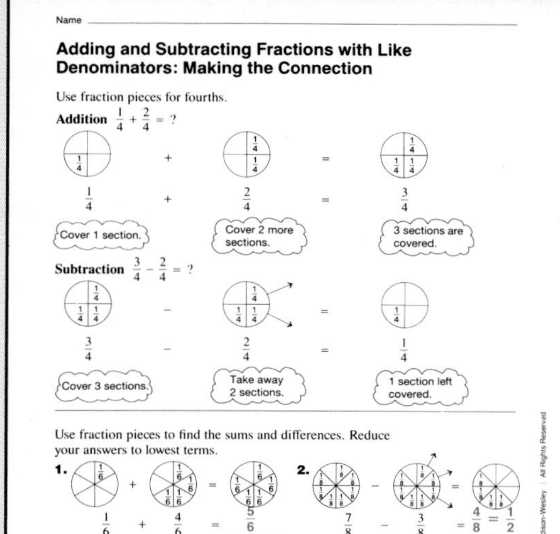

Reteaching

Manipulatives 15-1

Name ______

Adding and Subtracting Fractions with Like Denominators: Making the Connection

Use fraction pieces for fourths.

Addition $\frac{1}{4} + \frac{2}{4} = ?$

$\frac{1}{4} + \frac{2}{4} = \frac{3}{4}$

Cover 1 section.
Cover 2 more sections.
3 sections are covered.

Subtraction $\frac{3}{4} - \frac{2}{4} = ?$

$\frac{3}{4} - \frac{2}{4} = \frac{1}{4}$

Cover 3 sections.
Take away 2 sections.
1 section left covered.

Use fraction pieces to find the sums and differences. Reduce your answers to lowest terms.

1. $\frac{1}{6} + \frac{4}{6} = \frac{5}{6}$
2. $\frac{7}{8} - \frac{3}{8} = \frac{4}{8} = \frac{1}{2}$
3. $\frac{2}{5} + \frac{1}{5} = \frac{3}{5}$
4. $\frac{6}{7} - \frac{4}{7} = \frac{2}{7}$
5. $\frac{2}{6} + \frac{2}{6} = \frac{4}{6} = \frac{2}{3}$
6. $\frac{2}{3} - \frac{1}{3} = \frac{1}{3}$
7. $\frac{1}{4} + \frac{1}{4} = \frac{2}{4} = \frac{1}{2}$
8. $\frac{4}{5} - \frac{2}{5} = \frac{2}{5}$

146 Use with text pages 406-407. RS-4

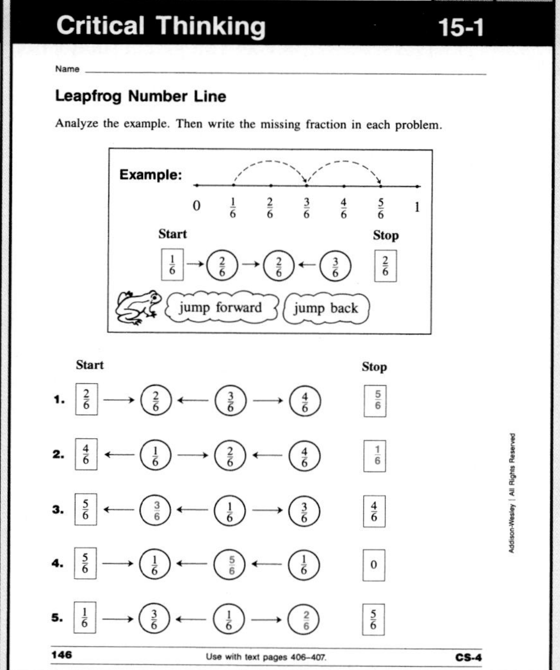

Challenges

Critical Thinking 15-1

Name ______

Leapfrog Number Line

Analyze the example. Then write the missing fraction in each problem.

Example: 0, $\frac{1}{6}$, $\frac{2}{6}$, $\frac{3}{6}$, $\frac{4}{6}$, $\frac{5}{6}$, 1

Start $\frac{1}{6}$ → $\frac{2}{6}$ → $\frac{2}{6}$ ← $\frac{3}{6}$ Stop $\frac{2}{6}$

jump forward
jump back

	Start				Stop
1.	$\frac{2}{6}$ →	$\frac{2}{6}$ ←	$\frac{3}{6}$ →	$\frac{4}{6}$	$\frac{5}{6}$
2.	$\frac{4}{6}$ ←	$\frac{1}{6}$ →	$\frac{2}{6}$ ←	$\frac{4}{6}$	$\frac{1}{6}$
3.	$\frac{5}{6}$ ←	$\frac{3}{6}$ ←	$\frac{1}{6}$ →	$\frac{3}{6}$	$\frac{4}{6}$
4.	$\frac{5}{6}$ →	$\frac{1}{6}$ ←	$\frac{5}{6}$ ←	$\frac{1}{6}$	0
5.	$\frac{1}{6}$ →	$\frac{3}{6}$ ←	$\frac{1}{6}$ →	$\frac{2}{6}$	$\frac{5}{6}$

146 Use with text pages 406-407. CS-4

Options for Individual Needs

Basic

Exercises 1-5
Skills Bank, pp. 466, 467

Supplements
Reteaching 146 or
Practice 146

Average

Exercises 1-5
Skills Bank, pp. 466, 467

Supplements
Practice 146
Challenges 146 or
Thinking Skills 146

Extended

Exercises 1-5

Supplements
Challenges 146
Thinking Skills 146

Other Resources:
Problem-Solving Experiences in Mathematics, Grade 4, Problems 96, 97
Mathematics, Book A, Teachers' Edition, pp. 70, 71
Mathematics, A Way of Thinking, Lessons 11-2, 11-4
Using the Math Explorer Calculator: A Sourcebook for Teachers, Chapter 14

15-1

LESSON PLAN 15-1

OBJECTIVE 15-1
To use objects to develop an understanding of adding and subtracting fractions with like denominators

Materials: fraction pieces

Alternative Materials: TA 21 (Fraction Strips)

Grouping Suggestions: small groups, pairs

1. MOTIVATE AND TEACH

LEARN ABOUT IT

EXPLORE ▶ **How are the fractions alike? Explain.** (same denominators; Both show some part of 8 total parts.)
▶ **Explain how covering sections relates to adding.** (You put together fraction pieces to cover sections, which is the addition action.)
▶ **Link the number of pieces needed to cover both sections to a fraction for the sum. Explain its meaning.** ($\frac{5}{8}$; 5 pieces, each is $\frac{1}{8}$)

TALK ABOUT IT ▶ **Explain how the numerators relate to your actions.** (Numerators tell how many pieces cover each section and how many are used in all.)
▶ **What rule could you use to add fractions with like denominators?** (Add numerators; use the same denominator of the addends.)
▶ **Use logical reasoning to explain how to subtract fractions with like denominators.** (Subtract numerators, then use the same denominator.)
Student Edition answers: **1-2.** Answers will vary.

2. CHECK UNDERSTANDING

TRY IT OUT

ERROR ALERT Failing to reduce answers to lowest terms. Adding or subtracting denominators.

Adding and Subtracting Fractions with Like Denominators
Making the Connection

LEARN ABOUT IT

EXPLORE Use Fraction Pieces
Work in groups. Use fraction pieces for eighths.

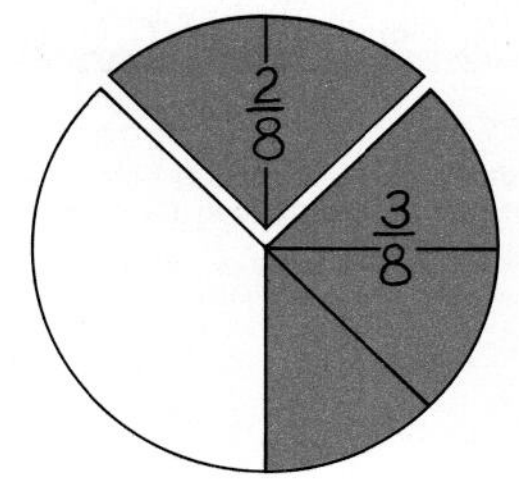

- Put some eighth pieces on the whole to cover one section. Record the number of eighths you use in a table like the one shown. Do the same thing again to cover another section.

1st section cover	2nd section cover	Number of pieces needed to cover both sections
$\frac{2}{8}$	$\frac{3}{8}$	$\frac{5}{8}$

- Try this process again with different eighths pieces. Then try it using sixth fraction pieces.

TALK ABOUT IT See teaching notes.

1. Look at one row of your table. Can you give an addition equation for that row?
2. Cover two sections of the whole. Now take the pieces from one of the sections. Can you give a subtraction equation that records this? Start over and take the pieces from the other section. Can you give another subtraction equation that records this?

406

TEACHING OPTIONS

RETEACHING TIPS Have students use fraction pieces to represent fractions, such as $\frac{2}{6}$. Then have them find a single fraction piece that is equivalent. Ask them to write the resulting equation. ($\frac{2}{6} = \frac{1}{3}$) Repeat with other fractions. Assign Reteaching Supplement 146.

ENRICHMENT Have students use fraction pieces to add or subtract mixed numbers with like denominators.
1. $1\frac{3}{5} + 1\frac{1}{5}$ ($2\frac{4}{5}$)
2. $1\frac{1}{4} + 1\frac{1}{4}$ ($2\frac{1}{2}$)
3. $3\frac{7}{8} - 1\frac{3}{8}$ ($2\frac{1}{2}$)
4. $2\frac{11}{12} - 2\frac{7}{12}$ ($\frac{1}{3}$)

You have put fraction pieces together and taken them away to understand how to add or subtract fractions. Now you will see a way to record what you have done. This process can help you find sums and differences in problems such as $\frac{2}{8} + \frac{3}{8}$ and $\frac{5}{8} - \frac{3}{8}$.

What You Do | **What You Record**

Addition

1. Cover two sections of the whole.

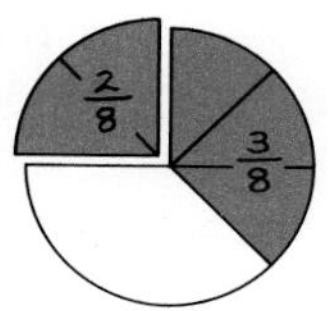

$\frac{2}{8} + \frac{3}{8}$

2. Count the number of eighths in all.

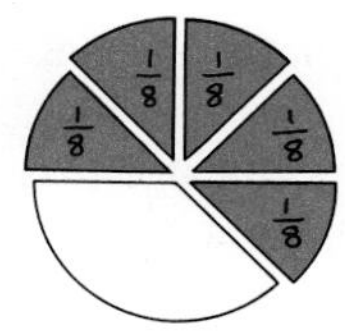

$\frac{2}{8} + \frac{3}{8} = \frac{5}{8}$

Subtraction

1. Cover two sections of the whole. Choose a section to take away.

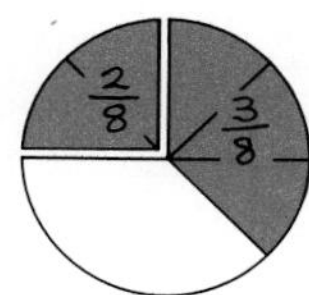

$\frac{5}{8} - \frac{3}{8}$

2. Show how many eighths are left.

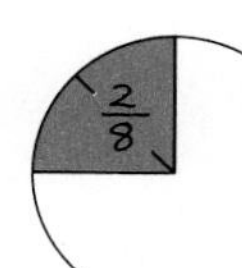

$\frac{5}{8} - \frac{3}{8} = \frac{2}{8}$

TRY IT OUT

Use fraction pieces to find the sums and differences. Reduce the answers to lowest terms.

1. $\frac{5}{8} + \frac{2}{8}$ $\frac{7}{8}$ **2.** $\frac{5}{6} - \frac{3}{6}$ $\frac{1}{3}$ **3.** $\frac{3}{4} - \frac{1}{4}$ $\frac{1}{2}$ **4.** $\frac{1}{5} + \frac{3}{5}$ $\frac{4}{5}$ **5.** $\frac{1}{3} + \frac{2}{3}$ 1

407

for pages 406-407

3. Practice and Apply

Basic	1-5
Average	1-5
Extended	1-5

PRACTICE

Examine the addition and subtraction examples on page 407. Explain the connection between What You Do and What You Record. ($\frac{2}{8}$ covering one section plus $\frac{3}{8}$ covering the other section gives $\frac{5}{8}$ in all; $\frac{5}{8}$ covering both sections minus $\frac{3}{8}$ taken away leaves $\frac{2}{8}$ of the whole.)
Continue working in small groups to complete the Try It Out exercises, using fraction pieces or fraction strips. Compare sums and differences to see that they are expressed in lowest terms.

15-1

Close and Assess

WRITE WHAT YOU KNOW

Have students list the steps they would use to add $\frac{4}{10}$ and $\frac{3}{10}$ with fraction pieces and the steps they would use to find the difference of those fractions. Then ask students to trade papers with a classmate. Pairs follow each other's steps to verify that the steps make sense.

QUICK QUIZ

Use fraction pieces to find the sum or difference. Give answers in lowest terms.

1. $\frac{7}{8} - \frac{3}{8}$ ($\frac{1}{2}$)
2. $\frac{1}{6} + \frac{5}{6}$ (1)

LESSON OPTIONS 15-2

Adding and Subtracting Fractions: Like Denominators

OBJECTIVE 15-2 To add and subtract fractions with like denominators

PREBOOK ACTIVITIES

QUICK REVIEW

Simplify and reduce each fraction to lowest terms.

1. $\frac{5}{10}$ $(\frac{1}{2})$	**2.** $\frac{8}{12}$ $(\frac{2}{3})$	**3.** $\frac{12}{16}$ $(\frac{3}{4})$
4. $\frac{13}{10}$ $(1\frac{3}{10})$	**5.** $\frac{11}{8}$ $(1\ \frac{3}{8})$	**6.** $\frac{14}{28}$ $(\frac{1}{2})$
7. $\frac{12}{8}$ $(1\frac{1}{2})$	**8.** $\frac{6}{9}$ $(\frac{2}{3})$	**9.** $\frac{12}{9}$ $(1\ \frac{1}{3})$

PRIOR KNOWLEDGE

Have students suggest real-life situations in which fractional amounts might be added or subtracted. (Possible answers: adding fractional weights of grocery items or fractions of a mile; subtracting fractions of an hour or fractions of an inch) Tell students that in this lesson they will add or subtract fractions and mixed numbers that have like denominators.

COMMUNICATION

Discussing and Writing Math Write *simplify* on the chalkboard and ask students to identify the root of the word. (*simple*) In their Math Journals, have students write an explanation of what it means to simplify a fraction. (Reduce it to lowest terms to make it easier to understand.) Have them write a distinction between simplifying an improper fraction, such as $\frac{13}{10}$, and simplifying a fraction less than 1, such as $\frac{8}{10}$. (To simplify $\frac{13}{10}$, first change it to a mixed number and fraction, then reduce the fraction part, if possible; improper fractions often require 2 steps to simplify, but you can often simplify a proper fraction in one step.)

EXPLORE AND CONNECT

Materials: TA 21 (Fraction Strips), TA 2 (Number Cubes numbered 1-6), TA 3 (Number Cards 1-12, Operation Cards, + and −)

Grouping Suggestion: cooperative learning groups of 4

Students explore adding and subtracting fractions and reducing answers to lowest terms. One student picks a number card as a denominator and an operation card for the group. Another student rolls the number cube twice to see how many pieces of that denominator to add or subtract. A third student models the problem as a fourth student records it. The group members check the problem for accuracy and discuss whether the answer can be simplified. Groups do the activity 4 times, trading tasks and using a different denominator each time to create 2 addition and 2 subtraction problems. Have groups summarize their actions and their methods for checking that answers were in simplest form. (Answers will vary.)

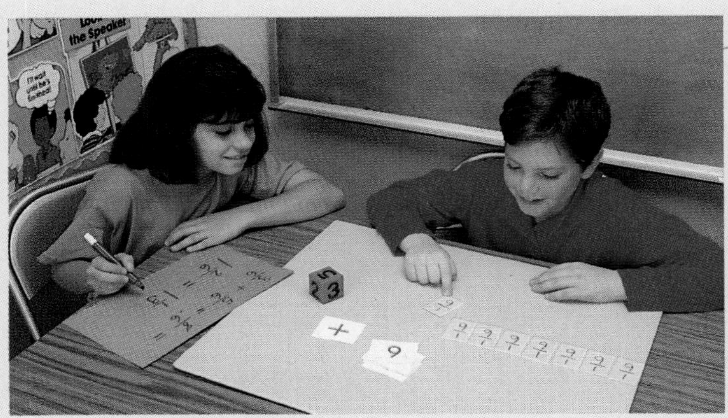

CONNECTIONS Use these anytime.

Problem of the Day

Visual Problem Solving Visualize fraction models and use number sense to explain how you could subtract $\frac{3}{8}$ from 1 whole. (Possible answer: Think of 1 whole as $\frac{8}{8}$, then take away $\frac{3}{8}$, which leaves $\frac{5}{8}$.)

Math Connection

Calculator Find a way to add $\frac{3}{4} + \frac{3}{4}$ on a calculator that cannot work with fractions. (Possible answer: Add the decimal equivalents 0.75 + 0.75 = 1.5; change 1.5 to the equivalent fraction $1\frac{1}{2}$.)

Number Sense

Reasoning Determine which sum is closer to 1 and explain your reasoning: $\frac{4}{11} + \frac{6}{11}$ or $\frac{10}{20} + \frac{9}{20}$. ($\frac{19}{20}$; each sum is one fractional unit less than 1, but since $\frac{1}{20}$ is a smaller piece than $\frac{1}{11}$, $\frac{19}{20}$ is closer to 1 than $\frac{10}{11}$.)

Classwork and Homework Supplements

Practice

Skills Maintenance 15-2

Name

Adding and Subtracting Fractions: Like Denominators

Find these sums and differences. Simplify.

1. $\frac{5}{9} + \frac{2}{9} = \frac{7}{9}$
2. $\frac{7}{8} - \frac{3}{8} = \frac{4}{8} = \frac{1}{2}$
3. $\frac{5}{7} - \frac{4}{7} = \frac{1}{7}$
4. $\frac{3}{5} + \frac{1}{5} = \frac{4}{5}$
5. $\frac{4}{6} + \frac{5}{6} = \frac{9}{6} = 1\frac{1}{2}$
6. $\frac{8}{9} - \frac{5}{9} = \frac{3}{9} = \frac{1}{3}$
7. $\frac{5}{8} - \frac{3}{8} = \frac{2}{8} = \frac{1}{4}$
8. $\frac{3}{4} + \frac{3}{4} = \frac{6}{4} = 1\frac{1}{2}$
9. $\frac{2}{3} - \frac{1}{3} = \frac{1}{3}$
10. $\frac{3}{5} + \frac{4}{5} = \frac{7}{5} = 1\frac{2}{5}$
11. $2\frac{1}{4} + 1\frac{1}{4} = 3\frac{2}{4} = 3\frac{1}{2}$
12. $\frac{6}{10} - \frac{5}{10} = \frac{1}{10}$
13. $7\frac{3}{4} - 4\frac{1}{4} = 3\frac{2}{4} = 3\frac{1}{2}$
14. $\frac{1}{5} + \frac{2}{5} = \frac{3}{5}$
15. $9\frac{2}{3} - 6\frac{1}{3} = 3\frac{1}{3}$
16. $\frac{7}{10} - \frac{3}{10} = \frac{4}{10} = \frac{2}{5}$
17. $1\frac{1}{2} + 3\frac{1}{2} = 4\frac{2}{2} = 5$
18. $6\frac{2}{3} + 3\frac{2}{3} = 9\frac{4}{3} = 10\frac{1}{3}$
19. $4\frac{4}{5} - 3\frac{1}{5} = 1\frac{3}{5}$
20. $3\frac{1}{4} + 4\frac{1}{4} = 7\frac{2}{4} = 7\frac{1}{2}$
21. $\frac{2}{5} + \frac{2}{5} = \frac{4}{5}$
22. $4\frac{9}{10} - 3\frac{3}{10} = 1\frac{6}{10} = 1\frac{3}{5}$

PS-4 Use with text pages 408-409. 147

Building Thinking Skills

Data Analysis 15-2

Name

Around Town

Study the map. The distance between dots on the map is $\frac{1}{10}$ of a kilometer. Add or subtract to find the distances. Reduce your answers to lowest terms.

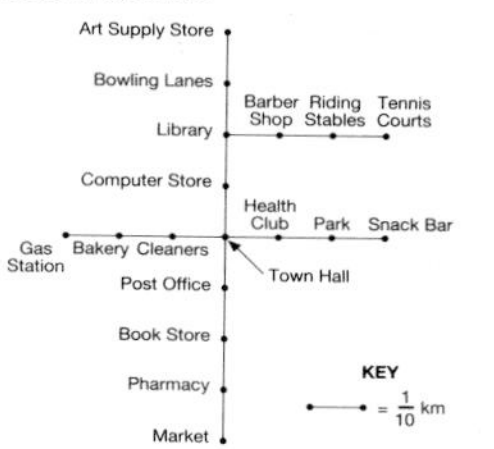

1. How far is it from the Post Office to the Snack Bar? $\frac{2}{5}$ km
2. How far is it from the Health Club to the Cleaners and then to the Tennis Courts? $\frac{4}{5}$ km
3. How far is it from the Riding Stables to the Bookstore and then to the Bakery? 1 km
4. How much closer is the Art Supply Store to the Computer Store than is the Gas Station to the Computer Store? $\frac{1}{10}$ km
5. How much closer is the Barber Shop to the Bowling Lanes than it is to the Park? $\frac{3}{10}$ km
6. How much closer is the Cleaners to the Town Hall than is the Pharmacy to the Town Hall? $\frac{1}{5}$ km

TS-4 Use with text pages 408-409. 147

Reteaching

Skills Review 15-2

Name

Adding and Subtracting Fractions: Like Denominators

Look at the denominators. → Add or subtract the numerators. → Write the sum or difference over the denominator. Simplify.

$\frac{8}{9} + \frac{5}{9}$ (The denominators are alike.) $8 + 5 = 13$ $\frac{8}{9} + \frac{5}{9} = \frac{13}{9} = 1\frac{4}{9}$

$\frac{3}{4} - \frac{1}{4}$ $3 - 1 = 2$ $\frac{3}{4} - \frac{1}{4} = \frac{2}{4} = \frac{1}{2}$

To add mixed numbers

$4\frac{2}{8} + 3\frac{1}{8} = ?$ (First add the whole numbers. $4 + 3 = 7$ Then add the fractions. $\frac{2}{8} + \frac{1}{8} = \frac{3}{8}$)

$4\frac{2}{8} + 3\frac{1}{8} = 7\frac{3}{8}$

Find these sums and differences. Simplify.

1. $\frac{2}{5} + \frac{1}{5} = \frac{3}{5}$ (2 + 1)
2. $\frac{5}{7} - \frac{2}{7} = \frac{3}{7}$ (5 − 2)
3. $\frac{7}{8} - \frac{5}{8} = \frac{2}{8} = \frac{1}{4}$
4. $\frac{1}{6} + \frac{3}{6} = \frac{4}{6} = \frac{2}{3}$
5. $1\frac{2}{10} + 4\frac{5}{10} = 5\frac{7}{10}$
6. $2\frac{1}{8} + 1\frac{5}{8} = 3\frac{6}{8} = 3\frac{3}{4}$
7. $5\frac{5}{6} - 3\frac{4}{6} = 2\frac{1}{6}$
8. $3\frac{8}{10} - 2\frac{3}{10} = 1\frac{5}{10} = 1\frac{1}{2}$
9. $\frac{4}{5} + \frac{2}{5} = \frac{6}{5} = 1\frac{1}{5}$
10. $1\frac{2}{3} + 3\frac{1}{3} = 4\frac{3}{3} = 5$
11. $\frac{5}{6} - \frac{2}{6} = \frac{3}{6} = \frac{1}{2}$
12. Add $\frac{4}{9}$ and $\frac{7}{9}$. $\frac{11}{9} = 1\frac{2}{9}$
13. Find the difference of $\frac{6}{7}$ and $\frac{2}{7}$. $\frac{4}{7}$

RS-4 Use with text pages 408-409. 147

Challenges

Mental Math 15-2

Name

Volcano Fractions

Write the missing fraction or mixed number in each problem. Then use your answer to solve the volcano puzzles below.

1. $\frac{3}{4} - \frac{2}{4} = \frac{1}{4}$ (C)
2. $\frac{7}{8} - \frac{2}{8} = \frac{5}{8}$ (G)
3. $\frac{3}{10} + \frac{4}{10} = \frac{7}{10}$ (A)
4. $\frac{2}{6} + \frac{3}{6} = \frac{5}{6}$ (M)
5. $\frac{5}{7} - \frac{1}{7} = \frac{4}{7}$ (R)
6. $\frac{4}{9} - \frac{2}{9} = \frac{2}{9}$ (O)
7. $1\frac{1}{8} + \frac{6}{8} = 1\frac{7}{8}$ (E)
8. $3\frac{5}{7} - 2\frac{2}{7} = 1\frac{3}{7}$ (N)
9. $2\frac{5}{11} + 1\frac{2}{11} = 3\frac{7}{11}$ (L)
10. $3\frac{5}{12} + 2\frac{2}{12} = 5\frac{7}{12}$ (U)

What is the world's largest active volcano?

M	A	U	N	A		L	O	A
$\frac{2}{6}$	$\frac{4}{10}$	$3\frac{5}{12}$	$3\frac{5}{7}$	$\frac{4}{10}$		$1\frac{2}{11}$	$\frac{4}{9}$	$\frac{4}{10}$

What is the world's highest extinct volcano?

C	E	R	R	O
$\frac{2}{4}$	$\frac{6}{8}$	$\frac{5}{7}$	$\frac{5}{7}$	$\frac{4}{9}$

A	C	O	N	C	A	G	U	A
$\frac{4}{10}$	$\frac{2}{4}$	$\frac{4}{9}$	$3\frac{5}{7}$	$\frac{2}{4}$	$\frac{4}{10}$	$\frac{2}{8}$	$3\frac{5}{12}$	$\frac{4}{10}$

CS-4 Use with text pages 408-409. 147

Options for Individual Needs

Basic

Exercises 1-6; 11-25
Data Bank, p. 483
Skills Bank, pp. 466, 467
Calculator Bank, p. 491
Computer Bank, p. 497
More Practice, p. 510, set A

Supplements
Reteaching 147 or
Practice 147
Challenges 147

Average

Exercises 1-26
Data Bank, p. 483
Skills Bank, pp. 466, 467
Calculator Bank, p. 491
Computer Bank, p. 497
More Practice, p. 510, set A

Supplements
Practice 147
Challenges 147 or
Thinking Skills 147

Extended

Exercises 3-26
Data Bank, p. 483
Calculator Bank, p. 491
Computer Bank, p. 497

Supplements
Challenges 147
Thinking Skills 147

Other Resources:
Problem-Solving Experiences in Mathematics, Grade 4, Problem 98
Mathematics, Book A, Teacher's Edition, pp 71-73
Mathematics, A Way of Thinking, Lessons 11-11, 11-12
Using the Math Explorer Calculator: A Sourcebook for Teachers, Chapter 14

15-2

LESSON PLAN 15-2

OBJECTIVE 15-2
To add and subtract fractions with like denominators

> **Materials:** fraction pieces
>
> **Alternative Materials:** TA 21 (Fraction Strips)

1. MOTIVATE AND TEACH

LEARN ABOUT IT

▶ **Summarize the purpose of the map.** (It shows the distances between locations at a volleyball camp).
▶ **Explain how the fractions are related.** (All are given in tenths.)
▶ **Visualize fraction pieces to justify why you do not add or subtract denominators.** (Possible answer: The denominator names the total number of pieces, which does not change; the numerators change.)

TALK ABOUT IT ▶ **How many tenths do you need to show the addition with fraction pieces? Explain why.** (15, because 7 tenths plus 8 tenths equals 15 tenths.)
▶ **Compare that to 1 whole.** (It is 5 more tenths than 1 whole.)
Student Edition answers: **1.** Possible answer: Each addend is more than 5 tenths, so the sum must be greater than $\frac{10}{10}$. **2.** Jorie jogged $1\frac{1}{2}$ mi from the cabins, past the swimming pool, and to the courts. The distance from the cabins to the pool is $\frac{1}{5}$ mi farther than that from the cabins to the dining hall.

2. CHECK UNDERSTANDING

TRY IT OUT

ERROR ALERT Adding or subtracting denominators. Failing to simplify answers.

Adding and Subtracting Fractions
Like Denominators

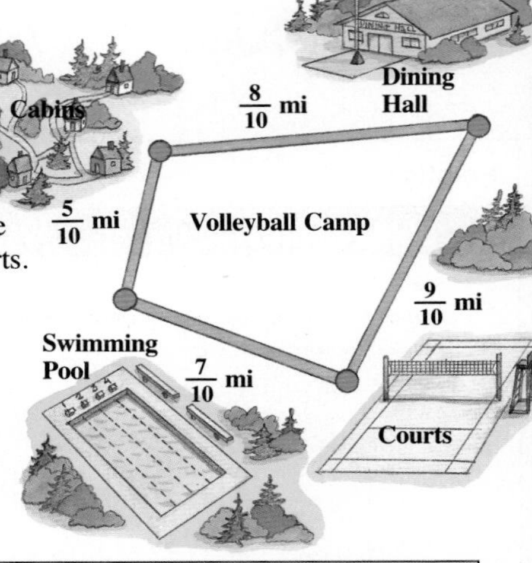

LEARN ABOUT IT

EXPLORE Think About the Process
At volleyball camp, Jorie jogged from the cabins past the swimming pool to the courts. How far is this? How much farther is it from the cabins to the dining hall than from the cabins to the swimming pool?

When two distances are combined, you add. To compare distances, you subtract.

Look at the denominators.	Add or subtract the numerators.	Write the sum or difference over the denominator. Simplify.
A $\frac{7}{10} + \frac{8}{10}$	$\frac{7}{10} + \frac{8}{10} = 15$	$\frac{7}{10} + \frac{8}{10} = \frac{15}{10} = 1\frac{5}{10} = 1\frac{1}{2}$
B $\frac{7}{10} - \frac{5}{10}$	$\frac{7}{10} - \frac{5}{10} = 2$	$\frac{7}{10} - \frac{5}{10} = \frac{2}{10} = \frac{1}{5}$

TALK ABOUT IT See teaching notes.

1. How could you estimate to decide if the sum in A is more than 1?
2. Use complete sentences to give reasonable answers to the story problem.

TRY IT OUT

Add or subtract. Reduce to lowest terms.

1. $\frac{2}{6} + \frac{3}{6}$ $\frac{5}{6}$ **2.** $\frac{5}{10} + \frac{6}{10}$ $1\frac{1}{10}$ **3.** $\frac{8}{9} - \frac{3}{9}$ $\frac{5}{9}$ **4.** $\frac{10}{12} - \frac{4}{12}$ $\frac{1}{2}$

TEACHING OPTIONS

RETEACHING TIPS Allow students to use models when they do the computations to reinforce that only the numerators are added or subtracted. Students should record each sum or difference with the like denominator, then simplify it if possible. Assign Reteaching Supplement 147.

COMPUTER Math Practice Level II, IBM Educational Systems, Copyright 1985 For all levels of students. In lessons 22 and 23, students practice solving addition and subtraction problems with like denominators, then simplify their answers. Each lesson takes 15 min.

PRACTICE

Find these sums and differences. Simplify.

1. $\frac{2}{4} - \frac{1}{4}$ $\frac{1}{4}$

2. $\frac{3}{8} + \frac{4}{8}$ $\frac{7}{8}$

3. $\frac{4}{7} - \frac{2}{7}$ $\frac{2}{7}$

4. $5\frac{4}{10} + 2\frac{5}{10}$ $7\frac{9}{10}$

5. $\frac{5}{8} + \frac{4}{8}$ $1\frac{1}{8}$

6. $\frac{2}{6} + \frac{5}{6} + \frac{3}{6}$ $1\frac{2}{3}$

7. $1\frac{3}{4} + 2\frac{1}{4}$ 4

8. $\frac{7}{8} - \frac{3}{8}$ $\frac{1}{2}$

9. Add $\frac{3}{5}$ and $\frac{4}{5}$. $1\frac{2}{5}$

10. Find the difference of $\frac{7}{9}$ and $\frac{2}{9}$. $\frac{5}{9}$

APPLY

MATH REASONING Which sum is greater? Use mental math.

11. (a) $\frac{3}{4} + \frac{1}{4}$ b $\frac{3}{10} + \frac{6}{10}$

12. a $\frac{1}{8} + \frac{3}{8}$ (b) $\frac{4}{12} + \frac{3}{12}$

Which difference is smaller? Use mental math.

13. a $\frac{5}{8} - \frac{1}{8}$ (b) $\frac{8}{10} - \frac{7}{10}$

14. a $\frac{7}{8} - \frac{3}{8}$ (b) $\frac{3}{4} - \frac{2}{4}$

PROBLEM SOLVING

15. Jeanette played volleyball for $2\frac{3}{4}$ hours before lunch. She played for $1\frac{3}{4}$ hour after lunch. How much longer did she play before lunch than after lunch? 1 hour

16. **Health and Fitness Data Bank** DATA BANK How much higher does a basketball bounce than a volley ball when dropped from a height of 6 ft? See page 483. $1\frac{1}{4}$ ft

MIXED REVIEW

Write the fraction that does not belong.

17. $\frac{1}{2}$ $\frac{2}{4}$ $\frac{1}{3}$ $\frac{1}{3}$

18. $\frac{4}{6}$ $\frac{6}{12}$ $\frac{2}{3}$ $\frac{6}{12}$

19. $\frac{4}{16}$ $\frac{4}{8}$ $\frac{1}{4}$ $\frac{4}{8}$

20. $\frac{5}{6}$ $\frac{3}{9}$ $\frac{1}{3}$ $\frac{5}{6}$

21. $\frac{4}{12}$ $\frac{8}{16}$ $\frac{2}{6}$ $\frac{8}{16}$

22. $\frac{1}{10}$ $\frac{2}{5}$ $\frac{8}{20}$ $\frac{1}{10}$

Write a decimal for the amount.

23. one and forty-four hundredths 1.44

24. thirty-five and two tenths 35.2

25. twenty and one hundredth 20.01

26. six and eight tenths 6.8

More Practice, page 510, set A

409

3. PRACTICE AND APPLY

Basic	1-6, 11-25
Average	1-26
Extended	3-26

PRACTICE

What must you remember to check in all the exercises? (that answers are in simplest form)

APPLY

MATH REASONING ► Explain how you can compare answers with unlike denominators. (Possible answer: Find equivalent fractions, then compare numerators.)

PROBLEM SOLVING ► Justify the operation to use to solve Problem 15. (Subtract to compare two amounts of time.)

MIXED REVIEW ► Explain how you would solve Exercises 17-22. (Look for a pair of equivalent fractions.) **► Explain how you know the number of decimal places to include in Exercises 23-26.** (Exercises with hundredths have 2 decimal places; those with tenths have 1.)

CLOSE AND ASSESS

SHOW WHAT YOU KNOW

Have students use fraction pieces to show the sum and difference of $\frac{5}{8}$ and $\frac{7}{8}$. Have them write an equation for each problem, give the sum or difference, then reduce answers to lowest terms if possible. (sum: $1\frac{1}{2}$; difference: $\frac{1}{4}$)

QUICK QUIZ

Find the sums or differences, then simplify.

1. $\frac{7}{8} - \frac{1}{8}$ ($\frac{3}{4}$)

2. $3\frac{2}{9} + 2\frac{4}{9}$ ($5\frac{2}{3}$)

3. $\frac{5}{12} + \frac{1}{12}$ ($\frac{1}{2}$)

15-2

LESSON OPTIONS 15-3

Problem Solving: Data from a Recipe

OBJECTIVE 15-3 To solve problems using data from a recipe

PREBOOK ACTIVITIES

QUICK REVIEW

Add or subtract. Reduce to lowest terms.

1. $\frac{3}{8} + \frac{5}{8}$ (1) **2.** $\frac{6}{7} - \frac{4}{7}$ ($\frac{2}{7}$)
3. $\frac{7}{12} + \frac{7}{12}$ ($1\frac{1}{6}$) **4.** $3\frac{3}{4} - 2\frac{1}{4}$ ($1\frac{1}{2}$)
5. $1\frac{5}{6} - 1\frac{1}{6}$ ($\frac{2}{3}$) **6.** $4\frac{1}{2} + 3\frac{1}{2}$ (8)

PRIOR KNOWLEDGE

Have students share experiences they may have had following a cooking recipe. (Answers will vary.) Ask them to give examples of fractions or mixed numbers a recipe might use to indicate amounts. (Possible answers: $\frac{1}{2}$ teaspoon, $\frac{3}{4}$ pound, $1\frac{1}{2}$ cups, $4\frac{1}{2}$ ounces)

COMMUNICATION

Reading and Writing Math Provide cookbooks or copies of recipes for students to use. Based on any chosen recipe, have students identify measurement amounts less than, equal to, and greater than 1 whole. Have students summarize their findings in their Math Journals by writing a list of the measurements that fit each category. (Answers will vary; check students' writing.)

EXPLORE AND CONNECT

COOPERATIVE ACTIVITY

Grouping Suggestion: small groups

A bread recipe calls for 1 $\frac{3}{4}$ cups wheat flour and 1 $\frac{1}{4}$ cups rye flour. How much more wheat flour does the recipe use?

TEACHING ACTIONS

Have students work together to discuss the situation and determine a sensible solution.

► **Explain the situation in your own words.** (A recipe uses two amounts of two different kinds of flour.)

► **Analyze what the question is asking.** (Find the difference in the amounts of flour.)

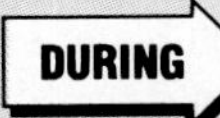

► **Decide on a solution method.** (Subtract to compare the amounts of flour.)

► **Analyze the problem to identify the data you need.** (1 $\frac{3}{4}$ cups wheat flour − 1 $\frac{1}{4}$ cups rye flour)

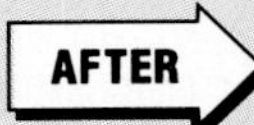

► **Evaluate your solution to see if it makes sense.** ($1\frac{3}{4} - 1\frac{1}{4} = \frac{2}{4}$, which reduces to $\frac{1}{2}$; check by using models.)

► **Explain how you would solve the same problem given the entire bread recipe.** (Find the necessary data about the flour from among the list of all ingredients, then follow the same solution steps.)

CONNECTIONS Use these anytime.

Problem of the Day

Use Your Head A cole slaw recipe takes 16 cups of shredded cabbage. Lionel knows that if he shreds an average head of cabbage, he will get about 8 cups. If Lionel wants to double the recipe for the class picnic, how many heads of cabbage should he buy? (4 heads)

Life Skills

Cooking The school cafeteria's recipe for alphabet vegetable soup calls for 3 quarts of tomato juice, 1 quart of carrot juice, and 2 gallons of water, along with other ingredients. How much liquid is used? (12 quarts or 3 gallons)

Math Connection

Measurement A recipe for tropical fruit party punch serves 60 people at 150 mL of punch per serving. Determine how many liters of punch the recipe makes. (9 L)

Classwork and Homework Supplements

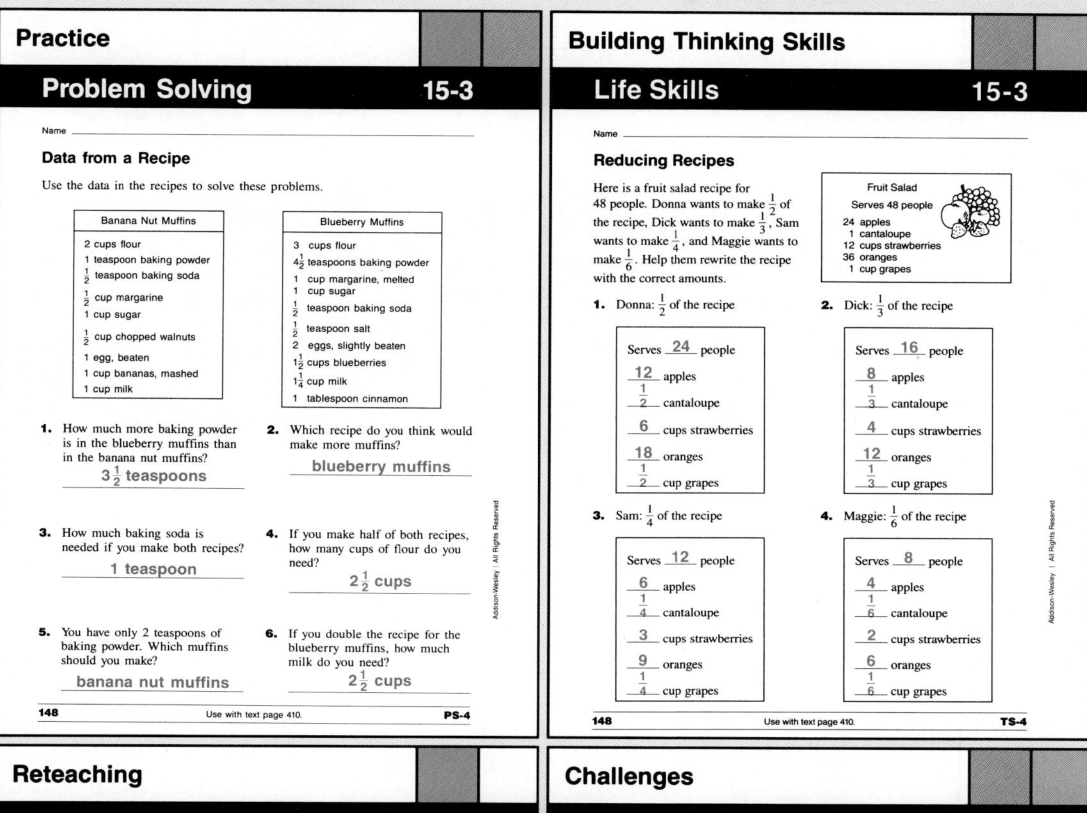

Practice

Problem Solving 15-3

Name ______________________

Data from a Recipe

Use the data in the recipes to solve these problems.

Banana Nut Muffins
2 cups flour
1 teaspoon baking powder
$\frac{1}{2}$ teaspoon baking soda
$\frac{1}{2}$ cup margarine
1 cup sugar
$\frac{1}{2}$ cup chopped walnuts
1 egg, beaten
1 cup bananas, mashed
1 cup milk

Blueberry Muffins
3 cups flour
$4\frac{1}{2}$ teaspoons baking powder
1 cup margarine, melted
1 cup sugar
$\frac{1}{2}$ teaspoon baking soda
$\frac{1}{2}$ teaspoon salt
2 eggs, slightly beaten
$1\frac{1}{2}$ cups blueberries
$1\frac{1}{4}$ cup milk
1 tablespoon cinnamon

1. How much more baking powder is in the blueberry muffins than in the banana nut muffins? $3\frac{1}{2}$ teaspoons
2. Which recipe do you think would make more muffins? blueberry muffins
3. How much baking soda is needed if you make both recipes? 1 teaspoon
4. If you make half of both recipes, how many cups of flour do you need? $2\frac{1}{2}$ cups
5. You have only 2 teaspoons of baking powder. Which muffins should you make? banana nut muffins
6. If you double the recipe for the blueberry muffins, how much milk do you need? $2\frac{1}{2}$ cups

148 Use with text page 410. PS-4

Building Thinking Skills

Life Skills 15-3

Name ______________________

Reducing Recipes

Here is a fruit salad recipe for 48 people. Donna wants to make $\frac{1}{2}$ of the recipe, Dick wants to make $\frac{1}{3}$, Sam wants to make $\frac{1}{4}$, and Maggie wants to make $\frac{1}{6}$. Help them rewrite the recipe with the correct amounts.

Fruit Salad Serves 48 people
24 apples
1 cantaloupe
12 cups strawberries
36 oranges
1 cup grapes

1. Donna: $\frac{1}{2}$ of the recipe

Serves 24 people; 12 apples; $\frac{1}{2}$ cantaloupe; 6 cups strawberries; 18 oranges; $\frac{1}{2}$ cup grapes

2. Dick: $\frac{1}{3}$ of the recipe

Serves 16 people; 8 apples; $\frac{1}{3}$ cantaloupe; 4 cups strawberries; 12 oranges; $\frac{1}{3}$ cup grapes

3. Sam: $\frac{1}{4}$ of the recipe

Serves 12 people; 6 apples; $\frac{1}{4}$ cantaloupe; 3 cups strawberries; 9 oranges; $\frac{1}{4}$ cup grapes

4. Maggie: $\frac{1}{6}$ of the recipe

Serves 8 people; 4 apples; $\frac{1}{6}$ cantaloupe; 2 cups strawberries; 6 oranges; $\frac{1}{6}$ cup grapes

148 Use with text page 410. TS-4

Reteaching

Problem Solving 15-3

Name ______________________

Data from a Recipe

Clair is making carrot bread and cranberry muffins for her 4-H bake sale.

Carrot Bread
$2\frac{1}{2}$ cups flour
1 cup sugar
$3\frac{1}{2}$ teaspoons baking powder
1 teaspoon salt
3 tablespoons salad oil
$\frac{3}{4}$ cup milk
1 egg
1 cup grated carrots

Cranberry Muffins
1 egg
$\frac{1}{2}$ cup milk
4 tablespoons salad oil
$1\frac{1}{2}$ cups flour
$\frac{3}{4}$ cup sugar
2 teaspoons baking powder
$\frac{1}{2}$ teaspoon salt
1 cup cranberries

Use the data from these recipes to answer the following questions.

1. How much milk does Clair need for both recipes?
   - ► Milk for bread: $\frac{3}{4}$ cup
   - ► Milk for muffins: $\frac{1}{2}$ cup
   - ► Total needed: $\frac{3}{4}+\frac{1}{2}=1\frac{1}{4}$ cups
2. How much more flour is in the bread than the muffins? 1 cup
3. How much baking powder would Clair need if she doubled both recipes? 11 teaspoons
4. How much sugar would Clair need if she doubled both recipes? $3\frac{1}{2}$ cups
5. 3 carrots are used to make 1 cup of grated carrots. How many carrots are needed to make 4 cups of grated carrots? 12 carrots

148 Use with text pages 410-411. RS-4

Challenges

Math Reasoning 15-3

Name ______________________

Missing Ingredients

Use the clues in the box to fill in the missing ingredients.

Muffins	Pancakes
2 eggs	2 eggs
$1\frac{3}{4}$ cup flour	$\frac{3}{4}$ cup flour
$\frac{1}{4}$ or $\frac{1}{2}$ teaspoon salt	$\frac{1}{4}$ teaspoon salt
$\frac{1}{4}$ cup sugar	$\frac{1}{4}$ cup sugar
$2\frac{1}{2}$ teaspoons baking powder	4 teaspoons baking powder
$\frac{1}{4}$ cup margarine	$\frac{1}{4}$ cup margarine
$1\frac{1}{3}$ cup milk	$1\frac{1}{3}$ cup milk

There are $1\frac{3}{4}$ cups of flour in the muffins.	There is $\frac{2}{4}$ cup of sugar in both recipes together.	There is $\frac{3}{4}$ teaspoon of salt in both recipes together.	There are $6\frac{1}{2}$ teaspoons of baking powder altogether.
There is the same amount of margaine in each recipe.	There is $\frac{1}{4}$ teaspoon of salt in the pancakes	There are $1\frac{1}{3}$ cups of milk in the muffins.	There is 1 cup less flour in the pancakes than the muffins.
There is the same amount of sugar in each recipe.	There is $\frac{2}{4}$ cup margarine in both recipes together.	There are $2\frac{1}{2}$ teaspoons of baking powder in the muffins.	There are $2\frac{2}{3}$ cups of milk in both recipes together.

148 Use with text page 410. CS-4

Options for Individual Needs

Basic

Exercises 1-8
More Practice, p. 527, set B

Supplements
Reteaching 148 or
Practice 148

Average

Exercises 1-8
More Practice, p. 527, set B

Supplements
Practice 148
Challenges 148 or
Thinking Skills 148

Extended

Exercises 1-8

Supplements
Challenges 148
Thinking Skills 148

Other Resources:
Problem-Solving Experiences in Mathematics, Grade 4, Problem 150
Mathematics, Book A, Teacher's Edition, p. 74
Mathematics, A Way of Thinking, Lessons 11-13, 11-14

15-3

LESSON PLAN 15-3

OBJECTIVE 15-3
To solve problems using data from a recipe

Materials: blank index cards, assorted recipe cards or cookbooks

1. MOTIVATE AND TEACH

LEARN ABOUT IT

BEFORE ▶ **Explain the question by stating it another way.** (What is the total amount of drained tomatoes both recipes use?)

DURING ▶ **Explain the steps you would follow to solve the problem.** (Find the amount of tomatoes per recipe; add to find a total.)

▶ **Analyze the recipes to find the data you need.** ($2\frac{1}{2}$ cups for lasagna, $1\frac{1}{2}$ cups for spaghetti)

▶ **Explain how to add the mixed numbers.** (Add the fractions: add the whole numbers; combine and reduce.)

▶ **Explain how to verify your solution.** ($2 + 1 = 3$; $\frac{1}{2} + \frac{1}{2} = 1$; $3 + 1 = 4$, so 4 cups of tomatoes makes sense.)

▶ **Explain why you should examine a recipe before you cook.** (to make sure you have enough of each ingredient you need)

2. CHECK UNDERSTANDING

TRY IT OUT

ERROR ALERT Misreading recipe amounts.

Problem Solving
Data from a Recipe

UNDERSTAND
FIND DATA
PLAN
ESTIMATE
SOLVE
CHECK

LEARN ABOUT IT

The fourth graders at Tubman School are having an Italian dinner. They are making lasagna and spaghetti. How many cups of drained tomatoes will they need?

Lasagna
$\frac{1}{2}$ pound ground beef
2 cups mozzarella cheese
$\frac{1}{2}$ cup grated parmesan cheese
$\frac{1}{2}$ cup chopped onion
$2\frac{1}{2}$ cups drained tomatoes
$\frac{3}{8}$ ounce tomato paste
$\frac{1}{2}$ pound package lasagna noodles
$\frac{1}{4}$ cup mushrooms

Spaghetti
$2\frac{1}{2}$ pounds ground beef
$\frac{1}{3}$ cup grated parmesan cheese
$\frac{1}{4}$ cup chopped parsley
$1\frac{1}{4}$ cups mushrooms
$1\frac{1}{2}$ cups chopped onion
$1\frac{1}{2}$ cups drained tomatoes
$1\frac{1}{8}$ ounces tomato paste
$1\frac{1}{2}$ lb. spaghetti noodles

I'll find the data I need in the recipes.

Lasagna: $2\frac{1}{2}$ cups drained tomatoes

Spaghetti: $1\frac{1}{2}$ cups drained tomatoes

Now I can add to solve the problem.

$$\begin{array}{r} 2\frac{1}{2} \\ +\ 1\frac{1}{2} \\ \hline 3\frac{2}{2} = 4 \end{array}$$

The fourth graders will need 4 cups of drained tomatoes.

TRY IT OUT

Use the data in the recipes to solve these problems.

1. How many ounces of tomato paste do they need? $1\frac{1}{2}$ ounces

2. How many more cups of mushrooms are in the spaghetti than the lasagna? 1 cup

410

TEACHING OPTIONS

RETEACHING TIPS Have students scan the lasagna and spaghetti recipes to find the name of the ingredient they need for each problem. Then have them underscore the amount in question with an index card to help them copy it correctly. Assign Reteaching Supplement 148.

ENRICHMENT **Family Math** Have students try this activity at home. They choose a recipe they like from a family cookbook. Then they rewrite the amount of each ingredient, as if they needed to double the recipe to serve a large group. Students should ask a family member to check their figures.

PRACTICE

Use fraction pieces to help you find each sum. Copy and complete the equation.

1. $\frac{1}{2} + \frac{1}{6}$ $\frac{2}{3}$ **2.** $\frac{2}{4} + \frac{3}{8}$ $\frac{7}{8}$ **3.** $\frac{1}{8} + \frac{1}{2}$ $\frac{5}{8}$ **4.** $\frac{2}{6} + \frac{1}{3}$ $\frac{2}{3}$

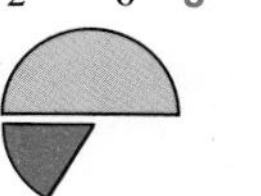

5. $\frac{1}{4} + \frac{2}{8}$ $\frac{1}{2}$ **6.** $\frac{4}{6} + \frac{1}{3}$ 1 **7.** $\frac{2}{4} + \frac{1}{2}$ 1 **8.** $\frac{2}{3} + \frac{1}{6}$ $\frac{5}{6}$

APPLY

MATH REASONING For each pair, use number sense to decide which will have the greater sum. Do not find the sums.

9. $\frac{5}{6} + \frac{1}{3}$ or $\underline{\frac{5}{6} + \frac{2}{3}}$ **10.** $\frac{3}{8} + \frac{1}{4}$ or $\underline{\frac{3}{8} + \frac{3}{4}}$

PROBLEM SOLVING

11. Jill practiced pitching for $\frac{1}{2}$ of an hour. She practiced hitting for $\frac{1}{4}$ of an hour. What part of an hour did she spend practicing?
$\frac{3}{4}$ of an hour

12. **Missing Data** Tell what data is needed to solve the problem. Tim played basketball for $\frac{3}{4}$ hour and then rode his bike to the store and back. How many hours did he exercise? For how long did he ride his bike?

▶ **MENTAL MATH**

Sometimes you can use mental math and compatible numbers to find fraction sums like $\frac{1}{3} + \frac{1}{5} + \frac{2}{3}$. $\frac{1}{3}$ and $\frac{2}{3}$ are compatible since they combine to make a whole number. Try these.

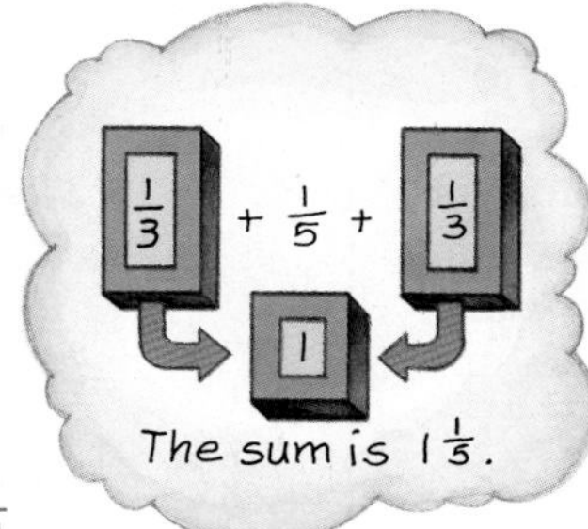

13. $\frac{4}{5} + \frac{3}{8} + \frac{1}{5}$ $1\frac{3}{8}$ **14.** $\frac{7}{8} + \frac{5}{6} + \frac{1}{8}$ $1\frac{5}{6}$

15. $\frac{9}{10} + \frac{1}{2} + \frac{1}{2}$ $1\frac{9}{10}$ **16.** $\frac{3}{4} + \frac{1}{4} + \frac{3}{10}$ $1\frac{3}{10}$

More Practice, page 510, set B

3. Practice and Apply

Basic	3-16
Average	1-16
Extended	5-16

PRACTICE

What do you notice about the addends in Exercise 7? (Both equal $\frac{1}{2}$.)

APPLY

MATH REASONING ▶ **Explain what is similar about both pairs.** (Each pair has one fraction that is an addend in both equations.)
▶ **How can this help you predict the greater sum?** (The equation whose unlike addend is greater will have the greater sum.)

PROBLEM SOLVING ▶ **Explain your solution method for Problem 11.** (Add to get a total practice time.)
▶ **Justify the need for more data in Problem 12.** (You cannot find a *total* with only one addend.)

MENTAL MATH ▶ **Summarize a relationship between the numerators and denominator in compatible fractions.** (If two fractions are compatible, the sum of the numerators will equal the denominator.)

Close and Assess

SHOW WHAT YOU KNOW

Have students use 3 different combinations of fraction pieces to show that $\frac{1}{2} + \frac{1}{4} = \frac{3}{4}$. They should write an equation for each solution. (Combinations may vary. Students may show $\frac{2}{4} + \frac{1}{4}$, $\frac{4}{8} + \frac{2}{8}$, or $\frac{6}{12} + \frac{3}{12}$; all reduce to $\frac{3}{4}$.)

Quick Quiz

Use models to find each sum. Simplify.

1. $\frac{1}{2} + \frac{1}{12}$ $(\frac{7}{12})$
2. $\frac{1}{6} + \frac{1}{3}$ $(\frac{1}{2})$
3. $\frac{2}{5} + \frac{3}{10}$ $(\frac{7}{10})$
4. $\frac{3}{4} + \frac{2}{8}$ (1)

15-4

LESSON OPTIONS 15-5

Subtracting Fractions with Models: Unlike Denominators

OBJECTIVE 15-5 To use objects to subtract fractions with unlike denominators

PREBOOK ACTIVITIES

QUICK REVIEW

Subtract. Simplify all differences.

1. $\frac{4}{5} - \frac{1}{5}$ $\left(\frac{3}{5}\right)$ **2.** $\frac{5}{8} - \frac{4}{8}$ $\left(\frac{1}{8}\right)$
3. $\frac{3}{6} - \frac{1}{6}$ $\left(\frac{1}{3}\right)$ **4.** $\frac{9}{10} - \frac{4}{10}$ $\left(\frac{1}{2}\right)$
5. $\frac{6}{7} - \frac{4}{7}$ $\left(\frac{2}{7}\right)$ **6.** $\frac{3}{4} - \frac{1}{4}$ $\left(\frac{1}{2}\right)$
7. $\frac{11}{12} - \frac{7}{12}$ $\left(\frac{1}{3}\right)$ **8.** $\frac{2}{3} - \frac{1}{3}$ $\left(\frac{1}{3}\right)$
9. $\frac{7}{9} - \frac{4}{9}$ $\left(\frac{1}{3}\right)$ **10.** $\frac{9}{14} - \frac{2}{14}$ $\left(\frac{1}{2}\right)$

PRIOR KNOWLEDGE

Have students review the steps to follow to subtract fractions with like denominators. (Subtract the numerators, write the difference over the like denominator, simplify if possible.) Have students imagine what they might do in order to subtract fractions with unlike denominators. (Trade one of the fractions for an equivalent fraction with the same denominator as the other, then subtract the like-denominator fractions the usual way.) Tell students that in this lesson they will use models to subtract fractions with unlike denominators.

COMMUNICATION

Writing in Math In their Math Journals, have students write the steps, in order, that they would follow to add fractions with unlike denominators. Then have them apply the same reasoning to visualize subtracting fractions with unlike denominators and to write a predicted order of steps. Ask volunteers to share their steps with the group. (Check students' writing.)

EXPLORE AND CONNECT

Materials: fraction pieces, fraction list (see below)
Alternative Materials: TA 21 (Fraction Strips)
Grouping Suggestion: cooperative learning pairs
Using assorted fraction pieces, students explore subtracting fractions with unlike denominators. Post this list of fractions for all students to use: $\frac{3}{4}$, $\frac{5}{6}$, $\frac{7}{8}$, $\frac{9}{10}$, $\frac{11}{12}$. Pairs model each fraction, then determine how to subtract $\frac{1}{2}$ from each one. They write fraction subtraction equations for every situation. Partners should discuss any possible trades to make, record what they do, and give each difference. For instance, students might write $\frac{3}{4} - \frac{1}{2} = \frac{3}{4} - \frac{2}{4} = \frac{1}{4}$. Conclude by having students summarize how they subtracted fractions with unlike denominators. (Possible answer: Trade $\frac{1}{2}$ for an equivalent fraction with the same denominator as the other fraction, subtract numerators, then write the difference of numerators over the like denominator.)

CONNECTIONS Use these anytime.

Problem of the Day

Creative Thinking Use the digits 1, 2, 3, and 6, then 2, 4, 6, and 12 to complete two subtraction problems.
$\frac{\square}{\square} - \frac{\square}{\square} = 0$
($\frac{1}{2} - \frac{3}{6} = 0$, $\frac{1}{3} - \frac{2}{6} = 0$; $\frac{2}{4} - \frac{6}{12} = 0$, $\frac{2}{6} - \frac{4}{12} = 0$; order of fractions in each equation may be reversed.)

Patterns

Subtract from $\frac{1}{2}$ Discover the pattern, then continue it three more times. Notice all differences are not in lowest terms.
$\frac{1}{2} - \frac{1}{4} = \frac{1}{4}$
$\frac{1}{2} - \frac{1}{6} = \frac{2}{6}$
$\frac{1}{2} - \frac{1}{8} = \frac{3}{8}$
$\frac{1}{2} - \frac{1}{10} = \frac{4}{10}$
($\frac{1}{2} - \frac{1}{12} = \frac{5}{12}$; $\frac{1}{2} - \frac{1}{14} = \frac{6}{14}$; $\frac{1}{2} - \frac{1}{16} = \frac{7}{16}$)

Number Sense

Mental Math Think about compatible numbers to find the differences mentally.
$1 - \frac{4}{7}$ $\left(\frac{3}{7}\right)$ $1 - \frac{5}{6}$ $\left(\frac{1}{6}\right)$
$1 - \frac{5}{8}$ $\left(\frac{3}{8}\right)$ $1 - \frac{1}{8}$ $\left(\frac{7}{8}\right)$
$1 - \frac{7}{10}$ $\left(\frac{3}{10}\right)$ $1 - \frac{1}{4}$ $\left(\frac{3}{4}\right)$

Classwork and Homework Supplements

Practice

Manipulatives 15-5

Name ____________

Subtracting Fractions with Models: Unlike Denominators

Use fraction pieces to find each difference.

1. $\frac{7}{8} = \frac{7}{8}$; $-\frac{1}{4} = \frac{2}{8}$; $\frac{5}{8}$
2. $\frac{1}{2} = \frac{3}{6}$; $-\frac{1}{6} = \frac{1}{6}$; $\frac{2}{6} = \frac{1}{3}$
3. $\frac{2}{3} = \frac{4}{6}$; $-\frac{1}{6} = \frac{1}{6}$; $\frac{3}{6} = \frac{1}{2}$
4. $\frac{5}{8} = \frac{5}{8}$; $-\frac{1}{2} = \frac{4}{8}$; $\frac{1}{8}$
5. $\frac{5}{9} = \frac{5}{9}$; $-\frac{1}{3} = \frac{3}{9}$; $\frac{2}{9}$
6. $\frac{9}{10} = \frac{9}{10}$; $-\frac{1}{2} = \frac{5}{10}$; $\frac{4}{10} = \frac{2}{5}$
7. $\frac{3}{4} = \frac{6}{8}$; $-\frac{3}{8} = \frac{3}{8}$; $\frac{3}{8}$
8. $\frac{1}{2} = \frac{2}{4}$; $-\frac{1}{4} = \frac{1}{4}$; $\frac{1}{4}$
9. $\frac{2}{3} = \frac{6}{9}$; $-\frac{2}{9} = \frac{2}{9}$; $\frac{4}{9}$
10. $\frac{4}{5} = \frac{8}{10}$; $-\frac{3}{10} = \frac{3}{10}$; $\frac{5}{10} = \frac{1}{2}$
11. $\frac{7}{8} = \frac{7}{8}$; $-\frac{3}{4} = \frac{6}{8}$; $\frac{1}{8}$
12. $\frac{1}{2} = \frac{4}{8}$; $-\frac{3}{8} = \frac{3}{8}$; $\frac{1}{8}$
13. $\frac{1}{3} = \frac{2}{6}$; $-\frac{1}{6} = \frac{1}{6}$; $\frac{1}{6}$
14. $\frac{9}{10} = \frac{9}{10}$; $-\frac{3}{5} = \frac{6}{10}$; $\frac{3}{10}$

Building Thinking Skills

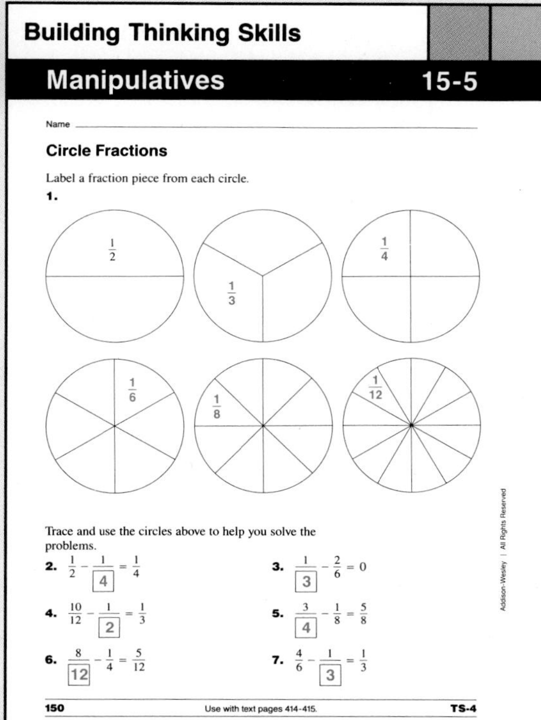
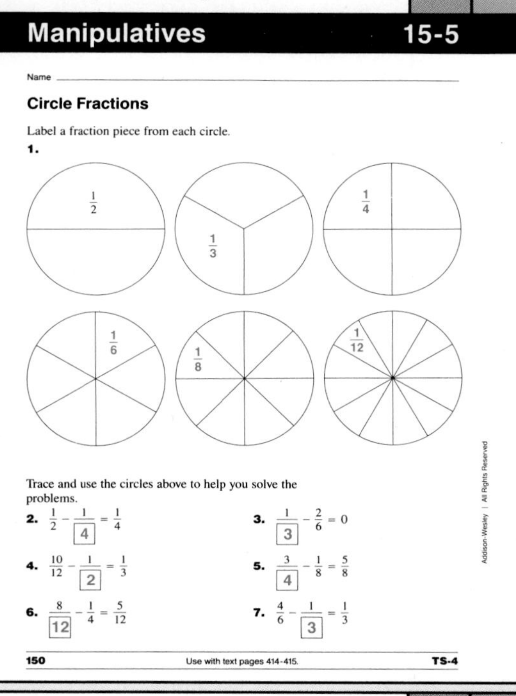

Manipulatives 15-5

Name ____________

Circle Fractions

Label a fraction piece from each circle.

1. $\frac{1}{2}$ $\frac{1}{3}$ $\frac{1}{4}$ $\frac{1}{6}$ $\frac{1}{8}$ $\frac{1}{12}$

Trace and use the circles above to help you solve the problems.

2. $\frac{1}{2} - \frac{1}{\boxed{4}} = \frac{1}{4}$
3. $\frac{1}{\boxed{3}} - \frac{2}{6} = 0$
4. $\frac{10}{12} - \frac{1}{\boxed{2}} = \frac{1}{3}$
5. $\frac{3}{\boxed{4}} - \frac{1}{8} = \frac{5}{8}$
6. $\frac{8}{\boxed{12}} - \frac{1}{4} = \frac{5}{12}$
7. $\frac{4}{6} - \frac{1}{\boxed{3}} = \frac{1}{3}$

Reteaching

Manipulatives 15-5

Name ____________

Subtracting Fractions with Models: Unlike Denominators

Subtract. $\frac{2}{3} - \frac{1}{6} = ?$

Cover up $\frac{2}{3}$. → Trade $\frac{2}{3}$ for $\frac{4}{6}$. → Take away $\frac{1}{6}$. → Decide what part is left.

$\frac{2}{3}$; $\frac{2}{3} = \frac{4}{6}$; $\frac{4}{6} - \frac{1}{6} =$; $\frac{3}{6}$ or $\frac{1}{2}$

Use fraction pieces to find each difference.

1. $\frac{1}{2} - \frac{1}{4}$: $\frac{1}{2}$; $\frac{1}{2} = \frac{2}{4}$; $\frac{2}{4} - \frac{1}{4} = \frac{1}{4}$; $\frac{1}{2} - \frac{1}{4} = \frac{1}{4}$
2. $\frac{5}{8} - \frac{1}{2}$: $\frac{5}{8}$; $\frac{1}{2} = \frac{4}{8}$; $\frac{5}{8} - \frac{4}{8} = \frac{1}{8}$; $\frac{5}{8} - \frac{1}{2} = \frac{1}{8}$

   This time we renamed the we took away.

3. $\frac{1}{3} - \frac{1}{6} = \frac{1}{6}$
4. $\frac{7}{8} - \frac{1}{2} = \frac{3}{8}$
5. $\frac{2}{3} - \frac{1}{6} = \frac{3}{6} = \frac{1}{2}$
6. $\frac{5}{6} - \frac{1}{3} = \frac{3}{6} = \frac{1}{2}$
7. $\frac{7}{8} - \frac{1}{4} = \frac{5}{8}$
8. $\frac{1}{3} - \frac{2}{6} = \frac{0}{6} = 0$
9. $\frac{1}{2} - \frac{1}{6} = \frac{2}{6} = \frac{1}{3}$
10. $\frac{3}{4} - \frac{3}{8} = \frac{3}{8}$
11. $\frac{5}{6} - \frac{1}{2} = \frac{2}{6} = \frac{1}{3}$

Challenges

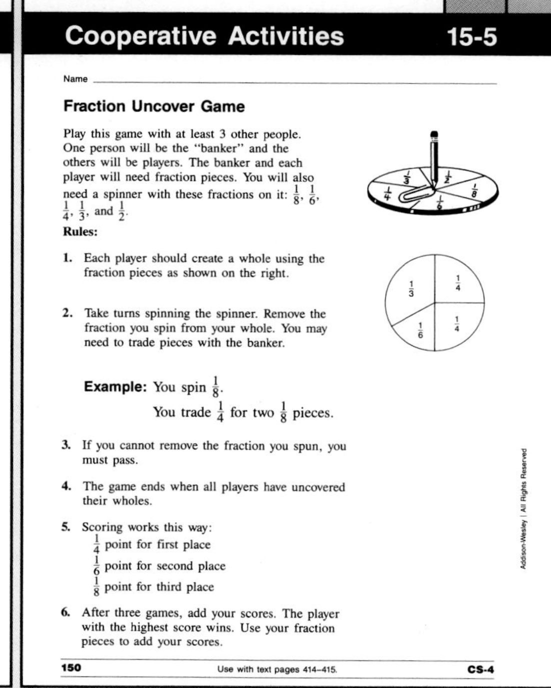

Cooperative Activities 15-5

Name ____________

Fraction Uncover Game

Play this game with at least 3 other people. One person will be the "banker" and the others will be players. The banker and each player will need fraction pieces. You will also need a spinner with these fractions on it: $\frac{1}{8}$, $\frac{1}{6}$, $\frac{1}{4}$, $\frac{1}{3}$, and $\frac{1}{2}$.

Rules:

1. Each player should create a whole using the fraction pieces as shown on the right.
2. Take turns spinning the spinner. Remove the fraction you spin from your whole. You may need to trade pieces with the banker.

   Example: You spin $\frac{1}{8}$.
   You trade $\frac{1}{4}$ for two $\frac{1}{8}$ pieces.

3. If you cannot remove the fraction you spun, you must pass.
4. The game ends when all players have uncovered their wholes.
5. Scoring works this way:
   $\frac{1}{4}$ point for first place
   $\frac{1}{6}$ point for second place
   $\frac{1}{8}$ point for third place
6. After three games, add your scores. The player with the highest score wins. Use your fraction pieces to add your scores.

Options for Individual Needs

Basic

Exercises 1-6, 9-15
Skills Bank, p. 467
Calculator Bank, p. 491
Computer Bank, p. 497
More Practice, p. 510, set C

Supplements
Reteaching 150 or
Practice 150

Average

Exercises 1-17
Calculator Bank, p. 491
Computer Bank, p. 497
More Practice, p. 510, set C

Supplements
Practice 150
Challenges 150 or
Thinking Skills 150

Extended

Exercises 4-17
Calculator Bank, p. 491
Computer Bank, p. 497

Supplements
Challenges 150
Thinking Skills 150

Other Resources:
Problem-Solving Experiences in Mathematics, Grade 4, Problem 102
Math In Stride, Grade 4, p. 216
Mathematics, A Way of Thinking, Lesson 11-19
Using the Math Explorer Calculator: A Sourcebook for Teachers, Chapter 14

LESSON PLAN 15-5

OBJECTIVE 15-5
To use objects to subtract fractions with unlike denominators

Materials: fraction pieces

Alternative Materials: TA 21 (Fraction Strips)

Grouping Suggestions: pairs

1. MOTIVATE AND TEACH

LEARN ABOUT IT

EXPLORE ► **Explain the relationship between thirds and sixths.** (A third is twice the size of a sixth.)
► **Explain how the picture and the equation are related.** ($\frac{5}{6}$ of the whole is covered, then $\frac{1}{3}$ of the whole is removed.)
► **Justify the trade of $\frac{1}{3}$ for $\frac{2}{6}$.** ($\frac{1}{3}$ and $\frac{2}{6}$ are equivalent fractions; the trade makes both fractions have like denominators.)
► **Why is the answer shown as $\frac{3}{6}$ or $\frac{1}{2}$?** ($\frac{3}{6}$ reduces to $\frac{1}{2}$.)

TALK ABOUT IT ► **Explain how to use equivalent fractions to subtract with unlike denominators.** (Trade one fraction for an equivalent fraction with the same denominator as the second fraction.)
► **Why is it easier to subtract fractions with like denominators?** (You only have to subtract the numerators, then write the difference over the like denominator.)
Student Edition answers: **1.** $\frac{2}{6}$, because it is the smaller fraction **2.** $\frac{2}{3}$

2. CHECK UNDERSTANDING

TRY IT OUT

ERROR ALERT Adding rather than subtracting. Making incorrect trades.

Subtracting Fractions with Models
Unlike Denominators

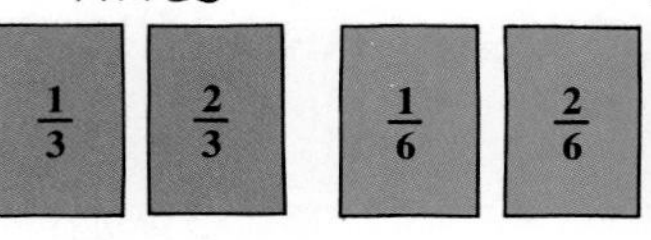

LEARN ABOUT IT

EXPLORE Use Fraction Pieces
Use the thirds and sixths fraction pieces and these fraction cards. Follow the steps several times and record your results.

- Choose a thirds and a sixths fraction card. The larger fraction is the *cover* fraction. The smaller is the *take away* fraction.
- With fraction pieces, cover up the section of the whole shown on the *cover* fraction card, in this case, 5 sixths.
- Trade the *take away* card for another card with an equivalent fraction that has the same denominator as the *cover* fraction.
- Take away the part of the covered section shown on the new *take away* card.
- Decide what part of the section is left. Complete an equation.

Cover | Take Away

$\frac{5}{6}$ | $\frac{1}{3}$

$\frac{5}{6} - \frac{1}{3} = ?$

Trade

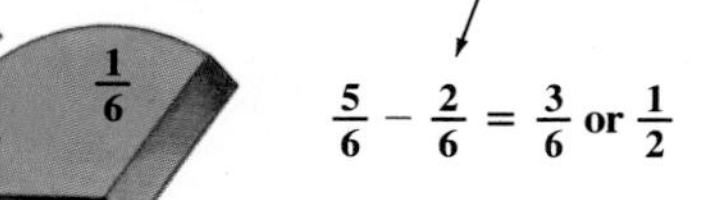

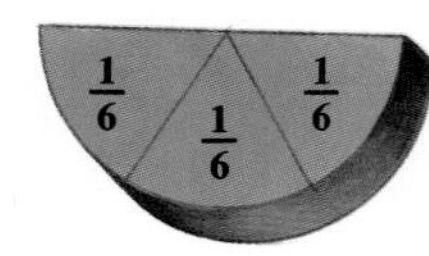

TALK ABOUT IT See teaching notes.

1. If you choose the $\frac{2}{6}$ piece and the $\frac{2}{3}$ piece, which is the *take away* piece? Explain.
2. When finding $\frac{2}{3} - \frac{1}{6}$, what piece will you trade to make the denominators the same?

You can subtract fractions by changing them so that the denominators are alike.

TRY IT OUT

Use fraction pieces to find each difference.

1. $\frac{5}{8} - \frac{1}{4}$ $\frac{3}{8}$ **2.** $\frac{1}{2} - \frac{3}{8}$ $\frac{1}{8}$ **3.** $\frac{3}{4} - \frac{1}{8}$ $\frac{5}{8}$ **4.** $\frac{1}{3} - \frac{1}{6}$ $\frac{1}{6}$

414

TEACHING OPTIONS

RETEACHING TIPS Students use the greater denominator in each exercise as the like denominator. They model the first number using an equivalent fraction with that denominator to simplify the subtraction and help find the difference. Assign Reteaching Supplement 150.

ENRICHMENT Have students apply the ideas of equivalent fractions and like denominators to subtract. Then have them check to make sure each answer is in lowest terms.
1. $\frac{8}{9} - \frac{1}{2}$ $(\frac{7}{18})$ **2.** $\frac{5}{7} - \frac{1}{2}$ $(\frac{3}{14})$
3. $\frac{4}{5} - \frac{1}{3}$ $(\frac{7}{15})$ **4.** $\frac{7}{10} - \frac{1}{4}$ $(\frac{9}{20})$
(All fractions are in lowest terms.)

PRACTICE

Use fraction pieces to find each difference.

1. $\frac{5}{8} - \frac{1}{2}$ $\frac{1}{8}$
2. $\frac{5}{6} - \frac{2}{3}$ $\frac{1}{6}$
3. $\frac{2}{3} - \frac{1}{6}$ $\frac{3}{6}$
4. $\frac{3}{8} - \frac{1}{4}$ $\frac{1}{8}$
5. $\frac{4}{6} - \frac{1}{2}$ $\frac{1}{6}$
6. $\frac{7}{8} - \frac{3}{4}$ $\frac{1}{8}$
7. $\frac{2}{3} - \frac{1}{2}$ $\frac{1}{6}$
8. $\frac{3}{4} - \frac{1}{2}$ $\frac{1}{4}$

APPLY

MATH REASONING For each pair, use number sense to decide which will have the greater difference. Do not subtract.

9. $\frac{5}{8} - \frac{1}{4}$ or $\frac{5}{8} - \frac{2}{4}$
10. $\frac{3}{10} - \frac{1}{5}$ or $\frac{7}{10} - \frac{1}{5}$

PROBLEM SOLVING

11. Bill did $\frac{1}{2}$ of his homework at school. He did $\frac{1}{4}$ of it before supper. What part of his homework did Bill have left to do after supper?
$\frac{1}{4}$ of his homework

12. **Extra Data** Solve. Then tell what data is not needed. Tina played $\frac{3}{4}$ of the basketball game, Ann played $\frac{1}{2}$ of the game, and Jackie played $\frac{1}{8}$ of the game. How much more did Tina play than Jackie?
$\frac{5}{8}$, how long Ann played

ESTIMATION

13. Write a fraction for the colored part of each strip. Tell if each fraction is closest to 0, closest to $\frac{1}{2}$, or closest to 1 whole. See Additional Answers.

A
C
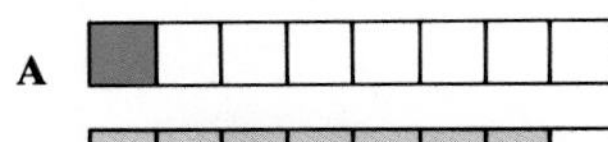

B
D
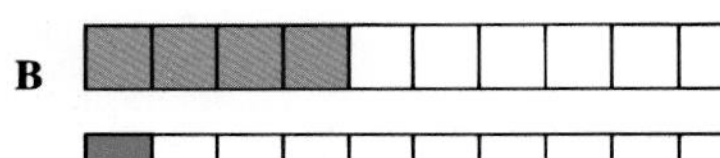

Replace each fraction below with 0, $\frac{1}{2}$, or 1 to estimate the sum or difference.

14. $\frac{9}{10} - \frac{1}{8}$ 1
15. $\frac{4}{10} + \frac{7}{8}$ $1\frac{1}{2}$
16. $\frac{3}{8} + \frac{4}{10}$ 1
17. $\frac{9}{10} - \frac{7}{8}$ 0

More Practice, page 510, set C

3. PRACTICE AND APPLY

Basic	1-6, 9-15
Average	1-17
Extended	4-17

Additional Answers: See p. T79.

PRACTICE

How will you solve Exercises 1-8? (Use fraction pieces, trading to make like denominators.)

APPLY

MATH REASONING ▶ **Explain how the pairs are similar in Exercises 9 and 10.** (One fraction is the same in each subtraction pair.)

PROBLEM SOLVING ▶ **How many operations are needed to solve Problem 11? Explain.** (Possible answer: Two: add to find out how much homework is done; subtract from 1 to find what part is still left to do.)
▶ **What operation would you use to solve Problem 12? Why?** (Subtract to compare two amounts.)

ESTIMATION ▶ **Explain how to quickly identify fractions near 1.** (If the numerator is almost the same as the denominator, often a fraction is near 1.)

CLOSE AND ASSESS

SHOW WHAT YOU KNOW

Have students work in pairs. Each creates a fraction subtraction problem for the partner to solve with fraction pieces. Have each student record the solution as a subtraction equation, then have the partner verify the answer. (Check pairs' problems and answers.)

QUICK QUIZ

Find each difference with fraction pieces.

1. $\frac{7}{8} - \frac{1}{2}$ $(\frac{3}{8})$
2. $\frac{5}{6} - \frac{2}{3}$ $(\frac{1}{6})$
3. $\frac{5}{8} - \frac{1}{4}$ $(\frac{3}{8})$

15-5

Exploring Algebra/Midchapter Review/Quiz

OBJECTIVE 15-6 To explore algebra to state verbal patterns and to understand that a variable can represent

PREBOOK ACTIVITIES

QUICK REVIEW

Find the pattern, then continue it three times.

1. 3, 6, 9, 12, (15), (18), (21)

2. 98, 87, 76, 65, (54), (43), (32)

3. 132, 243, 354, 465, (576), (687), (798)

4. $\frac{1}{2}$, $\frac{2}{3}$, $\frac{3}{4}$, $\frac{4}{5}$, ($\frac{5}{6}$), ($\frac{6}{7}$), ($\frac{7}{8}$)

PRIOR KNOWLEDGE

Have students identify problem-solving strategies they know that could be particularly useful for arranging and organizing data that changes. (Possible answers: Make a Table; Find a Pattern) Have them formulate a relationship between patterns and tables. (Possible answer: Once you notice number patterns, you can list the numbers in a table to see the relationships more easily.)

COMMUNICATION

Discussing Math Have students listen to this sentence to suggest synonyms for the phrase **stand for**: In algebra, letters are often used to **stand for** numbers. (Possible answers: *represent; mean the same as; be equivalent to*) Ask students to use the phrase to describe how a code might work. (Possible answer: In Morse Code, --- stands for the letter *o*.)

EXPLORE AND CONNECT

Materials: red and yellow counters

Grouping Suggestion: cooperative learning pairs

Students explore making symmetrical patterns, increasing the size of the patterns and recording the changes in table form. The first partner uses red and yellow counters to form a simple symmetrical pattern. The second records how many red and yellow counters are used in the pattern by making a table in which a code letter, such as *R* or *Y*, **stands for** each color. Then the first partner increases the basic pattern, keeping the symmetry, as the second records the new number of red and yellow counters. Partners increase and record the pattern twice more. Then they trade tasks to repeat with a new symmetrical pattern and table. Have students tell why the table shows a range of numbers. (As you increase the pattern, the table shows numbers increasing by the same amounts, so the numbers *stand for* different versions of the pattern.)

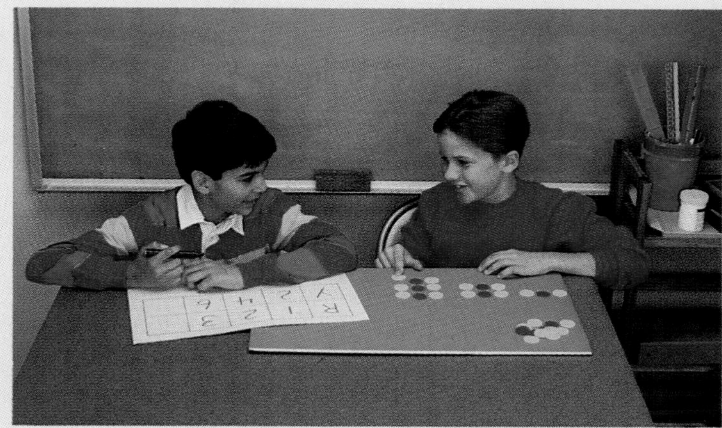

CONNECTIONS Use these anytime.

Problem of the Day

Stand By Find 2 different ways to make the addition problem work. Each letter stands for the same number 0 to 9 whenever it is used. HE + ME = WE (Possible answers: any combination of 2 multiples of 10 from 10 to 80 that equal a maximum of 90, such as 10 + 20 = 30.)

Patterns

Double Duty Find the pattern to complete the table.

A	12	24	36	48	(60)	(72)
B	7	13	19	(25)	(31)	(37)

(Row A: multiples of 12; Row B: half of A, plus 1)

Subject Integration

Social Studies Find out about Morse Code, which was first used in 1844 to send a telegraph message from Washington, D.C., to Baltimore. Figure out how to send your name in Morse Code signals.

represent a range of numbers

Classwork and Homework Supplements

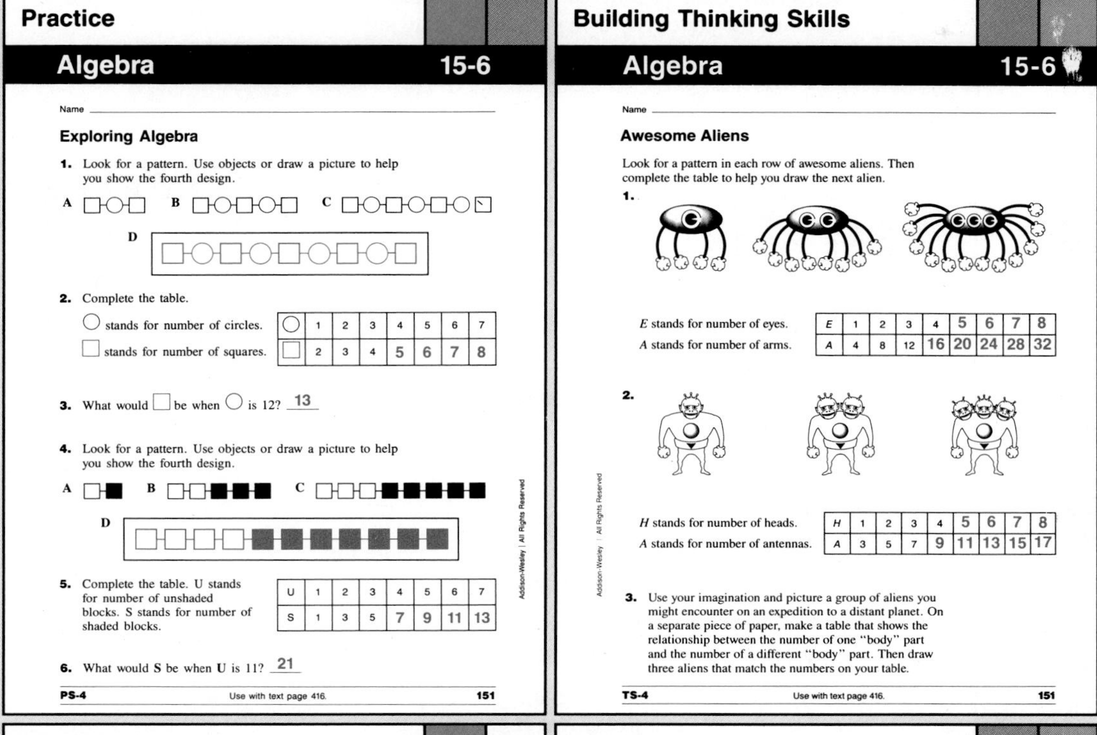

Practice

Algebra 15-6

Name

Exploring Algebra

1. Look for a pattern. Use objects or draw a picture to help you show the fourth design.

A B C D

2. Complete the table.

○ stands for number of circles.
□ stands for number of squares.

○	1	2	3	4	5	6	7
□	2	3	4	5	6	7	8

3. What would □ be when ○ is 12? 13

4. Look for a pattern. Use objects or draw a picture to help you show the fourth design.

A B C D

5. Complete the table. U stands for number of unshaded blocks. S stands for number of shaded blocks.

U	1	2	3	4	5	6	7
S	1	3	5	7	9	11	13

6. What would S be when U is 11? 21

PS-4 Use with text page 416. 151

Addison-Wesley | All Rights Reserved

Building Thinking Skills

Algebra 15-6

Name

Awesome Aliens

Look for a pattern in each row of awesome aliens. Then complete the table to help you draw the next alien.

1.

E stands for number of eyes.
A stands for number of arms.

E	1	2	3	4	5	6	7	8
A	4	8	12	16	20	24	28	32

2.

H stands for number of heads.
A stands for number of antennas.

H	1	2	3	4	5	6	7	8
A	3	5	7	9	11	13	15	17

3. Use your imagination and picture a group of aliens you might encounter on an expedition to a distant planet. On a separate piece of paper, make a table that shows the relationship between the number of one "body" part and the number of a different "body" part. Then draw three aliens that match the numbers on your table.

TS-4 Use with text page 416. 151

Addison-Wesley | All Rights Reserved

Reteaching

Algebra 15-6

Name

Exploring Algebra

Patterns can be represented by objects or drawing pictures. A chart can be used to organize the data.

1st 2nd 3rd

N stands for the number of the Vs.
D stands for the number of dots needed for each V.

N	1	2	3	4	5
D	3	5	7		

As the number of the V increases by 1, the number of dots increases by 2.

Look for a pattern. Fill in the blanks.

1st 2nd 3rd 4th

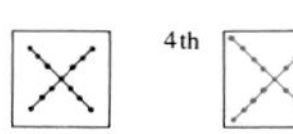

1. The first uses 5 dots.
2. The second uses 9 dots.
3. The third uses 13 dots.
4. Complete the chart using these data.

N	1	2	3	4	5
D	5	4	13	17	21

5. Draw the next X design in the box.
6. How does the number of the X relate to the number of dots needed? As the number of the X increases 1, the number of dots increases by 4.
7. What would *D* be when *N* is 9? 37

RS-4 Use with text page 416. 151

Challenges

Algebra 15-6

Name

Graphing Patterns

1. Look for a pattern. Use objects or draw a picture to help you complete the table below.

N stands for number of squares.
P stands for perimeter.

N	1	2	3	4	5	6	7
P	4	6	8	10	12	14	16

2. Change the pairs of numbers in the table into ordered pairs (*N*,*P*) and graph them on the graph below. The first one, (1,4), has been done for you.

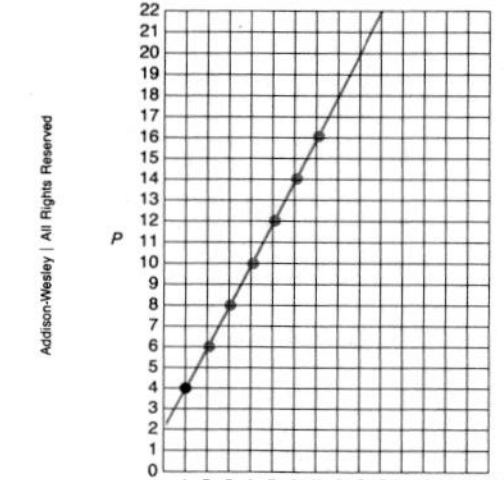

3. Draw a straight line to connect all the points. Make the line as high as the graph.
4. In the table above, an ordered pair of (10, ___) would mean that there were 10 squares in a row. Use the line you drew on your graph to tell the perimeter of 10 squares in a row. 22

CS-4 Use with text page 416. 151

Options for Individual Needs

Basic

Exercises 1-2, 17-22

Supplements
Reteaching 151 or
Practice 151

Average

Exercises 1-23

Supplements
Practice 151
Challenges 151 or
Thinking Skills 151

Extended

Exercises 5-23

Supplements
Challenges 151
Thinking Skills 151

Other Resources:
Problem-Solving Experiences in Mathematics, Grade 4, Problem 100
Math In Stride, Grade 4, pp. 151-156
Mathematics, A Way of Thinking, Lesson 11-15

15-6

LESSON PLAN 15-6

OBJECTIVE 15-6
To explore algebra to state verbal patterns and to understand that a variable can represent a range of numbers

Materials: red and yellow counters

1. MOTIVATE AND TEACH

LEARN ABOUT IT

▶ **Analyze the first pattern in terms of squares and rectangles.** (4 rectangles surround 1 square.)
▶ **Explain how the pattern changes.** (It takes 5 rectangles to surround 2 squares, then 6 rectangles to surround 3 squares.)
▶ **Explain the code used to record data in the table.** (*S* stands for how many squares in the pattern and *R* stands for how many rectangles.)

TALK ABOUT IT ▶ **Analyze the changing number of squares and rectangles.** (Both increase by 1.)
▶ **If the rate of change is the same, explain why the rows show different numbers.** (There are more rectangles than squares to begin with, so they increase from different numbers.)
Student Edition answers: **1.** increase by 1 **2.** increase by 1 **3.** There are always 3 more rectangles than squares.

2. CHECK UNDERSTANDING

TRY IT OUT

ERROR ALERT Failing to notice the pattern.

Exploring Algebra

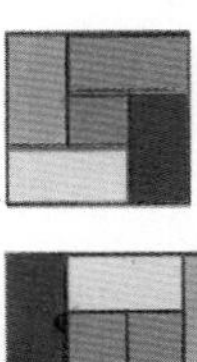

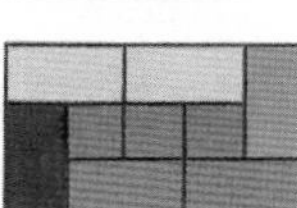

LEARN ABOUT IT

Notice how these patterns of geometric shapes grow. Continue the pattern by using objects or drawing pictures. Copy and complete the table.

S stands for the number of squares.
R stands for the number of rectangles.

S	1	2	3	4	5	6	7
R	4	5	6	||||	||||	||||	||||

TALK ABOUT IT See teaching notes.

1. How do the numbers of squares in the table change?
2. How do the numbers of rectangles in the table change?
3. How do the numbers of rectangles relate to the numbers of squares?

TRY IT OUT

Look for a pattern. Use objects or draw a picture to help you show the next *T* design.

1. Copy and complete the table.
2. What would P be when N is 10? 31

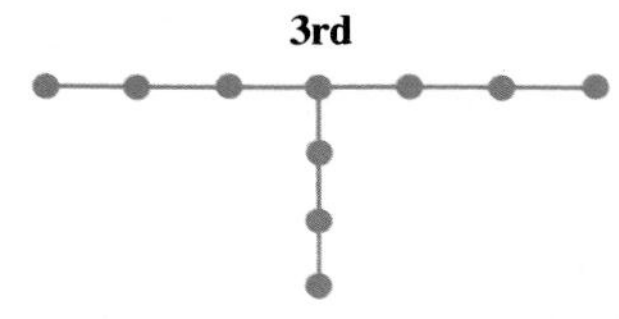

N stands for the number of the *T*.
P stands for the number of pegs needed to make it.

N	1	2	3	4	5	6	7
P	4	7	10	|||| 13	|||| 16	|||| 19	|||| 22

TEACHING OPTIONS

RETEACHING TIPS Have students make the first *T* pattern using 4 red counters. Then have them make the next *T* with 4 red counters and as many more yellow counters as necessary to complete the pattern. They use this plan to highlight each change in *P*. Assign Reteaching Supplement 151.

ENRICHMENT Students draw squares of increasing size on dot paper (TA 15) to complete a table comparing the number of perimeter dots and the numbers of inside dots. Sample table:

P	4	8	12	16	20
I	0	1	4	9	16

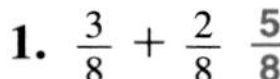

MIDCHAPTER REVIEW/QUIZ

Use fraction pieces if needed to find the lowest-terms sums and differences.

1. $\frac{3}{8}+\frac{2}{8}$ $\frac{5}{8}$
2. $\frac{2}{3}+\frac{1}{3}$ 1
3. $\frac{7}{10}-\frac{3}{10}$ $\frac{2}{5}$
4. $\frac{4}{5}-\frac{1}{5}$ $\frac{3}{5}$
5. $\frac{4}{9}+\frac{7}{9}$ $1\frac{2}{9}$
6. $\frac{7}{9}-\frac{4}{9}$ $\frac{1}{3}$
7. $\frac{5}{8}-\frac{3}{8}$ $\frac{1}{4}$
8. $\frac{2}{4}+\frac{3}{4}+\frac{1}{4}$ $1\frac{1}{2}$
9. $\frac{2}{5}+\frac{3}{10}$ $\frac{7}{10}$
10. $\frac{1}{9}+\frac{2}{3}$ $\frac{7}{9}$
11. $\frac{3}{8}+\frac{3}{4}$ $1\frac{1}{8}$
12. $\frac{11}{12}+\frac{5}{6}$ $1\frac{3}{4}$
13. $\frac{8}{10}-\frac{3}{10}$ $\frac{1}{2}$
14. $\frac{4}{7}+\frac{3}{7}$ 1
15. $\frac{7}{8}+\frac{4}{8}$ $1\frac{3}{8}$
16. $\frac{3}{4}-\frac{1}{4}$ $\frac{1}{2}$
17. $3\frac{3}{5}+2\frac{2}{5}$ 6
18. $1\frac{4}{9}+\frac{2}{9}$ $1\frac{2}{3}$
19. $4\frac{11}{12}-1\frac{5}{12}$ $3\frac{6}{12}$
20. $7\frac{2}{3}-3\frac{2}{3}$ 4

PROBLEM SOLVING

21. A cheese fondue recipe requires $1\frac{1}{4}$ pounds sharp Cheddar and $2\frac{3}{4}$ pounds Monterey Jack cheese. How many pounds of cheese is that all together? How much more Jack cheese than Cheddar cheese is needed? **4 pounds; $1\frac{1}{2}$ pounds**

22. A bread recipe calls for $2\frac{5}{8}$ cups wheat flour and $1\frac{1}{8}$ cups rice flour. How much flour is that all together? How much more wheat flour than rice flour is needed? **$3\frac{3}{4}$ cups; $1\frac{1}{2}$ cups**

23. When Kathryn went from her house to the store and back, she jogged a total of $3\frac{7}{10}$ miles and walked a total of $2\frac{3}{10}$ miles. How much farther did she jog than walk? How far is it between her house and the store? **$1\frac{2}{5}$ mi; 3 mi**

417

3. PRACTICE AND APPLY

Basic	1-12, 17-22
Average	1-23
Extended	5-23

PRACTICE

Compare Exercises 1 to 8 with Exercises 9 to 16. (Exercises 1 to 8 have like denominators; Exercises 9 to 16 have unlike denominators) *How are Exercises 17 to 20 related?* (All have like denominators and are in vertical form.) *How are the 3 story problems alike?* (Each asks for a sum and a difference based on the mixed numbers given.)

ITEM ANALYSIS The following table correlates the Midchapter Review/Quiz items with the lesson objectives.

Items	Objectives
1-8	15-1
9-12	15-4
(1-8), 13-20	15-2
21, 22	15-3
23	15-4

CLOSE AND ASSESS

WRITE WHAT YOU THINK

Have students pretend that they can slice oranges in halves or in sixths. Have them complete a table to compare the number of parts they could cut as the number of oranges increase.

Halves	2	4	6	8	10
Sixths	(6)	(12)	(18)	(24)	(30)

QUICK QUIZ

Complete the table.

Spider	1	2	3	(4)	(5)
Legs	8	16	24	(32)	(40)

15-6

Lesson Options 15-7

Adding and Subtracting Decimals: Making the Connection

OBJECTIVE 15-7 To use objects to develop an understanding of adding and subtracting decimals

Prebook Activities

Quick Review

What decimal comes *after* each number when you count by hundredths?

1. 5.67 (5.68) **2.** 10.05 (10.06) **3.** 0.89 (0.90)

What decimal comes *before* each number when you count by hundredths?

4. 3.51 (3.50) **5.** 22.02 (22.01) **6.** 0.30 (0.29)

PRIOR KNOWLEDGE

Ask students to recall what decimal numbers are. (another way to write fractions or mixed numbers that include tenths or hundredths) Have volunteers write some decimals in tenths and hundredths on the chalkboard. Ask students to express each decimal as an equivalent mixed number or fraction and to order them from least to greatest. (Answers will vary.) Have students suggest situations when they might add or subtract decimals. (Possible answers: to find total weight or price; to compare weights, measurements, or prices)

COMMUNICATION

Writing in Math Draw a simple decimal place value chart, with ones, tenths, and hundredths places, on the chalkboard. Have students describe each place in their Math Journals, giving the place's position with respect to the decimal point and its relationship to the other two places. For example, to describe the ones place, students might write the following: *The ones place is to the left of the decimal point. 1 one equals 10 tenths or 100 hundredths.* Ask volunteers to share their completed descriptions with the group. (Check students' writing.)

Explore and Connect

Materials: place value blocks, TA 3 (Number Cards 1-5), TA 22 (Decimal Place Value Charts)
Alternative Materials: TA 6 (Place Value Models)
Grouping Suggestion: cooperative learning groups of 4
Students build and order decimals to explore adding and subtracting them. One student draws 3 number cards and forms the least and greatest possible decimals. For instance, 2.45 and 5.42 could be formed with 4, 2, and 5. A second student verifies and records the decimals as two others each show one of the decimals with place value materials. The group decides how to find the decimal sum and the difference of the two decimals, modeling the actions and recording the results. Groups repeat three times, trading tasks. Students summarize the actions to compare decimal and whole number adding and subtracting. (Possible summary: Both use the same actions and trading rules.)

Connections Use these anytime.

Problem of the Day

Calculator Use a calculator to find the missing addend: 6.59 + □ = 8.36 + 0.4. (2.17)

Patterns

Adding Decimals Discover the pattern, then continue it three more times. 3.00, 3.15, 3.30, 3.45, ______, ______, ______. (pattern: increase by 0.15 each time; 3.60, 3.75, 3.90)

Math Connection

Fraction Equivalents Find the pair of numbers that, when written as mixed numbers with fractions, have a sum of $6\frac{4}{5}$ and a difference of 3.

0.8	1.7	1.9	3.8
4.7	4.9	5.5	8.5

(1.9 and 4.9; $1\frac{9}{10} + 4\frac{9}{10} = 5\frac{18}{10} = 6\frac{8}{10} = 6\frac{4}{5}$; $4\frac{9}{10} - 1\frac{9}{10} = 3$)

Classwork and Homework Supplements

Practice

Manipulatives 15-7

Name ______________________

Adding and Subtracting Decimals: Making the Connection

Use blocks to find these sums and differences.

1. 5.8 + 2.4 = 8.2
2. 3.16 + 7.45 = 10.61
3. 8.68 − 4.35 = 4.33
4. 5.45 − 2.81 = 2.64
5. 4.36 − 3.28 = 1.08
6. 6.8 + 9.3 = 16.1
7. 6.14 − 1.83 = 4.31
8. 7.45 + 2.88 = 10.33
9. 6.58 + 1.84 = 8.42
10. 5.15 + 8.85 = 14.00
11. 9.48 − 7.35 = 2.13
12. 4.28 + 6.36 = 10.64
13. 8.4 − 6.2 = 2.2
14. 8.33 − 2.45 = 5.88
15. 4.86 + 5.74 = 10.60
16. 6.03 + 7.08 = 13.11
17. 5.93 − 1.79: 5.93 − 1.79 = 4.14
18. 2.73 + 6.91: 2.73 + 6.91 = 9.64
19. 7.83 − 5.37: 7.83 − 5.37 = 2.46
20. 5.37 + 8.56: 5.37 + 8.56 = 13.93
21. 5.67 − 2.75: 5.67 − 2.75 = 2.92
22. 3.85 − 2.76: 3.85 − 2.76 = 1.09

Building Thinking Skills

Number Sense 15-7

Name ______________________

Which Purse?

Look at each exercise. Decide to which purse the sum or difference belongs. Write which method you used and then put ✓ under the picture of the correct purse.

To help you decide, use one of the following methods:

- place value blocks
- estimation
- mental math
- paper and pencil

Methods will vary.

		Method Used	Less than $10	Between $10 and $20	Greater than $20
1.	$7.22 + $2.86			✓	
2.	$12.04 − $1.95			✓	
3.	$11.87 + $9.68				✓
4.	$12.91 − $2.99		✓		
5.	$15.25 − $5.94		✓		
6.	$4.06 + $6.40			✓	
7.	$22.01 − $1.95				✓
8.	$6.29 + $3.70		✓		
9.	$8.86 + $11.86				✓

Reteaching

Manipulatives 15-7

Name ______________________

Adding and Subtracting Decimals
Making the Connection

Addition

1.65
+ 1.48

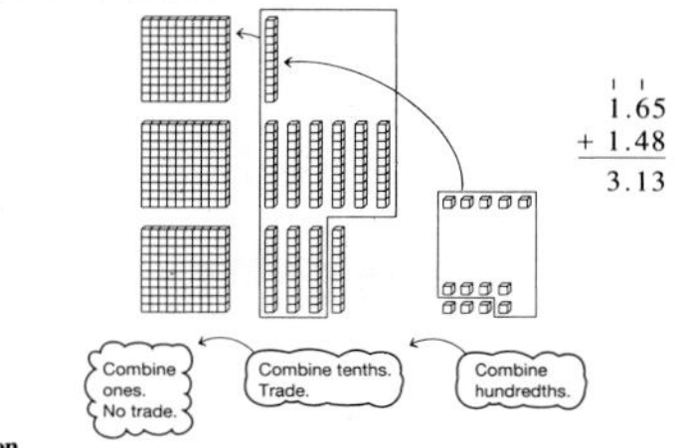

1.65
+ 1.48
3.13
Combine ones. No trade.
Combine tenths. Trade.
Combine hundredths.

Subtraction

4.42

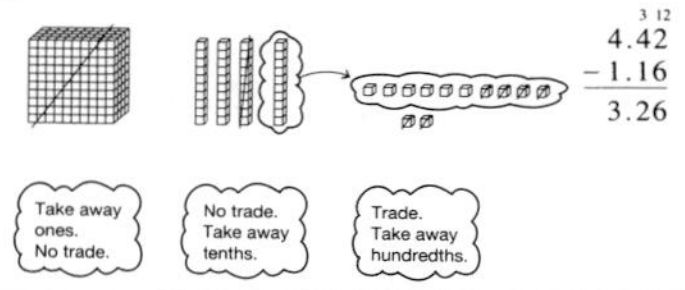

4.42
− 1.16
3.26
Take away ones. No trade.
No trade. Take away tenths.
Trade. Take away hundredths.

Use blocks to find these sums or differences.

1. 4.5 + 3.6 = 8.1
2. 1.36 + 4.26 = 5.62
3. 1.74 + 1.48 = 3.22
4. 6.2 − 4.7 = 1.5
5. 4.52 − 1.28 = 3.24
6. 6.34 − 2.61 = 3.73
7. 3.54 + 2.62 = 6.16
8. 5.81 − 3.54 = 2.27
9. 7.35 − 4.84 = 2.51
10. 2.98 + 6.34 = 9.32
11. 9.45 − 3.87 = 5.58
12. 2.59 + 3.87 = 6.46

Challenges

Manipulatives 15-7

Name ______________________

Decimal Guessimal Game

Play this game with 2 or more players.
You will need a spinner with the digits 0–9.

Rules

1. Take turns spinning the spinner 7 times.
2. Write each number that is spun in one of the boxes below. You can write one of the numbers in the "reject" box.
3. Use models to find the sum or difference.
4. Notice that in Games 1 and 2 the player with the largest answer wins. In Games 3 and 4, the player with the smallest answer wins.

Largest sum or difference

Game 1: ☐.☐☐ + ☐.☐☐ Reject ☐

Game 2: ☐.☐☐ − ☐.☐☐ Reject ☐

Smallest sum or difference

Game 3: ☐.☐☐ + ☐.☐☐ Reject ☐

Game 4: ☐.☐☐ − ☐.☐☐ Reject ☐

Options for Individual Needs

Basic

Exercises 1-4
Skills Bank, p. 460
Calculator Bank, p. 490

Supplements
Reteaching 152 or
Practice 152

Average

Exercises 1-4
Skills Bank, p. 460
Calculator Bank, p. 490

Supplements
Practice 152
Challenges 152 or
Thinking Skills 152

Extended

Exercises 1-4
Calculator Bank, p. 490

Supplements
Challenges 152
Thinking Skills 152

Other Resources:
Problem-Solving Experiences in Mathematics, Grade 4, Problems 136, 137
Math In Stride, Grade 4, pp. 190, 191
Mathematics, A Way of Thinking, Lesson 12-5
Using the Math Explorer Calculator: A Sourcebook for Teachers, Chapter 14

15-7

LESSON PLAN 15-7

OBJECTIVE 15-7
To use objects to develop an understanding of adding and subtracting decimals

Materials: place value blocks, TA 11 (Blank Spinners filled in with digits 0-9), TA 22 (Decimal Place Value Charts)

Alternative Materials: TA 6 (Place Value Models)

Grouping Suggestion: groups

1. MOTIVATE AND TEACH

LEARN ABOUT IT

EXPLORE ▶ **Analyze how the blocks are used to represent decimal values.** (Ones blocks are used as hundredths, tens are used as tenths, and hundreds represent 1 whole.)
▶ **Describe Activities 1 and 2 as number operations. Explain your reasoning.** (Activity 1 is addition because you are putting together groups; Activity 2 is subtraction because you are taking an amount away.)

TALK ABOUT IT ▶ **Explain how places relate for making trades.** (10 hundredths equal 1 tenth; 10 tenths equal 1 whole.)
▶ **Explain how you know when to trade.** (Use the same rules as with whole numbers: trade 10 of a place for 1 of the next greater place to add; trade 1 of a greater place for 10 of the next smaller place to subtract.)
Student Edition answers: **1.** Ones are greater than tenths or hundredths. **2.** 1 one, 6 tenths

2. CHECK UNDERSTANDING

ERROR ALERT Confusing the decimal value of the blocks with their whole-number value. Failing to make all possible trades.

Adding and Subtracting Decimals
Making the Connection

LEARN ABOUT IT

EXPLORE **Use a Place Value Model**
Work in groups. Use a spinner with the digits 0–9 and make piles of blocks.

Activity 1
- Spin three times to give the number of ones, tenths, and hundredths blocks for a pile. Do this twice. Write the number for each pile in a table like the one shown.
- Push the two piles together and make all possible trades. Write the number for the combined pile in the table.

Ones	Tenths	Hundredths

Trades
10 hundredths = 1 tenth
10 tenths = 1

Activity 2
- Spin 3 times to give the number of hundredths, tenths, and ones blocks for a pile. Write the total number of blocks in the table.
- Spin to get the number of hundredths, tenths, and ones to take away from the pile. Re-spin as needed until the take-away number is less than the first number. Write the take-away number in the table.
- Take that number of blocks from the pile. Trade if needed. In a third row of the table, write how many are left.
- Do each of the activities several times. Make a separate table each time.

TALK ABOUT IT See teaching notes.

1. Why is the ones column placed before the tenths and hundredths columns in the table?
2. Suppose you put 9 tenths with 7 tenths. What blocks would you have after you made a trade?

TEACHING OPTIONS

RETEACHING TIPS Students make an equivalency guide to recall the decimal value of the blocks. Students draw models to show that 10 hundredths (ones blocks) = 1 tenth (tens block) and 10 tenths (tens blocks) = 1 one (hundreds block). Assign Reteaching Supplement 152.

ENRICHMENT Have students add or subtract the decimals using models. They should record all necessary trades.
1. 0.08 + 0.09 (0.17)
2. 0.3 + 0.04 (0.34)
3. 0.11 − 0.07 (0.04)
4. 0.4 − 0.16 (0.24)

You have pushed blocks together, traded, and figured out how many in all or how many are left. Now you will see a way to record what you have done to find sums or differences.

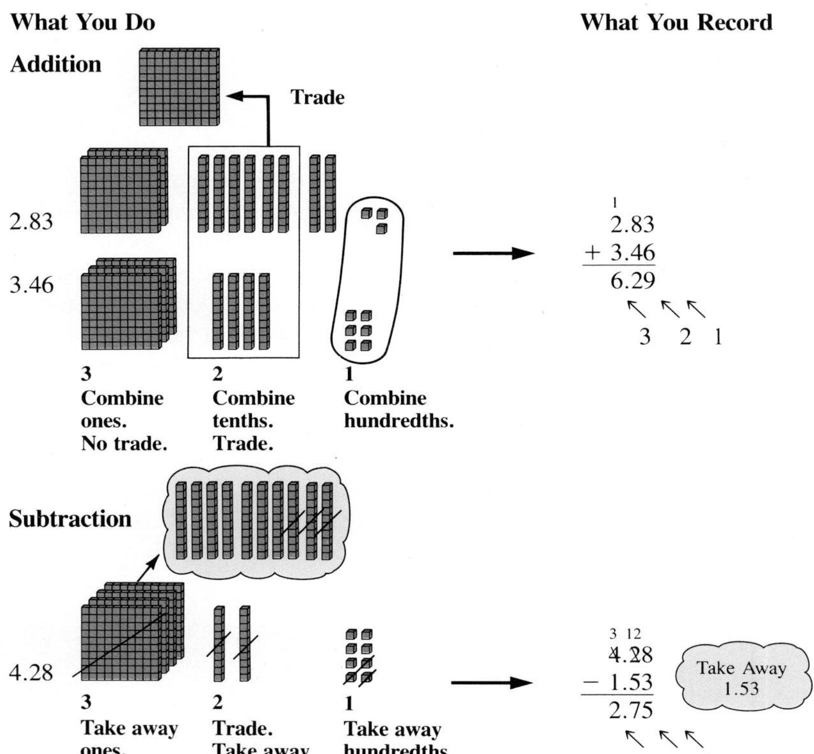

TRY IT OUT

Use blocks to find these sums or differences. Record what you did.

1. 6.2 + 3.8 **10** **2.** 1.64 + 5.37 **7.01** **3.** 6.73 − 2.46 **4.27** **4.** 4.37 − 1.75 **2.62**

419

3. Practice and Apply

Basic	1-4
Average	1-4
Extended	1-4

PRACTICE

Analyze the addition and subtraction examples on page 419 to connect What You Do and What You Record. (For addition, start by adding hundredths. No trade is needed, so record 9 hundredths. Add tenths, trade 10 tenths for 1 one, and record the trade by writing 2 tenths and a 1 over the ones place. Then add all ones, record 6 ones, and write a decimal point in the sum. For subtraction, start by subtracting hundredths. No trade is needed, so record 5 hundredths. Trade 1 one for 10 tenths to subtract tenths. Record the trade by crossing out 1 one and showing 12 tenths, then record 7 tenths. Finish subtracting, record 2 ones, and write a decimal point in the difference.) *What block would you need to show a trade of 10 ones for 1 ten?* (thousands block)
Have groups work the Try It Out exercises together, recording all trades.

Close and Assess

WRITE WHAT YOU THINK Ask students to agree or disagree with this statement: Adding and subtracting decimals is exactly like adding and subtracting whole numbers. Have them write their opinions and give examples to support their views. (Responses may vary. Check students' writing.)

QUICK QUIZ

Add or subtract with blocks and record what you find.

1. 5.3 − 3.5 (1.8)
2. 4.07 + 3.24 (7.31)
3. 1.68 + 2.53 (4.21)

15-7

LESSON OPTIONS 15-8

Adding and Subtracting Decimals

OBJECTIVE 15-8 To add and subtract decimals

PREBOOK ACTIVITIES

QUICK REVIEW

Add or subtract.

1. \$57.48 + 33.55 (\$91.03) **2.** \$4.08 + 8.75 (\$12.83) **3.** \$97.40 − 90.76 (\$6.64) **4.** \$11.98 + 57.04 (\$69.02)

5. \$6.00 − \$3.57 (\$2.43) **6.** \$38.50 + \$41.55 (\$80.05)

PRIOR KNOWLEDGE

Have students identify a common application of decimal addition and subtraction. (money calculations) Have students review how to add or subtract money amounts or any other decimals. (Possible answer: Add or subtract as you would whole numbers; trade as necessary; place the decimal point—and dollar sign for money amounts—in the sum or difference.) Tell students that in this lesson they will add and subtract decimal amounts without models, with and without trading.

COMMUNICATION

Discussing Math Write the phrase **line up** on the chalkboard. Have students use the phrase in sentences that suggest its general and mathematical meanings. (Samples: *Line up to get into the movies. Line up places when you add or subtract numbers.*) Have students explain why it is important to line up places when adding or subtracting whole numbers or decimals. (Possible answer: You must work with equivalent places to get answers that are correct.) Have students visualize a clue that may help them line up decimal places correctly. (the decimal point)

EXPLORE AND CONNECT

Materials: place value blocks, TA 3 (Number Cards 0-9), TA 22 (Decimal Place Value Charts)
Alternative Materials: TA 6 (Place Value Models)
Grouping Suggestion: cooperative learning groups of 3
Students create decimal addition and subtraction problems requiring trading in a given place. One student chooses 6 number cards and arranges them into 2 decimals to add that will require trading only in hundredths. (Sample: 3.47 + 2.39) The group checks that like decimal places **line up** properly. The next student models the addition and finds the sum. The third student uses any method he or she wants to verify the sum. Group members trade tasks to do 4 more problems: add, trading only tenths, then trading only ones; subtract, trading only ones, then trading only tenths. Groups discuss how they predicted and performed trades, how they **lined up** decimal places, and how they verified answers.

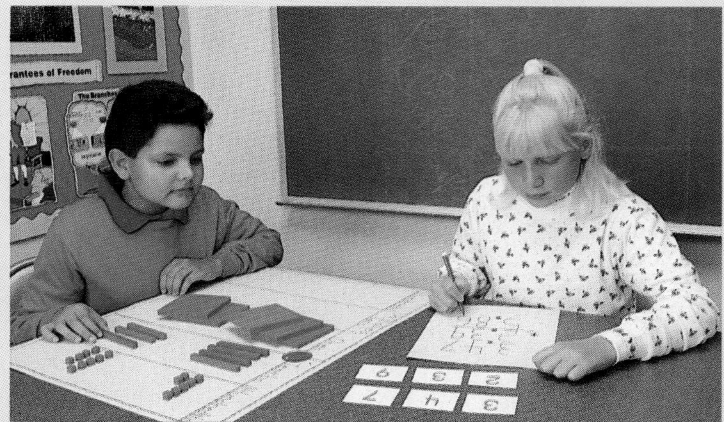

CONNECTIONS Use these anytime.

Problem of the Day

Magic Square Use logical reasoning to complete the magic square. Hint: Find the magic sum first. (4.2)

1.1	(1.6)	1.5
(1.8)	1.4	(1.0)
1.3	(1.2)	1.7

Number Sense

Mental Math Formulate an addition and a subtraction problem with decimal numbers in tenths with answers that are equivalent to one half. Repeat, using decimals in hundredths. (Answers may vary. Samples: 0.2 + 0.3 = 0.5; 1.4 − 0.9 = 0.5; 0.25 + 0.25 = 0.50; 0.75 − 0.25 = 0.50)

Math Connection

Calculator Enter any decimal number on a calculator. Find a number to add to or subtract from that decimal to make the display show the nearest whole number that is not zero. (Answers will vary. Samples: Enter 1.68; add 0.32 to show 2; enter 4.44; subtract 0.44 to show 4.)

Classwork and Homework Supplements

Practice

Skills Maintenance 15-8

Name ______

Adding and Subtracting Decimals

Find the sums and differences.

1. 3.4 + 6.1 = 9.5
2. 45.3 + 21.9 = 67.2
3. 67.4 + 40.8 = 108.2
4. 47.5 + 55.6 = 103.1
5. $53.70 + $85.68 = $139.38
6. 0.68 + 0.48 = 1.16
7. 43.75 + 82.19 = 125.94
8. $0.67 + $0.81 = $1.48
9. 8.4 − 6.2 = 2.2
10. 7.7 − 4.6 = 3.1
11. 83.3 − 24.5 = 58.8
12. 71.6 − 55.5 = 16.1
13. 8.04 − 3.26 = 4.78
14. 0.76 − 0.59 = 0.17
15. 3.58 − 1.79 = 1.79
16. 62.83 − 29.77 = 33.06
17. 82.60 − 14.48 = 68.12
18. $63.00 + $ 7.27 = $70.27
19. 51.0 − 6.4 = 44.6
20. 0.90 − 0.44 = 0.46
21. 15.90 + 6.85 = 22.75
22. 74.10 − 9.39 = 64.71
23. 92.93 + 16.00 = 108.93
24. $65.09 − $ 1.99 = $63.10
25. 6.24 + 3.51 — 6.24 + 3.51 = 9.75
26. $24.36 − $18.43 — $24.36 − $18.43 = $ 5.93
27. 0.75 − 0.47 — 0.75 − 0.47 = 0.28

Building Thinking Skills

Math Reasoning 15-8

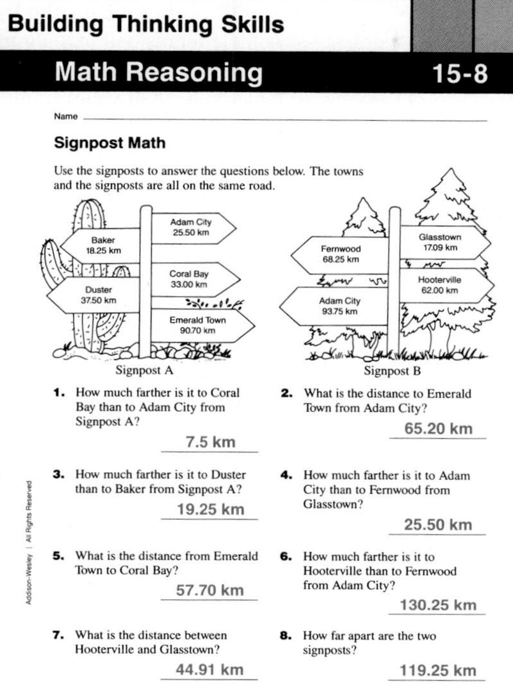
Name ______

Signpost Math

Use the signposts to answer the questions below. The towns and the signposts are all on the same road.

1. How much farther is it to Coral Bay than to Adam City from Signpost A? 7.5 km
2. What is the distance to Emerald Town from Adam City? 65.20 km
3. How much farther is it to Duster than to Baker from Signpost A? 19.25 km
4. How much farther is it to Adam City than to Fernwood from Glasstown? 25.50 km
5. What is the distance from Emerald Town to Coral Bay? 57.70 km
6. How much farther is it to Hooterville than to Fernwood from Adam City? 130.25 km
7. What is the distance between Hooterville and Glasstown? 44.91 km
8. How far apart are the two signposts? 119.25 km

Reteaching

Skills Review 15-8

Name ______

Adding and Subtracting Decimals

Line up the decimal points. → Add or subtract hundredths. Trade if necessary. → Add or subtract tenths. Trade if necessary. → Add or subtract whole numbers. Place the decimal point.

10.75 + 2.38 → 3 → 13 → 13.13 (decimal point)

13.42 − 8.93 → 9 → 49 → 4.49 (decimal point)

Add or subtract.

1. 56.3 + 14.5 = 70.8
2. 43.8 + 38.2 = 82.0
3. $13.13 − $ 6.27 = $6.86
4. 0.84 − 0.49 = 0.35
5. 19.47 − 7.09 = 12.38
6. 31.50 − 14.90 = 16.60
7. $64.72 + $38.26 = $102.98
8. 40.28 + 24.95 = 65.23
9. 57.04 − 8.16 = 48.88
10. 85.49 − 26.95 = 58.54

Line up the decimal points. Then add or subtract.

11. 0.64 + 0.69 — 0.64 + 0.69 = 1.33
12. $4.09 − $0.79 — $4.09 − $0.79 = $3.30
13. 48.06 + 3.41 — 48.06 + 3.41 = 51.47

Challenges

Critical Thinking 15-8

Name ______

Triple Sums

Complete the puzzles below. Each straight line of three decimals must have the same sum.

1.

1.4	0.9	1.0
0.7	1.1	1.5
1.2	1.3	0.8

Row sums: 3.3, 3.3, 3.3; column sums: 3.3, 3.3, 3.3; diagonals: 3.3, 3.3

Triple Sum 3.3

2.

3.6	3.1	3.8
3.7	3.5	3.3
3.2	3.9	3.4

Row sums: 10.5, 10.5, 10.5; column sums: 10.5, 10.5, 10.5; diagonals: 10.5, 10.5

Triple Sum 10.5

3.

12.21	2.76	9.51
5.46	8.16	10.86
6.81	13.56	4.11

Triple Sum 24.48

4.

1.20	5.19	2.34
4.05	2.91	1.77
3.48	0.63	4.62

Triple Sum 8.73

Options for Individual Needs

Basic

Exercises 1-14, 19, 20, 23-27
Skills Bank, pp. 462, 464
Calculator Bank, p. 489
More Practice, p. 511, set A

Supplements
Reteaching 153 or
Practice 153

Average

Exercises 1-30
Skills Bank, pp. 462, 464
Calculator Bank, p. 489
More Practice, p. 511, set A

Supplements
Practice 153
Challenges 153 or
Thinking Skills 153

Extended

Exercises 8-26
Calculator Bank, p. 489

Supplements
Challenges 153
Thinking Skills 153

Other Resources:
Problem-Solving Experiences in Mathematics, Grade 4, Problems 141, 142
Math In Stride, Grade 4, pp. 192, 193
Mathematics, A Way of Thinking, Lesson 12-6
Using the Math Explorer Calculator: A Sourcebook for Teachers, Chapter 14

15-8

LESSON PLAN 15-8

OBJECTIVE 15-8
To add and subtract decimals

Materials: calculators, TA 12 (Centimeter Graph Paper)

Grouping Suggestion: pairs

1. MOTIVATE AND TEACH

LEARN ABOUT IT

EXPLORE ► **Justify how balls nearly the same size could have such different weights.** (Possible answer: A table-tennis ball is hollow.)
► **Explain how the decimal point helps you line up places properly.** (Possible answer: If you line up decimal points, the related places will line up also.)
► **Why do you begin to add or subtract in the hundredths place?** (It is the smallest place and farthest to the right.)

TALK ABOUT IT ► **Explain why trades are needed when adding or subtracting.** (When adding, each place can have only 1 digit; you cannot subtract a larger digit from a smaller.)
► **What is the nearest whole number to each weight? Explain.** (46, 3; round up because the digits in the tenths places are 9 and 5.)
Student Edition answers: **1.** To add, trade 10 tenths for 1 one; to subtract, trade 1 tenth for 10 hundredths. **2.** Answers may vary. **3.** Together, the balls weigh 48.43 g. A golf ball weighs 43.37 g more than a table-tennis ball.

2. CHECK UNDERSTANDING

TRY IT OUT

ERROR ALERT Incorrectly lining up places. Leaving out the decimal point in answers.

Adding and Subtracting Decimals

LEARN ABOUT IT

EXPLORE Think About the Process

A table tennis ball and a golf ball are nearly the same size. But a golf ball can weigh 45.90 grams and a table tennis ball weighs only 2.53 grams. How much do the two balls weigh together? How much more does the golf ball weigh than the table tennis ball?

When you add and subtract decimals, you must keep the decimal points in the proper place.

Line up the decimal points.	Add or subtract the hundredths. Trade if necessary.	Add or subtract the tenths. Trade if necessary.	Add or subtract the whole numbers. Place the decimal point.
45.90 + 2.53	45.90 + 2.53 3	1 45.90 + 2.53 43	1 45.90 + 2.53 48.43
45.90 − 2.53	10 45.90 − 2.53 7	8 10 45.90 − 2.53 37	8 10 45.90 − 2.53 43.37

TALK ABOUT IT See teaching notes.

1. What trades did you make?
2. How would you have estimated the sum?
3. Use complete sentences to give reasonable answers to the story problems.

TRY IT OUT

1. 36.4 + 27.8 = 64.2
2. 15.45 + 6.19 = 21.64
3. 76.20 − 4.34 = 71.86
4. $7.02 − 2.65 = $4.37

420

TEACHING OPTIONS

RETEACHING TIPS Have students write each exercise on graph paper, putting each digit and the decimal point in a separate box. This will help students correctly line up places and remind them to include a decimal point in all decimal answers. Assign Reteaching Supplement 153.

ENRICHMENT **Family Math** Students do this activity with a family member. They search old newspapers, magazines, and catalogs for pairs of decimals that fit the clues. They cut out each pair.
1. Their sum is between 10 and 15.
2. Their difference is less than 1.
3. Their sum is a whole number.

PRACTICE

1. 64.2 + 28.7 = 92.9
2. 33.8 + 17.6 = 51.4
3. 40.5 + 39.5 = 80
4. $57.20 − 4.84 = $52.36
5. 0.72 − 0.59 = 0.13
6. 0.89 + 0.53 1.42
7. $6.02 − $0.69 $5.33
8. 24.61 + 16.18 40.79
9. 35.09 − 2.73 32.36
10. 42.30 − 18.80 = 23.50
11. $72.14 + 28.35 = $100.49
12. 36.05 − 9.18 = 26.87
13. 60.47 + 35.64 = 96.11
14. 56.58 − 29.74 = 26.84
15. 5.31 − 0.82 4.49
16. 43.00 + 17.06 60.06
17. 0.65 − 0.37 0.28
18. 30.54 − 8.38 22.16

APPLY

MATH REASONING Use mental math to find these sums. It may help to think of money or fractions.

19. 3.50 + 2.50 6
20. 0.25 + 0.75 1
21. 6.35 + 2.05 8.40
22. 3.04 + 5.01 8.05

PROBLEM SOLVING

23. Kevin's bowling ball weighed 5.44 kilograms. His sister Anne's weighed 4.08 kilograms. When Kevin carried both balls, how many kilograms did he carry? 9.52 kilograms

24. **Health and Fitness Data Bank** How much greater is the maximum weight of a baseball than the maximum weight of a tennis ball? See page 483. 97.4 g

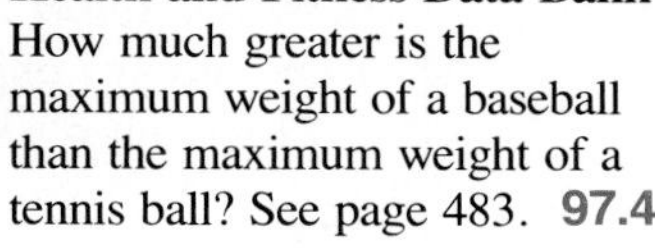

► CALCULATOR

What numbers could you put between these calculator key codes to make the number sentences true?

25. [ON/AC] 4.0 [+] |||| [=] 5.5 1.5
26. [ON/AC] 3 [−] |||| [=] 2.99 0.01
27. [ON/AC] 3.5 [−] |||| [=] 3 0.5
28. [ON/AC] 2.9 [+] |||| [=] 3.2 0.3
29. [ON/AC] 4.99 [+] |||| [=] 5 0.01
30. [ON/AC] 6 [−] |||| [=] 5.9 0.1

More Practice, page 510, set D

3. Practice and Apply

Basic	1-14, 19, 20, 23-27
Average	1-30
Extended	8-26

PRACTICE

How do Exercises 1-3 differ from the rest of the exercises in the set? (They have decimals in tenths, while all other exercises have decimals in hundredths.)

APPLY

MATH REASONING ► **Explain how breaking apart addends might help you find sums.** (Add the decimal part; add to the sum of the whole number part.)

PROBLEM SOLVING ► **What operation is needed in Problem 23? Explain.** (addition, because you need the total weight of the two bowling balls) ► **Explain what *maximum* means in Problem 24.** (''greatest possible'')

CALCULATOR ► **Justify using mental math and number sense to solve Exercises 25-30.** (Possible answer: You could count on or back, break apart addends, or compensate to make sense of the missing numbers.)

Close and Assess

SAY WHAT YOU THINK Have students work in pairs. First one student tells the partner how to add 39.05 to 56.78 and how to subtract 39.05 from 70.16. Then the other partner tells how to add 32.08 to 63.29 and how to subtract 32.08 from 60.19. (95.83, 31.11, 95.37, 28.11)

Quick Quiz

Add or subtract.

1. 70.6 + 25.7 (96.3)
2. 18.23 − 12.77 (5.46)
3. 0.78 + 0.26 (1.04)
4. $2.10 − $0.55 ($1.55)

LESSON OPTIONS 15-9

More Adding and Subtracting Decimals

OBJECTIVE 15-9 To add and subtract decimals in situations involving annexation of zeros

PREBOOK ACTIVITIES

QUICK REVIEW

Add or subtract.

1. 2.7 + 7.2 (9.9)
2. 35.8 + 83.5 (119.3)
3. 94.4 − 49.9 (44.5)
4. 7.87 − 3.29 (4.58)
5. 0.17 + 0.86 (1.03)
6. 0.80 − 0.36 (0.44)
7. 31.85 + 58.15 (90.00)
8. 5.7 + 83.8 (89.5)
9. 42.66 − 9.08 (33.58)
10. $50.98 − $2.40 ($48.58)

PRIOR KNOWLEDGE

Have volunteers write 5 dollars two different ways. ($5.00, $5) Have students analyze differences in the way the same money amount can be written. ($5.00 shows two decimal places with zeros in them, meaning that there are no cents; $5 means the same amount but shows no decimal places at all.) Tell students that in this lesson they will add and subtract decimals that may have unequal numbers of decimal places.

COMMUNICATION

Discussing and Reading Math Have students express 3.5 lb of rice as a mixed number. ($3\frac{1}{2}$ lb) Then write the following sentences on the chalkboard: I buy 3.5 pounds of rice. If I **annex** a zero to the decimal to show 3.50 pounds, I still have $3\frac{1}{2}$ pounds of rice. Have students infer the meaning of *annex*. ("to add on") Have them use the verb *annex* to compare $5 and $5.00. (Possible answer: You can annex two zeros to $5 to show $5.00, but both are exactly the same amount of money.)

EXPLORE AND CONNECT

Materials: TA 22 (Decimal Place Value Charts), TA 9 (Play Money—Coins and Dollars)
Grouping Suggestion: cooperative learning groups of 5
Students explore **annexing** zeros. Post these prices on the chalkboard: $1.61, $2.33, $3.48. The first student picks any whole dollar amount from $4 to $8 from which to subtract the first price. The next student writes a subtraction equation in which the whole dollar has no decimal places. The third student models the subtraction with play money. The fourth student writes the problem in vertical form, *annexing* zeros to line up the decimal places, and completes the subtraction. The fifth student verifies the difference. Trading tasks, students subtract the other prices the same way. Conclude by discussing how **annexed** zeros affected the money amount. (no effect) Have groups explain how *annexing* zeros helped in subtracting. (It lined up places.)

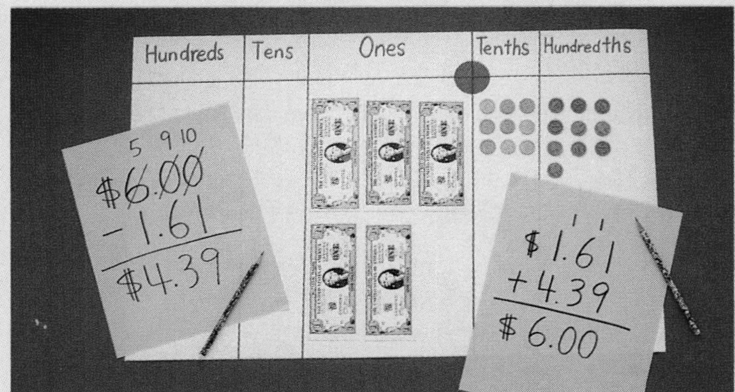

CONNECTIONS Use these anytime.

Problem of the Day

Super Snowfall As of February 10 one winter, Albany, New York, had received 37.82 in. of snow. The next day, a blizzard dropped 14.9 in. of new snow on Albany. What was the total snowfall in inches after that blizzard? (52.72 in.)

Life Skills

Money Gavin gave the cashier a $20 bill to pay for a new baseball bat that costs $13.79. Is there enough change for Gavin to buy a new baseball that costs $6.50? Explain. (No; the change is $6.21, so Gavin is 29¢ short.)

Math Connection

Calculator Start at 0.80. Count by 5 hundredths 10 times on a calculator. Enter 0.80 + 0.05 =. Continue to press the equals sign, and watch the display. Explain what happens. (It does not annex zeros for decimals; it shows a whole number without a decimal point if no tenths or hundredths; it shows an equivalent decimal in tenths.)

Classwork and Homework Supplements

Practice

Calculators 15-9

Name ______

More Adding and Subtracting Decimals

Find the sums and differences using a pencil. Time yourself. Then use a calculator to do the same exercises and time it. Compare the time and accuracy of each method.

1. 36.80 + 4.72 = 41.52
2. 47.20 − 16.35 = 30.85
3. 7.71 + 9.00 = 16.71
4. 42.0 − 18.8 = 23.2
5. 8.43 + 52.00 = 60.43
6. 39.90 − 12.41 = 27.49
7. 15.60 + 16.75 = 32.35
8. 44.7 + 85.0 = 129.7
9. 51.80 + 2.65 = 54.45
10. 77.30 − 12.95 = 64.35
11. 9.14 + 7.00 = 16.14
12. 36.0 − 19.8 = 16.2
13. 9.45 + 33.00 = 42.45
14. 63.60 − 27.27 = 36.33
15. 84.20 − 71.76 = 12.44
16. 25.6 + 58.0 = 83.6
17. 52.4 + 7.8 = 6.02
18. 4.09 − 2.80 = 1.29
19. 15.34 + 7.89 = 23.23
20. 60.0 − 48.3 = 11.7
21. 41.3 + 18 — 41.3 + 18.0 = 59.3
22. 12.5 − 5.39 — 12.50 − 5.39 = 7.11
23. 56.7 + 32.15 — 56.70 + 32.15 = 88.85

Time for paper and pencil ______

Time for calculator ______

Building Thinking Skills

Math Reasoning 15-9

Name ______

What Is Your Problem?

Complete the addition or subtraction problems using only these numerals: 2, 4, 5, 6, 9. You must also use a zero in each problem. Answers may vary.

1. 9.40 − 6.25 = 3.15
2. 6.04 + 2.95 = 8.99
3. 9.65 − 2.04 = 7.61
4. 5.06 − 2.49 = 2.57
5. 6.09 − 2.54 = 3.55
6. 2.45 + 9.60 = 12.05
7. 5.94 + 2.06 = 8.00
8. 9.52 + 4.60 = 14.12
9. 4.06 − 2.95 = 1.11

Decide whether each problem is an addition or subtraction problem. Write + or − in the ◯. Then fill in the boxes so that the problem is correct. One digit must be a zero. Answers will vary.

10. □.□□ ◯ □.□□ = 6.42
11. □□.□□ ◯ □.□□ = 8.15

Reteaching

Skills Review 15-9

Name ______

More Adding and Subtracting Decimals

Line up the decimal points. → Annex a zero to show both decimal parts as hundredths. → Add or subtract. Place the decimal point.

13.4 + 2.78 (13.4 is the same as 13.40.) 13.40 + 2.78 = 16.18

23.28 − 12.3 (12.3 is the same as 12.30.) 23.28 − 12.30 = 10.98

Find the sums and differences. Annex zeros when you need them.

1. 17.6 + 2.45 = 20.05
2. 25.26 − 11.4 = 13.86
3. 6.42 + 5. = 11.42
4. 17.6 + 4.38 = 21.98
5. 52.6 − 34 = 18.6
6. 67 − 23.4 = 43.6
7. 30.08 + 2.4 = 32.48
8. 28.7 − 12.76 = 15.94
9. 38.4 + 7.65 = 46.05
10. 68.4 − 12.36 = 56.04
11. 3.78 + 2. = 5.78
12. 85 − 12.6 = 72.4
13. 36.3 + 8.51 — 36.30 + 8.51 = 44.81
14. 40.08 + 0.6 — 40.08 + 0.60 = 40.68
15. 68 − 24.25 — 68.00 − 24.25 = 43.75

Challenges

Family Math 15-9

Name ______

Hexagon Puzzlers

Dear Family,
We have been learning how to add decimals. Work with your child to solve these decimal puzzlers.

Starting with the outer hexagon, go clockwise from circle to circle to complete all the hexagon puzzlers.
HINT: The same decimal has been added to the number in each circle to get the next number.

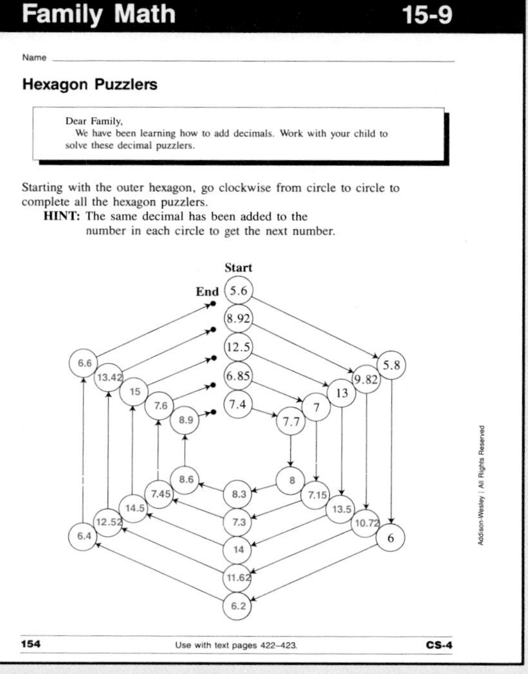

Options for Individual Needs

Basic

Exercises 4-23
Data Bank, p. 483
Skills Bank, pp. 462, 464
Computer Bank, p. 492
More Practice, p. 510, set D

Supplements
Reteaching 154 or
Practice 154
Thinking Skills 154

Average

Exercises 1-24
Data Bank, p. 483
Skills Bank, pp. 462, 464
Computer Bank, p. 492
More Practice, p. 510, set D

Supplements
Practice 154
Challenges 154 or
Thinking Skills 154

Extended

Exercises 6-24
Data Bank, p. 483
Computer Bank, p. 492

Supplements
Challenges 154
Thinking Skills 154

Other Resources:
Problem-Solving Experiences in Mathematics, Grade 4, Problem 23
Math In Stride, Grade 4, pp. 197, 198
Kids Are Consumers, Too!, pp. 112, 113
Using the Math Explorer Calculator: A Sourcebook for Teachers, Chapter 14

LESSON PLAN 15-9

OBJECTIVE 15-9
To add and subtract decimals in situations involving annexation of zeros

Materials: TA 22 (Decimal Place Value Charts), place value blocks

Alternative Materials: TA 6 (Place Value Models)

1. MOTIVATE AND TEACH

LEARN ABOUT IT

EXPLORE ► **Analyze the data in the table to identify the driest and wettest cities. Explain.** (driest: Phoenix with smallest amount; wettest: Atlanta with largest amount)
► **Describe how 14.2 and 7.62 are lined up.** (by their decimal points; 7.62 has a hundredths place that 14.2 does not; 14.2 has a tens place that 7.62 does not.)
► **Justify the annexed zero on 14.2.** (14.2 and 14.20 in. of rain are equal amounts; the annexed 0 gives a place from which to subtract the 2 hundredths of 7.62.)

TALK ABOUT IT ► **Explain how the picture proves that an annexed zero does not change the value of a decimal.** (It shows 0.2 and 0.20 are the same part of the square.)
Student Edition answers: **1.** The picture shows 0.2 = 0.20. **2.** Answers may vary. **3.** Denver averages 6.58 inches more rain per year than Phoenix.

2. CHECK UNDERSTANDING

TRY IT OUT

ERROR ALERT Failing to annex zeros. Lining up decimal places incorrectly.

More Adding and Subtracting Decimals

LEARN ABOUT IT

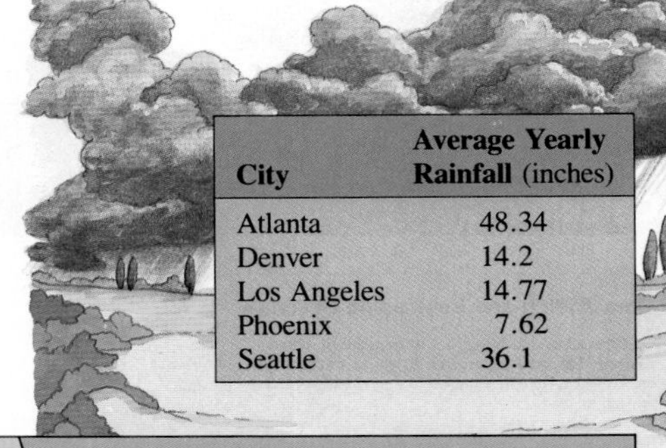

EXPLORE Think About the Process
The chart shows the average yearly rainfall for some cities. How much greater is the average rainfall for Denver than for Phoenix?

City	Average Yearly Rainfall (inches)
Atlanta	48.34
Denver	14.2
Los Angeles	14.77
Phoenix	7.62
Seattle	36.1

Since you are comparing two amounts, you subtract.

Write the problem. Line up the decimal points.

$$\begin{array}{r} 14.2 \\ -\ 7.62 \\ \hline \end{array}$$

14.2 is the same as 14.20.

Annex a zero to show both decimal parts as hundredths.

$$\begin{array}{r} 14.20 \\ -\ 7.62 \\ \hline 6.58 \end{array}$$

TALK ABOUT IT See teaching notes.

1. How could this picture help you explain why you can annex a zero and not change the value of the decimal number?
2. How would you have estimated the answer?
3. Use a complete sentence to give a reasonable answer to the story problem.

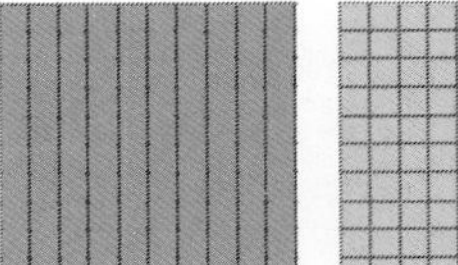

TRY IT OUT

Find the sums and differences. Annex zeros when you need them.

1. $\begin{array}{r} 42.7 \\ +\ 8.69 \\ \hline 51.39 \end{array}$
2. $\begin{array}{r} 64.8 \\ -\ 21.34 \\ \hline 43.46 \end{array}$
3. $\begin{array}{r} 2.69 \\ +\ 8 \\ \hline 10.69 \end{array}$
4. $\begin{array}{r} 64 \\ -\ 18.3 \\ \hline 45.7 \end{array}$
5. $\begin{array}{r} 93 \\ -\ 75.46 \\ \hline 17.54 \end{array}$

422

TEACHING OPTIONS

RETEACHING TIPS Have students use decimal place value charts to line up given decimal places correctly and to see where zeros can be annexed. They write each digit in its correct place, then annex as many zeros as needed to complete the calculation. Assign Reteaching Supplement 154.

ENRICHMENT Have students decide where the missing decimal point belongs in each addend below to equal the sum.
1. 1234 + 56 = 17.94 (12.34 + 5.6)
2. 17 + 162 = 3.32 (1.7 + 1.62)
3. 603 + 205 = 62.35 (60.3 + 2.05)

PRACTICE

Find the sums and differences.

1.	2.	3.	4.	5.
14.2 + 8.19 = 22.39	32.7 − 12.43 = 20.27	8.96 + 4 = 12.96	26.1 + 4.27 = 30.37	48.72 − 2.3 = 46.42

6. 56.6 − 21.63 **34.97** 7. 40.07 + 9.9 **49.97** 8. 65.2 − 46 **19.2**

9. 29.1 + 4.52 **33.62** 10. 60.07 + 0.5 **60.57** 11. 47 − 28.34 **18.66**

APPLY

MATH REASONING Use mental math to find these sums and differences.

12. 2 − 1.5 **0.5** 13. 5 − 3.5 **1.5** 14. 14 − 8.5 **5.5** 15. 25 + 15.5 **40.5**

PROBLEM SOLVING

16. Use the table on page 422. Atlanta received 5.7 inches of rain in April and 6.4 inches in May. How much rain needs to fall during the rest of the year for Atlanta's rainfall to equal the yearly average? **36.24 inches**

17. **Data Hunt** What is the average yearly rainfall in your state? How much more or less rainfall does your state get than the wettest state? the driest state? **Answers will vary.**

MIXED REVIEW

Tell which weighs the most.

18. nuts 326 grams; detergent 1,200 g; rice 1 kg

19. applesauce 725 g; pot roast 3 kg; potatoes 3,642 kg

20. tapioca 600 g; peaches 4 kg; vanilla 16 g

21. filet of sole 520 g; onion 435 g; butter 1 kg

Write L or mL for the unit you would use to measure each thing.

22. a raindrop **mL** 23. a pitcher of milk **L** 24. a spoonful of honey **mL**

More Practice, page 511, set A 423

3. Practice and Apply

Basic	4-23
Average	1-24
Extended	6-24

PRACTICE

What must you remember to do as you try the Practice exercises? (Line up the decimal places correctly, check operation signs, annex zeros as necessary.)

APPLY

MATH REASONING ▶ **Explain how you could make Exercises 12-15 easier to calculate mentally.** (Possible answer: Visually annex zeros to think of the numbers as money amounts.)

PROBLEM SOLVING ▶ **Explain the steps you would follow to solve Problem 16.** (Add 5.7 and 6.4, then subtract that sum from 48.34.)

MIXED REVIEW ▶ **Explain the relationship of grams to kilograms and of liters to milliliters.** (1,000 g = 1 kg; 1,000 mL = 1 L)
▶ **How would you compare the weights?** (Think of each item in grams to see which is the greatest.)

Close and Assess

SHOW WHAT YOU KNOW
Have students show how to annex zeros to solve 3.42 + 1.5 and 2 − 0.89. Then have them use place value materials to demonstrate that annexing zeros does not change the value of decimals. (4.92, 1.11; Check students' models.)

Quick Quiz

Find the sums and differences.
1. 4.62 + 8.6 (13.22)
2. 27.05 − 6.3 (20.75)
3. 0.75 + 24.2 (24.95)
4. 35 − 21.42 (13.58)

15-9

LESSON OPTIONS 15-10

Estimating Decimal Sums and Differences

OBJECTIVE 15-10 To use the estimation techniques of rounding and front-end estimation

QUICK REVIEW

Round each decimal to the nearest whole number.

1. 5.8 (6)	**2.** 33.5 (34)	**3.** 0.7 (1)
4. 3.07 (3)	**5.** 12.40 (12)	**6.** 1.36 (1)
7. 15.28 (15)	**8.** 2.61 (3)	**9.** 43.05 (43)
10. 20.49 (20)	**11.** 62.51 (63)	**12.** 79.72 (80)

PRIOR KNOWLEDGE

Have students suggest occasions when they might round decimals. (Possible answers: to estimate total cost; to compare estimated weights or distances) Ask students to use the decimals 4.3 and 8.9 to formulate a realistic situation that could be solved by estimation. (Sample: *My cat weighs 4.3 kg, and my dog weighs 8.9 kg. About how much heavier is my dog?*) Have volunteers tell how they would estimate the answer. (Methods may vary. Sample: Round each decimal to the nearest whole number, then subtract: 9 − 4 = 5 kg.)

COMMUNICATION

Discussing Math Review the method of front-end estimation and apply it to one of the situations students made up. (Add or subtract only the whole number part of the decimal.) Ask students how to choose an estimation method when solving a problem. (Possible answers: Use one that gives a reasonably close estimate; use one that suits the numbers to work with.) Have students explain the difference between overestimates and underestimates. (Overestimates are greater than and underestimates are less than the actual answer.)

EXPLORE AND CONNECT

Materials: blank index cards, calculators

Grouping Suggestion: cooperative learning groups of 4

Students compare estimation methods to find decimal sums. Groups copy these decimals on separate index cards: 3.8, 4.3, 6.58, 7.09. The first student picks 2 number cards and rounds them *down* by the front-end digits. The second student rounds the same decimals *up* by the front-end digits, while the third student rounds each decimal to the nearest whole number. They find the estimated sum based on their particular rounding method and record what they did, and the fourth student finds the exact sum with a calculator. Students compare estimates to exact sum to determine which method worked best for the given decimals. Groups repeat 3 times, trading tasks. Students summarize what they found. (Certain estimation methods work better with some numbers, while others work better with other numbers.)

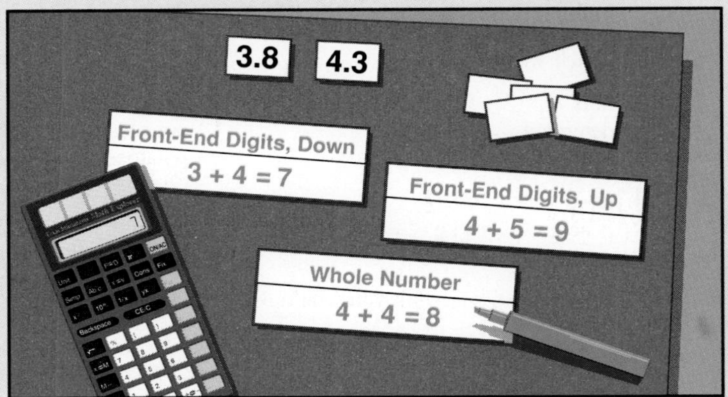

CONNECTIONS Use these anytime.

Problem of the Day

Logical Reasoning Solve the riddle. I am a 3-digit decimal with a digit sum that is 15. To the nearest whole number, I round to 9. Using front-end digits, I round up to 10. If you double me, I can be written with 1 less decimal place. What number am I? (9.15)

Number Sense

Estimation Winona estimated the sum of 6.7 and 4.5 two ways, both using front-end digits. She saw that if she rounded up, the estimated sum was 2 more than if she rounded down. Tell why. (Possible answer: If you round a decimal *up*, you add 1 to each front-end digit; with two addends, the sum includes adding 2.)

Life Skills

Weight Loss Henry weighed 58.7 kg when he started a new diet and exercise plan. After a month, he had lost 2.4 kg. What was Henry's weight at the end of the month? What was it to the nearest whole kg? (56.3 kg; 56 kg)

To estimate the sum or difference of two decimals and compare to a reference point

CLASSWORK AND HOMEWORK SUPPLEMENTS

Practice

Estimation 15-10

Name

Estimating Decimal Sums and Differences

Round down. Then estimate the sum.

1.	2.3 + 5.4 = 7	**2.**	21.32 + 7.43 = 28	**3.**	13.39 + 6.11 = 19	**4.**	4.42 + 6.21 = 10
5.	45.23 + 12.17 = 57	**6.**	72.15 + 10.45 = 82	**7.**	62.25 + 5.36 = 67	**8.**	20.19 + 32.35 = 52
9.	19.49 + 8.32 = 27	**10.**	37.16 + 4.44 = 41	**11.**	62.45 + 7.12 = 69	**12.**	13.01 + 26.47 = 39

Round up. Then estimate the difference.

13.	8.7 − 7.6 = 1	**14.**	79.97 − 39.55 = 40	**15.**	47.5 − 17.7 = 30	**16.**	9.62 − 3.58 = 6
17.	29.9 − 14.7 = 15	**18.**	6.75 − 3.58 = 3	**19.**	36.8 − 16.9 = 20	**20.**	35.76 − 25.62 = 10

Use rounding to estimate each sum or difference. Then write whether the actual sum or difference is **over** or **under** the reference point 20.

21. 10.4 + 10.1 — 20, over
22. 49.4 − 30.1 — 19, under
23. 50.75 − 29.25 — 22, over

PS-4 Use with text pages 424–425. 155

Building Thinking Skills

Estimation 15-10

Name

Central City Sports

Study the map of the Central City Sports Complex. Estimate each answer by rounding the distances as indicated in parentheses.

1. How far is it from the stadium to the swimming pool? (round down, using front-end digits) 8 mi

2. How far is it from the volleyball courts to the stadium? (round up to nearest tenth) 5.8 mi

3. How much farther is it from the fitness center to the basketball courts than to the softball field? (round up, using front-end digits) 4 mi

4. How much farther is it from the soccer field to the softball field than from the paddleball courts to the basketball courts? (round to the nearest whole number) 4 mi

5. What usually happens to estimates when you round down? They are less than the actual distances.

6. What usually happens to estimates when you round up? They are over the actual distances.

TS-4 Use with text pages 424–425. 155

Reteaching

Skills Review 15-10

Name

Estimating Decimal Sums and Differences

A Round up. → Round each number up to next whole number. → Estimate the difference.

6.7 − 4.2: 6.7 rounds up to 7; 4.2 rounds up to 5; 7 − 5 = 2

B Round down. → Round each number down to next whole. → Estimate the sum.

4.7 + 3.4: 4.7 rounds down to 4; 3.4 rounds down to 3; 4 + 3 = 7

C Round to the nearest whole number. 5.6 → 6; 4.3 → 4; 6 + 4 = 10

Round down. Then estimate the sum.

1. 7.4 + 2.1 = 9 **2.** 10.13 + 6.42 = 16 **3.** 14.36 + 7.21 = 21 **4.** 8.63 + 5.78 = 13 **5.** 32.27 + 12.21 = 44

Round up. Then estimate the difference.

6. 6.7 − 2.6 = 4 **7.** 32.5 − 16.3 = 16 **8.** 99.95 − 46.43 = 53 **9.** 6.42 − 2.46 = 4 **10.** 16.8 − 10.6 = 6

Use rounding to estimate each sum or difference. Then write whether the actual sum or difference is **over** or **under** the reference point 20.

11. 11.36 + 9.27 — 20; under
12. 6.2 + 18.8 — 25; over
13. 33.7 − 9.6 — 24; over

RS-4 Use with text pages 424–425. 155

Challenges

Calculators 15-10

Name

Decimal Clues

Write a decimal sentence that fits each clue. Use a calculator to help you. The first one has been done for you.
Answers to all problems except 4 will vary. Sample answers given.

Time yourself:
Record your starting time. ____
When you are finished, record your ending time. ____
How long did it take you? ____

Clue	Solution
1. three decimals whose sum is 15.8	5.3 + 5.4 + 5.1 = 15.8
2. two decimals whose sum is 27.9	13.5 + 14.4 = 27.9
3. two decimals whose difference is 3.4	6.8 − 3.4 = 3.4
4. three identical decimals whose sum is 24.9	8.3 + 8.3 + 8.3 = 24.9
5. two decimals with a difference of 2.73	9.98 − 7.25 = 2.73
6. three decimals whose sum is 72.5	21.1 + 31.2 + 20.2 = 72.5
7. two decimals with a difference between 2 and 3	10.9 − 8.2 = 2.7
8. two decimals with a sum between 6 and 7	4.23 + 2.12 = 6.35

CS-4 Use with text pages 424–425. 155

OPTIONS FOR INDIVIDUAL NEEDS

Basic

Exercises 3-8, 11-17
More Practice, p. 511, set B

Supplements
Reteaching 155 or
Practice 155

Average

Exercises 1-17
More Practice, p. 511, set B

Supplements
Practice 155
Challenges 155 or
Thinking Skills 155

Extended

Exercises 4-7, 11-17

Supplements
Challenges 155
Thinking Skills 155

Other Resources:
Problem-Solving Experiences in Mathematics, Grade 4, Problem 24
Math In Stride, Grade 4, pp. 181, 182
Kids Are Consumers, Too!, pp. 114, 115

LESSON PLAN 15-10

OBJECTIVE 15-10
To use the estimation techniques of rounding and front-end estimation to estimate the sum or difference of two decimals and compare to a reference point

Grouping Suggestion: pairs

1. MOTIVATE AND TEACH

LEARN ABOUT IT

EXPLORE ► **How are the distances measured on the trail map? Explain how you know.** (to the nearest tenth of a kilometer; Only one place after the decimal point is filled.)
► **Analyze the map to find the distance data you need. Explain your reasoning.** (3.7 + 4.8 + 2.3; You need to find the sum of these distances to see if they are greater than or less than 15 km.)

TALK ABOUT IT ► **Analyze how rounding up or down relates to over- or underestimates.** (Rounding down usually gives underestimates; rounding up usually gives overestimates.)
► **Explain why you might not be able to tell if certain estimates are over or under.** (If one number rounds up and the other down, they may seem to balance out.)
► **Can Megan make the hike? Explain your reasoning.** (Yes, all the estimation methods give sums below 15 km.)
Student Edition answers: **1.** 4 km; 3.7 is over halfway to 4, so round up.
2. underestimate

2. CHECK UNDERSTANDING

TRY IT OUT

ERROR ALERT Misjudging overestimates and underestimates.

Estimating Decimal Sums and Differences

LEARN ABOUT IT

EXPLORE **Study the Map**
Megan is planning a backpacking trip. She does not want to hike more than 15 km a day. Can she hike from the Ranger Station to Eagle Rock Ridge in one day?

TALK ABOUT IT See teaching notes.

1. Is the distance from the Ranger Station to the Boat Dock closer to 3 or 4 kilometers? Explain.
2. To estimate the distance from the Ranger Station to Bear Mountain Pass, you could add front-end digits and get 3 + 4, or 7 km. Is this an overestimate or an underestimate?

You can round decimals when you want to estimate a sum to decide if it is close to a reference point.

3.7 km + 4.8 km + 2.3 km = ||||

- round down, using front-end digits — 3 + 4 + 2 = 9
- round up — 4 + 5 + 3 = 12
- round to a chosen place — 4 + 5 + 2 = 11 (rounded to the nearest whole number)

The estimates are under 15 km.

TRY IT OUT

Estimate these sums or differences by rounding as indicated. Tell whether the answer is an *overestimate* or an *underestimate*. See Additional Answers.

1. 5.8 + 6.7 (up) **2.** 17.4 − 6.5 (down) **3.** 9.56 + 8.78 (up)

TEACHING OPTIONS

RETEACHING TIPS Have students focus on the front-end digits by crossing out the decimal places. They increase the front-end digits by 1 if the indication is *up* and leave them as is if the indication is *down*. Then they add or subtract the rounded numbers. Assign Reteaching Supplement 155.

ENRICHMENT Have students create a treasure map with distances indicated in tenths of kilometers. They make up one addition and one subtraction problem related to the map that can be solved by estimation. They trade maps with a partner and solve each other's problems.

PRACTICE

Round down. Then estimate the sum.

1. 6.4 + 3.3 = **9** **2.** 12.25 + 9.36 = **21** **3.** 15.45 + 5.28 = **20** **4.** 7.53 + 6.41 = **13** **5.** 23.21 + 10.19 = **33**

Round up. Then estimate the difference.

6. 7.8 − 3.7 = **4** **7.** 99.99 − 59.36 = **40** **8.** 27.5 − 17.3 = **10** **9.** 5.45 − 2.63 = **3** **10.** 14.9 − 12.8 = **2**

Use rounding to estimate each sum or difference. Then decide whether the actual sum or difference is over or under the reference point 30.

11. 16.45 + 14.01 **30, over** **12.** 12.3 + 19.7 **32, over** **13.** 35.6 − 5.9 **30, under**

APPLY

MATH REASONING

14. Megan bought a backpack for $29.58 and some wool socks for $5.25. She gave the clerk $40. Without counting, tell how much change she got.

a $4.17 (b) $5.17 c $3.17

PROBLEM SOLVING

15. Use the map on page 424 to solve this problem. Megan planned to hike from the Ranger Station to River Camp in two days. Is that distance more or less than 20 km? **less**

16. The backpackers took five tents on the trip. Two tents could hold 4 people each, and 3 tents could hold 2 people each. How many people all together could the tents hold? **14 people**

▶ COMMUNICATION Write Your Own Problem

17. Write your own story problem. The problem should involve estimating and adding or subtracting decimals. It should have people in it and should have a reasonable answer. **Answers will vary.**

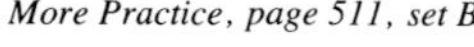

More Practice, page 511, set B

425

3. Practice and Apply

Basic	3-8, 11-17
Average	1-17
Extended	4-7, 11-17

Additional Answers, See p. T79.

PRACTICE

What 2 things will you do differently in Exercises 1-5 and 6-10? (Round *down* and add in Exercises 1-5, round *up* and subtract in Exercises 6-10.)

APPLY

MATH REASONING ▶ Explain how you could use estimation to solve Exercise 14. (Estimate the sum of the 2 items, subtract from $40, pick the answer nearest that difference.)

PROBLEM SOLVING ▶ Explain how you can use prior data to help solve Problem 15. (Start with the estimated sum for the distance from the Ranger Station to Eagle Rock Ridge, then add the estimate of 6.5.)

COMMUNICATION ▶ How can you test that your story problem makes sense? (Have a partner try it to see if any information is missing.)

Close and Assess

SHOW WHAT YOU KNOW

Have students work with a partner. Each pair uses 3 different rounding methods to estimate the sum and difference of 7.8 and 3.2. Partners write an equation for each method and give the estimated answers. (Sums may vary from 10-12; differences may be 4 or 5.)

Quick Quiz

Give the estimated answer and tell whether the estimate is *over, under,* or you *cannot tell.*

1. 12.7 − 5.8 (7; over)
2. 77.16 + 9.82 (87; cannot tell)

15-10

LESSON OPTIONS 15-11

Using Critical Thinking/Problem Solving

OBJECTIVE 15-11 To use critical thinking to analyze and follow a flow chart

PREBOOK ACTIVITIES

QUICK REVIEW

Find the sums.

1. 3.6 + 2.8 + 0.1 (6.5)
2. 0.7 + 3.3 + 2.6 (6.6)
3. 3.1 + 1.2 + 0.7 + 1.7 (6.7)
4. 1.5 + 2.3 + 3 (6.8)
5. 0.8 + 1.7 + 2.6 + 1.8 (6.9)

PRIOR KNOWLEDGE

Ask students if they have ever seen or heard of a special kind of diagram called a **flow chart.** (Students may have seen flow charts in computer manuals or as directions for games or for repairs.) Students who have seen flow charts may describe what they are or how they organize information. (Possible answer: A flow chart is a diagram of steps to follow from start to finish, including decisions to make.)

COMMUNICATION

Discussing Math Have students suggest ideas that relate to the general meaning of the verb *flow*. (Possible answers: move along like a river; travel in 1 direction) Then have them use logical reasoning to imagine how a flow chart might show steps. (Answers will vary.)

EXPLORE AND CONNECT

Materials: blank index cards
Grouping Suggestion: small groups
Students use logical reasoning to create a simple **flow chart.** On the chalkboard, write: Hang up. Dial. Stop. Start. Hear a busy signal. Look up the number. Pick up the receiver. Tell students that the list represents steps for calling a theater to ask about movie times. Have groups write each step on a separate index card, then put the steps in an order that makes sense. (Start. Look up the number. Pick up the receiver. Dial. Hear a busy signal. Hang up. Stop.) Have groups tell how they determined the order. (Answers will vary.) Have them analyze which steps would be the same regardless of the particular task. (Start. Stop.) Then ask students how to continue the process of making the call without starting back at the beginning. (Possible answer: Press disconnect button while holding receiver, so you go back only as far as Dial step.)

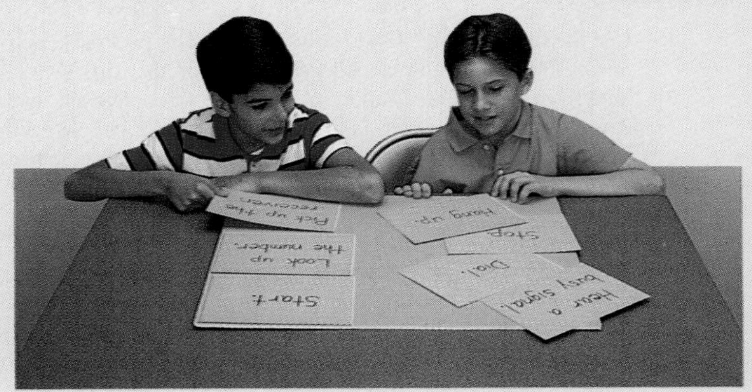

CONNECTIONS Use these anytime.

Problem of the Day

Flip Answer Dave and Maeve are flipping a coin to see who goes first in a game. "Heads, I win, tails you lose," says Dave. "No way!" says Maeve. Figure out why Maeve does not agree to Dave's plan. (He wins no matter how the flip comes out.)

Math Connection

Logical Reasoning The steps for using a battery-operated pencil sharpener are mixed up. Put them in a sensible order.

(4) Remove sharpened pencil.
(2) Put pencil in hole.
(3) Gently push.
(1) Put batteries in power pack.

Life Skills

Forms Harriet is opening a new bank account. At the end of a form she must complete, it says, "If you are under 18, a parent or guardian must sign." Since Harriet was born in 1972, what should she do? (She may sign it herself.)

Classwork and Homework Supplements

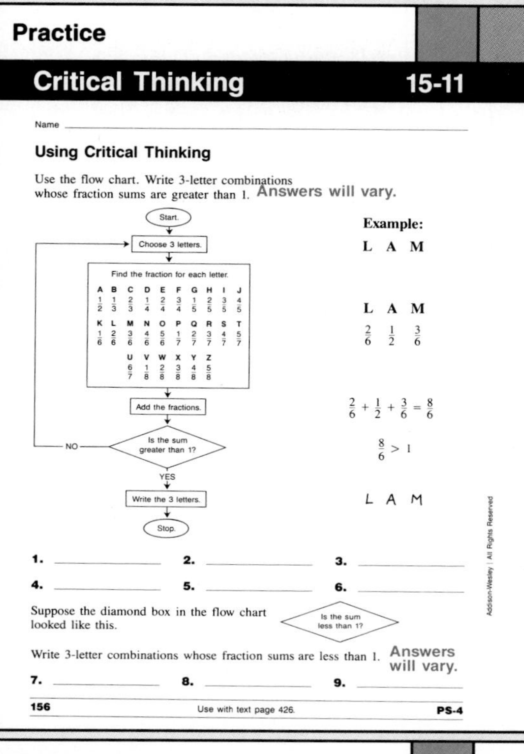

Practice

Critical Thinking 15-11

Name ______________________

Using Critical Thinking

Use the flow chart. Write 3-letter combinations whose fraction sums are greater than 1. Answers will vary.

Start. → Choose 3 letters. → Find the fraction for each letter.

A	B	C	D	E	F	G	H	I	J
$\frac{1}{2}$	$\frac{1}{3}$	$\frac{2}{3}$	$\frac{1}{4}$	$\frac{2}{4}$	$\frac{3}{4}$	$\frac{1}{5}$	$\frac{2}{5}$	$\frac{3}{5}$	$\frac{4}{5}$

K	L	M	N	O	P	Q	R	S	T
$\frac{1}{6}$	$\frac{2}{6}$	$\frac{3}{6}$	$\frac{4}{6}$	$\frac{5}{6}$	$\frac{1}{7}$	$\frac{2}{7}$	$\frac{3}{7}$	$\frac{4}{7}$	$\frac{5}{7}$

U	V	W	X	Y	Z
$\frac{6}{7}$	$\frac{1}{8}$	$\frac{2}{8}$	$\frac{3}{8}$	$\frac{4}{8}$	$\frac{5}{8}$

→ Add the fractions. → Is the sum greater than 1? NO → Choose 3 letters. YES → Write the 3 letters. → Stop.

Example:

L A M

L A M

$\frac{2}{6}$ $\frac{1}{2}$ $\frac{3}{6}$

$\frac{2}{6} + \frac{1}{2} + \frac{3}{6} = \frac{8}{6}$

$\frac{8}{6} > 1$

L A M

1. ________ **2.** ________ **3.** ________

4. ________ **5.** ________ **6.** ________

Suppose the diamond box in the flow chart looked like this. [Is the sum less than 1?]

Write 3-letter combinations whose fraction sums are less than 1. Answers will vary.

7. ________ **8.** ________ **9.** ________

156 Use with text page 426. PS-4

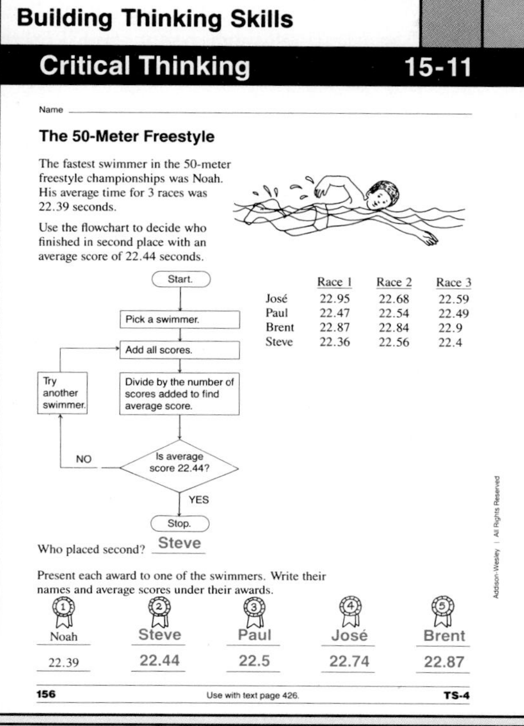

Building Thinking Skills

Critical Thinking 15-11

Name ______________________

The 50-Meter Freestyle

The fastest swimmer in the 50-meter freestyle championships was Noah. His average time for 3 races was 22.39 seconds.

Use the flowchart to decide who finished in second place with an average score of 22.44 seconds.

	Race 1	Race 2	Race 3
José	22.95	22.68	22.59
Paul	22.47	22.54	22.49
Brent	22.87	22.84	22.9
Steve	22.36	22.56	22.4

Start. → Pick a swimmer. → Add all scores. → Divide by the number of scores added to find average score. → Is average score 22.44? NO → Try another swimmer. YES → Stop.

Who placed second? Steve

Present each award to one of the swimmers. Write their names and average scores under their awards.

1	2	3	4	5
Noah	Steve	Paul	José	Brent
22.39	22.44	22.5	22.74	22.87

156 Use with text page 426. TS-4

Reteaching

Critical Thinking 15-11

Name ______________________

Using Critical Thinking

Flow charts show a step-by-step way of doing things. Different shapes are used for the different steps.

(Start.) or (Stop.) [Instruction] <Question>

Use the flowchart to answer these questions.

1. What is the first step? Write a word.

2. What is the question in the flow chart? Is the word even?

3. If the word is even, what do you do next? stop

4. What is the sum of the word DOG? 26

5. Is the word DOG even or odd? even

6. The word is DUCK. Is this word even? no What is the next step? Go back and write a word.

Start. → Write a word. → Find the number for each letter in the word. (A → 1, B → 2, C → 3 ... X → 24, Y → 25, Z → 26) → Add the numbers. → Is the word even? NO → Write a word. YES → Stop.

156 Use with text page 426. RS-4

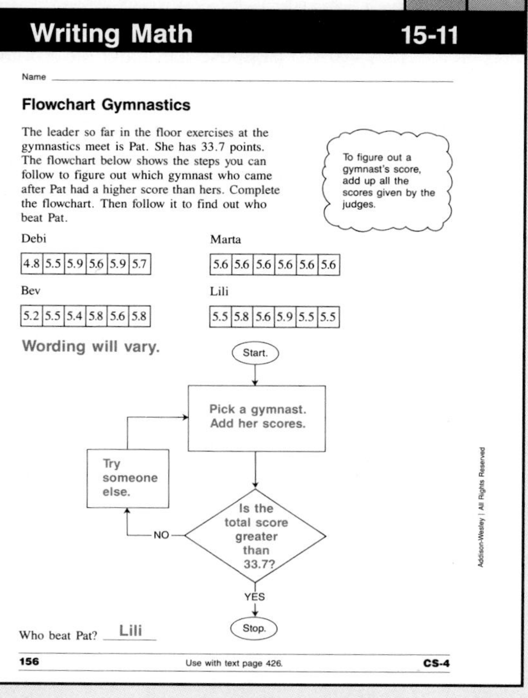

Challenges

Writing Math 15-11

Name ______________________

Flowchart Gymnastics

The leader so far in the floor exercises at the gymnastics meet is Pat. She has 33.7 points. The flowchart below shows the steps you can follow to figure out which gymnast who came after Pat had a higher score than hers. Complete the flowchart. Then follow it to find out who beat Pat.

To figure out a gymnast's score, add up all the scores given by the judges.

Debi

4.8	5.5	5.9	5.6	5.9	5.7

Marta

5.6	5.6	5.6	5.6	5.6	5.6

Bev

5.2	5.5	5.4	5.8	5.6	5.8

Lili

5.5	5.8	5.6	5.9	5.5	5.5

Wording will vary.

Start. → Pick a gymnast. Add her scores. → Is the total score greater than 33.7? NO → Try someone else. YES → Stop.

Who beat Pat? Lili

156 Use with text page 426. CS-4

Options for Individual Needs

Basic

Exercises 1-3, 5-8
More Practice, p. 527, set C

Supplements
Reteaching 156 or
Practice 156

Average

Exercises 1-8
More Practice, p. 527, set C

Supplements
Practice 156
Challenges 156 or
Thinking Skills 156

Extended

Exercises 1-7

Supplements
Challenges 156
Thinking Skills 156

Other Resources:
Problem-Solving Experiences in Mathematics, Grade 4, Problem 81
Math In Stride, Grade 4, pp. 199, 200
Kids Are Consumers, Too!, pp. 6, 7

15-11

LESSON PLAN 15-11

OBJECTIVE 15-11
To use critical thinking to analyze and follow a flow chart

Materials: calculators

1. MOTIVATE AND TEACH

LEARN ABOUT IT

▶ **Identify shapes in the flow chart.** (rectangle, diamond)
▶ **Compare shapes by the type of directions in each.** (Rectangles give basic steps to follow; the diamond asks a *YES/NO* question.)
▶ **Identify another guide in the flow chart.** (Arrows show in which direction to move.)
▶ **Decide which arrows are most important.** (*YES* or *NO* arrows from the diamond show what to do next, based on an answer to the question.)

TALK ABOUT IT
▶ **Summarize the plan of the flow chart.** (Possible answer: to find decimal sums for various words)
▶ **Analyze the steps in the largest rectangle.** (Count by tenths starting with A to give every letter its own decimal value.)
▶ **Explain the question in the diamond.** (A whole word has a whole number sum with no tenths.)
Student Edition answers: **1.** how to know whether a word is "whole" **2.** Start. Write a word. **3.** 4.1 **4.** The letters in *stop* have a whole number sum of 7.

2. CHECK UNDERSTANDING

TRY IT OUT

ERROR ALERT Substituting incorrect decimal values for the letters or adding incorrectly. Misinterpreting flow-chart steps.

Using Critical Thinking

LEARN ABOUT IT

Ellie showed this **flow chart** to Rosa. "Let's try to figure it out," said Rosa. "It might be fun, so I'll try the word *fun*!"

"What does *Is the word whole?* mean?" asked Ellie.

"I don't know," said Rosa, "but let's try the word *stop* before we stop!"

"Oh, now I see what it means!" said Ellie.

Start.
Write a word.
Find the decimal for each letter in the word.
A B C D . . . W X Y Z
0.1 0.2 0.3 0.4 2.3 2.4 2.5 2.6
Add the decimals.
Is the word whole?
NO
YES
Stop.

TALK ABOUT IT See teaching notes.

1. A flow chart gives directions for doing something. What does this flow chart tell you how to do?
2. It is important to do the steps in order. What is the first step in this flow chart? What is the second step?
3. What is the decimal value for the word *fun*?
4. How did trying the word *stop* help Jill see what *Is the word whole?* means?

TRY IT OUT

Does the word rate a perfect 10?

Suppose the diamond box in the flow chart looked like this. Which of these words would rate a perfect 10?

1. wizards **yes** 2. fourth **no** 3. squares **no** 4. problems **yes**

TEACHING OPTIONS

RETEACHING TIPS Have students who use incorrect values for the letters list each letter with its decimal equivalent. Such a list can help increase students' speed and accuracy. Allow them to use a calculator for the decimal column addition. Assign Reteaching Supplement 156.

COMPUTER Blockers and Finders, Sunburst Communications, Copyright 1987 Vary the number of obstacles for all. The "Finder" travels through a 4-by-4 grid. The location of the "tilties," arrows, and detours are found based on their effect on the "Finder." Allow 10 to 20 min.

Problem Solving

MIXED PRACTICE

Solve. Use any problem solving strategy.

Sizes of Penguins		
Penguin	Height	Weight
Fairy	35 cm	0.9 kg
Emperor	100 cm	45 kg at the most
extinct	?	135 kg

1. How much heavier than a fairy penguin is an emperor penguin? **44.1 kg**
2. One type of large penguin is now extinct. It was 10 cm shorter than 4 times the height of a fairy penguin. How tall was the penguin that is now extinct? **130 cm**
3. Emperors usually dive about 21 meters under water. They have been known to dive 13 times that deep to find large squid. How deep have they dived? **273 meters**
4. When a penguin pops 2 meters out of the water into the air, it is jumping 3 times its own height. For a tall man to jump 3 times his height, he would have to jump $5\frac{1}{2}$ meters out of the water. How much higher than the penguin does the human need to jump to jump 3 times his height? **$3\frac{1}{2}$ meters**
5. Roberto can do a report on adelie, emperor, or little blue penguins. He can write it alone or with a partner. How many different choices does he have? **6 choices**
6. When a penguin toboggans, it can go as fast as 3.2 kilometers in 15 minutes. Estimate how far it could get in an hour. **12 kilometers**
7. The zookeeper divided the fish for the penguins into 6 buckets. Each bucket had 9 fish. She also put 15 fish into a bag. When the fish in the buckets and the bag had been fed to the penguins, the zookeeper still had 8 fish left in her pocket. How many fish did she start out with? **77 fish**
8. Penguin parents sometimes feed their young as much as 907 grams of food an hour. At that rate, how much food would a baby get in 12 hours? **10,884 grams**

More Practice, page 527, set C

3. PRACTICE AND APPLY

Basic	1-3, 5-8
Average	1-8
Extended	1-7

Sample Solutions: See p. T79.

MIXED PRACTICE

► **Identify 2 one-step problems you can solve by using the same operation.** (Multiply to solve Problems 3 and 8.)

► **Explain how Problems 1 and 2 are related.** (Both use data from the table.)

► **Decide on a useful strategy for Problem 5.** (Make an Organized List)

► **Identify an important relationship to know to solve Problem 6.** (1 h = 60 min)

CLOSE AND ASSESS

WRITE WHAT YOU THINK

Have students write an explanation of how a flow chart presents a decision-making step. They should use the flow chart on page 426 as a guide. (Sample answer: A diamond box gives *yes* and *no* paths to follow, depending on which answer fits the question.)

QUICK QUIZ

For a computer game, make a flow chart that gives addition facts to solve. One step is *Enter the sum*. Use the flow-chart shapes pictured on page 426. See p. T79 for sample anno.

15-11

CHAPTER 15

APPLIED PROBLEM SOLVING GROUP DECISION MAKING

OBJECTIVE To analyze, organize, and make decisions using relevant data

FACTS TO CONSIDER

► **Analyze the directions to determine the materials you need to make the kite as described.** (scissors, knife or saw, balsa wood sticks, wrapping paper, glue, fabric for the tail, string)

► **Explain how this list might affect the total cost.** (You might need to buy balsa wood, glue, wrapping paper, string, or tools.)

► **Identify measurement relationships that will help you evaluate the data.** (12 in. = 1 ft; $\frac{1}{2}$ ft = 6 in.)

► **Explain how changing all measurements to inches may help.** (It is easier to compare sizes in the same unit of measurement.)

Applied Problem Solving
Group Decision Making

UNDERSTAND
FIND DATA
PLAN
ESTIMATE
SOLVE
CHECK

Group Skill:
Disagree in an Agreeable Way

Your group wants to enter the school's kite-flying contest. You need to figure out how many kites the group will make, what materials you will need, and how much your kites will cost.

Facts to Consider

You will need to follow these directions to make one kite.

1. Cut a balsa wood stick 24 inches long and another one 30 inches long.
2. Cut notches in the ends of the sticks.

428

TEACHING OPTIONS

COOPERATIVE LEARNING

Grouping Suggestion: cooperative learning groups of 4 to 6

Divide the class into groups in which at least 1 student has flown a kite or, if possible, has built a kite. To begin the process, help students list the tasks involved: understand construction directions, work with measurement units, make sketches or plans, compare various costs and materials, find money totals, and generate questions to consider what may not be clearly understood. You may wish to provide graph paper, rulers, and calculators to help students analyze the data.

Cost of Materials		
wrapping paper rolls small large extra large	 $1.78 $2.40 $3.50	 4 feet long and $2\frac{1}{2}$ feet wide 6 feet long and $2\frac{1}{2}$ feet wide 6 feet long and 3 feet wide
balsa wood sticks	$0.40 each $0.45 each $0.52 each	3 feet long 4 feet long 5 feet long
kite string, 1 ball	$1.46	

3. Tie the sticks together so they make a small letter *t*.
4. Run 1 piece of string through all the notches and tie it. Now you have a frame.
5. Cut a piece of wrapping paper to cover your frame. Make it $\frac{1}{2}$ inch taller and $\frac{1}{2}$ inch wider than the frame so you can fold it over.
6. Glue the wrapping paper to the frame.
7. Punch 2 holes in the paper and attach the flying string.
8. Make a tail.

Some Questions to Answer

1. How many kite sticks can you cut from a 3-foot balsa wood stick? a four-foot stick? a five-foot stick?
2. How many kites can you cut from one small roll of wrapping paper? from a large roll? from an extra-large roll?
3. How many kites will your group make?
4. Do you need more than one ball of kite string?
5. Can you think of a way to save money when you buy your materials? Hint: It might help to draw a picture or diagram to plan the least wasteful use of materials.

What Is Your Decision?

Make a list of the materials you will need. Tell how much it will cost to make the kites.

429

EXTENSION Investigate costs of ready-made kites that are about the same size as the one described in the Group Decision Making situation. Compare and contrast making and buying kites. Evaluate advantages and disadvantages of each possibility based on cost, effort, and any other important factors. (Answers will vary.)

SOME QUESTIONS TO ANSWER

▶ **Explain the operation to use to change the lengths from feet to inches.** (Multiply the number of feet by 12 to change to inches.)
▶ **Decide the dimensions of each roll of wrapping paper in inches.** (48 × 30; 72 × 30; 72 × 36)
▶ **Explain why you may consider making more than 1 kite.** (Possible answers: for an extra kite with which to practice; to enter the kite that flies better; to have a backup kite)
▶ **Decide what you need to know about the string.** (how much string is on the ball)

WHAT IS YOUR DECISION?

Have groups present their conclusions orally as they display any sketches or plans they used in making their decisions. Allow time for groups to question one another to clarify why they may have drawn different conclusions and to understand the justifications behind each decision. Guide groups to discuss other factors they might consider in planning a kite-making project, such as work time and space or prior experience making kites.

CHAPTER 15

WRAP UP

INTRODUCTION The Wrap Up provides activities emphasizing math language and thinking skills for the chapter and a project that integrates those skills with other math strands.

USING PAGE 430

What Comes First? Have students complete this section independently, then share their results in small groups to discuss any discrepancies.

Sometimes, Always, Never

▶ **Explain how to add or subtract fractions.** (Be sure fractions have like denominators, but add or subtract numerators only.)

▶ **Identify an example and a counterexample for Exercise 5.** (Samples: $3\frac{1}{4} + 1\frac{1}{4} = 4\frac{1}{2}$; $3\frac{3}{4} + 1\frac{1}{4} = 5$)

▶ **Explain what it means to annex zeros to a decimal.** (Add zeros after the last decimal place.)

Project Provide a collection of recipes or cookbooks, or have students do the project as a homework assignment so they may use favorite family recipes.

▶ **Decide on a plan for rewriting each recipe amount.** (Write the amount for each ingredient twice, find the sum of the doubles, then reduce to lowest terms.)

Have students illustrate their recipes on sheets of colored construction paper. Display the recipes on a bulletin board or collate all into a class cookbook.

WRAP UP

What Comes First?

Choose the phrase that correctly completes the sentence.

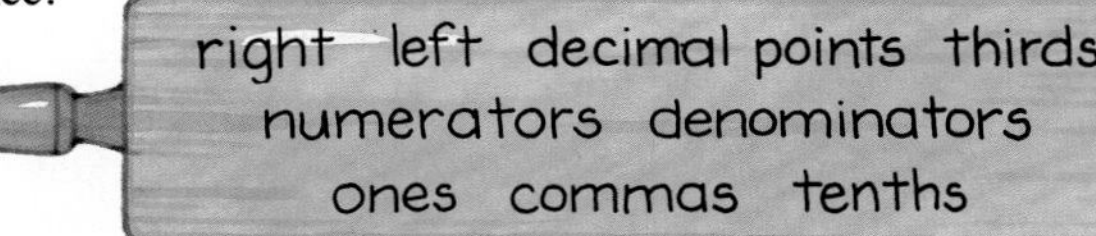

1. When you add or subtract fractions, first look at the __?__. denominators
2. When you add or subtract decimals, first line up the __?__. decimal points
3. When you add or subtract fractions with like denominators, first add the __?__ and write the sum over the denominator. numerators

Sometimes, Always, Never

Which word should go in the blank, sometimes, always, or never? Explain your choices. Explanations will vary.

4. To add or subtract fractions, you __?__ add or subtract denominators. never
5. The sum of two mixed numbers is __?__ a mixed number. sometimes
6. If you annex extra zeros to the right of the last decimal point, the value of the decimal __?__ stays the same. always

Project

Find a recipe for making something special you like to eat. Rewrite the recipe so it will make twice as much as the original recipe.

430

TEACHING OPTIONS

ENRICHMENT Have students use number sense to increase a recipe to make 4 times its original amount. (Double each amount, then double that amount.) Challenge them to adjust a recipe to make half the amount. Allow them to use fraction models or fraction strips (TA 21) to help them make adjustments.

CHAPTER REVIEW/TEST

Part 1 Understanding

1. Use fractions to tell how much of the pentagon is red and how much is blue. $\frac{3}{5}$, $\frac{2}{5}$

2. Explain what trade you could make to subtract $\frac{1}{2}$ from $\frac{7}{8}$. Then find the difference. See Additional Answers.

3. Find a pattern. Give the next 3 numbers in each row. P stands for perimeter and A stands for area. See Additional Answers.

P (in cm)	4	8	12	16	?	?	?
A (in sq cm)	1	4	9	16	?	?	?

Part 2 Skills

Add or subtract. Reduce answers to lowest terms.

4. $\frac{7}{10} - \frac{2}{10}$ $\frac{1}{2}$
5. $\frac{5}{6} + \frac{5}{6}$ $1\frac{2}{3}$
6. $\frac{6}{7} + \frac{4}{7}$ $1\frac{3}{7}$
7. $\frac{1}{4} + \frac{1}{2}$ $\frac{3}{4}$
8. $\frac{1}{8} + \frac{3}{4}$ $\frac{7}{8}$
9. $\frac{2}{3} - \frac{2}{9}$ $\frac{4}{9}$

Add or subtract.

10. 0.63 − 0.28 = 0.35
11. 3.74 + 8.26 = 12.00
12. 42.22 + 30.89 = 73.11
13. $23.50 − $ 9.62 = $13.88
14. 4.52 + 7.7 12.22
15. 44 − 35.01 8.99
16. 13.7 + 0.68 14.38

Part 3 Applications

17. At breakfast time, Dan was 20 km from his goal of hiking 500 km per month. If he hiked 12.9 km before lunch and 7.4 km after lunch, did he reach his goal? Yes; he passed it by 0.3 km.

18. **Challenge** A campfire stew recipe calls for $2\frac{1}{2}$ cups of water. Dan doubles the recipe. His canteen holds $1\frac{1}{4}$ cups. How many times must he fill it to make the stew? 4 times

431

CHAPTER REVIEW/TEST

INTRODUCTION The Review/Test is provided to review and evaluate the skills and concepts presented in Chapter 15.

USING PAGE 431
If you prefer to use this page for review, you may want to use the **Multiple-Choice Posttest** (pages 59-60) or the **Free-Response Posttest** (pages 59-60) to evaluate mastery of Chapter objectives.

ITEM ANALYSIS The table below correlates the Chapter Review/Test items with the lesson objectives for the chapter.

Items	Objectives
1	15-1
2	15-4
3	15-6
4-6	15-2
7-9	15-4
10-13	15-8
14-16	15-9
17	15-10
18	15-3

Additional Answers: See p. T79.

INFORMAL ASSESSMENT

Using Manipulatives Have students use fraction pieces or fraction strips (TA 21) to demonstrate how to add and subtract the following fraction pairs, then record the sums and differences in lowest terms: $\frac{3}{4}$ and $\frac{1}{8}$, $\frac{5}{6}$ and $\frac{1}{3}$, $\frac{7}{10}$ and $\frac{1}{2}$. ($\frac{7}{8}$, $\frac{5}{8}$; $1\frac{1}{6}$, $\frac{1}{2}$; $1\frac{1}{5}$, $\frac{1}{5}$)

Communication *Tell why you can annex 1 or more zeros when you add or subtract decimals without changing their value.* (When you annex a zero to the right of a decimal point or last decimal place, you indicate an empty place and do not add to or take away from the decimal value.)

Critical Thinking *Tell why a flow chart is useful for giving clear instructions.* (Possible answer: A flow chart tells you the exact order in which to follow a set of steps and what to do with a *yes* or *no* choice.)

CHAPTER 15

ENRICHMENT

INTRODUCTION In this activity, students will increase their understanding of geometry concepts, visual problem solving, and fraction computation.

USING PAGE 432
This Enrichment page is provided for all students. You may wish to use it after they have completed the Chapter Review/Test on page 431.

▶ **Identify each shape that is a fractional part of the hexagon.** (equilateral triangle; trapezoid; parallelogram)

▶ **Decide on a method for determining the relationship between the hexagon and each other shape.** (Visualize the hexagon filled with as many of each shape as may fit; use pattern blocks or tracing paper.)

▶ **Explain how to consider Exercises 2-5 as addition situations.** (Find the sum of all fractional parts used in the figures.)

▶ **Decide on a plan for finding the fraction sums.** (Use equivalent fractions so that all have like denominators, add, then reduce to lowest terms.)

▶ **Explain a way to check your addition.** (Possible answer: Reconstruct each shape over a hexagon to see whether it fills the same fractional amount of the hexagon as the sum.)

Additional Answers: See p. T79.

ENRICHMENT
Puzzling Fractions

Think of this hexagon as one unit.

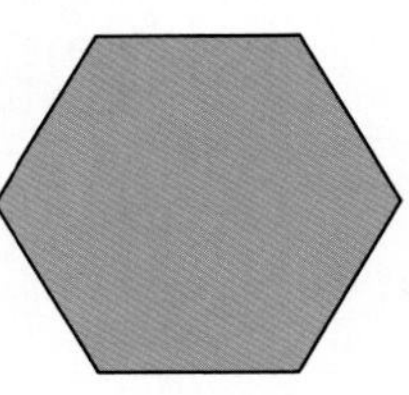

These shapes are fractional parts of the hexagon.

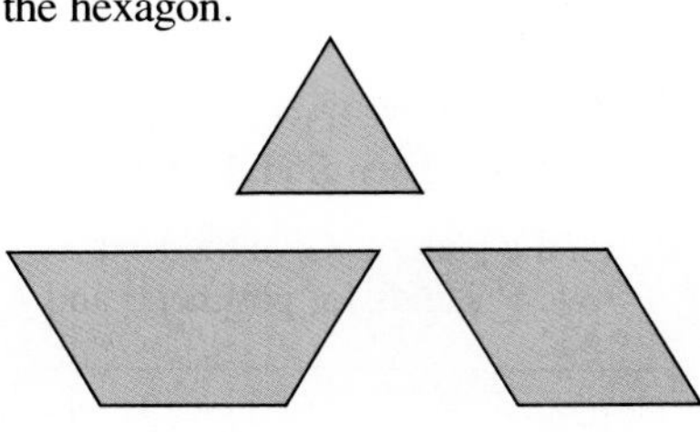

See Additional Answers.

1. Tell what fractional part of the hexagon each piece is. Use pattern blocks or tracing paper if you need help.

Write what fractional part of the original hexagon each of these pieces is. Then add the fractions in each problem. Write the sum as a fraction in lowest terms, a whole number, or a mixed number.

2. 

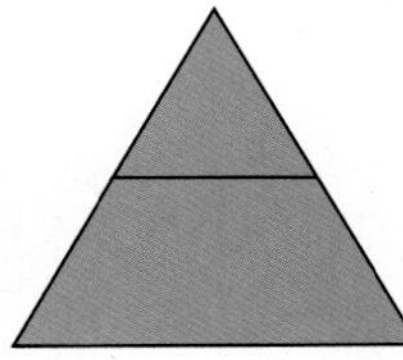

3.

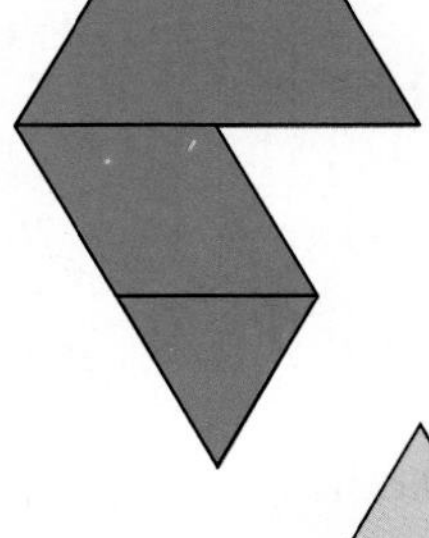

4.

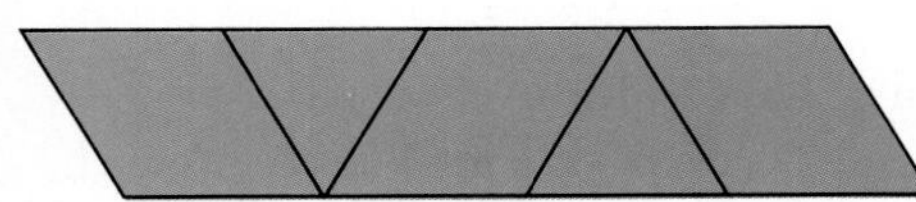

5.

6. Make a 3-piece quadrilateral, the sum of whose pieces is $\frac{5}{6}$.

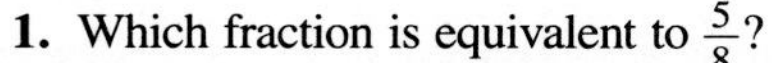

Cumulative Review

1. Which fraction is equivalent to $\frac{5}{8}$?

   A $\frac{8}{5}$ (B) $\frac{40}{64}$ C $\frac{10}{24}$ D $\frac{25}{32}$

2. Which fraction is reduced to lowest terms?

   (A) $\frac{9}{14}$ B $\frac{9}{12}$ C $\frac{9}{15}$ D $\frac{9}{27}$

3. Find $\frac{4}{5}$ of 40.

   A 24   B 10   C 8   (D) 32

4. Which is a reasonable estimate of 12 × $3.09?

   A $27   B $15   C $30   (D) $36

5. Which number has 5 in the tenths place?

   A 54.2   B 2.54   (C) 2.54   D 50.03

6. Which decimal is less than 3.1?

   A 3.10   (B) 3.08   C 3.21   D 4.0

7. Find a decimal equal to $\frac{4}{5}$.

   (A) 0.8   B 0.5   C 0.4   D 0.1

8. Which is a reasonable length for a watermelon?

   A 48 km   B 48 m   C 48 dm   (D) 48 cm

9. About what air temperature is reasonable for a swim in an outdoor pool?

   A 10°C   B 100°C   (C) 43°C   D −5°C

10. Which weighs about 3 kg?

    A a balloon   B a stove   C a crayon   (D) a kitten

11. A juice bottle holds 200 mL. How many bottles are needed to hold 1 L of juice?

    A 10   B 4   (C) 5   D 50

12. A string bean is just under 4 cm. Which could be its length in mm?

    A 45 mm   B 4 mm   (C) 38 mm   D 387 mm

433

Cumulative Review

INTRODUCTION The purpose of this Cumulative Review is to maintain previously taught skills and concepts. The emphasis in this Cumulative Review is on fraction concepts, Chapter 12; on decimal concepts, Chapter 13; and on metric measurement, Chapter 14.

ITEM ANALYSIS The table below correlates the Cumulative Review items with the lesson objectives.

Items	Objectives
1	12-4
2	12-6
3	12-9
4	13-7
5	13-1
6	13-3
7	13-6
8	14-1
9, 10	14-9
11	14-8
12	14-3

CHAPTER 16 DIVISION: 2-DIGIT DIVISORS

Chapter Management

OVERVIEW

Lesson	Pages	Objectives	Subject Integration	Strand Integration
Chapter Opener	434-435	To introduce chapter 16	language arts-*Twenty-One Balloons*	computation
Mental Math: Special Quotients	436-437	16-1 To use mental math to divide by 2-digit divisors that are multiples of 10	health/fitness-Fun Park	estimation
Dividing by Tens: 1-Digit Quotients	438-439	16-2 To find 1-digit quotients by dividing with 2-digit divisors that are multiples of 10	social studies-air transportation	graphing
Dividing: 1-Digit Quotients	440-441	16-3 To find 1-digit quotients by dividing with 2-digit divisors	language arts-*Twenty-One Balloons*	critical thinking
Changing Estimates	442-443	16-4 To change the estimated quotient when actual division proves it to be too large or too small	social studies-wax museum	algebra
Problem Solving: Mixed Practice/Midchapter Review/Quiz	444-445	16-5 To practice problem solving	science-Monarch butterfly	measurement
Dividing by Tens: 2-Digit Quotients	446-447	16-6 To find 2-digit quotients by dividing with 2-digit divisors that are multiples of 10	language arts-*Twenty-One Balloons*	problem solving
Dividing: 2-Digit Quotients	448-449	16-7 To find 2-digit quotients by dividing with 2-digit divisors that are not rounded	health/fitness-milk	calculators
Problem Solving: Using a Calculator	450-451	16-8 To solve 2-digit division problems using a calculator	social studies-school fair	consumer math
Data Collection and Analysis: Group Decision Making	452-453	16-9 To collect, organize, and analyze data	social studies-group skills	statistics

MATHEMATICAL BACKGROUND

Division
Students learn how to divide larger numbers. They first divide 2-digit divisors into 3-digit dividends to get 1-digit quotients, then 2-digit quotients.

Estimation
In Lesson 16-4, students are taught how to recognize when they need to change an initial estimate of a quotient.

Mental Math
Students learn a strategy for mentally finding the quotient of a multiple of 10 divided by a multiple of 10.

Problem Solving
Students practice strategies learned in previous chapters, as well as solving problems using a calculator.

TIPS FROM TEACHERS

Gather several different items, such as a block, toothpicks, keys, and a can of soup. Place one item on a scale and weigh it. Hold up a second item and ask students to predict whether it will weigh more, less, or the same as the first item. Weigh it to check, then discuss the accuracy of students' predictions. Repeat with other items.

Marilyn Majer
Kings Highway School
Clearwater, FL

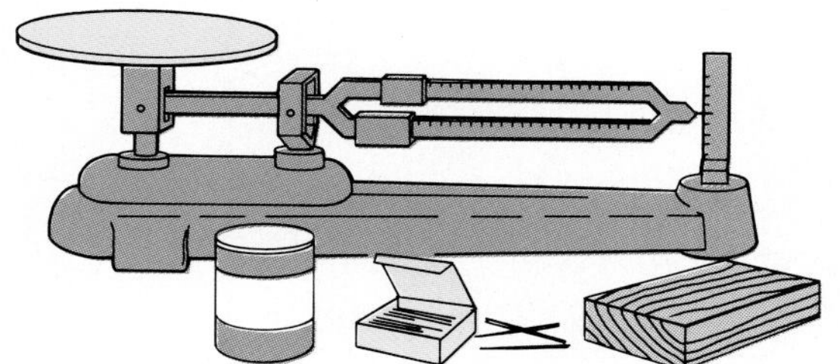

ASSESSMENT

Pretest — Chapter 16, page 1

Multiple-Choice Format

Name ______

1. Use mental math to find 400 ÷ 20. You can check by multiplying.
   a. 2 b. 20 c. 200 d. 800 — 1. b
2. Use mental math to find 150 ÷ 30.
   a. 5 b. 50 c. 500 d. 450 — 2. a
3. Divide. 30)89
   a. 29 R2 b. 2 R9 c. 2 R19 d. 2 R29 — 3. d
4. Divide. 90)730
   a. 80 R10 b. 8 R10 c. 81 R1 d. 8 R1 — 4. b
5. Divide. 38)289
   a. 7 R9 b. 7 R23 c. 9 R9 d. 9 R6 — 5. b
6. Divide. 81)$6.48
   a. $0.80 b. $8.00 c. $0.07 d. $0.08 — 6. d
7. Divide. 26)85
   a. 2 R33 b. 3 R7 c. 2 R5 d. 3 R5 — 7. b
8. Divide. 34)273
   a. 8 R1 b. 9 R3 c. 6 R33 d. 8 R3 — 8. a

Pretest — Chapter 16, page 2

Multiple-Choice Format

Name ______

9. Barbara had a 32-inch roll of ribbon. She cut as many 9-inch ribbon strips as she could from the roll. How many inches of ribbon did she have left?
   a. 23 in. b. 41 in. c. 3 in. d. 5 in. — 9. d
10. Divide. 40)964
   a. 21 R24 b. 28 R4 c. 24 R14 d. 24 R4 — 10. d
11. Divide. 40)$3.90
   a. $0.03 b. $0.13 c. $0.30 d. $1.30 — 11. b
12. Divide. 47)589
   a. 12 R25 b. 10 R19 c. 1 R9 d. 12 R9 — 12. a
13. Divide. 17)$8.16
   a. $0.42 b. $0.48 c. $4.80 d. $0.50 — 13. b
14. Divide. 61)358
   a. 51 R8 b. 6 R8 c. 5 R53 d. 59 R4 — 14. c
15. Choose the correct answer. There are 110 people who need rides to the Math Contest. Suppose each car holds 6 people. How many cars will they need? Your calculator shows: 18.333333
   a. 18 cars b. 19 cars c. Can't tell — 15. b

Posttest — Chapter 16, page 1

Multiple-Choice Format

Name ______

1. Use mental math to find 630 ÷ 90. You can check by multiplying.
   a. 7 b. 70 c. 700 d. 5,690 — 1. a
2. Use mental math to find 800 ÷ 20.
   a. 4 b. 40 c. 400 d. 1,600 — 2. b
3. Divide. 60)79
   a. 1 R13 b. 1 R3 c. 1 R19 d. 1 R9 — 3. c
4. Divide. 70)476
   a. 6 R56 b. 6 R8 c. 7 R6 d. 6 R9 — 4. a
5. Divide. 29)196
   a. 9 R6 b. 9 R16 c. 6 R12 d. 6 R22 — 5. d
6. Divide. 93)$7.44
   a. $0.80 b. $8.00 c. $0.07 d. $0.08 — 6. d
7. Divide. 36)74
   a. 1 R28 b. 2 R4 c. 2 R2 d. 1 R4 — 7. c
8. Divide. 73)641
   a. 9 R11 b. 8 R57 c. 8 R67 d. 9 R1 — 8. b

Posttest — Chapter 16, page 2

Multiple-Choice Format

Name ______

9. Alice had a 35-inch roll of ribbon. She cut as many 9-inch ribbon strips as she could from the roll. How many inches of ribbon did she have left?
   a. 26 in. b. 4 in. c. 3 in. d. 8 in. — 9. d
10. Divide. 20)738
   a. 32 R8 b. 36 R1 c. 36 R18 d. 31 R18 — 10. c
11. Divide. 40)$4.80
   a. $0.12 b. $0.01 c. $0.10 d. $1.12 — 11. a
12. Divide. 35)784
   a. 2 R4 b. 26 R4 c. 22 R4 d. 22 R14 — 12. d
13. Divide. 18)$9.36
   a. $0.48 b. $0.52 c. $4.13 d. $4.28 — 13. b
14. Divide. 71)482
   a. 6 R56 b. 68 R4 c. 60 R2 d. 6 R66 — 14. a
15. Choose the correct answer. Jack has a roll of twine that is 338 feet long. He wants to cut 21-feet pieces from the roll. How many pieces can he cut? Your calculator shows: 16.095238
   a. 16 pieces b. 17 pieces c. Can't tell — 15. a

ITEM ANALYSIS

Items	Objectives
1, 2	16-1
3, 4	16-2
5, 6	16-3
7, 8	16-4
9	16-5
10, 11	16-6
12-14	16-7
15	16-8

Note: The item analysis is the same for all pretests and posttests for this chapter.

ALSO AVAILABLE

- Free Response Tests
- Alternative Tests
- Thinking Strategies
- Concrete Materials

Optional Chapter Activities

PROJECT AND BULLETIN BOARD

Prepare two large, colorful shapes that resemble hydrogen balloons. Label one basket *1-Digit Quotients* and the other *2-Digit Quotients*. Then prepare a number of division problems of varying degrees of difficulty that follow the progression of the lessons in the chapter. Write them on blank index cards or on small construction-paper shapes. Then scatter them around the bottom of the bulletin board and tack them on. As students complete each lesson, they may pick a division problem to solve and tack inside the appropriate balloon. When all the prepared division problems have been solved and sorted, have students prepare new division cards with problems they formulate themselves for their classmates to solve and sort.

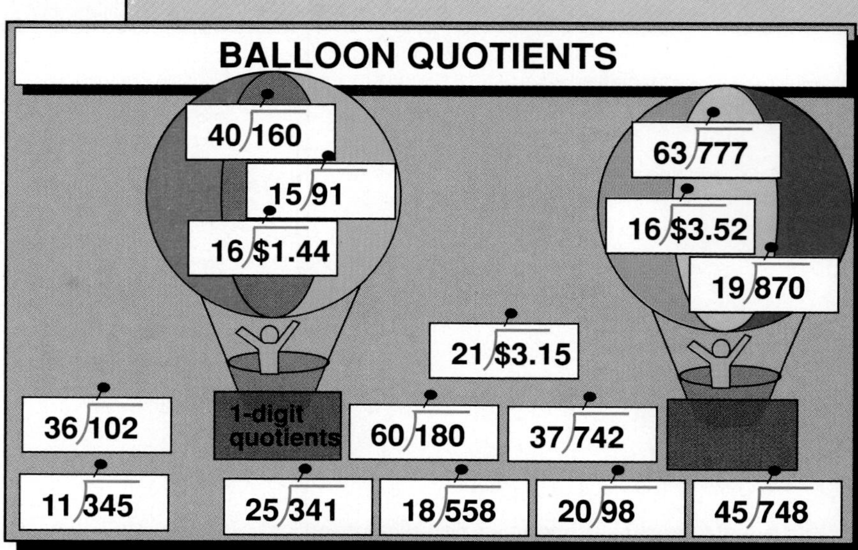

COOPERATIVE LEARNING

Divide the class into groups of three or four. Identify the group skill: explain and summarize. Appoint group leaders. Give each group some 3-digit numbers ending in either 0 or 5. Include some decimal numbers. Have one student divide these numbers by 5 and another student divide them by 10. The group should draw conclusions about which numbers can be divided evenly by which divisors. Then each group should come up with two rules they can remember that will help them with division problems. (Any number ending in 0 or 5 can be divided evenly by 5. Any number ending in 0 can be divided evenly by 10. Some groups may also notice that to divide by 10 they can simply move the decimal point one place to the left.) Students should agree on the wording of the rules; one student should write them next to examples. Have groups present their rules to the rest of the class for discussion or display.

You will find grouping suggestions and cooperative learning activities in most lessons throughout this chapter.

LITERATURE

Adler, David A. *Calculator Fun.* New York: Franklin Watts, 1981.

This beginner's book on calculators shows children how to use them and have fun at the same time. There are calculator riddles, surprises, puzzles, and games. Children will enjoy discussing the games described in the book. Then the children could select a game and pair off and play.

Bitter, Gary and Thomas Metes. *Exploring with Pocket Calculators.* New York: Julian Messner, 1977.

Simon, Seymour. *Computer Sense Computer Nonsense.* New York: J. B. Lippincott, 1984.

English as a Second Language

Use these teaching hints and the accompanying lesson to help ESL students review the division algorithm.

- Be sure children understand the vocabulary.
- Relate the notation to concrete examples.
- Explore division in relation to multiplication.
- Discuss reasons for rounding and estimating.
- Check for errors at every step in the algorithm.

Introduce a number of objects to be distributed, such as 100 marbles among 27 children. Write $27\overline{)100}$ on the chalkboard, labeling the dividend and divisor. As you point to each number, say *The dividend, 100, is divided by the divisor, 27.* Have students do the algorithm. Check comprehension by asking children to identify each step in the division and have a volunteer do the algorithm on the chalkboard. Have students identify the quotient, 3, and the remainder, 19. Then have another volunteer write the multiplication check on the chalkboard. Encourage them to identify factors, product, addend, and sum and to compare check steps to the division algorithm.

Gifted

Instruct your students to choose a partner. Have each pair cut three index cards into thirds and number each third with a multiple of ten, from 20 to 90. They should place the cards spread out and face down. Have them number a blank spinner (TA 11) from 1 to 9.

Each pair chooses one of the face down cards as the divisor for a division problem. Next, have them take turns spinning the spinner four times. Each number will represent a digit in the 4-digit number which will be the dividend in the division problem. Have them write down the division problem. One player solves the problem in a specified period of time, such as one minute. If the problem is solved correctly within the allotted amount of time, that player receives one point. An additional point is scored if the problem is solved mentally. Remind students to remember to include remainders in their answers.

Players rotate turns. One player solves the division problem while the other player checks for accuracy. The pair with the most combined points wins.

Students at Risk

Division by 2-digit divisors is one of the most problematic algorithms students must master. Students with memory, sequence, spatial, or visual organization deficits may encounter many obstacles to success.

An error students make involves incorrect placement of quotient digits. Show students how to group places in the dividend to make the first division step. They draw a small box for each digit of the quotient, then perform the steps of the algorithm. You may use color-coded worksheets to highlight this method.

$$71\overline{)347} \quad \text{but} \quad 71\overline{)836} \qquad 71\overline{)\boxed{347}} \qquad 71\overline{)\boxed{83}6}$$

Provide frequent review of the multiplication and subtraction skills involved in long division. You may allow students to use calculators to perform some intermediary calculations.

You may also use the Reteaching Supplements and the specific Reteaching Tips from each lesson in this chapter.

CHAPTER 16

INTRODUCING THE CHAPTER

SUBJECT INTEGRATION The photograph of the annual balloon festival in Reno, Nevada, suggests the chapter theme of language arts. Several lessons use division situations based on the novel *Twenty-One Balloons* by William Pene du Bois, including information on hydrogen balloons and on the Pacific island of Krakatoa, which was destroyed by a violent volcanic eruption in 1883.

USING DATA The Language Arts Data Bank on page 478 of the Student Edition provides statements of fact and fiction from the book *Twenty-One Balloons* by William Pene du Bois. It also shows a labeled diagram of the parts of a hydrogen balloon.

QUESTION 1 ► **Evaluate the statement you must use to solve the problem to plan a solution method.** (If there are 80 people in families of 4, you must divide 80 by 4 to find the number of families; when you know the number of families, multiply by 2 to find the total number of children.)
Student Edition answer: 20, 40

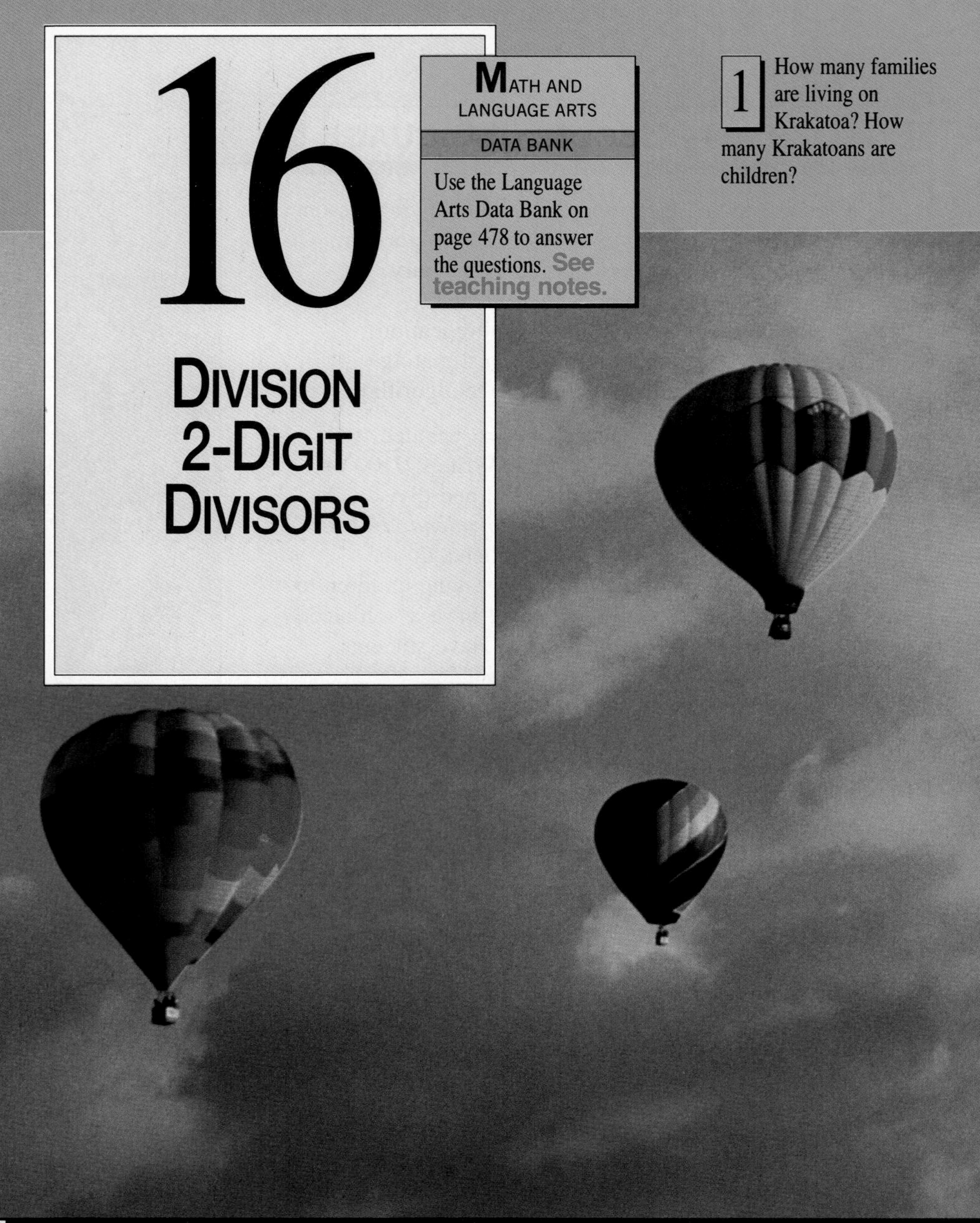

16
DIVISION
2-DIGIT
DIVISORS
MATH AND
LANGUAGE ARTS
DATA BANK
Use the Language Arts Data Bank on page 478 to answer the questions. See teaching notes.
1 How many families are living on Krakatoa? How many Krakatoans are children?

TEACHING OPTIONS

LANGUAGE DEVELOPMENT
Write the verb **alternate** on the chalkboard. Have students infer its meaning by listening to this sentence: Large and small balloons *alternate* around the platform. (Possible answers: ''take turns''; are in a pattern of large, small, large, small . . .) Ask students to describe a number pattern that alternates. (Answers may vary. Sample answers: counting consecutive numbers alternates odd and even; endings of multiples of 5 alternate in 5 or 0.)

2 Krakatoan inventions include a balloon merry-go-round. How many children can ride the balloon merry-go-round at a time?

3 The book *Twenty-One Balloons* was first published in 1947. How many years after the actual explosion of Krakatoa was this?

4 **Use Critical Thinking** Everyone escapes the volcano on a balloon platform. How many of each size balloon are on each side of the platform?

435

QUESTION 2 ▶ **Identify the data you need to solve the problem.** (A balloon merry-go-round had 8 boats, each of which held 2 children.)
▶ **Choose the operation to use and explain your decision.** (Multiplication to put together same-size groups.)
Student Edition answer: 16 children

QUESTION 3 ▶ **Explain how you answered the question.** (Subtract 1883, the date of the explosion, from 1947.)
▶ **Decide how many years have passed since Krakatoa exploded.** (Answers may vary.)
Student Edition answer: 64 years

QUESTION 4 ▶ **Decide which problem-solving strategy makes sense to use to understand how the balloon platform looked.** (Draw a Picture)
▶ **Analyze the data to help you draw the picture.** (Possible answer: Draw a rectangle, then draw a large balloon at each corner. Counting the balloon at each corner, show a total of 3 large balloons on each shorter side, then work backward to see how many large balloons remain for the longer sides. Draw a small balloon between each large balloon, then check that there are 10 of each size balloon.)
Student Edition answer: long sides have 4 large and 3 small balloons; short sides have 3 large and 2 small balloons.

SUBJECT INTEGRATION PROJECT Have small groups pick research topics related to hot-air or hydrogen balloons. Brainstorm a list of questions students might wish to answer about balloons, such as how balloons fly, where balloon festivals are held, how the balloon is made, what balloon-flight records there are, how you learn to fly a balloon, when the first balloons flew, or what are scientific uses for balloons. Conclude by having groups display their findings on colorful balloon shapes.

LESSON OPTIONS 16-1

Mental Math: Special Quotients

OBJECTIVE 16-1 To use mental math to divide by 2-digit divisors that are multiples of 10

PREBOOK ACTIVITIES

QUICK REVIEW

Divide using mental math.

1. 320 ÷ 8 (40) **2.** 240 ÷ 3 (80) **3.** 180 ÷ 6 (30)
4. 280 ÷ 7 (40) **5.** 360 ÷ 9 (40) **6.** 300 ÷ 6 (50)
7. 160 ÷ 4 (40) **8.** 420 ÷ 7 (60) **9.** 450 ÷ 9 (50)

PRIOR KNOWLEDGE

Have students review the concept of special sums, differences, products, and quotients by giving examples of each based on the digits 2 and 4. (Answers may vary. Samples: 200 + 200 = 400; 4,000 − 2,000 = 2,000; 20 × 20 = 400; 400 ÷ 2 = 200) Have students explain why special calculations such as these are easy to do using mental math. (Possible answer: Use basic number facts, then adjust for place value.) Tell students that in this lesson they will find special quotients in which the divisors are multiples of ten.

COMMUNICATION

Discussing and Writing Math In their Math Journals, have students write a statement in which they summarize, then generalize how basic number facts in division relate to special quotients. (Possible response: If you know that 4 ÷ 2 = 2, you can use that fact to find special quotients mentally, such as 400 ÷ 2 = 200 or 4,000 ÷ 2 = 2,000.) Ask volunteers to read their statements aloud. Then have students discuss situations in which they might find special quotients. (Possible answers: making estimates; checking answers)

EXPLORE AND CONNECT

Materials: play money $10 bills, blank index cards
Alternative Materials: TA 10 (Play Money—Larger Bills)
Grouping Suggestion: cooperative learning groups of 6
Students explore special quotients with play money. One member of each group writes a basic division fact, such as 21 ÷ 7, on an index card. A second student adjusts the fact by changing the dividend and divisor to multiples of ten: 210 ÷ 70. A third student counts out 21 play $10 bills so that a fourth student can model the division. A fifth student decides how to record the division (21 tens ÷ 7 tens; 210 ÷ 70; 70)210), as the last student uses any means to check the quotient. Groups repeat the activity for 5 other division facts, trading tasks. Have students generalize to describe the quotient when you divide a multiple of ten by a smaller multiple of ten. (Possible answer: If you divide a multiple of ten by a multiple of ten with 1 less place, the quotients are 1-digit numbers.)

CONNECTIONS Use these anytime.

Problem of the Day

Contest Winners Hundreds of people paid $5 each to enter a contest to win $7,500. 10 people tied for the prize, so they shared it equally. How much money did each lucky winner get? What was each one's profit? ($750; $745)

Number Sense

Mental Math Create 4 division equations with dividends that are multiples of ten and 1-digit divisors whose quotients are 40. (Answers may vary. Samples: 160 ÷ 4, 240 ÷ 6, 280 ÷ 7, and 320 ÷ 8.)

Patterns

Special Quotients Discover the pattern, then continue it 3 more times.
42,000,000 ÷ 60 = 700,000
4,200,000 ÷ 60 = 70,000
420,000 ÷ 60 = 7,000
(dividend decreases by one place each time; 42,000 ÷ 60 = 700; 4,200 ÷ 60 = 70; 420 ÷ 60 = 7)

Classwork and Homework Supplements

Practice

Mental Math 16-1

Name ____________________

Special Quotients

Divide, using mental math. Check by multiplying.

1. 80 ÷ 20 = 4
2. 540 ÷ 60 = 9
3. 300 ÷ 50 = 6
4. 720 ÷ 80 = 9
5. 240 ÷ 60 = 4
6. 450 ÷ 50 = 9
7. 210 ÷ 70 = 3
8. 140 ÷ 70 = 2
9. 420 ÷ 70 = 6
10. 490 ÷ 70 = 7
11. 120 ÷ 40 = 3
12. 450 ÷ 90 = 5
13. 60)60 — 1
14. 80)640 — 8
15. 30)270 — 9
16. 20)160 — 8
17. 70)350 — 5
18. 40)160 — 4
19. 50)350 — 7
20. 90)810 — 9
21. 80)480 — 6
22. How many 90s are in 180? 2
23. How many 60s are in 360? 6
24. What is 180 divided by 30? 6
25. What is 480 divided by 60? 8
26. What is 320 divided by 40? 8
27. What is 720 divided by 90? 8

Building Thinking Skills

Mental Math 16-1

Name ____________________

Bags of Gold

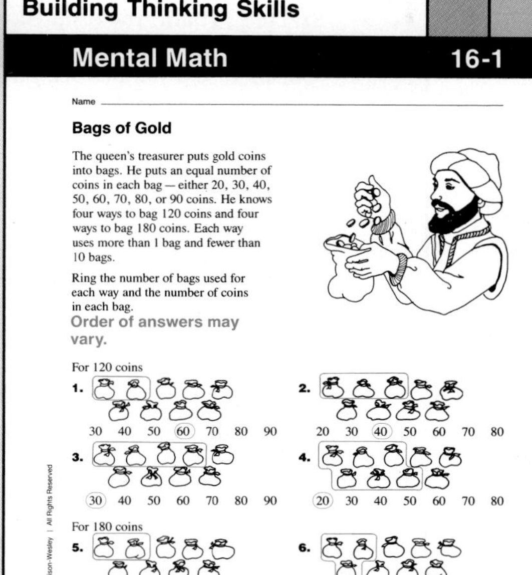

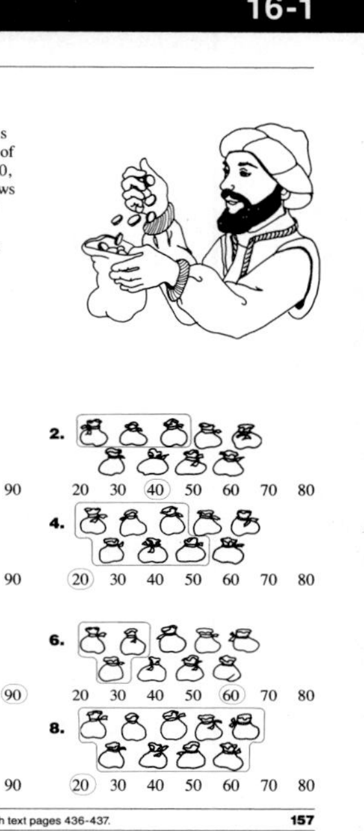

The queen's treasurer puts gold coins into bags. He puts an equal number of coins in each bag — either 20, 30, 40, 50, 60, 70, 80, or 90 coins. He knows four ways to bag 120 coins and four ways to bag 180 coins. Each way uses more than 1 bag and fewer than 10 bags.

Ring the number of bags used for each way and the number of coins in each bag.

Order of answers may vary.

For 120 coins

1. 30 40 50 (60) 70 80 90
2. 20 30 (40) 50 60 70 80
3. (30) 40 50 60 70 80 90
4. (20) 30 40 50 60 70 80

For 180 coins

5. 30 40 50 60 70 80 (90)
6. 20 30 40 50 (60) 70 80
7. (30) 40 50 60 70 80 90
8. (20) 30 40 50 60 70 80

Reteaching

Mental Math 16-1

Name ____________________

Special Quotients

How many wrappers are needed to put 120 coins into rolls of 40 coins each?

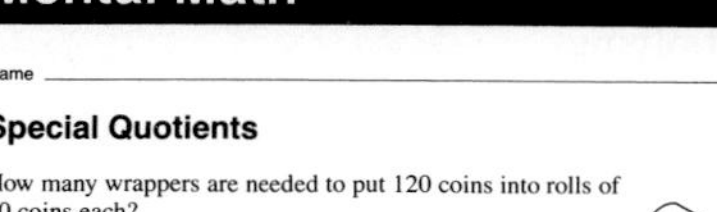

(120) (40)
12 tens ÷ 4 tens = 3
120 ÷ 40 = 3

or

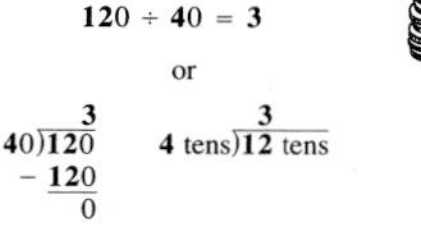

40)120 — 3
− 120
0

4 tens)12 tens — 3

Divide.

1. 30)240 — 8 (3 tens)24 tens — 8); −240; 0
2. 50)350 — 7 (5 tens)35 tens — 7); − 350; 0
3. 80)560 — 7 (8 tens)56 tens — 7); − 560; 0

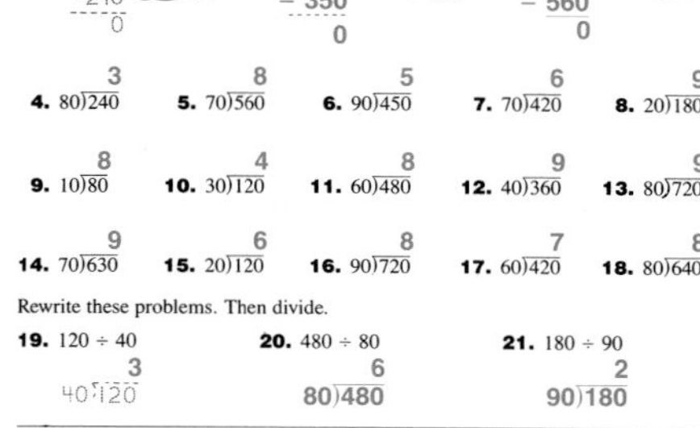

4. 80)240 — 3
5. 70)560 — 8
6. 90)450 — 5
7. 70)420 — 6
8. 20)180 — 9
9. 10)80 — 8
10. 30)120 — 4
11. 60)480 — 8
12. 40)360 — 9
13. 80)720 — 9
14. 70)630 — 9
15. 20)120 — 6
16. 90)720 — 8
17. 60)420 — 7
18. 80)640 — 8

Rewrite these problems. Then divide.

19. 120 ÷ 40 — 40)120 — 3
20. 480 ÷ 80 — 80)480 — 6
21. 180 ÷ 90 — 90)180 — 2

Challenges

Mental Math 16-1

Name ____________________

Zeroing In

Write zeros only. Make each equation correct but different.
Answers may vary. Some possible answers are given.

1. 2,400 ÷ 6 ____ = 4 00
   2,400 ÷ 6 00 = 4 ____
   2,400 ÷ 6 0 = 4 0
2. 5,600 ÷ 8 ____ = 7 00
   5,600 ÷ 8 0 = 7 0
   5,600 ÷ 8 00 = 7 ____
3. 1,400 ÷ 7 ____ = 2 00
   1,400 ÷ 7 0 = 2 0
   1,400 ÷ 7 00 = 2 ____
4. 3,200 ÷ 4 ____ = 8 00
   3,200 ÷ 4 0 = 8 0
   3,200 ÷ 4 00 = 8 ____
5. 4,000 ÷ 5 0 = 8 0
   4,000 ÷ 5 ____ = 8 00
   4,000 ÷ 5 00 = 8 ____
6. 7,200 ÷ 8 ____ = 9 00
   7,200 ÷ 8 0 = 9 0
   7,200 ÷ 8 00 = 9 ____
7. 45,000 ÷ 9 ____ = 5 ,000
   45,000 ÷ 9 0 = 5 00
   45,000 ÷ 9 00 = 5 0
   45,000 ÷ 9 ,000 = 5 ____
8. 30,000 ÷ 5 ____ = 6 ,000
   30,000 ÷ 5 0 = 6 00
   30,000 ÷ 5 00 = 6 0
   30,000 ÷ 5 ,000 = 6 ____
9. 54 ÷ 6 ____ = 9 ____
   540 ÷ 6 ____ = 9 0
   5,400 ÷ 6 0 = 9 0
   54,000 ÷ 6 0 = 9 00
10. 10 ÷ 2 ____ = 5 ____
    100 ÷ 2 ____ = 5 0
    1,000 ÷ 2 0 = 5 ____
    10,000 ÷ 2 0 = 5 00

Options for Individual Needs

Basic

Exercises 6-21, 24-29, 34-36
Skills Bank, p. 460
More Practice, p. 511, set C

Supplements
Reteaching 157 or
Practice 157

Average

Exercises 1-36
Skills Bank, p. 460
More Practice, p. 511, set C

Supplements
Practice 157
Challenges 157 or
Thinking Skills 157

Extended

Exercises 7-15, 18-22, 24-35

Supplements
Challenges 157
Thinking Skills 157

Other Resources:
Problem-Solving Experiences in Mathematics, Grade 4, Problems 125, 126
Mathematics, Book A, Teacher's Edition, pp. 54, 55
Mathematics, A Way of Thinking, Lesson 10-11
Using the Math Explorer Calculator: A Sourcebook for Teachers, Chapter 14

LESSON PLAN 16-1

OBJECTIVE 16-1
To use mental math to divide by 2-digit divisors that are multiples of 10

Materials: tens place value blocks

Alternative Materials: TA 6 (Place Value Models)

1. MOTIVATE AND TEACH

LEARN ABOUT IT

EXPLORE ► **Summarize the situation at the Log Water Slide in a question.** (Possible answer: If 20 people at once can ride the slide, how many slide rides are needed for 180 people?)

TALK ABOUT IT ► **Explain a way to solve the problem without dividing.** (Possible answers: Keep subtracting 20 from 180 until you reach 0; skip count by 20s to 180; think about what number times 20 equals 180.)
► **What similarity do 180 and 20 share? Explain your reasoning.** (The 0 indicates that both 180 and 20 are multiples of ten; they relate to the basic division fact 18 ÷ 2.)
► **Analyze how a basic division fact can help you find the special quotient mentally.** (If you know 18 ÷ 2 = 9, then think of 180 ÷ 20 as 18 tens ÷ 2 tens = 9.)
Student Edition answers: **1.** Guess a missing factor; adjust the guess as needed. **2.** 18; think of 18 tens ÷ 2 tens = 9.

2. CHECK UNDERSTANDING

TRY IT OUT

ERROR ALERT Giving the quotient as another multiple of ten. Failing to notice basic facts.

Mental Math
Special Quotients

LEARN ABOUT IT

EXPLORE Think About the Situation
You can use basic division facts and mental math to help you find special quotients. At an amusement park 20 people can ride the Log Water Slide at once. Jane wondered how many rides it would take for the 180 people waiting in line.

TALK ABOUT IT See teaching notes.

1. How can you use multiplication and the guess and check strategy to answer Jane's question?
2. How many groups of ten people are waiting in line? How could thinking of tens help you find the quotient?

Here is a quick way to find quotients like 180 ÷ 20 using mental math.

To find 180 ÷ 20, find 18 ÷ 2.

18 tens ÷ 2 tens = 9 $2 \text{ tens}\overline{)18 \text{ tens}}$ = 9

180 ÷ 20 = 9 $20\overline{)180}$ = 9

TRY IT OUT

Divide, using mental math. Check by multiplying.

1. 90 ÷ 30 **3**
2. 320 ÷ 40 **8**
3. 280 ÷ 70 **4**
4. 560 ÷ 80 **7**
5. 400 ÷ 50 **8**
6. 420 ÷ 60 **7**
7. 450 ÷ 90 **5**
8. 810 ÷ 90 **9**

TEACHING OPTIONS

RETEACHING TIPS Students use place value blocks to show the division, then verbalize what they see. For instance, for Exercise 1, students would show 9 tens in piles with 3 tens in each pile. They would say, *9 tens divided by 3 tens is 3 piles, so the quotient is 3*. Assign Reteaching Supplement 157.

ENRICHMENT Have students use metric measurement relationships to find these special products.
1. 24 cm ÷ 30 mm = (8) mm
2. 14 dm ÷ 20 cm = (7) cm
3. 3 m ÷ 60 cm = (5) cm
4. 4 km ÷ 50 m = (80) m
5. 1 L ÷ 50 mL = (20) mL

PRACTICE

Divide, using mental math. Check by multiplying.

1. 40 ÷ 20 2	2. 600 ÷ 6 100	3. 400 ÷ 80 5	4. 810 ÷ 9 90
5. 180 ÷ 6 30	6. 280 ÷ 40 7	7. 630 ÷ 70 9	8. 250 ÷ 50 5
9. 160 ÷ 20 8	10. 540 ÷ 90 6	11. 720 ÷ 80 9	12. 120 ÷ 30 4
13. 50)300 6	14. 90)90 1	15. 60)180 3	16. 70)490 7

17. How many 40s are in 160? 4
18. How many 80s are in 320? 4
19. What is 480 divided by 60? 8

APPLY

MATH REASONING Use mental math to decide if the quotients are equal or unequal.

20. 200 ÷ 2 and 2,000 ÷ 20 equal
21. 600 ÷ 60 and 6,000 ÷ 60 unequal
22. 400 ÷ 5 and 4,000 ÷ 50 equal
23. 210 ÷ 7 and 2,100 ÷ 70 equal

PROBLEM SOLVING

24. There are 30 seats on the ferris wheel. 240 people are waiting in line. If the ferris wheel is full for each ride, how many rides will it take for everyone to have a turn? 8 rides

25. Toby's father bought 4 five-day passes to Fun Park. The total cost was $160. How much did each pass cost? $40

▶ ESTIMATION

Estimate the quotients using front-end digits. Substitute a compatible basic fact when helpful.

26. 22)183 9	27. 67)487 8	28. 81)324 4	29. 82)641 8
30. 42)359 9	31. 78)236 3	32. 53)324 6	33. 34)122 4
34. 456 ÷ 94 5	35. 284 ÷ 31 9	36. 133 ÷ 62 2	

More Practice, page 511, set C

3. Practice and Apply

Basic	6-21, 24-29, 34-36
Average	1-36
Extended	7-15, 18-22, 24-35

PRACTICE

How can basic facts help you with Exercises 1 to 36? (Imagine basic facts in multiples of ten.) *In Exercises 1 to 16, which exercises have divisors that are not multiples of ten?* (Exercises 2, 4, 5)

APPLY

MATH REASONING ▶ **Explain how to decide if the quotients are equal or unequal without dividing.** (Find a relationship between the number of zeros in each pair of division problems.)

PROBLEM SOLVING ▶ **Explain how multiplication can be used to solve Problem 24.** (Think about the number of groups of 30 that equal 240.)

ESTIMATION ▶ **Explain how the strategy of finding compatible numbers can help you estimate Exercises 26-36.** (Think of basic division facts that are close to the numbers, then use special quotient division.)

Close and Assess

SHOW WHAT YOU KNOW

Have students create 3 different special quotient division equations: 1 with a divisor of 50, 1 with a dividend of 560, and 1 with a quotient of 9. Have them show how to use basic facts to find the quotients. (Possible answers: 250 ÷ 50 = 5; 560 ÷ 70 = 8; 810 ÷ 90 = 9)

QUICK QUIZ

Divide using mental math.

1. 640 ÷ 80 (8)	**2.** 120 ÷ 40 (3)
3. 350 ÷ 70 (5)	**4.** 300 ÷ 50 (6)
5. 90)450 (5)	**6.** 40)40 (1)
7. 80)320 (4)	**8.** 60)360 (6)

LESSON OPTIONS 16-2

Dividing by Tens: 1-Digit Quotients

OBJECTIVE 16-2 To find 1-digit quotients by dividing with 2-digit divisors that are multiples of 10

PREBOOK ACTIVITIES

QUICK REVIEW

Divide using mental math.

1. 540 ÷ 90 (6) **2.** 400 ÷ 80 (5) **3.** 270 ÷ 90 (3)
4. 360 ÷ 40 (9) **5.** 70 ÷ 70 (1) **6.** 280 ÷ 70 (4)
7. 720 ÷ 80 (9) **8.** 420 ÷ 70 (6) **9.** 160 ÷ 20 (8)

PRIOR KNOWLEDGE

Have students explain what a remainder is in division. (amount left over after making as many equal groups as possible) Ask them to give examples of remainders in real-life situations. (Possible answer: Divide 22 baseball cards among 4 children to give each child 5 cards, with 2 left over.)

COMMUNICATION

Discussing Math Have students analyze the relationship between the divisor and the remainder in a division problem. (Possible answer: The remainder must be less than the divisor.) Ask students to determine the greatest possible remainder with a divisor of 30. (29) Then have them imagine a divisor if the remainder is 57. (58 or more)

EXPLORE AND CONNECT

Materials: place value blocks (tens only)
Alternative Materials: TA 6 (Place Value Models)
Grouping Suggestion: cooperative learning groups of 3
Students explore 2-digit division with remainders. List these dividends on the chalkboard: 100, 130, 170. Groups should divide each number by 30 with place value materials, record the quotient and any possible remainder, and check answers by multiplication. Students take turns showing the division, recording the quotient, and checking the answer. When they finish, ask volunteers to share the quotients they found and to justify the remainders. (3 R10, 4 R10, 5 R20; dividends and the divisor are multiples of ten, but because they do not relate to basic facts, they do not divide completely.)

CONNECTIONS Use these anytime.

Problem of the Day

Missing Digits Use the digits 0, 1, 2, and 3 to complete the division problem.

$$\begin{array}{r} \square \text{ R } \square \\ \square\square\overline{)6\ 1} \end{array}$$

(61 ÷ 20 = 3 R1 or 61 ÷ 30 = 2 R1)

Number Sense

Mental Math 190 teachers and students are taking a field trip to the Airplane Museum. They will go in buses that seat 40 people each. Determine how many buses are needed. (190 ÷ 40 = 4 R30, but 4 buses would mean that 30 students would get left behind, so 5 buses are needed.)

Math Connection

Measurement Darcy has 195 cm of ribbon. She is going to cut it into equal-length pieces to use to make 20 cat toys to donate to the local animal shelter. What is the longest she can make each piece of ribbon? How much extra ribbon, if any, will she have left? (9 cm; 15 cm left over)

Classwork and Homework Supplements

Practice

Skills Maintenance 16-2

Name

Dividing by Tens: 1-Digit Quotients

Divide and check.

1. 40)84 = 2 R4; − 80; 4
2. 20)51 = 2 R11; − 40; 11
3. 30)76 = 2 R16; − 60; 16
4. 40)332 = 8 R12; − 320; 12
5. 70)413 = 5 R63; − 350; 63
6. 80)249 = 3 R9; − 240; 9
7. 60)375 = 6 R15; − 360; 15
8. 90)650 = 7 R20; − 630; 20
9. 80)594 = 7 R34; − 560; 34
10. 70)624 = 8 R64; − 560; 64
11. 20)186 = 9 R6; − 180; 6
12. 40)83 = 2 R3; − 80; 3
13. 50)467 = 9 R17; − 450; 17
14. 30)95 = 3 R5; − 90; 5
15. 60)565 = 9 R25; − 540; 25
16. 70)580 = 8 R20; − 560; 20
17. 90)572 = 7 R32; − 540; 32
18. 80)375 = 4 R55; − 320; 55
19. 60)252 = 4 R12; − 240; 12
20. 40)298 = 7 R18; − 280; 18
21. 90)343 = 3 R73; − 270; 73
22. 30)86 = 2 R26; − 60; 26
23. 50)309 = 6 R9; − 300; 9
24. 70)542 = 7 R52; − 490; 52

158 Use with text pages 438–439. PS-4

Building Thinking Skills

Family Math 16-2

Name

Treasure Hunt

Dear Family,
Your child has been learning how to divide by divisors that are multiples of 10. Here is an activity you can complete with your child.

Find the treasure chest. Begin at **Start.** Choose the path where the remainders increase from 1 through 8 to reach **Finish.** Draw arrows along your path.

START, 20)41, 80)370, 30)92, 40)298, 60)252, 40)82, 80)375, 90)572, 90)273, 50)501, 70)564, 60)488, 30)249, 80)725, 50)794, 60)546, 20)242, 40)847, 50)258, 70)559, FINISH

158 Use with text pages 438–439. TS-4

Reteaching

Skills Review 16-2

Name

Dividing by Tens: 1-Digit Quotients

Decide where to start. → Dividing Ones: • Divide • Multiply • Subtract • Compare

40)316

- Try hundreds. 40)3 — not enough hundreds
- Try tens. 40)31 — not enough tens
- Try ones. 40)316 — 316 ones is enough.

40)316 = 7 R36; 280; 36 (4 tens)31 tens, 7 tens, − 28 tens

Check: 40 × 7 = 280; + 36 ← remainder; 316

Divide and check.

1. 30)286 = 9 R16; −270 ← (3 tens)28 tens, 9, − 27 tens; 16. Check: 30 × 9 = 270; + 16; 286
2. 50)237 = 4 R37; − 200 ← (5 tens)23 tens, 4, − 20 tens; 37. Check: 50 × 4 = 200; + 37; 237
3. 30)223 = 7 R13; − 210; 13. Check: 30 × 7 = 210; + 13; 223
4. 50)473 = 9 R23; − 450; 23. Check: 50 × 9 = 450; + 23; 473
5. 70)565 = 8 R5; − 560; 5. Check: 70 × 8 = 560; + 5; 565

Rewrite these problems. Then divide and check.

6. 293 ÷ 40: 40)293 = 7 R13; × 280; 13. Check: 40 × 7 = 280; + 13; 293
7. 327 ÷ 60: 60)327 = 5 R27; − 300; 27. Check: 60 × 5 = 300; + 27; 327
8. 256 ÷ 30: 30)256 = 8 R16; − 240; 16. Check: 30 × 8 = 240; + 16; 256

158 Use with text pages 438-439. RS-4

Challenges

Estimation 16-2

Name

Magic Divider

If you could use a Magic Divider for every problem, dividing would be a snap. The Magic Divider helps you estimate the quotient. Study the example. Then use the Magic Divider for 60 to solve Problems 1 through 4.

Example: 60)439 = 7 ← Estimated quotient. 439 is between 420 and 480. 60)439 = 7 R19 ← Actual quotient; − 420; 19

Magic Divider for 60

1	2	3	4	5	6	7	8	9	10
× 60	× 60	× 60	× 60	× 60	× 60	× 60	× 60	× 60	× 60
60	120	180	240	300	360	420	480	540	600

1. 60)203 = 3 R23; − 180; 23
2. 60)415 = 6 R55; − 360; 55
3. 60)275 = 4 R35; − 240; 35
4. 60)532 = 8 R52; − 480; 52

Finish this Magic Divider for 30. Then use it to do Problems 5 through 8.

1	2	3	4	5	6	7	8	9	10
× 30	× 30	× 30	× 30	× 30	× 30	× 30	× 30	× 30	× 30
30	60	90	120	150	180	210	240	270	300

5. 30)200 = 6 R20; − 180; 20
6. 30)242 = 8 R2; − 240; 2
7. 30)182 = 6 R2; − 180; 2
8. 30)105 = 3 R15; − 90; 15

158 Use with text pages 438–439. CS-4

Options for Individual Needs

Basic

Exercises 1-10, 18-29
More Practice, p. 511, set D

Supplements
Reteaching 158 or
Practice 158
Challenges 158

Average

Exercises 1-29
More Practice, p. 511, set D

Supplements
Practice 158
Challenges 158 or
Thinking Skills 158

Extended

Exercises 11-17, 20-29

Supplements
Challenges 158
Thinking Skills 158

Other Resources:
Problem-Solving Experiences in Mathematics, Grade 4, Problem 127
Mathematics, A Way of Thinking, Lesson 10-13
Math In Stride, Grade 4, p. 160
Using the Math Explorer Calculator: A Sourcebook for Teachers, Chapter 14

16-2

LESSON PLAN 16-2

OBJECTIVE 16-2
To find 1-digit quotients by dividing with 2-digit divisors that are multiples of 10

Grouping Suggestion: pairs

1. MOTIVATE AND TEACH

LEARN ABOUT IT

EXPLORE ► **Explain the meaning of the graph scale labeled mph.** (*mph* means "miles per hour"; it has jet speeds between 500 and 660 mph.)

TALK ABOUT IT ► **Find a relationship between miles per hour and distance flown in 1 min. Explain your reasoning.** (1 h = 60 min; divide 580 mph by 60 for miles per minute.)
► **Explain how to estimate using front-end digits.** (Use front-end digits to find the closest basic facts to estimate the quotient.)
► **When would 90 be an appropriate estimate for a dividend of 580? Explain.** (if the divisor were 6—540 ÷ 6 = 90)
► **Explain how to check a division problem.** (Multiply the quotient by the divisor, then add the remainder to equal the dividend.)
► **Why are there remainders in the Other Examples.** (None of the examples uses basic facts.)
Student Edition answers: **1.** Multiply the quotient by the divisor; add the remainder. **2.** A Boeing 737 jet flies more than 9 miles in 1 min.

2. CHECK UNDERSTANDING

TRY IT OUT

ERROR ALERT Omitting remainders from the quotient. Giving quotients as multiples of ten.

Dividing by Tens
1-Digit Quotients

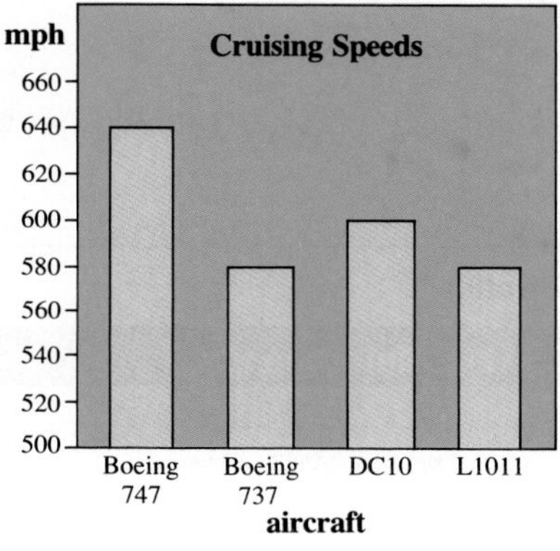

LEARN ABOUT IT

EXPLORE Think About the Process. The table shows the cruising speed of some modern jet aircraft. How far does the Boeing 737 fly in 1 minute?

This is how to find the correct quotient.

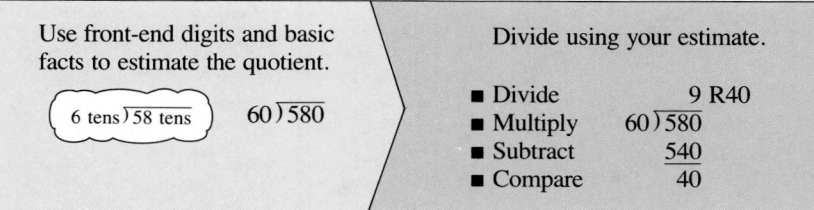

Use front-end digits and basic facts to estimate the quotient.

6 tens)58 tens 60)580

Divide using your estimate.

- Divide
- Multiply
- Subtract
- Compare

```
    9 R40
60)580
   540
    40
```

TALK ABOUT IT See teaching notes.

1. How can you use multiplication to see if your answer is reasonable?
2. Answer the question in the complete sentence.

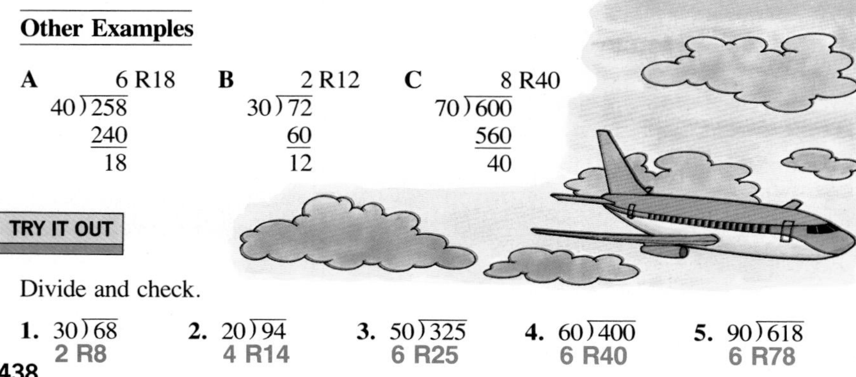

Other Examples

```
A     6 R18     B    2 R12     C     8 R40
  40)258          30)72          70)600
     240             60             560
      18             12              40
```

TRY IT OUT

Divide and check.

1. 30)68 2 R8
2. 20)94 4 R14
3. 50)325 6 R25
4. 60)400 6 R40
5. 90)618 6 R78

TEACHING OPTIONS

RETEACHING TIPS Partners verbalize the steps in the division process: divide, multiply, subtract, compare. Have them examine each other's exercises for evidence of every step. If there are remainders, partners should remind each other to write them beside the quotient. Assign Reteaching Supplement 158.

ENRICHMENT Family Math At home, students use a clock with a second hand to time how high they and at least 1 other family member can count in 1 min, then record the highest number each counter reaches. Then they divide to find how many numbers each person said per second.

PRACTICE

Divide and check.

1. $10\overline{)93}$ 9 R3
2. $20\overline{)67}$ 3 R7
3. $40\overline{)83}$ 2 R3
4. $20\overline{)54}$ 2 R14
5. $60\overline{)248}$ 4 R8
6. $30\overline{)159}$ 5 R9
7. $50\overline{)313}$ 6 R13
8. $80\overline{)500}$ 6 R20
9. $90\overline{)193}$ 2 R13
10. $30\overline{)251}$ 8 R11
11. $70\overline{)400}$ 5 R50
12. $60\overline{)195}$ 3 R15
13. $30\overline{)285}$ 9 R15
14. $50\overline{)491}$ 9 R41
15. $10\overline{)79}$ 7 R9

APPLY

MATH REASONING Estimate these quotients.

16. $60\overline{)372}$ 6
17. $20\overline{)126}$ 60
18. $30\overline{)189}$ 6
19. $50\overline{)449}$ 9
20. Find at least three numbers that when divided by 30 do not have a remainder. Answers will vary. Sample answers: 90, 300, 270

PROBLEM SOLVING

21. **Determining Reasonable Answers**
There were 16 people in one row of an airplane. The row had 6 more adults than children. How many children were there? Decide which answer is reasonable.

a 2 children **b** 4 children

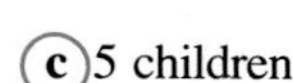

(c) 5 children **d** 6 children

22. How far does the DC 10 airplane fly in one minute? Use the data from the graph on page 438. 10 miles

MIXED REVIEW

Use mental math to divide.

23. 40 ÷ 20 2
24. 26 ÷ 13 2
25. 36 ÷ 12 3
26. 63 ÷ 21 3
27. 90 ÷ 30 3
28. Write 4 decimals with a number in the tenths place that rounds to 5. Answers will vary.
29. Write 4 decimals with numbers in the tenths and hundredths places that round to 10. Answers will vary.

More Practice, page 511, set D

3. PRACTICE AND APPLY

Basic	1-10, 18-29
Average	1-29
Extended	11-17, 20-29

PRACTICE

How can you predict that the division will include remainders? (No dividends are multiples of 10, but all divisors are.)

APPLY

MATH REASONING ► Explain how you can use compatible numbers to solve Exercises 16-20. (Round dividends to numbers that you can easily divide by the given multiple of ten.)

PROBLEM SOLVING ► Explain a strategy to use with Problem 21. (Guess and Check; look for a possible answer, then test it to see if it works with the other data.)

MIXED REVIEW ► Explain how Exercises 23 and 27 differ from Exercises 24-26. (Possible answers: Exercises 23 and 27 use special quotients; 23 and 27 have dividends and divisors that are multiples of 10.)

CLOSE AND ASSESS

WRITE WHAT YOU THINK

Have students work in pairs. Each partner writes the steps to follow to divide by a multiple of ten, using $40\overline{)273}$ as a sample problem. Then partners each read what the other wrote to verify the answer and that the steps make sense. (6 R33; Check students' writing.)

QUICK QUIZ

Divide and check.

1. $50\overline{)317}$ (6 R17)
2. $30\overline{)242}$ (8 R2)
3. 380 ÷ 60 (6 R20)
4. 261 ÷ 30 (8 R21)

16-2

LESSON OPTIONS 16-3

Dividing: 1-Digit Quotients

OBJECTIVE 16-3 To find 1-digit quotients by dividing with 2-digit divisors

PREBOOK ACTIVITIES

QUICK REVIEW

Divide.

1. $40\overline{)316}$	(7 R36)	**2.** $50\overline{)149}$	(2 R49)
3. $20\overline{)120}$	(6)	**4.** $90\overline{)800}$	(8 R80)
5. $60\overline{)384}$	(6 R24)	**6.** $70\overline{)523}$	(7 R33)
7. $10\overline{)44}$	(4 R4)	**8.** $30\overline{)55}$	(1 R25)
9. $80\overline{)666}$	(8 R26)	**10.** $50\overline{)171}$	(3 R21)

PRIOR KNOWLEDGE

Have students suggest real-life situations that might require dividing by a 2-digit number. (Possible answers: dividing objects among many people; sharing money amounts; finding gas mileage per gallon.) Have students describe the 2-digit divisors they have worked with so far. (All have been multiples of ten.)

COMMUNICATION

Discussing and Writing Math On the chalkboard, have a volunteer list the steps for dividing by multiples of ten. (divide, multiply, subtract, compare) Ask students to relate such division to basic facts. (Possible answer: Before you divide, compare front-end digits to the nearest basic fact to estimate the quotient; then follow the other steps.) Have students use logical reasoning to guess how to use basic facts when divisors are *not* multiples of ten. (Possible answer: Round divisors to the nearest multiple of ten, then use all the same steps.)

EXPLORE AND CONNECT

Materials: TA 3 (Number Cards 0-9), TA 6 (Place Value Models), calculators

Grouping Suggestion: cooperative learning groups of 4

Cooperative groups explore and compare various division methods. The first student picks 4 number cards and arranges them to form the greatest and the smallest possible 2-digit numbers for a division problem—the greater number will be the dividend, the smaller number the divisor. The next student shows the division with place value blocks, while the third student rounds the numbers to the nearest ten and writes out the estimated division. The fourth student divides with a calculator. When all methods are complete, group members compare and discuss their results. Groups should repeat the activity 3 times, trading tasks. Have students generalize about working with divisors that are not multiples of ten. (Possible answer: Use the same steps as in any other division.)

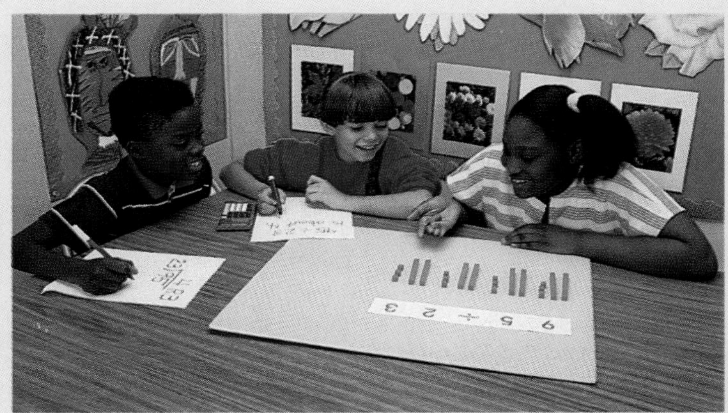

CONNECTIONS Use these anytime.

Problem of the Day

Measurement Gloria buys a 10-yd roll of glow tape. She uses it to decorate firefly costumes for a school play. One costume takes 40 in. of glow tape. How many costumes can Gloria decorate with the roll of tape? (9)

Creative Thinking

A Weedy Deal Enrique has $7.50 to pay 3 friends who helped him weed his garden. He will pay them $0.50 for each row they weeded. Since they did 3, 5, and 7 rows, how much money should each helper get? ($1.50; $2.50; $3.50)

Math Connection

Calculator Find a way to divide 296 by 37 without ever pressing the ÷ key. (8; Guess and Check to find a missing factor or count how many times you subtract 37 from 296 until you reach 0.)

Classwork and Homework Supplements

Practice

Estimation 16-3

Name ______

Dividing: 1-Digit Quotients

Write the number to which you would round the divisor when estimating the quotient.

1. 37)123 — 40
2. 16)81 — 20
3. 12)78 — 10
4. 42)$6.50 — 40

Divide and check.

5. 19)58 = 3 R1 (− 57, 1)
6. 31)95 = 3 R2 (− 93, 2)
7. 22)73 = 3 R7 (− 66, 7)
8. 43)2.58 = $0.06 (− 258, 0)
9. 34)77 = 2 R9 (− 68, 9)
10. 41)375 = 9 R6 (− 369, 6)
11. 56)493 = 8 R45 (− 448, 45)
12. 26)65 = 2 R13 (− 52, 13)
13. 51)381 = 7 R24 (− 357, 24)
14. 24)75 = 3 R3 (− 72, 3)
15. 45)$3.15 = $0.07 (− 3 15, 0)
16. 33)88 = 2 R22 (− 66, 22)
17. 28)59 = 2 R3 (− 56, 3)
18. 44)268 = 6 R4 (− 264, 4)
19. 27)159 = 5 R24 (− 135, 24)
20. 25)70 = 2 R20 (− 50, 20)
21. 36)85 = 2 R13 (− 72, 13)
22. 82)367 = 4 R39 (− 328, 39)
23. 57)$4.56 = $0.08 (− 4 56, 0)
24. 78)567 = 7 R21 (− 546, 21)

Building Thinking Skills

Estimation 16-3

Name ______

Waste Not

Ring the purchase that is closest to the amount you need. Make sure you have enough.

1. You need 15 hot dog buns.
   - A 3 packages of 6
   - **B 2 packages of 8** (ringed)
   - C 1 package of 6 and 1 package of 12
2. You need 25 hot dog buns.
   - A 5 packages of 6
   - B 4 packages of 8
   - **C 1 package of each size** (ringed)

3. You need 65 granola bars.
   - A 3 packages of 25
   - B 1 package of 50 and 1 package of 20
   - **C 1 package of 25 and 2 packages of 20** (ringed)
4. You need 55 granola bars.
   - A 2 packages of 20 and 1 package of 25
   - **B 3 packages of 20** (ringed)
   - C 1 package of 50 and 1 package of 20

CHEESE 50 SLICES · CHEESE 36 SLICES · CHEESE 24 SLICES

5. You need 80 slices of cheese.
   - **A 2 packages of 24 and 1 package of 36** (ringed)
   - B 4 packages of 24
   - C 2 packages of 50
6. You need 60 slices of cheese.
   - A 2 packages of 36
   - B 3 packages of 24
   - **C 1 package of 36 and 1 package of 24** (ringed)

Reteaching

Skills Review 16-3

Name ______

Dividing: 1-Digit Quotients

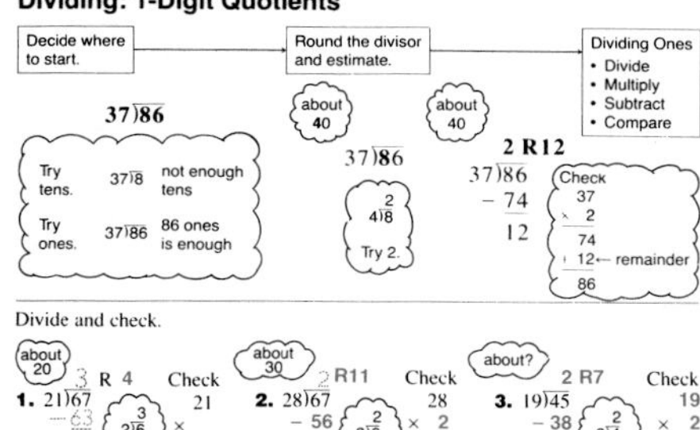

Divide and check.

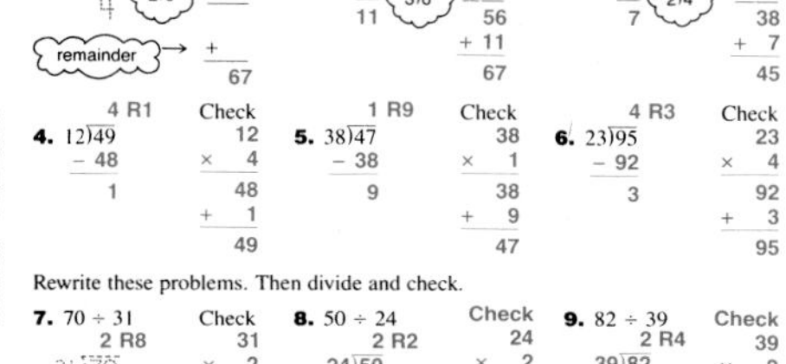

4. 12)49 = 4 R1 (− 48, 1); Check 12 × 4 = 48 + 1 = 49
5. 38)47 = 1 R9 (− 38, 9); Check 38 × 1 = 38 + 9 = 47
6. 23)95 = 4 R3 (− 92, 3); Check 23 × 4 = 92 + 3 = 95

Rewrite these problems. Then divide and check.

7. 70 ÷ 31 — 31)70 = 2 R8 (− 62, 8); Check 31 × 2 = 62 + 8 = 70
8. 50 ÷ 24 — 24)50 = 2 R2 (− 48, 2); Check 24 × 2 = 48 + 2 = 50
9. 82 ÷ 39 — 39)82 = 2 R4 (− 78, 4); Check 39 × 2 = 78 + 4 = 82

Challenges

Writing Math 16-3

Name ______

Truth Detective

quotient / divisor) dividend

In Problems 1, 2, and 3, decide if the statements are true or false. Then complete the examples. In Problems 4 and 5, write a true statement to fit the examples.

Statement	True or False?	Examples
1. If you double the dividend, the quotient will double.	True	3)6 = 2 → 3)12 = 4; 18)54 = 3 → 18)108 = 6
2. If you halve (make half) the divisor, you halve the quotient.	False	6)12 = 2 → 3)12 = 4; 22)132 = 6 → 11)132 = 12
3. If you triple both the divisor and the dividend, the quotient stays the same.	True	2)6 = 3 → 6)18 = 3; 12)48 = 4 → 36)144 = 4
4. If you halve the dividend, you halve the quotient.	True	24)144 = 6 → 24)72 = 3
5. If you double the divisor and the dividend, the quotient stays the same.	True	32)96 = 3 → 64)192 = 3

Options for Individual Needs

Basic

Exercises 1-12, 18-26
Data Bank, p. 478
Calculator Bank, p. 487
More Practice, p. 511, set E

Supplements
Reteaching 159 or
Practice 159

Average

Exercises 1-26
Data Bank, p. 478
Calculator Bank, p. 487
More Practice, p. 511, set E

Supplements
Practice 159
Challenges 159 or
Thinking Skills 159

Extended

Exercises 3-6, 12-18, 22-26
Data Bank, p. 478
Calculator Bank, p. 487

Supplements
Challenges 159
Thinking Skills 159

Other Resources:
Problem-Solving Experiences in Mathematics, Grade 4, Problem 128
Kids Are Consumers, Too!, pp. 118, 119
Math In Stride, Grade 4, p. 204
Using the Math Explorer Calculator: A Sourcebook for Teachers, Chapter 14

LESSON PLAN 16-3

OBJECTIVE 16-3
To find 1-digit quotients by dividing with 2-digit divisors

Grouping Suggestions: pairs

1. MOTIVATE AND TEACH

LEARN ABOUT IT

EXPLORE ▶ **Explain the situation in your own words.** (Possible answer: With 265 lb of sand, how many 33-lb bags could the professor make?)
▶ **Analyze why it may help to round the divisor.** (Rounding the divisor makes it easier to use front-end digits and basic facts to estimate the quotient.)
▶ **Predict a possible error in the Multiply step.** (Possible answer: multiplying 8 by 30 instead of by 33)

TALK ABOUT IT ▶ **Justify using division.** (You divide to make equal-sized bags.)
▶ **When would 80 be an appropriate estimate if the dividend is 265? Explain.** (if the divisor were 3; 80 × 3 = 240)
Student Edition answers: **1.** 80 is too big. **2.** Sample sentence: The professor could make 8 ballast bags with 1 lb of sand left over.

2. CHECK UNDERSTANDING

TRY IT OUT

ERROR ALERT Exercises 2 and 3: Making subtraction errors. Exercise 4: Forgetting to show the quotient as a money amount.

Dividing
1-Digit Quotients

LEARN ABOUT IT

EXPLORE **Think About the Process**
In the book *Twenty-One Balloons*, a hydrogen balloon such as the *Globe* must carry bags of sand. These bags, called ballast, weigh 33 pounds each. How many bags of ballast could the professor make from 265 pounds of sand?

Use rounding to help you find the quotient.

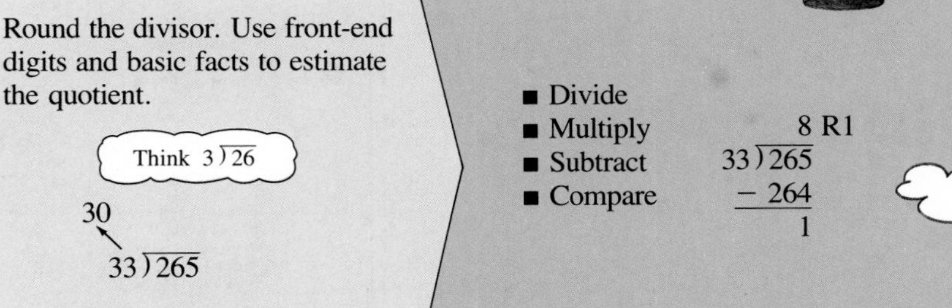

TALK ABOUT IT See teaching notes.

1. Why is 8 a better estimate than 80?
2. Use a complete sentence to give a reasonable answer to the story problem.

TRY IT OUT

Divide and check.

1. 18)37 **2 R1**
2. 23)86 **3 R17**
3. 13)34 **2 R8**
4. 57)$2.28 **$0.04**
5. 90)369 **4 R9**
6. 96 ÷ 45 **2 R6**
7. 48 ÷ 36 **1 R12**
8. 425 ÷ 85 **5**

440

TEACHING OPTIONS

RETEACHING TIPS To show money quotients, students write the dollar sign and decimal point directly above those places in the dividend *before* dividing. After they find the 1-digit quotient, have them place it in the pennies place, then write a zero to hold the dimes place. Assign Reteaching Supplement 159.

ENRICHMENT Have students create 2 division problems with 2-digit divisors and 1-digit quotients according to these rules: 1) odd divisor, even quotient and remainder 2) even dividend and divisor, odd quotient, no remainder. (Answers will vary. Samples: 29)130, 4 R14; 38)190, 5)

PRACTICE

To what number would you round the divisor when estimating the quotient?

1. 28)68 30 **2.** 64)93 60 **3.** 23)76 20 **4.** 85)$8.76 90

Divide and check.

5. 29)92 3 R5 **6.** 18)42 2 R6 **7.** 32)53 1 R21 **8.** 54)83 1 R29

9. 72)377 5 R17 **10.** 21)85 4 R1 **11.** 19)143 7 R10 **12.** 64)$5.76 $0.09

13. 63)260 4 R8 **14.** 25)$2.00 $0.08 **15.** 47)255 5 R20 **16.** 32)$2.24 $0.07

APPLY

BALLOON RIDES

MATH REASONING Use mental math to solve these problems.

17. 12)24 2 **18.** 25)50 2 **19.** 15)30 2 **20.** 25)75 3

Guess and check to solve these equations.

21. $9 \times n = 108$ 12 **22.** $96 = 4 \times n$ 24 **23.** $7 \times n = 98$ 14

PROBLEM SOLVING

24. For stopping, a hydrogen balloon needs 2 mooring ropes each 33 feet long. How many mooring ropes could be cut from a rope 325 feet long? 9 ropes

25. Language Arts Data Bank DATA BANK The valve for letting out the hydrogen should require a pull of between 33 and 44 pounds. About how many times more than the greatest recommended pull was the pull of each balloon's valve on the flying platform? See page 478. about 4 times

▶ **USING CRITICAL THINKING Support Your Conclusion**

Decide if this statement is sometimes true, always true, or never true. Show some examples to support your conclusion. Start with a 1-digit divisor. Then try a 2-digit divisor. never; sample answers: $78 \div 3 = 26$, $78 \div 6 = 13$

> If you double the divisor in a problem, the quotient will also double.

More Practice, page 511, set E

3. Practice and Apply

Basic	1-12, 18-26
Average	1-26
Extended	3-6, 12-18, 22-26

PRACTICE

In Exercises 1-4, which divisors would you round up and which would you round down? (up: 1, 4; down: 2, 3)

APPLY

MATH REASONING ▶ **Explain how thinking about money may help with Exercises 18 and 20.** (Visualize quarters, which are familiar and easy to work with.)

PROBLEM SOLVING ▶ **How will you interpret a remainder in Problem 24?** (Ignore it; only whole ropes count.) ▶ **Explain a strategy to solve Problem 25.** (Possible answer: Choose a reasonable divisor between 33 and 44, then divide the valve pull number by it to make a comparison.)

USING CRITICAL THINKING ▶ **How could you model the situation?** (Make up a problem; double the divisor to see what happens.)

Close and Assess

SAY WHAT YOU THINK Have students work in pairs. One partner talks the other through the steps to follow to divide 321 by 52. Then partners switch roles, and the other student explains how to divide 567 by 93. Partners verify each other's answers. (6 R9 for both)

Quick Quiz

Divide and check.

1. 19)79 (4 R3)
2. 71)$4.97 ($0.07)
3. $222 \div 35$ (6 R12)
4. $247 \div 27$ (9 R4)

16-3

LESSON OPTIONS 16-4

Changing Estimates

OBJECTIVE 16-4 To change the estimated quotient when actual division proves it to be too large or too small

PREBOOK ACTIVITIES

QUICK REVIEW

Check each division exercise to find the ones that are wrong. Correct any errors you find.

1. 37 ÷ 43 = 1 R 6 (wrong; should be 0 R37)
2. 245 ÷ 67 = 2 R111 (wrong; should be 3 R44)
3. 626 ÷ 89 = 7 R3 (correct)
4. 273 ÷ 30 = 9 (wrong; should be 9 R3)

PRIOR KNOWLEDGE

Have students suggest real-life situations when they have made what they considered to be reasonable estimates that actually turned out to be too large or too small. (Answers will vary. Possible answers: making too much food for a meal; planning too little time to finish a chore)

COMMUNICATION

Discussing and Reading Math Have students summarize the estimation used at the start of a division problem. (Round the divisor; use front-end digits to estimate a quotient.) Have students compare the divisors used for estimating and the exact divisors. (Divisors used for estimating may be greater or smaller than the exact divisors, depending on whether you rounded up or rounded down.) Then write this problem on the chalkboard: 319 ÷ 33; estimated: 319 ÷ 30 = 10; exact: 319 ÷ 33 = 9 R22. Challenge students to analyze why an estimated quotient based on a correctly rounded divisor could turn out to be too big, like this one, or too small. (Possible answer: You base an estimated quotient on only front-end digits; the quotient really uses all digits of the exact divisor.)

EXPLORE AND CONNECT

Materials: calculators
Grouping Suggestion: cooperative learning pairs
Students explore adjusting quotients. On the chalkboard, write: 16)142, 27)240, 33)281. Pairs work together. The first student begins by rounding a divisor to the nearest ten, then uses front-end digits to estimate the quotient. The partner uses a calculator to test the estimated quotient. If the product is *less* than the dividend and the difference less than the divisor, the first student can continue dividing. If the difference is greater than the divisor or the product is *greater* than the dividend, the first student adjusts the estimate. Partners trade tasks to work all 3 problems. Ask students to summarize the estimates. (16)142 was too small, 27)240 worked as predicted, 33)281 was too large.) Have students notice *when* they knew that an estimate needed adjustment. (too small: after the Subtract step; too large: after the Multiply step)

CONNECTIONS Use these anytime.

Problem of the Day

Moving Videos A video store is moving to a new location. Taylor must decide how to pack 192 tapes so that they all fit in moving boxes. He has boxes that can hold 22, 24, or 26 tapes. Explain which size is best for the job. (192 ÷ 24 = 8 with no remainder; the boxes that hold 24 tapes)

Creative Thinking

Number Riddle How can you make three 3s equal 11? (33 ÷ 3 = 11)

Number Sense

Estimation The following mixed-up numbers make a division problem: 5, 6, 17, 91. Use estimation to decide how the numbers go together, then divide to check your estimate. (91 ÷ 17 = 5 R6)

Classwork and Homework Supplements

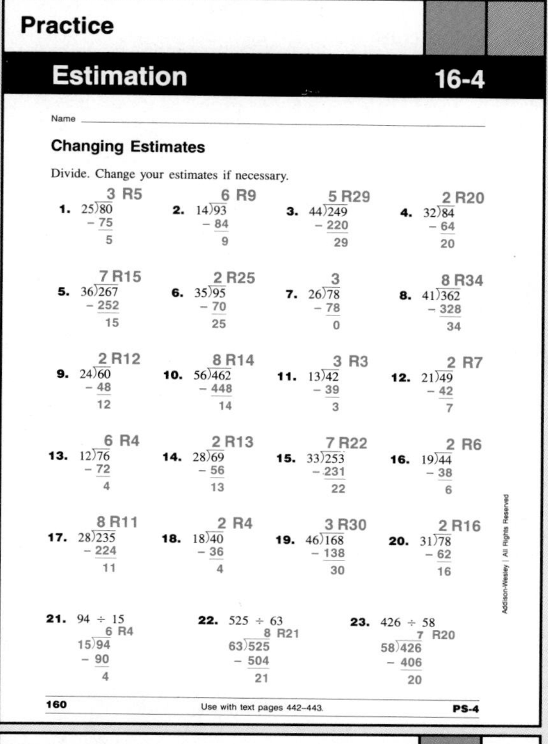

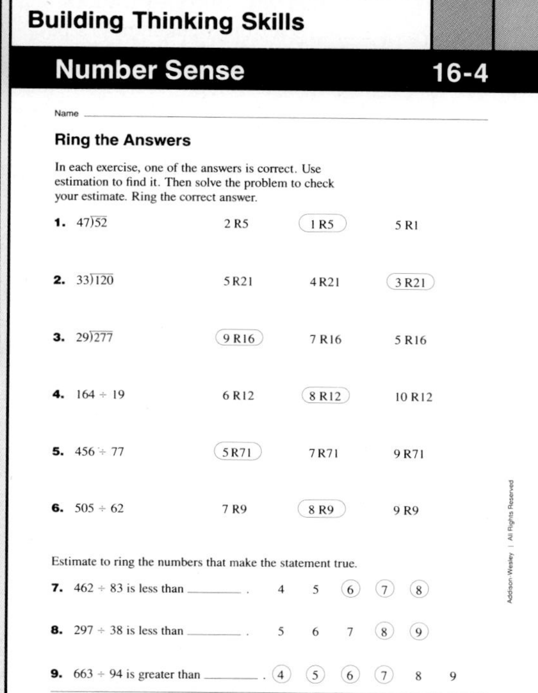

Reteaching

Estimation 16-4

Name ______

Changing Estimates

If your estimated quotient is too small or too large, you have to change the estimate.

Decide how to change the estimates. Then divide again.

Divide. Change your estimates if necessary.

160 Use with text pages 442-443. RS-4

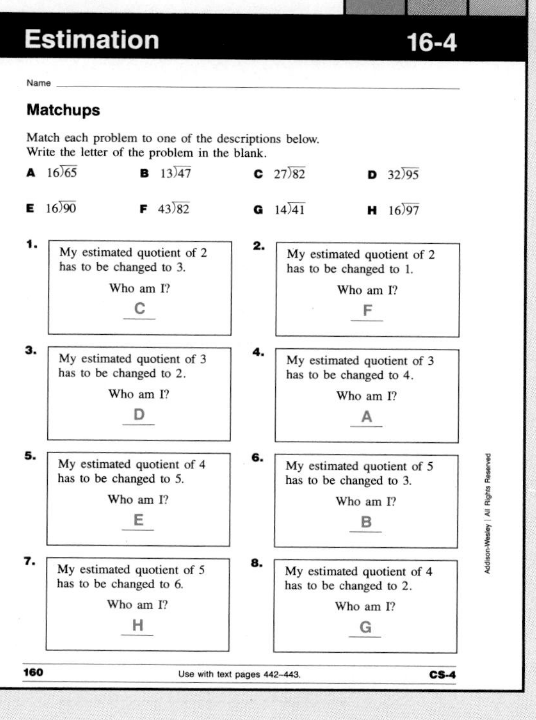

Options for Individual Needs

Basic

Exercises 6-19, 24-31
More Practice, p. 511, set F

Supplements
Reteaching 160 or
Practice 160
Challenges 160

Average

Exercises 1-31
More Practice, p. 511, set F

Supplements
Practice 160
Challenges 160 or
Thinking Skills 160

Extended

Exercises 10-15, 20-31

Supplements
Challenges 160
Thinking Skills 160

Other Resources:
Problem-Solving Experiences in Mathematics, Grade 4, Problem 129
Mathematics, Book A, Teacher's Edition, p. 55

16-4

LESSON PLAN 16-4

OBJECTIVE 16-4
To change the estimated quotient when actual division proves it to be too large or too small

Materials: index cards

1. MOTIVATE AND TEACH

LEARN ABOUT IT

EXPLORE ▶ **Explain how to classify the data to make the situation clearer.** (495 people for double-decker bus tours, 72 per bus; 325 people for single-decker, 46 per bus)

TALK ABOUT IT ▶ **Justify using division to solve the problem.** (Divide to make same-size groups.)
▶ **Explain how you know to divide 495 by 72 and 325 by 46.** (You are looking for the total number of each type of bus needed to carry the number of same-type ticket holders.)
▶ **Explain how you will interpret any remainders.** (A remainder of any size means another bus is needed.)
▶ **In Examples A and B, explain when and why you know that the estimates must be changed.** (A: after you multiply; the product is greater than the dividend, so you cannot subtract. B: after you subtract; the difference is greater than the divisor, so you could make another group.)
Student Edition answers: **1.** to make same-sized groups **2.** 495 ÷ 72; 325 ÷ 46

2. CHECK UNDERSTANDING

TRY IT OUT

ERROR ALERT Failing to notice when an adjustment must be made. Continuing to divide with the given quotient without adjustment.

Changing Estimates

LEARN ABOUT IT

EXPLORE Solve to Understand
Over the weekend, 495 people bought tickets for a double-decker bus tour. 325 people bought tickets for the single-decker bus tour. A double-decker bus holds 72 passengers and a single-decker bus holds 46 passengers. How many full buses will the company need for each tour and how many people will be on a partly filled bus?

TALK ABOUT IT See teaching notes.

1. How do you know that you should divide in this problem?
2. Which pairs of numbers will you need to divide?

When you divide you will sometimes discover that you need to change your estimate.

A

70 → 72)495, quotient 7; − 504 ← Too large

70 → 72)495, quotient 6 R63; − 432; 63

B

50 → 46)325, quotient 6; − 276 ← Too small; 49 ← more than 46

50 → 46)325, quotient 7 R3; − 322; 3

6 full double-decker buses and an extra bus with 63 people are needed. 7 full single-decker buses and an extra bus with 3 people are needed.

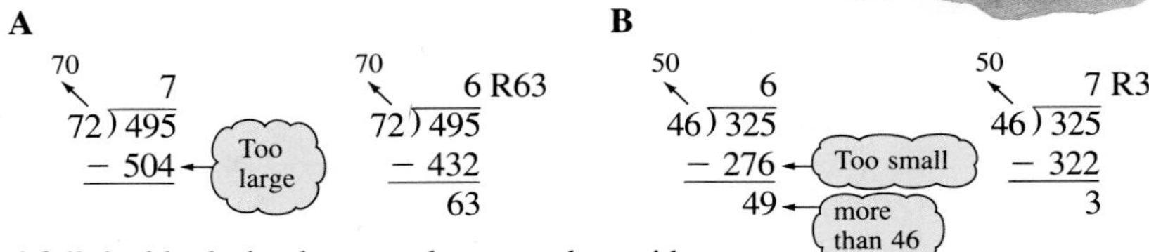

TRY IT OUT

Decide which estimates must be changed. Then finish the division.

1. 17)88, estimate 4 — 5 R3
2. 28)86, estimate 2 — 3 R2
3. 16)97, estimate 4 — 6 R1
4. 42)82, estimate 2 — 1 R40

TEACHING OPTIONS

RETEACHING TIPS Have students write flowchart questions on index cards to test estimates. One card says: Multiply. Product greater than dividend? If *yes*, estimate is too large. The other card says: Subtract. Difference greater than divisor? If *yes*, estimate is too small. Assign Reteaching Supplement 160.

ENRICHMENT Have students use number sense to arrange the division problems in order from smallest to largest quotient. Tell them *not* to divide.
a. 39)43 **b.** 61)436
c. 45)127 **d.** 54)278
(a, c, d, b)

PRACTICE

Divide. Change your estimate if necessary.

1. $38\overline{)46}$ 1 R8
2. $22\overline{)85}$ 3 R19
3. $53\overline{)125}$ 2 R19
4. $44\overline{)243}$ 5 R23
5. $64\overline{)312}$ 4 R56
6. $32\overline{)248}$ 7 R24
7. $35\overline{)142}$ 4 R2
8. $19\overline{)184}$ 9 R13
9. $77\overline{)543}$ 7 R4
10. $93\overline{)651}$ 7
11. $42\overline{)289}$ 6 R37
12. $85\overline{)686}$ 8 R6
13. $65\overline{)391}$ 6 R1
14. $29\overline{)133}$ 4 R17
15. $74\overline{)636}$ 8 R44
16. 182 ÷ 27 6 R20
17. 167 ÷ 54 3 R5
18. 364 ÷ 39 9 R13
19. 332 ÷ 82 4 R4
20. 428 ÷ 56 7 R36
21. 895 ÷ 93 9 R58
22. 85 ÷ 26 3 R7
23. 646 ÷ 91 7 R9
24. Find 543 divided by 61. 8 R55
25. Find 699 divided by 86. 8 R11

APPLY

MATH REASONING Decide which quotient is larger without solving the problem.

26. 2,383 ÷ 42 or 2,383 ÷ 52

27. 423 ÷ 17 or 323 ÷ 17

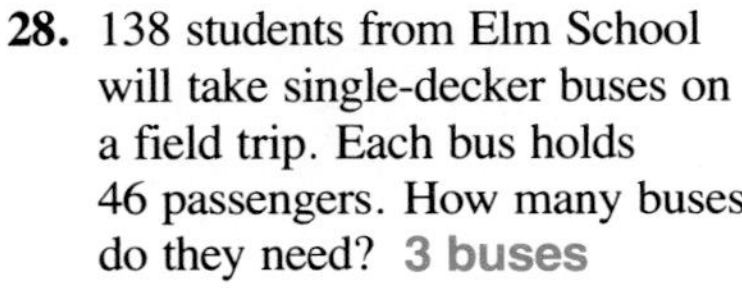

PROBLEM SOLVING

28. 138 students from Elm School will take single-decker buses on a field trip. Each bus holds 46 passengers. How many buses do they need? 3 buses

29. The wax museum is very popular. In one day it averages 424 visitors. About how many visitors does it average every 2 weeks? 5,936 visitors

► **ALGEBRA** See Additional Answers.

Find at least 5 pairs of numbers for the □ and △ in each problem.

30. □ ÷ △ = 40

31. □ ÷ △ = 20

More Practice, page 511, set F

3. Practice and Apply

Basic	6-19, 24-31
Average	1-31
Extended	10-15, 20-31

Additional Answers: See p. T79.

PRACTICE

When can you tell if your estimate is too large? (after the Multiply step)

APPLY

MATH REASONING ► **Explain a relationship between the size of the dividend or the divisor and the quotient.** (When the dividend remains the same, the smaller the divisor, the larger the quotient because smaller-sized groups mean more groups can be made; when the divisor remains the same, the larger the dividend, the larger the quotient because there is more to divide.)

PROBLEM SOLVING ► **Explain how to solve Problem 29.** (multiply to combine same-size groups)

ALGEBRA ► **Explain how special products can help solve Exercises 30 and 31.** (Think of the quotient as a factor; find another factor and the product using basic facts and multiples of 10.)

Close and Assess

WRITE WHAT YOU THINK

Have students write paragraphs about how to recognize estimates that are too large or too small. They should explain *when* they would notice the need to adjust, *what* they would notice, and *how* they would make any necessary changes. (Check students' writing.)

QUICK QUIZ

Divide. Change your estimate if necessary.

1. $44\overline{)342}$ (7 R34)
2. $25\overline{)241}$ (9 R16)
3. $18\overline{)153}$ (8 R9)

LESSON OPTIONS 16-5

Problem Solving: Mixed Practice/Midchapter Review/Quiz

OBJECTIVE 16-5 To practice problem solving

PREBOOK ACTIVITIES

QUICK REVIEW

Solve the miniproblems using any appropriate strategy.

1. 45 seats per bus, 360 passengers—how many buses? (8)
2. 78 tickets at $5.75 each—how much money spent? ($448.50)
3. Project began in 1967, ended in 1981—how many years? (14)
4. 3.65 km each way—how long a round trip? (7.3 km)

PRIOR KNOWLEDGE

Have students explain the thinking they generally use to help them choose an operation to solve a story problem. (Possible answer: Visualize the action suggested by the situation, then choose the operation that represents that action.) Have them tell how they choose a calculation method. (Answers may vary.)

COMMUNICATION

Writing in Math In their Math Journals, have students write a paragraph summarizing general solution methods that can apply to any story problem. (Possible example: Choose an Operation) Volunteers may read their paragraphs aloud. (Answers will vary. Check students' writing.)

EXPLORE AND CONNECT

COOPERATIVE ACTIVITY

Grouping Suggestion: small groups

Al has twice as many fish as Cal, who has 2 fewer than Hal. Hal has named his fish after all the days of the week. How many fish does each boy have?

TEACHING ACTIONS

Have students work together to discuss reasonable strategies and find a solution that makes sense.

BEFORE

▶ **Explain the situation.** (3 boys have different amounts of fish.)

▶ **Analyze the given data.** (Hal has 7 fish if he has 1 for each day of the week.)

DURING

▶ **Decide on a reasonable solution strategy.** (Possible answers: Work Backward; Use Logical Reasoning; Guess and Check; Use Objects; Choose an Operation)

▶ **Decide how to apply the strategy you chose to solve the problem.** (Methods may vary; Hal has 7 fish, Cal has 5, Al has 10.)

AFTER

▶ **Evaluate your solution to see whether it makes sense.** (Based on Hal having 7 fish, Cal has 2 less, which is 5, and Al has twice as many as Cal, which is 10.)

▶ **Justify the solution method you chose.** (Answers will vary.)

CONNECTIONS Use these anytime.

Problem of the Day

How Old? When Dana asked Granny her age, Granny answered with a riddle. Use the clues to find Granny's age today. I am not yet 80, but I am over 50. Last year my age was a multiple of 7, but this year it is a multiple of 6. (78)

Number Sense

Estimation Estimate the product: $9 \times 8 \times 7 \times 6 \times 5 \times 4 \times 3 \times 2 \times 1$. Explain how you made your estimate, then find the exact answer with a calculator. (Estimates may vary: 362,880)

Creative Thinking

Clever Change Tran discovered that he can combine the 10 coins he has to pay the exact price for anything from $.01 to $.99. What coins does Tran have? (3 quarters, 2 dimes, 1 nickel, 4 pennies)

Classwork and Homework Supplements

Practice

Problem Solving 16-5

Name

Mixed Practice

Choose a strategy from the strategies list to solve these problems. Strategies used will vary.

Some Strategies

Act It out	Guess and Check
Use Objects	Make a Table
Choose an Operation	Look for a Pattern
Draw a Picture	Use Logical Reasoning
Make an Organized List	Work Backward

1. Keiko took the commuter train from Trenton to Deal on 3 days. She spent $7 a day on tickets. The third day she bought snacks for $1.35. She had $1.65 left. She spent no other money. How much money did she start with? $24
2. There are 2 commuter trains with a total of 32 cars. Train A has 2 more cars than Train B. How many cars does Train B have? 15 cars
3. The train ride from Eastport to Milltown takes 17 minutes. The ride from Eastport to Landon takes 3 times as long. How long is the trip from Eastport to Landon? 51 minutes
4. The commuter train has 15 cars. Each car holds 40 passengers. How many passengers can the train hold in all? 600 passengers
5. Westbury is 3 stops after Clearview. Ashton is 2 stops before Golden. Golden is 1 stop before Clearview. Which of the stops comes last? Westbury
6. 65 train tickets were sold between Lorb and Monroe. 43 were sold from Monroe to Lorb. 37 were sold from Lorb to Monroe. How many were round-trip tickets? 15 tickets

PS-4 Use with text page 444. 161

Building Thinking Skills

Problem Solving 16-5

Name

The Problem with Zeppelins

Choose a strategy from the list to solve each problem. Write the number of the problem next to the strategy you used. Then solve the problem. Choose from these strategies:
Answers for strategies used may vary.

Work Backward 4	Make a Table 1
Draw a Picture 3	Choose an Operation 2
Use Logical Reasoning ___	Make an Organized List ___

1. In 1899 in Germany Count von Zeppelin developed an airship called a zeppelin. In calm air, it could travel 80 miles per hour. How many hours did it take to travel 160 miles? 240 miles? 400 miles? 2, 3, 5
2. The *Hindenburg*, the largest zeppelin, measured 135 feet in length. How many times longer was it than a 30-foot zeppelin? $4\frac{1}{2}$ times
3. The *Hindenburg* contained fuel and water tanks and the crew's rooms on the front end. The rudders were located at the other end. 16 gas bags and the propellers were in the portion next to the rudders. Next to this section were the lounge and double-berth cabins. What section was next to the fuel and water tanks and crew's quarters? lounge and cabins
4. In April a zeppelin carried 50 passengers and a crew of 60. In May it carried 75 passengers and 25 crew members. During the months of March, April, and May the passengers and crew members totaled 312. How many passengers and crew members did the zeppelin carry in March? 102

TS-4 Use with text page 444. 161

Reteaching

Problem Solving 16-5

Name

Mixed Practice

Many strategies can be used to solve problems. Here is a list of strategies.

Act It Out	Guess and Check
Use Objects	Make a Table
Choose an Operation	Look for a Pattern
Draw a Picture	Use Logical Reasoning
Make an Organized List	Work Backward

Example: Theo is taller than Pedro. Dave is shorter than Pedro. Kirk is taller than Theo. Who is the tallest?

Read the problem. Decide which strategy to use. → Draw a line. → Show Theo taller than Pedro. → Show Dave shorter than Pedro. → Show Kirk taller than Theo.

Theo, Pedro | Theo, Pedro, Dave | Kirk, Theo, Pedro, Dave

Drawing a picture will help.

Kirk is the tallest.

Choose a strategy from the list to solve each problem.
Strategies used will vary.

1. Sierra bought 8 records. Each record cost $6. Then she spent $5 for a tape. How much money did Sierra start with if she had $2 left? $55
2. Arif has saved $14. He bought a book for $5. Then he earned $8 baby-sitting. How much money does he have now? $17
3. The teacher asked for 1 boy and 1 girl to help him. 3 boys and 2 girls wanted to help. How many ways could the teacher choose? 6 ways
4. There were 3 beans in the first bag, 6 beans in the second bag, 9 beans in the third bag, and so on. How many beans were in the sixth bag? 18 beans

RS-4 Use with text page 444. 161

Challenges

Problem Solving 16-5

Name

Making a Plan

Many problems can be solved using more than one strategy.

Example: At his party, Tim can have punch or lemonade. He can serve lunch, dinner, or a snack. How many drink and food combinations are there? Here are two strategies Tim can use to solve his problem:

Make an Organized List

punch—snack	lemonade—snack
punch—lunch	lemonade—lunch
punch—dinner	lemonade—dinner

Draw a Picture

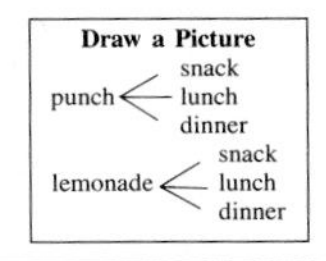

Name 2 strategies you could use to solve each problem. Then choose one and solve. Choose from these strategies: Strategies used will vary.

Use Objects	Make an Organized List
Draw a Picture	Make a Table
Guess and Check	Choose an Operation

1. Jeff can buy tickets for 2 miniature golf games for $2.25. How much would 8 games cost? $9
2. Anita swung at 25 balls altogether at the batting cage. She hit 7 more than she missed. How many did she hit? 16
3. For his birthday, Joe could go to the water slides, the pool, or miniature golf. He could go on January 15 or January 22. How many possibilities are there? 6
4. At miniature golf, Marcos was ahead of Kim. Denise was between Kim and Marcos. Marcos was behind Jeff. Who was first in line? Jeff

CS-4 Use with text page 444. 161

Options for Individual Needs

Basic

Exercises 1-7; 1-16, 21-32
Computer Bank, p. 494
More Practice, p. 527, set D

Supplements
Reteaching 161 or
Practice 161

Average

Exercises 1-7; 1-32
Computer Bank, p. 494
More Practice, p. 527, set D

Supplements
Practice 161
Challenges 161 or
Thinking Skills 161

Extended

Exercises 1-7; 5-32
Computer Bank, p. 494

Supplements
Challenges 161
Thinking Skills 161

Other Resources:
Problem-Solving Experiences in Mathematics, Grade 4, Problem 131
Mathematics, A Way of Thinking, Lesson 10-14
Challenge, A Program for the Mathematically Talented, Teacher's Edition, Activity 61
Using the Math Explorer Calculator: A Sourcebook for Teachers, Chapter 14

16-5

LESSON PLAN 16-5

OBJECTIVE 16-5
To practice problem solving

Grouping Suggestion: pairs

1. MOTIVATE AND TEACH

LEARN ABOUT IT

▶ **For Problem 2, explain the situation in your own words.** (A trip involves a drive and hike in each direction.)

DURING

▶ **Identify data you need to solve the problem.** (Drive 45.75 miles each way; hike 1.2 miles each way.)

▶ **Decide on a sensible solution strategy.** (Possible answer: Double each distance, then find the total; add both distances, then double the sum.)

▶ **Explain how to estimate the answer.** (Possible answer: Round 45.75 to 46; multiply by 2 = 92; round 1.2 to 1; multiply by 2; 92 + 2 = estimate of 94.)

▶ **Evaluate your answer to see if it makes sense.** (45.75 doubled is 91.5, 1.2 doubled is 2.4, 91.5 + 2.4 = 93.9; or 45.75 + 1.2 = 46.95, 46.95 doubled is 93.9; 93.9 miles fits the estimate that the total trip was 94 miles.)

2. CHECK UNDERSTANDING

TRY IT OUT

ERROR ALERT Misinterpreting the situation, leading to an incorrect solution strategy.

Problem Solving
Mixed Practice

Choose a strategy from the strategies list to solve these problems.

Some Strategies
Act It Out
Use Objects
Choose an Operation
Draw a Picture
Make an Organized List
Guess and Check
Make a Table
Look for a Pattern
Use Logical Reasoning
Work Backward

1. Teresa's school took a field trip to see the Monarch Butterfly Refuge. 108 students went on the trip. 12 students went in each van. How many vans made the trip? **9 vans**

2. The drive to the monarch refuge was 45.75 miles. The students hiked 1.2 miles to get to the grove. Then they hiked back to the vans and drove home. How far did they go in all? **93.9 miles**

3. To get to the preserve for the winter, one monarch flew 216 miles. Another flew 13 times as far. How far did the second monarch fly? **2,808 miles**

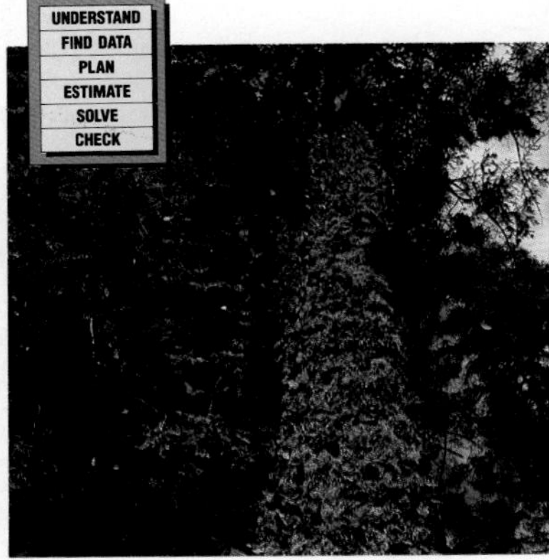

4. When a caterpillar hatches from its egg, its length is $\frac{3}{16}$ of an inch. The guide said one caterpillar grew to be $1\frac{1}{16}$ inches long. How much did it grow? **$\frac{14}{16}$ or $\frac{7}{8}$ inch**

5. At the nature store, the students bought a total of 12 souvenir keychains. They paid $24 in all. How much did each keychain cost? **$2**

6. Jose bought peanuts at the nature store. He gave 5 peanuts to each of the 6 people in his group. He ate 7. Then he had 9 peanuts left. How many peanuts did he buy? **46 peanuts**

7. The largest known butterfly has an 11.02 inch wingspan and weighs 0.88 ounces. The smallest known butterfly has a wingspan of 0.26 inches. What is the difference in their wingspans? **10.76 inches**

More Practice, page 527, set D

TEACHING OPTIONS

RETEACHING TIPS Have students work in pairs to discuss and restate each problem in their own words. This will help students clarify each situation and visualize the suggested actions. Assign Reteaching Supplement 161.

COMPUTER **Path Tactics, MECC, Copyright 1986** For use with all levels of students. Choose the operation to practice. Given 3 numbers, create an equation whose solution tells the Robot how many steps to take to reach the end of the path. Allow 5 to 10 min to complete the game.

Midchapter Review/Quiz

Find each quotient.

1. 30)150 5	**2.** 80)560 7	**3.** 60)360 6	**4.** 50)200 4
5. 20)80 4	**6.** 40)160 4	**7.** 70)420 6	**8.** 90)810 9

Divide and check.

9. 10)27 2 R7	**10.** 30)275 9 R5	**11.** 80)410 5 R10	**12.** 70)608 8 R48
13. 14)98 7	**14.** 39)245 6 R11	**15.** 82)600 7 R26	**16.** 54)387 7 R9
17. 45)337 7 R22	**18.** 68)540 7 R64	**19.** 27)190 7 R1	**20.** 74)435 5 R65
21. 24)\$1.44 \$0.06	**22.** 51)32 0 R32	**23.** 64)435 6 R51	**24.** 35)99 2 R29
25. 30)260 8 R20	**26.** 90)580 6 R40	**27.** 20)149 7 R9	**28.** 47)\$2.35 \$0.05

PROBLEM SOLVING

A nickel wrapper holds 20 nickels and a penny wrapper holds 50 pennies.

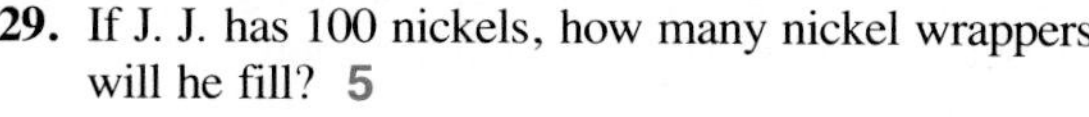

29. If J. J. has 100 nickels, how many nickel wrappers will he fill? 5

30. How many penny wrappers will Rita fill with 487 pennies? How many pennies will be left over? 9 wrappers, 37 left over

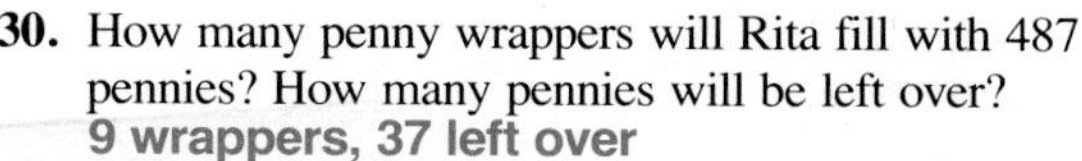

31. Gina has 320 pennies and 144 nickels. How many coin wrappers will she need? How much money will be left over? 13 wrappers, 40¢ left over

32. How many nickel wrappers will Tony fill if he has \$1.00 in nickels? 1 wrapper

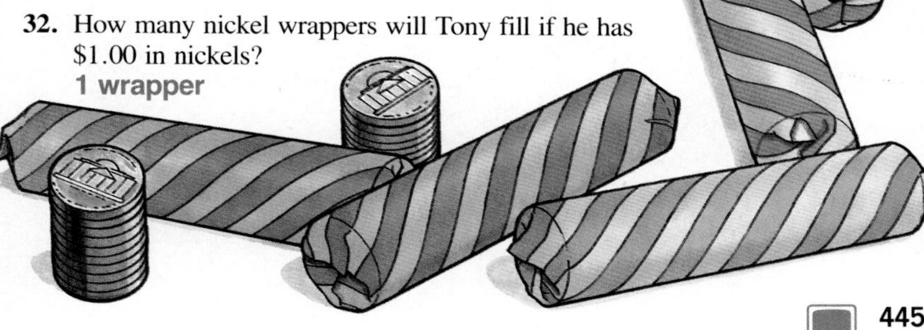

445

Close and Assess

WRITE WHAT YOU THINK
Have students write a paragraph explaining how they can check the solution to a problem to determine if it is reasonable. Have them use any problem solved on page 444 as an example of their method.

Quick Quiz

Sven saved \$27.50 this month from his baby-sitting money. His mother saved 9 times that much this month. What is the total they saved this month? (\$275.00)

3. Practice and Apply

Basic	1-7; 1-16, 21-32
Average	1-7; 1-32
Extended	1-7; 5-32

PRACTICE

How could you use special quotients to solve Exercises 1 to 8? (Find basic facts related to the division problems.) *How do Exercises 9 to 12 differ from Exercises 13 to 24?* (Divisors in 9 to 12 are multiples of 10; in 13 to 24, divisors are other 2-digit numbers.)

ITEM ANALYSIS The following table correlates the Midchapter Review/Quiz items with the lesson objectives.

Items	Objectives
1-8, 29, 32	16-1
9-12, 25-27, 30, 31	16-2
13-16, 22, 24	16-3
17-21, 23, 28	16-4
(29-32)	16-5

16-5

LESSON OPTIONS 16-6

Dividing by Tens: 2-Digit Quotients

OBJECTIVE 16-6 To find 2-digit quotients by dividing with 2-digit divisors that are multiples of 10

PREBOOK ACTIVITIES

QUICK REVIEW

Divide.

1. $5\overline{)79}$ (15 R4)	**2.** $6\overline{)314}$ (52 R2)	**3.** $3\overline{)188}$ (62 R2)
4. $8\overline{)437}$ (54 R5)	**5.** $2\overline{)138}$ (69)	**6.** $9\overline{)638}$ (70 R8)
7. $4\overline{)301}$ (75 R1)	**8.** $7\overline{)293}$ (41 R6)	**9.** $5\overline{)450}$ (90)

PRIOR KNOWLEDGE

Have students estimate the population of the school, or tell them the number. Then have them imagine situations in which that number might be divided into equal groups. (number of students per class, number of students in the lunchroom at one time, number of buses needed to take everyone on a trip) Tell students that in this lesson they will practice division with 2-digit divisors, resulting in 2-digit quotients.

COMMUNICATION

Discussing Math Write $10\overline{)56}$ on the chalkboard and have students find the quotient. (5 R6) Then revise the problem as $10\overline{)560}$ and have students describe the change. (The dividend is now 10 times greater.) Ask students to predict how the change in the dividend will affect the size of the quotient. (Students will probably say that the quotient must be 10 times greater.) Have them determine, without dividing, how many digits the new quotient will have. (2)

EXPLORE AND CONNECT

Materials: calculators
Grouping Suggestion: cooperative learning pairs
Pairs explore the relationship between dividends and 1- and 2-digit quotients. Using paper and pencil, students divide each number on this list by 20: 52, 64, 96. (2 R12, 3 R4, 4 R16) Next, partners multiply each dividend by 10, rewrite the problems ($20\overline{)520}$, $20\overline{)640}$, $20\overline{)960}$), and predict new quotients. Then they use the calculator to divide the new problems and compare the actual 2-digit quotients to their predictions. (26, 32, 48) If partners notice discrepancies between the two, challenge them to use logical reasoning and their understanding of the division process to try to relate the 2-digit quotient to the problem. Conclude by having pairs share their findings. (Students may discover that the remainder with the 1-digit quotient becomes part of the bring-down step when there are 2-digit quotients.)

CONNECTIONS Use these anytime.

Problem of the Day

Calculator Find the pattern and missing numbers with a calculator.

11	(22)	(33)	(44)	(55)	66	77
121	242	(363)	484	605	(726)	(847)

(Across the top row, numbers increase by 11 each time; then they are multiplied by 11 to equal the numbers on the bottom row.)

Creative Thinking

Number Riddle How can you make eight 5s equal 1? (5,555 ÷ 5,555 = 1)

Number Sense

Estimation Find the missing digits in the division problem. (604 ÷ 63 = 9 R37)

```
      9 R□7
6□)□0□
    5□7
     □7
```

Classwork and Homework Supplements

Practice — Skills Maintenance 16-6

Name ____________

Dividing by Tens: 2-Digit Quotients

Divide and check.

1. 40)556 — 13 R36; −40, 156, −120, 36
2. 20)792 — 39 R12; −60, 192, −180, 12
3. 50)643 — 12 R43; −50, 143, −100, 43
4. 30)810 — 27; −60, 210, −210, 0
5. 10)311 — 31 R1; −30, 11, −10, 1
6. 30)415 — 13 R25; −30, 115, −90, 25
7. 40)562 — 14 R2; −40, 162, −160, 2
8. 20)391 — 19 R11; −20, 191, −180, 11
9. 50)961 — 19 R11; −50, 461, −450, 11
10. 20)503 — 25 R3; −40, 103, −100, 3
11. 70)862 — 12 R22; −70, 162, −140, 22
12. 30)770 — 25 R20; −60, 170, −150, 20
13. 30)$7.20 — $0.24; −60, 120, −120, 0
14. 60)$8.40 — $0.14; −60, 240, −240, 0
15. 20)$4.00 — $0.20; −40, 00, −0, 0
16. 40)$8.80 — $0.22; −80, 80, −80, 0

Building Thinking Skills — Math Reasoning 16-6

Name ____________

Divide and Add

Find quotients for the first two problems. Then use these quotients to find the quotient for the third problem. Check by multiplying.

				Check
1.	70)700 = 10	70)210 = 3	70)910 = 13	13 × 70 = 910
2.	40)800 = 20	40)160 = 4	40)960 = 24	24 × 40 = 960
3.	30)900 = 30	30)60 = 2	30)960 = 32	32 × 30 = 960
4.	50)500 = 10	50)250 = 5	50)750 = 15	15 × 50 = 750
5.	20)400 = 20	20)120 = 6	20)520 = 26	26 × 20 = 520
6.	30)600 = 20	30)150 = 5	30)750 = 25	25 × 30 = 750
7.	80)800 = 10	80)160 = 2	80)960 = 12	12 × 80 = 960
8.	60)600 = 10	60)360 = 6	60)960 = 16	16 × 60 = 960

Reteaching — Skills Review 16-6

Name ____________

Dividing by Tens: 2-Digit Quotients

Divide the tens.
- Estimate
- Divide
- Multiply
- Subtract
- Compare

Divide the ones.
- Bring down
- Divide
- Multiply
- Subtract
- Compare

Example: 40)568 — 14 R8; −40, 168, −160, 8. Check: 40 × 14 = 160 + 400 = 560; 560 + 8 = 568

Divide and check.

1. 30)476 — 15 R26; −30, 176, −150, 26. Check: 30 × 15 = 150 + 300 = 450; 450 + 26 = 476
2. 20)517 — 25 R17; −40, 117, −100, 17. Check: 20 × 25 = 100 + 400 = 500; 500 + 17 = 517
3. 40)458 — 11 R18; −40, 58, −40, 18. Check: 40 × 11 = 40 + 400 = 440; 440 + 18 = 458
4. 50)613 — 12 R13; −50, 113, −100, 13. Check: 50 × 12 = 100 + 500 = 600; 600 + 13 = 613
5. 30)900 — 30; −90, 00. Check: 30 × 30 = 00 + 900 = 900
6. 10)854 — 85 R4; −80, 54, −50, 4. Check: 10 × 85 = 50 + 800 = 850; 850 + 4 = 854

Challenges — Cooperative Activities 16-6

Name ____________

Name That Quotient

Work in small groups. Complete each problem below using only the numbers 2, 3, 4, and 5. You may use each number only once in each problem.

1. You want the largest quotient possible. — 20)543 = 27 R3
2. You want the smallest quotient possible. — 50)234 = 4 R34
3. You want a quotient between 20 and 30. **Answers will vary. Possible answer shown.** — 20)435 = 21 R15
4. You want the quotient to be 8 with a remainder. **Answers will vary. Possible answer shown.** — 40)325 = 8 R5
5. You want the quotient to be between 10 and 20. **Answers will vary. Possible answer shown.** — 30)425 = 14 R5

Options for Individual Needs

Basic

Exercises 5-28
Data Bank, p. 478
More Practice, p. 512, set A

Supplements
Reteaching 162 or
Practice 162

Average

Exercises 1-31
Data Bank, p. 478
More Practice, p. 512, set A

Supplements
Practice 162
Challenges 162 or
Thinking Skills 162

Extended

Exercises 7-22, 27-31
Data Bank, p. 478

Supplements
Challenges 162
Thinking Skills 162

Other Resources:

Problem-Solving Experiences in Mathematics, Grade 4, Problem 132
Mathematics, A Way of Thinking, Lesson 10-15
Math In Stride, Grade 4, p. 105
Using the Math Explorer Calculator: A Sourcebook for Teachers, Chapter 14

16-6

LESSON PLAN 16-6

OBJECTIVE 16-6
To find 2-digit quotients by dividing with 2-digit divisors that are multiples of 10

Materials: lined paper

1. MOTIVATE AND TEACH

LEARN ABOUT IT

EXPLORE ▶ **Summarize differences between our calendar and the Krakatoan calendar.** (Ours has 365 d with 12 mo of different lengths; the Krakatoan calendar has 360 d with 20 same-size mo.)
▶ **Justify division to solve the problem.** (divide, because all months have the same number of days)
▶ **Explain why 16 is not a remainder.** (There are still ones to bring down and divide.)
▶ **Explain how 16 tens relate to 160.** (160 is 16 tens with 0 ones brought down.)

TALK ABOUT IT ▶ **Using compatible numbers, would an estimate be high or low? Explain.** (high, because rounding 360 to 400 ÷ 20 = 20)
Student Edition answers: **1.** There are not enough hundreds to divide, so divide the tens and write the first quotient digit above the tens. **2.** Answers will vary. **3.** Each month has 18 d.

2. CHECK UNDERSTANDING

TRY IT OUT

ERROR ALERT Forgetting to keep dividing after finding the first digit of the quotient. Making estimates too large or too small.

Dividing by Tens
2-Digit Quotients

LEARN ABOUT IT

EXPLORE **Think About the Process**
Our year has 365 days. In the book *Twenty-One Balloons* the Krakatoan calendar has 20 months in a year and only 360 days. If the months all have the same number of days, how many days are in each Krakatoan month?

Here is how to divide by a multiple of 10.

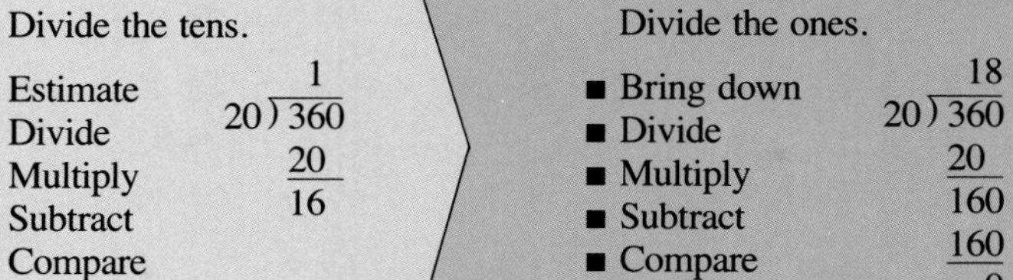

TALK ABOUT IT See teaching notes.

1. How do you decide where to write the first quotient digit?
2. How would you have estimated the answer?
3. Use a complete sentence to give a reasonable answer to the story problem.

TRY IT OUT

Divide and check.

1. 10)673 **67 R3**	**2.** 50)617 **12 R17**	**3.** 60)875 **14 R35**	**4.** 40)$4.80 **$0.12**
5. 40)932 **23 R12**	**6.** 50)835 **16 R35**	**7.** 20)$6.00 **$0.30**	**8.** 70)864 **12 R24**

446

TEACHING OPTIONS

RETEACHING TIPS Have students work on lined paper turned sideways so each number in the dividend has its own column. After they divide tens, students draw an arrow down from the ones place to show the bring-down step. They divide until all columns are used. Assign Reteaching Supplement 162.

ENRICHMENT Students continue the pattern 3 times.
600 ÷ 30 = 20
630 ÷ 30 = 21
(660) ÷ 30 = 22
(690) ÷ 30 = (23)
(dividend increases by 30, quotient by 1; 720 ÷ 30 = 24; 750 ÷ 30 = 25; 780 ÷ 30 = 26)

PRACTICE

Divide and check.

1. $60\overline{)255}$ 4 R15
2. $30\overline{)742}$ 24 R22
3. $20\overline{)285}$ 14 R5
4. $50\overline{)750}$ 15
5. $10\overline{)678}$ 67 R8
6. $20\overline{)400}$ 20
7. $30\overline{)386}$ 12 R26
8. $40\overline{)495}$ 12 R15
9. $675 \div 50$ 13 R25
10. $\$9.60 \div 80$ \$0.12
11. $526 \div 40$ 13 R6
12. $921 \div 30$ 30 R21
13. How many 40s are in 810? 20 R10
14. How many 20s are in 665? 33 R5

APPLY

MATH REASONING Estimate each quotient. Answers may vary. Sample answers given.

15. $790 \div 10$ 79
16. $420 \div 30$ 14
17. $800 \div 40$ 20
18. $900 \div 50$ 18

Write each example using both kinds of division symbols. Do not solve.

19. 38 divided into 423
$38\overline{)423}$ or $423 \div 38$
20. 174 divided by 83
$83\overline{)174}$ or $174 \div 83$

PROBLEM SOLVING

21. It takes about 700 cubic feet of free hydrogen to lift 50 pounds. How many cubic feet of hydrogen does it take to lift one pound?
14 cubic feet

22. **Language Arts Data Bank** DATA BANK The size of Professor Sherman's balloon, the *Globe*, was 10 times the size of the standard balloon in 1883. What was the size of the *Globe*? See page 478.
6,000 cubic yards

MIXED REVIEW

Find the sums. Then write the answers as mixed numbers and reduce them to lowest terms. See Additional Answers.

23. $\frac{2}{3} + \frac{4}{3}$
24. $\frac{4}{10} + \frac{8}{10}$
25. $\frac{3}{6} + \frac{5}{6}$
26. $\frac{8}{9} + \frac{1}{9}$

27. $7\frac{5}{10} + 3\frac{3}{10}$
28. $2\frac{5}{11} + 5\frac{6}{11}$
29. $4\frac{2}{8} + 1\frac{4}{8}$
30. $2\frac{6}{7} + 3\frac{5}{7}$
31. $1\frac{4}{15} + 7\frac{14}{15}$

More Practice, page 512, set A

3. PRACTICE AND APPLY

Basic	5-28
Average	1-31
Extended	7-22, 27-31

Additional Answers: See p. T79.

PRACTICE

Scan the Practice exercises to find 3 that have no remainders. (Exercises 4, 6, 10)

APPLY

MATH REASONING ► **Explain how you can estimate Exercises 15-18.** (Possible answer: Break apart factors, as in Exercise 16: 300 ÷ 30 = 10; 120 ÷ 30 = 4; 10 + 4 = 14.)

PROBLEM SOLVING ► **Justify the operation to use to solve Problem 21.** (Divide; you know 700 cubic ft lifts 50 lb, so 700 ÷ 50 tells how many cubic feet lift 1 lb.)

► **Before using the Data Bank, justify using mental math to solve Problem 22.** (Whatever the standard size is, multiply it by 10, which is easy to do mentally.)

MIXED REVIEW ► **Make a generalization about the Mixed Review exercises.** (All require adding fractions with like denominators.)

CLOSE AND ASSESS

SHOW WHAT YOU KNOW

Have students find and correct the error in the example below and show its check:

```
     20 R6
40)936
   80
    6
```

(Subtract step not done before bringing down 6; 23 R 16; 23 × 40 = 920 + 16 = 936.)

QUICK QUIZ

Divide and check.

1. $70\overline{)980}$ (14)
2. $20\overline{)534}$ (26 R14)
3. $40\overline{)175}$ (4 R15)
4. $80\overline{)\$9.60}$ (\$0.12)

LESSON OPTIONS 16-7

Dividing: 2-Digit Quotients

OBJECTIVE 16-7 To find 2-digit quotients by dividing with 2-digit divisors that are not rounded

PREBOOK ACTIVITIES

QUICK REVIEW

Divide.

1. $20\overline{)678}$	(33 R18)	**2.** $30\overline{)678}$	(22 R18)
3. $40\overline{)678}$	(16 R38)	**4.** $50\overline{)812}$	(16 R12)
5. $60\overline{)812}$	(13 R32)	**6.** $70\overline{)812}$	(11 R42)
7. $20\overline{)797}$	(39 R17)	**8.** $40\overline{)797}$	(19 R37)
9. $60\overline{)797}$	(13 R17)	**10.** $80\overline{)987}$	(12 R27)

PRIOR KNOWLEDGE

Review the division process. (Estimate, divide, multiply, subtract, compare, bring down.) Ask students to explain what to do after the bring-down step. (Repeat the original steps in the same order until there are no more digits to bring down.)

COMMUNICATION

Reading and Writing Math Have students copy and complete the following statements in their Math Journals.

1. Before you start to divide, a helpful strategy is to (estimate) using (front-end) digits.

2. An amount that does not divide completely is shown as a (remainder) .

3. A remainder can never be (greater) than the divisor.

4. You may change an estimate if the quotient is (too high or too low) .

5. Divide money amounts as you would divide any other numbers, but show the quotient with (a dollar sign, decimal point, and two decimal places) .

6. Check division by multiplying the (quotient) by the (divisor) , then (adding the remainder) . The sum should equal the (dividend) .

EXPLORE AND CONNECT

Materials: TA 3 (Number Cards 0-9)

Grouping Suggestion: cooperative learning groups of 3

Students formulate division problems with 2-digit divisors and 3-digit dividends that will have 1- or 2-digit quotients. One student picks 5 number cards. The second student arranges the cards to create a division problem with a 1-digit quotient. The first student records the problem. Then the third student rearranges the same 5 digits to form another division problem that has a 2-digit quotient. Again, the first student records the problem. The team uses any means they think of to verify the quotients. Groups repeat 3 times, trading tasks. Have students find a link between the dividend and the divisor to help them determine quotient size. (If the first 2 digits of a dividend are equal to or greater than the divisor, the quotient will have 2 digits; if the first 2 digits of a dividend are smaller than the divisor, the quotient will have 1 digit.)

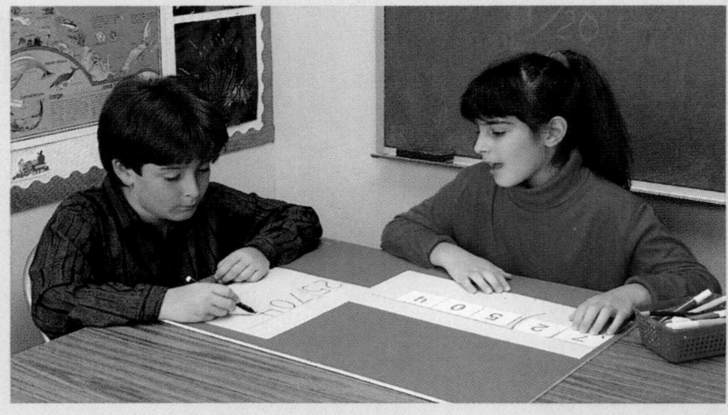

CONNECTIONS Use these anytime.

Problem of the Day

Missing Digits Use the digits 0, 1, 4, 5 and 9 in the division problem so that the quotient will be 12 R39.

□□)□□□

($40\overline{)519}$)

Patterns

Calculator Quotients Enter 99,999,999 in a calculator, divide by 11, and record the quotient. Enter 88,888,888, divide by 11, and record the quotient. Now predict the quotients for dividing 77,777,777 by 11, 66,666,666 by 11, and so on down to 11,111,111 divided by 11. (7,070,707; 6,060,606; 5,050,505; and so on to 1,010,101)

Math Connection

Money In the first hour of the Spring Fair, the Water Balloon Toss collected \$4.60. At \$0.20 per toss, how many water balloons were thrown? At that rate, how much money can the game expect to earn by the end of the 6-h fair? (23; \$27.60)

Classwork and Homework Supplements

Practice

Skills Maintenance 16-7

Name ________________

Dividing: 2-Digit Quotients

Find tl s. Check y rs.

1. 27)725 = 26 R23 (− 54, 185, − 162, 23)
2. 44)673 = 15 R13 (− 44, 233, − 220, 13)
3. 46)634 = 13 R36 (− 46, 174, − 138, 36)
4. 51)870 = 17 R3 (− 51, 360, − 357, 3)
5. 32)650 = 20 R10 (− 64, 10, − 0, 10)
6. 17)473 = 27 R14 (− 34, 133, − 119, 14)
7. 65)800 = 12 R20 (− 65, 150, − 130, 20)
8. 13)277 = 21 R4 (− 26, 17, − 13, 4)
9. 41)562 = 13 R29 (− 41, 152, − 123, 29)
10. 51)827 = 16 R11 (− 51, 317, − 306, 11)
11. 67)724 = 10 R54 (− 67, 54, − 0, 54)
12. 39)407 = 10 R17 (− 39, 17, − 0, 17)
13. 19)$2.85 = $0.15 (− 19, 95, − 95, 0)
14. 36)$7.92 = $0.22 (− 72, 72, − 72, 0)
15. 22)$8.80 = $0.40 (− 88, 00, − 0, 0)
16. 51)$6.63 = $0.13 (− 51, 153, − 153, 0)

PS-4 Use with text pages 448–449. 163

Building Thinking Skills

Problem Solving 16-7

Name ________________

Balloon Bazaar

Use the price list to solve each problem. Round each answer.

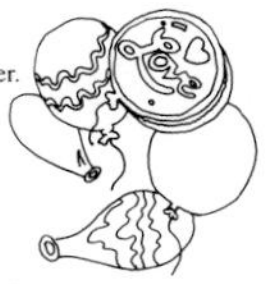

single-color latex balloons	$ 2.25 a dozen
single-color latex balloons, inflated	$ 5.15 a dozen
multicolored latex balloons	$ 2.75 a dozen
multicolored latex balloons, inflated	$ 5.25 a dozen
silver mylar balloons, inflated	$14.99 a dozen
mylar balloons with message, inflated	$20.99 a dozen

1. Lorenzo plans to give red latex balloons he blows up himself to each of 24 friends on Valentine's Day. About how much does each balloon cost? **about 19¢**

2. Ali bought 3 dozen multicolored latex balloons for the end-of-year party at school. She plans to blow up the balloons herself. What is the approximate cost of each balloon? **about 23¢**

3. Mrs. Lopez is buying 24 multicolored, inflated balloons to surprise her students on the last day of school. Each student will receive 1 balloon. About how much is Mrs. Lopez paying for each balloon? **about 44¢**

4. Mr. and Mrs. Chang are celebrating their thirteenth anniversary. Mr. Chang wants to buy his wife 13 mylar balloons with a Happy Anniversary message on them. About how much does he have to pay? **$23; if only by the dozen: $42**

5. Daniel is ordering 1 dozen silver mylar balloons, already inflated, for his birthday party. About how much does each balloon cost? **about $1.25**

6. The school basketball team ordered 1 dozen orange and 1 dozen blue inflated latex balloons for the coach. 13 players are sharing the cost. About how much does each player have to contribute? **about 80¢**

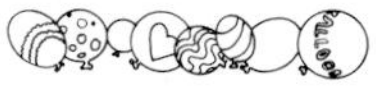

TS-4 Use with text pages 448–449. 163

Reteaching

Skills Review 16-7

Name ________________

Dividing: 2-Digit Quotients

Decide where to start. → Divide the tens if possible. → Divide the ones.

tens	ones

24)57|8

Try hundreds 24)5 not enough hundreds.
Try tens 24)57 57 tens is enough.

think: 20)57

2
24)57|8
− 48
9

think: 20)98

24 R2
24)57|8
− 48↓
9|8
− 9|6
2

Check: 24 × 24 = 96 + 48 = 576; 576 + 2 = 578

Find the quotients. Check your answers.

1. (20) 21)446 = 21 R5 (42↓, 26, − 21, 5) Check: 21 × 21 = 21 + 42 = 441; + 5 = 446
2. (50) 46)785 = 17 R3 (46, 325, 322, 3) Check: 46 × 17 = 322 + 46 = 782; + 3 = 785
3. (40) 37)892 = 24 R4 (74, 152, 148, 4) Check: 37 × 24 = 148 + 74 = 888; + 4 = 892
4. 29)788 = 27 R5 (− 58, 208, − 203, 5) Check: 29 × 27 = 203 + 58 = 783; + 5 = 788
5. 34)538 = 15 R28 (− 34, 198, − 170, 28) Check: 34 × 15 = 170 + 34 = 510; + 28 = 538
6. 65)671 = 10 R21 (− 65, 21) Check: 65 × 10 = 650; + 21 = 671

RS-4 Use with text pages 448-449. 163

Challenges

Family Math 16-7

Name ________________

Clones

Dear Family,
Your child has been learning how to divide when the divisor and the quotient are 2-digit numbers. Play the "Clones" game with your child.

Fill in the blanks. The divisor and the quotient must be the same number. Use a calculator if you wish. The first one has been done for you.

16 ← quotient
16)256
↑ divisor

1. [1][0] / [1][0]) 100
2. [ ][ ] / [ ][ ]) 121
3. [ ][ ] / [ ][ ]) 225
4. [ ][ ] / [ ][ ]) 144
5. [ ][ ] / [ ][ ]) 625
6. [ ][ ] / [ ][ ]) 169
7. [ ][ ] / [ ][ ]) 400
8. [ ][ ] / [ ][ ]) 196
9. [ ][ ] / [ ][ ]) 484
10. [ ][ ] / [ ][ ]) 900

Answers: 2. 11 3. 15 4. 12 5. 25 6. 13 7. 20 8. 14 9. 22 10. 30

CS-4 Use with text pages 448–449. 163

Options for Individual Needs

Basic

Exercises 5-24
More Practice, p. 512, set B

Supplements
Reteaching 163 or
Practice 163

Average

Exercises 1-24
More Practice, p. 512, set B

Supplements
Practice 163
Challenges 163 or
Thinking Skills 163

Extended

Exercises 6-24

Supplements
Challenges 163
Thinking Skills 163

Other Resources:
Problem-Solving Experiences in Mathematics, Grade 4, Problem 133
Mathematics, A Way of Thinking, Lesson 10-16
Kids Are Consumers, Too!, pp. 152, 153
Using the Math Explorer Calculator: A Sourcebook for Teachers, Chapter 14

16-7

LESSON PLAN 16-7

OBJECTIVE 16-7
To find 2-digit quotients by dividing with 2-digit divisors that are not rounded

Materials: calculators

Grouping Suggestion: pairs

1. MOTIVATE AND TEACH

LEARN ABOUT IT

EXPLORE ► **Explain a measurement relationship you need to solve the problem.** (12 mo = 1 y; You are finding gallons per month.)
► **Explain why you cannot divide hundreds first.** (There are only 9 hundreds, so you cannot make 12 groups.)

TALK ABOUT IT ► **Explain why it is necessary to use the bring-down step.** (to divide the ones)
► **Explain how to use front-end digits to estimate the answer.** (Round the divisor to a compatible number; 900 ÷ 10 = 90.)
Student Edition answers: **1.** The bring-down step was used to divide the ones. **2.** Answers may vary. **3.** Sample sentence: A Jersey cow gives 75 gal of milk per month.

2. CHECK UNDERSTANDING

TRY IT OUT

ERROR ALERT Incorrectly deciding where to start the division.

Dividing
2-Digit Quotients

LEARN ABOUT IT

EXPLORE Think About the Process
A Jersey cow needs about 300 gallons of water and 3,750 pounds of grass per month. She gives about 900 gallons of milk a year. How much milk does she give in a month?

Decide where to start.	Divide the tens if possible.	Divide the ones.
$12\overline{)900}$	$12\overline{)900}$ quotient 7; − 84; 6	$12\overline{)900}$ quotient 75; − 84; 60; − 60; 0
12 > 9 There are not enough hundreds. 12 < 90 Start by dividing 10s.		

TALK ABOUT IT See teaching notes.

1. Explain how you used the "bring down" step.
2. How would you have estimated the final quotient?
3. Give a reasonable answer using a complete sentence.

TRY IT OUT

Divide. Decide if you start with the hundreds or the tens.

1. $30\overline{)674}$ 22 R14
2. $60\overline{)275}$ 4 R35
3. $40\overline{)384}$ 9 R24
4. $80\overline{)945}$ 11 R65
5. $38\overline{)745}$ 19 R23
6. $43\overline{)875}$ 20 R15
7. $67\overline{)540}$ 8 R4
8. $16\overline{)\$9.28}$ $0.58

448

TEACHING OPTIONS

RETEACHING TIPS Have students predict the size of the quotient. They compare the divisor with the first two digits of the dividend. If those digits are *equal to* or *greater than* the divisor, the quotient has 2 digits. If those digits are *less*, the quotient has 1 digit. Assign Reteaching Supplement 163.

ENRICHMENT Family Math Students ask an adult in their family to estimate the yearly cost for telephone, food, or other expenses their family pays regularly. Then they divide to find the average expense per month and per week in each category. They may use a calculator.

PRACTICE

Find the quotients. Check your answers.

1. 28)793 **28 R9** **2.** 52)523 **10 R3** **3.** 36)582 **16 R6** **4.** 70)856 **12 R16** **5.** 42)652 **15 R22**

6. 23)477 **20 R17** **7.** 57)704 **12 R20** **8.** 35)986 **28 R6** **9.** 88)935 **10 R55** **10.** 13)$8.32 **$0.64**

11. $3.57 ÷ 17 **$0.21** **12.** 894 ÷ 43 **20 R34** **13.** $8.36 ÷ 44 **$0.19** **14.** 483 ÷ 24 **20 R3**

15. What is 500 divided by 28? **17 R24**

16. How many 12s are in 908? **75 R8**

APPLY

MATH REASONING Use estimation to decide which of these cannot be correct.

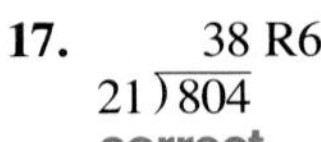

17. 21)804 = 38 R6 **correct** **18.** 19)572 = 38 R2 **incorrect** **19.** 48)820 = 17 R4 **correct** **20.** 32)645 = 10 R4 **incorrect**

PROBLEM SOLVING

21. If you bought 5 quarts of milk for $4.80, how much did you pay per quart? **$0.96**

22. Ted poured the milk from his two cows, Bossie and Daisy, together to make a gallon of milk. Bossie always gives twice as much milk as Daisy. What fraction of the gallon of milk did each cow give? **Bossie $\frac{2}{3}$ gallon, Daisy $\frac{1}{3}$ gallon**

▶ CALCULATOR

A number is divisible by another number if their quotient is a whole number and the remainder is 0. Use your calculator to answer these questions.

23. Which of these numbers is divisible by 4?
252 187 72 356 234

24. 224 is divisible by which of these numbers?
2 4 24 46 56

More Practice, page 512, set B

3. PRACTICE AND APPLY

Basic	5-24
Average	1-24
Extended	6-24

PRACTICE

What must you decide before you can divide Exercises 1-16? (where to place the first digit in the quotient) *Examine Exercise 6 to predict how many digits in its quotient.* (2)

APPLY

MATH REASONING ▶ Explain what to consider when you evaluate Exercises 17-20. (Possible answers: Compare the dividends and divisors; multiply the given quotients by the divisors.)

PROBLEM SOLVING ▶ Estimate whether Problem 21's quotient is over or under $1.00. Explain why. (under; 5 qt at $1.00 each would be $5.00, so they must be under $1.00 each to total $4.80.)

CALCULATOR ▶ In Exercise 23, explain how you can tell quickly which number cannot be divisible by 4. (187; 4 cannot evenly divide an odd number.)

CLOSE AND ASSESS

SHOW WHAT YOU KNOW

Have students work in pairs to discuss and predict how many digits each quotient will have. Pairs should *not* divide.

1. 42)268 (1) **2.** 37)716 (2)
3. 15)143 (1) **4.** 68)689 (2)
5. 29)789 (2) **6.** 92)724 (1)

QUICK QUIZ

Divide and check.

1. 24)513 (21 R9)
2. 41)264 (6 R18)
3. 58)592 (10 R12)
4. 62)$8.06 ($0.13)

LESSON OPTIONS 16-8

Problem Solving: Using a Calculator

OBJECTIVE 16-8 To solve 2-digit division problems using a calculator

PREBOOK ACTIVITIES

QUICK REVIEW

Use this problem to answer the questions: 451 ÷ 36 = 12 R19

1. How many complete groups of 36 can be made? (12)
2. What amount was separated into same-size groups (451)
3. If the quotient tells how many equal groups there are, what does the divisor represent? (the number in each group)
4. Explain the 19. (remainder; amount left over)

PRIOR KNOWLEDGE

Have students recall two ways to interpret a remainder in division. (how many left; make an extra grouping) Then have students analyze the meaning of the decimal number 46.7. (Possible answers: 46.7 means 46 7/10; it is greater than 46 but less than 47.) Have students suggest decimals greater than 5 but less than 6. (Answers may vary; samples include 5.1, 5.47, 5.99.)

COMMUNICATION

Discussing Math Have students evaluate the quotient in the division 213 ÷ 9 = 23 R6. (Possible answer: You could make 23 groups of 9 with 6 left over, which is not enough to form another same-size group.) Challenge students to give a broad explanation of how the same quotient might appear as a decimal. (Possible explanation: The whole number part of the quotient would be 23, then there would be a decimal part to show that it is over 23 but not 24.)

EXPLORE AND CONNECT

COOPERATIVE ACTIVITY

Grouping Suggestion: small groups

Jay makes bracelets. To find how many 48-bead bracelets he can make with 360 beads, he uses a calculator to divide 360 by 48. The display shows 7.5. What does the quotient tell Jay?

TEACHING ACTIONS

Have students work together to discuss the situation and determine a reasonable interpretation.

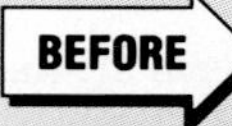

► **Explain Jay's situation in your own words.** (Jay wants to know how many 48-bead bracelets 360 beads will make.)

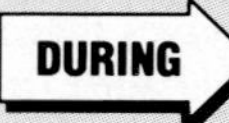

► **Explain why Jay uses division to try to answer his question.** (He wants to separate the 360 beads into same-size groups of 48 beads per group, so division makes sense.)

► **Evaluate the meaning of the decimal 7.5.** (It is halfway between 7 and 8.)

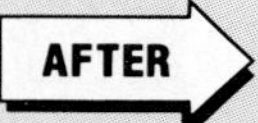

► **Explain how the decimal quotient relates to Jay's question.** (7.5 means that 360 does not divide evenly by 48; the decimal quotient means there is a remainder.)

► **Explain how to interpret the decimal quotient.** (Jay can make 7 complete bracelets with some beads left over.)

CONNECTIONS Use these anytime.

Problem of the Day

Logical Thinking Brad cannot do 794 ÷ 2 on his calculator because the ÷ key is broken. Using number sense and an understanding of decimals, determine how Brad can find the answer with the × key. (Dividing by 2 is the same as finding half; 0.5 is a decimal that means half, so multiply 794 by 0.5; 397.)

Math Connection

Calculator Try this calculator trick.

1. Enter any 3 digits, then repeat the same 3 digits in the same order to form a 6-digit number, such as 473,473.
2. Divide the 6-digit number by 7.
3. Divide the quotient by 11.
4. Divide the new quotient by 13.
5. What number is in the display? (You always get the original 3 digits.)

Number Sense

Mental Math Brianna used a calculator to divide 348 by 20, and the display showed a quotient of 174. Use mental math to evaluate her answer, then explain what Brianna did. (The quotient is too large; it should be around 17; Brianna divided by 2, not 20. The correct answer is 17.4.)

Classwork and Homework Supplements

Practice

Calculators 16-8

Name

Problem Solving: Using a Calculator

Use a calculator to help solve these problems. Remember to interpret the decimal quotient and write the answer in a complete sentence.

1. On "Group Night," the movie theater sold tickets to 262 people. If every group had 12 people, how many groups bought tickets?
   21 groups; there are not enough people left to make another group.
2. The theater is open daily for 11 hours. The movie currently showing is 90 minutes long. How many times can the movie be shown in one day?
   7 times; there are not enough minutes to show the movie one more time.
3. The refreshment stand manager needs 650 popcorn boxes for the weekend. If one carton contains 48 boxes, how many cartons should the manager order?
   14 cartons; 13 would not be enough.
4. The manager wants plastic runners to cover parts of the carpeting. Each runner will be 15 ft long. How many runners can be made from a 125 ft-roll of plastic?
   8 runners; there is not enough left over to make a 9th.
5. The refreshment stand sells about 500 drinks a weekend. If there are 30 paper cups in each box, how many boxes are needed for the weekend?
   17 boxes; 16 boxes would not be enough.
6. There are 375 seats in the theater. New seat covers are to be installed. The covers come 24 to a box. How many boxes should be ordered?
   16 boxes; 15 would not be enough.

164 Use with text page 450. PS-4

Building Thinking Skills

Calculators 16-8

Name

Balloon Project

Michiko and her brothers are making hot-air balloon models. They have collected the following materials:

string, balloons, half-pint milk cartons, construction paper, netting, wire rings

Use your calculator to solve each problem. Change decimal quotients to mixed numbers when it makes sense. Give whole-number answers when necessary.

1. Michiko has a ball of string that is 92 inches long. If she wants to support her balloon with 8 suspension strings, what is the greatest length each piece of string can be?
   $11\frac{1}{2}$ in.
2. A half-pint milk carton can be used for the basket of a model balloon. If a strip of paper 11 inches long can be used to cover the 4 sides of the carton, what is the length of each side?
   $2\frac{3}{4}$ in.
3. If a strip of paper 11 inches long can be used to cover the 4 sides of a milk carton, how many milk cartons can be covered from a roll of paper 60 inches long?
   5 cartons
4. Wire rings can be used for suspension hoops on the model. The model needs 8 rings. If a bag of 18 rings cost \$1.44, what is the cost of the rings needed for the model?
   \$0.64

164 Use with text page 450. TS-4

Reteaching

Problem Solving 16-8

Name

Using a Calculator

For some division problems, a calculator shows the quotient as a decimal number. You need to interpret it to solve the problems.

Jane bought 1,250 apples. A bag holds 34 apples.

Questions:
- How many bags can Jane completely fill?
- How many bags does Jane need to carry all 1,250 apples?

1,250 ÷ 34

Answers:
Jane can completely fill 36 bags.
Jane needs 37 bags.

Use a calculator to help solve these problems. Remember to interpret the decimal quotient.

1. The cook bought 543 rolls. Each package holds 1 dozen rolls.
   - How many packages can he completely fill? 45 packages
   - How many packages does he need to get all 543 rolls in packages? 46 packages
2. There are 1,247 balloons for the festival. Each hour 24 balloons are let go. How many hours will it take before all the balloons are let go?
   52 hours
3. Leno has 1,420 words to type. He can type 36 words a minute. Will he be finished in 9 minutes?
   no
4. There are 265 campers signed up for volleyball teams. Each team needs 15 players. How many complete teams can be formed?
   17 teams
5. Juice comes in packages of 16 bottles. 154 people have to be served. How many packages of juice are needed?
   10 packages

164 Use with text page 450. RS-4

Challenges

Math Reasoning 16-8

Name

Remainder Puzzles

When you use a calculator to divide, sometimes it makes sense to change a decimal quotient to a mixed number. Sometimes neither a decimal nor a mixed number makes sense and you need to give your answer as a whole number.

Example:
Meimei is building a display case for her trophies. She wants the case to be 102 inches high with 4 shelves, each the same height. How high will each shelf be?

$102 \div 4 = 25.5$ $\quad 25.5 = 25\frac{5}{10} = 25\frac{1}{2}$

Each shelf will be $25\frac{1}{2}$ inches high.

Inches and feet are usually expressed as a mixed number, not as a decimal.

Use your calculator to solve these problems. Change decimal quotients to mixed numbers when it makes sense. Give whole number answers when necessary.

1. Jeremy sawed up a tree that was 567 inches long into 6 equal pieces to make a raft. How long was each piece?
   $94\frac{1}{2}$ inches
2. Greg needs pieces of wood 32 inches long to carve kachina dolls. How many can he cut from a piece of wood 120 inches long?
   3
3. Betty has a piece of wood 148 inches long. She wants to make 16 miniature totem poles all the same height. How high can each one be?
   $9\frac{1}{4}$ inches
4. Sonia made steps for her tree house. She cut up a board that was 135 inches long into 12-inch-wide steps. How many steps could she make?
   11

164 Use with text page 450. CS-4

Options for Individual Needs

Basic

Exercises 1-8
Calculator Bank, p. 487
Computer Bank, pp. 493, 494
More Practice, p. 527, set E

Supplements
Reteaching 164 or
Practice 164

Average

Exercises 1-9
Calculator Bank, p. 487
Computer Bank, pp. 493, 494
More Practice, p. 527, set E

Supplements
Practice 164
Challenges 164 or
Thinking Skills 164

Extended

Exercises 1-9
Calculator Bank, p. 487
Computer Bank, pp. 493, 494

Supplements
Challenges 164
Thinking Skills 164

Other Resources:
Problem-Solving Experiences in Mathematics, Grade 4, Problem 135
Mathematics, A Way of Thinking, Lessons 10-17, 10-18, 10-19
Challenge, A Program for the Mathematically Talented, Teacher's Edition, Activities 65 and 66.
Using the Math Explorer Calculator: A Sourcebook for Teachers, Chapter 14

16-8

LESSON PLAN 16-8

OBJECTIVE 16-8
To solve 2-digit division problems using a calculator

Materials: calculators

1. MOTIVATE AND TEACH

LEARN ABOUT IT

BEFORE ► **Analyze each problem to restate it in other words.** (Cut some number of 30-inch pieces from a 144-inch board; find how many dozen bags of prizes to buy for a total of 750 prizes.)

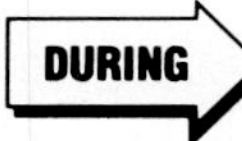

► **Justify using division to solve the problems.** (Divide to separate same-size groups or to find how many groups can be made.)

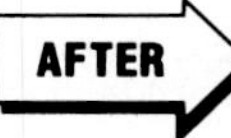

► **Evaluate the meaning of the decimal numbers in each quotient.** (4.8 is greater than 4 but less than 5; 62.5 is halfway between 62 and 63.)

► **Explain how the decimal quotients relate to the situations.** (4.8 means students can cut only 4 30-inch pieces, with some wood left over; 62.5 means that 62 bags of 1 dozen prizes is less than the 750 needed, so they must buy 63 bags.

2. CHECK UNDERSTANDING

TRY IT OUT

ERROR ALERT Misinterpreting decimal remainders. *Problem 3:* Failing to perform all steps of the multiple-step problem.

Problem Solving Using a Calculator

UNDERSTAND
FIND DATA
PLAN
ESTIMATE
SOLVE
CHECK

LEARN ABOUT IT

For some division problems, a calculator shows the quotient as a decimal number. It is helpful to know how to use these quotients.

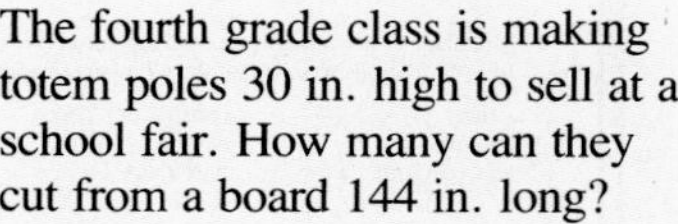
The fourth grade class is making totem poles 30 in. high to sell at a school fair. How many can they cut from a board 144 in. long?

144 ÷ 30 [4.8]

They can make 4 totem poles. There is not enough wood to make a fifth.

Everyone who plays a game at the fair will receive a prize. The organizing committee wants to buy 750 prizes, which come in bags of 1 dozen each. How many bags of prizes should they buy?

750 ÷ 12 [62.5]

62 bags will not be enough. The committee should buy 63 bags.

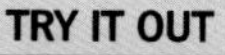

Use a calculator to help solve these problems. Remember to interpret the decimal quotient and write the answer in a complete sentence.

1. Some students are making ribbons for awards. Each award uses 15 in. of ribbon. How many awards can they make from a roll of ribbon 110 in. long? **7 awards**
2. The third graders need 450 cups for the refreshment booth. If 1 bag of cups contains 36 cups, how many bags should they buy? **13 bags**
3. One class is going to sell strawberries in baskets. They plan to pick 12 dozen and put them into 20 baskets. How many strawberries will be in each basket? **7**
4. Aiko cut a 365 ft string into 15 ft pieces for the Amazing Maze booth. How many 15 ft pieces did she cut? **24 pieces**

450

TEACHING OPTIONS

RETEACHING TIPS In Problem 3, students must multiply before dividing. Students verbalize how many objects are in a dozen (12), then tell how to find the number of strawberries in 12 dozen. (12 × 12) Then they may divide the total number of strawberries (144) by 20. Use Reteaching Supplement 164.

ENRICHMENT Have students use number sense to match each decimal quotient with its division problem, using calculators to check their estimates. (1c, 2a, 3b)

1. 51.4	**a.** 54)783
2. 14.5	**b.** 16)532
3. 33.25	**c.** 35)1,799

MIXED PRACTICE

Use any problem solving strategy to solve these problems.

1. 38 fourth graders worked at the fair. 17 worked at the refreshment booths and 25 at the game booths. How many students worked at both types of booth? 4 students

2. Everyone tried the Obstacle Course booth. Danielle was 3.5 seconds slower than Diego going around the course. Use the table to find out what her time was. 58.3 seconds

Obstacle Course	
Name	Time
Diego	54.8 seconds
Mary	54.9 seconds
Barney	57.2 seconds

3. The second time around the obstacle course Mary went 2.3 seconds faster than the first time. How fast did she go the second time around? 52.6 seconds

4. Michael worked at the ticket booth. He sold 127 tickets at $0.25 each. How much money did he collect? $31.75

5. The school made $1,062 by selling 581 raffle tickets for a handmade quilt. The quilt cost $178 to make. How much did the school profit by selling the quilt? $884

6. Students formed teams of 12 for the tug-of-war. 136 students wanted to play. How many complete teams could they form? 11 teams

7. Large balloons cost $0.75 and small balloons cost $0.50. Chapa sold 32 large and 17 small balloons. How much money did she earn for the school? $32.50

8. The students at the Make-Your-Own Button booth needed 248 stickers. Each package has 16 stickers. How many packages did they need to buy? 16 packages

9. The police department registered 57 bicycles at the fair. There were 11 more racing bikes than mountain bikes. How many racing bikes did they register? 34 racing bikes

More Practice, page 527, set E

3. Practice and Apply

Basic	1-8
Average	1-9
Extended	1-9

Sample Solutions: See p. T79.

MIXED PRACTICE

► **Analyze Problem 1 to choose a solution strategy.** (Use Logical Reasoning)

► **In Problem 2, explain what it means that Danielle was 3.5 seconds slower than Diego.** (Danielle's time was 3.5 seconds greater.)

► **Compare and contrast Problems 4 and 7.** (Both use multiplication; Problem 4 has one step, Problem 7 is a multiple-step problem.)

► **Analyze Problem 5 to identify extra data.** (581 tickets sold)

► **Explain how problems 6 and 8 are related.** (Both use division.)

Close and Assess

WRITE WHAT YOU THINK

Have students write a paragraph to summarize how to interpret a decimal quotient when solving a division problem with a calculator. (Answers may vary. Check students' writing.)

Quick Quiz

Solve with a calculator: Pullet Surprise Farm ships 36-packs of eggs to restaurants. How many full 36-packs can be shipped today if 3,220 eggs were gathered? (89)

CHAPTER 16

DATA COLLECTION AND ANALYSIS

GROUP DECISION MAKING

OBJECTIVE To collect, organize, and present data

COLLECTING DATA

▶ **Decide how to determine reasonable categories for ways students spend money.** (Possible method: Begin by listing ways group members spend their money, then look for any gaps.)

▶ **Explain why it may help to offer the same number of choices for each question.** (It will make it easier to graph the results when you finish the survey.)

▶ **Explain why it is important to question an equal number of boys and girls.** (They may spend their money differently, but by questioning an equal number of each, you will still get balanced results.)

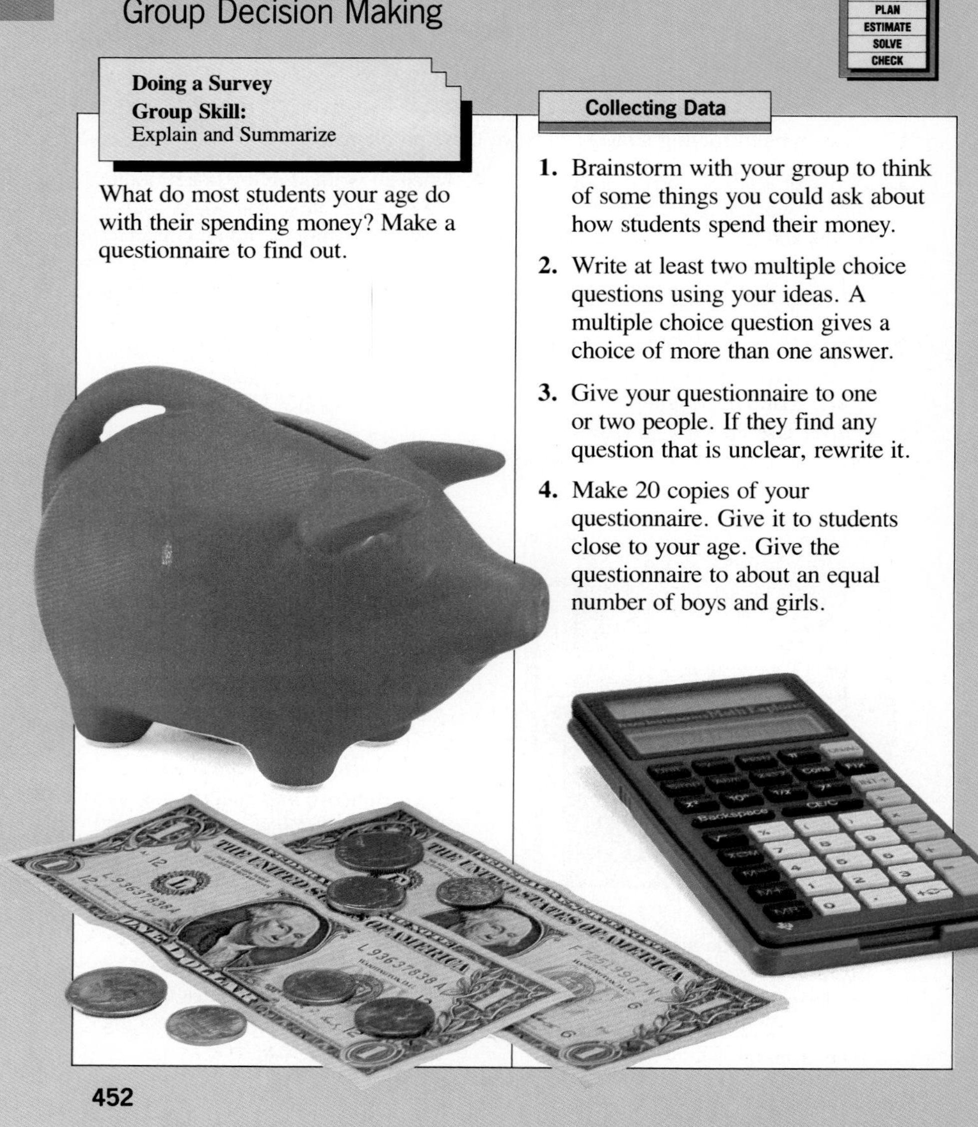

Data Collection and Analysis
Group Decision Making

Doing a Survey
Group Skill:
Explain and Summarize

What do most students your age do with their spending money? Make a questionnaire to find out.

Collecting Data

1. Brainstorm with your group to think of some things you could ask about how students spend their money.
2. Write at least two multiple choice questions using your ideas. A multiple choice question gives a choice of more than one answer.
3. Give your questionnaire to one or two people. If they find any question that is unclear, rewrite it.
4. Make 20 copies of your questionnaire. Give it to students close to your age. Give the questionnaire to about an equal number of boys and girls.

452

TEACHING OPTIONS

COOPERATIVE LEARNING

Grouping Suggestion: cooperative learning groups of 4 to 6
Have groups divide the tasks involved in the project: plan, write, test, edit, and copy the questionaire; distribute, then collect the surveys; tally results; design and make a bar graph to display the findings; and prepare summarizing statements for presenting the analysis. Group members may work individually or in pairs on some parts of the project, but the full group should agree on the questions they wish to ask. Provide graph paper and strips of colored paper for the bar graph.

Organizing Data

5. Make a table to record the information from your questionnaire.

Sample Table

	Answer A	Answer B	Answer C
Question 1	𝍸	𝍸 IIII	IIII
Question 2	𝍸 𝍸 𝍸 I	III	II

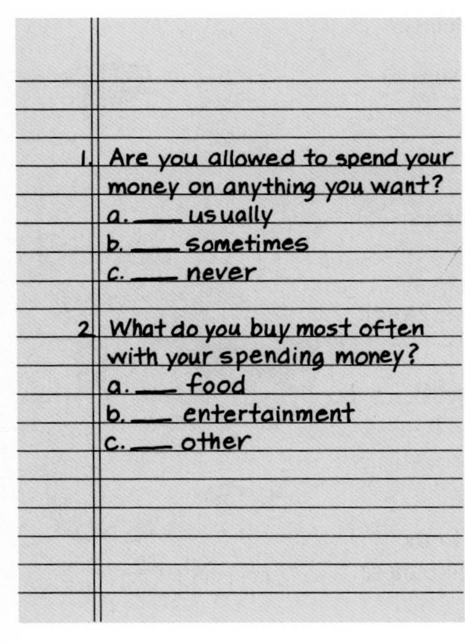

6. Copy and complete a bar graph to show the results for each question.

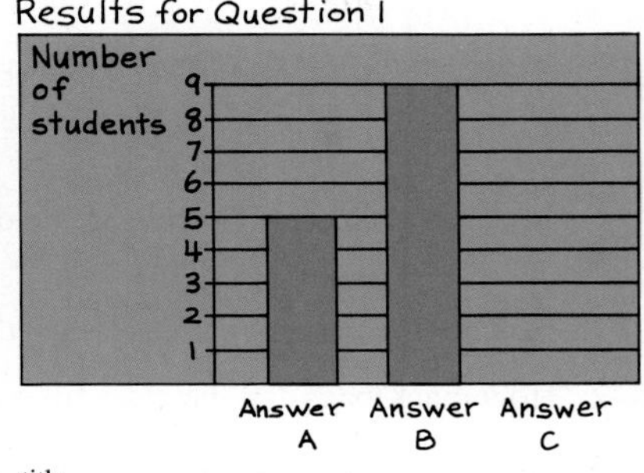

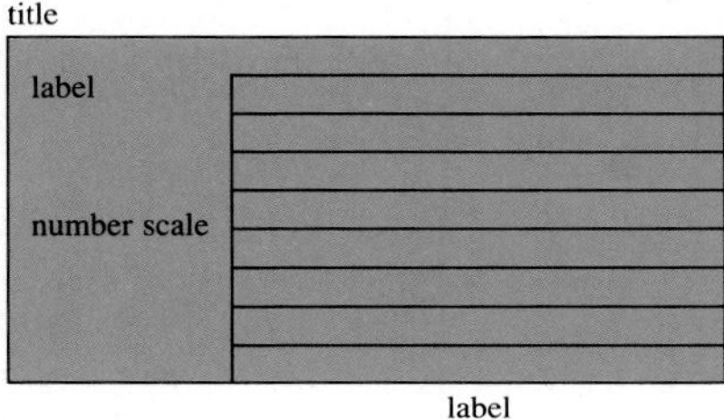

Presenting Your Analysis

7. What was the most popular answer for your first question? For the second question?

8. Prepare to tell the class three or four things you learned from your questionnaire.

 453

EXTENSION Students may enjoy doing a companion questionnaire to determine the most common sources of students' spending money. Typical questions might include: Do you get an allowance? Do you earn money for chores? Do you ask your parents for money?

COMPUTER **Teasers By Tobbs, Sunburst Communications, Copyright 1982** For pairs of students at all levels. Choose division and difficulty level 2 or 3. Students work backward to fill the empty squares on an incomplete 2-by-2 table. Allow 10 to 15 min to complete the puzzle.

ORGANIZING DATA

▶ **Analyze the sample table to justify its design.** (The 3 columns provide separate spaces in which to tally each answer possibility for every question in the survey.)

▶ **Evaluate the answer choices *usually* and *sometimes* in Sample Question 1.** (Possible answer: *Usually* means more often than *sometimes*.)

▶ **Evaluate the choices given for Sample Question 2.** (Opinions may vary. Students might decide to provide different answer choices.)

▶ **Explain how to complete the bar graph for Question 1.** (Check the Sample Table to count the tallies for Answer C in Question 1, then add a bar for Answer C that goes as high as the line that represents 4 students.)

PRESENTING YOUR ANALYSIS

Have each group member plan a statement based on the questionnaire. Some students may summarize the findings while others explain possible problems or issues that arose during the survey. Provide display space for the completed graphs and allow time for groups to ask questions of one another.

CHAPTER 16

WRAP UP

INTRODUCTION The Wrap Up provides activities emphasizing math language and thinking skills for the chapter and a project that integrates those skills with other math strands.

USING PAGE 454

Answers in Division Have students complete this section independently, then share their answers in small groups to justify their decisions.

Sometimes, Always, Never

► **Identify examples and counterexamples for Exercise 5.** (Answers will vary.)

► **Explain the relationship between a divisor and any possible remainder.** (A remainder must be less than the divisor; if it is not, you can make another group.)

Project Have students work in pairs to complete the project.

► **Explain a relationship between the divisor and the dividend to predict how many digits will be in the quotient.** (If the divisor is greater than the first 2 digits of the dividend, the quotient will have 1 digit; if the divisor is less than the first 2 digits of the dividend, the quotient will have 2 digits.) Have students share their answers, using number cards to demonstrate some quotients.

Additional Answers: See p. T79.

WRAP UP

Answers in Division

To answer a division word problem you must understand which of the following is needed.

A quotient and remainder **B** quotient only

C remainder only **D** quotient, increased by 1

In these exercises, tell whether you need to use A, B, C, or D. Then give the answer. Use this division exercise to help you.

$$\begin{array}{r} 29 \text{ R}11 \\ 25\overline{)736} \\ -\underline{50} \\ 236 \\ -\underline{225} \\ 11 \end{array}$$

Colin's class collected 736 cans in the clean-up drive. They put 25 cans in each bag.

1. How many bags does the class need in all? **D, 30 bags**
2. How many bags can the class fill completely? **B, 29 bags**
3. How many cans are left over when 29 bags are filled? **C, 11 cans**

Sometimes, Always, Never

Which word should go in the blank, sometimes, always, or never? Explain your choices. **Explanations may vary.**

4. Dividing by a 2-digit divisor __?__ gives a 2-digit quotient. **sometimes**
5. If a remainder has 2 digits, the divisor will __?__ be a 1-digit number. **never**

Project

Make cards for the digits 1–5. Place them in the pattern shown to create division examples like these. You may use a calculator to help. **Answers will vary.**

□□)□□□

A a 1-digit quotient **B** a 2-digit quotient

C an even remainder **D** an odd remainder

454

TEACHING OPTIONS

ENRICHMENT Have students use calculators, number sense, and their understanding of the relationship between multiplication and division to formulate division problems with 2-digit divisors that will produce each of these quotients: 4 R6, 9 R54, 12 R17, 23 R34, 47 R11. (Answers will vary. Samples: 114 ÷ 27 = 4 R6; 549 ÷ 55 = 9 R54; 257 ÷ 20 = 12 R17; 839 ÷ 35 = 23 R34; 622 ÷ 13 = 47 R11.)

CHAPTER REVIEW/TEST

Part 1 Understanding

1. Explain how to use basic division facts and mental math to divide 360 by 40. See Additional Answers.
2. Why is rounding an important first step when you are finding a quotient? See Additional Answers.
3. Give two general rules for when you should change an estimated quotient in division. See Additional Answers.
4. Determine the number of digits in the quotients of $40\overline{)295}$ and $31\overline{)726}$ without dividing 1, 2

Part 2 Skills

Divide and check.

5. 480 ÷ 60 8
6. 97 ÷ 20 4 R17
7. 318 ÷ 60 5 R18
8. 175 ÷ 23 7 R14
9. $48\overline{)303}$ 6 R15
10. $56\overline{)\$3.92}$ $0.07
11. $33\overline{)128}$ 3 R29
12. $46\overline{)419}$ 9 R5
13. $60\overline{)791}$ 13 R11
14. $73\overline{)952}$ 13 R3
15. $38\overline{)270}$ 7 R4
16. $51\overline{)\$3.57}$ $0.07

Part 3 Applications

17. When Tina divided 138 by 8, her calculator showed 17.25 as the quotient. What does this tell about her answer? There is a remainder.
18. When Randy used mental math to divide 525 by 52, he got 100 R3 as the quotient. How can you tell that his answer is not reasonable? See Additional Answers.
19. Gary used up 2 boxes of toothpicks to build 5 identical houses. If a box had 475 toothpicks, how many toothpicks were in each house? 190 toothpicks
20. **Challenge** 12 women shared a $750 prize, then each gave $5 of her winnings to charity. What did each person win? How much did the group give to charity? $57.50, $60

455

INFORMAL ASSESSMENT

Using Manipulatives Have students use any 5 number cards (TA 3) to formulate division problems with 2-digit divisors that will have a 1-digit quotient and a 2-digit quotient. Have them multiply to check. (Answers will vary. Check students' work.)

Communication *State a relationship between remainders and divisors.* (Remainder may range from 0 to 1 less than the divisor size.)

Critical Thinking *Use number sense to interpret a decimal quotient of 6.5 for the problem $40\overline{)260}$.* (You can make 6 complete groups; since 5 tenths is equivalent to $\frac{1}{2}$ and $\frac{1}{2}$ of 40 is 20, there are 20 left over.)

CHAPTER REVIEW/TEST

INTRODUCTION The Review/Test is provided to review and evaluate the skills and concepts presented in Chapter 16.

USING PAGE 455
If you prefer to use this page for review, you may want to use the **Multiple-Choice Posttest** (pages 63-64) or the **Free-Response Posttest** (pages 63-64) to evaluate mastery of Chapter objectives.

ITEM ANALYSIS The table below correlates the Chapter Review/Test items with the lesson objectives for the chapter.

Items	Objectives
1	16-1
2	16-3
3	16-4
4	16-6
5	16-1
6, 7	16-2
8-10	16-3
11, 12	16-4
13	16-6
14, 15	16-7
16	16-3
17	16-8
18	16-6
19, 20	16-5

Additional Answers: See p. T79.

ENRICHMENT

INTRODUCTION Students will sharpen their ability to use number sense and logical reasoning as they solve digit-substitution puzzles.

USING PAGE 456
This Enrichment page is provided for all students. You may wish to use it after they have completed the Chapter Review/Test on page 455.

▶ **Examine the first tool puzzle to identify a number relationship.** (The quotient and the ones place of the dividend are equal.)

▶ **Analyze this division and explain your reasoning.** (It is a basic fact because the divisor and quotient are 1-digit numbers and it has no remainder.)

▶ **Explain why 36 ÷ 6 does not work.** (The quotient and the divisor must be different digits.)

▶ **Decide how to solve the second puzzle.** (Plans may vary.)

▶ **List 4 possible divisions and explain your reasoning.** (11, 22, 33, 44; *saw* cannot be 1, so any higher divisor times 2 or more will not give a 2-digit product.)

▶ **Explain to verify your solution.** (See if your solution works for each digit substitution.)

EXTENSION Challenge students to formulate a similar division puzzle that uses a symbol or letter for each digit. After students confirm that their puzzles work, partners can solve each other's puzzles.

Additional Answers: See p. T79.

ENRICHMENT
Division Tools

What is going on in this division puzzle? Hint: Each tool stands for a different digit from 1 to 9.

1. Solve the division puzzle by replacing each tool with a digit. Be sure your solution works. See Additional Answers.
2. Compare your solution with a classmate's. Explain why your solutions might be different. Then work with your classmate to show another way the puzzle could be solved.
3. Try this division puzzle. Remember, each tool stands for a different digit from 1 to 9. Hint: Find a relationship between the screwdriver and the hammer.

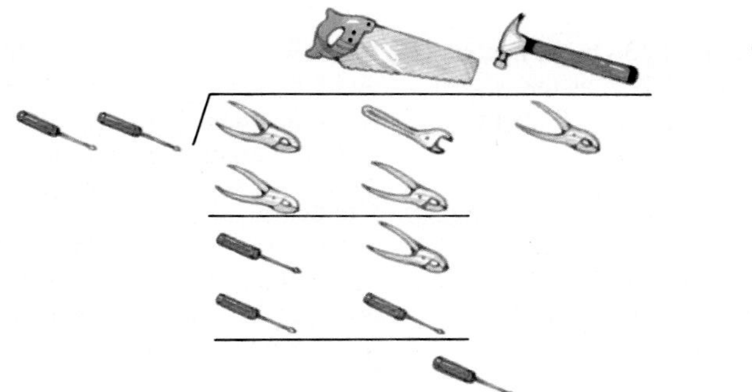

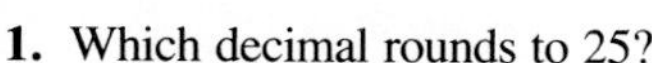

CUMULATIVE REVIEW

1. Which decimal rounds to 25?

   A 26.35 B 25.61
   (C) 25.09 D 20.7

2. Which decimal belongs between 0.7 and 0.72?

   A 0.8 B 0.69
   C 0.70 (D) 0.71

3. Theo estimated 9 cm for the length of part of a stick. About how long is the stick?

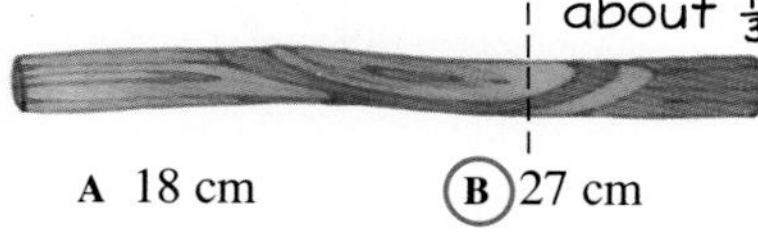

   A 18 cm (B) 27 cm
   C 36 cm D 3 cm

4. Choose a reasonable measure for the height of a table.

   (A) 75 cm B 75 dm
   C 75 m D 75 km

5. The shading shows how many sixths remain. What fraction tells how much is not shaded?

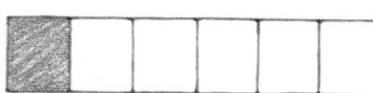

   A $\frac{4}{5}$ B $\frac{1}{6}$
   (C) $\frac{5}{6}$ D $\frac{1}{2}$

6. $\frac{9}{12} + \frac{5}{12}$

   A $\frac{1}{3}$ (B) $1\frac{1}{6}$
   C $1\frac{1}{2}$ D $\frac{12}{14}$

7. A recipe asks for $\frac{5}{8}$ cup orange juice and $\frac{1}{8}$ cup lemon juice. How much more orange juice is needed?

   A $\frac{3}{4}$ cup B $\frac{5}{8}$ cup
   (C) $\frac{1}{2}$ cup D $\frac{1}{4}$ cup

8. 0.62 + 0.89

   A 0.51 B 1.41
   C 0.151 (D) 1.51

9. 53 − 4.26

   A 57.26 (B) 48.74
   C 49.26 D 49.64

10. A bus holds 60 people. How many buses are needed to take 288 people on a field trip?

    (A) 5 B 6
    C 4 D 5 R12

11. Gino paid $8.64 for a dozen cans of oil. What was the cost per can?

    A $0.86 B $7.20
    (C) $0.72 D $0.70

457

CUMULATIVE REVIEW

INTRODUCTION The purpose of this Cumulative Review is to maintain previously taught skills and concepts. The emphasis in this Cumulative Review is on decimal concepts, Chapter 13; on metric measurement, Chapter 14; on addition and subtraction of fractions and decimals, Chapter 15; and on division with 2-digit divisors, Chapter 16.

ITEM ANALYSIS The table below correlates the Cumulative Review items with the lesson objectives.

Items	Objectives
1	13-5
2	13-3
3	14-2
4	14-1
5	15-1
6, 7	15-2
8	15-8
9	15-9
10	16-2
11	16-7

RESOURCE BANK AND APPENDIX

RESOURCE BANK

APPENDIX

SKILLS REVIEW BANK

Place Value: Hundreds, Tens, and Ones

These models help you understand numbers.

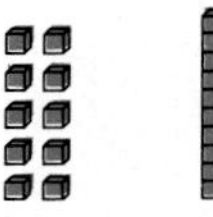

ten ones = one ten (10)

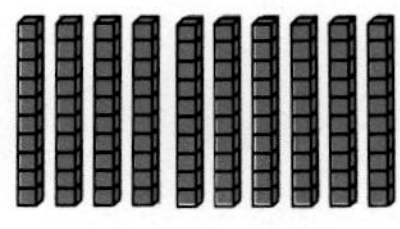

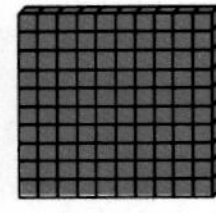

ten tens = one hundred (100)

This model shows the meaning of 232.

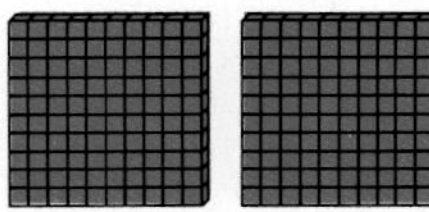

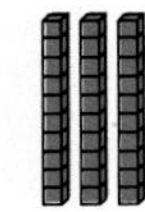

2 hundreds , 3 tens , 2 ones = 232

TRY IT OUT Read each number. Tell the meaning of the red digit.

Example: 426 The 2 means 2 tens.

1. 342 **4 tens**
2. 639 **6 hundreds**
3. 19 **9 ones**
4. 401 **4 hundreds**
5. 823 **3 ones**
6. 436 **6 ones**
7. 808 **0 tens**
8. 42 **4 tens**
9. 791 **9 tens**
10. 92 **2 ones**

Practice the Facts: Addition

During the Apollo 12 moon mission Charles Conrad walked for 8 hours on the moon. Alan Bean walked for 7 hours. What is the total number of hours they walked on the moon?

Since we want the total number of hours, we add.

7	+	8	=	15
Addend		Addend		Sum

$$\begin{array}{rl} 7 & \text{Addend} \\ +\ 8 & \text{Addend} \\ \hline 15 & \text{Sum} \end{array}$$

They walked for a total of 15 hours on the moon.

Practice. Add.

1. 4 + 9 = **13** **2.** 6 + 5 = **11** **3.** 3 + 2 = **5**

4. 6 + 3 = **9** **5.** 1 + 9 = **10** **6.** 5 + 7 = **12**

7. 8 + 5 = **13** **8.** 4 + 3 = **7** **9.** 7 + 6 = **13**

Practice. Add.

10. $\begin{array}{r} 5 \\ +\ 6 \\ \hline 11 \end{array}$ **11.** $\begin{array}{r} 9 \\ +\ 1 \\ \hline 10 \end{array}$ **12.** $\begin{array}{r} 8 \\ +\ 5 \\ \hline 13 \end{array}$ **13.** $\begin{array}{r} 4 \\ +\ 4 \\ \hline 8 \end{array}$ **14.** $\begin{array}{r} 3 \\ +\ 7 \\ \hline 10 \end{array}$

15. $\begin{array}{r} 0 \\ +\ 8 \\ \hline 8 \end{array}$ **16.** $\begin{array}{r} 8 \\ +\ 2 \\ \hline 10 \end{array}$ **17.** $\begin{array}{r} 6 \\ +\ 4 \\ \hline 10 \end{array}$ **18.** $\begin{array}{r} 7 \\ +\ 8 \\ \hline 15 \end{array}$ **19.** $\begin{array}{r} 1 \\ +\ 6 \\ \hline 7 \end{array}$

Adding: One Trade

Emma plays on a women's basketball team. In the championship game she scores 38 points in the first half and 26 points in the second half. How many points does she score in all?

Since we want the total, we add.

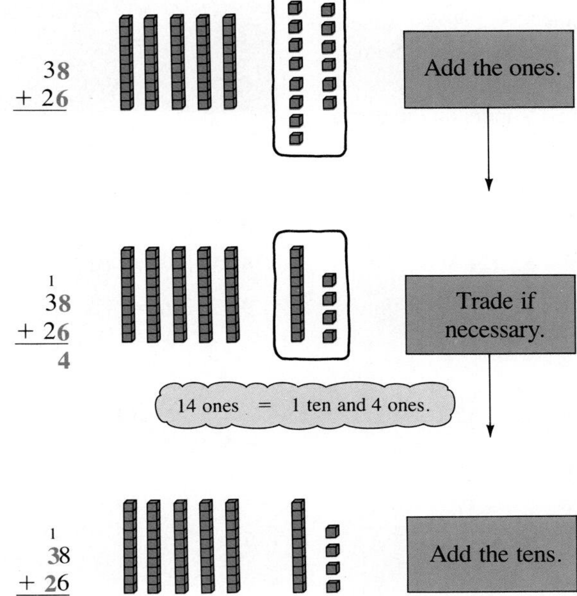

38
+ 26
Add the ones.
1
38
+ 26
4
Trade if necessary.
14 ones = 1 ten and 4 ones.
1
38
+ 26
64
Add the tens.

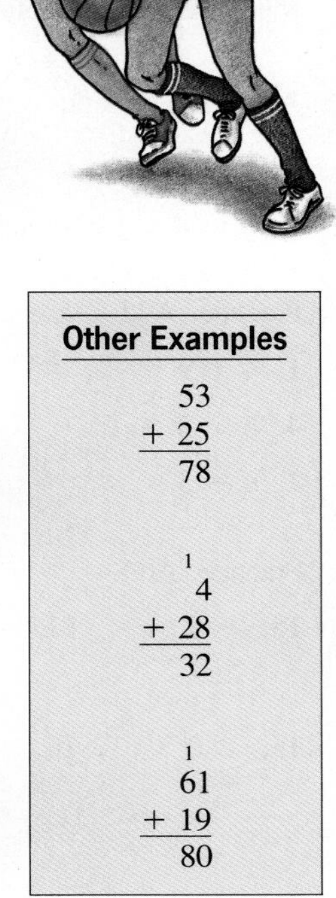

Other Examples

$$\begin{array}{r} 53 \\ +\ 25 \\ \hline 78 \end{array}$$

$$\begin{array}{r} {}^{1}\ \\ 4 \\ +\ 28 \\ \hline 32 \end{array}$$

$$\begin{array}{r} {}^{1}\ \ \\ 61 \\ +\ 19 \\ \hline 80 \end{array}$$

Emma scores 64 points in the championship game.

Try it out. Add.

1. 24 + 18 = 42	**2.** 91 + 41 = 132	**3.** 26 + 36 = 62	**4.** 9 + 79 = 88	**5.** 38 + 38 = 76

SKILLS REVIEW BANK

Practice the Facts: Subtraction

Jane Goodall studied chimpanzees in Africa. One group of chimps had 13 members. Another group had 7 members. How many more chimps were in the larger group?

Since we want to find how many more, we subtract.

$13 - 7 = 6$ (difference)

$$\begin{array}{r} 13 \\ -\ 7 \\ \hline 6 \end{array} \text{ difference}$$

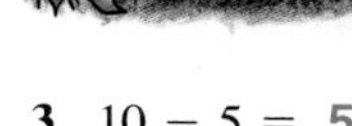

Practice. Subtract.

1. 15 − 6 = **9**	**2.** 17 − 8 = **9**	**3.** 10 − 5 = **5**
4. 11 − 4 = **7**	**5.** 13 − 2 = **11**	**6.** 7 − 0 = **7**
7. 9 − 7 = **2**	**8.** 16 − 8 = **8**	**9.** 6 − 6 = **0**

Practice. Subtract.

10. 12 − 8 = **4**	**11.** 10 − 3 = **7**	**12.** 7 − 5 = **2**	**13.** 13 − 6 = **7**	**14.** 17 − 9 = **8**
15. 9 − 4 = **5**	**16.** 11 − 2 = **9**	**17.** 5 − 5 = **0**	**18.** 8 − 3 = **5**	**19.** 6 − 4 = **2**

Subtracting: One Trade

Elizabeth bought 36 stamps of famous American women. She traded 18 of them with her friends. How many American women stamps did she have left?

Since we want to find how many she had left, we subtract.

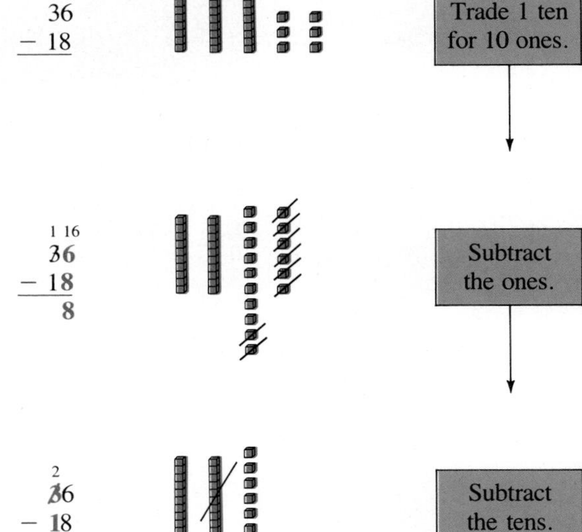

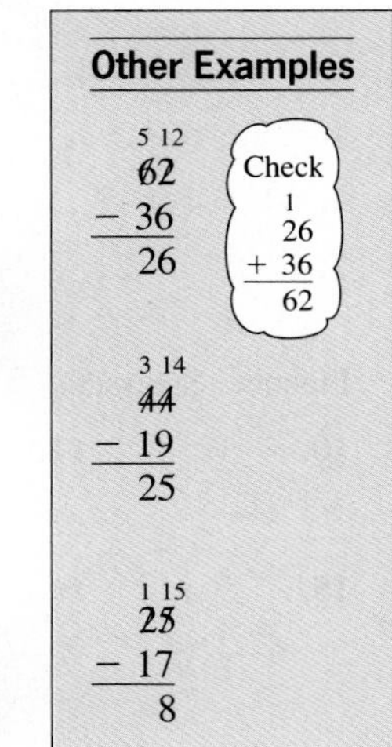

She had 18 stamps of American women left.

Try it out. Subtract. Check by adding.

1. 74 − 29 = 45	**2.** 58 − 18 = 40	**3.** 66 − 48 = 18	**4.** 21 − 8 = 13	**5.** 85 − 56 = 29

SKILLS REVIEW BANK

Multiplying: Trading Ones

Antoine throws 25 clay bowls each day on his pottery wheel. How many bowls will he make in 3 days?

Since we want the total for equal amounts, we multiply.

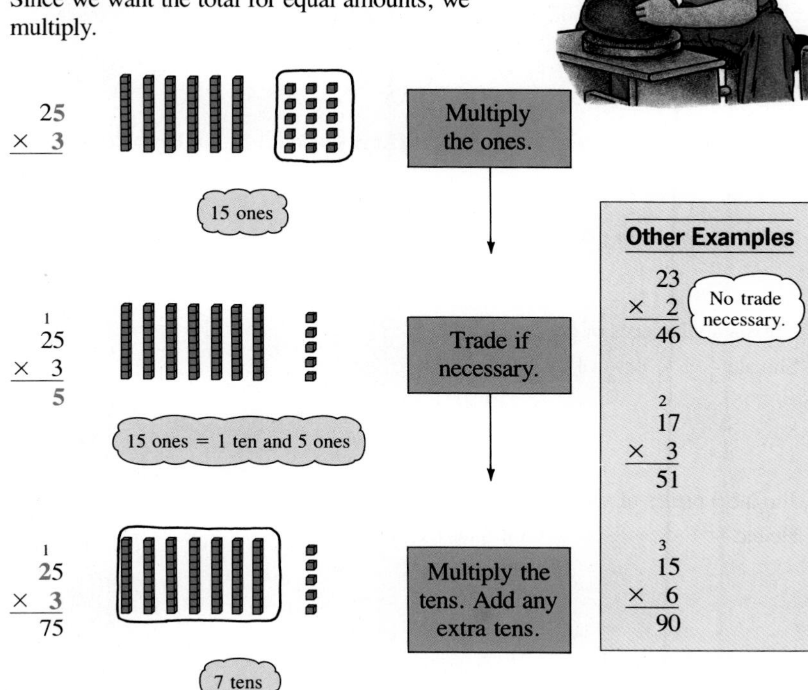

Other Examples

$$\begin{array}{r} 23 \\ \times\ 2 \\ \hline 46 \end{array}$$

No trade necessary.

$$\begin{array}{r} {}^{2} \\ 17 \\ \times\ 3 \\ \hline 51 \end{array}$$

$$\begin{array}{r} {}^{3} \\ 15 \\ \times\ 6 \\ \hline 90 \end{array}$$

Antoine makes 75 bowls in 3 days.

Try it out. Multiply.

1. $\begin{array}{r} 22 \\ \times\ 3 \\ \hline 66 \end{array}$ **2.** $\begin{array}{r} 36 \\ \times\ 2 \\ \hline 72 \end{array}$ **3.** $\begin{array}{r} 17 \\ \times\ 3 \\ \hline 51 \end{array}$ **4.** $\begin{array}{r} 14 \\ \times\ 6 \\ \hline 84 \end{array}$ **5.** $\begin{array}{r} 19 \\ \times\ 2 \\ \hline 38 \end{array}$

SKILLS REVIEW BANK

Adding Fractions: Like Denominators

You can write fractions to describe a part of something.

cheese pizza	sausage pizza	pineapple pizza
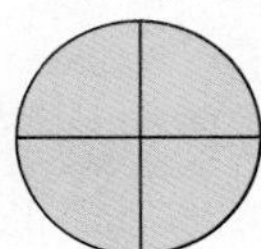	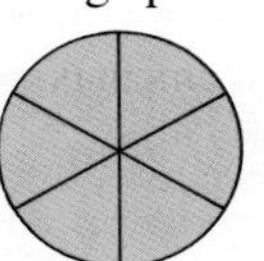	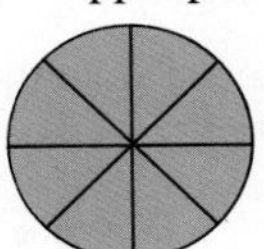
$\frac{1}{4}$ of the pizza is shaded.	$\frac{1}{6}$ of the pizza is shaded.	$\frac{1}{8}$ of the pizza is shaded.

1. Which piece of pizza is the largest? $\frac{1}{4}$

2. Which piece of pizza is the smallest? $\frac{1}{8}$

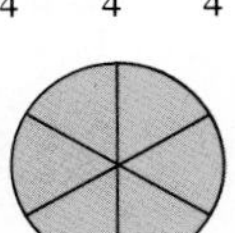

Christa ate 2 pieces of cheese pizza.
She ate $\frac{1}{4} + \frac{1}{4}$ or $\frac{2}{4}$ of the cheese pizza.

$\frac{1}{4} + \frac{1}{4} = \frac{2}{4}$

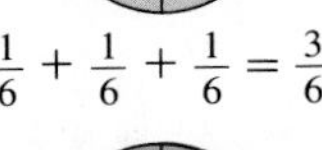

Jim ate 3 pieces of sausage pizza.
He ate $\frac{1}{6} + \frac{1}{6} + \frac{1}{6}$ or $\frac{3}{6}$ of the sausage pizza.

$\frac{1}{6} + \frac{1}{6} + \frac{1}{6} = \frac{3}{6}$

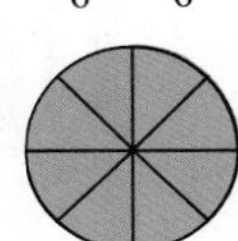

Quan ate 4 pieces of pineapple pizza.
She ate $\frac{1}{8} + \frac{1}{8} + \frac{1}{8} + \frac{1}{8}$ or $\frac{4}{8}$ of the pineapple pizza.

$\frac{1}{8} + \frac{1}{8} + \frac{1}{8} + \frac{1}{8} = \frac{4}{8}$

Find the sums. Add.

1. $\frac{5}{10} + \frac{4}{10} = \frac{9}{10}$ **2.** $\frac{2}{9} + \frac{6}{9} = \frac{8}{9}$ **3.** $\frac{1}{6} + \frac{2}{6} = \frac{3}{6}$

4. $\frac{1}{3} + \frac{1}{3} = \frac{2}{3}$ **5.** $\frac{2}{5} + \frac{2}{5} = \frac{4}{5}$ **6.** $\frac{3}{7} + \frac{2}{7} = \frac{5}{7}$

Subtracting Fractions: Like Denominators

The fourth grade class sold pieces of pizza at the school fair. Jose cut the cheese pizza into 4 equal pieces. He sold 2 pieces. How many pieces did he have left?

Since we want to find how many, we subtract.

cheese pizza

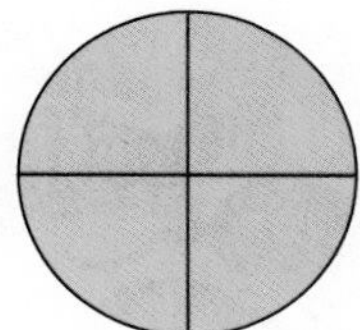

$\frac{4}{4} - \frac{2}{4} = \frac{2}{4}$

sausage pizza

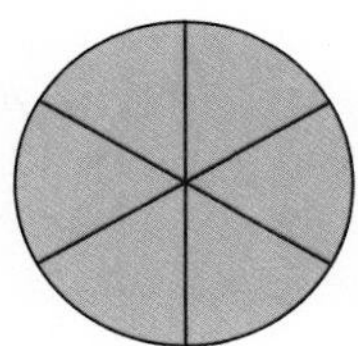

$\frac{6}{6} - \frac{2}{6} = \frac{4}{6}$

pineapple pizza

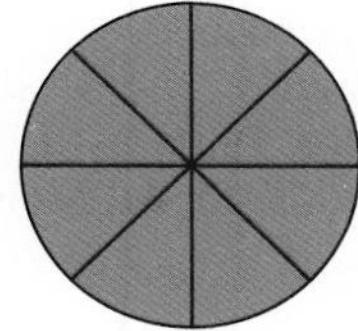

$\frac{8}{8} - \frac{5}{8} = \frac{3}{8}$

He had 2 pieces or $\frac{2}{4}$ of the cheese pizza left.

1. Michelle sold 2 pieces of sausage pizza. How many pieces did she have left?
2. James sold 5 pieces of pineapple pizza. How many pieces did he have left?

Find the differences. Subtract.

1. $\frac{7}{10} - \frac{2}{10} = \frac{5}{10}$
2. $\frac{3}{5} - \frac{2}{5} = \frac{1}{5}$
3. $\frac{3}{8} - \frac{1}{8} = \frac{2}{8}$
4. $\frac{6}{9} - \frac{4}{9} = \frac{2}{9}$
5. $\frac{5}{6} - \frac{4}{6} = \frac{1}{6}$
6. $\frac{2}{3} - \frac{1}{3} = \frac{1}{3}$

Math and Science Data Bank

Life Spans of Small Wild Animals

Because of predators, hunters, and automobiles, in the wild most of these animals live an average of one year. But they can live longer.

	In the Wild	In Captivity
	Years Possible	Years Possible
Cottontail Rabbit	3	5
Raccoon	6	14
Squirrel	12	20
Box Turtle	80	123
White-footed Mouse	2	8

Daytime Activity of Red-Backed Salamander

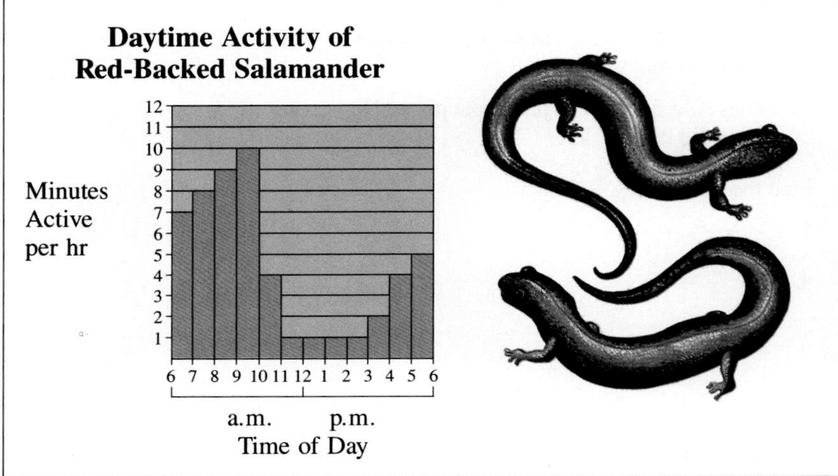

Math and Science Data Bank

Heartbeat Rates of Birds

Bird	Heartbeats per minute
Sparrow	500
Starling	390
Crow	379
Ostrich	65
Peregrine Falcon	347

Wingbeats Per Second

Hummingbird weighing 2 g	50
Hummingbird weighing 4 g	32
Hummingbird weighing 6 g	24

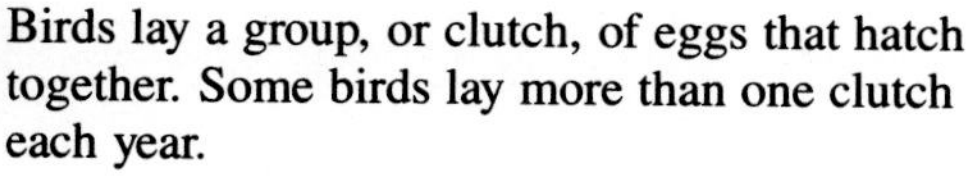

Birds lay a group, or clutch, of eggs that hatch together. Some birds lay more than one clutch each year.

Number of Eggs Laid

Bird	Usual Number of Eggs in a Clutch	Usual Number of Clutches Laid in a Year
Barn Owl	5	2
Coot	8	2
Peregrine Falcon	3	1
Hummingbird	2	2
Lark	4	3
King Penguin	1	1
Ostrich	14	1
Starling	6	2

Math and Science Data Bank

Planets in Our Solar System

Planet	Number of Earth days to go around the sun	Number of Satellites	Diameter in km
Mercury	88	0	5,000
Venus	225	0	12,000
Earth	365	1	13,000
Mars	687	2	7,000
Jupiter	4,333	16	143,000
Saturn	10,759	23	121,000
Uranus	30,685	15	51,000
Neptune	60,188	2	45,000
Pluto	90,700	1	3,000

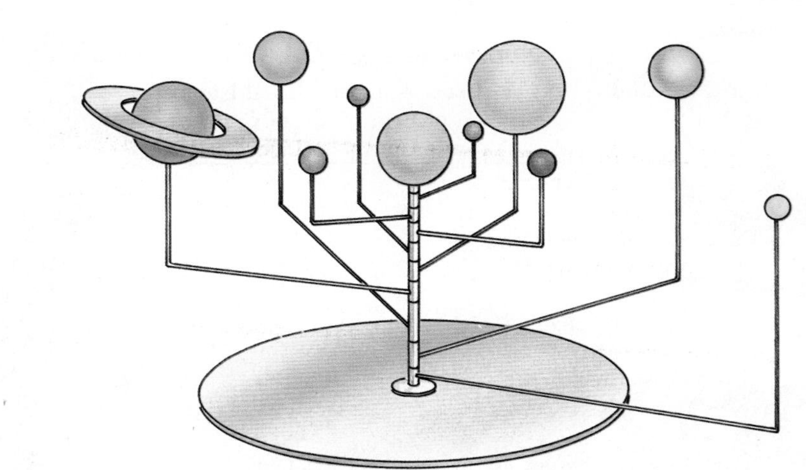

DATA BANK

Math and Science Data Bank

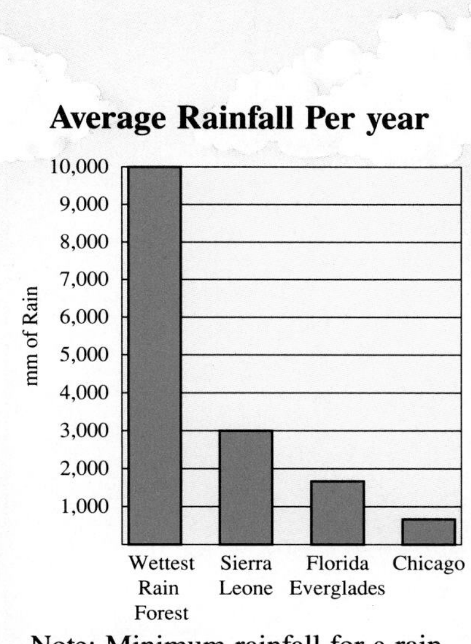

Note: Minimum rainfall for a rain forest is 2,000 mm per year.

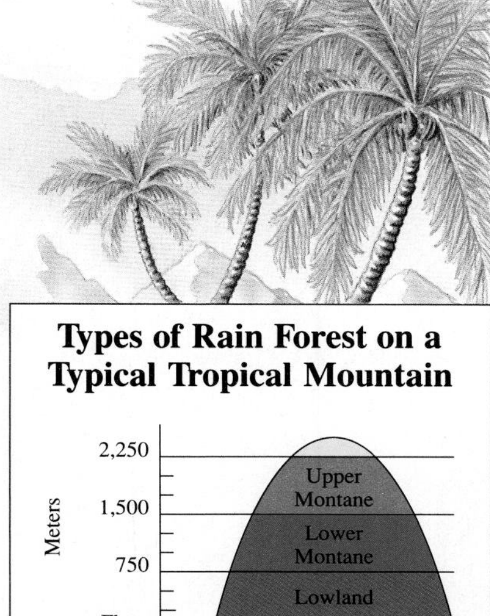

Layers of Vegetation in a Tropical Rain Forest

Emergent Layer

Canopy Layer

Understory

Floor

Math and Social Studies Data Bank

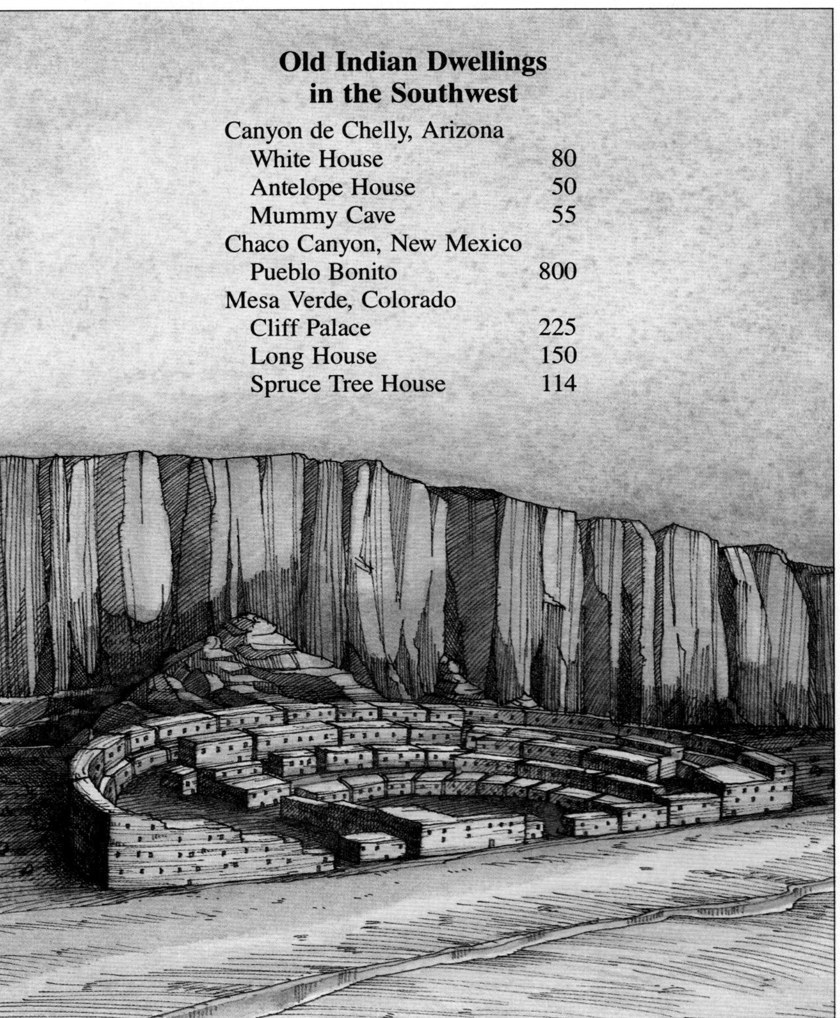

Old Indian Dwellings in the Southwest	
Canyon de Chelly, Arizona	
White House	80
Antelope House	50
Mummy Cave	55
Chaco Canyon, New Mexico	
Pueblo Bonito	800
Mesa Verde, Colorado	
Cliff Palace	225
Long House	150
Spruce Tree House	114

DATA BANK

Math and Social Studies Data Bank

U.S. Peaks More Than 14,000 Feet Above Sea Level

State	Number of Peaks
Alaska	18
California	12
Colorado	53
Washington	1

Some Rivers Formed in the Rocky Mountains

River	Length in Miles	Direction of Flow	Mouth
Colorado	1,400	west	Gulf of California
Missouri	2,714	east	Mississippi
Rio Grande	1,800	east	Gulf of Mexico
Arkansas	1,400	east	Mississippi River
Snake	1,038	west	Columbia River

473

Math and Social Studies Data Bank

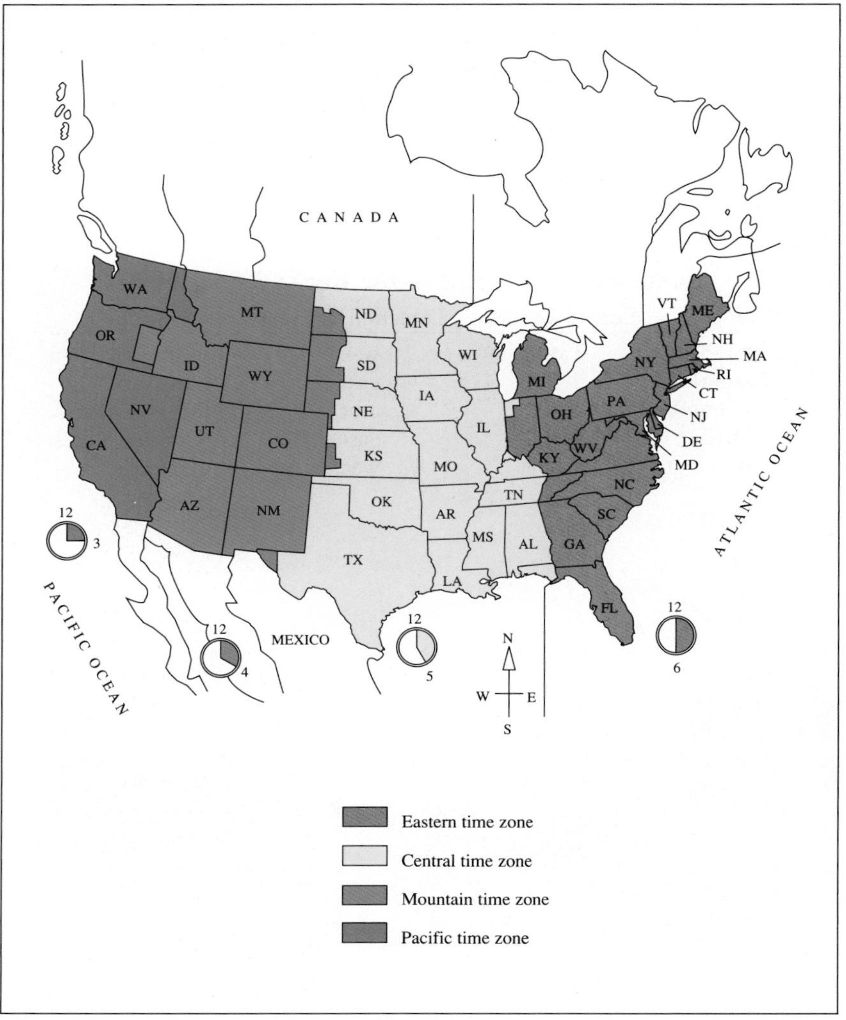

Math and Social Studies Data Bank

Lengths of Historical Ships

Kind of ship	Length
Viking longship	150 ft
Viking cargo ship	54 ft
Man-of-war carrack	120 ft
Merchant carrack	100 ft
Columbus' *Santa María*	90 ft
Columbus' *Pinta*	75 ft

Crew Sizes of Historical Ships

Kind of ship	Size of crew
Small Viking ship	6 sailors
Viking longship	70 sailors
Viking cargo ship	30 sailors
Columbus' *Santa María*	50 sailors
Columbus' *Pinta*	30 sailors

Math and Language Arts Data Bank

Tall Facts from American Tall Tales

Pecos Bill

Pecos Bill was the make-believe hero of the cowboys of the Southwest.

- During a drought, Pecos Bill had to lasso 9 miles of the Rio Grande River each morning to feed his cattle.
- Bill could rope a herd of cattle at one throw.

Paul Bunyan

Loggers made up stories about a giant, Paul Bunyan, and Babe, his blue ox.

- To grease Paul's hotcake griddle, 5 men skated on it with a slab of bacon tied to each foot.
- The Gumbaroo Paul captured in the woods had 16 pairs of rubber legs.

Joe Magarac, the Steel Man

Joe was a folk hero of men who worked in steel mills.

- Joe made 4 steel rails at a time with one hand by squeezing them out between his fingers.

Alfred Bulltop Stormalong

Alfred was a hero in stories told by deep-water sailors.

- He was 4 fathoms tall. He fought a sea monster 10 fathoms long. A fathom is a sailor's measure equal to 6 feet.
- Once Alfred tied an octopus's arms in knots that took a month of Sundays to untie.

Math and Language Arts Data Bank

Books by Laura Ingalls Wilder

	Year of Publication
Little House in the Big Woods	1932
Farmer Boy	1933
Little House on the Prairie	1935
On the Banks of Plum Creek *(Newberry Honor Book)*	1937
By the Shores of Silver Lake *(Newberry Honor Book)*	1939
The Long Winter *(Newberry Honor Book)*	1940
Little Town on the Prairie	1941
These Happy Golden Years	1943
The First Four Years	1971

Recipe for Johnny Cake

Served at threshing time in *Little House in the Big Woods*

1 egg	½ teaspoon salt
¾ cup corn meal	1½ cups buttermilk
½ teaspoon baking soda	1 tablespoon melted butter

Beat the egg. Stir in the corn meal, baking soda, salt, and buttermilk. Pour the mixture into a 1-quart baking dish greased with the melted butter. Bake at 400° for 20 to 25 minutes. *Amount: 6 servings.*

Math and Language Arts Data Bank

Fact and Fiction
from the book *Twenty-One Balloons*
by William Pene du Bois

Fact

- The standard size of a hydrogen balloon in 1883 was 600 cubic yards.
- The volcanic island of Krakatoa in the Pacific Ocean blew up in 1883 in the greatest explosion ever. The sound was heard 3,000 miles away.

Fiction

- 80 people live on Krakatoa in families of 4 with 2 children in each family.
- A balloon merry-go-round made of 8 boats connected in a circle could land on the ocean. Each boat held 2 children and was attached to a balloon.
- The rectangular balloon platform on which the Krakatoans and the professor escaped was lifted by 10 large balloons alternating with 10 smaller balloons. A large balloon was at each corner. Each shorter side had 3 large balloons.
- To land the platform, Professor Sherman had to pull apart the valves that let the hydrogen out of the balloons. Each valve required a 150-pound pull.

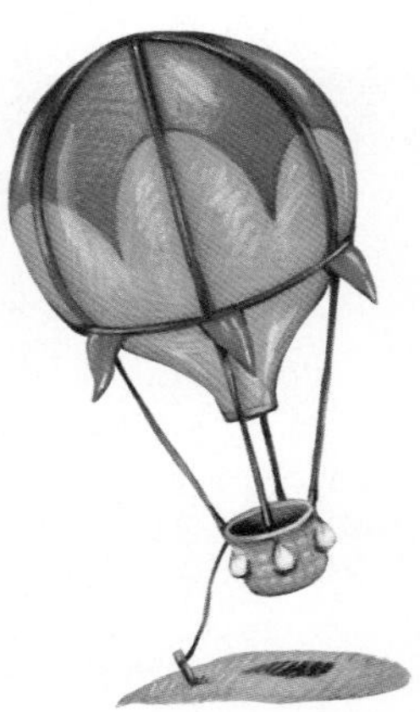

DATA BANK

Math and Fine Arts Data Bank

"Double Airplane" Controller for 9-String Marionette

To make the 2 T bars you need 2 wood strips that are 10 inches long and 2 wood strips that are 7 inches long. Each of the 9 strings in the diagram is labeled by the part of the puppet to which it is to be attached. To string the puppet you need 2 pieces of string that are 60 inches long and 5 pieces of string that are 30 inches long.

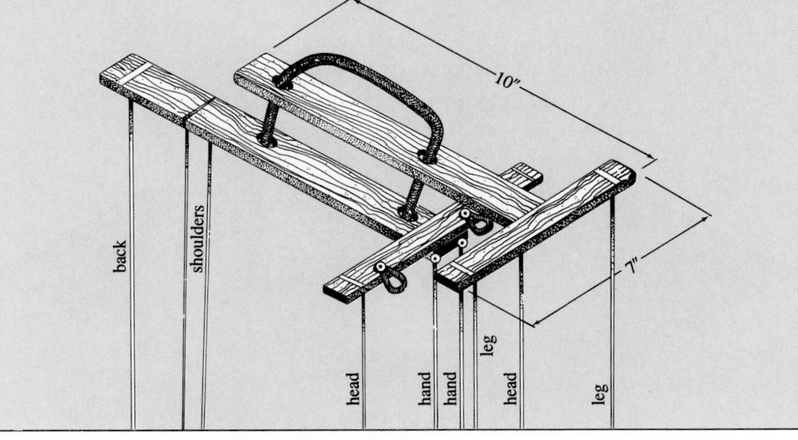

Japanese Bunraku Puppet Theater

The puppets weigh about 70 pounds each and are between 3 and 4 feet tall.
The female puppets are each worked by 3 people.
The male puppets are each worked by 4 people.
The people working the puppets are dressed in black and can be seen on the stage as they work the puppets.
Singers and readers present the story.

Math and Fine Arts Data Bank

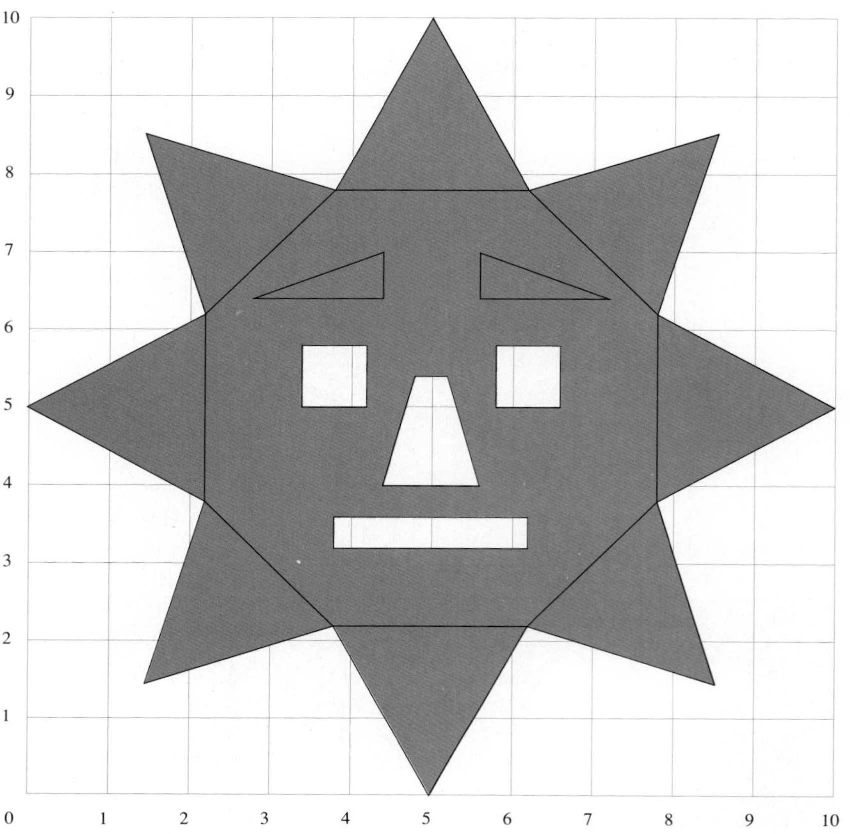

Math and Health and Fitness Data Bank

World Records for Fourth Graders Single Rope Skills Events

Event	Number of jumps
Single Speed	272
Double Speed	292
Double Unders	296
Double Unders/Crosses	53
Triple Unders	39
Pogo Jumping	5,064
Hoppity Hop Jumping	390

NOTE: Single Speed has a time limit of 1 minute. Double Speed allows 30 seconds for each partner. The other events have no time limit.

Aerobic Points for Energy Used in Exercise

Activity	Aerobic Points for 1 hour of activity
Jumping Rope	24
Running	30
Walking	3
Swimming	15
Baseball	2

Average Resting Heartbeat Levels Heartbeats Per Minute

DATA BANK

Math and Health and Fitness Data Bank

Facts about Winter Olympic Games

- The first Winter Olympic Games were held in 1924.
- The race course for the Men's Slalom skiing event must have between 55 and 75 gates. The course for the Women's Slalom must have between 40 and 60 gates.

Speed Skating: Women's 500-Meter Race

Year	Winner of Gold Medal	Time
1960	Helga Haase	45.9 seconds
1964	Lydia Skoblikova, USSR	45.0 seconds
1968	Ludmila Titova, USSR	46.1 seconds
1972	Anne Henning, United States	43.33 seconds
1976	Sheila Young, United States	42.76 seconds
1980	Karin Enke, East Germany	41.78 seconds
1984	Crista Rothenburger, East Germany	41.02 seconds
1988	Bonnie Blair, United States	39.10 seconds

Alpine Skiing: Men's Slalom

Year and Medal	Winner	Minutes	Seconds
1980			
Gold Medal	Ingemar Stenmark, Sweden	1	44.26
Silver Medal	Phil Mahre, United States	1	44.76
Bronze Medal	Jacques Luethy, Switzerland	1	45.06
1984			
Gold Medal	Phil Mahre, United States	1	39.41
Silver Medal	Steve Mahre, United States	1	39.62
Bronze Medal	Didier Bouvet, France	1	40.20
1988			
Gold Medal	Alberto Tomba, Italy	1	39.47
Silver Medal	Frank Woerndl, East Germany	1	39.53
Bronze Medal	Poul Frommelt, Liechtenstein	1	39.84

DATA BANK

Math and Health and Fitness Data Bank

Official Weights of Sport Balls

	Minimum	Maximum
Lawn Tennis	56.7 grams	58.5 grams
Baseball	141.7 grams	155.9 grams
Softball	177.2 grams	198.4 grams
Croquet	461.0 grams	477.0 grams
Table Tennis	2.4 grams	2.53 grams

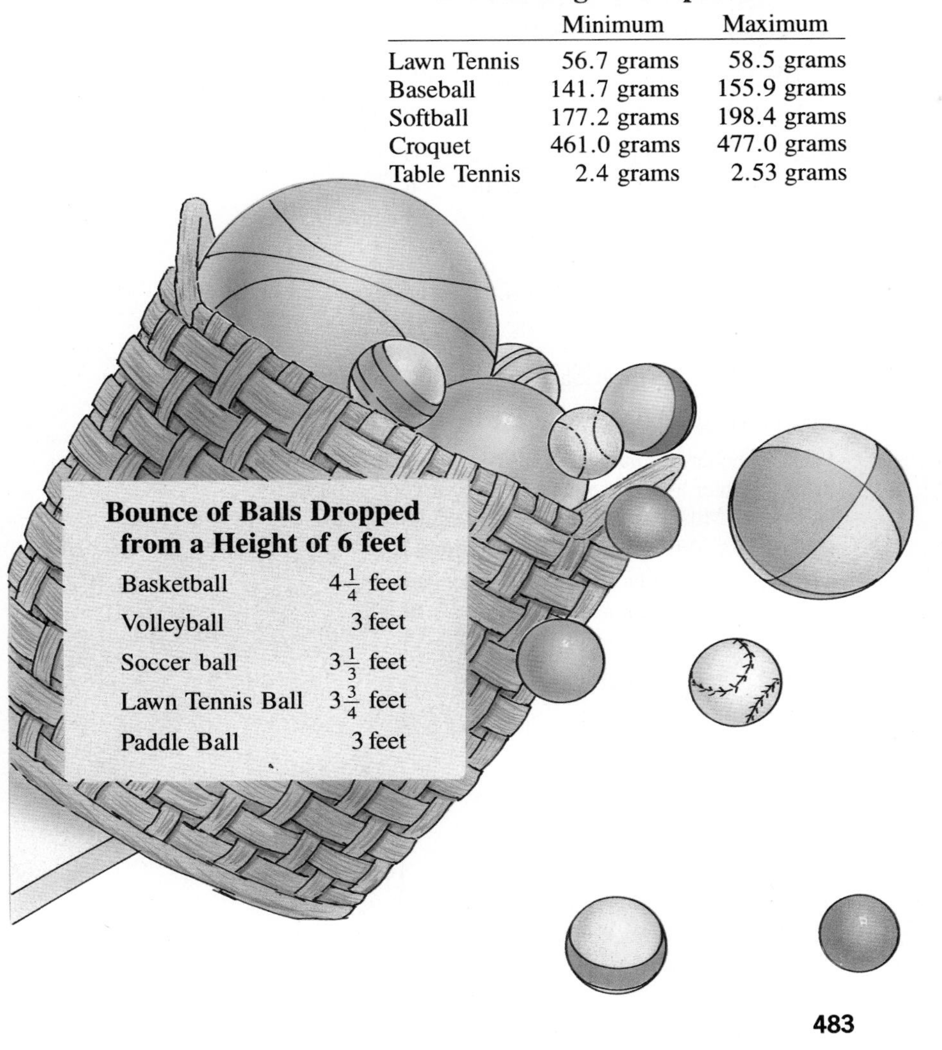

Bounce of Balls Dropped from a Height of 6 feet

Basketball	$4\frac{1}{4}$ feet
Volleyball	3 feet
Soccer ball	$3\frac{1}{3}$ feet
Lawn Tennis Ball	$3\frac{3}{4}$ feet
Paddle Ball	3 feet

Counting and Counting Patterns

Try these key codes to make your calculator count on by twos.

[ON/AC] [+] 2 [=] [=] [=] [=] . . .

[ON/AC] [+] 2 [Cons] [Cons] [Cons] [Cons] . . .

Entering [+] 2 or [+] 2 [Cons] sets up a **constant**, a number that stays the same. Each time you press [=] or [Cons] the calculator will add 2 to the number in the display.

Now try counting backward by 4s. Start at 70.

Enter [ON/AC] 70 [−] 4 [=] [=] [=] [=] . . .

or [ON/AC] [−] 4 [Cons] 70 [Cons] [Cons] [Cons] [Cons] . . .

The display should show 66, 62, 58, 54, and so on.

What is the largest number your calculator can display? Enter as many 9s as you can on your calculator. Most calculators can display eight 9s, or 99,999,999. What happens when you add 1? The number is too large for many calculators. The display shows an **overflow error**.

Activity

Is the target number in the counting pattern? Write yes or no.

	Start at	Count	Target Number
1.	20	on by 8	68 **yes**
2.	14,000	on by 96,000	700,000 **no**
3.	700,000	on by 7,000,000	Error **yes**
4.	5,000	back by 64	4,680 **yes**
5.	17,000	back by 810	560,000 **no**

CALCULATOR BANK

Whole Number Addition and Subtraction

To do an addition or subtraction problem, enter the key code just the way you say the problem. Try these.

Say	Enter	Display
four plus eight equals	[ON/AC] 4 [+] 8 [=]	12
twenty minus five equals	[ON/AC] 20 [−] 5 [=]	15
eighty-nine minus fourteen equals	[ON/AC] 89 [−] 14 [=]	75
sixty-nine plus thirty equals	[ON/AC] 69 [+] 30 [=]	99
six hundred six minus fifty equals	[ON/AC] 606 [−] 50 [=]	556
four thousand seven plus fifty equals	[ON/AC] 4007 [+] 50 [=]	4057

Addition and subtraction problems with more than two numbers work the same way. Try these.

Problem	Enter	Display
$23 + 45 + 91 =$	[ON/AC] 23 [+] 45 [+] 91 [=]	159
$97 + 11 + 67 - 22 =$	[ON/AC] 97 [+] 11 [+] 67 [−] 22 [=]	153
$93 - 21 - 16 - 30 =$	[ON/AC] 93 [−] 21 [−] 16 [−] 30 [=]	26
$345 - 45 + 16 - 6 =$	[ON/AC] 345 [−] 45 [+] 16 [−] 6 [=]	310

Activity

Complete the web. The outside ring is the sum of the three inside rings.

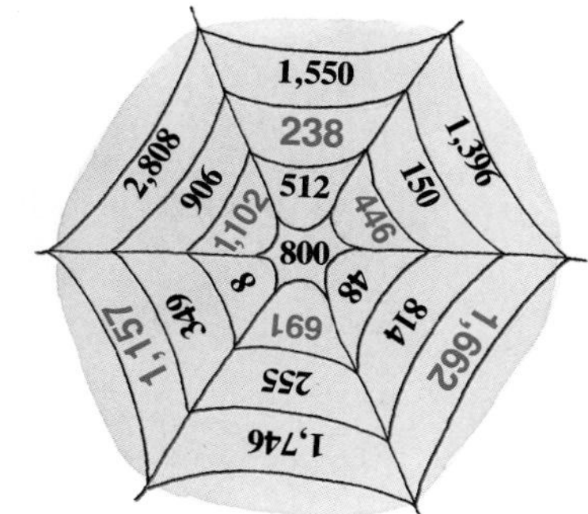

CALCULATOR BANK

Whole Number Multiplication

Here are some ways you can find the total of 5 sevens.

[ON/AC] 0 [+] 7 [=] [=] [=] [=] [=]

[ON/AC] 7 [+] 7 [+] 7 [+] 7 [+] 7 [=]

[ON/AC] 5 [×] 7 [=]

Use your calculator to find 9 eights, 32 twelves, and 215 nineteens.

Suppose you want to multiply 22, 45, 113, and 2,045 each by 15. If your calculator has a **multiplication constant**, you can enter the constant, [×] 15, and then multiply each number by the constant.

[ON/AC] 22 [×] 15 [=] 45 [=] 113 [=] 2045 [=]

[ON/AC] [×] 15 [Cons] 22 [Cons] 45 [Cons] 113 [Cons] 2045 [Cons]

Your display should show 330, 675, 1,695, and 30,675.

Multiply 12, 33, 432, 2,341, and 44,153 by 1. Is your display the same as the number multiplied? That is because 1 is the **identity** number for multiplication.

Multiply 14, 65, 315, 3,516, and 47,936 by 0. Does your display show 0 after each operation? The product of any number and 0 is 0.

Activity

Can you solve all of these problems in less than two minutes?

1. $16 \times 16 = $ **256**
2. $41 \times 1 = $ **41**
3. $0 \times 55 = $ **0**
4. $1{,}600 \times 16 = $ **25,600**
5. $1 \times 213 = $ **213**
6. $14 \times 16 = $ **224**
7. $88 \times 0 = $ **0**
8. $16 \times 14 = $ **224**
9. $8{,}564 \times 1 = $ **8,564**
10. $765 \times 0 = $ **0**

CALCULATOR BANK

Whole Number Division

How many 9s are there in 45? You can count the number of times you can subtract 9 from 45.

Enter [ON/AC] 45 [−] 9 [=] [=] [=] [=] [=]

or [ON/AC] 45 [−] 9 [=] [−] 9 [=] [−] 9 [=] [−] 9 [=] [−] 9 [=]

Or divide 45 by 9. Enter [ON/AC] 45 [÷] 9 [=].

To divide 96, 88, 80, 48, and 16 each by 8, you can enter the **division constant**, [÷] 8, and then divide each number by that constant.

Enter [ON/AC] 96 [÷] 8 [=] 88 [=] 80 [=] 48 [=] 16 [=]

or [ON/AC] [÷] 8 [Cons] 96 [Cons] 88 [Cons] 80 [Cons] 48 [Cons] 16 [Cons]

Your display should show 12, 11, 10, 6, and 2.

Divide 174 by 5. Your display should show 34.8. With the Math Explorer calculator, you can use the [INT ÷] key to do division with remainders.

Enter	Display
[ON/AC] 174 [INT ÷] 5 [=]	34 (Q) 4 (R)

The quotient is 34. The remainder is 4.

Divide 9, 56, 179, and 6,543 by 0. Dividing by zero is not logical. The calculator will display a **logic error**.

Activity

Find the number in each row that cannot be divided evenly by the divisor. What is the remainder?

Divisor								
7	14	105	147	91	318	574	182	**45 R3**
13	52	325	533	107	858	533	221	**8 R3**
41	82	205	574	902	2,091	1,025	297	**7 R10**
23	92	391	322	690	1,079	598	1,863	**46 R21**

Order of Operations: Memory Keys

To do a problem involving more than one operation, first multiply and divide, then add and subtract. For example, to do 6 × 7 + 4 × 13 you first find 6 × 17. Next find 4 × 13. Then add the two products.

Enter	Display
[ON/AC] 6 [×] 17 [=]	102
[ON/AC] 4 [×] 13 [=]	52
[ON/AC] 102 [+] 52 [=]	154

Sometimes you will want to remember the result of one calculation while you another one. This can be done with **memory keys**.

[M+] adds the display to the calculator's memory
[M−] subtracts the display from the calculator's memory
[MR] recalls the total in memory

Find 6 × 17 + 4 × 13.

Enter	Display
[ON/AC] 6 [×] 17 [=] [M+]	102
4 [×] 13 [=] [M+]	52
[MR]	154

Unlike some calculators, the Math Explorer does operations in the correct order. You can enter the problem just as it is written.

[ON/AC] 6 [×] 17 [+] 4 [×] 13 [=] 154

Activity

Match each expression in Column A with the expression in Column B which equals it. Remember to use the correct order of operations.

A		B	
152 ÷ 4 + 16 × 4	**102**	88 + 166 − 16 × 5	**174**
12 × 12 − 32 ÷ 8	**140**	8 × 5 + 5 × 20	**140**
180 − 77 ÷ 7 + 5	**174**	19 × 3 + 180 ÷ 4	**102**

CALCULATOR BANK

Decimals

Enter decimals on your calculator in the same way you enter whole numbers. Remember to press the decimal key. Enter these decimals.

Decimal Number	Key Code	Display
three tenths	[ON/AC] [.] 3	0.3
three hundredths	[ON/AC] [.] 03	0.03
four and one tenth	[ON/AC] 4 [.] 1	4.1

Notice that the calculator places a zero in front of the decimal point if no whole number is entered.

Add and subtract decimals just like you add and subtract whole numbers. Enter money amounts as decimals. Try these.

Problem	Key Code	Display
6 − 0.43 =	[ON/AC] 6 [−] .43 =	5.57
\$7.05 + \$23.62 =	[ON/AC] 7.05 [+] 23.62 =	30.67
\$6.58 − \$3.18 =	[ON/AC] 6.58 [−] 3.18 =	3.4

The display for the last problem shows 3.4, which in dollars is \$3.40.

Activity

Find the mistake Carlos made in his checkbook. His ending balance should be \$646.64. Make any necessary corrections in his balances.

Check No.	Date	To	Checks	Deposits	Balance	
					546.12	
324	4/1	AP Auto	450.00		96.12	
	4/7	(Pay Check)		757.18	853.30	
325	4/9	Al Barr	276.89		585.41	**576.41**
326	4/9	Sam's Food	81.12		504.29	**495.29**
327	4/11	Cable TV	29.90		474.39	**465.39**
	4/13	(Interest)		217.40	691.79	**682.79**
328	4/15	Sal's Toys	36.15		655.64	**646.64**

Fractions and Decimals

To find the decimal equivalent of a fraction, you can use your calculator to divide the numerator by the denominator.

Find the decimal for $\frac{1}{2}$, $\frac{3}{8}$, and $\frac{12}{5}$. Your calculator should show 0.5, 0.375, and 2.4.

The [F↔D] key on the Math Explorer calculator is a fraction/decimal key. To change $\frac{1}{4}$ to a decimal, enter [ON/AC] 1 [/] 4 [F↔D].

Find the decimals for $\frac{1}{2}$, $\frac{3}{8}$, and $\frac{12}{5}$ using the [F↔D] and [/] keys.

Now find the decimal for $\frac{3}{4}$.

Enter	Display
[ON/AC] 3 [/] 4 [F↔D]	0.75
Press [F↔D] again.	$\frac{75}{100}$

Pressing [F↔D] the second time changes the decimal 0.75 back to a fraction. The N/D → n/d in the display means that the fraction is not in simplest form. To simplify the fraction, enter [Simp] [=] until N/D → n/d disappears from the display.

Activity

Find the one fraction that does not have an equivalent decimal, and the one decimal that does not have an equivalent fraction.

Fractions

$\frac{21}{24}$ $\frac{36}{16}$ $\frac{5}{2}$

$\frac{35}{50}$ $\frac{33}{20}$

<u>$\frac{20}{24}$</u> $\frac{24}{32}$ $\frac{20}{25}$

Decimals

2.5 .7 1.65

.75 <u>1.7</u> 2.25

.8 .875

CALCULATOR BANK

Adding and Subtracting Fractions

To add or subtract fractions on a calculator, change them to decimals.

Add $\frac{1}{2} + \frac{7}{8}$.	Enter	Display
	[ON/AC] 1 [÷] 2 [=]	0.5
	[ON/AC] 7 [÷] 8 [=]	0.875
	[ON/AC] .5 [+] .875 [=]	1.375

To add or subtract mixed numbers, first change the mixed number to an improper fraction. For example, $2\frac{1}{2} + 1\frac{4}{5} = \frac{5}{2} + \frac{9}{5}$.

[ON/AC] 5 [÷] 2 [=] [M+]	2.5
9 [÷] 5 [=] [M+]	1.8
[MR]	4.3

To add or subtract fractions on the Math Explorer, enter the key code just the way you write the problem. Here are some examples to try.

Problem	Key Code	Display
$\frac{5}{6} - \frac{1}{3}$	5 [/] 6 [−] 1 [/] 3 [=]	$\frac{3}{6}$
	[Simp] [=]	$\frac{1}{2}$
$2\frac{7}{8} + \frac{6}{16}$	2 [Unit] 7 [/] 8 [+] 6 [/] 16 [=]	2 u $\frac{20}{16}$
	[Ab/c]	3 u $\frac{4}{16}$
	[Simp] 4 [=]	3 u $\frac{1}{4}$

Note that the [Ab/c] key changes improper fractions to mixed numbers.

Activity

Use the digits 1, 2, 3, 4, 5, 6, 7, 8, and 9. Make a true equation.
(Hint: The sum and differences are equal to $2\frac{1}{4}$ or 2.25.) **Answers will vary.**

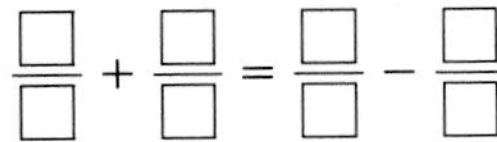

491

This program is available on disk.

Computer Technology: Finding Total Amounts

Daryl was in the checkout counter at the supermarket. He had 5 items in his cart. He had only $10. He decided to estimate the total cost of the 5 items to see if he had enough money.

Bread	$1.39
Ground Beef	2.96
Apples	1.39
Cereal	2.49
Milk	1.15

Estimate the total cost. Do you think Daryl had enough money? **A good estimate of the total is $9.00. The exact amount is $9.38.**

You can use the computer program below to practice your addition estimation skills.

```
10  PRINT "ESTIMATING TOTAL AMOUNTS": PRINT "SELECT HOW MANY
    NUMBERS TO ADD. THE": PRINT "COMPUTER WILL DISPLAY THE
    NUMBERS.": PRINT "ESTIMATE THE TOTAL. DO NOT USE": PRINT "PAPER
    AND PENCIL."
20  T = 0
30  PRINT : INPUT "HOW MANY NUMBERS TO ADD? ";N
40  PRINT : FOR I = 1 TO N
50  P = INT (995 * RND (1))/100: PRINT "$";P
60  T = T + P
70  NEXT I
80  PRINT : INPUT "ESTIMATE THE TOTAL. ";T1
90  PRINT : PRINT "THE EXACT TOTAL IS ";T
100 PRINT : PRINT "YOU MISSED THE TOTAL BY ";INT (100 * ABS (T-T1))/100
110 END
```

COMPUTER BANK

Estimating Length

Choose something in your classroom to measure. It can be a chalkboard, your desk or table, or even a book. Estimate the length in centimeters. Now measure to find the actual length. How close was your estimate? **Answers will vary.**

The computer program below will give you more practice in estimating length. You will be given a unit segment and an unmarked segment. You must estimate the length of the unmarked segment. The computer will tell you how close your estimate was to the actual length.

```
 10  PRINT : PRINT : PRINT "ESTIMATING PRODUCTS"
 20  F1 = INT (90 * RND (1) + 1):F2 = INT (90 * RND (1) + 1)
 30  P = F1 * F2
 40  PRINT "ESTIMATING THIS PRODUCT."
 50  PRINT : PRINT TAB(15 - LEN (STR$ (F1)))F1: PRINT
 60  PRINT TAB(12)"x"; TAB(15 - LEN (STR$ (F2)))F2
 70  PRINT TAB(12)"___"
 80  PRINT : INPUT "ESTIMATE = ";P1
 90  PRINT : PRINT "THE EXACT PRODUCT IS ";P"."
100  D = ABS (P - P1): IF D < 10 THEN GOTO 120
110  PRINT "YOUR ESTIMATE IS OFF BY ";D: GOTO 130
120  PRINT P1;" IS A VERY GOOD ESTIMATE."
130  PRINT : INPUT "DO YOU WANT TO TRY ANOTHER PROBLEM? ";Y$
140  IF LEFT$ (Y$,1) = "Y" THEN GOTO 10
150  END
```


This program is available on disk.

This program is available on disk.

Estimating Capacity

Kristy made a graph to show the number of gallons of water in a tank. Each ☆ shows one gallon of water. Count the stars to find how many gallons are in the tank. How many gallons are there?
The full tank shows 40 gallons.

Now estimate how many gallons the empty tank will hold. **The empty tank will hold about 60 gallons.**

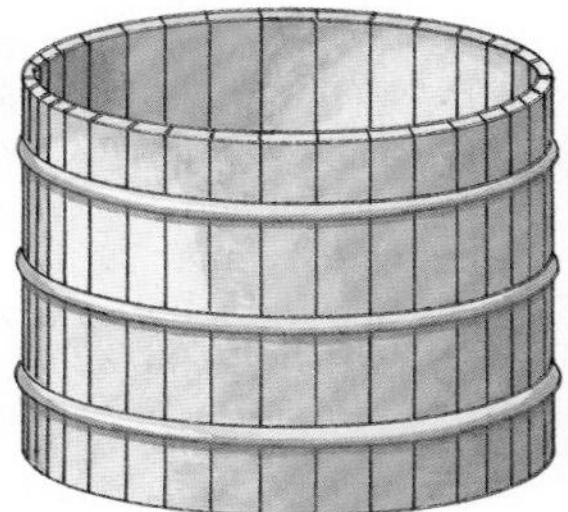

You can use the computer program below to try other estimation problems.

```
10  PRINT : PRINT : PRINT "ESTIMATING PRODUCTS"
20  F1 = INT (90 * RND (1) + 1):F2 = INT (90 * RND (1) + 1)
30  P = F1 * F2
40  PRINT "ESTIMATE THIS PRODUCT."
50  PRINT : PRINT TAB(15 − LEN (STR$ (F1)))F1: PRINT
60  PRINT TAB(12)"x"; TAB(15 − LEN (STR$ (F2)))F2
70  PRINT TAB(12)"___"
80  PRINT : INPUT "ESTIMATE = ";P1
90  PRINT : PRINT "THE EXACT PRODUCT IS ";P"."
100 D = ABS (P − P1): IF D < 10 THEN GOTO 120
110 PRINT "YOUR ESTIMATE IS OFF BY ";D: GOTO 130
120 PRINT P1;" IS A VERY GOOD ESTIMATE."
130 PRINT : INPUT "DO YOU WANT TO TRY ANOTHER PROBLEM? ";Y$
140 IF LEFT$ (Y$1) = "Y" THEN GOTO 10
150 END
```

COMPUTER BANK

Function Tables

Can you see a pattern between the input and output numbers in the function table?

What are the two missing output numbers for the table? What is the rule that is used to get the output numbers? **The rule is: input × 3 = output. The two missing numbers are 24 and 30.** The computer program below will give you more practice in finding rules and numbers for function tables.

Function Table

Input	Output
12	36
3	9
11	33
8	?
10	?

```
10  FOR I = 1 TO 5:X(I) = INT (20 * RND (1) + 1)
20  IF X(I) = X(I - 1) THEN 10
30  NEXT I
40  A = INT (10 * RND (1) + 1)
50  PRINT : PRINT : PRINT "INPUT | OUTPUT": PRINT "______|______": PRINT " |"
60  GOSUB 190
70  IF X(5) < 10 THEN PRINT " "X(5)" | ?": GOTO 90
80  PRINT " "X(5)" | ?"
90  PRINT : PRINT : PRINT "FUNCTION TABLES": PRINT "THERE IS A
    PATTERN BETWEEN THE INPUT": PRINT "AND OUTPUT NUMBERS IN THE
    FUNCTION": PRINT "TABLE. STUDY THE TABLE AND SEE IF YOU": PRINT
    "CAN FIND THE PATTERN. WHAT IS THE"
100 INPUT "MISSING NUMBER IN THE TABLE? ";M: PRINT : IF (J = 1) AND
    (M = X(5) + A) THEN PRINT "CORRECT.": GOTO 140
110 IF (J = 2) AND (M = X(5) * A) THEN PRINT "CORRECT.": GOTO 150
120 IF J = 1 THEN PRINT "NOT CORRECT.": GOTO 140
130 IF J = 2 THEN PRINT "NOT CORRECT.": GOTO 150
140 PRINT "THE RULE IS: INPUT + ";A:" = OUTPUT": GOTO 160
150 PRINT "THE RULE IS: INPUT X";A;" = OUTPUT"
160 INPUT "DO YOU WANT ANOTHER FUNCTION TABLE? ";Y$
170 IF LEFT$ (Y$,1) = "Y" THEN GOTO 10
180 END
190 J = INT (2 * RND (1) + 1)
200 ON J GOTO 210,230
210 FOR N = 1 TO 4: IF X(N) < 10 THEN PRINT " "X(N)" |"X(N) + A: NEXT N:
    RETURN
220 PRINT " "X(N)" | "X(N) + A: NEXT N: RETURN
230 FOR N = 1 TO 4: IF X(N) < 10 THEN PRINT " "X(N)" | "X(N) * A: NEXT N:
    RETURN
240 PRINT " "X(N)" | "X(N) * A: NEXT N: RETURN
```


This program is available on disk.

This program is available on disk.

Smallest Difference

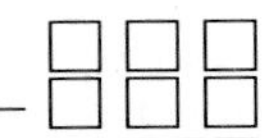

Joan and Nikko wre playing the game of Smallest Difference. Joan had the 6 digits, 3, 5, 3, 2, 0, 7 to put in the boxes in the subtraction problem. She wanted the answer to be as small as possible. Nikko had the digits 4, 3, 9, 9, 7, 0. She wanted to get a smaller difference than Joan.

What problem would you make with Joan's digits? What would you make with Nikko's digits? Who would win?

Joan: 325 − 307 = 18
Nikko: 940 − 937 = 3
Nikko would win.

You can play the game of Smallest Difference on the computer. Think about some strategies that may help you win some games.

```
 10  PRINT "SMALLEST DIFFERENCE GAME"
 20  PRINT "EACH PLAYER RECEIVES 6 DIGITS. USE THE": PRINT "6 DIGITS
     TO CREATE A SUBTRACTION"
 30  PRINT "PROBLEM WITH THE SMALLEST POSSIBLE": PRINT
     "DIFFERENCE. THE PLAYER WITH THE": PRINT "SMALLEST DIFFERENCE
     WINS THE GAME."
 40  FOR P = 1 TO 2
 50  PRINT : PRINT "PLAYER ";P;", YOUR NUMBERS ARE:": PRINT
 60  FOR C = 1 TO 6:B = INT (10 * RND (1))
 70  PRINT B" ";: NEXT C: PRINT : PRINT
 80  INPUT "TYPE THE TOP NUMBER. ";T(P)
 90  INPUT "TYPE THE BOTTOM NUMBER. ";B(P)
100  IF B(P) > T(P) THEN GOTO 80
110  D(P) = T(P) - B(P): NEXT P
120  PRINT : PRINT "PLAYER 1","PLAYER 2": PRINT
130  PRINT TAB(6 - LEN (STR$ (T(1))))T(1); TAB(22 - LEN (STR$ (T(2))))T(2):
     PRINT: PRINT TAB(2)"-"; TAB(6 - LEN (STR$(B(1))))B(1); TAB(18)"-";
     TAB(22 - LEN(STR$ (B(2))))B(2)
140  PRINT TAB(2)"___"; TAB(18)"___": PRINT : PRINT TAB(6 - LEN (STR$
     (D(1))))D(1); TAB(22 - LEN (STR$ (D(2))))D(2)
150  PRINT : IF D(1) = D(2) THEN PRINT "TIE SCORE OF ";D(1): GOTO 180
160  IF D(1) < D(2) THEN PRINT "PLAYER 1 WINS.": GOTO 180
170  PRINT "PLAYER 2 WINS."
180  PRINT : INPUT "WANT TO PLAY ANOTHER GAME?(Y/N) ";Y$
190  IF LEFT$ (Y$,1) = "Y" THEN 40
200  END
```

COMPUTER BANK

Fractions of a Number

There are 24 students in Melissa's music class. $\frac{3}{8}$ of the students can play a musical instrument. How many students can play a musical instrument?

$\frac{3}{8}$ of 24 = 9

You can use the set of 24 stars to help you think about the problem. There are 8 stars in each row. There are 3 rows of stars. What is $\frac{3}{8}$ of 24?

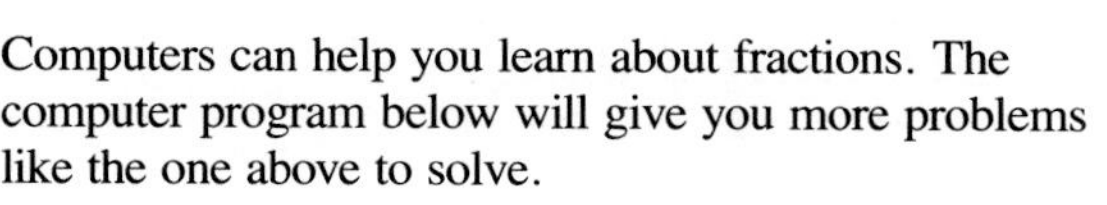

Computers can help you learn about fractions. The computer program below will give you more problems like the one above to solve.

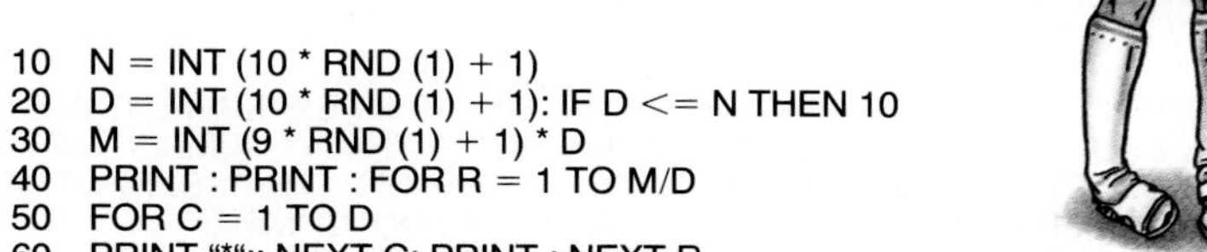

```
10  N = INT (10 * RND (1) + 1)
20  D = INT (10 * RND (1) + 1): IF D <= N THEN 10
30  M = INT (9 * RND (1) + 1) * D
40  PRINT : PRINT : FOR R = 1 TO M/D
50  FOR C = 1 TO D
60  PRINT "*";: NEXT C: PRINT : NEXT R
70  PRINT : PRINT : PRINT "FINDING FRACTIONS OF A WHOLE NUMBER":
    PRINT "THERE ARE ";M;" TOTAL STARS. THERE ARE ";D
80  PRINT "STARS IN EACH ROW. THERE ARE ";M/D;" ROWS OF": PRINT
    "STARS. WHAT IS ";N;"/";D;" OF ";M;
90  INPUT "STARS? ";A:A1 = (N/D) * M: PRINT
100 IF A = A1 THEN PRINT "CORRECT."
110 IF A <> A1 THEN PRINT "SORRY."
120 PRINT N:"/";D;" OF ";M;" = ";A1: PRINT
130 FOR R = 1 TO M/D
140 FOR C = 1 TO N
150 PRINT "*";: NEXT C: PRINT : NEXT R
160 PRINT : INPUT "DO YOU WANT ANOTHER PROBLEM? ";Y$
170 IF LEFT$ (Y$,1) = "Y" THEN 10
180 END
```

497

This program is available on disk.

This program is available on disk.

Probability Spinner

Raymond used a spinner divided into 10 sectors of equal size for a probability experiment. He decided to spin the spinner 100 times and record the number for each spin. He thought that each of the numbers 1 to 10 would come up 10 times. Do you think this will happen? What would happen in 1,000 spins?

One run of the program for 100 spins produced these outcomes: 1—12, 2—13, 3—10, 4—6, 5—11, 6—11, 7—11, 8—7, 9—11, 10—8

Computers can be programmed to simulate some probability problems. The program below can be used to simulate a spinner with any number of equal sectors. It can simulate the number cube by choosing a spinner with 6 sectors. To simulate a coin toss, choose a spinner with 2 sectors. You can choose any number of trials.

```
10  PRINT "PROBABILITY SPINNER": PRINT "THIS IS AN EXPERIMENT IN
    PROBABILITY.": PRINT "CHOOSE A SPINNER WITH ANY NUMBER OF":
    PRINT "EQUAL PARTS. CHOOSE ANY NUMBER OF": PRINT "SPINS. THE
    COMPUTER WILL QUICKLY GIVE": PRINT "THE OUTCOME."
20  PRINT : INPUT "HOW MANY SECTORS OF EQUAL SIZE? ";X
30  DIM D(X)
40  FOR N = 1 TO X:D(N) = 0: NEXT N
50  INPUT "HOW MANY SPINS DO YOU WANT? ";Y
60  FOR I = 1 TO Y:R = INT (X * RND (1)) + 1
70  LET D(R) = D(R) + 1: NEXT I
80  PRINT "NUMBER","FREQUENCY"
90  FOR N = 1 TO X: PRINT N,D(N): NEXT N
100 END
```

COMPUTER BANK

Computer Graphs

Joyce wanted to make a graph of the data in a table of record animal ages. She decided to show a star, *, for every 2 years of age for each of the animals.

Make a graph of the data in the table. Use Joyce’s plan. **See Additional Answers.**

Computers can be used to quickly and accurately show data in graph form. The program below is a simple example. You must make some choices when using the program.

Record Ages of Animals	
Elephant	62
Hippopotamus	54
Rhinoceros	40
Bear	34
Monkey	26

```
10  PRINT : PRINT : PRINT “COMPUTER GRAPHING“: PRINT “ENTER THE
    FOLLOWING INFORMATION AND THE“: PRINT “COMPUTER WILL CREATE
    A GRAPH.“
20  PRINT : INPUT “HOW MANY NUMBERS FOR THE GRAPH? “;N
30  DIM N$(N): DIM X(N)
40  PRINT “FOR EACH ITEM, TYPE THE NAME AND THE“: PRINT “NUMBER
    SEPARATED BY A COMMA.“
50  FOR I = 1 TO N: INPUT N$(I),X(I): NEXT I
60  S = 1: FOR Q = 1 TO N:S1 = INT (X(Q)/23 + 1): IF S1 > S THEN S = S1
70  NEXT Q: INPUT “TYPE THE NAME OF THE GRAPH. “;G$
80  PRINT : PRINT TAB(20)G$
90  PRINT “______________________________________“
100 FOR I = 1 TO N: PRINT N$(I),
110 FOR J = 1 TO INT (X(I)/S + .5): PRINT “*“;: NEXT J
120 PRINT : NEXT I
130 PRINT “______________________________________“: PRINT
140 PRINT “EACH * = “;S
150 END
```


This program is available on disk.

MORE PRACTICE BANK

Set A For use following page 7.

Find these sums.

1.	2.	3.	4.	5.	6.
6	7	8	9	0	4
+ 5	+ 7	+ 3	+ 7	+ 8	+ 6
11	14	11	16	8	10

7. (3 + 9) + 4 16

8. 3 + (9 + 4) 16

Set B For use following page 15.

Add. Break apart an addend if needed.

1.	2.	3.	4.	5.	6.	7.
14	15	10	12	7	16	11
+ 7	+ 7	+ 3	+ 4	+ 0	+ 9	+ 2
21	22	13	16	7	25	13

Set C For use following page 17.

Add. Use compensation if needed.

1.	2.	3.	4.	5.	6.	7.
13	10	17	18	6	12	15
+ 6	+ 4	+ 8	+ 9	+ 2	+ 7	+ 6
19	14	25	27	8	19	21

Set D For use following page 31.

Write > or < for each ▥.

1. 73,112 ▥ 73,211 <
2. 468,101 ▥ 468,011 >
3. 676 ▥ 667 >
4. 538 ▥ 358 >

Set E For use following page 37.

Round to the nearest ten or hundred.

1. 28 ▥ 30
2. 83 ▥ 80
3. 65 ▥ 70
4. 34 ▥ 30
5. 295 ▥ 300
6. 703 ▥ 700

Set F For use following page 39.

Round to the nearest thousand or dollar.

1. 4,499 4,000
2. 8,207 8,000
3. 2,600 3,000
4. 5,653 6,000
5. $1.79 $2.00
6. $68.16 $68.00

500

MORE PRACTICE BANK

Set A For use following page 55.

Find these sums and differences.

1.	2.	3.
300	80	700
+ 600	− 40	+ 500
900	40	1,200

4.	5.	6.
16,000	1,200	800
− 8,000	+ 1,500	+ 600
8,000	2,700	1,400

Set B For use following page 57.

Estimate the sums and differences by rounding.

1.	2.	3.	4.	5.	6.
75	42	242	318	683	1,684
+ 34	− 33	+ 757	− 186	− 321	+ 7,450
110	10	1,000	100	400	10,000

Set C For use following page 61.

Find the sums.

1.	2.	3.	4.	5.	6.
715	685	263	702	457	375
+ 916	+ 77	+ 98	+ 859	+ 382	+ 829
1,631	672	361	1,561	839	1,204

Set D For use following page 63.

Add.

1.	2.	3.	4.	5.	6.
64	$3.83	746	563	$1.95	52
47	5.35	75	87	6.28	43
28	7.68	434	412	1.39	18
+ 35	+ 0.54	+ 8	+ 29	+ .97	+ 77
174	$17.40	1,263	1,091	$10.59	190

Set E For use following page 66.

Estimate the sums. Use front-end estimation.

1.	2.	3.	4.	5.	6.
24	46	342	602	630	312
33	38	+ 461	+ 813	742	403
+ 14	+ 17	700	1,400	+ 253	+ 614
60	80			1,500	1,300

501

MORE PRACTICE BANK

Set A For use following page 71.

Subtract.

1.	2.	3.	4.	5.	6.
529	615	7,136	148	390	370
− 179	− 340	− 472	− 95	− 36	− 114
350	275	6,664	53	354	156

Set B For use following page 73.

Subtract.

1.	2.	3.	4.	5.	6.
508	605	1,006	505	2,001	402
− 179	− 346	− 788	− 149	− 135	− 58
329	259	218	356	1,866	344

Set C For use following page 75.

Use compensation to find these sums and differences.

1.	2.	3.	4.	5.	6.
763	596	841	589	687	386
+ 97	+ 35	− 499	− 405	+ 163	− 79
860	631	342	184	850	307

Set D For use following page 79.

Find the sums and differences. Use a calculator if necessary.

1.	2.	3.	4.	5.	6.
2,964	6,587	4,532	4,430	6,429	7,000
+ 5,682	+ 2,744	+ 1,607	− 726	− 5,161	− 2,674
8,646	9,331	6,139	3,704	1,268	4,326

Set E For use following page 119.

Find the products.

1.	2.	3.	4.	5.	6.
4	1	2	0	2	5 × 4 = 20
× 1	× 3	× 0	× 3	× 1	4 × 5 = n 20
4	3	0	0	2	

Set F For use following page 121.

Find the products.

1.	2.	3.	4.	5.	6.	7.
2	2	2	4	5	5	5
× 2	× 7	× 8	× 2	× 2	× 3	× 8
4	14	16	8	10	15	40

502

MORE PRACTICE BANK

Set A For use following page 123.

Multiply.

1.	2.	3.	4.	5.	6.	7.
6	7	9	9	2	1	9
× 9	× 9	× 0	× 9	× 9	× 9	× 5
54	63	0	81	18	9	45

Set B For use following page 125.

Multiply.

1.	2.	3.	4.	5.	6.	7.
6	3	5	3	4	3	7
× 3	× 4	× 4	× 9	× 3	× 3	× 4
18	12	20	27	12	9	28

Set C For use following page 131.

Find the products. Break apart one of the factors if needed.

1.	2.	3.	4.	5.	6.	7.
7	8	6	7	7	9	5
× 6	× 5	× 8	× 7	× 8	× 9	× 6
42	40	48	49	56	81	30

Set D For use following page 133.

Find the products.

1.	2.	3.	4.	5.	6.
6	8	6	6	8	6
× 9	× 8	× 7	× 6	× 6	× 7
54	64	42	36	48	42

Set E For use following page 135.

Copy and complete each set of multiples.

1.

×	0	1	2	3	4	5
5	0	5	10	▥	▥	▥

15 20 25

2.

×	0	1	2	3	4	5
2	0	2	4	▥	▥	▥

6 8 10

Set F For use following page 147.

Find the products. Write answers only.

1. 5 × 30 **150**
2. 2 × 700 **1,400**
3. 3 × 200 **600**
4. 6 × 1,000 **6,000**
5. 2 × 8,000 **16,000**

503

MORE PRACTICE BANK

Set A For use following page 151.

Multiply and then add 4. Write answers only.

1. 2 × 5 **14**
2. 6 × 7 **46**
3. 3 × 2 **10**
4. 7 × 4 **32**
5. 8 × 7 **60**

Set B For use following page 155.

Find the products.

1. 53 × 4 **212**
2. 72 × 5 **360**
3. 24 × 4 **96**
4. 45 × 6 **270**
5. 86 × 5 **480**
6. 12 × 8 **96**

Set C For use following page 157.

Find the products.

1. 130 × 4 **520**
2. 161 × 7 **1,127**
3. 128 × 3 **384**
4. 116 × 5 **580**
5. 411 × 8 **3,288**
6. 247 × 2 **494**

Set D For use following page 159.

Find the products.

1. 605 × 3 **1,815**
2. 250 × 7 **1,750**
3. 708 × 2 **1,416**
4. 435 × 8 **3,480**
5. 582 × 5 **2,910**
6. 641 × 5 **3,205**

Set E For use following page 162.

Find the products.

1. (2 × 3) × 3 **18**
2. (4 × 1) × 10 **40**
3. 5 × (4 × 2) **40**
4. 4 × (2 × 100) **800**
5. 5 × (2 × 3) **30**
6. (3 × 3) × 10 **90**

Set F For use following page 163.

Find the missing numbers using your calculator.

1. 382 + 526 + 55 = 261 + 118 + □ **584**
2. 407 + 89 + 281 = 292 + 43 + □ **442**

504

MORE PRACTICE BANK

Set A For use following page 165.

Find the products.

1. 4,512 × 7 **31,584**
2. 1,475 × 6 **8,850**
3. 7,004 × 5 **35,020**
4. 2,359 × 3 **7,077**
5. 5,267 × 8 **42,136**

Set B For use following page 167.

Multiply.

1. $0.45 × 7 **$3.15**
2. $5.26 × 8 **$42.08**
3. $3.02 × 4 **$12.08**
4. $8.59 × 9 **$77.31**
5. $12.78 × 5 **$63.90**

Set C For use following page 179.

Find the products. Write answers only.

1. 90 × 50 **4,500**
2. 50 × 60 **3,000**
3. 60 × 40 **2,400**
4. 80 × 30 **2,400**
5. 20 × 60 **1,200**

Set D For use following page 181.

Estimate the products. Round numbers to the nearest ten.

1. 12 × 29 **3,000**
2. 38 × 21 **8,000**
3. 61 × 49 **3,000**
4. 352 × 19 **8,000**
5. 18 × 19 **4,000**

Set E For use following page 183.

Multiply.

1. 63 × 80 **5,040**
2. 48 × 30 **1,440**
3. 75 × 40 **3,000**
4. 43 × 10 **430**
5. 27 × 60 **1,620**
6. 38 × 20 **760**

Set F For use following page 185.

Find the products.

1. 12 × 23 **276**
2. 31 × 42 **1,302**
3. 43 × 11 **473**
4. 30 × 24 **720**
5. 14 × 12 **168**
6. 44 × 34 **1,496**

505

MORE PRACTICE BANK

Set A For use following page 193.

Find the amounts.

1. $4.73 × 36 = $170.28
2. $9.06 × 53 = $480.18
3. $5.61 × 42 = $235.62
4. $8.34 × 16 = $133.44
5. $3.10 × 45 = $139.50

Set B For use following page 239.

Use counters to find the quotients.

1. 8 ÷ 2 = 4
2. 24 ÷ 3 = 8
3. 14 ÷ 2 = 7
4. 2)16 8
5. 3)21 7
6. 2)12 6

Set C For use following page 243.

Divide.

1. 3)21 7
2. 2)18 9
3. 3)27 9
4. 2)8 4
5. 3)12 4
6. 2)16 8
7. 3)24 8
8. 2)14 7
9. 3)9 3
10. 2)12 6

Set D For use following page 245.

Divide.

1. 20 ÷ 5 = 4
2. 16 ÷ 4 = 4
3. 10 ÷ 5 = 2
4. 40 ÷ 5 = 8
5. 25 ÷ 5 = 5
6. 36 ÷ 4 = 9

Set E For use following page 248.

Find the quotients.

1. 0 ÷ 8 0
2. 9 ÷ 1 9
3. 0 ÷ 2 0
4. 4 ÷ 1 4
5. 87 ÷ 87 1
6. 0 ÷ 6 0

Set F For use following page 251.

Find the quotients.

1. 35 ÷ 7 = 5
2. 54 ÷ 6 = 9
3. 12 ÷ 6 = 2
4. 21 ÷ 7 = 3
5. 30 ÷ 6 = 5
6. 42 ÷ 7 = 6
7. 28 ÷ 7 = 4
8. 18 ÷ 6 = 3

506

MORE PRACTICE BANK

Set A For use following page 253.

Divide.

1. 8 ÷ 8 = 1
2. 27 ÷ 9 = 3
3. 56 ÷ 8 = 7
4. 81 ÷ 9 = 9
5. 32 ÷ 8 = 4
6. 63 ÷ 9 = 7

Set B For use following page 267.

Find the quotients and remainders. Check your answers.

1. 2)13 6 R1
2. 4)22 5 R1
3. 7)16 2 R2
4. 6)15 2 R3
5. 8)65 8 R1
6. 9)39 4 R3
7. 5)47 9 R2

Set C For use following page 269.

Find the quotients. Write answers only.

1. 80 ÷ 4 20
2. 80 ÷ 8 10
3. 60 ÷ 2 30
4. 40 ÷ 2 20
5. 360 ÷ 4 90
6. 560 ÷ 8 80

Set D For use following page 271.

Estimate by rounding to the nearest ten. Write estimated answers only.

1. 91 ÷ 3 30
2. 75 ÷ 4 20
3. 58 ÷ 2 30
4. 49 ÷ 5 10
5. 252 ÷ 5 50
6. 423 ÷ 7 60
6. 357 ÷ 9 40
8. 182 ÷ 3 60

Set E For use following page 275.

Find the quotients and remainders.

1. 5)68 13 R3
2. 8)94 11 R6
3. 2)91 45 R1
4. 6)53 8 R5
5. 4)79 16 R3
6. 3)55 18 R1
7. 7)81 11 R4
8. 9)86 9 R5
9. 3)92 30 R2
10. 8)82 10 R2

507

MORE PRACTICE BANK

Set A For use following page 279.

Find the quotients and remainders.

1. $7\overline{)884}$ 126 R2 2. $6\overline{)893}$ 148 R5 3. $4\overline{)450}$ 112 R2 4. $2\overline{)335}$ 167 R1 5. $8\overline{)889}$ 111 R1 6. $6\overline{)696}$ 116 7. $4\overline{)510}$ 127 R2

Set B For use following page 283.

Divide and check.

1. $3\overline{)124}$ 41 R1 2. $7\overline{)810}$ 115 R5 3. $6\overline{)200}$ 33 R2 4. $2\overline{)137}$ 68 R1 5. $4\overline{)543}$ 135 R3 6. $9\overline{)425}$ 47 R2 7. $5\overline{)663}$ 132 R3

Set C For use following page 285.

Divide.

1. $7\overline{)636}$ 90 R6 2. $6\overline{)604}$ 100 R4 3. $9\overline{)98}$ 10 R8 4. $2\overline{)801}$ 400 R1 5. $5\overline{)750}$ 150 6. $3\overline{)91}$ 30 R1 7. $4\overline{)431}$ 107 R3

Set D For use following page 289.

Divide.

1. $4\overline{)\$5.92}$ \$1.48 2. $7\overline{)\$4.41}$ \$0.63 3. $8\overline{)\$8.00}$ \$1.00 4. $3\overline{)\$0.78}$ \$0.26 5. $6\overline{)\$2.70}$ \$0.45

Set E For use following page 335.

Fill in the ▦ to create an equivalent fraction.

1. $\frac{2}{3} = \frac{▦}{6}$ 4 2. $\frac{3}{6} = \frac{▦}{12}$ 6 3. $\frac{1}{4} = \frac{▦}{8}$ 2 4. $\frac{1}{2} = \frac{2}{▦}$ 2 5. $\frac{3}{5} = \frac{▦}{10}$ 6

Set F For use following page 337.

Multiply the numerator and denominator by 2, 3, and 4 to find a set of equivalent fractions.

1. $\frac{3}{8} = \frac{▦}{▦} = \frac{▦}{▦} = \frac{▦}{▦}$ $\frac{6}{16}$ $\frac{9}{24}$ $\frac{12}{32}$ 2. $\frac{3}{4} = \frac{▦}{▦} = \frac{▦}{▦} = \frac{▦}{▦}$ $\frac{6}{8}$ $\frac{9}{12}$ $\frac{12}{16}$ 3. $\frac{5}{9} = \frac{▦}{▦} = \frac{▦}{▦} = \frac{▦}{▦}$ $\frac{10}{18}$ $\frac{15}{27}$ $\frac{20}{36}$

Set G For use following page 339.

Reduce each fraction to lowest terms.

1. $\frac{6}{8}$ $\frac{3}{4}$ 2. $\frac{3}{9}$ $\frac{1}{3}$ 3. $\frac{4}{16}$ $\frac{1}{4}$ 4. $\frac{18}{24}$ $\frac{3}{4}$ 5. $\frac{8}{12}$ $\frac{2}{3}$ 6. $\frac{15}{25}$ $\frac{3}{5}$

508

MORE PRACTICE BANK

Set A For use following page 341.

Write >, <, or = for each ▦.

1. $\frac{1}{5}$ ▦ $\frac{1}{3}$ < 2. $\frac{1}{2}$ ▦ $\frac{1}{3}$ > 3. $\frac{1}{10}$ ▦ $\frac{1}{5}$ < 4. $\frac{1}{4}$ ▦ $\frac{1}{5}$ > 5. $\frac{2}{4}$ ▦ $\frac{5}{10}$ =

Set B For use following page 345.

Solve.

1. $\frac{2}{5}$ of 5 2 2. $\frac{3}{4}$ of 24 18 3. $\frac{4}{5}$ of 15 14 4. $\frac{2}{4}$ of 16 8 5. $\frac{3}{8}$ of 24 9 6. $\frac{3}{4}$ of 16 12

Set C For use following page 347.

Write each fraction as a whole number or a mixed number. Reduce all fractions to lowest terms.

1. $\frac{40}{6}$ $6\frac{2}{3}$ 2. $\frac{12}{2}$ 6 3. $\frac{11}{4}$ $2\frac{3}{4}$ 4. $\frac{15}{2}$ $7\frac{1}{2}$ 5. $\frac{9}{3}$ 3 6. $\frac{39}{9}$ $4\frac{1}{3}$

Set D For use following page 365.

Give > or < for each ▦.

1. 2.27 ▦ 2.35 < 2. 7.6 ▦ 7.54 > 3. 9.4 ▦ 9.36 >
4. 4.8 ▦ 3.9 > 5. 6.27 ▦ 6.29 < 6. 2.5 ▦ 2.6 <

Set E For use following page 367.

Round each decimal number to the nearest whole number.

1. 64.53 65 2. 11.4 11 3. 29.5 30 4. 6.8 7 5. 5.25 5 6. 93.1 93 7. 9.2 9

Set F For use following page 369.

Write the decimal for each fraction.

1. $\frac{1}{4} =$ 0.25 2. $\frac{2}{10} =$ 0.20 3. $\frac{3}{5} =$ 0.60 4. $\frac{4}{10} =$ 0.40 5. $\frac{1}{2} =$ 0.50 6. $\frac{2}{5} =$ 0.40

509

MORE PRACTICE BANK

Set A For use following page 409.

Add or subtract. Reduce to lowest terms.

1. $\frac{3}{5} + \frac{1}{5}$ — $\frac{4}{5}$
2. $\frac{11}{10} - \frac{6}{10}$ — $\frac{5}{10}$ or $\frac{1}{2}$
3. $4\frac{5}{8} + 4\frac{2}{8}$ — $8\frac{7}{8}$
4. $8\frac{6}{10} - 7\frac{3}{10}$ — $1\frac{3}{10}$
5. $3\frac{1}{2} + 2\frac{1}{2}$ — 6

Set B For use following page 413.

Add. Use models if necessary.

1. $\frac{1}{6} + \frac{2}{3}$ — $\frac{5}{6}$
2. $\frac{6}{10} + \frac{3}{5}$ — $1\frac{2}{10}$ or $1\frac{1}{5}$
3. $\frac{2}{8} + \frac{2}{4}$ — $\frac{6}{8}$ or $\frac{3}{4}$
4. $\frac{1}{3} + \frac{5}{6}$ — $1\frac{1}{6}$
5. $\frac{3}{10} + \frac{3}{5}$ — $\frac{9}{10}$
6. $\frac{4}{10} + \frac{1}{2}$ — $\frac{9}{10}$

Set C For use following page 415.

Subtract.

1. $\frac{5}{8} - \frac{1}{2}$ — $\frac{1}{8}$
2. $\frac{1}{2} - \frac{1}{8}$ — $\frac{3}{8}$
3. $\frac{2}{3} - \frac{2}{6}$ — $\frac{2}{6}$ or $\frac{1}{3}$
4. $\frac{6}{8} - \frac{1}{2}$ — $\frac{2}{8}$ or $\frac{1}{4}$
5. $\frac{7}{8} - \frac{3}{4}$ — $\frac{1}{8}$
6. $\frac{7}{10} - \frac{1}{5}$ — $\frac{5}{10}$ or $\frac{1}{2}$

Set D For use following page 421.

Add or subtract.

1. 53.68 + 4.19 — 57.87
2. 42.7 + 69.1 — 111.8
3. 4.83 + 1.47 — 6.30
4. 58.26 + 17.35 — 75.61
5. 8.3 + 7.2 — 15.5
6. 7.64 − 3.16 — 4.48
7. \$47.20 − 19.80 — \$27.40
8. 47.52 − 8.73 — 38.79
9. 47.60 − 17.82 — 29.78
10. 32.75 − 12.08 — 10.67

510

MORE PRACTICE BANK

Set A For use following page 423.

Add or subtract.

1. 42.7 + 8.69 — 51.39
2. 64.8 − 21.34 — 43.46
3. 2.69 + 8 — 10.69
4. 64 − 18.3 — 45.7
5. 93 − 75.46 — 17.54

Set B For use following page 425.

Round to the nearest whole number, then add or subtract.

1. 32.46 − 17.83 — 14
2. 26.41 − 14.82 — 11
3. 13.40 + 6.17 — 19
4. 28.65 + 19.82 — 49
5. 67.62 − 53.46 — 15

Set C For use following page 437.

Divide.

1. 20)80 — 4
2. 60)180 — 3
3. 10)90 — 9
4. 40)240 — 6
5. 90)360 — 4
6. 70)420 — 6

Set D For use following page 439.

Divide.

1. 50)285 — 5 R35
2. 30)95 — 3 R5
3. 90)508 — 5 R58
4. 60)185 — 3 R5
5. 20)99 — 4 R19
6. 70)383 — 5 R33

Set E For use following page 441.

Divide and check.

1. 15)48 — 3 R3
2. 47)96 — 2 R2
3. 33)47 — 1 R14
4. 25)56 — 2 R6
5. 39)34 — 0 R34
6. 14)30 — 2 R2

Set F For use following page 443.

Divide. Change your estimates if necessary.

1. 13)35 — 2 R9
2. 12)49 — 4 R1
3. 19)427 — 22 R5
4. 18)72 — 4
5. 23)45 — 1 R22
6. 31)91 — 2 R29
7. 27)588 — 21 R21
8. 14)83 — 5 R13
9. 35)80 — 2 R10
10. 42)813 — 19 R15

511

MORE PRACTICE BANK

Set A For use following page 447.

Divide and check.

1. 20)$7.00 **$0.35**
2. 70)955 **13 R45**
3. 30)812 **27 R2**
4. 40)579 **14 R19**
5. 50)805 **16 R5**

Set B For use following page 449.

Divide and check.

1. 14)279 **19 R13**
2. 22)354 **16 R2**
3. 41)892 **21 R31**
4. 35)961 **27 R16**
5. 46)703 **15 R13**

Set C For use following page 5.

Use counters to help you solve these problems.

1. Steve has saved $11. He bought a record for $5. Then he earned $7 more. How much money does he have now? **$13**
2. Jack has $12. Jin has $15. Jin spends $7. Jack does not spend any money. Now how much more money does Jack have than Jin? **$4**

Set D For use following page 9.

Write the fact family for each pair of addends.

1. 5, 9
   5 + 9 = 14 14 − 5 = 9
   9 + 5 = 14 14 − 9 = 5
2. 3, 4
   3 + 4 = 7 7 − 4 = 3
   4 + 3 = 7 7 − 3 = 4

Set E For use following page 11.

Solve.

1. Mike wanted to spot a dozen blue jays on his hike. By noon he had seen 5 blue jays. How many more blue jays does he have to spot? **7 blue jays**
2. Holly found 11 acorns in the forest. Her brother Ted found 16 acorns. How many fewer acorns did Holly find than Ted? **5 acorns**

Set F For use following page 27.

Write the place value of each red number.

1. 3,620 **thousands**
2. 739 **ones**
3. 19 **tens**
4. 402 **tens**
5. 924 **hundreds**
6. 589 **tens**

512

MORE PRACTICE BANK

Set A For use following page 29.

Write the standard number. Use a comma to separate thousands.

1. thirty-six thousand **36,000**
2. five hundred seventy-nine thousand **579,000**

Set B For use following page 35.

Solve.

1. Riku is shorter than Betty. Fran is taller than Betty. Donna is shorter than Riku. Who is the tallest girl? **Fran**
2. Nadine is younger than Garrett. Joan is older than Garrett. Ed's age is between Garrett's and Joan's. Who is the youngest? **Nadine**

Set C For use following page 41.

Write the standard number.

1. eight million, seven hundred twelve thousand **8,712,000**
2. forty-nine million **49,000,000**

Set D For use following page 43.

Pretend you gave the clerk $10.00 to buy some items. The prices are below. Tell what coins and bills the clerk would give you for change. **See Additional Answers.**

1. $7.78
2. $8.82
3. $5.65
4. $9.22
5. $4.38
6. $2.15

Set E For use following page 45.

Decide without counting if each amount can buy a $2.00 kite.

1. **no**
2. **yes**

513

MORE PRACTICE BANK

Set A For use following page 77.

1. At the store, Rebecca selected a bag of apples that cost $1.05, a bunch of bananas that cost $1.50, and several pears that cost $2.30. At the checkout counter, Rebecca found she only had $4.00. What is the difference between the money she had and the total cost of the apples, bananas, and pears? **$0.85**
2. There are 10 boys and 12 girls in Domingo's class. The classroom had 20 desks. How many people in Domingo's class had to sit at a table? **2 people**

Set B For use following page 81.

Tell if you need an exact answer or an estimate. Explain why.

1. You are a checkout clerk at a grocery store. The customer pays for his $8.95 purchase with a $10.00 bill. How much change do you give the customer? **exact answer—need to give exact change**

Set C For use following page 91.

Use the graphs on page 90 to answer these questions.

1. One autumn the snow could be found as low as 11,000 ft. Which mountains on the bar graph were capped with snow? **Mt. Whitney and Mt. McKinley**
2. If 200 of the campers from the pictograph stayed in trailers that year, how many campers stayed in tents? **300 campers**

Set D For use following page 93.

1. Make a bar graph like the one on page 90 with the data from this table. **Check students' graphs.**

	Blue Spins in 300 tries
Spinner 1	90
Spinner 2	140
Spinner 3	50

514

MORE PRACTICE BANK

Set A For use following page 97.

1. Copy the line graph on page 96. Then draw these points and connect them to the line. Add to the graph if necessary. **Check students' graphs.**

More Mountain Temperatures (°F)

6,000 ft up	39°	7,000 ft up	35°

2. How many points on the graph are above 50°F? **3 points**

Set B For use following page 101.

1. At the annual spelling bee, only 3 of the 62 students on Team A misspelled a word. There were 35 boys and 27 girls on Team A. How many students on Team A spelled every word correctly? **59 students**
2. Team B won the contest with 185 points. Team A scored 140 points and Team C scored 176 points. By how many points did Team A beat Team C? **9 points**

Set C For use following page 103.

1. At the count of three, Debbie and Ian each hold up 1 to 5 fingers. If the number of fingers they each hold up matches, Debbie gets a point. If the number of fingers does not match, Ian gets a point. Is this a fair or unfair game? Why? **unfair—the chances of winning are not equal**
2. Ian and Debbie change the rules. They decide to hold up 1 or 2 fingers each time. If the number of fingers matches, Debbie gets a point. If the number of fingers does not match, Ian gets a point. Is this game fair or unfair. Why? **fair—the chances of winning are equal**

Set D For use following page 105.

1. Clarinda wrote the letters of the alphabet on a piece of paper so that the entire page was covered. Then she shut her eyes and put her finger on the paper. Do you think it was more likely that she picked out a consonant or a vowel? Why? **consonant—there are more consonants than vowels in the alphabet**

515

Set A For use following page 117.

Tell whether addition or multiplication is best and why.

1. José has 6 dollars. Each dollar is worth 4 quarters. How many quarters can José get for his dollars? **multiplication—not adding more money to what already have**

2. James has 1 quarter, 2 dimes, and 3 nickels. What is the total amount of money he has? **addition—want to find how much there is in all**

Set B For use following page 129.

Write each question in a different way. Then solve.

1. Abdul's softball team won 9 games each year for 3 years in a row. What is the total number of games that Abdul's team won over the 3-year period? **How many games did they win in all? 27 games**
2. In July Abdul hit 15 home runs. In August he hit 3 home runs. What is the difference in the number of home runs? **How many more home runs did he hit in July? 12 home runs**

Set C For use following page 137.

Fill in the data needed to complete the table. Then solve.

1. Muffins cost $1.50 for a "baker's dozen" at the bakery. There are 13 muffins, or one extra muffin in a "baker's dozen." How many muffins can you buy for $6.00? **52 muffins**

cost	$1.50	$3.00	**$4.50**	**$6.00**
muffins	13	26	**39**	**52**

Set D For use following page 169.

Make a table to help solve the problems.

1. Dan decided to do 5 more push-ups each week to get ready for the swim meet. How many push-ups was he doing after 8 weeks? **40 push-ups**
2. Carol added 2 more laps to her workout each week. How many laps was she running after 6 weeks? **12 laps**

Set A For use following page 195.

Tell which calculation method you would choose. Then solve.

1. The fourth grade class held a car wash. They charged $3.75 to wash each car. On Saturday, they washed 52 cars. How much money did they collect on Saturday? **calculator, $195.00**
2. An additional $5.75 was charged to wax a car after it was washed. What was the total charge to wash and wax a car? **paper and pencil; $9.50**

Set B For use following page 197.

1. Movie companies use cameras that shoot 24 pictures each second. If a camera has shot 1,348 pictures, how many more pictures does it need to have shot a full minute? (60 second = 1 minute) **92 pictures**
2. A slow-motion camera takes 54 pictures each second. If a director puts one minute of slow-motion pictures with 720 regular-speed pictures, how many pictures does he have? (60 seconds = 1 minute) **3,960 pictures**

Set C For use following page 207.

Write each time.

1.

▯ : ▯▯ **4:35**
▯ minutes to ▯ **25, 5**

2.

▯▯ : ▯▯ **10:27**
▯ minutes to ▯ **27, 10**

3.

▯ : ▯▯ **8:53**
▯ minutes to ▯ **7, 9**

Set D For use following page 208.

Write whether each time is a.m. or p.m.

1. Lois got up early and ate breakfast at 7:00 ▯. **a.m.**
2. Guy was out of school and roller-skating by 3:15 ▯. **p.m.**

MORE PRACTICE BANK

Set A For use following page 209.

Use the August calendar on page 209 to name these dates.

1. On August 16 the parade committee decided to meet again in a week. When will they next meet? **the 23rd or August 23**
2. The parade and street fair will be held the last Saturday in August. What date should everyone circle on their calendars? **the 26th or August 26**

Set B For use following page 211.

Give the times.

1. What time was it 5 hours before 2:00 p.m.? **10 a.m.**
2. What time will it be 25 minutes after 8:50 a.m.? **9:15 a.m.**

Set C For use following page 213.

Solve. Find as many answers as you can.

1. Which coins make $0.25?
2. Pilar has 24 pennies. Into how many rows can she arrange the coins and still have an equal number of coins in each row? **Answers will vary.**

Set D For use following page 215.

Solve.

1. Mr. Blacksmith's draft horse is 4 cubits tall. When he compares a hand span and a cubit, he finds there are about 4 hand spans in 1 cubit. How many hand spans tall is his horse? **16 hand spans**
2. Mr. Blacksmith paced around the horse corral to find its size. He found it was 20 steps wide and 22 steps long. What was the perimeter of the corral? **84 steps**

Set E For use following page 217.

Write <u>inches</u>, <u>feet</u>, or <u>yards</u> to make the statement reasonable.

1. The basketball player is 6 __?__ tall. **feet**
2. The classroom is 5 __?__ wide. **yards**

MORE PRACTICE BANK

Set A For use following page 220.

1. On a map of South Carolina, 1 thumb width stands for 75 miles. There are 13 thumb widths between Middleton and Seaside City. How many miles apart are the two towns? **975 miles**

Set B For use following page 222.

Find the perimeter of each figure.

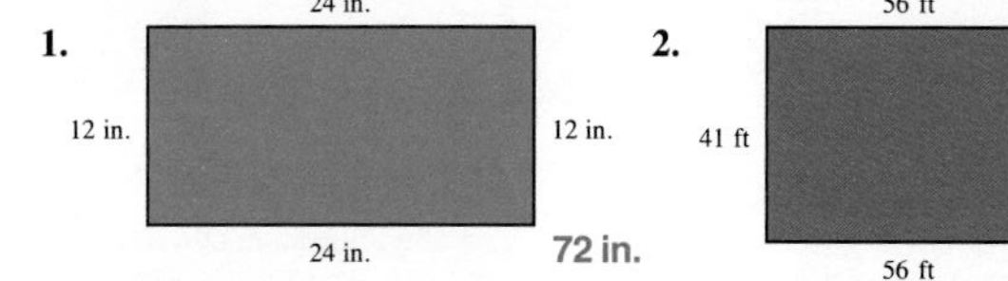

1. **72 in.**
2. **194 ft**

Set C For use following page 223.

Choose the better estimate.

1. How wide is the desk?
   A 1 foot (B) 1 yard
2. How long is the street?
   A 4 yards (B) 4 miles

Set D For use following page 225.

Solve using data from the chart on page 224.

1. What is the total population of the two cities that get the most rainfall in Texas? **1,941,028**
2. Which city has about 3 times as many people as Austin? **Dallas**

Set E For use following page 227.

Use the relationships shown on page 226 to solve.

1. The cook made 5 gallons of vegetable soup. How many quarts is this? **20 quarts**
2. The cook made 8 quarts of fruit punch for a party. How many pints is this? **16 pints**

MORE PRACTICE BANK

Set A For use following page 228.

Choose pounds or ounces to estimate these weights.

1. Portable TV
   20 _?_ **pounds**
2. Orange
   8 _?_ **ounces**

Set B For use following page 229.

Choose the best estimate.

1. Hot water faucet
   A 60°F
   B 90°F
   (C) 150°F
2. Cool fall day
   A 90°F
   (B) 40°F
   C 10°F
3. Inside a freezer
   (A) 10°F
   B 40°F
   C 60°F

Set C For use following page 241.

Find the products and quotients.

1. $4 \times 3 = n$ **12**; $3 \times 4 = n$ **12**; $12 \div 3 = n$ **4**; $12 \div 4 = n$ **3**
2. $5 \times 2 = n$ **10**; $2 \times 5 = n$ **10**; $10 \div 2 = n$ **5**; $10 \div 5 = n$ **2**
3. $3 \times 5 = n$ **15**; $5 \times 3 = n$ **15**; $15 \div 5 = n$ **3**; $15 \div 3 = n$ **5**
4. $2 \times 4 = n$ **8**; $4 \times 2 = n$ **8**; $8 \div 4 = n$ **2**; $8 \div 2 = n$ **4**

Set D For use following page 247.

Estimate the answer. Then solve.

1. 4 friends earned $36 for unloading firewood from a truck. How much money did each get? **about $10; exactly $9**
2. A cord of firewood costs $127. If Mountain Ski Lodge burns 5 cords of firewood each winter, how much do they spend on firewood?
   about $500; exactly $635

Set E For use following page 257.

1. A bus left the downtown station and traveled 2 hours before stopping. The rest stop lasted 20 minutes. The bus then traveled an hour and a half before arriving in Middletown at 4:30 p.m. What time did the bus leave for Middletown?
   12:40 p.m.

520

MORE PRACTICE BANK

Set A For use following page 277.

Solve.

1. Noriko wants to take 250 photographs of the wedding. On her portrait camera she can take 7 photographs for each roll of film. How many rolls of film does she need? **36 rolls of film**

Set B For use following page 280.

Find the average of these numbers.

1. 233, 205, 248, 258 **236**
2. 91, 85, 119, 103, 142, 132 **112**

Set C For use following page 287.

Tell which calculation method you will use. Then solve.

1. A hot-air balloon traveled 86 mi in 3 hours. If on the average the balloon traveled the same distance each hour, about how many miles did it travel each hour?
   paper and pencil, 28 miles
2. It costs $6.85 for each person to ride in a hot-air balloon. About how much would it cost altogether for 8 people to ride in a hot-air balloon?
   mental math, about $56

Set D For use following page 299.

Name each space figure or plane figure.

1. **cube**
2. **cone**
3. **cylinder**
4. **pyramid**
5. **square**
6. **circle**

Set E For use following page 301.

Name each polygon.

1. **quadrilateral**
2. **pentagon**
3. **octagon**
4. **hexagon**

521

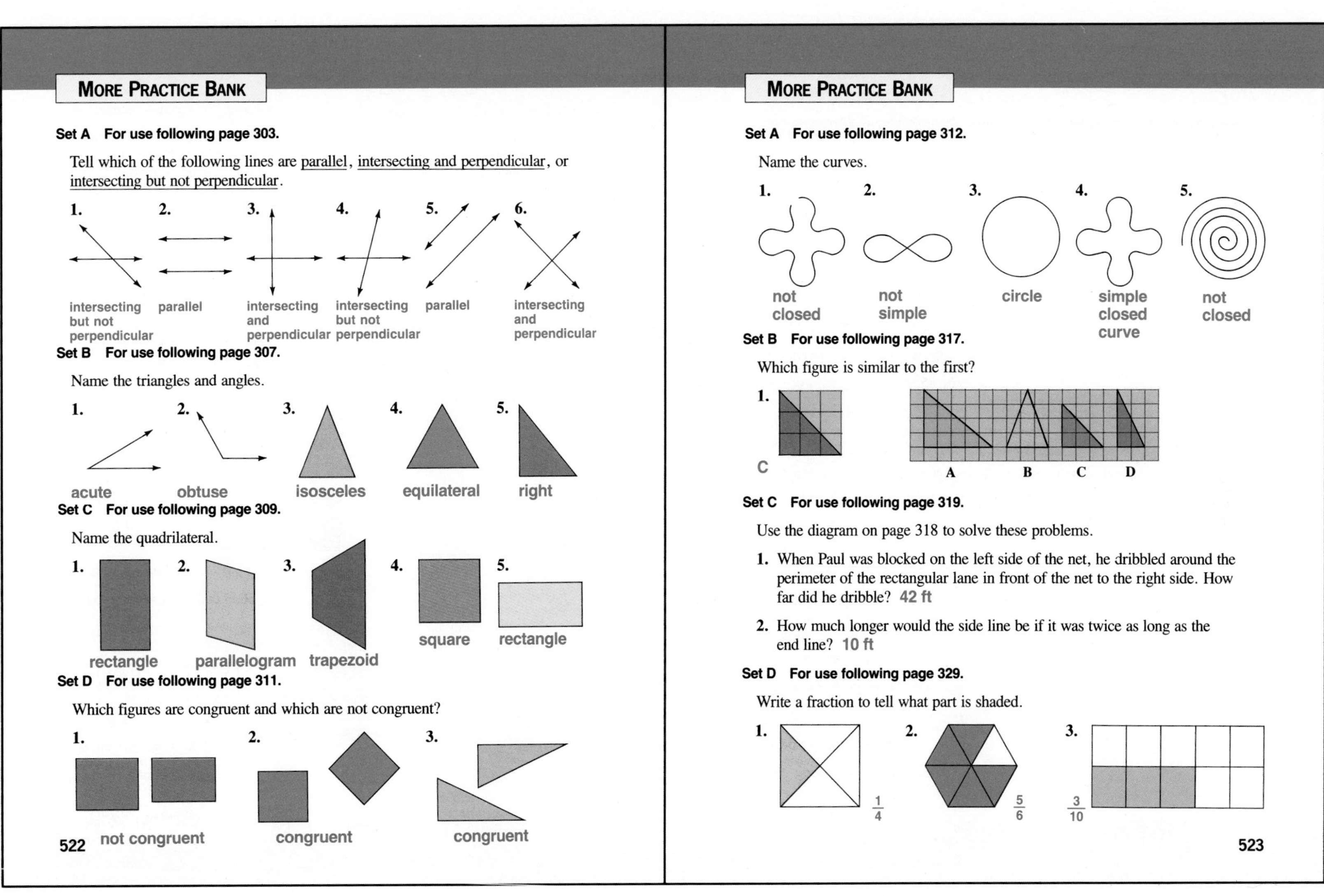

MORE PRACTICE BANK

Set A For use following page 303.

Tell which of the following lines are parallel, intersecting and perpendicular, or intersecting but not perpendicular.

1. intersecting but not perpendicular
2. parallel
3. intersecting and perpendicular
4. intersecting but not perpendicular
5. parallel
6. intersecting and perpendicular

Set B For use following page 307.

Name the triangles and angles.

1. acute
2. obtuse
3. isosceles
4. equilateral
5. right

Set C For use following page 309.

Name the quadrilateral.

1. rectangle
2. parallelogram
3. trapezoid
4. square
5. rectangle

Set D For use following page 311.

Which figures are congruent and which are not congruent?

1. not congruent
2. congruent
3. congruent

522

MORE PRACTICE BANK

Set A For use following page 312.

Name the curves.

1. not closed
2. not simple
3. circle
4. simple closed curve
5. not closed

Set B For use following page 317.

Which figure is similar to the first?

1. C

A B C D

Set C For use following page 319.

Use the diagram on page 318 to solve these problems.

1. When Paul was blocked on the left side of the net, he dribbled around the perimeter of the rectangular lane in front of the net to the right side. How far did he dribble? 42 ft
2. How much longer would the side line be if it was twice as long as the end line? 10 ft

Set D For use following page 329.

Write a fraction to tell what part is shaded.

1. $\frac{1}{4}$
2. $\frac{5}{6}$
3. $\frac{3}{10}$

523

MORE PRACTICE BANK

Set A For use following page 331.

Write a fraction for each ||||.

1. 

$\frac{1}{3}$ |||| of the papers have an X.

2. 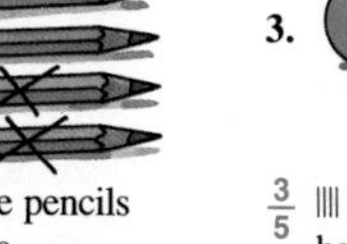

$\frac{2}{4}$ |||| of the pencils have Xs.

3. $\frac{3}{5}$ |||| of the balls have Xs.

Set B For use following page 332.

Estimate what part of each figure is shaded.

1. $\frac{1}{3}$

2. $\frac{1}{2}$

3. $\frac{1}{4}$

Set C For use following page 333.

1. Don had 10 checkers. He made two stacks. One stack had 2 more checkers than the other. How many checkers were in each stack? **4 checkers and 6 checkers**

2. At the end of the checker contest, Bernie had won more games than Emily. Emily won more games than Dale. Kate won more games than Emily but was not in second place. In what order did they finish? **Kate, Bernie, Emily, Dale**

Set D For use following page 349.

1. Lila knitted a row this long in 2 minutes. She wants to try again and keep up this speed for 10 minutes. If she succeeds, how long will her knitted row be? Measure to the nearest $\frac{1}{4}$ inch. **10 inches**

2. Jonathan was gluing a path made of beans onto his picture. To stretch from the house to the pond the path needed to be about 9 inches long. How many more beans will he need? Measure to the nearest $\frac{1}{2}$ inch. **27 beans**

MORE PRACTICE BANK

Set A For use following page 361.

Write a decimal for each.

1. three and six hundredths **3.06**
2. two and thirty-six hundredths **2.36**

Set B For use following page 362.

Write the decimal that comes after each number when you count by hundredths.

1. 9.25	2. 10.1	3. 6.36	4. 7.79	5. 5.98	6. 8.99
9.26	10.11	6.37	7.8	5.99	9

Set C For use following page 371.

Do not solve the problems. Tell why the answers are reasonable or not reasonable.

1. $\frac{7}{8}$ of Lincoln Public School voted for class president. 1,992 students go to the school. How many students voted in the election? [1743]
reasonable—because $\frac{7}{8}$ is nearly all the students

2. One candidate sold campaign buttons for $0.89 each and donated the money to the school orchestra. The donation was $426.31. How many buttons did the candidate sell? **not reasonable—because $400 ÷ $1 = 400** [133]

Set D For use following page 383.

Fill in each blank with cm, dm, m, or km.

1. The distance across town is 20 __?__. **km**
2. My piano is 2 __?__ high. **m**
3. Her necklace is 3 __?__ long. **dm**
4. The caterpillar is 6 __?__ long. **cm**

Set E For use following page 383.

Use unitizing to estimate these lengths in centimeters.

1. **6 centimeters**

2. **9 centimeters**

MORE PRACTICE BANK

Set A For use following page 389.

Use cm graph paper to draw these figures. **Check students' drawings.**

1. a rectangle of 28 square centimeters.
2. an area of 14 square centimeters.

Set B For use following page 391.

Give the volume of the following.

1. A stack of blocks with 4 rows, 4 boxes in each row, and 2 layers = ▥ cubic centimeters. **32**
2. A stack of blocks with 6 rows, 3 boxes in each row, and 3 layers = ▥ cubic centimeters. **54**

Set C For use following page 393.

Solve these problems. Then tell how they are related. **Both use the same strategy—choose an operation.**

1. Ana built a rectangular yard fence. Two sides were 98 m and two sides 105 m. How much fence was this? **406 m**
2. Ian has a square bulletin board. Each side is 96 cm. What is the perimeter of the bulletin board? **384 cm**

Set D For use following page 395.

Choose the better estimate of capacity.

1. (A) 4 L   B 4 mL
2. A 1 L   (B) 1 mL
3. 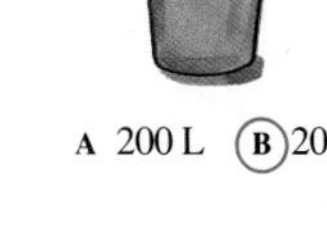 A 200 L   (B) 200 mL

Set E For use following page 396.

Estimate the weight of each object.

1. (A) 6 g   B 6 kg
2. A 2 g   (B) 2 kg
3. (A) 8 g   B 8 kg

526

MORE PRACTICE BANK

Set A For use following page 397.

Record each temperature.

1. 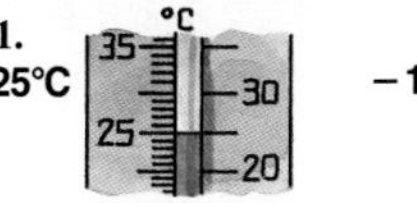 **25°C**
2.  **−13°C**
3. **70°C**

Set B Use following page 411.

Use the recipes on page 410 to answer these questions.

1. How much ground beef do you need to make both spaghetti and lasagne? **3 pounds**
2. The spaghetti recipe calls for how many more ounces of tomato paste than the lasagne recipe? **$\frac{3}{4}$ oz.**

Set C For use following page 427.

1. A bus going to the city had 3 empty seats—1 in front, 1 in back, and 1 in the middle. It stopped at Island Shopping Mall to pick up a man and a woman. How many ways could they sit down? **6 ways**
2. There were 20 passengers left on the bus when it got to the city. There were 2 more men than women. How many men were on the bus? **11 men**

Set D For use following page 444.

1. Hawaii has an average of 177.6 cm of rain per year. Nevada has an average of 18.8 cm. What is the difference in average rainfall between Hawaii and Nevada? **158.8 cm**
2. Chicago had 85.1 cm of rain one year. The following year 96.62 cm of rain fell. How much rain did Chicago have in the two years? **181.72 cm**

Set E For use following page 451.

Use a calculator to help solve these problems.

1. Louise divided 81 old comic books among 5 friends. How many comic books did each friend get? **16 comic books**
2. Mr. Lopez read a book to his grandchildren. He read 11 pages per day. The book had 75 pages. How many days did it take Mr. Lopez to finish the book? **7 days**

527

TABLE OF MEASURES

Metric System		Customary System	
Length			
1 centimeter (cm)	10 millimeters (mm)	1 foot (ft)	12 inches (in.)
1 decimeter (dm)	100 millimeters (mm) 10 centimeters (cm)	1 yard (yd)	36 inches (in.) 3 feet (ft)
1 meter (m)	1,000 millimeters (mm) 100 centimeters (cm) 10 decimeters (dm)	1 mile (m)	5,280 feet (ft) 1,760 yards (yd)
1 kilometer (km)	1,000 meters (m)		
Area			
1 square meter (m^2)	100 square decimeters (dm^2) 10,000 square centimeters (cm^2)	1 square foot (ft^2)	144 square inches ($in.^2$)
Volume			
1 cubic decimeter (dm^3)	1,000 cubic centimeters (cm^3) 1 liter (L)	1 cubic foot (ft^3)	1,728 cubic inches ($in.^3$)
Capacity			
1 teaspoon	5 milliliters (mL)	1 cup (c)	8 fluid ounces (fl oz)
1 tablespoon	12.5 milliliters (mL)	1 pint (pt)	16 fluid ounces (fl oz) 2 cups (c)
1 liter (L)	1,000 milliliters (mL) 1,000 cubic centimeters (cm^3) 1 cubic decimeter (dm^3) 4 metric cups	1 quart (qt)	32 fluid ounces (fl oz) 4 cups (c) 2 pints (pt)
		1 gallon (gal)	128 fluid ounces (fl oz) 16 cups (c) 8 pints (pt) 4 quarts (qt)
Weight			
1 gram (g)	1,000 milligrams (mg)	1 pound (lb)	16 ounces (oz)
1 kilogram (kg)	1,000 grams (g)		
Time			
1 minute	60 seconds (s)	1 year (yr)	365 days 52 weeks 12 months
1 hour (h)	60 minutes (min)		
1 day (d)	24 hours (h)		
1 week (w)	7 days (d)	1 decade	10 years
1 month	about 4 weeks	1 century	100 years

GLOSSARY

a.m. A way to indicate the times from 12:00 midnight to 12:00 noon.

acute angle An angle that is smaller than a right angle and measures less than 90°.

addends Numbers that are added together to form a sum.

Example:

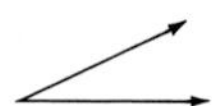

angle Two rays from a single point.

area The measure of a region, expressed in square units.

associative property See grouping property.

average The quotient obtained when the sum of the numbers in a set is divided by the number of addends.

bar graph A graph that shows information by using bars.

benchmark A point of reference from which measures can be estimated.

capacity The volume of a space figure given in terms of liquid measurement.

centimeter (cm) A unit of length in the metric system. 100 centimeters equal 1 meter.

⊢——⊣ ← 1 centimeter

circle A closed curve in which all the points are the same distance from a point called the center.

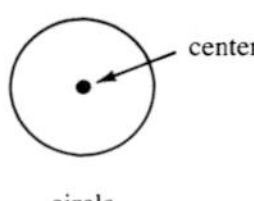

circle

clustering Using numbers that are close to, or cluster around, a rounded number, making it easy to estimate.

commutative property See order property.

compatible numbers Pairs of numbers that "go together" to make mental math easier.

compensation A mental math technique in which a sum or difference is changed into an easier sum or difference with the same answer. In addition, one addend is increased and the other decreased. In subtraction, each number is increased or decreased the same amount.

cone A solid figure that has a circular bottom.

congruent figures Figures that have the same size and shape.

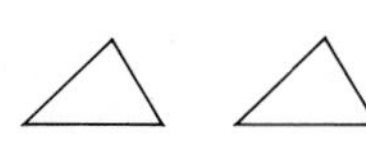

congruent triangles

constant A number entered on a calculator which allows you to do operations using that number without re-entering it.

coordinates The two numbers in a number pair.

cube A space figure that has squares for all of its faces.

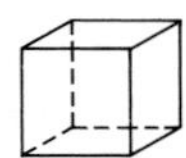

cup (c) A unit for measuring capacity. 4 cups equal 1 quart.

cylinder A space figure that has a circle for a face.

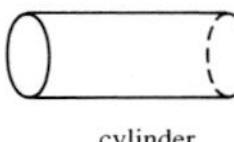

cylinder

decimal A number that uses a decimal point to show tenths, hundredths, and so on.

3.2 ← decimal
↑
decimal point

GLOSSARY

decimeter (dm) A unit of length in the metric system. 1 decimeter equals 10 centimeters.

degree Celsius (°C) A unit for measuring temperature in the metric system.

degree Fahrenheit (°F) A unit for measuring temperature in the customary system of measurement.

denominator The number below the line in a fraction.

$\frac{3}{4}$ ← denominator

difference The number obtained by subtracting one number from another.

digits The symbols used to write numerals: 0, 1, 2, 3, 4, 5, 6, 7, 8, and 9.

display The window on a calculator that shows the numbers as they are entered and the results of the calculations.

dividend A number to be divided.

$7\overline{)28}$ with quotient 4 ← dividend

divisor The number by which a dividend is divided.

divisor → $7\overline{)28}$ with quotient 4

edge One of the segments making up any of the faces of a space figure.

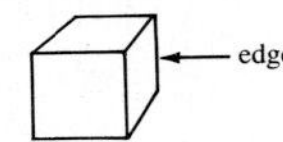

END An instruction in a computer program that tells the computer to stop.

equation A number sentence that uses the equal sign.

Examples: $9 + 2 = 11$
$8 - 4 = 4$

equilateral triangle A triangle with all sides the same length.

equivalent fractions Fractions that name the same amount.

Example: $\frac{1}{2}$ and $\frac{2}{4}$

estimate To find an answer that is close to the exact answer.

even number A whole number that has 0, 2, 4, 6, or 8 in the ones place.

face One of the plane figures (regions) making up a space figure.

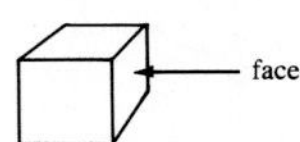

fact family A group of related facts using the same set of digits.

factors Numbers that are multiplied together to form a product.

factors → $6 \times 7 = 42$

flowchart A chart that shows a step-by-step way of doing something.

foot (ft) A unit for measuring length. 1 foot equals 12 inches.

fraction A number that expresses parts of a whole or a set.

Example: $\frac{3}{4}$

front-end estimation The estimation technique of adding the leading digits of addends, then using the other places to adjust the estimate.

gallon (gal) A unit for measuring capacity. 1 gallon equals 4 quarts.

GOTO An instruction in a computer program that tells the computer to jump to a specified line.

gram (g) The basic unit for measuring mass in the metric system. The mass of a paper clip is about 1 gram.

graph A picture that shows information in an organized way.

grouping property When the grouping of addends or factors is changed, the sum or product is the same.

greater than The relationship of one number being larger than another number.

Example: $6 > 5$, read "6 is greater than 5."

GLOSSARY

half gallon A unit for measuring capacity. 1 half gallon equals 2 quarts.

hexagon A polygon with six sides.

improper fraction A fraction in which the numerator is greater than or equal to the denominator.

inch (in.) A unit for measuring length. 12 inches equal 1 foot.

intersecting lines Lines that meet in a point.

isosceles triangle A triangle that has at least 2 sides the same length.

key codes An arrangement of letters and numbers that tell what order to press the keys on a calculator to find an answer.

kilogram (kg) A unit of mass in the metric system. 1 kilogram is 1,000 grams.

kilometer A unit of length in the metric system. 1 kilometer is 1,000 meters.

length The measure of distance from one end to the other end of an object.

less than The relationship of being smaller than another number.
Example: $5 < 6$, read "5 is less than 6."

line A straight path that is endless in both directions.

line graph A graph that shows information by using lines.

line of symmetry A line on which a figure can be folded so that the two parts fit exactly.

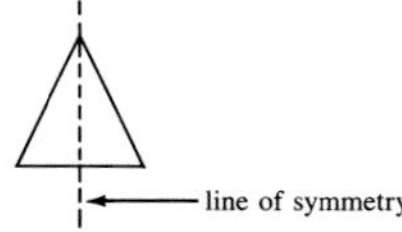

liter (L) A metric unit used to measure capacity. 1 liter equals 1,000 milliliters.

logic error The message on a calculator display that shows an operation is not logical.

Logo A special computer language that is used for computer graphics.

lowest terms A fraction is in lowest terms if the numerator and denominator have no common factor greater than 1.

memory keys The keys marked with M that instruct the calculator to remember the result of one calculation while you do another one.

meter (m) A unit of length in the metric system. 1 meter is 100 centimeters.

mile (mi) A unit for measuring length. 1 mile equals 5,280 feet.

milliliter (mL) A metric unit for measuring capacity. 1,000 milliliters equal 1 liter.

millimeter (mm) A unit of length in the metric system. 10 millimeters equal 1 centimeter.

mixed number A number that has a whole number part and a fractional part, such as $2\frac{3}{4}$.

multiple A number that is the product of a given number and a whole number.

multiple-choice question A written question that gives more than one choice for an answer.

negative number A number that is less than zero.

number pair Two numbers that are used to give the location of a point on a graph.
Example: (3,2)

numeral A symbol for a number.

numerator The number above the line in a fraction.

$\frac{3}{4}$ ← numerator

obtuse angle An angle that is greater than a right triangle and measures more than 90°.

octagon A polygon with eight sides.

odd number A whole number that has 1, 3, 5, 7, or 9 in the ones place.

one property In multiplication, when either factor is 1, the product is the other factor. In division, when 1 is the divisor, the quotient is the same as the dividend.

GLOSSARY

order property When the order of addends or factors is changed, the sum or product is the same.

ordinal number A number that is used to tell order. Example: first, fifth

ounce (oz) A customary unit for measuring weight. 16 ounces equal 1 pound.

overflow error The message on a calculator display showing that a number is too large for the display window.

p.m. A way to indicate the times from 12:00 noon to 12:00 midnight.

parallel lines Lines that do not intersect.

parallelogram A quadrilateral with 2 pairs of same-length sides and two pairs of parallel sides.

pentagon A polygon with five sides.

perimeter The distance around a figure.

period A group of three digits set off by a comma in larger numbers.

perpendicular lines Lines that intersect to form a right angle.

pictograph A graph that uses pictures to show quantities.

pint (pt) A unit for measuring capacity. 2 pints equal 1 quart.

place value The value given to the place a digit occupies in a number.

Example: 3 5 6

- 3: hundreds' place
- 5: tens' place
- 6: ones' place

plane figures Figures that lie on a flat surface.

Examples:

square triangle circle

point A single, exact location, often represented by a dot.

polygon A closed figure formed by line segments.

pound (lb) A customary unit for measuring weight. 1 pound equals 16 ounces.

prime number A whole number greater than 1, whose only factors are itself and 1.

PRINT An instruction in a computer program that tells the computer to print something.

probability The chance that something will or will not happen.

product The result of the multiplication operation.

$6 \times 7 = 42$ ← product

program The set of instructions that tells a computer what to do.

quadrilateral A polygon with four sides.

quart (qt) A unit for measuring capacity. 1 quart equals 4 cups.

questionnaire A written list of questions used to gather information.

quotient The number (other than the remainder) that is the result of the division operation.

$45 \div 9 = 5$ (5 ← quotient)

$7\overline{)45}$ = 6 ← quotient; -42; remainder 3

rectangle A plane figure with two pairs of same-length sides and four right angles.

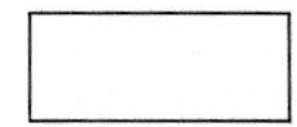

rectangular prism A space figure with six faces. It has the shape of a box.

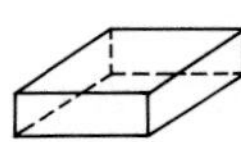

reference point A point from which something is measured or to which something is compared.

GLOSSARY

remainder The number less than the divisor that remains after the division process is completed.

Example:
```
  6
7)47
- 42
   5 ← remainder
```

right angle An angle that has the same shape as the corner of a square.

right angle protractor A tool used to measure right angles.

rounding Replacing a number with a number that tells about how many.

Example: 23 rounded to the nearest 10 is 20.

RUN What appears on the video screen when a computer program is used.

similar figures Two or more figures having the same shape but not necessarily the same size.

space figure A figure that is not flat but that has volume.

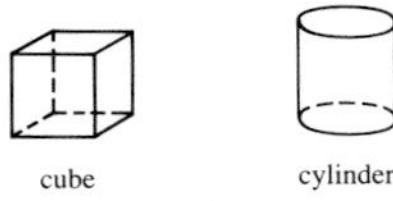

sphere A space figure that has the shape of a round ball.

square A plane figure that has four equal sides and four equal corners.

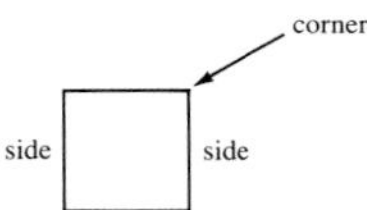

sum The number obtained by adding numbers.
Example:
```
  3
+ 2
  5 ← sum
```

symmetric figure A plane figure that can be folded in half so that the two halves match.

ton A unit for measuring weight. 1 ton equals 2,000 pounds.

trading To make a group of ten from one of the next highest place value, or one from ten of the next lowest place value.
Examples: 1 hundred can be traded for 10 tens; 10 ones can be traded for 1 ten.

trapezoid A quadrilateral with exactly one pair of parallel sides.

triangle A plane figure with three segments as sides.

unit An amount or quantity used as a standard of measurement.

unitizing Visually or physically dividing an object into equal parts to estimate length.

vertex (vertices) The common point of any two sides of a polygon.

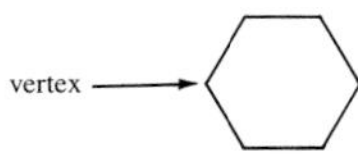

volume The number of units of space that a space figure holds.

yard (yd) A unit for measuring length. 1 yard equals 3 feet.

zero property In addition, when one addend is 0, the sum is the other addend. In multiplication, when either factor is 0, the product is 0.

Teacher's Edition references are in italics.

A

B

C

D

E

ACKNOWLEDGEMENTS

PHOTO CREDITS

Lillian Gee: pp. 2D, 25D, 52D, 88D, 92A, 102A, 114D, 176D, 204D, 236D, 264D, 268A, 274A, 296D, 312A, 326D, 330A, 334A, 344A, 356D, 358A, 362A, 368A, 378D, 384A, 388A, 396A, 404D, 406A, 408A, 412A, 416A, 418A, 420A, 426A, 434D, 436A, 438A, 440A, 446A, 444A.

Michael Groen: pp. 6A, 16A, 32A, 44A, 96A, 104A, 118A, 122A, 154A, 166A, 206A, 210A, 216A, 222A, 228A, 266A, 278A, 284A, 302A, 308A, 314A, 328A, 338A, 342A, 346A, 364A, 366A, 380A, 382A, 390A, 422A.

Michal Heron: pp. 148A, 150A, 152A, 160A, 162A, 164A.

Ken Karp: pp. 8A, 14A, 26A, 30A, 36A, 38A, 42A, 54A, 56A, 58A, 60A, 62A, 66A, 68A, 70A, 72A, 74A, 90A, 94A, 120A, 124A, 130A, 132A, 184A, 188A, 208A, 214A, 220A, 226A, 240A, 244A, 250A, 252A, 254A, 270A, 272A, 280A, 282A, 288A, 298A, 300A, 304A, 306A, 310A, 316A, 332A, 340A, 360A, 394A, 414A.

ART CREDITS

Electronic Publishing Center, Inc.: pp. 12A, 28A, 40A, 78A, 98A, 126A, 134A, 146A, 156A, 158A, 178A, 180A, 182A, 186A, 192A, 242A, 248A, 336A, 424A, 442A.

Networkgraphics: pp. 2A, 7, 14A, 24A, 24D, 52D, 54A, 72, 88A, 91, 94A, 99, 114A, 114D, 144A, 144D, 162, 163, 166A, 176A, 176D, 204A, 236A, 264A, 266A, 274, 296A, 298A, 300A, 302, 305, 306A, 306, 308A, 308, 310A, 311, 316A, 318A, 326A, 328A, 329, 330A, 331, 332A, 333, 334A, 335, 336A, 343, 352, 356A, 356D, 378A, 388, 389, 391, 404A, 404D, 406A, 420A, 434A, 434D, T79, T88, T89.

Laslo Vespremi: pp. 2C, 24C, 52C, 88C, 114C, 144C, 176C, 204C, 236C, 264C, 296C, 326C, 356C, 378C, 404C, 434C.

ACKNOWLEDGMENTS

Illustration Acknowledgments

Anthony Accardo p. 461, 462, 463, 465, 493, 497.
Angela Adams p. 91, 92, 93, 94, 95.
Randy Chewning p. 43, 44, 54, 55, 58, 63, 65, 68, 70, 71, 722, 73, 74, 75, 84, 152, 228, 229, 272, 352, 353, 354, 382, 383, 387, 396, 397, 418, 522, 524, 525, 526, 527.
Suzanne Clee p. 147, 149, 151, 155, 158, 159, 164, 165.
Daniel Del Valle p. 381, 384, 385, 391, 394, 395.
Len Ebert p. 28, 29, 30, 34, 35, 36, 37, 39, 40, 41, 110, 112, 160, 200, 202, 374, 376, 377.
Andrea Fong p. 472, 481.
Simon Galkin p. 359, 360, 362, 364, 365, 366, 368, 369, 370, 371, 408, 413, 414, 416, 422, 424, 426, 427, 464, 485, 494, 497, 498.
Jeff Hukill p. 470, 483.
Arlan Jewel p. 334, 335, 336, 337, 338, 339, 340, 343, 348, 349.
Heather King p. 4, 5, 6, 7, 8, 9, 10, 15, 16, 17, 21, 298, 299, 300, 301, 302, 304, 305, 306, 309, 312, 314, 315, 316, 318.
Barbara Lanza p. 260, 274, 276, 277, 402, 430.
Morissa Lipstein p. 48, 50, 90, 91, 95, 102, 103, 208, 209, 210, 211, 212, 213, 232, 233, 234, 246, 386, 388, 392, 393, 396.
Laura Lydecker p. 329, 330, 331, 332, 344, 345, 346, 347.
Laurie Marks p. 146, 150, 152, 157, 162, 167, 168, 178, 179, 184, 186, 190, 191, 194, 195, 196.
Jane McCreary p. 119, 122, 126, 130, 132, 134, 135, 136, 137, 140, 142, 143, 156, 166, 187, 192, 214, 215, 216, 217, 172, 282, 283.
Susan Nelson p. 438, 439, 440, 441, 442, 443, 444, 445, 446, 448, 449, 450, 451.
Rik Olson p. 96, 97, 98, 99, 100, 101, 102, 104, 11105, 109, 266, 267, 270, 271, 278, 284, 285, 286.
Rick Sams p. 475, 479.
Margaret Sanfilippo p. 168, 169.
Ed Sauk p. 20, 181, 247, 254, 255, 302, 316, 318, 319, 328, 333, 361, 367, 369, 371, 406, 418, 420, 425.
Nancy Schill p. 12, 15, 58, 60, 61, 64, 66, 68, 76, 77, 80, 81.
Blanche Sims p. 6, 14.
Rosiland Solomon p. 468, 469, 471.
Rhonda Voo p. 473, 476, 477, 482.
Ann Wilson p. 207, 220, 221, 223, 226, 227, 238, 239, 240, 241, 242, 243, 245, 249, 252, 253, 257, 262, 292, 294, 322, 400, 401, 402, 403, 430, 431, 454, 456, 457.
Jeannie Winston p. 116, 117, 118, 120, 121, 123, 124, 131, 133.

Photo Acknowledgments

Chapter 1: David M. Dennis/Tom Stack & Associates; 5 John Gerlach/Animals, Animals; 9 Wayland Lee*/Addison-Wesley Publishing Company; 11 Jeff Foott/Tom Stack & Associates

Chapter 2: 24-25 Craig Aurness/West Light;38T John Running

Chapter 3: 52-53 Roger Ressmeyer/Starlight; 78 NASA; 79 Jet Propulsion Lab

Chapter 4: 88-89 Spencer Swanger/Tom Stack & Associates;100 Wayland Lee*/Addison-Wesley Publishing Company; 106 Wayland Lee*/Addison-Wesley Publishing Company; 107 Wayland Lee*/Addison-Wesley Publishing Company; 108 Wayland Lee*/Addison-Wesley Publishing Company

Chapter 5: 114-15 Bradley Smith/Animals, Animals; 120 Wayland Lee*/Addison-Wesley Publishing Company; 124-125 Wayland Lee*/Addison-Wesley Publishing Company; 128T Wayland Lee*/Addison-Wesley Publishing Company

Chapter 6: 144-45 Charles & Elizabeth Schwartz/Animals, Animals

Chapter 7: 176-77 Eric Bakke

Chapter 8: 204-05 Bill Gallery/Stock, Boston; 211 Wayland Lee*/Addison-Wesley Publishing Company; 223B Wayland Lee*/Addison-Wesley Publishing Company; 224 Wes Thompson/The Stock Market; 225 Matt Bradley/Tom Stack & Associates

Chapter 9: 250B Ben Simmons/The Stock Market; 250T Martine Franck/Magnum Photos; 251 Ben Simmons/The Stock Market

Chapter 10: 264-65 E. R. Degginger/Bruce Coleman Inc.; 268B Wayland Lee*/Addison-Wesley Publishing Company; 269 Wayland Lee*/Addison-Wesley Publishing Company; 287 Bob McKeever/Tom Stack & Associates; 289B Wayland Lee*/Addison-Wesley Publishing Company; 290 Wayland Lee*/Addison-Wesley Publishing Company

Chapter 11: 296-97 Aldo Tutino/Art Resource; 320 Clare Smith/Bruce Coleman Inc.

Chapter 12: 326-27 Rod Planck/Tom Stack & Associates

Chapter 13: 356-57 Mike Powell/Allsport; 372 Wayland Lee*/Addison-Wesley Publishing Company

Chapter 14: 378-79 D. H. Hessel/Stock, Boston; 385 Wayland Lee*/Addison-Wesley Publishing Company

Chapter 15: 404-05 Focus On Sports

Chapter 16: 434-35 Phillip Wallick/The Stock Market; 436 Michele Burgess/The Stock Market; 437 Wendell Metzen/Bruce Coleman Inc.; 442 Wayland Lee*/Addison-Wesley Publishing Company; 444 W. Perry Conway/Tom Stack & Associates; 449 Wayland Lee*/Addison-Wesley Publishing Company; 452 Wayland Lee*/Addison-Wesley Publishing Company

All other photographs taken by Janice Sheldon*

Special thanks to California School for the Deaf; Chabot Elementary School; Hawthorne Elementary School; Whitton Elementary School; Albany Bowl; Dr. Richard Kennedy; Lewis Mahlmann; Randal Metz; Pizza Rustica.

*Photographs taken expressly for the publisher

ASSESSMENT

Placement Test — Page 1

Multiple-Choice Format

Name ____________________

1. Find: 6 + 7.

a. 15 **b.** 12 **c.** 13 **d.** 1 — **1.** c

2. Choose > or < for the ●: 294 ● 297.

a. > **b.** < — **2.** b

3. Sari started mowing the yard at 3:00 p.m. She finished one and a half hours later. What time did she finish mowing the yard?

a. 4:00 p.m. **b.** 3:15 p.m. **c.** 4:15 p.m. **d.** 4:30 p.m. — **3.** d

4. Find: 376 + 495.

a. 871 **b.** 761 **c.** 771 **d.** 861 — **4.** a

5. Find: 742 − 367.

a. 475 **b.** 375 **c.** 485 **d.** 385 — **5.** b

6. Roger had $15. He bought a flower for $3 and a vase for $6. How much did Roger have left?

a. $3 **b.** $12 **c.** $6 **d.** $9 — **6.** c

7. Maria saved 1¢ the first day, 3¢ the second day, 5¢ the third day, and so on. How much did she save the fifth day?

a. 1¢ **b.** 5¢ **c.** 9¢ **d.** 7¢ — **7.** c

8. Find the perimeter.

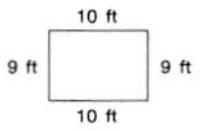

a. 19 ft **b.** 9 ft
c. 10 ft **d.** 38 ft — **8.** d

9. Find: 5 × 9.

a. 45 **b.** 14 **c.** 40 **d.** 35 — **9.** a

MCT 4 A

Placement Test — Page 2

Multiple-Choice Format

Name ____________________

10. Which numbers are all multiples of 6?

a. 0, 3, 6, 9 **b.** 0, 4, 8, 12
c. 0, 6, 12, 18 **d.** 0, 8, 16, 24 — **10.** c

11. Which polygon has 4 sides and 4 right angles?

11. a

12. Find: 30 ÷ 5.

a. 3 **b.** 4 **c.** 5 **d.** 6 — **12.** d

13. Find: 64 ÷ 8.

a. 5 **b.** 6 **c.** 7 **d.** 8 — **13.** d

14. Multiply. $\begin{array}{r} 37 \\ \times\ 2 \\ \hline \end{array}$

a. 64 **b.** 74 **c.** 614 **d.** 35 — **14.** b

15. Give the area of the shape in square centimeters.

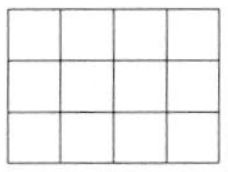

a. 7 cm^2 **b.** 1 cm^2
c. 12 cm^2 **d.** 24 cm^2 — **15.** c

16. Find: $\frac{3}{8} + \frac{4}{8}$.

a. $\frac{7}{8}$ **b.** $\frac{1}{8}$ **c.** $\frac{12}{8}$ **d.** $\frac{3}{4}$ — **16.** a

17. Find: 23 ÷ 3.

a. 72 **b.** 20 **c.** 7 R2 **d.** 6 R5 — **17.** c

B MCT 4

ITEM ANALYSIS

Items	Objectives
1	1-2
2	1-3
3	2-3
4	2-5
5	2-7
6	3-4
7	3-9
8	3-12
9	4-2
10	4-9
11	5-4
12	5-5
13	6-5
14	6-7
15	7-3
16	7-4
17	8-6
18	8-9

ASSESSMENT

Mid-Year Test — Chapters 1-8, page 1

Multiple-Choice Format

Name ______

1. Find: (3 + 5) + 4.
   a. 7 **b.** 12 **c.** 4 **d.** 19 — 1. b
2. Find: 10 − 3. Think about finding the missing addend.
   a. 13 **b.** 3 **c.** 7 **d.** 6 — 2. c
3. Choose <, >, or = for the ●: 723 ● 713
   a. > **b.** < **c.** = — 3. a
4. Four runnners were in a line. Joey was behind Frank and in front of Larry. Bobby was first in the line. Who was in second place?
   a. Joey **b.** Frank **c.** Larry **d.** Bobby — 4. b
5. Round 2,541 to the nearest thousand.
   a. 2,600 **b.** 2,500 **c.** 2,000 **d.** 3,000 — 5. d
6. Find: 241 + 463.
   a. 242 **b.** 701 **c.** 184 **d.** 704 — 6. d
7. Find: 824 − 341.
   a. 483 **b.** 403 **c.** 1,185 **d.** 505 — 7. a
8. Lupi had $7.00. He bought a notebook for $3.75 and a pen for $1.30. How much did Lupi have left?
   a. $1.95 **b.** $2.95 **c.** $5.05 **d.** $3.25 — 8. a
9. Suppose you tossed a coin several times and used your data to make this graph. How many times did tails come up?
   Record of 25 Coin Tosses (Heads, Tails; 0 5 10 15)
   a. 15 **b.** 10 **c.** 5 **d.** 25 — 9. b

Mid-Year Test — Chapters 1-8, page 2

Multiple-Choice Format

Name ______

10. The sum of two numbers is 35. Their difference is 7. What are the two numbers?
    a. 7 and 42 **b.** 28 and 42
    c. 14 and 21 **d.** 28 and 35 — 10. c
11. Find: 9 × 5.
    a. 35 **b.** 14 **c.** 45 **d.** 4 — 11. c
12. Find: 3 × 4.
    a. 14 **b.** 7 **c.** 1 **d.** 12 — 12. d
13. Find: 3 × 27.
    a. 81 **b.** 30 **c.** 24 **d.** 61 — 13. a
14. Find: 4 × 376.
    a. 1,204 **b.** 380 **c.** 1,504 **d.** 1,484 — 14. c
15. Find: 23 × 30.
    a. 53 **b.** 690 **c.** 69 **d.** 260 — 15. b
16. Find 36 × 18.
    a. 54 **b.** 224 **c.** 648 **d.** 2 — 16. c
17. Tell which measurement is longer.
    a. 2 yd **b.** 5 ft — 17. a
18. Find the perimeter. (125 ft, 25 ft, 25 ft, 125 ft)
    a. 150 ft **b.** 125 ft
    c. 625 ft **d.** 300 ft — 18. d

ITEM ANALYSIS

Items	Objectives
1	1-2
2	2-3
3	3-9
4	3-12
5	4-2
6	5-5
7	6-6
8	7-5
9	8-9
10	9-7
11	10-7
12	11-7
13	12-6
14	13-5
15	14-1
16	15-2
17	16-3

End-of-Year Test — Chapters 1-16, page 1

Multiple-Choice Format

Name ______

1. Find: (6 + 2) + 3.
   a. 8 **b.** 36 **c.** 11 **d.** 24 — 1. c
2. Choose <, >, or = for the ●: 236 ● 264.
   a. > **b.** < **c.** = — 2. b
3. Find: 871 − 263.
   a. 618 **b.** 608 **c.** 1,134 **d.** 602 — 3. b
4. Darrel had $9.00. He bought a postcard for $2.00 and a greeting card for $2.65. How much did Darrel have left?
   a. $4.35 **b.** $4.65 **c.** $7.00 **d.** $5.35 — 4. a
5. Suppose you tossed a coin and used your data to make this graph. How many times did heads come up?
   Record of Coin Tosses (Heads, Tails; 0 10 20 30)
   a. 20 **b.** 30 **c.** 10 **d.** 50 — 5. a
6. Find: 4 × 9.
   a. 13 **b.** 36 **c.** 5 **d.** 45 — 6. b
7. Find: 2 × 316.
   a. 318 **b.** 314 **c.** 622 **d.** 632 — 7. d
8. Find: 127 × 24.
   a. 3,048 **b.** 762 **c.** 151 **d.** 2,048 — 8. a
9. Find the perimeter. (6 ft, 4 ft, 4 ft, 6 ft)
   a. 10 ft **b.** 20 ft
   c. 6 ft **d.** 24 ft — 9. b

End-of-Year Test — Chapters 1-16, page 2

Multiple-Choice Format

Name ______

10. Find: 63 ÷ 7.
    a. 6 **b.** 7 **c.** 8 **d.** 9 — 10. d
11. Find: 732 ÷ 3.
    a. 244 **b.** 234 **c.** 728 **d.** 134 — 11. a
12. Which two figures are congruent?
    a. **b.** **c.** **d.** — 12. b
13. Reduce the fraction to lowest terms. $\frac{28}{42}$
    a. $\frac{2}{3}$ **b.** $\frac{7}{6}$ **c.** $\frac{4}{6}$ **d.** $\frac{1}{2}$ — 13. a
14. Round 4.45 to the nearest whole number.
    a. 4.5 **b.** 4.4 **c.** 5 **d.** 4 — 14. d
15. Tell which measurement is longer or if they are the same length: 3,000 cm or 3 km.
    a. Same length **b.** 3,000 cm **c.** 3 km — 15. c
16. Find: $\frac{5}{8} - \frac{4}{8}$.
    a. $\frac{3}{8}$ **b.** $\frac{2}{8}$ **c.** 1 **d.** $\frac{1}{8}$ — 16. d
17. Find: $21\overline{)84}$.
    a. 40 **b.** 4 **c.** 42 **d.** 63 — 17. b

ASSESSMENT

Basic-Facts Test — Addition Facts

Name ____________________

Add.

	A	B	C	D	E	F	G	H	I	J
1.	1 + 1 = 2	4 + 1 = 5	2 + 3 = 5	5 + 2 = 7	0 + 1 = 1	3 + 3 = 6	1 + 2 = 3	3 + 1 = 4	2 + 2 = 4	3 + 0 = 3
2.	6 + 2 = 8	1 + 3 = 4	5 + 1 = 6	2 + 4 = 6	6 + 3 = 9	1 + 5 = 6	3 + 4 = 7	6 + 1 = 7	0 + 2 = 2	4 + 2 = 6
3.	3 + 2 = 5	2 + 1 = 3	0 + 3 = 3	5 + 3 = 8	1 + 4 = 5	3 + 5 = 8	4 + 3 = 7	1 + 0 = 1	6 + 4 = 10	2 + 5 = 7
4.	2 + 0 = 2	3 + 6 = 9	2 + 7 = 9	1 + 6 = 7	5 + 4 = 9	7 + 1 = 8	0 + 4 = 4	3 + 7 = 10	2 + 6 = 8	4 + 4 = 8
5.	7 + 2 = 9	0 + 5 = 5	8 + 1 = 9	2 + 8 = 10	4 + 5 = 9	1 + 7 = 8	3 + 8 = 11	6 + 0 = 6	5 + 5 = 10	0 + 8 = 8
6.	4 + 0 = 4	6 + 5 = 11	2 + 9 = 11	5 + 6 = 11	3 + 9 = 12	0 + 6 = 6	8 + 2 = 10	7 + 0 = 7	1 + 8 = 9	4 + 6 = 10
7.	5 + 9 = 14	7 + 3 = 10	1 + 9 = 10	8 + 0 = 8	4 + 7 = 11	6 + 6 = 12	5 + 0 = 5	6 + 8 = 14	0 + 7 = 7	8 + 3 = 11
8.	4 + 8 = 12	9 + 1 = 10	8 + 8 = 16	7 + 5 = 12	8 + 4 = 12	9 + 0 = 9	4 + 9 = 13	7 + 8 = 15	9 + 2 = 11	8 + 5 = 13
9.	9 + 8 = 17	0 + 9 = 9	7 + 4 = 11	9 + 3 = 12	6 + 9 = 15	5 + 7 = 12	9 + 4 = 13	8 + 7 = 15	7 + 6 = 13	9 + 6 = 15
10.	6 + 7 = 13	8 + 9 = 17	9 + 7 = 16	0 + 0 = 0	5 + 8 = 13	9 + 5 = 14	7 + 9 = 16	8 + 6 = 14	7 + 7 = 14	9 + 9 = 18

MCT 4 69

Basic-Facts Test — Subtraction Facts

Name ____________________

Subtract.

	A	B	C	D	E	F	G	H	I	J
1.	2 − 1 = 1	4 − 2 = 2	6 − 3 = 3	1 − 1 = 0	5 − 3 = 2	2 − 2 = 0	7 − 1 = 6	3 − 2 = 1	5 − 1 = 4	1 − 0 = 1
2.	7 − 2 = 5	9 − 3 = 6	2 − 0 = 2	8 − 3 = 5	6 − 1 = 5	9 − 2 = 7	3 − 1 = 2	9 − 8 = 1	3 − 3 = 0	8 − 1 = 7
3.	5 − 2 = 3	8 − 0 = 8	9 − 9 = 0	7 − 3 = 4	5 − 0 = 5	10 − 4 = 6	6 − 2 = 4	9 − 1 = 8	4 − 4 = 0	7 − 5 = 2
4.	4 − 3 = 1	10 − 7 = 3	6 − 4 = 2	3 − 0 = 3	4 − 1 = 3	6 − 5 = 1	8 − 2 = 6	5 − 4 = 1	4 − 0 = 4	10 − 9 = 1
5.	9 − 0 = 9	5 − 5 = 0	12 − 6 = 6	11 − 8 = 3	7 − 4 = 3	10 − 1 = 9	14 − 7 = 7	8 − 4 = 4	10 − 6 = 4	7 − 0 = 7
6.	7 − 6 = 1	10 − 8 = 2	8 − 5 = 3	10 − 3 = 7	12 − 4 = 8	6 − 0 = 6	11 − 9 = 2	9 − 6 = 3	14 − 5 = 9	10 − 5 = 5
7.	12 − 3 = 9	11 − 7 = 4	6 − 6 = 0	12 − 7 = 5	9 − 5 = 4	13 − 9 = 4	7 − 7 = 0	10 − 2 = 8	16 − 7 = 9	8 − 8 = 0
8.	13 − 8 = 5	8 − 6 = 2	11 − 4 = 7	15 − 8 = 7	13 − 7 = 6	11 − 5 = 6	14 − 6 = 8	9 − 7 = 2	12 − 8 = 4	11 − 6 = 5
9.	13 − 4 = 9	17 − 9 = 8	12 − 5 = 7	11 − 3 = 8	8 − 7 = 1	15 − 9 = 6	9 − 4 = 5	13 − 6 = 7	0 − 0 = 0	16 − 9 = 7
10.	14 − 8 = 6	15 − 6 = 9	16 − 8 = 8	14 − 9 = 5	17 − 8 = 9	12 − 9 = 3	15 − 7 = 8	18 − 9 = 9	11 − 2 = 9	13 − 5 = 8

MCT 4 71

Basic-Facts Test — Multiplication Facts

Name ____________________

Find the products.

	A	B	C	D	E	F	G	H	I	J
1.	6 × 2 = 12	4 × 4 = 16	7 × 2 = 14	5 × 4 = 20	0 × 0 = 0	3 × 5 = 15	6 × 3 = 18	3 × 8 = 24	0 × 8 = 0	7 × 3 = 21
2.	5 × 5 = 25	6 × 4 = 24	3 × 9 = 27	8 × 3 = 24	6 × 5 = 30	0 × 1 = 0	3 × 6 = 18	8 × 2 = 16	7 × 5 = 35	6 × 0 = 0
3.	8 × 4 = 32	3 × 7 = 21	1 × 6 = 6	7 × 6 = 42	9 × 2 = 18	4 × 8 = 32	4 × 6 = 24	9 × 3 = 27	4 × 7 = 28	5 × 0 = 0
4.	0 × 3 = 0	5 × 8 = 40	9 × 4 = 36	5 × 7 = 35	2 × 1 = 2	9 × 5 = 45	5 × 6 = 30	1 × 5 = 5	5 × 9 = 45	9 × 8 = 72
5.	7 × 7 = 49	7 × 9 = 63	8 × 8 = 64	6 × 6 = 36	8 × 7 = 56	1 × 2 = 2	9 × 6 = 54	9 × 9 = 81	8 × 6 = 48	1 × 9 = 9
6.	9 × 1 = 9	2 × 5 = 10	1 × 1 = 1	3 × 4 = 12	3 × 0 = 0	1 × 3 = 3	8 × 0 = 0	8 × 1 = 8	0 × 9 = 0	8 × 9 = 72
7.	9 × 0 = 0	5 × 1 = 5	3 × 2 = 6	4 × 0 = 0	2 × 2 = 4	7 × 1 = 7	6 × 8 = 48	2 × 6 = 12	6 × 7 = 42	0 × 5 = 0
8.	8 × 5 = 40	4 × 1 = 4	2 × 8 = 16	9 × 7 = 63	0 × 6 = 0	1 × 7 = 7	2 × 9 = 18	7 × 4 = 28	0 × 2 = 0	6 × 9 = 54
9.	1 × 0 = 0	5 × 2 = 10	3 × 3 = 9	2 × 4 = 8	4 × 9 = 36	7 × 0 = 0	4 × 2 = 8	4 × 3 = 12	1 × 4 = 4	2 × 3 = 6
10.	0 × 7 = 0	6 × 1 = 6	7 × 8 = 56	5 × 3 = 15	2 × 7 = 14	1 × 8 = 8	4 × 5 = 20	0 × 4 = 0	3 × 1 = 3	2 × 0 = 0

MCT 4 73

Basic-Facts Test — Division Facts

Name ____________________

Find the quotients.

	A	B	C	D	E	F	G	H	I	J
1.	2)2 → 1	3)9 → 3	8)32 → 4	7)49 → 7	5)10 → 2	4)0 → 0	1)1 → 1	4)8 → 2	2)12 → 6	9)54 → 6
2.	1)3 → 3	1)2 → 2	2)4 → 2	2)14 → 7	8)8 → 1	7)63 → 9	8)40 → 5	5)0 → 0	4)4 → 1	1)0 → 0
3.	4)12 → 3	9)45 → 5	9)0 → 0	6)6 → 1	3)12 → 4	1)7 → 7	3)0 → 0	1)9 → 9	2)16 → 8	3)3 → 1
4.	3)15 → 5	5)20 → 4	3)18 → 6	3)6 → 2	5)15 → 3	7)0 → 0	9)27 → 3	4)16 → 4	7)21 → 3	8)0 → 0
5.	4)20 → 5	7)28 → 4	8)16 → 2	6)0 → 0	3)21 → 7	9)18 → 2	4)24 → 6	2)6 → 3	1)8 → 8	5)35 → 7
6.	7)35 → 5	3)27 → 9	6)36 → 6	3)24 → 8	2)0 → 0	4)32 → 8	9)9 → 1	4)36 → 9	6)42 → 7	5)40 → 8
7.	8)64 → 8	7)14 → 2	6)30 → 5	8)56 → 7	1)5 → 5	4)28 → 7	9)63 → 7	7)56 → 8	8)24 → 3	6)24 → 4
8.	9)81 → 9	6)48 → 8	6)18 → 3	7)42 → 6	2)10 → 5	6)54 → 9	9)36 → 4	5)45 → 9	8)72 → 9	2)8 → 4
9.	9)72 → 8	1)6 → 6	5)25 → 5	5)5 → 1	2)18 → 9	5)30 → 6	6)12 → 2	1)4 → 4	8)48 → 6	7)7 → 1

MCT 4 75

BIBLIOGRAPHY

BOOKS FOR THE TEACHER

Ashlock, R. *Error Patterns in Computation: Semi-Programmed Approach,* 3rd ed. Columbus, OH: Merrill, 1982.

Baratta-Lorton, Mary. *Mathematics Their Way.* Menlo Park, CA: Addison-Wesley, 1972.

Baratta-Lorton, Robert. *Mathematics . . . A Way of Thinking.* Menlo Park, CA: Addison-Wesley, 1977.

Barnett, Carne and Sharon Young. *Teaching Kids Math: Problem-Solving Activities to Help Young Children Learn and Enjoy Mathematics.* Englewood Cliffs, NJ: Prentice Hall, 1982.

Bitter, G., and J. Mikesell. *Sourcebook for Teachers Using the TI-12 Math Explorer™ Calculator.* Menlo Park, CA: Addison-Wesley, 1989.

Buxton, L. *Do You Panic About Maths? Coping with Maths Anxiety.* Exeter, NH: Heinemann Educational Books, 1981.

Chamot, A., and J. M. O'Malley. *Mathematics Book A.* Menlo Park, CA: Addison-Wesley, 1988.

Charles, R., et al. *Problem-Solving Experiences in Mathematics.* Menlo Park, CA: Addison-Wesley, 1989.

———, and Frank Lester. *Problem Solving: What, Why, and How.* Palo Alto, CA: Dale Seymour, 1982.

Clark, Clare, Betsy Y. Carter, and Betty J. Sternberg. *Math in Stride.* Menlo Park, CA: Addison-Wesley, 1988.

Davidson, N., editor. *Cooperative Learning in Mathematics: A Handbook for Teachers.* Menlo Park, CA: Addison-Wesley, 1990.

Doerr, Carol. *Microcomputers and the Three R's: A Guide for Teachers.* Rochelle Park, NJ: Hayden, 1979.

Dumas, Enoch. *Arithmetic Games,* 2nd ed. Belmont, CA: Pitman Learning, 1960.

———, and C. W. Schminke. *Math Activities for Child Involvement.* 2nd ed. Boston: Allyn and Bacon, 1977.

Eicholz, R., consultant. *Skillseekers Series.* Menlo Park, CA: Addison-Wesley, 1989.

Greenes, Carole, John Gregory, and Dale Seymour. *Successful Problem-Solving Techniques.* Palo Alto, CA: Creative Publications, 1977.

Haag, Vincent, et al. *Challenge: A Program for the Mathematically Talented.* Menlo Park, CA: Addison-Wesley, 1986.

Heimer, R., and C.R. Trueblood. *Strategies for Teaching Children Mathematics.* Reading, MA: Addison-Wesley, 1977.

Lerch, H. *Active Learning Experiences for Teaching Elementary School Mathematics.* Boston: Houghton Mifflin, 1981.

Lund, Chuck, and Margaret A. Smart. *Focus on Calculator Math.* Hayward, CA: Activity Resources, 1979.

Meyer, Carol, and Tom Sallee. *Make It Simpler.* Menlo Park, CA: Addison-Wesley, 1983.

National Council of Teachers of Mathematics. *Applications in School Mathematics, 1979 Yearbook.* Reston, VA: 1979.

———. *Computers in Mathematics Education, 1984 Yearbook.* Reston, VA: NCTM, 1984.

———. *Developing Computational Skills, 1978 Yearbook.* Reston, VA: NCTM, 1978.

———. *Estimation and Mental Computation, 1986 Yearbook.* Reston, VA: NCTM, 1986.

———. *Measurement in School Mathematics, 1976 Yearbook.* Reston, VA: NCTM, 1976.

———. *New Directions for Elementary School Mathematics, 1989 Yearbook.* Reston, VA: NCTM, 1989.

———. *Problem Solving in School Mathematics, 1980 Yearbook.* Reston, VA: NCTM, 1980.

O'Daffer, P., and S. Clemens. *Geometry: An Investigative Approach.* Menlo Park, CA: Addison-Wesley, 1976.

———. *Metric Measurement for Teachers: An Activity Approach.* Menlo Park, CA: Addison-Wesley, 1976.

Papert, Seymour. *Mindstorms: Children, Computers, and Powerful Ideas.* New York: Basic Books, 1980.

Ploutz, Paul F. *The Metric System: Content and Methods,* 2nd ed. Columbus, OH: Merrill, 1977.

Reisman, Fredricka K. *A Guide to the Diagnostic Teaching of Arithmetic,* 3rd ed. Columbus, OH: Merrill, 1982.

Sentlowitz, Michael, and Margaret Trivisone. *Dice and Dots.* Menlo Park, CA: Addison-Wesley, 1979.

Shoecraft, Paul Joseph, and Terry James Clukey. *The Mad Minute.* Menlo Park, CA: Addison-Wesley, 1981.

Skolnick, Joan, Carol Langbort, and Lucille Day. *How to Encourage Girls in Math and Science.* Englewood Cliffs, NJ: Prentice Hall, 1982.

Steffe, Leslie P., ed. *Research on Mathematical Thinking of Young Children.* Reston, VA: NCTM, 1975.

Stenmark, J., V. Thompson, and R. Cossey. *Family Math.* Berkeley, CA: Lawrence Hall of Science, 1986.

Thornburg, D. *Picture This! An Introduction to Computer Graphics for Kids of All Ages.* Menlo Park, CA: Addison-Wesley, 1982.

———. *Picture This Too! An Introduction to Computer Graphics for Kids of All Ages.* Menlo Park, CA: Addison-Wesley, 1982.

Thornton, Carol, et al. *Teaching Mathematics to Children with Special Needs.* Menlo Park, CA: Addison-Wesley, 1983.

Walker, M. *Addison-Wesley ESL Program.* Menlo Park, CA: Addison-Wesley, 1989.

Westley, J., and M. Randolph. *Windows on Mathematics.* Sunnyvale, CA: Creative Publications, 1987.

RECOMMENDED PERIODICALS

Arithmetic Teacher. Reston, VA: NCTM.

Mathematics Teacher. Reston, VA: NCTM.

BOOKS FOR THE STUDENT

Adler, David A. *Calculator Fun*. New York: Franklin Watts, 1981.

Anno, Masaichiro, and Mitsumasa Anno. *Anno's Mysterious Multiplying Jar*. New York: Philomel Books, The Putnam Publishing Group, 1983.

Anno, Mitsumasa. *Anno's Math Games*. New York: Philomel Books, Putnam & Grosset, 1987.

———. *The King's Flower*. Cleveland, OH: William Collins, 1979.

Barnstone, Aliki. "Numbers" from: *Zero Makes Me Hungry; A Collection of Poems for Today*. Compiled by Leuders & St. John. New York: Lothrop, Lee & Shepard, 1976.

Barson, Alan. *Motivational Games for Mathematics*. Warrington, PA: Fabmath, 1981.

Blume, Judy. *Tales of a Fourth Grade Nothing*. New York: Dell Publishing, 1972.

Branley, Franklyn M. *How Little and How Much: A Book About Scales*. New York: Thomas Y. Crowell, 1976.

———. *Measure with Meter*. New York: Thomas Y. Crowell, 1975.

Breiter, Herta S. *Time and Clocks,* Read About Science Series. Milwaukee, WI: Raintree, 1978.

Brooke, Maxey. *Coin Games and Puzzles*. New York: Dover Publications, 1973.

Brown, Marcia. *One Two Three: An Animal Counting Book*. Boston: Little, Brown, 1976.

———. *Listen to a Shape*. New York: Franklin Watts, 1979.

Burns, Marilyn. *This Book Is About Time*. Boston: Little, Brown, 1978.

Cartwright, Sally. *What's in a Map?* New York: Coward, McCann & Geoghegan, 1976.

Clark, Clare, Betsy Y. Carter, and Betty J. Sternberg. *Math in Stride*. Menlo Park, CA: Addison-Wesley, 1988.

Conaway, Judith. *The Discovery Book of Time*. Milwaukee, WI: Milwaukee Publishers, 1979.

D'Amato, Alex, and Janet D'Amato. *Galaxy Games*. New York: Doubleday, 1981.

Dennis, Richard J. *Fractions are Parts of Things*. New York: Thomas Y. Crowell, 1971.

Eager, Edward. *The Time Garden*. New York: Voyager/Harcourt Brace Jovanovich, 1958.

Eicholz, Robert E., consultant. *Skillseekers Series*. Menlo Park, CA: Addison-Wesley, 1977.

Elwood, A. and C. Orsag. "Starting Your Own Business" from Chapter 9, "Money and Work," *Macmillan Illustrated Almanac for Kids*. New York: Macmillan, 1981.

Farber, Norma. *Up the Down Elevator*. Reading, MA: Addison-Wesley, 1979.

Fritz, Jean. *What's the Big Idea, Ben Franklin?* New York: Coward, McCann & Geoghegan, 1976.

Froman, Robert. *Angles Are Easy as Pie*. New York: Thomas Y. Crowell, 1976.

———. *The Greatest Guessing Game: A Book About Dividing*. New York: Thomas Y. Crowell, 1978.

Gag, Wanda. *Wanda Gag's Jorinda and Joringel*. New York: Coward, McCann & Geogehegan, 1975.

Gersting, Judith L., and Joseph E. Kuczkowski. *Yes-No, Stop-Go: Some Patterns in Mathematical Logic*. New York: Thomas Y. Crowell, 1977.

Gilson, Jamie. *4B Goes Wild*. New York: Lothrop, Lee & Shepard, 1983.

Goeller, Lee. *How to Make an Adding Machine: That Even Adds Roman Numerals*. New York: Harcourt, Brace, Jovanovich, 1979.

Heller, Ruth. *Designs for Coloring*. New York: Grosset and Dunlap, 1976.

Hertzberg, Hendrik. *One Million*. New York: Simon & Schuster, 1970.

Hooks, William H. *The 17 Gerbils of Class 4A*. New York: Coward, McCann & Geogehegan, 1976.

James, Elizabeth, and Carol Barkin. *How to Grow 100 Dollars*. New York: Lothrop, Lee & Shepard, 1979.

———. *What Do You Mean by "Average"? Means, Medians, and Modes*. New York: Lothrop, Lee & Shepard, 1978.

Larsen, Sally G. *Computers for Kids*. Morristown, NJ: Creative Computing, 1980.

Leaf, Munro. *Metric Can Be Fun*. New York: J. B. Lippincott, 1976.

Leighton, R., and C. Feynman. *How to Count Sheep Without Falling Asleep*. Englewood Cliffs, NJ: Prentice Hall, 1976.

Levy, Elizabeth. *Something Queer at the Lemonade Stand*. New York: Dell/Yearling, 1982.

Madison, Arnold, and David L. Drotar. *Pocket Calculators: How to Use and Enjoy Them*. New York: Lodestar, 1979.

Mathews, Louise. *Bunches and Bunches of Bunnies*. New York: Dodd, Mead, 1979.

———. *Gator Pie*. New York: Dodd, Mead, 1979.

Murphy, Elaine C. *Developing Skills with Tables and Graphs,* Book A. Palo Alto, CA: Dale Seymour, 1981.

Nentl, Jerolyn Ann. *The Celsius Thermometer Is*. Mankato, MN: Crestwood, 1976.

———. *The Metric System Is*. Mankato, MN: Crestwood, 1976.

O'Connor, Vincent F. *Mathematics on the Playground*. Milwaukee, WI: Raintree, 1978.

Phillips, Jo. *Exploring Triangles: Paper Folding Geometry*. New York: Harper & Row, 1975.

Robertson, Keith. *Henry Reed, Inc*. New York: Puffin Books, Viking Penguin, 1989.

Sachar, Louise. "Dana." from: *Sideways Stories from Wayside School*. New York: Avon Books, 1985.

BIBLIOGRAPHY

Sandburg, Carl. "Arithmetic." from *Reflections on a Gift of Watermelon Pickle . . . and Other Modern Verse*. Compiled by Dunning, Leuders & Smith. New York: Lothrop, Lee & Shepard, 1967.

Sarnoff, Jane, and Reynold Ruffins. *The Code and Cipher Book*. New York: Charles Scribner's Sons, 1975.

Schneider, Herman, and Nina Schneider. *How Big is Big? From Stars to Atoms*. New York: William R. Scott, 1950.

Sharmat, Marjorie Weinman. *The 329th Friend*. New York: Four Winds Scholastic Book Service, 1979.

Shoecraft, Paul Joseph, and Terry James Clukey. *The Mad Minute*. Menlo Park, CA: Addison-Wesley, 1981.

Shotwell, Louisa R. *Roosevelt Grady*. New York: Dell, 1977.

Simon, Seymour. *Computer Sense Computer Nonsense*. New York: J. B. Lippincott, 1984.

Sloan, Sara. *The Brown Bag Cookbook: Nutritious Portable Lunches for Kids and Grownups*. Charlotte, VT: Williamson Publishing, 1984.

Smith, David E. *Number Stories of Long Ago*. Detroit: Gala Research Co., 1979.

Srivastava, Jane Jonas. *Averages*. New York: Thomas Y. Crowell, 1975.

———. *Number Families*. New York: Thomas Y. Crowell, 1980.

———. *Spaces, Shapes, and Sizes*. New York: Thomas Y. Crowell, 1980.

Stallworth, Lyn. *Wond'rous Fare: A Classic Childrens Cookbook*. Chicago: Contemporary Books, 1988.

Stern, David P. *Math Squared: Graph Paper Activities for Fun and Fundamentals*. New York: Teachers College Press, 1981.

Strelich, Tom, and Virginia Strelich. *Mathdroid*. Menlo Park, CA: Addison-Wesley, 1985.

Tongren, Sally. *What's for Lunch: Animal Feeding at the Zoo*. New York: EMG Publishing, 1981.

Viorst, Judith. *Alexander, Who Used to be Rich Last Sunday*. New York: Atheneum, 1978.

Wahl, John, and Stacey Wahl. *I Can Count the Petals of a Flower*. Reston, VA: NCTM, 1985.

Watson, Clyde. *Binary Numbers*. New York: Thomas Y. Crowell, 1977.

Weiss, Malcolm E. *666 Jelly Beans! All That?* New York: Thomas Y. Crowell, 1976.

———. *Solomon Grundy, Born on One Day*. New York: Thomas Y. Crowell, 1977.

Wyler, Rose, and Eva-Lee Baird. *Nutty Number Riddles*. New York: Doubleday, 1977.

Wyler, Rose, and Gerald Ames. *Funny Number Tricks: Easy Magic with Arithmetic*. New York: Parents Magazine Press, 1976.

Youldon, Gillian. *Numbers*. New York: Franklin Watts, 1979.

SOFTWARE

Addition Logician (Apple II series). MECC, 1984.

Addition Magician (Apple II series, Commodore 64, IBM PC/PCjr and PS/2, Tandy 1000; color monitor desirable). Learning Company, 1984.

Blockers and Finders (Apple II series, Commodore 64; color monitor desirable). Sunburst Communications, 1987.

Building Perspective (Apple II series, IBM PC/PCjr and PS/2, Tandy 1000; color monitor required). Sunburst Communications, 1986.

Bumble Games (Apple II series). Addison-Wesley, 1985.

Explorer Metros: A Metric Adventure (Apple II series). Sunburst Communications, 1981.

Fraction Munchers (Apple II series; color monitor desirable). MECC, 1987.

Geometric preSupposer: Points and Lines (Apple II series). Sunburst Communications, 1986.

Logo Works (available for nearly all computers). Terrapin, 1985.

Magic Cash Register. (Apple II series). Avant-Garde, 1983.

Math Practice Level II (IBM PC/PCjr and PS/2; color monitor required). IBM Educational Systems, 1985.

Math Strategies: Estimation (Apple II series). SRA, 1985.

Metric and Problem Solving (Apple II series, Atari 800). MECC, 1982.

Number Munchers (Apple II series; color monitor desirable). MECC, 1986.

Path Tactics (Apple II series, Commodore 64, IBM PC/PCjr and PS/2, Tandy 1000; color monitor desirable). MECC, 1986.

Pond: Explorations in Problem Solving (Apple II series, Atari, Commodore 64, IBM PC/PCjr and PS/2, TRS-80 Color and Tandy 1000; color monitor required). Sunburst Communications, 1985.

Problem Solving Strategies. MECC, 1983.

Puzzle Tanks (Apple II series, TRS-80, 3, 4). Sunburst Communications, 1985.

Right Turn (Apple II series, Commodore 64, IBM PC/PCjr and PS/2; color monitor required). Sunburst Communications, 1985.

Safari Search (Apple II series). Sunburst Communications, 1985.

Teasers by Tobbs (Apple II series, Atari, Commodore 64, IBM PC/PCjr and PS/2, TRS-80 Color and Tandy 1000; color monitor required). Sunburst Communications, 1982.

Trading Post (Apple II series, IBM PC/PCjr and PS/2, TRS-80 Color and Tandy 1000; color monitor required). Sunburst Communications, 1985.

Zandar III & IV (Apple II series; color monitor required). SVE, 1984.

Page 9, Ex. 27-30

27. 4 + 9 = 13
13 − 9 = 4
9 + 4 = 13
13 − 4 = 9

28. 6 + 8 = 14
14 − 8 = 6
8 + 6 = 14
14 − 6 = 8

29. 3 + 6 = 9
9 − 6 = 3
6 + 3 = 9
9 − 3 = 6

30. 7 + 7 = 14
14 − 7 = 7

Sample Solution, Page 11, Ex. 4

Understand the situation: The owl monkey has already slept some of the usual time he sleeps in a day. You must find how much more sleep he will get. Find the data: Use the table to see how long an owl monkey usually sleeps—17 hours. The problem says he has already slept 9 of those hours. Plan a solution: Choose an operation to decide how to find how many more hours of sleep the monkey will get; subtraction is the sensible operation. Estimate: 20 − 10 = 10. Solve: 17 − 9 = 8; the owl monkey will sleep 8 more hours. Check: Combine 9 hours already slept and 8 more hours to go, which gives 17 hours; the answer makes sense.

Page 20, Ex. 14

Problems will vary. Sample problems for the first fact: How much longer can a snail go without food than a tarantula spider? (3 y) How much longer can a tarantula spider go without food than without water? (17 mo) Sample problem for the second fact: If 2 brothers and their dog were sprayed by a skunk, how many large cans of tomato juice would it take to get rid of the smell? (9)

Page 21, Ex. 5, 13-15

5. △ + ○ = □
□ − △ = ○
□ − ○ = △

13. 4 + 7 = 11
7 + 4 = 11
11 − 4 = 7
11 − 7 = 4

14. 5 + 9 = 14
9 + 5 = 14
14 − 5 = 9
14 − 9 = 5

15. 6 + 6 = 12
12 − 6 = 6

Page 22. Ex. 1, 2

1.

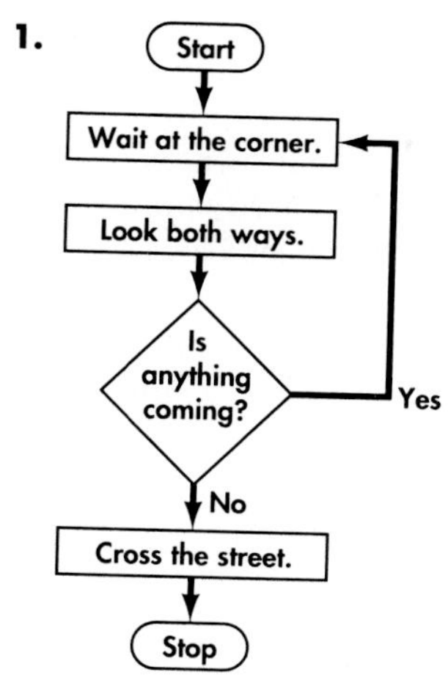

2.

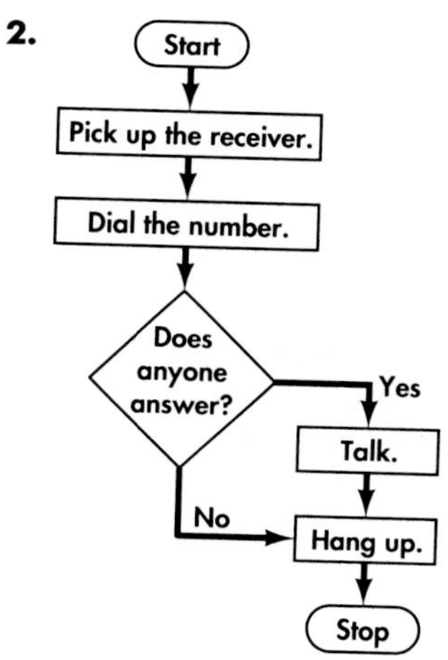

Page 27, Ex. 1, 2

1. 2 thousands, 3 hundreds, 3 tens, 4 ones; 2,334
2. 1 thousand, 5 hundreds, 2 tens, 0 ones; 1,520

Page 29, Ex. 7-10

7. 221,378; 645,318
8. 385,219; 308,467
9. 443,276; 463,218
10. 832,104; 538,425

Page 30, Ex. 7

Least to greatest: 587, 5,817, 5,819, 5,871
Greatest to least: 5,871, 5,819, 5,817, 587

Page 31, Ex. 7-11

7. 369, 1,487, 1,501, 1,522
8. 4,967, 5,867, 34,867, 34,967
9. 10,000; 9,035
10. 3,218; 3,692; 5,411; 2,480
11. 7,081; 5,500; 5,411; 9,035

Page 33, Ex. 13
2,989; 13,289; 26,341; 26,355

Sample Solution, Page 35, Ex. 3
Read the problem. Restate the situation in your own words: A beaver's head is 17 in. high, but 8 in. of the head is in the mouth. Plan a solution: If you find the difference between the total height of the beaver's head and the height of its mouth, that will give the height of the rest; subtract 8 from 17. Solve the problem: $17 - 8 = 9$. Check: Since $8 + 9 = 17$, the answer makes sense.

Page 41, Ex. 9-16
9. 576,908,442; 235,975,762
10. 639,817,430; 89,540,813
11. 98,345,012; 493,003,561
12. 387,592,041; 194,318
13. 24,418,000; 22,418,000
14. 517,050,000; 515,050,000
15. 10,300,000; 8,300,000
16. 50,750,000; 48,750,000

Page 43, Ex. 3, 4, 6
Answers may vary. Sample answers given use the least number of bills and coins. **3.** 1 ten-dollar bill, 1 five-dollar bill, 2 one-dollar bills, 1 quarter, 1 dime, 4 pennies; 1 penny, 1 dime, 2 quarters, 2 one-dollar bills; **4.** 1 five-dollar bill, 2 one-dollar bills, 2 quarters, 3 pennies; 2 pennies, 2 dimes, 1 quarter, 2 one-dollar bills, 1 ten-dollar bill; **6.** \$3.43; \$5.00; 2 pennies, 1 nickel, 2 quarters, 1 one-dollar bill

Page 45, Ex. 3, 4
3. No. Answers may vary, but the most the coins could be worth is \$3.50: 8 quarters = \$2.00, 10 dimes = \$1.00, and 10 nickels = \$0.50. **4.** Yes. Answers may vary, but 4 quarters = \$1 and 30 dimes = \$3, so already there is \$4.

Page 49, Ex. 14
Cube order, from top to bottom, is red, blue, green, pink.

Page 50, Ex. 1-3
1. Answers will vary. Sample: When the symbol to the right in the numeral has the same or less value than the symbol to the left of it, the two symbols are added. When the symbol to the left in the numeral has less value than the symbol to the right of it, the smaller symbol is subtracted from the larger symbol.
2. Answers will vary. Sample: III = $1 + 1 + 1$; VI = $5 + 1$
3. Answers will vary. Sample: IV = $5 - 1$; XL = $50 - 10$

Page 55, Ex. 25
Answers will vary. Sample: Nan scored 300 points less in the second game than she did in the first game. She scored 500 points in the second game. How much did she score in the first game? (800 points)

Page 59, Ex. 5
Answers will vary. Sample:

$$\begin{array}{r} 360 \\ +254 \\ \hline 4 \end{array}$$ There are not enough ones to trade.

$$\begin{array}{r} \overset{1}{3}60 \\ +254 \\ \hline 614 \end{array}$$ Ten tens are traded for 1 hundred.

Page 61, Ex. 33
Answers will vary. Sample: To show $346 + 182 = 528$ using place value blocks, lay out the blocks. ($346 =$ 3 hundreds, 4 tens, 6 ones; $182 =$ 1 hundred, 8 tens, 2 ones) Put the ones together ($6 + 2 = 8$; there are not enough ones to trade.) Put the tens together. ($4 + 8 = 12$; trade 10 tens for 1 hundred.) Put the hundreds together. ($1 + 3 + 1 = 5$; no trade needed.) The total is 5 hundreds, 2 tens, and 8 ones, which is a sum of 528 written in standard form.

Page 63, Ex. 15, 17-20
15. *Windows to the Universe, All About Telescopes,* and *How Big Is Space?* for a total of \$18.79
17. $11 - 3 = 8$ or $11 - 8 = 3$
18. $15 - 8 = 7$ or $15 - 7 = 8$
19. $15 - 9 = 6$ or $15 - 6 = 9$
20. $18 - 9 = 9$

Sample Solution, Page 65, Ex. 4
Read the problem, then state the situation in your own words: Shirley had a goal of writing 50 star facts by New Year's Day. Find the given data: She wrote 21 facts in October and 15 in November. Plan a solution strategy: Find how many facts Shirley has to write in December to reach her goal of 50 facts. Since that amount of star facts is a missing addend of the sum 50, it makes sense to subtract. Solution takes 2 operations: First add $21 + 15 = 36$, then subtract $50 - 36 = 14$. Check solution: Add $21 + 15 + 14 = 50$, so the answer makes sense.

Page 67, Ex. 31
Becky used 3 tens and 2 ones pieces to show 32 and 1 hundred, 6 tens, and 8 ones pieces to show 168, for a total of 1 hundred, 9 tens, and 10 ones pieces; after trading 10 ones for 1 ten, then 10 tens for 1 hundred, Becky needed 2 hundreds blocks to show the sum.

Page 69, Ex. 1-5

1. $\begin{array}{r} {\scriptstyle 7\ 12} \\ \not{8}\,\not{2} \\ -\ 3\ 7 \\ \hline 4\ 5 \end{array}$ **2.** $\begin{array}{r} {\scriptstyle 6\ 15} \\ 1\ \not{7}\,\not{5} \\ -\ 5\ 8 \\ \hline 1\ 1\ 7 \end{array}$ **3.** $\begin{array}{r} {\scriptstyle 5\ 12} \\ 3\ \not{6}\,\not{2} \\ -\ 1\ 3\ 7 \\ \hline 2\ 2\ 5 \end{array}$ **4.** $\begin{array}{r} {\scriptstyle 3\ 13} \\ 4\ \not{3}\,\not{6} \\ -\ 2\ 7\ 1 \\ \hline 1\ 6\ 5 \end{array}$

5. Answers will vary. Sample:

$\begin{array}{r} {\scriptstyle 7\ 14} \\ \not{8}\,\not{4}\ 5 \\ -\ 6\ 6\ 1 \\ \hline 1\ 8\ 4 \end{array}$

Page 71, Ex. 16-18

Students may use estimation to determine whether the differences are correct; **16.** 142 rounds to 140; 59 rounds to 60; 140 − 60 = 80, answer is incorrect; **17.** 356 rounds to 360; 28 rounds to 30; 360 − 30 = 330; answer is incorrect; **18.** 532 rounds to 530; 216 rounds to 220; 530 − 220 = 310; answer is close enough to be correct.

Page 73, Ex. 15-18

15. 104 − 67 = 37 **16.** 204 − 167 = 37
17. 304 − 267 = 37 **18.** 404 − 367 = 37
Each has a difference of 37. The next 3 examples are 504 − 467 = 37, 604 − 567 = 37, and 704 − 667 = 37.

Page 75, Ex. 21-28

21. 328 + 547 = 875 **22.** 329 − 182 = 147
23. 305 + 448 = 753 **24.** 662 + 409 = 1,071
25. 405 − 216 = 189 **26.** 855 + 427 = 1,282
27. 586 − 432 = 154 **28.** 174 + 635 = 809

Page 77, Ex. 8

Answers will vary. Sample: The long table can seat 14 people. Each smaller table seats 8 people, 2 at each end. When 2 tables are pushed together, 2 ends "disappear," so that 2 possible seats are lost.

Sample Solution, Page 77, Ex. 6

Read the problem to restate the situation: *Compare the total number of milk cartons sold on Tuesday and Wednesday with the total sold on Thursday and Friday.* Find the data: 173 milk cartons sold on Tuesday, 148 sold on Wednesday, 131 sold on Thursday, and 138 sold on Friday. Plan how to solve: Add 173 and 148; add 131 and 138; subtract to compare the 2 totals. Estimate: 300 − 250 = 50. Solve: 173 + 148 = 321; 131 + 138 = 269; 321 − 269 = 52. Examine the solution: 52 more milk cartons sold on Tuesday and Wednesday makes sense.

Page 79, Ex. 11, 12

11. Jupiter has 7 fewer satellites than Saturn, or Saturn has 7 more satellites than Jupiter; **12.** 63,280 km/h faster

Page 80, Ex. 1, 2

1. Estimate: I need to know whether I have enough money. I can estimate the total cost; yes. **2.** Exact: The ticket taker must get the right amount of money; $5.25.

Page 81, Ex. 1-10

1. Estimate; Janell's mother needs a general idea; 300.
2. Estimate; the newspaper needs an approximate report; $300.
3. Estimate; Mr. Thornquist needs to know if he has enough money; yes. **4.** Estimate; Megan needs to order about twice as many; 160. **5.** Exact; the ticket seller needs the exact amount; $5.00. **6.** Exact; the ticket takers and the person figuring profits both need exact figures; 53, yes. **7.** Estimate; Sue's friend needs to know about how much the shirts cost; $10.00.
8. Exact; Jake should return exact change to his father; (The amount of money Jake received is unknown, so it is not possible to list an answer.) **9.** Estimate; Bo's friend needs to know about how long he was there; 90 minutes longer.
10. Not reasonable; by rounding each ticket price and estimating, we find $2 + $2 + $1 + $1 + $3 = $9.

Sample Solution, Page 81, Ex. 4

Understand the situation: Megan wants twice as many balloons this year as last year. Find the data: 78 balloons last year. Plan a solution: Find a number twice as much as 78. Decide whether to estimate or to find an exact answer: Since the problem does not indicate that an exact number of balloons is needed, it makes sense to estimate about how many Megan should order. Solve: 78 is about 80; to double 80, think 8 + 8 = 16, so 80 + 80 = 160. Examine your solution: If Megan orders 160 balloons, that is a little more than twice what she used last year.

Page 84, Ex. 9

Other patterns: If you add or subtract 2 even numbers, the answer is even. If you add or subtract an even and an odd number, the answer is odd.

Page 85, Ex. 1-3

Answers may vary. Samples: **1.** compensate up-down: 400 + 463 = 863; **2.** Subtract special differences: think of 15 hundreds − 7 hundreds = 8 hundreds, or 800; **3.** Group the compatible numbers 400 and 600, which is 1,000, then add 335, for a sum of 1,335.

Page 86, Ex. 1, 2, 4

1. The letters or numbers read the same forward and backward. **2.** 12,345; yoyo; and moon are not palindromes because they do not read the same forward and backward.
4. The number of steps may vary, but you eventually reach a palindrome.

Page 91, Ex. 1-4
1. Length of Some Mountain Hiking Trails; **2.** Answers may vary. Possible answers: Swing Along; Lonesome Snake; Craggy Ridge; Short Stretch; **3.** It is only 1 mile long. **4.** Lonesome Snake

Page 99, Ex. 9
The temperature rose steadily throughout the morning. The sun is most directly overhead at noon.

Page 101, Ex. 1
6 possible pairs: Jim and David, Jim and Rod, Jim and Li, David and Rod, David and Li, Rod and Li

Sample Solution, Page 101, Ex. 5
Understand the situation: Carmina cannot hear sounds less than 82 decibels without a hearing aid. Analyze the data: Use the pictograph, which compares sounds in decibels. Plan a solution: Find the row for people talking nearby, then use the symbol to determine how many decibels of loudness that sound has. (65 decibels) Use the data to answer the question: Talking nearby is only 65 decibels, so Carmina cannot hear it. Examine your solution: The answer should be "no."

Page 107, Ex. 5
3 choices: *Racer* and *Triple Dragon, Racer* and *Baseball Player, Triple Dragon* and *Baseball Player*

Sample Solution, Page 107, Ex. 4
Understand the situation: Jeff worked a total of 14 weeks to win two different computer games. Analyze the given information: It took 4 weeks longer to win *Triple Dragon* than to win *Crystal Search,* and the total time was 14 weeks. Plan a solution strategy: Use the Guess and Check method to find two addends, one 4 more than the other, that have a sum of 14. Try 5 for the first guess: $5 + 4 = 9$, $5 + 9 = 14$. The guess of 5 checks with the facts of the situation. Examine the solution: It took Jeff 5 weeks to win *Crystal Search* and 9 weeks to win *Triple Dragon*. 9 is 4 more than 5, and $9 + 5 = 14$, so the solution makes sense.

Page 111, Ex. 2, 8, 16
2. Answers may vary. Sample: The rules do not favor any 1 player. **8.** the number of servings sold of various school lunches; **16.** No, there is a higher probability of getting one of each, based on the possible outcomes: HH, TT, HT, TH.

Page 112, Ex. 3, 4
3.

Sum	Ways to Roll Sum			Total Number of Ways
0	0, 0			1
1	0, 1			1
2	0, 2	1, 1		2
3	0, 3	1, 2		2
4	0, 4	1, 3	2, 2	3
5	0, 5	1, 4	2, 3	3
6	1, 5	2, 4	3, 3	3
7	2, 5	3, 4		2
8	3, 5	4, 4		2
9	4, 5			1
10	5, 5			1

4. Most often: 4, 5, 6; least often, 0, 1, 9, 10; Sums that can be made by the most combinations of numbers are most likely to occur; sums that can be made only 1 way are least likely to occur.

Page 128, Ex. 3, 4
Questions may vary. Sample questions and exact answer given. **3.** How many more patients did Dr. Verne see in August? 78; **4.** How many pictures are displayed in all? 81

Page 129, Ex. 1-8
Questions may vary. Sample questions and exact answer given. **1.** How many fewer children than adults did Dr. Fisher see in 1990? 790; **2.** What is the total number of children Dr. Fisher saw from 1989 to 1991? 4,175; **3.** Is the number of adults Dr. Fisher saw from 1989 to 1991 less than 6,000? No, you can estimate to see that the total number of patients is greater than 6,000. **4.** What is the total number of hours Charlie wore his headgear? 50 h; **5.** What is the total number of rings Dr. Rose bought? 40; **6.** How long was Jose at the dentist? 65 min, or 1 h 5 min; **7.** What is Mrs. Osawa's total number of teeth? 32; **8a.** If Judy makes an appointment during school, she can see 3 doctors: Dr. Brown, Dr. Pan, or Dr. Bernstein. If she makes an appointment after school, she can see 3 doctors: Dr. Brown, Dr. Pan, or Dr. Bernstein; **8b.** Judy has 6 choices; **8c.** Make an Organized List

Sample Solution, Page 129, Ex. 3
Understand the question: Compare the number of adults Dr. Fisher saw over those years with a reference point of 6,000. Use the table to find necessary data: $2{,}177 + 2{,}189 + 2{,}161$. Plan a solution strategy: Estimate the sum, then compare the estimate with the reference point. Solve: 6,000; the answer is no. Examine the solution to see if it is reasonable: Since 6,000 is an *under*estimate, Dr. Fisher actually saw over 6,000 adults, so the answer makes sense.

Page 134, Ex. 2

2.

×	0	1	2	3	4	5	6	7	8	9	10
3	0	3	6	9	12	15	18	21	24	27	30

Page 135, Ex. 8-12

8.

×	0	1	2	3	4	5	6	7	8	9	10
8	0	8	16	24	32	40	48	56	64	72	80

9.

×	0	1	2	3	4	5	6	7	8	9	10
9	0	9	18	27	36	45	54	63	72	81	90

10.

×	0	1	2	3	4	5	6	7	8	9	10
12	0	12	24	36	48	60	72	84	96	108	120

11.

×	0	1	2	3	4	5	6	7	8	9	10
13	0	13	26	39	52	65	78	91	104	117	130

12.

×	0	1	2	3	4	5	6	7	8	9	10
15	0	15	30	45	60	75	90	105	120	135	150

Sample Solution, Page 137, Ex. 3

Read the problem carefully to understand the situation: Jimbo made 2 different sizes of bubble chains. He made 7-bubble chains, 3 of each, then he made 9-bubble chains, 5 of each. Analyze what question to answer: How many bubbles did he make in all? Plan a solution strategy: The problem requires 3 steps: first multiply to put together 2 sets of same-size groups; then add the products for a final total. Solve: $3 \times 7 = 21$; $5 \times 9 = 45$; $21 + 45 = 66$. Examine the answer: The basic facts are correct, an estimated sum would be 70, so the answer of 66 bubbles makes sense.

Page 141, Ex. 21

How many meals did Amir's Restaurant serve in all? 821

Page 142, Ex. 1, 5, 7, 8

1. Answers will vary. Sample answers: If you put a finger on a number row and another finger on a number column and move across the row and down the column, the place where your fingers meet is the product of the two numbers with which you started. If you move along a number row, you will see the multiples of that number. If you stop on any multiple and look to the top of the column, you will find the second factor of that multiple. **5.** There are 35 other possible pairs. You find identical pairs because each digit is multiplied in two directions. For example, you have $5 \times 4 = 20$ and $4 \times 5 = 20$.

7. No; Answers will vary, samples given by row:
Pattern of digit sums in the 2 row: 2, 4, 6, 8, 1, 3, 5, 7, 9.
Pattern of digit sums in the 3 row: 3, 6, 9, 3, 6, 9, 3, 6, 9.
Pattern of digit sums in the 4 row: 4, 8, 3, 7, 2, 6, 10, 5, 9.
Pattern of digit sums in the 5 row: 5, 1, 6, 2, 7, 3, 8, 4, 9.
Pattern of digit sums in the 6 row: 6, 3, 9, 6, 3, 9, 6, 12, 9.
Pattern of digit sums in the 7 row: 7, 5, 3, 10, 8, 6, 13, 11, 9.
Pattern of digit sums in the 8 row: 8, 7, 6, 5, 4, 12, 11, 10, 9.
8. The sum equals the product just below the second addend because 1 times a number + 2 times a number = 3 times the number; no.

Page 153, Ex. 1-6

1. $\begin{array}{r} 42 \\ \times\ 3 \\ \hline 126 \end{array}$ **2.** $\begin{array}{r} {}^{2} \\ 17 \\ \times\ 4 \\ \hline 68 \end{array}$ **3.** $\begin{array}{r} {}^{3} \\ 16 \\ \times\ 5 \\ \hline 80 \end{array}$ **4.** $\begin{array}{r} {}^{1} \\ 72 \\ \times\ 8 \\ \hline 576 \end{array}$ **5.** $\begin{array}{r} {}^{4} \\ 58 \\ \times\ 6 \\ \hline 348 \end{array}$

6. Answers will vary. Sample:

$$\begin{array}{r} {}^{3} \\ 95 \\ \times\ 7 \\ \hline 665 \end{array}$$

Page 155, Ex. 28

Answers will vary. Sample: To solve the equation 24×3 using blocks, lay out 3 groups of 24 (2 tens blocks and 4 ones blocks in each group). Put together same-size groups by multiplying the ones ($4 \times 3 = 12$) and trading (10 ones for 1 ten). Count tens (7) and ones (2). So, the product of 24 and 3 is 72.

Page 165, Ex. 20-25

Methods may vary. Samples:
20. 6,030; breaking apart numbers; **21.** 7,800; choosing compatible numbers; **22.** 2,201; counting on; **23.** 3,531; using compensation; **24.** 8,400; breaking apart numbers; **25.** 4,498; counting back

Page 169, Ex. 1, 2

1.

Day	1	2	3	4	5	6
Boxes	1	2	4	8	16	32

32 boxes

2.

Bin	1	2	3	4	5	6	7
Price	\$1.50	\$1.75	\$2.00	\$2.25	\$2.50	\$2.75	\$3.00

\$3.00

Sample Solution, Page 169, Ex. 5
First, identify the known facts: Joe draws a 4-frame comic strip every day. Then determine what you must find: How many frames does he draw in a year? Find the important measurement fact needed to solve the problem: 1 y = 365 d. Choose a sensible operation: Multiply. Decide on a reasonable calculation method: Pencil and Paper. Multiply: $4 \times 365 =$ 1,460. Give the answer in a complete sentence: Joe draws 1,460 comic frames in a year.

Page 173, Ex. 3
Answers may vary. Sample: You can multiply any 2 factors first, but it is easier to find $4 \times 5 = 20$, then multiply $20 \times 7 = 140$ mentally.

Page 174
Questions will vary. Samples: **Sand castle:** How wide was it? How long did it take to build it? How many people worked on it? **Rocking chair:** Did the man eat or sleep? How many times did he rock per minute? How many complete rocks did he make? **Pogo stick:** What distance did the man cover during that time? How high was the average bounce? How many bounces were made during that time?

Page 179, Ex. 13
b; The products of **c** and **d** would be too small, and the product of **a** would be too large.

Page 180, Ex. 1-5
1. 4,000; underestimate; closer estimate: $50 \times 90 = 4{,}500$; **2.** 800; can't tell; **3.** 12,000; overestimate; closer estimate: $300 \times 30 = 9{,}000$; **4.** 30,000; can't tell; **5.** \$200; can't tell

Page 181, Ex. 1-12
1. 2,100; overestimate; closer estimate: $20 \times 70 = 1{,}400$; **2.** 2,000; can't tell; **3.** \$180; overestimate; closer estimate: \$5.00 × 30 = \$150; **4.** 10,000; can't tell; **5.** 16,000; underestimate; closer estimate: $20 \times 900 = 18{,}000$; **6.** 4,800; can't tell; **7.** 63,000; can't tell; **8.** \$240; can't tell; **9.** 48,000; can't tell; **10.** \$240; underestimate; **11.** 2,500; underestimate; **12.** 50,000; can't tell

Page 189, Ex. 5-8
5. overestimate; closer estimate: $35 \times 30 = 1{,}050$;
6. underestimate; closer estimate: 30 × \$6.00 = \$180.00;
7. overestimate; closer estimate: $80 \times 400 = 32{,}000$;
8. underestimate; closer estimate: $240 \times 100 = 24{,}000$

Sample Solution, Page 191, Ex. 4
Read the problem to understand the situation and restate it in your own words: Some boy scouts ordered 12 medium and 11 large frozen yogurts. Analyze what question you must answer: What is the total number of ounces of frozen yogurt they ordered? Find the data: Using the frozen yogurt table and the facts in the problem, 12 scouts got medium yogurts, which are 10 oz each; 11 scouts got large yogurts, which are 14 oz each. Plan a solution strategy: Multiply to put together same-size groups for each size of yogurt, then add both products for the total number of ounces. Estimate the answer: $12 \times 10 = 120$; $11 \times 14 =$ about 150, so the estimated sum is about 270 oz. Solve: $12 \times 10 = 120$; $11 \times 14 = 154$; $120 + 154 = 274$. Examine the solution: 274 is close to the estimate; it makes sense that 274 oz of frozen yogurt were ordered in all.

Page 194, Try It Out, Ex. 1-5
Answers may vary. Sample: **1.** mental math (special products); 700; **2.** mental math (compensation); 263; **3.** mental math (break-apart factors); 39; **4.** mental math (compatible numbers); \$10.00; **5.** calculator; 205,920

Page 195, Ex. 1-12
Answers may vary. Sample: **1.** mental math (compatible numbers); 6,800; **2.** mental math (compensation); 101; **3.** calculator; 334,582; **4.** mental math (special products); 2,400; **5.** mental math (break-apart factors); 369; **6.** mental math (compatible numbers); 300; **7.** paper and pencil; 775; **8.** calculator; \$928.31; **9.** mental math (compensation); 91; **10.** mental math (break-apart factors); 63; **11.** mental math (special products); 620; **12.** paper and pencil; 1,170

Sample Solution, Page 195, Ex. 14
Read and understand the problem, then explain what to find: Total rest time the balancer got. Find the data: The Wacky Records table says that the balancer got a 5-minute rest break after each hour. Plan a solution: Multiply to find the time in all 5-minute breaks. Estimate: $5 \times 30 = 150$, so the product should be over 150 minutes. Solve: Use paper and pencil, multiply $34 \times 5 = 170$. Examine the solution: Adjust the product because the balancer would not take the same kind of rest break *after* setting the record; subtract 5 minutes. The balancer rested a total of 165 minutes.

Sample Solution, Page 197, Ex. 2
Understand the situation: You need to compare what the fourth graders spent on book club orders last month with this month. Analyze the data to plan a solution strategy: Use the table to find out how much the fourth graders spent this month: $129.83. Then subtract that amount from $136.98 to find the difference. Estimate: $140.00 − $130.00 = $10.00, which is an overestimate. Solve: $136.98 − $129.83 = $7.15. Examine your answer: $7.15 is under the overestimate of $10.00. You can also check by adding $129.83 + $7.15 = $136.98, so the answer makes sense.

Page 206, Ex. 1-4
Answers will vary. Samples: **1.** 9:24, nine-twenty-four, 24 minutes past 9; **2.** 4:45, four-forty-five, quarter to five; **3.** 6:30, six-thirty, half past six; **4.** 11:50, 50 minutes past 11, 10 minutes to 12

Page 212, Ex. 1, 2
1. 9 bicycles and 1 tricycle or 5 tricycles and 3 bicycles or 6 bicycles and 3 tricycles; **2.** 1 50-pound bag and 2 25-pound bags or 2 50-pound bags or 4 25-pound bags

Page 213, Ex. 2, 5
2. 8 possible answers: 1 row of 24 bars, 2 rows of 12 bars, 3 rows of 8 bars, 4 rows of 6 bars, 6 rows of 4 bars, 8 rows of 3 bars, 12 rows of 2 bars, 24 rows of 1 bar; **5.** two 6-foot boards and one 5-foot board

Sample Solution, Page 213, Ex. 2
Understand the facts: There are 24 bars to be put in rows with the same number of bars per row. Analyze the situation: You can have any number of rows and any number of bars per row. This is the action of multiplication, with 24 as the product, so you must find factor pairs. Plan a solution strategy: List as many factor pairs as possible that produce 24. Solve the problem: 1 row of 24 bars, 2 rows of 12 bars, 3 rows of 8 bars, 4 rows of 6 bars, 6 rows of 4 bars, 8 rows of 3 bars, 12 rows of 2 bars, 24 rows of 1 bar. Examine the solution: Since all the combinations listed use 24 bars, they make sense.

Page 218, Ex. 1, 2
1. Actual measurement; the dog should not eat more or less than 1 pound of food. **2.** Actual measurement; the doctor needs to know your exact temperature.

Page 219, Ex. 1-9
1. Measure; the place mat needs to fit exactly; measurements will vary. **2.** Estimate; the picture only needs to be about at eye level. **3.** Measure; you need to know exactly what the cost of the package will be. **4.** Measure; the yarn must fit exactly; measurements will vary. **5.** Estimate; the ribbon does not need to be an exact length, just long enough to go around the present. **6.** Measure; you do not want to underbake or overbake the cupcakes. **7.** Estimate; you can guess about how much each friend will drink. **8.** Measure; data for the graph should be accurate; measurements will vary. **9.** Measure; the ladder must fit the cage; answers will vary.

Sample Solution, Page 219, Ex. 3
Understand the situation: The Box It Up Shop charges $0.25/lb. to wrap packages. Analyze the question: You want to know the cost of wrapping a certain package. Plan what to consider: What measurement is needed? (weight) How is the measurement used? (to determine cost) Decide how to solve the problem: Measure. Examine your decision: If you estimate the weight, you may not pay the right amount; you need to know the exact weight to determine the correct price.

Page 221, Ex. 17
Answers may vary. Possibilities: 2 rows of 14 plants, 14 rows of 2 plants, 4 rows of 7 plants, 7 rows of 4 plants

Sample Solution, Page 225, Ex. 5
Understand the question: Find the tallest and shortest buildings, then compare them to find the difference in their heights. Decide how to use the chart to locate the necessary data: Look in the Tallest Buildings column for the largest and smallest buildings. The tallest is the Texas Commerce Tower at 1,002 ft, and the shortest is the One American Center building at 395 ft. Plan a solution method: Subtract to compare; find 1,002 − 395, which is 607. Examine the solution to see if it makes sense: Round and estimate to check. 1,000 − 400 = 600, so 607 is a reasonable answer.

Page 233, Ex. 17
six 5-pen packets and ten 3-pen packets; five 3-pen packets and nine 5-pen packets

Page 234, Ex. 4
−1°F, −5°F; −5°F is colder because the lower the temperature falls below 0°F, the colder it is.

ADDITIONAL ANSWERS

Page 241, Ex. 2-12

2. $2 \times 3 = 6$, $6 \div 2 = 3$, $6 \div 3 = 2$
3. $8 \times 2 = 16$, $16 \div 8 = 2$, $16 \div 2 = 8$
4. $18 \div 6 = 3$, $6 \times 3 = 18$, $3 \times 6 = 18$

5. $2 \times 5 = 10$, $5 \times 2 = 10$, $10 \div 5 = 2$, $10 \div 2 = 5$
6. $3 \times 6 = 18$, $6 \times 3 = 18$, $18 \div 3 = 6$, $18 \div 6 = 3$
7. $2 \times 9 = 18$, $9 \times 2 = 18$, $18 \div 9 = 2$, $18 \div 2 = 9$

8. $4 \times 3 = 12$, $3 \times 4 = 12$, $12 \div 4 = 3$, $12 \div 3 = 4$
9. $3 \times 3 = 9$, $9 \div 3 = 3$
10. $2 \times 6 = 12$, $6 \times 2 = 12$, $12 \div 6 = 2$, $12 \div 2 = 6$

11. $3 \times 7 = 21$, $7 \times 3 = 21$, $21 \div 7 = 3$, $21 \div 3 = 7$
12. $4 \times 8 = 32$, $8 \times 4 = 32$, $32 \div 4 = 8$, $32 \div 8 = 4$

Ex. 9 is different from the others because the fact family for doubles such as 3×3 has only 2 equations.

Sample Solution, Page 247, Ex. 3

Understand the situation: Bev has saved some money toward the cost of a new guitar. Summarize what the problem asks: Find the cost of the new guitar; compare it with how much money Bev has now to find how much more she needs. Find the data: Bev saved \$87.75; the guitar costs \$169.99. Plan a solution method: Round both amounts; subtract to estimate the difference; find an exact answer. \$170 − \$90 = \$80; \$169.99 − \$87.75 = \$82.24. Evaluate the solution: Since \$82.24 is near the estimate of \$80, the answer is reasonable.

Page 249, Ex. 1-10, 25-27

1. share equally; 3; check students' drawings; **2.** separate same-size groups; 6; check students' drawings

3. $3 \times 4 = 12$, $4 \times 3 = 12$, $12 \div 3 = 4$, $12 \div 4 = 3$
4. $4 \times 7 = 28$, $7 \times 4 = 28$, $28 \div 4 = 7$, $28 \div 7 = 4$
5. $6 \times 5 = 30$, $5 \times 6 = 30$, $30 \div 5 = 6$, $30 \div 6 = 5$

6. $1 \times 2 = 2$, $2 \times 1 = 2$, $2 \div 1 = 2$, $2 \div 2 = 1$
7. $5 \times 8 = 40$, $40 \div 8 = 5$, $40 \div 5 = 8$
8. $2 \times 5 = 10$, $10 \div 5 = 2$, $10 \div 2 = 5$

9. $27 \div 9 = 3$, $3 \times 9 = 27$, $9 \times 3 = 27$
10. $8 \div 2 = 4$, $4 \times 2 = 8$, $2 \times 4 = 8$

25-27: Answers may vary. Samples: **25.** 8 photos per page, 3 pages; 3 photos per page, 8 pages; 6 photos per page, 4 pages; 4 photos per page, 6 pages; **26.** 7 teams of 3 players; 3 teams of 4 players plus 3 teams of 3 players; **27.** 10 + 10 + 0; 8 + 8 + 4; 10 + 5 + 5

Page 251, Ex. 21

5. $6 \times 6 = 36$
10. $6 \times 5 = 30$ or $5 \times 6 = 30$
15. $7 \times 4 = 28$ or $4 \times 7 = 28$
20. $8 \times 7 = 56$ or $7 \times 8 = 56$
25. $3 \times 7 = 21$ or $7 \times 3 = 21$

Page 255, Ex. 10-21

10. 30
11. 54
12. 42
13. 0
14. Divide by 3.
15. 8
16. 6
17. 5
18. 9
19. 12
20. Multiply by 2 and Add 1.
21. 21

Sample Solution, Page 257, Ex. 4

Understand the situation: You know the number of pins that Marco knocked down in the second and third frames of a bowling game. Analyze the question: You must find the number of pins he knocked down in the first frame. Plan a solution strategy: Work Backward from the known total to find the number of pins Marco knocked down in the first frame. Organize the data: 4 pins in the second frame, twice that many, or 8 pins, in the third frame. Solve: 21 − 4 = 17; 17 − 8 = 9; so Marco knocked down 9 pins in the first frame. Examine your solution: If Marco did knock down 9 pins in the first frame, his 3-frame total would be 9 + 4 + 8, which is 21; the solution checks.

Page 260, Projects 10a, 10b

10a. Possible answers: 7 large tables of 4 students each and no small tables = 28; 8 small tables of 3 students each and 1 large table of 4 students = 28; 4 large tables of 4 students each and 4 small tables of 3 students each equals 28; **10b.** 16, 12; 4 of each size table; check students' drawings.

Page 261, Ex. 1, 2, and 4

1. Check students' drawings. $18 \div 3 = 6$
XXX XXX XXX XXX XXX XXX
2. Check students' drawings. $15 \div 5 = 3$
||| ||| ||| ||| |||
4. $6 \times 7 = 42$; $7 \times 6 = 42$; $42 \div 6 = 7$; $42 \div 7 = 6$

Page 262, Ex. 1, 3, 4

1. 4 ways; check students' work; factor pairs: 1, 24; 2, 12; 3, 8; 4, 6; **3.** Check students' work; factor pairs: 1, 16; 2, 8; 4,4 factors in order: 1, 2, 4, 8, 16

4.

1	1	just right
2	1, 2	hungry
3	1, 3	hungry
4	1, 2, 4	hungry
5	1, 5	hungry
6	1, 2, 3, 6	just right
7	1, 7	hungry
8	1, 2, 4, 8	hungry
9	1, 3, 9	hungry
10	1, 2, 5, 10	hungry
11	1, 11	hungry
12	1, 2, 3, 4, 6, 12	too full
13	1, 13	hungry
14	1, 2, 7, 14	hungry
15	1, 3, 5, 15	hungry
16	1, 2, 4, 8, 16	hungry
17	1, 17	hungry
18	1, 2, 3, 6, 9, 18	too full
19	1, 19	hungry
20	1, 2, 4, 5, 10, 20	too full

Page 267, Ex. 26

Answers are given for 8½-by-11 in. tablet paper. **a.** 9 pictures, **b.** 3 pictures, **c.** 1 picture; **a.** 9 tablet sheets, **b.** 27 tablet sheets, **c.** 81 tablet sheets

Page 269, Ex. 25-28

25. $6 \times 3 = 18$
$3 \times 6 = 18$
$18 \div 6 = 3$
$18 \div 3 = 6$

26. $7 \times 4 = 28$
$4 \times 7 = 28$
$28 \div 7 = 4$
$28 \div 4 = 7$

27. $5 \times 9 = 45$
$45 \div 9 = 5$
$45 \div 5 = 9$

28. $7 \times 8 = 56$
$8 \times 7 = 56$
$56 \div 7 = 8$
$56 \div 8 = 7$

Page 275, Ex. 19-20

Problems may vary. Samples:
19. 0; $36 \div 2 = 18$; $12 \div 2 = 6$; $20 \div 2 = 10$
20. 1; $35 \div 2 = 17$ R1; $179 \div 2 = 89$ R1; $19 \div 2 = 9$ R1

Sample Solution, Page 277, Ex. 8

Understand the situation: Some friends have $39 for renting wetsuits at $9 per suit. Analyze the question: How many wetsuits can they afford to rent? Plan a solution: Divide, then interpret the remainder; $39 \div 9 = 4$ R3. Examine the solution: They can rent 4 wetsuits, which costs $36; R3 means they will have $3 left, which is not enough money to rent another suit.

Sample Solution, Page 287, Ex. 16

Understand the situation: A ship had 5 masts, with 12 sails per mast, and 1 extra sail at the front and at the back. Analyze the question: You must find the total number of sails. Find the data you need: 5 masts $\times$ 12 sails per mast + 1 sail in front + 1 sail in back. Plan a solution method: Use mental math to multiply 5×12, which is 60, then add $1 + 1 = 62$. Examine the solution: Check with paper and pencil: $5 \times 12 = 60$; $60 + 2 = 62$.

Page 292, Project

Average height: 37 in; Robots X40 and J91 are taller than average; TC3 and Q44 are shorter than average; no robot is exactly average.

Page 293, Ex. 1, 3

1. When you divide 38 into 5 equal groups, there are 7 in each group, with a remainder of 3. To check, multiply 5×7, which is 35, and add the remainder: $35 + 3 = 38$. The answer checks. **3.** Possible answer: If you round 413 to 400, you cannot divide easily by 6. But if you substitute 420 for 413, you can easily divide by 6 using the basic fact $42 \div 6 = 7$. The quotient of 70 would be a close overestimate.

Page 294, Ex. 3, 5

3. 11, 13, 17, 19, 23; factor pair tables: 1×11, 1×13, 1×17, 1×19, 1×23. **5.** 10, 12, 14, 15, 16; factor pair tables: 1×10, 2×5, 1×12, 2×6, 3×4; 1×14, 2×7; 1×15, 3×5; 1×16, 2×8, 4×4.

Page 298, Try It Out, Ex. 1

rectangular prism: 6 faces, 12 edges, 8 vertices; triangular prism: 5 faces, 9 edges, 6 vertices; pyramid: 5 faces, 8 edges, 5 vertices

Page 301, Ex. 6, 7

6. 1. triangle, 3 sides; 2. quadrilateral, 4 sides; 3. pentagon, 5 sides; 4. hexagon, 6 sides; 5. triangle, 3 sides

7. 1. 1 right angle; 2. 2 right angles; 3. 2 right angles; 4. 3 right angles; 5. 0 right angles

Page 303, Ex. 1-3, 9, 10

1. parallel; **2.** intersecting but not perpendicular; **3.** intersecting and perpendicular
9, 10: Answers may vary. Samples: **9.** . . . the books might fall off. **10.** . . . you would fall straight down.

Page 305, Ex. 10
Some symmetric words are BIKE, BED, HIKE, KID, DIKE, KICK, CHICK, BOX, DICE, and DECIDE; B, C, D, E, H, I, K, O, X are symmetric capital letters that have a horizontal line of symmetry. H and O also have vertical lines of symmetry.

Page 311, Ex. 4
rectangle, parallelogram; they are alike because both have 2 pairs of parallel sides; they are different because a rectangle has 4 right angles and a parallelogram has 2 acute and 2 obtuse angles.

Page 313, Ex. 1, 5
1. A, triangular prism; B, square pyramid; C, cone; D, rectangular prism; E, cylinder; F, sphere; **5. A,** triangle; 3; **B,** pentagon, 5; **C,** quadrilateral, 4

Page 315, Ex. 10
Check students' graphs. Pattern: The first coordinate increases by 1; the second coordinate increases by 2. The next two coordinates will be (5, 10) and (6, 12).

Page 317, Ex. 3
Possible answers: squares, circles, equilateral triangles

Sample Solution, Page 319, Ex. 7
Understand the situation: The pass went from the middle of the court to the middle of the free throw line. Analyze the question: You must find a distance not given on the diagram. Find the data you need: 37 ft from center line to end line, minus 4 ft from basket to end line and 15 ft from free throw line to basket is $38 - 4 - 15 = 18$ ft; Check the answer against the diagram: $18 + 15 + 4 = 37$, so 18 ft makes sense.

Page 323, Ex. 3, 4, 18
3. Both have 4 sides and 4 right angles. A rectangle has 2 pairs of same-length sides but a square has all equal sides.
4. A trapezoid has only 1 pair of parallel sides, but a parallelogram has 2 pairs of parallel sides. **18.** Answers may vary; check that students draw 2 sides of equal length and that when added to the third side will total a measurement of 30, such as $11 + 11 + 8$ or $9 + 9 + 12$.

Page 329, Ex. 4-7
4. $\frac{5}{12}$ shaded, $\frac{7}{12}$ unshaded; **5.** $\frac{3}{8}$ shaded, $\frac{5}{8}$ unshaded;
6. $\frac{1}{2}$ shaded, $\frac{1}{2}$ unshaded; **7.** $\frac{2}{3}$ shaded, $\frac{1}{3}$ unshaded

Sample Solution, Page 333, Ex. 1
Understand the question: In all the years a school has been training guide dogs, how many dogs have been trained? Identify the necessary data: 95 dogs per year for 38 years. Find extra data: They train 3 different kinds of dogs. Choose an operation: Multiply to put together same-size groups. Estimate the product: $100 \times 40 = 4{,}000$, which is an overestimate. Choose a calculation method: Use paper and pencil or a calculator: $95 \times 38 = 3{,}610$. Examine the answer: 3,610 fits the overestimate of 4,000, so it makes sense that 3,610 dogs have been trained.

Page 343, Ex. 1-3
1. $\frac{2}{5}, \frac{3}{5}$ **2.** $\frac{3}{6}, \frac{3}{6}$ **3.** $\frac{3}{4}, \frac{1}{4}$

Sample Solution, Page 349, Ex. 1
Understand the situation: Sheryl has made part of a bracelet that will be 6 in. long. Analyze the question: Compare the amount now done to $\frac{1}{3}$ of the total length. Find the data: The bracelet is now $2\frac{1}{2}$ in. long. Plan a strategy: Find $\frac{1}{3}$ of 6, then compare with $2\frac{1}{2}$ in. Solve: $\frac{1}{3}$ of $6 = 2$: $2\frac{1}{2} > 2$. Examine the solution: The bracelet is $2\frac{1}{2}$ in. long, which is longer than $\frac{1}{3}$ of 6, so the answer makes sense.

Page 352, Project

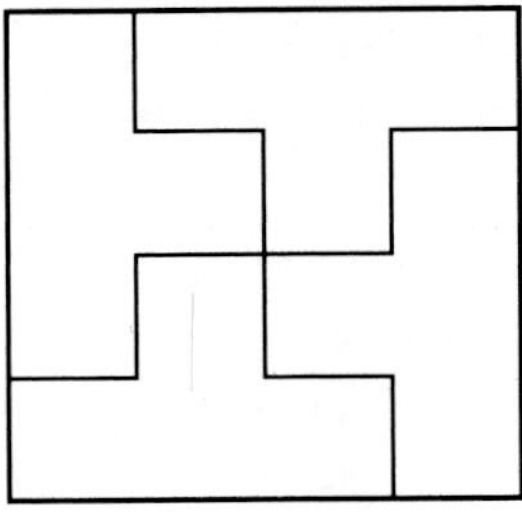

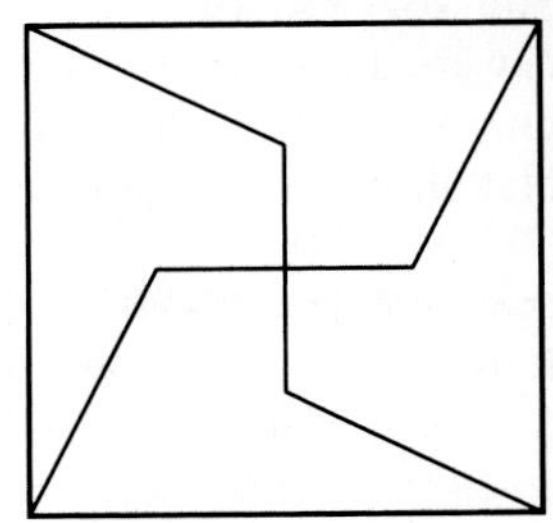

Page 354, Ex. 2
a. $\frac{1}{3}, \frac{2}{6}, \frac{4}{12}$ **b.** $\frac{3}{4}, \frac{9}{12}$ **c.** $\frac{2}{3}, \frac{4}{6}, \frac{8}{12}$

Page 365, Ex. 12
12 possible decimals: 30.15, 30.51, 31.05, 31.50, 35.01, 35.10, 50.13, 50.31, 51.03, 51.30, 53.01, 53.10

Sample Solution, Page 371, Ex. 4
Understand the situation: Mrs. Chung needs a dozen rolls of wallpaper that each cost the same amount. Decide how to solve the problem: Multiply to combine same-size groups. Pick a calculation method: Use paper and pencil. Estimate the answer: Round \$11.95 to \$12; round 12 to 10; $10 \times \$12 = \$120$, which represents an underestimate. Solve: $\$11.95 \times 12 = \$143.40$. Check the answer to see whether it makes sense: Compared with underestimate of \$120, \$143.40 makes sense.